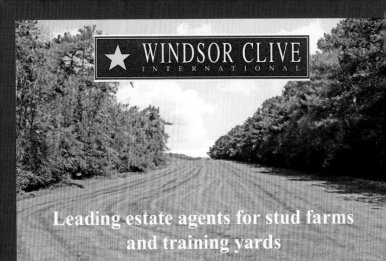

CELEBRATING

70 YEARS

ROA

RACEHORSE OWNERS
ASSOCIATION

WORKING FOR
OWNERS SINCE 1945

TOP-NOTCH BENEFITS FOR OWNERS

ROA membership is the equivalent of just 63p*
a day but the benefits are immense

- SIS sponsorship (worth an average of £4,000 against
  ownership costs alone – annually per horse)

- Free racecourse admission
  and priority car parking
  (worth over £200 a year)

- Automatic third-party insurance
  (worth £290 a year)

- BHA 20% fee discounts
  (worth £55 on average)

- Thoroughbred Owner & Breeder
  magazine (worth £55 for 12 issues)

Plus much more

Join 7,500 owners today.
Call 020 7152 0200
or visit roa.co.uk

*£230/365 days - £0.63
Terms and conditions may apply to benefits

HORSES
IN TRAINING 2016

126th YEAR OF PUBLICATION

Raceform

INDEX TO GENERAL CONTENTS

Editor	Richard Lowther; Raceform Ltd., 27 Kingfisher Court, Hambridge Road, Newbury, RG14 5SJ Fax: 01635 578101 E-mail: richard.lowther@racingpost.com
Assistant Editor	Simon Turner
Production Editor	Adrian Gowling; Bloodstock Services, Weatherbys
Production Assistants	Kerry D'Elia, Chris Hill, Alan Mosley, Gary Bivens and Chris Bennett
Typesetting	Maggie Elvie; Printing Services, Weatherbys, Sanders Road, Wellingborough, NN8 4BX.
Orders	Raceform Ltd., Sanders Road, Wellingborough, Northants NN8 4BX. Tel: 01933 304858 www.racingpost.com/shop E-mail: Shop@racingpost.com
Advertisements	Keith Haggerty, Archant Dialogue, Prospect House, Rouen Road, Norwich, NR1 1RE Tel: 01603 772864 E-mail: keith.haggerty@archantdialogue.co.uk
ISBN	978-1-910498-58-3

INDEX TO ADVERTISERS

2016

RACING FIXTURES

AND SALE DATES

(SUBJECT TO ALTERATION)

Flat fixtures are in **Black Type**; Jump in Light Type; Irish in *Italic;*
asterisk (☆) indicates an evening or Twilight meeting;
† indicates an All Weather meeting. Sale dates are at foot of fixtures

MARCH

Sun	Mon	Tues	Wed	Thur	Fri	Sat
		1	**2**	**3**	**4**	**5**
		Catterick Bridge Leicester **Lingfield Park†**	Bangor-On-Dee *Downpatrick* **Kempton Park†☆** Wincanton **Wolverhampton†**	**Chelmsford City†☆** *Clonmel* Ludlow **Southwell†** Taunton	Doncaster **Dundalk†☆** **Lingfield Park†** Newbury **Wolverhampton†☆**	Doncaster *Gowran Park* Kelso **Lingfield Park†** Newbury Stratford-On-Avon
6	**7**	**8**	**9**	**10**	**11**	**12**
Huntingdon *Naas* Sedgefield	Lingfield Park Southwell **Wolverhampton†**	Exeter Newcastle **Southwell†**	Catterick Bridge Fontwell Park **Kempton Park†☆** **Lingfield Park†**	Carlisle **Chelmsford City†☆** **Southwell†** Wincanton	Ayr **Chelmsford City†☆** *Dundalk†☆* Leicester Sandown Park	Ayr Chepstow *Limerick* Sandown Park **Wolverhampton†**
13	**14**	**15**	**16**	**17**	**18**	**19**
Limerick Market Rasen *Navan* Warwick	*Cork* Plumpton Stratford-On-Avon Taunton	Cheltenham Sedgefield **Southwell†** **Wolverhampton†☆**	Cheltenham Huntingdon **Kempton Park†☆** **Southwell†**	**Chelmsford City†☆** Cheltenham *Down Royal* Hexham Towcester *Wexford* Cheltenham Sale	Cheltenham *Dundalk†☆* Fakenham **Lingfield Park†** **Wolverhampton†☆**	Fontwell Park *Gowran Park* Kempton Park Newcastle Uttoxeter **Wolverhampton†☆**
20	**21**	**22**	**23**	**24**	**25**	**26**
Carlisle *Curragh* *Downpatrick* Ffos Las	Kelso Southwell Taunton	Exeter **Southwell†** Wetherby	*Dundalk†☆* Haydock Park **Kempton Park†☆** **Southwell†** Warwick	Chepstow Ludlow *Thurles* **Wolverhampton†**	**Lingfield Park†** **Musselburgh**	Carlisle *Cork* Haydock Park **Kempton Park†** Newton Abbot Stratford-On-Avon
27	**28**	**29**	**30**	**31**		
Cork *Fairyhouse* **Musselburgh** Plumpton Sedgefield **Wolverhampton†**	Chepstow *Cork* *Fairyhouse* Fakenham Huntingdon Market Rasen Plumpton **Redcar**	Fairyhouse Hexham Southwell **Wolverhampton†**	Exeter **Kempton Park†☆** **Lingfield Park†** **Southwell†**	Bangor-On-Dee **Chelmsford City†☆** *Clonmel☆* Ffos Las **Wolverhampton†**		

APRIL

Sun	Mon	Tues	Wed	Thur	Fri	Sat
					1	**2**
					Dundalk†☆ Fontwell Park **Lingfield Park†** Newbury Wetherby **Wolverhampton†☆**	**Doncaster** Kelso **Kempton Park†** *Navan* Newbury Uttoxeter
3	**4**	**5**	**6**	**7**	**8**	**9**
Ascot Carlisle *Curragh* **Doncaster** *Limerick*	**Lingfield Park†** Warwick Wincanton	*Fairyhouse* Ludlow Newton Abbot **Pontefract**	**Catterick Bridge** **Kempton Park†☆** *Leopardstown* **Lingfield Park†** **Nottingham** Ascot Sale	Aintree **Chelmsford City†** *Limerick* **Southwell†☆** Taunton Doncaster Sale at Aintree	Aintree *Dundalk†☆* **Leicester** Newcastle *Wexford☆* **Wolverhampton†☆**	Aintree Chepstow *Gowran Park* **Lingfield Park†** Sedgefield **Wolverhampton†☆**
10	**11**	**12**	**13**	**14**	**15**	**16**
Ffos Las Leopardstown Market Rasen *Tramore*	Kelso **Redcar** *Tramore☆* **Windsor** Tattersalls Sale Keeneland Sale	Exeter **Newmarket** **Southwell†** *Tipperary☆* Tattersalls Sale	**Beverley** Cheltenham **Kempton Park†☆** **Newmarket** Tattersalls Sale	**Chelmsford City†☆** Cheltenham *Limerick* **Newmarket** **Ripon** Tattersalls Sale	Ayr *Ballinrobe☆* **Bath☆** *Dundalk†☆* Fontwell Park **Newbury** Southwell☆	Ayr Bangor-On-Dee *Cork* **Newbury** **Nottingham☆** **Thirsk** **Wolverhampton†☆**
17	**18**	**19**	**20**	**21**	**22**	**23**
Navan Stratford-On-Avon Wetherby Wincanton	Hexham Huntingdon☆ Newton Abbot **Pontefract** **Windsor☆** Ascot Sale	**Brighton☆** Kempton Park Ludlow Sedgefield☆ **Wolverhampton†** Doncaster Sale	**Catterick Bridge** **Epsom Downs** *Fairyhouse☆* **Lingfield Park†☆** Perth Taunton☆ Doncaster Sale	**Beverley** Exeter☆ Market Rasen☆ Perth *Tipperary☆* Warwick	Chepstow☆ **Doncaster** *Dundalk†☆* *Kilbeggan☆* Perth Plumpton☆ **Sandown Park** Cheltenham Sale	**Doncaster☆** **Haydock Park** **Leicester** *Limerick* **Ripon** Sandown Park **Wolverhampton†☆**
24	**25**	**26**	**27**	**28**	**29**	**30**
Gowran Park **Musselburgh** **Thirsk**	**Ayr** **Chelmsford City†** *Naas☆* **Southwell†** **Windsor☆** **Wolverhampton†☆**	**Bath** **Brighton** **Lingfield Park†☆** **Nottingham** *Punchestown☆* **Wolverhampton†☆**	**Ascot** **Brighton☆** Cheltenham☆ **Pontefract** *Punchestown☆* **Wolverhampton†**	**Chelmsford City†☆** **Lingfield Park†** *Punchestown☆* **Redcar** Sedgefield☆ Towcester Goffs Sale	Bangor-On-Dee☆ **Chepstow** Fontwell Park☆ **Lingfield Park†** **Musselburgh** Punchestown☆ Tattersalls Sale	**Doncaster☆** **Goodwood** Hexham☆ **Newmarket** *Punchestown* **Thirsk** Uttoxeter

MAY

Sun	Mon	Tues	Wed	Thur	Fri	Sat
1	**2**	**3**	**4**	**5**	**6**	**7**
Hamilton Park **Newmarket** **Salisbury** *Sligo*	**Bath** **Beverley** Curragh *Down Royal* Kempton Park Warwick **Windsor**	*Ballinrobe☆* **Brighton** **Catterick Bridge☆** Exeter☆ Fakenham Sedgefield	**Chelmsford City†☆** **Chester** Kelso Newton Abbot Wetherby☆	Carlisle☆ **Chester** *Clonmel☆* Newton Abbot Uttoxeter Wincanton☆	**Ascot☆** **Chester** *Cork☆* *Downpatrick☆* **Lingfield Park** Market Rasen **Nottingham☆** **Ripon☆**	**Ascot** **Haydock (Mixed)** Hexham **Lingfield Park** **Nottingham** **Thirsk☆** Warwick☆ Wexford
		Osarus Sale				
8	**9**	**10**	**11**	**12**	**13**	**14**
Leopardstown *Limerick* Ludlow Plumpton	**Brighton** **Musselburgh** *Roscommon☆* Towcester☆ **Windsor☆** **Wolverhampton†**	**Beverley** **Chepstow☆** Sedgefield Southwell☆ Wincanton	**Bath☆** **Lingfield Park†** *Naas☆* *Perth☆* Worcester **York**	Fontwell Park☆ **Newmarket☆** Perth **Salisbury** *Tipperary☆* **York**	Aintree☆ *Dundalk☆* **Hamilton Park☆** *Kilbeggan☆* **Newbury** **Newmarket** **York**	Bangor-On-Dee **Doncaster☆** **Newbury** **Newmarket** *Punchestown* **Thirsk** Uttoxeter☆
						Arqana Sale
15	**16**	**17**	**18**	**19**	**20**	**21**
Killarney Market Rasen *Navan* **Ripon** Stratford-On-Avon	**Brighton** Kempton Park *Killarney☆* **Leicester☆** **Redcar** **Windsor☆**	Huntingdon☆ *Killarney☆* **Lingfield Park†** **Newcastle†** **Nottingham** **Wetherby☆**	**Ayr** **Bath** *Dundalk☆* **Kempton Park†☆** Southwell☆ Warwick	*Clonmel☆* **Goodwood** **Lingfield Park** **Ripon☆** **Sandown Park☆** Worcester	**Carlisle** **Catterick Bridge☆** *Cork☆* *Downpatrick☆* **Goodwood** Stratford-On-Avon☆ **Wolverhampton†**	**Chepstow☆** *Curragh* **Goodwood** **Haydock Park** **Newmarket** Stratford-On-Avon☆ **York**
	Doncaster Sale	Doncaster Sale	Doncaster Sale	Goresbridge Sale	Goresbridge Sale	
22	**23**	**24**	**25**	**26**	**27**	**28**
Curragh Fakenham **Nottingham**	**Ayr** **Carlisle☆** **Leicester** *Sligo☆* **Windsor☆**	Hexham Southwell☆ **Wetherby☆** **Wolverhampton†**	*Gowran Park☆* **Hamilton Park** **Kempton Park†☆** **Lingfield Park** Market Rasen Newton Abbot☆	Bangor-On-Dee **Chelmsford City†** **Haydock Park** Newcastle☆ **Sandown Park☆** *Tipperary☆*	**Bath** **Brighton** *Down Royal☆* **Haydock Park** **Musselburgh☆** **Pontefract☆** Worcester☆	**Beverley** Cartmel **Catterick Bridge** **Chester** *Flos Las☆* **Haydock Park** *Navan* **Salisbury☆**
				Cheltenham Sale	Baden-Baden Sale	
29	**30**	**31**				
Fontwell Park Kelso *Naas* Uttoxeter	*Ballinrobe☆* Cartmel Huntingdon **Leicester** **Redcar** **Windsor**	*Ballinrobe☆* **Leicester** **Lingfield Park†☆** **Redcar** Towcester **Wolverhampton†☆**				
		Ascot Sale				

JUNE

Sun	Mon	Tues	Wed	Thur	Fri	Sat
			1 Cartmel **Chelmsford City**†☆ Fontwell Park **Nottingham** *Punchestown*☆ **Ripon**☆	**2** *Fairyhouse*☆ Ffos Las☆ **Hamilton Park**☆ **Kempton Park**†☆ **Lingfield Park** Ripon	**3** **Bath**☆ **Catterick Bridge** **Doncaster**☆ **Epsom Downs** **Goodwood**☆ *Leopardstown*☆ Market Rasen *Tramore*☆	**4** *Curragh*☆ **Doncaster** **Epsom Downs** Hexham **Lingfield Park**☆ **Musselburgh** **Newcastle**†☆ *Tramore* Worcester
5 *Goodwood* Kilbeggan *Listowel* Perth	**6** Ayr **Brighton** *Gowran Park* *Listowel* **Pontefract**☆ **Windsor**☆	**7** Fontwell Park **Lingfield Park**☆ **Salisbury** Southwell☆	**8** **Beverley** *Fairyhouse* **Hamilton Park**☆ **Haydock Park** **Kempton Park**†☆ **Yarmouth** Goff's Sale	**9** **Haydock Park**☆ *Leopardstown*☆ **Newbury** **Nottingham** Uttoxeter☆ **Yarmouth** Goff's Sale	**10** Aintree☆ **Chepstow**☆ *Clonmel*☆ **Goodwood**☆ Newton Abbot **Sandown Park** **York**	**11** **Bath** **Chester** Hexham **Leicester**☆ *Limerick*☆ **Lingfield Park**☆ **Musselburgh** *Navan* **Sandown Park** **York**
12 *Cork* **Doncaster** *Downpatrick* **Salisbury**	**13** Carlisle **Nottingham**☆ *Roscommon*☆ **Thirsk** **Windsor**☆ Goff's Sale (London)	**14** **Royal Ascot** **Beverley** **Brighton**☆ *Roscommon*☆ Stratford-On-Avon☆ **Thirsk**	**15** **Royal Ascot** **Chelmsford City**†☆ **Hamilton Park** **Ripon**☆ Uttoxeter Wexford☆	**16** **Royal Ascot** **Chelmsford City**† Ffos Las☆ **Leicester**☆ *Leopardstown*☆ **Lingfield Park**†☆ **Ripon**	**17** **Royal Ascot** Ayr☆ *Down Royal*☆ **Goodwood**☆ *Limerick*☆ Market Rasen **Newmarket**☆ Redcar	**18** **Royal Ascot** **Ayr** *Down Royal* *Gowran Park* **Haydock Park**☆ **Lingfield Park**☆ **Newmarket** Redcar
19 *Gowran Park* Hexham **Pontefract** Worcester	**20** **Chepstow** *Kilbeggan*☆ Southwell **Windsor**☆ **Wolverhampton**†☆	**21** *Ballinrobe*☆ **Beverley** **Brighton** **Leicester**☆ Newton Abbot☆	**22** **Bath**☆ **Carlisle** **Kempton Park**†☆ *Naas*☆ **Salisbury** Worcester Tattersalls (IRE) Sale	**23** **Hamilton Park**☆ *Leopardstown*☆ **Newbury**☆ **Newcastle**† **Newmarket** **Nottingham** Tattersalls (IRE) Sale	**24** Cartmel **Chester**☆ *Curragh*☆ **Doncaster** **Newcastle**†☆ **Newmarket**☆ **Yarmouth** Tattersalls (IRE) Sale	**25** **Chester** *Curragh* **Doncaster**☆ **Lingfield Park**☆ **Newcastle**† **Newmarket** **Windsor**
26 Cartmel *Curragh* Uttoxeter **Windsor**	**27** **Musselburgh**☆ **Pontefract** **Windsor**☆ **Wolverhampton**†	**28** **Brighton** **Chepstow**☆ **Hamilton Park** *Sligo*☆ Stratford-On-Avon☆	**29** **Bath**☆ **Catterick Bridge** *Fairyhouse* **Kempton Park**†☆ Perth Worcester Arqana Sale	**30** *Bellewstown*☆ **Epsom Downs**☆ **Haydock Park** **Newbury**☆ Perth *Tipperary*☆ **Yarmouth** Arqana Sale		

JULY

Sun	Mon	Tues	Wed	Thur	Fri	Sat
31					**1**	**2**
Chepstow **Chester** *Galway* Market Rasen					*Bellewstown*☆ **Beverley**☆ **Doncaster** **Haydock Park**☆ Newton Abbot **Sandown Park** *Wexford*☆	*Bellewstown*☆ **Beverley** **Carlisle**☆ **Haydock Park** **Leicester** **Nottingham**☆ **Sandown Park**
					Arqana Sale	
3	**4**	**5**	**6**	**7**	**8**	**9**
Ayr *Limerick* Market Rasen *Naas*	**Ayr** **Ripon**☆ *Roscommon*☆ **Windsor**☆ Worcester	**Brighton**☆ **Pontefract** *Roscommon*☆ Uttoxeter **Wolverhampton**†	**Bath**☆ **Catterick Bridge** **Kempton Park**† **Lingfield Park** Yarmouth	**Carlisle** **Doncaster** **Epsom Downs**☆ *Leopardstown*☆ **Newbury**☆ **Newmarket**	**Ascot** **Chepstow**☆ **Chester**☆ *Cork*☆ **Musselburgh** *Navan*☆ **Newmarket** **York**	**Ascot** **Chester** **Hamilton Park**☆ **Newmarket** **Salisbury**☆ *Tipperary* **York**
		Tattersalls Sale	*Tattersalls Sale*	*Tattersalls Sale*	*Tattersalls Sale*	
10	**11**	**12**	**13**	**14**	**15**	**16**
Fairyhouse Perth *Sligo* Southwell Stratford-On-Avon	**Ayr** **Chelmsford City**† *Killarney*☆ **Windsor**☆ **Wolverhampton**†☆	**Bath** **Beverley** *Dundalk*† *Killarney*☆ **Thirsk**☆ Worcester	**Catterick Bridge** *Downpatrick* *Killarney*☆ **Lingfield Park** **Sandown Park**☆ Uttoxeter **Yarmouth**☆	**Chepstow** **Doncaster**☆ **Epsom Downs**☆ **Hamilton Park** *Killarney* **Leicester** *Leopardstown*☆	**Hamilton Park**☆ **Haydock Park** *Kilbeggan*☆ **Newbury** **Newmarket**☆ **Nottingham** **Pontefract**☆	Cartmel *Curragh* **Haydock Park**☆ **Lingfield Park**☆ Market Rasen **Newbury** **Newmarket** **Ripon**
		Ascot Sale *Fasig-Tipton Sale*				
17	**18**	**19**	**20**	**21**	**22**	**23**
Curragh Newton Abbot **Redcar** Stratford-On-Avon *Tipperary*	**Ayr** *Ballinrobe*☆ **Beverley**☆ Cartmel **Windsor**☆	*Ballinrobe*☆ **Chelmsford City**☆ **Ffos Las** **Musselburgh** **Nottingham**☆	**Bath** **Catterick Bridge** **Leicester**☆ **Lingfield Park**† *Naas*☆ **Sandown Park**☆	**Doncaster**☆ *Leopardstown*☆ *Limerick*☆ **Newbury**☆ **Sandown Park** Worcester **Yarmouth**	**Ascot** **Chepstow**☆ *Down Royal*☆ **Newmarket**☆ **Thirsk** Uttoxeter *Wexford*☆ **York**☆	**Ascot** **Chester** **Lingfield Park**☆ **Newcastle**† **Newmarket** **Salisbury**☆ *Wexford* **York**
					Goresbridge Sale	
24	**25**	**26**	**27**	**28**	**29**	**30**
Carlisle **Pontefract** Uttoxeter	**Ayr** *Galway*☆ Newton Abbot **Windsor**☆ **Wolverhampton**†☆	**Beverley** *Galway*☆ **Goodwood** Perth☆ Worcester☆ **Yarmouth**	*Galway*☆ **Goodwood** **Leicester**☆ Perth **Redcar** **Sandown Park**☆	**Epsom Downs**☆ **Ffos Las**☆ *Galway* **Goodwood** **Nottingham** Stratford-On-Avon	Bangor-On-Dee **Bath**☆ *Galway*☆ **Goodwood** **Musselburgh**☆ **Newmarket**☆ **Thirsk**	**Doncaster** *Galway* **Goodwood** **Hamilton Park**☆ **Lingfield Park**☆ **Newmarket** **Thirsk**

AUGUST

Sun	Mon	Tues	Wed	Thur	Fri	Sat
	1 Carlisle☆ *Cork* **Kempton Park†** *Naas* **Ripon** **Windsor☆**	**2** **Catterick Bridge** **Chelmsford City†☆** *Cork☆* **Nottingham☆** *Roscommon☆* **Salisbury** *Doncaster Sale*	**3** **Bath** **Brighton** **Kempton Park†☆** **Pontefract** *Sligo☆* **Yarmouth☆** *Doncaster Sale*	**4** **Brighton** **Haydock Park** *Leopardstown☆* **Newcastle†☆** **Sandown Park☆** *Sligo☆* **Wolverhampton†☆** **Yarmouth**	**5** **Brighton** **Haydock Park☆** **Musselburgh** **Newmarket☆** *Tipperary☆* **Wolverhampton†**	**6** **Ascot** **Ayr☆** **Haydock Park** *Kilbeggan☆* **Lingfield Park☆** **Newmarket** **Redcar**
7 **Chelmsford City†** *Curragh* *Downpatrick* **Leicester** **Windsor**	**8** **Ayr☆** *Ballinrobe☆* **Ffos Las ☆** **Windsor☆** **Wolverhampton†** *Fasig-Tipton Sale*	**9** **Chepstow** **Lingfield Park☆** **Nottingham☆** **Thirsk** *Tattersalls (IRE) Sale* *Fasig-Tipton Sale*	**10** **Bath☆** **Beverley** *Gowran Park☆* **Kempton Park†☆** *Newton Abbot* **Salisbury** *Tattersalls (IRE) Sale*	**11** **Beverley** *Leopardstown☆* **Salisbury** **Stratford-On-Avon☆** *Tramore☆* **Worcester** **Yarmouth☆** *Tattersalls (IRE) Sale*	**12** **Catterick Bridge☆** **Newbury** **Newcastle☆** **Newmarket☆** **Nottingham** *Tramore☆*	**13** **Doncaster** **Lingfield Park☆** *Market Rasen☆* **Newbury** **Newmarket** **Ripon** *Tramore☆*
14 *Dundalk†* **Pontefract** Southwell *Tramore* *Arqana Sale*	**15** **Ayr☆** *Roscommon☆* **Thirsk** **Windsor☆** *Arqana Sale*	**16** **Kempton Park†** **Leicester☆** **Ripon** *Sligo☆* **Wolverhampton†☆** *Arqana Sale*	**17** **Carlisle** **Chepstow** **Kempton Park†☆** *Killarney☆* **Worcester☆** **York** *Ascot Sale* *Arqana Sale*	**18** **Chepstow** *Fontwell Park☆* **Hamilton Park☆** *Killarney☆* **Stratford-On-Avon** **York**	**19** *Bangor-On-Dee* *Kilbeggan☆* *Killarney☆* **Salisbury☆** **Sandown Park** **Wolverhampton†☆** **York**	**20** **Bath☆** **Chelmsford City†☆** **Chester** *Curragh* *Killarney* *Newton Abbot* *Perth* **Sandown Park** **York**
21 **Brighton** **Chelmsford City†** *Curragh* **Worcester**	**22** **Brighton** **Carlisle** **Kempton Park†☆** **Thirsk☆**	**23** *Ballinrobe☆* **Chelmsford City†☆** **Newbury☆** Southwell **Yarmouth** *Doncaster Sale*	**24** *Bellewstown☆* **Catterick Bridge** **Kempton Park†☆** **Lingfield Park** **Musselburgh** **Stratford-On-Avon☆** *Doncaster Sale*	**25** *Bellewstown☆* *Fontwell Park* **Leicester** **Musselburgh** *Sedgefield☆* *Tipperary☆* **Wolverhampton†☆** *Doncaster Sale*	**26** *Down Royal☆* **Ffos Las** **Goodwood☆** **Hamilton Park☆** **Newcastle†☆** **Newmarket** **Thirsk**	**27** **Beverley** *Cartmel* **Goodwood** **Newmarket** *Redcar☆* *Wexford* **Windsor☆**
28 **Beverley** *Cork* *Curragh* **Goodwood** **Yarmouth**	**29** *Cartmel* **Chepstow** *Downpatrick* **Epsom Downs** **Newcastle†** **Ripon** *Roscommon☆*	**30** **Epsom Downs** **Goodwood** **Hamilton Park** **Ripon☆** **Worcester☆**	**31** **Bath** **Carlisle☆** *Gowran Park☆* **Lingfield Park** *Newton Abbot☆* Southwell		

SEPTEMBER

Sun	Mon	Tues	Wed	Thur	Fri	Sat
				1 **Chelmsford City**†☆ **Haydock Park** **Salisbury** Sedgefield	**2** **Ascot** **Haydock Park** **Kempton Park**☆ *Kilbeggan*☆ **Musselburgh**☆ **Newcastle**† *Baden-Baden Sale*	**3** **Ascot** **Haydock Park** **Kempton Park**† *Navan* Stratford-On-Avon **Thirsk** **Wolverhampton**†☆
4 *Dundalk*† Fontwell Park **York**	**5** **Brighton** *Galway*☆ Perth **Windsor** *Doncaster Sale*	**6** *Galway*☆ **Leicester** Perth☆ **Redcar** Worcester *Doncaster Sale*	**7** **Carlisle** **Doncaster** **Kempton Park**†☆ Uttoxeter	**8** **Chelmsford City**†☆ **Chepstow** *Clonmel*☆ **Doncaster** **Epsom Downs**	**9** **Chester** **Doncaster** *Down Royal*☆ **Salisbury**☆ **Sandown Park**	**10** **Bath** **Chester** **Doncaster** *Leopardstown* **Lingfield Park** **Musselburgh**☆ *Goffs Sale*
11 **Bath** **Chelmsford City**† *Curragh* **Ffos Las** *Listowel* *Keeneland Sale*	**12** **Brighton** **Kempton Park**† *Listowel* Worcester **Wolverhampton**†☆ *Keeneland Sale*	**13** **Carlisle**☆ **Chepstow** *Laytown* *Listowel* **Thirsk** Yarmouth *Keeneland Sale*	**14** **Beverley** *Kelso*☆ *Listowel* **Sandown Park** Yarmouth *Keeneland Sale*	**15** **Ayr** **Chelmsford City**†☆ *Listowel* **Pontefract** Yarmouth *Keeneland Sale* *Osarus Sale*	**16** **Ayr** Hexham☆ *Listowel* **Newbury** Newton Abbot *Keeneland Sale* *Osarus Sale* *SGA Sale*	**17** **Ayr** **Catterick Bridge** *Listowel* **Newbury** **Newmarket** **Wolverhampton**†☆ *Keeneland Sale*
18 *Gowran Park* Plumpton Uttoxeter *Keeneland Sale*	**19** **Hamilton Park** **Kempton Park**† **Leicester** *Keeneland Sale*	**20** *Ballinrobe* **Beverley** **Ffos Las**☆ **Lingfield Park**† Warwick *Keeneland Sale* *Tattersalls (IRE) Sale*	**21** **Goodwood** **Kempton Park**†☆ *Naas* Perth **Redcar** *Keeneland Sale* *Tattersalls (IRE) Sale*	**22** **Chelmsford City**†☆ **Newmarket** Perth **Pontefract** *Keeneland Sale* *Tattersalls (IRE) Sale*	**23** *Downpatrick* *Dundalk*†☆ **Haydock Park** **Newcastle**†☆ **Newmarket** Worcester *Keeneland Sale*	**24** **Chester** **Hamilton Park**☆ **Haydock Park** Market Rasen *Navan* **Newmarket** **Ripon** *Keeneland Sale*
25 *Curragh* **Epsom Downs** **Musselburgh**	**26** **Bath** **Hamilton Park** Newton Abbot *Roscommon*	**27** **Ayr** *Fairyhouse* Sedgefield Southwell **Wolverhampton**†☆ *Goffs Sales*	**28** Bangor-On-Dee **Kempton Park**†☆ **Nottingham** **Salisbury** *Sligo* *Goffs Sales*	**29** **Brighton** **Chelmsford City**†☆ *Clonmel* **Newcastle**† Warwick *Goffs Sale*	**30** **Ascot** *Dundalk*†☆ Fontwell Park *Gowran Park* Hexham **Newcastle**†☆ *Goffs Sale*	

OCTOBER

Sun	Mon	Tues	Wed	Thur	Fri	Sat
30	**31**					**1**
Carlisle *Galway* Huntingdon *Leopardstown*	*Galway* Hereford **Kempton Park**† Plumpton *Wexford*					**Ascot** Fontwell Park *Gowran Park* **Newmarket** **Redcar** **Wolverhampton**†☆ *Arqana Sale*
2	**3**	**4**	**5**	**6**	**7**	**8**
Huntingdon Kelso *Tipperary* Uttoxeter	**Pontefract** Southwell **Windsor**	**Brighton** **Catterick Bridge** **Kempton Park**†☆ **Leicester** *Tipperary* *Tattersalls Sale* *Ascot Sale*	**Kempton Park**†☆ Ludlow *Navan* **Nottingham** Towcester *Tattersalls Sale*	**Ayr** **Chelmsford City**†☆ Exeter Hereford *Tramore* *Tattersalls Sale*	*Dundalk*†☆ **Newcastle**†☆ **Newmarket** Newton Abbot **York**	Chepstow Fairyhouse Hexham *Limerick* **Newcastle**†☆ **Newmarket** York
9	**10**	**11**	**12**	**13**	**14**	**15**
Chepstow *Curragh* **Goodwood** *Limerick* *Tattersalls Sale*	**Chelmsford City**†☆ *Curragh* **Salisbury** **Windsor** **Yarmouth** *Tattersalls Sale*	*Galway* Huntingdon **Leicester** Musselburgh **Wolverhampton**†☆ *Tattersalls Sale*	**Bath** **Kempton Park**†☆ **Nottingham** *Punchestown* Wetherby *Tattersalls Sale*	**Brighton** Carlisle **Chelmsford City**†☆ *Punchestown* Uttoxeter *Tattersalls Sale*	Downpatrick *Dundalk*†☆ Fakenham **Haydock Park** **Newcastle**†☆ **Redcar** Wincanton *Tattersalls Sale*	**Ascot** **Catterick Bridge** *Cork* Ffos Las Market Rasen Stratford-On-Avon **Wolverhampton**†☆
16	**17**	**18**	**19**	**20**	**21**	**22**
Cork Kempton Park *Naas* **Newcastle**†	Plumpton **Pontefract** **Windsor**	Exeter *Gowran Park* **Kempton Park**†☆ **Newcastle**† **Yarmouth** *Arqana Sale*	Fontwell Park **Kempton Park**†☆ *Navan* **Newmarket** Worcester *Arqana Sale*	Carlisle **Chelmsford City**†☆ Ludlow Newton Abbot *Thurles* *Arqana Sale*	Cheltenham **Doncaster** *Dundalk*†☆ **Newbury** **Wolverhampton**†☆ *Arqana Sale* *Baden-Baden Sale*	**Chelmsford City**†☆ Cheltenham **Doncaster** Kelso **Newbury** *Punchestown* *Baden-Baden Sale*
23	**24**	**25**	**26**	**27**	**28**	**29**
Aintree *Leopardstown* Wincanton	Ayr **Leicester** **Redcar**	Bangor-On-Dee **Catterick Bridge** Chepstow **Newcastle**†☆ *Tattersalls Sale*	**Chelmsford City**† *Dundalk*†☆ Fakenham **Kempton Park**†☆ **Nottingham** *Tattersalls Sale*	**Chelmsford City**†☆ *Clonmel* **Lingfield Park**† Sedgefield Stratford-On-Avon *Tattersalls Sale*	*Dundalk*†☆ **Newcastle**†☆ **Newmarket** Uttoxeter Wetherby *Tattersalls Sale* *Goresbridge Sale*	Ascot Ayr **Chelmsford City**†☆ **Newmarket** Wetherby *Wexford*

NOVEMBER

Sun	Mon	Tues	Wed	Thur	Fri	Sat
		1	**2**	**3**	**4**	**5**
		Exeter Kempton Park†☆ **Redcar** Wolverhampton†	Chepstow Kempton Park†☆ Musselburgh **Nottingham**	**Chelmsford City**†☆ Market Rasen Musselburgh Newbury *Thurles*	Down Royal *Dundalk*†☆ Fontwell Park Hexham **Newcastle**†☆ Warwick	Aintree **Chelmsford City**†☆ **Doncaster** *Down Royal* Kelso Wincanton
		Ascot Sale Doncaster Sale	Ascot Sale Doncaster Sale	Doncaster Sale Osarus Sale	Goffs Sale Osarus Sale	Tattersalls (IRE) Sale SGA Sale
6	**7**	**8**	**9**	**10**	**11**	**12**
Cork Ffos Las *Naas* Sandown Park	Carlisle Kempton Park **Newcastle**†	*Fairyhouse* Huntingdon Lingfield Park **Newcastle**†☆ Sedgefield	Ayr Bangor-On-Dee *Dundalk*☆ Exeter **Kempton Park**†☆	**Chelmsford City**†☆ Ludlow **Southwell**† Taunton	Cheltenham *Dundalk*☆ **Lingfield Park**† Newcastle **Wolverhampton**†☆	Cheltenham **Lingfield Park**† *Naas* Uttoxeter Wetherby **Wolverhampton**†☆
Tattersalls (IRE) Sale	Tattersalls (IRE) Sale	Tattersalls (IRE) Sale Keeneland Sale	Tattersalls (IRE) Sale Keeneland Sale	Tattersalls (IRE) Sale Keeneland Sale	Tattersalls (IRE) Sale Keeneland Sale Cheltenham Sale	Tattersalls (IRE) Sale Keeneland Sale
13	**14**	**15**	**16**	**17**	**18**	**19**
Cheltenham Fontwell Park *Navan*	Leicester **Newcastle**† Plumpton	Fakenham **Lingfield Park**† Southwell	Chepstow *Fairyhouse* Hexham **Kempton Park**†☆ Warwick	**Chelmsford City**†☆ *Clonmel* Market Rasen **Newcastle**† Wincanton	Ascot *Dundalk*☆ Ffos Las Haydock Park **Newcastle**†☆	Ascot Haydock Park Huntingdon **Lingfield Park**† *Punchestown* **Wolverhampton**†☆
Tattersalls (IRE) Sale Keeneland Sale	Goffs Sale Arqana Sale Keeneland Sale	Goffs Sale Arqana Sale Keeneland Sale	Goffs Sale Keeneland Sale	Goffs Sale Keeneland Sale	Goffs Sale Keeneland Sale	Goffs Sale Keeneland Sale
20	**21**	**22**	**23**	**24**	**25**	**26**
Cork Exeter *Punchestown* Uttoxeter	**Chelmsford City**† Kempton Park Ludlow	Lingfield Park Sedgefield **Southwell**† *Wexford*	Hereford **Kempton Park**†☆ Wetherby **Wolverhampton**†	**Chelmsford City**†☆ Musselburgh Taunton *Thurles* Towcester	Doncaster *Dundalk*†☆ Newbury **Newcastle**† **Wolverhampton**†☆	Bangor-On-Dee Doncaster *Gowran* Newbury Newcastle **Wolverhampton**†☆
Goffs Sale	Tattersalls Sale	Tattersalls Sale	Tattersalls Sale	Tattersalls Sale	Doncaster Sale at Newbury Tattersalls Sale	Tattersalls Sale
27	**28**	**29**	**30**			
Carlisle Leicester *Navan*	Ludlow **Newcastle**† Plumpton	Lingfield Park **Newcastle**† Southwell	Catterick Bridge Ffos Las **Kempton Park**†☆ **Lingfield Park**†			
	Tattersalls Sale	Tattersalls Sale	Tattersalls Sale			

DECEMBER

Sun	Mon	Tues	Wed	Thur	Fri	Sat
				1 **Chelmsford City**†☆ Leicester Market Rasen *Thurles* Wincanton *Tattersalls Sale*	**2** Dundalk†☆ Exeter *Limerick* Sandown Park Sedgefield **Wolverhampton**†☆ *Tattersalls Sale*	**3** Aintree Chepstow *Fairyhouse* Sandown Park Wetherby **Wolverhampton**†☆ *Arqana Sale*
4 *Fairyhouse* Huntingdon Kelso *Arqana Sale*	**5** Ayr **Lingfield Park**† Ludlow *Arqana Sale* *Ascot Sale*	**6** Fontwell Park **Southwell**† Uttoxeter *Arqana Sale*	**7** Hexham **Kempton Park**†☆ Leicester **Lingfield Park**† *Goffs Sale*	**8** **Chelmsford City**†☆ *Clonmel* Newcastle Taunton Warwick *Goffs Sale*	**9** Bangor-On-Dee Cheltenham Doncaster *Dundalk*†☆ **Newcastle**†☆ *Cheltenham Sale*	**10** Cheltenham Doncaster Lingfield Park *Navan* **Newcastle**† **Wolverhampton**†☆
11 Carlisle *Cork* Punchestown Southwell	**12** Ffos Las Plumpton **Wolverhampton**†	**13** Catterick Bridge **Southwell**† Wincanton	**14** **Kempton Park**†☆ **Lingfield Park**† Musselburgh Newbury	**15** **Chelmsford City**†☆ Exeter **Newcastle**† Towcester *Tramore*	**16** Ascot *Dundalk*†☆ **Newcastle**† Uttoxeter **Wolverhampton**†☆	**17** Ascot *Fairyhouse* Haydock Park **Lingfield Park**† Newcastle
18 Fakenham **Lingfield Park**† *Navan* *Thurles*	**19** Ayr **Chelmsford City**† Hereford	**20** **Kempton Park**† **Southwell**† Taunton	**21** Ffos Las Ludlow **Newcastle**†	**22** Bangor-On-Dee **Chelmsford City**† **Wolverhampton**†	**23** *Dundalk*†☆	**24**
25	**26** *Down Royal* Fontwell Park Huntingdon Kempton Park Leopardstown *Limerick* Market Rasen Sedgefield Wetherby Wincanton	**27** Chepstow Kempton Park Leopardstown *Limerick* Wetherby **Wolverhampton**† **Wolverhampton**†	**28** Catterick Bridge Leicester *Leopardstown* *Limerick* **Lingfield Park**†	**29** Doncaster Kelso *Leopardstown* *Limerick* **Southwell**†	**30** Haydock Park **Newcastle**† Taunton	**31** **Lingfield Park**† Newbury Punchestown Uttoxeter Warwick

DATES OF PRINCIPAL RACES

(SUBJECT TO ALTERATION)

JANUARY

Dornan Engineering Relkeel Hurdle (Cheltenham)	1st
Betbright Novices' Chase (Cheltenham)	1st
Betbright Handicap Chase (Cheltenham)	1st
EBF Stallions & Cheltenham Pony Club Standard Open National Hunt Flat Race (Cheltenham)	1st
Wilf Dooly Chase (Tramore)	1st
32Red Tolworth Novices' Hurdle (Sandown Park)	2nd
32Red.com Mares Hurdle Race (Sandown Park)	2nd
32Redsport.com Veterans Handicap Steeplechase Final (Sandown Park)	2nd
Slaney Novices' Hurdle (Naas)	3rd
Native Upmanship Steeple Chase (Thurles)	4th
Lanzarote Handicap Hurdle (Kempton Park)	9th
Williamhill.com Steeple Chase (Kempton Park)	9th
Moscow Flyer Novices' Hurdle (Punchestown)	9th
Dan Moore Memorial Handicap Chase (Fairyhouse)	10th
Kinloch Brae Chase (Thurles)	14th
Coolmore EBF Mares Novices' Chase (Thurles)	14th
Betfred Classic Handicap Chase (Warwick)	16th
Neptune Investment Management Novices' Hurdle (Warwick)	16th
Betfred Hampton Novices' Steeplechase (Warwick)	16th
Woodlands Park 100 Naas Novices' Steeple Chase (Naas)	16th
Limestone Lad Hurdle (Naas)	16th
Leopardstown Chase (Leopardstown)	17th
Killiney Novices' Steeple Chase (Leopardstown)	17th
Leopardstown Handicap Hurdle (Leopardstown)	17th
Goffs Theyestes Handicap Chase (Gowran Park)	21st
Galmoy Hurdle (Gowran Park)	21st
Peter Marsh Handicap Chase (Haydock Park)	23rd
Sodexo Clarence House Chase (Ascot)	23rd
OLBG.com Mares' Hurdle (Ascot)	23rd
Keltbray Holloway's Hurdle (Ascot)	23rd
Stanjames.com Champion Hurdle Trial (Haydock Park)	23rd
Peter Marsh Chase (Haydock Park)	23rd
CE Facilities Novices' Chase (Haydock Park)	23rd
Sky Bet Supreme Trial Novices' Hurdle (Haydock Park)	23rd
Frank Ward Solicitors Arkle Novices' Chase (Leopardstown)	24th
BHP Irish Champion Hurdle (Leopardstown)	24th
Nathaniel Lacy Golden Cygnet Novices' Hurdle (Leopardstown)	24th
Betbright Cup Cotswold Chase (Cheltenham)	30th
Galliardhomes.com Cleeve Hurdle (Cheltenham)	30th
Freebets.com Trophy Chase (Cheltenham)	30th
Neptune Investment Management Novices' Hurdle (Cheltenham)	30th
JCB Triumph Hurdle Trial (Cheltenham)	30th
Sky Bet Chase (A Handicap) (Formerly The Great Yorkshire Chase) (Doncaster)	30th
OLBG.com Mares Hurdle (Doncaster)	30th
Lightning Novices' Chase (Doncaster)	30th
Albert Bartlett Novices' Hurdle (Doncaster)	30th
Solerina Mares Novice Hurdle (Fairyhouse)	30th
Tied Cottage Chase (Punchestown)	31st
Grand National Trial Handicap Chase (Punchestown)	31st
EBF Novices' Hurdle (Punchestown)	31st

FEBRUARY

Powerstown Novice Hurdle (Clonmel)	4th
Winter Derby Trial Stakes (Lingfield Park)	6th
Cleves Stakes (Lingfield Park)	6th
Welsh Champion Hurdle (Ffos Las)	6th
Betfred TV Scilly Isles Novices' Chase (Sandown Park)	6th
Betfred Mobile Heroes Handicap Hurdle (Sandown Park)	6th
Betfred Contenders Hurdle (Sandown Park)	6th
Totepool Towton Novices' Chase (Wetherby)	6th
Irish Gold Cup (Leopardstown)	6th
Spring 4yo Hurdle (Leopardstown)	6th
Flogas Novices' Chase (Leopardstown)	6th
Deloitte Novices' Hurdle (Leopardstown)	6th
Opera Hat Mares Chase (Naas)	7th
Betfair Hurdle (Newbury)	13th
Betfair Denman Chase (Newbury)	13th

Betfair Price Rush Chase (Newbury) 13th
Kingmaker Novices' Chase (Warwick) 13th
Red Mills Chase (Gowran Park) 13th
Red Mills Trial Hurdle (Gowran Park) 13th
Ladbrokes Boyne Hurdle (Navan) 14th
Flyingbolt Novices' Chase (Navan) 14th
Ten Up Novices' Chase (Navan) 14th
Jane Seymour Novices' Hurdle (Sandown Park) 19th
Betfair Ascot Chase (Ascot) 20th
Reynoldstown Novices' Chase (Ascot) 20th
Betfred Grand National Trial (Haydock Park) 20th
Betfred 'Still Treble Odds On Lucky 15's' Hurdle (Haydock Park) 20th
Albert Bartlett Novices' Hurdle (Haydock Park) 20th
Bathwick Tyres Kingwell Hurdle (Wincanton) 20th
At The Races Bobbyjo Chase (Fairyhouse) 20th
Winning Fair Juvenile Hurdle (Fairyhouse) 20th
Paddy Power Newlands Chase (Naas) 21st
Paddy Power Johnstown Novices' Hurdle (Naas) 21st
Nas na Riogh Novices' Handicap Chase (Naas) 21st
Michael Purcell Novices' Hurdle (Thurles) 25th
Hever Sprint Stakes (Lingfield Park) 27th
Betbright Chase (Kempton Park) 27th
Betbright Best For Festival Betting Pendil Novices' Chase (Kempton Park) 27th
Sky Bet Dovecote Novices' Hurdle (Kempton Park) 27th
Betbright Cheltenham Festival Fund Adonis Juvenile Hurdle (Kempton Park) 27th
Coral.co.uk Winter Derby (Lingfield Park) 27th
Carrickmines Handicap Steeple Chase (Leopardstown) 28th
Totepool National Spirit Hurdle (Fontwell Park) 28th

MARCH

Spring Cup Stakes (Lingfield Park) 5th
Stanjames.com Supporting Greatwood Gold Cup Handicap Chase (Newbury) 5th
Totescoop6 Premier Kelso Hurdle (Kelso) 5th
Shamrock Handicap Steeple Chase (Gowran Park) 5th
Irish Racing Writers Kingsfurze Novice Hurdle (Naas) 6th
Directors Plate Novice Chase (Naas) 6th
Leinster National Steeple Chase (Naas) 6th
Lady Wulfruna Stakes (Wolverhampton) 12th
Imperial Cup Handicap Hurdle (Sandown Park) 12th
European Breeders' Fund 'National Hunt' Novices' Handicap Hurdle Final (Sandown Park) 12th
Dawn Run EBF Mares' Novice Steeple Chase (Limerick) 13th
Shannon Spray EBF Mares' Novice Hurdle (Limerick) 13th
EBF Novices' Final Handicap Steeple Chase (Navan) 13th
Stan James Champion Hurdle (Cheltenham) 15th
OLBG Mares' Hurdle (Cheltenham) 15th
Racing Post Arkle Challenge Trophy Chase (Cheltenham) 15th
Sky Bet Supreme Novices' Hurdle (Cheltenham) 15th
Ultima Business Solutions Handicap Chase (Cheltenham) 15th
Neptune Investment Management Novices' Hurdle (Cheltenham) 16th
Coral Cup Handicap Hurdle (Cheltenham) 16th
Fred Winter Juvenile Handicap Hurdle (Cheltenham) 16th
Betway Queen Mother Champion Chase (Cheltenham) 16th
RSA Chase (Cheltenham) 16th
Weatherbys Champion Bumper (Cheltenham) 16th
Ryanair Chase (Cheltenham) 17th
Ladbrokes World Hurdle (Cheltenham) 17th
JLT Novices' Chase (Cheltenham) 17th
Brown Advisory & Merriebelle Plate Handicap Chase (Cheltenham) 17th
Trull House Stud Mares' Novices' Hurdle (Cheltenham) 17th
Timico Cheltenham Gold Cup Chase (Cheltenham) 18th
Albert Bartlett Novices' Hurdle (Cheltenham) 18th
JCB Triumph Hurdle (Cheltenham) 18th
Johnny Henderson Grand Annual Chase (Cheltenham) 18th
Vincent O'Brien County Hurdle (Cheltenham) 18th
EBF Park Express Stakes (Curragh) 20th
Magnolia Stakes (Kempton Park) 26th
Ryanair Gold Cup (Fairyhouse) 27th
Coolmore NH Sires Festival Novices' Hurdle (Fairyhouse) 27th
EBF Mares Novices' Hurdle Final (Fairyhouse) 27th
John Fowler Memorial Mares Chase (Fairyhouse) 27th
INHSO Final Novices' Handicap Hurdle (Fairyhouse) 27th
Imperial Call Steeple Chase (Cork) 27th
Easter Handicap Hurdle (Cork) 27th
Cork Sprint Stakes (Cork) 28th
Rathbarry Novices' Hurdle (Fairyhouse) 28th

Greenogue Novices' Handicap Chase (Fairyhouse) 28th
Keelings Hurdle (Fairyhouse) 28th
Boylesports Irish Grand National Grade A Steeplechase (Fairyhouse) 28th
Percy Maynard 4yo Hurdle (Fairyhouse) 29th
Normans Grove Steeple Chase (Fairyhouse) 29th
thetote.ie Handicap Hurdle (Fairyhouse) 29th

APRIL

Patton Stakes (Dundalk) 1st
Doncaster Mile Stakes (Doncaster) 2nd
Cammidge Trophy Stakes (Doncaster) 2nd
Betway Lincoln (Doncaster) 2nd
William Hill Spring Mile (Doncaster) 2nd
Snowdrop Stakes (Kempton Park) 2nd
Doom Bar Juvenile Hurdle (Newbury) 2nd
An Uaimh Chase (Navan) 2nd
Gladness Stakes (Curragh) 3rd
Alleged Stakes (Curragh) 3rd
Kevin McManus Bumper (Limerick) 3rd
Hugh McMahon Memorial Novices' Chase (Limerick) 3rd
Further Flight Stakes (Nottingham) 6th
Noblesse Stakes (Leopardstown) 6th
Doom Bar Aintree Hurdle (Aintree) 7th
Betfred Bowl Chase (Aintree) 7th
Anniversary 4yo Juvenile Hurdle (Aintree) 7th
Manifesto Novices' Chase (Aintree) 7th
Red Rum Handicap Chase (Aintree) 7th
Aintree Handicap Hurdle (Aintree) 7th
Crabbie's Topham Handicap Chase (Aintree) 8th
Melling Chase (Aintree) 8th
Doom Bar Sefton Novices' Hurdle (Aintree) 8th
Mildmay Novices' Chase (Aintree) 8th
The Top Novices' Hurdle (Aintree) 8th
Alder Hey Children's Charity Handicap Hurdle (Aintree) 8th
Weatherbys Wealth Management Champion Standard Open National Hunt Flat (Aintree) 8th
International Stakes (Lingfield Park) 9th
Betfred Handicap Chase (Aintree) 9th
Crabbie's Grand National Chase (Aintree) 9th
Silver Cross Stayers' Hurdle (Aintree) 9th
Doom Bar Maghull Novices' Chase (Aintree) 9th
Mersey Novices' Hurdle (Aintree) 9th
Pinsent Masons Nickel Coin Mares' Standard Open National Hunt Flat (Aintree) 9th
Leopardstown 2000 Guineas Trial (Leopardstown) 10th
Ballysax Stakes (Leopardstown) 10th
Leopardstown 1000 Guineas Trial (Leopardstown) 10th
Feilden Stakes (Newmarket) 12th
Ceres Silver Trophy Chase (Cheltenham) 13th
CSP European Free Handicap (Newmarket) 13th
Lanwades Stud Nell Gwyn Stakes (Newmarket) 13th
Weatherbys General Stud Book Earl Of Sefton Stakes (Newmarket) 14th
Novae Bloodstock Insurance Craven Stakes (Newmarket) 14th
Connaught Access Flooring Abernant Stakes (Newmarket) 14th
EBF Lansdown Stakes (Bath) 15th
Coral Scottish Grand National Chase (Ayr) 16th
QTS Scottish Champion Hurdle (Ayr) 16th
Jordan Electrics Ltd Future Champion Novices' Chase (Ayr) 16th
Dubai Duty Free Finest Surprise Stakes (Newbury) 16th
AON Greenham Stakes (Newbury) 16th
Dubai Duty Free Stakes (Newbury) 16th
Heritage Stakes (Cork) 16th
Bet365 Mile (Sandown Park) 22nd
Bet365 Gordon Richards Stakes (Sandown Park) 22nd
Bet365 Classic Trial (Sandown Park) 22nd
EBF Richard III Stakes (Leicester) 23rd
Bet365 Gold Cup Chase (Sandown Park) 23rd
Bet365 Celebration Chase (Sandown Park) 23rd
Bet365 Oaksey Chase (Sandown Park) 23rd
Martin Molony Stakes (Limerick) 23rd
Victor McCalmont Stakes (Gowran Park) 24th
Woodlands Sprint Stakes (Naas) 25th
Boylesports Champion Chase (Punchestown) 26th
Growise Novices' Chase (Punchestown) 26th
Evening Herald Champion Novices' Hurdle (Punchestown) 26th
Kilashee Handicap Hurdle (Punchestown) 26th
Longines Sagaro Stakes (Ascot) 27th

Paradise Stakes (Ascot)..27th
Bibby Financial Punchestown Gold Cup (Punchestown)...27th
Attheraces Champion Bumper (Punchestown)..27th
Guinness Handicap Chase (Punchestown)..27th
Irish Daily Mirror War Of Attrition Novice Hurdle (Punchestown)...27th
Ryanair Novices' Chase (Punchestown)..28th
Ladbrokes World Series Hurdle (Punchestown)...28th
Ballymore Eustace Handicap Hurdle (Punchestown)...28th
Three.ie Handicap Steeplechase (Punchestown)...28th
Punchestown Novice Handicap Chase (Punchestown)...29th
Tattersalls Ireland Champion Novice Hurdle (Punchestown)...29th
Punchestown Champion Hurdle (Punchestown)...29th
Liss A Paoraigh Mares Bumper (Punchestown)...29th
Glencarraig Lady Mares Handicap Chase (Punchestown)...29th
QIPCO 2000 Guineas Stakes (Newmarket)...30th
Dunaden At Overbury Jockey Club Stakes (Newmarket)..30th
Pearl Bloodstock Palace House Stakes (Newmarket)...30th
Newmarket Stakes (Newmarket)...30th
Daisy Warwick Stakes (Goodwood)...30th
EBF Conqueror Stakes (Goodwood)..30th
Aes Champion 4Yo Hurdle (Punchestown)...30th
EBF Mares Champion Hurdle (Punchestown)..30th
Palmerstown House Pat Taaffe Handicap Chase (Punchestown)..30th
Setanta Sport Handicap Hurdle (Punchestown)...30th

MAY

QIPCO 1000 Guineas Stakes (Newmarket)...1st
Charm Spirit Dahlia Stakes (Newmarket)..1st
Pretty Polly Stakes (Newmarket)...1st
Prix Ganay (Saint Cloud)...1st
Mooresbridge Stakes (Curragh)...2nd
Athasi Stakes (Curragh)...2nd
Tetrach Stakes (Curragh)...2nd
Cheshire Oaks Stakes (Chester)...4th
Betway Chester Cup (Heritage Handicap) (Chester)...4th
MBNA Chester Vase Stakes (Chester)...5th
Betfair Huxley Stakes (Chester)..5th
Boodles Diamond Ormonde Stakes (Chester)..6th
Dee Stakes (Chester)..6th
Buckhounds Stakes (Ascot)...7th
Victoria Cup Handicap (Ascot)...7th
Spring Trophy Stakes (Haydock Park)..7th
Pertemps Network Handicap Hurdle (Haydock Park)..7th
Derby Trial Stakes (Lingfield Park)...7th
Oaks Trial Stakes (Lingfield Park)..7th
Betfred Chartwell Fillies' Stakes (Lingfield Park)...7th
EBF Kilvington Stakes (Nottingham)..7th
Amethyst Stakes (Leopardstown)...8th
Derrinstown Derby Trial (Leopardstown)..8th
Derrinstown 1000 Guineas Trial (Leopardstown)...8th
Royal Windsor Stakes (Windsor)..9th
Duke Of York Clipper Stakes (York)..11th
Tattersalls Musidora Stakes (York)...11th
Blue Wind Stakes (Naas)..11th
Betfred Dante Stakes (York)...12th
Betfred Middleton Stakes (York)...12th
Hambleton Handicap Stakes (York)...12th
EBF Westow Stakes (York)..12th
Betway Yorkshire Cup (York)...13th
Michael Seely Stakes (York)...13th
EBF Marygate Stakes (York)...13th
Al Shaqab Lockinge Stakes (Newbury)..14th
Fillies' Trial Stakes (Newbury)..14th
Carnarvon Stakes (Newbury)..14th
King Charles II Stakes (Newmarket)..14th
Vintage Crop Stakes (Navan)..15th
Ladbrokes Handicap Hurdle (Killarney)..15th
Poule d'Essai des Poulains (Deauville)...15th
Poule d'Essai des Pouliches (Deauville)...15th
Coolmore Prix Saint Alary (Deauville)..16th
The New EBF Stakes (Ayr)..18th
Cantor Fitzgerald Investment Trusts Henry II Stakes (Sandown Park)..19th
Cantor Fitzgerald Research Brigadier Gerard Stakes (Sandown Park)..19th
Height of Fashion Stakes (Goodwood)..19th
EBF Cocked Hat Stakes (Goodwood)...20th

888Sport Sandy Lane Stakes (Haydock Park) 21st
888Sport Pinnacle Stakes (Haydock Park) 21st
Timeform Jury Stakes (Haydock Park) 21st
EBF Cecil Frail Stakes (Haydock Park) 21st
Tapster Stakes (Goodwood) 21st
888 Festival Stakes (Goodwood) 21st
Fairway Stakes (Newmarket) 21st
Grand Cup Stakes (York) 21st
Weatherbys Greenlands Stakes (Curragh) 21st
Lanwades Ridgewood Pearl Stakes (Curragh) 21st
Tattersalls Irish 2000 Guineas (Curragh) 21st
Marble Hill Stakes (Curragh) 21st
Airlie Gallinule Stakes (Curragh) 22nd
Tattersalls Gold Cup (Curragh) 22nd
Tattersalls Irish 1000 Guineas (Curragh) 22nd
Leisure Stakes (Windsor) 23rd
Prix d'Ispahan (Chantilly) 24th
Heron Stakes (Sandown Park) 26th
National Stakes (Sandown Park) 26th
Achilles Stakes (Haydock Park) 27th
Betfred.com Temple Stakes (Haydock Park) 28th
Lacken Stakes (Naas) 29th
Whitehead Memorial Stakes (Navan) 29th
Rochestown Stakes (Navan) 29th
Coolmore Stud Juvenile Fillies Stakes (Naas) 29th

JUNE

EBF Notts Oaks Stakes (Nottingham) 1st
Investec Oaks (Epsom Downs) 3rd
Princess Elizabeth Stakes (Epsom Downs) 3rd
Investec Diomed Stakes (Epsom Downs) 3rd
Surrey Stakes (Epsom Downs) 3rd
Woodcote Stakes (Epsom Downs) 3rd
Nijinsky (for King George V Cup) Stakes (Leopardstown) 3rd
Seamus & Rosemary McGrath Memorial Savel Beg Stakes (Leopardstown) 3rd
Investec Corporate Banking 'Dash' Handicap (Epsom Downs) 4th
Investec Derby (Epsom Downs) 4th
Investec Coronation Cup (Epsom Downs) 4th
Ballyogan Stakes (Curragh) 4th
Silver Stakes (Curragh) 4th
Prix du Jockey Club (Chantilly) 5th
Ballymacoll Stud Stakes (Newbury) 9th
Glencairn Stakes (Leopardstown) 9th
Scurry Stakes (Sandown Park) 11th
Ganton Stakes (York) 11th
William Hill Scottish Sprint Cup (A Heritage Handicap) (Musselburgh) 11th
EBF Cathedral Stakes (Salisbury) 12th
Munster Oaks (Cork) 12th
Midsummer Sprint Stakes (Cork) 12th
Queen Anne Stakes (Ascot) 14th
St James Palace Stakes (Ascot) 14th
King's Stand Stakes (Ascot) 14th
Coventry Stakes (Ascot) 14th
Windsor Castle Stakes (Ascot) 14th
Royal Hunt Cup (Heritage Handicap) (Ascot) 15th
Prince Of Wales's Stakes (Ascot) 15th
Duke Of Cambridge Stakes (Ascot) 15th
Queen Mary Stakes (Ascot) 15th
Jersey Stakes (Ascot) 15th
Sandringham Handicap Stakes (Ascot) 15th
Gold Cup (Ascot) 16th
Ribblesdale Stakes (Ascot) 16th
Norfolk Stakes (Ascot) 16th
Tercentenary Stakes (Ascot) 16th
Ballycorus Stakes (Leopardstown) 16th
Coronation Stakes (Ascot) 17th
Commonwealth Cup (Ascot) 17th
King Edward VII Stakes (Ascot) 17th
Albany Stakes (Ascot) 17th
Queen's Vase Stakes (Ascot) 17th
Diamond Jubilee Stakes (Ascot) 18th
Hardwicke Stakes (Ascot) 18th
Wokingham Stakes (Heritage Handicap) (Ascot) 18th
Wolferton Handicap Stakes (Ascot) 18th
Chesham Stakes (Ascot) 18th

Land O'Burns Stakes (Ayr) 18th
Pontefract Castle Stakes (Pontefract) 19th
Prix de Diane Longines (Chantilly) 19th
EBF Eternal Stakes (Carlisle) 22nd
Naas Oaks Trial Stakes (Naas) 22nd
EBF Hoppings Stakes (Newcastle) 24th
John Smith's Northumberland Plate (Heritage Handicap) (Newcastle) 25th
Betfred Chipchase Stakes (Newcastle) 25th
Criterion Stakes (Newmarket) 25th
Fred Archer Stakes (Newmarket) 25th
Empress Stakes (Newmarket) 25th
Midsummer Stakes (Windsor) 25th
Gain Railway Stakes (Curragh) 25th
Dubai Duty Free Irish Derby (Curragh) 25th
Dubai Duty Free Belgrave Stakes (Curragh) 25th
Dubai Duty Free Celebration Stakes (Curragh) 25th
Grangecon Stud Balanchine Stakes (Curragh) 26th
At The Races Curragh Cup (Curragh) 26th
Pretty Polly Stakes (Curragh) 26th
International Stakes (Curragh) 26th

JULY

Ambant Gala Stakes (Sandown Park) 1st
Dragon Stakes (Sandown Park) 1st
Bet365 Old Newton Cup (Heritage Handicap) (Haydock Park) 2nd
Bet365 Lancashire Oaks (Haydock Park) 2nd
Coral-Eclipse Stakes (Sandown Park) 2nd
Coral Charge (Sandown Park) 2nd
Coral Esher Stakes (Sandown Park) 2nd
Coral Distaff Stakes (Sandown Park) 2nd
Grand Prix de Saint Cloud (Saint Cloud) 3rd
Lenebane Stakes (Roscommon) 4th
Weatherbys Pipalong Stakes (Pontefract) 5th
Princess Of Wales's Arqana Racing Club Stakes (Newmarket) 7th
Bahrain Trophy (Newmarket) 7th
Arqana July Stakes (Newmarket) 7th
Sir Henry Cecil Stakes (Newmarket) 7th
Betfred Mobile (Heritage Handicap) (Newmarket) 8th
QIPCO Falmouth Stakes (Newmarket) 8th
Duchess of Cambridge Stakes (Newmarket) 8th
888Sport Summer Stakes (York) 8th
City Plate Stakes (Chester) 9th
Totescoop6 Heritage Handicap (Ascot) 9th
Summer Mile Stakes (Ascot) 9th
Darley July Cup Stakes (Newmarket) 9th
Bet365 Superlative Stakes (Newmarket) 9th
Bet 365 Bunbury Cup (Heritage Handicap) (Newmarket) 9th
Silver Cup Handicap Stakes (York) 9th
City Walls Stakes (York) 9th
57th John Smiths Cup (Heritage Handicap) (York) 9th
Grimes Hurdle (Tipperary) 9th
Tipperary Stakes (Tipperary) 9th
Brownstown Stakes (Fairyhouse) 10th
Prix Jean Prat (Chantilly) 10th
Cairn Rouge Stakes (Killarney) 11th
Bourn Vincent Memorial Handicap Steeplechase (Killarney) 12th
Meld Stakes (Leopardstown) 14th
Challenge Stakes (Leopardstown) 14th
Juddmonte Grand Prix de Paris (Saint Cloud) 14th
EBF Glasgow Stakes (Hamilton Park) 15th
Rose Bowl Stakes (Newbury) 15th
Al Basti Equiworld Hackwood Stakes (Newbury) 16th
Steventon Stakes (Newbury) 16th
Aphrodite Stakes (Newmarket) 16th
Darley Irish Oaks (Curragh) 16th
Jebel Ali Anglesey Stakes (Curragh) 16th
Sapphire Stakes (Curragh) 16th
Kilboy Estate Stakes (Curragh) 17th
Minstrel Stakes (Curragh) 17th
Sweet Mimosa Stakes (Naas) 20th
EBF Star Stakes (Sandown Park) 21st
Tyros Stakes (Leopardstown) 21st
Silver Flash Stakes (Leopardstown) 21st
EBF Valiant Stakes (Ascot) 22nd
EBF Lyric Stakes (York) 22nd

Gigaset International Stakes (Heritage Handicap) (Ascot) 23rd
King George VI And Queen Elizabeth Stakes (Ascot) 23rd
Princess Margaret Juddmonte Stakes (Ascot) 23rd
Winkfield Stakes (Ascot) 23rd
Sky Bet York Stakes (York) 23rd
Skybet Pomfret Stakes (Pontefract) 24th
Qatar Lennox Stakes (Goodwood) 26th
Qatar Vintage Stakes (Goodwood) 26th
Qatar Sussex Stakes (Goodwood) 27th
Neptune Investment Management Gordon Stakes (Goodwood) 27th
Fairmont Molecomb Stakes (Goodwood) 27th
Thetote.com Galway Plate (Galway) 27th
Qatar Goodwood Cup Stakes (Goodwood) 28th
Qatar Richmond Stakes (Goodwood) 28th
Markel Insurance Fillies' Stakes (Goodwood) 28th
Guinness Galway Hurdle (Galway) 28th
Corrib EBF Fillies Stakes (Galway) 28th
Betfred Mile (Heritage Handicap) (Goodwood) 29th
Qatar King George Stakes (Goodwood) 29th
Betfred Glorious Stakes (Goodwood) 29th
Bonhams Thoroughbred Stakes (Goodwood) 29th
L'Ormarins Queen's Plate Stakes (Goodwood) 29th
Qatar Stewards' Cup (Heritage Handicap) (Goodwood) 30th
Qatar Nassau Stakes (Goodwood) 30th
EBF Chalice Stakes (Newmarket) 30th
Ladbrokes Mervue Handicap Hurdle (Galway) 30th
Queensferry Stakes (Chester) 31st
Prix Rothschild (Deauville) 31st

AUGUST

Give Thanks Stakes (Cork) 2nd
Platinum Stakes (Cork) 2nd
Ballyroan Stakes (Leopardstown) 4th
Abergwaun Stakes (Tipperary) 5th
El Gran Senor Stakes (Tipperary) 5th
Betfred Rose Of Lancaster Stakes (Haydock Park) 6th
EBF Dick Hern Stakes (Haydock Park) 6th
German-Thoroughbred.com Sweet Solera Stakes (Newmarket) 6th
Keeneland Phoenix Stakes (Curragh) 7th
QREC Phoenix Sprint (Curragh) 7th
LARC Prix Maurice de Gheest (Deauville) 7th
EBF Upavon Stakes (Salisbury) 10th
Hurry Harriet Stakes (Gowran Park) 10th
Totepool Sovereign Stakes (Salisbury) 11th
Desmond Stakes (Leopardstown) 11th
St Hugh's Stakes (Newbury) 12th
William Hill Great St Wilfrid Stakes (Ripon) 13th
Betfred Hungerford Stakes (Newbury) 13th
Betfred Geoffrey Freer Stakes (Newbury) 13th
Washington Singer Stakes (Newbury) 13th
Flying Fillies' Stakes (Pontefract) 14th
Prix du Haras de Fresnay le Buffard - Jacques Le Marois (Deauville) 14th
Juddmonte International Stakes (York) 17th
Betway Great Voltigeur Stakes (York) 17th
Tattersails Acomb Stakes (York) 17th
Ruby Stakes (Killarney) 17th
Darley Yorkshire Oaks (York) 18th
Pinsent Masons Lowther Stakes (York) 18th
EBF Galtres Stakes (York) 18th
Coolmore Nunthorpe Stakes (York) 19th
Weatherbys Hamilton Lonsdale Cup Stakes (York) 19th
EBF Stonehenge Stakes (Salisbury) 19th
Lough Leane Handicap Steeple Chase (Killarney) 19th
Thoroughbred Breeders' Association Atalanta Stakes (Sandown Park) 20th
888Sport Solario Stakes (Sandown Park) 20th
Betfred Ebor (Heritage Handicap) (York) 20th
Irish Thoroughbred Marketing Gimcrack Stakes (York) 20th
Betfred Strensall Stakes (York) 20th
Roses Stakes (York) 20th
Chester Handicap Stakes (Chester) 20th
Renaissance Stakes (Curragh) 20th
Brandon Handicap Hurdle (Killarney) 20th
Ballycullen Stakes (Curragh) 21st
Galileo EBF Futurity Stakes (Curragh) 21st
Debutante Stakes (Curragh) 21st

Royal Whip Stakes (Curragh) 21st
Darley Prix Morny (Deauville) 21st
Darley Prix Jean Romanet (Deauville) 21st
Fairy Bridge Stakes (Tipperary) 25th
Doom Bar Celebration Mile (Goodwood) 27th
888Sport Prestige Stakes (Goodwood) 27th
March Stakes (Goodwood) 27th
Beverley Bullet Stakes (Beverley) 27th
Hopeful Stakes (Newmarket) 27th
Unibet Winter Hill Stakes (Windsor) 27th
August Stakes (Windsor) 27th
Doom Bar Supreme Stakes (Goodwood) 28th
Round Tower Stakes (Curragh) 28th
Dance Design Stakes (Curragh) 28th
Flame of Tara Stakes (Curragh) 28th
Champion 2-Year-Old Trophy (Ripon) 29th

SEPTEMBER

Country Gentlemen's Association Dick Poole Stakes (Salisbury) 1st
Appletiser Handicap (Heriatge Handicap) (Ascot) 3rd
Betfred Sprint Cup (Haydock Park) 3rd
Betfred.com Superior Mile (Haydock Park) 3rd
Ascendant Stakes (Haydock Park) 3rd
Toteexacta Sirenia Stakes (Kempton Park) 3rd
Totescoop6 September Stakes (Kempton Park) 3rd
Garrowby Stakes (York) 4th
Oyster Stakes (Galway) 5th
Ballybrit Novices' Chase (Galway) 6th
Scarbrough Stakes (Doncaster) 7th
DFS Park Hill Stakes (Doncaster) 8th
Japan Racing Association Sceptre Stakes (Doncaster) 8th
Socialites E-Cigarettes Expert Doncaster Cup (Doncaster) 9th
1stsecuritysolutions.co.uk May Hill Stakes (Doncaster) 9th
Fly Aer Lingus From Doncaster Sheffield Flying Childers Stakes (Doncaster) 9th
Flying Scotsman Stakes (Doncaster) 9th
Ladbrokes St Leger Stakes (Doncaster) 10th
Saint Gobain Weber Park Stakes (Doncaster) 10th
At The Races Champagne Stakes (Doncaster) 10th
Stand Cup Stakes (Chester) 10th
Coolmore Matron Stakes (Leopardstown) 10th
Willis Golden Fleece (Leopardstown) 10th
Qipco Irish Champion Stakes (Leopardstown) 10th
KPMG Kilternan Stakes (Leopardstown) 10th
Clipper Logistics Solonoway Stakes (Leopardstown) 10th
Goffs Vincent O'Brien National Stakes (Curragh) 11th
Palmerstown House St Leger Stakes (Curragh) 11th
Moyglare Stud Blandford Stakes (Curragh) 11th
Moyglare Stud Stakes (Curragh) 11th
Derrinstown Stud Flying Five Stakes (Curragh) 11th
Qatar Prix du Moulin de Longchamp (Chantilly) 11th
Qatar Prix Vermeille (Chantilly) 11th
Latrigue 4yo Handicap Hurdle (Listowel) 13th
Fortune Stakes (Sandown Park) 14th
EBF John Musker Stakes (Yarmouth) 14th
Guinness Kerry National (Listowel) 14th
Listowel Stakes (Listowel) 14th
Ladbrokes Handicap Hurdle (Listowel) 15th
Harry Rosebery Stakes (Ayr) 16th
Dubai Duty Free Cup (Newbury) 16th
William Hill Ayr Gold Cup (Heritage Handicap) (Ayr) 17th
William Hill Firth Of Clyde Stakes (Ayr) 17th
Doonside Cup Stakes (Ayr) 17th
Dubai Duty Free Mill Reef Stakes (Newbury) 17th
Dubai Duty Free Legacy Cup (Newbury) 17th
Dubai International Airport World Trophy Stakes (Newbury) 17th
Cordell Lavarack Stakes (Gowran Park) 18th
Foundation Stakes (Goodwood) 21st
Somerville Tattersall Stakes (Newmarket) 22nd
Rose Bowl Stakes (Newmarket) 22nd
Shadwell Rockfel Stakes (Newmarket) 23rd
Shadwell Joel Stakes (Newmarket) 23rd
Godolphin Stakes (Newmarket) 23rd
Princess Royal Stakes (Newmarket) 23rd
Rosemary Stakes (Newmarket) 23rd
Betfred Cambridgeshire (Heritage Handicap) (Newmarket) 24th

OCTOBER

NOVEMBER

DECEMBER

Neptune Investment Management Novices' Hurdle (Sandown Park) 2nd
Betfred Becher Handicap Chase (Aintree) 3rd
888Sport Tingle Creek Chase (Sandown Park) 3rd
Racing Post Henry VIII Novices' Chase (Sandown Park) 3rd
New Stand Handicap Hurdle (Fairyhouse) 3rd
Ballyhack Handicap Chase (Fairyhouse) 3rd
Betfred Peterborough Chase (Huntingdon) 4th
Bar One Drinmore Novices' Chase (Fairyhouse) 4th
Bar One Hattons Grace Hurdle (Fairyhouse) 4th
Bar One Royal Bond Novices' Hurdle (Fairyhouse) 4th
Winter Festival Juvenile Hurdle (Fairyhouse) 4th
Porterstown Handicap Chase (Fairyhouse) 4th
December Handicap Chase (Cheltenham) 9th
Caspian Caviar Gold Cup (Cheltenham) 10th
Stanjames.com International Hurdle (Cheltenham) 10th
Albert Bartlett Novices' Hurdle (Cheltenham) 10th
December Novices' Chase (Doncaster) 10th
Summit Juvenile Hurdle (Doncaster) 10th
Klairon Davis EBF Novices' Chase (Navan) 10th
John Durkan Memorial Chase (Punchestown) 11th
Kerry Group Hilly Way Chase (Cork) 11th
Kerry Group Cork Stayers Novice Hurdle (Cork) 11th
Lombardstown EBF Mares Novice Chase (Cork) 11th
Mitie Novices' Chase (Ascot) 16th
Sky Bet Supreme Trial Novices' Hurdle (Ascot) 16th
Quebec Stakes (Lingfield Park) 17th
Ascot Handicap Hurdle (Ascot) 17th
JLT Long Walk Hurdle (Ascot) 17th
Navan Novice Hurdle (Navan) 18th
Future Champions Bumper (Navan) 18th
Tara Handicap Hurdle (Navan) 18th
Foxrock Handicap Chase (Navan) 18th
Rowland Meyrick Chase (Wetherby) 26th
William Hill King George VI Chase (Kempton Park) 26th
Williamhill.com Christmas Hurdle (Kempton Park) 26th
Kauto Star Novices' Chase (Kempton Park) 26th
Racing Post Novices' Chase (Leopardstown) 26th
Knight Frank Juvenile Hurdle (Leopardstown) 26th
Greenmount Park Novices' Chase (Limerick) 26th
Coral Welsh Grand National (Chepstow) 27th
Coral.co.uk Future Champions Finale Juvenile Hurdle (Chepstow) 27th
Williamhill.com Desert Orchid Chase (Kempton Park) 27th
Williamhill.com Novices' Chase (Kempton Park) 27th
Paddy Power Dial A Bet Chase (Leopardstown) 27th
Paddy Power Future Champions Novices' Hurdle (Leopardstown) 27th
Paddy Power Handicap Chase (Leopardstown) 27th
Tim Duggan Memorial Handicap Chase (Limerick) 27th
Christmas Hurdle (Leopardstown) 28th
Lexus Chase (Leopardstown) 28th
Sporting Limerick 4yo Hurdle (Limerick) 28th
Ryanair December Hurdle (Leopardstown) 29th
Topaz Fort Leney Novices' Chase (Leopardstown) 29th
EBF Mares Hurdle (Leopardstown) 29th
Dorans Pride Novice Hurdle (Limerick) 29th
Betfred Goals Galore Challow Novices' Hurdle (Newbury) 31st

The list of Principal Races has been supplied by the BHA and Horse Racing Ireland and is provisional. In all cases, the dates, venues, and names of sponsors are correct at time of going to press, but also subject to possible alteration.

INDEX TO TRAINERS

†denotes Permit to train under N.H. Rules only

†BREWIS, MISS RHONA 061
BRIDGER, MR JOHN 062
BRIDGWATER, MR DAVID 063
BRISBOURNE, MR MARK 064
BRISLAND, MR ROBYN 065
BRITTAIN, MR ANTONY 066
†BROOKE, LADY 067
BROOKS, MRS ANNA 068
BROTHERTON, MR ROY 069
BROWN, MR ALAN 070
BROWN, MR ANDI 071
BROWN, MR DAVID 072
†BRYANT, MISS MICHELLE 073
†BUCKETT, MRS KATE 074
BUCKLER, MR BOB 075
BURCHELL, MR DAI 076
BURGOYNE, MR PAUL 077
BURKE, MR K. R. 078
†BURNS, MR HUGH 079
BURROWS, MR OWEN 080
BUTLER, MR PADDY 081
†BUTTERWORTH, MRS BARBARA .082
BYCROFT, MR NEVILLE 083

C

CAMACHO, MISS JULIE 084
CAMPION, MR MARK 085
CANDLISH, MS JENNIE 086
CANDY, MR HENRY 087
CANN, MR GRANT 088
CANTILLON, MR DON 089
CARBERRY, MRS LOUISA 090
CARR, MRS RUTH 091
CARROLL, MR DECLAN 092
CARROLL, MR TONY 093
CARSON, MR TONY 094
CARTER, MR LEE 095
CASE, MR BEN 096
CHAMINGS, MR PATRICK 097
CHANNON, MR MICK 098
CHAPMAN, MR MICHAEL 099

CHAPPLE-HYAM, MS JANE 100
CHAPPLE-HYAM, MR PETER 101
CHARALAMBOUS, MR PETER 102
CHARLTON, MR GEORGE 103
CHARLTON, MR ROGER 104
CHISMAN, MR HARRY 105
CLEMENT, MR NICOLAS 106
COAKLEY, MR DENIS J. 107
COLE, MR PAUL 108
COLTHERD, MR STUART 109
COOGAN, MR ALAN 110
COOMBE, MR JOHN 111
CORBETT, MRS SUSAN 112
CORCORAN, MR LIAM 113
†CORNWALL, MR JOHN 114
COWELL, MR ROBERT 115
COX, MR CLIVE 116
COYLE, MR TONY 117
CRAGGS, MR RAY 118
CRATE, MR PETER 119
CRISFORD, MR SIMON 120
CROOK, MR ANDREW 121
CROWLEY, MISS JO 122
CUMANI, MR LUCA 123
CUNNINGHAM, MR MICHAEL 124
CUNNINGHAM-BROWN, MR KEN .125
CURTIS, MISS REBECCA 126
CUTHBERT, MR THOMAS 127

D

D'ARCY, MR PAUL 128
DACE, MR LUKE 129
DALGLEISH, MR KEITH 130
DALTON, MS HEATHER 131
DALY, MR HENRY 132
DANDO, MR PHILLIP 133
DARTNALL, MR VICTOR 134
DASCOMBE, MR TOM 135
DAVIDSON, MR TRISTAN 136
DAVIES, MR JOHN 137
†DAVIES, MR PAUL 138

Name	Team No.
FORSTER, MISS SANDY	216
FOSTER, MISS JOANNE	217
FOX, MR JIMMY	218
FRANCE, MISS SUZZANNE	219
†FRANKLAND, MR DEREK	220
FROST, MR JAMES	221
FROST, MR KEVIN	222
FROUD, MR HUGO	223
FRY, MR HARRY	224
FRYER, MISS CAROLINE	225
FURTADO, MR IVAN	226

G

Name	Team No.
GALLAGHER, MR JOHN	227
GANSERA-LÉVÊQUE, MRS ILKA	228
GARDNER, MRS SUSAN	229
GASK, MR JEREMY	230
†GASSON, MRS ROSEMARY	231
†GATES, MR MICHAEL	232
GEAKE, MR JONATHAN	233
GEORGE, MR TOM	234
GIFFORD, MR NICK	235
GILLARD, MR MARK	236
GIVEN, MR JAMES	237
†GLEDSON, MR J. L.	238
GOLDIE, MR JIM	239
†GOLDIE, MR ROBERT	240
GOLLINGS, MR STEVE	241
GORDON, MR CHRIS	242
GORMAN, MR J T	243
GOSDEN, MR JOHN	244
GRAHAM, MRS HARRIET	245
GRANT, MR CHRIS	246
GRASSICK, MR JAMES	247
GRASSICK, MR LIAM	248
GRASSICK, MR M. C.	249
GRAY, MR CARROLL	250
GRAYSON, MR PETER	251
GREATREX, MR WARREN	252
GREEN, MR PAUL	253
GRETTON, MR TOM	254

Name	Team No.
GRIFFIN, MR PATRICK	255
GRIFFITHS, MR DAVID C.	256
†GRIFFITHS, MR SIRRELL	257
GRISSELL, MRS DIANA	258
GROUCOTT, MR JOHN	259
GUEST, MR RAE	260
GUEST, MR RICHARD	261
GUNDRY, MS POLLY	262

H

Name	Team No.
HAGGAS, MR WILLIAM	263
HALES, MR ALEX	264
HALFORD, MR MICHAEL	265
HALL, MISS SALLY	266
HAMBRO, MRS MARY	267
HAMER, MRS DEBRA	268
HAMILTON, MRS ALISON	269
†HAMILTON, MR ANDREW	270
†HAMILTON, MRS ANN	271
HAMILTON, MR B. R.	272
HAMMOND, MR MICKY	273
HAMMOND, MR MIKE	274
HANMER, MR GARY	275
HANNON, MR RICHARD	276
HARKER, MR GEOFFREY	277
†HARPER, MR RICHARD	278
HARRINGTON, MRS JESSICA	279
HARRIS, MISS GRACE	280
HARRIS, MR RONALD	281
HARRIS, MR SHAUN	282
HARRISON, MISS LISA	283
HARTY, MR EDWARD P.	284
HASLAM, MR BEN	285
HAWKE, MR NIGEL	286
HAWKER, MR RICHARD	287
†HAYNES, MR JONATHAN	288
HAYWOOD, MISS GAIL	289
HEAD-MAAREK, MRS C.	290
HEDGER, MR PETER	291
HENDERSON, MR NICKY	292
HENDERSON, MR PAUL	293

Name	Team No.
HERRINGTON, MR MICHAEL	294
HIATT, MR PETER	295
HIDE, MR PHILIP	296
HILL, MRS LAWNEY	297
HILL, MR MARTIN	298
HILLS, MR CHARLES	299
HOAD, MR MARK	300
HOBBS, MR PHILIP	301
†HOBSON, MISS CLARE	302
HOBSON, MR RICHARD	303
†HODGE, MR JOHN	304
HODGES, MR RON	305
HODGSON, MR SIMON	306
HOGAN, MR EAMONN M.	307
†HOGARTH, MR HENRY	308
HOLLINGSWORTH, MR ALAN	309
HOLLINSHEAD, MR ANDREW	310
HOLLINSHEAD, MISS SARAH	311
HOLLINSHEAD, MRS STEPH	312
HOLMES, MR PATRICK	313
HOLT, MR JOHN	314
HONEYBALL, MR ANTHONY	315
HOWE, MR STUART	316
†HUGHES, MR JAMES	317
HUGHES, MRS JO	318
HUGHES, MR RICHARD	319
HUGHES, MRS SANDRA	320
HUGO, MS N. M.	321
HUMPHREY, MRS SARAH	322
†HUNTER, MR KEVIN	323
†HURLEY, MISS LAURA	324
HUTCHINSON, MISS ALISON	325

I

Name	Team No.
†IKIN, MRS CAROLE	326
INGRAM, MR ROGER	327
IVORY, MR DEAN	328

J

Name	Team No.
JACKSON, MISS TINA	329

Name	Team No.
†JACKSON, MRS VALERIE	330
JAMES, MR LEE	331
JARDINE, MR IAIN	332
JARVIS, MR WILLIAM	333
JEFFERSON, MR MALCOLM	334
JENKINS, MR J. R.	335
†JESSOP, MR ALAN	336
JEWELL, MRS LINDA	337
JOHNSON, MR BRETT	338
JOHNSON HOUGHTON, MISS EVE	339
JOHNSON, MR KENNY	340
†JOHNSON, MRS SUSAN	341
JOHNSTON, MR MARK	342
JONES, MR ALAN	343
†JONES, MR MALCOLM	344
JORDAN, MRS VIOLET M.	345

K

Name	Team No.
KEEVIL, MRS CAROLINE	346
KEIGHLEY, MR MARTIN	347
KELLETT, MR CHRISTOPHER	348
KELLEWAY, MISS GAY	349
†KENDALL, MISS LYNSEY	350
KENT, MR NICK	351
KING, MR ALAN	352
KING, MR NEIL	353
KINSEY, MR WILLIAM	354
KIRBY, MR PHILIP	355
KIRK, MR SYLVESTER	356
KITTOW, MR STUART	357
KNIGHT, MR WILLIAM	358
KUBLER, MR DANIEL	359

L

Name	Team No.
LACEY, MR TOM	360
LAFFON-PARIAS, MR CARLOS	361
LAMPARD, MR NICK	362
LANIGAN, MR DAVID	363
LAVELLE, MISS EMMA	364
LEAVY, MR BARRY	365

Name	Team No.
LEE, MISS KERRY	366
LEECH, MRS SOPHIE	367
†LEWIS, MRS SHEILA	368
LINES, MR CLIFFORD	369
LLEWELLYN, MR BERNARD	370
LLOYD-BEAVIS, MISS NATALIE	371
LOCKWOOD, MR ALAN	372
LODER, MR DAVID	373
LONG, MR JOHN E.	374
LONGSDON, MR CHARLIE	375
LOUGHNANE, MR DANIEL MARK	376
LOUGHNANE, MR DAVID	377
LYCETT, MR SHAUN	378

M

Name	Team No.
MACKIE, MR JOHN	379
MACTAGGART, MR BRUCE	380
†MADDISON, MR PETER	381
MADGWICK, MR MICHAEL	382
MAIN, MRS HEATHER	383
†MAKIN, MRS JANE	384
MALZARD, MRS ALYSON	385
MANGAN, MR JAMES JOSEPH	386
MANN, MR CHARLIE	387
MARGARSON, MR GEORGE	388
MARTIN, MR A. J.	389
†MARTIN, MR ANDREW J.	390
MASON, MR CHRISTOPHER	391
MASON, MRS JENNIFER	392
†MATHIAS, MISS JANE	393
†MAUNDRELL, MR G. C.	394
MAYS, MR GRAHAM	395
MCBRIDE, MR PHILIP	396
MCCAIN, MR DONALD	397
MCCARTHY, MR TIM	398
MCCORMICK, MISS DANIELLE	399
MCENTEE, MR PHIL	400
MCGRATH, MR MURTY	401
MCGREGOR, MRS JEAN	402
MCLINTOCK, MS KAREN	403
MCMAHON, MR ED	404

Name	Team No.
MCMATH, MR BRIAN	405
MCPHERSON, MR GRAEME	406
MEADE, MR MARTYN	407
MEADE, MR NOEL	408
MEEHAN, MR BRIAN	409
MENUISIER, MR DAVID	410
MENZIES, MISS REBECCA	411
MIDDLETON, MR PHIL	412
MIDGLEY, MR PAUL	413
MILLMAN, MR ROD	414
MITCHELL, MR NICK	415
MITCHELL, MR PHILIP	416
MITCHELL, MR RICHARD	417
MOFFATT, MR JAMES	418
MOHAMMED, MR ISMAIL	419
MONGAN, MRS LAURA	420
MOORE, MR ARTHUR	421
MOORE, MR GARY	422
MOORE, MR J. S.	423
MORGAN, MR KEVIN	424
MORGAN, MR PAUL	425
MORRIS, MR DAVE	426
MORRIS, MR M. F.	427
MORRIS, MR PATRICK	428
MORRISON, MR HUGHIE	429
MOSS, MR GARRY	430
MUIR, MR WILLIAM	431
MULHALL, MR CLIVE	432
MULHOLLAND, MR NEIL	433
MULLANEY, MR LAWRENCE	434
MULLINEAUX, MR MICHAEL	435
MULLINS, MR SEAMUS	436
MULLINS, MR WILLIAM P.	437
MURPHY, MRS ANABEL K.	438
MURPHY, MR MIKE	439
MURPHY, MR PAT	440
MURTAGH, MR BARRY	441
MUSSON, MR WILLIE	442

Name	Team No.
N	
NAYLOR, DR JEREMY	443
†NEEDHAM, MR JOHN	444
NELMES, MRS HELEN	445
†NENADICH, MR CHRIS	446
NEWCOMBE, MR TONY	447
NEWLAND, DR RICHARD	448
NEWTON-SMITH, MISS ANNA	449
NICHOLLS, MR DAVID	450
NICHOLLS, MR PAUL	451
NIVEN, MR PETER	452
NORMILE, MRS LUCY	453
NORTON, MR JOHN	454
NOSEDA, MR JEREMY	455
O	
O'BRIEN, MR A. P.	456
O'BRIEN, MR DANIEL	457
O'BRIEN, MR FERGAL	458
O'GRADY, MR EDWARD J.	459
O'KEEFFE, MR JEDD	460
O'MEARA, MR DAVID	461
O'NEILL, MR JOHN	462
O'NEILL, MR JONJO	463
O'SHEA, MR JOHN	464
OLDROYD, MR GEOFFREY	465
OLIVER, MR HENRY	466
OSBORNE, MR JAMIE	467
OWEN, MISS EMMA	468
P	
PALMER, MR HUGO	469
PANTALL, MR H. A.	470
PANVERT, MR JOHN	471
†PARROTT, MRS HILARY	472
PAULING, MR BEN	473
PEACOCK, MR RAY	474
PEARCE, MRS LYDIA	475
PEARS, MR OLLIE	476
PECKHAM, MR GEORGE	477

Name	Team No.
PERRATT, MISS LINDA	478
PERRETT, MRS AMANDA	479
PHELAN, MR PAT	480
PHILLIPS, MR ALAN	481
†PHILLIPS, MR PAUL	482
PHILLIPS, MR RICHARD	483
PICKARD, MISS IMOGEN	484
PIPE, MR DAVID	485
PITMAN, MR MARK	486
POGSON, MR CHARLES	487
†POLLOCK, MR KEITH	488
POMFRET, MR NICHOLAS	489
PORTMAN, MR JONATHAN	490
POULTON, MR JAMIE	491
POWELL, MR BRENDAN	492
POWELL, MR TED	493
PRESCOTT BT, SIR MARK	494
PRICE, MISS KATY	495
PRICE, MR RICHARD	496
PRITCHARD, MR PETER	497
PURDY, MR PETER	498
Q	
QUINN, MR DENIS	499
QUINN, MR JOHN	500
QUINN, MR MICK	501
R	
RANDELL, MISS SALLY	502
REED, MR W. T.	503
†REED, MR WILLIAM	504
REES, MR DAVID	505
†REES, MRS HELEN	506
REGAN, MR SEAN	507
REID, MR ANDREW	508
†RETTER, MRS JACQUELINE	509
REVELEY, MR KEITH	510
RICHARDS, MRS LYDIA	511
RICHARDS, MR NICKY	512
RICHES, MR JOHN DAVID	513

Name	Team No.
RIMELL, MR MARK	514
ROBERTS, MR DAVE	515
ROBERTS, MR MIKE	516
ROBINSON, MISS SARAH	517
ROBSON, MISS PAULINE	518
†ROSS, MR R. A.	519
ROTHWELL, MR BRIAN	520
ROUGET, MR J. - C.	521
ROWE, MR RICHARD	522
ROWLAND, MISS MANDY	523
ROYER-DUPRE, MR A. DE	524
RUSSELL, MS LUCINDA	525
RYALL, MR JOHN	526
RYAN, MR JOHN	527
RYAN, MR KEVIN	528

S

Name	Team No.
SADIK, MR AYTACH	529
SANDERSON, MRS DEBORAH	530
†SANDERSON, MRS KATHLEEN	531
SANTOS, MR JOSE	532
SAUNDERS, MR MALCOLM	533
SAYER, MRS DIANNE	534
SCARGILL, DR JON	535
†SCOTT, MR DERRICK	536
SCOTT, MR GEORGE	537
SCOTT, MR JEREMY	538
SCOTT, MISS KATIE	539
SCUDAMORE, MR MICHAEL	540
SHAW, MR DEREK	541
SHAW, MRS FIONA	542
†SHAW, MRS PATRICIA	543
†SHEARS, MR MARK	544
SHEPPARD, MR MATT	545
SHERWOOD, MR OLIVER	546
†SHIELS, MR RAYMOND	547
SIDDALL, MISS LYNN	548
SIMCOCK, MR DAVID	549
SKELTON, MR DAN	550
†SLACK, MR KENNETH	551
SLY, MRS PAM	552

Name	Team No.
SMAGA, MR DAVID	553
SMART, MR BRYAN	554
SMITH, MR CHARLES	555
SMITH, MR JULIAN	556
SMITH, MR MARTIN	557
SMITH, MR MICHAEL	558
SMITH, MR R. MIKE	559
SMITH, MR RALPH	560
SMITH, MRS SUE	561
SMITH, MISS SUZY	562
SMYLY, MR GILES	563
SNOWDEN, MR JAMIE	564
SOWERSBY, MR MIKE	565
SPEARING, MR JOHN	566
SPILLER, MR HENRY	567
STACK, MR TOMMY	568
STANFORD, MR EUGENE	569
†STEELE, MR DANIEL	570
STEPHEN, MRS JACKIE	571
†STEPHENS, MRS KATIE	572
STEPHENS, MR ROBERT	573
STOKELL, MISS ANN	574
STONE, MR WILLIAM	575
STOREY, MR BRIAN	576
STOREY, MR WILF	577
STOUTE, SIR MICHAEL	578
STRONGE, MRS ALI	579
STUBBS, MISS KRISTIN	580
SUMMERS, MR ROB	581
SWINBANK, MR ALAN	582
SYMONDS, MR TOM	583

T

Name	Team No.
TATE, MR JAMES	584
TATE, MR TOM	585
†TAYLOR, MRS SUE	586
TEAGUE, MR COLIN	587
TEAL, MR ROGER	588
TETT, MR HENRY	589
THOMAS, MR SAM	590
†THOMASON-MURPHY, MRS JOANNE	591

Name	Team No.
THOMPSON, MR DAVID	592
THOMPSON, MR RONALD	593
†THOMPSON, MR VICTOR	594
THOMSON, MR SANDY	595
TINKLER, MR NIGEL	596
TIZZARD, MR COLIN	597
TODHUNTER, MR MARTIN	598
TOMPKINS, MR MARK	599
TREGONING, MR MARCUS	600
TUER, MR EDWIN	601
TUITE, MR JOSEPH	602
TURNER, MR BILL	603
TURNER, MR JAMES	604
TUTTY, MRS KAREN	605
TWISTON-DAVIES, MR NIGEL	606

U

Name	Team No.
UNETT, MR JAMES	607
UPSON, MR JOHN	608
USHER, MR MARK	609

V

Name	Team No.
VARIAN, MR ROGER	610
VAUGHAN, MR ED	611
VAUGHAN, MR TIM	612
VON DER RECKE, MR CHRISTIAN	613

W

Name	Team No.
WADE, MR JOHN	614
WADHAM, MRS LUCY	615
WAGGOTT, MISS TRACY	616
WAINWRIGHT, MR JOHN	617
†WALEY-COHEN, MR ROBERT	618
WALFORD, MR MARK	619
WALFORD, MR ROBERT	620
WALKER, MR ED	621
WALL, MR CHRIS	622
WALL, MR MARK	623
WALLIS, MR CHARLIE	624
WALTON, MRS JANE	625

Name	Team No.
†WALTON, MR JASON	626
WALTON, MRS SHEENA	627
WARD, MR JASON	628
†WATKINS, MISS TRACEY	629
WATSON, MR FREDERICK	630
WATT, MRS SHARON	631
WAUGH, MR SIMON	632
WEBBER, MR PAUL	633
WELD, MR D. K.	634
WEST, MISS SHEENA	635
WEST, MR SIMON	636
†WESTON, MR DAVID	637
WESTON, MR TOM	638
†WESTWOOD, MISS JESSICA	639
WEYMES, MR JOHN	640
WHEELER, MR ERIC	641
WHILLANS, MR ALISTAIR	642
WHILLANS, MR DONALD	643
WHITAKER, MR RICHARD	644
†WHITEHEAD, MR ARTHUR	645
†WHITING, MR ARTHUR	646
†WHITTAKER, MR CHARLES	647
WHITTINGTON, MR HARRY	648
WIGHAM, MR MICHAEL	649
WILESMITH, MR MARTIN	650
WILLIAMS, MR DAI	651
WILLIAMS, MR EVAN	652
WILLIAMS, MR IAN	653
WILLIAMS, MR NICK	654
WILLIAMS, MR NOEL	655
WILLIAMS, MR OLLY	656
WILLIAMS, MR STUART	657
WILLIAMS, MISS VENETIA	658
WILLIAMSON, MRS LISA	659
†WILSON, MR ANDREW	660
WILSON, MR CHRISTOPHER	661
WILSON, MR JIM	662
†WILSON, MISS MAIRI	663
WILSON, MR NOEL	664
WINGROVE, MR KEN	665
†WINKS, MR PETER	666

Name	Team No.
WINTLE, MR ADRIAN	667
WOODMAN, MR STEVE	668
WOOLLACOTT, MR RICHARD	669

Y

YORK, MR RAYMOND	670
YOUNG, MRS LAURA	671
†YOUNG, MR WILLIAM	672

PROPERTY OF HER MAJESTY

The Queen

Colours: Purple, gold braid, scarlet sleeves, black velvet cap with gold fringe

Trained by **Sir Michael Stoute**, Newmarket

  1 DARTMOUTH, 4, b c Dubawi (IRE)—Galatee (FR)

THREE-YEAR-OLDS
  2 CLEAR EVIDENCE, b c Cape Cross (IRE)—Rainbow's Edge
  3 DIPLOMA, b f Dubawi (IRE)—Enticement
  4 FORTH BRIDGE, b c Bernardini (USA)—Sally Forth
  5 HAMMER GUN (USA), b c Smart Strike (CAN)—Caraboss
  6 LABYRINTH (IRE), b f Lawman (FR)—Kerry Gal (IRE)
  7 MAINSTREAM, b c Dansili—Golden Stream (IRE)

TWO-YEAR-OLDS
  8 FRONTISPIECE, b c 6/2 Shamardal (USA)—Free Verse (Danehill Dancer (IRE))
  9 MISSED, b c 7/3 So You Think (NZ)—Daring Aim (Daylami (IRE))

Trained by **William Haggas**, Newmarket

  10 PICK YOUR CHOICE, 4, b g Elusive Quality (USA)—Enticement

THREE-YEAR-OLDS
  11 DAPHNE, b f Duke of Marmalade (IRE)—Daring Aim
  12 GUY FAWKES, b g Big Bad Bob (IRE)—Flight of Fancy
  13 LIGHT MUSIC, b f Elusive Quality (USA)—Medley
  14 ORIENTAL CROSS (IRE), b f Cape Cross (IRE)—Orion Girl (GER)
  15 WISHPOINT (USA), b c Street Cry (IRE)—Key Point (IRE)

TWO-YEAR-OLDS
  16 CALL TO MIND, b c 5/2 Galileo (IRE)—Memory (IRE) (Danehill Dancer (IRE))
  17 QUINQUEREME, b f 24/1 Elusive Quality (USA)—Finding Neverland (FR) (Green Desert (USA))

Trained by **Richard Hannon**, Marlborough

THREE-YEAR-OLDS
  18 PATENT, b g Paco Boy (IRE)—Film Script

TWO-YEAR-OLDS
  19 MAYAN GOLD, b f 23/3 Paco Boy (IRE)—Flash of Gold (Darshaan)
  20 WITH ONE ACCORD, b f 15/3 Acclamation —Raymi Coya (CAN)(Van Nistelrooy (USA))

PROPERTY OF HER MAJESTY

The Queen

Trained by **Roger Charlton**, Beckhampton

THREE-YEAR-OLDS
21 FINAL CHOICE, b g Makfi—Anasazi (IRE)
22 PURE FANTASY, b f Fastnet Rock (AUS)—Fictitious

TWO-YEAR-OLDS
23 MATHS PRIZE, b c 3/2 Royal Applause —Hypoteneuse (IRE) (Sadler's Wells (USA))

Trained by **Michael Bell**, Newmarket

24 FABRICATE, 4, b g Makfi—Flight of Fancy

THREE-YEAR-OLDS
25 BONHOMIE, b f Shamardal (USA)—Bonnie Doon (IRE)
26 FORECASTER, b f Fastnet Rock (AUS)—Aurore (IRE)

TWO-YEAR-OLDS
27 ELEMENTARY, b c 25/2 Exceed And Excel (AUS)—Humdrum (Dr Fong (USA))
28 GLASSALT, b f 1/2 Medaglia d'Oro (USA) —Abergeldie (USA) (Street Cry (IRE))
29 MERLIN, b c 1/2 Oasis Dream —Momentary (Nayef (USA))

Trained by **Andrew Balding**, Kingsclere

THREE-YEAR-OLDS
30 MAKE FAST, b f Makfi—Raymi Coya (CAN)
31 MOLTEN GOLD, b c New Approach (IRE)—Flash of Gold (Darshaan)

TWO-YEAR-OLDS
32 APPRECIATING, b f 15/4 New Approach (IRE)—Star Value (IRE) (Danehill Dancer (IRE))

Trained by **Richard Hughes**, Upper Lambourn

TWO-YEAR-OLDS
33 PATCHWORK, ch c 29/4 Paco Boy (IRE)—Medley (Danehill Dancer (IRE))

Trained by **Nicky Henderson**, Lambourn

34 CLOSE TOUCH, 8, ch g Generous (IRE)—Romantic Dream
35 COMELY, 4, b f Midnight Legend—Belle Magello
36 KNOCK CASTLE, 4, b g Kayf Tara —Bella Macrae
37 SPECIAL AGENT, 7, b g Invincible Spirit (IRE)—Flight of Fancy
38 TAKE TO HEART, 4, b g Sakhee (USA) —Romantic Dream
39 WISHING WIND, 6, b m Kayf Tara—Romantic Dream

Trained by **Charlie Longsdon**, Chipping Norton

40 LUCKY ESCAPE, 4, b g Lucarno (USA) —Spring Flight
41 SPORTS DAY, 4, b f Beat Hollow —Midsummer Magic

SOME TRAINERS' STRINGS ARE TAKEN FROM THE BHA RACING ADMINISTRATION WEBSITE AND INCLUDE HORSES LISTED ON THERE AS 'AT GRASS' OR 'RESTING'

---

1 MR N. W. ALEXANDER, Kinneston
Postal: Kinneston, Leslie, Glenrothes, Fife, KY6 3JJ
Contacts: PHONE (01592) 840774 MOBILE (07831) 488210
E-MAIL nicholasalexander@kinneston.com WEBSITE www.kinneston.com

1 **AFTERCLASS (IRE)**, 8, b g Stowaway—Afsana (IRE) **N. W. Alexander**
2 **ALWAYS TIPSY**, 7, b g Dushyantor (USA)—French Pick (USA) **JJ Cockburn AJ Wight P Home**
3 **ANOTHER MATTIE (IRE)**, 9, b g Zagreb (USA)—Silver Tassie (FR) **Quandt & Cochrane**
4 **BACK ON THE ROAD (IRE)**, 14, bl g Broken Hearted—Special Trix (IRE) **J. F. Alexander**
5 **BEEN DECIDED (IRE)**, 6, b g Flemensfirth (USA)—Laboc **JJ Cockburn AJ Wight P Home**
6 **BENNY'S SECRET (IRE)**, 6, br g Beneficial—Greenhall Rambler (IRE) **Mr B. C. Castle**
7 **BERTALUS (IRE)**, 7, b g City Honours (USA)—Deep Dalus (IRE) **Lord Cochrane & Partners**
8 **BRACING**, 7, ch m Alflora (IRE)—Sports Express **Bissett Racing**
9 **CALIVIGNY (IRE)**, 7, b g Gold Well—Summer Holiday (IRE) **Hugh Hodge Ltd**
10 4, B f Getaway (GER)—Call Her Again (IRE) **Hugh Hodge Ltd**
11 **CELESTINO (FR)**, 5, b g Leeds (IRE)—Evamoon (FR) **More Madness**
12 **CLAN CHIEF**, 7, ch g Generous (IRE)—Harrietfield **Clan Gathering**
13 **CLAN LEGEND**, 6, ch g Midnight Legend—Harrietfield **Clan Gathering**
14 **DUTCH CANYON (IRE)**, 6, b g Craigsteel—Chitabe (IRE) **E Barlow, R Cundall & W Kennedy**
15 **FAREWELLTOCHEYENNE (IRE)**, 8, b g Zagreb (USA)—
    Valerie Ellen (IRE) **Turcan Barber Douglas Miller Dunning**
16 **FRANKIE'S PROMISE (IRE)**, 8, ch g Fruits of Love (USA)—According To Molly (IRE) **Mr B. C. Castle**
17 **GOLD OPERA (IRE)**, 7, b g Gold Well—Flute Opera (IRE) **Macdonalds, Cardwell, Castle & Davies**
18 **HEILAN REBEL (IRE)**, 6, b g Where Or When (IRE) **Alexander, Macdonald and Stanistreet**
    Nordice Equity (IRE) **Alexander, Macdonald and Stanistreet**
19 **HERE'S TO HARRY**, 9, b g Helissio (FR)—Harrietfield **N. W. Alexander**
20 **ISLA PEARL FISHER**, 13, br g Supreme Sound—Salem Beach **Mrs P. M. Gammell**
21 **JANE'S FANTASY (IRE)**, 6, br m Robin des Pres (FR)—
    Trendy Attire (IRE) **Turcan Barber Douglas Miller Dunning**
22 **JET MASTER**, 10, b g Brian Boru—Whats The Reason (IRE) **Mr HW Turcan & Sir Simon Dunning**
23 **LAKE VIEW LAD (IRE)**, 6, gr g Oscar—Missy O'brien (IRE) **Mr A. Cochrane**
24 **LANDECKER (IRE)**, 8, br g Craigsteel—Winsome Breeze (IRE) **Hugh Hodge Ltd**
25 **LITTLE GLENSHEE (IRE)**, 10, gr m Terimon—Harrietfield **Turcan Barber Douglas Miller Dunning 1**
26 **MARLEE MASSIE (IRE)**, 7, b g Dr Massini (IRE)—Meadstown Miss (IRE) **N. W. Alexander**
27 **MASSINI'S LADY**, 5, b m Dr Massini (IRE)—Lady du Bost (FR) **Kinneston Racing**
28 **MCGINTY'S DREAM (IRE)**, 5, b g Flemensfirth (USA)—Laboc **Mr B. C. Castle**
29 **MORE MADNESS (IRE)**, 9, b g Dr Massini (IRE)—Angelic Angel (IRE) **More Madness**
30 **PRESENTING ROSE (IRE)**, 6, b m Presenting—Berkeley House (IRE) **Mr A. Cochrane**
31 **ROAD TO GOLD (IRE)**, 7, b br g Gold Well—Haut de Gamme (IRE) **Mrs J. Douglas Miller**
32 **ROSSINI'S DANCER**, 11, b g Rossini (USA)—Bint Alhabib **N. W. Alexander**
33 **ROYAL CHATELIER (FR)**, 11, b g Video Rock (FR)—Attualita (FR) **J. F. Alexander**
34 **SECRET ACT (IRE)**, 7, b g Milan—Rose of Salome (IRE) **N. W. Alexander**
35 **SPINNING AWAY**, 8, ch m Alflora (IRE)—Minora (IRE) **Horsindae Syndicate**
36 6, Ch m Black Sam Bellamy (IRE)—Sports Express **Bissett Racing**
37 **THE BISHOP (IRE)**, 8, b g Winged Love (IRE)—Charlie's Mary (IRE) **Turcan Barber Fletcher Dunning**
38 **THE ORANGE ROGUE (IRE)**, 9, br g Alderbrook—Classic Enough **Mrs S. M. Irwin**
39 **TITIAN BOY (IRE)**, 7, ch g Spadoun (FR)—Leodotcom (IRE) **Hardie & Robb**

Other Owners: Mrs Nicholas Alexander, Mr David T. Alexander, Mr Jamie Alexander, Mr Nicholas Alexander, Mr James Barber, Miss Emma Barlow, Mr A. A. Bissett, Mrs J. Bissett, Mr Neil Cardwell, Mr Brian Castle, The Hon Thomas Cochrane, Lord Cochrane of Cults, Mr J. J. Cockburn, Mr Darren Davies, Mrs J. Douglas Miller, Mr John Dudgeon, Mr Andrew Duncan, Sir Simon Dunning, Miss F. M. Fletcher, Mr Timothy Hardie, Mrs S. Irwin, Mrs Michelle Macdonald, Mr Dan Macdonald, Miss S. Quandt, Mrs L. Robb, Mrs David Stanistreet, Mr H. W. Turcan, Mr A. J. Wight.

Assistant Trainer: Catriona Bissett

Jockey (NH): Lucy Alexander. **Conditional:** Stephen Mulqueen. **Apprentice:** Lucy Alexander.
Amateur: Mr Kit Alexander.

2 | MR CONRAD ALLEN, Newmarket
Trainer did not wish details of his string to appear

3 | MR JIM ALLEN, Reigate
Postal: **Tin Tin Cottage, Littleton Manor, Littleton Lane, Reigate, Surrey, RH2 8LB**
Contacts: **MOBILE (07973) 243369**

1 BEACH RHYTHM (USA), 9, ch g Footstepsinthesand—Queen's Music (USA) **J. P. Allen**
2 TWELFTH DAN, 4, ch g Proclamation (IRE)—Mythical Charm **J. P. Allen**

TWO-YEAR-OLDS

3 B f 20/3 Paco Boy (IRE)—Mythical Charm (Charnwood Forest (IRE)) **J. P. Allen**

4 | MR ERIC ALSTON, Preston
Postal: **Edges Farm Stables, Chapel Lane, Longton, Preston, Lancashire, PR4 5NA**
Contacts: **PHONE (01772) 612120 FAX (01772) 619600 MOBILE (07879) 641660**
E-MAIL eric1943@supanet.com

1 BUSH BEAUTY (IRE), 5, b m Bushranger (IRE)—Scottendale **Mr D. Charlesworth**
2 KNOW YOUR NAME, 5, ch g Halling (USA)—Lady Agnes **Livvys Racing Group**

THREE-YEAR-OLDS

3 AUTRE PRINCESS (IRE), b f Strategic Prince—Molly Marie (IRE) **T. J. Hemmings**
4 B g Acclamation—Dani Ridge (IRE) **C. F. Harrington**
5 B f Zamindar (USA)—Quiet Elegance **Mr & Mrs G. Middlebrook**

TWO-YEAR-OLDS

6 REDROSEZORRO, b g 23/4 Foxwedge (AUS)—Garter Star (Mark of Esteem (IRE)) (19047)

Other Owners: Mr D. J. Lockwood, Mr Fred Lockwood, Mr G. Middlebrook, Mrs L. Middlebrook.

Assistant Trainer: Mrs Sue Alston

5 | MR CHARLIE APPLEBY, Newmarket
Postal: **Godolphin Management Co Ltd, Moulton Paddocks, Newmarket, Suffolk, CB8 7YE**

> This list doesn't include horses based in Dubai for the 2016 Carnival which may return to Britain - see **www.godolphin.com**

1 ALDGATE (USA), 7, ch g Street Cry (IRE)—Adonesque (IRE)
2 ANGLOPHILE, 5, ch g Dubawi (IRE)—Anna Palariva (IRE)
3 ANTIQUARIUM (IRE), 4, b g New Approach (IRE)—Antillia
4 BOW AND ARROW, 4, b g Iffraaj—Isobel Archer
5 CHARMING THOUGHT, 4, b c Oasis Dream—Annabelle's Charm (IRE)
6 ENDLESS TIME (IRE), 4, b f Sea The Stars (IRE)—Mamonta
7 FESTIVE FARE, 4, b g Teofilo (IRE)—Al Joza
8 GAME SHOW, 4, b g Dubawi (IRE)—Dream Play (IRE)
9 GOLD TRAIL (IRE), 5, ch h Teofilo (IRE)—Goldthroat (IRE)
10 GOLDEN HERITAGE, 5, b g Halling (USA)—Summertime Legacy
11 HOLIDAY MAGIC (IRE), 5, gr g Dark Angel (IRE)—Win Cash (IRE)
12 LATHARNACH (USA), 4, b c Iffraaj—Firth of Lorne (IRE)
13 OCEANOGRAPHER, 4, b g Sea The Stars (IRE)—Que Puntual (ARG)
14 OUTLAW COUNTRY (IRE), 4, br c Teofilo (IRE)—Neverletme Go (IRE)
15 PALLISTER, 4, b g Pivotal—Punctilious
16 PATHWAY TO HONOUR, 4, ch g New Approach (IRE)—Cheerleader
17 PINZOLO, 5, b g Monsun (GER)—Pongee
18 PORTAMENTO (IRE), 4, gr c Shamardal (USA)—Octave (USA)

MR CHARLIE APPLEBY - Continued

19 **RARE RHYTHM**, 4, b c Dubawi (IRE)—Demisemiquaver
20 **RAZOR WIND (IRE)**, 5, b g Dubawi (IRE)—Tender Is Thenight (IRE)
21 **SKY CAPE**, 4, b g Cape Cross (IRE)—Green Swallow (FR)
22 **SPACE AGE (IRE)**, 4, ch g New Approach (IRE)—Historian (IRE)
23 **SPARRING (IRE)**, 4, b g Teofilo (IRE)—Henties Bay (IRE)
24 **WENTWORTH FALLS**, 4, gr g Dansili—Strawberry Morn (CAN)

THREE-YEAR-OLDS

25 **AL VALORE (IRE)**, b r Shamardal (USA)—Kind Words (USA)
26 **ALBERNATHY**, ch c Dubawi (IRE)—La Pelegrina (USA)
27 **ALDRIN (FR)**, b c New Approach (IRE)—Trip To The Moon
28 **ANTIMO**, b g Dubawi (IRE)—Anna Palariva (IRE)
29 **BACHELORHOOD**, b g New Approach (IRE)—Most Charming (FR)
30 **BACK TO LOVE (CAN)**, b f Street Cry (IRE)—Song and Danz (USA)
31 **BINT AL REEM (IRE)**, b f Elusive Quality (USA)—Causeway Lass (AUS)
32 **BLANCHE NEIGE**, b f Halling (USA)—White Star (IRE)
33 **BLOSSOMTIME**, b f Shamardal (USA)—Bal de La Rose (IRE)
34 **BOCHART**, ch g Dubawi (IRE)—Camlet
35 **BOMBILATE (USA)**, b f Kitten's Joy (USA)—Wild Chant (USA)
36 **BRAMBLES**, ch f Street Cry (IRE)—Peace Camp (USA)
37 **BROOKE'S POINT**, b c Cape Cross (IRE)—Forest Pearl (USA)
38 **BY THE LAW**, b g New Approach (IRE)—Walk On Bye (IRE)
39 **CARRINGTON (FR)**, b g New Approach (IRE)—Winning Family (IRE)
40 **CATCHPHRASE (IRE)**, gr f Dubawi (IRE)—Miss Jean Brodie (USA)
41 **CHESS MASTER (IRE)**, br c Shamardal (USA)—Cassandra Go (IRE)
42 **CITY CHIC (USA)**, b br f Street Cry (IRE)—Divine Dixie (USA)
43 **CLOCK WATCHER**, b c Shamardal (USA)—Hypnology (USA)
44 **CUBOMANIA (IRE)**, ro gr c Halling (USA)—Surrealism
45 **CULTURATI**, b c Dubawi (IRE)—Whazzis
46 **DANCE ROCK**, b c Oasis Dream—Zee Zee Top
47 **DINSDALE**, b c Cape Cross (IRE)—Emmy Award (IRE)
48 **DISOBEDIENCE (USA)**, b g Street Cry (IRE)—Rosa Parks (USA)
49 **DUFAY (IRE)**, b f Dubawi (IRE)—White Moonstone (USA)
50 **EMOTIONLESS (IRE)**, b c Shamardal (USA)—Unbridled Elaine (USA)
51 **EPIC EMIRATES**, b f Dubawi (IRE)—Nabati (USA)
52 **FIRNAS**, b c Dubawi (IRE)—Crystal Music (USA)
53 **FIRST VOYAGE (IRE)**, ch c Dubawi (IRE)—Concordia
54 **FOLKSWOOD**, b c Exceed And Excel (AUS)—Magic Nymph (IRE)
55 **FRONTIERSMAN**, br c Dubawi (IRE)—Ouija Board
56 **G K CHESTERTON (IRE)**, ch c Poet's Voice—Neptune's Bride (USA)
57 **HORNSBY**, b c Dubawi (IRE)—Moonlife (IRE)
58 **HOWILAT (USA)**, b f Cape Cross (IRE)—Vine Street (IRE)
59 **ISTIQLAAL**, b c Oasis Dream—Independence
60 **LITERATOR**, b c Oasis Dream—Titivation
61 **LOVELL**, b c Dubawi (IRE)—Cosmodrome (USA)
62 **LUSORY**, b c Shamardal (USA)—Playful Act (IRE)
63 **MA PETITE (USA)**, b br f Distorted Humor (USA)—Caressive (USA)
64 **MALAGASI**, b c Street Cry (IRE)—Meeznah (USA)
65 **MANDRELL (USA)**, b f Dubawi (IRE)—Country Star (USA)
66 **MAXIMIAN (IRE)**, ch c Shamardal (USA)—Via Milano (FR)
67 **MENDACITY (IRE)**, gr ro f Invincible Spirit (IRE)—Half Truth (IRE)
68 **MISE EN ROSE (IRE)**, b br f War Front (USA)—Buy The Barrel (USA)
69 **MONDIAL (IRE)**, b f Shamardal (USA)—Mannington (AUS)
70 **MORSIAN**, ch f Dubawi (IRE)—Misheer
71 **MOTCOMB STREET (USA)**, b c Street Cry (IRE)—Zaeema
72 **MUSEO**, ch f Teofilo (IRE)—Historian (IRE)
73 **NEW DISCOVERY**, b c New Approach (IRE)—Copperbeech (IRE)
74 **PARLIAMENTARIAN (IRE)**, b g Dubawi (IRE)—Forum Floozie (NZ)
75 **PENTHESILEA (USA)**, b br f Bernardini (USA)—Folklore (USA)
76 **PERGAMINO**, b g Dubawi (IRE)—Pryka (ARG)
77 **PICTOGRAPH (USA)**, b c Lonhro (AUS)—Puppet Queen (USA)
78 **PSYCHOLOGY**, b c Shamardal (USA)—Emotion Parade (ARG)
79 **ROARING FORTIES (IRE)**, b g Invincible Spirit (IRE)—Growling (IRE)
80 **ROUNDSMAN**, b c Pivotal—Forgotten Dreams (IRE)
81 **SKIFFLE**, b f Dubawi (IRE)—Princesse Dansante (IRE)

MR CHARLIE APPLEBY - Continued

82 **SONG OF SHADOWS**, b g Invincible Spirit (IRE)—Lyrique (IRE)
83 **SPENNITHORNE (IRE)**, b f Shamardal (USA)—Two Marks (USA)
84 **TAUTOLOGY**, b c Dubawi (IRE)—Portmanteau
85 **THIEL**, br f Teofilo (IRE)—Vista Bella
86 **TRENCHES (USA)**, b c War Front (USA)—Sangrita (USA)
87 **VENTUROUS (IRE)**, ch c Raven's Pass (USA)—Bold Desire
88 **WHITE WITCH (USA)**, b f Invincible Spirit (IRE)—Ishitaki (ARG)

TWO-YEAR-OLDS

89 B f 6/2 Shamardal (USA)—Affectionate (Distorted Humor (USA))
90 B f 1/4 Shamardal (USA)—Akrivi (IRE) (Tobougg (IRE)) (260000)
91 B br c 25/2 Candy Ride (ARG)—Androeah (USA) (Arch (USA)) (231990)
92 Ch c 27/4 Teofilo (IRE)—Artisia (IRE) (Peintre Celebre (USA))
93 B c 28/2 Shamardal (USA)—Assabiyya (IRE) (Cape Cross (IRE)) (550000)
94 Ch c 12/4 More Than Ready (USA)—Baffled (USA) (Distorted Humor (USA)) (457875)
95 B f 12/5 Bernardini (USA)—Bedazzle (USA) (Dixieland Band (USA))
96 B c 28/2 Lope de Vega (IRE)—Bristol Bay (IRE) (Montjeu (IRE)) (400000)
97 Ch f 31/1 Dubawi (IRE)—Calando (USA) (Storm Cat (USA))
98 Ch c 5/3 Shamardal (USA)—Celestial Girl (Dubai Destination (USA)) (450000)
99 B f 8/3 Frankel (USA)—Colour (AUS) (More Than Ready (USA))
100 B c 13/1 Redoute's Choice (AUS)—Copernica (IRE) (Galileo (IRE)) (332225)
101 B c 20/2 Invincible Spirit (IRE)—Dark Promise (Shamardal (USA)) (575000)
102 B f 1/2 Dubawi (IRE)—Discourse (USA) (Street Cry (IRE))
103 Ch c 18/4 Discreet Cat (USA)—Emirates Girl (USA) (Unbridled's Song (USA))
104 Ch c 6/5 Sepoy (AUS)—Fading Light (King's Best (USA))
105 B f 10/2 Street Cry (IRE)—Floristry (Fasliyev (USA))
106 B f 9/2 Oasis Dream—Hypnology (USA) (Gone West (USA)) (130000)
107 B br c 10/3 Lonhro (AUS)—Janetstickettocats (USA) (Storm Cat (USA)) (109890)
108 B c 16/3 Dubawi (IRE)—La Pelegrina (USA) (Redoute's Choice (AUS))
109 B f 30/3 Dubawi (IRE)—Lady of Everest (IRE) (Montjeu (IRE)) (420000)
110 B c 12/2 Shamardal (USA)—Lavande Violet (GER) (Hurricane Run (IRE)) (531561)
111 B c 8/3 Dubawi (IRE)—Love Charm (Singspiel (IRE))
112 Ch f 18/3 Shamardal (USA)—M'oubliez Pas (USA) (El Corredor (USA))
113 B c 7/4 Kitten's Joy (USA)—Maid Service (USA) (Arch (USA)) (228937)
114 B f 1/3 Street Cry (IRE)—Mialuna (Zafonic (USA))
115 B c 11/4 Dubawi (IRE)—Moyesii (USA) (Diesis)
116 B c 11/2 Lonhro (AUS)—Pure Illusion (Danehill (USA))
117 B c 4/5 Cape Cross (IRE)—Queen Consort (USA) (Kingmambo (USA))
118 B f 13/3 Dark Angel (IRE)—Rumline (Royal Applause) (81210)
119 B f 1/2 Shamardal (USA)—Scarlet Belle (Sir Percy) (250000)
120 B br c 6/4 Dubawi (IRE)—Silkwood (Singspiel (IRE))
121 **SWORD EXCEED (GER)**, b c 28/4 Exceed And Excel (AUS)—Sword Roche (GER) (Laroche (GER)) (59062)
122 B f 22/3 Invincible Spirit (IRE)—Tajriba (IRE) (Teofilo (IRE))
123 Ch f 9/2 Dubawi (IRE)—Whazzis (Desert Prince (IRE))
124 B c 8/3 Shamardal (USA)—White Moonstone (USA) (Dynaformer (USA))
125 Ch f 11/2 Dubawi (IRE)—Wild Wind (GER) (Danehill Dancer (IRE)) (580000)

Jockey (flat): William Buick.

---

6 **MR MICHAEL APPLEBY, Newark**
Postal: **Stubby Nook Lodge Bungalow, Danethorpe Lane, Danethorpe, Newark, Nottinghamshire, NG24 2PD**
Contacts: **MOBILE (07884) 366421**
E-MAIL appleby477@aol.com WEBSITE www.mickapplebyracing.com

1 **ALYS ROCK (IRE)**, 7, gr m Medaaly—Rock Slide (IRE) **M. Appleby**
2 **ANSAAB**, 8, b g Cape Cross (IRE)—Dawn Raid (IRE) **Mr C. Buckingham**
3 **APACHE STORM**, 4, ch f Pivotal—Best Side (IRE) **Ferrybank Properties Limited**
4 **APOLLO ELEVEN (IRE)**, 7, b g Manduro (GER)—Arlesienne (IRE) **Mr F. McAleavy**
5 **ARSENALE (GER)**, 5, b m Nicaron (GER)—Alte Rose (GER) **Mr C. Bacon**
6 **ART SCHOLAR (IRE)**, 9, b g Pyrus (USA)—Marigold (FR) **Mick Appleby Racing**
7 **ASTRA HALL**, 7, ch m Halling (USA)—Star Precision **From The Front Racing**
8 **BANCNUANAHEIREANN (IRE)**, 9, b g Chevalier (IRE)—Alamanta (IRE) **Mr W. J. Sewell**

MR MICHAEL APPLEBY - Continued

9 **BE ROYALE**, 6, b m Byron—Sofia Royale **Mr Wayne Brackstone, Mr Steve Whitear**
10 **BEYEH (IRE)**, 8, b m King's Best (USA)—Cradle Rock (IRE) **T. R. Pryke**
11 **BOGNOR (USA)**, 5, b g Hard Spun (USA)—Ms Blue Blood (USA) **Richard and Nicola Hunt**
12 **BOUNTY TIME**, 4, b g Bahamian Bounty—Pressed For Time (IRE) **Mr P. A. Cafferty**
13 **BRASSBOUND (USA)**, 8, b g Redoute's Choice (AUS)—In A Bound (AUS) **Ferrybank Properties Limited**
14 **BRIGADOON**, 9, b g Compton Place—Briggsmaid **Castle Racing**
15 **BUNKER HILL LASS**, 4, ch f Kheleyf (USA)—Incony **Mr C. A. Blyth**
16 **CABLE STREET**, 4, gr c Street Cry (IRE)—Cable (USA) **Mr T. Al Nisf**
17 **CALL OUT LOUD**, 4, b c Aqlaam—Winner's Call **Kings Head Duffield Racing Partnership**
18 **CAPELITA**, 5, b m Cape Cross (IRE)—Zamhrear **Richard and Nicola Hunt**
19 **CELESTIAL DANCER (FR)**, 4, b br f Dr Fong (USA)—Rabeera **Kinder & Golding**
20 **CHEROKEE PRINCESS (IRE)**, 6, ch m Iffraaj—Radiancy (IRE) **Ferrybank Properties Limited**
21 **CLOUDED GOLD**, 4, ch g Resplendent Glory (IRE)—Segretezza (IRE) **Mrs B. A. Matthews**
22 **COMANCHE CHIEFTAIN (CAN)**, 4, b g Broken Vow (USA)—
                        Platinum Preferred (CAN) **Ferrybank Properties Limited**
23 **CORDITE (IRE)**, 5, ch g Footstepsinthesand—Marion Haste (IRE) **Shaw, Greaves, Day, Appleby**
24 **DANZENO**, 5, b g Denounce—Danzanora **Mr A. M. Wragg**
25 **DEMORA**, 7, b m Deportivo—Danzanora **Mr A. M. Wragg**
26 **DENALA**, 5, ch m Denounce—Fuwala **Mr A. M. Wragg**
27 **DEWALA**, 7, b m Deportivo—Fuwala **Mr A. M. Wragg**
28 **ESCALATING**, 4, ch c Three Valleys (USA)—Pure Joy **The Horse Watchers**
29 **EURYSTHEUS (IRE)**, 7, b g Acclamation—Dust Flicker **Midest Partnership**
30 **FALCON'S REIGN (FR)**, 7, ch g Haafhd—Al Badeya (IRE) **Mr W. J. Sewell**
31 **FANTASY GLADIATOR**, 10, b g Ishiguru (USA)—Fancier Bit **The Fantasy Fellowship**
32 **FATHER PROBUS**, 10, ch g Fleetwood (IRE)—Nearly At Sea **Mr A. R. Coney**
33 **FAVORITE GIRL (GER)**, 8, b m Shirocco (GER)—Favorite (GER) **T. R. Pryke**
34 **GOLDEN HIGHWAY (USA)**, 4, ch g Elusive Quality (USA)—Awesome Chic (USA) **Mr T. Al Nisf**
35 **GUISHAN**, 6, b m Ishiguru (USA)—Fareham **B. D. Cantle**
36 **HALL OF BEAUTY**, 4, ch f Halling (USA)—Victorian Era **Mrs L. Huntley**
37 **HELL HATH NO FURY**, 7, b m Oratorio (IRE)—Sagamartha **Mr C. Bacon**
38 **HESKA (IRE)**, 5, b g Rock of Gibraltar (IRE)—Sweet Sioux **Appleby & Woodward**
39 **IT MUST BE FAITH**, 6, b g Mount Nelson—Purple Rain (IRE) **M. Appleby**
40 **JEFFERSON CITY (IRE)**, 5, b g Montjeu (IRE)—Reina Blanca **Mr C. Bacon**
41 **JOHN COFFEY (IRE)**, 7, b g Acclamation—Appleblossom Pearl **Mick Appleby Racing**
42 **KATIE GALE**, 5, b f Shirocco (GER)—Karla June **Ferrybank Properties Limited**
43 **KELLY'S FINEST (IRE)**, 4, ch f Intense Focus—Priory Rock (IRE) **Richard and Nicola Hunt**
44 **KOPTOON**, 4, b g Rip Van Winkle (IRE)—Mania (IRE) **Richard and Nicola Hunt**
45 **LAUGHING ROCK (IRE)**, 6, b m Rock of Gibraltar (IRE)—The Last Laugh **Mick Appleby Racing**
46 **LLYN**, 4, ch f Dutch Art—Makara **Mr A. Gray**
47 **LOUMARIN (IRE)**, 4, b f Bushranger (IRE)—Masela (IRE) **Looksarnteverything Partnership**
48 **LULU THE ZULU (IRE)**, 8, ch m Danroad (AUS)—Timbervati (USA) **The Ab Kettlebys**
49 **LUV U LUCKY**, 4, b g Multiplex—Lady Suesanne (IRE) **Richard and Nicola Hunt**
50 **LUV U WHATEVER**, 6, b g Needwood Blade—Lady Suesanne (IRE) **Richard and Nicola Hunt**
51 **MAGGIE PINK**, 7, b m Beat All (USA)—Top Notch **Mr A. W. Bult**
52 **MARMOOZ**, 4, ch f Piccolo—Aegean Mystery **Tykes & Terriers Racing Club**
53 **MAWAQEET (USA)**, 7, b g Dynaformer (USA)—Lady Ilsley (USA) **Mr F. McAleavy**
54 **MOON RIVER (IRE)**, 4, b f Exceed And Excel (AUS)—Dame Blanche (IRE) **Mr C. Buckingham**
55 **MOONADEE (IRE)**, 4, gr g Haafef (USA)—Again Royale (IRE) **The Golden Horse Racing Club**
56 **MOPS ANGEL**, 5, b m Piccolo—Tanning **Sarnian Racing**
57 **MR RED CLUBS (IRE)**, 7, b g Red Clubs (IRE)—Queen Cobra (IRE) **Ferrybank Properties Limited**
58 **MS EBORACUM (IRE)**, 4, b f Vale of York (IRE)—Ms Victoria (IRE) **Mr D. A. Creighton**
59 **NAVAJO CHANT**, 4, b f Cape Cross (IRE)—Bezant (IRE) **Ferrybank Properties Limited**
60 **NOTOURSORTDEAR**, 4, b f Monsieur Bond (IRE)—Jasmine Breeze **T. R. Pryke**
61 **PEACE LILLY (USA)**, 4, b br f Distorted Humor (USA)—Julia Tuttle (USA) **Richard and Nicola Hunt**
62 **PEARL NATION (USA)**, 7, b g Speightstown (USA)—
                        Happy Nation (USA) **Iddon, M & C Dixon, Taylor, Finn, O'Brien**
63 **PERCYS PRINCESS**, 5, b m Sir Percy—Enford Princess **Mr C. A. Blyth**
64 **PERLE EXPRESS**, 4, b f Rail Link—Perle d'or (IRE) **The Perle d'Or Partnership**
65 **PERSONAL TOUCH**, 7, ch g Pivotal—Validate **Mr M. C. Elvin**
66 **PHILBA**, 4, b g Cockney Rebel (IRE)—Hisaronu (IRE) **Mr T. Johnson**
67 **POWERFULSTORM**, 4, b f Bertolini (USA)—Frisson **Houghton Bloodstock**
68 **POYLE VINNIE**, 6, b g Piccolo—Poyle Dee Dee **Mr C. Bacon**
69 **QUEEN OF SKIES (IRE)**, 7, b m Shamardal (USA)—Attractive Crown (USA) **Ferrybank Properties Limited**
70 **RED UNICO (IRE)**, 4, b g Vale of York (IRE)—Testa Unica (ITY) **Racing Daily**
71 **RESILIENCY (IRE)**, 5, ch g Mastercraftsman (IRE)—Euroceleb (IRE) **Mr F. McAleavy**

MR MICHAEL APPLEBY - Continued

72 **RESPONSE**, 6, ch g New Approach (IRE)—Spotlight **Racing Daily 1**
73 **ROYAL PECULIAR**, 8, b g Galileo (IRE)—Distinctive Look (IRE) **T. R. Pryke**
74 **ROYAL SIGNALLER**, 5, b g Dylan Thomas (IRE)—Whirly Bird **Mr Archibald Hargie & Mr Brian Hargie**
75 **RURAL AFFAIR**, 5, b m Pastoral Pursuits—Torcross **T. R. Pearson**
76 **SECRET LIGHTNING (FR)**, 4, ch f Sakhee's Secret—Dimelight **Richard and Nicola Hunt**
77 **SELLINGALLTHETIME (IRE)**, 5, ch g Tamayuz—Anthyllis (GER) **Mr R. Oliver**
78 **SHAW TING**, 4, b f Winker Watson—Shawhill **T. R. Pryke**
79 **SHIPYARD (USA)**, 7, ch g Pivotal—Nadia **Mr C. Buckingham**
80 **SLEET (IRE)**, 5, b g Amadeus Wolf—Secret Justice (USA) **The Golden Horse Racing Club**
81 **STREET FORCE (USA)**, 5, b h Street Cry (IRE)—Maskunah (IRE) **Mr T. Al Nisf**
82 **SUPERSTA**, 5, ch g Pivotal—Resort **Rod In Pickle Partnership**
83 **TANGERINE TREES**, 11, b g Mind Games—Easy To Imagine (USA) **Tangerine Trees Partnership**
84 **TARTAN TRIP**, 9, b g Selkirk (USA)—Marajuana **The Golden Horse Racing Club**
85 **TAYSH (USA)**, 4, b br g Bernstein (USA)—Normandy's Nell (USA) **Mr C. Buckingham**
86 **TEAJAYBE (USA)**, 8, b br g Street Cry (IRE)—Wild Heaven **Mick Appleby Racing**
87 **THE LOCK MASTER (IRE)**, 9, b g Key of Luck (USA)—Pitrizza (IRE) **Kenneth George Kitchen**
88 **THERMAL COLUMN (IRE)**, 4, b g Vale of York (IRE)—Swiss Roll (IRE) **Mr M. C. Elvin**
89 **TOBOUGGAN RUN**, 4, b g Tobougg (IRE)—Justbetweenfriends (USA) **The Rain Dancers**
90 **TWO JABS**, 6, b g Teofilo (IRE)—Red Bravo (USA) **The Horse Watchers**
91 **VENUS GRACE**, 5, b m Royal Applause—Basque Beauty **Richard and Nicola Hunt**
92 **VIEWPOINT (IRE)**, 7, b g Exceed And Excel (AUS)—Lady's View (USA) **M. Appleby**
93 **VILLA ROYALE**, 7, b m Val Royal (FR)—Villa Carlotta **David Kuss & Tim Pakyurek**
94 **WALK LIKE A GIANT**, 5, b g Sir Percy—Temple of Thebes (IRE) **Mr C. Bacon**
95 **WEALD OF KENT (USA)**, 4, b g Successful Appeal (USA)—Apple of Kent (USA) **Mr T. Al Nisf**
96 **WIN LOSE DRAW (IRE)**, 4, b g Dark Angel (IRE)—Caherassdotcom **MIDEST 1**
97 **ZIGGYS STAR**, 4, b g Compton Place—Ziggy Zaggy **Mr T. Al Nisf**

THREE-YEAR-OLDS

98 **BADALONA BREEZE (IRE)**, br f Big Bad Bob (IRE)—Rose Mandarin (IRE) **The Horse Watchers & Dan Creighton**
99 B f Royal Applause—Carollan (IRE) **Houghton Bloodstock**
100 **DREAM SERENADE**, b f Dream Eater (IRE)—Lady Santana (IRE) **Tykes & Terriers Racing Club**
101 **GIANT BRADLEY**, ch c Monsieur Bond (IRE)—Cut Back
102 **KINGFISHER GIRL**, gr f Hellvelyn—Caribbean Star **Dorans & Sutton**
103 **MACKIRI (IRE)**, b c Makfi—Inchiri **Mr C. Buckingham**
104 **MOLLIE'S GIRL (IRE)**, b f Elusive Pimpernel (USA)—Ebony Star **Mr L A Hill & Mr C L Bacon**
105 **NAVAJO STORM (IRE)**, gr f Dark Angel (IRE)—Strike Lightly **Ferrybank Properties Limited**
106 **PICCACARD**, b f Piccolo—All Business **From The Front Racing**
107 **PURSUIT OF TIME**, br f Pastoral Pursuits—Pressed For Time (IRE) **Mr P. A. Cafferty**
108 **RAINBOW LAD (IRE)**, b g Lilbourne Lad (IRE)—Carmona **Mr C. Buckingham**
109 **ROCETTE**, ch f Prime Defender—Makindi **PD Legacy Partnership**
110 **SAKHEE STAR**, ch c Sakhee's Secret—Forrest Star **New Kids On The Trot**
111 **SEA OF UNCERTAINTY**, b g Kyllachy—Moving Sea (IRE) **Mr C. Buckingham**
112 **SECRET CLAUSE**, b c Sakhee's Secret—Claws **Almond, Burns**
113 **STAR OF KHELEYF**, b g Kheleyf (USA)—Semplicita (IRE) **Mr C. Bacon**
114 **STARS N ANGELS (IRE)**, gr f Dark Angel (IRE)—Passage To India (IRE) **Mr C. Bacon**
115 **TAN ARABIQ**, b c Arabian Gleam—Tanning **Sarnian Racing**
116 **YOUNG TOM**, b g Sir Percy—Enford Princess **Formulated Polymer Products Ltd**

TWO-YEAR-OLDS

117 **OUR GRETA (IRE)**, gr f 8/3 Exchange Rate (USA)—
Academicienne (CAN) (Royal Academy (USA)) (66666) **Mr A. Gray**

Other Owners: Mr S. Almond, Mrs P. Barrell, Mr N. Berrisford, A. M. Blewitt, Mr W. M. Brackstone, Mr K. Bradley, M. Bryson, Mr G. Burns, Mr A. Clarke, Mr V. H. Coleman, P. Coll, Mrs N. M. Cooper, Mr A. J. T. D'Arcy, Mr M. Dixon, Mr C. Dixon, Mr P. Dorans, Mr D. Finn, Mr M. N. Franklin, A. R. Franklin, Mr S. Franks, Mr D. R. Gardner, Mr A. N. Gargan, Mr M. Golding, Mr D. Greaves, Mr M. B. Gromett, Mr A. Grummitt, Mr A. C. Hargie, Mr B. Hargie, Mr M. Harris, Mr L. A. Hill, Mr N. C. Hoare, Mr R. Hoiles, Mr R. A. Hunt, Mrs N. Hunt, Mr C. Iddon, Mrs V. Kinder, Mr P. Kirton, Mr D. Kuss, Mr A. W. Le Page, Mr C. Le Page, Mr S. J. Lee, Mr M. Matthews, Mr I. McAleavy, Mr S. Nightingale, Mr R. O'Brien, Mr J. O'Shaughnessy, Mr L. T. Pakyurek, Mr D. Parkinson, Mr W. D. Pick, R. W. Sharp, Mr P. J. Shaw, Mr J. Sumsion, Mr S. Sutton, Mr B. Tait, Mr M. J. Taylor, Mr J. R. Theaker, Mr B. Totty, Mr S. Wain, Mr M. O. Ward, Mr R. Wherritt, Mr M. White, Mr S. J. Whitear, Mr D. Woodward.

MR MICHAEL APPLEBY - Continued

Head Lad: Niall Nevin

Jockey (flat): Liam Jones, Luke Morris, Andrew Mullen. **Jockey (NH):** Richard Johnson, Charlie Poste.

Conditional: Jonathan England. **Apprentice:** Jane Elliott, Alistair Rawlinson, Ryan Tate.

Amateur: Miss Serena Brotherton.

---

7 | ### MR DAVID ARBUTHNOT, Beare Green
Postal: **Henfold House Cottage, Henfold Lane, Beare Green, Dorking, Surrey, RH5 4RW**
Contacts: **PHONE (01306) 631529 FAX (01306) 631529 MOBILE (07836) 276464**
E-MAIL **dwparbuthnot@hotmail.com** WEBSITE **www.henfoldracing.co.uk**

1 AMBIVALENT ABOUT, 5, b m Josr Algarhoud (IRE)—Peppermint Plod **The Kykie Allsopp Partnership**
2 DANGLYDONTASK, 5, b g Lucky Story (USA)—Strat's Quest **P. Banfield**
3 DARING DEPLOY (IRE), 10, b g Deploy—Daring Perk (IRE) **The Daring Partnership**
4 DOASUWOULDBEDONEBY (IRE), 5, b g Robin des Champs (FR)—Sarah Princess (IRE) **A. T. A. Wates**
5 FOLLOWMYBUTTONS (IRE), 6, br g Kalanisi (IRE)—Clondalee (IRE) **Mr A T A Wates & Mrs S Wates**
6 GANDALFE (FR), 11, b br g Laveron—Goldville (FR) **A. T. A. Wates**
7 MAX MILAN (IRE), 7, b g Milan—Sunset Leader (IRE) **Mr P. M. Claydon**
8 SNOWBALL (IRE), 9, gr g Alderbrook—Rosafi (IRE) **The Daring Partnership**
9 STARLUCK (IRE), 11, gr g Key of Luck (USA)—Sarifa (IRE) **A. T. A. Wates**
10 STROLLAWAYNOW (IRE), 9, b g Oscar (IRE)—Rose of Salome (IRE) **A. T. A. Wates**
11 TINGO IN THE TALE (IRE), 7, b g Oratorio (IRE)—Sunlit Skies **G. S. Thompson**
12 TOPOLSKI (IRE), 10, b g Peintre Celebre (USA)—Witching Hour (IRE) **Mr P. M. Claydon**
13 URCALIN (FR), 8, b g Network (GER)—Caline So (FR) **Mr A T A Wates & Mrs S Wates**
14 WELLUPTOSCRATCH (FR), 5, b br g Irish Wells (FR)—Aulne River (FR) **Mr A T A Wates & Mrs S Wates**

Other Owners: Mr W. P. Harriman, Mrs J. E. B. Leigh-Pemberton, Mrs S. M. Wates, Mr K. Wiggert.

Jockey (NH): Tom Cannon, Daryl Jacob.

---

8 | ### MR PETER ATKINSON, Northallerton
Postal: **Yafforth Hill Farm, Yafforth, Northallerton, North Yorkshire, DL7 0LT**
Contacts: **PHONE (01609) 772598 MOBILE (07751) 131215**

1 IRISH ROE (IRE), 5, b m Vinnie Roe (IRE)—Betty's The Best (IRE) **Mr P. G. Atkinson**
2 REVERANT CUST (IRE), 5, gr g Daylami (IRE)—Flame Supreme (IRE) **Mr P. G. Atkinson**

---

9 | ### MR MICHAEL ATTWATER, Epsom
Postal: **Tattenham Corner Stables, Tattenham Corner Road, Epsom Downs, Surrey, KT18 5PP**
Contacts: **PHONE (01737) 360066 MOBILE (07725) 423633**
E-MAIL **Attwaterracing@hotmail.co.uk** WEBSITE **www.attwaterracing.com**

1 ASK THE GURU, 6, b g Ishiguru (USA)—Tharwa (IRE) **Canisbay Bloodstock**
2 BRAVO ECHO, 10, b g Oasis Dream—Bold Empress (USA) **Canisbay Bloodstock**
3 BRONZE PRINCE, 9, b g Oasis Dream—Sweet Pea **Canisbay Bloodstock**
4 CANCELLARA, 4, b c Kheleyf (USA)—Royal Ivy **Canisbay Bloodstock**
5 EL TREN (IRE), 5, b g Danehill Dancer (IRE)—Dhamma (USA) **The Attwater Partnership**
6 EMBANKMENT, 7, b g Zamindar (USA)—Esplanade **Canisbay Bloodstock**
7 FIRESTORM (GER), 5, b g Dylan Thomas (IRE)—Fitness (IRE) **The Attwater Partnership**
8 FLEETWOOD BELLA, 5, ch m Byron—Royal Ivy **Canisbay Bloodstock**
9 FLEETWOOD POPPY, 4, br f Kheleyf (USA)—Steppin Out **Canisbay Bloodstock**
10 KNIGHT MUSIC, 4, b g Sir Percy—Lyric Art (USA) **The Attwater Partnership**
11 LET'S CONFER, 7, ch m Doyen (IRE)—Vrennan **Canisbay Bloodstock**
12 LION'S MAID, 7, b m Iceman—Steppin Out **Canisbay Bloodstock**
13 LORD OF THE STORM, 8, b g Avonbridge—Just Run (IRE) **Mrs M. Teversham**
14 MAJOR FRANKO, 4, ch g Major Cadeaux—Royal Future (IRE) **The Attwater Partnership & Sussex Racing**
15 NOBLE DEED, 6, ch g Kyllachy—Noble One **Canisbay Bloodstock**
16 ORKNEY ISLAND, 5, gr g Dubawi (IRE)—Ronaldsay **The Attwater Partnership**
17 OST WIND, 4, b g Oasis Dream—Maroussies Wings (IRE) **Mr C. Main**
18 PALACE MOON, 11, b g Fantastic Light (USA)—Palace Street (USA) **Canisbay Bloodstock**

MR MICHAEL ATTWATER - Continued

19 PLOVER, 6, b m Oasis Dream—Short Dance (USA) **Canisbay Bloodstock**
20 POLAR KITE (IRE), 8, b g Marju (IRE)—Irina (IRE) **Mr A. C. D. Main**
21 PROFESSOR, 6, ch h Byron—Jubilee **Canisbay Bloodstock**
22 PURFORD GREEN, 7, ch m Kyllachy—Mo Stopher **Canisbay Bloodstock**
23 SALIENT, 12, b g Fasliyev (USA)—Savannah Belle **Canisbay Bloodstock**
24 SQUIRE, 5, b g Teofilo (IRE)—Most Charming (FR) **The Attwater Partnership**
25 SUNSHINE ALWAYS (IRE), 10, b gr g Verglas (IRE)—Easy Sunshine (IRE) **Miss M. E. Stopher**
26 SYMPHONY OF KINGS, 5, b g Lucarno (IRE)—Flying Lion **Mr C. Main**

THREE-YEAR-OLDS

27 B g Rail Link—Anastasia Venture **Canisbay Bloodstock**
28 BUZZ LIGHTYERE, b c Royal Applause—Lady Gloria **The Attwater Partnership**
29 OAK FOREST, b g Mullionmileanhour (IRE)—Lady Royal Oak (IRE) **A. C. Maylam**
30 B c Authorized (IRE)—Steppin Out **Canisbay Bloodstock**

Other Owners: Mr M. J. Attwater, Mr B. M. Attwater, Mr Scott Brown, Mr James Michael Duggan, Mr R. F. Kilby, Mr W. P. L. Smith, Miss Maureen Stopher, Mr Antony Waters.

Assistant Trainer: S. Sawyer

---

10 MR ALAN BAILEY, Newmarket
Postal: **Cavendish Stables, Hamilton Road, Newmarket, Suffolk, CB8 7JQ**
Contacts: **PHONE (01638) 664546 FAX (01638) 664546 MOBILE (07808) 734223**
WEBSITE www.alanbaileyracing.co.uk

1 BADDILINI, 6, b g Bertolini (USA)—Baddi Heights (FR) **Mrs M. Shone**
2 FRANGARRY (IRE), 4, b g Lawman (FR)—Divert (IRE) **Dr S. P. Hargreaves**
3 GLENBUCK LASS (IRE), 4, gr f Dandy Man (IRE)—Certainlei (IRE) **North Cheshire Trading & Storage Ltd**
4 GO FAR, 6, b g Dutch Art—Carranita (IRE) **Mr R. J. H. West**
5 HIGH RAIL, 4, b g High Chaparral (IRE)—Cool Catena (USA) **Dr S. P. Hargreaves**
6 HONEY REQUIRED, 4, b f Makfi—Tiger Mist (IRE) **Mrs A Shone & Mr P Baker**
7 MASTERPAVER, 5, gr g Mastercraftsman (IRE)—Most-Saucy **Mrs A. M. Riney**
8 MIMI LUKE (USA), 5, b m U S Ranger (USA)—Hard As Nails (USA) **Dr S. P. Hargreaves**
9 MRS EVE (IRE), 4, ch f Bahamian Bounty—Catbells (IRE) **Mr C. M. & Mrs S. A. Martin**
10 SCHOTTISCHE, 6, ch m Pastoral Pursuits—Calligraphy **AB Racing Limited**
11 VIMY RIDGE, 4, ch g American Post—Fairy Shoes **Mr J. F. Stocker**
12 WAROFINDEPENDENCE (USA), 4, b br g War Front (USA)—My Dear Annie (USA) **Mr J. F. Stocker**

THREE-YEAR-OLDS

13 BAZZAT (IRE), ch g Roderic O'Connor (IRE)—Compradore **Mr J. F. Stocker**
14 CAPPY BROWN, b g Showcasing—Corndavon (USA) **Dr S. P. Hargreaves**
15 ESSPEEGEE, b g Paco Boy—Goldrenched (IRE) **The Skills People Group Ltd**
16 STRICTLY ART (IRE), b g Excellent Art—Sadinga (IRE) **A J McNamee & L C McNamee**
17 STRICTLY CARTER, b g Multiplex—Compolina **A J McNamee & L C McNamee**

Other Owners: Mr P. Baker, C. M. Martin, Mrs S. A. Martin, A. J. McNamee, Mr L. McNamee.

Assistant Trainer: J. Parr

Apprentice: Tim Clark.

---

11 MRS CAROLINE BAILEY, Holdenby
Postal: **37 Eastfield Road, Brixworth, Northamptonshire, NN6 9ED**
Contacts: PHONE **(01604) 883729 (Home) (01604) 770234 (Yard) FAX (01604) 770423**
MOBILE **(07831) 373340**
E-MAIL caroline.bailey4@btinternet.com WEBSITE www.carolinebaileyracing.co.uk

1 BALLYVAUGHN (IRE), 6, b br g Robin des Pres (FR)—Countessdee (IRE) **C. W. Booth**
2 BEING GLOBAL (FR), 5, b g Epalo (GER)—Haida IV (FR) **Mrs S. Carsberg**
3 BIG GENERATOR, 10, ch g Generous (IRE)—Frizzball (IRE) **G. T. H. Bailey**
4 CARLO ROCKS (IRE), 6, b g Carlo Bank (IRE)—Rock Garden (IRE) **Mrs S. Tucker**
5 CROSSPARK, 6, b g Midnight Legend—Blue Shannon (IRE) **C. W. Booth**
6 DEALING RIVER, 9, b g Avonbridge—Greensand **Mr S. A. Richards**

MRS CAROLINE BAILEY - Continued

7 **DENALI HIGHWAY (IRE),** 9, ch g Governor Brown (USA)—Amaretto Flame (IRE) **Ian Payne & Kim Franklin**
8 **DIG DEEPER,** 7, b g Overbury (IRE)—Tickle The Tiller (IRE) **C. C. Shand Kydd**
9 **EARLY RETIREMENT (IRE),** 4, b g Daylami (IRE)—Deep Lilly **Mr J. M. B. Strowbridge**
10 **EDWARD ELGAR,** 5, ch g Avonbridge—Scooby Dooby Do **Mrs J. M. Dixon Smith**
11 **GALWAY JACK (IRE),** 11, b g Witness Box (USA)—Cooldalus (IRE) **Mrs M. E. Moody**
12 **GLOBAL BONUS (IRE),** 7, b g Heron Island (IRE)—That's The Bonus (IRE) **Mrs S. Carsberg**
13 **GLOBAL DOMINATION,** 8, b g Alflora (IRE)—Lucia Forte **G. T. H. Bailey**
14 **GLOBAL DREAM,** 6, ch g Lucarno (USA)—Global Girl **Mrs S. Carsberg**
15 **GOLD INGOT,** 9, ch g Best of The Bests (IRE)—Realms of Gold (USA) **Mr J Cowan & Mr B Jessop**
16 **HIGH RON,** 11, b g Rainbow High—Sunny Heights **Mrs G. A. Burke**
17 **MISS MACARNO,** 5, b m Lucarno—Shady Minx **G. T. H. Bailey**
18 **NOBLE LEGEND,** 9, b g Midnight Legend—Elmside Katie **Mr P. Dixon Smith**
19 **PRINCE DES MARAIS (FR),** 13, b br g Network (GER)—Djeba Royale (FR) **C. W. Booth**
20 **RYDE BY KNIGHT,** 8, b g Grape Tree Road—Knight Ryde **Mrs N. S. Tregaskes**
21 **SIR BENTLEY,** 6, b g Flemensfirth (USA)—Silk Rope (IRE) **Mr & Mrs R. Scott**
22 **SMARTMAX (FR),** 7, ch g Until Sundown—Quendora (FR) **C. Flinton**
23 **THE FRUGAL STAR,** 8, ch g Fraam—Star of Heaven **Mr & Mrs L. E. Bird**

Other Owners: Mr L. E. Bird, Mrs M. Bird, Mr James E. Cowan, Miss K. M. Franklin, Mr B. P. Jessup, Mr I. T. Payne, R. Scott, Mrs P. M. Scott.

Jockey (NH): Tom Messenger, Adam Pogson, Andrew Thornton. **Amateur:** Mr Jonathan Bailey.

---

12 MR KIM BAILEY, Cheltenham
Postal: **Thorndale Farm, Withington Road, Andoversford, Cheltenham, Gloucestershire, GL54 4LL**
Contacts: **PHONE (01242) 890241 FAX (01242) 890193 MOBILE (07831) 416859**
E-MAIL info@kimbaileyracing.com WEBSITE www.kimbaileyracing.com

1 **ABBREVIATE (GER),** 5, b g Authorized (IRE)—Azalee (GER) **Mr & Mrs K. R. Ellis**
2 4, B g Flemensfirth (USA)—Accordian Rules (IRE) **Mr K. C. Bailey**
3 **ALIANDY (IRE),** 5, b g Presenting—Water Rock **A & S Enterprises Ltd**
4 **ALLEZ ENCORE (IRE),** 7, b m Turtle Island (IRE)—Glebe Beauty (IRE) **GSTTKPA Charity Partnership**
5 **ASCOTDEUX NELLERIE (FR),** 6, ch g Network (GER)—Jumper Nellerie (FR) **The Lucky Nelleries**
6 4, B g Shantou (USA)—Bally Bolshoi (IRE) **Mr & Mrs Paul & Clare Rooney**
7 **BALLYKNOCK LAD (IRE),** 7, b g Bach (IRE)—Ballyknock Lass (IRE) **Mrs Julie Martin & David R. Martin**
8 **BANDON ROC,** 5, b g Shirocco (GER)—Azur (IRE) **The WOW Partnership**
9 **BATTLE DUST (IRE),** 7, b g Portrait Gallery—Katie O'toole (IRE) **Mr & Mrs Mark Laws**
10 **BOOLAVARD KING (IRE),** 7, b g Winged Love (IRE)—Eastender **Kim Bailey Racing Partnership II**
11 **BOY IN A BENTLEY (IRE),** 6, b g Kayf Tara—All Our Blessings (IRE) **The Cool Silk Partnership**
12 **BRAW ANGUS,** 6, b g Alflora (IRE)—Suilven **I. F. W. Buchan**
13 **BY THE BOARDWALK (IRE),** 8, br g Presenting—Peripheral Vision (IRE) **J. F. Perriss**
14 **CASCAYE (FR),** 4, b br f Merlino Mago—Castyana (IRE) **Mr M. J. D. Lambert**
15 **CHARBEL (IRE),** 5, b g Iffraaj—Eoz (IRE) **Mrs Julie Martin & David R. Martin**
16 **CRACKED REAR VIEW (IRE),** 6, b g Portrait Gallery—Trip To Knock **Mr & Mrs Paul & Clare Rooney**
17 **CRAZY JACK (IRE),** 8, b g Royal Anthem (USA)—
Cindy's Fancy (IRE) **May We Never Be Found Out Partnership 2**
18 **CRESWELL LEGEND (IRE),** 5, b g Midnight Legend—Cresswell Willow (IRE) **Mrs Julie Martin & David R. Martin**
19 **DARNA,** 10, b g Alflora (IRE)—Dutch Dyane **Mrs Julie Martin & David R. Martin**
20 **DERRINTOGHER BLISS (IRE),** 7, b g Arcadio (GER)—His Fair Lady (IRE) **The Irrational Group**
21 **DIDNTITELLYA (IRE),** 7, b g Presenting—Beauty Star (IRE) **Timewilltell**
22 **DUELING BANJOS,** 6, b gr g Proclamation (IRE)—Kayf Lady **J. F. Perriss**
23 **EMILY GRAY (IRE),** 8, b m Flemensfirth (USA)—Rose Island **J. F. Perriss**
24 **FAERIE REEL (FR),** 6, b m Country Reel (USA)—Final Whistle (FR) **Mrs E. A. Kellar**
25 **FIFTY BOB (IRE),** 5, b g Witness Box (USA)—Slogan (IRE)
26 **FIZZY DANCER,** 6, ch m Norse Dancer (IRE)—Mrs Fizziwig **A & R Racing Club Partnership**
27 **FLEMENSMIX (IRE),** 8, gr g Flemensfirth (USA)—Perfect Mix (FR) **The Perfect Mix Racing Club**
28 **FORGOTTEN HERO (IRE),** 7, b g High Chaparral (IRE)—Sundown **Mrs Julie Martin & David R. Martin**
29 **GAELIC MYTH,** 6, b g Midnight Legend—Shannon Native (IRE) **A. N. Solomons**
30 **GALLERY EXHIBITION (IRE),** 9, b g Portrait Gallery (IRE)—Good Hearted (IRE) **The GFH Partnership**
31 **GOLD MAN (IRE),** 7, ch g Presenting—Mama Jaffa (IRE) **Mr K. C. Bailey**
32 **GRAND MARCH,** 7, b g Beat All (USA)—Bora Bora **Mme J. B. Baldanza**
33 **HARRY TOPPER,** 9, b g Sir Harry Lewis (USA)—Indeed To Goodness (IRE) **A. N. Solomons**
34 **JIMMY THE JETPLANE (IRE),** 8, b g Jimble (FR)—C'est Cool (IRE) **The Cool Silk Partnership**
35 **KALANISI GLEN (IRE),** 6, br g Kalanisi (IRE)—Glen Ten (IRE) **Mr & Mrs Paul & Clare Rooney**

MR KIM BAILEY - Continued

36 **KILTY CAUL (IRE)**, 7, b m Beneficial—Gale Johnston (IRE) **The Boom Syndicate**
37 **KING SIMBA (IRE)**, 5, b g Let The Lion Roar—Anaaween (USA) **GSTTKPA Charity Partnership**
38 **KNOCKANRAWLEY (IRE)**, 8, gr g Portrait Gallery (IRE)—Hot Lips (IRE) **Kim Bailey Racing Partnership VIII**
39 **LADY OF LLANARMON**, 5, b m Yeats (IRE)—One Gulp **R J McAlpine & Mrs David Johnson**
40 **LAVAL NOIR (FR)**, 5, b g Laveron—Vale of Honor (FR) **The Mindy Partnership**
41 **MAGIC MONEY**, 8, b m Midnight Legend—Sticky Money **M. D. C. Jenks**
42 **MILORD (GER)**, 7, br g Monsun (GER)—Montserrat (GER) **Kim Bailey Racing Partnership VII**
43 **MOLLY'S A DIVA**, 9, ch m Midnight Legend—Smokey Diva (IRE) **J. F. Perriss**
44 **MONKHOUSE (IRE)**, 6, b g Scorpion (IRE)—Gold Shot **Mrs V. W. H. Johnson**
45 **MOR BROOK**, 8, b g Kayf Tara—Miss Quickly (IRE) **Mor Fun Partnership**
46 **MY COUSIN RACHEL (IRE)**, 5, br m Presenting—Countess Camilla **Huw & Richard Davies**
47 **NAM HAI (IRE)**, 5, b g Fastnet Rock (AUS)—Bowstring (IRE) **This Horse Is For Sale Partnership**
48 **NET WORK ROUGE (FR)**, 7, b g Network (GER)—
                                   Lychee de La Roque (FR) **John Wills & David Reid Scott Ptnership**
49 **OUR BELLE AMIE**, 4, b f Black Sam Bellamy (IRE)—Very Special One (IRE) **Chasing Hopefuls**
50 **PATSYS CASTLE (IRE)**, 9, ch g Windsor Castle—Annienoora (IRE) **Mr P. P. Moorby**
51 **POLICY BREACH (IRE)**, 5, b g Kayf Tara—Just Stunning (IRE) **D. A. Hall**
52 **PULLING POWER**, 6, br m Erhaab (USA)—Pulling Strings (USA) **Turf Club 2014 & The Real Partnership**
53 **QUEER TIMES (IRE)**, 7, b g Zagreb (USA)—Lucy Walters (IRE) **Mrs P. A. Perriss**
54 **RED SPINNER (IRE)**, 6, b g Redback—Massalia (IRE) **Mr & Mrs Paul & Clare Rooney**
55 **RHIANNA**, 5, b m Robin des Champs (FR)—La Harde (FR) **Mr N. Carter**
56 **ROYAL SUPREMO (IRE)**, 5, b g Beneficial—Slaney Athlete (IRE) **The Cool Silk Partnership**
57 **SAINTE LADYLIME (IRE)**, 5, b m Saint des Saints (FR)—Lady Pauline (FR) **Mr & Mrs Paul & Clare Rooney**
58 **SAME OLE TRIX (IRE)**, 5, gr g King's Theatre (IRE)—Reklame's Gorl (GER) **The Young Pretenders**
59 **SILVER EAGLE (IRE)**, 8, gr g Presenting—Lady Lincon (IRE) **Kim Bailey Racing Partnership IV**
60 **SILVER KAYF**, 4, gr g Kayf Tara—Silver Spinner **The Lucky Spinners**
61 **SONNEOFPRESENTING (IRE)**, 6, b br g Presenting—Sonne Cinq (IRE) **Mr & Mrs Paul & Clare Rooney**
62 **SUCH A LEGEND**, 8, ch g Midnight Legend—Mrs Fizziwig **The Real Partnership**
63 **SUNBLAZER (IRE)**, 6, gr g Dark Angel (IRE)—Damask Rose (IRE) **Mr N. Carter**
64 **TARA'S RAINBOW**, 6, b m Kayf Tara—Nile Cristale (IRE) **Kim Bailey Racing Partnership**
65 **TEXAS FOREVER (IRE)**, 7, b g Heron Island (IRE)—Gravinis (FR) **Mrs IC Sellars & Major & Mrs P Arkwright**
66 **THE LAST SAMURI (IRE)**, 8, ch g Flemensfirth (USA)—Howaboutthis (IRE) **Mr & Mrs Paul & Clare Rooney**
67 **THE SCARLETT WOMAN**, 7, b m Kayf Tara—Double Red (IRE) **Mrs P. A. Perriss**
68 **THEDRINKYMEISTER (IRE)**, 7, b g Heron Island—Keel Row **J. F. Perriss**
69 **TROJAN STAR (IRE)**, 6, b g Tikkanen (USA)—Mystical Queen (IRE) **Mr M. J. D. Lambert**
70 **TWELVE ROSES**, 8, ch g Midnight Legend—Miniature Rose **Jones Broughtons Wilson Weaver**
71 **UN ACE (FR)**, 8, b g Voix du Nord (FR)—First Ball (USA) **Ace In The Pack Partnership**
72 **VIADUCT JACK (IRE)**, 7, b g King's Theatre (IRE)—Back Market Lass (IRE) **Viajack Partnership**
73 **WIDOW ON THE RUN (IRE)**, 5, b m Milan—O Mio My (IRE) **Mrs P. A. Perriss**
74 **YOUNEVERCALL (IRE)**, 5, b g Yeats (IRE)—Afarka (IRE) **Youneverknow Partnership**

Other Owners: Major P. W. F. Arkwright, Mrs Sandra G. E. Arkwright, Mr P. J. Bailey, Mrs C. Bailey, Mr O. S. W. Bell, Mr A. N. C. Bengough, Sir M. F. Broughton, Mr S. W. Broughton, Mr S. R. Cannon, Mr D. M. Clancy, Mr K. T. Clancy, Mr R. Connolly, Mr R. L. Davies, H. G. Davies, Mr P. F. Dibben, Mrs S. F. Dibben, Mrs E. Ellis, K. R. Ellis, Mr G. C. Farr, Mrs L. H. Field, Lady M. P. Hatch, Mrs N. Jones, Mr P. S. Kerr, D. J. Keyte, Mr H. Kimbell, Mrs J. M. Laws, Mr J. Laws, Mrs J. M. T. Martin, D. R. Martin, Mr C. W. Mather, R. J. McAlpine, Mr P. R. Monger, Mr D. A. C. Reid Scott, Mr P. A. Rooney, Mrs C. Rooney, Mrs N. P. Sellars, Mr J. A. Stanley, Dr J. M. Steer-Fowler, Mrs S. J. Steer-Fowler, Mr C. G. Straghalis, P. Swann, Mr G. D. W. Swire, Mrs C. A. T. Swire, Turf Club 2014, Mrs N. Van Dijk, Mrs R. B. Weaver, Mrs B. E. Wilkinson, Mr D. R. Williams, Mr J. H. Wills, T. C. Wilson, Mr S. J. Winter.

Assistant Trainer: Mathew Nicholls

Jockey (NH): David Bass, Jason Maguire. **Amateur:** Mr J. Morris.

---

13   **MISS EMMA BAKER, Cheltenham**
Postal: **Brockhill, Naunton, Cheltenham, Gloucestershire, GL54 3BA**
Contacts: **FAX (01451) 850199 MOBILE (07887) 845970**
E-MAIL **emmajbakerracing@hotmail.co.uk** WEBSITE **www.emmabakerracing.com**

1 **ARQUEBUSIER (FR)**, 6, bl g Discover d'auteuil (FR)—Djurjura (FR) **Miss E. J. Baker**
2 **BACK BY MIDNIGHT**, 7, ch g Midnight Legend—Roberta Back (IRE) **Select Racing Club & Mrs M. J. Arnold**
3 **BOURDELLO**, 7, b m Milan—Haudello (FR) **Mrs J. Arnold**
4 **BRINESTINE (USA)**, 5, b g Bernstein (USA)—Miss Zafonic (FR) **Brians Buddies**
5 **CHURCH HALL (IRE)**, 8, b g Craigsteel—Island Religion (IRE) **Mrs J. Arnold**
6 **GLANCE BACK**, 5, b g Passing Glance—Roberta Back (IRE) **Mrs J. Arnold**

MISS EMMA BAKER - Continued

7 **GREY MESSENGER (IRE)**, 7, gr g Heron Island (IRE)—Turlututu (FR) **Miss E. J. Baker**
8 **MIDNIGHT CHARMER**, 10, b g Midnight Legend—Dickies Girl **Mrs J. Arnold**
9 **SNOWELL (IRE)**, 9, b g Well Chosen—Snow Water (IRE) **Miss E. J. Baker**
10 **SUBTLE APPROACH (IRE)**, 11, b g Subtle Power (IRE)—Rotoruasprings (IRE) **Mrs J. Arnold**

Other Owners: Mr M. J. Arnold, Mrs M. J. Arnold, Miss E. J. Baker, Mr Jock Cullen, www.Select-Racing-Club.co.uk.

---

14 MR GEORGE BAKER, Manton

Postal: **Barton Yard, Manton House Estate, Marlborough, Wiltshire, SN8 4HB**
Contacts: **PHONE OFFICE: (01672) 515493 (01672) 516234 FAX (01672) 514938**
MOBILE (07889) 514881
E-MAIL gbakerracing@gmail.com WEBSITE www.georgebakerracing.com

1 **ALCATRAZ (IRE)**, 4, b g Camacho—Spring Opera (IRE) **Riverdee I**
2 **ANCIENT GREECE**, 9, b g Pivotal—Classicism **George Baker & Partners**
3 **AQUA ARDENS (GER)**, 8, b g Nayef (USA)—Arduinna (GER) **Mrs C. E. S. Baker**
4 **BARWICK**, 8, b g Beat Hollow—Tenpence **Michael H. Watt**
5 **BEAUSANT**, 4, ch g Orientor—Hanella (IRE) **Mr G. Baker & Mr Tom Earl**
6 **BELGIAN BILL**, 8, b h Exceed And Excel (AUS)—Gay Romance **PJL, Byrne & Baker**
7 **BOOMSHACKERLACKER (IRE)**, 6, gr g Dark Angel (IRE)—Allegrina (IRE) **PJL Racing**
8 **BOUNTYBEAMADAM**, 6, b m Bahamian Bounty—Madamoiselle Jones **Whitsbury Hopefuls**
9 **COMMODORE (IRE)**, 4, b g Kodiac—Deportment **Highclere Thoroughbred Racing - Trinity**
10 **DESTINY'S GOLD (IRE)**, 6, b g Millenary—Knockhouse Rose (IRE) **Delancey & Mrs V. Finegold**
11 **DESTINY'S SHADOW (IRE)**, 4, gr g Dark Angel (IRE)—
　　　　　　　　　　　　Lunar Love (IRE) **Delancey Real Estate Asset Management Limited**
12 **ETON RAMBLER (USA)**, 6, b br g Hard Spun (USA)—Brightbraveandgood (USA) **The Eton Ramblers**
13 **FIFTYSHADESFREED (IRE)**, 5, gr g Verglas (IRE)—Vasilia **Team Fifty**
14 **FIFTYSHADESOFGREY (IRE)**, 5, gr g Dark Angel (IRE)—Wohaida (IRE) **Team Fifty**
15 **FLUTTERBEE**, 4, b f Equiano (FR)—Dunya **PJL Racing**
16 **FORCED FAMILY FUN**, 6, b g Refuse To Bend (IRE)—Juniper Girl (IRE) **George Baker & Partners**
17 **FOUR NATIONS (USA)**, 8, ch g Langfuhr (CAN)—Kiswahili **The Transatlantic USA Syndicate**
18 **GEORGE BAKER (IRE)**, 9, b g Camacho—Petite Maxine **George Baker & Partners**
19 **GONE VIRAL (IRE)**, 5, ch g Virtual—Dorinda Gray (IRE) **Ivy Up A Wall Partnership**
20 **GUARD OF HONOUR (IRE)**, 5, b g Galileo (IRE)—Queen of France (USA) **Mrs L. M. Sherwood**
21 **HARRY HURRICANE**, 4, b g Kodiac—Eolith **PJL Racing**
22 **HEISMAN (IRE)**, 5, b g Teofilo (IRE)—Luminata (IRE) **Mr G. Baker**
23 **HERECOMESTHEBAND**, 4, b g Bertolini (USA)—Green Supreme **Herecomestheband Partnership**
24 **HOPONANDSEE**, 5, b m Nomadic Way (USA)—Jago's Girl **Kate & Clive Giles**
25 **HUMIDOR (IRE)**, 9, b g Camacho—Miss Indigo **Delancey Real Estate Asset Management Limited**
26 **I'M FRAAM GOVAN**, 8, ch g Fraam—Urban Dancer (IRE) **Sir A. Ferguson**
27 **I'M HARRY**, 7, b g Haafhd—First Approval **Wickfield Stud & Hartshill Stud**
28 **INTIBAAH**, 6, b g Elnadim (USA)—Mawaared **Delancey Real Estate Asset Management Limited**
29 **ISHIAMBER**, 6, ch m Ishiguru (USA)—Black And Amber **Mrs P. A. Scott-Dunn**
30 **JACK'S REVENGE (IRE)**, 8, br g Footstepsinthesand—Spirit of Age (USA) **PJL Racing**
31 **JOEY'S DESTINY (IRE)**, 6, ch g Kheleyf (USA)—
　　　　　　　　　　　　Maid of Ailsa (USA) **Delancey Real Estate Asset Management Limited**
32 **LADY BEE (IRE)**, 4, b f Lawman (FR)—Rainbow Lyrics (IRE) **The Countess of Bathurst**
33 **MENDACIOUS HARPY (IRE)**, 5, b m Dark Angel (IRE)—Idesia (IRE) **Mr R. Curry**
34 **MR ROCK**, 5, b g Galileo (IRE)—Kitza (IRE) **Sir A. Ferguson**
35 **MRS WARREN**, 6, b m Kyllachy—Bold Bunny **On The Game Partnership**
36 **MUIR LODGE**, 5, ch g Exceed And Excel (AUS)—Miss Chaussini (IRE) **Turf Club 2014**
37 **NOVA CHAMP (IRE)**, 5, ch g Intikhab (USA)—Baby Bunting **PJL Racing**
38 **PILGRIMS REST (IRE)**, 7, ch g Rock of Gibraltar (IRE)—Holly Blue **Pittam, Mather & Baker**
39 **PRESELI STAR (IRE)**, 6, b g Scorpion (IRE)—Horner Hill (IRE) **The Ramblers Racing Syndicate**
40 **RED FOUR**, 6, ch m Singspiel (IRE)—Protectorate **Lady Cobham**
41 **SECULAR SOCIETY**, 6, b g Royal Applause—Fantastic Santanyi **Mrs S. C. Head**
42 **SINBAD THE SAILOR**, 11, b g Cape Cross (IRE)—Sinead (USA) **Baker, Coleman, Wand & Williams**

THREE-YEAR-OLDS

43 **AFRICAN SHOWGIRL**, ch f Showcasing—Georgie The Fourth (IRE) **PJL Racing 1**
44 **BOUTAN**, b f Tobougg (IRE)—High Tan **Seaton Partnership**
45 **FUNNY OYSTER (IRE)**, gr f Dark Angel (IRE)—Carpet Lover (IRE) **Skinner, Baker & Partners**
46 **MAGNIFICENT MADIBA**, b g Mount Nelson—Mrs Penny (AUS) **PJL Racing 1**

MR GEORGE BAKER - Continued

47 **MAMILLIUS**, b c Exceed And Excel (AUS)—Laika Lane (USA) **The Mamillius Partnership**
48 **MANTON GRANGE**, b c Siyouni (FR)—Emulate **Goltz, Finegold & McGeever**
49 **MAVROS**, br g Authorized (IRE)—Barley Bree (IRE) **PJL Racing**
50 **NAG'S WAG (IRE)**, b f Approve (IRE)—Street Kitty (IRE) **Mr G. Baker**
51 **PAPOU TONY**, b g Raven's Pass (USA)—Lukrecia (IRE) **PJL, Clark & Moore**
52 **RED TROOPER (FR)**, ch g Shamardal (USA)—Solar Midnight (USA) **PJL Racing 1**
53 **TG BOY**, ch g Monsieur Bond (IRE)—Formidable Girl (USA) **Mr M. D. McGeever**

TWO-YEAR-OLDS

54 B c 28/4 Kodiac—Altishaan (Darshaan) (32500) **Paul Bowden**
55 B f 8/4 Exceed And Excel (AUS)—Blinking (Marju (IRE)) (80000) **Mr & Mrs Bailye & Partners**
56 **DANCING DRAGON (IRE)**, b f 10/4 Dragon Pulse (IRE)—
                    Abbeyleix Lady (IRE) (Montjeu (IRE)) (10335) **Robinson Strategic Planning Ltd**
57 Gr f 15/2 Dark Angel (IRE)—First Lady (IRE) (Indian Ridge) (66666) **Earl Of Brecknock & Partners**
58 Ch c 28/4 Excelebration (IRE)—Gay Romance (Singspiel (IRE)) (45000) **George Baker**
59 B f 10/3 Dark Angel (IRE)—
                    Jasmine Flower (Kyllachy) (95000) **Delancey Real Estate Asset Management Limited**
60 B f 22/4 Quality Road—Kinda Wonderful (USA) (Silver Train (USA) (73260) **George Baker**
61 B c 9/3 Miesque's Son (USA)—Lisselan Firefly (IRE) (Monashee Mountain (USA)) (33960) **Allez France**
62 B c 30/4 Kyllachy—Ragazza Mio (IRE) (Generous (IRE)) (62000) **George Baker**
63 B f 7/5 Lope de Vega (IRE)—Shemissa (IRE) (Fairy King (USA)) (50000) **Chriselliam Partnership**
64 B c 25/1 Elusive Quality (USA)—Sovereign Crisis (USA) (Congrats (USA)) (53113) **George Baker**
65 **TAP TAP BOOM**, br c 5/4 Foxwedge (AUS)—
                    Exclusive Approval (USA) (With Approval (CAN)) (20952) **Steve & Jolene De'Lemos**
66 B f 16/4 Aqlaam—Velma Kelly (Vettori (IRE)) (11812) **Allez France**
67 **WIND IN THE TREES (FR)**, b f 29/4 Sunday Break (JPN)—Swift Winged (Motivator) (19195) **Allez France**

Other Owners: Miss E. Asprey, Mr M. Atherton, Mr Steve Avery, Mrs C. E. S. Baker, Mr George Baker, Mrs V. P. Baker, Mr P. Bowden, Mrs Karlene Boyce, Mr Norton Brookes, Mrs Lindsey Bull, Mr Alex Bull, Mr Justin Byrne, Mr Ken Carter, Mr Sean Clancy, Mr Nick Clark, Mr A. Coleman, Mr Peter M. Crane, Mr J. Dale, Mrs Jolene de'Lemos, Mr A. de'Lemos, Mr Steve De'Lemos-Pratt, Mr P. Deal, Delancey, Miss L. Egerton, Colonel Richard Evans, Mrs Virginia Finegold, Mr A. Flintoff, Mr Clive Giles, Mr Mark Grier, The Hon H. Herbert, Highclere Thoroughbred Racing Ltd, Miss L. Hurley, Mrs E. L. James, Mr David Jenks, Mrs Jonathan Leigh, Sir I. Magee, Mr Craig Mather, Mr Bobby McAlpine, Mr Mike McGeever, Mr R. Moore, Mrs Milly Phillips, Mr J. Pittam, Mrs Peter Robinson, Mr Peter Russell, Mr Peter W. Skinner, Earl Spencer, Mrs A. V. J. Spencer, Mrs Fiona Stonehouse, Mr Robert Turner, Mr Toby Wand, Mrs P. H. Williams.

Assistant Trainer: Patrick Murphy, Valerie Murphy

Jockey (flat): Pat Cosgrave. **Jockey (NH):** Andrew Tinkler. **Apprentice:** Alfie Davies, Chris Meehan.

---

15   MR ANDREW BALDING, Kingsclere
Postal: Park House Stables, Kingsclere, Newbury, Berkshire, RG20 5PZ
Contacts: **PHONE** (01635) 298210 **FAX** (01635) 298305 **MOBILE** (07774) 633791
E-MAIL admin@kingsclere.com **WEBSITE** www.kingsclere.com

1 **ABSOLUTELY SO (IRE)**, 6, b g Acclamation—Week End **The George Smith Family Partnership**
2 **ARABIAN ILLUSION (FR)**, 4, ch g Makfi—Arabian Spell (IRE) **Mrs F. H. Hay**
3 **BALLYNANTY (IRE)**, 4, gr c Yeats (IRE)—Reina Blanca **Mr R. J. C. Wilmot-Smith**
4 **BERKSHIRE BEAUTY**, 4, b f Aqlaam—Salim Toto **Berkshire Parts & Panels Ltd**
5 **BLOND ME (IRE)**, 4, ch f Tamayuz—Holda (IRE) **Mrs B. M. Keller**
6 **BRANDON CASTLE**, 4, b g Dylan Thomas (IRE)—Chelsey Jayne (IRE) **R P B Michaelson & Dr E Harris**
7 **BREAKHEART (IRE)**, 9, b g Sakhee (USA)—Exorcet (FR) **I. A. Balding**
8 **CAPE SPIRIT (IRE)**, 4, b f Cape Cross (IRE)—Fearless Spirit (USA) **I. A. Balding**
9 **COMMUNICATOR**, 8, b g Motivator—Goodie Twosues **Lady S. Davis**
10 **COOL STRUTTER (IRE)**, 4, b g Kodiac—Cassava (IRE) **Mr A. Gemmell**
11 **COUNTERMAND**, 4, b g Authorized (IRE)—Answered Prayer **Ms K Gough Mr R Wilmot-Smith Mr K Ghaly**
12 **DANCE OF FIRE**, 4, b g Norse Dancer (IRE)—Strictly Dancing (IRE) **J. C. Smith**
13 **DOCTOR BONG**, 4, b g Sleeping Indian—Vax Rapide **The Pink Star Racing Partnership**
14 **DUNGANNON**, 9, b g Monsieur Bond (IRE)—May Light **Dr E. Harris**
15 **DURETTO**, 4, ch g Manduro (GER)—Landinium (ITY) **Lord J. Blyth**
16 **ELBERETH**, 5, b m Mount Nelson—Masandra (IRE) **D. Taylor**
17 **ELM PARK**, 4, b c Phoenix Reach (IRE)—Lady Brora **Qatar Racing Limited**
18 **GUIDING LIGHT (IRE)**, 4, b g Acclamation—Venus Rising **Thurloe Thoroughbreds XXXIV**
19 **HAINES**, 5, ch g Shirocco (GER)—Spring Dream (IRE) **Bow River Racing**

MR ANDREW BALDING - Continued

20 **HALA MADRID**, 4, ch f Nayef (USA)—Ermine (IRE) **N. M. Watts**
21 **HAVISHAM**, 4, b g Mount Nelson—Ile Deserte **D. E. Brownlow**
22 **HEARTLESS**, 4, ch f New Approach (IRE)—Honorine (IRE) **Qatar Racing Limited**
23 **HERE COMES WHEN (IRE)**, 6, b g Danehill Dancer (IRE)—Quad's Melody (IRE) **Mrs F. H. Hay**
24 **HIGH ADMIRAL**, 4, b g New Approach (IRE)—Wosaita **D. E. Brownlow**
25 **HIGHLAND COLORI (IRE)**, 8, b g Le Vie Dei Colori—Emma's Star (ITY) **Mr E.M. Sutherland**
26 **HIT LIST (IRE)**, 4, ch g Makfi—Kassiopeia (IRE) **Another Bottle Racing 2**
27 **INTRANSIGENT**, 7, b g Trans Island—Mara River **Kingsclere Racing Club**
28 **MAN LOOK**, 4, b g Nayef (USA)—Charlecote (IRE) **C. C. Buckley**
29 **MAN OF HARLECH**, 5, b g Dansili—Ffestiniog (IRE) **Elite Racing Club**
30 **MELVIN THE GRATE (IRE)**, 6, b g Danehill Dancer (IRE)—Hawala (IRE) **Fromthestables.com & I. A. Balding**
31 **MERRY ME (IRE)**, 5, b m Invincible Spirit (IRE)—Thought Is Free **Mrs F. H. Hay**
32 **MONTALY**, 5, b g Yeats (IRE)—Le Badie (IRE) **Farleigh Racing**
33 **MYMATECHRIS (IRE)**, 5, br g High Chaparral (IRE)—Splendeur (FR) **D. E. Brownlow**
34 **NABATEAN (IRE)**, 5, b g Rock of Gibraltar (IRE)—Landinium (ITY) **Lord J. Blyth**
35 **OPERA LAD (IRE)**, 4, b g Teofilo (IRE)—Opera Glass **J. C. Smith**
36 **PASSOVER**, 5, b g Passing Glance—Floriana **Kingsclere Racing Club**
37 **PEARL SPECTRE (USA)**, 5, ch g Street Cry (IRE)—Dark Sky (USA) **Pearl Bloodstock Limited**
38 **ROCKY RIDER**, 4, b c Galileo (IRE)—Blue Symphony **Qatar Racing Limited**
39 **ROSE ABOVE**, 4, b f Yeats (IRE)—Sabah **Sir Roger Buckley, Mr Gerald Oury**
40 **ROYAL NORMANDY**, 4, b g Royal Applause—Border Minstral (IRE) **M. Payton**
41 **SCARLET MINSTREL**, 4, b g Sir Percy—Sweet Mandolin **J. C., J. R & S. R. Hitchins**
42 **SCOTLAND (GER)**, 5, b g Monsun (GER)—Sqillo (IRE) **Mrs F. H. Hay**
43 **SCOTTISH (IRE)**, 4, b g Teofilo (IRE)—Zeiting (IRE) **Mrs F. H. Hay**
44 **SECRET HINT**, 5, b m Oasis Dream—Teeky **Mr John Drew & Mr D. H. Caslon**
45 **SMILING STRANGER (IRE)**, 5, br g Nayef (USA)—Carraigoona (IRE) **N. M. Watts**
46 **TULLIUS (IRE)**, 8, ch g Le Vie Dei Colori—Whipped Queen (USA) **Kennet Valley Thoroughbreds VI**
47 **VICTORIA POLLARD**, 4, b f Sir Percy—Victoria Montoya **Kingsclere Racing Club**

THREE-YEAR-OLDS

48 **ABLE JACK**, b g Iffraaj—Solva **Happy Valley Racing & Breeding Limited**
49 **ALHAJJAJ**, gr c Cacique (IRE)—Strawberry Morn (CAN) **Mr S. Rashid**
50 **ATALANTE**, b f Cape Cross (IRE)—Sabria (USA) **W. R. J. Swinburn**
51 **BERNIE'S BOY**, b c Lilbourne Lad (IRE)—Stoney Cove (IRE) **Mr B. P. McGuire**
52 **BINGO GEORGE (IRE)**, b g Holy Roman Emperor (IRE)—Kalleidoscope **The George Smith Family Partnership**
53 **BLUFF CRAG**, b g Canford Cliffs (IRE)—Camp Riverside (USA) **James/Michaelson/Greenwood 1**
54 **BOTH SIDES**, b g Lawman (FR)—Pearl Dance (USA) **G. Strawbridge**
55 **BRIEF VISIT**, b f Fastnet Rock (AUS)—Brevity (USA) **Cliveden Stud Ltd**
56 **BROROCCO**, b g Shirocco (GER)—Lady Brora **Kingsclere Racing Club**
57 **CALLIOPE**, b f Poet's Voice—Costa Brava (IRE) **Thurloe Thoroughbreds XXXVI**
58 **CHARMY**, b f Yeats (IRE)—Saturday Girl **Mr R. J. C. Wilmot-Smith**
59 **DANCING STAR**, b f Aqlaam—Strictly Dancing **J. C. Smith**
60 **DARK SHOT**, b c Acclamation—Dark Missile **J. C. Smith**
61 **DEEP DREAM**, b f Dream Ahead (USA)—Jessica's Dream (IRE) **Qatar Racing Limited**
62 **DREAM OF SUMMER (IRE)**, b c Canford Cliffs (IRE)—
                                             Danehill's Dream (IRE) **Happy Valley Racing & Breeding Limited**
63 **EMPEROR NAPOLEON**, b c Champs Elysees—Amarullah (FR) **The Napoleon Partnership**
64 **EXCELLENT ALIBI**, ch c Exceed And Excel (AUS)—Indian Love Bird **Mr S. Rashid**
65 **FACTION**, b g Champs Elysees—Belladera (IRE) **Qatar Racing Limited & Mr A M Balding**
66 **FLEETING GLIMPSE**, b f Passing Glance—Perfect Act **Mildmay Racing & Mr D. H. Caslon**
67 **FORT JEFFERSON**, br g Passing Glance—Florida Heart **Kingsclere Racing Club**
68 **FRENCH LEGEND**, b f Pour Moi (IRE)—Fast Flow (IRE) **J. C. Smith**
69 **GONE GIRL**, b f Arcano (IRE)—Siren's Gift **J. C. Smith**
70 **GREAT AND SMALL**, b f Galileo (IRE)—Gryada **N. M. H. Jones**
71 **HAIRDRYER**, b c Motivator—Londonnetdotcom (IRE) **Sir A Ferguson, P Done, G Mason**
72 **IAN FLEMING**, b g Makfi—High Cross (IRE) **Chelsea Thoroughbreds - Cagnes Sur Mer**
73 **IBERICA ROAD (USA)**, b br g Quality Road (USA)—Field of Clover (CAN) **The Mucho Men Racing Partnership**
74 **ISAAK (FR)**, b g Dalghar (FR)—Ela's Giant **Mr N Botica, Mr Rex & Mrs Wendy Gorell**
75 **KINGSTON KURRAJONG**, b c Authorized (IRE)—Kingston Acacia **Mr R. C. Hains**
76 **LADY BLANCO (USA)**, b br f Cape Blanco (IRE)—War Clan (USA) **Mrs F. H. Hay**
77 **LADY PERIGNON**, b f Poet's Voice—Amalina **Mrs F. H. Hay**
78 **LE TISSIER**, ch g Sir Percy—Incarnation (IRE) **Mrs L. E. Ramsden & Mr R. Morecombe**
79 **LOADED (IRE)**, b g Kodiac—Fikrah **Mr & Mrs R. M. Gorell**
80 **LORD ASLAN (IRE)**, b c Thewayyouare (USA)—Lunar Lustre **D. E. Brownlow**
81 **LORD HUNTINGDON**, b g Lord of England (GER)—Marajuana **Kingsclere Racing Club**

MR ANDREW BALDING - Continued

82 **LORELINA**, b f Passing Glance—Diktalina **Mr Tim Wixted & Mr Tony Anderson**
83 **MAKE FAST**, b f Makfi—Raymi Coya (CAN) **Her Majesty The Queen**
84 **MAKE MUSIC**, b f Acclamation—Come What May **Mrs E. A. M. Balding**
85 **MOLTEN GOLD**, b c New Approach (IRE)—Flash of Gold **Her Majesty The Queen**
86 **MONTAGUE WAY (IRE)**, b g Rock of Gibraltar (IRE)—Shanghai Lily (IRE) **Martin & Valerie Slade & Partners**
87 **MOON OVER MOBAY**, b f Archipenko (USA)—Slew The Moon (ARG) **Miss K. Rausing**
88 **MR ANDROS**, b g Phoenix Reach (IRE)—Chocolada **Winterbeck Manor Stud Ltd**
89 **MYSTIC BLAZE (IRE)**, ch c Arcano (IRE)—Star Approval (IRE) **Sheikh J. D. Al Maktoum**
90 **NODACHI (IRE)**, b c Rip Van Winkle (IRE)—Jabroot (IRE) **Mrs F. H. Hay**
91 **ORMITO (GER)**, b c Mamool (IRE)—Ormita (GER) **Mr R Morecombe & Mrs L E Ramsden**
92 **PARIS BOUND**, b c Champs Elysees—Averami **Kingsclere Racing Club**
93 **PICKAPOCKET (IRE)**, b c Fast Company (IRE)—Ann's Annie (IRE) **Mrs Susan Roy & Mr N M Watts**
94 **PREDETERMINED (IRE)**, b g Lope de Vega (IRE)—Queen Bodicea (IRE) **Mrs F. H. Hay**
95 **REAL DOMINION (USA)**, b br c Cape Blanco (IRE)—Real Doll (USA) **Mick and Janice Mariscotti**
96 **REHEARSE (IRE)**, b c Big Bad Bob (IRE)—And Again (USA) **Highclere Thoroughbred Racing (Disraeli)**
97 **ROCK OPERA**, b f Fastnet Rock (AUS)—Opera Glass **J. C. Smith**
98 **SHONGOLOLO (IRE)**, b g Manduro (GER)—Nipping (IRE) **Martin & Valerie Slade & Partner**
99 **SHOWDAISY**, ch f Showcasing—Darling Daisy **Mrs P. A. Scott-Dunn**
100 **SIGHT SEA**, b f Passing Glance—Seaflower Reef (IRE) **Kingsclere Racing Club**
101 **SIGNAL HILL (IRE)**, b g Rock of Gibraltar (IRE)—Izzy Lou (IRE) **Kennet Valley Thoroughbreds VIII**
102 **SIR PASS I AM**, b g Passing Glance—Orbital Orchid **Mrs J. S. Newton**
103 **ST MARY'S**, b f Siyouni (FR)—Once Over **Kingsclere Racing Club**
104 **SUMMER CHORUS**, b f Exceed And Excel (AUS)—Soviet Terms **Sheikh J. D. Al Maktoum**
105 **SUNFLOWER**, ch f Dutch Art—Swan Wings **N. M. H. Jones**
106 **SWASHBUCKLE**, b c Dashing Blade—Inhibition **Kingsclere Racing Club**
107 **THE GRADUATE (IRE)**, gr c Mastercraftsman (IRE)—Ballyvarra (IRE) **Mick and Janice Mariscotti**
108 **THIS IS FOR YOU**, b g Paco Boy (IRE)—Waypoint **Persaud & Partners**
109 **THREE LOVES (IRE)**, b f Duke of Marmalade (IRE)—
                    Three Moons (IRE) **Happy Valley Racing & Breeding Limited**
110 **TOUCHDOWN BANWELL (USA)**, b br g Fairbanks (USA)—Friendly Thunder (USA) **Mr L. L. Register**
111 **VANISHING POINT**, b c Pivotal—Hyperspectra **Castle Down Racing**
112 **VERNE CASTLE**, gr f Sakhee's Secret—Lochangel **J. C. Smith**
113 **VISCOUNT BARFIELD**, b c Raven's Pass (USA)—Madonna Dell'orto **D. E. Brownlow**
114 **WENSARA DREAM**, b f Lilbourne Lad (IRE)—Emerald Fire **Martin & Valerie Slade**
115 **WHITE POPPY (IRE)**, b f Frozen Power (IRE)—Symbol of Peace (IRE) **Qatar Racing Limited**
116 **WYNFORD (IRE)**, ch g Dylan Thomas (IRE)—Wishing Chair (USA) **Mr I A Balding & Mr P Fox**
117 **ZOFFANYS PRIDE (IRE)**, b c Zoffany (IRE)—Lioness **Axom LXII**

TWO-YEAR-OLDS

118 **APPRECIATING**, b f 15/4 New Approach (IRE)—Star Value (IRE) (Danehill Dancer (IRE)) **Her Majesty The Queen**
119 B c 4/4 Passing Glance—Averami (Averti (IRE)) **Kingsclere Racing Club**
120 Ch c 13/2 Mastercraftsman (IRE)—Avon Lady (Avonbridge) (40000) **Mick & Janice Mariscotti**
121 **BERKSHIRE BOY (IRE)**, b c 23/4 Elzaam (AUS)—
                    Circuit City (IRE) (Exit To Nowhere (USA)) (50000) **Berkshire Parts & Panels**
122 B c 2/4 Thewayyouare (IRE)—Betrothed (IRE) (Oratorio (IRE)) (14765)
123 B c 19/4 Galileo (IRE)—Birmanie (IRE) (Aldebaran (USA)) (75000) **D. E. Brownlow**
124 Ch c 20/4 Casamento (IRE)—Call Later (USA) (Gone West (USA)) (50000) **Kennet Valley Thoroughbreds XII**
125 B c 9/3 Mount Nelson—Carsulae (IRE) (Marju (IRE)) (80000) **Sheikh J. D. Al Maktoum**
126 B c 6/2 Pour Moi (IRE)—Casual Glance (Sinndar (IRE)) **Kingsclere Racing Club**
127 Ch c 14/4 Rio de La Plata (USA)—Cosabawn (IRE) (Barathea (IRE)) (40000) **D. E. Brownlow**
128 B c 1/5 Arcano (IRE)—Dune Breeze (IRE) (Azamour (IRE)) (12550) **Mr P. Fox**
129 B c 11/2 Manduro (GER)—Garmerita (FR) (Poliglote) (28054) **DJT**
130 **GEORGIO (GER)**, br c 16/4 Approve (IRE)—Gillenia (GER) (Greinton) (13289)
131 B c 13/3 Mastercraftsman (IRE)—Gift Dancer (Imperial Dancer) (40000) **Owners Group 015**
132 B f 19/3 Footstepsinthesand—Hidden Valley (Haafhd) **Kingsclere Racing Club**
133 B c 21/4 Frankel—Honorine (IRE) (Mark of Esteem (IRE)) **Qatar Racing Limited**
134 **HORSEPLAY**, b f 26/3 Cape Cross (IRE)—Mischief Making (USA) (Lemon Drop Kid (USA)) **Cliveden Stud**
135 **HOT LICK**, b c 3/3 Phoenix Reach (IRE)—Sweet Mandolin (Soviet Star (USA)) **J. C., J. R. & S. R. Hitchins**
136 B c 2/4 Shirocco (GER)—Inhibition (Nayef (USA)) **Kingsclere Racing Club**
137 Ch c 6/2 Dutch Art—Intimacy (IRE) (Teofilo (IRE)) (66445) **Thurloe T/Breds XXXIX**
138 **INVESTIGATION**, gr c 10/2 Rip Van Winkle (IRE)—Syann (IRE) (Daylami (IRE)) (22148) **Martin & Valerie Slade**
139 Ch c 21/4 Born To Sea (IRE)—Islandagore (IRE) (Indian Ridge) (40000) **Mick and Janice Mariscotti**
140 Ch c 12/4 Bated Breath—Jakarta Jade (IRE) (Royal Abjar (USA)) (27000) **Mick and Janice Mariscotti**
141 **KINGSTON MALALEUCA**, b c 17/4 Dream Ahead (USA)—
                    Kingston Acacia (King of Roses (AUS)) **Mr Richard Hains**

MR ANDREW BALDING - Continued

142 **KINGSTON TASMANIA**, b c 16/4 Kheleyf (USA)—Derartu (AUS) (Last Tycoon) **Mr Richard Hains**
143 B br f 6/4 Passing Glance—Lady Brora (Dashing Blade) **Kingsclere Racing Club**
144 Ch c 6/3 Equiano (FR)—Le Badie (IRE) (Spectrum (IRE)) (48000) **Farleigh Racing**
145 Ch c 19/3 Lope de Vega (IRE)—Let It Be Me (USA) (Mizzen Mast (USA)) (145000) **Qatar Racing Limited**
146 Br f 2/4 Kyllachy—Life Rely (USA) (Maria's Mon (USA)) (100000) **Sheikh J. D. Al Maktoum**
147 Ch c 11/3 Raven's Pass (USA)—Magic America (USA) (High Yield (USA)) **George Strawbridge**
148 B c 17/1 Lilbourne Lad (IRE)—Make Amends (IRE) (Indian Ridge) (25000) **Sheikh J. D. Al Maktoum**
149 **MANOLITO DE MADRID (GER)**, b c 25/3 Soldier Hollow—
                         Molly Maxima (GER) (Big Shuffle (USA)) (38390) **Mr N. M. Watts**
150 B c 19/1 Sakhee's Secret—Marajuana (Robellino) (USA)) **Kingsclere Racing Club**
151 **MAX ZORIN (IRE)**, b c 8/5 Cape Cross (IRE)—My (King's Best) (USA)) (37000) **Chelsea Thoroughbreds**
152 Gr f 11/5 Makfi—Mintly Fresh (USA) (Rubiano (USA)) (59062) **Jon Haseler**
153 **MUCHO APPLAUSE (IRE)**, b c 24/4 Acclamation—Pediment (Desert Prince (IRE)) (73827) **Transatlantic Racing**
154 **MUNSTEAD STAR**, ch f 30/3 Sir Percy—Royal Patron (Royal Academy (USA)) **Sir Gordon Brunton**
155 B f 14/3 Lawman (FR)—Night Carnation (Sleeping Indian) **George Strawbridge**
156 Ch c 1/2 Cape Blanco (IRE)—Nimue (USA) (Speightstown (USA)) **Mrs F. Hay**
157 Ch g 28/2 Manduro (GER)—Oekaki (FR) (Martillo (GER)) (25101)
158 Ch c 23/1 Dubawi (IRE)—Opera Gal (IRE) (Galileo (IRE)) **J. C. Smith**
159 B f 2/4 Nathaniel (IRE)—Opera Glass (Barathea (IRE)) **J. C. Smith**
160 B f 18/5 Camacho—Passata (FR) (Polar Falcon (USA)) (50000) **Sheikh J. D. Al Maktoum**
161 B c 2/3 Shamardal (USA)—Pearl Dance (USA) (Nureyev (USA)) **George Strawbridge**
162 B c 30/4 Teofilo (IRE)—Pellinore (USA) (Giant's Causeway (USA)) (160000) **Qatar Racing Limited**
163 Ch gr g 12/4 Mastercraftsman (IRE)—Penny Cross (Efisio) (25000) **Mr P. Fox**
164 **PERFECT ANGEL (IRE)**, br f 13/3 Dark Angel (IRE)—
                         The Hermitage (IRE) (Kheleyf (USA)) (17000) **Mildmay Racing & D. H. Caslon**
165 **QUEEN MOON (IRE)**, b br f 21/4 Lawman (FR)—Movie Queen (Danehill (USA)) (5906) **Mr L. L. Register**
166 B c 3/4 Zoffany (IRE)—Red Japonica (Daylami (IRE)) (33222) **Kennet Valley Thoroughbreds II**
167 Ch c 8/3 Paco Boy (IRE)—Robema (Cadeaux Genereux) (33000) **D. E. Brownlow**
168 B c 31/1 Casamento (IRE)—Rohlindi (Red Ransom (USA)) (85000) **Qatar Racing Limited**
169 B c 26/4 Deep Impact (JPN)—Rumba Boogie (Rainbow Quest (USA)) **Qatar Racing Limited**
170 Ch f 28/1 Rip Van Winkle (IRE)—Sabah (Nashwan (USA)) **Sir Roger Buckley**
171 B br f 1/5 Street Cry (IRE)—Satulagi (Officer (USA)) **Mrs F. Hay**
172 B f 24/3 Lawman (FR)—Snow Key (USA) (Cozzene (USA)) **George Strawbridge**
173 B f 13/4 Exceed And Excel (AUS)—Speed Cop (Cadeaux Genereux) **J. C. Smith**
174 B c 29/3 Mount Nelson—Susi Wong (IRE) (Selkirk (USA)) (35000) **Mick and Janice Mariscotti**
175 B f 4/4 Shamardal (USA)—Thought Is Free (Cadeaux Genereux) **Mrs F. H. Hay**
176 B c 14/5 Born To Sea (IRE)—Three Days In May (Cadeaux Genereux) (77519) **Qatar Racing Limited**
177 B f 10/2 Poet's Voice—Vanity (IRE) (Thatching) (200000) **Mrs M. E. Wates**
178 B c 2/5 Rip Van Winkle (IRE)—Wedding Cake (IRE) (Groom Dancer (USA)) (19195) **Mr P. Fox**
179 **WINE LIST**, ch c 28/4 Champs Elysees—Masandra (IRE) (Desert Prince (IRE)) (50000) **Another Bottle Register**

Other Owners: Mr Tony Anderson, Axom, Mr I. A. Balding, Mrs I. A. Balding, Mr A. M. Balding, Mr Paul Blaydon, Mr N. Botica, Mr Peter Box, Mr John Bridgman, Sir Roger Buckley, Mr D. H. Caslon, Chelsea Thoroughbreds Ltd, Mr Carl Conroy, Mr N. A. Coster, Mrs G. Cullen, Mr J. Da Vega, Mr Peter Done, Mr Dan Downie, Mrs Natasha Dwyer, Mrs H. S. Ellingsen, Mr P. E. Felton, Sir Alex Ferguson, Mr S. G. Friend, Mr Karim Ghaly, Mr R. Gorell, Mrs W. Gorell, Ms Karen Gough, Mr B. Greenwood, Mr S. Harding, Mr N. G. R. Harris, Dr E. Harris, Mr D. A. Hazell, The Hon H. Herbert, Highclere Thoroughbred Racing Ltd, Mr Tony Hill, Mr J. Hitchins, Mr J. C. Hitchins, Mr S. R. Hitchins, Sir C. J. S. Hobhouse, Lady Hobhouse, Mr R. S. Hoskins, Mr G. R. Ireland, Ms Kate James, Mr John Karter, Mr Luke Lillingston, Mrs J. K. Lukas, Mr J. Maldonado, Mrs Janice Mariscotti, Mr Mick Mariscotti, Mr I. G. Martin, Mr Ged Mason, Mr R. P. B. Michaelson, Mrs T. L. Miller, Mr Richard Morecombe, Miss M. Noden, Mr Gerald Oury, Mr O. J. W. Pawle, Mr David F. Powell, Mr James Ramsden, Mrs L. E. Ramsden, Mr N. J. F. Robinson, Mrs Susan Roy, Mr D. M. Slade, Mrs V. J. M. Slade, Mr M. Smith (Leicester), Mr J. A. B. Stafford, Mrs P. I. Veenbaas, Mr M. Weinfeld, Mr Richard Wilmot-Smith, Mr Tim Wixted.

Assistant Trainer: Chris Bonner

Jockey (flat): Liam Keniry, David Probert, Jimmy Fortune, Oisin Murphy. **Apprentice:** Ed Greatrex, Rob Hornby, Kieran Shoemark, Daniel Wright.

---

16   **MR JOHN BALDING, Doncaster**
      Postal: **Mayflower Stables, Saracens Lane, Scrooby, Doncaster, South Yorkshire, DN10 6AS**
      Contacts: **HOME (01302) 710096 FAX (01302) 710096 MOBILE (07816) 612631**
      E-MAIL j.balding@btconnect.com

1 **FORTINBRASS (IRE)**, 6, b g Baltic King—Greta d'argent (IRE) **Mr W. Herring**
2 **JACOBS SON**, 8, ch g Refuse To Bend (IRE)—Woodwin (IRE) **The Rain Dancers**

MR JOHN BALDING - Continued

3 **LUCKY MARK (IRE)**, 7, b g Moss Vale (IRE)—Vracca **Mr C. Priestley**
4 **POINT NORTH (IRE)**, 9, b g Danehill Dancer (IRE)—Briolette (IRE) **Mr W. Herring**
5 **RAZIN' HELL**, 5, b g Byron—Loose Caboose (IRE) **Timms, Timms & McCabe**
6 **ROCKY HILL RIDGE**, 5, gr g Auction House (USA)—Amwell Star (USA) **Lucky Heather**
7 **SHOWBOATING (IRE)**, 8, b g Shamardal—Sadinga (IRE) **Mr M & Mrs L Cooke & Mr A McCabe**
8 **SLEEPY BLUE OCEAN**, 10, b g Oasis Dream—Esteemed Lady (IRE) **Mr W. Herring**
9 **SOV (IRE)**, 5, gr g Duke of Marmalade (IRE)—Exotic Mix (FR) **P Smith (PC Coaches), A Timms, D Warke**

THREE-YEAR-OLDS

10 **ANAGALLIS (IRE)**, b f Elusive Pimpernel (USA)—Adjtiya (IRE) **The Centurions**
11 **GETTIN' LUCKY**, ch g Bertolini (USA)—Loose Caboose (IRE) **Timms, Timms, Baker & McCabe**

Other Owners: Mr A. D. Baker, Miss H. P Chellingworth, Mr M. Cooke, Mrs N. M. Cooper, A. J. McCabe, P C Coaches of Lincoln Limited, Mr J. R. Theaker, Mr A. C. Timms, Mr M. E. Timms, Mr M. G. Warke.

Assistant Trainer: Claire Edmunds, Jason Edmunds

---

17 **MR MICHAEL BANKS, Sandy**
Postal: Manor Farm, Manor Farm Road, Waresley, Sandy, Bedfordshire, SG19 3BX
Contacts: PHONE (01767) 650563 FAX (01767) 652988 MOBILE (07860) 627370
E-MAIL waresleyfarms@btconnect.com

1 **CLERK'S CHOICE (IRE)**, 10, b g Bachelor Duke—Credit Crunch (IRE) **M. C. Banks**
2 **LOMBARDY BOY (IRE)**, 11, b g Milan—Horner Water (IRE) **M. C. Banks**
3 **MAX LAURIE (FR)**, 11, bl g Ungaro (GER)—Laurie Mercurialle (FR) **Mrs R. L. Banks**
4 **ROGUE DANCER (FR)**, 11, b g Dark Moondancer—Esperanza IV (FR) **M. C. Banks**

THREE-YEAR-OLDS

5 **QUICK LOOK**, b g Kheleyf (USA)—Weqaar (USA) **M. C. Banks**

Assistant Trainer: Nicola Banks

---

18 **MRS TRACEY BARFOOT-SAUNT, Wotton-under-Edge**
Postal: Cosy Farm, Huntingford, Charfield, Wotton-under-Edge, Gloucestershire, GL12 8EY
Contacts: PHONE (01453) 520312 FAX (01453) 520312 MOBILE (07976) 360626

1 4, B c Sulamani (IRE)—Maxilla (IRE)
2 **TAKE OF SHOC'S (IRE)**, 12, ch g Beneficial—Dear Dunleer (IRE) **BS Racing**

Other Owners: Mr G. C. Barfoot-Saunt, Mrs T. M. Barfoot-Saunt.

---

19 **MR MAURICE BARNES, Brampton**
Postal: Tarnside, Farlam, Brampton, Cumbria, CA8 1LA
Contacts: PHONE/FAX (01697) 746675 MOBILE (07760) 433191
E-MAIL anne.barnes1@btinternet.com

1 **APACHE PILOT**, 8, br g Indian Danehill (IRE)—Anniejo **Mr Gibson & Mr Wilson**
2 **BARNEY'S CAULKER**, 5, b g Captain Gerrard (IRE)—Little Cascade **M. A. Barnes**
3 **BOBS LADY TAMURE**, 9, b m Tamure (IRE)—Bob Back's Lady (IRE) **J. R. Wills**
4 **CARRIGDHOUN (IRE)**, 11, gr g Goldmark (USA)—Pet Tomjammar (IRE) **M. A. Barnes**
5 **DEE BEES GIFT**, 5, gr g Firebreak—Josie May (USA) **M. A. Barnes**
6 **DESERT ISLAND DUSK**, 5, b g Superior Premium—Desert Island Disc **Miss A. P. Lee**
7 **DYNAMIC DRIVE (IRE)**, 9, b g Motivator—Biriyani (IRE) **Ring Of Fire**
8 **FLYING JACK**, 6, b g Rob Roy (USA)—Milladella (FR) **Exors of the Late Mr M. D. Townson**
9 **HARRYS WHIM**, 11, b m Sir Harry Lewis (USA)—Whimbrel **J. R. Wills**
10 **HOPE FOR GLORY**, 7, b g Proclamation (IRE)—Aissa **Mr R. E. Wharton**
11 **INDIAN VOYAGE (IRE)**, 8, b g Indian Haven—Voyage of Dreams (USA) **Mr D Carr & Mr M Carlyle**
12 **JOVIAL JOEY (IRE)**, 5, b g St Jovite (USA)—Like A Bird (IRE) **The Edinburgh Woollen Mill Ltd**
13 **LENEY COTTAGE (IRE)**, 9, b g Witness Box (USA)—Fleur de Tal
14 **LOULOUMILLS**, 6, b m Rob Roy (USA)—Etching (USA) **Exors of the Late Mr M. D. Townson**
15 **MY IDEA**, 10, b g Golan (IRE)—Ghana (GER) **M. A. Barnes**

MR MAURICE BARNES - Continued

16 **OISHIN**, 4, b g Paco Boy (IRE)—Roshina (IRE) **M. A. Barnes**
17 **QUICK BREW**, 8, b g Denounce—Darjeeling (IRE) **The Wizards**
18 **RED MYSTIQUE (IRE)**, 7, b g Red Clubs (IRE)—Sacred Love (IRE) **Mr M. Barnes, Mr Scott Lowther**
19 **SKIDDAW POPPY**, 5, b m Byron—Skiddaw Wolf **J. R. Wills**
20 **SPINNING SCOOTER**, 6, b g Sleeping Indian—Spinning Coin **M. A. Barnes**
21 **STORMONT BRIDGE**, 8, b g Avonbridge—Stormont Castle (USA) **M. A. Barnes**
22 **TOLEDO GOLD (IRE)**, 10, ch g Needwood Blade—Eman's Joy **Mr M. Barnes, Mr Scott Lowther**
23 **TRANSLUSCENT (IRE)**, 6, b g Trans Island—Little Miss Diva (IRE) **M. A. Barnes**
24 **TURTLEPLEX**, 5, b m Multiplex—Turtle Bay **G & J Park**

Other Owners: Mr M. Barnes, Mr J. M. Carlyle, Mr David Carr, Mr J. H. Gibson, Mr Keith Greenwell, Mr Stevan Houliston, Mr Scott Lowther, Mr Nigel North, Mr Gordon Park, Miss Jill Park, Mr R. Towler, Mr P. Wilson.

Jockey (NH): Michael McAlister. **Conditional:** Stephen Mulqueen.

---

20   MR BRIAN BARR, Sherborne
Postal: **Tall Trees Stud, Longburton, Sherborne, Dorset, DT9 5PH**
Contacts: PHONE **(01963) 210173** MOBILE **(07826) 867881**
E-MAIL **brianbarrracing@hotmail.com** WEBSITE **www.brianbarrracing.co.uk**

1 **ANN MARIES REJECT (IRE)**, 7, br m Sendawar (IRE)—Charlestown Lass **Kieran O'Toole**
2 **CANIVER QUEEN (IRE)**, 6, ch m Sendawar (IRE)—Sharp Dancer **Kieran O'Toole**
3 **CASTLEMORRIS KING**, 8, br g And Beyond (IRE)—Brookshield Baby **Mr Kevin Radcliffe**
4 **FOLLOW THE TRACKS (IRE)**, 8, b b g Milan—Charming Mo (IRE) **Brian Barr Racing Club**
5 **HEAD SPACE (IRE)**, 8, b g Invincible Spirit (IRE)—Danzelline **Miss D. Hitchins**
6 **JOPAAN (IRE)**, 9, ch g Pierre—No Precedent (IRE) **NDS Ltd**
7 **MADAM BE**, 6, b m Kayf Tara—Mrs Be (IRE) **Brian Barr Racing Club**
8 **MARTY'S MAGIC**, 7, b g Tale of The Cat (USA)—Steno (USA)
9 **NORFOLK SKY**, 7, ch m Haafhd—Cayman Sound **Mr G. Hitchins**
10 **SHANANDOA**, 5, b m Shamardal (USA)—Divisa (GER) **Excel Racing**
11 **SKY WATCH (IRE)**, 9, b g Flemensfirth (USA)—The Shining Force (IRE) **Miss D. Hitchins**
12 **STEPHEN HERO (IRE)**, 6, br g Celtic Swing—Albaiyda (IRE) **Miss D. Hitchins**
13 **TUFFSTUFF**, 8, b g Generous (IRE)—Life Line **Brian Barr Racing Club**
14 **VENTURE LAGERTHA (IRE)**, 7, ch m Fruits of Love (USA)—Millmounts Tara (IRE) **Kieran O'Toole**
15 , Br g Milan—Wychnor Dawn (IRE) **Mr G. Hitchins**

Other Owners: Mrs Katrina Hitchins.

Assistant Trainer: Daisy Hitchins (07975) 754622

Jockey (flat): Dougie Costello. **Jockey (NH):** Dave Crosse, Gavin Sheehan. **Conditional:** Tom Garner, Mikey Heard.
Amateur: Mr Eddie Doggrell.

---

21   MR RON BARR, Middlesbrough
Postal: **Carr House Farm, Seamer, Stokesley, Middlesbrough, Cleveland, TS9 5LL**
Contacts: PHONE **(01642) 710687** MOBILE **(07711) 895309**
E-MAIL **christinebarr1@aol.com**

1 **A J COOK (IRE)**, 6, b g Mujadil (USA)—Undertone (IRE) **Mrs V. G. Davies**
2 **FOREIGN RHYTHM (IRE)**, 11, ch m Distant Music (USA)—Happy Talk (IRE) **R. E. Barr**
3 **GRACEFUL ACT**, 8, b m Royal Applause—Minnina (IRE) **D. Thomson**
4 **MIDNIGHT WARRIOR**, 6, b g Teofilo (IRE)—Mauri Moon **Mr K. Trimble**
5 **MITCHUM**, 7, b g Elnadim (USA)—Maid To Matter **P. Cartmell**
6 **OROBAS (IRE)**, 4, b g Dark Angel (IRE)—Miss Mujadil (IRE) **Mrs C. Barr**
7 **PLAYBOY BAY**, 4, b g Indesatchel—Dim Ofan **P. Cartmell**

THREE-YEAR-OLDS

8 **TWEETHEART**, ch f Dutch Art—Strictly (USA) **Mrs V. G. Davies**

Other Owners: Mrs R. E. Barr.

MR RON BARR - Continued

Assistant Trainer: Mrs C. Barr

Amateur: Miss V. Barr.

---

22 **MR DAVID BARRON, Thirsk**
Postal: Maunby House, Maunby, Thirsk, North Yorkshire, YO7 4HD
Contacts: PHONE (01845) 587435 FAX (01845) 587331
E-MAIL david@harrowgate.wanadoo.co.uk

1 **ABOVE THE REST (IRE)**, 5, b g Excellent Art—Aspasias Tizzy (USA) **L. G. O'Kane**
2 **ART OBSESSION (IRE)**, 5, b g Excellent Art—Ghana (IRE) **Mr D. Pryde & Mr J. Cringan**
3 **BAHAMA MOON (IRE)**, 4, b g Lope de Vega (IRE)—Bahama Bay (GER) **Pryde, Van Der Hoeven & Beaumont**
4 **BERTIEWHITTLE**, 8, ch g Bahamian Bounty—Minette **Norton Common Farm Racing II&JKB Johnson**
5 **BILLYOAKES (IRE)**, 4, b g Kodiac—Reality Check (IRE) **D. E. Cook**
6 **CHILWORTH BELLS**, 4, ch g Sixties Icon—Five Bells (IRE) **Harrowgate Bloodstock Ltd**
7 **DUTCH DESCENT (IRE)**, 5, b g Royal Applause—Wagtail **Twinacre Nurseries Ltd**
8 **ESTEAMING**, 6, b g Sir Percy—Night Over Day **L. G. O'Kane**
9 **FAST TRACK**, 5, b g Rail Link—Silca Boo **R. C. Miquel**
10 **FIELDGUNNER KIRKUP (GER)**, 8, b g Acclamation—Fire Finch **Mr J. Knotts**
11 **FREE CODE (IRE)**, 5, b g Kodiac—Gerobies Girl (USA) **Ron Hull & Laurence O'Kane**
12 **HANDSOME DUDE**, 4, b g Showcasing—Dee Dee Girl (IRE) **Mr W D & Mrs D A Glover**
13 **INDY (IRE)**, 5, b g Indian Haven—Maddie's Pearl (IRE) **White Rose Racing**
14 **JAMESBO'S GIRL**, 6, ch m Refuse To Bend (IRE)—Donna Anna **Hardisty Rolls**
15 **LAWYER (IRE)**, 5, b g Acclamation—Charaig **Laurence O'Kane & Ron Hull**
16 **LONG AWAITED (IRE)**, 8, b g Pivotal—Desertion (IRE) **Harrowgate Bloodstock Ltd**
17 **MONEY TEAM (IRE)**, 5, b g Kodiac—Coral Dawn (IRE) **White Rose Racing**
18 **NEW BIDDER**, 5, b br g Auction House (USA)—Noble Nova **Mrs J. A. Watts**
19 **NEWSTEAD ABBEY**, 6, b g Byron—Oatcake **Let's Be Lucky Partnership**
20 **PEARL SECRET**, 7, ch h Compton Place—Our Little Secret (IRE) **Qatar Racing Limited**
21 **PLAY NICELY**, 4, ch g Naaqoos—Aalya (IRE) **Lets Be Lucky Racing 5**
22 **RED TYCOON (IRE)**, 4, b g Acclamation—Rugged Up (IRE) **Lets Be Lucky Racing 4**
23 **ROBOT BOY (IRE)**, 6, ch g Shamardal (USA)—Pivotal's Princess (IRE) **Mr Laurence O'Kane & Paul Murphy**
24 **SIR RUNS A LOT**, 4, b g Sir Percy—Monjouet (IRE) **Harrowgate Bloodstock Ltd**
25 **STEELRIVER (IRE)**, 6, b g Iffraaj—Numerus Clausus (FR) **Go Orange Stars**
26 **SWIFT EMPEROR (IRE)**, 4, b g Holy Roman Emperor (IRE)—Big Swifty (IRE) **DC Racing Partnership**
27 **TWIN APPEAL (IRE)**, 5, b g Oratorio (IRE)—Velvet Appeal (IRE) **Twinacre Nurseries Ltd**
28 **WAR GIRL (IRE)**, 4, b br f War Front (USA)—Valarchos Destiny (USA) **Harrowgate Bloodstock Ltd**
29 **ZAC BROWN (IRE)**, 5, b g Kodiac—Mildmay (USA) **Mr R. G. Toes**

THREE-YEAR-OLDS

30 Ch g Mount Nelson—Bella Beguine **Mr M. J. Rozenbroek**
31 **BERLIOS (IRE)**, b g Excellent Art—Endless Peace (IRE) **Lets Be Lucky Racing 6**
32 B g Bushranger (IRE)—Coming Home **Harrowgate Bloodstock Ltd**
33 **EVENLODE (IRE)**, b c Elnadim (USA)—Escudo (IRE) **Qatar Racing Limited**
34 **GRACEFUL FAVOUR**, gr f Hellvelyn—Pontressina (USA) **Harrowgate Bloodstock Ltd**
35 **HALLUX**, ch g Sakhee (USA)—Jaconet (USA) **Mr R. G. Toes**
36 **KOOTHRAPPALI**, b g Sakhee's Secret—Grandmas Dream **Harrowgate Bloodstock Ltd**
37 **LA ASOMADA**, b f Arabian Gleam—Morristown Music (IRE) **J. G. Brown**
38 **PEGGY JOYCE**, b f Aussie Rules (USA)—Ashtaroute (USA) **Mr M. J. Rozenbroek**
39 **POET'S PRIZE**, b c Compton Place—La Gessa **L. G. O'Kane**
40 **RANTAN (IRE)**, b g Kodiac—Peace Talks **Mr H. D. Atkinson**
41 **SEMANA SANTA**, b f Arabian Gleam—La Zamora **J. G. Brown**
42 **WOLOWITZ (IRE)**, b g Intense Focus (USA)—Tranquil Sky **Mrs S. C. Barron**

TWO-YEAR-OLDS

43 **ARABELLA ROSE**, b f 29/3 Monsieur Bond (IRE)—Moorhouse Girl (Makbul) **Mr R. Hull**
44 Ch c 13/3 Compton Place—Arley Hall (Excellent Art) (15000) **Harrowgate Bloodstock Ltd**
45 B c 5/3 Clodovil (IRE)—Art of Gold (Excellent Art) (25000) **Elliot Brothers & Peacock & Partner**
46 B c 21/2 Sleeping Indian—Ashtaroute (USA) (Holy Bull (USA)) (3809) **Mr M. J. Rozenbroek**
47 Ch c 21/2 Kheleyf (USA)—Barbieri (IRE) (Encosta de Lago (AUS)) **Dr N. J. Barron**
48 B c 21/3 Power—Bawaakeer (USA) (Kingmambo (USA)) (35437) **Elliot Brothers & Peacock & Partner**
49 B c 6/3 Compton Place—Beautiful Lady (IRE) (Peintre Celebre (USA)) (28000) **Dr N. J. Barron**
50 **BOB MAXWELL (IRE)**, b c 5/3 Big Bad Bob (IRE)—Catching Stars (IRE) (Halling (USA)) (19000) **Peter Jones**

MR DAVID BARRON - Continued

51 B f 9/3 Royal Applause—Canukeepasecret (Mind Games) (8095) **Rozenbroek, Berry & Partner**
52 Br c 4/4 Big Bad Bob (IRE)—
  Causeway Charm (USA) (Giant's Causeway (USA)) (55000) **Kangyu International Racing (HK) Limited**
53 CLEAN CUT, b f 7/5 Kheleyf (USA)—Regal Asset (USA) (Regal Classic (CAN)) **Mr R. Hull**
54 Br f 1/3 Big Bad Bob (IRE)—Colourpoint (USA) (Forest Wildcat (USA)) (8121) **Harrowgate Bloodstock Ltd**
55 Ch ro c 7/2 Kheleyf (USA)—Elbow Beach (Choisir (AUS)) (27000) **Harrowgate Bloodstock Ltd**
56 GAVAL, b c 26/3 Major Cadeaux—Bold Bidder (Indesatchel (IRE)) (5500) **Bearstone Stud Limited**
57 B f 18/4 Bahamian Bounty—Hulcote Rose (IRE) (Rock of Gibraltar (IRE)) (22000) **Mr M. J. Rozenbroek**
58 B c 31/1 Sakhee's Secret—London Welsh (Cape Cross (IRE)) (23624) **Dr N. J. Barron**
59 B c 2/3 Equiano (FR)—Marine Girl (Shamardal (USA)) (26666) **All About York II & Partner**
60 B c 21/3 Delegator—Pelican Key (Mujadil (USA)) (45000) **Kangyu International Racing (HK) Limited**
61 Ch c 13/4 Zoffany (IRE)—Playful Promises (IRE) (Elnadim (USA)) (38095) **Mr R. Hull**
62 B c 16/4 Tamayuz—Red Planet (Pivotal) (15503) **Harrowgate Bloodstock Ltd**
63 B c 11/3 Showcasing—Reel Cool (Reel Buddy (USA)) (43809) **Elliot Brothers & Peacock & Partner**
64 C 11/2 Kyllachy—Responsive (Dutch Art) (31428) **Mr M. J. Rozenbroek**
65 RONNIE THE ROOSTER, b c 2/4 Captain Gerrard (IRE)—Piranha (IRE) (Exceed And Excel (AUS)) **Mr R. Hull**
66 Br c 18/1 Big Bad Bob (IRE)—Teodelight (IRE) (Teofilo (IRE)) (21410) **Elliot Brothers & Peacock & Partner**
67 B c 27/2 Stimulation (IRE)—Timeless Elegance (IRE) (Invincible Spirit (IRE)) (7619) **Harrowgate Bloodstock Ltd**
68 B f 22/1 Sir Prancealot (IRE)—Too Close (IRE) (Danehill Dancer (IRE)) **Harrowgate Bloodstock Ltd**
69 B c 23/4 Dandy Man (IRE)—Warm Welcome (Motivator) (26666) **Elliot Brothers & Peacock & Partner**
70 ZANDRADEE (IRE), br f 3/3 Zebedee—Annie Beach (IRE) (Redback) **Harrowgate Bloodstock Ltd**
71 ZONE IN, b c 20/3 Equiano (FR)—Donna Giovanna (Mozart (IRE)) **Mr R. Hull**

Other Owners: T. D. Barron, J. J. Beaumont, Mr P. R. Bentley, J. Berry, Mr C. Blaymire, R. J. Cornelius, J. A. Cringan, C. R. Elliott, J. M. Elliott, Mr D. B. Ellis, Mr W. D. Glover, Mrs D. A. Glover, Mr S. T. Gorrie, Mr R. A. Gorrie, Mrs J. Ingham, Mr G. M. C. Johnson, Mr P. A. Murphy, Norton Common Farm Racing Ltd, D. G. Pryde, Mr P. Rolls, Mrs J. Rolls, Mr D. P. van der Hoeven.

Assistant Trainer: Nicola-Jo Barron

---

23 MR P. BARY, Chantilly
Postal: **5 Chemin des Aigles, 60500 Chantilly, France**
Contacts: **PHONE (0033) 3445 71403 FAX (0033) 3446 72015 MOBILE (0033) 6075 80241**
E-MAIL p-bary@wanadoo.fr

1 BILLABONG (MOR), 7, ch h Gentlewave (IRE)—Lunattori **Jalobey Stud**
2 JULES ET JIM, 4, b c Teofilo (IRE)—Alsace **Hspirit**
3 LAUNCHED (IRE), 4, b c Galileo (IRE)—Apsara (FR) **Niarchos Family**
4 MAGNETICJIM (IRE), 4, br gr c Galileo (IRE)—Dibenoise (FR) **Hspirit**
5 MENARDAIS (FR), 7, b g Canyon Creek (IRE)—Madeleine's Blush (USA) **G. Sandor**
6 SAMIRE (FR), 4, ch c American Post—Semire (FR) **G. Sandor**
7 SILVERWAVE (FR), 4, b c Silver Frost (IRE)—Miss Bio (FR) **Hspirit**
8 SORIANO, 5, ch g Halling (USA)—Sureyya (GER) **Ecurie La Boetie**
9 STRIX, 6, ch h Muhtathir—Serandine (IRE) **Flaxman Stables Ireland**
10 ZHIYI (USA), 6, b g Henrythenavigator (USA)—Burning Sunset **Niarchos Family**

THREE-YEAR-OLDS

11 ALEGRIA ALEGRIA (FR), b f Elusive City (USA)—Abeille (IRE) **Haras du Mezeray**
12 ANGEL ERIA (IRE), b f Siyouni (FR)—Arcangela **Ecurie J. L. Bouchard**
13 ANTONOE (USA), b f First Defence (USA)—Ixora (USA) **K. Abdullah**
14 BATLADY (FR), gr f Slickly (FR)—Belga Wood (USA) **G. Sandor**
15 BEYOND APOLLO (FR), b br c Sea The Stars (IRE)—Celestial Lagoon (JPN) **Niarchos Family**
16 BIDDER, b c Oasis Dream—Love The Rain **K. Abdullah**
17 ELIDE (IRE), b f Wootton Bassett—Elodie **Skymarc Farm Inc.**
18 EMPIRIC, b c Holy Roman Emperor (IRE)—Sierra Slew **Emmeline de Waldner**
19 FARCEUR (FR), b g Iffraaj—Zomorroda (IRE) **Ecurie J. L. Bouchard**
20 GOLD VIBE (IRE), ch c Dream Ahead (USA)—Whisper Dance (USA) **Sutong Pan**
21 GOLDEN TEMPO (IRE), b f Canford Cliffs (IRE)—Haute Volta (FR) **Sutong Pan**
22 GOOD WAY OFF (USA), b f Northern Afleet (USA)—Out of Reach **K. Abdullah**
23 HIORT (IRE), b f Rip Van Winkle (IRE)—Gifts Galore (IRE) **Laghi France**
24 LE PIN (FR), gr g Holy Roman Emperor (IRE)—Night Dhu **Ecurie La Boetie II**
25 LILY PASSION, ch gr f Sea The Stars (IRE)—Alix Road (FR) **Ecurie des Charmes**
26 LOW SUN, b c Champs Elysees—Winter Solstice **K. Abdullah**
27 MANGO TANGO (FR), b f Siyouni (FR)—Alexandrina (GER) **Galileo Racing**

MR P. BARY - Continued

28 **MARLINGFORD,** b f Oasis Dream—Imbabala **K. Abdullah**
29 **MAX'S SPIRIT (IRE),** b g Invincible Spirit (IRE)—My Uptown Girl **Ecurie J. L. Bouchard**
30 **MILITATE,** b f Oasis Dream—Orford Ness **K. Abdullah**
31 **MOONLIGHT MAGIC (FR),** b f Wootton Bassett—Cracking Melody **Galileo Racing**
32 **MOVING (USA),** b c War Front (USA)—Visions of Clarity (IRE) **Flaxman Stables Ireland**
33 **MYTHOLOGICAL (USA),** b f Bernardini (USA)—Witching Hour (FR) **Flaxman Stables Ireland**
34 **NEW GRANADA,** b c Zamindar (USA)—Costa Rica (IRE) **K. Abdullah**
35 **NOMADIC (FR),** b f Duke of Marmalade (IRE)—Teepee (JPN) **Niarchos Family**
36 **ONLYJIM (FR),** b c Manduro (GER)—Dansilady (IRE) **Hspirit**
37 **PHIDIAN (IRE),** b c Galileo (IRE)—Divine Proportions (USA) **Flaxman Stables Ireland**
38 **RECEPTIVE (USA),** b c Afleet Alex (USA)—Brief Look **K. Abdullah**
39 **ROLLER,** b g Rail Link—Buffering **K. Abdullah**
40 **SABLEROSE (IRE),** b f Dubawi (IRE)—Sandbar **Lady O'Reilly**
41 **SECRETJIM (FR),** b c Equiano (FR)—Hometown **Hspirit**
42 **SEE YOU (FR),** b f Siyouni (FR)—Chic Retreat (USA) **Emmeline de Waldner**
43 **SPRING BOK (FR),** b c Turtle Bowl (IRE)—Rock Harmonie (FR) **Ecurie La Boetie**
44 **SPRING MASTER,** b c Mastercraftsman (IRE)—Cracovie **Ecurie J. L. Bouchard**
45 **SWEET ELECTRA (FR),** gr f Sea The Stars (IRE)—Ysoldina (FR) **Hspirit**
46 **TRANCOSO (FR),** b g Rock of Gibraltar (IRE)—Tropa de Elite (USA) **Arthur Mendes**
47 **TUILERIES,** b f Cape Cross (IRE)—Toi Et Moi (IRE) **Grundy Bloodstock Ltd**
48 **VITAL SUN (FR),** ch c Pivotal—Burning Sunset **Niarchos Family**

TWO-YEAR-OLDS

49 B f 30/4 Redoute's Choice (AUS)—All Is Vanity (FR) (Gold Away (IRE)) (73827) **Ecurie J. L. Bouchard Sarl**
50 **ANNASANDRA (FR),** ch f 16/4 Pounced (USA)—Annaly (ITY) (Kirkwall) **Razza Dormello Olgiata**
51 B c 24/2 Frankel—Apsara (FR) (Darshaan) **Niarchos Family**
52 B c 13/2 Lawman (FR)—Ares Flight (IRE) (Hernando (FR)) **Niarchos Family**
53 Gr f 21/1 Rajsaman (FR)—Aviane (GER) (Winged Love (IRE)) (5906) **Moise Ohana**
54 **BELLE WALKER (FR),** ch f 1/1 Tamayuz—Huroof (IRE) (Pivotal) (31007) **Angeville Racing Club**
55 **BOSNORMAND (FR),** gr c 22/1 Rajsaman (FR)—Sardinelle (FR) (Verglas (IRE)) **Franklin Finance SA**
56 **CARDARA (FR),** b c 8/5 Soldier of Fortune (IRE)—
                              Cool Woman (IRE) (One Cool Cat (USA)) **Razza Dormello Olgiata**
57 **CROZET (FR),** ch f 27/2 Zoffany (IRE)—Teoris (IRE) (Bachelor Duke (USA)) (35437) **Laghi France**
58 B c 16/5 Excelebration (IRE)—Denebola (USA) (Storm Cat (USA)) **Flaxman Stables Ireland**
59 B c 2/4 Acclamation—Dolphina (USA) (Kingmambo (USA)) **Niarchos Family**
60 **FALAISE (FR),** b f 1/1 Canford Cliffs (IRE)—Amonita (Anabaa (USA)) **Haras du Mezeray**
61 B f 14/2 Acclamation—Fleur de Sel (Linamix (FR)) (66445) **Ecurie des Charmes**
62 B c 1/1 Holy Roman Emperor (IRE)—Folle Allure (FR) (Poliglote) (73827) **Ecurie J. L. Bouchard Sarl**
63 **GLICOURT (FR),** b c 31/1 Rajsaman (FR)—Fusee Francaise (FR) (Anabaa (USA)) (31007) **Franklin Finance SA**
64 B f 14/3 First Defence (USA)—Helstra (USA) (Nureyev (USA)) **K. Abdullah**
65 **KITTY JONES (IRE),** b f 11/4 Nathaniel (IRE)—Di Moi Oui (Warning) (45000) **Scuderia Vittadini Srl**
66 B f 24/4 Invincible Spirit (IRE)—Lumiere Noire (FR) (Dashing Blade) (118124) **Ecurie J. L. Bouchard Sarl**
67 B f 26/3 Makfi—Lune Rose (High Chaparral (IRE)) (55370) **Ecurie J. L. Bouchard Sarl**
68 B c 25/1 Galileo (IRE)—Moonlight's Box (USA) (Nureyev (USA)) **Flaxman Stables Ireland**
69 **MYFRIENDRICH,** gr c 14/4 Mastercraftsman (IRE)—Abandagold (IRE) (Orpen (USA)) (47988) **Galileo Racing**
70 **OBEDIENT,** ch f 21/2 Motivator—Namaskar (Dansili) **K. Abdullah**
71 **ORIVAL (FR),** b c 1/1 Le Havre (FR)—Sallen (IRE) (Oratorio (IRE)) **Franklin Finance SA**
72 **ORRERY (USA),** b f 10/2 Smart Strike (CAN)—It's Midnight (USA) (Shamardal (USA)) **Flaxman Stables Ireland**
73 **PARTICIPATE,** b c 28/5 Bated Breath—Imroz (USA) (Nureyev (USA)) **K. Abdullah**
74 B f 24/2 Siyouni (FR)—Pluie d'or (IRE) (Bering) (110741) **Ecurie J. L. Bouchard Sarl**
75 B f 5/4 Motivator—Pomonia (FR) (Anabaa (USA)) (55370) **Ecurie J. L. Bouchard Sarl**
76 B c 9/2 Lawman (FR)—Rajastani (IRE) (Zamindar (USA)) (51679) **Ecurie J. L. Bouchard Sarl**
77 **ROVETTA (FR),** b f 1/1 So You Think (NZ)—Rosa Brett (ITY) (Green Tune (USA)) **Razza Dormello Olgiata**
78 B f 10/5 Galileo (IRE)—Royal Highness (GER) (Monsun (GER)) (228866) **Ecurie des Monceaux**
79 **SENGA (USA),** b f 15/3 Blame (USA)—Beta Leo (USA) (A P Indy (USA)) **Flaxman Stables Ireland**
80 B f 3/3 Champs Elysees—Starfan (USA) (Lear Fan (USA)) **K. Abdullah**
81 **THAIS (FR),** b f 1/1 Rio de La Plata (USA)—Tianshan (FR) (Lahint (USA)) (103359) **G. Sandor**
82 Ch f 5/3 Medicean—Virtuosity (Pivotal) (95976) **Ecurie J. L. Bouchard Sarl**

Assistant Trainer: Baratti Mario

Jockey (flat): Stephane Pasquier, Christophe Soumillon. **Apprentice:** Pierre Bazire.

24 MISS REBECCA BASTIMAN, Wetherby
Postal: **Goosemoor Farm, Warfield Lane, Wetherby, West Yorkshire, LS22 5EU**
Contacts: PHONE **(01423) 359783 (01423) 359397 MOBILE (07818) 181313**
E-MAIL **rebeccabastiman@hotmail.co.uk**

1 BE BOLD, 4, ch g Assertive—Marysienka **Mrs P. Bastiman**
2 BIG RED, 4, ch f Sakhee's Secret—Hickleton Lady (IRE) **Ms M. Austerfield**
3 CLERGYMAN, 4, b g Pastoral Pursuits—Doctor's Note **Mrs P. Bastiman**
4 GONE WITH THE WIND (GER), 5, b g Dutch Art—Gallivant **Mrs P. Bastiman**
5 GREEN HOWARD, 8, ch g Bahamian Bounty—Dash of Lime **Ms M. Austerfield**
6 HARBOUR PATROL (IRE), 4, b c Acclamation—Traou Mad (IRE) **Mrs P. Bastiman**
7 INDIAN CHIEF (IRE), 6, b g Montjeu (IRE)—Buck Aspen (USA) **Castle Construction (North East) Ltd**
8 JOHN CAESAR (IRE), 5, b g Bushranger (IRE)—Polish Belle **Mrs K. Hall**
9 KYLLACHYKOV (IRE), 8, ch g Kyllachy—Dance On **Austerfield, Hall, Dickson & Bastiman**
10 LIZZY'S DREAM, 8, ch g Choisir (AUS)—Flyingit (USA) **Mrs P. Bastiman**
11 MADAM MAI TAI, 4, ch f Compton Place—Dash of Lime **Ms M. Austerfield**
12 NOVALIST, 8, ch g Avonbridge—Malelane (IRE) **Mr E. N. Barber**
13 ROYAL ACCLAIM (IRE), 4, b g Acclamation—Top Row **Ms M. Austerfield**
14 ROYAL BRAVE (IRE), 5, b g Acclamation—Daqtora **Mr James Edgar**
15 SECRET CITY (IRE), 10, b g City On A Hill (USA)—Secret Combe (IRE) **Ms M. Austerfield**
16 SEE VERMONT, 8, b g Kyllachy—Orange Lily **Mr J. Smith**
17 SHIKARI, 5, ch g Sakhee's Secret—Hickleton Lady (IRE) **Ms M. Austerfield**
18 SINGEUR (IRE), 9, b g Chineur (FR)—Singitta **Ms M. Austerfield**
19 ZESHOV (IRE), 5, b g Acclamation—Fathoming (USA) **Mrs P. Bastiman**

THREE-YEAR-OLDS

20 ANOTHER DESPERADO (IRE), b g Approve (IRE)—Kind Regards (IRE) **I. B. Barker**
21 DONNELLY'S RAINBOW (IRE), b c Lilbourne Lad (IRE)—Donnelly's Hollow (IRE) **Miss R. Bastiman**

Other Owners: Ms M. Austerfield, Mrs P. Bastiman, Mr David Dickson, Mrs K. Hall.

Assistant Trainer: Harvey Bastiman

Jockey (flat): Paul Mulrennan.

25 MRS ALISON BATCHELOR, Petworth
Postal: **Down View Farm, Burton Park Road, Petworth, West Sussex, GU28 0JT**
Contacts: PHONE **(01798) 343090 FAX (01798) 343090**
E-MAIL **alison@alisonbatchelorracing.com** WEBSITE **www.alisonbatchelorracing.com**

1 AMBRE DES MARAIS (FR), 6, ch m Network (GER)—Fee des Marais (FR) **Mrs A. M. Batchelor**
2 GRAPHICAL (IRE), 7, b g High Chaparral (IRE)—Woopi Gold (IRE) **Mrs A. M. Batchelor**
3 MR LANDO, 7, b g Shirocco (GER)—Capitana (GER) **Mrs A. M. Batchelor**
4 POLISHED ROCK (IRE), 6, ch g Rock of Gibraltar (IRE)—Where We Left Off **Mrs A. M. Batchelor**
5 SEVENTH HUSSAR, 10, b g Alflora (IRE)—Shuil Do (IRE) **Mrs A. M. Batchelor**
6 TAGGIA (FR), 9, b m Great Pretender (IRE)—Ecossaise II (FR) **Mrs A. M. Batchelor**
7 TARA DOVE, 8, gr m Kayf Tara—Kildee Lass **Mrs A. M. Batchelor**
8 TRY CATCH ME (IRE), 11, b g Commander Collins (IRE)—Misty River (IRE) **Mrs A. M. Batchelor**
9 YUR NEXT (IRE), 8, br m Definite Article—Listen Up **Mrs A. M. Batchelor**

Amateur: Mr S. Hanson.

26 MR BRIAN BAUGH, Crewe
Postal: **Meadow Cottage, 47 Scot Hay Road, Alsagers Bank, Stoke-On-Trent, Staffordshire, ST7 8BW**
Contacts: PHONE **(01782) 706222 MOBILE (07547) 495236**
E-MAIL **bpjbaugh@aol.com**

1 CONSISTANT, 8, b g Reel Buddy (USA)—Compact Disc (IRE) **Miss J. A. Price**
2 JOHN POTTS, 11, b g Josr Algarhoud (IRE)—Crown City (USA) **Miss S. M. Potts**

MR BRIAN BAUGH - Continued

THREE-YEAR-OLDS

3 **DAVID'S BEAUTY (IRE)**, b f Kodiac—Thaisy (USA) **Mr G. B. Hignett**
4 **LUVLY**, b g Multiplex—Luv U Too **Richard and Nicola Hunt**

Other Owners: Mr R. A. Hunt, Mrs N. Hunt, Mr G. Ratcliffe.

Assistant Trainer: S Potts

---

27 **MR CHRIS BEALBY, Grantham**
Postal: **North Lodge, Barrowby, Grantham, Lincolnshire, NG32 1DH**
Contacts: OFFICE **(01476) 564568** FAX **(01476) 572391** MOBILE **(07831) 538689**
E-MAIL **chris@northlodgeracing.co.uk** WEBSITE **www.northlodgeracing.co.uk**

1 **BENEFIT OF LUCK (IRE)**, 4, ch g Beneficial—Shamrock Miss (IRE) **J. H. Henderson**
2 **BLACK LILY (IRE)**, 8, b m Quws—Sandaluna (IRE) **Triumph In Mind**
3 **CROSSLANES (IRE)**, 5, b m Brian Boru—Threecrossmammies (IRE) **C. C. Bealby**
4 **CUL DEALGA (IRE)**, 7, b m Kalanisi (IRE)—Yes Boss (IRE) **The Rann Family**
5 **DIEGO SUAREZ (FR)**, 6, b g Astarabad (USA)—Shabada (FR) **Mrs M. J. Pepperdine**
6 **EQUUS SECRETUS (IRE)**, 4, b g Brian Boru—Bodega Bay (IRE) **A. J. Taylor**
7 **FARRELLS DESTINY (IRE)**, 4, gr g Proclamation (IRE)—Hello Hello **Mr E. E. A. Buddle**
8 **FIRE (IRE)**, 6, ch g Royal Anthem (USA)—Patsy's Choice (IRE) **Read Williams & Hilton**
9 **LEGENDARY HOP**, 10, b m Midnight Legend—Hopping Mad **Messrs Duke,Umpleby,Holmes & Bealby**
10 **RUARAIDH HUGH (IRE)**, 7, b g Craigsteel—Decent Shower **C. C. Bealby**
11 **SEND FOR KATIE (IRE)**, 8, b m Kayf Tara—Katsura **J. H. Henderson**
12 **SIR LYNX (IRE)**, 9, gr g Amilynx (FR)—Minilus (IRE) **Sir Lynx Partnership**
13 **SPRING HILL (IRE)**, 4, b g Stowaway—Miss The Post **A. J. Taylor**
14 **THE PURCHASER (IRE)**, 8, b g Definite Article—Cash Customer (IRE) **Sir Lynx Partnership**
15 **TOUCH BACK (IRE)**, 10, b g Shantou (USA)—Back Log (IRE) **Miss L. Morgan**
16 **VINTAGE RED**, 8, ch g Grape Tree Road—Simply Stunning **North Lodge Racing Club**
17 **WINGS ATTRACT (IRE)**, 7, b g Winged Love—Huncheon Siss (IRE) **The Rann Family**

Other Owners: Mr D. M. Cook, B. G. Duke, Mrs R. J. Hilton, F. M. Holmes, Mr G. P. D. Rann, Mrs L. E. Rann, Mr P. L. Read, Mr P. Umpleby, Mr T. Wendels, Mrs A. M. Williams, R. F. Wright.

Jockey (NH): Tom Messenger, Noel Fehily, Adam Wedge.

---

28 **MR RALPH BECKETT, Andover**
Postal: **Kimpton Down Stables, Kimpton Down, Andover, Hampshire, SP11 8QQ**
Contacts: PHONE **(01264) 772278** MOBILE **(07802) 219022**
E-MAIL **trainer@rbeckett.com**

1 **AIR PILOT**, 7, b g Zamindar (USA)—Countess Sybil (IRE) **Lady Cobham**
2 **AIR SQUADRON**, 6, b g Rail Link—Countess Sybil (IRE) **Lady Cobham**
3 **ARGUS (IRE)**, 4, b c Rip Van Winkle (IRE)—Steel Princess (IRE) **Qatar Racing Ltd**
4 **BELLAJEU**, 4, b f Montjeu (IRE)—Arbella **Qatar Racing Partnership**
5 **DESDICHADO**, 4, ch g Pivotal—Murrieta **Anstock, Dunn, Richnell & Barker**
6 **ENCORE L'AMOUR**, 4, b f Azamour (IRE)—Centime **Eclipse Partnership**
7 **GREAT GLEN**, 4, b g High Chaparral (IRE)—Grand Opening (IRE) **J. H. Richmond Watson**
8 **GREEN LIGHT**, 5, b g Authorized (IRE)—May Light **Sceptre**
9 **HAAF A SIXPENCE**, 7, b g Haafhd—Melody Maker **Melody Racing**
10 **LACAN (IRE)**, 5, b h New Approach (IRE)—Invincible Isle (IRE) **China Horse Club Ltd**
11 **MAGIC CIRCLE (IRE)**, 4, b g Makfi—Minkova (IRE) **Mr & Mrs D. Aykroyd**
12 **MASTER OF IRONY (IRE)**, 4, b g Makfi—Mother of Pearl (IRE) **Qatar Racing Ltd**
13 **MOONRISE LANDING (IRE)**, 5, gr m Dalakhani (IRE)—Celtic Slipper (IRE) **P. D. Savill**
14 **MR BOSSY BOOTS (IRE)**, 5, b g Teofilo—Zelding (IRE) **P. J. Scargill & Partner**
15 **NICEOFYOUTOTELLME**, 7, b g Hernando (FR)—Swain's Gold (USA) **R. Roberts**
16 **PACIFY**, 4, b g Paco Boy (IRE)—Supereva (IRE) **Prince of Wales & Duchess of Cornwall**
17 **PARNELL'S DREAM**, 4, b f Oasis Dream—Kitty O'shea **Mr & Mrs D. Aykroyd**
18 **REDSTART**, 4, b f Cockney Rebel (IRE)—Ecstasy **A. D. G. Oldrey & G. C. Hartigan**
19 **RIVERS RUN (IRE)**, 4, b f High Chaparral (IRE)—Quiet Waters (USA) **Ballymore Sterling Syndicate**
20 **SHE IS NO LADY**, 4, b f Lope de Vega (IRE)—Capestar (IRE) **D & J Newell**
21 **SIMPLE VERSE (IRE)**, 4, b f Duke of Marmalade (IRE)—Guantanamera (IRE) **Qatar Racing Partnership**

MR RALPH BECKETT - Continued

22 **SIZZLER**, 6, ch g Hernando (FR)—Gino's Spirits **Heseltine, Henley & Jones**
23 **SOUTHERN STORM (IRE)**, 4, b f Cape Cross (IRE)—Stormy Blessing (USA) **Chris McHale**

THREE-YEAR-OLDS

24 **ABACO RIDGE**, b f Bahamian Bounty—Echo Ridge (IRE) **J. C. Smith**
25 **ALYSSA**, b f Sir Percy—Almiranta **Miss K. Rausing**
26 **ANDASTRA (GER)**, b f Kamsin (GER)—Arpista (GER) **H.H. Sheikh Mohammed bin Khalifa Al Thani**
27 **ANOTHER BOY**, ch g Paco Boy (IRE)—Kurtanella **Mrs P. Snow & Partners**
28 **BLYTHBURGH**, ch f Lord of England (GER)—Brisk Breeze (GER) **Ennismore Racing I**
29 **CAPE BANJO (USA)**, ch g Cape Blanco (IRE)—Magic of Love **ABB Partnership**
30 **CARNTOP**, b c Dansili—Milford Sound **Prince of Wales & Duchess of Cornwall**
31 **CAUSE AND EFFECT (IRE)**, b g Big Bad Bob (IRE)—Special Cause (IRE) **Mr R. Robert, Mr P. A. Deal & Partner**
32 **CHICADORO**, b f Paco Boy (IRE)—Going For Gold **James Ortega Bloodstock**
33 **COSMIC STORM**, b f Sea The Stars (IRE)—Riotous Applause **Eclipse Partnership**
34 **CROWNING GLORY (FR)**, b f Speightstown (USA)—Forest Crown **The Eclipse Partnership**
35 **CUSTARD THE DRAGON**, b g Kyllachy—Autumn Pearl **Mr & Mrs Kevan Watts**
36 **DESERT HAZE**, br f New Approach (IRE)—Ensemble (FR) **H.H. Sheikh Mohammed bin Khalifa Al Thani**
37 **DESERT WAY (IRE)**, ch f Giant's Causeway (USA)—Desert Sage **J. H. Richmond-Watson**
38 **DIAMONDS POUR MOI**, b f Pour Moi (IRE)—Diamond Light (USA) **Pearl Bloodstock Ltd**
39 **EASTER MATE (IRE)**, b g Acclamation—Greek Easter (IRE) **Robert Ng**
40 **EMERALD LOCH**, ch f Danehill Dancer (IRE)—Loch Verdi **J. C. Smith**
41 **GIRLING (IRE)**, b f Rock of Gibraltar (IRE)—Gravitation **Gillian, Lady Howard De Walden**
42 **GOLD FAITH (IRE)**, gr g Dark Angel (IRE)—Livadream (IRE) **Sutong Pan**
43 **GOLDEN CHAPTER**, b f Danehill Dancer (IRE)—Farfala (FR) **Sutong Pan**
44 **GOLDEN STUNNER (IRE)**, ch f Dream Ahead (USA)—Pina Colada **Sutong Pan**
45 **HEREAWI**, b f Dubawi (IRE)—Look Here **J. H. Richmond-Watson**
46 B f New Approach (IRE)—Hobby **Larksborough Stud**
47 **INSWING (IRE)**, b f Intikhab (USA)—Vampire Blues (IRE) **Millennium Madness**
48 **JUSTICE GRACE (IRE)**, b g Kodiac—Right After Noon **Robert Ng**
49 **LITTLE AVON**, b f Makfi—Bahamamia **Qatar Racing Ltd**
50 **MADAME CHOW (IRE)**, b f Galileo (IRE)—Landmark (USA) **Sheikh Khalifa, Sheikh Suhaim & QRL**
51 **MATCH MY FIRE**, ch g Makfi—High Lite **Kennet Valley Thoroughbreds VII**
52 **MATIDIA**, ch f Manduro (GER)—Caesarea (GER) **J. L. Rowsell**
53 **MOUNTAIN BELL**, b f Mount Nelson—Shenir **Qatar Racing Ltd**
54 **NASSUVIAN PEARL**, br f Bahamian Bounty—Melody Maker **Melody Racing**
55 **NIGHT TO REMEMBER (IRE)**, b g Dark Angel (IRE)—Night Club **Thurloe Thoroughbreds XXXII**
56 **POINT OF WOODS**, b g Showcasing—Romantic Myth **Mr & Mrs D. Aykroyd**
57 **PURE ART**, b f Dutch Art—Pure Song **R. Barnett**
58 **PURE INNOCENCE (IRE)**, b f Montjeu (IRE)—Festoso (IRE) **Clipper Logistics**
59 **RAIN IN THE FACE**, b g Naaqoos—Makaaseb (USA) **P. K. Gardner**
60 **ROCAVERDE (IRE)**, b f Rock of Gibraltar (IRE)—Green Room (FR) **Nigel & Carolyn Elwes**
61 **SECRET SENSE (USA)**, b f Shamardal (USA)—Shastye (USA) **Newsells Park Stud**
62 **SEPTEMBER STARS (IRE)**, ch f Sea The Stars (IRE)—
Altesse Imperiale (IRE) **Andrew Rosen & Edward W. Easton**
63 **SHADAD (IRE)**, b g Zamindar (USA)—Tender Morn (USA) **H.H. Sheikh Mohammed bin Khalifa Al Thani**
64 **SHINE**, ch f Exceed And Excel (AUS)—Sensational Mover (USA) **P. K. Gardner**
65 **SHORT WORK**, ch g Kyllachy—Agony Aunt **The Pickford Hill Partnership**
66 **SIGHTLINE**, b f Rock of Gibraltar (IRE)—Look So **J. H. Richmond-Watson**
67 **SPARRING QUEEN (USA)**, b f War Front (USA)—Spa Break (USA) **Lofts Hall Stud & Mr P. Freedman**
68 **STEAM AHEAD**, b g Dream Ahead (USA)—Tropical Treat **J. C. Smith**
69 **THE KING'S STEED**, b c Equiano (FR)—King's Siren **J. C. Smith**
70 **WAVELESS**, b f Three Valleys (USA)—Wemyss Bay **K. Abdullah**

TWO-YEAR-OLDS

71 **ALBIZZIA**, b f 21/4 Archipenko (USA)—Altitude (Green Desert (USA)) **Miss K. Rausing**
72 B f 2/4 Medicean—Altruiste (Montjeu (USA)) (90000) **Miss K. Rausing**
73 **AUREANA**, b f 19/4 Kyllachy—Going For Gold (Barathea (IRE)) (9500) **James Ortega Bloodstock**
74 B f 27/4 Showcasing—Azita (Tiger Hill (IRE)) (85000) **Thurloe Thoroughbreds XXXVIII**
75 B f 4/4 Archipenko (USA)—Bassinet (USA (Stravinsky (USA)) (18000) **Dr Bridget Drew & Mr R. A. Farmiloe**
76 **BELLE ABOVE ALL**, ch f 25/2 New Approach (USA)—Foodbroker Fancy (IRE) (Halling (USA)) **Normandie Stud Ltd**
77 B f 1/3 Cacique (IRE)—Blast Furnace (IRE) (Sadler's Wells (USA)) **Chasemore Farm**
78 **BRIMHAM ROCKS**, b c 17/5 Fastnet Rock (AUS)—Colima (IRE) (Authorized (IRE)) **Mr & Mrs David Aykroyd**
79 B c 23/4 Rail Link—Brisk Breeze (GER) (Monsun (GER)) **Ennismore Racing I**
80 Gr f 16/2 Lawman (FR)—Bruxcalina (FR) (Linamix (FR)) (40000) **Newsells Park Stud**

MR RALPH BECKETT - Continued

81 CHARITY, br f 31/3 Azamour (IRE)—Feis Ceoil (IRE) (Key of Luck (USA)) **R. Allcock**
82 B f 21/3 Fastnet Rock (AUS)—Days of Summer (IRE) (Bachelor Duke (USA)) (59062) **Clipper Logistics**
83 Ch f 28/3 Frankel—Discreet Brief (IRE) (Darshaan) **Qatar Racing Ltd**
84 DR JULIUS NO, b c 15/1 Dick Turpin (IRE)—Royal Assent (Royal Applause) (28571) **Chelsea Thoroughbreds**
85 EARTHLY (USA), b c 24/3 Spring At Last (USA)—Geographic (USA) (Empire Maker (USA)) **K. Abdullah**
86 B f 29/3 Harbour Watch (IRE)—Elektra Marino (Mount Nelson) (29531) **Qatar Racing Ltd**
87 Ch f 25/4 Lope de Vega (IRE)—Fairnilee (Selkirk (USA)) (44296) **Clipper Logistics**
88 HARAKA (IRE), b f 17/4 Fastnet Rock (AUS)—
                                    Luna Wells (IRE) (Sadler's Wells (USA)) (50000) **Andy Smith & Friends**
89 HAREBELL (IRE), ch f 5/3 Halling (USA)—Prairie Flower (IRE) (Zieten (USA)) **J. H. Richmond-Watson**
90 HERE AND NOW, b c 18/4 Dansili—Look Here (Hernando (FR)) **J. H. Richmond-Watson**
91 B f 7/3 Teofilo (IRE)—Intapeace (IRE) (Intikhab (USA)) (70000) **Qatar Racing Ltd**
92 B f 11/2 Nathaniel (IRE)—Ivory Rose (Green Desert (USA)) (129198) **Qatar Racing Ltd**
93 B c 8/2 Foxwedge (AUS)—King's Siren (IRE) (King's Best (USA)) **J. C. Smith**
94 B f 22/1 Poet's Voice—Limber Up (IRE) (Dansili) (55000) **Warm Words Partnership**
95 B c 13/3 Makfi—Lixian (Linamix (FR)) (51679) **Qatar Racing Ltd**
96 Br f 27/4 Elusive City (USA)—Lochridge (Indian Ridge) **J. C. Smith**
97 B f 25/4 Galileo (IRE)—Louvain (IRE) (Sinndar (IRE)) **H.H. Sheikh Mohammed bin Khalifa Al Thani**
98 B f 1/4 Deep Impact (JPN)—Love And Bubbles (USA) (Loup Sauvage (USA)) **Qatar Racing Ltd**
99 B f 16/4 Oasis Dream—Magic Tree (UAE) (Timber Country (USA)) **Alvediston Stud & Madams Farm**
100 MAID TO REMEMBER, b f 29/3 Redoute's Choice (AUS)—
                                    Maid To Believe (Galileo (IRE)) (147655) **Normandie Stud Ltd**
101 MANNERS MAKETH MAN (IRE), b c 18/2 Lope de Vega (IRE)—
                                    Dabawiyah (IRE) (Intikhab (USA)) (36913) **R. Roberts**
102 MANNERS PLEASE, b c 30/1 Sixties Icon—Humility (Polar Falcon (USA)) (15000) **R. Roberts**
103 Ch c 24/4 Mastercraftsman (IRE)—Mary Boleyn (IRE) (King's Best (USA)) (42000) **Black, Morecombe & Roberts**
104 B f 26/1 Fastnet Rock (AUS)—
                                    Maryinsky (IRE) (Sadler's Wells (USA)) (610500) **H. H. Sheikh Mohammed bin Khalifa Al Thani**
105 B c 3/5 Royal Applause—Melody Maker (Diktat) **Melody Racing**
106 B gr f 8/4 Makfi—Miss Universe (Warning) (110000) **Qatar Racing Ltd**
107 MISTRESS QUICKLY (IRE), b f 13/2 Mastercraftsman (IRE)—
                                    In My Life (IRE) (Rainbow Quest (USA)) (110000) **Mrs M. E. Slade**
108 B f 28/1 Galileo (IRE)—Mohican Princess (Shirley Heights) (400000) **China Horse Club**
109 MOUNT MORIAH, b c 17/3 Mount Nelson—Rule Britannia (Night Shift (USA)) (22148) **Norman Brunskill**
110 MUNRO, b c 21/3 Kyllachy—Meddle (Diktat) (35000) **Emma Capon & Mrs Simon Marsh**
111 NATHALIE, b f 15/3 Nathaniel (IRE)—Deirdre (Dubawi (IRE)) **Normandie Stud Ltd**
112 NOBELIUM (USA), br c 1/4 Sky Mesa—Striking Example (Empire Maker (USA)) **K. Abdullah**
113 PIAFFE (USA), b f 10/5 Successful Appeal (USA)—Palisade (USA) (Gone West (USA)) **K. Abdullah**
114 PLEASELETMEWIN (IRE), b c 4/4 Power—Jacaranda Ridge (Indian Ridge) (34285) **R. Roberts**
115 B f 7/5 Makfi—Pop Alliance (IRE) (Entrepreneur) (118124) **Qatar Racing Ltd**
116 B f 27/4 Nathaniel (IRE)—Quad's Melody (IRE) (Spinning World (USA)) (95976) **Qatar Racing Ltd**
117 B f 24/1 Dark Angel (IRE)—Red Intrigue (IRE) (Selkirk (USA)) (180000) **Qatar Racing Ltd & China Horse Club**
118 REIGN ON, ch c 8/3 Equiano (FR)—Queens Jubilee (Cayman Kai (IRE)) (30476) **What Asham Partnership**
119 RISTRETTO (USA), b f 13/4 Medaglia d'oro (USA)—Visit (Oasis Dream) **K. Abdullah**
120 B f 27/4 Galileo (IRE)—Saoire (Pivotal) **Andrew Rosen**
121 B f 9/2 Deep Impact (JPN)—Shamrocker (NZ) (O'reilly (NZ)) **Qatar Racing Ltd**
122 B f 17/2 Street Cry (IRE)—Shastye (IRE) (Danehill (USA)) (800000) **Newsells Park Stud**
123 Ch c 6/5 Power—Silver Skates (IRE) (Slip Anchor) (36913) **The Outlaws**
124 Ch c 8/5 Cape Blanco (IRE)—Skip a Dare (USA) (Skip Away (USA)) (18315) **Rat Pack Partnership**
125 SKIPINNISH, b f 28/2 Exceed And Excel (AUS)—Ceilidh House (Selkirk (USA)) **J. H. Richmond-Watson**
126 B f 28/2 Lawman (FR)—Smart Step (Montjeu (IRE)) (190000) **H.H. Sheikh Mohammed bin Khalifa Al Thani**
127 B c 10/4 Dandy Man (IRE)—Soranna (IRE) (Compton Place) (44296) **Kennet Valley Thoroughbreds III**
128 SOUND BAR, b c 13/2 Oasis Dream—Milford Sound (Barathea (IRE)) **K. Abdullah**
129 STEAMING (IRE), ch c 22/3 Rail Link—Dazzling Day (Hernando (FR)) (23624) **A. D. Oldrey & G. C. Hartigan**
130 B f 9/2 Sea The Stars (IRE)—Stylish One (IRE) (Invincible Spirit (IRE)) (130000) **Qatar Racing Ltd**
131 SYNDICATE, b f 14/3 Dansili—Indication (Sadler's Wells (USA)) **K. Abdullah**
132 B f 16/2 Fastnet Rock (AUS)—The Thrill Is Gone (Bahamian Bounty) (52380) **Qatar Racing Ltd**
133 B f 11/4 Fastnet Rock (AUS)—Tropical Treat (Bahamian Bounty) **J. C. Smith**
134 ULYSSES (GER), b c 5/2 Sinndar (IRE)—Ungarin (GER) (Goofalik (USA)) (49464) **Norman Brunskill**
135 B c 25/2 Cacique (IRE)—Wemyss Bay (Sadler's Wells (USA)) **K. Abdullah**
136 WHAT A BOY, b c 13/4 Paco Boy (IRE)—Kurtanella (Pastoral Pursuits) **Mrs P. Snow & Partners**
137 B c 15/3 High Chaparral (IRE)—Witch of Fife (USA) (Lear Fan (USA)) (31746) **James McHale & Partners**
138 YOUR LADYSHIP (IRE), b f 15/4 Lawman (FR)—Bufera (IRE) (King's Best (USA)) (230000) **Normandie Stud Ltd**
139 ZILLA, ch f 4/5 Zamindar (USA)—Caesarea (GER) (Generous (IRE)) **J. L. Rowsell**

MR RALPH BECKETT - Continued

Other Owners: Mr A. R. Adams, Mr M. A. A. M. K. Al - Kubaisi, Sheikh K. A. K. H. Al Thani, Sheikh S. A. K. H. Al Thani, Mr Fergus Anstock, Mr J. Ashley, Mrs L. M. Aykroyd, D. P. Aykroyd, Mrs Ralph Beckett, Mr J. J. Brummitt, Mr H. M. Butler, Mrs E. Capon, Chelsea Thoroughbreds Ltd, Cliveden Stud Ltd, Duchess of Cornwall, Mr P. A. Deal, Mr D. W. Dennis, J. R. Drew, Dr S. B. Drew, Mr Nigel Elwes, Mrs Carolyn Elwes, Mr J. M. O. Evans, Mr R. A. Farmiloe, Mr N. J. Forman Hardy, Mrs M. R. Gregory, G. C. Hartigan, The Hon H. Herbert, Mr I. J. Heseltine, Highclere Thoroughbred Racing Ltd, Mr J. Hillier, Mr R. S. Hoskins, Mrs J. C. Lascelles, Mrs J. F. Marsh, Mr Michael D. Moroney, Mrs K. J. Morton, Mr Paul Gerard Murphy, Mrs J. Newell, D. J. M. Newell, S. F. Oldrey, Mr A. D. G. Oldrey, Mr O. J. W. Pawle, Mr Geoffrey Pooley, Mr T. J. Ramsden, N. J. F. Robinson, Mr G. Schoeningh, Miss Barbara Snow, Mrs Philip Snow, Mr J. A. B. Stafford, The Hon Sir Mathew Thorpe, H.R.H. The Prince Of Wales, Mrs Prudence Watts, Mr Kevan Watts, Mr R. Weston, Mr T. Wilkinson.

Assistant Trainer: Adam Kite, Stephen Thorne

Apprentice: Patrick O'Donnell. **Amateur:** Mrs Victoria Wood.

---

29   MR MICHAEL BELL, Newmarket
Postal: **Fitzroy House, Newmarket, Suffolk, CB8 0JT**
Contacts: **PHONE** (01638) 666567 **FAX** (01638) 668000 **MOBILE** (07802) 264514
E-MAIL office@fitzroyhouse.co.uk **WEBSITE** www.michaelbellracing.co.uk

1 **BIG ORANGE**, 5, b g Duke of Marmalade (IRE)—Miss Brown To You (IRE) **W. J. and T. C. O. Gredley**
2 **FABRICATE**, 4, b g Makfi—Flight of Fancy **Her Majesty The Queen**
3 **FRANKLIN D (USA)**, 4, b c Medaglia d'oro (USA)—Kissed By A Star (USA) **W. J. and T. C. O. Gredley**
4 **GIANT REDWOOD (IRE)**, 4, b c Galileo (IRE)—Gwynn (IRE) **Middleham Park Racing III & Partners**
5 **GRACELAND (FR)**, 4, b bf Mastercraftsman (IRE)—Jeunesse Lulu (IRE) **The Chriselliam Partnership**
6 **INDEPENDENT ROSE**, 4, ch f Mount Nelson—Red Roses Story (FR) **Chippenham Lodge Stud Limited**
7 **INSTANT KARMA (IRE)**, 5, b g Peintre Celebre (USA)—Kotdiji **L. Caine & J. Barnett**
8 **NEYMAR**, 4, ch g New Approach (IRE)—Just Like A Woman **Mascalls Stud**
9 **ROCK OF MAX**, 4, b g Royal Applause—Poldhu **Karmaa Racing Ltd**
10 **TAPER TANTRUM (IRE)**, 4, b g Azamour (IRE)—Maramba (USA) **Secular Stagnation**

THREE-YEAR-OLDS

11 **AID TO AFRICA (IRE)**, b c Big Bad Bob (IRE)—El Soprano (IRE) **Wildcard Racing Syndicate**
12 **ALCANAR (USA)**, ch c Teofilo (IRE)—Badalona **Sheikh Marwan Al Maktoum**
13 **BATTS ROCK (IRE)**, b c Fastnet Rock (AUS)—Be My Queen (IRE) **Lady Bamford**
14 **BLUE MOON RISING (IRE)**, ch f Dream Ahead (USA)—
                                   Wedding Gown **Miss Emily Asprey & Christopher Wright**
15 **BOCKING END (IRE)**, b c Paco Boy (IRE)—Miss Wells (IRE) **W. J. and T. C. O. Gredley**
16 **BONHOMIE**, b f Shamardal (USA)—Bonnie Doon (IRE) **Her Majesty The Queen**
17 **CHELABELLA**, b f Medicean—Agrippina **Mr Paddy Barrett**
18 **DALESIDE**, b f Vale of York (IRE)—Al Cobra (IRE) **Saif Ali**
19 **DAVEY BOY**, ch g Paco Boy (IRE)—She's So Pretty (IRE) **Mr David Lockwood & Mr Fred Lockwood**
20 **DUCHY**, b f Kyllachy—Albavilla **Mr Michael & Mrs Michelle Morris**
21 **DUCK A L'ORANGE (IRE)**, ch g Duke of Marmalade (IRE)—Incheni (IRE) **J. Barnett**
22 **FORECASTER**, b f Fastnet Rock (AUS)—Aurore (IRE) **Her Majesty The Queen**
23 **GENERAL HAZARD (IRE)**, gr g Cacique (IRE)—In The Soup (USA) **Mr R. P. B. Michaelson**
24 **KAISAN**, b g Rip Van Winkle (IRE)—Orinoco (IRE) **Lady Bamford**
25 **MACHINE LEARNER**, b g Sir Percy—My First Romance **The Deflators**
26 **MARCH PAST (IRE)**, ch c Teofilo (IRE)—Blue Parade (IRE) **Saif Ali**
27 **MIDNIGHT MYSTIC**, b f Fastnet Rock (AUS)—In The Mist **Lady Bamford**
28 **MODEST**, b f Kyllachy—Coy (IRE) **Mr T Hyde and Mr David Graham**
29 **PURPLE MAGIC**, b f Rip Van Winkle (IRE)—Discerning **Lady Bamford**
30 **PURPLE RAVEN**, b f Poet's Voice—Juniper Girl (IRE) **Mr M. B. Hawtin**
31 **ROSECOMB (IRE)**, b f Rip Van Winkle (IRE)—Malyana **M. L. W. Bell Racing Ltd**
32 **SCHOOL FETE (IRE)**, b c Authorized (IRE)—Local Spirit (USA) **Sheikh Marwan Al Maktoum**
33 **SCIARRA**, ch f Monsieur Bond (IRE)—Tibesti **Qatar Racing Ltd**
34 **SHOW LEGEND**, ch g Showcasing—Dubai Legend **Three Desperate Housewives**
35 **SORORAL (IRE)**, b f Dream Ahead (USA)—Sister Sylvia **M. L. W. Bell Racing Ltd**
36 **STETCHWORTH PARK**, b g Duke of Marmalade (IRE)—Perseida (IRE) **W. J. and T. C. O. Gredley**
37 **STRATHEARN (IRE)**, b g Halling (USA)—Polska (USA) **Mr Colin Bryce**
38 **TAUREAN STAR (IRE)**, b g Elnadim (USA)—Marhaba **Mr Brian Goodyear**
39 **THE MAJOR**, b g Major Cadeaux—Ballerina Suprema (IRE) **Lady Clare Law**

MR MICHAEL BELL - Continued

40 **TOWERLANDS PARK (IRE)**, b c Danehill Dancer (IRE)—Strategy **W. J. and T. C. O. Gredley**
41 **WAR DEPARTMENT (IRE)**, b g Frozen Power (IRE)—On My Kness (FR) **W. J. and T. C. O. Gredley**

TWO-YEAR-OLDS

42 **ABACUS**, b c 29/3 Sixties Icon—Friendlier (Zafonic (USA)) **W. J. and T. C. O. Gredley**
43 **ABBU RAHY**, b c 8/4 Mayson—Abandon (USA) (Rahy (USA)) (35000) **Jaber Abdullah**
44 **AIR MINISTRY (IRE)**, b c 4/4 High Chaparral (IRE)—
        Hadarama (IRE) (Sinndar (IRE)) (55000) **W. J. and T. C. O. Gredley**
45 **AMERICAN PATROL (IRE)**, ch c 15/3 Rio de La Plata (USA)—
        Gutter Press (IRE) (Raise A Grand (IRE)) (105000) **W. J. and T. C. O. Gredley**
46 Ch c 17/2 Mayson—Arch of Colours (Monsun (GER)) (19000) **Mascalls Stud**
47 B f 5/3 Henrythenavigator (USA)—Babycakes (IRE) (Marju (IRE)) (51679) **Mr James Acheson**
48 B f 16/4 Elusive Quality (USA)—Badalona (Cape Cross (IRE)) **Sheikh Marwan Al Maktoum**
49 B c 6/3 Pivotal—Constitute (USA) (Gone West (USA)) (45000) **The Royal Ascot Racing Club**
50 Ch f 19/5 Raven's Pass (USA)—Dancing Abbie (USA) (Theatrical) **Sheikh Marwan Al Maktoum**
51 **DANCING ELEGANCE**, ch f 27/2 Nathaniel (IRE)—
        Parisian Elegance (Zilzal (USA)) (31000) **Chippenham Lodge Stud**
52 **ELEMENTARY**, b c 25/2 Exceed And Excel (AUS)—Humdrum (Dr Fong (USA)) **Her Majesty The Queen**
53 B f 12/5 Sepoy (AUS)—Fairy Efisio (Efisio) (60000) **Highclere Thoroughbred Racing**
54 Ch f 7/3 Nathaniel (IRE)—Fleur de Lis (Nayef (USA)) **W. J. & T. C. O. Gredley**
55 Br c 3/3 Arcano (IRE)—Folle Blanche (Elusive Quality (USA)) (28054) **Fish, Fox and Ware**
56 **GLASSALT**, b f 1/2 Medaglia d'oro (USA)—Abergeldie (USA) (Street Cry (IRE)) **Her Majesty The Queen**
57 B c 21/3 Sir Prancealot (IRE)—Hapipi (Bertolini (USA)) (24761) **Fish, Fox and Ware**
58 Ch f 15/2 Zebedee—Hawattef (IRE) (Mujtahid (USA)) (280000) **Lady Bamford**
59 Ch f 30/3 Rip Van Winkle (IRE)—In The Soup (USA) (Alphabet Soup (USA)) (8000) **Sibbertoft Bloodstock Ltd**
60 Ch f 26/3 Zoffany (IRE)—Inis Boffin (Danehill Dancer (IRE)) (33222) **Mrs B. V. Sangster**
61 B c 23/2 Firebreak—Island Rhapsody (Bahamian Bounty) (24761) **Fish, Fox and Ware**
62 **JE SUIS CHARLIE**, b c 12/3 High Chaparral (IRE)—
        Fin (Groom Dancer (USA)) (21000) **Mrs G. Rowland-Clark & Mr C. M. Budgett**
63 B f 8/4 Poet's Voice—Juniper Girl (IRE) (Revoque (IRE)) (40000) **Mr M. B. Hawtin**
64 **KSCHESSINSKA**, b f 31/3 Sir Percy—Les Hurlants (IRE) (Barathea (USA)) (32000) **W. J. and T. C. O. Gredley**
65 Ch c 2/4 Dream Ahead (USA)—Last Cry (FR) (Peintre Celebre (USA)) (60000) **Mr J Barnett & Mr Timmy Hyde**
66 Br f 12/2 Sayif (IRE)—Lough Mewin (IRE) (Woodman (USA)) (59062) **Saleh Al Homaizi & Imad Al Sagar**
67 **MAORI BOB (IRE)**, b c 15/4 Big Bad Bob (IRE)—
        Tekhania (IRE) (Dalakhani (IRE)) (45773) **Mr P Philipps, Mr C Philipps, Mr T Redman**
68 **MERLIN**, b c 1/2 Oasis Dream—Momentary (Nayef (USA)) **Her Majesty The Queen**
69 Ch f 23/2 Notnowcato—Ming Meng (IRE) (Intikhab (USA)) **Mr Paddy Barrett**
70 **PREOBRAJENSKA**, b f 4/2 Paco Boy (IRE)—Unex Mona Lisa (Shamardal (USA)) **W. J. and T. C. O. Gredley**
71 Gr ro f 25/1 Stay Thirsty (USA)—
        Primrose Hill (USA) (Giant's Causeway (USA)) (65000) **The Hon. Mrs J. M. Corbett and Mr C. Wright**
72 **PRINCE MONOLULU**, ch c 28/1 Kyllachy—Corrine (IRE) (Spectrum (IRE)) (90000) **W. J. and T. C. O. Gredley**
73 B c 15/3 Henrythenavigator (USA)—Princess Danah (IRE) (Danehill (USA)) **Saleh Al Homaizi & Imad Al Sagar**
74 B c 29/1 Raven's Pass (USA)—Rainbow Desert (USA) (Dynaformer (USA)) (70000) **Saif Ali & Saeed H. Altayer**
75 B c 25/3 Dragon Pulse (IRE)—Riymaisa (IRE) (Traditionally (USA)) (33000)
76 **RONALD R (IRE)**, ch c 1/2 Nathaniel (IRE)—
        Amazon Beauty (IRE) (Wolfhound (USA)) (130000) **W. J. and T. C. O. Gredley**
77 **SHE**, ch f 8/4 Dubawi (IRE)—First City (Diktat) (75000) **W. J. & T. C. O. Gredley**
78 B c 16/1 Henrythenavigator (USA)—Station House (IRE) (Galileo (IRE)) (20000)
79 **STICKS MCKENZIE**, b c 16/3 Sepoy (AUS)—
        Bended Knee (Refuse To Bend (IRE)) (65000) **W. J. and T. C. O. Gredley**
80 B c 10/3 Pivotal—Striving (IRE) (Danehill Dancer (IRE)) (72000) **Mr Michael Lowe**
81 **THREE DUCHESSES**, b f 26/4 Dutch Art—Three Ducks (Diktat) (20000) **The Hon Major James Broughton**
82 **WAR OFFICE (IRE)**, b c 27/1 Dutch Art—
        Slieve Mish (IRE) (Cape Cross (IRE)) (110000) **W. J. and T. C. O. Gredley**
83 **WINSTON C (IRE)**, b c 11/3 Rip Van Winkle (IRE)—
        Pitrizza (IRE) (Machiavellian (USA)) (55000) **W. J. and T. C. O. Gredley**

Assistant Trainer: Ben James

Jockey (flat): Jamie Spencer. **Apprentice:** Louis Steward.

30 MR JAMES BENNETT, Wantage
Postal: 2 Filley Alley, Letcombe Bassett, Wantage, Oxfordshire, OX12 9LT
Contacts: PHONE (01235) 762163 MOBILE (07771) 523076
E-MAIL jabennett345@btinternet.com

1 IDOL DEPUTY (FR), 10, gr g Silver Deputy (CAN)—Runaway Venus (USA) Miss J. C. Blackwell
2 THE LAST MELON, 4, ch g Sir Percy—Step Fast (USA) Miss J. C. Blackwell
3 ZAC COURAGEOUS (IRE), 4, b g Mastercraftsman (IRE)—Thats Your Opinion Miss J. C. Blackwell

Assistant Trainer: Miss J. Blackwell

Jockey (flat): Racheal Kneller.

31 MR ALAN BERRY, Cockerham
Postal: Moss Side Racing Stables, Crimbles Lane, Cockerham, Lancashire, LA2 0ES
Contacts: PHONE (01524) 791179 FAX (01524) 791958 MOBILE (07880) 553515
E-MAIL mosssideracing@tiscali.co.uk WEBSITE www.alanberryracing.co.uk

1 AMIS REUNIS, 7, b m Bahamian Bounty—Spring Clean (FR) A. Berry
2 BUSY BIMBO (IRE), 7, b m Red Clubs (IRE)—Unfortunate
3 ECONOMIC CRISIS (IRE), 7, ch m Excellent Art—Try The Air (IRE) J Berry/ W Burns
4 I'LL BE GOOD, 7, b g Red Clubs (IRE)—Willisa Do Well Racing
5 JORDAURA, 10, br g Primo Valentino (IRE)—Christina's Dream A. Berry
6 KAY GEE BE (IRE), 12, b g Fasliyev (USA)—Pursuit of Truth (USA) A. Berry
7 LICENCE TO TILL (USA), 9, b g War Chant (USA)—With A Wink (USA) Spectral Racing
8 MACARTHURS PARK (IRE), 4, b f Equiano (FR)—La Tintoretta (IRE) A. Berry
9 MARGOT ROSE, 4, b f Kheleyf (USA)—Sanjuna A. Berry
10 MYSTIFIED (IRE), 13, b g Raise A Grand (IRE)—Sunrise (IRE) A. Berry
11 PARTNER'S GOLD (IRE), 6, b g Red Clubs (IRE)—Unfortunate Partner's Brewery
12 PENNY PURSUITS, 5, b m Pastoral Pursuits—Sattelight A. R. White
13 PLUNDER, 6, ch g Zamindar (USA)—Reaching Ahead (USA) A. Berry
14 RAISE A BILLION, 5, b g Major Cadeaux—Romantic Destiny T Blane, F Flynn, H Rocks & M Rocks
15 RED FOREVER, 5, ch g Major Cadeaux—Spindara (IRE) Sporting Kings
16 RED LUCK (IRE), 4, b f Thousand Words—Mirandassister (IRE) R Lennon & S Allen
17 SHAMKHANI, 4, b g Mullionmileanhour (IRE)—Matilda Peace Do Well Racing
18 TENHOO, 10, b g Reset (AUS)—Bella Bambina M. Watkinson & Mr P. Steadman

THREE-YEAR-OLDS

19 OH WHAT A SPECIES (IRE), b f Captain Rio—Aspired (IRE) Mojo Partnership
20 ROMAN TIMES (IRE), b f Holy Roman Emperor (IRE)—Timeless Dream A. B. Parr
21 TIHANA, b f Lawman (FR)—La Bocca (USA) Mojo Partnership

Other Owners: Mr S. J. Allen, J. Berry, T. W. Blane, Mr G. D. Brown, W. Burns, Mr F. G. Flynn, Mr D. P. Gallagher, Mr I. Griffiths, Mr B. K. Hopson, Mr I. D. Johnson, Mr R. J. Lennon, Mr B. J. Maxted, Mr A. McGennis, Mr H. Rocks, Mr M. Rocks, Mr N. Sharp, Mr D. P. Steadman, Mr T. Suttle, Mr M. Watkinson.

32 MR J. A. BERRY, Blackwater
Postal: Ballyroe, Blackwater, Enniscorthy, Co. Wexford, Ireland
Contacts: MOBILE (00353) 8625 57537
E-MAIL johnaberry@eircom.net

1 ABBEY MAGIC (IRE), 5, b m Beneficial—Magical Theatre (IRE) G. Halley
2 BALLYROE RAMBLER (IRE), 9, br g Lahib (USA)—Victoria's Rose (IRE) Fire & Ice Syndicate
3 BORDEAUX BILL (IRE), 5, b br g Craigsteel—Laura Croft (IRE) P. Laffin
4 CATCH MY DRIFT (IRE), 7, ch g Subtle Power (IRE)—Deliga Lady (IRE) J. A. Berry
5 COOTAMUNDRA (IRE), 13, ch g Broken Hearted—Sigginstown Turbine Syndicate
6 DAY DAY (IRE), 6, b m Hurricane Run (IRE)—Mem O'rees J. P. McManus
7 FAMOUS BALLERINA (IRE), 8, b m Golan (IRE)—World of Ballet (IRE) J. A. Berry
8 PRIMROSE LADY (IRE), 5, b m Craigsteel—Raheen River (IRE) Mrs J. Berry
9 RIGHTY RUE (IRE), 6, b m Mountain High (IRE)—Last of Many (IRE) Mrs A. Berry
10 TELL ME THIS, 7, b g High-Rise (IRE)—Gallic Flame Mrs A. Berry
11 WHATS ON THE MENU (IRE), 12, ch g Anshan—Leading Dream (IRE) Mrs J. Berry

MR J. A. BERRY - Continued

Assistant Trainer: B. Parnell

Amateur: Mr J. P. Berry.

---

33   MR JOHN BERRY, Newmarket
Postal: Beverley House Stables, Exeter Road, Newmarket, Suffolk, CB8 8LR
Contacts: PHONE (01638) 660663
WEBSITE www.beverleyhousestables.com

1 BLUE SEA OF IBROX (IRE), 8, gr m Subtle Power (IRE)—Jerpoint Rose (IRE) **Mr S. Brown**
2 COTTESLOE (IRE), 7, b g Teofilo (IRE)—Vignelaure (IRE) **Mr S. Brown**
3 FEN LADY, 4, b f Champs Elysees—Query (USA) **Mr D. Tunmore**
4 GRAND LIAISON, 7, b m Sir Percy—Dancinginthedark **Mr D. Tunmore**
5 INDIRA, 5, ch m Sleeping Indian—Forever Loved **Severn Crossing Partnership**
6 KOREEN (IRE), 5, b g Samum (GER)—Pony Girl (FR) **J. C. De P. Berry**
7 MAGIC ICE, 6, b m Royal Applause—Winter Ice **J. C. De P. Berry**
8 NEAR WILD HEAVEN, 5, b m Robin des Champs (FR)—Love Supreme (IRE) **The Beverley Hillbillies**
9 PLATINUM PROOF (USA), 6, b br g Smart Strike (CAN)—Keeper Hill (USA) **J. C. De P. Berry**
10 ROY ROCKET (FR), 6, gr g Layman (USA)—Minnie's Mystery (FR) **McCarthy & Berry**
11 RUSSIAN LINK, 6, b m Rail Link—Zathonia **Mrs E. L. Berry**
12 SENATOR MATT, 6, b h Joe Bear (IRE)—Anytime Anywhere **Mrs M. Lethbridge-Brown**
13 SO MUCH WATER (IRE), 4, gr f Le Havre (IRE)—Minnie's Mystery (FR) **McCarthy & Berry**
14 ZAROSA (IRE), 7, b m Barathea (IRE)—Shantalla Peak (IRE) **Mr R. G. Vicarage**

THREE-YEAR-OLDS

15 HYMN FOR THE DUDES, br g Sakhee's Secret—Hermione's Dream **C. V. Wentworth**
16 SACRED ROCK (IRE), b g Rock of Gibraltar (IRE)—Snowpalm **Raffles Thoroughbred Racing**
17 SIRLI (FR), b f Carlotamix (FR)—Tailzie **The Beverley House Stables Partnership**
18 WHITE VALIANT (FR), gr g Youmzain (IRE)—Minnie's Mystery (FR) **J. C. De P. Berry**

Other Owners: Mr A. W. Fordham, Mr R. Jones, Miss L. I. McCarthy, Mrs M. L. Parry, Mr B. M. Sherwin, P. M. Steele-Mortimer, L. J. Stratton, L. C. Wadey.

Jockey (flat): John Egan. Jockey (NH): Will Kennedy, Jack Quinlan.

---

34   MR JIM BEST, Lewes
Postal: Grandstand Stables, The Old Racecourse, Lewes, East Sussex, BN7 1UR
Contacts: PHONE (01435) 882073 (01273) 480249 FAX (01435) 882073 MOBILE (07968) 743272
E-MAIL jimandtombest@btinternet.com WEBSITE www.jimandtombestracing.co.uk

1 ACE FIGHTER PILOT, 10, b g Silver Patriarch (IRE)—Vedra (IRE) **Odds On Racing**
2 ALBERTA (IRE), 7, ch g Choisir (AUS)—Akita (IRE) **Allen B Pope, S&A Mares, Jamie Donnelly**
3 ARAMADYH, 5, gr m Authorized (IRE)—Swift Dispersal **Mr & Mrs F. W. Golding**
4 AUSTIN FRIARS, 4, b g New Approach (IRE)—My Luigia (IRE) **Austin Friars Partnership**
5 BOBBY BENTON (IRE), 5, b g Invincible Spirit (IRE)—Remarkable Story **M. J. Benton**
6 BORU'S BROOK (IRE), 8, b g Brian Boru (IRE)—Collybrook Lady (IRE) **Cheltenham Dreamers**
7 BRIAC (FR), 5, b g Kapgarde (FR)—Jarwin Do (FR) **Mr O. S. Harris**
8 BROTHER BENNETT (FR), 6, gr g Martaline—La Gaminerie (FR) **The Best Elite Partnership**
9 ECHO BRAVA, 6, gr g Proclamation (IRE)—Snake Skin **M. J. Benton**
10 GAS LINE BOY (IRE), 10, b g Blueprint (IRE)—Jervia **The Three Graces**
11 GENEROUS JACK (IRE), 7, ch g Generous (IRE)—Yosna (FR) **Mr J. J. Callaghan**
12 INCH WING (IRE), 8, b m Winged Love (IRE)—Incharder (IRE) **Mr & Mrs F. W. Golding**
13 INDIAN SECRET (IRE), 6, ch m Indian River (FR)—Secret Leave **Mr J. J. Callaghan**
14 JAZZY LADY (IRE), 5, b m Intikhab (USA)—Lock's Heath (CAN) **Wishful Thinkers Partnership**
15 KIAMA BAY (IRE), 10, b g Fraam—La Panthere (USA) **Chris Dillon & Barry Reilly**
16 LITTLE BUXTED (USA), 6, b br g Mr Greeley (USA)—Mo Cheoil Thu (IRE) **Elten Barker & Chris Dillon**
17 MARIA'S CHOICE (IRE), 7, b g Oratorio (IRE)—Amathusia **Mr P. J. Arrow**
18 MISSILE MAN (IRE), 7, b g Winged Love (IRE)—Miss Ondee (IRE) **Jack Callaghan & Christopher Dillon**
19 MY LORD, 8, br g Ishiguru (USA)—Lady Smith **M. J. Benton**
20 NEW STREET (IRE), 5, gr h Acclamation—New Deal **Mr J. J. Callaghan**
21 OFFICER DRIVEL (IRE), 5, b g Captain Rio—Spiritville (IRE) **M. J. Benton**
22 OUTRATH (IRE), 6, b g Captain Rio—Silver Grouse (IRE) **Outrath Partnership**

MR JIM BEST - Continued

23 **PLANETOID (IRE)**, 8, b g Galileo (IRE)—Palmeraie (USA) **Planetoid Partnership**
24 **RED ORATOR**, 7, ch g Osorio (GER)—Red Roses Story (FR) **Wishful Thinkers Partnership**
25 **SIX GUN SERENADE (IRE)**, 5, b g Kalanisi (IRE)—Zenaide (IRE) **Mr J. J. Callaghan**
26 **SLOWFOOT (GER)**, 8, b h Hernando (FR)—Simply Red (GER) **Slowfoot Partnership**
27 **THATS MY RABBIT (IRE)**, 7, b g Heron Island (IRE)—Minnie Turbo (IRE) **The Best Elite Partnership**
28 **THEHILL OFTHE ROCK (IRE)**, 6, ch g Indian River (FR)—Ballyburn Lady (IRE) **Mr & Mrs F. W. Golding**
29 **WAYWARD FROLIC**, 10, br g Fair Mix (IRE)—Mighty Frolic **JAG Racing Elite**
30 **WILLSHEBETRYING**, 5, b m Act One—Precedence (IRE) **Willshebetrying Partnership**

Other Owners: Mr A. Achilleous, Mr E. Barker, Mr J. J. Best, Mr M. Callow, Mr J. Cumber, Mr C. J. Dillon, Mr J. Donnelly, Mr D. Edmonston, Mr P. J. Gardner, Mrs M. J. Golding, Mr F. W. Golding, Mr J. Haste, Mr M. Jackson, Mr P. J. Legros, Mr A. A. Maloney, Mr S. Mares, Mrs A. Mares, A. B. Pope, Mr B. Reilly, Mr G. C. Sales, Mr P. Thwaites.

Assistant Trainer: Mr Tom Best

Jockey (flat): William Twiston-Davies.

35　**MR JOHN BEST, Borden**
Postal: **Eyehorn Farm, Munsgore Lane, Borden, Sittingbourne, Kent, ME9 8JU**
Contacts: **MOBILE (07889) 362154**
E-MAIL john.best@johnbestracing.com WEBSITE www.johnbestracing.com

1 **AUTHORIZED SPIRIT**, 4, b f Authorized (IRE)—World Spirit **Stapleford Racing Ltd**
2 **BERRAHRI (IRE)**, 5, b g Bahri (USA)—Band of Colour (IRE) **Curtis, Malt & Wykes**
3 **BIG WHISKEY (IRE)**, 6, ch g Ad Valorem (USA)—El Opera (IRE) **Mr N. Dyshaev**
4 **CHARLIES MATE**, 5, br g Myboycharlie (IRE)—Retainage (USA) **Mrs J. O. Jones**
5 **FAST SPRITE (IRE)**, 4, b g Fast Company (IRE)—Salty Air (IRE) **N Dyshaev & The Boys Partnership**
6 **FEARLESS LAD (IRE)**, 6, b g Excellent Art—Souffle **Mrs J. O. Jones**
7 **GUNG HO JACK**, 7, b g Moss Vale (IRE)—Bijan (IRE) **Best, Paine & Woodward**
8 **HIORNE TOWER (FR)**, 5, b g Poliglote—Hierarchie (FR) **Mrs J. O. Jones**
9 **LUPO D'ORO (IRE)**, 7, b g Amadeus Wolf—Vital Laser (USA) **Mr S. Malcolm, Mr M. Winwright & Mr P. Tindall**
10 **MONCARLO**, 6, b g Lucarno (USA)—Sparkling Jewel **David & Elaine Long**
11 **MOSSGO (IRE)**, 6, b g Moss Vale (IRE)—Perovskia (USA) **Hucking Horses V**
12 **MULLIONHEIR**, 4, b g Mullionmileanhour (IRE)—Peyto Princess **Mr S. D. Malcolm**
13 **PRINCESS SPIRIT**, 7, b m Invincible Spirit (IRE)—Habariya (IRE) **Mr N. Dyshaev**
14 **REVISION (FR)**, 4, b br g Vision d'etat (FR)—Karmibola (FR) **Curtis, Malt & Williams**
15 **SHEIKH THE REINS (IRE)**, 7, b g Iffraaj—Wychwood Wanderer (IRE) **Williams & Harris**
16 **VALE OF IRON (IRE)**, 4, b c Vale of York (IRE)—Lady Van Gogh **Lingfield Park Owners Group I**

THREE-YEAR-OLDS

17 **BALLYLARE**, b g Mullionmileanhour (IRE)—Retainage (USA) **Curtis, Malt & Williams**
18 **MULLED WINE**, b c Mullionmileanhour (IRE)—Numanthia (IRE) **Last Orders Racing**
19 **MULLOVER**, b f Mullionmileanhour (IRE)—Daughters World **Williams & Harris**
20 **RUBY WEDNESDAY**, b f Mullionmileanhour (IRE)—Cheap N Chic **Harris, Beckett & Millen**
21 **SANTIBURI SPRING**, b f Mullionmileanhour (IRE)—Santiburi Girl **Best, Paine, Hill & Young**
22 **TRIDENT TESTED**, gr g Arabian Gleam—Neptune's Girl (IRE) **Curtis & Williams Bstk, Paine & Malt**
23 **WHITSTABLE PEARL (IRE)**, b f Kodiac—Amber's Bluff **Bruce Woodward & Mark Wellbelove**

TWO-YEAR-OLDS

24 Ch c 5/2 Muhtathir—Abondante (USA) (Thunder Gulch (USA)) (44296) **Curtis & Williams Bloodstock**
25 B f 24/4 Mullionmileanhour (IRE)—
　　　　　　　　　　　　Balletlou (IRE) (Peintre Celebre (USA)) **Simon Malcolm & Malcolm Winwright**
26 **BANTA BAY**, b c 21/4 Kheleyf (USA)—Atnab (USA) (Riverman (USA)) **Jones, Fuller & Paine**
27 B f 22/2 American Post—Elle S'voyait Deja (USA) (Carson City (USA))
28 B c 1/4 Mullionmileanhour (IRE)—Hannah's Dream (IRE) (King's Best (USA))
29 B c 7/3 Dream Ahead (USA)—
　　　　　　　　　　　　Kerry Gal (IRE) (Galileo (IRE)) (32000) **Mr & Mrs H Jarvis and Mr & Mrs S Malcolm**
30 **NECESSARY**, b c 21/2 Mullionmileanhour (IRE)—Neissa (USA) (Three Wonders (USA))
31 **NOBLE ATTITUDE (FR)**, b c 20/3 Dunkerque (FR)—
　　　　　　　　　　　　Silent Flight (FR) (Sicyos (USA)) **Mr H J Jarvis & Mrs P Jarvis**
32 **PADRINHO (IRE)**, b c 23/3 High Chaparral (IRE)—Belanoiva (IRE) (Motivator) **Mr S. D. Malcolm**
33 B c 27/3 Tagula (IRE)—Peninsula Girl (IRE) (Cape Cross (IRE)) (15000) **Keaveney & Butcher**
34 B c 8/4 Mullionmileanhour (IRE)—Queen Ranavola (USA) (Medaglia d'oro (USA))

MR JOHN BEST - Continued

35 B c 1/5 Casamento (IRE)—
      Sense of Greeting (IRE) (Key of Luck (USA)) (28000) **Mr & Mrs S Malcolm and Mr & Mrs H Jarvis**
36 STAPLEFORD, b f 20/1 Equiano (FR)—World Spirit (Agnes World (USA)) **Stapleford Racing Ltd**

Other Owners: Mr J. R. Best, Mr P. Butcher, Mr M. B. Curtis, Mrs P. Jarvis, H. J. Jarvis, Mr G. R. Jones, Mr M. Keaveney,
Mr A. Keaveney, Mrs E. Long, D. J. Long, Mrs L. C. G. Malcolm, Mr R. C. Malt, Mr M. J. Wellbelove, Miss H. J. Williams,
Mr M. J. Winwright, Mr B. Woodward.

Jockey (flat): Kieren Fox.

---

36   MISS HARRIET BETHELL, Arnold
Postal: **Arnold Manor, Black Tup Lane, Arnold, Hull, North Humberside, HU11 5JA**

1 EL MASSIVO (IRE), 6, b b br g Authorized (IRE)—Umtoulah (IRE) **W. A. Bethell**
2 FRESH BY NATURE (IRE), 9, b m Flemensfirth (USA)—Star Alert (IRE) **W. A. Bethell**
3 KUDA HURAA (IRE), 8, b g Montjeu (IRE)—Healing Music (FR) **W. A. Bethell**
4 MIAMI PRESENT (IRE), 6, b br g Presenting—Miami Nights (GER) **W. A. Bethell**
5 MONEY FOR NOTHING, 7, b g Kayf Tara—Top of The Dee **W. A. Bethell**
6 NALIM (IRE), 10, b g Milan—Hati Roy (IRE) **W. A. Bethell**

---

37   MR JAMES BETHELL, Middleham
Postal: **Thorngill, Coverham, Middleham, North Yorkshire, DL8 4TJ**
Contacts: **PHONE (01969) 640360 FAX (01969) 640360 MOBILE (07831) 683528**
E-MAIL james@jamesbethell.co.uk WEBSITE www.jamesbethell.com

1 BELLE DE LAWERS, 5, b m Black Sam Bellamy (IRE)—Scotland The Brave **Mr J. Tabet**
2 BRIARDALE (IRE), 4, b g Arcano (IRE)—Marine City (JPN) **J. Carrick&Clarendon Thoroughbred Racing**
3 BURNESTON, 4, br g Rock of Gibraltar (IRE)—Grain of Gold **Clarendon Thoroughbred Racing**
4 DECLAN, 4, ch g Dylan Thomas (IRE)—Fleurissimo **Normandie Stud Ltd**
5 LAST SUPPER, 7, b m Echo of Light—Scotland The Brave **R. F. Gibbons**
6 MISTER BOB (GER), 7, ch g Black Sam Bellamy (IRE)—Mosquera (GER) **Mr R. Gibbons**
7 NOBBLY BOBBLY (IRE), 4, br c High Chaparral (IRE)—Rock Queen (IRE) **Mr J. S. Lambert**
8 PRINCESS PEACHES, 4, ch f Notnowcato—Miss Apricot **D. Kilburn**
9 RICH AGAIN (IRE), 7, b g Amadeus Wolf—Fully Fashioned (IRE) **R. T. Vickers**
10 THANKYOU VERY MUCH, 6, b m Lucky Story (USA)—Maid of Perth **Mr R. Gibbons**

THREE-YEAR-OLDS

11 AIRTON, b g Champs Elysees—Fly In Style **Clarendon Thoroughbred Racing**
12 CHIRINGUITA (USA), gr f Hard Spun (USA)—Silver Games (IRE) **C. N. Wright**
13 FAST AND FURIOUS (IRE), b c Rock of Gibraltar (IRE)—Ocean Talent (USA) **Mr A. Buckingham**
14 FRUIT SALAD, ch f Monsieur Bond (IRE)—Miss Apricot **Clarendon Thoroughbred Racing**
15 HAPPY BIRTHDAY, b f Schiaparelli (GER)—Shazana **Mr R. Gibbons**
16 HAZELY, b f Cape Cross (IRE)—Sentimental Value (USA) **Clarendon Thoroughbred Racing**
17 LADY CANFORD (IRE), b f Canford Cliffs (IRE)—Soul Mountain (IRE) **Clarendon Thoroughbred Racing**
18 LUKOUTOLDMAKEZEBAK, b g Arabian Gleam—Angelofthenorth **Mr P. McMahon**
19 MON AMI BOB, ch g Schiaparelli (GER)—Maid of Perth **Mr J. Tabet**
20 ON FIRE, b c Olden Times—La Notte **Mrs C. M. Holliday**
21 RICH PURSUIT, ch g Pastoral Pursuits—Salvia **Mr R. Vickers**
22 RONALDJAMESSACH (IRE), ch g Lord Shanakill (USA)—Boschendal (IRE) **Market Avenue Racing Club Ltd**
23 SICILIANO (IRE), b f Tagula (IRE)—Akatib (IRE) **Mr J. A. Tabet**
24 SS VEGA, b f Kheleyf (USA)—Annie Gee **F. Brady**

TWO-YEAR-OLDS

25 B c 6/5 Rock of Gibraltar (IRE)—Ajiaal (Cape Cross (IRE)) (23624) **Mr J. Dance**
26 B c 17/4 Rip Van Winkle (IRE)—Amaya (USA) (Kingmambo (USA)) (18000) **Clarendon Thoroughbred Racing**
27 CONISTONE, ch f 19/2 Poet's Voice—
      Protectress (Hector Protector (USA)) (22000) **Clarendon Thoroughbred Racing**
28 Ch c 23/5 Pivotal—Dorelia (IRE) (Efisio) (30000) **Clarendon Thoroughbred Racing**
29 HAWORTH, b c 6/2 Showcasing—Some Diva (Dr Fong (USA)) (30000) **Clarendon Thoroughbred Racing**
30 JESSINAMILLION, b c 5/5 Mine (IRE)—Miss Apricot (Indian Ridge) **David Kilburn**
31 B br c 1/4 Bated Breath—Mark Too (IRE) (Mark of Esteem (IRE)) (20000) **Clarendon Thoroughbred Racing**

MR JAMES BETHELL - Continued

32 **PORTLEDGE (IRE)**, b c 18/4 Acclamation—Off Chance (Olden Times) (60000) **Mr T. Buckingham**
33 **QUIET WEEKEND**, b c 9/3 Mawatheeq (USA)—Maid of Perth (Mark of Esteem (IRE)) **Mr R. Gibbons**
34 Ch f 16/4 Mastercraftsman (IRE)—Zagreb Flyer (Old Vic) (25000) **Mr J. Lund**

Other Owners: Mr J. D. Bethell, Mrs James Bethell, Mr J. Carrick.

---

38 **MR EDWARD BEVAN, Hereford**
Postal: **Pullen Farm, Ullingswick, Herefordshire, HR1 3JQ**
Contacts: **PHONE/FAX (01432) 820370 MOBILE (07970) 650347**

1 **BOLD CROSS (IRE)**, 13, b g Cape Cross (IRE)—Machikane Akaiito (IRE) **E. G. Bevan**
2 **BOLD DUKE**, 8, b g Sulamani (IRE)—Dominant Duchess **E. G. Bevan**
3 **BOLD GROVE**, 4, b g Proclamation (IRE)—Trysting Grove (IRE) **E. G. Bevan**
4 **HENRYHUDSONBRIDGE (USA)**, 4, b g Henrythenavigator (USA)—Harlan Ash (USA) **E. G. Bevan**
5 **LOOKING ON**, 8, b g Observatory (USA)—Dove Tree (FR) **Mr R. A. Thomas**

Assistant Trainer: Michelle Byrom

---

39 **MR GEORGE BEWLEY, Hawick**
Postal: **South Dean Farm, Bonchester Bridge, Hawick, Roxburghshire, TD9 8TP**
Contacts: **PHONE (01450) 860651 MOBILE (07704) 924783**
E-MAIL southdean.farm@btconnect.com WEBSITE www.georgebewleyracing.co.uk

1 **BANNOW STORM (IRE)**, 5, b m Presenting—Bannow Girl (IRE) **martingrayracing**
2 **BRAE ON (IRE)**, 8, ch g Presenting—Raphuca (IRE) **West Coast Racing Partnership**
3 **CHICAGO OUTFIT (IRE)**, 11, b g Old Vic—Lambourne Lace (IRE) **G. T. Bewley**
4 **DIAMOND D'AMOUR (IRE)**, 10, gr g Danehill Dancer (IRE)—
Diamond Line (FR) **Mr J Hope,Mr K Twentyman & Mr J Gibson**
5 **DR WEST (IRE)**, 5, b g Westerner—Contessa Messina (IRE) **Bewley, M Robson, W Rayment & L Davidson**
6 **FLYING NATIVE (IRE)**, 7, b g Winged Love (IRE)—Native Success (IRE) **Mr L. B. Kerr**
7 **GRAYS CHOICE (IRE)**, 5, b g Well Chosen—Pennyworth (IRE) **martingrayracing**
8 **HUNTERS BELT (IRE)**, 12, b g Intikhab (USA)—Three Stars **Mr R. A. Fisher**
9 **INNIS SHANNON (IRE)**, 6, br m Stowaway—Put On Hold (IRE) **Mrs Lesley Bewley & Mr John Gibson**
10 **MESSINA STRAIGHTS**, 8, br g Blueprint (IRE)—Calabria **Southdean Racing Club**
11 **OUR MORRIS (IRE)**, 5, b g Milan—Broken Gale (IRE) **G. T. Bewley**
12 **QUEST MAGIC (IRE)**, 10, ch g Fantastic Quest (IRE)—Magic Sign (IRE) **West Coast Racing Partnership**
13 **REV UP RUBY**, 8, b m Revoque (IRE)—Kingennie **Mr A Kerr, L Kerr, K Twentyman & Bewley**
14 **SILVER TRIX (IRE)**, 6, gr m Mahler—Sika Trix (IRE) **G. T. Bewley**
15 **SYBIL GREY**, 7, gr m Fair Mix (IRE)—Gimme Shelter (IRE) **Mrs E. Annett**
16 4, Gr f Black Sam Bellamy (IRE)—Tikk Tokk (IRE) **G. T. Bewley**
17 **WARDEN LAW (IRE)**, 5, b h Definite Article—Mrs Avery (IRE) **martingrayracing**
18 **WHATS UP WOODY (IRE)**, 11, b g Beneficial—Lady Noellel (IRE) **G. T. Bewley**

Other Owners: Mrs L. Bewley, Mr L. J. Davidson, Mr J. H. Gibson, Mrs G. Gray, Mr I. M. Gray, J. Hope, Mr D. Kerr, Mr A. M. Kerr, Mr W. Rayment, Mr M. Robson, Mr K. Twentyman, Mr A. L. Wilson.

Jockey (NH): Jonathon Bewley.

---

40 **MR JOSEPH BEWLEY, Jedburgh**
Postal: **Newhouse Cottage, Camptown, Jedburgh, Roxburghshire, TD8 6RW**
Contacts: **PHONE (01835) 840273 MOBILE (07758) 783910**
E-MAIL bewley18@tiscali.co.uk

1 **MAJOR RIDGE (IRE)**, 7, b g Indian Danehill (IRE)—Native Novel (IRE) **J. R. Bewley**
2 **VEINARD (FR)**, 7, ch g Shaanmer (IRE)—Ombline (FR) **J. R. Bewley**

Assistant Trainer: Mrs K Bewley

Conditional: Callum Bewley.

41

MRS PIPPA BICKERTON, Almington
Postal: Almington House, Pinfold Lane, Almington, Market Drayton, Shropshire, TF9 2QR

1 TROPICAL SUNSHINE (IRE), 8, b g Bachelor Duke (USA)—Tropical Coral (IRE) **Mrs P. F. Bickerton**

42

MR SAEED BIN SUROOR, Newmarket
Postal: Godolphin Office, Snailwell Road, Newmarket, Suffolk, CB8 7YE
Contacts: PHONE (01638) 569956

> This list doesn't include horses based in Dubai for the 2016 Carnival which may return to Britain - see **www.godolphin.com**

1 **ALWAYS SMILE (IRE)**, 4, b f Cape Cross (IRE)—Eastern Joy
2 **BASEM**, 5, b h Pivotal—Gonbarda (GER)
3 **BEAUTIFUL ROMANCE**, 4, b f New Approach (IRE)—Mazuna (IRE)
4 **BEST EXAMPLE (USA)**, 4, ch g King's Best (USA)—Born Something (IRE)
5 **BEST OF TIMES**, 4, b c Dubawi (IRE)—Nabati (USA)
6 **CLASSIC COLLECTION**, 4, b g Cape Cross (IRE)—Local Spirit (USA)
7 **ELITE ARMY**, 5, b g Authorized (IRE)—White Rose (GER)
8 **EMIRATES AIRLINE**, 4, b g Dubawi (IRE)—Moonlife (IRE)
9 **FLIGHT OFFICER**, 4, b h New Approach (IRE)—Danuta (USA)
10 **FUTURE EMPIRE**, 4, ch g New Approach (IRE)—Fann (USA)
11 **FUTURE REFERENCE (IRE)**, 6, ch g Raven's Pass (USA)—Mike's Wildcat (USA)
12 **GLOBAL FORCE (IRE)**, 4, b g Shamardal (USA)—Pioneer Bride (USA)
13 **GOOD JUDGE (USA)**, 4, gr g Cape Cross (IRE)—Summer Fete (IRE)
14 **GREATEST PLACE (IRE)**, 4, ch f Shamardal (USA)—Texas Tammy (USA)
15 **HOLD TIGHT**, 4, ch g Exceed And Excel (AUS)—Kangra Valley
16 **IMPORTANT MESSAGE**, 4, b br c New Approach (IRE)—Plaza (USA)
17 **IMPORTANT POINT (USA)**, 4, b br g Street Cry (IRE)—Zofzig (USA)
18 **KICKBOXER (IRE)**, 5, gr g Clodovil (IRE)—Ajig Dancer
19 **LOVELY MEMORY (IRE)**, 4, b f Shamardal (USA)—Folk Opera (IRE)
20 **MEMORIAL DAY (IRE)**, 5, b g Cape Cross (IRE)—Reunite (IRE)
21 **MOVIE SET (USA)**, 4, b br g Dubawi (IRE)—Short Skirt
22 **MY CALL**, 4, b f Shamardal (USA)—Hush Money (CHI)
23 **NEW STRATEGY (IRE)**, 4, b g Lawman (FR)—Kate The Great
24 **POWER GAME**, 4, ch g Shamardal (USA)—Counterclaim
25 **RACING HISTORY (IRE)**, 4, b c Pivotal—Gonbarda (GER)
26 **SUPER KID**, 4, b g Exceed And Excel (AUS)—Crimson Year (USA)
27 **TIME CHECK (USA)**, 4, ch f Shamardal (USA)—Alizes (NZ)
28 **WILD STORM**, 4, b f Dubawi (IRE)—The World
29 **WINTER HOUSE**, 4, b g Cape Cross (IRE)—Villarrica (USA)

THREE-YEAR-OLDS

30 **AARAAMM (USA)**, b f Street Cry (IRE)—Aryaamm (IRE)
31 **AFNAAN**, ch c Raven's Pass (USA)—Almansoora (USA)
32 **AHAZEEJ (IRE)**, b f Dubawi (IRE)—Albaraari
33 **AL FATTAN**, b g Dubawi (IRE)—Ocean Silk (USA)
34 **ALMUNJID (USA)**, b g Street Cry (USA)—Hatheer (USA)
35 **ANNA PLATINI**, ch f Dubawi (IRE)—Antara (GER)
36 **ARCARIUS**, ch c Dubawi (IRE)—Isobel Archer
37 **AZHAR**, b f Exceed And Excel (AUS)—Nitya (FR)
38 **BARRETINA (IRE)**, b f Street Cry (IRE)—Picture Hat (USA)
39 **BRABBLE (USA)**, b f Bernardini (USA)—Well Chosen (USA)
40 **BRAVE HERO**, b c Poet's Voice—Classical Dancer
41 **BRAVE TIMES**, b f Exceed And Excel (AUS)—Marie de Medici (USA)
42 **CLEAR LEADER (USA)**, b c Hard Spun (USA)—Laureldean Gale (USA)
43 **CLEAR WATER (USA)**, b f Hard Spun (USA)—Storm Lily (USA)
44 **COME BACK KING (IRE)**, ch c Pivotal—Queen Consort (USA)
45 **CONFIDENT KID**, b c Dubawi (IRE)—Longing To Dance
46 **DIFFERENT JOURNEY**, b c Poet's Voice—Vintage Gardenia
47 **EBTIHAAL (IRE)**, ch c Teofilo (IRE)—Dance Troupe
48 **FINAL STAGE**, ch f Street Cry (IRE)—Moyesii (USA)

MR SAEED BIN SUROOR - Continued

49 FIRST START, b c Street Cry (IRE)—Measured Tempo
50 FIRST VICTORY (IRE), b f Teofilo (IRE)—Eastern Joy
51 GLOBAL RACING (IRE), ch c Hard Spun (USA)—Dancing Abbie (USA)
52 GOOD MAN (IRE), ch c New Approach (IRE)—Garden City (FR)
53 GOOD RUN (FR), ch c Iffraaj—Tadawul (USA)
54 GOOD TRIP (IRE), b c Dansili—Counterclaim
55 GREAT ORDER (USA), b br c Distorted Humor (USA)—Michita (USA)
56 GREAT RETURN, b c New Approach (IRE)—Under The Rainbow
57 HARDEST PART, b c Hard Spun (USA)—Born Something (IRE)
58 HARLECH, ch f Pivotal—Zoowraa
59 HUGE FUTURE, b c Shamardal (USA)—Time Honoured
60 HUMAN NATURE (IRE), b c Kodiac—Sundown
61 IMPRESSIVE DAY (IRE), b f Cape Cross (IRE)—Shieldmaiden (USA)
62 JUFN, b c Nayef (USA)—Deyaar (USA)
63 LACEY'S LANE, b f Street Cry (IRE)—Hibaayeb
64 LATEST PLAN (USA), ch f Dubawi (IRE)—Badminton
65 LIFE OF LUXURY, b g Shamardal (USA)—Champagnelifestyle
66 LOOKS GREAT, b f New Approach (IRE)—Danehill Dreamer (USA)
67 MOST CELEBRATED (IRE), b c New Approach (IRE)—Pietra Santa (FR)
68 NATURAL SCENERY, b f Dubawi (IRE)—Argentina (IRE)
69 NATURE'S BEAUTY (USA), b f Bernardini (USA)—Channel (USA)
70 NEW LIST, ch c Pivotal—Angel's Tears
71 NEXT LIFE, b f Oasis Dream—Silkwood
72 NEXT MEETING (USA), gr ro f Street Cry (IRE)—Summer Fete (IRE)
73 NEXT STAGE, ch c Dubawi (IRE)—Dash To The Front
74 NICE FUTURE (IRE), b c Dubawi (IRE)—Comic (IRE)
75 PRIZE MONEY, b c Authorized (IRE)—Dresden Doll (USA)
76 QUALITY TIME (IRE), b f Exceed And Excel (AUS)—Crinoline (USA)
77 RACE DAY (IRE), ch c Dubawi (IRE)—Nadia
78 RACE TIME (USA), b br f Street Sense (USA)—Well At The Top (IRE)
79 SENSHI (IRE), ch c Pivotal—Crimson Year (USA)
80 SHARE THE HONOUR, ch c Shamardal (USA)—Hometime
81 SHORT DISTANCE (USA), b br c Smart Strike (CAN)—Ransomed Bride
82 SILENT ATTACK, b c Dream Ahead (USA)—Chanterelle (FR)
83 SIMPLE ATTACK, b g Invincible Spirit (IRE)—Princess Taise (USA)
84 SOOFIAH, b f King's Best (USA)—Anaamil (USA)
85 SPELLCRAFT, b f Dubawi (IRE)—Siyasa (USA)
86 STREET OF DREAMS, b c Shamardal (USA)—Express Way (ARG)
87 STRONG CHALLENGE (IRE), ch c Exceed And Excel (AUS)—Miss Brief (IRE)
88 STRONG FORCE, b g Sea The Stars (IRE)—Rhadegunda
89 STRONG TEAM (IRE), b c Exceed And Excel (AUS)—Star Blossom (USA)
90 SUGAR STRAND (USA), b br f Hard Spun (USA)—Siyaadah
91 TEAM TALK, b c Teofilo (IRE)—Native Blue
92 TIMEKEEPING (IRE), ch c New Approach (IRE)—Midnight Line (USA)
93 TOWN'S HISTORY (USA), ch c Hard Spun (USA)—Smooth Charmer (USA)
94 VALERIA VICTRIX (IRE), ch f Dubawi (IRE)—Vallericca (USA)
95 VERY TALENTED (IRE), b c Invincible Spirit (IRE)—Crystal House (CHI)
96 WINNING STORY, b c New Approach (IRE)—Tanzania (IRE)
97 YATTWEE (USA), b br g Hard Spun (USA)—Alzerra (UAE)
98 YOU'RE BACK (USA), b f Street Cry (USA)—Nawaiet (USA)

TWO-YEAR-OLDS

99 B f 22/2 Distorted Humor (USA)—Achieving (USA) (Bernardini (USA)) (335775)
100 Gr c 8/3 Dark Angel (IRE)—Admire The View (IRE) (Dubawi (IRE)) (150000)
101 B c 17/4 Kodiac—Al Andalyya (USA) (Kingmambo (USA)) (90000)
102 B c 7/3 Champs Elysees—Al Cobra (IRE) (Sadler's Wells (USA)) (55000)
103 B c 2/2 Dubawi (IRE)—Alsindi (Acclamation) (750000)
104 Ch f 12/2 Nathaniel (IRE)—Amallna (Green Desert (USA))
105 AMTHAAL, b f 14/2 Exceed And Excel (AUS)—Darajaat (USA) (Elusive Quality (USA))
106 Ch f 11/2 Distorted Humor (USA)—Angel Craft (USA) (A P Indy (USA))
107 Ch c 20/3 Street Cry (IRE)—Aryaamm (IRE) (Galileo (IRE))
108 Ch f 3/2 Casamento (IRE)—Ashirah (USA) (Housebuster (USA)) (200000)
109 B f 2/3 Elusive Quality (USA)—Aviacion (BRZ) (Know Heights (IRE))
110 B f 30/1 Sepoy (AUS)—Baheeja (Dubawi (IRE))
111 B c 14/2 Dutch Art—Bahia Emerald (IRE) (Bahamian Bounty) (280000)

MR SAEED BIN SUROOR - Continued

112 B f 4/3 Invincible Spirit (IRE)—Ballantrae (IRE) (Diktat)
113 B br c 7/4 War Front (USA)—Bauble Queen (USA) (Arch (USA)) (549450)
114 B c 18/3 Dubawi (IRE)—Birjand (Green Desert (USA))
115 B c 25/2 Dark Angel (IRE)—Bugie d'amore (Rail Link) (100000)
116 B f 3/3 Exceed And Excel (AUS)—Calipatria (Shamardal (USA))
117 B c 28/2 Acclamation—Carioca (IRE) (Rakti) (200000)
118 B f 24/2 Shamardal (USA)—Catchline (USA) (Bertolini (USA)) (260000)
119 Ch c 18/2 Sepoy (AUS)—Cheyenne Star (IRE) (Mujahid (USA)) (110000)
120 B f 18/4 Hard Spun (USA)—Chilukki's Song (USA) (Elusive Quality (USA))
121 DECEMBER SECOND (IRE), b br c 12/3 Teofilo (IRE)—Bulbul (IRE) (Shamardal (USA))
122 B f 27/3 Exceed And Excel (AUS)—Dresden Doll (Elusive Quality (USA))
123 B f 6/3 Invincible Spirit (IRE)—Dubai Smile (USA) (Pivotal)
124 B br c 14/3 Street Cry (IRE)—Element of Truth (USA) (Atticus (USA)) (335775)
125 B f 3/3 Dubawi (IRE)—Elusive Sparkle (USA) (Elusive Quality (USA))
126 Ch f 4/3 Dubawi (IRE)—Express Way (ARG) (Ahmad (ARG))
127 B f 26/2 Street Cry (IRE)—First Blush (IRE) (Pivotal)
128 B f 9/1 Bernardini (USA)—Game Face (USA) (Menifee (USA))
129 Gr c 9/4 Dark Angel (IRE)—Golden Rosie (IRE) (Exceed And Excel (AUS)) (228571)
130 B f 9/3 Dansili—Gossamer (Sadler's Wells (USA))
131 B f 21/2 Dubawi (IRE)—Ihsas (USA) (Rahy (USA))
132 B f 22/3 Dubawi (IRE)—Independence (Selkirk (USA))
133 B f 13/4 Dubawi (IRE)—Inner Secret (USA) (Singspiel (IRE))
134 B f 15/2 Shamardal (USA)—Irish History (IRE) (Dubawi (IRE))
135 B f 17/3 Dubawi (IRE)—Khawlah (IRE) (Cape Cross (IRE))
136 B c 20/3 Lonhro (AUS)—Kydd Gloves (USA) (Dubai Millennium)
137 B c 29/1 Dark Angel (IRE)—Layla Jamil (IRE) (Exceed And Excel (AUS)) (257142)
138 B c 17/4 Distorted Humor (USA)—Love Theway Youare (USA) (Arch (USA)) (122100)
139 B f 6/3 Dubawi (IRE)—Maids Causeway (IRE) (Giant's Causeway (USA))
140 B f 22/3 Frankel—Marie de Medici (USA) (Medicean)
141 Ch f 2/3 Distorted Humor (USA)—Michita (USA) (Dynaformer (USA))
142 B c 6/3 Lonhro (AUS)—Midnight Music (IRE) (Dubawi (IRE)) (152625)
143 B c 9/5 Raven's Pass (USA)—Miss Lucifer (FR) (Noverre (USA))
144 B br c 28/2 Lonhro (AUS)—My Dubai (IRE) (Dubai Millennium)
145 B c 15/2 Dubawi (IRE)—Nahrain (Selkirk (USA))
146 B c 6/2 Lonhro (AUS)—Nasmatt (Danehill (USA))
147 Ch c 1/3 Shamardal (USA)—Next Holy (IRE) (Holy Roman Emperor (IRE)) (103359)
148 B f 12/4 Elusive Quality (USA)—Pamona Ball (USA) (Pleasantly Perfect (USA))
149 B f 16/3 Dubawi (IRE)—Pimpernel (IRE) (Invincible Spirit (IRE))
150 B br f 9/3 Street Cry (IRE)—Pulitzer (USA) (Bernardini (USA))
151 B f 8/2 Dubawi (IRE)—Rainfall (IRE) (Oasis Dream)
152 B f 24/2 Shamardal (USA)—Rumh (GER) (Monsun (GER))
153 Gr f 6/3 Invincible Spirit (IRE)—Scenica (ARG) (Interprete (ARG))
154 Ch c 21/3 Distorted Humor (USA)—Silent Moment (USA) (Giant's Causeway (USA))
155 Ch f 2/4 Sepoy (AUS)—Some Sunny Day (Where Or When (IRE)) (200000)
156 SUTOOR (IRE), b c 7/2 Cape Cross (USA)—Yanabeeaa (USA) (Street Cry (IRE))
157 B br c 10/4 Exceed And Excel (AUS)—Sylvan Song (USA) (Street Cry (IRE))
158 B c 3/5 Lonhro (AUS)—Tamarillo (Daylami (IRE))
159 B f 25/2 Bernardini (USA)—Victorian Beauty (USA) (Rahy (USA))
160 B f 7/3 Exceed And Excel (AUS)—Vincennes (King's Best (USA))
161 Ch c 18/3 Street Cry (IRE)—Vine Street (IRE) (Singspiel (IRE))
162 B f 5/3 Cape Cross (IRE)—Waitress (USA) (Kingmambo (USA))
163 B f 4/4 Lonhro (AUS)—Well At The Top (IRE) (Sadler's Wells (USA)) (140415)
164 B c 25/2 Hard Spun (USA)—Windsor County (USA) (Elusive Quality (USA))
165 B c 27/3 Lemon Drop Kid (USA)—Winner (USA) (Horse Chestnut (SAF)) (195360)
166 B f 19/3 Manduro (GER)—Zahrat Dubai (Unfuwain (USA))
167 Ch f 27/4 Poet's Voice—Zayn Zen (Singspiel (IRE))
168 B c 18/3 Exceed And Excel (AUS)—Zoowraa (Azamour (IRE))

Jockey (flat): James Doyle.

43 MR KEVIN BISHOP, Bridgwater

Postal: **Barford Park Stables, Spaxton, Bridgwater, Somerset, TA5 1AF**
Contacts: **PHONE/FAX (01278) 671437 MOBILE (07816) 837610**
E-MAIL hevbishop@hotmail.com

1 BLACKDOWN BABE, 8, b m Weld—Blackdown Beauty **M. J. Coate**
2 COLUMBANUS (IRE), 5, b g Jeremy (USA)—Shamah **Miss H. P. Tate**
3 CRUISE IN STYLE (IRE), 10, b m Definite Article—Henrietta Street (IRE) **Mr S. G. Atkinson**
4 GENEROUS PET (IRE), 7, ch g Generous (IRE)—Sarahs Music (IRE) **Miss H. P. Tate**
5 JANESMERLIN, 4, b g Jelani (IRE)—Janes Allweather **Miss J. Nicholls**
6 LETS GO DUTCHESS, 6, b m Helissio (FR)—Lets Go Dutch **K. Bishop**
7 PRECIOUS GROUND, 6, b g Helissio (FR)—Wild Ground (IRE) **Jim Kilduff & Ken Jones**
8 SHADY GREY, 6, gr m Helissio (FR)—Compton Amica (IRE) **Mr A. S. Meaden**
9 SOMERSET JEM, 7, b g Sir Harry Lewis (USA)—Monger Lane **Slabs & Lucan**
10 TARA TAVEY (IRE), 11, gr m Kayf Tara—Slieve League (IRE) **K. Bishop**

Other Owners: Mr Ken Jones, Mr K. J. Kilduff, Miss Sarah Macey, Mr C. J. Macey.

Assistant Trainer: Heather Bishop

Jockey (NH): James Best. Conditional: Conor Smith.

44 MISS LINDA BLACKFORD, Tiverton

Postal: **Shortlane Stables, Rackenford, Tiverton, Devon, EX16 8EH**
Contacts: **PHONE (01884) 881589 MOBILE (07887) 947832**
E-MAIL overthelast@talktalk.net WEBSITE www.overthelast.com

1 KAYF CHARMER, 6, b m Kayf Tara—Silver Charmer **Mrs V. W. Jones**
2 LURE DES PRES (IRE), 4, br g Robin des Pres (FR)—Pinkeen Lady (IRE) **Mr J. S. Wood**
3 MOUNTAIN OF MOURNE (IRE), 7, ch g Mountain High (IRE)—Katies Native (IRE) **Over The Last Racing**
4 PRIMARY SUSPECT (IRE), 6, br gr g Primary (USA)—Charismatique (GER) **Over The Last Racing**
5 STEEL EXPRESS (IRE), 4, b g Craigsteel—Assidua (IRE) **Mrs Susan Quick**

Other Owners: Miss L. A. Blackford, Mr Stuart Howe, Mr B. P. Jones, Mr M. J. Vanstone.

Assistant Trainer: M. J. Vanstone.

Jockey (NH): Nick Scholfield, Micheal Nolan. Conditional: Conor Smith.
Amateur: Mr Joshua Guerriero, Mr S. Houlihan.

45 MR ALAN BLACKMORE, Hertford

Postal: **'Chasers', Stockings Lane, Little Berkhamsted, Hertford**
Contacts: **PHONE (01707) 875060 MOBILE (07803) 711453**

1 COCKER, 4, b g Shirocco (GER)—Treble Heights (IRE) **A. G. Blackmore**
2 COOL CHIEF, 7, b g Sleeping Indian—Be Bop Aloha **A. G. Blackmore**
3 OCCASIONALLY YOURS (IRE), 12, b g Moscow Society (USA)—Kristina's Lady (IRE) **A. G. Blackmore**

Assistant Trainer: Mrs P. M. Blackmore

Jockey (NH): Marc Goldstein. Amateur: Miss Tabitha Worsley.

46 MR MICHAEL BLAKE, Trowbridge

Postal: **Staverton Farm, Trowbridge, Wiltshire, BA14 6PE**
Contacts: **PHONE (01225) 782327 MOBILE (07971) 675180**
E-MAIL mblakestavertonfarm@btinternet.com WEBSITE www.michaelblakeracing.co.uk

1 ABLE DASH, 6, ch g Dutch Art—Evasive Quality (FR) **West Wilts Hockey Lads**
2 BARTON ROSE, 7, b m Midnight Legend—Barton Flower **Mrs J. M. Haines**
3 CAPTAIN GEORGE (IRE), 5, b g Bushranger (IRE)—High Society Girl (IRE) **Staverton Owners Group**
4 DOUBLY CLEVER (IRE), 4, ch g Iffraaj—Smartest (USA) **Mr F. Tieman**
5 HASSADIN, 10, ch g Reset (AUS)—Crocolat **H. M. W. Clifford**
6 HIGH ASPIRATIONS (IRE), 8, b g Dr Massini (IRE)—Divining (IRE) **Mrs J. M. Haines**
7 MICK DUGGAN, 6, ch g Pivotal—Poppy Carew (IRE) **Mr M. A. Muddiman**

MR MICHAEL BLAKE - Continued

8 **NEBULA STORM (IRE)**, 9, b g Galileo (IRE)—Epping **West Wilts Hockey Lads**
9 **PALADIN (IRE)**, 7, b g Dubawi (IRE)—Palwina (FR) **D. J. S. Ffrench Davis**
10 **PICK A LITTLE**, 8, b g Piccolo—Little Caroline (IRE) **Mrs J. M. Haines**
11 **ROCKY REBEL**, 8, b g Norse Dancer (IRE)—Gulchina (USA) **Mrs J. M. Haines**
12 **SINNDAR'S MAN**, 5, b g Sinndar (IRE)—Relish (IRE) **H. M. W. Clifford**
13 **WELD ARAB (IRE)**, 5, b g Shamardal (USA)—Itqaan (USA) **The Moonlighters**

Other Owners: M. J. Blake, Mrs S. E. Blake, Mrs V. A. Butcher, Mr R. C. Butcher.

Assistant Trainer: Sharon Blake (07812) 599904

47

MR MICHAEL BLANSHARD, Upper Lambourn
Postal: **Lethornes Stables, Upper Lambourn, Hungerford, Berkshire, RG17 8QP**
Contacts: **PHONE (01488) 71091 FAX (01488) 73497 MOBILE (07785) 370093**
E-MAIL blanshard.racing@btconnect.com WEBSITE www.michaelblanshard.co.uk

1 **ABERTILLERY**, 4, b g Shamardal (USA)—Nantyglo **Lady E. Mays-Smith**
2 **AMALFI DOUG (FR)**, 6, gr g Network (GER)—Queissa (FR) **Mr D. W. J. Garrett**
3 **COPPER CAVALIER**, 5, ch g Haafhd—Elle Crystal **The Reignmakers**
4 **DISHY GURU**, 7, ch g Ishiguru (USA)—Pick A Nice Name **The Reignmakers**
5 **FAIR COMMENT**, 6, b m Tamayuz—Cliche (USA) **Fair Comment Partnership**
6 **GAVARNIE ENCORE**, 4, b c Intikhab (USA)—Greeley Bright (USA) **Hill, Price & Blanshard**
7 **GRACESOME (IRE)**, 5, b m Shirocco (GER)—Simonda **W. Murdoch**
8 **IVANHOE**, 6, b g Haafhd—Marysienka **The Ivanhoe Partnership**
9 **JUST ISLA**, 6, ch m Halling (USA)—Island Rapture **D. A. Poole**
10 **MILLY ROYALE**, 4, b f Royal Applause—Milly Fleur **The Reignmakers**
11 **MY BUBBA**, 4, b g Dutch Art—Moyoko (IRE) **Mrs N. Young**
12 **RED DRAGON (IRE)**, 6, b g Acclamation—Delphie Queen (IRE) **Lady E. Mays-Smith**
13 **STELLARTA**, 5, b m Sakhee's Secret—Torgau (IRE) **Mr V. G. Ward**
14 **THE COMPOSER**, 14, b g Royal Applause—Superspring **A. D. Jones**

THREE-YEAR-OLDS

15 **COMMANDING ROLE**, ch f Major Cadeaux—Cultural Role **J. Gale, J. Cover & V. Ward**
16 **MAJESTICA**, b f Royal Applause—Snake's Head **The Reignmakers**
17 **PACA PUNCH**, b f Paco Boy (IRE)—Plumage **Mrs N. Young**
18 **PROSPERITEE**, b f Paco Boy (IRE)—Goodie Twosues **J K Racing Club**

TWO-YEAR-OLDS

19 B f 22/4 Paco Boy (IRE)—Arculinge (Paris House)
20 B c 26/3 Famous Name—Daffodil Walk (IRE) (Captain Rio) (7500)
21 B c 20/3 Excelebration (IRE)—Emeralds Spirit (IRE) (Rock of Gibraltar (IRE)) (15000) **J. Gale & Partner**
22 B f 15/2 Delegator—Harryana To (Compton Place) (4500)
23 B f 10/4 Sakhee's Secret—Witness (Efisio) (1000)

Other Owners: Mr S. Beccle, Mr M. Blanshard, Mr D. Cannings, Mrs Emma Clarke, Dr Andrew Gay, Mr Lloyd Hill, Mr Ian Lewis, Mr Brian Mitchell, Mrs W. Murdoch, Mrs S. Oldham, Mr Charles Phillips, Mrs D. Pickering, Mr M. J. Prescott, Mr Nick Price, Mrs Ginny Rusher.

48

MR J. S. BOLGER, Carlow
Postal: **Glebe House, Coolcullen, Carlow, Ireland**
Contacts: **PHONE (00353) 56 4443150 (00353) 56 4443158 FAX (00353) 56 4443256**
E-MAIL racing@jsb.ie

1 **BRIDLE PATH (IRE)**, 4, b f Teofilo (IRE)—Twin Sails (USA) **Mrs J. S. Bolger**
2 **CLUB WEXFORD (IRE)**, 5, b g Lawman (FR)—Masnada (IRE) **Dave Bernie**
3 **ELUSIVE APPROACH (IRE)**, 4, b f New Approach (IRE)—Soilse Na Cathrach (IRE) **Mrs J. S. Bolger**
4 **EMPEROR'S PALACE (IRE)**, 4, ch c Teofilo (IRE)—Lia (IRE) **Godolphin**
5 **FLIGHT RISK (IRE)**, 5, ch h Teofilo (IRE)—Raghida (IRE) **Mrs J. S. Bolger**
6 **LUCIDA (IRE)**, 4, b f Shamardal (USA)—Lura (USA) **Godolphin**
7 **MCGUIGAN (IRE)**, 4, ch c Teofilo (IRE)—Scribonia (IRE) **Mrs J. S. Bolger**
8 **PARISH BOY**, 4, gr c New Approach (IRE)—Requesting **Godolphin**
9 **PARISH HALL (IRE)**, 7, b h Teofilo (IRE)—Halla Siamsa (IRE) **Mrs J. S. Bolger**

MR J. S. BOLGER - Continued

10 PLEASCACH (IRE), 4, b f Teofilo (IRE)—Toirneach (USA) **Godolphin**
11 STEIP AMACH (IRE), 4, b f Vocalised (USA)—Ceist Eile (IRE) **Mrs J. S. Bolger**
12 STELLAR GLOW (IRE), 4, b f Sea The Stars (IRE)—Glinting Desert (IRE) **Mrs Patricia J. Burns**

THREE-YEAR-OLDS

13 ADMODUM (USA), ch c Majestic Warrior (USA)—Unbridled Treasure (USA) **Mrs J. S. Bolger**
14 AEGEUS (IRE), b c Shamardal (USA)—Magna Graecia (IRE) **Godolphin**
15 AL MOHALHAL (IRE), b c Acclamation—Secret Question (USA) **Mubarak Al Naemi**
16 ALYSSUM (IRE), ch f New Approach (IRE)—Alasha (IRE) **Mrs Patricia J. Burns**
17 AN CAILIN ORGA (IRE), ch f Galileo (IRE)—Finsceal Beo (IRE) **Mr M. D. Ryan**
18 BALANCED APPROACH (IRE), b c New Approach (IRE)—Soilse Na Cathrach (IRE) **Godolphin**
19 BURNING BULLET, b c Zamindar (USA)—Miliana (IRE) **Mubarak Al Naemi**
20 BURNING SWORD (IRE), b c Zoffany (IRE)—Trinity Fair **Mubarak Al Naemi**
21 CEOL AN GHRA (IRE), b f Teofilo (IRE)—Key To Coolcullen (IRE) **Mrs J. S. Bolger**
22 CEOL NA NOG (IRE), b f Teofilo (IRE)—Ard Fheis (IRE) **Mrs J. S. Bolger**
23 CIRIN TOINNE (IRE), ch f Galileo (IRE)—Sister Angelina (IRE) **Mrs J. S. Bolger**
24 CLEAR CUT, b c Acclamation—Claiomh Solais (IRE) **Mrs J. S. Bolger**
25 CLINICAL APPROACH (IRE), b c New Approach (IRE)—My Girl Sophie (USA) **Godolphin**
26 DYNAMIC FOCUS (IRE), b f Intense Focus (USA)—Super Hoofer (USA) **Mrs J. S. Bolger**
27 FIUNTACH (IRE), ch f Intense Focus (USA)—Ceist Eile (IRE) **Mrs J. S. Bolger**
28 FOUNTAIN (IRE), b c Pour Moi (IRE)—Teolane (IRE) **Mrs J. S. Bolger**
29 GIRL OF THE HOUR, b f Makfi—American Spirit (IRE) **Mrs June Judd**
30 GLAMOROUS APPROACH (IRE), ch f New Approach (IRE)—Maria Lee (IRE) **Mrs J. S. Bolger**
31 HERALD THE DAWN (IRE), b c New Approach (IRE)—Hymn of The Dawn (USA) **Godolphin**
32 INTENSE STYLIST (IRE), ch f Intense Focus (USA)—Style Queen (IRE) **Mrs J. S. Bolger**
33 KING OF SAXONY (IRE), b c Pivotal—Turmalin (IRE) **Godolphin**
34 LABHANDAR (IRE), b f Authorized (IRE)—Lavender Blue **Mrs J. S. Bolger**
35 LANDLOCKED, b c Street Cry (IRE)—Land of Dreams **Godolphin**
36 LANSEOL (IRE), b f Teofilo (IRE)—Twin Sails (USA) **Mrs J. S. Bolger**
37 LEAFY SHADE (IRE), b f New Approach (IRE)—Dublin Six (USA) **Mrs J. S. Bolger**
38 LIGHTNING BULLET (IRE), b c New Approach (IRE)—La Conquistadora **Mubarak Al Naemi**
39 LORENDANO (IRE), b f Teofilo (IRE)—Altarejos (IRE) **Mrs J. S. Bolger**
40 MANDARIN MONARCH (IRE), ch c Manduro (GER)—Abigail Pett **Mrs June Judd**
41 MAOINEAS (IRE), ch f Teofilo (IRE)—Maoineach (USA) **Mrs J. S. Bolger**
42 MIMICKING (IRE), b f Invincible Spirit (IRE)—Her Own Kind (JPN) **Godolphin**
43 MOONLIGHT MAGIC, b c Cape Cross (IRE)—Melikah (IRE) **Godolphin**
44 MRS KING (IRE), b f Dubawi (IRE)—Coretta (IRE) **Godolphin**
45 PARI PASSU (IRE), ch c New Approach (IRE)—Tiz The Whiz (USA) **Godolphin**
46 PARTY FOR EVER (IRE), b f Iffraaj—Miss Party Line (USA) **Mrs June Judd**
47 PLEADINGS (USA), ch c Street Cry (IRE)—Say No Now (IRE) **Godolphin**
48 QATARI HUNTER (IRE), b c Footstepsinthesand—Inis Boffin **Mubarak Al Naemi**
49 QUEEN OF SICILY (USA), b br f Cape Cross (IRE)—Jealous Again (USA) **Godolphin**
50 REFERIO (IRE), b f Teofilo (IRE)—Tiffed (USA) **Mrs J. S. Bolger**
51 ROUND TWO (IRE), b c Teofilo (IRE)—Khazina (USA) **Godolphin**
52 SAAFARR, b c Teofilo (IRE)—Hall Hee (IRE) **Godolphin**
53 SANUS PER AQUAM (IRE), b c Teofilo (IRE)—Fainne (IRE) **Mrs J. S. Bolger**
54 SIAMSAIOCHT (IRE), b f Teofilo (IRE)—Halla Siamsa (IRE) **Mrs J. S. Bolger**
55 SOLOMON THE WISE (IRE), b c Lawman (FR)—Imeall Na Speire (USA) **Mrs J. S. Bolger**
56 SPECIAL FOCUS (IRE), b f Intense Focus (USA)—Arjooch (IRE) **Mrs J. S. Bolger**
57 SPLIT DECISION (IRE), b f Teofilo (IRE)—Night Visit **Mrs J. S. Bolger**
58 STELLAR MASS (IRE), b c Sea The Stars (IRE)—Juno Marlowe (IRE) **Mrs June Judd**
59 STENOGRAPHER (USA), ch c Distorted Humor (USA)—Sadler's Secretary (IRE) **Godolphin**
60 TAISCE NAISIUNTA (IRE), b f Lawman (FR)—Ciste Naisiunta (IRE) **Mrs J. S. Bolger**
61 THEODORICO (IRE), b c Teofilo (IRE)—Yes Oh Yes (USA) **Godolphin**
62 THEODOTUS (IRE), b c Teofilo (IRE)—Gearanai (USA) **Mrs J. S. Bolger**
63 TIPSTAFF, b c Street Cry (IRE)—Firth of Lorne (IRE) **Godolphin**
64 TRIBAL BEAT (IRE), b c Street Cry (IRE)—Tashelka (FR) **Godolphin**
65 TURRET ROCKS (IRE), b f Fastnet Rock (AUS)—Beyond Compare (IRE) **Mrs J. S. Bolger**
66 TWILIGHT PAYMENT (IRE), b c Teofilo (IRE)—Dream On Buddy (IRE) **Godolphin**
67 WEXFORD VOICE (IRE), b g Vocalised (USA)—Have A Heart (IRE) **Mrs J. S. Bolger**
68 WORKING LEATHER (IRE), b c Teofilo (IRE)—Masnada (IRE) **Godolphin**

TWO-YEAR-OLDS

69 ABBEY SQUARE (IRE), b c 29/3 Intense Focus (USA)—Beyond Compare (IRE) (Galileo (IRE)) **Mrs J. S. Bolger**
70 B f 1/3 Frankel—Alexander Goldrun (IRE) (Gold Away (IRE)) (1255075) **China Horse Club**

MR J. S. BOLGER - Continued

71 **ALL AND SINGULAR (IRE),** b c 2/5 Lawman (FR)—Solas Na Greine (IRE) (Galileo (IRE)) **Mrs J. S. Bolger**
72 B f 1/3 New Approach (IRE)—Anayid (A P Indy (USA)) **Godolphin**
73 **BRUINNEALL (IRE),** ch f 27/2 New Approach (IRE)—
My Fere Lady (USA) (Mr Greeley (USA)) (14765) **Mrs J. S. Bolger**
74 **CASHLESS (IRE),** b c 1/3 Intense Focus (USA)—Snas (USA) (Bernstein (USA)) **Mrs J. S. Bolger**
75 B f 27/3 Lawman (FR)—Ciste Naisiunta (IRE) (Galileo (IRE)) **Mrs J. S. Bolger**
76 **CLEONA (IRE),** b c 4/3 Pour Moi (IRE)—Cleofila (IRE) (Teofilo (IRE)) **Mrs J. S. Bolger**
77 **COMEDIENNE,** ch f 4/3 Archipenko (USA)—Claiomh Solais (IRE) (Galileo (IRE)) **Miss K. Rausing**
78 **CONSTANT COMMENT,** b f 21/1 Fastnet Rock (AUS)—
Livia Galilei (IRE) (Galileo (IRE)) (75000) **Mrs June Judd**
79 **CONTESSA CONFESSA (IRE),** b f 20/1 Lope de Vega (IRE)—
Pardoven (Clodovil (IRE)) (100000) **Mrs June Judd**
80 B br c 30/1 Lonhro (AUS)—Danelagh (AUS) (Danehill (USA)) **Godolphin**
81 **DAWN OF A NEW ERA (IRE),** b f 28/5 New Approach (IRE)—
Hymn of The Dawn (USA) (Phone Trick (USA)) (354374) **Mrs J. S. Bolger**
82 **DELIGHTFUL FOCUS (IRE),** b f 15/3 Intense Focus (USA)—Tamra Delight (USA) (Diesis) **Mrs J. S. Bolger**
83 **DREAM FOCUS (IRE),** b c 24/4 Intense Focus (USA)—Dream On Buddy (IRE) (Oasis Dream) **Mrs J. S. Bolger**
84 **DUBAI SAND (IRE),** ch c 6/3 Teofilo (IRE)—Bring Back Matron (IRE) (Rock of Gibraltar (IRE)) **Godolphin**
85 **EIRIAMACH NA CASCA (IRE),** b f 7/4 Intense Focus (USA)—Night Visit (Sinndar (IRE)) **Mrs J. S. Bolger**
86 **FALLACIA (IRE),** b f 22/5 Teofilo (IRE)—Intriguing Humor (CAN) (Distorted Humor (USA)) **Mrs J. S. Bolger**
87 B f 5/2 New Approach (IRE)—Favourable Terms (Selkirk (USA)) **Godolphin**
88 **FIOR CLISTE (IRE),** b c 5/2 Pour Moi (IRE)—Fionnuar (IRE) (Teofilo (IRE)) **Mrs J. S. Bolger**
89 **FIORUISCE (IRE),** b c 3/5 Vocalised (USA)—Teacht An Earraig (USA) (Galileo (IRE)) **Mrs J. S. Bolger**
90 **FOCUS ON GRASS (IRE),** b c 23/5 Intense Focus (USA)—Sanaara (USA) (Anabaa (USA)) **Mrs J. S. Bolger**
91 **FOCUS ON TAPIT (IRE),** ch c 26/4 Intense Focus (USA)—Gilded Butterfly (USA) (Tapit (USA)) **Mrs J. S. Bolger**
92 **FUARAN (IRE),** br f 16/3 Intense Focus (USA)—Foinse (IRE) (Teofilo (IRE)) **Mrs J. S. Bolger**
93 **FUSACHT (IRE),** b f 30/3 Intense Focus (USA)—Furasta (USA) (Leroidesanimaux (BRZ)) **Mrs J. S. Bolger**
94 **FUTURE FOCUS (IRE),** b c 9/4 Intense Focus (USA)—Ard Fheis (IRE) (Lil's Boy) **Mrs J. S. Bolger**
95 **GALUMINOUS (IRE),** b f 14/5 Intense Focus (USA)—Luminous One (IRE) (Galileo (IRE)) **Mrs J. S. Bolger**
96 **GLOVES ON (IRE),** b c 18/2 Teofilo (IRE)—Tiffed (USA) (Seattle Slew (USA)) **Godolphin**
97 **GOLDEN HANDCUFFS (IRE),** ch f 13/2 New Approach (IRE)—Tiffilia (IRE) (Macho Uno (USA)) **Mrs J. S. Bolger**
98 B f 20/2 Shamardal (USA)—Hairpin (USA) (Bernardini (USA)) **Godolphin**
99 B f 2/4 Pivotal—Halle Bop (Dubai Millennium) **Godolphin**
100 **HOLISTIC APPROACH (IRE),** b c 23/2 New Approach (IRE)—
Sway Me Now (USA) (Speightstown (USA)) **Godolphin**
101 B f 5/2 Teofilo (IRE)—Huma Bird (Invincible Spirit (IRE)) **Godolphin**
102 B f 9/5 Invincible Spirit (IRE)—Hush Money (CHI) (Hussonet (USA)) **Godolphin**
103 **IN SOMNO (IRE),** ch f 23/3 Dream Ahead (USA)—Maoineach (USA) (Congaree (USA)) **Mrs J. S. Bolger**
104 Ch f 11/4 New Approach (IRE)—Innuendo (IRE) (Caerleon (USA)) **Godolphin**
105 **INTENSELY FOCUSSED (IRE),** b c 2/4 Intense Focus (USA)—
Soilse Na Cathrach (IRE) (Elusive City (USA)) **Mrs J. S. Bolger**
106 **INTROIBO (IRE),** b f 3/4 Intense Focus (USA)—Excuse Me (USA) (Distorted Humor (USA)) **Mrs J. S. Bolger**
107 **LATCHET (IRE),** b f 19/3 Intense Focus (USA)—Teolane (IRE) (Teofilo (IRE)) **Mrs J. S. Bolger**
108 **LEGITIMUS (IRE),** b f 8/3 Lawman (FR)—Imeall Na Speire (USA) (Galileo (IRE)) **Mrs J. S. Bolger**
109 **LEVEL OF INTENSITY (IRE),** b c 8/5 Intense Focus (USA)—
Teofolina (IRE) (Teofilo (IRE)) (5167) **Mrs J. S. Bolger**
110 **LITIR GHRA (IRE),** b c 3/3 Intense Focus (USA)—Christmas Letter (IRE) (Galileo (IRE)) (7382) **Mrs J. S. Bolger**
111 **MARIORA (IRE),** b f 13/2 Teofilo (IRE)—Maria Lee (IRE) (Rock of Gibraltar (IRE)) **Mrs J. S. Bolger**
112 **MODERN APPROACH (IRE),** b f 3/3 New Approach (IRE)—Janey Muddles (IRE) (Lawman (FR)) **Mrs June Judd**
113 B c 22/1 Shamardal (USA)—Movin' Out (AUS) (Encosta de Lago (AUS)) **Godolphin**
114 **MUININEACH (IRE),** b f 25/4 Intense Focus (USA)—
National Swagger (IRE) (Giant's Causeway (USA)) **Mrs J. S. Bolger**
115 Ch c 6/5 Street Cry (IRE)—Najoum (USA) (Giant's Causeway (USA)) **Godolphin**
116 **OBEY THE LAW (IRE),** b f 16/2 Lawman (FR)—Lavender Blue (Galileo (IRE)) **Mrs J. S. Bolger**
117 **OH GRACE (IRE),** b f 17/4 Lawman (FR)—Flea Cheoil (IRE) (Galileo (IRE)) **Mrs J. S. Bolger**
118 Ch c 25/2 New Approach (IRE)—Peace Camp (USA) (Storm Cat (USA)) **Godolphin**
119 B c 4/2 New Approach (IRE)—Punctilious (Danehill (USA)) **Godolphin**
120 B c 21/4 Lope de Vega (IRE)—Purple Tigress (Dubai Destination (USA)) **Mrs June Judd**
121 **QUEEN OF THE RING (IRE),** b f 17/5 Teofilo (IRE)—Aiseiri (IRE) (Rock of Gibraltar (IRE)) **Mrs J. S. Bolger**
122 **REALTA (IRE),** b f 20/4 Intense Focus (USA)—Starland (IRE) (Galileo (IRE)) **Mrs J. S. Bolger**
123 **RENEWED FOCUS (IRE),** b c 28/1 Intense Focus (USA)—
Lonrach (IRE) (Holy Roman Emperor (IRE)) **Mrs J. S. Bolger**
124 **RINGSIDE FOCUS (IRE),** b c 8/4 Intense Focus (USA)—Amhrasach (IRE) (Teofilo (IRE)) **Mrs J. S. Bolger**
125 **RINGSIDE SEAT (IRE),** b c 19/5 Teofilo (IRE)—Key To Coolcullen (IRE) (Royal Academy (USA)) **Godolphin**
126 **RINGSIDE SUPPORT (IRE),** b c 5/5 Teofilo (IRE)—Halla Siamsa (IRE) (Montjeu (IRE)) **Godolphin**

MR J. S. BOLGER - Continued

127 B f 11/3 Cape Cross (IRE)—Rose Trail (USA) (Kingmambo (USA)) **Godolphin**
128 B c 7/4 Teofilo (IRE)—Scatina (IRE) (Samum (GER)) **Godolphin**
129 SIN SIN (IRE), b f 8/4 Intense Focus (USA)—Saor Sinn (IRE) (Galileo (IRE)) **Mrs J. S. Bolger**
130 SLANEY STREET (IRE), ch c 27/4 Intense Focus (USA)—
                                            Halla Na Saoire (IRE) (Teofilo (IRE)) (15503) **Mrs J. S. Bolger**
131 B f 6/4 Dubawi (IRE)—Speirbhean (IRE) (Danehill (USA)) **Godolphin**
132 SUAIMHNEAS (IRE), ch f 23/3 Intense Focus (USA)—Oiche Ghealai (IRE) (Galileo (IRE)) **Mrs J. S. Bolger**
133 B f 26/1 High Chaparral (IRE)—Take Flight (IRE) (Pivotal) (190000) **Mrs J. S. Bolger**
134 TEO'S MUSIC (IRE), b f 13/4 Intense Focus (USA)—Teo's Sister (IRE) (Galileo (IRE)) **Mrs J. S. Bolger**
135 THEODOSIA (IRE), b c 16/5 Teofilo (IRE)—Tiz The Whiz (USA) (Tiznow (USA)) **Godolphin**
136 TWO BY TWO (IRE), b f 17/5 Roderic O'Connor (IRE)—Astralai (IRE) (Galileo (IRE)) **Mrs J. S. Bolger**
137 B f 3/5 New Approach (IRE)—Victoria Star (IRE) (Danehill (USA)) **Godolphin**
138 VOCAL ACTIVITY (IRE), b c 7/3 Vocalised (USA)—Rachida (IRE) (Hurricane Run (IRE)) **Mrs J. S. Bolger**
139 VOCAL RESPONSE (IRE), b c 22/3 Vocalised (USA)—Super Hoofer (IRE) (Shamardal (USA)) **Mrs J. S. Bolger**
140 B c 22/2 Kitten's Joy (USA)—Wave of Applause (Royal Applause) (110741) **Godolphin**
141 B c 10/4 Smart Strike (CAN)—Zofzig (USA) (Danzig (USA)) **Godolphin**

Other Owners: Mr John Corcoran, Mr Tom McGurk.

Jockey (flat): R. P. Cleary, Kevin Manning, R. P. Whelan. **Apprentice:** Daniel Redmond.

---

49 **MRS MYRIAM BOLLACK-BADEL, Lamorlaye**
Postal: **20 Rue Blanche, 60260 Lamorlaye, France**
Contacts: **(0033) 9774 89044 FAX (0033) 3442 13367 MOBILE (0033) 6108 09347**
E-MAIL myriam.bollack@gmail.com WEBSITE www.myriam-bollack.com

1 HEY JOE (FR), 4, b c Redback—Manon **Manfred Hofer**
2 INDIAN ICON (FR), 6, b g Indian Rocket—Playing Star (FR) **Mr J. P. Dunne**
3 IRON SPIRIT (FR), 6, b h Turtle Bowl (IRE)—Irish Vintage (FR) **M. Motschmann**
4 MADIVA (FR), 4, gr f Aussie Rules (USA)—Mahradva (GER) **Turf Syndikat 2014**
5 NORSE KING (FR), 7, ch g Norse Dancer (IRE)—Angel Wing **J. C. Smith**
6 ROYAL PRIZE, 6, ch g Nayef (USA)—Spot Prize (USA) **J. C. Smith**
7 SPORTLOBSTER (IRE), 4, b c Strategic Prince—First Bank (FR) **A. Badel**
8 TIZIANA (FR), 4, b f Touch Down (GER)—Tizia (IRE) **Manfred Hofer**
9 VIKING RUNNER (FR), 4, b f Norse Dancer (IRE)—Speed of Sound **J. C. Smith**
10 WAVE POWER (FR), 4, b c Motivator—Wave Goodbye (FR) **J. C. Smith**
11 ZAHAB (FR), 4, b f Naaqoos—Zython (FR) **Ecurie Noel Forgeard**
12 ZAMIYR (FR), 4, b f Naaqoos—Zayine (IRE) **A. Badel**
13 ZIMRI (FR), 12, b g Take Risks (FR)—Zayine (IRE) **Mme M. Bollack-Badel**

THREE-YEAR-OLDS

14 AVEC LAURA, ch c Manduro (GER)—Sign of Life **Mme M. Bollack-Badel**
15 DORSET DREAM (FR), b f Canford Cliffs (IRE)—Fontcia (FR) **J. C. Smith**
16 ELUSIVE GIRL (FR), b f Elusive City—Wave Goodbye **J. C. Smith**
17 FANCY GEM (FR), b f American Post—Figurelibre (IRE) **M. Motschmann**
18 INCITATOR (FR), b c Motivator—Summer Wave (IRE) **Ecurie Noel Forgeard**
19 KORIANDRE (FR), b f Kouroun—Knout **Mrs G. de Chatelperron**
20 MONTEGO (FR), ch c Excellent Art—Massaye (IRE) **M. Motschmann**
21 PRESIDENT'S SEAL, b f Aqlaam—White House **Mrs D. Swinburn**
22 SIRINSKA (FR), b c Sir Percy—Rinskia **J. C. Smith**

TWO-YEAR-OLDS

23 ALLURE OF LIGHT (FR), b f 4/3 Lord of England (GER)—City of Light (Singspiel (IRE)) (14765) **Mr J. P. Dunne**
24 FARADIBA (FR), gr f 8/2 Motivator—Figurelibre (IRE) (Verglas (IRE)) **M. Motschmann**
25 FAST SHADOW (FR), b c 13/3 Mastercraftsman (IRE)—
                             Flores Del Lago (IRE) (Encosta de Lago (AUS)) (44296) **Mr J. P. Dunne**
26 FLICKER FLAME (IRE), b f 14/4 Born To Sea (IRE)—Xaloc (IRE) (Shirocco (GER)) (25839) **Mr J. P. Dunne**
27 GRIOTTE (FR), gr f 10/4 Excelebration (IRE)—Grande Rousse (FR) (Act One) (32484) **Mrs G. de Chatelperron**
28 KORSAIRE (FR), b c 6/5 Youmzain (IRE)—Knout (Kendor (FR)) **Mme M. Bollack-Badel**
29 NOUS TROIS (FR), b f 1/1 Motivator—Numerologie (FR) (Numerous (USA)) **Andrew Barber**
30 VUE DE L'ESPRIT (FR), b f 16/3 Poet's Voice—Srinagar Girl (Shamardal (USA)) **Ecurie Noel Forgeard**

MRS MYRIAM BOLLACK-BADEL - Continued

31 Gr f 5/4 American Post—Wave Goodbye (FR) (Linamix (FR)) **J. C. Smith**
32 ZOHAR (FR), b c 1/1 Naaqoos—Zayine (IRE) (Polish Patriot (USA)) **Mme M. Bollack-Badel**

Assistant Trainer: Alain Badel

---

50 **MR MARTIN BOSLEY, Chalfont St Giles**
Postal: **Bowstridge Farm, Bowstridge Lane, Chalfont St. Giles, Buckinghamshire, HP8 4RF**
Contacts: **PHONE (01494) 875533 FAX (01494) 875533 MOBILE (07778) 938040**
E-MAIL martin@martinbosley.com WEBSITE www.martinbosleyracing.com

1 **AIR OF GLORY (IRE)**, 6, ch g Shamardal (USA)—Balloura (USA) **Walid & Paula Marzouk**
2 **BURNT CREAM**, 9, b m Exceed And Excel (AUS)—Basbousate Nadia **Mrs P. M. Brown**
3 **CAROBELLO (IRE)**, 9, b g Luso—Vic's Queen (IRE) **Mr A. Randle**
4 **COUNTERFEITER**, 6, b g Singspiel (IRE)—Grain of Truth **J. Carey**
5 **DELAIRE**, 4, b g Sakhee's Secret—Moody Margaret **Dr J. Wilson**
6 **EXCEEDING POWER**, 5, b g Exceed And Excel (AUS)—Extreme Beauty (USA) **The Chalfonts**
7 **FRONT FIVE (IRE)**, 4, b g Teofilo (IRE)—Samdaniya **Mr A. Randle**
8 **MISS BISCOTTI**, 8, ch m Emperor Fountain—Bellacaccia (IRE) **Mrs C. Herbert**
9 **NAMED ASSET**, 4, b g Invincible Spirit (IRE)—Sabria (USA) **The Chalfonts**
10 **SUMEIDA (USA)**, 4, b br c Street Sense (USA)—Camargue (USA) **G. Lansbury**
11 **TOPTHORN**, 10, gr g Silver Patriarch (IRE)—Miss Traxdata **Bosley - Vollaro - Clark**

THREE-YEAR-OLDS

12 B g Tagula (IRE)—Dualagi **Bayard Racing**

TWO-YEAR-OLDS

13 Ch f 3/2 Firebreak—Dualagi (Royal Applause) **Bayard Racing**

Other Owners: Mr M. R. Bosley, Mr G. F. Clark, Mr J. R. Hazeldine, Mrs Paula Marzouk, Mr Walid Marzouk, Ms L. Vollaro, Mrs K. Whitaker.

Jockey (flat): George Baker, Robert Havlin. **Jockey (NH):** Sam Twiston-Davies. **Amateur:** Mr Zac Baker.

---

51 **MR MARCO BOTTI, Newmarket**
Postal: **Prestige Place, Snailwell Road, Newmarket, Suffolk, CB8 7DP**
Contacts: **PHONE (01638) 662416 FAX (01638) 662417 MOBILE (07775) 803007**
E-MAIL office@marcobotti.co.uk WEBSITE www.marcobotti.co.uk

1 **ALFAJER**, 4, b f Mount Nelson—Sakhee's Song (IRE) **Saleh Al Homaizi & Imad Al Sagar**
2 **AZRAFF (IRE)**, 4, b g Paco Boy (IRE)—Gee Kel (USA) **Saleh Al Homaizi & Imad Al Sagar**
3 **BRANDYBEND (IRE)**, 4, b f Galileo (IRE)—Elusive Wave (IRE) **A J Suited Partnership**
4 **CRAZY CHIC (IRE)**, 5, gr g Exceed And Excel (AUS)—Martines (FR) **Scuderia Vittadini SRL**
5 **DYLAN MOUTH (IRE)**, 5, b h Dylan Thomas (IRE)—Cottonmouth (IRE) **Scuderia Effevi SRL**
6 **EMERALD (ITY)**, 4, b g High Chaparral (IRE)—Ekta **La Tesa Spa & Mr J Allison**
7 **EURO CHARLINE**, 5, b m Myboycharlie (IRE)—Eurolink Artemis **Team Valor LLC**
8 **FANCIFUL ANGEL (IRE)**, 4, gr g Dark Angel (IRE)—Fanciful Dancer **Scuderia Blueberry SRL**
9 **GOLDEN STEPS (FR)**, 5, b g Footstepsinthesand—Kocooning (USA) **Mr M. A. A. Al-Mannai**
10 **GRENDISAR (IRE)**, 6, b h Invincible Spirit (IRE)—Remarkable Story **Mr M. A. M. Albousi Alghufli**
11 **GREY MIRAGE**, 7, b g Oasis Dream—Grey Way (USA) **G. Manfredini**
12 **KURIOSA (IRE)**, 4, ch f Rip Van Winkle—Kite Mark **Mrs L. Botti**
13 **KYLLACHY QUEEN (IRE)**, 4, b br f Kyllachy—Queen Sensazione (IRE) **Scuderia Blueberry SRL**
14 **LAT HAWILL (IRE)**, 5, b g Invincible Spirit (IRE)—Arbella **G. Manfredini**
15 **LATIN CHARM (IRE)**, 5, b g Cape Cross (IRE)—Di Moi Oui **Grundy Bloodstock Ltd**
16 **MOOHAARIB (IRE)**, 5, b g Oasis Dream—Evita **Sheikh M. B. K. Al Maktoum**
17 **NAADIRR (IRE)**, 5, b g Oasis Dream—Beach Bunny (IRE) **Sheikh M. B. K. Al Maktoum**
18 **SOLAR DEITY (IRE)**, 7, b h Exceed And Excel (AUS)—Dawn Raid (IRE) **Mr G Manfredini & Mr A Tinkler**
19 **SOUND OF FREEDOM (IRE)**, 4, ch f Duke of Marmalade (IRE)—Paint In Green (IRE) **Scuderia Effevi SRL**
20 **SPICY JAM**, 4, b br f Holy Roman Emperor (IRE)—Jalys (IRE) **Scuderia Blueberry SRL**

THREE-YEAR-OLDS

21 **ALJAZZI**, b f Shamardal (USA)—Nouriya **Saleh Al Homaizi & Imad Al Sagar**
22 **ANGELICAL DANCER (FR)**, gr g Dark Angel (IRE)—Sundancer **Mr R. Ng**

MR MARCO BOTTI - Continued

23 **APPROCAILLIS (IRE),** ch c New Approach (IRE)—Capercaillie (USA) **Mr V. Vartanov**
24 **CANFORD THOMPSON,** b c Canford Cliffs (IRE)—Sadie Thompson (IRE) **Scuderia Blueberry SRL**
25 **DANDY STAR (IRE),** b g Dandy Man (IRE)—Mount Street (IRE) **Mr A. N. Mubarak**
26 **DARKSITEOFTHEMOON (IRE),** b g Dark Angel (IRE)—Moon Club (IRE) **G. Manfredini**
27 **DHAHMAAN (IRE),** b c Kodiac—Heroine Chic (IRE) **Sheikh N. M. H. Al Khalifa**
28 **DIVINE JOY,** b f Rip Van Winkle (IRE)—Joyeaux **Mr W. A. Tinkler**
29 **DREAM FACTORY (IRE),** ch g Manduro (GER)—Istishaara (USA)
30 **DREAM LORD (IRE),** ch c Dream Ahead (USA)—Silent Secret (IRE) **K. A. Dasmal**
31 **DREAM MOVER (IRE),** ch c Dream Ahead (USA)—Maramba (USA) **Team Valor LLC**
32 **ENCORE MOI,** b f Exceed And Excel (AUS)—Di Moi Oui **Scuderia Vittadini SRL**
33 **FEEL THIS MOMENT (IRE),** b g Tamayuz—Rugged Up (IRE) **Mrs L. Botti**
34 **FREESIA (IRE),** b f Dansili—Field of Hope (IRE) **Grundy Bloodstock Ltd**
35 **HAWEEYA (IRE),** b f Iffraaj—Yin **Sheikh M. B. K. Al Maktoum**
36 **HIDE YOUR FIRES (IRE),** b f Frozen Power (IRE)—Omanah (USA) **Mr S. M. Al Sabah**
37 **ICE ALERT (IRE),** b c Frozen Power (IRE)—Karenka (IRE) **Miss H. M. Turner**
38 **IL SASSICAIA,** b g Dick Turpin (IRE)—Step Fast (USA) **Mrs L. Botti**
39 **ILZAM (IRE),** b g Holy Roman Emperor (IRE)—Let's Pretend **Sheikh K. A. I. S. Al Khalifa**
40 **IMASUMAQ (IRE),** b f Teofilo (IRE)—Miss Dela (IRE) **El Catorce**
41 **JASSUR,** b c Canford Cliffs (IRE)—Child Bride (USA) **Saleh Al Homaizi & Imad Al Sagar**
42 **JUST FAB (IRE),** b f Canford Cliffs (IRE)—Unlock (USA) **D Bellamy, M Holman, J Allison & Fabfive**
43 **KNIFE EDGE (IRE),** ch c Zoffany (IRE)—Attalea (IRE) **Mrs J Magnier, Mr M Tabor & Mr D Smith**
44 **KUWAIT CANDY (USA),** b c Candy Ride (ARG)—Panthera (USA) **Mr S. M. Al Sabah**
45 **LAZZAM,** ch c Archipenko (USA)—Empire Rose (ARG) **Sheikh M. B. K. Al Maktoum**
46 **LILY TRICKS,** b f Authorized (IRE)—Trick of Ace (USA) **Mr I. Wilson**
47 **MAJESTIQUE (IRE),** br f High Chaparral (IRE)—Germane **Miss Y. M. G. Jacques**
48 **MALMOSTOSA,** b f Intikhab (USA)—Tell Mum **Promenade Bloodstock Limited**
49 **MAY ROSE (IRE),** b f Lawman (FR)—Rose de France (IRE) **Saleh Al Homaizi & Imad Al Sagar**
50 **MILETAKETHEBALL (IRE),** b g Vale of York (IRE)—Carrauntoohil (IRE) **Fabfive**
51 **MISTY LORD (IRE),** b c Lilbourne Lad (IRE)—Misty Night (IRE) **Fabfive**
52 **MR KHALID,** b c Pour Moi (IRE)—Island Dreams (IRE) **Saleh Al Homaizi & Imad Al Sagar**
53 **ONESIE (IRE),** b g Dandy Man (IRE)—Easee On (IRE) **Mr W. A. Tinkler**
54 **PACOMMAND,** b c Paco Boy (IRE)—Indian Story (IRE) **G. Manfredini**
55 **PIACERE (IRE),** b f New Approach (IRE)—Aneedah (IRE) **The Great Partnership**
56 **PRINCESS RAIHANA,** br f Cape Cross (IRE)—Raihana (AUS) **Sheikh M. B. K. Al Maktoum**
57 **PUSHAQ (IRE),** b g Roderic O'Connor (IRE)—Et Dona Ferentes **El Catorce**
58 **RASASEE (IRE),** gr c Rip Van Winkle (IRE)—Gleaming Silver (IRE) **Sheikh M. B. K. Al Maktoum**
59 **RASMEE,** b c Fastnet Rock (AUS)—Reem (AUS) **Sheikh M. B. K. Al Maktoum**
60 **RECONSIDER (IRE),** ch g Approve (IRE)—Singora Lady (IRE) **Mrs L. Botti**
61 **REFULGENCE (FR),** b f Azamour (IRE)—Ares Flight (USA) **Niarchos Family**
62 **ROCKSPIRIT (IRE),** b f Fastnet Rock (AUS)—Phillippa (IRE) **G. Manfredini**
63 **SAEEDAN (IRE),** b c Tagula (IRE)—Sharadja (IRE) **Sheikh A. Z. A. M. Al Khalifa**
64 **SAHALIN,** b f Red Rocks (IRE)—Tamathea (IRE) **Immobiliare Casa Paola SRL**
65 **SCIACCA (IRE),** b f Royal Applause—With Colour **Promenade Bloodstock Limited**
66 **SEMRA (USA),** b f Candy Ride (ARG)—Smara (USA) **Sheikh M. B. K. Al Maktoum**
67 **SHAHBAR,** b g Champs Elysees—Dahama **Al Shaqab Racing UK Limited**
68 **SISANIA (IRE),** ch f Mastercraftsman (IRE)—Avril Rose (IRE) **Scuderia Rencati SRL**
69 **SMIRNOVA (IRE),** b f Dylan Thomas (IRE)—Seminova **Mrs L. Botti**
70 **TRISHULI ROCK (IRE),** b f Fastnet Rock (AUS)—Trishuli **Scuderia Blueberry SRL**
71 **ULFAH DREAM,** b f Oasis Dream—Ulfah (USA) **Sheikh M. B. K. Al Maktoum**
72 **URBAN BEAUTY (IRE),** ch f Sea The Stars (IRE)—One Day In Spain **Mr V. Vartanov**
73 **VELVET REVOLUTION,** ch c Pivotal—Gino's Spirits **Heart Of The South Racing & Partner**
74 **VICTORIOUS LAUGH (IRE),** b c High Chaparral (IRE)—Last Laugh (USA) **Mr V. Vartanov**
75 **VOGUEATTI (USA),** b f Arch (USA)—Not Here (USA) **Sheikh K. A. I. S. Al Khalifa**
76 **WILD HACKED (USA),** b c Lemon Drop Kid (USA)—Dance Pass (IRE) **Sheikh K. A. I. S. Al Khalifa**
77 **XCEEDINGLY XCITED (IRE),** b f Exceed And Excel (USA)—Alamouna (IRE) **Sheikh M. B. K. Al Maktoum**
78 **ZAHID (IRE),** ch c Zoffany (IRE)—Opinionated (IRE) **Sheikh M. B. K. Al Maktoum**

TWO-YEAR-OLDS

79 B f 16/5 Frankel—Amanee (AUS) (Pivotal) **Sheikh M. B. K. Al Maktoum**
80 **BAHAMAS (IRE),** b c 12/4 Rip Van Winkle (IRE)—Gwyllion (USA) (Red Ransom (USA)) (57142)
81 **BOBBIO (IRE),** ch c 17/2 Choisir (AUS)—
   Balladiene (IRE) (Noverre (USA)) (36913) **Promenade Bloodstock Limited**
82 **BORNTOSIN (IRE),** b c 1/5 Born To Sea (IRE)—Mrs Beeton (IRE) (Dansili) (8859) **G. Manfredini**
83 **DO YOU KNOW (IRE),** b f 15/4 So You Think (NZ)—Queen of Lyons (USA) (Dubai Destination (USA)) (11073)

MR MARCO BOTTI - Continued

84 **DRIVER'S GIRL (USA)**, b br f 3/2 Candy Ride (ARG)—
    Sharbat (USA) (Dynaformer (USA)) (27472) **Gute Freunde Partnership**
85 B c 17/2 Kodiac—Easy Times (Nayef (USA)) (42000) **Sheikh A. Z. A. M. Al Khalifa**
86 B c 28/3 Tamayuz—Empire Rose (ARG) (Sunray Spirit (USA)) **Sheikh M. B. K. Al Maktoum**
87 Ch gr f 30/3 Poet's Voice—Expedience (USA) (With Approval (CAN)) (47619) **Saleh Al Homaizi & Imad Al Sagar**
88 B f 2/2 Sayif (IRE)—Island Dreams (USA) (Giant's Causeway (USA)) **Saleh Al Homaizi & Imad Al Sagar**
89 B f 17/2 Royal Applause—Lady Artemisia (IRE) (Montjeu (IRE)) **Mr M. G. Moretti**
90 B f 9/2 High Chaparral (IRE)—Last Laugh (USA) (Smart Strike (CAN)) **Mr V. Vartanov**
91 **MAGICAL FOREST (IRE)**, b f 29/4 Casamento (IRE)—
    Hurry Home Hydee (USA) (Came Home (USA)) (20952) **Mr J. Allison**
92 B c 14/2 Dubawi (IRE)—Mahbooba (AUS) (Galileo (IRE)) **Sheikh M. B. K. Al Maktoum**
93 **MANDARIN (GER)**, ch c 31/3 Lope de Vega (IRE)—
    Margarita (GER) (Lomitas) (55000) **Sheikh M. B. K. Al Maktoum**
94 **MIO RAGAZZO**, b c 27/4 Mayson—Mia Diletta (Selkirk (USA)) **Scuderia Blueberry SRL**
95 B c 23/2 Dutch Art—Miss Quality (USA) (Elusive Quality (USA)) (280000) **Saleh Al Homaizi & Imad Al Sagar**
96 B c 7/4 Sayif (IRE)—Missy O' Gwaun (IRE) (King's Best (USA)) **Saleh Al Homaizi & Imad Al Sagar**
97 B f 18/3 Henrythenavigator (USA)—Moonboat (Starcraft (NZ))
98 Ch c 10/4 Casamento (IRE)—Nightswimmer (IRE) (Noverre (USA)) (58000) **Scuderia Rencati SRL**
99 B f 6/2 Galileo (IRE)—Nouriya (Danehill Dancer (IRE)) **Saleh Al Homaizi & Imad Al Sagar**
100 **PIRATE LOOK (IRE)**, b c 8/4 Canford Cliffs (IRE)—Gerika (FR) (Galileo (IRE)) (47988) **La Tesa SPA**
101 Ch f 3/5 Raven's Pass (USA)—Pivotal Lady (Pivotal) (38000)
102 B f 28/3 Tamayuz—Qilaada (USA) (Bernardini (USA)) **Sheikh M. B. K. Al Maktoum**
103 B f 17/3 Oasis Dream—Raihana (AUS) (Elusive Quality (USA)) **Sheikh M. B. K. Al Maktoum**
104 B c 7/3 Dubawi (IRE)—Reem (AUS) (Galileo (IRE)) **Sheikh M. B. K. Al Maktoum**
105 B c 21/4 Pivotal—Rivara (Red Ransom (USA)) (12000)
106 B f 30/1 Fastnet Rock (AUS)—Shegotloose (USA) (Dynaformer (USA)) **Sheikh M. B. K. Al Maktoum**
107 **SHIFT CROSS**, br f 10/2 Cape Cross (IRE)—Rose Shift (IRE) (Night Shift (USA)) **Scuderia Blueberry SRL**
108 **SLICEOFLIFE**, b c 1/3 Sayif (IRE)—Cherrego (AUS) (Borrego (USA)) (19195) **G. Manfredini**
109 **SOUNDS OF APRIL (IRE)**, b f 8/4 Exceed And Excel (AUS)—Wickwig (In The Wings) **La Tesa SPA**
110 B f 11/4 High Chaparral (IRE)—
    Special Assignment (USA) (Lemon Drop Kid (USA)) (22148) **Scuderia Rencati SRL**
111 B c 23/2 Galileo (IRE)—Sweet Cecily (IRE) (Kodiac)

Other Owners: Mr P. C. Aberg, Mrs E. Adamski, I. J. Al-Sagar, D. Bellamy, Mr L. Biffi, Mrs Catherine Cashman, Saleh Al Homaizi, Mrs S. Magnier, Mr T. Muller, Mr J. M. Nicholson, A. Panetta, J. R. Penny, Mrs K. Pizarro, Mr C. Pizarro, D. Smith, M. Tabor.

Assistant Trainers: Lucie Botti, Karen Paris

Apprentice: Marc Monaghan, Daniel Muscutt.

---

52   MR PETER BOWEN, Haverfordwest
Postal: **Yet-Y-Rhug, Letterston, Haverfordwest, Pembrokeshire, SA62 5TB**
Contacts: **PHONE (01348) 840486 FAX (01348) 840486 MOBILE (07811) 111234**
E-MAIL **info@peterbowenracing.com** WEBSITE **www.peterbowenracing.com**

1 **AL CO (FR)**, 11, ch g Dom Alco (FR)—Carama (FR) **F. Lloyd**
2 **ALF 'N' DOR (IRE)**, 5, ch g Flemensfirth (USA)—Greenflag Princess (IRE) **Mr J. Andrews**
3 **AWAYWITHTHEGREYS (IRE)**, 9, gr g Whipper (USA)—
    Silver Sash (GER) **Karen Bowen, Saith O Ni & The Hedonists**
4 **BEGGAR'S WISHES (IRE)**, 5, b g Oscar (IRE)—Strong Wishes (IRE) **Roddy Owen & Paul Fullagar**
5 **BEREA BORU (IRE)**, 8, b g Brian Boru—Wayward Venture (IRE) **Mr H. Jones**
6 **BISHOP WULSTAN (IRE)**, 5, b g Oratorio (IRE)—Laurentine (USA) **The Hedonists & Karen Bowen**
7 **BUACHAILL ALAINN (IRE)**, 9, b g Oscar (IRE)—Bottle A Knock (IRE) **Roddy Owen & Paul Fullagar**
8 **CLASSI MASSINI**, 5, b m Dr Massini (IRE)—Classi Maureen **Mr C. W. Pyne**
9 **COUGAR'S GOLD (IRE)**, 5, b g Oscar (IRE)—Top Her Up (IRE) **Mr W. E. V. Harries**
10 **COURT KING (IRE)**, 5, b g Indian River (FR)—Eliza Everett (IRE) **Mr J. G. Morris**
11 **CURIOUS CARLOS**, 7, b g Overbury (IRE)—Classi Maureen **Mr C. W. Pyne**
12 **DEADLY MOVE (IRE)**, 7, b g Scorpion (IRE)—Sounds Attractive (IRE) **R. D. J. Swinburne**
13 **DESERTMORE HILL (IRE)**, 6, b g Beneficial—Youngborogal (IRE) **West Coast Haulage Limited**
14 **DIPITY DOO DAH**, 12, b m Slip Anchor—Lyra **C. G. R. Booth**
15 **DR ROBIN (IRE)**, 6, b g Robin des Pres (FR)—Inter Alia (IRE) **David Robbins & Karen Bowen**
16 **DREAMS OF MILAN (IRE)**, 8, b g Milan—Joe's Dream Catch (IRE) **Paul Duffy, David Semmens, Viv Williams 1**
17 **FAIR TO MIDDLING**, 6, gr g Fair Mix (IRE)—Mtilly **Mrs S. McDonald**
18 **FLYING EAGLE (IRE)**, 8, b g Oscar (IRE)—Fille d'argent (IRE) **West Coast Haulage Limited**

MR PETER BOWEN - Continued

19 **GHOST RIVER**, 6, ch g Flemensfirth (USA)—Cresswell Native (IRE) **Mr J. Andrews**
20 **GRAPE TREE FLAME**, 8, ch m Grape Tree Road—Althrey Flame (IRE) **F. Lloyd**
21 **HENLLAN HARRI (IRE)**, 8, br g King's Theatre (IRE)—Told You So (IRE) **Mr W. E. V. Harries**
22 **HENRI PARRY MORGAN**, 8, b g Brian Boru—Queen of Thedaises **Ednyfed & Elizabeth Morgan**
23 **HOLLIES PEARL**, 6, b m Black Sam Bellamy (IRE)—Posh Pearl **R. D. J. Swinburne**
24 **KINARI (IRE)**, 6, b g Captain Rio—Baraza (IRE) **Mr J. Andrews**
25 **LETBESO (IRE)**, 8, ch g Vinnie Roe (IRE)—Go Hunting (IRE) **Roddy Owen & Paul Fullagar**
26 **LORD BRYAN (IRE)**, 5, b g Brian Boru—Run Cat (IRE) **Mrs K. Bowen**
27 **MINELLA DADDY (IRE)**, 6, b g Flemensfirth (USA)—Old Moon (IRE) **Roddy Owen & Paul Fullagar**
28 **PEARL SWAN (FR)**, 8, b g Gentlewave (IRE)—Swanson (USA) **Roddy Owen & Paul Fullagar**
29 **PRINCESS TARA (IRE)**, 6, b m Kayf Tara—Oscars Vision (IRE) **David Perkins & Kate Perkins**
30 **RED LECTRA**, 6, b g Beat All (USA)—Coronation Queen **Mr R. Quinn**
31 **RED SIX (IRE)**, 5, ch g Flemensfirth (USA)—Glacial Missile (IRE) **Roddy Owen & Paul Fullagar**
32 **REGAL DIAMOND (IRE)**, 8, b g Vinnie Roe (IRE)—
Paper Money (IRE) **Roddy Owen,Paul Fullagar & Karen Bowen**
33 **ROLLING MAUL (IRE)**, 8, b g Oscar (IRE)—Water Sports (IRE) **Roddy Owen & Paul Fullagar**
34 **RONS DREAM**, 6, b m Kayf Tara—Empress of Light **Mrs T. S. P. Stepney**
35 **STRUMBLE HEAD (IRE)**, 11, b g Anshan—Milan Moss **Mr J. A. Martin**
36 **UNIVERSAL SOLDIER (IRE)**, 11, b g Winged Love (IRE)—Waterland Gale (IRE) **Mrs L. M. King**
37 **WHAT A DIVA**, 5, b m Kayf Tara—Land of Glory **Mrs T. S. P. Stepney**

Other Owners: Mr B. G. Bowen, D. P. Duffy, P. G. Fullagar, Mr E. O. Morgan, Mrs E. Morgan, R. R. Owen, Mrs L. K. Perkins, Mr D. J. Perkins, B. S. Port, S. D. Reeve, D. J. Robbins, Mr D. M. Semmens, Mr P. R. Williams.

Assistant Trainers: Karen Bowen, Michael Bowen

Jockey (NH): Sean Bowen, Donal Devereux, Jamie Moore, Tom O'Brien.

---

53 **MR ROY BOWRING, Edwinstowe**
Postal: **Fir Tree Farm, Edwinstowe, Mansfield, Nottinghamshire, NG21 9JG**
Contacts: **PHONE (01623) 822451 MOBILE (07973) 712942**
E-MAIL bowrings@btconnect.com

1 **ACE MASTER**, 8, ch g Ballet Master (USA)—Ace Maite **S. R. Bowring**
2 **CLUBLAND (IRE)**, 7, b g Red Clubs (IRE)—Racjilanemm **Mr L. P. Keane**
3 **COOL BEANS**, 4, b g Kyllachy—Stellar Brilliant (USA) **Mr L. P. Keane**
4 **DANCING MAITE**, 11, ch g Ballet Master (USA)—Ace Maite **S. R. Bowring**
5 **DIVERTIMENTI (IRE)**, 12, b g Green Desert (USA)—Ballet Shoes (IRE) **K. Nicholls**
6 **DOUGLAS BANK (IRE)**, 4, b g Dandy Man (IRE)—Balance The Books **Mr L. P. Keane**
7 **FIRST EXCEL**, 4, ch g First Trump—Exceedingly Good (IRE) **S. R. Bowring**
8 **FOOLAAD**, 5, ch g Exceed And Excel (AUS)—Zayn Zen **K. Nicholls**
9 **HICKSTER (IRE)**, 5, br g Intense Focus (USA)—Surrender To Me (USA) **Mr L. P. Keane**
10 **LITTLE CHOOSEY**, 6, ch m Cadeaux Genereux—Little Nymph **K. Nicholls**
11 **MARINA BALLERINA**, 8, b br m Ballet Master (USA)—Marinaite **S. R. Bowring**
12 4, B g Resplendent Glory (IRE)—Marinaite **S. R. Bowring**
13 **MASTER OF SONG**, 9, ch g Ballet Master (USA)—Ocean Song **S. R. Bowring**
14 **REASSERT**, 4, b g Assertive—Zonta Zitkala **Mr L. P. Keane**
15 **SOFIAS NUMBER ONE (USA)**, 8, b br g Silver Deputy (CAN)—Storidawn (USA) **S. R. Bowring**
16 **SOLARMAITE**, 7, b m Needwood Blade—Marinaite **S. R. Bowring**
17 **THREE MMM'S**, 5, b m Milk It Mick—Marinaite **S. R. Bowring**

THREE-YEAR-OLDS

18 **RIO GLAMOROUS**, b g Aussie Rules (USA)—Glamorous Spirit (IRE) **K. Nicholls**

---

54 **MR JIM BOYLE, Epsom**
Postal: **South Hatch Stables, Burgh Heath Road, Epsom, Surrey, KT17 4LX**
Contacts: **PHONE (01372) 748800 FAX (01372) 739410 MOBILE (07719) 554147**
E-MAIL info@jamesboyle.co.uk & jimboylesec@hotmail.co.uk (Secretary)
WEBSITE www.jamesboyle.co.uk

1 **ARTISTIC FLIGHT (IRE)**, 4, b g Art Connoisseur (IRE)—Robin **Inside Track Racing Club**
2 **DUKE OF NORTH (IRE)**, 4, b g Danehill Dancer (IRE)—Althea Rose (IRE) **The Paddock Space Partnership 2**

MR JIM BOYLE - Continued

3 **EMPTY THE TANK (IRE)**, 6, b g Lawman (FR)—Asian Alliance (IRE) **The "In Recovery" Partnership**
4 **GIOVANNI DI BICCI**, 4, b g Medicean—Marula (IRE) **M Khan X2**
5 **INKE (IRE)**, 4, br f Intikhab (USA)—Chifney Rush (IRE) **Harrier Racing 2**
6 **NEVER TO BE (USA)**, 5, b g Thewayyouare (USA)—Kitty Foille (USA) **M Khan X2**
7 **ONORINA (IRE)**, 4, b f Arcano (IRE)—Miss Honorine (IRE) **Sir D. J. Prosser**
8 **PERFECT PASTIME**, 8, ch g Pastoral Pursuits—Puritanical (IRE) **The Paddock Space Partnership 2**
9 **PYROCLASTIC (IRE)**, 4, b g Tagula (IRE)—Gypsy Royal (IRE) **The "In Recovery" Partnership**
10 **RIPINTO (IRE)**, 4, ch g Rip Van Winkle (IRE)—For Evva Silca **The "In Recovery" Partnership**
11 **ROYAL OCCASSION**, 4, b c Royal Applause—Stagecoach Jade (IRE) **Mrs J. Thompson**
12 **SEARCHLIGHT**, 5, b g Kyllachy—Baralinka (IRE) **Elite Racing Club**
13 **SHOWTIME BLUES**, 4, b g Showcasing—Night Symphonie **Mr M. B. Spence**
14 **WHAT A DANDY (IRE)**, 5, b g Dandy Man (IRE)—Ibtihal (IRE) **Inside Track Racing Club**

THREE-YEAR-OLDS

15 **BLACK BESS**, br f Dick Turpin (IRE)—Spring Clean (FR) **The Clean Sweep Partnership**
16 **EBBISHAM (IRE)**, b g Holy Roman Emperor (IRE)—Balting Lass (IRE) **The "In Recovery" Partnership**
17 **KRISTOFF (IRE)**, b c Frozen Power (IRE)—Easter Girl **Inside Track Racing Club**
18 **MASTER OF HEAVEN**, b g Makfi—Maid In Heaven (IRE) **Maid In Heaven Partnership**
19 **NORTHMAN (IRE)**, b g Frozen Power (IRE)—Chifney Rush (IRE) **Harrier Racing 3**

TWO-YEAR-OLDS

20 Ch c 20/2 Tagula (IRE)—April Green (FR) (Green Tune (USA)) (36913) **The "In Recovery" Partnership**
21 Ch f 14/2 Harbour Watch (IRE)—Blonde (IRE) (Pivotal) (25839) **The "In Recovery" Partnership**
22 Ch c 18/3 Sir Prancealot (IRE)—Tides (Bahamian Bounty) (60538) **Mr C. C. A. Kwok**
23 B f 23/3 Paco Boy (IRE)—Zia (GER) (Grand Lodge (USA)) **Mr W. J. Hayford**

Other Owners: Mr K. Booth, Mrs P. Boyle, J. R. Boyle, A. J. Chambers, M. C. Cook, Ms J. E. Harrison, Mr A. J. Hill, Mr J. Hillier, Ms T. Keane, M. Khan, M. Khan, Mr P. O. Mooney, Miss M. Noden, Mr R. O'Dwyer, E. Sames, Mr R. Stanbridge, Mr P. A. Taylor.

Apprentice: Nathan Alison.

---

55 **MR RICHARD BRABAZON, Curragh**
Postal: Rangers Lodge, The Curragh, Co. Kildare, Ireland
Contacts: **PHONE 00353 (0) 45 441259 FAX 00353 (0) 45 441906 MOBILE 00353 (0) 87 2515626**
E-MAIL richardbrabazon@eircom.net WEBSITE www.richardbrabazon.ie

1 **KORBOUS (IRE)**, 7, ch g Choisir (AUS)—Puppet Play (IRE) **Mrs F. D. McAuley**
2 **PLACERE (IRE)**, 8, ch m Noverre (USA)—Puppet Play (IRE) **Mrs F. D. McAuley**
3 **RYAN'S HILL**, 4, b g Archipenko (USA)—Flor Y Nata (USA) **Richard Brabazon**

THREE-YEAR-OLDS

4 **ARCHER'S UP**, ch g Archipenko (USA)—Nadeszhda **Richard Brabazon**

TWO-YEAR-OLDS

5 Gr g 11/5 Stormy River (FR)—Happy (JPN) (Bago (FR)) (10705) **David Moran / Richard Brabazon**

---

56 **MR DAVID BRACE, Bridgend**
Postal: Llanmihangel Farm, Pyle, Bridgend, Mid-Glamorgan, CF33 6RL
Contacts: **PHONE (01656) 742313**

1 **BAJAN BLU**, 8, b g Generous (IRE)—Bajan Girl (FR) **D. Brace**
2 **BENNIE O CONNOR (IRE)**, 6, b g Brian Boru—Moneygall (IRE) **D. Brace**
3 **BOB THE BUTCHER**, 7, b g Needle Gun (IRE)—Brydferth Ddu (IRE) **D. Brace**
4 **COLORADO DOC**, 5, b g Dr Massini (IRE)—First Royal (GER) **D. Brace**
5 **DBOBE**, 7, br g Needle Gun (IRE)—Braceys Girl (IRE) **D. Brace**
6 **DOC CODY**, 5, b g Dr Massini (IRE)—Brydferth Ddu (IRE) **D. Brace**
7 **DOC LILY**, 5, b m Dr Massini (IRE)—Branston Lily **D. Brace**
8 **DOCTOR BRAVEHEART (IRE)**, 7, b g Dr Massini (IRE)—Letimavit (IRE) **D. Brace**
9 **DONT TELL PA (IRE)**, 9, b g Oscar (IRE)—Glacial Snowboard (IRE) **D. Brace**
10 **DUNRAVEN DOC**, 5, b g Dr Massini (IRE)—Aphrodisias (FR) **D. Brace**

MR DAVID BRACE - Continued

11 **DUNRAVEN ROYAL,** 6, b g Black Sam Bellamy (IRE)—First Royal (GER) **D. Brace**
12 **GERALDO THE SPARKY (IRE),** 6, ch g Araafa (IRE)—Little Firefly (IRE) **D. Brace**
13 **IT'S PICALILLY,** 6, b m Needle Gun (IRE)—Branston Lily **D. Brace**
14 **PINK EYED PEDRO,** 5, b g Dr Massini (IRE)—Poacher's Paddy (IRE) **D. Brace**

Assistant Trainer: Robbie Llewellyn

---

57 **MR MILTON BRADLEY,** Chepstow
Postal: **Meads Farm, Sedbury Park, Chepstow, Gwent, NP16 7HN**
Contacts: **PHONE (01291) 622486 FAX (01291) 626939**

1 **BURAUQ,** 4, b g Kyllachy—Riccoche (IRE) **D. Smith**
2 **COMPTON PRINCE,** 7, ch g Compton Place—Malelane (IRE) **E. A. Hayward**
3 **DIVINE CALL,** 9, b g Pivotal—Pious **E. A. Hayward**
4 **ENGLISHMAN,** 6, b g Royal Applause—Tesary **E. A. Hayward**
5 **HAMIS AL BIN (IRE),** 7, b g Acclamation—Paimpolaise (IRE) **P. Banfield**
6 **INDIAN AFFAIR,** 6, b h Sleeping Indian—Rare Fling (USA) **J. M. Bradley**
7 **INDIAN TIM,** 4, b g Sleeping Indian—River City Moon (USA) **J. M. Bradley**
8 **JAZRI,** 5, b g Myboycharlie (IRE)—Read Federica **J. M. Bradley**
9 **NOBLE ASSET,** 5, ch g Compton Place—Chance For Romance **E. A. Hayward**
10 **QUICKASWECAN,** 5, b g Shamardal (USA)—Arctic Air **E. A. Hayward**
11 **SPIRIT OF GONDREE (IRE),** 8, b g Invincible Spirit (IRE)—
Kristal's Paradise (IRE) **Paul & Ann de Weck & Partner**
12 **TEMPLE ROAD (IRE),** 8, b g Street Cry (IRE)—Sugarhoneybaby (IRE) **J. M. Bradley**
13 **TRIPLE DREAM,** 11, ch g Vision of Night—Triple Joy **J. M. Bradley**

THREE-YEAR-OLDS

14 **BUSHWISE (IRE),** b f Bushranger (IRE)—Validate **E. A. Hayward**
15 **INDIAN GOLD,** b g Sleeping Indian—Hiraeth **E. A. Hayward**

Other Owners: P. Chapman, Mrs C. A. Chapman, Mrs A. De Weck, Mr M. A. Glassett, Mr S. G. Morris, P. L. de Weck.

Jockey (flat): Luke Morris, Franny Norton.

---

58 **MR MARK BRADSTOCK,** Wantage
Postal: **The Old Manor Stables, Letcombe Bassett, Wantage, Oxfordshire, OX12 9NB**
Contacts: **PHONE (01235) 760780 MOBILE (07887) 686697**
E-MAIL mark.bradstock@btconnect.com WEBSITE www.markbradstockracing.co.uk

1 **BALINROAB (IRE),** 9, b g Milan—Gentle Eyre (IRE) **Miss C. Fordham**
2 **BLACKDOWN HILLS,** 6, b m Presenting—Lady Prunella (IRE) **Mrs P. de W. Johnson**
3 **BLOODY NOSE (IRE),** 4, b g Kalanisi (IRE)—Renvyle Society (IRE) **Mr E. P. K. Weatherall**
4 **COJACK (IRE),** 4, b g Presenting—In The Waves (IRE) **Colin Elgram & Jack Rowlands**
5 **CONEYGREE,** 9, b g Karinga Bay—Plaid Maid (IRE) **The Max Partnership**
6 **DAMBY'S STAR (IRE),** 6, b g Kayf Tara—She Took A Tree (FR) **The Eric Partnership**
7 **FLINTHAM,** 7, b g Kayf Tara—Plaid Maid (IRE) **The Rasher Partnership**
8 **GREY SWIFT,** 8, gr g Terimon—Swift Settlement **Mr J. E. Bond-Smith**
9 **HORTENSE MANCINI,** 7, ch m King's Best (USA)—Have Fun **The Woughton Partnership**
10 **JAISALMER (IRE),** 4, b g Jeremy (USA)—Shara (IRE) **The Jeremy Partnership**
11 **KATARRHINI,** 7, b m Kayf Tara—Dedrunknmunky (IRE) **Mrs K. Casini**
12 4, B f King's Theatre (IRE)—Kon Tiky (FR) **Kiki Partnership**
13 **LADY OVERMOON,** 7, b m Overbury (IRE)—Lady Fleur **The Lady Overmoon Partnership**
14 4, B f Ask—Lady Shackleton (IRE) **Colin Elgram & Jack Rowlands**
15 **LORD VALENTINE,** 8, b g Overbury (IRE)—Lady Fleur **The Lady Overmoon Partnership & Partners**
16 **PLANTAGENET,** 4, b g Midnight Legend—Marsh Court **Mrs P. de W. Johnson**
17 **ROBERT'S STAR (IRE),** 6, b g Oscar (IRE)—Halona **North Star Partnership**
18 **STAR RIDE,** 7, b g Kayf Tara—Star Diva (IRE) **Dorchester On Thames Syndicate**
19 **TALKSALOT (IRE),** 5, b g Thousand Words—Lady Piste (IRE) **Mr J. E. Bond-Smith**

MR MARK BRADSTOCK - Continued

Other Owners: M. F. Bradstock, Mrs A. Bridge, Mrs L. Burgess, Mrs S. Crean, Mr A. C. Dolbey, R. C. Douglas, Lady Dundas, C. Elgram, Mr S. A. D. Hall, Mrs M. J. Kelsey Fry, J. Kelsey-Fry, Mrs S. Kelsey-Fry, D. King, Mrs B. Lockhart-Smith, Dr P. M. Milligan, Mrs S. Robinson, Mr J. R. Rowlands, Miss J. Seaman, M. S. Tamburro, Mr R. W. Tyrrell, C. A. Vernon.

Assistant Trainer: Sara Bradstock

Jockey (NH): Nico De Boinville.

MR GILES BRAVERY, Newmarket
Postal: **Green Ridge House, Hamilton Road, Newmarket, Suffolk, CB8 7JQ**
Contacts: **PHONE (01638) 810231 MOBILE (07711) 112345**
E-MAIL Braverygc@aol.com WEBSITE www.gilesbravery.com Twitter: @GilesBravery

1 **DAN'S PRINCESS**, 4, b f Authorized (IRE)—Piedmont (UAE)
2 **DARRELL RIVERS**, 4, b f Hellvelyn—First Term
3 **GREYFRIARSCHORISTA**, 9, ch g King's Best (USA)—Misty Heights
4 **MOORSTONE**, 4, b f Manduro (GER)—Pan Galactic (USA)
5 **MR MOROCCO**, 4, b g Shirocco (GER)—Moxby
6 **MS ARSENAL**, 4, b f Mount Nelson—Magical Dancer (IRE)
7 **PANOPTICON**, 5, ch m Lucky Story (USA)—Barnacla (IRE)
8 **SUBTLE KNIFE**, 7, ch m Needwood Blade—Northern Bows

THREE-YEAR-OLDS

9 B c Majestic Missile (IRE)—Bold Bunny
10 **LUCIA SCIARRA**, ch f Monsieur Bond (IRE)—Oke Bay
11 **MODELLO (IRE)**, b f Intikhab (USA)—Precious Citizen (USA)
12 **SUMMERTIME LUCY (IRE)**, ch f Frozen Power (IRE)—Sanfrancullinan (IRE)
13 B gr c Hellvelyn—Surprise Statement
14 **TIGSERIN (IRE)**, ch f Approve (IRE)—Mairead Anne (USA)

TWO-YEAR-OLDS

15 Ch f 27/3 Choisir (AUS)—Alchemilla (Dubai Destination (USA))
16 B c 2/2 Aqlaam—Applauding (IRE) (Royal Applause) (5000)
17 B f 9/2 Requinto (IRE)—Aspasias Tizzy (USA) (Tiznow (USA)) (12000)
18 B f 12/2 Danehill Dancer (IRE)—Blanche Dubawi (IRE) (Dubawi (IRE)) (90000)
19 B f 5/4 Foxwedge (AUS)—Crinolette (IRE) (Sadler's Wells (USA)) (60000)
20 B f 7/4 Kyllachy—Let My People Go (FR) (Country Reel (USA)) (19195)
21 B f 5/4 Teofilo (IRE)—Musical Bar (IRE) (Barathea (IRE))
22 Ch f 13/4 Pastoral Pursuits—Northern Bows (Bertolini (USA))
23 B f 12/3 Royal Applause—Our Gal (Kyllachy) (5000)
24 B f 25/3 Sir Percy—Parsonagehotelyork (IRE) (Danehill (USA)) (900)
25 B f 29/4 Lilbourne Lad (IRE)—Sail With The Wind (Saddlers' Hall (IRE)) (21000)
26 B f 12/4 Intikhab (USA)—Solace (USA) (Langfuhr (CAN)) (6000)
27 B c 20/4 Kentucky Dynamite (USA)—Teatime (FR) (Loup Solitaire (USA)) (5167)
28 B c 22/3 Lilbourne Lad (IRE)—Timber Tops (UAE) (Timber Country (USA)) (14285)

Assistant Trainer: Noel Quinlan

MR BARRY BRENNAN, Kingston Lisle
Postal: **Little Farm, Fawler Road, Kingston Lisle, Wantage, Oxfordshire, OX12 9QH**
Contacts: **MOBILE (07907) 529780**
E-MAIL barrybrennan2@hotmail.co.uk WEBSITE www.barrybrennanracing.co.uk

1 **BOOK OF EXCUSES (IRE)**, 8, b g Brian Boru—Out of Danger (IRE) **D. R. T. Gibbons**
2 **CHANGING THE GUARD**, 10, b g King's Best (USA)—Our Queen of Kings **M. J. Hills**
3 **FLASH CRASH**, 7, b g Val Royal (FR)—Tessara (GER) **M. J. Hills**
4 **HANNINGTON**, 5, ch g Firebreak—Manderina **M. J. Hills**
5 **HOPE'S WISHES**, 6, b m Kayf Tara—Otarie (FR) **M. J. Hills**
6 **IRONDALE EXPRESS**, 5, b m Myboycharlie (IRE)—Olindera (GER) **D. R. T. Gibbons**
7 **NOUJOUD (IRE)**, 4, b f Teofilo (IRE)—Penang (IRE) **M. J. Hills**
8 **PUT THE BOOT IN (IRE)**, 4, ch g Duke of Marmalade (IRE)—Mubkera (IRE) **M. J. Hills**

MR BARRY BRENNAN - Continued

9 **UNFORGIVING MINUTE**, 5, b h Cape Cross (IRE)—Ada River **L. M. Power**
10 **VICKY'S CHARM (IRE)**, 7, b m Old Vic—Sweet Charm (IRE) **Dr I. A. Cragg**

61　**MISS RHONA BREWIS, Belford**
Postal: **Chester Hill, Belford, Northumberland, NE70 7EF**
Contacts: **PHONE (01668) 213239/213281**

1 **CLOVELLY**, 6, b m Midnight Legend—Chantilly Rose **Miss R. G. Brewis**

62　**MR JOHN BRIDGER, Liphook**
Postal: **Upper Hatch Farm, Liphook, Hampshire, GU30 7EL**
Contacts: **PHONE (01428) 722528 MOBILE (07785) 716614**
E-MAIL jbridger@btconnect.com

1 **BOOKMAKER**, 6, b g Byron—Cankara (IRE) **T Wallace & J J Bridger**
2 **BYRD IN HAND (IRE)**, 9, b g Fasliyev (USA)—Military Tune (IRE) **Marshall Bridger**
3 **CHORAL FESTIVAL**, 10, b m Pivotal—Choirgirl **Mrs E. Gardner**
4 **FAIRY MIST (IRE)**, 9, b g Oratorio (IRE)—Prealpina (IRE) **Mr J. J. Bridger**
5 **LILY EDGE**, 7, b m Byron—Flaming Spirt **Mr J. J. Bridger**
6 **PETTOCHSIDE**, 7, b g Refuse To Bend (IRE)—Clear Impression (IRE) **P. Cook**
7 **RENNIE MACKINTOSH (IRE)**, 4, b g Excellent Art—Mac Melody (IRE) **W. A. Wood**
8 **SHIFTING STAR (IRE)**, 11, ch g Night Shift (USA)—Ahshado **Night Shadow Syndicate**
9 **WELSH INLET (IRE)**, 8, br m Kheleyf (USA)—Ervedya (IRE) **Mr J. J. Bridger**

THREE-YEAR-OLDS

10 **ARCTIC FLOWER (IRE)**, gr f Roderic O'Connor (IRE)—Just In Love (FR) **Mr & Mrs K. Finch**
11 **DEER SONG**, b g Piccolo—Turkish Delight **The Deer's Hut**
12 **FINE SHARE (IRE)**, b g Art Connoisseur (IRE)—Novel Fun (IRE) **P. Cook**
13 **NIDNOD**, b f Myboycharlie (IRE)—Littlemisstutti (IRE) **Mr J. J. Bridger**

TWO-YEAR-OLDS

14 **CRYSTAL SECRET**, b f 26/3 Sayif (IRE)—Laser Crystal (IRE) (King's Theatre (IRE)) (1714) **Mr & Mrs K. Finch**
15 B f 22/3 Delegator—Desert Kiss (Cape Cross (IRE)) **T. Ellison**
16 Ch g 29/4 Medicean—Priena (IRE) (Priolo (USA)) (1000) **Mr & Mrs K. Finch**
17 **RIESCO**, b f 1/3 Hellvelyn—Lola Sapola (IRE) (Benny The Dip (USA)) (761) **Mr & Mrs K. Finch**
18 **TAURIAN GOLD**, b g 15/5 Piccolo—Elsie's Orphan (Pastoral Pursuits) **Mr & Mrs K. Finch**

Other Owners: Mr J. J. Bridger, Mrs Diane Ellison, Mr K. Finch, Mr David Higgs, Mr C. Marshall, Mr F. R. Northcott, Mrs Diane Stewart, Mr Trevor Wallace.

Assistant Trainer: Rachel Cook

63　**MR DAVID BRIDGWATER, Stow-on-the-Wold**
Postal: **Wyck Hill Farm, Wyck Hill, Stow-on-the-Wold, Cheltenham, Gloucestershire, GL54 1HT**
Contacts: **PHONE (01451) 830349 FAX (01451) 830349 MOBILE (07831) 635817**
E-MAIL sales@bridgwaterracing.co.uk WEBSITE www.bridgwaterracing.co.uk

1 **ACCORDING TO TREV (IRE)**, 10, ch g Accordion—Autumn Sky (IRE) **Building Bridgies**
2 **AMBER SPYGLASS**, 6, ch g Act One—Northern Bows **Mrs J. A. Chenery & Mr R. J. Chenery**
3 **ASKNOTWHAT (IRE)**, 5, ch g Dylan Thomas (IRE)—Princess Roseburg (USA) **In It For The Crack No.1**
4 **BAWDEN ROCKS**, 7, b g Anabaa (USA)—Late Night (GER) **Mr S. Hunt**
5 **BELMONT PARK (FR)**, 5, b br g Al Namix (FR)—Goldoulyssa (FR) **Terry & Sarah Amos**
6 **BIG TALK**, 9, b g Selkirk (USA)—Common Request (USA) **Deauville Daze Partnership**
7 **CELTIC INTRIGUE (IRE)**, 9, b g Celtic Swing—Macca Luna (IRE) **Mrs J. Smith**
8 **CLEEVE HILL LAD**, 8, b g Overbury (IRE)—Lady Prunella (IRE) **Mr P. J. Williams**
9 **COLLODI (GER)**, 7, b g Konigstiger (GER)—Codera (GER) **MMG Racing**
10 **DE KERRY MAN (IRE)**, 8, b g Westerner—Fishy Fishy (IRE) **In It For The Crack**
11 **DONT DO MONDAYS (IRE)**, 9, b g Rashar (USA)—Bit of A Chance **F. W. K. Griffin**
12 **DR CUDDLES (IRE)**, 8, b g Dr Massini (IRE)—Native Emigrant (IRE) **MMG Racing**
13 **EDGAR (GER)**, 6, b g Big Shuffle (USA)—Estella (GER) **K J McCourt & Partners**

MR DAVID BRIDGWATER - Continued

14 **EMPEROR COMMODOS**, 9, b g Midnight Legend—Theme Arena **R. Mathew**
15 **ENGAI (GER)**, 10, b g Noroit (GER)—Enigma (GER) **D. G. Bridgwater**
16 **FERGAL MAEL DUIN**, 8, gr g Tikkanen (USA)—Fad Amach (IRE) **James Messenger Jean-Marie Buob-Aldorf**
17 **GINO TRAIL (IRE)**, 9, br g Perugino (USA)—Borough Trail (IRE) **Mrs J. Smith**
18 **GOLAN DANCER (IRE)**, 8, b g Golan (IRE)—Seductive Dance **S Hunt, R Butler, D Ward, S Girardier**
19 **HIPPIART**, 4, ch g Dutch Art—Hippogator (USA) **Michael & Gerry Worcester**
20 **JOT'EM DOWN (IRE)**, 5, b g Kalanisi (IRE)—Shuil A Hocht (IRE) **Mr S. Hunt**
21 **LAKESHORE LADY (IRE)**, 6, b m Lakeshore Road (IRE)—Chiminee Chime (IRE) **Simon & Liz Hunt**
22 **LOST ARCA (FR)**, 10, b g Lost World (IRE)—Luarca (IRE) **R. Mathew**
23 **MAHLERS STAR (IRE)**, 6, ch g Mahler—Celestial Rose (IRE) **Simon Hunt & Jack Hunt**
24 **MON PETIT ANGE (FR)**, 5, b g Ultimately Lucky (IRE)—Line Tzigane (FR) **Terry & Sarah Amos**
25 **NAMPARAROO**, 7, b m Kayf Tara—Silk Stockings (FR) **The Happy Horse Partnership**
26 **NO BUTS**, 8, b g Kayf Tara—Wontcostalotbut **Wontcostalot Partnership**
27 **NOMADIC STORM**, 10, b g Nomadic Way (USA)—Cateel Bay **Mrs V. Williams**
28 **OPECHEE (IRE)**, 5, b g Robin des Champs (FR)—Falcons Gift (IRE) **AM Bostock DG Bostock**
29 **ORCHESTRATED (IRE)**, 5, b g Mahler—Rose Island **Feasibility Limited**
30 **ORIONS GOLD**, 5, b g Proclamation (IRE)—Charm of Gold **The Lucky Seven**
31 **OSCAR HILL (IRE)**, 10, b g Oscar (IRE)—Elizabeth Tudor (IRE) **K. W. Bradley**
32 **PULLED ANOTHER**, 5, b m Tobougg (IRE)—Mini Mandy **Mr B. P. Keogh**
33 **SAFFRON PRINCE**, 8, b g Kayf Tara—Jan's Dream (IRE) **Mrs J. A. Chenery**
34 **SAGE MONKEY (IRE)**, 7, br g Craigsteel—Braw Lass **Mrs J. Smith**
35 **SID'S TOPPER (FR)**, 6, b br g Anabaa Blue—Last Sicyos (FR) **Chemipetro Limited**
36 **SIR PITT**, 9, b g Tiger Hill (IRE)—Rebecca Sharp **G. D. Kendrick**
37 **TEMPURAN**, 7, b gr g Unbridled's Song (USA)—Tenderly (IRE) **Mr D. J. Smith**
38 **THE GIANT BOLSTER**, 11, b g Black Sam Bellamy (IRE)—Divisa (GER) **Simon Hunt & Gary Lambton**
39 **THE YANK**, 7, b g Trade Fair—Silver Gyre (IRE) **Mr G. Attwood**
40 **THEATRE FLAME (IRE)**, 6, b g King's Theatre (IRE)—Bob's Flame (IRE) **CWB LLP**
41 **WAHWONAISA**, 4, b g Kalanisi (IRE)—Clandestine **AM Bostock DG Bostock**
42 **WALDEN PRINCE (IRE)**, 9, b g Saffron Walden (FR)—Kahyasi Princess (IRE) **Mr G. Attwood**
43 **WYCK HILL (IRE)**, 12, b g Pierre—Willow Rose (IRE) **J. P. McManus**

Other Owners: T. P Amos, Mrs S. P Amos, Mrs C. H. Borghoff, D. G. Bostock, Mrs A. M. Bostock, R. J. Brennan, Mr J. P. R. Buob-Aldorf, Mr R. J. Chenery, Mr G. J. Clarkson, A. A. Clifford, R. L. Clifford, Mrs A. Field, Mr A. Gunn, Miss L. M. Haywood, Mr M. V. Hill, Mr J. Hunt, Mrs E. A. Hunt, Mr B. Knight, Mr G. Lambton, C. D. Massey, Mr K. J. McCourt, J. M. Messenger, Ms L. E. Moore, Mr T. J. Payton, Mr A. R. Pigott, Miss E. L. Walker, Mr D. J. Ward, Mr N. J. Witts-Hewinson, Mr M. G. Worcester, Mrs G. S. Worcester.

Assistant Trainer: Mrs Lucy K. Bridgwater

Jockey (NH): Tom Scudamore. **Conditional:** Jake Hodson. **Amateur:** Miss Poppy Bridgwater.

---

64 **MR MARK BRISBOURNE, Nesscliffe**
Postal: Ness Strange Stables, Great Ness, Shrewsbury, Shropshire, SY4 2LE
Contacts: **PHONE** (01743) 741599 **MOBILE** (07803) 019651

1 **DUTCH BARNEY**, 6, b g Dutch Art—Celeb Style (IRE) **Celeb Style Racing**
2 **ELLE REBELLE**, 6, b m Cockney Rebel (IRE)—Lille Ida **The Bourne Connection**
3 **FOSSA**, 6, b g Dubai Destination (USA)—Gayanula (USA) **Mark Brisbourne**
4 **GAMESTERS LAD**, 4, br g Firebreak—Gamesters Lady **The Gamesters Partnership**
5 4, B g Kirkwall—Makeover **Mr Gordon Kendrick**
6 **MYSTICAL MAZE**, 5, br m Multiplex—Musical Maze **Mr Marshall Barnett**
7 **OMOTESANDO**, 6, b g Street Cry (IRE)—Punctilious **Mr P. G. Evans**
8 **ROYAL TROOPER (IRE)**, 10, b g Hawk Wing (USA)—Strawberry Roan (IRE) **Mark Brisbourne**
9 **SAKHRA**, 5, b g Nayef (USA)—Noble Desert (FR) **P. R. Kirk**
10 **STORM LIGHTNING**, 7, b g Exceed And Excel (AUS)—All For Laura **Law Abiding Citizens**
11 **TARO TYWOD (IRE)**, 7, br m Footstepsinthesand—Run To Jane (IRE) **Rasio Cymru Racing**

THREE-YEAR-OLDS

12 B g Captain Gerrard (IRE)—Ensign's Trick **Mark Brisbourne**
13 **GAMESTERS BOY**, b g Firebreak—Gamesters Lady **The Gamesters Partnership**
14 **LONG ISLAND**, b f Firebreak—Fakhuur **Mark Brisbourne**
15 **PIVOTAL DREAM (IRE)**, br f Excellent Art—Oasis Fire (IRE) **The Bourne Connection**

MR MARK BRISBOURNE - Continued

TWO-YEAR-OLDS

16 Ch f 3/4 Captain Gerrard (IRE)—Ensign's Trick (Cayman Kai (IRE)) **Mark Brisbourne**

Other Owners: Mr A. J. Banton, Mr Derek Dean, Mrs C. M. Gibson, Mr Raymond McNeil, Mr Peter Mort, Mr Mike Murray, Mrs C. A. Naylor, Mr John Owen, Mr A. Pitt, Mr Raymond Tooth.

Jockey (flat): Ryan Clark, Cam Hardie, Shane Kelly. **Jockey (NH):** Liam Treadwell.
Apprentice: Charlie Bennett, Becky Brisbourne.

---

65 MR ROBYN BRISLAND, Newmarket
Postal: **Cadland Cottage Stables, Moulton Road, Newmarket, Suffolk, CB8 8DU**
Contacts: **MOBILE (07771) 656081**
E-MAIL robbris@me.com

1 **AMAZE ME**, 4, ch f Aqlaam—Princess Miletrian (IRE) **Franconson Partners**
2 **BAKER**, 4, b g Teofilo (IRE)—Meydan Princess (IRE) **Franconson Partners**
3 **BARNABY BROOK (CAN)**, 6, b g North Light (IRE)—Mascara (USA) **Franconson Partners**
4 **BETHNAL GREEN**, 4, ch f Cockney Rebel (IRE)—Exodia **Franconson Partners**
5 **ENRICHING (USA)**, 8, ch g Lemon Drop Kid (USA)—Popozinha (USA) **Franconson Partners**
6 **MAGNUS MAXIMUS**, 5, b g Holy Roman Emperor (IRE)—Chanrossa (IRE) **Franconson Partners**

THREE-YEAR-OLDS

7 **BIG MAJOR**, ch c Aqlaam—Ermine (IRE) **Franconson Partners**
8 **BLAZING MIGHTY**, ch f Mighty—Exodia **Franconson Partners**
9 **BOSSA NOVA**, b f High Chaparral (IRE)—Marcellinas Angel **Franconson Partners**
10 **BRICK LANE**, ch f Bahamian Bounty—Medicea Sidera **Franconson Partners**
11 **E FOURTEEN**, b f Nayef (USA)—Pale Blue Eyes (IRE) **Franconson Partners**
12 **ELTHAM**, ch f Kheleyf (USA)—Baddi Heights (FR) **Franconson Partners**
13 **HACKNEY ROAD**, b f Aqlaam—West Lorne (USA) **Franconson Partners**
14 **LEMONADE MONEY**, b f Mighty—Stormy Weather **Franconson Partners**
15 **MIGHTY LADY**, ch f Mighty—Spia (USA) **Franconson Partners**
16 **PACIFICA (IRE)**, b f Aqlaam—Raggiante (IRE) **Franconson Partners**
17 **POPLAR**, b c Hellvelyn—Amelie Pouliche (FR) **Franconson Partners**
18 **VALLANCE ROAD**, b f Kheleyf (USA)—Last Romance (USA) **Franconson Partners**

TWO-YEAR-OLDS

19 B c 16/4 Sir Prancealot (IRE)—Bond Deal (IRE) (Pivotal) (13000) **Franconson Partners**
20 B c 14/4 Poet's Voice—Foreign Language (USA) (Distant View (USA)) (10000) **Franconson Partners**
21 B c 10/2 Intense Focus (USA)—Green Tambourine (Green Desert (USA)) (4500) **Franconson Partners**
22 B f 15/4 Lilbourne Lad (IRE)—Lilakiya (IRE) (Dr Fong (USA)) (5500) **Franconson Partners**
23 B c 21/4 Warrior's Reward (USA)—Maidstone (USA) (Aptitude (USA)) (3500) **Franconson Partners**
24 Ch f 4/4 Dutch Art—Meydan Princess (IRE) (Choisir (AUS)) **Franconson Partners**
25 B f 16/5 Big Bad Bob (IRE)—Morena Park (Pivotal) (1500) **Franconson Partners**
26 B f 27/3 Kheleyf (USA)—Reeling N' Rocking (IRE) (Mr Greeley (USA)) (1200) **Franconson Partners**
27 Ch f 21/2 Showcasing—Spritzeria (Bigstone (IRE)) (8500) **Franconson Partners**

Other Owners: D. Curran, Mrs D. Curran.

---

66 MR ANTONY BRITTAIN, Warthill
Postal: **Northgate Lodge, Warthill, York, North Yorkshire, YO19 5XR**
Contacts: **PHONE (01759) 371472 FAX (01759) 372915**
E-MAIL email@antonybrittain.co.uk WEBSITE www.antonybrittain.co.uk

1 **CARRAGOLD**, 10, b g Diktat—Shadow Roll (IRE) **Mr Antony Brittain**
2 **COOL MUSIC (IRE)**, 6, b m One Cool Cat (USA)—Musicology (USA) **Mr Antony Brittain**
3 **DESKTOP**, 4, b g Desideratum—First Harmony **Mr Antony Brittain**
4 **DREAM SCENARIO**, 6, b m Araafa (IRE)—Notjustaprettyface (USA) **Northgate Black**
5 **GENEROUS DREAM**, 8, ch m Generous (IRE)—First Harmony **Mr Antony Brittain**
6 **GREY DESTINY**, 8, gr g Desideratum—Mother Corrigan (IRE) **Mr Antony Brittain**
7 **HUSSAR BALLAD (USA)**, 7, b g Hard Spun (USA)—Country Melody (USA) **Mr Antony Brittain**
8 **JOALDO**, 4, b g Monsieur Bond (IRE)—Labba **Mr Antony Brittain**
9 **LUCKY LODGE**, 6, b g Lucky Story (USA)—Melandre **Mr Antony Brittain**

MR ANTONY BRITTAIN - Continued

10 **MAYFIELD BOY,** 5, b g Authorized (IRE)—Big Pink (IRE) **Mr Antony Brittain**
11 **MAYFIELD GIRL (IRE),** 6, br m One Cool Cat (USA)—Rose of Mooncoin (IRE) **Mr Antony Brittain**
12 **MISTER MARCASITE,** 6, gr g Verglas (IRE)—No Rehearsal (FR) **S. J. Box**
13 **MISTER YORK,** 4, b g Monsieur Bond (IRE)—Knavesmire (IRE) **Mr Antony Brittain**
14 **SLEEPING STAR,** 5, ch m Sleeping Indian—Silver Purse **Mr Antony Brittain**
15 **SOOQAAN,** 5, bl g Naaqoos—Dream Day (FR) **Mr Antony Brittain**
16 **STANGHOW,** 4, b g Monsieur Bond (IRE)—Melandre **Mr Antony Brittain**
17 **STEEL STOCKHOLDER,** 10, b g Mark of Esteem (IRE)—Pompey Blue **Mr Antony Brittain**

THREE-YEAR-OLDS

18 **FRENCH,** ch f Monsieur Bond (IRE)—Guadaloup **Mr Antony Brittain**
19 **MISS YORK,** ch f Monsieur Bond (IRE)—Knavesmire (IRE) **Mr Antony Brittain**
20 **MOZIMBA,** ch f Monsieur Bond (IRE)—Mozayada (USA) **Mr Antony Brittain**
21 **ROCK OF MONACO,** b f Monsieur Bond (IRE)—Melandre **Mr Antony Brittain**

TWO-YEAR-OLDS

22 B c 31/3 Monsieur Bond (IRE)—Caranbola (Lucky Story (USA)) **The How Rude Partnership**
23 Ch f 26/4 Monsieur Bond (IRE)—Guadaloup (Loup Sauvage (USA)) **Great Brittain Partnership**
24 Ch c 6/5 Monsieur Bond (IRE)—Knavesmire (IRE) (One Cool Cat (USA))
25 Ch f 31/3 Monsieur Bond (IRE)—Lujiana (Lujain (USA)) **Northgate Grey**
26 B c 5/5 Monsieur Bond (IRE)—Melandre (Lujain (USA)) **Northgate White**

Other Owners: Mr Paul Chambers, Mr A. Jarvis, Mr J. Jarvis.

Apprentice: Mathew Still.

 LADY BROOKE, Llandrindod Wells
Postal: **Tyn-y-Berth Farm, Dolau, Llandrindod Wells, Powys, LD1 5TW**
Contacts: **PHONE (01597) 851190 MOBILE (07977) 114834**
E-MAIL suebrooke@live.co.uk

1 **AMERICAN WORLD (FR),** 12, b br g Lost World (IRE)—Rose Laura (FR) **Lady Brooke**
2 **CROWD CONTROL (IRE),** 7, b g Oscar (IRE)—Apollo Lady **Lady Brooke**
3 **FREE WORLD (FR),** 12, b g Lost World (IRE)—Fautine (FR) **Lady Brooke**
4 **OVER TO MIDNIGHT,** 6, b m Midnight Legend—Makeover **Lady Brooke**
5 **RADUIS BLEU (FR),** 11, gr g Dadarissime (FR)—Regence Bleue (FR) **Lady Brooke**
6 **SATU (IRE),** 12, b g Marju (IRE)—Magic Touch **Lady Brooke**

Assistant Trainer: Lorna Brooke (07786) 962911

Amateur: Miss Lorna Brooke.

 MRS ANNA BROOKS, Towcester
Postal: **Horton House, Alderton, Towcester, Northamptonshire, NN12 7LN**
Contacts: **PHONE (01327) 811354 FAX (01327) 811496 MOBILE (07802) 541294**
E-MAIL onespotracing@hotmail.com

1 **BANDERITOS,** 7, b g Revoque (IRE)—Orchid **T. L. Brooks**
2 **DROMBEG WEST,** 9, b m Westerner—Quinag **Mrs J. M. Owen**
3 4, Ch f Black Sam Bellamy (IRE)—Letitia's Loss (IRE) **T. L. Brooks**
4 **VINEGAR HILL,** 7, b g Kayf Tara—Broughton Melody **Theshouldhavehadabiggerbudgetgroup**

Other Owners: Mr S. E. Tate.

 MR ROY BROTHERTON, Pershore
Postal: **Mill End Racing Stables, Netherton Road, Elmley Castle, Pershore, Worcestershire, WR10 3JF**
Contacts: **PHONE/FAX (01386) 710772 MOBILE (07973) 877280**

1 **FILAMENT OF GOLD (USA),** 5, b g Street Cry (IRE)—Raw Silk (USA) **Mr M. A. Geobey**
2 **IN THE CROWD (IRE),** 7, ch g Haafhd—Eliza Gilbert **Mrs T. J. Byrne**

MR ROY BROTHERTON - Continued

   3 **KAABER (USA)**, 5, b g Daaher (CAN)—Taseel (USA) **Mr J. Holt**
   4 **MIRACLE GARDEN**, 4, ch g Exceed And Excel (AUS)—Sharp Terms **Mr M. A. Geobey**
   5 **RENEWING**, 5, b g Halling (USA)—Electric Society (IRE) **Mr J. Holt**
   6 **RUGGERO**, 6, b g Tiger Hill (IRE)—Bergamask (USA) **Mr S. E. Cambridge**
   7 **UP YOUR GAME (IRE)**, 8, b g Milan—Katie Snurge (IRE) **Millend Racing Club**

THREE-YEAR-OLDS

   8 **BLUE BLAZE**, ch c Sleeping Indian—Lilly Blue (IRE) **Mr A. T. L. Clayton**
   9 **MASTER PEKAN**, b c Piccolo—Lady Pekan **Mr A. T. L. Clayton**
10 **MILLADY PERCY**, b f Sir Percy—Steady Rain **Mrs C. A. Newman**

Other Owners: Mr Roy Brotherton, Mr T. L. Martin.

Assistant Trainer: Justin Brotherton

Jockey (flat): Tom Eaves. **Jockey (NH):** James Banks. **Conditional:** Ryan Hatch. **Amateur:** Mr Sam Drinkwater.

---

70   MR ALAN BROWN, Malton
Postal: **Lilac Farm, Yedingham, Malton, North Yorkshire, YO17 8SS**
Contacts: **PHONE (01944) 728090 MOBILE (07970) 672845**
E-MAIL **ad.brownn@hotmail.co.uk** WEBSITE **www.alanbrownracing.co.uk**

   1 **JEBEL TARA**, 11, b g Diktat—Chantilly (FR) **Miss E. Johnston**
   2 **KALANI'S DIAMOND**, 6, ch m Kalani Bay (IRE)—Cryptonite Diamond (USA) **The Armstrong Family**
   3 **LAZARUS BELL**, 8, ch g Bahamian Bounty—Snake's Head **Mr Frank Reay**
   4 **MEANDMYSHADOW**, 8, ch m Tobougg (IRE)—Queen Jean **Mr G. Morrill**
   5 **POPPY IN THE WIND**, 4, b f Piccolo—Vintage Steps (IRE) **Mrs M Doherty & Mrs W Craven**
   6 **RED SHADOW**, 7, b m Royal Applause—Just A Glimmer **S. E. Pedersen**
   7 **REDALANI (IRE)**, 6, b m Redback—Zafaraya (IRE) **S. E. Pedersen**
   8 **ROUGH JUSTICE (IRE)**, 8, b g Beneficial—Ringzar (IRE) **Mr D. J. Sturdy**
   9 **SHOULD I STAY (FR)**, 8, b g Muhtathir—Dusky Royale (FR) **Mr D. J. Sturdy**
10 **WESTERN JO (IRE)**, 8, b g Westerner—Jenny's Jewel (IRE) **Mr D. J. Sturdy**

THREE-YEAR-OLDS

11 **NEFETARI**, b f Kodiac—Town And Gown **Mr Frank Reay**

Other Owners: Mr R. Armstrong, Mr N. Armstrong.

---

71   MR ANDI BROWN, Newmarket
Postal: **Southfields Stables, Hamilton Road, Newmarket, Suffolk, CB8 7JQ**

   1 **KIRTLING**, 5, gr g Araafa (IRE)—Cape Maya **Faith Hope and Charity**
   2 5, B m Virtual—Loriner's Lass
   3 **VICTORIOUSLY**, 4, b g Azamour (IRE)—Ambria (GER) **Miss L. Knocker**
   4 **VOICE OF A LEADER (IRE)**, 5, b g Danehill Dancer (IRE)—Thewaytosanjose (IRE) **Miss L. Knocker**

TWO-YEAR-OLDS

   5 B f 21/2 Nathaniel (IRE)—Enchufla (Danehill Dancer (IRE)) **Miss L. Knocker**

Other Owners: A. S. Brown.

---

72   MR DAVID BROWN, Averham
Postal: **The Old Stables, Averham Park, Newark, Nottinghamshire, NG23 5RU**
Contacts: **PHONE (01636) 613793 MOBILE (07889) 132931**
E-MAIL **david@davidbrownracing.com**

   1 **BRIGHT FLASH**, 4, ch f Dutch Art—Quadri **J. C. Fretwell**
   2 **CLUMBER STREET**, 5, ch g Compton Place—Tinnarinka **J. C. Fretwell**
   3 **DEVON DRUM**, 8, b g Beat Hollow—West Devon (USA) **Mr D. Carrington**
   4 **DUTCH GARDEN**, 4, b g Fastnet Rock (AUS)—Swan Wings **J. C. Fretwell**

MR DAVID BROWN - Continued

5 **EXCHEQUER (IRE)**, 5, ch g Exceed And Excel (AUS)—Tara's Force (IRE) **J. C. Fretwell**
6 **HENRY MORGAN**, 9, ch g Bahamian Bounty—Hill Welcome **Mrs F. Denniff**
7 **LADY ATLAS**, 4, ch f Dutch Art—Paquerettza (FR) **Miss C. A. Carr**
8 **MEDRANO**, 4, b c Archipenko (USA)—Trick Or Treat **Peter Onslow & Mr & Mrs Gary Middlebrook**
9 **MUHAAFIZ (IRE)**, 4, br g Lord Shanakill (USA)—Yasmin Satine (IRE) **J. C. Fretwell**
10 **MUNFALLET (IRE)**, 5, b g Royal Applause—Princess Mood (GER) **J. C. Fretwell**
11 **RUBY'S DAY**, 7, ch m Vital Equine (IRE)—Isabella's Best (IRE) **Mrs R. A. Archer**
12 **SAMHAIN**, 5, b g Compton Place—Athboy Nights (IRE) **J. C. Fretwell**
13 **ST QUINTIN**, 6, b g Act One—Gloriana **Lady Legard**
14 **TSEO**, 4, ch g Mount Nelson—Pasithea (IRE) **Lady Legard**
15 **X RAISE (IRE)**, 4, gr f Aussie Rules (USA)—Raise (USA) **Onslow, Hughlock, Brooke & Brown**

THREE-YEAR-OLDS

16 **ARIZE (IRE)**, b f Approve (IRE)—Raise (USA) **Mrs Sandra Brown & Mrs Ann Harrison**
17 **ARIZONA SUNRISE**, b c Sakhee's Secret—Phoenix Rising **Miss C. A. Carr**
18 **BIT OF A LAD (IRE)**, b g Lilbourne Lad (IRE)—Sacred Love (IRE) **Brown, Bolland, Goforth & Watson**
19 **CLICK AND ROLL (USA)**, b f Smart Strike (CAN)—More Hennessy (USA) **Qatar Racing Limited**
20 **CONTINENTAL LADY**, ch f Medicean—Paquerettza (FR) **Qatar Racing Limited**
21 **GINGER JOE**, ch g Medicean—Susi Wong (IRE) **J. C. Fretwell**
22 **LUATH**, ch g Archipenko (USA)—Delaware Dancer (IRE) **Miss Kate Dobb & Mr Stuart Dobb**
23 **MIDNIGHT MACCHIATO (IRE)**, b c Dark Angel (IRE)—Lathaat **D. A. West**
24 **PALPITATION (IRE)**, b g Fast Company (IRE)—Sensation **D. A. West**
25 **SIMPLY CLEVER**, ch f Stimulation (IRE)—Well of Echoes **Mr J. R. Atherton**
26 **SWIRRAL EDGE**, b f Hellvelyn—Pizzarra **Mr D. H. Brown**
27 **TAKE CHARGE**, b c Showcasing—Be Decisive **J. C. Fretwell**
28 **TICKING AWAY**, gr g Monsieur Bond (IRE)—Pendulum **J. C. Fretwell**
29 **TIKTHEBOX (IRE)**, b g Approve (IRE)—Nicene (USA) **Brown, Bolland, Goforth & Watson**
30 **TIME AGAIN**, b f Kyllachy—Record Time **P. Onslow**
31 **TURN TIDE**, ch c Medicean—Quadri **J. C. Fretwell**

TWO-YEAR-OLDS

32 B c 13/3 Bahamian Bounty—Alice Alleyne (IRE) (Oasis Dream) (45000) **J. C. Fretwell**
33 B f 16/2 Distorted Humor (USA)—Bootery (USA) (Storm Boot (USA)) **Qatar Racing Limited**
34 B f 11/2 Bahamian Bounty—Brick Tops (Danehill Dancer (IRE)) (34000) **J. C. Fretwell**
35 B f 23/4 Royal Applause—Creative Mind (IRE) (Danehill Dancer (IRE)) **Mrs R. A. Archer**
36 B f 7/4 Harbour Watch (IRE)—Dee Dee Girl (IRE) (Primo Dominie) (32380) **Qatar Racing Limited**
37 **DONNY LAD**, b c 31/3 Doncaster Rover (USA)—Ashover Amber (Green Desert (USA)) **Doncaster Racing Team**
38 B f 9/3 Tamayuz—Dream Day (Oasis Dream) (34285) **J. C. Fretwell**
39 B f 11/4 Royal Applause—Dubai Bounty (Dubai Destination (USA)) (44523) **Mrs F. Denniff**
40 B c 20/3 Iffraaj—Effigie (IRE) (Oratorio (IRE)) (43809) **J. C. Fretwell**
41 Ch c 25/4 Mayson—Ellablue (Bahamian Bounty) (8000) **Mr D. H. Brown**
42 B c 25/2 Fast Company (IRE)—French Doll (Titus Livius (FR)) (32380) **J. C. Fretwell**
43 B c 19/3 Elzaam (AUS)—Kiralik (Efisio) (35000) **J. C. Fretwell**
44 Ch c 11/2 Shirocco (GER)—Pasithea (IRE) (Celtic Swing) **Lady Legard**
45 Ch c 30/4 Bated Breath—Quadri (Polish Precedent (USA)) (9500) **Lady Legard**
46 Gr ro f 14/4 Zebedee—Speckled Hen (IRE) (Titus Livius (FR)) (30000) **J. C. Fretwell**
47 **STEVIE BROWN**, b c 15/4 Bushranger (IRE)—
                                        Oriental Romance (IRE) (Elusive City (USA)) (2857) **Brown, Bolland, Goforth & Watson**
48 Ch c 7/4 Equiano (FR)—Trinny (Rainbow Quest (USA)) (20000) **Just For Girls Partnership**
49 B f 17/4 Kodiac—Virevolle (FR) (Kahyasi) (23000) **Mr D. H. Brown, Mr Clive Watson**
50 **WIGAN WARRIOR**, b c 15/2 Doncaster Rover (USA)—Rattleyurjewellery (Royal Applause) **P. Onslow**
51 **YORKSHIRE ROVER**, b c 6/4 Doncaster Rover (USA)—Mother Jones (Sleeping Indian) **Mr Browns Boys**

Other Owners: Mr Steve Bolland, Mr D. M. Brooke, Mrs Sandra Brown, Mr D. H. Brown, Mrs F. Denniff, Miss K. M. Dobb, Mr Stuart Dobb, Mr Graham G. Goforth, Mrs Ann Harrison, Mr Roger J. Hughlock, Mrs L. Middlebrook, Mr G. Middlebrook, Mr Peter Onslow, Mr Ian Raeburn, Mr Clive Watson, Mrs Judy Youdan.

Assistant Trainer: Dushyant Dooyea

Jockey (flat): Tom Eaves, Philip Makin, Oisin Murphy, Jamie Spencer.

73 **MISS MICHELLE BRYANT, Lewes**
Postal: **Bevern Bridge Farm Cottage, South Chailey, Lewes, East Sussex, BN8 4QH**
Contacts: **PHONE/FAX (01273) 400638 MOBILE (07976) 217542**

1 **ALL OR NOTHIN (IRE)**, 7, b g Majestic Missile (IRE)—
Lady Peculiar (CAN) **Miss M. P. Bryant, David & Eileen Bryant**
2 **HAWK GOLD (IRE)**, 12, ch g Tendulkar (USA)—Heiress of Meath (IRE) **Miss M. P. Bryant**
3 **SUTTON SID**, 6, ch g Dutch Art—Drastic Measure **Miss M. P. Bryant**

Other Owners: Miss M. Bryant, Mrs Eileen Bryant, Mr David Bryant.

Amateur: Miss M. P. Bryant.

---

74 **MRS KATE BUCKETT, Bishops Waltham**
Postal: **Woodlocks Down Farm, Upham, Bishops Waltham, Hampshire, SO32 1JN**
Contacts: **PHONE (01962) 777557**

1 **BOARDWALK EMPIRE (IRE)**, 9, b g Overbury (IRE)—Mighty Mandy (IRE) **Mrs K. A. Buckett**
2 **JOIN THE NAVY**, 11, b g Sea Freedom—Join The Parade **Mrs K. A. Buckett**
3 **UPHAM ATOM**, 13, b g Silver Patriarch (IRE)—Upham Lady **Mrs K. A. Buckett**
4 **UPHAM RUNNING (IRE)**, 8, b g Definite Article—Tara Brooch (IRE) **Mrs K. A. Buckett**

Jockey (NH): Mark Grant, Liam Treadwell. Amateur: Miss Chloe Boxall.

---

75 **MR BOB BUCKLER, Bridgwater**
Postal: **Gibb Hill, Courtway, Spaxton, Bridgwater, Somerset, TA5 1DR**
Contacts: **PHONE (01278) 671268 MOBILE (07785) 773957**
E-MAIL rbuckler@btconnect.com WEBSITE www.robertbucklerracing.co.uk

1 **BALLYEGAN (IRE)**, 11, b g Saddlers' Hall (IRE)—Knapping Princess (IRE) **R. H. Buckler**
2 **HOO BALLY DIVA (IRE)**, 5, b m Scorpion (IRE)—Dr Sandra (IRE) **Golden Cap**
3 **SAY MY NAME (IRE)**, 5, ch g Fleetwood (IRE)—River Reine (IRE) **Mr T. S. Macdonald**
4 **SOMERSET LIAS (IRE)**, 8, b g Golan (IRE)—Presenting Gayle (IRE) **D. R. Fear**
5 **TINKER TIME (IRE)**, 8, b g Turtle Island (IRE)—Gypsys Girl (IRE) **Golden Cap**
6 **UGOLIN DE BEAUMONT (FR)**, 8, b g Alberto Giacometti (IRE)—Okarina de Beaumont (FR) **A. J. Norman**
7 **UP TO AL (IRE)**, 8, b g Heron Island (IRE)—Pretonic **R. H. Buckler**

Other Owners: Mr R. H. Buckler, Mrs H. E. Shane.

Head Lad: Giles Scott (07774) 033246

Jockey (NH): Liam Heard.

---

76 **MR DAI BURCHELL, Ebbw Vale**
Postal: **Drysiog Farm, Briery Hill, Ebbw Vale, Gwent, NP23 6BU**
Contacts: **PHONE (01495) 302551 MOBILE (07980) 482860**

1 **ACAPULCO BAY**, 12, b g Pursuit of Love—Lapu-Lapu **J. Parfitt**
2 **APPROACHING STAR (FR)**, 5, ch m New Approach (IRE)—Madame Arcati (IRE) **Mr A. P. Shinton**
3 **BLUE TOP**, 7, b g Millkom—Pompey Blue **B. M. G. Group**
4 **CROPLEY (IRE)**, 7, gr g Galileo (IRE)—Niyla (IRE) **Miss S. Carter**
5 **CRUCHAIN (IRE)**, 13, ch g Shernazar—Mack Tack (IRE) **Mr & Mrs A. J. Mutch**
6 **FUSE WIRE**, 9, b g Tamayaz (CAN)—Zaffaranni (IRE) **Mr D. A. Smerdon**
7 **GUANCIALE**, 9, b g Exit To Nowhere (USA)—Thenford Lass (IRE) **The Beefeaters**
8 **ONE FOR THE BOSS (IRE)**, 9, b g Garuda (IRE)—Tell Nothing (IRE) **J. E. Mutch**
9 **PRIM AND PROPER**, 5, b m Sleeping Indian—Quite Fantastic (IRE) **Mr & Mrs A. J. Mutch**
10 **RATIFY**, 12, br g Rakaposhi King—Sea Sky **Mr J. J. King**
11 **REBECCAS CHOICE (IRE)**, 13, b g Religiously (USA)—Carolin Lass (IRE) **J. E. Mutch**
12 **SYMPHONY OF PEARLS**, 5, b m Lucarno (USA)—Echostar **B. J. Williams**

MR DAI BURCHELL - Continued

13 **UJAGAR (IRE)**, 5, gr g Dalakhani (IRE)—No Secrets (USA) **J. Parfitt**
14 **VINNIE THE FISH (IRE)**, 8, br g Vinnie Roe (IRE)—Darwin Angel (IRE) **Mr & Mrs A Mutch & Mr & Mrs J King**

Other Owners: Mr W. R. A. Davies, Mrs A. Davies, Mrs V. C. King, Mr A. J. Mutch, Mrs S. Mutch.

Assistant Trainer: Ruth Burchell

Jockey (NH): Robert Dunne. **Amateur:** Miss Jodie Hughes.

---

77 **MR PAUL BURGOYNE, Wincanton**
Postal: **Knowle Rock, Shepton Montague, Wincanton, Somerset, BA9 8JA**
Contacts: **PHONE (01963) 32138 MOBILE (07894) 081008**
E-MAIL knowlerockracing@hotmail.co.uk

1 **BLACKTHORN STICK (IRE)**, 7, b g Elusive City (USA)—Hi Lyla (IRE) **Knowle Rock Racing**
2 **RUNAIOCHT (IRE)**, 6, ch g Teofilo (IRE)—Julie Girl (USA) **Knowle Rock Racing**
3 **SAMMY'S CHOICE**, 4, ch g Pastoral Pursuits—Diane's Choice **Mr A. J. Taylor**
4 **SUDDEN WISH (IRE)**, 7, b m Jeremy (USA)—Fun Time **Mr F. Ingram**
5 **WEST LEAKE (IRE)**, 10, b g Acclamation—Kilshanny **Mrs C. E. E. Turner**

THREE-YEAR-OLDS

6 **BRIDGET KENNET**, b f Kier Park (IRE)—Kathleen Kennet **Miss Bridget Floyd**

Other Owners: Mr M. Burgoyne, Mrs C. Leigh-Turner.

Assistant Trainer: Mrs C. Leigh-Turner

Jockey (flat): Liam Keniry, Jimmy Quinn. **Apprentice:** David Parkes.

---

78 **MR K. R. BURKE, Leyburn**
Postal: **Spigot Lodge, Middleham, Leyburn, North Yorkshire, DL8 4TL**
Contacts: **PHONE (01969) 625088 FAX (01969) 625099 MOBILE (07778) 458777**
E-MAIL karl@karlburke.co.uk WEBSITE www.karlburke.co.uk

1 **CAPRIOR BERE (FR)**, 4, b g Peer Gynt (JPN)—Hush Hush (USA) **Mr D J Mackay & Mrs E Burke**
2 **CHEVALLIER**, 4, b g Invincible Spirit (IRE)—Magical Romance (IRE) **Mr T. J. Dykes**
3 **DALMARELLA DANCER (IRE)**, 5, gr m Mastercraftsman (IRE)—Ting A Greeley **Dr M E Glaze & Mr I Mcinnes**
4 **DOYNOSAUR**, 9, b m Doyen (IRE)—Daring Destiny **Mrs E. M. Burke**
5 **FELIX LEITER**, 4, ch g Monsieur Bond (IRE)—Spiralling **Mr T Dykes & Mrs E Burke**
6 **FIDELMA MOON (IRE)**, 4, b f Dylan Thomas (IRE)—Ridiforza (FR) **The Mount Racing Club & Mrs E Burke**
7 **GEORGIAN BAY (IRE)**, 6, b g Oratorio (IRE)—Jazzie (FR) **Market Avenue Racing Club & Mrs E Burke**
8 **INTENSE TANGO**, 5, b m Mastercraftsman (IRE)—Cover Look (SAF) **Cosy Seal Racing Limited**
9 **JOLIEVITESSE (FR)**, 4, b g Elusive City (USA)—Volvoreta **Owners For Owners: Jolievitesse**
10 **LITTLE LADY KATIE (IRE)**, 4, b f Lord Shanakill (USA)—Akarita (IRE) **Ontoawinner 5, M Hulin & Mrs E Burke**
11 **LORD BEN STACK (IRE)**, 4, b g Dylan Thomas (IRE)—Beringold **Owners For Owners: Lord Ben Stack**
12 **LOSTOCK HALL (IRE)**, 4, b g Lord Shanakill (USA)—Cannikin (IRE) **Tim Dykes & Partner**
13 **MALLYMKUN**, 4, b f Kheleyf (USA)—Harriet's Girl **R. Bailey**
14 **MOTHERS FINEST (IRE)**, 4, ch f Tamayuz—Sheer Glamour (IRE) **Mr H. J. Strecker**
15 **PEARL CASTLE (IRE)**, 6, b g Montjeu (IRE)—Ghurra (USA) **Cosy Seal Racing Limited**
16 **RIVELLINO**, 6, b g Invincible Spirit (IRE)—Brazilian Bride (IRE) **Mrs M. Bryce**
17 **TOOCOOLFORSCHOOL (IRE)**, 4, b g Showcasing—Spring Surprise **Ontoawinner 6, M Hulin, E Burke**
18 **WE'LL SHAKE HANDS (IRE)**, 5, b g Excellent Art—
                                           Amou Daria (FR) **Market Avenue Racing Club & Mrs E Burke**
19 **WHAT SAY YOU (IRE)**, 4, b f Galileo (IRE)—Alta Anna (FR) **Mr H. J. Strecker**
20 **YANKEE MAIL (FR)**, 4, br f American Post—Mercredi (FR) **Mrs E. M. Burke**
21 **YEEOOW (IRE)**, 7, b g Holy Roman Emperor (IRE)—Taraya (IRE) **Ontoawinner 7 & Mrs E Burke**
22 **YOU'RE FIRED (IRE)**, 5, b g Firebreak—My Sweet Georgia **Market Avenue Racing Club & Tim Dykes**
23 **YOURARTISONFIRE**, 6, ch g Dutch Art—Queens Jubilee **Mr J O'Shea,Mr W Rooney & Ontoawinner**

THREE-YEAR-OLDS

24 **ADA MISOBEL (IRE)**, b f Alfred Nobel (IRE)—Startarette (USA) **Middleham Park Racing XXXV & Mrs E Burke**
25 **BANDIT BOB (IRE)**, b c Manduro (GER)—Neat Shilling (IRE) **Mr T. J. Dykes**
26 **BIODYNAMIC (IRE)**, b c New Approach (IRE)—Doctrine **Mr H. J. Strecker**
27 **BONJOUR BABY**, ch f Duke of Marmalade (IRE)—Briery (IRE) **Mr H. A. A. M. Al-Abdulmalik**

MR K. R. BURKE - Continued

28 **CARBUTT'S RIDGE (IRE)**, br g Alfred Nobel (IRE)—Tallassee **Ontoawinner 9 & Mrs E Burke**
29 **DAISY BERE (FR)**, b f Peer Gynt (JPN)—Jackette (USA) **Mrs E. M. Burke**
30 **EXPLOSIVE POWER (IRE)**, gr c Alfred Nobel (IRE)—
My Girl Lisa (USA) **Market Avenue Racing Club & Mr P Garvey**
31 **FATHERLY FRIEND (USA)**, b br c Scat Daddy (USA)—Grimace (USA) **Mr H. J. Strecker**
32 **FORGIVING FLOWER**, ch f New Approach (IRE)—Dance Lively (USA) **Mr H. J. Strecker**
33 **HIGH DRAW (FR)**, ch g Falco (USA)—Augusta Lucilla (USA) **Mr T Dykes & Mrs E Burke**
34 **KADOOMENT DAY (IRE)**, ch g Lord Shanakill (USA)—Four Poorer (IRE) **Mrs E. M. Burke**
35 **KATIE'S DIAMOND (FR)**, b f Turtle Bowl (IRE)—Aaliyah (GER) **Qatar Racing Ltd & Barbara Keller**
36 **KELLY'S DINO (FR)**, b g Doctor Dino (FR)—Sabolienne (FR) **Mr Liam Kelly & Mrs E Burke**
37 **LILLY VEGA (IRE)**, ch f Lope de Vega (IRE)—Salpiglossis (GER) **Mrs Z. Wentworth**
38 **LONDON PROTOCOL (FR)**, ch g Muhtathir—Troiecat (FR) **Ontoawinner, Mr R Mckeown & E Burke**
39 **MASTERFUL MAN (IRE)**, gr g Mastercraftsman (IRE)—Lamanka Lass (USA) **Mr H. A. A. M. Al-Abdulmalik**
40 **MONPAZIER (IRE)**, br g Tamayuz—Wicked Maria (IRE) **Ontoawinner 14 & Mrs E Burke**
41 **MOONDYNE JOE (IRE)**, b g Bushranger (IRE)—Golden Shine **Mr J Burley & Mrs E Burke**
42 **NOTION OF BEAUTY (USA)**, b f Harlan's Holiday (USA)—Gypsy Monarch (USA) **Mr H. J. Strecker**
43 **OCEANELLA (IRE)**, b f Canford Cliffs (IRE)—Mundus Novus (USA) **Ontoawinner 7, M Hulin, E Burke**
44 **PERCY STREET**, br c Sir Percy—Star of Gibraltar **Mr J Henderson & Mrs E Burke**
45 **QUEEN ELSA (IRE)**, b f Frozen Power (IRE)—Spring Surprise **Clipper Group Holdings Ltd**
46 **QUIET REFLECTION (IRE)**, b f Showcasing—My Delirium **Ontoawinner, Strecker & Burke**
47 **SISTER DUDE**, ch f Notnowcato—Inaminute (IRE) **R. Bailey**
48 B f Invincible Spirit (IRE)—Skiphall **Clipper Group Holdings Ltd**
49 **SOUTHERN GAILES (IRE)**, ch c Frozen Power (IRE)—
Pardoned (IRE) **PalatinateRacing Chandler Westwood Bryce**
50 **SPORTY YANKEE (USA)**, gr ro g Paddy O'prado (USA)—I Insist (USA) **The Mount Racing Club & Mrs E Burke**
51 **TABIKAT ELLE (IRE)**, ch f Showcasing—Mansiya **Ontoawinner, SDH Project Services Ltd 1**
52 **TAP THE HONEY**, b g Fastnet Rock (AUS)—Balladonia **Mrs E. M. Burke**
53 **THANKYOU STARS**, b f Exceed And Excel (AUS)—Magic Music (IRE) **R. Bailey**
54 **TIMELESS ART (IRE)**, b c Medicean—Bellona (IRE) **Owners For Owners: Timeless Art**
55 **TRAP QUEEN (IRE)**, b f Nayef (USA)—Quiritis **Mr J Henderson & Mrs E Burke**
56 **UNDERTOW (IRE)**, b g Arcano—Tides **Middleham Park Racing CXVII & Mrs Burke**
57 **WAYWARD HOOF (IRE)**, b g Equiano (FR)—Mystical Spirit (IRE) **Palatinate Racing A Chandler L Westwood**
58 **WHOLESOME (USA)**, b br f Lemon Drop Kid (USA)—Nite in Rome (CAN) **Mr H. J. Strecker**
59 **WINGS OF ESTEEM (IRE)**, b f Sir Percy—Wings of Fame (IRE) **Mr M Nelmes-Crocker & Mrs E Burke**
60 **ZAINAT (IRE)**, b g Masterofthehorse (IRE)—Think Fast (IRE) **Mr H. A. A. M. Al-Abdulmalik**

TWO-YEAR-OLDS

61 B c 24/3 Elzaam (IRE)—Adaptation (Spectrum (IRE)) (25101) **Ontoawinner 14 & Mrs E Burke**
62 **ALL OF ME**, b f 1/3 Teofilo (IRE)—Madonna Dell'orto (Montjeu (IRE)) (100000) **Mr H. J. Strecker**
63 B f 23/2 Tin Horse (IRE)—Anaphora (IRE) (Goofalik (USA)) (31007) **Unregistered Partnership**
64 **ANGEL PALANAS**, b c 18/4 Mayson—
Scottish Exile (IRE) (Ashkalani (IRE)) (20000) **Mr Mark Bates & Mrs E Burke**
65 B f 19/2 Wootton Bassett—Angel Voices (IRE) (Tagula (IRE)) (18456) **Mrs E. M. Burke**
66 **BAIE D'AMOUR (FR)**, ch f 13/2 Never On Sunday (FR)—
Baie des Fleurs (FR) (Chelsea Manor) (16980) **Ontoawinner, SDH Project Services Ltd 1**
67 Ch f 20/4 Casamento—Bonne (Namid) (24761)
68 **BOUNTY BRIDGE (IRE)**, ch c 29/3 Bahamian Bounty—
Miss Cambridge (Dubawi (IRE)) (16000) **Mr T Dykes & Mrs E Burke**
69 **BOURNVILLE (IRE)**, b f 25/4 Casamento (IRE)—
Passaggio (Pivotal) (20952) **Ontoawinner, J Farmer & Mrs E Burke**
70 B f 14/1 Harbour Watch (IRE)—
Brazilian Breeze (IRE) (Invincible Spirit (IRE)) (9523) **Middleham Park Racing LXIX & Mrs Burke**
71 B f 22/1 Acclamation—Dutch Diamond (Dutch Art) (38390) **Mrs Z. Wentworth**
72 **ENGLAND EXPECTS**, b f 23/2 Mount Nelson—
Fanny's Fancy (Groom Dancer (USA)) (20671) **Tim Dykes & Jon Hughes**
73 B c 1/3 Lord Shanakill (USA)—Four Poorer (IRE) (Oasis Dream)
74 **FREE TO DANCE (IRE)**, b f 25/2 Tamayuz—Flurry of Hands (IRE) (Acclamation) (24761) **Mr H. J. Strecker**
75 **GRATON (IRE)**, ch c 10/2 Camacho—Deslaya (IRE) (Green Desert (USA)) **P & L Partners**
76 B f 5/3 Harbour Watch (IRE)—Khumba Mela (IRE) (Hero's Honor (USA)) (18456)
77 B c 23/4 Born To Sea (IRE)—La Belle Maison (IRE) (Titus Livius (FR)) (59062)
78 Ch c 18/4 Authorized (IRE)—Magic Music (IRE) (Magic Ring (IRE)) (30000) **Mr R Bailey & Mr J Hughes**
79 B c 2/3 Showcasing—Maid To Dance (Pyramus (IRE)) (20000) **Hambleton Racing Ltd Trio & E Burke**
80 **MEDICI BANCHIERE**, ch c 18/4 Medicean—Fairy Shoes (Kyllachy) (40000) **Mr D J Mackay & Mrs E Burke**
81 **MICOLYS (FR)**, b f 30/3 Myboycharlie (IRE)—
Lady Sadowa (Nayef (USA)) (11074) **Hambleton Racing Ltd Trio & E Burke**

MR K. R. BURKE - Continued

82 Ch c 10/5 Evasive—Moon Tree (FR) (Groom Dancer (USA)) (14765) **Hambleton Racing Ltd Trio & E Burke**
83 B c 20/4 Kheleyf (USA)—New Romantic (Singspiel (IRE)) (7013) **Ontoawinner 9 & Mrs E Burke**
84 **NICK VEDDER**, b c 22/1 Rip Van Winkle (IRE)—Devotion (IRE) (Dylan Thomas (IRE)) (50000) **Mr S. Burns**
85 B f 12/2 Sir Prancealot (IRE)—Pandoras Secret (IRE) (Monashee Mountain (USA)) (5167)
86 Gr c 6/2 Excelebration (IRE)—Pinch of Posh (IRE) (Pivotal) **Mrs M. Bryce**
87 B f 2/5 Iffraaj—Right Ted (IRE) (Mujadil (USA)) (8859) **Mr H. J. Strecker**
88 **RIVIERE ARGENTEE (FR)**, gr f 20/4 Hurricane Cat (USA)—
                                        River Trebor (USA) (Myrakalu (FR)) (13289) **Mr D J Mackay & Mrs E Burke**
89 **SAN SEBASTIANA**, b f 30/4 Power—Spanish Quest (Rainbow Quest (USA)) (7000) **Mr T Dykes & Mrs E Burke**
90 **SARNANO STAR**, b f 9/4 Harbour Watch (IRE)—Clifton Dancer (Fraam) (40000) **Mr Steve Lock & Mrs E Burke**
91 **SATISFY (IRE)**, b f 26/4 New Approach (IRE)—Venturi (Danehill Dancer (USA)) (60000) **Ms J. J. Murphy**
92 **SEDUCE ME**, b f 8/2 Dutch Art—Deep Bleu (Kyllachy) (18000) **Ontoawinner, Mr R Mckeown & E Burke**
93 B f 15/5 Never On Sunday (FR)—Shakila (Cadeaux Genereux) (14765) **Unregistered Partnership**
94 **SHENG CHI DRAGON (IRE)**, ch c 26/3 Dragon Pulse (IRE)—
                                        Shin Feign (USA) (El Prado (IRE)) (20952) **Ontoawinner, SDH Project Services Ltd 1**
95 **SUNDAY PROSPECT (FR)**, ch c 8/4 Sunday Break (JPN)—
                                        Green Shadow (FR) (Green Tune (USA)) (35437) **Owners For Owners: Sunday Prospect**
96 **TESTBOURNE (IRE)**, b c 15/3 Big Bad Bob (IRE)—
                                        Magnificent Bell (IRE) (Octagonal (NZ)) (18000) **Mr T. J. Dykes**

Other Owners: Mr D. C. Bacon, Mr M. Bates, Mr S. Bridge, C. Bryce, J. Burley, Mr A. Chandler, Mr T. Dal, Mr P. K. Davis, Mr A. N. Eaton, Dr C. I. Emmerson, Mr J. Fairrie, Mr K. Flanagan, P Garvey, Dr M. E. Glaze, Hambleton Racing Ltd, Mr J. Henderson, Mr G. W. Holden, Mrs J. Hughes, Mr E. J. Hughes, Mr M. A. S. Hulin, Mrs B. M. Keller, Mr L. Kelly, Mr A. T. Larkin, Mr S. Lock, Mr D. J. MacKay, Market Avenue Racing Club Ltd., I. McInnes, Mr R. C. McKeown, Mrs S. M. Morley, M. Nelmes-Crocker, Mr J. Nolan, Mr N. J. O'Brien, Mr J. O'Shea, Palatinate Thoroughbred Racing Limited, T. S. Palin, G. Pickering, M. Prince, Qatar Racing Limited, Mr W. Rooney, Mr G. A. Shields, Mr S. R. H. Turner, Mr L. J. Westwood.

Assistant Trainer: Mrs E. Burke

Jockey (flat): Dougie Costello, Joey Haynes. **Apprentice:** Clifford Lee, Jordan Vaughan.

---

79 · MR HUGH BURNS, Alnwick
Postal: **Rose Cottage, Hedgeley Hall, Powburn, Alnwick, Northumberland, NE66 4HZ**
Contacts: **PHONE (01665) 578972 MOBILE (07914) 018987**
E-MAIL hughburns123@hotmail.co.uk

1 BROOKE'S BOUNTY, 6, ch g Bahamian Bounty—Choysia **Mr H. Burns**
2 HOP 'N POP (IRE), 9, b m Millenary—Rivita Princess (IRE) **Mr H. Burns**
3 LUCKY VIOLET (IRE), 4, b f Dandy Man (IRE)—Rashida **Mr H. Burns**
4 4, B f Overbury (IRE)—Ma Dame Mytton **Mr H. Burns**

---

80 · MR OWEN BURROWS, Lambourn
Postal: **Kingwood House Stables, Lambourn, Berkshire, RG17 7RS**
Contacts: **PHONE (01488) 73144**
E-MAIL oburrows@kingwoodhousestables.co.uk

1 ALGAITH (USA), 4, b g Dubawi (IRE)—Atayeb (USA) **Hamdan Al Maktoum**
2 ERHAAF (USA), 4, b g Street Sense (USA)—Saraama (USA) **Hamdan Al Maktoum**
3 LABAIK (FR), 5, gr g Montmartre (FR)—Avanguardia (GER) **Hamdan Al Maktoum**
4 MARKAZ (IRE), 4, gr c Dark Angel (IRE)—Folga **Hamdan Al Maktoum**
5 MAZAAHER, 6, b g Elnadim (USA)—Elutrah **Hamdan Al Maktoum**
6 MEZEL, 6, b g Tamayuz—Mumayeza **Hamdan Al Maktoum**
7 MOHATEM (USA), 4, ch c Distorted Humor (USA)—Soul Search (USA) **Hamdan Al Maktoum**

THREE-YEAR-OLDS

8 BASMA, b f Exceed And Excel (AUS)—Miss Chicane **Hamdan Al Maktoum**
9 DHEYAA (IRE), b f Dream Ahead (USA)—Lady Livius (IRE) **Hamdan Al Maktoum**
10 EHTIRAAS, b c Oasis Dream—Kareemah (IRE) **Hamdan Al Maktoum**
11 FAWAAREQ (USA), b c Invincible Spirit (IRE)—Ghandoorah (USA) **Hamdan Al Maktoum**
12 JABBAAR, ch g Medicean—Echelon **Hamdan Al Maktoum**
13 MASARZAIN (IRE), br g Kodiac—Cache Creek (IRE) **Hamdan Al Maktoum**
14 MASSAAT (IRE), b c Teofilo (IRE)—Madany (IRE) **Hamdan Al Maktoum**

MR OWEN BURROWS - Continued

15 **MIDHMAAR,** b g Iffraaj—Merayaat (IRE) **Hamdan Al Maktoum**
16 **MITHQAAL (USA),** ch c Speightstown (USA)—Bestowal (USA) **Hamdan Al Maktoum**
17 **MUBAJAL,** br c Dubawi (IRE)—Jadhwah **Hamdan Al Maktoum**
18 **MUNTAZAH,** b c Dubawi (IRE)—Rumoush **Hamdan Al Maktoum**
19 **MUSTAJEER,** b c Medicean—Qelaan **Hamdan Al Maktoum**
20 **RAAQY (IRE),** gr f Dubawi (IRE)—Natagora (FR) **Hamdan Al Maktoum**
21 **SIRDAAL (USA),** b c Medaglia d'oro (USA)—Sarayir (USA) **Hamdan Al Maktoum**
22 **TANASOQ (IRE),** b c Acclamation—Alexander Youth (IRE) **Hamdan Al Maktoum**
23 **WAQAAD (IRE),** b c New Approach (IRE)—Kitty Kiernan **Hamdan Al Maktoum**

TWO-YEAR-OLDS

24 **AKHLAAQ,** b c 10/4 New Approach (IRE)—Misheer (Oasis Dream) (400000) **Hamdan Al Maktoum**
25 **ALFAWARIS,** b c 15/4 Frankel—Kareemah (IRE) (Peintre Celebre (USA)) **Hamdan Al Maktoum**
26 **ALNASL (IRE),** b f 15/2 Tamayuz—Arwaah (IRE) (Dalakhani (IRE)) **Hamdan Al Maktoum**
27 **ALWAATHEQ (IRE),** ch c 16/5 Frankel—Tariysha (IRE) (Daylami (IRE)) (700000) **Hamdan Al Maktoum**
28 **ALWAFAA (IRE),** b f 12/5 Invincible Spirit (IRE)—Ghandoorah (USA) (Forestry (USA)) **Hamdan Al Maktoum**
29 **AROOSAH (IRE),** b f 9/3 Dansili—Dhelaal (Green Desert (USA)) **Hamdan Al Maktoum**
30 **ARZAAK (IRE),** br c 3/3 Casamento (IRE)—Dixieland Kiss (USA) (Dixie Union (USA)) **Hamdan Al Maktoum**
31 **AZALY (IRE),** ch c 23/3 Sepoy (AUS)—Azzoom (IRE) (Cadeaux Genereux) (110000) **Hamdan Al Maktoum**
32 **FIKHAAR,** b f 15/2 Oasis Dream—Fawaayed (IRE) (Singspiel (IRE)) **Hamdan Al Maktoum**
33 **HATHIQ (IRE),** b c 7/4 Exceed And Excel (AUS)—Madany (IRE) (Acclamation) **Hamdan Al Maktoum**
34 **JAAZEM (IRE),** b c 30/4 Dark Angel (IRE)—Miss Indigo (Indian Ridge) (265780) **Hamdan Al Maktoum**
35 **JAZAALAH (USA),** ch f 20/4 Hard Spun (USA)—Teeba (USA) (Seeking The Gold (USA)) **Hamdan Al Maktoum**
36 **MAFAAHEEM (IRE),** b c 16/3 Shamardal (USA)—Hammiya (IRE) (Darshaan) **Hamdan Al Maktoum**
37 **MIRDHAK,** br f 11/4 Dansili—Muthabara (IRE) (Red Ransom (USA)) **Hamdan Al Maktoum**
38 **MOHALLELA (USA),** b f 28/2 Teofilo (IRE)—Zaroof (USA) (Street Cry (IRE)) **Hamdan Al Maktoum**
39 **MUHAJJAL,** b c 25/1 Cape Cross (IRE)—Muqantara (USA) (First Samurai (USA)) (180000) **Hamdan Al Maktoum**
40 **NAJASHEE (IRE),** gr c 22/3 Invincible Spirit (IRE)—Tonnara (IRE) (Linamix (FR)) (516795) **Hamdan Al Maktoum**
41 **OKOOL (FR),** b c 30/1 Cape Cross (IRE)—Seschat (IRE) (Sinndar (IRE)) (236249) **Hamdan Al Maktoum**
42 **QULOOB,** b c 15/3 New Approach (IRE)—Jadhwah (Nayef (USA)) **Hamdan Al Maktoum**
43 **TALAAYEB,** b f 27/2 Dansili—Rumoush (USA) (Rahy (USA)) **Hamdan Al Maktoum**
44 **TAWAAFEEJ (IRE),** gr c 19/4 Zebedee—Absolutely Cool (IRE) (Indian Ridge) (133333) **Hamdan Al Maktoum**
45 **TEQANY (IRE),** gr c 1/3 Dark Angel (IRE)—Capulet Monteque (IRE) (Camacho) (380000) **Hamdan Al Maktoum**
46 **THAMMIN,** b c 30/1 Dark Angel (IRE)—
                        Gimme Some Lovin (IRE) (Desert Style (IRE)) (161904) **Hamdan Al Maktoum**
47 **TUREYTH (IRE),** b f 2/2 Street Cry (USA)—Garmoosha (USA) (Kingmambo (USA)) **Hamdan Al Maktoum**

Other Owners: Mr Khalil Al Sayegh, Mr Hadi Al-Tajir.

Head Lad: John Lake

Jockey (flat): Dane O'Neill, Paul Hanagan. **Apprentice:** Tommy O'Connor.

---

81 **MR PADDY BUTLER, Lewes**
Postal: Homewood Gate Racing Stables, Novington Lane, East Chiltington, Lewes,
East Sussex, BN7 3AU
Contacts: PHONE/FAX (01273) 890124 MOBILE (07973) 873846
E-MAIL homewoodgate@aol.com

1 **ALL OR NOTHIN (IRE),** 7, b g Majestic Missile (IRE)—
                        Lady Peculiar (CAN) **Miss M P Bryant, David & Eileen Bryant**
2 **ATHENIAN GARDEN (USA),** 9, b m Royal Academy (USA)—Webee (USA) **Mrs E. Lucey-Butler**
3 **ESTIBDAAD (IRE),** 6, b g Haatef (USA)—Star of Siligo (USA) **Miss M. P. Bryant**
4 **GENEROUS JUNE (IRE),** 8, ch m Generous (IRE)—Outo'theblue (IRE) **C. W. Wilson**
5 **HAWK GOLD (IRE),** 12, ch g Tendulkar (USA)—Heiress of Meath (IRE) **Miss M. P. Bryant**
6 **INVESTISSEMENT,** 10, b g Singspiel (USA)—Underwater (USA) **Homewoodgate Racing Club**
7 **KILLABRAHER CROSS (IRE),** 9, gr g Kasmayo—Enoughrose (IRE) **Homewoodgate Racing Club**
8 **PICCOLO TED,** 5, ch g Piccolo—Quality Street **Mr D. M. Whatmough**
9 **QUERIDO (GER),** 12, b g Acatenango (GER)—Quest of Fire (FR) **Miss M. P. Bryant**
10 **RON WAVERLY (IRE),** 6, ch g Haatef—Mermaid Beach **Miss M P Bryant, David & Eileen Bryant**
11 **SPICE BOAT,** 4, ch g Shamardal (USA)—Frizzante **Mrs E. Lucey-Butler**
12 **STAR ANISE (FR),** 5, b m Astronomer Royal (USA)—Sasicha (IRE) **The Winning Tipster Ltd**
13 **SWEET PICCOLO,** 6, ch g Piccolo—Quality Street **Mr D. M. Whatmough**

MR PADDY BUTLER - Continued

THREE-YEAR-OLDS
14 **LITTLE LIZZIE,** ch f Sleeping Indian—Quality Street

Other Owners: Mrs E. Bryant, Mr D. Bryant.

Assistant Trainer: Mrs E Lucey-Butler

Amateur: Miss M. Bryant, Miss J. Oliver.

---

82   **MRS BARBARA BUTTERWORTH, Appleby**
Postal: **Bolton Mill, Bolton, Appleby-in-Westmorland, Cumbria, CA16 6AL**
Contacts: **PHONE (01768) 361363 MOBILE (07778) 104118**

1 **CHERRY PRINCESS,** 6, gr m Act One—Francia **Mrs B. Butterworth**
2 **KNIGHT VALLIANT,** 13, gr g Dansili—Aristocratique **Mrs B. Butterworth**

Assistant Trainer: Miss Elizabeth Butterworth

Jockey (NH): Sean Quinlan. **Amateur:** Miss Elizabeth Butterworth.

---

83   **MR NEVILLE BYCROFT, Malton**
Postal: **Cotman Rise, Brandsby, York, YO61 4RN**
Contacts: **PHONE (01347) 888641 MOBILE (07802) 763227**

1 **ADIATOR,** 8, b m Needwood Blade—Retaliator **N. Bycroft**
2 **DUAL MAC,** 9, br g Paris House—Carol Again **N. Bycroft**
3 **EIUM MAC,** 7, b g Presidium—Efipetite **N. Bycroft**
4 **EURO MAC,** 4, ch f Sir Percy—Oomph **N. Bycroft**
5 **GURU MAC,** 6, b m Ishiguru (USA)—Zacinta (USA) **N. Bycroft**
6 **MILU MAC,** 5, b m Milk It Mick—Efipetite **N. Bycroft**
7 **MISU MAC,** 6, b m Misu Bond (IRE)—Umbrian Gold (IRE) **Mr J. D. Martin**
8 **ROLEN SLY,** 7, b g Tillerman—Feiticeira (USA) **N. Bycroft**
9 **WILL MAC,** 5, b g Misu Bond (IRE)—Zacinta (USA) **N. Bycroft**
10 **WILLBEME,** 8, b m Kyllachy—Befriend (USA) **Mr P. D. Burrow**

Assistant Trainer: Seb Spencer

Jockey (flat): Franny Norton, Jimmy Quinn.

---

84   **MISS JULIE CAMACHO, Malton**
Postal: **Star Cottage, Welham Road, Norton, Malton, North Yorkshire, YO17 9QE**
Contacts: **PHONE (01653) 696205 FAX (01653) 696205 MOBILE (07779) 318135 / (07950) 356440**
E-MAIL julie@jacracing.co.uk WEBSITE www.juliecamacho.com

1 **BURTONWOOD,** 4, b g Acclamation—Green Poppy **Judy & Richard Peck & Julie Camacho**
2 **CITY OF NIGHT (IRE),** 4, b g Elusive City (USA)—Testama (FR) **Julie Camacho**
3 **ILLUSTRIOUS PRINCE (IRE),** 9, b g Acclamation—Sacred Love (IRE) **G. Howard & Partners**
4 **JUDICIAL (IRE),** 4, b g Iffraaj—Marlinka **Elite Racing Club**
5 **SPIRIT OF WEDZA (IRE),** 4, b g Footstepsinthesand—Sampers (IRE) **Owners Group**
6 **SWAHEEN,** 4, b g Lawman (FR)—Whole Grain **Judy & Richard Peck**
7 **TOM SAWYER,** 8, b g Dansili—Cayman Sunset (IRE) **L. Bolingbroke & Partners**
8 **WILDE INSPIRATION (IRE),** 5, ch g Dandy Man (IRE)—Wishing Chair (USA) **Judy & Richard Peck**
9 **YULONG XIONGBA (IRE),** 4, b g Kodiac—Moon Legend (USA) **Owners Group 006**

THREE-YEAR-OLDS
10 **BINT ARCANO (FR),** ch f Arcano (IRE)—Rosa Mundi **G. B. Turnbull Ltd**
11 **DEANSGATE (IRE),** b g Dandy Man (IRE)—Romarca (IRE) **Axom**
12 **GILT EDGED (IRE),** br f Big Bad Bob (IRE)—Caona (USA) **Axom**
13 **KIRKHAM,** b g Pastoral Pursuits—Royal Grace **Kirkham Partnership**
14 **MEDIA WORLD (IRE),** ch g Medicean—Panoptic **Media World Partnership**
15 **OSCAR HUGHES (IRE),** br g Frozen Power (IRE)—Pedra Ona (IRE) **Julie Camacho**
16 **WILDE EXTRAVAGANCE (IRE),** ch g Dandy Man (IRE)—Castanetta (IRE) **Judy & Richard Peck**

MISS JULIE CAMACHO - Continued

TWO-YEAR-OLDS

17 B f 11/4 Exceleration (IRE)—Marlinka (Marju (IRE)) **Elite Racing Club**
18 B c 23/4 Intikhab (USA)—Panoptic (Dubawi (IRE)) (12380) **Kirkham Partners**

Other Owners: Mr Dan Downie, Mr Tony Hill, Mr B. M. Hillier, Miss M. Noden.

Assistant Trainer: Mr S. Brown

Jockey (flat): Tom Eaves, Barry McHugh.

---

85 **MR MARK CAMPION, Malton**
Postal: **Whitewell House Stables, Whitewall, Malton, North Yorkshire, YO17 9EH**
Contacts: **PHONE** (01653) 692729 **FAX** (01653) 600066 **MOBILE** (07973) 178311
E-MAIL info@markcampion-racing.com **WEBSITE** www.markcampion-racing.com

1 CHARMING GRACE (IRE), 10, b m Flemensfirth (USA)—Lady Laureate
2 COSMIC BLUE (IRE), 4, b f Kalanisi (IRE)—Gift of Freedom (IRE)
3 DESERT NOVA (IRE), 14, ch g Desert King (IRE)—Assafiyah (IRE)
4 MINKIE MOON (IRE), 8, b g Danehill Dancer (IRE)—Minkova (IRE)
5 SADDLERS' SECRET (IRE), 11, b m Saddlers' Hall (IRE)—Birdless Bush (IRE)
6 THE MASTERS CHOICE (IRE), 4, b g High Chaparral (IRE)—Final Legacy (USA)

Owners: Mr V. B. Coleman, Mr G. Nurse.

Assistant Trainer: Mrs F. Campion

---

86 **MS JENNIE CANDLISH, Leek**
Postal: **Basford Grange Racing Stables, Basford, Leek, Staffordshire, ST13 7ET**
Contacts: **PHONE** (07889) 413639 (07976) 825134 **FAX** (01538) 360324
E-MAIL jenniecandlish@yahoo.co.uk **WEBSITE** www.jenniecandlishracing.co.uk

1 ASTAROLAND (FR), 6, b g Astarabad (USA)—Orlandaise (FR) **Ms J. Candlish**
2 BARAFUNDLE (IRE), 12, ch g Flemensfirth (USA)—Different Dee (IRE) **Mrs J. M. Ratcliff**
3 BASFORD BEN, 8, b g Trade Fair—Moly (FR) **A. J. Baxter**
4 BEAUBOREEN (IRE), 9, b g Revoque (IRE)—Roseboreen (IRE) **Mrs A. V. Hall**
5 BEEVES (IRE), 9, b g Portrait Gallery (IRE)—Camas North (IRE) **Mr & Mrs Paul & Clare Rooney**
6 BRYDEN BOY (IRE), 6, b g Craigsteel—Cailin Vic Mo Cri (IRE) **Alan Baxter & Brian Hall**
7 FEARLESS TUNES (IRE), 8, b g Shantou—Miss Snapdragon (IRE) **Mr & Mrs Paul & Clare Rooney**
8 GRANVILLE ISLAND (IRE), 9, b g Flemensfirth (USA)—Fox Glen **Mr P. & Mrs G. A. Clarke**
9 GREENWORLDSOLUTION, 4, b g Lucarno (USA)—Basford Lady (IRE) **Brian Hall, Jen Candlish & Alan Baxter**
10 GROVE SILVER (IRE), 7, gr g Gamut (IRE)—Cobbler's Well (USA) **Alan Baxter Anthony Bloor Dave Cheetham**
11 MAOI CHINN TIRE (IRE), 9, b g Mull of Kintyre (USA)—Primrose And Rose **Ms J. Candlish**
12 PARTY ROCK (IRE), 9, b g Vinnie Roe (IRE)—Garryduff Eile (IRE) **Mrs P. M. Beardmore**
13 RESTRAINT OF TRADE (IRE), 6, br g Authorized (IRE)—Zivania (IRE) **A. J. Baxter**
14 RIO FALLS (IRE), 4, b g Captain Rio—Swallow Falls (IRE) **A. J. Baxter**
15 SECRETSISTA (IRE), 4, b f Presenting—Princess Rainbow (FR) **Mr P. & Mrs G. A. Clarke**
16 SLEEPY HAVEN (IRE), 6, b g Indian Haven—
                                                      High Society Girl (IRE) **Alan Baxter Anthony Bloor Dave Cheetham**
17 SPIRIT OF HALE (IRE), 5, ch g Stowaway—Roseboreen (IRE) **Mrs A. V. Hall**
18 ST LEWIS, 6, b g Erhaab (USA)—Miss Lewis **The Portchester Lads**
19 STAR ASCENDING (IRE), 4, ch g Thousand Words—Sakaka **Mr P. Wright-Bevans**
20 TANARPINO, 5, ch g Tobougg (IRE)—Got Tune (FR) **Mr P. & Mrs G. A. Clarke**
21 THEFLYINGPORTRAIT (IRE), 7, gr g Portrait Gallery (IRE)—Skule Hill Lass (IRE) **The Mere Partnership**
22 TIMEFORFIRTH (IRE), 6, b m Flemensfirth (USA)—Don't Be Upset (IRE) **A Baxter M Barrett B Cant & S Rogers**
23 TOMMY THE RASCAL, 6, b g Multiplex—Tina Gee **A. J. White**
24 WAKE YOUR DREAMS (IRE), 8, b g Oscar (IRE)—Rose Karanja **Pam Beardmore & Alan Baxter**
25 WINTERED WELL (IRE), 8, b g Milan—Stratosphere **A. J. White**
26 WINTERLUDE (IRE), 6, b g Street Cry (IRE)—New Morning (IRE) **Brian Verinder & Alan Baxter**

THREE-YEAR-OLDS

27 SHOW PALACE, ch c Showcasing—Palais Polaire **Mr P. & Mrs G. A. Clarke**
28 SIBERIAN POWER (IRE), b c Frozen Power (IRE)—Novosibirsk (USA) **Mr P. & Mrs G. A. Clarke**

MS JENNIE CANDLISH - Continued

Other Owners: Mr M. Barrett, Mr H. A. E. Bloor, Mr R. J. Cant, Mr D. A. Cheetham, Mr P. Clarke, Mrs G. A. Clarke, Mr B. H. Dolan, Mr B. J. Hall, Mr J. P. Naylor, Mrs S. Rogers, Mrs C. Rooney, Mr P. A. Rooney, Mr B. W. Verinder.

Assistant Trainer: Alan O'Keeffe

Jockey (flat): Joe Fanning, Paul Hanagan.

87	**MR HENRY CANDY, Wantage**

Postal: **Kingston Warren, Wantage, Oxfordshire, OX12 9QF**
Contacts: **PHONE (01367) 820276 / 820514 FAX (01367) 820500 MOBILE (07836) 211264**
E-MAIL henrycandy@btconnect.com

1 ANYA, 7, b m Monsieur Bond (IRE)—Dyanita **Mrs L. M. Alexander**
2 CHAIN OF DAISIES, 4, b f Rail Link—Puya **Girsonfield Ltd**
3 DINKUM DIAMOND (IRE), 8, b h Aussie Rules (USA)—Moving Diamonds **Eight Star Syndicate**
4 EXOPLANET BLUE, 4, b f Exceed And Excel (AUS)—Tut (IRE) **One Too Many Partners**
5 GREENSIDE, 5, b h Dubawi (IRE)—Katrina (IRE) **Clayton, Frost, Kebell & Turner**
6 HAROLD LLOYD, 4, b g Cape Cross—Silent Act (USA) **Mr & Mrs R. Scott**
7 ICONIC (IRE), 4, b f Kodiac—Christa Maria **First Of Many And Turner**
8 LIGHT OF LOVE, 4, b f Dylan Thomas (IRE)—May Light **Brightwalton Bloodstock Limited**
9 LIMATO (IRE), 4, b g Tagula (IRE)—Come April **P. G. Jacobs**
10 OAT COUTURE, 4, b f Kyllachy—Oat Cuisine **Mrs G. E. Rowland-Clark**
11 PEDRO SERRANO (IRE), 6, b g Footstepsinthesand—Shaiyadima (IRE) **Six Too Many**
12 PERCEIVED, 4, ch f Sir Percy—New Light **Candy, Pritchard & Thomas**
13 POSTBAG, 4, b f Three Valleys (USA)—Postage Stampe **Major M. G. Wyatt**
14 SON OF AFRICA, 4, b g Equiano (FR)—Generously Gifted **One Too Many Partners**
15 SPRING FLING, 5, b m Assertive—Twilight Mistress **Six Too Many/T A Frost/ G Wilson**
16 STOIC BOY, 4, ch g Paco Boy (IRE)—Dramatic Turn **Mrs David Blackburn & Mr M. Blackburn**
17 TWILIGHT SON, 4, b c Kyllachy—Twilight Mistress **Mr Godfrey Wilson & Cheveley Park Stud**
18 UELE RIVER, 4, b f Refuse To Bend (IRE)—Baddi Heights (FR) **Mrs A. R. Ruggles**

THREE-YEAR-OLDS

19 AFRICAN FRIEND (IRE), b g Equiano (FR)—Fontanally Springs (IRE) **Henry D. N. B. Candy**
20 ARTISTS MODEL (IRE), b f Dutch Art—Zarwala (IRE) **Girsonfield Ltd**
21 BEAR CHEEK (IRE), b f Kodiac—See Nuala (IRE) **Miss J. Barnett**
22 BOUNCE, b f Bahamian Bounty—Black Belt Shopper (IRE) **Landmark Racing Limited**
23 DENHAM SOUND, ch f Champs Elysees—Presbyterian Nun (IRE) **The Earl Cadogan**
24 FREE PASSAGE, ch g Medicean—Free Offer **The Earl Cadogan**
25 HAMILTON TERRACE, b gr f Mount Nelson—Striking Pose (IRE) **The Ace Partnership**
26 JACK NEVISON, b g Dick Turpin (IRE)—Creative Mind (IRE) **Henry Candy & Partners III**
27 JAUNTY JOH (IRE), b f Zoffany (IRE)—Don't Care (IRE) **Mr Geoff Buck & Mr Henry Candy**
28 LA RIOJA, b f Hellvelyn—Talampaya (USA) **Qatar Racing Limited**
29 LIMONATA (IRE), b f Bushranger (IRE)—Come April **P. G. Jacobs**
30 MEDICIMAN, b c Medicean—Quintrell **One Too Many/Mr N Agran/Mr M Silver**
31 NICARRA (IRE), b f Kodiac—Nassma (IRE) **Mrs P. J. Burns**
32 NOBLE PEACE, b c Kyllachy—Peace Concluded **One Too Many & Candy**
33 PAST MASTER, gr c Mastercraftsman (IRE)—Millestan (IRE) **Mr D B Clark/Mr A R Bentall/Mr H Candy**
34 POOLE BELLE (IRE), b f Canford Cliffs (IRE)—Anbella (FR) **Sir E. J. Loder**
35 ROSIE ROYCE, b f Acclamation—Rebecca Rolfe **Hunscote Stud**
36 SANTORINI (IRE), b g Tagula (IRE)—Rags (IRE) **One Too Many Partners**
37 SHAMISA (IRE), b f Art Connoisseur (IRE)—Shakeeba (IRE) **Candy, Pritchard & Thomas**
38 SHOWING OFF (IRE), ch g Notnowcato—Walk On Water **Bloomsbury Stud**
39 SQUIGGLEY, b f Sir Percy—Oat Cuisine **Mrs G. E. Rowland-Clark**
40 STAR JEANIE, b f Kyllachy—Floating **Potensis Bloodstock Limited**
41 TERESAR, ch f Dandy Man (IRE)—High Chart **Potensis Bloodstock Limited**
42 TIME TO EXCEED (IRE), b f Exceed And Excel (AUS)—In Your Time **Hunscote Stud**
43 VIBRANT CHORDS, b g Poet's Voice—Lovely Thought **P. G. Jacobs**
44 WHERE NEXT, b g Compton Place—Neqaawi **Mr H Candy**

TWO-YEAR-OLDS

45 B c 14/3 Duke of Marmalade (IRE)—Aweebounce (IRE) (Dubawi (IRE)) (22148) **Potensis Bloodstock Limited**
46 BECK AND CALL, b f 21/3 Holy Roman Emperor (IRE)—Gosbeck (Dubawi (IRE)) **Major M. G. Wyatt**
47 B f 7/4 Harbour Watch (IRE)—Black Belt Shopper (IRE) (Desert Prince (IRE)) (26000) **First Of Many**

MR HENRY CANDY - Continued

48 **CANFORD TOR (IRE)**, b c 13/5 Canford Cliffs (IRE)—
Igreja (ARG) (Southern Halo (USA)) (22148) **Simon Broke & Partners**
49 **DIMITRE**, gr c 20/2 Showcasing—Devoted (IRE) (Dalakhani (IRE)) **Landmark Racing Limited**
50 **DRAMA DIVA (IRE)**, b f 25/4 Acclamation—Khibraat (Alhaarth (IRE)) (18095) **P. G. Jacobs**
51 B c 22/3 Kyllachy—Falling Angel (Kylian (USA)) (24761) **Thurloe Thoroughbreds XX**
52 B c 18/3 Medicean—Free Offer (Generous (IRE)) **The Earl Cadogan**
53 Ch f 2/4 Sir Prancealot (IRE)—Fuerta Ventura (IRE) (Desert Sun) (100000) **Qatar Racing Limited**
54 **GREY THOU ART (IRE)**, gr f 16/3 Canford Cliffs (IRE)—Roystonea (Polish Precedent (USA)) **Sir Edmund Loder**
55 **KING OF NEPAL**, b c 31/1 Sepoy (AUS)—Empress Anna (IRE) (Imperial Ballet (IRE)) (38000) **First Of Many**
56 **LET RIP (IRE)**, b c 18/5 Rip Van Winkle (IRE)—Al Ihsas (Danehill (USA)) (13289) **P. G. Jacobs**
57 **MADELEINE BOND**, ch f 30/3 Monsieur Bond (IRE)—Spin A Wish (Captain Rio) (14285) **Henry D. N. B. Candy**
58 **MORELLO (IRE)**, b f 9/4 Medicean—Mullein (Oasis Dream) **Landmark Racing Limited**
59 **OUR OYSTERCATCHER**, br c 24/1 Pastoral Pursuits—
The Dark Eider (Superlative) **Mrs F. A. Veasey & GB Partnership**
60 B c 3/3 High Chaparral (IRE)—Presbyterian Nun (IRE) (Daylami (IRE)) **The Earl Cadogan**
61 **REBECCA ROCKS**, b f 25/1 Exceed And Excel (AUS)—Rebecca Rolfe (Pivotal) **Hunscote Stud**
62 B c 8/5 Dandy Man (IRE)—Ride A Rainbow (Rainbow Quest (USA)) (7382) **Henry D. N. B. Candy**
63 B c 15/4 Kodiac—Shamarlane (Shamardal (USA)) (35437) **Mr Geoff Buck & Mr Henry Candy**
64 Ch f 27/4 Zebedee—Sportsticketing (IRE) (Spectrum (IRE)) (13289) **Potensis Bloodstock Limited**
65 B f 20/1 Iffraaj—Still I'm A Star (IRE) (Lawman (FR)) (81210) **Qatar Racing Limited**
66 B f 3/3 Showcasing—Tremelo Pointe (IRE) (Trempolino (USA)) (75000) **Andrew Whitlock Racing**
67 **TURNPIKE TRIP**, b c 25/3 Champs Elysees—Neqaawi (Alhaarth (IRE)) **Mrs D. Blackburn**
68 Ch f 21/3 Power—Uvinza (Bertolini (USA)) (11000) **Mrs A. R. Ruggles**
69 B f 21/3 Dark Angel (IRE)—Yazmin (IRE) (Green Desert (USA)) (23624) **Potensis Bloodstock Limited**

Other Owners: Mr Alexander Acloque, Mr N. Agran, Mr A. Bentall, Mr Mark Blackburn, Mrs David Blackburn, Mr S. Broke, Mr Geoff Buck, Mr Henry Candy, Cheveley Park Stud, Mr D. B. Clark, Mr S. Clayton, Mr W. R. Collins, Mrs Amanda Dixon, Mr Frederick Ellis, Mr D. J. Erwin, Mr Richard Farquhar, Mr Alexander Frost, Mr T. A. F. Frost, Mr T. Gould, Mr J. Inverdale, Mr J. Kebell, Mr T. J. Le Blanc-Smith, Mr R. Maynard, Mr H. McNeill, Mr D. Norris, Mrs Angela Pinder, Mrs C. M. Poland, Mr Roy Pritchard, Mr M. J. Silver, Mr S. M. Smith, Mrs L. A. Smith, Mrs Jenny Snowball, Mr Gerry Thomas, Mr Godfrey Wilson.

Assistant Trainer: David Pinder

---

88 **MR GRANT CANN**, Bath
Postal: **Park Field, Hall Lane, Lower Hamswell, Bath, Gloucestershire, BA1 9DE**
Contacts: **PHONE (01225) 891674 MOBILE (07968) 271118**

1 **ASTER'S APPROVAL**, 6, b g With Approval (CAN)—Aster (IRE) **P. J. Cave**
2 **CAILIN (IRE)**, 8, b m Golan (IRE)—Castle Arms Cailin (IRE) **J. G. Cann**
3 **I'M IN CHARGE**, 10, b g Rakaposhi King—Cloudy Pearl **J. G. Cann**
4 **MASTER TODD (IRE)**, 11, ch g Dream Well (FR)—Falika (FR)
5 **MILLER'S MAVERICK**, 8, b g Millkom—Gables Girl **P. J. Cave**
6 7, B g Millenary—Slievemhuire (IRE) **Miss A. M. Bush**
7 **UNIFY**, 6, b m Midnight Legend—Holy Smoke **J. G. Cann**

---

89 **MR DON CANTILLON**, Newmarket
Postal: **63 Exeter Road, Newmarket, Suffolk, CB8 8LP**
Contacts: **PHONE (01638) 668507 MOBILE (07709) 377601**

1 **BEYOND MEASURE (IRE)**, 5, ch m Flemensfirth (USA)—Faucon **D. E. Cantillon**
2 **DRUIDS LODGE**, 5, b g Tiger Hill (IRE)—Mimiteh (USA) **D. E. Cantillon**
3 **IT IS I (IRE)**, 6, b g Presenting—Nivalf **D. E. Cantillon**
4 **LA ESTRELLA (USA)**, 13, b g Theatrical—Princess Ellen **D. E. Cantillon**
5 **WESTERN WAY (IRE)**, 7, b g Westerner—Faucon **D. E. Cantillon**
6 **WHATS NOT TO LIKE (GER)**, 5, b g Saddex—Wild Girl (GER) **D. E. Cantillon**

THREE-YEAR-OLDS

7 **ESPRIT DE TAUBER (IRE)**, b f Zoffany (IRE)—Trois Graces (USA) **Mrs C. Reed**
8 **HINT OF GREY (IRE)**, gr f Mastercraftsman (IRE)—Anamarka **Mrs C. Reed**
9 **HOLLYWOOD ROAD (IRE)**, b c Kodiac—Rinneen (IRE) **Mrs C. Reed**

90 MRS LOUISA CARBERRY, Pouance

Postal: Le Rivage, 49420 Pouance, France
Contacts: MOBILE (0033) 624 866369
E-MAIL louisacarberryracing@gmail.com WEBSITE www.carberryracing.com

1 **A POSTERIORI (FR)**, 6, ch g Michel Georges—Kinshasac (FR) **Tony Killoran, Mark Flood, Louisa Carberry**
2 **ANNE OF BRITTANY (FR)**, 4, b f King's Best (USA)—Abyaan (IRE) **Peter Spiller**
3 **ASTRE DE BALLON (FR)**, 7, b g Astarabad (USA)—Nile Altesse (FR) **Mme Robert Gasche Luc**
4 **BEAU DE BALLON (FR)**, 7, ch g Discover d'auteuil (FR)—Lady Apatry (FR) **Mme Robert Gasche Luc**
5 **BEN ER D'EL PAZ (FR)**, 5, gr g Ange Gabriel (FR)—Princess d'elpaz (FR) **Mme Marie Jose Corbin**
6 **BETISE BEAUCHENE (FR)**, 5, b m Peer Gynt (JPN)—Adria de Clermont (FR) **Elevage De Clermont**
7 **BONHEUR DE STARA (FR)**, 6, b m Astarabad (USA)—Nile Bonheur (FR) **Mme Robert Gasche Luc**
8 **BUCKENHILL**, 6, gr g Intikhab (USA)—Trauquebise (FR) **Mr and Mrs A. Russel**
9 **CARMEN DES BORDES (FR)**, 4, br f Network (GER)—
                              Miss Berry (FR) **Gerard Hanquiez, Anthony Allot, Hubert Chalivoy, Bruno Marisy**
10 **CHAPO DE BALLON (FR)**, 9, b g Turgeon (USA)—Chapohio (FR) **Mme Robert Gasche Luc**
11 **CHIC ALORS (FR)**, 4, ch f Turgeon (USA)—Standing Around (FR) **Mme Henri Devin**
12 **CHIFFRE D'AFFAIRES (FR)**, 7, b g Kahyasi—Affaire de Moeurs (FR) **Mme Henri Devin**
13 **COTTON WOOD'S (FR)**, 4, b g Vendangeur (IRE)—Toscane des Fleurs (FR) **John Riley**
14 **CREATION (FR)**, 4, ch f Vendangeur (IRE)—Oasaka (FR) **Patrice Vagne**
15 **DINETTE DE BALLON (FR)**, 4, b f Doctor Dino (FR)—Nile Altesse (FR) **Mme Robert Gasche Luc**
16 **DOCTEUR DE BALLON (FR)**, 4, ch g Doctor Dino (FR)—Nile Breeze (FR) **Mme Robert Gasche Luc**
17 **EVER LAD (FR)**, 5, b g Linda's Lad—Best Ever (FR) **Regis Girardin**
18 **GRACIE HART**, 5, b m Sakhee's Secret—Dictatrix **Jackie Penny**
19 **HUDSON RIVER (FR)**, 4, gr g Turgeon (USA)—Heritage River (FR) **Mme Henri Devin**
20 **IT'S JENNIFER (FR)**, 4, b f Martaline—Shanxi Girl **Tim Johnson**
21 **JOE DE CLERMONT (IRE)**, 5, b g Westerner—Joe's Dream Catch (IRE) **Elevage De Clermont**
22 **MARVELLOSO**, 8, b g Tobougg (IRE)—Qudrah (IRE) **Louisa Carberry**
23 **NILE KHALKEVIE (FR)**, 6, b m Khalkevi (FR)—Nile Altesse (FR) **Mme Robert Gasche Luc**
24 **PATGARY (FR)**, 4, b g Ballingarry (IRE)—Maylady Pat (FR) **Fenton Archer**
25 **PEARSE (FR)**, 12, ch g River Bay (USA)—Little Rocket **Tony Killoran, Louisa Carberry**
26 **SOLDIERS FORTUNE (FR)**, 5, b m Soldier of Fortune (IRE)—
                              Villa Joyeuse (FR) **Mme Henri Devin, Mrs Ashbrooke**
27 **TECTONA (IRE)**, 5, b m Shirocco (GER)—Too Marvelous (FR) **EPDS racing**
28 **TOUCH OF VELVETT (FR)**, 4, gr f Proclamation (IRE)—Rose Bien **Harry Wheeler**
29 **TURLOUGH (FR)**, 4, gr g Turgeon (USA)—Vanilla Sky (FR) **Mme Henri Devin**
30 **TZAR DE L'ELFE (FR)**, 6, b g Satri (IRE)—Rue Tournefort (FR) **Lord Clinton, Adrian Pratt**
31 **WONDER FLIGHT (FR)**, 4, b f Ballingarry (IRE)—Lili Flight (FR) **Lord Harrington**
32 **ZANZIBELLE (FR)**, 4, ch f Zanzibari (USA)—Audebelle (FR) **Mme Henri Devin**

THREE-YEAR-OLDS

33 **ACHERA (FR)**, gr f Silver Frost (IRE)—Luckiest (IRE) **Patricia Morin Paye**

TWO-YEAR-OLDS

34 **ANAARUS (FR)**, b g 28/2 Anabaa Blue—Russian Beauty (USA) (Diesis) (5167) **David Reynolds**

Assistant Trainer: Philip Carberry

91 MRS RUTH CARR, Stillington

Postal: Mowbray House Farm, Easingwold Road, Stillington, York, North Yorkshire, YO61 1LT
Contacts: PHONE (01347) 823776 (home) (01347) 821683 (yard) MOBILE (07721) 926772
E-MAIL ruth@ruthcarrracing.co.uk WEBSITE www.ruthcarrracing.co.uk

1 **ABUSHAMAH (IRE)**, 5, b g Nayef (USA)—Adaala (USA) **Grange Park Racing & Mrs R Carr**
2 **ADVENTUREMAN**, 4, b g Kyllachy—Constitute (USA) **The Venturers & Mrs R Carr**
3 **ALMUHALAB**, 5, b br g Dansili—Ghanaati (USA) **Michael Hill**
4 **AMAZING BLUE SKY**, 10, b g Barathea (IRE)—Azure Lake (USA) **G Scruton, D Williamson & R Carr**
5 **ANNIGONI (IRE)**, 4, b g Excellent Art—Aspen Falls (IRE) **Michael Hill**
6 **ASIAN TRADER**, 7, b g Acclamation—Tiger Waltz **Mrs R Carr & The Bottom Liners**
7 **BE PERFECT (USA)**, 7, b g Street Cry (IRE)—Binya (GER) **The Beer Stalkers & Ruth Carr**
8 **BROWNSEA BRINK**, 6, b g Cadeaux Genereux—Valiantly **The Bottom Liners & Mrs R. Carr**
9 **CHAPLIN BAY (IRE)**, 4, b g Fastnet Rock (AUS)—Green Castle (IRE) **Mrs M. Chapman**
10 **CHEECO**, 4, ch g Shami—Mandarin Lady **Mrs A. Clark**
11 **COSMIC CHATTER**, 6, b g Paris House—Paradise Eve **Grange Park Racing**

MRS RUTH CARR - Continued

12 **DANISH DUKE (IRE)**, 5, ch g Duke of Marmalade (IRE)—Bridge Note (USA) **Michael Hill**
13 **DUBAI DYNAMO**, 11, b g Kyllachy—Miss Mercy (IRE) **The Bottom Liners**
14 **ELLAAL**, 7, b g Oasis Dream—Capistrano Day (USA) **The Bottom Liners & Paul Saxton**
15 **EXOTIC GUEST**, 6, ch g Bahamian Bounty—Mamoura (IRE) **21st Century Racing,A Swinburne,R Carr**
16 **EXPLAIN**, 4, ch g Kyllachy—Descriptive (IRE) **The Beer Stalkers & Ruth Carr**
17 **FAVOURITE TREAT (USA)**, 6, b g Hard Spun (USA)—Truart (USA) **Paul Saxton & The Bottom Liners**
18 **FLASH CITY (ITY)**, 8, b g Elusive City (USA)—Furnish **Mr S. R. Jackson**
19 **FOXTROT KNIGHT**, 4, b g Kyllachy—Rustam **The Double 'A' Partnership**
20 **FROSTY THE SNOWMAN (IRE)**, 5, gr g Mastercraftsman (IRE)—
Sleeveless (USA) **Bruce Jamieson, Barbara Dean, Ruth Carr**
21 **HAB REEH**, 8, gr g Diktat—Asian Love **Grange Park Racing & Mrs B Taylor**
22 **INTENSIFIED (IRE)**, 5, b br g Intense Focus (USA)—Sway Me Now (USA) **Mrs R. A. Carr**
23 **LEXINGTON PLACE**, 6, ch g Compton Place—Elidore **Mrs M. Chapman**
24 **MAGICAL EFFECT (IRE)**, 4, ch g New Approach (IRE)—Purple Glow (IRE) **Miss V. A. Church**
25 **MERDON CASTLE (IRE)**, 4, b g Acclamation—Siren's Gift **Mrs R. A. Carr**
26 **MESHARDAL (GER)**, 6, b g Shamardal (USA)—Melody Fair (IRE) **The Hollinbridge Partnership & Ruth Carr**
27 **MININGROCKS (FR)**, 4, b g Lawman (FR)—Fashion School **Miss B Houlston, Mrs M Chapman & Mrs R Carr**
28 **MUTAFAAKIR (IRE)**, 7, b g Oasis Dream—Moon's Whisper (USA) **Mrs M. Chapman**
29 **ORIENTAL SPLENDOUR (IRE)**, 4, br g Strategic Prince—Asian Lady **Mr M Baldam & Mrs R Carr**
30 **SAN CASSIANO (IRE)**, 9, b g Bertolini (USA)—Celtic Silhouette (FR) **Mr S Jackson, Mr L Shaw, Mrs R Carr**
31 **SLEMY (IRE)**, 5, b g Raven's Pass (USA)—Wolf Cleugh (IRE) **J. A. Swinburne**
32 **TANAWAR (IRE)**, 6, b g Elusive City (USA)—Parakopi (IRE) **G Scruton, D Williamson & R Carr**
33 **VALLARTA (IRE)**, 6, b g Footstepsinthesand—Mexican Miss (IRE) **D. C. Renton**
34 **VICTOIRE DE LYPHAR (IRE)**, 9, b g Bertolini (USA)—Victory Peak **The Beer Stalkers & Ruth Carr**
35 **YORK GLORY (USA)**, 8, gr ro h Five Star Day (USA)—
Minicolony (USA) **Wildcard Racing Syndicate & Ruth Carr**

THREE-YEAR-OLDS

36 **DYLLAN (IRE)**, b g Zebedee—Luvmedo (IRE) **RHD & Ruth Carr**
37 Ch g Haafhd—Mandarin Lady **Mrs A. Clark**

TWO-YEAR-OLDS

38 Ch g 25/4 Pastoral Pursuits—China Cherub (Inchinor) **Mrs A. Clark**
39 **FOXY REBEL**, ch g 24/3 Cockney Rebel (IRE)—Foxholes Lodge (Nasheet) **Mr G. Scruton & Mr D. Williamson**

Other Owners: Mr M. Baldam, Mr A. J. Bonarius, Mr N. J. Bonarius, T. J. E. Brereton, A. W. Catterall, Mrs B. Catterall, A. D. Crombie, Mr T. W. Deadman, Mrs B. I. Dean, Mr C. Dufferwiel, Mr F. H. Eales, J. P. Hames, Miss B. J. Houlston, Mr A. B. Jamieson, Mr D. R. Kelly, Mr P. Newell, R J H Limited, RHD Research Limited, P. A. Saxton, Mr G. Scruton, Mr L. D. Shaw, Mr E. Surr, Mrs B. Taylor, S. L. Walker, Mr D. J. Williamson, Mr R. W. Wilson.

Assistant Trainer: Mrs M. Chapman

Jockey (flat): P. J. McDonald, James Sullivan. **Jockey (NH):** Jake Greenall. **Amateur:** Miss Serena Brotherton.

---

92 MR DECLAN CARROLL, Malton
Postal: **The Office, Norton Grange Stables, Park Road, Norton, Malton, North Yorkshire, YO17 9EA**
Contacts: **PHONE** (01653) 698517 **FAX** (01653) 698577 **MOBILE** (07801) 553779
E-MAIL declancarrollracing@gmail.com

1 **BEAUTY'S FORTE (IRE)**, 5, b g Kyllachy—Viking Fair **R. J. Flegg**
2 **BOLD SPIRIT**, 5, b g Invincible Spirit (IRE)—Far Shores (USA) **Mrs S. A. Bryan**
3 **BUONARROTI (IRE)**, 5, b g Galileo (IRE)—Beauty Is Truth (IRE) **D. Hardy**
4 **ETERNAL**, 4, ch c New Approach (IRE)—Sharp Mode (USA) **Mr Steve Ryan**
5 **FARANG JAI DEE (IRE)**, 4, b g Approve—Fruit O'the Forest (IRE) **Dreams**
6 **GOD WILLING**, 5, b g Arch (USA)—Bourbon Ball **Bee Health Ltd**
7 **LIGHTNING STEPS**, 4, b g Champs Elysees—Fairy Steps **The Commissioning Team**
8 **LLEWELLYN**, 8, b g Shamardal (USA)—Ffestiniog (IRE) **Mrs S. A. Bryan**
9 **MONSIEUR JIMMY**, 4, ch g Monsieur Bond (IRE)—Artistic License (IRE) **Mr Ray Flegg & Mr H J Bousfield**
10 **MRS BIGGS**, 4, ch f Paco Boy (IRE)—Hoh Chi Min **Mr D. Carroll**
11 **MUSHARRIF**, 4, b g Arcano (IRE)—Cefira (USA) **Ray Flegg & John Bousfield**
12 **MYSTERIAL**, 6, b g Invincible Spirit (IRE)—Diamond Dilemma (IRE) **Mrs S. A. Bryan**
13 **PULL THE PLUG (IRE)**, 5, b m Sleeping Indian—Babylonian **Mr C. J. Harding**
14 **SAIGON CITY**, 6, b g Mount Nelson—Hoh Chi Min **C. H. Stephenson & Partners 1**
15 **SAVE THE BEES**, 8, b g Royal Applause—Rock Concert **Mr Steve Ryan**

MR DECLAN CARROLL - Continued

16 **STONEBOAT BILL**, 4, ch g Virtual—Applauding (IRE) **Mr D. J. O'Reilly**
17 **WHOZTHECAT (IRE)**, 9, b g One Cool Cat (USA)—Intaglia (GER) **Mr S. R. Bean**

THREE-YEAR-OLDS

18 **ISA**, b f Approve (IRE)—Ha'penny Beacon **Mr J. G. Johnson**

TWO-YEAR-OLDS

19 **REBOUNDED**, ch c 11/4 Mayson—Winter Dress (Haafhd) (7619) **Mr J. G. Johnson**

Apprentice: Lee Byrne, Ger O'Neil.

---

93 MR TONY CARROLL, Cropthorne

Postal: **The Cropthorne Stud, Field Barn Lane, Cropthorne, Pershore, Worcestershire, WR10 3LY**
Contacts: **PHONE (01386) 861020 FAX (01386) 861628 MOBILE (07770) 472431**
E-MAIL a.w.carroll@btconnect.com WEBSITE www.awcarroll.co.uk

1 **ADMIRABLE ART (IRE)**, 6, b g Excellent Art—Demi Voix **Mr D. S. G. Morgan**
2 **ALTAIRA**, 5, b h Dubawi (IRE)—Peach Pearl **Mrs S. R. Keable**
3 **AMBITIOUS ROSIE**, 5, b m Striking Ambition—Cerulean Rose **Mr J. Loftus**
4 **ASSERTIVE AGENT**, 6, b m Assertive—Agent Kensington **Wedgewood Estates**
5 **BALTIC PRINCE**, 6, b g Baltic King—Brunswick **Mr A. Mills**
6 **BE MY SEA (IRE)**, 5, b g Sea The Stars (IRE)—Bitooh **Mr G. Attwood**
7 **BEAU MISTRAL (IRE)**, 7, ch m Windsor Knot (IRE)—Carpet Lover (IRE) **Mr A. Mills**
8 **BELLATRIX**, 6, b m Motivator—Haladiya (IRE) **No Fools And Horses Partnership**
9 **BLACK HOLE SUN**, 4, ch f Black Sam Bellamy (IRE)—Black Annie (IRE) **The Ferandlin Peaches**
10 **BLISTERING DANCER (IRE)**, 6, b g Moss Vale (IRE)—Datura **Mrs E. Madden**
11 **BOOM THE GROOM (IRE)**, 5, b g Kodiac—Ecco Mi (IRE) **Mr G. Attwood**
12 **BOSTON BLUE**, 9, b g Halling (USA)—City of Gold (IRE) **Mr B. J. Millen**
13 **BOUCLIER (IRE)**, 6, ch h Zamindar (USA)—Bastet (IRE) **Mr M. Chung**
14 **BY RIGHTS**, 5, b m Byron—Legend House (FR) **Last Day Racing Partnership**
15 **CERULEAN SILK**, 6, b m Striking Ambition—Cerulean Rose **Mr D Lowe & Mr J Loftus**
16 **CITISONSMITH (IRE)**, 4, b g Amadeus Wolf—Ink Pot (USA) **Mr A. Mills**
17 **DISTRICT TWELVE (FR)**, 4, b f Aqlaam—Zanna (FR) **A. W. Carroll**
18 **DUSTY BLUE**, 4, ch f Medicean—Jazz Jam **Mr M. Chung**
19 **EASYDOESIT (IRE)**, 8, b g Iffraaj—Fawaayid (USA) **Six Pack**
20 **ESSAKA (IRE)**, 4, b g Equiano (FR)—Dream Vision (USA) **Mrs J. Carrington**
21 **EVIDENT (IRE)**, 6, b g Excellent Art—Vestavia (IRE) **Mr Morgan, Bright, Clarke & Parris**
22 **EXPANDING UNIVERSE (IRE)**, 9, b g Galileo (IRE)—Uliana (USA) **A. W. Carroll**
23 **FIRST REBELLION**, 7, ch g Cockney Rebel (IRE)—First Dawn **Brian, Mark & Carolynn Day**
24 **HANG FIRE (IRE)**, 6, ch m Shirocco (GER)—Ambrosine **Mrs P. J. Clark**
25 **HEURTEVENT (FR)**, 7, b br g Hold That Tiger (USA)—Sybilia (GER) **L. T. Cheshire**
26 **INNOKO (FR)**, 6, gr g Carlotamix (FR)—Chalana **Mill House Racing Syndicate**
27 **JESTER JET**, 6, br m Overbury (IRE)—Hendre Hotshot **Mrs T. P. James**
28 **KING OLAV (UAE)**, 11, ch g Halling (USA)—Karamzin (USA) **Cover Point Racing**
29 **KINGS CROSS (FR)**, 6, b br g King's Theatre (IRE)—Ladies Choice (FR) **A. W. Carroll**
30 **KINGSTON (GER)**, 7, bl g Dylan Thomas (IRE)—Katy Carr **Three Counties Racing**
31 **LARAGHCON BOY (IRE)**, 7, ch g Stowaway—Hannah Mooney (IRE) **Mr M. S. Cooke**
32 **LEONARD THOMAS**, 7, b g Singspiel (IRE)—Monawara (IRE) **Mrs E. S. Arundel**
33 **LET IT GO**, 4, b f Halling (USA)—Kisses **Wedgewood Estates**
34 **MALANOS (IRE)**, 8, b br g Lord of England (GER)—Majorata (GER) **Mr B. J. Millen**
35 **MAN OF MUSIC**, 5, b g Piccolo—Blue Goddess (IRE) **G. A. Wilson**
36 **MONSIEUR VALENTINE**, 4, ch g Monsieur Bond (IRE)—Minnina (IRE) **Mayden Stud**
37 **MR MAFIA (IRE)**, 7, b g Zerpour (IRE)—Wizzy (IRE) **Three Counties Racing**
38 **NOUVELLE ERE**, 5, b g Archipenko (USA)—Sinister Ruckus (USA) **Lady Jennifer Green & Martyn C Palmer**
39 **OCEAN BENTLEY (IRE)**, 4, b g Amadeus Wolf—Bentley's Bush (IRE) **Mr P Shields and Mr S Barton**
40 **OCEAN LEGEND (IRE)**, 11, b g Night Shift (USA)—Rose of Mooncoin (IRE) **Mr W. McLuskey**
41 **OEIL DE TIGRE (FR)**, 5, b g Footstepsinthesand—Suerte **Miss C. A. Baines**
42 **PAR THREE (IRE)**, 5, b br g Azamour (IRE)—Little Whisper (IRE) **Property Players**
43 **POUR LA VICTOIRE (IRE)**, 6, b g Antonius Pius (USA)—Lady Lucia (IRE) **Curry House Corner**
44 **PRAIRIE TOWN (IRE)**, 5, b g High Chaparral (IRE)—Lake Baino **Cooke & Millen**
45 **PROMINNA**, 6, ch g Proclamation (IRE)—Minnina (IRE) **Mayden Stud**
46 **QUEEN AGGIE (IRE)**, 6, b m Elnadim (USA)—Catfoot Lane **Shropshire Wolves 4**
47 **RIGHTWAY (IRE)**, 5, b g Cockney Rebel (IRE)—Caeribland (IRE) **Mr B. J. Millen**

MR TONY CARROLL - Continued

48 **RISING BREEZE (FR)**, 5, b g Shirocco (GER)—Moon Tree (FR) **Mr D. W. Brookes**
49 **SAINT POIS (FR)**, 5, b g Le Havre (IRE)—Our Dream Queen **Mr P. A. Downing**
50 **SALVADO (IRE)**, 6, b g Invincible Spirit (IRE)—Easter Fairy (USA) **Contubernium Racing Club**
51 **SCRAFTON**, 5, b g Leporello (IRE)—Some Diva **Mrs P. J. Clark**
52 **SHALAMBAR (IRE)**, 10, gr g Dalakhani (IRE)—Shalama (IRE) **Mr B. J. Millen**
53 4, B f Top Line Dancer (IRE)—Sita (IRE)
54 **SMART CATCH (IRE)**, 5, b g Pivotal—Zafaraniya (IRE) **Cover Point Racing**
55 **SMOKY HILL (IRE)**, 7, gr g Galileo (IRE)—Danaskaya (IRE) **Millen & Cooke**
56 **SPIRITOFTOMINTOUL**, 7, gr g Authorized (IRE)—Diamond Line (FR) **The Sunday Players**
57 **SPRAY TAN**, 6, b m Assertive—Even Hotter **Silks Racing Partnership**
58 **STAND TO REASON (IRE)**, 8, ch g Danehill Dancer (IRE)—Ho Hi The Moon (IRE) **Montpellier Racing**
59 **SUNI DANCER**, 5, b m Captain Gerrard (IRE)—Sunisa (IRE) **Mr I. Furlong**
60 **SUPA SEEKER (USA)**, 10, b br g Petionville (USA)—Supamova (USA) **A. W. Carroll**
61 **SYMPHONY OF ANGELS**, 4, b g Sulamani (IRE)—Flying Lion **T. R. Pearson**
62 **TIME MEDICEAN**, 10, gr g Medicean—Ribbons And Bows (IRE) **A. W. Carroll**
63 **TIME SQUARE (FR)**, 9, b g Westerner—Sainte Parfaite (FR) **Mr M. S. Cooke**
64 **TONI'S A STAR**, 4, b f Avonbridge—Canina **A Star Recruitment Limited**
65 **VEDANI (IRE)**, 7, b g Dalakhani (IRE)—Velandia (IRE) **Six Pack**
66 **VERTUEUX (FR)**, 11, gr g Verglas (IRE)—Shahrazad (FR) **A. W. Carroll**
67 **WARM ORDER**, 5, b m Assertive—Even Hotter **Mrs V. C. Gilbert**
68 **WEDGEWOOD ESTATES**, 5, ch m Assertive—Heaven **Wedgewood Estates**
69 **WOWEE**, 5, b g Archipenko (USA)—Katya Kabanova **Wedgewood Estates**
70 **YOUM JAMIL (USA)**, 9, gr g Mizzen Mast (USA)—Millie's Choice (IRE) **Neville Statham & Family**
71 **ZETEAH**, 6, b m Passing Glance—Ajeebah (IRE) **Ms E. A. Judd**

THREE-YEAR-OLDS

72 **BOOM JUNIOR**, b c Compton Place—Khyber Knight (IRE) **Mr G. Attwood**
73 **CLOUD NINE (FR)**, b f Sakhee (USA)—Heaven **Wedgewood Estates**
74 **HOT STUFF**, b g Assertive—Even Hotter **Lady Whent**
75 **MACHU PICHU**, b g Sir Percy—Play Bouzouki **A. W. Carroll**
76 **TAHITI ONE**, b f Bertolini (USA)—Club Tahiti **Seasons Holidays**

TWO-YEAR-OLDS

77 **COMPTON POPPY**, b f 19/2 Compton Place—Miss Poppy (Averti (IRE)) (11428) **Mr P. A. Downing**
78 **HENRY DID IT (IRE)**, b c 1/3 Henrythenavigator (USA)—
⠀⠀⠀⠀⠀⠀⠀⠀⠀⠀⠀⠀⠀⠀⠀⠀⠀⠀⠀⠀The Fairies Did It (USA) (Elusive Quality (USA)) **D. Boocock**
79 **JACKMAN**, b gr c 9/4 Aussie Rules (USA)—Fit To Burst (Pastoral Pursuits) (6000) **Mr P. A. Downing**
80 **LILLY BALLERINA (IRE)**, b f 15/2 Lilbourne Lad (IRE)—Entrechat (Green Desert (USA)) (5714) **Mr P. A. Downing**
81 B f 2/3 Assertive—Mabel's Song (Sakhee (USA)) **Lady Whent**
82 **PAPA DELTA**, b c 1/4 Makfi—Step Softly (Golan (IRE)) (5500) **Mr P. A. Downing**

Other Owners: Mr J. Babb, Mr S. Barton, Mr D. R. Blake, Mr A. D. Bright, N. A. Brimble, Miss A. Bryan, Mr G. Bryan, Mr R. Buckland, Mr C. E. Carroll, Mr M. B. Clarke, Mr J. R. Daniell, Mr M. S. Day, Miss C. J. Day, Mrs D. S. Dewhurst, J. A. Dewhurst, Mr A. J. Gilder, Lady J. Green, Ms K. A. Gwilliam, Ms R. J. Harris, P. V. Harris, Mr S. J. Hill, Mr J. Lawrence, D. J. Lowe, Mr T. R. Mennell, R. J. Millen, Mr M. Nichol, Mr W. G. Nixon, Mr M. C. Palmer, Mr K. J. Parris, Dr A. D. Rogers, N. Scanlan, Mr P. Shields, D. T. Shorthouse, R. Simpson, Mr N. J. Statham, Mrs P. Statham, Mr J. A. Sullivan, Mr C. G. Taylor, Mr L. C. Thomas.

Jockey (NH): Lee Edwards. **Conditional:** Josh Hamer. **Apprentice:** George Downing.

---

94 **MR TONY CARSON, Newmarket**
Postal: **5 Churchill Avenue, Newmarket, Suffolk, CB8 0BZ**
Contacts: PHONE **(01638) 660947** MOBILE **(07837) 601867**
E-MAIL **southgatestables@outlook.com**

1 **CRAZY QUEEN**, 4, ch f Le Fou (IRE)—Queen of Norway (USA) **W. F. H. Carson**
2 **DECISIVE (IRE)**, 4, ch f Iffraaj—Guarantia **Hugh & Mindi Byrne & W H Carson**
3 **DEEP BLUE SEA**, 4, b f Rip Van Winkle (IRE)—Semaphore **Minster Stud**
4 **DESERT MORNING (IRE)**, 4, b f Pivotal—Arabian Mirage **W. F. H. Carson**
5 **GULLAND ROCK**, 5, b g Exceed And Excel (AUS)—Sacre Coeur **W. F. H. Carson**
6 **MARY MY SECRET (IRE)**, 5, b m Court Cave—Secret Can't Say (IRE) **Mrs Elizabeth Lloyd**
7 **MAY HAY**, 6, b m Dubai Destination (USA)—Trounce **W. F. H. Carson**
8 **MAY'S SISTER**, 5, b m Tiger Hill (IRE)—Trounce **W. F. H. Carson**

MR TONY CARSON - Continued

  9 **SHE'S NO BIMBO,** 4, ch f Recharge (IRE)—Senorita Parkes **Mr G. P. Taylor**
10 **SPIRITUAL STAR (IRE),** 7, b g Soviet Star (USA)—Million Spirits (IRE) **Hugh and Mindi Byrne & Macattack**

THREE-YEAR-OLDS

11 Ch c Pivotal—Celeste **Hugh & Mindi Byrne & W. H. Carson**
12 **CURIOUS FOX,** b f Bertolini (USA)—Doric Lady **Carson, Francis, Ghauri & Percy**
13 B f High Chaparral (IRE)—Langoustine (AUS) **Dave Newman & W. H. Carson**
14 **MOSSY'S LODGE,** b f Royal Applause—Tee Cee **MacAttack**
15 B br f Street Cry (IRE)—Real Fancy Runner (USA) **Hugh & Mindi Byrne & W. H. Carson**
16 **TULIP DRESS,** ch f Dutch Art—White Dress (IRE) **Hugh & Mindi Byrne & Minster Stud**

TWO-YEAR-OLDS

17 **FLYING FOXY,** b f 18/4 Foxwedge (AUS)—Fauran (IRE) (Shamardal (USA)) **Mrs Elizabeth Lloyd**
18 B f 28/1 Equiano (FR)—Love Me Tender (Green Desert (USA)) (4000) **Minster Stud**
19 Ch f 28/2 Medicean—Munchkin (Tiger Hill (IRE)) **Minster Stud**
20 B c 18/4 Tamayuz—White Dress (IRE) (Pivotal) (30000) **Minster Stud**

Other Owners: Mr Hugh Byrne, Mrs Mindi Byrne, Mrs E. Carson, Mr A. Carson, Mr M. R. Francis, Mr T. J. McLoughlin, Mr A. Percy.

Assistant Trainer: Graham Carson

Jockey (flat): William Carson. **Amateur:** Mr Graham Carson.

---

95   **MR LEE CARTER, Epsom**
Postal: **The Old Yard, Clear Height Stables, Epsom, Surrey, KT18 5LB**
Contacts: **PHONE (01372) 740878 FAX (01372) 740898 MOBILE (07539) 354819**
E-MAIL leecarterracing@aol.co.uk WEBSITE www.leecarterracing.com

  1 **ANGEL FLORES (IRE),** 5, b m Art Connoisseur (IRE)—Emmas Princess (IRE) **Mr J. J. Smith**
  2 **BENNELONG,** 10, b g Bahamian Bounty—Bundle Up (USA) **Mr J. J. Smith**
  3 **BLUE AMAZON (IRE),** 4, b f Acclamation—Amazon Beauty (IRE) **Tattenham Corner Racing IV**
  4 **FIRST EXPERIENCE,** 5, b m Tamayuz—Lolla's Spirit (IRE) **Clear Racing**
  5 **FOOTSTEPSINTHERAIN (IRE),** 6, b g Footstepsinthesand—Champagne Toni (IRE) **Mr J. Turner**
  6 **GLORIOUS DANCER,** 4, br g Royal Applause—Provence **Mrs I. Marshall**
  7 **INDUS VALLEY (IRE),** 9, ch g Indian Ridge—Gloriously Bright (USA) **Clear Racing**
  8 **KING TORUS (IRE),** 8, b g Oratorio (IRE)—Dipterous (IRE) **Mr J. J. Smith**
  9 **LEDBURY (IRE),** 4, b g Lawman (FR)—Truly Magnificent (USA) **Mr J. J. Smith**
10 **MAURITIUS,** 4, b g Zamindar (USA)—Mascarene (USA) **Mr J. J. Smith**
11 **MEZZOTINT (IRE),** 7, b g Diamond Green (FR)—Aquatint **Ewell Never Know**
12 **MISLEADING,** 4, ch g Footstepsinthesand—Danny's Choice **Mr R. Cooper**
13 **MUNSARIM (IRE),** 9, b g Shamardal (USA)—Etizaaz (USA) **Wackey Racers Harefield**
14 **NOT YOUR CALL (IRE),** 5, b g Balmont (USA)—Cafe Lassere (USA) **Clear Racing**
15 **PARISIAN PYRAMID (IRE),** 10, gr g Verglas (IRE)—Sharadja (IRE) **Mr R. Cooper**
16 **ROBERT THE PAINTER (IRE),** 8, b g Whipper (USA)—Lidanna **Mr J. J. Smith**
17 **SEEK THE FAIR LAND,** 10, b g Noverre (USA)—Duchcov **Mr J. J. Smith**
18 **STATE OF THE UNION (IRE),** 4, ch g Approve (IRE)—First Lady (IRE) **Mr S. C. Crane**
19 **TABLA,** 4, b f Rail Link—Questa Nova **Mr J. J. Smith**
20 **TAKEITFROMALADY (IRE),** 7, b g Intikhab—Pinheiros (IRE) **Only One Bid Partnership**
21 **TIDAL'S BABY,** 7, b g Dutch Art—Tidal **Mrs B. Quinn**

Other Owners: N. Boyce, Mrs K. T. Carter, Mr R. Cooper, Ewell Never Know Ptns, Mr Gus Gordon, Mrs M. M. Greening, B. J. Greening, Mrs I. Marshall, Mr J. O'Hara, Mrs B. Quinn, Tattenham Corner Racing, Mr D. Wood.

---

96   **MR BEN CASE, Banbury**
Postal: **Wardington Gate Farm, Edgcote, Banbury, Oxfordshire, OX17 1AG**
Contacts: **PHONE (01295) 750959 FAX (01295) 758840 MOBILE (07808) 061223**
E-MAIL info@bencaseracing.com WEBSITE www.bencaseracing.com

1 **BALLAGH (IRE),** 7, b g Shantou (USA)—Go Along (IRE) **Mrs C. Kendrick**
2 **BEBINN (IRE),** 9, b m Brian Boru—Windmill Star (IRE) **The Polk Partnership**
3 **BREAKING THE BANK,** 7, ch g Medicean—Russian Dance (USA) **Exors of the Late Mr D. C. R. Allen**
4 **COCHINILLO (IRE),** 7, b g Shantou (USA)—Nut Touluze (IRE) **Goodman, Case & Case**

MR BEN CASE - Continued

5 CROCO BAY (IRE), 9, b g Croco Rouge (IRE)—April Thistle (IRE) **Lady Jane Grosvenor**
6 CROOKSTOWN (IRE), 9, b g Rudimentary (USA)—Millview Lass (IRE) **Mrs C. Wallace**
7 4, B g Robin des Champs (FR)—Dawn Court **Mrs C. Bailey**
8 DEEP TROUBLE (IRE), 9, b g Shantou (USA)—Out of Trouble (IRE) **Lady Jane Grosvenor**
9 EASTERN MAGIC (IRE), 8, b m Observatory (USA)—Inchtina **Mrs C. A. Stevenson**
10 FORTUNATA FASHIONS, 6, b m Kayf Tara—Aniston (IRE) **Swanee River Partnership**
11 GAMAIN (IRE), 7, b g Gamut (IRE)—Glass Curtain (IRE) **Exors of the Late Mr D. C. R. Allen**
12 GINGER FIZZ, 9, ch m Haafhd—Valagalore **Mrs A. D. Bourne**
13 GRACEFUL LEGEND, 5, b m Midnight Legend—Clover Green (IRE) **Exors of the Late Mr D. C. R. Allen**
14 HANDAZAN (IRE), 7, b g Nayef (USA)—Handaza (IRE) **John L Marriott & Albert L Marriott**
15 IMPRESSIVELY FAIR, 7, gr g Fair Mix (IRE)—Rock Xaar (IRE) **Miss Margo Key**
16 LILLY OF THE MOOR, 8, b m Flemensfirth (USA)—Serenique **Exors of the Late S. D. Hemstock**
17 MIDNIGHT JAZZ, 6, b m Midnight Legend—Ring Back (IRE) **Exors of the Late Mr D. C. R. Allen**
18 MOVIE LEGEND, 6, b g Midnight Legend—Cyd Charisse **Dale Hing & Nicole Langstaff**
19 MR GREY (IRE), 8, gr g Great Palm (USA)—Presenting Shares (IRE) **Exors of the Late Mr D. C. R. Allen**
20 MY NOSY ROSY, 8, b m Alflora (IRE)—Quiz Night **Case Racing Partnership**
21 MY RENAISSANCE, 6, b m g Medicean—Lebenstanz **N. S. Hutley**
22 ON THE PROWL (IRE), 4, b g Kalanisi (IRE)—Prowler (USA) **Lady Jane Grosvenor**
23 ORANGEADAY, 9, b g Kayf Tara—One of Those Days **Exors of the Late Mr D. C. R. Allen**
24 OSKI (IRE), 4, b g Oscar (IRE)—Mossville (FR) **Mrs C. Kendrick**
25 PETERPANOPIRATEMAN (IRE), 7, b g Kalanisi (IRE)—Year'fthehorse (IRE) **Mrs C. Kendrick**
26 PETROU (IRE), 6, b g Mountain High (IRE)—Evnelu (IRE) **J. Wright**
27 PHARE ISLE (IRE), 11, b g Turtle Island (IRE)—Pharennia (IRE) **Nicholson Family Moore Moore & Kendrick**
28 PRETTY ROSE (IRE), 6, b m King's Theatre (IRE)—Rosies All The Way **Case Racing Partnership**
29 4, B f Yeats (IRE)—Rhapsody Rose **Exors of the Late Mr D. C. R. Allen**
30 ROLLO'S REFLECTION (IRE), 6, b g Shantou (USA)—Lola's Reflection **T. W. Moore**
31 ROYAL CAPTAIN (IRE), 7, br g Presenting—Dunahall Queen (IRE) **J. Wright**
32 RUSHVALE (IRE), 7, b g Moss Vale (IRE)—Evidence **Mrs C. Kendrick**
33 SHARP GETAWAY (IRE), 4, b g Getaway (GER)—Thanks Noel (IRE) **Mrs C. Kendrick**
34 SILENT ENCORE (IRE), 4, ch g Curtain Time (IRE)—What Can I Say (IRE) **North & South Racing Partnership**
35 SNOWY DAWN, 6, gr g Notnowcato—Tereyna **Mrs C. A. Stevenson**
36 4, B g King's Theatre (IRE)—Temptation (FR) **Lady Jane Grosvenor**
37 THEMANFROM MINELLA (IRE), 7, b g Shantou (USA)—Bobomy (IRE) **Mrs C. Kendrick**
38 VESUVHILL (FR), 7, ch g Sabrehill (USA)—L'orchidee (FR) **Case Racing Partnership**
39 WESTON FLAME, 6, b m Westerner—Rocheflamme (FR) **E. R. Hanbury**
40 WIN IN A WELL (IRE), 7, b g Gamut (IRE)—Lady Bellingham (IRE) **Case Racing Partnership**

THREE-YEAR-OLDS

41 B f Kalanisi (IRE)—Dee Two O Two (IRE) **Ben Case**

Other Owners: Mr D. Baines, Mr N. Biggs, Mr E. Bland, Mrs P. Bonner, Mr T. Boylan, Mr R. Bray, Mrs S. Case, Mrs Robert Case, Mr B. I. Case, Mrs A. Charlton, Mr C K Crossley Cooke, Mr J. Deeley, Mr O. Denny, Mr W. Duffin, Mr J. English, Mr D. Foulk, Mrs A. Gladden, Mr E. Gladden, Mr John Goodman, Mr J. Grindlay, Mr R. Hagen, Mr R. Harper, Mrs S. Harrison, Mr Dale Hing, Mrs M. Howlett, Mr & Mrs R. Howlett, Mrs J. Hulse, Dr C. Ilsley, Mrs B. Joice, Mrs Carolyn Kendrick, Miss Nicole Langstaff, Mrs H. Loggin, Mrs L. Lovell, Miss A. Lush, Mr P. Lush, Mr Albert L. Marriott, Mr John L. Marriott, Mr M. Marshall, Mr M. Matthews, Mr T. W. Moore, Mrs Wendy Moore, Mr D. Muffitt, Mrs P. Murray, Mr Grahame Nicholson, Mr C. Nixey, Mr J. Nowell-Smith, Mr R. Palmer, Mr G. D. Payne, Mrs K. Perrem, Mr James Polk, Mr John Polk, Mr J. Shaw, Mr & Mrs D. Smith, Mrs J. Snell, Mr & Mrs J. Sullivan, Mrs F. Unich-Wagg, Mrs C. Wallace, Mr David Watson, Mr N. Wellington.

Jockey (NH): Daryl Jacob, Kielan Woods. **Amateur:** Mr M. J. P. Kendrick.

---

97 MR PATRICK CHAMINGS, Basingstoke
Postal: **Inhurst Farm Stables, Baughurst, Tadley, Hampshire, RG26 5JS**
Contacts: PHONE **(01189) 814494 FAX (01189) 820454 MOBILE (07831) 360970**
E-MAIL chamingsracing@talk21.com

1 BENTWORTH BOY, 5, b g Archipenko (USA)—Maria di Scozia **Robinson,Wiggin,Hayward-Cole,Roberts**
2 BIG CHILL (IRE), 4, b g Acclamation—Royal Consort (IRE) **Trolley Action**
3 BLAKESON (IRE), 4, b g Presenting—Sleepless Eye **Mr O. S. Harris**
4 CHARLES MOLSON, 5, b g Monsieur Bond (IRE)—Arculinge **Trolley Action**
5 CHELWOOD GATE (IRE), 6, b gr g Aussie Rules (USA)—Jusoor (USA) **K. W. Tyrrell**
6 CHURCH LEAP (IRE), 5, gr g High Chaparral (IRE)—Alambic **Robinson,Wiggin,Hayward-Cole,Roberts**
7 DIRECTORSHIP, 10, br g Diktat—Away To Me **Mrs R. Lyon**

MR PATRICK CHAMINGS - Continued

8 **DOUBLE CZECH (IRE)**, 5, b g Bushranger (IRE)—Night of Joy (IRE) **P. R. Chamings**
9 **FOXFORD**, 5, b m Clodovil (IRE)—Pulau Pinang (IRE) **The Foxford House Partnership**
10 **FOXHAVEN**, 14, ch g Unfuwain (USA)—Dancing Mirage (IRE) **The Foxford House Partnership**
11 **JUST WHEN**, 7, b g Dalakhani (IRE)—Cape Grace (IRE) **Inhurst Players**
12 **PERFECT ALCHEMY (IRE)**, 5, b m Clodovil (IRE)—
Desert Alchemy (IRE) **The Perfect Partnership & D H Caslon**
13 **PERFECT BOUNTY**, 4, ch f Bahamian Bounty—Perfect Cover (IRE) **Mildmay Racing & D. H. Caslon**
14 **PERFECT RHYTHM**, 5, b m Halling (USA)—Bassinet (USA) **Dr Bridget Drew & Partners**
15 **PURPLE GENIE (GR)**, 4, ch f Tiantai (USA)—Purple Way (GR) **Mrs A. J. Chandris**
16 **REGAL MISS**, 4, b f Royal Applause—Pretty Miss **Mrs J. E. L. Wright**
17 **SCOTTISH GLEN**, 10, ch g Kyllachy—Dance For Fun **The Foxford House Partnership**
18 **TAKE A NOTE**, 7, b g Singspiel (IRE)—Ela Paparouna **The Foxford House Partnership**
19 **THE REEL WAY (GR)**, 5, br m Reel Buddy (USA)—Nephetriti Way (IRE) **The Foxford House Partnership**
20 **UNCLE RUFUS (IRE)**, 5, ch g Iffraaj—Astuti (IRE) **P. R. Chamings**

THREE-YEAR-OLDS

21 **WILD DANCER**, b f Mawatheeq (USA)—Pretty Miss **The Foxford House Partnership**

Other Owners: D. H. Caslon, J. R. Drew, Dr S. B. Drew, Mrs N. Hayward-Cole, Mr S. Hill, F. T. Lee, Mrs M. Roberts, Mr N. R. Robinson, Mr M. R. Stewart, Mr R. C. Thomas, Mr D. P. Wiggin, Mr W. Womersley.

Assistant Trainer: Phillippa Chamings

---

98   **MR MICK CHANNON**, West Ilsley
Postal: **West Ilsley Stables, West Ilsley, Newbury, Berkshire, RG20 7AE**
Contacts: **PHONE (01635) 281166 FAX (01635) 281177**
E-MAIL mick@mick-channon.co.uk/susan@mick-channon.co.uk WEBSITE www.mickchannon.tv

1 **AL MANAAL**, 6, b m Echo of Light—Mall Queen (USA) **M. R. Channon**
2 **AMAHORO**, 5, b m Sixties Icon—Evanesce **Dave & Gill Hedley**
3 **ARNOLD LANE (IRE)**, 7, b h Footstepsinthesand—Capriole **Mr J. M. Mitchell**
4 **BOSSY GUEST (IRE)**, 4, b c Medicean—Ros The Boss (IRE) **John Guest Racing Ltd**
5 **BRIDIE FFRENCH**, 5, b m Bahamian Bounty—Wansdyke Lass **M. R. Channon**
6 **DIVINE (IRE)**, 5, b m Dark Angel (IRE)—Carallia (IRE) **Mr M. Al-Qatami & Mr K. M. Al-Mudhaf**
7 **EL CHE**, 4, gr f Winker Watson—Rose Cheval (USA) **P. Taplin**
8 **ELIDOR**, 6, br g Cape Cross (IRE)—Honorine (IRE) **Jon & Julia Aisbitt**
9 **EXENTRICITY**, 4, b f Paco Boy (IRE)—Wansdyke Lass **Mr W. G. Parish**
10 **FINGAL'S CAVE (IRE)**, 4, ch g Fast Company (IRE)—Indiannie Moon **The Motley Cru I**
11 **FITZWILLIAM**, 4, ch g Sixties Icon—Canadian Capers **Bargate**
12 **FITZWILLY**, 5, b g Sixties Icon—Canadian Capers **P. Taplin**
13 **FOLLOW THE FAITH**, 4, b f Piccolo—Keeping The Faith (IRE) **M. R. Channon**
14 **FOSTER'S ROAD**, 7, b g Imperial Dancer—Search Party **Dave & Gill Hedley**
15 **GRATZIE**, 5, b m Three Valleys—La Gazzetta (IRE) **C Corbett, David Hudd, Chris Wright**
16 **HIGHLIFE DANCER**, 8, br g Imperial Dancer—Wrong Bride **The Highlife Racing Club**
17 **IFICANIWILL (IRE)**, 4, b f Mastercraftsman (IRE)—Hollow Hill (IRE) **The Motley Cru I**
18 **ISABELLA BIRD**, 5, b m Invincible Spirit (IRE)—Meetyouthere (IRE) **Jon & Julia Aisbitt**
19 **JAYWALKER (IRE)**, 5, b g Footstepsinthesand—Nipping (IRE) **Insignia Racing (Crest)**
20 **KING CRIMSON**, 4, ch g Captain Gerrard—Elegant Lady **Mr W. G. Parish**
21 **KNIGHT OF THE AIR**, 4, b g Bushranger (IRE)—Picolette **Insignia Racing (Crescent)**
22 **KNOCK HOUSE (IRE)**, 7, ch g Old Vic—Lady's Gesture (IRE) **Mr T. P. Radford**
23 **LINCOLN (IRE)**, 5, b g Clodovil (IRE)—Gilt Linked **Mr W. G. Parish**
24 **LOCH BA (IRE)**, 10, b g Craigsteel—Lenmore Lisa (IRE) **Peter Taplin, Susan Bunney & Partners**
25 **LUNARIAN**, 5, ch m Bahamian Bounty—One Giant Leap (IRE) **Mrs A. C. Black**
26 **MISTER WHITAKER (IRE)**, 4, b g Court Cave (IRE)—Benbradagh Vard (IRE)
27 **MISTIC MAGIC (IRE)**, 9, b m Orpen (USA)—Mistic Sun
28 **MOBSTA (IRE)**, 4, b c Bushranger (IRE)—Sweet Nicole
29 **MOONRAKER**, 4, ch c Starspangledbanner (AUS)—Licence To Thrill **Christopher Wright & Miss Emily Asprey**
30 **NEEDLESS SHOUTING (IRE)**, 5, b g Footstepsinthesand—
Ring The Relatives **Lord Ilsley Racing (Russell Syndicate)**
31 **PERSUN**, 4, ch f Sir Percy—Sunley Shines **M. R. Channon**
32 **POTTERNELLO (IRE)**, 4, b f Captain Marvelous (IRE)—Purepleasureseeker (IRE) **M. R. Channon**
33 **ROUGH COURTE (IRE)**, 5, b m Clodovil (IRE)—Straight Sets (IRE) **Mr W. G. Parish**
34 **SARMADEE (IRE)**, 4, b g Fast Company (IRE)—Veronica Cooper (IRE) **M. R. Channon**
35 **SGT RECKLESS**, 9, b g Imperial Dancer—Lakaam **Mr T. P. Radford**

MR MICK CHANNON - Continued

36 **SHORE STEP (IRE)**, 6, br g Footstepsinthesand—Chatham Islands (USA) **Jon & Julia Aisbitt**
37 **SOMERSBY (IRE)**, 12, b g Second Empire (IRE)—Back To Roost (IRE) **Mr T. P. Radford**
38 **THE BLUE BOMBER**, 4, b g Stimulation (IRE)—Mar Blue (FR) **M. R. Channon**
39 **THE LAST CAVALIER (IRE)**, 6, br g Presenting—All Set (IRE) **Mr T. P. Radford**
40 **TIDAL MOON**, 4, b f Sea The Stars (IRE)—Miss Riviera Golf **Jon & Julia Aisbitt**
41 **VIVA STEVE**, 8, b g Flemensfirth (USA)—Eluna **Mr T. P. Radford**
42 **VOLUNTEER POINT (IRE)**, 4, b f Footstepsinthesand—Piffling **Box 41**
43 **WALRUS GUMBOOT**, 4, b g Sixties Icon—Nedwa **M. R. Channon**
44 **WARDEN HILL (IRE)**, 8, br g Presenting—Moon Storm (IRE) **Mr T. P. Radford**

THREE-YEAR-OLDS

45 **ANGELIC GUEST (IRE)**, gr f Dark Angel (IRE)—Kelsey Rose **John Guest Racing Ltd**
46 **ASHJAN**, b c Medicean—Violet (IRE) **J. Alharbi**
47 **BLACKLISTER**, br g Lawman (FR)—Lebenstanz **Box 41 Racing**
48 **BRESLIN**, ch g Atlantic Sport (USA)—Aries (GER)
49 **CZABO**, b f Sixties Icon—Fiumicino **Norman Court Stud**
50 **EPSOM ICON**, b f Sixties Icon—Hairspray **Epsom Stars Racing I**
51 **ETTIE HART (IRE)**, b f Bushranger (IRE)—Miss Megs (IRE) **Lord Ilsley Racing (Marsden Syndicate)**
52 **GANDVIK (IRE)**, b g Baltic King—Regal Lustre **Lord Ilsley Racing (Charles Syndicate)**
53 **HARLEQUEEN**, b f Canford Cliffs (IRE)—Aurelia **Mrs S. Brandt**
54 **HARLEQUIN TWIST**, b f Acclamation—Triton Dance (IRE) **Harlequin Direct Ltd**
55 **HARRISON**, b c Sixties Icon—Excellent Day (IRE) **M. R. Channon**
56 **JAADU (FR)**, b c Holy Roman Emperor (IRE)—Reine Violette (FR) **Mr P. C. N. Chan**
57 **JERSEY BREEZE (IRE)**, gr f Dark Angel (IRE)—Sixfields Flyer (IRE) **Mrs S. G. Bunney**
58 **KASSIA (IRE)**, b f Acclamation—Speedy Sonata (USA) **Jon & Julia Aisbitt**
59 **KERRY ICON**, b f Sixties Icon—La Gifted **Norman Court Stud**
60 **LILLYPUT (IRE)**, b f Lilbourne Lad (IRE)—Bellacoola (GER) **Box 41 Racing**
61 **MALAIKA**, b f Sixties Icon—Evanesce **Dave & Gill Hedley**
62 **MARMONT**, ch g Winker Watson—Five Bells **Norman Court Racing I**
63 **MASTERSON (IRE)**, gr g Lawman (FR)—Indian Dumaani **Box 41 Racing**
64 **MOTDAW**, b f Motivator—Dawnus (IRE) **Mr & Mrs D. D. Clee**
65 **MUTHRAAB ALDAAR (IRE)**, b c Baltic King—Vertigo On Course (IRE) **J. Alharbi**
66 **OCTOBER STORM**, br c Shirocco (GER)—Cyber Star **Jon & Julia Aisbitt**
67 **OPAL TIARA (IRE)**, b f Thousand Words—Zarafa **Qatar Racing & The Sweet Partnership**
68 **PACCHES (IRE)**, b f Clodovil (IRE)—Ringarooma **The Wentworth Amigos**
69 **PC DIXON**, ch g Sixties Icon—Lakaam **M. R. Channon**
70 **ROCKLIFFE**, b g Notnowcato—Hope Island (IRE) **Mrs M. Forsyth**
71 **SCRUTINEER (IRE)**, b c Intense Focus (USA)—Royal Esteem **Malih L. Al Basti**
72 **SHAHAAMA**, br f Showcasing—Oystermouth **Mr M. Al-Qatami & Mr K. M. Al-Mudhaf**
73 **SHINE LIKEADIAMOND**, ch f Atlantic Sport (USA)—Solmorin **M. R. Channon**
74 **SILCA STAR**, ch c Medicean—Silca Chiave **Aldridge Racing Partnership**
75 **SIRI**, br f Atlantic Sport (USA)—Search Party **Dave & Gill Hedley**
76 **SIXTIES IDOL**, b f Sixties Icon—Fading Away **P. Taplin**
77 **SIXTIES SUE**, gr f Sixties Icon—Rose Cheval (USA) **Norman Court Stud**
78 **SPECIAL QUEEN (IRE)**, gr f Clodovil (IRE)—Special Lady (FR) **J. Alharbi**
79 **STAR BLAZE**, b c Shamardal (USA)—Gallic Star (IRE) **Jon & Julia Aisbitt**
80 **SUMMER ICON**, b f Sixties Icon—Summer Cry (USA) **Allen, Porter, Voute Partnership 1**
81 **THE BIG GUY**, b g Atlantic Sport (USA)—Linda Green **Norman Court Racing I**
82 **TIGERWOLF (IRE)**, br c Dream Ahead (USA)—Singing Field (IRE) **George Materna & Roger Badley**
83 **VISAGE BLANC**, b f Champs Elysees—Russian Empress (IRE) **Norman Court Stud**
84 **WILLSY**, b g Sakhee's Secret—Blakeshall Rose **E & R Bastian**

TWO-YEAR-OLDS

85 B f 1/5 Sayif (IRE)—Alice's Girl (Galileo (IRE))
86 B f 13/4 Sixties Icon—Altona (IRE) (Redback)
87 B f 30/4 Fast Company (IRE)—Amazing Win (IRE) (Marju (IRE)) (19047) **M. R. Channon**
88 B c 16/4 Foxwedge (AUS)—And I (Inchinor) (32000)
89 Ch c 20/3 Harbour Watch (IRE)—April (IRE) (Rock of Gibraltar (IRE)) (30000)
90 B f 8/5 Rip Van Winkle (IRE)—Ayla (IRE) (Daylami (IRE)) **Barry Walters Catering**
91 B c 1/5 Sayif (IRE)—Aziz Presenting (Charnwood Forest (IRE))
92 Ch c 17/4 Sixties Icon—Blakeshall Rose (Tobougg (IRE))
93 B f 23/2 Arcano (IRE)—Capriole (Noverre (USA)) (22148)
94 **CARAVELA (IRE)**, b f 23/3 Henrythenavigator (USA)—Stella Point (IRE) (Pivotal) **Jon & Julia Aisbitt**
95 **CHICAGO STAR**, b f 12/5 Exceed And Excel (AUS)—Librettista (AUS) (Elusive Quality (USA)) **Jon & Julia Aisbitt**
96 B f 1/5 Sayif (IRE)—Daisy Crazy (Auction House (USA))

MR MICK CHANNON - Continued

97 **DEWAN (IRE)**, b c 20/4 Elzaam (AUS)—
So Blissful (IRE) (Cape Cross (IRE)) (30476) **Nick & Olga Dhandsa & John & Zoe Webster**
98 **ESTRELLADA**, b f 5/3 Oasis Dream—Gallic Star (IRE) (Galileo (IRE)) **Jon & Julia Aisbitt**
99 Ch f 8/3 Sixties Icon—Excellent Day (IRE) (Invincible Spirit (IRE)) **M. R. Channon**
100 B f 3/3 Winker Watson—Fading Away (Fraam) **P. Taplin**
101 **FATHER MCKENZIE**, b c 28/1 Sixties Icon—Queen of Narnia (Hunting Lion (IRE)) **M. R. Channon**
102 Ch f 27/4 Sixties Icon—Five Bells (IRE) (Rock of Gibraltar (IRE)) **Norman Court Stud I**
103 B c 10/4 Arabian Gleam—Floral Beauty (Shamardal (USA)) (19000) **M. R. Channon**
104 **HALDAW**, b f 23/4 Halling (USA)—Dawnus (IRE) (Night Shift (USA)) (25000) **Mr & Mrs D. D. Clee**
105 **HARLEQUIN ROSE (IRE)**, ch f 21/2 Dutch Art—
Miss Chaussini (IRE) (Rossini (USA)) (50000) **Harlequin Direct Ltd**
106 **HARMONISE**, b f 2/5 Sakhee's Secret—Composing (IRE) (Noverre (USA)) **Wood Street Syndicate II**
107 **INGLEBY MACKENZIE**, b c 4/5 Sixties Icon—Natalie Jay (Ballacashtal (CAN)) **M. R. Channon**
108 B f 3/4 Harbour Watch (IRE)—Jules (IRE) (Danehill (USA)) (15238) **Mr M. Stewkesbury**
109 Ch f 14/4 Arcano (IRE)—Kirunavaara (IRE) (Galileo (USA)) (14000)
110 **KOEMAN**, b c 22/2 Dutch Art—Angelic Note (IRE) (Excellent Art) (60000) **Taplin & Bunney Partnership**
111 Ch c 7/3 Paco Boy (IRE)—La Gifted (Fraam) (10000) **Norman Court Stud**
112 Ch f 16/2 Kyllachy—Lady Scarlett (Woodman (USA))
113 Gr c 20/4 Dark Angel (IRE)—Leceile (USA) (Forest Camp (USA)) (180000) **John Guest Racing Ltd**
114 B c 23/4 Sayif (IRE)—Lily Le Braz (Montjeu (IRE))
115 Gr f 16/4 Mastercraftsman (IRE)—Luxie (IRE) (Acclamation) (33222)
116 B c 17/4 Sayif (IRE)—Mar Blue (FR) (Marju (IRE))
117 B f 5/4 Sixties Icon—Mistic Magic (IRE) (Orpen (USA)) (761) **M. R. Channon**
118 B c 14/2 Bushranger (IRE)—Money Note (Librettist (USA)) (4000) **M. R. Channon**
119 **MYLADYJANE (IRE)**, b f 18/4 Mastercraftsman (IRE)—
Candlehill Girl (IRE) (Shamardal (USA)) (73827) **Nick & Olga Dhandsa & John & Zoe Webster**
120 B f 19/4 Clodovil (IRE)—Nadinska (Doyen (IRE)) **Norman Court Stud**
121 B f 31/3 Approve (IRE)—Passage To India (IRE) (Indian Ridge) (20000) **Insignia Racing Limited**
122 **PERFECT IN PINK**, ch f 27/4 Raven's Pass (USA)—
Fashion Rocks (IRE) (Rock of Gibraltar (IRE)) (100000) **G. D. P. Materna**
123 B c 19/2 Sayif (IRE)—Pesse (IRE) (Eagle Eyed (USA)) (5500) **M. R. Channon**
124 B f 8/2 Born To Sea (IRE)—Puerto Oro (IRE) (Entrepreneur) (19047)
125 Ch f 7/4 Sixties Icon—Quinzey's Best (IRE) (King's Best (USA)) **Norman Court Stud**
126 **RAFFLE KING (IRE)**, b c 19/3 Kodiac—
Tap The Dot (IRE) (Sharp Humor (USA)) (48000) **Taplin & Bunney Partnership**
127 Br gr c 19/2 Bushranger (IRE)—Sandtail (IRE) (Verglas (IRE)) (8120) **Insignia Racing Limited**
128 B f 10/2 Indian Haven—Selinda (Piccolo) **Dave & Gill Hedley**
129 B c 18/4 Tagula (IRE)—Sharadja (IRE) (Doyoun) (22147)
130 B f 17/4 New Approach (IRE)—Silver Touch (IRE) (Dansili)
131 Ch c 31/3 Winker Watson—Solmorin (Fraam) **M. R. Channon**
132 Ch c 27/3 Kyllachy—Sonny Sunshine (Royal Applause) (60000) **Malih L. Al Basti**
133 B c 30/4 Stimulation (IRE)—Sophies Heart (Hurricane Run (IRE))
134 B c 17/4 New Approach (IRE)—Sweet Lilly (Tobougg (IRE)) (60000)
135 B f 13/4 Sixties Icon—The Screamer (IRE) (Insan (USA)) **Norman Court Stud**
136 B f 8/3 Acclamation—Valeur (Rock of Gibraltar (IRE)) **Prince A. A. Faisal**
137 B c 23/4 Sixties Icon—Vilnius (Imperial Dancer)
138 B f 17/3 Pour Moi (IRE)—Visanilla (FR) (Danehill (USA)) **Barry Walters Catering**
139 **WHITELEY (IRE)**, b f 19/2 Dark Angel (IRE)—
Carallia (IRE) (Common Grounds) (45000) **Peter Taplin & Susan Bunney**

Other Owners: J. R. Aisbitt, Mrs J. M. Aisbitt, K. M. Al-Mudhaf, Mohammed Jasem Al-Qatami, Mrs C. T. Aldridge, E. Aldridge, Mr T. J. Allen, Emily Charlotte Asprey, Mr R. Badley, Mr R. W. Bastian, Mr E. I. R. Bastian, Mrs J. P. Clee, D. D. Clee, The Hon Mrs C. Corbett, Dr N. Dhandsa, Mr T. V. Drayton, Ms G. H. Hedley, Mr D. L. Hudd, Mrs A. M. Jones, Mike Channon Bloodstock Ltd, Mrs J. Pearce, Mr S. Pearce, Qatar Racing Limited, J. P. Repard, Mr M. R. Stokes, Mrs T. G. Trant, Mr Simon Trant, Mr P. Trant, Mrs G. Voute, Mr J. Webster, J. A. Williams, C. N. Wright.

---

99 | **MR MICHAEL CHAPMAN, Market Rasen**
Postal: **Woodlands Racing Stables, Woodlands Lane, Willingham Road, Market Rasen, Lincolnshire, LN8 3RE**
Contacts: PHONE/FAX (01673) 843663 MOBILE (07971) 940087
E-MAIL woodlands.stables@btconnect.com WEBSITE www.woodlandsracingstables.co.uk

1 4, B g Bushranger (IRE)—Cayambe (IRE) **Mrs M. M. Chapman**
2 **DUC DE SEVILLE (IRE)**, 4, b g Duke of Marmalade (IRE)—Splendid (IRE) **Mr S. A. Richards**

MR MICHAEL CHAPMAN - Continued

3 **FEELING PECKISH (USA)**, 12, ch g Point Given (USA)—Sunday Bazaar (USA) **J. E. Reed**
4 **KHESKIANTO (IRE)**, 10, b m Kheleyf (USA)—Gently (IRE) **F. A. Dickinson**
5 **L'ES FREMANTLE (FR)**, 5, b g Orpen (USA)—Grand Design **Mrs M. M. Chapman**
6 **MONZINO (USA)**, 8, b br g More Than Ready (USA)—Tasso's Magic Roo (USA) **Mrs M. M. Chapman**
7 **ORACLE BOY**, 5, b g Mount Nelson—Snow Princess (IRE) **Mrs A. M. Binns**
8 **PEAK SEASONS (IRE)**, 13, ch g Raise A Grand (IRE)—Teresian Girl (IRE) **J. E. Reed**
9 **SANTO SUBITO (IRE)**, 15, b g Presenting—Shinora (IRE) **Mrs M. M. Chapman**
10 **SIMPLIFIED**, 13, b m Lend A Hand—Houston Heiress (USA) **Mrs M. M. Chapman**
11 **SOPHIE'S BEAU (USA)**, 9, b g Stormy Atlantic (USA)—Lady Buttercup (USA) **Mrs M. M. Chapman**
12 **STRIKING NIGELLA**, 6, b m Striking Ambition—Fiona Fox **F. A. Dickinson**
13 **TAYARAT (IRE)**, 11, b g Noverre (USA)—Sincere (IRE) **Mrs M. M. Chapman**
14 **THE SOCIETY MAN (IRE)**, 9, ch g Moscow Society (USA)—Redruth (IRE) **A. Mann**
15 **VOGARTH**, 12, ch g Arkadian Hero (USA)—Skara Brae **Mrs M. M. Chapman**
16 **VOLCANIC JACK (IRE)**, 8, b g Kodiac—Rosaria Panatta (IRE) **A. Mann**

Assistant Trainer: Mr S. Petch

Conditional: Joe Cornwall, Alice Mills.

---

100   MS JANE CHAPPLE-HYAM, Newmarket
Postal: Rose Cottage, The Street, Dalham, Newmarket, Suffolk, CB8 8TF
Contacts: PHONE (01638) 500451 FAX (01638) 661335 MOBILE (07899) 000555
E-MAIL janechapplehyam@hotmail.co.uk / janechapplehyamracing@outlook.com

1 **AVENUE DES CHAMPS**, 4, b g Champs Elysees—Penang Cry **The Tuesday Club**
2 **DOLPHIN VILLAGE (IRE)**, 6, b g Cape Cross (IRE)—Reform Act (USA) **Mr M. W. Sellars**
3 **ENERGIA DAVOS (BRZ)**, 8, gr g Torrential (USA)—
Star Brisingamen (USA) **Bryan Hirst Ltd & Jane Chapple-Hyam**
4 **GOOLAGONG GIRL (IRE)**, 4, b f Avonbridge—Lady Berta **Essex Racing Club**
5 **INJUN SANDS**, 5, b g Halling (USA)—Serriera (FR) **Mrs H. H. Morriss**
6 **JUNGLE BAY**, 9, b g Oasis Dream—Dominica **Brewster/Harding & Essex Racing Club**
7 **THE TWISLER**, 4, b g Motivator—Panna **Kwikdelivery Limited**
8 **TOMMY'S SECRET**, 6, gr g Sakhee's Secret—La Gessa **The Tuesday Club & Jane Chapple-Hyam**
9 **VALBCHEK (IRE)**, 7, b g Acclamation—Spectacular Show (IRE) **Bryan Hirst Limited**

THREE-YEAR-OLDS

10 **BULLINGTON BEAR (FR)**, b c Youmzain (IRE)—Maternelle (FR) **Bryan Hirst Ltd & Jane Chapple-Hyam**
11 **CAT ROYALE (IRE)**, b c Lilbourne Lad (IRE)—Call This Cat (IRE) **Bryan Hirst Ltd & S&G Refurbishments Ltd**
12 **CLEVERCONVERSATION (IRE)**, ro f Thewayyouare (USA)—Monet's Lady (IRE) **The Hon A. S. Peacock**
13 **LONE BLACK RANGER**, b c Bushranger (IRE)—Bravada (GER) **Agata Startek**
14 **NORFOLK TAVERNER**, b g Firebreak—Miss Elegance **Essex Racing Club**
15 **ROYAL MIGHTY**, b f Mighty—Royal Hush **Mr John McGuire & Jane Chapple-Hyam**
16 **ZEBADIAH (IRE)**, b c Zebedee—Kiva **Jane Chapple-Hyam & Westward Bloodstock Limited**

TWO-YEAR-OLDS

17 **BOMBAY ROLL**, br f 2/5 Bated Breath—
Labisa (IRE) (High Chaparral (IRE)) (10000) **Bradley, KwikDelivery, S&G Refurbishment**
18 **DONT TELL HIM PIKE**, b c 5/2 Vale of York (IRE)—Reem Star (Green Tune (USA)) (4000) **Jane Chapple-Hyam**
19 **HOW'S LUCY**, b f 7/4 Approve (IRE)—Murielle (Diktat) **Close Syndicate Lucy**
20 B c 15/2 Sir Percy—Shesells Seashells (Tiger Hill (IRE)) (11000) **Smarden Thoroughbreds**
21 **SOMES SOUND (IRE)**, b c 6/3 Big Bad Bob (IRE)—Zapping (IRE) (Lycius (USA)) (31007) **Mrs H. H. Morriss**
22 **TWIGGY**, b f 5/5 Sixties Icon—Queen's Pudding (IRE) (Royal Applause) **Anglia Bloodstock**
23 **UBER COOL (IRE)**, b c 10/5 Born To Sea (IRE)—
My Uptown Girl (Dubai Destination (USA)) (36913) **Westward Bloodstock Limited**

Other Owners: Mr Paul Body, Mr P. Bottomley, Mr Steve Bradley, Mr Simon Brewster, Brian Hirst Limited, Mrs Jane Chapple-Hyam, Mr Chris Fahy, Mrs Hilary Fitzsimmons, Mrs C. Harding, Mr Jordan Harris, Mr Mark Hodsoll, Mr John McGuire, Mr James O'Dwyer, Mrs Joan Root, Mr Barry Root, S&G Refurbishments & Maintenance Ltd.

Assistant Trainer: Abigail Harrison

Apprentice: Danny Brock.

101   MR PETER CHAPPLE-HYAM, Newmarket
Postal: **St Gatien Stables, All Saints Road, Newmarket, Suffolk, CB8 8HJ**
Contacts: **PHONE (01638) 560827 FAX (01638) 561908 MOBILE (07770) 472774**
E-MAIL **pchapplehyam@yahoo.com** WEBSITE **www.peterchapplehyam.com**

1 **AROD (IRE)**, 5, b h Teofilo (IRE)—My Personal Space (USA) **Qatar Racing Limited**
2 **BUCKSTAY (IRE)**, 6, b g Lawman (FR)—Stella Del Mattino (USA) **Mrs Fitri Hay**
3 **DIRECT TIMES (IRE)**, 5, b g Acclamation—Elegant Times (IRE) **Mr A. Belshaw**
4 **FARQUHAR (IRE)**, 5, ch g Archipenko (USA)—Pointed Arch (IRE) **Mr T Elliott & Mr P Cunningham**
5 **MURGAN**, 4, b c Galileo (IRE)—Approach **Qatar Racing Limited**
6 **WASHINGTON WINKLE**, 4, b g Rip Van Winkle (IRE)—Bluebelle Dancer (IRE) **Mr D. Hanafin**

THREE-YEAR-OLDS

7 **AHRAAM (IRE)**, b g Roderic O'Connor (IRE)—Simla Sunset (IRE) **Mr A. R. Elliott**
8 **BEAST MODE (IRE)**, b c Cape Cross (IRE)—Faithful One (IRE) **Qatar Racing Limited**
9 **DANCING HEARTS**, b f Makfi—Danceabout **Qatar Racing Limited**
10 **GEMMULAL**, b f Acclamation—Elvira Delight (IRE) **Saleh Al Homaizi & Imad Al Sagar**
11 **GUNNERY (FR)**, ch c Le Havre (IRE)—Loup The Loup (FR) **Mrs Fitri Hay**
12 **HESTINA (FR)**, b f Soldier of Fortune (IRE)—Diagora (FR) **Mr P. Hancock**
13 **MARCEL (IRE)**, b c Lawman (FR)—Mauresmo (IRE) **Mr P. Hancock**
14 **MARSHAL DAN TROOP (IRE)**, b c Lawman (FR)—Corrozal (GER) **High Rollers**
15 **PERICLES (IRE)**, ch g Danehill Dancer (IRE)—Althea Rose (IRE) **Mrs Fitri Hay**
16 **PLEASURE DOME**, b f Makfi—Nouvelle Lune **J. G. Davis & Star Pointe Ltd**
17 **SABRE SQUADRON (IRE)**, b g Lope de Vega (IRE)—Caravan of Dreams (IRE) **Mrs Fitri Hay**
18 **SAUTTER**, b c Kyllachy—Regency Rose **Saleh Al Homaizi & Imad Al Sagar**
19 **TIMES LEGACY**, b c Cape Cross (IRE)—Simply Times (USA) **Mr A. Belshaw**

TWO-YEAR-OLDS

20 B c 26/2 Lawman (FR)—Amorama (FR) (Sri Pekan (USA)) (40605) **Mrs Fitri Hay**
21 **CLASSICAL TIMES**, b f 10/2 Lawman (FR)—Sunday Times (Holy Roman Emperor (IRE)) **Mr A. Belshaw**
22 B f 30/1 Excelebration (IRE)—Connote (Oasis Dream) (38000) **Mrs Fitri Hay**
23 B f 25/2 Dutch Art—Crazy Too (IRE) (Invincible Spirit (IRE)) **Saleh Al Homaizi & Imad Al Sagar**
24 B f 21/4 Holy Roman Emperor (IRE)—Grain Only (Machiavellian (USA)) (22000)
25 **HOTCAKE**, ch f 6/5 Archipenko (USA)—Heat of The Night (Lear Fan (USA)) **Miss K. Rausing**
26 B f 26/3 Kheleyf (USA)—Kalinova (IRE) (Red Ransom (USA)) (24000) **Mrs Clodagh McStay**
27 B c 22/4 Sayif (IRE)—Keep Dancing (IRE) (Distant Music (USA)) **Saleh Al Homaizi & Imad Al Sagar**
28 Ch f 16/3 Casamento (IRE)—Lady Caprice (Kyllachy) (8000) **Mr Tony Elliott**
29 B c 30/3 Intikhab (USA)—Miss Latina (IRE) (Mozart (IRE)) (24000) **Mr P. Hancock**
30 **NO PAIN NO GAIN (FR)**, b c 4/5 Myboycharlie (IRE)—
                   Rascafria (USA) (Johannesburg (USA)) (5167) **Mr P. Hancock**
31 B c 20/2 Teofilo (IRE)—Nyarhini (Fantastic Light (USA)) (58000) **Mr Tony Elliott**
32 **REDICEAN**, b c 14/3 Medicean—Red Halo (IRE) (Galileo (IRE)) (34000) **High Rollers**
33 B f 30/4 Authorized (IRE)—Sagina (Shernazar) (1000) **FOMO Syndicate**
34 **TIMES SPIRIT**, b c 21/3 Redoute's Choice (AUS)—Forever Times (So Factual (USA)) (20000) **Mr A. Belshaw**
35 B c 18/4 Dandy Man (IRE)—Why Now (Dansili) (50000) **Mrs Fitri Hay**

102   MR PETER CHARALAMBOUS, Newmarket
Postal: **6 Barn, Calder Park, Hamilton Road, Newmarket, Suffolk, CB8 0NY**
Contacts: **PHONE (01638) 730415 MOBILE (07921) 858421**
E-MAIL **info@pcracing.co.uk** WEBSITE **www.pcracing.co.uk**

1 **BOONGA ROOGETA**, 7, b m Tobougg (IRE)—Aberlady Bay (IRE) **pcracing.co.uk**
2 **ELA GOOG LA MOU**, 7, b m Tobougg (IRE)—Real Flame **pcracing.co.uk**
3 **KALON BRAMA**, 5, b m Kodiac—Gilded Truffle (IRE) **pcracing.co.uk**
4 **THEYDON BOIS**, 4, b f Three Valleys (USA)—Velvet Waters **pcracing.co.uk**
5 **THEYDON THUNDER**, 4, b g Virtual—Lady Agnes **pcracing.co.uk**
6 **TRULEE SCRUMPTIOUS**, 7, b m Strategic Prince—Morning Rise (GER) **pcracing.co.uk**

MR PETER CHARALAMBOUS - Continued

THREE-YEAR-OLDS

7 B f Poet's Voice—Match Point **P. Charalambous**
8 THEYDON GREY, gr g Champs Elysees—Cheerfully **Mr E. O'Riordan**
9 THEYDON PARK, b g Royal Applause—Velvet Waters **P. Charalambous**

Other Owners: Miss T. L. Tideswell.

---

103 MR GEORGE CHARLTON, Stocksfield
Postal: Mickley Grange Farm, Stocksfield, Northumberland, NE43 7TB
Contacts: PHONE (01661) 843247 MOBILE (07808) 955029
E-MAIL gcharlton@fsmail.net

1 BALLYVOQUE (IRE), 10, b g Revoque (IRE)—Timissa (IRE) **J. I. A. Charlton**
2 DARSI DA FARE (IRE), 7, b g Darsi (FR)—Enchanted Valley (IRE) **Northumbria Leisure Ltd**
3 FAIRLEE GRACE, 5, b m Fair Mix (IRE)—Halo Flora **J. L. Gledson**
4 FAIRLEE PEARL, 5, b m Fair Mix (IRE)—Cloudy Pearl **J. L. Gledson**
5 HUBAL (POL), 4, b g Safety Wire (IRE)—Hebra (POL) **G. A. G. Charlton**
6 KNOCKARA BEAU (IRE), 13, b g Leading Counsel (USA)—Clairabell (IRE) **J. I. A. Charlton**
7 LORD USHER (IRE), 9, b g Lord Americo—Beet Five (IRE) **G. A. G. Charlton**
8 SHEPHERD'S BIGHT (IRE), 4, b g Court Cave (IRE)—Orador Sur Glane (IRE) **Mrs A. R. Wood**

Assistant Trainer: Mr J. I. A. Charlton

Jockey (NH): Jan Faltejsek.

---

104 MR ROGER CHARLTON, Beckhampton
Postal: Beckhampton House, Marlborough, Wiltshire, SN8 1QR
Contacts: OFFICE (01672) 539533 HOME (01672) 539330 FAX (01672) 539456
MOBILE (07710) 784511
E-MAIL roger@beckhamptonstables.com / office@beckhamptonstables.com
WEBSITE www.rogercharlton.com

1 AYRAD (IRE), 5, ch h Dalakhani (IRE)—Sweet Firebird (IRE) **Saleh Al Homaizi & Imad Al Sagar**
2 CAPTAIN CAT (IRE), 7, b g Dylan Thomas (IRE)—Mother of Pearl (IRE) **Seasons Holidays**
3 CLOWANCE ONE, 4, b g Oasis Dream—Clowance **Seasons Holidays**
4 COUNTERMEASURE, 4, b c American Post—Namaskar **K. Abdullah**
5 DECORATED KNIGHT, 4, ch c Galileo (IRE)—Pearling (USA) **Saleh Al Homaizi & Imad Al Sagar**
6 ELITE FORCE (IRE), 5, ch g Medicean—Amber Queen (IRE) **H.R.H. Sultan Ahmad Shah**
7 HUNTSMANS CLOSE, 6, b g Elusive Quality (USA)—Badminton **Brook House**
8 MARZANTE (USA), 8, gr g Maria's Mon (USA)—Danzante (USA) **Beckhampton Stables Ltd**
9 MOUNTAIN RESCUE (IRE), 4, b g High Chaparral (IRE)—Amber Queen (IRE) **Lady Richard Wellesley**
10 OOTY HILL, 4, gr c Dubawi (IRE)—Mussoorie (FR) **A. E. Oppenheimer**
11 QUEST FOR MORE (IRE), 6, b g Teofilo (IRE)—No Quest (IRE) **H.R.H. Sultan Ahmad Shah**
12 TIME TEST, 4, b c Dubawi (IRE)—Passage of Time **K. Abdullah**

THREE-YEAR-OLDS

13 ARNICA, b c Champs Elysees—Cordoba **K. Abdullah**
14 BANHAM (USA), gr c Exchange Rate (USA)—Palisade (USA) **K. Abdullah**
15 BATTLEMENT, b gr f Dansili—Scuffle **K. Abdullah**
16 BLAKENEY POINT, b c Sir Percy—Cartoon **Axom**
17 BLUE BUTTERFLY, b f Kyllachy—Raysiza (IRE) **A and S Brudenell**
18 BLUE SILK, b f Compton Place—Silky Dawn (IRE) **D. J. Deer**
19 CHESTER STREET, b c Invincible Spirit (IRE)—Expressive **H.R.H. Sultan Ahmad Shah**
20 CLODIANNA (IRE), gr f Clodovil (IRE)—Indiannie Moon **Paul Inglett & Partners**
21 CLOUDBERRY, b c Pivotal—Clouded Leopard (USA) **Lady Rothschild**
22 B f Dansili—Clowance **Seasons Holidays**
23 DE AGUILAR (IRE), b c Cape Blanco (IRE)—Golden Aster (USA) **Jane Allison / Hugo Merry**
24 EXECUTOR, b c Cacique (IRE)—Star Cluster **K. Abdullah**
25 FINAL CHOICE, b c Makfi—Anasazi (IRE) **Her Majesty The Queen**
26 HIGH SHIELDS (IRE), b c Shamardal (USA)—Marine City (JPN) **Michael Pescod**
27 HORRAH, b g Royal Applause—Aegean Shadow **Mrs H. Thomson Jones**
28 IMPERIAL AVIATOR, b c Paco Boy (IRE)—Telescopic **Daniel Hunt / Mrs Markham**

MR ROGER CHARLTON - Continued

29 **INTERMITTENT**, b f Cacique (IRE)—Innocent Air **K. Abdullah**
30 **IRREVOCABLE (IRE)**, b f Big Bad Bob (IRE)—Out of Time (IRE) **The Pyoneers**
31 B c Makfi—Kazeem **D. J. Deer**
32 **KUANTAN**, b c Acclamation—Gay Mirage (GER) **H.R.H. Sultan Ahmad Shah**
33 **KUMMIYA**, br g Dansili—Balisada **A. E. Oppenheimer**
34 **L'ETOILE (IRE)**, ch g Champs Elysees—Cross Your Fingers (USA) **Kessly Equine**
35 **LEAPING**, b f Oasis Dream—Avoidance (USA) **K. Abdullah**
36 **NOBLEWOMAN**, b f Showcasing—Rare Virtue (USA) **K. Abdullah**
37 **PACIFIC SALT (IRE)**, gr c Zebedee—Villa Nova (IRE) **Jon Kelly**
38 **PALING**, b c Zamindar (USA)—Solar Pursuit **K. Abdullah**
39 **PINA**, b f Dansili—Bourbonella **David Hearson**
40 **POPPYLAND**, b f Equiano (FR)—Follow Flanders **Bole, Carter, Deal, Hambro**
41 **PROJECTION**, b g Acclamation—Spotlight **The Royal Ascot Racing Club**
42 **PURE FANTASY**, b f Fastnet Rock (AUS)—Fictitious **Her Majesty The Queen**
43 **PURE VANITY**, b f New Approach (IRE)—Miss Pinkerton **A. E. Oppenheimer**
44 **QUEEN ATHENA (IRE)**, b f Royal Applause—Olimpic Girl (IRE) **Jane Allison**
45 **QUICK MARCH**, b f Lawman (FR)—Strut **Lady Rothschild**
46 **ROCK STEADY (IRE)**, ch g Intikhab (USA)—Mannsara (IRE) **Owners Group**
47 **SALAD DAYS**, b f Pivotal—Scarlet Runner **N. Jones**
48 **SCAMPER**, b f Oasis Dream—Wince **K. Abdullah**
49 **SHEARLING**, b f Rail Link—Casual **K. Abdullah**
50 **SNOBBERY (IRE)**, b g Duke of Marmalade (IRE)—Boast **Lady Rothschild**
51 **SOLWAY FIRTH**, b f Cacique (IRE)—Rule of Nature **K. Abdullah**
52 **TAMBOUR**, b c Notnowcato—Tamso (USA) **Lady Rothschild**

TWO-YEAR-OLDS

53 B f 19/3 Poet's Voice—Acquifer (Oasis Dream) (58000) **Axom**
54 B f 1/5 Nathaniel (IRE)—Amber Queen (IRE) (Cadeaux Genereux) (50000) **Lady Richard Wellesley**
55 **AMENTA (IRE)**, b f 17/4 Roderic O'Connor (IRE)—Pale Light (USA) (Lemon Drop Kid (USA)) (8000) **Liam Norris**
56 B f 13/2 Makfi—Azeema (IRE) (Averti (IRE)) **D. J. Deer**
57 **BLAZED (IRE)**, gr c 20/4 Dark Angel (IRE)—
Sudden Blaze (IRE) (Soviet Star (USA)) (125000) **H.R.H. Sultan Ahmad Shah**
58 B f 29/1 Rip Van Winkle (IRE)—Bristol Fashion (Dansili) (30000) **Bradley Racing**
59 **CARACAS**, b c 6/3 Cacique (IRE)—Bourbonella (Rainbow Quest (USA)) **David Hearson**
61 **CASEMENT (IRE)**, b c 23/2 Casamento (IRE)—Kirk Wynd (Selkirk (USA)) (60000) **Beckhampton Racing**
61 **COMRADE (IRE)**, b c 12/4 Canford Cliffs (IRE)—View (IRE) (Galileo (IRE)) (57585) **Michael Pescod**
62 B c 31/1 Bated Breath—Condition (Deploy) (230000) **Al Shaqab**
63 **DAGONET (IRE)**, b c 18/4 Sir Prancealot (IRE)—Dubai Diamond (Octagonal (NZ)) (37000) **Michael Pescod**
64 **DISCOVERED (IRE)**, ch c 25/3 Bated Breath—Sandglass (Zafonic (USA)) (160000) **H.R.H. Sultan Ahmad Shah**
65 **DISTANT (USA)**, b br f 13/3 First Defence (USA)—Ventoux (Galileo (IRE)) **K. Abdullah**
66 **ESPRIT DE CORPS**, b c 21/2 Sepoy (AUS)—Corps de Ballet (IRE) (Fasliyev (USA)) (80000) **Hearson and Inglett**
67 B c 23/3 Medicean—Estrela (Authorized (IRE)) **Seasons Holidays**
68 **FAIR EVA**, ch f 12/4 Frankel—African Rose (Observatory (USA)) **K. Abdullah**
69 **FIREGATE (USA)**, b f 10/2 First Defence (USA)—Media Fire (USA) (Bernardini (USA)) **K. Abdullah**
70 **FOREWARNING**, b c 21/3 Cacique (IRE)—Buffering (Beat Hollow) **K. Abdullah**
71 **GALACTUS**, b c 6/5 Notnowcato—Tamso (USA) (Seeking the Gold (USA)) **Lady Rothschild**
72 Ch c 22/2 Casamento (IRE)—Glyndebourne (USA) (Rahy (USA)) (75000) **Inglett & Hearson**
73 B c 12/3 Avonbridge—Go Between (Daggers Drawn (USA)) **D. J. Deer**
74 **HANDFUL (IRE)**, b f 9/1 Dark Angel (IRE)—Delia Eria (IRE) (Zamindar (USA)) **Trevor Stewart**
75 B c 9/2 Sea The Stars (IRE)—Hector's Girl (Hector Protector (USA)) **Mrs D. Swinburn**
76 B c 17/4 Frankel—Icon Project (USA) (Empire Maker (USA)) **Andrew Rosen**
77 B c 14/5 Bated Breath—Iwunder (IRE) (King's Best (USA)) (115000) **Highclere Racing**
78 Ch c 9/4 Dubawi (IRE)—Kazeem (Darshaan) **D. J. Deer**
79 B f 8/2 Equiano (FR)—Lavinia's Grace (USA) (Green Desert (USA)) **James Stewart**
80 B f 31/3 Nathaniel (IRE)—Longing To Dance (Danehill Dancer (IRE)) **D. J. Deer**
81 **MATHS PRIZE**, b c 3/2 Royal Applause—Hypoteneuse (IRE) (Sadler's Wells (USA)) **Her Majesty The Queen**
82 **MISS ANTICIPATION**, b f 3/4 Bated Breath—Dusting (IRE) (Acclamation) (36913) **Humber and Inglett**
83 B f 14/4 Zamindar (USA)—Moonlight Rhapsody (IRE) (Danehill Dancer (IRE)) **Diane Englehardt**
84 **NUNCIO**, b c 12/2 Authorized (IRE)—Sweet Pilgrim (Talkin Man (CAN)) **Mrs Sandy Hames**
85 **OCCURRENCE**, b f 5/3 Frankel—Arrive (Kahyasi) **K. Abdullah**
86 **ORANGE GIN (IRE)**, b c 2/2 Bushranger (IRE)—Gin Twist (Invincible Spirit (IRE)) **A. Bengough**
87 Ch f 24/3 Nathaniel (IRE)—Our Queen of Kings (Arazi (USA)) (600000) **K. Abdullah**
88 **PRINCESS DE LUNE (IRE)**, gr f 9/3 Shamardal (USA)—
Princess Serena (USA) (Unbridled's Song (USA)) (300000) **Round Hill Stud**
89 **QUITE SHARP**, ch f 21/2 New Approach (IRE)—Balisada (Kris) **A. E. Oppenheimer**

MR ROGER CHARLTON - Continued

90 B c 10/4 Sir Prancealot (IRE)—Rindiseyda (IRE) (Arakan (USA)) **Jane Allison**
91 B c 27/2 Nathaniel (IRE)—Ronaldsay (Kirkwall) (152380) **R. J. McCreery & Partners**
92 **SAND SHOE,** b f 19/2 Footstepsinthesand—Dolma (FR) (Marchand de Sable (USA)) **Lady Rothschild**
93 **SFUMATO,** br c 5/2 Bated Breath—Modern Look (Zamindar (USA)) **K. Abdullah**
94 **SILENT ECHO,** b c 20/2 Oasis Dream—Quiet (Observatory (USA)) **K. Abdullah**
95 **SOLAR CROSS,** b c 10/4 Sea The Stars (IRE)—
                    Nantyglo (Mark of Esteem (IRE)) (75000) **De Zoete, Inglett, Mercer, Smartt**
96 **SOLAR SHOWER,** b c 6/3 Oasis Dream—Solar Pursuit (Galileo (IRE)) **K. Abdullah**
97 **STONE THE CROWS,** b c 19/3 Cape Cross (IRE)—Stars In Your Eyes (Galileo (IRE)) **A. E. Oppenheimer**
98 **TIME CHASER,** b f 12/3 Dubawi (IRE)—Passage of Time (Dansili) **K. Abdullah**
99 Ch c 3/2 Frankel—Turama (Pivotal) **Saleh Al Homaizi & Imad Al Sagar**

Other Owners: Lady Agnew, Adie Bamboye, Doug and Maurine Bauckham, William Bole, Ken Carter, Sophia Dale, Peter Deal, Paul Dean, Mary Hambro, David Hues, Edward Kessly, David Ludlow, Hugo Merry, Syed Inayath Mornin, Lady Morrison, Andrew Parker Bowles (OBE), John Phelan, Hugh Shipton, Alexander Sparks, Richard and Elizabeth Stephens, Richard Stephens, Lady Tidbury, Taj Uddin, Geoff Webber.

Assistant Trainer: Harry Charlton

---

105 **MR HARRY CHISMAN, Stow-on-the-Wold**
Postal: **The Retreat Stables, Maugersbury, Cheltenham, Gloucestershire, GL54 1HP**
Contacts: **PHONE (07787) 516723**
WEBSITE www.harrychisman.co.uk

1 **ALL RILED UP,** 8, b m Dr Massini (IRE)—Martha Reilly (IRE) **McClean Baker Flint Wood Welch**
2 **AUGHCARRA (IRE),** 11, b g High Chaparral (IRE)—Pearly Brooks **Baker Waggott Byrne Madden Kirkland**
3 **CAPTAIN KENDALL (IRE),** 7, b g Clodovil (IRE)—Queen's Lace (IRE) **S Kirkland D Welch P Baker M Atherton**
4 **FOYLESIDEVIEW (IRE),** 4, b g Dark Angel (IRE)—Showerproof **B. J. McClean**

TWO-YEAR-OLDS

5 B f 14/3 Delegator—Hip Hip Hooray (Monsieur Bond (IRE)) (571)

Other Owners: Mr M. Atherton, Mr P. M. Baker, Mrs H. Byrne, Mr Harry Chisman, Mr V. R. Cooke, Mr Michael Flint, Mr S. Kirkland, Mr M. Madden, Mrs Maggie McClean, Mr J. W. Waggott, Mr D. Welch, Mr Duncan Wood.

Jockey (flat): Cathy Gannon. **Jockey (NH):** Tom O'Brien, Sean Quinlan, Andrew Tinkler. **Conditional:** Daniel Hiskett.

---

106 **MR NICOLAS CLEMENT, Chantilly**
Postal: **37, Avenue de Joinville, 60500 Chantilly, France**
Contacts: **PHONE (0033) 3445 75960 FAX (0033) 3445 77084 MOBILE (0033) 6072 34640**
E-MAIL office@nicolasclement.com WEBSITE www.nicolasclement.com

1 **CHALMONT (IRE),** 4, gr g Dalakhani (IRE)—Gadalka (USA)
2 **DUKE OF ELLINGTON (FR),** 4, b g Duke of Marmalade (IRE)—Abime (USA)
3 **ELUSIVE DANCER (FR),** 4, b g Elusive City (USA)—Snake Dancer (IRE)
4 **FAWLEY (IRE),** 4, b c Makfi—The Wise Lady (FR)
5 **GAME THEORY (IRE),** 4, b f Aussie Rules (USA)—Atullia (GER)
6 **LUXE VENDOME (FR),** 4, gr g Kendargent (FR)—Place Vendome (FR)
7 **MA CAGNOTTE (FR),** 4, b f King's Best (USA)—Masaya (SWI)
8 **MAKE MERRY,** 4, b f Teofilo (IRE)—Contare
9 **MER ET JARDIN,** 4, b f Lord Shanakill (USA)—Mirandola's Dream (FR)
10 **MINOTAUR (IRE),** 4, b g Azamour (IRE)—Mycenae
11 **MORGENLICHT (GER),** 4, b f Sholokhov (IRE)—Monbijou (GER)
12 **NOW WE CAN,** 7, b g Martillo (GER)—Notre Dame (GER)
13 **PRESTIGE VENDOME (FR),** 5, gr g Orpen (USA)—Place Vendome (FR)

THREE-YEAR-OLDS

14 **ALASKA DANCER (FR),** b g Elusive City (USA)—Aliyeska (IRE)
15 **ALSUSHA (FR),** gr f Kendargent (FR)—Heleniade (FR)

MR NICOLAS CLEMENT - Continued

16 **BELLE DAUPHINE,** gr f Dalakhani (IRE)—Bruxcalina (FR)
17 **BENGALI DREAM (IRE),** b f Acclamation—Gems of Araby
18 **BLANC DE NOIR (FR),** gr f Myboycharlie (IRE)—Sardinelle (FR)
19 **BOYISSIME (FR),** ch g Exceed And Excel (AUS)—Caprarola (USA)
20 **CHAMPAGNE CHARLEY (FR),** b g Myboycharlie (IRE)—Age of Refinement (IRE)
21 **CLASSE VENDOME (FR),** gr f Kendargent (FR)—Place Vendome (FR)
22 **DALGARNO (FR),** b c Sea The Stars (IRE)—Jakonda (USA)
23 **EASY VICTORY (FR),** b f Muhtathir—Easy Sundae (IRE)
24 **EL ISSIDRO,** ch f Beat Hollow—Atiza (IRE)
25 **EMERALD ISLE (IRE),** b f Duke of Marmalade (IRE)—Lady Causeway (USA)
26 **FASTNET VAGANOVA (IRE),** b c Fastnet Rock (AUS)—Ballet School (IRE)
27 **FASTNET WHIRLWIND (IRE),** b c Fastnet Rock (AUS)—Crazy Volume (IRE)
28 **FLEUR D'IPANEMA (FR),** b f Le Havre (IRE)—Anthropologie (FR)
29 **FLOJO (USA),** b f Exchange Rate (USA)—Gingivere (USA)
30 **FLYING FLEUR (FR),** b f Lawman (FR)—Fleur de Sel
31 **GARRI LE ROI (FR),** ch c Linngari (IRE)—Kikinda (FR)
32 **HARDNESS (IRE),** b c Makfi—Hideaway (FR)
33 **ILLUSTRISSIME (USA),** b g Mizzen Mast (USA)—Ghost Friendly (USA)
34 **JEU D'OMBRES (IRE),** b c Lawman (FR)—The Wise Lady (FR)
35 **KARSA JET (FR),** b f Acclamation—Karsabruni (FR)
36 **KENSHABA (FR),** b f Kendargent (FR)—Sabasha (FR)
37 **L'EMIR D'ART (FR),** ch c Dubai Destination (USA)—Art Machine (USA)
38 **LA DAUPHINE (FR),** b f King's Best (USA)—Lady of Akita (USA)
39 **LAW DEPUTY (IRE),** b c Pour Moi (IRE)—Laramie (USA)
40 **LAW GIRL (FR),** b f Lawman (FR)—Lamarsa (FR)
41 **MANAMITE (FR),** b c Kentucky Dynamite (USA)—Masaya (CHI)
42 **MARCASSIN,** b c Lawman (FR)—Mirina (FR)
43 **MERI DEVIE (FR),** b f Spirit One (FR)—Folle Biche (FR)
44 **MIRABELL (IRE),** ch f Manduro (GER)—Mycenae
45 **MT OF BEATITUDES (IRE),** b f Fastnet Rock (AUS)—Treasure The Lady (IRE)
46 **NESSUN DORMA (GER),** b f Lawman (FR)—Notre Dame (GER)
47 **OAKMONT (FR),** ch c Turtle Bowl (IRE)—Onega Lake (IRE)
48 **ONCEUPONASTAR (IRE),** b f Sea The Stars (IRE)—Main Spring
49 **PRIVATE AFFAIR (FR),** b c Pour Moi (IRE)—Private Eye (FR)
50 **ROCK DARGENT (FR),** b br c Kendargent (FR)—Melinda (FR)
51 **SAINT ISIDORE (FR),** b f Le Havre (IRE)—Texalouna (FR)
52 **SHAKSTORMY (FR),** ch f Stormy River (FR)—Shaking
53 **THE JULIET ROSE (FR),** b f Monsun (GER)—Dubai Rose
54 **TRAFFIC JAM (IRE),** b f Duke of Marmalade (IRE)—Place de L'etoile (IRE)
55 **VIVE LE GRIS (FR),** gr g High Chaparral (IRE)—Viva Maria (FR)
56 **VODKA DOUBLE (FR),** ch f Peintre Celebre (USA)—Volga Volga (USA)

TWO-YEAR-OLDS

57 **AIGUILLON (IRE),** ch c 27/2 New Approach (IRE)—Aiglonne (USA) (Silver Hawk (USA)) (155038)
58 **BLOW MY MIND,** br f 3/3 Holy Roman Emperor (IRE)—Be My Lady (GER) (Be My Guest (USA))
59 **COMBLOT (FR),** b g 1/4 Rajsaman (FR)—Irish Cat (IRE) (One Cool Cat (USA))
60 **DOMFRONT (IRE),** b c 23/2 Royal Applause—Debuetantin (Big Shuffle (USA)) (66445)
61 **ETOILE BERE (FR),** b f 5/4 Hurricane Cat (USA)—L'ete (CHI) (Hussonet (USA)) (36913)
62 B f 26/4 Dark Angel (IRE)—Halong Bay (FR) (Montjeu (IRE)) (59062)
63 B c 10/3 Fastnet Rock (AUS)—Ideal (Galileo (IRE))
64 B f 7/5 Redoute's Choice (AUS)—Lockup (IRE) (Inchinor (USA)) (258397)
65 B f 12/4 Arcano (IRE)—Mary Spring Rice (IRE) (Saffron Walden (FR)) (7382)
66 B c 11/4 Halling (USA)—Mystic Spirit (IRE) (Invincible Spirit (IRE)) (22148)
67 Ch f 25/1 Dutch Art—On The Line (FR) (Green Tune (USA)) (51679)
68 **SEA OF LIGHTS (GER),** b f 21/3 Areion (GER)—Senaida (IRE) (Danehill Dancer (IRE)) (17718)
69 **SMART VENDOME,** gr c 30/3 Kendargent (FR)—Place Vendome (FR) (Dr Fong (USA)) (199335)
70 **TIKITIKI (FR),** b f 16/4 Fastnet Rock (AUS)—Green Diamond Lady (USA) (Johannesburg (USA)) (37652)
71 **TRICEPS (IRE),** br f 26/2 Excelebration (IRE)—Trip To The Moon (Fasliyev (USA)) (77519)
72 B f 18/4 Cacique (IRE)—Vienna View (Dalakhani (IRE)) (60538)
73 **WEEKENDER (FR),** ch c 3/4 Sunday Break (JPN)—Funny Crazy (FR) (Chichicastenango (FR)) (28054)

107 MR DENIS J. COAKLEY, West Ilsley

Postal: **Keeper's Stables, West Ilsley, Newbury, Berkshire, RG20 7AH**
Contacts: **PHONE (01635) 281622 MOBILE (07768) 658056**
E-MAIL racing@deniscoakley.com WEBSITE www.deniscoakley.com

1 **AUNTIE MAY (IRE)**, 4, b f Steppe Dancer (IRE)—Auntie Mame **J. C. Kerr**
2 **GABRIEL'S LAD (IRE)**, 7, b g Dark Angel (IRE)—Catherine Wheel **Killoran Ennis Conway**
3 **KING CALYPSO**, 5, ch g Sir Percy—Rosa de Mi Corazon (USA) **Pearlygems**
4 **MISS MARJURIE (IRE)**, 6, b m Marju (IRE)—Kazatzka **Chris van Hoorn Racing**
5 **SAUMUR**, 4, b f Mawatheeq (USA)—Sparkling Montjeu (IRE) **Sparkling Partners**
6 **STEPPE DAUGHTER (IRE)**, 5, b m Steppe Dancer (IRE)—Carmencita **Chris van Hoorn Racing**

THREE-YEAR-OLDS

7 **ELOCUTION**, b f Paco Boy (IRE)—Speech **Sue Huntingdon & Partners**
8 **JAN STEEN (IRE)**, b g Footstepsinthesand—Mi Rubina (IRE) **Chris van Hoorn Racing**
9 **JUST FRED (IRE)**, br g Excellent Art—Consignia (IRE) **Cargreen Racing**
10 Gr g Mount Nelson—Lady Friend **Mrs P. de W. Johnson**
11 **POURQUOI NON (IRE)**, b g Pour Moi (IRE)—Anyuta **Chris van Hoorn Racing**
12 **SHEILA'S TREAT (IRE)**, b g Frozen Power (IRE)—Bonny Rose **Styles, Whymark & Mountford**
13 **STAFFA (IRE)**, b f Rock of Gibraltar (IRE)—Gabriellina Klon (IRE) **The Good Mixers**

TWO-YEAR-OLDS

14 B f 10/4 Power—Ascendancy (Sadler's Wells (USA)) (10000) **Count Calypso Racing**
15 B f 26/4 Fastnet Rock (AUS)—Crystal Curling (IRE) (Peintre Celebre (USA)) (17000) **R. J. Styles**
16 B c 11/4 Elusive City (USA)—Dream For Life (FR) (Oasis Dream) (20000) **Chris van Hoorn Racing**
17 **HENRIQUA**, b f 16/2 Henrythenavigator (USA)—
Child Bride (USA) (Coronado's Quest (USA)) (12000) **West Ilsley Racing**
18 **KEEPER'S CHOICE (IRE)**, ch f 9/4 Intikhab (USA)—Crossing (Cape Cross (IRE)) (14000) **Keeper's 12**
19 Gr f 17/4 Beat Hollow—Lady Friend (Environment Friend) **Mrs P. de W. Johnson**

Other Owners: Mr A. P. Bloor, R. J. Bolam, Mr J. Carmichael, Mrs M. Carmichael, Mrs B. Coakley, P. M. Emery, J. T. Ennis, Mr D. B. Harris, Lady S. M. G. Huntingdon, Mr T. A. Killoran, Mr J. G. Mountford, Mr G. Oakley, J. G. Ross, Miss A. D. Swift, C. T. Van Hoorn, Mr J. K. Whymark, Mrs P. A. Williams.

108 MR PAUL COLE, Whatcombe

Postal: **Whatcombe Estate, Whatcombe, Wantage, Oxfordshire, OX12 9NW**
Contacts: **PHONE (01488) 638433 FAX (01488) 638609**
E-MAIL admin@paulcole.co.uk WEBSITE www.paulcole.co.uk

1 **AZILIAN**, 4, b c Azamour (IRE)—Zietory **The Fairy Story Partnership**
2 **BERKSHIRE (IRE)**, 5, b h Mount Nelson—Kinnaird (IRE) **H.R.H. Sultan Ahmad Shah**
3 **COMPLICIT (IRE)**, 5, b g Captain Rio—Molomo **9.36 from Paddington**
4 **DUTCH ART DEALER**, 5, b g Dutch Art—Lawyers Choice **P. F. I. Cole & Mr R. Green**
5 **EXPENSIVE DATE**, 4, ch f Monsieur Bond (IRE)—Cheap Thrills **Mr C. Wright**
6 **KUBEBA (IRE)**, 5, b g Kodiac—Brillano (FR) **Mr D. L. Hadley**
7 **LADURELLI (IRE)**, 4, b g Mastercraftsman—Chanter **Mrs F. H. Hay**
8 **LYFKA (IRE)**, 4, ch f Kheleyf (USA)—Tarkamara (IRE) **Mr A. H. Robinson**
9 **MOLTEN LAVA (IRE)**, 4, b g Rock of Gibraltar (IRE)—Skehana (IRE) **Red Run Racing**
10 **PENDO**, 5, b g Denounce—Abundant **Mr B. K. Hopson**
11 **ROCKAROUNDTHECLOCK (IRE)**, 4, ch c Starspangledbanner (AUS)—Lulawin **P. F. I. Cole & Mr C. Wright**
12 **ROTHERWICK (IRE)**, 4, ch c Starspangledbanner (AUS)—Pivotalia (IRE) **H.R.H. Sultan Ahmad Shah**
13 **RUSSIAN REWARD (IRE)**, 4, b g Iffraaj—Forever Times **Mr A. D. Spence**
14 **SILVERHEELS (IRE)**, 7, gr g Verglas—Vasilia **P. F. I. Cole**
15 **STORMBOUND (IRE)**, 7, b g Galileo (IRE)—A Footstep Away (USA) **P. F. I. Cole**
16 **TIOGA PASS**, 5, b m High Chaparral (IRE)—Seren Devious **The Fairy Story Partnership**
17 **UPSTAGING (IRE)**, 4, b g Mount Nelson—Corndavon (USA) **H.R.H. Sultan Ahmad Shah**

THREE-YEAR-OLDS

18 **AGAINST THE ODDS**, b c Champs Elysees—Generous Diana **Mr A. D. Spence**
19 **ARCHIMEDES (IRE)**, b c Invincible Spirit (IRE)—Waveband **Mrs F. H. Hay**
20 **BARON BOLT**, bl g Kheleyf (USA)—Scarlet Royal **Asprey, Wright, Meyrick, PJL, Wilcock**
21 **BATTLE OF BOSWORTH (IRE)**, b g Duke of Marmalade (IRE)—
Muskoka Dawn (USA) **Wright, Asprey, Meyrick, PJL, Wilcock**

MR PAUL COLE - Continued

22 **BRAVE ARCHIBALD (IRE)**, b c Arch (USA)—Muneefa (USA) **PJL Racing, Wright, Asprey, Meyrick, Wilcock**
23 **CAITIE (IRE)**, b f Canford Cliffs (IRE)—The Shrew **Mr A. H. Robinson**
24 **CHEMPEDAK BAY (IRE)**, ch g Exceed And Excel (AUS)—Snowdrops **Mr T. A. Rahman**
25 **CLIFFHANGER**, b f Canford Cliffs (IRE)—Copy-Cat **Mr F. P. Stella**
26 **DRAMATIC VOICE**, ch f Poet's Voice—Darwinia (GER) **Mrs E. A. Bass**
27 **HONIARA**, b c Rock of Gibraltar (IRE)—Indian Maiden (IRE) **Meyrick, Wright, Asprey, PJL, Wilcock**
28 **HOUSE OF COMMONS (IRE)**, b c Sea The Stars (IRE)—Reality (FR) **Mrs F. H. Hay**
29 **INDRAPURA (IRE)**, ch c Cape Blanco (IRE)—A Mind of Her Own (IRE) **H.R.H. Sultan Ahmad Shah**
30 **JAZZ CAT (IRE)**, ch f Tamayuz—Chelsea Rose (IRE) **Mrs F. H. Hay**
31 **MAROC**, b c Rock of Gibraltar (IRE)—Zietory **The Fairy Story Partnership**
32 **PILOT HILL (IRE)**, b f Intikhab (USA)—Song of Passion (USA) **H.R.H. Prince Faisal Salman**
33 **PINK ANGEL (IRE)**, gr f Dark Angel (IRE)—Xarzee (IRE) **Mrs F. H. Hay**
34 **RECENT ACQUISITION (IRE)**, b g Approve (IRE)—Dear Catch (IRE) **Mr R. Green**
35 **SHAH OF ARMAAN (IRE)**, b c Fastnet Rock (AUS)—Queen of Tara (IRE) **Mr T. A. Rahman**
36 **SHAKERATTLENROLL (IRE)**, b c Intikhab (USA)—Carolxaar (IRE) **P. F. I. Cole & Mr C. Wright**
37 **SWEET DRAGON FLY**, ch f Oasis Dream—Sweet Cecily (IRE) **Mrs F. H. Hay**
38 **TUOLUMNE MEADOWS**, b f High Chaparral (IRE)—Seren Devious **The Fairy Story Partnership**

TWO-YEAR-OLDS

39 B c 24/4 Iffraaj—Appletreemagic (IRE) (Indian Danehill (IRE)) (40000)
40 Ch c 5/2 Poet's Voice—Avril Rose (IRE) (Xaar) (35000)
41 **GALINI**, ch f 2/2 Medicean—Flashbang (Dubawi (IRE)) **Mr A. H. Robinson**
42 B c 4/3 Galileo (IRE)—Impressionist Art (IRE) (Giant's Causeway (USA)) **Mrs F. H. Hay**
43 B c 24/3 Frankel—Intrigued (Darshaan) **H.R.H. Prince Faisal Salman**
44 Ch c 2/2 Mayson—Intrusion (Indesatchel (IRE)) (30476)
45 Ch f 4/3 Power—Izzy Lou (IRE) (Spinning World (USA)) (25714)
46 Gr f 13/3 Helmet (AUS)—Lesotho (IRE) (Excellent Art) (44296) **Mr C. Wright, Miss E. Asprey**
47 B c 18/3 Acclamation—Midnight Martini (Night Shift (USA)) (58000) **Mr J. Gatley, Mr T. Baines**
48 **MUTOONDRESDASHORSE**, ch c 9/4 Harbour Watch (IRE)—
                      Mutoon (IRE) (Erhaab (USA)) (18000) **9.36 from Paddington**
49 **PACOFILHA**, b f 15/3 Paco Boy (IRE)—Seradim (Elnadim (USA)) **The Fairy Story Partnership**
50 **PERSEPHONE (IRE)**, b f 21/4 Kodiac—Demeter (USA) (Diesis) (115000) **Mr A. H. Robinson**
51 B c 27/4 Kodiac—Quickstyx (Night Shift (USA)) (110000) **Mrs F. H. Hay**
52 B c 1/5 Oasis Dream—Rainbow Dancing (Rainbow Quest (USA)) (58000) **Mrs F. H. Hay**
53 B c 10/4 Tagula (IRE)—Ten Spot (IRE) (Intikhab (USA)) (31428)

Other Owners: Miss E. Asprey, Mr Rory Colfer, Mr E. R. Goodwin, Mr R. A. Green, Mrs Josephine Green, Mr David Klein, Sir George Meyrick, Mr P. Mott, P. F. I. Cole Ltd, Mr Nicholas Wilcock, Miss H. E. Wright, Mr Christopher Wright.

Assistant Trainer: Oliver Cole

---

109 MR STUART COLTHERD, Selkirk
Postal: Clarilawmuir Farm, Selkirk, Selkirkshire, TD7 4QA
Contacts: PHONE (01750) 21251 FAX (01750) 21251 MOBILE (07801) 398199
E-MAIL wscoltherd@clarilawmuir.wanadoo.co.uk

1 **AMETHYST ROSE (IRE)**, 9, ch m Beneficial—Cap The Rose (IRE) **Coltherd Whyte Swinton Ruddy**
2 **ASH PARK (IRE)**, 8, b g Milan—Distant Gale (IRE) **W. S. Coltherd**
3 **AYE WELL**, 11, b g Overbury (IRE)—Squeeze Box (IRE) **Mrs C. Hogg**
4 **BYRONEGETONEFREE**, 5, b g Byron—Lefty's Dollbaby (USA) **Coltherd Conchar**
5 **CAPTAIN REDBEARD (IRE)**, 7, ch g Bach (IRE)—Diesel Dancer (IRE) **W. S. Coltherd**
6 **DARSI DANCER (IRE)**, 8, b g Darsi (FR)—Jaystara (IRE) **Coltherd Gillie**
7 **FORTY SOMETHING (IRE)**, 11, b g Moothyeb (USA)—Drumquin Girl (IRE) **Mr R. W. Powell**
8 **GAWN SID**, 5, b g Exceed And Excel (AUS)—Only In Dreams **W. S. Coltherd**
9 **GUNNER LINDLEY**, 9, ch g Medicean—Lasso **W. S. Coltherd**
10 **HATTON SPRINGS**, 5, b m Jeremy (USA)—Oopsadaisy (IRE) **Binnie Dunbar Murray Sheil**
11 **HURRICANE RITA (FR)**, 6, gr m Sagamix (FR)—Madonna da Rossi **Mr S. Shiel**
12 **KILLONE (IRE)**, 7, gr g Flemensfirth (USA)—Ceol Tire (IRE) **TurnbullHendersonFindlaterBoyceMacDougall**
13 **MIA MATRIARCH**, 10, ch m Silver Patriarch (IRE)—Youandi **A. Gilchrist**
14 **NORFOLK SOUND**, 5, b m Pastoral Pursuits—Cayman Sound **HoodMcKirganBoyceCawkwellMitchellBannon**
15 **OIL BURNER**, 11, b g Sir Harry Lewis (USA)—Quick Quote **Mr J. W. Clark**
16 **OVERAWED**, 5, b m Overbury (IRE)—Alleged To Rhyme (IRE) **Mrs E. A. Fletcher**
17 **QUICK DECISSON (IRE)**, 8, b g Azamour (IRE)—Fleet River (USA) **Whyte Scott Swinton Gillie**
18 **RESOLUTE REFORMER (IRE)**, 7, b g Arcadio (GER)—Booking Note (IRE) **D. Neale**

MR STUART COLTHERD - Continued

19 SCOTSMAN, 8, b g And Beyond (IRE)—Kariba Dream **W. S. Coltherd**
20 SEVENTEEN BLACK (IRE), 8, b g Subtle Power (IRE)—Snowbaby (IRE) **Whyte Jeffrey Hall**
21 SUPRISE VENDOR (IRE), 10, ch g Fath (USA)—Dispol Jazz **Mr A. Gunning**

Other Owners: Mr S. M. Bannon, Mr R. A. Binnie, Mr J. Boyce, Mrs S. F. Cawkwell, Mr T. Conchar, Mr D. L. Dunbar, Mr G. Findlater, Mr E. Gillie, Mr I. Hall, Mr G. E. K. Henderson, Mr M. J. Hood, J. B. Jeffrey, Mr G. E. MacDougall, Mrs S. M. McKirgan, Mr D. Mitchell, Mr I. A. J. Mitchell, Mr I. S. Murray, Mr J. Payne, Mr J. E. Ruddy, Mr M. J. Scott, Mr S. Swinton, Mr A. Turnbull, Mr A. G. Whyte.

Jockey (NH): Brian Harding, Henry Brooke.

---

110 **MR ALAN COOGAN, Ely**
Postal: **31 Hasse Road, Soham, Ely, Cambridgeshire, CB7 5UW**
Contacts: **PHONE (01353) 721673 FAX (01353) 721117**

1 ALLEGRI (IRE), 7, b g Key of Luck (USA)—Bermuxa (FR) **A B Coogan & Jane Chapple-Hyam**
2 JOE PALOOKA (IRE), 6, b g Galileo (IRE)—Glinting Desert (IRE) **A. B. Coogan**
3 SILVER DETAIL (IRE), 4, b f Youmzain (IRE)—Ayam Zainah **A. B. Coogan**

Other Owners: Ms J. F. Chapple-Hyam.

---

111 **MR JOHN COOMBE, Weymouth**
Postal: **Sea Barn Farm, Fleet, Weymouth, Dorset, DT3 4ED**
Contacts: **PHONE (01305) 761745 (0780) 3752831 FAX (01305) 775396 MOBILE (07796) 990760**
E-MAIL wib@seabarnracing.com WEBSITE www.seabarnracing.com

1 CHESIL BEACH BOY, 13, b g Commanche Run—Eatons **M. J. Coombe**
2 SAN MARINO (FR), 13, ch g Bering—Sienne (FR) **M. J. Coombe**

Assistant Trainer: Mr John Roberts

Amateur: Mrs M. Roberts.

---

112 **MRS SUSAN CORBETT, Otterburn**
Postal: **Girsonfield, Otterburn, Newcastle upon Tyne, Tyne and Wear, NE19 1NT**
Contacts: **PHONE (01830) 520771 FAX (01830) 520771 MOBILE (07713) 651215**
E-MAIL girsonfield@outlook.com WEBSITE www.girsonfield.co.uk

1 CUPID'S QUEST (IRE), 4, b f Jeremy (USA)—Lovers Nest **Castle View Racing**
2 DEFINITELY GLAD (IRE), 9, b m Definite Article—Gladys May (IRE) **Mr W. F. Corbett**
3 DUN TO PERFECTION, 9, ch g Endoli (USA)—Dun To A Tern **Mr W. F. Corbett**
4 EASTER SPIRIT (IRE), 6, gr g Ivan Denisovich (IRE)—Dumaani's Dream (USA) **Mr F. W. W. Chapman**
5 EBONY ROSE, 4, br f Kalanisi (IRE)—Cogolie (FR) **Enright, Goodfellow, Corbett**
6 HARLEYS MAX, 7, b g Winged Love (IRE)—Researcher **Girsonfield Racing Club**
7 MANBALLANDALL (IRE), 8, b g Flemensfirth (USA)—Omas Lady (IRE) **Mrs J. L. Corbett**
8 MISTER HENDRE, 8, gr g Fair Mix (IRE)—Bonne Anniversaire **Mr G. Foley**
9 RIPONIAN, 6, ch g Trade Fair—Dispol Katie **Girsonfield Racing Club**
10 SILVA SAMOURAI, 7, gr g Proclamation (IRE)—Ladykirk **Mr J. Goodfellow**
11 SPERANZA, 4, b f Bahri (USA)—Toarmandowithlove (IRE) **Ms R. Enright**
12 STAY IN MY HEART (IRE), 7, ch m Medicean—Christmas Cracker (FR) **Mr M. Kavanagh**
13 SUPER COLLIDER, 9, b g Montjeu (IRE)—Astorg (USA) **Mrs J. L. Corbett**
14 TOARMANDOWITHLOVE (IRE), 8, ch m Choisir (AUS)—Deadly Buzz (IRE) **Ms R. Enright**

THREE-YEAR-OLDS

15 IAMNOLADY, b f Millkom—Turbo Linn **Mr W. F. Corbett**
16 JODY, ch f Kheleyf (USA) Canis Star **Enright, Goodfellow, Corbett**
17 JOSEPHINE K, b f Bahri (USA)—Montrachet Belle **K. Eichler**
18 MY BROWN EYED GIRL, b f Ferrule (IRE)—Chalosse **Mr G. Satchwell**

MRS SUSAN CORBETT - Continued

19 THE AULD KIRK, b g Millkom—Lady Counsellor
20 THE WINNINGTIPSTER, ch g Kheleyf (USA)—Freedom Song **The Winning Tipster Ltd**

Other Owners: Mr D. J. Clarke, Mr S. Humphries.

Assistant Trainer: Mr W.F. Corbett

Conditional: James Corbett. **Apprentice:** James Corbett.

113
MR LIAM CORCORAN, Kingsbridge
Postal: **Court Cottage, Pittaford Farm, Slapton, Kingsbridge, Devon, TQ7 2QG**
Contacts: **MOBILE (07789) 368234**
E-MAIL corcoranracing@aol.co.uk

1 BARON'S BEST, 6, gr g Lucky Story (USA)—Dispol Isle (IRE) **Miss C. L. Bowles**
2 HARDTOROCK (IRE), 7, b g Mountain High (IRE)—Permissal (IRE) **Mr N. A. Eggleton**
3 6, Ch m Franklins Gardens—Launceston
4 SPENCER MOON (IRE), 8, b g Dr Massini (IRE)—Nana Moon (IRE) **Miss C. L. Bowles**
5 STERLING GENT (IRE), 9, gr g Cloudings (IRE)—Company Credit (IRE) **Miss C. L. Bowles**
6 WELCOME BACH (IRE), 7, ch g Bach (IRE)—Massini's Daughter (IRE) **Miss C. L. Bowles**

114
MR JOHN CORNWALL, Melton Mowbray
Postal: **April Cottage, Pasture Lane, Hose, Melton Mowbray, Leicestershire, LE14 4LB**
Contacts: **PHONE (01664) 444453 FAX (01664) 444754 MOBILE (07939) 557091**
E-MAIL johncornwall7@gmail.com

1 FLICHITY (IRE), 11, br g Turtle Island (IRE)—Chancy Gal **J. R. Cornwall**
2 NEXT EXIT (IRE), 11, b g Exit To Nowhere (USA)—Pilgrim Star (IRE) **J. R. Cornwall**
3 THAT'S THE DEAL (IRE), 12, b br g Turtle Island (IRE)—Sister Swing **J. R. Cornwall**
4 THE JUGOPOLIST (IRE), 9, b g Oscar (IRE)—Chance My Native (IRE) **J. R. Cornwall**

115
MR ROBERT COWELL, Newmarket
Postal: **Bottisham Heath Stud, Six Mile Bottom, Newmarket, Suffolk, CB8 0TT**
Contacts: **PHONE (01638) 570330 MOBILE (07785) 512463**
E-MAIL robert@robertcowellracing.co.uk WEBSITE www.robertcowellracing.co.uk

1 BAHAMIAN HEIGHTS, 5, b g Bahamian Bounty—Tahirah **Mrs J Morley & Mr A Rix**
2 CAPOLAVORO (FR), 5, b g Sulamani (IRE)—Farnesina (FR) **Mr Cyril Humphris & Partner**
3 CAPTAIN BOB (IRE), 5, b g Dark Angel (IRE)—Birthday Present **The Captain Bob Partnership**
4 DESERT COMMAND, 6, b g Oasis Dream—Speed Cop **Mrs J. Hadida**
5 EJBAAR, 4, b g Oasis Dream—Habaayib **Malih L. Al Basti**
6 ENCORE D'OR, 4, b c Oasis Dream—Entente Cordiale (IRE) **Newsells Park Stud Limited**
7 GOLDREAM, 7, b g Oasis Dream—Clizia (IRE) **Mr J Sargeant & Mrs J Morley**
8 GRAND BEAUTY (IRE), 4, ch f Kheleyf (USA)—Grand Zafeen **Mr J. Abdullah**
9 GREEN DOOR (IRE), 5, b g Camacho—Inourhearts (IRE) **Mrs F. H. Hay**
10 IFFRANESIA (FR), 6, ch m Iffraaj—Farnesina (FR) **C. Humphris**
11 IMMEDIATE, 4, b f Oasis Dream—Emergency **The Socrates Partnership**
12 INDIAN TINKER, 7, b g Sleeping Indian—Breakfast Creek **Mr J. Sargeant**
13 JAMES BOND GIRL (USA), 4, b f Giant's Causeway (USA)—Swan Nebula (USA) **Ecurie La Boetie**
14 JUST US TWO (IRE), 4, b c Royal Applause—Sarah's First **Mr A. Al Mansoori**
15 JUSTINEO, 3, b h Oasis Dream—Loulwa (IRE) **Saleh Al Homaizi & Imad Al Sagar**
16 KINGSGATE NATIVE (IRE), 11, b g Mujadil (USA)—Native Force (IRE) **Cheveley Park Stud Limited**
17 MARMALADY (IRE), 6, ch m Duke of Marmalade (IRE)—Grecian Glory (IRE) **Heart Of The South Racing**
18 MORE SPICE (IRE), 4, b g Exceed And Excel (AUS)—High Spice (USA) **Mr Khalifa Dasmal & Partner**
19 NORMAL EQUILIBRIUM, 6, b g Elnadim (USA)—Acicula (IRE) **The Morley Family**
20 OUTBACK TRAVELLER (IRE), 5, b g Bushranger (IRE)—Blue Holly (IRE) **Lordship Stud & Mrs J Morley**
21 RAINBOW ORSE, 4, b g Zebedee—Khafayif (USA) **Mr G. M. C. Johnson**
22 ROYAL BAJAN (USA), 8, gr ro g Speightstown (USA)—Crown You (USA) **The Cool Silk Partnership**
23 SECRETINTHEPARK, 6, ch g Sakhee's Secret—Lark In The Park (IRE) **Mia Racing**
24 SIR ROBERT CHEVAL, 5, b g Green Desert (USA)—Aunt Ruby (USA) **Heart Of The South Racing**

MR ROBERT COWELL - Continued

25 **SPEED HAWK (USA)**, 5, b br g Henny Hughes (USA)—Cosmic Wing (USA) **K. A. Dasmal**
26 **SPIRIT QUARTZ (IRE)**, 8, b g Invincible Spirit (IRE)—Crystal Gaze (IRE) **Ecurie La Boetie**
27 **TOOFI (FR)**, 5, b g Henrythenavigator (USA)—Silver Bark **Saleh Al Homaizi & Imad Al Sagar**
28 **WEBSITE**, 4, b g Oasis Dream—Homepage **Malih L. Al Basti**

THREE-YEAR-OLDS

29 **CHANDRESH,** b f Holy Roman Emperor (IRE)—Cloud's End **Manor Farm Stud (Rutland)**
30 **EDITH WESTON,** b f Showcasing—Twitch Hill **Miss S. Hoare**
31 **FINGERTIPS,** b f Royal Applause—Hanging On **The Fingertips Partnership**
32 **GWENDOLYN (GER),** b f Invincible Spirit (IRE)—Golden Whip (GER) **Sheikh Khalifa, Sheikh Suhaim, QRL**
33 **HORSESHOE BEND,** b g Fastnet Rock (AUS)—Ruby Rocket (IRE) **Mrs F. H. Hay**
34 **JOYFUL DAY (IRE),** b c Lilbourne Lad (IRE)—Blondie's Esteem (IRE) **Mr A. Al Mansoori**
35 **JUMEIRAH STAR (USA),** b f Street Boss (USA)—Cosmic Wing (USA) **Mr Khalifa Dasmal & Partner**
36 **JUST OVER,** b f Bahamian Bounty—Kassuta **Mr J. Sargeant**
37 **KING COLE (USA),** ch c Scat Daddy (USA)—Volver (IRE) **K. A. Dasmal**
38 **MAJESTIC GIRL (IRE),** b f Royal Applause—Pretty Majestic (IRE) **Mr Ahmed Jaber**
39 **MISS UPPITY,** ch f Notnowcato—Instructress **Bottisham Heath Stud**
40 **NEW LEGEND (IRE),** b c Lilbourne Lad (IRE)—Next To The Top **S. Ali**
41 **PRIVATE DONALD,** ch c Sakhee's Secret—Excello **Bottisham Heath Stud**
42 **ROCKING RUDOLPH (USA),** b f Discreetly Mine (USA)—Empire Spring (USA) **Mr G. M. C. Johnson**
43 **SABREWING (IRE),** b f Fast Company (IRE)—Tawaafur **Qatar Racing Limited**
44 B f Danehill Dancer (IRE)—Shaanara (IRE) **Mr A. Al Banwan**
45 **SOUTHERN BELLE (IRE),** b f Aqlaam—Areyaam (USA) **Mr A. Jaber**
46 **SPICE MILL (IRE),** b c Dream Ahead (USA)—High Spice (USA) **Mr Khalifa Dasmal & Partner**
47 **SUMMER MUSIC (IRE),** b f Elnadim (USA)—Startori **Mr M. Al Shafar**
48 **TANAASUB (IRE),** ch f Lope de Vega (IRE)—Corryvreckan (IRE) **Mr A. Al Mansoori**
49 **UPSTANDING,** ch f Pivotal—Virtuous **Cheveley Park Stud Limited**
50 **WESTBOURNE GROVE (USA),** b c Munnings (USA)—Catch Me Later (USA) **K. Quinn/ C. Benham**
51 **ZAIN CENTRE (IRE),** b c Holy Roman Emperor (IRE)—Love Thirty **Mr A. Al Banwan**

TWO-YEAR-OLDS

52 Ch c 12/3 Kyllachy—Amazed (Clantime) (65000) **Mr A. Al Mansoori**
53 B c 15/5 Invincible Spirit (IRE)—Areyaam (USA) (Elusive Quality (USA)) **Mr A. Jaber**
54 B c 2/4 Kodiac—Cakestown Lady (IRE) (Petorius) (55000) **Mr A. Al Mansoori**
55 B f 17/4 Dubawi (IRE)—Coyote (Indian Ridge) (200000) **The Cool Silk Partnership**
56 Gr f 15/2 Arcano (IRE)—Daliana (Verglas (IRE)) (10000) **Mr Jaber Abdullah**
57 B c 18/3 Hat Trick (JPN)—Desert Sky (IRE) (Green Desert (USA)) (32000) **Mr M. Al Shafar**
58 **ELLIPTICAL,** ch f 26/2 Foxwedge (AUS)—Gyroscope (Spinning World (USA)) **Cheveley Park Stud Limited**
59 Ch f 11/3 Pastoral Pursuits—Instructress (Diktat) **Bottisham Heath Stud**
60 B f 30/3 Compton Place—Khyber Knight (IRE) (Night Shift (USA)) (30476) **Mr Khalifa Dasmal & Partner**
61 Ch c 26/2 Helmet (AUS)—Lady Gorgeous (Compton Place) **Mr Jaber Abdullah**
62 Ch c 29/3 Sakhee's Secret—Lark In The Park (IRE) (Grand Lodge (USA)) **Mia Racing**
63 Gr f 15/4 Dark Angel (IRE)—Mickleberry (IRE) (Desert Style (IRE)) (34000) **Mr Jaber Abdullah**
64 B c 18/2 Equiano (FR)—Morning After (Emperor Jones (USA)) (32000) **Mr M. Al Shafar**
65 B c 5/5 Casamento (IRE)—Pretty Majestic (IRE) (Invincible Spirit (IRE)) **Mr A. Jaber**
66 Ch f 21/3 Mayson—Resistance Heroine (Dr Fong (USA)) (32000) **Mr Jaber Abdullah**
67 B f 29/4 Kodiac—Valmirez (USA) (Smart Strike (CAN)) (40000) **The Cool Silk Partnership**
68 **VISIONARY (IRE),** b c 27/1 Dream Ahead (USA)—Avodale (IRE) (Lawman (FR)) (20000) **K. A. Dasmal**
69 **WAISHBOOSHBASH,** ch f 15/4 Kheleyf (USA)—Crystal Moments (Haafhd) **Mr Mohammed Jaber**

Other Owners: Mr Jaber Abdullah, Mrs E. Adamski, Mr Malih L. Al Basti, Mr Abdullah Al Mansoori, Mr Mohammed Al Shafar, Sheikh Khalifa Al Thani, Sheikh Suhaim Al Thani, I. J. Al-Sagar, Mr S. Ali, Mr C. F. Benham, Bottisham Heath Stud, Captain Bob Partnership, Mr A. Chapman, Cheveley Park Stud, Cool Silks Partnership, Mr Khalifa Dasmal, Mr Finster, Mrs Fitri Hay, Heart of the South Racing, Miss S. Hoare, Saleh Al Homaizi, Mr Cyril Humphris, Mr M. Jaber, Mr Ahmed Jaber, Mr G. Johnson, Ecurie La Boetie, Manor Farm Stud (Rutland), T. W. Morley, Mrs M. J. Morley, Pearl Bloodstock, J. R. Penny, Qatar Racing Limited, K. J. Quinn, A. J. Rix, Mr J. Sargeant, Mr I. Saunders, P. Swann, Mrs D. M. Swinburn, A. Tickle, M. A. Tickle, Mrs I. M. Tickle, Mrs B. E. Wilkinson, Mrs S. Wright.

Assistant Trainers: Mr Ross Studholme, Mr Harry Hughes-Onslow

116 MR CLIVE COX, Hungerford

Postal: **Beechdown Farm, Sheepdrove Road, Lambourn, Hungerford, Berkshire, RG17 7UN**
Contacts: **OFFICE (01488) 73072 FAX (01488) 73500 MOBILE (07740) 630521**
E-MAIL clive@clivecox.com WEBSITE www.clivecox.com

1 **ARCHIE (IRE)**, 4, b g Fast Company (IRE)—Winnifred **Seamus Burns, Tom Flaherty, Sabina Kelly**
2 **BRAZEN SPIRIT**, 4, gr g Zebedee—Never Say Deya **Mr T. H. S. Fox**
3 **CALLENDULA**, 4, ch f Halling (USA)—Oatey **R. Haim**
4 **DUTCH S**, 5, ch m Dutch Art—Park Law (IRE) **Mondial Racing & Robert Haim**
5 **FEAR OR FAVOUR (IRE)**, 5, b g Haatef (USA)—Insaaf **A. G. Craddock**
6 **ICE LORD (IRE)**, 4, gr g Verglas (IRE)—Special Lady (IRE) **Hintlesham Racing Ltd**
7 **KODI BEAR (IRE)**, 4, br c Kodiac—Hawattef (IRE) **Mrs O. A. Shaw**
8 **LADY D'S ROCK (IRE)**, 4, gr f Aussie Rules (USA)—Za Za **Mrs A. M. Dawes**
9 **LAIDBACK ROMEO (IRE)**, 4, b g Kodiac—Belmora (USA) **Mr R. P. Craddock**
10 **LITTLE PALAVER**, 4, b g Showcasing—Little Nymph **Mr T. H. S. Fox**
11 **LOUIE DE PALMA**, 4, b c Pastoral Pursuits—Tahirah **P. N. Ridgers**
12 **MY DREAM BOAT (IRE)**, 4, b c Lord Shanakill (USA)—Betty Burke **Mr & Mrs Paul & Clare Rooney**
13 **OUTBACK RULER (IRE)**, 4, gr g Aussie Rules (USA)—My American Beauty **The Rulers**
14 **PERFECT CRACKER**, 8, ch g Dubai Destination (USA)—Perfect Story (IRE) **Mildmay Racing**
15 **PROFITABLE (IRE)**, 4, b c Invincible Spirit (IRE)—Dani Ridge (IRE) **Mr A. D. Spence**
16 **QUINTUS CERIALIS (IRE)**, 4, b g Vale of York (IRE)—Red Fox (IRE) **Brighthelm Racing**
17 **QUITE A STORY**, 4, ch f Equiano (FR)—Perfect Story (IRE) **Mildmay Racing & D. H. Caslon**
18 **SEEKING MAGIC**, 8, b g Haafhd—Atnab (USA) **The Seekers**
19 **SHALIMAH (IRE)**, 4, br g Dark Angel (IRE)—Jemima's Art **Mrs C. A. Craddock**
20 **ST GEORGES ROCK (IRE)**, 4, b g Camacho—Radio Wave **Mrs A. M. Dawes**
21 **TEARS OF THE SUN**, 5, b m Mastercraftsman (IRE)—Perfect Star **Dr Bridget Drew & Partners**
22 **WEETLES**, 4, b f High Chaparral (IRE)—Millestan (IRE) **Mr David Clark, Mr Alistair Bentall, Mrs M. A. Penfold**
23 **WINTER SPICE (IRE)**, 5, gr g Verglas (IRE)—Summer Spice (IRE) **Spice Traders**

THREE-YEAR-OLDS

24 **ANDAR**, gr ro c Hellvelyn—Rioliina (IRE) **Mr D. Russell**
25 **ANGIE'S GIRL**, b f Exceed And Excel (AUS)—Expedience (USA) **Mrs A. M. Dawes**
26 **ATTITUDE ROCKS**, b c Dansili—Dorelia (IRE) **Mrs A. M. Dawes**
27 **BEAUTY NIGHT**, b g Showcasing—Night Symphonie **One Carat Partnership**
28 **BOBBY WHEELER**, b c Pivotal—Regal Rose **P. N. Ridgers**
29 **BOND TRADER**, b g Monsieur Bond (IRE)—Bidding Time **Beechdown Double O Sevens**
30 **CARPE DIEM LADY (IRE)**, b f Acclamation—Greenisland (IRE) **Mrs A. M. Dawes**
31 **CHELSEA'S BOY (IRE)**, gr c Rip Van Winkle (IRE)—St Roch (IRE) **Mr D. J. Dawes**
32 **CORELLA (IRE)**, b f Dream Ahead (USA)—Nashira **Old Peartree Stud**
33 **DON'T BLAME ME**, b g Captain Gerrard (IRE)—Dragon Flyer (IRE) **Mr & Mrs Paul & Clare Rooney**
34 **FASTEN UP**, b f Fastnet Rock (AUS)—Marisa (GER) **Biddestone Stud**
35 **GO ON GO ON GO ON**, b f Medicean—Piranha (USA) **Mr & Mrs Paul & Clare Rooney**
36 **HE'S MY CRACKER**, ch g Captain Gerrard (IRE)—Dalmunzie (IRE) **Mr & Mrs Paul & Clare Rooney**
37 **INCLINATION (IRE)**, b f Acclamation—Interaction **Mr James Egan**
38 **JOANNE PARK**, b f Kheleyf (USA)—Sarah Park (IRE) **Mr & Mrs D Cash & Mr P Turner**
39 **LAND OF DUBAI (IRE)**, b f Dubai Destination (USA)—Land Army (IRE) **Mr F. Ryan**
40 **LITTLE SALAMANCA**, ch g Sakhee's Secret—Little Nymph **Mr T. H. S. Fox**
41 **MAGIC STRIKE (IRE)**, b c Zebedee—Artemis Culture (USA) **The Arrows**
42 **MAJOR ASSAULT**, b c Kyllachy—Night Premiere (IRE) **Mrs O. A. Shaw**
43 **PERFECT QUEST**, br f Bushranger (IRE)—Love Quest **Hants & Herts**
44 **PETER PARK**, b c Kheleyf (USA)—Go Go Girl **Mr & Mrs D Cash & Mr P Turner**
45 **PINE RIDGE**, b f Elusive City (USA)—Fisadara **Wood Hall Stud Limited**
46 **PRICELESS**, b f Exceed And Excel (AUS)—Molly Brown **Mr A. D. Spence**
47 **PRIME PURPOSE (IRE)**, b g Kodiac—Open Verse (USA) **Miss J. Deadman & Mr S. Barrow**
48 **QUEBEE**, b f Sir Percy—Tintac **Mr M. A. Collins**
49 **RHYTHM AND BLUES**, b f Poet's Voice—Golden Nun **Mr A. D. Spence**
50 B c Pour Moi (IRE)—Sallanches (USA) **C. V. Wentworth**
51 **SILKEN SKIES**, ch f Zoffany (IRE)—Sky Red **Hot To Trot Racing Club**
52 **SOAPY AITKEN**, b c Pastoral Pursuits—Littlemisssunshine (IRE) **Kenneth MacPherson**
53 **STAUNCH**, bl c Pivotal—Striving (IRE) **Cheveley Park Stud Limited**
54 **STRAWBERRY SORBET**, b f Street Cry (IRE)—Strawberrydaiquiri **Cheveley Park Stud Limited**
55 **THE SPECIAL ONE**, br f Cape Cross (IRE)—Capote West (USA) **Mr D. J. Dawes**
56 **THREAT ASSESSED (IRE)**, b c Holy Roman Emperor (IRE)—High Reserve **A. G. Craddock**
57 **TOTALLY COMMITTED**, b c Invincible Spirit (IRE)—Zanzibar (IRE) **C. F. Harrington**
58 **WANT THE FAIRYTALE**, b f Mount Nelson—Tattercoats (FR) **Mondial Racing**

MR CLIVE COX - Continued

59 **YOURE ALWAYS RIGHT (IRE)**, b f Pour Moi (IRE)—Zaraba (IRE) **Mr & Mrs Paul & Clare Rooney**
60 **ZEEHAN**, gr f Aussie Rules (USA)—Cross Current **Mondial Racing**
61 **ZONDERLAND**, ch c Dutch Art—Barynya **Cheveley Park Stud Limited**

TWO-YEAR-OLDS

62 Ch f 17/2 Foxwedge (AUS)—Ahwahnee (Compton Place) **The Racegoers Club**
63 B c 15/2 Myboycharlie (IRE)—Audrey Brown (Mind Games) (19047) **Biddestone Stud**
64 **B B QUEEN (IRE)**, br f 14/3 Big Bad Bob (IRE)—Gold Queen (Grand Lodge (USA) (24363) **Hintlesham Racing**
65 B c 8/2 Dark Angel (IRE)—Beatrix Potter (IRE) (Cadeaux Genereux) (41904) **P. N. Ridgers**
66 B gr f 5/3 Mastercraftsman (IRE)—Dani Ridge (IRE) (Indian Ridge) (110000) **C. F. Harrington**
67 B f 14/4 Kodiac—Dark Arts (USA) (Royal Anthem (USA)) (47619) **Wood Hall Stud Limited**
68 **FLOOD WARNING**, ch f 23/2 Pivotal—Sabreon (Caerleon (USA)) (130000) **Cheveley Park Stud**
69 **FOXCATCHER**, ch f 20/2 Foxwedge (AUS)—Copy-Cat (Lion Cavern (USA)) **Whitsbury Manor Stud**
70 B c 9/2 Elzaam (AUS)—Harvest Joy (IRE) (Daggers Drawn (USA)) (29531) **New Syndicate**
71 **HIGHLAND MINER (IRE)**, ch f 21/1 Zebedee—
                                         Red Blanche (IRE) (Red Clubs (IRE)) (32380) **Highland Thoroughbred Ltd**
72 B g 26/2 Bated Breath—Highland Jewel (IRE) (Azamour (IRE)) (33000) **Highland Thoroughbred Ltd**
73 Br gr c 24/2 Delegator—Ice Haven (IRE) (Verglas (IRE)) **Mrs O. A. Shaw**
74 Br f 14/4 Sir Prancealot (IRE)—Larkfield Empress (IRE) (Holy Roman Emperor (IRE)) (9523)
75 Ch f 17/2 Mayson—Lisieux Orchid (IRE) (Sadler's Wells (USA)) (47619) **Wood Hall Stud Limited**
76 B c 24/1 Kodiac—Magilini (IRE) (Bertolini (USA)) (30269) **B Allen, G Hill & N Wagland**
77 Ch f 19/4 Lawman (FR)—Miracle Seeker (Rainbow Quest (USA)) **Mr D. J. Burke**
78 **MISTER FREEZE (IRE)**, ch c 16/3 Frozen Power (IRE)—
                                         Beacon of Hope (IRE) (Barathea (IRE)) (25839) **Ken Lock Racing**
79 **MISTER SUNSHINE (IRE)**, ch c 26/4 Fast Company (IRE)—
                                         Second Omen (Rainbow Quest (USA)) (7619) **A. J. Perkins**
80 **PERFECT LADY**, b f 5/4 Excelebration (IRE)—Theladyinquestion (Dubawi (IRE)) **Mildmay Racing & D. H. Caslon**
81 B c 9/2 Makfi—Perfect Spirit (IRE) (Invincible Spirit (IRE)) (90000) **Dr Bridget Drew & Partners**
82 B c 13/3 Excelebration (IRE)—Quiritis (Galileo (IRE)) (162421) **Mr P. K. Siu**
83 B f 16/3 Helmet (AUS)—Red Fuschia (Polish Precedent (USA)) (36000) **Appletree Stud**
84 Ch f 17/2 Medicean—Regal Heiress (Pivotal) **Cheveley Park Stud**
85 Ch c 8/3 Helmet (AUS)—Reine de Romance (Vettori (IRE)) (54000) **Mr A. D. Spence**
86 **SEE THE MASTER (IRE)**, b c 13/2 Dutch Art—
                                         See Emily Play (IRE) (Galileo (IRE)) (95000) **Mr & Mrs P. Hargreaves**
87 Gr c 31/3 Dark Angel (IRE)—Sixfields Flyer (IRE) (Desert Style (IRE)) (59062) **A. G. Craddock**
88 B c 5/3 Delegator—Sparkle Park (Kyllachy) **Mr & Mrs D. Cash & Mr P. Turner**
89 **STAND N DELIVER**, br c 21/3 Dick Turpin (IRE)—Drifting Gold (Bold Edge) **Mr M. Oliver**
90 **TIS MARVELLOUS**, b c 1/2 Harbour Watch (IRE)—
                                         Mythicism (Oasis Dream) (49523) **Miss J. Deadman & Mr S. Barrow**
91 **TIS WONDERFUL (IRE)**, b c 10/4 Casamento (IRE)—
                                         Cosenza (Bahri (USA)) (33222) **Miss J. Deadman & Mr S. Barrow**
92 **WASHINGTON BLUE**, b f 19/4 Rip Van Winkle (IRE)—
                                         Powder Blue (Daylami (IRE)) (14000) **Cavendish Bloodstock Racing**
93 B c 19/1 Henrythenavigator (USA)—Wonderful Desert (Green Desert (USA)) (30000) **New Syndicate**

Assistant Trainer: Shaun Johnson

Jockey (flat): John Fahy, Adam Kirby. **Apprentice:** Josh Quinn, Ryan Tate.

---

117 **MR TONY COYLE, Norton**
Postal: **Long Row Stables, Beverley Road, Norton, Malton, North Yorkshire, YO17 9PJ**
Contacts: **MOBILE (07976) 621425**
E-MAIL tonycoyleracing@hotmail.co.uk

1 **BLING NOIR (IRE)**, 6, b m High Chaparral (IRE)—Tribal Princess (IRE) **Mr A. C. Coyle**
2 **FLICKA'S BOY**, 4, b g Paco Boy (IRE)—Selkirk Sky **Twenty Four Seven Recruitment Services Ltd**
3 **FLOWER POWER**, 5, br m Bollin Eric—Floral Rhapsody **Ms M. H. Matheson**
4 **HORSFORTH**, 4, b f Kyllachy—Lady McBeth **Morecool Racing**
5 **KEEP IT DARK**, 7, b g Invincible Spirit (IRE)—Tarneem (USA) **Exors of the Late Mr N. Hetherton**
6 **LENDAL BRIDGE**, 5, ch g Avonbridge—Dunloe (IRE) **Mrs V. C. Sugden**
7 **LUCKY LANDING (IRE)**, 10, b br g Well Chosen—Melville Rose (IRE) **Gary Dewhurst & Tony Coyle**
8 **MAGIC EMPRESS (IRE)**, 4, b f Baltic King—Red Trance (IRE) **Mr A. C. Coyle**
9 **MAUREB (IRE)**, 4, br f Excellent Art—Almost Blue (USA) **Gap Personnel & Tony Coyle**

MR TONY COYLE - Continued

10 **MOLLY APPROVE (IRE)**, 4, b f Approve (IRE)—Kathleen Rafferty (IRE) **Kerr's Cronies**
11 **OUR KYLIE (IRE)**, 4, b f Jeremy (USA)—Prakara (IRE) **Morecool & Cool Racing**
12 **PERFECT FIT (IRE)**, 4, ch f Teofilo (IRE)—Queen of Lyons (USA) **Plantation Stud**
13 **SAMSONITE (IRE)**, 4, ch g Pivotal—Silca's Sister **Antony Denham & Chris Green**
14 **SILVER DRAGON**, 8, gr g Silver Patriarch (IRE)—Gotogeton **Twenty Four Seven Recruitment Services Ltd**
15 **TAFFETTA**, 4, ch f Paco Boy (IRE)—Tarneem (USA) **Mrs H. B. Raw**
16 **THATCHERITE (IRE)**, 8, gr g Verglas (IRE)—Damiana (IRE) **Mr B. Kerr**
17 **WESTWOOD HOE**, 5, b g Oasis Dream—Disco Volante **Gap Personnel & Craig Buckingham**

THREE-YEAR-OLDS

18 **ADHERENCE**, b g Sir Percy—Straight Laced **M. A. Scaife**
19 **BALLYCOYLE GIRL (IRE)**, b f Manduro (GER)—Gwyllion (USA) **Gary Dewhurst & Tony Coyle**
20 B f Excellent Art—Granny Kelly (USA) **Mr A. C. Coyle**
21 **INDULGENT**, b c Makfi—Santa Agata (FR) **M. A. Scaife**
22 B g Haafhd—Jenise (IRE) **W. P. S. Johnson**
23 **LITTLE PIPPIN**, b f Sir Percy—Lady Le Quesne (IRE) **Mr A. C. Coyle**
24 **NEW ROAD SIDE**, b f Paco Boy (IRE)—Spring Green **Morecool Racing & Partner**
25 **PICKETT'S CHARGE**, b g Clodovil (IRE)—Chelsea Morning **Morecool Racing & Cool Racing**
26 **PROVEN POINT (IRE)**, b c Fastnet Rock (AUS)—Speciale (USA) **Mr A. C. Coyle**
27 **THE EXCEL QUEEN (IRE)**, br f Excellent Art—Gypsie Queen (IRE) **Chris Varley & Simon Parkinson**

TWO-YEAR-OLDS

28 Ch c 19/2 Paco Boy (IRE)—Branston Gem (So Factual (USA)) (24761) **Mr G. Dewhurst**

Other Owners: Mr S. Bland, Mr C. Buckingham, Mr J. J. Cosgrove, Mr A. Denham, Gap Personnel Franchises Limited, C. R. Green, Mr T. D. Nield, Mrs A. O'Leary, Mrs W. O'Leary, M. O'Leary, Mr S. J. Parkinson, Mr M. Sykes, Mr C. J. Varley, Mr A. Wilson.

Assistant Trainer: Jaimie Kerr

Jockey (flat): Stephen Craine, Barry McHugh. **Amateur:** Miss Harriet Dukes.

---

118 **MR RAY CRAGGS, Sedgefield**
Postal: **East Close Farm, Sedgefield, Stockton-On-Tees, Cleveland, TS21 3HW**
Contacts: **PHONE (01740) 620239 FAX (01740) 623476**

1 **CORAL QUEEN**, 5, b m Desideratum—Queen's Lodge (IRE) **R. Craggs**
2 **DOWNTOWN BOY (IRE)**, 8, br g Kheleyf (USA)—Uptown (IRE) **R. Craggs**
3 **FLEURTILLE**, 7, b m Tillerman—Miss Fleurie **R. Craggs**
4 **NEEDWOOD PARK**, 8, br g Needwood Blade—Waterpark **R. Craggs**
5 **PARK HOUSE**, 7, b g Tillerman—Rasin Luck **R. Craggs**
6 **TAKE A BREAK**, 5, b m Josr Algarhoud (IRE)—Waterpark **R. Craggs**
7 **WELL I NEVER**, 4, b g Josr Algarhoud (IRE)—Tour d'amour (IRE) **R. Craggs**

Assistant Trainer: Miss J N Craggs

---

119 **MR PETER CRATE, Dorking**
Postal: **Springfield Farm, Parkgate Road, Newdigate, Dorking, Surrey, RH5 5DZ**
Contacts: **MOBILE (07775) 821560**
E-MAIL peterdcrate@jandjfranks.com

1 **PICANSORT**, 9, b g Piccolo—Running Glimpse (IRE) **P. D. Crate**
2 **SANDFRANKSKIPSGO**, 7, ch g Piccolo—Alhufoof (USA) **P. D. Crate**
3 **SMOOTHTALKINRASCAL (IRE)**, 6, b g Kodiac—Cool Tarifa (IRE) **Peter Crate & Gallagher Equine Ltd**
4 **TAAJUB (IRE)**, 9, b g Exceed And Excel (AUS)—Purple Tiger (IRE) **P. D. Crate**

THREE-YEAR-OLDS

5 **FRANK SANDATRA**, b g Equiano (FR)—Alhufoof (USA) **P. D. Crate**
6 **SAND BY ME**, b g Piccolo—Marysienka **P. D. Crate**

MR PETER CRATE - Continued

TWO-YEAR-OLDS

7 B f 25/1 Piccolo—Ivory's Joy (Tina's Pet) **P. D. Crate**

Other Owners: Gallagher Equine Ltd.

Jockey (flat): George Baker, Shane Kelly. **Amateur:** Mr George Crate.

---

120 MR SIMON CRISFORD, Newmarket
Postal: **Calne Stables, 49A Bury Road, Newmarket, Suffolk, CB8 7BY**
Contacts: **PHONE (01638) 662661**
E-MAIL office@crisfordracing.com

1 **GANG WARFARE,** 5, b g Medicean—Light Impact (IRE)
2 **MUTAWATHEA,** 5, b g Exceed And Excel (AUS)—Esteemed Lady (IRE)
3 **PERIL,** 5, ch g Pivotal—Portodora (USA)
4 **WELD AL EMARAT,** 4, b g Dubawi (IRE)—Spirit of Dubai (IRE)

THREE-YEAR-OLDS

5 **ADEEB (IRE),** b g Iffraaj—Flamenco Red
6 **ANDANOTHERONE (IRE),** b f Kodiac—Itsanothergirl
7 **CELEBRATION DAY (IRE),** b g Raven's Pass (USA)—Bunting
8 **DAAFIK,** b g Shamardal (USA)—Princess Danah (IRE)
9 **DAME JUDI (IRE),** b f Shamardal (USA)—Miss Hepburn (USA)
10 **DAQEEQ (IRE),** b c New Approach (IRE)—Asawer (IRE)
11 **DELIGHTFUL BELLE (USA),** b f Elusive Quality (USA)—Delighted (IRE)
12 **DISCREET HERO (IRE),** ch c Siyouni (FR)—Alfaguara (USA)
13 **DONNERHALL (IRE),** b g Kendargent (FR)—Daidoo (IRE)
14 **FELIX ARTURO (IRE),** ch g Lope de Vega (IRE)—Rain Dancer (IRE)
15 **FIRST SELECTION (SPA),** b c Diktat—Villa Sonata
16 **FLOWER CUP,** b f Acclamation—Amber Queen (IRE)
17 **FLOWER OF LOVE,** br f Poet's Voice—Fragrancy (IRE)
18 **GREATEST VIRTUE,** b f Poet's Voice—Demerger (USA)
19 **HAPPY CALL,** b g Kodiac—Munaa's Dream
20 **IMPULSIVE DREAM (IRE),** b g Rip Van Winkle (IRE)—Grecian Dancer
21 **INCREDIBLE DREAM (IRE),** b g Vale of York (IRE)—Finnmark
22 **JAWAAYIZ,** b f Kodiac—Silkenveil (IRE)
23 **JETSTREAM EXPRESS (IRE),** b c New Approach (IRE)—Airline (USA)
24 **KENSINGTON STAR,** b c Pivotal—Wild Silk
25 **KINDLY,** b f Kyllachy—Touching (IRE)
26 B f Dubawi (IRE)—Lady Zonda
27 **LORD MARMADUKE,** ch c Duke of Marmalade (IRE)—Maid To Treasure (IRE)
28 **LUCKY LOT,** b f Exceed And Excel (AUS)—Sweetie Time
29 **NEW HAPPINESS (IRE),** b f Teofilo (IRE)—Anyaas (IRE)
30 **PALENVILLE (IRE),** ch f Rip Van Winkle (IRE)—Faithful Duchess (IRE)
31 **PENNY POET (IRE),** b f Intikhab (USA)—Mneme (FR)
32 **PHANTOM ISLE,** b g Teofilo (IRE)—Antillia
33 **PRIDE OF ANGELS,** gr f Dark Angel (IRE)—Openness
34 **RAASHDY (IRE),** b c Intikhab (USA)—Maghya (IRE)
35 **RED ARTIST,** b g Archipenko (USA)—Danceatdusk
36 **SAYEEDATY ANESATY,** b f Zamindar (USA)—Dubai Media (CAN)
37 **SENSES OF DUBAI,** b c Royal Applause—Umseyat (USA)
38 **SILK CRAVAT,** ch g Kyllachy—Polly Floyer
39 **TAFTEESH (IRE),** b g Kodiac—Mudalalah (USA)
40 **TAWDHEEF (IRE),** br g Zebedee—Duchess of Foxland (IRE)
41 **TIME TO BLOSSOM,** b f Cape Cross (IRE)—Time Over
42 **WAFI STAR (IRE),** b g Showcasing—Ophelia's Song
43 **WASSEEM (IRE),** ch g Approve (IRE)—Vintage Escape (IRE)
44 **ZANJABEEL,** b g Aussie Rules (USA)—Grain Only

Trainer did not wish details of his two-year-olds to appear

121 MR ANDREW CROOK, Leyburn

Postal: **Ashgill Stables (Yard 2), Tupgill Park, Coverham, Middleham, North Yorkshire, DL8 4TJ**
Contacts: PHONE **(01969) 640303** MOBILE **(07764) 158899**
E-MAIL **andycrookracing@fsmail.net** WEBSITE **www.andrewcrookracing.co.uk**

1 **AGESILAS (FR)**, 8, gr g Ultimately Lucky (IRE)—Aimessa du Berlais (FR) **R. P. E. Berry**
2 **AIR CHIEF**, 11, ch g Dr Fong (USA)—Fly For Fame **Lucky Catch Partnership**
3 **ALMAHOY**, 5, b m Martaline—Tokahy (FR) **Mr W. Henderson**
4 **ALONG CAME THEO (IRE)**, 6, b g Vertical Speed (FR)—Kachina (IRE) **Mr G. Heap**
5 **BAH LAMB**, 5, ch m Sakhee (USA)—Lucinda Lamb **Mrs D. S. Wilkinson**
6 **CERTIFICATION (IRE)**, 6, b g Authorized (IRE)—Most Charming (FR) **Mr W. Henderson**
7 **COOLCALMCOLLECTED (IRE)**, 4, b f Acclamation—Jalissa **Mr D. Hopper**
8 **CRAKEHALL LAD (IRE)**, 5, ch g Manduro (GER)—My Uptown Girl **Mrs K. M. Savage**
9 **CYRANO STAR (FR)**, 4, gr g Martaline—Quezac du Boulay (FR) **Leeds Plywood & Doors**
10 **DISTURB**, 4, ch g Halling (USA)—Ataraxy **Mr D. Carter**
11 **EARLY BOY (FR)**, 5, b g Early March—Eclat de Rose (FR) **R. P. E. Berry**
12 5, B m Afflora (IRE)—Fairlie **Margaret Hodgeson**
13 **FOUR BUCKS**, 4, b g Virtual—Jontys'lass **Ashgill Stud**
14 **HE WHO DARES**, 5, gr g Act One—Who Goes There **Lucky Catch Partnership**
15 **JACARNO**, 4, ch g Lucarno (USA)—Sparkling Jewel **Mrs V. Henderson**
16 **JIMMIE BROWN (USA)**, 8, b g Street Cry (IRE)—Vid Kid (CAN) **The 100 Club**
17 **LITTLE MISS FLOSSY**, 7, b m Kayf Tara—The Ginger Whinger **Mr A. W. Muir**
18 **NASHVILLE (IRE)**, 7, b g Galileo (IRE)—Brown Eyes **Mr D. Carter**
19 **ONE IN A ROW (IRE)**, 9, ch g Saffron Walden (FR)—Rostarr (IRE) **Lucky Catch Partnership**
20 **REMEDIO (IRE)**, 6, b g Ramonti (FR)—Cant Hurry Love **Lucky Catch Partnership**
21 **SHEILAS LADY**, 8, b m Tamure (IRE)—Ladies From Leeds **Mr Tom England**
22 **VENTUREPREDEMENTIA**, 5, b g Indian Danehill (IRE)—Sounds Familiar (IRE) **Elite Ladies Racing Club**
23 **ZAZAMIX (FR)**, 11, b g Sagamix (FR)—Ombre Bleue (FR) **Mrs C. Hopper**

THREE-YEAR-OLDS

24 B g Mount Nelson—Local Abbey (IRE) **Mr W. Henderson**
25 B g Alfred Nobel (IRE)—Twinberry (IRE) **Mr W. Henderson**

TWO-YEAR-OLDS

26 B f 13/4 Malinas (GER)—Jontys'lass (Tamure (IRE)) **Ashgill Stud**

Other Owners: John Sinclair Haulage, Helen Sinclair.

Assistant Trainer: Amy Crook

Jockey (flat): Neil Farley. **Conditional:** John Kington.

122 MISS JO CROWLEY, Whitcombe

Postal: **Whitcombe Moneymusk Racing Stables, Whitcombe, Dorchester, Dorset, DT2 8NY**
Contacts: PHONE **(01305) 265300** FAX **(01305) 265499** MOBILE **(07918) 735219**
E-MAIL **jocrowley61@hotmail.co.uk**

1 **COMADOIR (IRE)**, 10, ch g Medecis—Hymn of The Dawn (USA) **Exors of the Late Mrs E. A. M. Nelson**
2 **DREAM RULER**, 5, b g Holy Roman Emperor (USA)—Whatcameoverme (USA) **Mrs J. A. Cornwell**
3 **MUSIC MAN (IRE)**, 6, b g Oratorio (IRE)—Chanter **Mrs J. A. Cornwell**
4 **MYSTICAL SAPPHIRE**, 6, b m Sakhee's Secret—Nadyma (IRE) **Mrs J. A. Cornwell**
5 **SEA REGATTA (IRE)**, 7, b m Hurricane Run (IRE)—Regatta (USA) **Mrs J. A. Cornwell**
6 **TANZINA**, 4, b f Equiano (FR)—Pilcomayo (IRE) **Mrs J. A. Cornwell**
7 **THREAVE**, 8, b m Diktat—Bianca Sforza **Mrs J. A. Cornwell**
8 **WILFRED PICKLES (IRE)**, 10, ch g Cadeaux Genereux—Living Daylights (IRE) **Mrs J. A. Cornwell**

THREE-YEAR-OLDS

9 B c Lawman (FR)—Abunai **Mrs J. A. Cornwell**
10 Ch f Pastoral Pursuits—Bazelle **Mrs J. A. Cornwell**
11 Ch g Roderic O'Connor (IRE)—Bianca Sforza **Mrs J. A. Cornwell**
12 **EJAYTEEKAY**, b f Big Bad Bob (IRE)—Lovely Dream (IRE) **TMBS Solutions Ltd**
13 Ch c Frozen Power (IRE)—Eleanor Eloise **Mrs J. A. Cornwell**
14 B f Royal Applause—Merle **Mrs J. A. Cornwell**
15 Ch g Intikhab (USA)—Mistress Bailey (IRE) **Mrs J. A. Cornwell**

MISS JO CROWLEY - Continued

16 **SANDACRES**, b c Frozen Power (IRE)—Lady Golan (IRE) **Mrs J. A. Cornwell**
17 B f Iffraaj—Speak Softly To Me (USA) **Mrs J. A. Cornwell**
18 B f Kheleyf (USA)—Stravie (IRE) **Mrs J. A. Cornwell**
19 B f Dick Turpin (IRE)—Whatcameoverme (USA) **Mrs J. A. Cornwell**

TWO-YEAR-OLDS

20 B f 24/3 Excelebration (IRE)—Merle (Selkirk (USA)) **Mrs J. A. Cornwell**
21 Ch f 7/4 Sakhee's Secret—Porcelana (IRE) (Highest Honor (FR)) **Mrs J. A. Cornwell**

Assistant Trainer: Anthony Clark

Jockey (flat): Dane O'Neill, Fergus Sweeney.

---

123 MR LUCA CUMANI, Newmarket
Postal: **Bedford House Stables, Bury Road, Newmarket, Suffolk, CB8 7BX**
Contacts: **PHONE (01638) 665432 FAX (01638) 667160 MOBILE (07801) 225300**
E-MAIL luca@lucacumani.com WEBSITE www.lucacumani.com

1 **AL**, 4, b g Halling (USA)—Incarnation (IRE) **Hunter, Moulton, Ramsden**
2 **ARCHERY PEAK**, 4, b g Arch (USA)—Come Touch The Sun (IRE) **Mr J. S. Kelly**
3 **BERMONDSEY**, 4, b g Galileo (IRE)—Barter **Fittocks Stud**
4 **BESS OF HARDWICK**, 4, b f Dansili—Request **The Duke of Devonshire**
5 **DREAMLIKE**, 4, b f Oasis Dream—So Silk **Fittocks Stud & Andrew Bengough**
6 **FALLEN FOR A STAR**, 4, b g Sea The Stars (IRE)—Fallen Star **Normandie Stud**
7 **INTERSTELLA**, 4, b f Sea The Stars (IRE)—Hyperspectra **Helena Springfield Ltd**
8 **KOORA**, 4, b f Pivotal—Kithanga (IRE) **Fittocks Stud**
9 **LAURENCE**, 4, b g Dubawi (IRE)—Victoire Celebre (USA) **Fittocks Stud & Andrew Bengough**
10 **LOVING THINGS**, 4, b f Pivotal—Fallen In Love **Normandie Stud**
11 **MIZZOU (IRE)**, 5, b b Galileo (IRE)—Moments of Joy **Mr J. S. Kelly**
12 **PAMONA (IRE)**, 4, b f Duke of Marmalade (IRE)—Palanca **Highclere Thoroughbred Racing (Albany)**
13 **SECOND SPEAR (IRE)**, 5, b g Dalakhani (IRE)—My Dark Rosaleen **Merry Fox Stud Limited**
14 **SHAKOPEE**, 4, b g High Chaparral (IRE)—Tentpole (USA) **Kangyu International Racing (HK) Ltd**
15 **UNNOTICED**, 4, b g Observatory (USA)—Celestial Empire (USA) **Thrift Farm Stud**

THREE-YEAR-OLDS

16 **AL KHAFJI**, ch c New Approach (IRE)—Wadaat **Al Shaqab Racing UK Limited**
17 **ANGELA NORTH**, b f Canford Cliffs (IRE)—Vallota **Mrs M. Marinopoulos**
18 **BANKSEA**, b c Lawman (FR)—Stars In Your Eyes **L. Marinopoulos**
19 **BEAUTIFUL MORNING**, b f Galileo (IRE)—Date With Destiny (IRE) **Mr J. S. Kelly**
20 **BLIND FAITH (IRE)**, ch f Zoffany (IRE)—Guajira (FR) **Christopher Wright & Miss Emily Asprey**
21 **BRODIE**, gr f Sea The Stars (IRE)—Dali's Grey **Normandie Stud Ltd**
22 **CRYPTIC (IRE)**, br g Lord Shanakill (USA)—Privet (IRE) **Mrs A. S. Silver**
23 **DIAMOND GEYSER (IRE)**, b c Champs Elysees—Triomphale (USA) **L. Marinopoulos**
24 **EL VIP (IRE)**, b c Pivotal—Elle Danzig (GER) **Al Shaqab Racing UK Limited**
25 **FALLEN FOR ANOTHER**, b c Dansili—Fallen Star **Normandie Stud**
26 **FARANDINE**, ch f Rock of Gibraltar (IRE)—Rivara **Fittocks Stud**
27 **FASTNET MONSOON (IRE)**, b c Fastnet Rock (AUS)—Mona Lisa **O.T.I. Racing & Partner**
28 **FOUR ON EIGHT**, gr c Lawman (FR)—Pocket Watch **Mr S. A. Stuckey**
29 **GADWA**, b f Oasis Dream—Lady of Everest (IRE) **Saleh Al Homaizi & Imad Al Sagar**
30 **HAGGLE**, ch f Pivotal—Barter **Fittocks Stud**
31 **KILIM**, b f Dansili—Kibara **Fittocks Stud**
32 **MATERIALISTIC**, b f Oasis Dream—Pongee **Fittocks Stud**
33 **MYOPIC**, b f Teofilo (IRE)—Blinking **The Duke of Devonshire & The Duke of Roxburghe**
34 **ONLY ME (IRE)**, b f Galileo (IRE)—Danedrop (IRE) **Mr Michael Tabor & Mrs John Magnier**
35 **PACHARANA**, b f Oasis Dream—Cascata (IRE) **Mr S. A. Stuckey**
36 **PINSTRIPE**, br c Dansili—Paisley **Fittocks Stud**
37 **ROCK'N GOLD**, b g Fastnet Rock (AUS)—La Concorde (FR) **Bartisan Racing Ltd**
38 **ROYAL MAHOGANY (IRE)**, b c Kodiac—Chiba (UAE) **Emma Capon & Mrs Simon Marsh**
39 **SILK SUIT (FR)**, b c Rip Van Winkle (IRE)—Silk Gallery (USA) **Buxted Partnership**
40 **STANLEY**, ch c Sea The Stars (IRE)—Deirdre **Normandie Stud**
41 **TESTIMONIO**, b c Cacique (IRE)—Witness **O.T.I. Racing**
42 **TIPTREE (IRE)**, b f Duke of Marmalade (IRE)—Taking Liberties (IRE) **Mr Michael & Mrs Michelle Morris**
43 **VERY DASHING**, br f Dansili—Dash To The Top **Helena Springfield Ltd**
44 **VUELA**, ch f Duke of Marmalade (IRE)—Victoire Finale **Mr S. A. Stuckey**

MR LUCA CUMANI - Continued

45 **WANNABE FRIENDS**, ch c Dubawi (IRE)—Wannabe Posh (IRE) **Normandie Stud**
46 **WAR STORY (IRE)**, gr c Myboycharlie (IRE)—America Nova (FR) **Mr G. L. Grimish**
47 **YELLOW BAND (USA)**, ch f Dalakhani (IRE)—My Dark Rosaleen **Merry Fox Stud Limited**

TWO-YEAR-OLDS

48 Gr ro c 27/4 Dream Ahead (USA)—America Nova (FR) (Verglas (IRE)) (82000) **Buxted Partnership**
49 B f 10/2 Raven's Pass (USA)—
                    Aneedah (IRE) (Invincible Spirit (IRE)) (370000) **Saleh Al Homaizi & Imad Al Sagar**
50 B c 7/4 Pivotal—Atlantic Destiny (IRE) (Royal Academy (USA)) (150000) **Al Shaqab Racing**
51 Gr f 19/1 Galileo (IRE)—Bewitched (IRE) (Dansili) (360000) **Al Shaqab Racing**
52 **BEYOND RECALL**, b f 14/4 Cacique (IRE)—Forgotten Dreams (IRE) (Olden Times) **Fittocks Stud**
53 **BLONDIKOVA**, b f 27/4 Pivotal—Cosmodrome (USA) (Bahri) **Fittocks Stud**
54 **BUCKEYE**, b c 24/3 Shamardal (USA)—Tenderly (IRE) (Danehill (USA)) (103359) **Mr J. S. Kelly**
55 **CANNED HEAT**, b c 13/4 Dansili—One So Marvellous (Nashwan) **Castle Down Racing**
56 **CHAPPARAL**, gr c 17/3 High Chaparral (IRE)—Kassiyra (IRE) (Kendor (FR)) **Fittocks Stud**
57 B c 9/4 Zoffany (IRE)—Chocolate Mauk (USA) (Cozzene (USA)) (58000) **Dahab Racing**
58 Bl c 13/5 Pivotal—Contredanse (IRE) (Danehill Dancer (IRE)) (87000) **Mr S. A. Stuckey**
59 **CORNWALLIS**, b c 5/2 High Chaparral (IRE)—
                    Merry Jaunt (USA) (Street Sense (USA)) (110000) **Emma Capon & Mrs Simon Marsh**
60 **CROSSING PATHS (IRE)**, b f 14/4 Cape Cross (IRE)—
                    Rebelline (IRE) (Robellino (USA)) (420000) **Merry Fox Stud II Limited**
61 B c 15/2 Authorized (IRE)—Crystal Swan (IRE) (Dalakhani (IRE)) **Saleh Al Homaizi & Imad Al Sagar**
62 B f 29/1 Galileo (IRE)—Daneleta (IRE) (Danehill (USA)) (221483) **Clipper Logistics**
63 B c 30/3 Nathaniel (IRE)—Darinza (FR) (Dalakhani (IRE)) (45000) **Mr L. Marinopoulos**
64 B f 18/4 Teofilo (IRE)—Deep Winter (Pivotal) (66445) **Coolmore**
65 B c 23/4 Cacique (IRE)—Doggerbank (IRE) (Oasis Dream) **Mr G. Schoeningh**
66 **DUBARA**, b f 1/5 Dubawi (IRE)—Kibara (Sadler's Wells (USA)) **Fittocks Stud**
67 B f 1/3 Frankel (IRE)—Dynaforce (USA) (Dynaformer (USA)) (450000) **Al Shaqab Racing**
68 B c 2/2 Mastercraftsman (IRE)—Eurolink Raindance (IRE) (Alzao (USA)) (125000) **Mr J. D. Cotton**
69 B f 26/3 Nathaniel (IRE)—Ever Rigg (Dubai Destination (USA)) **St Albans Bloodstock**
70 B c 21/4 Zoffany (IRE)—Glympse (IRE) (Spectrum (IRE)) (200000) **Al Shaqab Racing**
71 **GREAT COURT**, gr f 11/4 Mastercraftsman (IRE)—
                    Neat Shilling (IRE) (Bob Back (USA)) (32000) **Mr J. Shack & Mr G. Barnard**
72 B f 30/3 Nathaniel (IRE)—Hazy Dancer (Oasis Dream) (150000) **Mr Michael & Mrs Michelle Morris**
73 **HIGHFALUTING (IRE)**, b c 12/2 High Chaparral (IRE)—
                    Walk On Water (Exceed And Excel (AUS)) (50000) **Mr L. Marinopoulos**
74 **HOUNDSTOOTH (IRE)**, b c 7/2 Dream Ahead (USA)—Baileys Gleam (Compton Place) (95976) **Mr J. S. Kelly**
75 B c 18/3 High Chaparral (IRE)—
                    Jewel In The Sand (IRE) (Bluebird (USA)) (125000) **Highclere T'Bred Racing-Edward Lear**
76 B f 16/3 Invincible Spirit (IRE)—Kitty Wells (Sadler's Wells (USA)) **Mr Stuart Stuckey**
77 **KNIGHT PROTECTOR**, b c 8/2 Dansili—Queen of Pentacles (IRE) (Selkirk (USA)) **Normandie Stud**
78 B f 24/3 Invincible Spirit (IRE)—Leavingonajetplane (IRE) (Danehill (USA)) (90000) **Apple Tree Stud**
79 **LIGHTABLE**, b f 5/3 Shamardal (USA)—Luminance (IRE) (Danehill Dancer (IRE)) **Fittocks Stud**
80 B c 29/3 Dansili—Loulwa (IRE) (Montjeu (IRE)) **Saleh Al Homaizi & Imad Al Sagar**
81 Ch f 20/2 Nathaniel (IRE)—Majestic Dancer (IRE) (Danehill Dancer (IRE)) (45000) **Dahab Racing**
82 **MARKETEER**, b f 11/4 Oasis Dream—Barter (Daylami) (240000) **Emma Capon & Fittocks Stud**
83 **MEDICEAN DREAM (IRE)**, br c 7/3 Medicean—Oasis Fire (IRE) (Oasis Dream) (42820) **Mr C. Bloor**
84 B c 2/3 Fastnet Rock (AUS)—Mona Lisa (Giant's Causeway (USA)) **OTI Racing & Partner**
85 B c 25/4 Rock of Gibraltar (IRE)—Muluk (IRE) (Rainbow Quest (USA)) (68000)
86 **PARISIAN CHIC (IRE)**, b f 30/4 Kodiac—
                    Divine Design (IRE) (Barathea (IRE)) (78000) **Bedford House Fillies Syndicate**
87 **PARTY NIGHTS**, b f 11/4 Lawman (FR)—
                    Funseeker (UAE) (Halling (USA)) (12000) **Bedford House Fillies Syndicate**
88 **PERFECT SPY**, b f 9/2 Nathaniel (IRE)—
                    Heavenly Whisper (IRE) (Halling (USA)) (65000) **Bedford House Fillies Syndicate**
89 **PINCHECK (IRE)**, b c 7/3 Invincible Spirit (IRE)—Arty Crafty (USA) (Arch (USA)) (273163) **Mr J. S. Kelly**
90 **PLEASANT SURPRISE (IRE)**, b f 15/3 Mastercraftsman (IRE)—
                    Ibiza Dream (Night Shift (USA)) (52000) **Bedford House Fillies Syndicate**
91 **QUEEN GWENDOLEN**, b f 6/3 Nathaniel (IRE)—Factice (USA) (Known Fact (USA)) (50000) **Emma Capon**
92 **RED LABEL (IRE)**, b c 13/4 Dubawi (IRE)—Born Something (IRE) (Caerleon (USA)) (375000) **Mr J. S. Kelly**
93 B f 20/1 Oasis Dream—Require (Montjeu (IRE)) **Duke Of Devonshire**
94 **RICKRACK (IRE)**, b f 28/1 Teofilo (IRE)—Arazena (USA) (Woodman (USA)) (260000) **Mr J. S. Kelly**
95 **ROMINA**, b f 30/1 Raven's Pass (USA)—Dolores (Danehill (USA)) **Normandie Stud**
96 **SIMPLY FATE**, b f 24/3 Pivotal—Alvee (IRE) (Key of Luck (USA)) **Merry Fox Stud**
97 B f 28/4 Lawman (FR)—So Silk (Rainbow Quest (USA)) (450000) **Lordship Stud**

MR LUCA CUMANI - Continued

98 SPINNAKA (IRE), b f 7/4 Invincible Spirit (IRE)—
Spinning Well (IRE) (Pivotal) (160000) **Fittocks Stud & Mr A. Bengough**
99 SPUN GOLD, ch c 27/4 Exceed And Excel (AUS)—
Victoire Celebre (USA) (Stravinsky (USA)) **Fittocks Stud & Mr A. Bengough**
100 SUMMIT DAY (USA), ch c 14/3 Distorted Humor (USA)—
My Dark Rosaleen (Sadler's Wells (USA)) **Merry Fox Stud**
101 B f 3/5 New Approach (IRE)—Time Saved (Green Desert (USA)) (230000) **Clipper Logistics**
102 TOTAL STAR, gr c 17/2 Pivotal—Millennium Star (IRE) (High Chaparral (IRE)) **Fittocks Stud**
103 B c 13/2 Bated Breath—Up And About (Barathea (IRE)) (35000) **Kangyu International Racing (HK) Ltd**
104 B f 6/5 Fastnet Rock (AUS)—Victoire Finale (Peintre Celebre (USA)) **Mr Stuart Stuckey**
105 B c 28/3 Zebedee—Warda (Pivotal) (45000)

Other Owners: Mr Imad Al-Sagar, Miss E. Asprey, The Dowager Duchess of Bedford, Mr A. N. C. Bengough, Mr C. Bird, Mr Daniel Boorer, Mr P. Booth, Mrs Emma Capon, Mrs Luca Cumani, Duke of Devonshire, Mrs H. S. Ellingsen, Fittocks Stud, Mr Jim Hanifin, Mr M. Heffernan, Mr T. Henderson, The Hon H. Herbert, Highclere Nominated Partner Limited, Highclere Thoroughbred Racing Ltd, Mr Saleh Al Homaizi, Prof John Hunter, Mrs John Magnier, Mrs Simon Marsh, Mrs Michelle Morris, Mr M. Morris, Mr Paul Moulton, Mr S. O'Donnell, Mr M. Quirke, Mrs L. E. Ramsden, Duke of Roxburghe, Mrs J. Ruthven, Mr Paul G. S. Silver, Mr M. Tabor, Ms Sylvia Vrska, Mr M. Weinfeld, Mr Christopher Wright.

Assistant Trainer: Amy Murphy

124

MR MICHAEL CUNNINGHAM, Navan
Postal: **Gormanstown Stables, Kildalkey, Navan, Co. Meath, Ireland**
Contacts: **PHONE (00353) 4694 31672 MOBILE (00353) 8625 93962**
E-MAIL cunninghamstables@gmail.com

1 COME DANCE WITH ME (IRE), 5, b m Flemensfirth (USA)—Sunset Queen (IRE) **Mrs Paul Shanahan**
2 CROWDED ROOM (IRE), 10, b g Oscar (IRE)—Leadamurraydance (IRE) **Mrs Michael Cunningham**
3 MARISE (IRE), 4, b f Azamour (IRE)—Singing Field (IRE) **Ms Marion Goodbody**

125

MR KEN CUNNINGHAM-BROWN, Stockbridge
Postal: **Danebury Place, Stockbridge, Hampshire, SO20 6JX**
Contacts: **PHONE (01264) 781061 FAX (01264) 781061 MOBILE (07802) 500059**
E-MAIL kcb@danebury.co.uk

1 AYE AYE SKIPPER (IRE), 6, b g Captain Marvelous (IRE)—Queenfisher **John Pearl**
2 BULLETPROOF (IRE), 10, b g Wareed (IRE)—Laura's Native (IRE) **Danebury Racing Stables**
3 LADY HARE (IRE), 4, b f Approve (IRE)—Peaceful Kingdom (USA) **Danebury Racing Stables**
4 LES DARCY, 5, b g Haafet (USA)—Overcome **Danebury Racing Stables**
5 LOVING YOUR WORK, 5, b g Royal Applause—Time Crystal (IRE) **Danebury Racing Stables**
6 MISS GERONIMO, 4, b f Hellvelyn—Churn Dat Butter (USA) **Danebury Racing Stables**
7 SECRET STRIKER, 4, ch f Sakhee's Secret—Silver Purse **Danebury Racing Stables**
8 TAMUJIN (IRE), 8, b g Elusive City (USA)—Arabian Princess **Danebury Racing Stables**
9 VINCENZO COCCOTTI (USA), 4, gr ro g Speightstown (USA)—Ocean Colors (USA) **Mr D. F. Henery**

Other Owners: Mr K. O. Cunningham-Brown, Mrs Beth Cunningham-Brown, John Pearl.

Assistant Trainer: Tony Charlton

Jockey (flat): Chris Catlin, Dane O'Neill. **Jockey (NH):** Tom Cannon.

126

MISS REBECCA CURTIS, Newport
Postal: **Fforest Farm, Newport, Pembrokeshire, SA42 0UG**
Contacts: **PHONE (01348) 811489 MOBILE (07970) 710690**
E-MAIL rebcurtis@hotmail.com

1 APACHE OUTLAW (IRE), 7, b g Westerner—Bermuda Bay (IRE) **Mr G. Costelloe**
2 AT FISHERS CROSS (IRE), 9, b g Oscar (IRE)—Fermoy Supreme (IRE) **J. P. McManus**
3 AUDACIOUS PLAN (IRE), 7, b g Old Vic—North Star Polly (IRE) **Mr A. McIver**
4 AURILLAC (FR), 6, gr g Martaline—Ombrelle (FR) **D Mossop, P John & R White**
5 AURORE D'ESTRUVAL (FR), 6, ch m Nickname (FR)—Option d'estruval (FR) **Mr C. S. Hinchy**
6 BALLYBANE (IRE), 6, gr g Acambaro (GER)—Madam Sophie (IRE) **Trembath, Obree & Beesley**

MISS REBECCA CURTIS - Continued

7 **BEAST OF BURDEN (IRE)**, 7, ch g Flemensfirth (USA)—Nuit des Chartreux (FR) **Mr C. S. Hinchy**
8 **BIGBADJOHN (IRE)**, 7, br g Vinnie Roe (IRE)—Celtic Serenade (IRE) **Mr N. D. Morris**
9 **BINGE DRINKER (IRE)**, 7, b g Spadoun (FR)—Our Honey (IRE) **Corsellis & Seyfried**
10 **BOB FORD (IRE)**, 9, b g Vinnie Roe (IRE)—Polar Lamb (IRE) **The JJ Partnership**
11 **BRAQUEUR D'OR (FR)**, 5, b g Epalo (GER)—Hot d'or (FR) **Corsellis & Seyfried**
12 **CAPTAIN MCGINLEY (IRE)**, 6, bl g Robin des Pres (FR)—Rocella (GER) **Mr A. McIver**
13 **CARNINGLI (IRE)**, 7, b g Old Vic—Name For Fame (USA) **The Newport Partnership**
14 **CLOUD BROOK (IRE)**, 8, b g Cloudings (IRE)—Stoney Brook (IRE) **Mr R. J. H. Geffen**
15 **CORNISH WARRIOR (IRE)**, 5, b g Oscar (IRE)—Ballylooby Moss (IRE) **Trembath, Outhart, Moran & Costelloe**
16 **DEFINITE OUTCOME (IRE)**, 7, b g Definite Article—Magical Theatre (IRE) **Mr C. S. Hinchy**
17   5, B m Scorpion (IRE)—Dipp In The Dark (IRE)
18 **DOING FINE (IRE)**, 8, b g Presenting—Howaya Pet (IRE) **Mr C. S. Hinchy**
19 **DRUID'S FOLLY (IRE)**, 6, b g Beneficial—Sweet Vale (IRE) **Mr C. R. Trembath**
20 **GEORDIE DES CHAMPS (IRE)**, 5, br g Robin des Champs (FR)—
                                Kilcoleman Lady (IRE) **Trembath, Outhart, Moran & Costelloe**
21 **GLENWOOD STAR (IRE)**, 8, b g Oscar (IRE)—Shuil Ar Aghaidh **Mr M. A. Sherwood**
22 **GLOBALISATION (IRE)**, 6, b g Tikkanen (USA)—On A Mission (IRE) **J. P. McManus**
23 **GOING FOR BROKE (IRE)**, 6, b g Gold Well—Kokopelli Star **J. P. McManus**
24 **GOLDEN MILAN (IRE)**, 8, b g Milan—Belle Provence (FR) **Mr M. A. Sherwood**
25 **HIGHWAY STORM (IRE)**, 6, b g Stowaway—Snow In Summer (IRE) **Mr C. S. Hinchy**
26 **HOLY CROSS (IRE)**, 5, b g Yeats (IRE)—Bleu Ciel Et Blanc (FR) **Mr N. D. Morris**
27 **HOW ABOUT IT (IRE)**, 7, b g Kayf Tara—Midnight Gift (IRE) **Mr C. S. Hinchy**
28 **IMAGINE THE CHAT**, 7, b g Kayf Tara—Be My Bird **J. P. McManus**
29 **IRISH CAVALIER (IRE)**, 7, gr ro g Aussie Rules (USA)—Tracker **Mr A. McIver**
30 **JESSIE WEBSTER (IRE)**, 7, b m Kayf Tara—Blueberry Bramble (IRE) **Miss R. Curtis**
31 **KANTURK BANK (IRE)**, 6, b g Carlo Bank (IRE)—Kanturk Belle (IRE) **Mr C. S. Hinchy**
32 **KILCULLEN FLEM (IRE)**, 6, ch g Flemensfirth (USA)—Cansalrun (IRE) **Tangledupinblue**
33 **KIT CASEY (IRE)**, 6, b g Robin des Pres (FR)—An Culainn Beag (IRE) **Conyers, O'Reilly, Roddis, Zeffman**
34 **KNIGHT TO OPEN (IRE)**, 6, b g Oscar (IRE)—Sunset View (IRE) **The Bruton Street Partnership**
35 **MASTER ALLY (IRE)**, 6, gr g Flemensfirth (USA)—
                                Ally Rose (IRE) **Greg Davies Ged Lynch Smith Emad Hussain**
36 **MINELLA ON LINE (IRE)**, 7, b g King's Theatre (IRE)—Bally Bolshoi (IRE) **AHB Racing Partnership**
37 **MONKEY KINGDOM**, 8, b g King's Theatre (IRE)—Blast Freeze (IRE) **Mr C. S. Hinchy**
38 **MYSTICAL KNIGHT**, 7, b g Kayf Tara—Dark Diva **J. P. McManus**
39   5, B h Robin des Champs (FR)—Native Wood (IRE) **Corsellis & Seyfried**
40 **O'FAOLAINS BOY (IRE)**, 9, b g Oscar (IRE)—Lisa's Storm (IRE) **Trembath, Hyde, Outhart & Hill**
41 **ONE TERM (IRE)**, 9, b g Beneficial—One Edge (IRE) **Miss L Reid & Mr G Costelloe**
42 **PICKAMIX (IRE)**, 5, b g Sagamix (FR)—Star of Wonder (FR) **Trembath, Outhart, Moran & Costelloe**
43 **POTTERS CROSS**, 9, b g Alflora (IRE)—Teeno Nell **Conyers, O'Reilly, Roddis, Zeffman**
44 **PRESELI NATIVE (IRE)**, 6, ch g Flemensfirth (USA)—Chantoue Royale (FR) **The Bruton Street Partnership**
45 **RACING PULSE (IRE)**, 8, b g Garuda (IRE)—Jacks Sister (IRE) **Mr C. S. Hinchy**
46 **RED DEVIL LADS (IRE)**, 7, b g Beneficial—Welsh Sitara (IRE) **Mr A. McIver**
47 **RELENTLESS DREAMER (IRE)**, 7, br g Kayf Tara—Full of Elegance (FR) **Mr N. D. Morris**
48 **ROYAL BOY (FR)**, 9, b br g Lavirco (GER)—Quintanilla (FR) **Mr C. S. Hinchy**
49 **SUMMER NAME (IRE)**, 4, b g Duke of Marmalade (IRE)—Summer's Eve **Mrs L. E. Ramsden**
50 **SWEETLITTLEKITTY (IRE)**, 6, b m Robin des Champs (FR)—Alcrea (IRE) **Sweet Little Kitty's**
51 **TARA ROAD**, 8, b g Kayf Tara—Sparkling Jewel **Mr N. D. Morris**
52 **THE ROMFORD PELE (IRE)**, 9, b g Accordion—Back And Fore (IRE) **Trembath & Outhart**
53   5, Ch g Spadoun (FR)—Twilight Vic (IRE) **Trembath, Outhart, Moran & Costelloe**
54 **VINTAGE VINNIE (IRE)**, 7, b g Vinnie Roe (IRE)—Bobby's Jet (IRE) **Trembath, Hyde, Outhart & Hill**
55 **WILD ROVER (IRE)**, 7, b g Scorpion (IRE)—Pandalute (IRE) **The Wild Rover Partnership**

Other Owners: Mr M. A. Beesley, Mr J. Conyers, Mrs J. C. Corsellis, Mr G. Davies, Mr D. Fitzwilliams, Mr L. Fitzwilliams, Mr M. D. Hankin, Mr J. C. I. Heilbron, M. Hill, Dr E. Hussain, Mr R. Hyde, JCM Retail Equipment Ltd, Mr P. D. H. John, Mr G. Lynch-Smith, Marwyn Asset Management SPC, R. H. W. Morecombe, A. J. Mossop, D. Mossop, Mr J. P. O'Reilly, Mr W. D. Obree, A. J. Outhart, Miss. L. Reid, Mr D. A. Robinson, Mr N. M. Roddis, Mr E. J. N. Seyfried, Mrs R. E. White, D. C. Zeffman.

Assistant Trainer: Paul Sheldrake

127 MR THOMAS CUTHBERT, Brampton
Postal: **Woodlands, Cowranbridge, How Mill, Brampton, Cumbria, CA8 9LH**
Contacts: **PHONE (01228) 560822 FAX (01228) 560822 MOBILE (07747) 843344**
E-MAIL **cuthbertracing@fsmail.net**

1 EDAS, 14, b g Celtic Swing—Eden (IRE) **Mrs J. Cuthbert**
2 LANDESHERR (GER), 9, b g Black Sam Bellamy (IRE)—Lutte Marie (GER) **Mrs J. Cuthbert**
3 YAIR HILL (IRE), 8, b g Selkirk (USA)—Conspiracy **T. A. K. Cuthbert**

Assistant Trainer: Helen Cuthbert

Amateur: Miss H. Cuthbert.

128 MR PAUL D'ARCY, Newmarket
Postal: **Charnwood Stables, Hamilton Road, Newmarket, Suffolk, CB8 7JQ**
Contacts: **PHONE (01638) 662000 MOBILE (07768) 807653**
E-MAIL **pauldarcy@fsmail.net** WEBSITE **www.pauldarcyracing.com**

1 ANASTAZIA, 4, br f Kyllachy—Meddle **Mr K. Snell**
2 RED INVADER (IRE), 6, b g Red Clubs (IRE)—Tifariti (USA) **C. M. Wilson**
3 SPRING LOADED (IRE), 4, gr g Zebedee—Nisriyna (IRE) **Rowley Racing**

THREE-YEAR-OLDS
4 MISS PHILLYJINKS (IRE), b f Zoffany (IRE)—Smoken Rosa (USA) **Mr N. Hartery**
5 MOOIZO (IRE), b f Rock of Gibraltar (IRE)—Skid (IRE) **Mr J. N. Reus**
6 ROCKLEY POINT, b c Canford Cliffs (IRE)—Statua (IRE) **Rowley Racing**
7 SHADOW HUNTER (IRE), b f Arcano (IRE)—Sweet Irish **Mrs J. Harris**
8 B g Shamardal (USA)—Tiffany Diamond (IRE)
9 TOTZO (IRE), b f Lilbourne Lad (IRE)—Later (IRE) **P. D'Arcy**

TWO-YEAR-OLDS
10 B f 27/3 Requinto (IRE)—Abbasharjah (GER) (Tiger Hill (IRE)) (38000) **Mrs A. Doyle**
11 Ch f 17/4 Rip Van Winkle (IRE)—Nick's Nikita (IRE) (Pivotal) **Mr N. Hartery**
12 B f 12/2 Canford Cliffs (IRE)—Night Lily (IRE) (Night Shift (USA)) **Mr K. Snell**
13 B f 22/2 Medicean—Nurai (Danehill Dancer (IRE)) **Mr K. Snell**
14 SHADOW WARRIOR, b c 27/2 Born To Sea (IRE)—Dolcetto (IRE) (Danehill Dancer (IRE)) (20000) **Mrs J. Harris**

Other Owners: Mrs Sue D'Arcy, Mrs M. Doyle.

Assistant Trainer: Sue D'Arcy

Apprentice: Stacey Kidd. **Amateur:** Mrs Rachel Wilson.

129 MR LUKE DACE, Billingshurst
Postal: **Copped Hall Farm and Stud, Okehurst House, Okehurst Lane, Billingshurst,
West Sussex, RH14 9HR**
Contacts: **FAX (01403) 612176 MOBILE (07949) 401085**
E-MAIL **lukedace@yahoo.co.uk** WEBSITE **www.lukedace.co.uk**

1 HIT THE HEADLINES (IRE), 10, b g Flemensfirth (USA)—Heather Breeze (IRE) **N. A. Dunger**
2 RAVENOUS, 5, b g Raven's Pass (USA)—Supereva (IRE) **M. C. S. D. Racing Partnership**
3 WESTERLY, 5, b m Rail Link—Humility **Mr G. Collacott**

THREE-YEAR-OLDS
4 BELEAVE, gr f Avonbridge—Grezie **R. L. Page**
5 STYLISTIK, ch f Sakhee's Secret—Passing Hour (USA) **M. J. Benton**

Other Owners: Mrs M. B. McClean, B. J. McClean.

Assistant Trainer: Mrs L Dace

Amateur: Mr J. Doe.

130 **MR KEITH DALGLEISH, Carluke**
Postal: Belstane Racing Stables, Carluke, Lanarkshire, ML8 5HN
Contacts: **PHONE (01555) 773335**

1 **ARCHIE'S ADVICE**, 5, b g Archipenko (USA)—Flylowflylong (IRE) **A. R. M Galbraith**
2 **ARGAKI (IRE)**, 6, ch g Strategic Prince—Amathusia **D. G. Savala**
3 **AWAY FOR SLATES (IRE)**, 4, b g Arcadio (GER)—Rumi **Equus Syndicate**
4 **AZRUR (IRE)**, 6, b g Sir Percy—Tiger Spice **Mr D. C. Moat**
5 **BEAUTIFUL STRANGER (IRE)**, 5, b g Iffraaj—Monarchy (IRE) **Weldspec Glasgow Limited**
6 **BIFF JOHNSON (IRE)**, 4, b g Dansili—Sagacious (IRE) **Mr R. Docherty**
7 **CHOOKIE ROYALE**, 8, ch g Monsieur Bond (IRE)—Lady of Windsor (IRE) **Raeburn Brick Limited**
8 **CORTON LAD**, 6, b g Refuse To Bend (IRE)—Kelucia (IRE) **Mr J. J. Hutton**
9 **DARK PROFIT (IRE)**, 4, gr g Dark Angel (IRE)—Goldthroat (IRE) **Weldspec Glasgow Limited**
10 **DEVONSHIRE PLACE (IRE)**, 4, b f Rip Van Winkle (IRE)—Councilofconstance (IRE) **Middleham Park Racing V**
11 **EDGAR BALTHAZAR**, 4, b g Pastoral Pursuits—Assistacat (IRE) **Middleham Park Racing XXII**
12 **FAST PICK (IRE)**, 4, b f Fastnet Rock (AUS)—Dream Time **Mr R. Docherty**
13 **FLEMENSFIRTHLEADER**, 7, b m Flemensfirth (USA)—National Leader (IRE) **Mr T. Young**
14 **FRIGHTENED RABBIT (USA)**, 4, b g Hard Spun (USA)—Champagne Ending (USA) **Equus Syndicate**
15 **GOLD FLASH**, 4, b g Kheleyf (USA)—My Golly **Mr R. Docherty**
16 **GOT THE NAC (IRE)**, 7, br g Beneficial—Hey Jude (IRE) **Richard & Katherine Gilbert**
17 **HITMAN HEARNS (IRE)**, 7, b g Milan—Desirable Asset (IRE) **Richard & Katherine Gilbert**
18 **HOME FOR TEA**, 7, b g Westerner—Wolnai **Richard & Katherine Gilbert**
19 **HUEHUECOYTLE**, 6, br g Turgeon (USA)—Azturk (FR) **Mr & Mrs Paul & Clare Rooney**
20 **INCURS FOUR FAULTS**, 5, b g Halling (USA)—Rapsgate (IRE) **J. S. Morrison**
21 **INVOKE (IRE)**, 5, b m Kodiac—Tides **Mr M. Beaumont**
22 **JACOB BLACK**, 5, b g Amadeus Wolf—First Eclipse (IRE) **Redgate Bloodstock & Charles Wentworth**
23 **JAMMY MOMENT**, 5, ch m Duke of Marmalade (IRE)—Special Moment (IRE) **J. K. McGarrity**
24 **LITTLE BELTER (IRE)**, 4, gr g Dandy Man (IRE)—On Thin Ice (IRE) **J. K. McGarrity**
25 **MALEFICENT QUEEN**, 4, b f Mount Nelson—Manila Selection (USA) **Weldspec Glasgow Limited**
26 **MIRSAALE**, 6, ch g Sir Percy—String Quartet (IRE) **Equus Syndicate**
27 **MIXBOY (FR)**, 6, gr g Fragrant Mix (IRE)—Leston Girl (FR) **Mr & Mrs Paul & Clare Rooney**
28 **MOON ARC (IRE)**, 4, b g Arcano (IRE)—Moon Unit (IRE) **Mr J. C. Higgins**
29 **NAM MA PROW**, 5, ch g Bahamian Bounty—Charlotte Vale
30 **NEW LEASE OF LIFE**, 7, b g Orientor—Primo Heights **Mr K. W. Dalgleish**
31 **PROPERUS (IRE)**, 4, b c Lord Shanakill (USA)—Amistad (GER) **Mr M. Beaumont**
32 **SANTEFISIO**, 10, b g Efisio—Impulsive Decision (IRE) **Weldspec Glasgow Limited**
33 **SEWN UP**, 6, ch g Compton Place—Broughton Bounty **Mr J. Kelly**
34 **SO IT'S WAR (FR)**, 5, b g Orpen (USA)—Impulsive Decision (IRE) **Weldspec Glasgow Limited**
35 **SOUND ADVICE**, 7, b g Echo of Light—Flylowflylong (IRE) **G L S Partnership**
36 **TOMMY DOCC (IRE)**, 4, b g Thewayyouare (USA)—Liturgy (IRE) **Mr R. Docherty**
37 **TOWNSVILLE**, 4, b c Zamindar (USA)—Rule of Nature (USA) **Mr K. W. Dalgleish**

THREE-YEAR-OLDS

38 **ALBA DAWN (IRE)**, ch f Compton Place—Pink Delight (IRE) **Alan & Barry Macdonald**
39 **AMY BLAIR**, b c Captain Gerrard (IRE)—Shalad'or **Mr J. Fyffe**
40 **CHARMED COMPANY (IRE)**, b f Fast Company (IRE)—Lucky Leigh **Richard & Katherine Gilbert**
41 **DOEADEER (IRE)**, b f Dandy Man (IRE)—Bloomsday Babe (USA) **Weldspec Glasgow Limited**
42 B f Rock of Gibraltar (IRE)—Ecusson **Mr J. C. Higgins**
43 **EEZ EH (IRE)**, b c Jeremy (USA)—Step With Style (USA) **Weldspec Glasgow Limited**
44 **FALCON'S FIRE (IRE)**, ch g Thewayyouare (USA)—Matadora (IRE) **Mr R. Docherty**
45 **FARKLE MINKUS**, b g Kheleyf (USA)—Majestic Diva (IRE) **Mr G. R. Leckie**
46 **FOREVER A LADY (IRE)**, b f Dark Angel (IRE)—Unicamp **Mr T. Young**
47 **GLENROWAN ROSE (IRE)**, b f Bushranger (IRE)—Choice House (USA) **Weldspec Glasgow Limited**
48 **HOLLYWOOD KEN (IRE)**, b g Arcano (IRE)—Third Dimension (FR) **Richard & Katherine Gilbert**
49 B c Monsieur Bond (IRE)—Lady McBeth (IRE) **Mrs J. M. MacPherson**
50 **LADY WOOTTON**, b f Wootton Bassett—Killer Class **F. Brady**
51 **LIVELLA FELLA (IRE)**, b f Strategic Prince—Ardent Lady **Middleham Park Racing XXIII**
52 **MAULESDEN MAY (IRE)**, b f Dark Angel (IRE)—Jemima's Art **The County Set (Two)**
53 **MR GRUMPY**, b g Sir Percy—Panna **Richard & Katherine Gilbert**
54 **OVERHAUGH STREET**, b g Bahri (USA)—Bom Chicka Wah Wah (USA) **Sharron & Robert Colvin**
55 **RESSURRETO (IRE)**, b f Frozen Power (IRE)—Silver Whale (FR) **Mrs F. E. Mitchell**
56 **ROBINNIELLY (IRE)**, b g Approve (IRE)—Beauty And Style (AUS) **Prestige Thoroughbred Racing**
57 **SATTELAC**, b f Kodiac—Sattelight **Mr T. Young**
58 **SHE'S ELECTRIC (IRE)**, b f Roderic O'Connor (IRE)—Maundays Bay (IRE) **Weldspec Glasgow Limited**

MR KEITH DALGLEISH - Continued

59 **TOMBE GIRL**, b f Royal Applause—Tahfeez (IRE) **Exchange Court Properties Ltd**
60 **UNDERDRESSED**, b f Elnadim (USA)—Bijan (IRE) **Ronnie Docherty & Partner**

TWO-YEAR-OLDS

61 Ch c 19/4 Dandy Man (IRE)—Alifandango (IRE) (Alzao (USA)) (19047)
62 B f 10/4 Bushranger (IRE)—Atishoo (IRE) (Revoque (IRE)) (7381) **Equus Syndicate**
63 B c 26/4 Pastoral Pursuits—Bijan (IRE) (Mukaddamah (USA)) (19047) **Mr A. G. MacLennan**
64 B c 13/2 Elusive Quality (USA)—Ebony Street (USA) (Street Cry (IRE)) (36913) **Weldspec Glasgow Limited**
65 Ch c 23/3 Intikhab (USA)—Fantastic Opinion (IRE) (Fantastic Light (USA)) (52380) **Weldspec Glasgow Limited**
66 B f 30/4 Bushranger (IRE)—Fatwa (IRE) (Lahib (USA)) (6053) **Equus Syndicate**
67 Bl c 2/4 Kheleyf (USA)—Impulsive Decision (IRE) (Nomination) (8000) **Weldspec Glasgow Limited**
68 B f 15/2 Dandy Man (IRE)—Italian Affair (Fumo di Londra (IRE)) (2857)
69 B c 31/3 Elzaam (AUS)—Lost Highway (IRE) (Danehill Dancer (IRE)) (14765)
70 B c 28/3 Dandy Man (IRE)—Miss Me (Marju (IRE)) (14285) **S. J. Macdonald**
71 Ch f 22/2 Bahamian Bounty—Moynsha Lady (IRE) (Namid) (14285)
72 Ch c 25/4 Camacho—Nigella (Band On The Run) (23000) **Weldspec Glasgow Limited**
73 B f 17/3 Elzaam (AUS)—Question (USA) (Coronado's Quest (USA)) (8121)
74 B f 7/4 Kodiac—Red Trance (IRE) (Soviet Star (USA)) (24761) **Equus Syndicate**
75 B f 16/2 Royal Applause—Samasana (IRE) (Redback) (11428)
76 B c 26/3 Delegator—Shore Light (USA) (Gulch (USA)) (3333) **Mr J. C. Higgins**
77 B c 14/2 Rip Van Winkle (IRE)—Sister Moonshine (Averti (IRE)) (21000) **Mr J S Morrison & Partner**
78 B c 19/4 Harbour Watch (IRE)—Spring Fashion (IRE) (Galileo (IRE)) (59062) **Weldspec Glasgow Limited**
79 Br c 25/4 Dark Angel (IRE)—Visual Element (USA) (Distant View (USA)) (59062) **Weldspec Glasgow Limited**

Other Owners: Mr W. Burke, A. Cadger, Mrs S. Colvin, R. Colvin, Mr D. Duncan, Mr D. C. Flynn, Miss E. Foley, Mr R. P. Gilbert, Mrs K. E. Gilbert, G. Godsman, E. D. Haggart, Mr A. W. Henderson, Mr J. S. Lessells, Mr B. N. MacDonald, Mr A. G. MacDonald, Mr M. G. Mellor, T. S. Palin, M. Prince, Mr S. C. Reay, Mrs C. Rooney, Mr P. A. Rooney, Mr A. Savage, Mr B. T. E. Shrubsall, A. W. Sinclair, Miss M. M. Smith, D. R. Tucker, C. V. Wentworth.

Assistant Trainer: Kevin Dalgleish

---

131   MS HEATHER DALTON, Market Drayton
Postal: **Kenfields, Childs Ercall, Market Drayton, Shropshire, TF9 2DA**

1 **ADOURA BELL**, 4, b f Bahri (USA)—Silent Treatment (IRE)
2 **ARTISTE DU GOUET (FR)**, 6, b br g Lavirco (GER)—Newhaven (FR) **D. R. T. Gibbons**
3 **BRAVO KING (IRE)**, 8, b g Sakhee (USA)—Ashbilya (USA) **Mr S. Arnold**
4 **CIARAS COOKIE (IRE)**, 4, b f Approve (IRE)—Preach (IRE) **Mr S. Arnold**
5 **COMMISSAR**, 7, b g Soviet Star (USA)—Sari **Mr S. Arnold**
6 **DANIEL THOMAS (IRE)**, 14, b g Dansili—Last Look **Mr S. Arnold**
7 **EMILY DAVISON (IRE)**, 5, gr m Moss Vale (IRE)—Carabine (USA) **Mrs M. S. Coles**
8 **HYPERLINK (IRE)**, 7, b g Cape Cross (IRE)—Surf The Web (IRE) **Dalton, Pattinson & Newton**
9 **LE DELUGE (FR)**, 6, b g Oratorio (IRE)—Princess Sofia (UAE) **Mr S. Arnold**
10 **LIKE A DIAMOND (IRE)**, 6, b g Antonius Pius (USA)—Silk Law (IRE) **Mr S. Arnold**
11 **MCCARTHY MOR (IRE)**, 5, b g Bushranger (IRE)—Alexander Anapolis (IRE) **Mr S. Arnold**
12 **MR MCGREGOR (IRE)**, 8, ch g Beneficial—Our Idol (IRE) **C. B. Compton**
13 **ON THE CUSP (IRE)**, 9, b g Footstepsinthesand—Roman Love (IRE) **Mr S. Arnold**
14 **OSCAR BRAVO (IRE)**, 5, br g Oscar (IRE)—Brave Commitment (IRE) **C. B. Compton**
15 **PULL THE PIN (IRE)**, 7, b g Kheleyf (USA)—Inscribed (IRE) **Mr S. Arnold**
16 **ROYAL RETTIE**, 4, b f Royal Applause—Bended Knee **Mr S. Arnold**
17 **SPECIAL CODE (IRE)**, 4, b g Iffraaj—Najmati **Mr S. Arnold**
18 4, B f Westerner—Thuringe (FR)
19 5, Ch g Majestic Missile (IRE)—Tough Chic (IRE) **Ms H. Dalton**
20 **TRUE SPIRIT**, 6, b g Shamardal (USA)—Petonellajill **Mr S. Arnold**
21 **WE HAVE A DREAM**, 11, b br g Oasis Dream—Final Shot **Mr S. Arnold**
22 **WHAT ABOUT MOLLY (IRE)**, 6, ch m Stowaway—Great Legacy (IRE) **Heather Dalton, Mr M Owen**
23 **ZUBAIDAH**, 4, b f Exceed And Excel (AUS)—Bedouin Bride (USA) **Mr S. Arnold**

THREE-YEAR-OLDS

24 **DOMINEENO**, b g Stimulation (IRE)—Shining Oasis (IRE) **Mr S. Arnold**
25 B f Dutch Art—Focal **Mr S. Arnold**

MS HEATHER DALTON - Continued

TWO-YEAR-OLDS

26 B c 28/3 Foxwedge (AUS)—Cut The Cackle (IRE) (Danetime (IRE)) (7619) **Mr S. Arnold**
Other Owners: Mr L. I. Newton, Mr M. Owen, Mrs P. M. Pattinson.

---

132 **MR HENRY DALY, Ludlow**
Trainer did not wish details of his string to appear

---

133 **MR PHILLIP DANDO, Peterston-Super-Ely**
Postal: **Springfield Court, Peterston-Super-Ely, Cardiff, South Glamorgan, CF5 6LG**
Contacts: **PHONE (01446) 760012 MOBILE (07872) 965395**

1 DRIFTWOOD HAZE, 8, b g Nomadic Way (USA)—Kristal Haze **P. C. Dando**
2 RAINBOW HAZE, 10, b g Rainbow High—Kristal Haze **Mr Phillip Dando & Dr Michael Armitage**
3 RIVER HAZE, 6, b g Lucarno (USA)—Kristal Haze **P. C. Dando**
4 SAHARA HAZE, 7, b m Rainbow High—Gypsy Haze **Mr Phillip Dando & Mr Anthony Brown**

Other Owners: Dr Michael Armitage, Mr H. A. Brown, Mr P. Dando.

Assistant Trainer: Mrs Rebecca Davies

---

134 **MR VICTOR DARTNALL, Barnstaple**
Postal: **Higher Shutscombe Farm, Charles, Brayford, Barnstaple, Devon, EX32 7PU**
Contacts: **PHONE (01598) 710280 FAX (01598) 710708 MOBILE (07974) 374272**
E-MAIL victordartnall@gmail.com **WEBSITE** www.victordartnallracing.com

1 ABYAAT (IRE), 5, b g Halling (USA)—Why Dubai (USA) **Edge Of Exmoor**
2 ADMIRAL'S SECRET, 5, b g Kayf Tara—Bobs Bay (IRE) **The Whacko Partnership**
3 AMBION LANE (IRE), 6, b g Scorpion (IRE)—Thrilling Prospect (IRE) **Mr O. C. R. Wynne & Mrs S. J. Wynne**
4 AMBION WOOD (IRE), 10, b g Oscar (IRE)—Dorans Grove **Mr O. C. R. Wynne & Mrs S. J. Wynne**
5 BINDON MILL, 7, b g Tamure—Singing Cottage **Mrs E. S. Weld**
6 BOLVING (IRE), 5, b g Stowaway—Kiniohio (FR) **Mrs C. M. Barber**
7 CORDEY WARRIOR, 6, b g Tobougg (IRE)—Aquavita **P. J. H. George**
8 DANCING SHADOW (IRE), 7, br g Craigsteel—Be My Shadow (IRE) **The Dancing Shadows**
9 DARLOA (IRE), 7, br g Darsi (FR)—Lady Lola (IRE) **Mr S. W. Campbell**
10 EXMOOR MIST, 8, gr g Kayf Tara—Chita's Flora **Exmoor Mist Partnership**
11 4, B g Mahler—Fridays Folly (IRE)
12 GOOD AUTHORITY (IRE), 9, b g Chineur (FR)—Lady Alexander (IRE) **Mrs J. Scrivens**
13 HOOPER'S LEGEND, 5, b g Midnight Legend—Norton Sapphire **Mr R. Harding**
14 JEZZA, 10, br g Pentire—Lara (GER) **Mrs J. Scrivens**
15 MARY LE BOW, 5, b m Sir Percy—Bermondsey Girl **Mrs J. Scrivens**
16 4, B f Getaway (GER)—Minnie Hill (IRE)
17 MOTHER MELDRUM (IRE), 7, b m Milan—Europet (IRE) **G. D. Hake**
18 OUEST OCEAN (FR), 5, b g Early March—Kalistina (FR) **Ms C. Carter**
19 RUN TO MILAN (IRE), 4, b g Milan—Run Supreme (IRE) **Barber, Birchenhough, De Wilde**
20 SEEBRIGHT, 9, b g Milan—Aranga (IRE) **Mrs D. J. Fleming**
21 SHAMMICK BOY (IRE), 11, b g Craigsteel—Dulcet Music (IRE) **First Brayford Partnership**
22 SIDBURY FAIR, 5, br m Fair Mix (IRE)—Manque Pas d'air (FR) **Mrs L. M. Northover**
23 SLEEPING CITY, 9, b br g Sleeping Car (FR)—City Prospect (FR) **Edge Of Exmoor**
24 4, B g Arvico (FR)—Storm Kitten (IRE)
25 4, B g Getaway (GER)—Third Wish (IRE)
26 TOLKEINS TANGO (IRE), 8, ch g Beneficial—Aule (FR) **Mrs S. M. Hall**
27 UN BLEU A L'AAM (FR), 8, b g Shaanmer (IRE)—Bleu Perle (FR) **F. R. Williamson**
28 UNEFILLE DE GUYE (FR), 8, b br m Voix du Nord (FR)—
Mascotte de Guye (FR) **The Second Brayford Partnership**
29 UT MAJEUR AULMES (FR), 8, ch g Northern Park (USA)—My Wish Aulmes (FR) **Mrs S. De Wilde**
30 WEE SAXON, 7, b g Kayf Tara—Countess Point **Mrs J. E. Purdie**

MR VICTOR DARTNALL - Continued

Other Owners: Mrs C. Barber, Mrs Kay Birchenhough, Mrs Paula Cunliffe, Mr Brian Dallyn, Mr V. R. A. Dartnall, Mr G. A. Dartnall, Mrs Jean Dartnall, Mrs S. De Wilde, Mr Jeffery Edelman, Mr N. P Haley, Mrs Sonia M. Hall, Mr Colston Herbert, Mr Michael Nicholls, Mr M. W. Richards, Mrs T. M. Scott, Mr Lee Singleton, Mr R. F. Willcocks, Mr O. C. R. Wynne, Mrs S. J. Wynne.

Assistant Trainer: G. A. Dartnall

Jockey (NH): Jack Doyle. **Conditional:** Jake Bament.

---

135 MR TOM DASCOMBE, Malpas
Postal: **Manor House Stables, Malpas, Cheshire, SY14 8AD**
Contacts: PHONE (01948) 820485 FAX (01948) 820495 MOBILE (07973) 511664
E-MAIL tom@manorhousestables.com WEBSITE www.manorhousestables.com

1 ANGELIC LORD (IRE), 4, b g Dark Angel (IRE)—Divine Design (IRE) **The Mad March Hares**
2 BALLISTA (IRE), 8, b g Majestic Missile (IRE)—Ancient Secret **Well Done Top Man Partnership**
3 BARRACUDA BOY (IRE), 6, b g Bahamian Bounty—Madame Boulangere **L. A. Bellman**
4 CAPO ROSSO (IRE), 6, b g Red Clubs (IRE)—Satin Cape (IRE) **Deva Racing Red Clubs Partnership**
5 CAPTAIN REVELATION, 4, ch g Captain Rio—Agony Aunt **Cheshire Racing**
6 CHOSEN CHARACTER (IRE), 8, b g Choisir (AUS)—Out of Thanks (IRE) **Aykroyd & Sons Limited**
7 COLOURFILLY, 4, ch f Compton Place—Where's Broughton **L. A. Bellman**
8 CYMRO (IRE), 4, gr g Dark Angel (IRE)—Dictatrice (FR) **Mr D. R. Passant & Hefin Williams**
9 DANA'S PRESENT, 7, ch g Osorio (GER)—Euro Empire (USA) **Mr Russell Jones & Partner**
10 DAWN'S EARLY LIGHT (IRE), 4, gr g Starspangledbanner (AUS)—Sky Red **Empire State Racing Partnership**
11 DEAUVILLE PRINCE (FR), 6, b g Holy Roman Emperor (IRE)—
Queen of Deauville (FR) **N & S Mather, C Ledigo, L Basran**
12 DIATOMIC (IRE), 4, b g Bushranger (IRE)—Gilded Truffle (IRE) **Mr J. D. Brown**
13 EXCILLY, 4, br f Excellent Art—Afra Tsitsi (FR) **Bellman Lowe O'Halloran Trowbridge**
14 HILLBILLY BOY (IRE), 6, b g Haafhd—Erreur (IRE) **Macguire's Bloodstock Ltd**
15 KINGSCROFT (IRE), 8, b g Antonius Pius (USA)—Handsome Anna (IRE) **Manor House Racing Club**
16 MR CHRISTOPHER (IRE), 4, b g Bahamian Bounty—Embassy Pearl (IRE) **Mrs M. C. Antrobus**
17 NEWERA, 4, ch g Makfi—Coming Home **Mr D. R. Passant**
18 ROUDEE, 4, b g Kodiac—Eau Rouge **Edwards Hughes Jenkins Roberts & Partner**
19 SEVE, 4, ch g Exceed And Excel (AUS)—Flamenco Dancer **The Blue Nuns**
20 SNAP SHOTS (IRE), 4, b g Kodiac—Refuse To Give Up (IRE) **Gap Personnel Franchises Limited**
21 THATABOY (IRE), 5, b g Green Desert (USA)—Hawas **Mr D. J. Lowe**
22 THE CHARACTER (IRE), 5, b g Bushranger (IRE)—Operissimo **Aykroyd & Sons Limited**

THREE-YEAR-OLDS
23 ABOVE N BEYOND, ch c Exceed And Excel (AUS)—
Hill Welcome **Chasemore Farm LLP & Owen Promotions Ltd**
24 ARCANADA (IRE), ch g Arcano (IRE)—Bond Deal (IRE) **The Arcanada Partnership**
25 BIG AMIGO (IRE), b c Bahamian Bounty—Goldamour (IRE) **L. A. Bellman**
26 BULGE BRACKET, b g Great Journey (JPN)—Baldovina **Chasemore Farm LLP**
27 CALDER PRINCE (IRE), gr c Dark Angel (IRE)—Flame of Ireland (IRE) **Mr P. G. Birbeck**
28 CANCAN KATY, b f Canford Cliffs (IRE)—Katy Nowaitee **Chasemore Farm LLP**
29 CAPONOVA (IRE), b g Bushranger (IRE)—Satin Cape (IRE) **Deva Racing Bushranger Partnership**
30 FILE OF FACTS (IRE), b g Iffraaj—Clever Day (USA) **Chasemore Farm LLP & Owen Promotions Ltd**
31 FIRE DIAMOND, b c Firebreak—Diapason (IRE) **Mr J. D. Brown**
32 FIRESNAKE (IRE), b g Dandy Man (IRE)—La Bataille (USA) **Pritchard & Woodward**
33 GAMBIT, b c New Approach (IRE)—Sospel **Laurence Bellman & Caroline Ingram**
34 GOLDEN GLIMMER (IRE), b f Danehill Dancer (IRE)—Gilded Vanity (IRE) **Chasemore Farm LLP**
35 HAPPY TIDINGS, b f Exceed And Excel (AUS)—
Helena Molony (IRE) **Newsells Park Stud & Manor House Stables**
36 KACHY, b c Kyllachy—Dubai Bounty **Jones Lowe Mound Trowbridge**
37 LA CELEBS VILLE (IRE), b f Sea The Stars (IRE)—Bryanstown (IRE) **Newport Rangers**
38 MICKEY (IRE), b c Zoffany (IRE)—Enchantment **Mrs Janet Lowe & Mr Tom Dascombe**
39 MONSIEUR GLORY, ch g Monsieur Bond (IRE)—Chuskka **Kangyu International Racing (HK) Limited**
40 OUR ELTON (USA), ch g Speightstown (USA)—Warsaw Ballet (CAN) **D Studholme, M Smyth & S Burns**
41 REFLEKTOR (IRE), ch g Bahamian Bounty—Baby Bunting **Mr D. J. Lowe**
42 SHARP JACK, ch c Pivotal—Sharp Terms **P Bamford, L Bellman & C McKee**
43 SIMPLY ME, b f New Approach (IRE)—Ego **L. A. Bellman**
44 SPEY SECRET (IRE), br g Kyllachy—Chiarezza (AUS) **Speyside Distillers Company Limited**
45 SWANSWAY, ch c Showcasing—Spring Stroll (USA) **M Smyth S Burns D Studholme & T Flaherty**

MR TOM DASCOMBE - Continued

46 TOP OF THE ROCKS (FR), b g Rock of Gibraltar (IRE)—Runaway Top **The Mad March Hares**
47 WALL OF LIGHT, b f Zamindar (USA)—Veiled Beauty (USA) **Chasemore Farm LLP**

TWO-YEAR-OLDS

48 B f 17/3 Elzaam (AUS)—Alchimie (IRE) (Sri Pekan (USA)) (5906) **The Roaring Twenties**
49 Ch c 5/2 Bahamian Bounty—Aliante (Sir Percy) (66666) **Manor House Stables LLP**
50 B f 6/3 Captain Gerrard (IRE)—All Fur Coat (Multiplex) (571) **Mr & Mrs Paul & Clare Rooney**
51 Ch c 3/4 Teofilo (IRE)—
    Altesse Imperiale (IRE) (Rock of Gibraltar (IRE)) (50203) **Laurence Bellman & Caroline Ingram**
52 Br f 23/2 Intikhab (USA)—Anyaas (IRE) (Green Desert (USA)) (10335) **The Roaring Twenties**
53 B f 28/1 Born To Sea (IRE)—Aquanaut (Dansili) **Chasemore Farm LLP**
54 B c 22/3 Fastnet Rock (AUS)—Be My Queen (IRE) (Sadler's Wells (USA)) (6000) **The Roaring Twenties**
55 B c 29/4 Art Connoisseur (IRE)—Be Special (IRE) (Sri Pekan (USA)) (6275) **The Roaring Twenties**
56 BLACKBELLE (IRE), br f 26/3 New Approach (IRE)—Wadaat (Diktat) (45000) **L. A. Bellman**
57 B f 2/4 Monsieur Bond (IRE)—Bollin Rita (Rambo Dancer (CAN)) (8571) **The Roaring Twenties**
58 B f 6/4 Tagula (IRE)—Bonny Rose (Zaha (CAN)) (10476) **The Roaring Twenties**
59 BROGAN, b f 12/3 Pivotal—Roger Sez (IRE) (Red Clubs (IRE)) **Chasemore Farm LLP**
60 CAJMERE, b c 14/3 Kyllachy—Percolator (Kheleyf (USA)) (36190) **Mr J. Dance**
61 CHEERFILLY (IRE), br f 10/4 Excelebration (IRE)—Classic Remark (IRE) (Dr Fong (USA)) (51679) **L. A. Bellman**
62 Br f 25/2 Sir Prancealot (IRE)—Dance On (Caerleon (USA)) (16242)
63 B c 4/4 Arcano (IRE)—Dolce Dovo (Medicean) (16242) **The Roaring Twenties**
64 Ch c 4/2 Showcasing—Douro (Manduro (GER)) (32000) **Manor House Stables LLP**
65 B f 21/3 Fast Company (IRE)—Easy Going (Hamas (IRE)) (8121) **The Roaring Twenties**
66 EXCITING TIMES, ch c 7/2 Tamayuz—Catwalk (IRE) (Pivotal) (44296) **Mr D. R. Passant**
67 B f 8/3 Born To Sea (IRE)—Eyrecourt (Efisio) (31000) **Mr John Dance & James Pak Racing**
68 FULL INTENTION, b c 16/4 Showcasing—My Delirium (Haafhd) (51428) **Mr J. Dance**
69 B c 25/3 Dragon Pulse (IRE)—Gala Spirit (IRE) (Invincible Spirit (IRE)) (12380) **The Roaring Twenties**
70 B c 1/1 Exceed And Excel (AUS)—Glory Power (IRE) (Medicean) (73827)
71 B f 25/2 Rip Van Winkle (IRE)—Goldamour (IRE) (Fasliyev (USA)) (42820) **Manor House Stables LLP**
72 B c 30/1 Kitten's Joy (USA)—Granny Franny (USA) (Grand Slam (USA)) (230000) **Burns Smyth Studholme**
73 Ch c 8/4 Thewayyouare (USA)—Grenouillere (USA) (Alysheba (USA)) (14765) **The Roaring Twenties**
74 HAZY MANOR (IRE), b f 23/4 Tagula (IRE)—Hazarama (IRE) (Kahyasi) (23624) **Excel Racing & Partners**
75 HEAVEN'S ROCK (IRE), b c 24/3 Requinto (IRE)—
    Rockfleet Castle (Rock of Gibraltar (IRE)) (38095) **Tom Cleverley & Stephen Mound**
76 Ch c 2/5 Dandy Man (IRE)—High Inthe Sky (IRE) (High Chaparral (IRE)) (11812) **The Roaring Twenties**
77 IMDANCINWITHURWIFE (IRE), b f 16/2 Sir Prancealot (IRE)—
    Bishop's Lake (Lake Coniston (IRE)) (32000) **Hong Kong Crew**
78 B c 22/4 Paco Boy (IRE)—Infectious (Mujadil (USA)) (4761) **The Roaring Twenties**
79 Br f 2/4 Dragon Pulse (IRE)—Intricate Dance (USA) (Aptitude (USA)) (13289) **The Roaring Twenties**
80 KACHESS, b f 19/4 Kyllachy—Fibou (USA) (Seeking The Gold (USA)) (38095) **Mr D. J. Lowe**
81 Ch c 2/5 Adlerflug (GER)—Lady Manners (USA) (Montbrook (USA)) (33960)
82 B f 4/4 Arcano (IRE)—Lady McBeth (IRE) (Avonbridge) (7619) **The Roaring Twenties**
83 LEGATO (IRE), ch c 19/4 Power—Lisa Gherardini (IRE) (Barathea (IRE)) (29531) **Alan & Sue Cronshaw**
84 B f 17/3 Approve (IRE)—Mar Sin De (IRE) (Danetime (IRE)) (9597) **The Roaring Twenties**
85 B c 4/3 Sepoy (AUS)—Max One Two Three (IRE) (Princely Heir (USA)) **Laurence Bellman & Chasemore Farm**
86 Ch f 18/2 Dragon Pulse (IRE)—Mysterious Girl (IRE) (Teofilo (IRE)) (28571)
87 B c 9/1 Excelebration (IRE)—Nigh (IRE) (Galileo (IRE)) (73827) **Trowbridge O'Halloran Lowe Jones**
88 Ch c 23/3 Nathaniel (IRE)—Quiet Protest (USA) (Kingmambo (USA)) (9000) **The Roaring Twenties**
89 RED SHANGHAI (IRE), ch f 10/4 Tamayuz—Rouge Noir (USA) (Saint Ballado (CAN)) (8859) **Mr B. W. Keswick**
90 B c 23/4 Majestic Missile (IRE)—Ron's Secret (Efisio) (25101)
91 Ch c 11/3 Arcano (IRE)—Royal Blush (Royal Applause) (35238) **Manor House Stables LLP**
92 B c 17/3 Dandy Man (IRE)—Royal Majestic (Tobougg (IRE)) (42857)
93 Ch f 15/4 Dandy Man (IRE)—Sesmen (Inchinor) (22148) **Deva Racing Dandy Man Partnership**
94 SHADOW WING (IRE), ch f 12/3 Sakhee's Secret—Go Maggie Go (IRE) (Kheleyf (USA)) (22886) **Mr J. Dance**
95 STAR OF RORY (IRE), b c 25/2 Born To Sea (IRE)—
    Dame Alicia (IRE) (Sadler's Wells (USA)) (80000) **Mr D. R. Passant & Hefin Williams**
96 Ch f 5/2 Paco Boy (IRE)—Sunday Bess (JPN) (Deep Impact (JPN)) (7500) **Chasemore Farm LLP**
97 B c 16/4 Bushranger (IRE)—Sweet Wind Music (Zamindar (USA)) (5714) **The Roaring Twenties**
98 Gr ro f 25/2 Hat Trick (JPN)—Tarika (USA) (Cozzene (USA)) (14765) **The Roaring Twenties**
99 B c 5/4 Sir Prancealot (IRE)—Toy Show (IRE) (Danehill (USA)) (9523) **The Roaring Twenties**
100 B c 7/5 Dream Ahead (USA)—Valandraud (IRE) (College Chapel) **Chasemore Farm LLP & Owen Promotions Ltd**

MR TOM DASCOMBE - Continued

Other Owners: Mr D. Athorn, Mr N. B. Attenborough, Mr C. Austin, P. Bamford, Mr L. S. Basran MBE, Mrs A. Biles, A. W. Black, Mrs J. E. Black, Mrs S. J. Bosanko, Mr S. Burns, Mr T. W. Cleverley, Mrs M. Coxon, Mr A. Cronshaw, Mrs S. P. Cronshaw, B. Dascombe, T. G. Dascombe, Mr D. Duncan, Mr N. C. Dunnington, Mr M. Edwards, Mr P. Fisher, Mr T. M. Flaherty, Mr M. D. Foster, Mr M. Foster, Mrs J. Foster, Mr N. J. Hughes, Mrs C. L. Ingram, Mr C. M. Ingram, Mr R. Jones, Mr S. L. Keswick, Mr C. Ledigo, Mr C. Lindley, Mrs J. Lowe, Mrs S. E. Mather, Mr N. P. Mather, Mr C. E. McKee, Mr S. N. Mound, Mrs A. C. Mound, Newsells Park Stud Limited, Mr M. O'Halloran, Mr M. Owen, Owen Promotions Limited, Mr J. Pak, Mr C. D. Pritchard, Mr A. S. Pritchard, S. E. Roberts, Mrs C. Rooney, Mr P. A. Rooney, Mr D. M. Shaw, Mr G. Shepherd, Mr J. M. Smart, Mr M. Smyth, Mr D. Studholme, K. P. Trowbridge, Mr H. Williams, Mr M. Wilmshurst, Mr J. Woodward.

Assistant Trainer: Colin Gorman

Jockey (flat): Richard Kingscote.

---

136 MR TRISTAN DAVIDSON, Carlisle
Postal: **Bellmount, Laversdale, Irthington, Carlisle, Cumbria, CA6 4PS**
Contacts: **MOBILE (07789) 684290**

1 **GOLIATH (IRE),** 4, br g Golan (IRE)—Lady Shanakill (IRE) **Adamson Bell Carruthers Davidson Etheridge**
2 **LEANNA BAN,** 9, b g Alflora (IRE)—Gurleigh (IRE) **E G Tunstall, P Nicholson, S M Grice**
3 **NAILER (IRE),** 6, b g Coroner (IRE)—Celtic Serenade (IRE) **G E Davidson, S M Grice, M McManus**
4 **ORCHARD ROAD (USA),** 9, b g Street Cry (IRE)—Aunt Mottz (USA) **The Not Very Likely Lads**

Other Owners: Mr Gordon Adamson, Mr Andrew G. Bell, Mr K. Carruthers, Mr Gordon E. Davidson, Mr George Brian Davidson, Mr Gary Etheridge, Mr S. M. Grice, Mr M. McManus, Mr P. S. Nicholson, Mr E. G. Tunstall.

---

137 MR JOHN DAVIES, Darlington
Postal: **Denton Grange, Piercebridge, Darlington, Co. Durham, DL2 3TZ**
Contacts: **PHONE (01325) 374366 MOBILE (07746) 292782**
E-MAIL johndavieshorses@live.co.uk WEBSITE www.johndaviesracing.com

1 **ARRIELLA,** 4, b f Dapper—Bedtime Blues **Mr C. W. Davies**
2 **IM DAPPER TOO,** 5, b g Dapper—Lonely One **Mr C. W. Davies**
3 **KOMMANDER KIRKUP,** 5, ch g Assertive—Bikini **K. Kirkup**
4 **LIFE STORY,** 4, b g New Approach (IRE)—Storyland (USA) **Mr & Mrs R. Scott**
5 **MAJOR ROWAN,** 5, b g Captain Gerrard (IRE)—Julie's Gift **David H. Cox**
6 **MCVICAR,** 7, b g Tobougg (IRE)—Aries (GER) **Ms D. Nicholson**
7 **MONTYDARKDESTROYER,** 5, b g Lucarno (USA)—Markila (FR) **Mrs M. S. Stone**
8 **OSTEOPATHIC REMEDY (IRE),** 12, ch g Inchinor—Dolce Vita (IRE) **K. Kirkup**
9 **THE OSTEOPATH (IRE),** 13, ch g Danehill Dancer (IRE)—Miss Margate (IRE) **K. Kirkup**
10 **THROCKLEY,** 5, b g Passing Glance—Porcelain (IRE) **The Maroon Stud**

THREE-YEAR-OLDS

11 **DAWN FLIGHT (IRE),** b g Cacique (IRE)—Ommadawn (IRE) **Mr & Mrs R. Scott**
12 **MANGO CHUTNEY,** b g Sleeping Indian—Crimson Topaz **Mr P. Taylor**
13 **QUIET APPROACH,** b g Makfi—Silent Act (USA) **Mr & Mrs R. Scott**
14 **SAXON GOLD (IRE),** ch f Zoffany (IRE)—Apple Brandy (USA) **J Davies & A Gitsham**

TWO-YEAR-OLDS

15 B f 8/4 Harbour Watch (IRE)—Elidore (Danetime (IRE)) (15238) **Ms D. Nicholson**
16 Ch c 26/5 Dapper—Vera Richardson (IRE) (Dutch Art) **K. Kirkup**

Other Owners: J. J. Davies, L. L. Dickman, A. Dickman, Mr A. Gitsham, Mrs P. M. Scott, R. Scott.

Jockey (flat): P. J. McDonald.

---

138 MR PAUL DAVIES, Bromyard
Postal: **20 Hatton Park, Bromyard, Herefordshire, HR7 4EY**

1 **EMMA SODA,** 11, b m Milan—Ms Trude (IRE) **Mr P. S. Davies**

139 **MISS SARAH-JAYNE DAVIES, Leominster**
Postal: **The Upper Withers, Hundred Lane, Kimbolton, Leominster, Herefordshire, HR6 0HZ**
Contacts: **PHONE (01584) 711780 MOBILE (07779) 797079**
E-MAIL sjdracing@live.co.uk

1 **ACCESSALLAREAS (IRE)**, 11, ch g Swift Gulliver (IRE)—Arushofgold (IRE) **Withers Winners**
2 **ANOTHER JOURNEY**, 7, b g Rail Link—Singasongosixpence **Gary Dewhurst & Sarah-Jayne Davies**
3 **BATTLESHIP BOY (IRE)**, 8, b g Kaieteur (USA)—Battle On **Loose Cannon Racing**
4 **CAPISCI (IRE)**, 11, br g Tikkanen (USA)—Dolce Notte (IRE) **K. E. Stait**
5 **CHANKILLO**, 7, ch g Observatory (USA)—Seasonal Blossom (IRE) **Mr A. J. Gough**
6 4, B g Fantastic Spain (USA)—Clarice Starling **Mr A. J. Gough**
7 **COURTING HARRY**, 5, b g Lucarno (USA)—Harry's Bride **W. S. Layton**
8 **DARKENING NIGHT**, 4, b g Cape Cross (IRE)—Garanciere (FR) **The Cannon Club**
9 **DEADLY APPROACH**, 5, b g New Approach (IRE)—Speirbhean (IRE) **Quadriga Racing**
10 **FOUR SHUCK MEN (IRE)**, 8, b g Spartacus (IRE)—Shed **Good Evans Racing Partnership**
11 **GIOS LAST (GER)**, 6, gr g Paolini (GER)—Giovanella (IRE) **Pump & Plant Services Ltd**
12 **HERR LARRY HEWIS**, 8, b g Sir Harry Lewis (USA)—Avenches (GER) **Mr R. A. Skidmore**
13 **KIMS OCEAN (IRE)**, 6, b g Urban Ocean (FR)—A Touch of Joy (IRE) **Mr T. J. Richards**
14 **MISS DIMPLES (IRE)**, 7, gr m Tikkanen (USA)—Scolboa House (IRE) **Pippin Bank Partnership**
15 **PASSING FIESTA**, 7, b m Passing Glance—Clarice Starling **Mr A. J. Gough**
16 **PEMBROKE HOUSE**, 9, gr g Terimon—Bon Coeur **Mr A. Mortimer**
17 **PETTAL**, 5, b m Indian Danehill (IRE)—Fields of Home (IRE) **Moorland Racing**
18 4, B f Multiplex—Romping Home **Mr G. Dewhurst**
19 **SPARKS (IRE)**, 4, br f Elusive City (USA)—Hambye **Pump & Plant Services Ltd**
20 **SPYDER**, 8, b g Resplendent Glory (IRE)—Collect **Miss S. J. Davies**
21 **TRAFALGAR (FR)**, 9, b g Laveron—Dzaoudzie (FR) **Moorland Racing**
22 **TWIN BARRELS**, 9, ch g Double Trigger (IRE)—Caballe (USA) **K. E. Stait**
23 4, Ch f Tobougg (IRE)—Two Aye Em **Mrs S. M. Davies**
24 5, B m Multiplex—Walton Money **Good Evans Racing Partnership**
25 **WHOS DE BABY (IRE)**, 8, gr g Bienamado (USA)—Beaus Rose (IRE) **Mrs C. J. Davies**

Other Owners: M. P. Bass, Mr M. Evans, Mr C. S. D. James, S. A. Mace, Mrs A. M. Mace, Mr J. H. M. Mahot, Mr K. J. Price, Mr D. Richardson, Mr O. Vaughan, Mr J. F. Vincent.

Assistant Trainer: Jeremy Mahot

Jockey (NH): Will Kennedy, Liam Treadwell. **Amateur:** Miss Sarah-Jayne Davies, Mr Jeremy Mahot.

140 **MISS JOANNA DAVIS, East Garston**
Postal: **1 Parson Close Stables, School Lane, East Garston, Hungerford, Berkshire, RG17 7HR**
Contacts: **PHONE (01488) 649977 FAX (01488) 649977 MOBILE (07879) 811535**
E-MAIL davisjo_007@hotmail.com WEBSITE www.jodavisracing.com

1 5, B m Rainbow High—Bright Spangle (IRE) **Jo Davis**
2 **CAPELLIAN CRUSADER (IRE)**, 7, b g Cape Cross (IRE)—Llia **Mrs P. M. Brown**
3 **CAPTAIN FLASH (IRE)**, 7, b g Indian River (FR)—Westgate Run **John L & Albert L Marriott & Jo Davis**
4 **DARK MUSIC (IRE)**, 5, br m Misu Bond (IRE)—Tender Moments **Mrs P. M. Brown**
5 **DOCTOR OF MUSIC (IRE)**, 10, ch g Dr Fong (USA)—Sublime Beauty (USA) **Mrs P. M. Brown**
6 **GALLIC DESTINY (IRE)**, 5, b g Champs Elysees—Cross Your Fingers (USA) **Mrs P. M. Brown**
7 **HEROES OR GHOSTS (IRE)**, 7, br g Indian River (FR)—Awomansdream (IRE) **Tony Worth & Vic Bedley**
8 **INDIEFRONT**, 7, b m Indesatchel (IRE)—Jonchee (FR) **Robbie Allsop**
9 **JOHN BISCUIT (IRE)**, 8, ch g Hawk Wing (USA)—Princess Magdalena **Mrs P. M. Brown**
10 **MR FITZROY (IRE)**, 6, ch g Kyllachy—Reputable **Mrs P. M. Brown**
11 **PASSATO (GER)**, 12, b g Lando (GER)—Passata (FR) **Robbie Allsop**
12 **PRAIRIE RANGER**, 6, b g Montjeu (IRE)—No Frills (IRE) **Mrs P. M. Brown**
13 **SPANISH DANSER (IRE)**, 4, ch f Lord Shanakill (USA)—
                                        Highwater Dancer (IRE) **Fiona Stonehouse & Peter Skinner**
14 **STAR FOOT (IRE)**, 5, b g Soviet Star (USA)—On The Backfoot (IRE) **John L Marriott & Albert L Marriott**
15 **WILLY BRENNAN (IRE)**, 5, br g Bushranger (IRE)—Miss Assertive **Mrs P. M. Brown**

TWO-YEAR-OLDS

16 Ch g 17/4 Malinas (GER)—Bright Spangle (IRE) (General Monash (USA)) **Jo Davis & Tony Hutchinson**
17 Br f 5/2 Oasis Dream—No Frills (IRE) (Darshaan) **Dr P. Brown**

MISS JOANNA DAVIS - Continued

Other Owners: V. R. Bedley, Miss J. Davis, Mr John L. Marriott, Mr Albert L. Marriott, Mr Peter W. Skinner, Mrs Fiona Stonehouse, Mr A. G. Worth.

141 MISS LOUISE DAVIS, Levedale

Postal: **The Stables, Hillcrest, Bradley Lane, Levedale, Stafford, Staffordshire, ST18 9AH**
Contacts: MOBILE **(07426) 316685**
E-MAIL **vky1971@yahoo.co.uk** WEBSITE **www.louisedavisracing.co.uk**

1 HAMBLE, 7, b g Librettist (USA)—Time For Tea (IRE) **Miss L. V. Davis**
2 MOUNT WELCOME (IRE), 12, b g Bach (IRE)—Be My Vixen (IRE) **Miss L. V. Davis**
3 NEVER PERFECT (IRE), 7, b g Galileo (IRE)—Dapprima (GER) **Miss L. V. Davis**
4 SAMAWI (IRE), 6, b g Street Cry (IRE)—Hi Dubai **Miss L. V. Davis**

Assistant Trainer: Mr J. Freeman

142 MISS ZOE DAVISON, East Grinstead

Postal: **Shovelstrode Racing Stables, Shovelstrode Lane, Ashurstwood, East Grinstead, West Sussex, RH19 3PN**
Contacts: PHONE **(01342) 300319** MOBILE **(07970) 839357 & (07812) 007554**
E-MAIL **andy01031976@yahoo.co.uk** WEBSITE **www.shovelstroderacing.co.uk**

1 ANNAKRISTA (GER), 8, b m Kallisto (GER)—Annabelle (GER) **A. J. Irvine**
2 ASKER (IRE), 8, b g High Chaparral (IRE)—Pay The Bank **The Secret Circle**
3 BOLD MAX, 5, b g Assertive—Jane's Payoff (IRE) **Mr K. C. Bennett**
4 BUSTER BROWN (IRE), 7, ch g Singspiel (IRE)—Gold Dodger (USA) **The Secret Circle**
5 CHILL (IRE), 8, b g Diamond Green (FR)—Time To Relax (IRE) **Mrs S. E. Colville**
6 DERRYOGUE (IRE), 11, b g Tikkanen (USA)—Snugville Sally **The Lump O'Clock Syndicate**
7 DYLANSEOGHAN (IRE), 7, b g Pierre—Sabbatical (IRE) **The Lump O'Clock Syndicate**
8 FINNEGAN'S GARDEN (IRE), 7, b g Definite Article—Tri Folene (FR) **Mr K. Corke**
9 FRANK N FAIR, 8, br m Trade Fair—Frankfurt (GER) **Miss Z. C. Davison**
10 GEORGE NYMPTON (IRE), 10, br g Alderbrook—Countess Camilla **The Secret Circle**
11 GEORGIESHORE (IRE), 8, b g Turtle Island (IRE)—Pride of St Gallen (IRE) **The Lump O'Clock Syndicate**
12 GUSTAV, 6, b g Mahler—Pakaradyssa (FR) **The Plum Merchants**
13 JUMEIRAH LIBERTY, 8, ch g Proclamation (IRE)—Gleam of Light (IRE) **The Secret Circle**
14 LINDSAY'S DREAM, 10, b m Montjeu (IRE)—Lady Lindsay (IRE) **Mr S. P. O'Loughlin**
15 NOIR GIRL, 7, b m Beat All (USA)—Forever Shineing **The Secret Circle**
16 PARADISE SPECTRE, 9, b g Firebreak—Amber's Bluff **The Secret Circle**
17 PIAZZA SAN PIETRO, 10, ch g Compton Place—Rainbow Spectrum (FR) **Mr K. Corke**
18 SHARENI (IRE), 7, b g Azamour (IRE)—Sharesha (IRE) **The Secret Circle**
19 STANDING STRONG (IRE), 8, b g Green Desert (USA)—Alexander Three D (IRE) **The Secret Circle**
20 THE GOLDEN HOUR (IRE), 6, b m Gold Well—Kirktonmoor Katie (IRE) **Miss Z. C. Davison**

Other Owners: S. J. Clare, A. C. Clift, T. M. Santry, A. N. Waters.

Assistant Trainer: A. Irvine

Jockey (NH): Gemma Gracey-Davison. **Amateur:** Mr M. G. Miller.

143 MR ANTHONY DAY, Hinckley

Postal: **Wolvey Fields Farm, Coalpit Lane, Wolvey, Hinckley, Leicestershire, LE10 3HD**
Contacts: PHONE **(01455) 220225** MOBILE **(07519) 828473**
E-MAIL **kathy197@btinternet.com**

1 CHARMING LAD (IRE), 11, b g Dushyantor (USA)—Glens Lady (IRE) **Mrs K. D. Day**
2 COOL FUSION, 7, b m Beat All (USA)—Fusion of Tunes **Mrs K. D. Day**
3 OHMS LAW, 11, b g Overbury (IRE)—Polly Live Wire **Mrs K. D. Day**
4 SOUND THE BUGLE, 6, b g Overbury (IRE)—Fusion of Tunes **Mrs K. D. Day**
5 VELVET EDGE, 7, b m Central Park (IRE)—Velvet Leaf **Mrs K. D. Day**

MR ANTHONY DAY - Continued

Assistant Trainer: Mrs K. D. Day (07546) 593485
Conditional: Jake Hodson.

---

144 **MR WILLIAM DE BEST-TURNER, Calne**
Postal: **8 North End, Calne, Wiltshire, SN11 9DQ**
Contacts: **PHONE (01249) 811944 HOME (01249) 813850 FAX (01249) 811955
MOBILE (07977) 910779**
E-MAIL debestracing@hotmail.co.uk

1 **BOSTON RED**, 4, ch g Schiaparelli (GER)—Maylan (IRE) **W. de Best-Turner**
2 **CHICAGO SOCKS**, 6, b h Catcher In The Rye (IRE)—Sachiko **W. de Best-Turner**
3 **NELSON'S HILL**, 6, b g Mount Nelson—Regal Step **W. de Best-Turner**
4 **SPARTACULOUS**, 8, b m Spartacus (IRE)—Sachiko **W. de Best-Turner**

Assistant Trainer: Mrs I. De Best

---

145 **MR ED DE GILES, Ledbury**
Postal: **Lilly Hall Farm, Little Marcle, Ledbury, Herefordshire, HR8 2LD**
Contacts: **PHONE (01531) 637369 MOBILE (07811) 388345**
E-MAIL ed@eddegilesracing.com WEBSITE www.eddegilesracing.com

1 **AKAVIT (IRE)**, 4, b g Vale of York (IRE)—Along Came Molly **Mr S. Treacher**
2 4, Bl f Halling (USA)—Candle **E. B. de Giles**
3 **CROQUEMBOUCHE (IRE)**, 7, b g Acclamation—Wedding Cake (IRE) **Mr P. J. Manser**
4 **FROSTY BERRY**, 7, gr m Proclamation (IRE)—Star Entry **Ms J. A. French**
5 **GO NANI GO**, 10, b g Kyllachy—Go Between **Tight Lines Partnership**
6 **GODDESS EPONA**, 4, b f Dylan Thomas (IRE)—Cloudchaser (IRE) **E. B. de Giles**
7 **KINGSGATE CHOICE (IRE)**, 9, b g Choisir (AUS)—Kenema (IRE) **T. Gould**
8 **LUCY THE PAINTER (IRE)**, 4, b f Excellent Art—Royal Bounty (IRE) **Mr J. P. Carrington**
9 **NAPOLEONIC (USA)**, 5, b g War Front (USA)—High Savannah **Mr S. Treacher**
10 **PRENDERGAST HILL (IRE)**, 4, b g Raven's Pass (USA)—Daraliya (IRE) **Gwyn & Samantha Powell**
11 **QUANTUM DOT (IRE)**, 5, ch g Exceed And Excel (AUS)—Jeed (IRE) **Mrs Y. Fleet**
12 **SHADES OF SILVER**, 6, b g Dansili—Silver Pivotal (IRE) **The Champion Family**
13 **SUN IN HIS EYES**, 4, ch g Compton Place—Sunset Lady (IRE) **Ms J. A. French**
14 **TEA GOWN (IRE)**, 5, ch m Iffraaj—Dignify (IRE) **Ms J. A. French**
15 **TIJUCA (IRE)**, 7, b m Captain Rio—Some Forest (IRE) **E. B. de Giles**
16 **TWENTY ONE CHOICE (IRE)**, 7, ch g Choisir (AUS)—Midnight Lace **T. Gould**
17 **WIND IN MY SAILS**, 4, b g Footstepsinthesand—Dylanesque **Mr P. J. Manser**
18 **ZUGZWANG (IRE)**, 5, b g Kodiac—Kris's Bank **Mr S. Treacher**

THREE-YEAR-OLDS

19 **ARQUUS (IRE)**, b c Lilbourne Lad (IRE)—Charaig **Lilly Hall Thoroughbreds**
20 **BELLA IMPERATRIX**, b f Holy Roman Emperor (IRE)—
Be Amazing (IRE) **Mrs Bernard Taylor and Mr John Manser**
21 **CARCHARIAS (IRE)**, b c Kodiac—Princess Atoosa (USA) **Boardman, Golder, Sercombe & Viall I**
22 **CAY LOCATION (IRE)**, b g Bahamian Bounty—Desert Location **Clarke, King & Lewis**
23 **CHILLI JAM**, b c Mastercraftsman (IRE)—Wosaita **Mr P. R. Jarvis**
24 **INCUS**, b c Bertolini (USA)—Cloudchaser (IRE) **E. B. de Giles**
25 **MARCLE (IRE)**, b c Kodiac—Mark One **Clarissa Casdagli & Simon Treacher**
26 **OPERATIVE**, ch c Pastoral Pursuits—Gilt Linked **Gwyn & Samantha Powell & Partner**
27 **PANKO (IRE)**, b c Iffraaj—Engraving **Mr S. Treacher**
28 **SWANTON BLUE (IRE)**, b c Kodiac—Cabopino (IRE) **I. W. Gibson**
29 **WAKAME (IRE)**, b c Kodiac—Awwal Malika (USA) **Mr S. Treacher**
30 **WASSAIL**, b f Shamardal (USA)—Gower Song **Mr A. Mortazavi**
31 **ZLATAN (IRE)**, b c Dark Angel (IRE)—Guard Hill (USA) **Gwyn Powell & Richard Meakes**

TWO-YEAR-OLDS

32 B c 19/4 Paco Boy (IRE)—Black Baroness (Ishiguru (USA)) (40000)
33 B f 10/3 Tamayuz—Coeur de La Mer (IRE) (Caerleon (USA)) (9000) **Mrs S. Powell**

MR ED DE GILES - Continued

34 B f 20/4 Lope de Vega (IRE)—Crossbreeze (USA) (Red Ransom (USA)) (42000) **Mrs S. Powell**
35 B c 13/3 Casamento (IRE)—Designed (Zamindar (USA)) (40000) **Mr S. Treacher**
36 Ch c 23/4 Kyllachy—Indian Belle (IRE) (Indian Ridge) (60000) **Mr S. Treacher**
37 B c 12/3 Dragon Pulse (IRE)—Mathool (IRE) (Alhaarth (IRE)) (34000)
38 B c 11/3 Vocalised (USA)—Tense (IRE) (Invincible Spirit (IRE)) (3690) **E. B. de Giles**

Other Owners: Mr R. J. Boardman, Mrs C. R. Casdagli, Mrs A. P. Champion, Mr N. C. Champion, Mr D. Clarke, Mr J. C. Golder, C. J. King, Mrs E. V. Lewis, Mr R. Meakes, G. E. Powell, Rycote Services Limited, Mr P. R. Sercombe, Mrs S. J. Taylor, A. J. Viall, Mrs C. R. de Giles.

---

146 MR BEN DE HAAN, Lambourn
Postal: 7 Newbury Road, Lambourn, Hungerford, Berkshire, RG17 7LL
Contacts: **PHONE (01488) 72163 FAX (01488) 71306 MOBILE (07831) 104574**
E-MAIL bendehaanracing@aol.com **WEBSITE** www.bendehaanracing.com

1 DECIDING MOMENT (IRE), 10, b g Zagreb (USA)—Fontaine Jewel (IRE) **W. A. Tyrer**
2 NATIVE GALLERY (IRE), 11, gr g Portrait Gallery (IRE)—Native Bev (IRE) **W. A. Tyrer**

THREE-YEAR-OLDS

3 KATH'S LEGACY, ch f Cockney Rebel (IRE)—It's Dubai Dolly **Mr M. M. Cox**

Jockey (flat): Adam Kirby. **Jockey (NH):** Daryl Jacob, Noel Fehily.

---

147 MR GEOFFREY DEACON, Compton
Postal: Hamilton Stables, Hockham Road, Compton, Newbury, Berkshire, RG20 6QJ
Contacts: **MOBILE (07967) 626757**
E-MAIL geoffdeacon@aol.com **WEBSITE** www.geoffreydeacontraining.com

1 BANKS ROAD (IRE), 11, b g Beneficial—Cecelia's Charm (IRE) **Mr C. W. Duckett**
2 CAPTAIN RYAN, 5, b g Captain Gerrard (IRE)—Ryan's Quest (IRE) **A.Lomax, B.Mortimer, W.H & J.Simpson**
3 DARK PHANTOM (IRE), 5, b g Dark Angel (IRE)—Stoneware **Mrs J. I. Simpson**
4 EARTHWINDORFIRE, 5, br g High Chaparral (IRE)—Elemental **Mr G. Deacon**
5 ESEEJ (USA), 11, ch g Aljabr (USA)—Jinaan (USA) **Miss S. J. Duckett**
6 EVIAS, 5, b g Tiger Hill (IRE)—Circadian Rhythm **J. W. Haydon**
7 GLASTONBERRY, 8, gr m Piccolo—Elderberry **Geoffrey Deacon Racing Club**
8 IZZY PICCOLINA (IRE), 8, b m Morozov (USA)—Chloara (IRE) **Geoffrey Deacon Racing Club**
9 LETTUCE SNOW (IRE), 4, b f Clodovil (IRE)—Lola Rosa (IRE) **The Stanford Dingleys**
10 MISS MITTENS, 4, b f Shirocco (GER)—River of Silence (IRE) **Mrs J. I. Simpson**
11 MOON TRIP, 7, b g Cape Cross (IRE)—Fading Light **The Moon Trip Partnership**
12 PICKET LINE, 4, b g Multiplex—Dockside Strike **Homegrown Partnership**
13 RAHMAH (IRE), 4, b c Vale of York (IRE)—Sweet Home Alabama (IRE) **Mr G. Deacon**
14 SPRINGHILL LAD, 9, b g Kayf Tara—Anouska **J. Davies**
15 SUITSUS, 5, b g Virtual—Point Perfect **Suitsus Partnership**

THREE-YEAR-OLDS

16 DRUMLIN, gr g Hellvelyn—Live To Tell **Bucklands Farm & Stud Ltd**
17 MAX BEDDOW (IRE), b c Tagula (IRE)—Copper Harbour (IRE) **Mr G. Deacon**
18 MONSIEUR PADDY, ch g Monsieur Bond (IRE)—Minnina (IRE) **J. A. Dewhurst**
19 REBEL WOODS (FR), b g Cockney Rebel (IRE)—In The Woods **Mr A. R. Pittman**
20 SILVER GHOST (IRE), gr c Dark Angel (IRE)—Aqualina (IRE) **Mr WH & Mrs Jennifer Simpson**
21 SIR JAMIE, ch c Monsieur Bond (IRE)—First Dawn **Mayden Stud & Associates**

Other Owners: Business Moves Group Ltd, P. D. Cundell, H. J. W. Davies, Mrs D. S. Dewhurst, Mr F. Hearty, R. Kent, Mr A. R. A. Lomax, Miss L. McGrath, Mr B. Mortimer, Mr W. H. Simpson.

Assistant Trainer: Sally Duckett

148 MR MIKEL DELZANGLES, Gouvieux

Postal: 16 Avenue Francois Mathet, 60270 Gouvieux, France
Contacts: PHONE (0033) 344573309 FAX (0033) 344219350 MOBILE (0033) 680387480
E-MAIL mikel.delzangles@worldonline.fr WEBSITE www.mikeldelzangles.com

1 ATAMAN ERMAK (IRE), 5, b g Galileo (IRE)—Missvinski (USA) V. Bukjtoyarov
2 BEATA (FR), 4, b f Silver Frost (IRE)—Bright Moon (USA) Wildenstein Stables
3 BILAPERFECTA (FR), 4, ch f Gentlewave (IRE)—Billette (FR) M. Delzangles
4 BOOKRUNNER (USA), 5, b h Tiznow (USA)—Take the Ribbon (USA) Papillon Stables
5 CHAMBOIS (FR), 4, gr g Whipper (USA)—Carmel (FR) G. Augustin-Normand
6 ELDACAR, 4, gr f Verglas (IRE)—Seracina Stud RDi
7 ERA UMA VEZ (FR), 4, ch f Galileo (IRE)—Pale Moon Rising (IRE) Stud RDi
8 EXCEEDINGLY RARE (IRE), 4, ch f Lope de Vega (IRE)—Pop Alliance (IRE) Qatar Racing
9 L'ARNACOEUR (FR), 4, ch g Makfi—Shapoura (FR) M. Delzangles
10 L'OBELISQUE (FR), 4, b g Soldier of Fortune (IRE)—Tintagel O. Carli
11 LADY PHLIZZ (FR), 4, gr f Soldier of Fortune (IRE)—Phlizz (FR) C. Lambert
12 MAIMARA (FR), 4, b f Makfi—Hideaway Heroine (IRE) A. Louis-Dreyfus
13 MING DYNASTY (FR), 4, b c King's Best (USA)—Memoire (FR) Qatar Racing
14 MURHIB (IRE), 4, b g Sea The Stars (IRE)—Mood Swings (IRE) Al Shaqab Racing
15 OATHKEEPER (USA), 4, b g Kitten's Joy (USA)—Canopy (USA) Papillon Stables
16 OLIVE D'HAGUENET (FR), 4, gr g Fragrant Mix (IRE)—Pauline d'haguenet (FR) M. Delzangles
17 PACIFIC ANGEL (IRE), 4, b f Dalakhani (IRE)—Perstrovka (IRE) Ballymore Thoroughbred Ltd
18 PEARL DRAGON (FR), 5, b h Nicobar—La Marlia (FR) Pearl Bloodstock
19 PEKAS, 4, b g Makfi—Singing Machine (USA) A. Louis-Dreyfus
20 SHALOUSHKA (IRE), 4, b f Dalakhani (IRE)—Shalama (IRE) S. A. Aga Khan
21 TAGHIR TASH (FR), 4, b g Siyouni (FR)—Queen Dream (FR) V. Bukhtoyarov
22 TOM TOM D'HAGUENET (FR), 4, gr g Apsis—Marie d'haguenet (FR) M. Delzangles
23 TRESORDARGENT (FR), 5, gr h Kendargent (FR)—Restia (FR) V. Bukhtoyarov
24 VARIANTE ALTA, 4, ch f Mastercraftsman (IRE)—Rinskia V. Bukhtoyarov
25 VEZILLON (FR), 4, b g Le Havre (IRE)—Veleza (FR) G. Augustin-Normand
26 VILLA KATSURA (IRE), 4, b f Peintre Celebre (USA)—Vieux Maisons (IRE) Jedburgh Stud
27 WAHIB (FR), 6, b h Invincible Spirit (IRE)—Wardat Allayl (IRE) Mr K. M. Al Attiyah

THREE-YEAR-OLDS

28 AMILIYA (IRE), b f Azamour (IRE)—Amen Desert (FR) H. H. Aga Khan
29 ANTEMIO (FR), b c Rip Van Winkle (IRE)—Peinture d'or (IRE) Ildefonso Leon-Sotelo Garcia
30 ARMURE BLEUE (FR), b f Invincible Spirit (IRE)—Aquarelle Rare Wildenstein Stables Limited
31 BADIYA (FR), gr f Rock of Gibraltar (IRE)—Beraviyna (IRE) H. H. Aga Khan
32 CAJARIAN (FR), b c Manduro (GER)—Carisamba (FR) H. H. Aga Khan
33 CANESSAR (FR), b c Kendargent (FR)—Candara (FR) H. H. Aga Khan
34 CIBOURE (FR), b f Sir Percy—Amou Daria (FR) E. Swyer
35 CLEOPHIS (FR), gr f Soldier of Fortune (IRE)—Our Dreams (IRE) O. Carli
36 DAZARI (FR), b g Paco Boy (IRE)—Darbaza (FR) Princess Z. Aga Khan
37 DESERT GALE (IRE), b f Pour Moi (IRE)—Await (IRE) H. H. Sheikh Mohammed Bin Khalif Al Thani
38 ENERYDA (FR), b f Sinndar (IRE)—Ensaya (IRE) S. A. Aga Khan
39 ESQUISITO (IRE), b f Fastnet Rock (AUS)—Floating Away (USA) D. Moodie
40 FALCAO NEGRO, b g Canford Cliffs (IRE)—Really Lovely (IRE) Stud RDi
41 FICA COMIGO, ch g Pivotal—Tudor Court (USA) Stud RDi
42 FOREST WONDER, b f Rip Van Winkle (IRE)—Pop Alliance (IRE) V. Bukhtoyarov
43 IRISH MAN (FR), ch g Muhtathir—Love And War (GER) V. Bukhtoyarov
44 KHAIRAGASH (FR), b c Sinndar (IRE)—Khazina (FR) S. A. Aga Khan
45 KHATERA (FR), b f Zamindar (USA)—Khelwa (FR) S. A. Aga Khan
46 L'ETOILE NOIRE (FR), b f Lope de Vega (IRE)—Black Dalhia (FR) F. Perree
47 LADY ALIENOR (IRE), b f Elusive Quality (USA)—Lady Aquitaine (USA) Wildenstein Stables Limited
48 LARGENT DU BONHEUR (FR), b c Kendargent (FR)—La Joie (FR) Qatar Racing Ltd
49 LAST FRONTIER (FR), gr f Kendargent (FR)—L'etoile de Moscou Wildenstein Stables Limited
50 LITTERALE CI (FR), b f Soldier of Fortune (IRE)—Cigalia F. Perree
51 LIVOYE (FR), b g Le Havre (IRE)—Lady Calido (USA) G. Augustin-Normand
52 MARAZA (IRE), b f Paco Boy (IRE)—Marque Royale H. H. Aga Khan
53 MIRASOL (FR), b f Makfi—Singing Machine (USA) A. Louis-Dreyfus
54 MONSTER MASH (FR), b f Zamindar (USA)—Monster Munchie (JPN) A. Black
55 MYSTERY OF QATAR (IRE), b f Dansili—Louvain (USA) H. H. Sheikh Mohammed Bin Khalifa Al Thani
56 PARANNGA (FR), b f Rock of Gibraltar (IRE)—Parandeh (FR) H. H. Aga Khan
57 PRIME SUSPECT (FR), gr c Silver Frost (IRE)—Premiere Danseuse Wildenstein Stables Limited

MR MIKEL DELZANGLES - Continued

58 **QATARI GOLD (USA)**, b g Lemon Drop Kid (USA)—
        Forest Valentine (USA) **H.H. Sheikh Mohammed Bin Khalifa Al Thani**
59 **RED ANGEL (IRE)**, gr g Dark Angel (IRE)—Love Green (FR) **Marquise De Moratalla**
60 **RIGEL STAR (IRE)**, ch c Danehill Dancer (IRE)—Rosa Bonheur (FR) **Wildenstein Stables Limited**
61 **ROCAGEL (FR)**, b c Rock of Gibraltar (IRE)—Sign of The Vine (FR) **B. Van Dalfsen**
62 **ROCKSTAR NIGHT (IRE)**, b f Fastnet Rock (AUS)—Starlight Night (USA) **V. Bukhtoyarov**
63 **ROYAL BOWL (FR)**, b c Turtle Bowl (IRE)—Monarquia (USA) **V. Bukhtoyarov**
64 **SANTORINA (FR)**, b f Trajano (USA)—Madinella (FR) **Ildefonso Leon-Soteco Garcia**
65 **SHALAKAR (FR)**, b c Cape Cross (IRE)—Shalanaya (IRE) **S. A. Aga Khan**
66 **SPRING PRINCESS (IRE)**, b f Nayef (USA)—Voie de Printemps (FR) **L. Roy**
67 **VENGEFUL (FR)**, b c Zoffany (IRE)—Miss Bex (IRE) **Qatar Racing Ltd**
68 **VERBAL LINK (FR)**, gr c King's Best (USA)—Verba (FR) **V. Bukhtoyarov**
69 **ZAWIYLA (FR)**, b f Azamour (IRE)—Zewara (FR) **S. A. Aga Khan**
70 **ZERKELA (FR)**, b f Cape Cross (IRE)—Zerkeriya (IRE) **S. A. Aga Khan**

TWO-YEAR-OLDS

71 **ACARI (IRE)**, b c 21/2 High Chaparral (IRE)—
        Abyssinie (IRE) (Danehill Dancer (IRE)) **Wildenstein Stables Limited**
72 **BERDIBEK (FR)**, gr c 1/2 Dark Angel (IRE)—Beravivna (IRE) (Zamindar (USA)) **H. H. Aga Khan**
73 B f 25/1 Bernardini (USA)—Changing Skies (IRE) (Sadler's Wells (USA)) **Al Shaqab Racing**
74 B c 24/4 War Front (USA)—
    Communique (USA) (Smart Strike (CAN)) (366300) **H.H. Sheikh Mohammed Bin Khalifa Al Thani**
75 **CORVILLE (FR)**, b f 26/3 Le Havre (FR)—Coutances (Shamardal (USA)) **G. Augustin-Normand**
76 **DARBUZAN (FR)**, gr c 23/3 Zamindar (USA)—Darbaza (FR) (Verglas (IRE)) **Princess Z. Aga Khan**
77 Ch f 15/3 Medicean—Ensaya (IRE) (Alhaarth (IRE)) **S. A. Aga Khan**
78 **GIPOIA (FR)**, ch f 31/1 Medicean—Really Lovely (IRE) (Galileo (IRE)) **Stud RDi**
79 B f 7/3 Nathaniel (IRE)—Grenade (FR) (Bering) (44296) **Robert Ng**
80 B c 12/2 Cape Cross (IRE)—Kasatana (IRE) (Hernando) **S. A. Aga Khan**
81 **NAHUEL (FR)**, b c 19/4 Mr Sidney (USA)—Singing Machine (USA) (Rossini (USA)) **A. Louis-Dreyfus**
82 B f 11/3 Oasis Dream—Petite Noblesse (FR) (Galileo (USA)) **Stud RDi**
83 **PRINZ HLODOWIG (FR)**, b c 4/2 Rajsaman (FR)—
      Princess Cheri (GER) (Mondrian (GER)) (27316) **OTI Management Ltd**
84 B c 16/4 Lawman (FR)—Secret Question (USA) (Rahy (USA)) **Al Shaqab Racing**
85 **SHAHJALAL (FR)**, b c 30/1 Excelebration (IRE)—Shanndiyra (IRE) (King's Best (USA)) **S. A. Aga Khan**
86 **SHAZIA (FR)**, ch f 21/3 New Approach (IRE)—Shalanaya (IRE) (Lomitas) **S. A. Aga Khan**
87 **SPECIAL GAL (FR)**, b f 17/4 Galileo (IRE)—
      Special Delivery (IRE) (Danehill (USA)) **Wildenstein Stables Limited**
88 **SPECIAL JOY (FR)**, b f 21/4 Rio de La Plata (USA)—
      Xcape To Victory (IRE) (Cape Cross (IRE)) (29531) **Robert Ng**
89 B c 8/2 Lope de Vega (IRE)—Sunrise Song (IRE) (Invincible Spirit (IRE)) (59062) **R. Harding**
90 **TAHIRA (FR)**, b f 15/2 Holy Roman Emperor (IRE)—Tazmiyna (FR) (Alhaarth (IRE)) **S. A. Aga Khan**
91 **VERDE RIVER (IRE)**, b f 29/1 Danehill Dancer (IRE)—
      Venetian Beauty (USA) (Lear Fan (USA)) **Wildenstein Stables Limited**
92 B f 2/5 Redoute's Choice (AUS)—Vermentina (FR) (Darshaan) **Stud RDi**
93 B f 31/1 Teofilo (IRE)—
    Walk In Beauty (IRE) (Shamardal (USA)) (130000) **H. H. Sheikh Mohammed Bin Khalifa Al Thani**
94 B f 20/3 Dalakhani (IRE)—Zalaiyka (FR) (Royal Academy (USA)) **S. A. Aga Khan**
95 **ZORAWAR (FR)**, c 1/1 Shamardal (USA)—Zerkeriya (IRE) (Soviet Star (USA)) **S. A. Aga Khan**

---

149 | **MR DAVID DENNIS, Hanley Swan**
Postal: Tyre Hill Racing Stables, Hanley Swan, Worcester, Worcestershire, WR8 0EQ
Contacts: **PHONE** (01684) 310565 **MOBILE** (07867) 974880
E-MAIL david@daviddennistrainer.co.uk **WEBSITE** www.ddracing.co.uk

1 **ANGINOLA (IRE)**, 7, b m Kodiac—Lady Montekin **Help With Numbers**
2 **ANGUS GLENS**, b g 2y Dalakhani (IRE)—Clara Bow (FR) **Favourites Racing (Syndication) Ltd 5**
3 **BEAUTIFUL WAR (IRE)**, 6, b br m Presenting—Dunahall Queen (IRE) **The Ferandlin Peaches**
4 **BORED OR BAD (IRE)**, 4, b g Oscar (IRE)—Siberiansdaughter (IRE) **Tyre Hill Farm Ltd**
5 **BRUNEL WOODS (IRE)**, 4, b g Oscar (IRE)—Golden Bay **The R C Partnership**
6 **CHANGE OR GO (IRE)**, 4, b g Kalanisi (IRE)—Teffia Rose (IRE) **Tyre Hill Farm Ltd**
7 **CRANK EM UP (IRE)**, 5, b g Royal Anthem (USA)—Carrawaystick (IRE) **Favourites Racing Ltd**
8 **CRAZY (GER)**, 7, b m Nicaron (GER)—Chato's Girl (GER) **The Joaly Partnership**
9 **CYCLOP (IRE)**, 5, b g King's Theatre (IRE)—Tasmani (FR) **DD Racing & Professor L P Hardwick**

MR DAVID DENNIS - Continued

10 **DAULYS ANTHEM (IRE)**, 8, br g Royal Anthem (USA)—Over Dubai **The Dobbin Club & Partner**
11 **DEAUVILLE DANCER (IRE)**, 5, b g Tamayuz—Mathool (IRE) **Favourites Racing Ltd**
12 4, Br g Kalanisi (IRE)—Eluna **Mr & Mrs Paul & Clare Rooney**
13 **FINAL NUDGE (IRE)**, 7, b g Kayf Tara—Another Shot (IRE) **Corbett Stud**
14 **FLED OR PLED (IRE)**, 4, b g Shantou (USA)—Desert Gail (IRE) **Tyre Hill Farm Ltd**
15 **GODSMEJUDGE (IRE)**, 10, b g Witness Box (USA)—Eliza Everett (IRE) **Favourites Racing Ltd**
16 **HAWDYERWHEESHT (IRE)**, 8, b g Librettist (USA)—Rapsgate (IRE) **Favourites Racing (Syndication) Ltd 7**
17 **HORIZONTAL SPEED (IRE)**, 8, b g Vertical Speed (FR)—Rockababy (IRE) **Favourites Racing Ltd**
18 **INDY FIVE (IRE)**, 6, b g Vertical Speed (FR)—Beesplease (IRE) **Favourites Racing Ltd**
19 **JUST SO COOL (IRE)**, 5, gr g Acambaro (GER)—Lauras Dote (IRE) **Favourites Racing Ltd**
20 **LUCKY JIM**, 5, b g Lucky Story (USA)—Lateralle (IRE) **DD Racing & Professor L P Hardwick 2**
21 **MARJU'S QUEST (IRE)**, 6, b g Marju (IRE)—Queen's Quest **Favourites Racing (Syndication) Ltd 1**
22 **MARQUIS OF CARABAS (IRE)**, 6, b br g Hurricane Run (IRE)—Miss Otis Regrets (IRE) **Favourites Racing Ltd**
23 **MY MO (FR)**, 4, b g Silver Frost (IRE)—Anna Ivanovna (FR) **Favourites Racing (Syndication) Ltd 3**
24 **NORSE LIGHT**, 5, ch g Norse Dancer (IRE)—Dimelight **The Dobbin Club & Partner**
25 **REBEL BEAT**, 5, b g Lucarno (USA)—Callitwhatyalike **The Ferandlin Peaches**
26 **REBEL BENEFIT (IRE)**, 8, b g Craigsteel—Tourmaline Girl (IRE) **Rose Farm Developments(UK) Ltd & Partner**
27 **RETRO VALLEY (IRE)**, 4, b g Vale of York (USA)—Retrato (USA) **Favourites Racing Ltd**
28 **RUSSIAN BOLERO (GER)**, 5, ch g Tertullian (USA)—Russian Samba (IRE) **BAA Management Ltd**
29 **SCOT DADDY (USA)**, 4, ch g Scat Daddy (USA)—Flor de Oro (USA) **Favourites Racing Ltd**
30 **SET THE TREND**, 10, br g Reset (AUS)—Masrora (USA) **Corbett Stud**
31 **SEVEN KINGDOMS (IRE)**, 4, b g Yeats (IRE)—Valrhona (IRE) **Professor L P Hardwick & Partner**
32 **THE BIG DIPPER**, 7, b g Alflora (IRE)—Pougatcheva (FR) **The Lucky Seven**
33 4, B g Sakhee's Secret—Vodka Shot (USA)
34 **WADE HARPER (IRE)**, 6, b g Westerner—Nosie Betty (IRE) **Favourites Racing (Syndication) Ltd 4**
35 **WINK OLIVER**, 4, b g Winker Watson—Nadinska **P & L Partners**
36 **ZAMMIA (FR)**, 4, b g Kingsalsa (USA)—Aisyacall (FR) **Mr M. N. Khan**

THREE-YEAR-OLDS

37 **DANECASE**, ch g Showcasing—Yding (IRE) **Favourites Racing (Syndication) Ltd 6**
38 **FATEH (IRE)**, b c Big Bad Bob (IRE)—Passarelle (USA) **Mr M. N. Khan**
39 **SHOW ME AGAIN**, ch g Showcasing—Broughtons Revival **Favourites Racing Ltd**

TWO-YEAR-OLDS

40 **ZEE MAN (FR)**, b c 9/5 Soldier of Fortune (IRE)—Sky High Flyer (Anabaa (USA)) **Mr M. N. Khan**

Other Owners: Mr M. J. S. Cockburn, Mr D. R. Dennis, D. W. Doolittle, Favourites Racing (Syndication) Ltd., Prof L. P. Hardwick, Ms R. J. Harris, P. V. Harris, M. Hingley, Mr A. T. Larkin, Mr R. R. Lester, Mrs J. Massey, C. D. Massey, G. Pickering, Mrs J. Rees, Mrs C. Rooney, Mr P. A. Rooney, Rose Farm Developments (UK) Ltd, Mr P. Sproson, Mrs A. J. Sproson, Mr D. R. Tribe, Mr N. J. Witts-Hewinson.

| 150 | **MR TIM DENNIS, Bude**
Postal: **Thorne Farm, Bude, Cornwall, EX23 0LU**
Contacts: **PHONE (01288) 352849 MOBILE (07855) 785781**
E-MAIL trainertwdennis@gmail.com |

1 **ANN'S LOTTERY**, 10, ch m Old Vic—Vallingale (IRE) **Mrs J. E. Dennis**
2 **ITS A LONG ROAD**, 8, b g Grape Tree Road—Blue Shannon (IRE) **Mrs J. E. Dennis**
3 **MOUNT PROSPEX (IRE)**, 7, ch g Golan (IRE)—No Blues (IRE) **Mrs J. E. Dennis**
4 **VALLEY ROAD**, 8, b m Grape Tree Road—Vallingale (IRE) **Mrs J. E. Dennis**

| 151 | **MR ROBIN DICKIN, Alcester**
Postal: **Alne Park, Park Lane, Great Alne, Alcester, Warwickshire, B49 6HS**
Contacts: **PHONE (01789) 488148 (01789) 488388 MOBILE (07979) 518593 / (07979) 518594**
E-MAIL claire@robindickinracing.org.uk WEBSITE www.robindickinracing.org.uk |

1 **ANTI COOL (IRE)**, 7, b g Heron Island (IRE)—Youngborogal (IRE) **EPDS Racing Partnership 10**
2 **BADGERS COVE (IRE)**, 9, b g Witness Box (USA)—Celestial Rose (IRE) **E. R. C. Beech & B. Wilkinson**
3 **BALLY LAGAN (IRE)**, 8, gr g Kalanisi (IRE)—Rose Palma (IRE) **Park Lane Partnership**
4 **BE MY WITNESS (IRE)**, 7, b m Witness Box (USA)—Smokey Firth (IRE) **Mrs A. L. Merry**
5 **BLACK COUNTRY BOY**, 4, b g Black Sam Bellamy (IRE)—Simple Glory (IRE) **E. R. C. Beech & B. Wilkinson**

MR ROBIN DICKIN - Continued

6 **DAN'S QUEST**, 6, b g Kalanisi (IRE)—Piedmont (UAE) **Mark James Bloodstock**
7 **DESROCHES (GER)**, 8, b m Royal Dragon (USA)—Dadrala (USA) **N. J. Allen**
8 **DONTMINDDBOYS (IRE)**, 7, gr g Portrait Gallery (IRE)—Native Ocean (IRE) **EPDS Racing Partnership 7**
9 **GALACTIC POWER (IRE)**, 6, ch g Gamut (IRE)—Celtic Peace (IRE) **EPDS Racing Twitterati Partnership**
10 **GARRAHALISH (IRE)**, 8, b g Presenting—Savu Sea (IRE) **Just 4 Fun**
11 **GET INVOLVED (IRE)**, 7, b g Milan—Strong Red **The Point Of Attack Partnership**
12 **JACKFIELD**, 6, b g Norse Dancer (IRE)—Small Amount **Mrs C. M. Dickin**
13 **KADDYS DREAM**, 5, b m Kadastrof (FR)—Symbiosis **More The Merrier, T Greig & P Whitehead**
14 **KADDYS GIRL**, 6, ch m Kadastrof (FR)—Dickies Girl **J. Rogers**
15 **KAWA (FR)**, 10, gr g Kouroun (FR)—Kulitch (FR) **Mrs C. M. Dickin**
16 **KAYF TIGER**, 7, b g Kayf Tara—La Marette **The Jameson Partnership**
17 **KITEGEN (IRE)**, 10, b g Milan—Keen Gale (IRE) **Paul Whitehead & Clare Spencer-Herbert**
18 **MUST MEET MRSGRATH (IRE)**, 5, b m Mustameet (USA)—Ladymcgrath (IRE) **C. M. Dickin**
19 **MYROUNDORURS (IRE)**, 6, b g Arakan (USA)—Six Bob (IRE) **John Nicholls (Trading) Ltd**
20 **ROUTINE PROCEDURE (IRE)**, 6, b g Arcadio (GER)—Wayward Bride (IRE) **More Of Us The Merrier**
21 **SOME FINISH (IRE)**, 7, b g Kayf Tara—Kylie Kaprice (GER) **Mrs C Dickin & The Some Finish Partners**
22 **SPURNED GIRL**, 6, b m Passing Glance—Highlight Girl **Mr T. P. Hitchman**
23 **STORMING HARRY**, 4, ch g Assertive—Miss Pebbles (IRE) **Mr Nigel Thick**
24 **TARA WELL (IRE)**, 6, b m Kayf Tara—Miss Baden (IRE) **N. J. Allen**
25 **THE LION MAN (IRE)**, 6, b g Let The Lion Roar—Just Smart (IRE) **Mrs M A Cooper & Mr J R Cooper**
26 **THOMAS CRAPPER**, 9, b g Tamure (IRE)—Mollycarrs Gambul **Apis.uk.com**
27 **TIMON'S TARA**, 7, br m Kayf Tara—Princess Timon **Mr M. J. James**
28 **TWYCROSS WARRIOR**, 4, b g Cockney Rebel (IRE)—Gaelic Roulette (IRE) **Graham & Lynn Knight**
29 **UNDER THE PHONE (IRE)**, 7, b g Heron Island (IRE)—Theo On The Bench (IRE) **The Tricksters**
30 **VOCALISER (IRE)**, 4, b c Vocalised (USA)—Bring Back Matron (IRE) **The Songsters**
31 **WILDMOOR BOY**, 5, b g Midnight Legend—Simple Glory (IRE) **E. R. C. Beech & B. Wilkinson**
32 **YOUNG LOU**, 7, b m Kadastrof (FR)—Wanna Shout **E. R. C. Beech & B. Wilkinson**

THREE-YEAR-OLDS

33 **NETHERTON BOY**, b g Black Sam Bellamy (IRE)—Simple Glory (IRE) **C. Beech & B. Wilkinson**

Other Owners: Mr E. R. Clifford Beech, Mr Hugh Brown, Mr R. A. Cockrell, Mrs M. A. Cooper, Mr J. R. Cooper, Mrs C. M. Dickin, Mr C. J. Dickin, Mr Matt FitzGerald, Mr D. Hern, Mrs V. Jameson, Miss N. A. Jameson, Mr S. Kirby, Mrs L. C. Knight, Mr G. Knight, Mr John Porter, Mr John Powell, Miss T. Sloan, Ms Clare Spencer-Herbert, Mrs Julia Venvell, Mr Paul Whitehead, Mr B. Wilkinson.

Assistant Trainer: Claire Dickin

Jockey (NH): Charlie Poste, Chris Ward. **Conditional:** Cathal Courtney. **Amateur:** Mr James Martin.

---

152 **MR JOHN DIXON, Carlisle**
Postal: **Moorend, Thursby, Carlisle, Cumbria, CA5 6QP**
Contacts: **PHONE (01228) 711019**

1 **CIRCUS STAR (USA)**, 8, b g Borrego (USA)—Picadilly Circus (USA) **Mrs S. F. Dixon**
2 **PISTOL (IRE)**, 7, b g High Chaparral (IRE)—Alinea (USA) **Mrs S. F. Dixon**

Amateur: Mr J. J. Dixon.

---

153 **MR SCOTT DIXON, Retford**
Postal: **Haygarth House Stud, Haygarth House, Babworth, Retford, Nottinghamshire, DN22 8ES**
Contacts: **PHONE (01777) 869300 (01777) 869079/701818 FAX (01777) 869326**
MOBILE (07976) 267019
E-MAIL scottdixon1987@hotmail.com / mrsyvettedixon@gmail.com
WEBSITE www.scottdixonracing.com

1 **ABI SCARLET (IRE)**, 7, b m Baltic King—Petarga **Ontoawinner 4 & Homecroft Wealth Racing**
2 **ARMELLE (FR)**, 5, b m Milk It Mick—Park Ave Princess (IRE) **The Friday Follies**
3 **BEST TAMAYUZ**, 5, ch g Tamayuz—Pink Ivory **P J Dixon & Partners**
4 **BOOTS AND SPURS**, 7, b g Oasis Dream—Arctic Char **Mr S. E. Chappell**
5 **CADEAUX PEARL**, 8, b g Acclamation—Anneliina **P J Dixon & Partners**
6 **CLOAK AND DEGAS (IRE)**, 4, b g Sakhee's Secret—Coup de Torchon (FR) **Homecroft Wealth Racing**
7 **COCK OF THE NORTH**, 4, ch g Cockney Rebel (IRE)—Camp Fire (IRE) **Cope Dixon Kennerly**

MR SCOTT DIXON - Continued

8 **COISTE BODHAR (IRE)**, 5, b g Camacho—Nortolixa (FR) **Miss Y. Lowe**
9 **CROSSE FIRE**, 4, b g Monsieur Bond (IRE)—Watersilk (IRE) **Chappell, Cope, Dixon**
10 **DR RED EYE**, 8, ch g Dr Fong (USA)—Camp Fire (IRE) **P J Dixon & Partners**
11 **FELICE (IRE)**, 6, b m Papal Bull—Tarabaya (IRE) **P J Dixon & Partners**
12 **HIGH INTENSITY**, 4, b g Sir Percy—Woodbeck **Homecroft Wealth Racing**
13 **HUGIE BOY (IRE)**, 4, ch g Art Connoisseur (IRE)—Piece Unique **Mr J. Radford**
14 **INCOMPARABLE**, 11, ch g Compton Place—Indian Silk (IRE) **P J Dixon & Partners**
15 **LE LAITIER (FR)**, 5, b g Milk It Mick—La Brigitte **Ms Yvonne Lowe, P J Dixon & Partners**
16 **MASKED DANCE (IRE)**, 9, gr g Captain Rio—Brooks Masquerade **P J Dixon & Partners**
17 **MORE MORE MORE**, 6, b g Milk It Mick—Snowmore
18 **PEARL NOIR**, 6, b g Milk It Mick—Cora Pearl (IRE) **P J Dixon & Partners**
19 **PENNINE WARRIOR**, 5, b g Lucky Story (USA)—Discoed **Yorkshire Exiles V**
20 **PENNY DREADFUL**, 4, b f Piccolo—Trina's Pet **Sexy Six Partnership**
21 **PICENO (IRE)**, 8, b g Camacho—Ascoli **P J Dixon & Partners**
22 **SIR GEOFFREY (IRE)**, 10, b g Captain Rio—Disarm (IRE) **General Sir G. H. W. Howlett**
23 **SPOWARTICUS**, 7, ch g Shamardal (USA)—Helen Bradley (IRE) **P J Dixon & Partners**
24 **THUNDERBIRD**, 4, b f Sakhee (USA)—Trustthunder **P J Dixon & Partners**
25 **WIMBOLDSLEY**, 5, ch g Milk It Mick—Chrystal Venture (IRE) **Paul J Dixon & The Chrystal Maze Ptn**

THREE-YEAR-OLDS

26 **ALBERT BOY (IRE)**, ch g Falco (USA)—Trumbaka (IRE) **Mr J. Radford**
27 **ALMOST SPANISH (IRE)**, b f Rock of Gibraltar (IRE)—Spanish Quest **D. Boocock**
28 **BOMBER ETCHES**, b c Hellvelyn—Little Greenbird **Ms Yvonne Lowe & Paul J Dixon**
29 **COMPARINKA**, ch f Compton Place—Tinnarinka **Grange Park Racing & Partner**
30 **KRYSTALLITE**, ch f Kheleyf (USA)—Chrystal Venture (IRE) **Paul J Dixon & The Chrystal Maze Ptn**
31 **LADY ELIZABETH (IRE)**, b f Dandy Man (IRE)—Disarm (IRE) **Gen Sir G Howlett Ms Yvonne Lowe & Ptnr**
32 B f Della Francesca (USA)—Loupana (FR) **Haygarth House**
33 **MISU MONEYPENNY**, b f Misu Bond (IRE)—Watersilk (IRE) **The Doncaster Racing Club**
34 **PILGRIMS PATH**, b g Sakhee (USA)—Scrooby Baby **P J Dixon & Partners**
35 **RED CHATTERBOX (IRE)**, b f Thousand Words—Red Empress **Mr D Sharp and Partners**
36 **RUPERT BOY (IRE)**, ch g Frozen Power (IRE)—Curious Lashes (IRE) **Mr J. Radford**
37 **SARABI**, b f Rip Van Winkle (IRE)—Xaphania **Paul J Dixon & Yvonne Lowe**
38 **SOCIALITES**, gr c Hellvelyn—Lola Sapola (IRE) **Socialites**
39 **SOCIALITES RED**, ch f Sakhee's Secret—Tipsy Girl **Socialites**
40 **THE KNAVE (IRE)**, b g Dick Turpin (IRE)—Bayswater **Derek Boocock & The Winners Enclosure**
41 Ch f Observatory (USA)—True Melody (IRE) **Andrew Middleton**
42 B f Roderic O'Connor (IRE)—Viscountess Brave (IRE) **Haygarth House**

TWO-YEAR-OLDS

43 B c 3/4 Kheleyf (USA)—Amouage Royale (IRE) (Mr Greeley) (USA)) (3809) **Helen Warboys**
44 Ch c 9/4 Sakhee (USA)—Chrystal Venture (IRE) (Barathea (IRE)) **Andrew Timms**
45 Ch c 11/2 Medicean—Cockney Fire (Cockney Rebel (IRE)) (21000) **Graham Amey, David Blunt**
46 **COMPASS ROSE (IRE)**, b f 3/4 Henrythenavigator (USA)—
                Raydaniya (IRE) (In The Wings) (19047) **Mrs J. Jackson**
47 B gr f 4/3 Aussie Rules (USA)—Cora Pearl (USA) (Montjeu (IRE)) **Haygarth House**
48 B f 14/3 Kheleyf (USA)—Edge of Light (Xaar) (9523) **Joe Sciza**
49 B c 31/3 Rip Van Winkle (IRE)—In A Silent Way (IRE) (Desert Prince (IRE)) (5500) **Haygarth House**
50 **NIGHT SHADOW**, ch c 16/3 Haafhd—Totally Trusted (Oasis Dream) **Glenn Morrill**
51 Ch c 10/2 Rip Van Winkle (IRE)—On The Dark Side (IRE) (Kheleyf (USA)) (3500) **C. Parker**
52 B f 17/4 Pastoral Pursuits—Royal Arruhan (Royal Applause) (1000) **Haygarth House**
53 B f 4/4 Delegator—Surprise Statement (Proclamation (IRE)) (3000) **Haygarth House**
54 B f 23/4 Compton Place—Tipsy Girl (Haafhd) (12500) **Sam Hoskins, Trickledown Stud, Socialites**
55 B f 31/3 Paco Boy (IRE)—Western Eyes (IRE) (Rock of Gibraltar (IRE)) (15000) **M. A. Parker**
56 B f 6/3 Mount Nelson—Xaphania (Sakhee (USA)) (8500) **Haygarth House**

Other Owners: Mr S. Atkinson, Mr A. D. Baker, Mr A. I. Cope, A. D. Crombie, Mrs Y. Dixon, J. S. Kennerley, Mr D. R. Lucas, Mr N. J. O'Brien, Mr M. Oxby, S. J. Piper, Mr N. Pogmore, Mr D. Sharp, Mr E. Surr, Mr A. C. Timms, Mr D. Wood, Mrs S. Woodcroft.

Assistant Trainer: Mr K. Locking (07835 360125)

Amateur: Mr Kevin Locking.

154 MR STEVEN DIXON, Winterslow
Postal: **Apple Tree Barn, Livery Road, Winterslow, Nr Salisbury, Wiltshire, SP5 1RJ**
Contacts: **PHONE (01980) 862930 MOBILE (07771) 963011**
E-MAIL **sarahjdixon@hotmail.co.uk**

1 RAGTIME LADY, 8, b m General Gambul—Pink Lady **Mr S. D. Dixon**
2 SHADOW BLUE (IRE), 7, br g Blueprint (IRE)—Rosie Belle (IRE) **Mr S. D. Dixon**
3 SUN QUEST, 12, b g Groom Dancer (USA)—Icaressa **Mr S. D. Dixon**
4 WARSAW PACT (IRE), 13, b g Polish Precedent (USA)—Always Friendly **Mr S. D. Dixon**

Assistant Trainer: Mrs Sarah Dixon

Jockey (NH): Jamie Moore. **Amateur:** Mr Luke Kilgarriff, Mr James King, Mr Bradley Paris-Crofts, Mr Gordon Treacy.

---

155 MRS ROSE DOBBIN, Alnwick
Postal: **South Hazelrigg Farm, Chatton, Alnwick, Northumberland, NE66 5RZ**
Contacts: **PHONE (01668) 215395 (office) (01668) 215151 (house) FAX (01668) 215114**
MOBILE (07969) 993563
E-MAIL **hazelriggracing1@btconnect.com WEBSITE www.rosedobbinracing.co.uk**

1 AMYS CHOICE (IRE), 6, b m Craigsteel—Tanya Thyne (IRE) **Mr & Mrs Paul & Clare Rooney**
2 ANOTHER DIMENSION (IRE), 10, b g Overbury (IRE)—Freshwater (IRE)
3 ATTENTION PLEASE (IRE), 6, b g Kalanisi (IRE)—
    Dangerous Dolly (IRE) **Mr Ronnie Jacobs & Mrs Rose Dobbin**
4 BAKO DE LA SAULAIE (FR), 5, b g Balko (FR)—Krickette (FR) **Mr & Mrs Duncan Davidson**
5 BENJAMIN BOGLE (IRE), 8, b g Yeats (IRE)—Zalama (FR) **Mr & Mrs Davidson & Sir Chips Keswick**
6 BENJAMIN TREE (IRE), 5, ch g Beneficial—Lady Millie (IRE) **Mr & Mrs Duncan Davidson**
7 BENNYLICIOUS (IRE), 7, b g Beneficial—Railstown Lady (IRE) **Mr & Mrs D Davidson & Miss J Matterson**
8 BIGIRONONHISHIP (IRE), 5, b g Beneficial—Portobello Lady (IRE) **Mr & Mrs Duncan Davidson**
9 DONAPOLLO, 8, b g Kayf Tara—Star of Wonder (FR) **Mrs R. Dobbin**
10 EVERYLASTING (IRE), 9, b g Millenary—All French (IRE) **Miss C. L. Jones**
11 FIBRE OPTIC, 4, b g Rip Van Winkle (IRE)—Wind Surf (USA) **Mr James Filmer Wilson & Mr Nagy El Azar**
12 FINAL FLING (IRE), 5, b g Milan—Supreme Singer (IRE) **J. M. & Mrs M. R. Edwardson**
13 GINGILI, 6, b g Beat All (USA)—Gentian **Mr & Mrs Paul & Clare Rooney**
14 GOLANS CHOICE (IRE), 7, b g Golan (IRE)—Sea Voyager (IRE) **Murph and the Magic Tones**
15 GREY STORM (IRE), 5, gr g September Storm (GER)—Lady Blayney (IRE) **Mr & Mrs Duncan Davidson**
16 JONNIESOFA (IRE), 6, b g Well Made (GER)—Lucky Sarah (IRE) **Mr R & Mrs A Houghton & Mr A Houghton**
17 MAC N CHEESE (IRE), 6, b g Milan—Fox Burrow (IRE) **Richard & Katherine Gilbert**
18 MARRAKECH TRADER (NZ), 9, ch g Pentire—Eastern Bazzaar (IRE) **Mr J. L. Dickson**
19 MINELLA SUITE (IRE), 5, br g Oscar (IRE)—Ballymaguirelass (IRE) **Mr & Mrs Duncan Davidson**
20 MISTER DON (IRE), 6, br g Presenting—Spring Flower (IRE) **Mr & Mrs D. Davidson & Mr R. Jacobs**
21 MONFASS (IRE), 5, b g Trans Island—Ajo Green (IRE) **Mrs Dobbin & The Dimhorns**
22 PROFESSOR PLUM (IRE), 7, b g Kalanisi (IRE)—Miss Plum **Mr & Mrs Duncan Davidson**
23 PROUD GAMBLE (IRE), 7, b g Brian Boru—Sister Anna **Major-Gen C. A. Ramsay**
24 ROCKING BLUES (FR), 11, b g Lavirco (GER)—Herbe de La Roque (FR) **The Friday Lions**
25 SCIMON TEMPLAR (FR), 8, b br g Saint des Saints (FR)—
    Made In Law (FR) **Mr & Mrs Raymond Anderson Green**
26 SHADY SADIE (IRE), 9, b m Dushyantor (USA)—Beltane Queen (IRE) **Mrs M. C. Coltman**
27 SMUGGLER'S STASH (IRE), 6, ch g Stowaway—Sweetasanu (IRE) **Mr & Mrs Duncan Davidson**
28 SPIRIT DAME (IRE), 5, ch m Beneficial—Drama Chick **Mr & Mrs D Davidson & Miss J Matterson**
29 SPITZ (FR), 8, b g Enrique—Spezzia (FR) **Mr R. A. Jacobs**
30 TRELIVER MANOR (IRE), 8, b g Flemensfirth (USA)—Loch Lomond (IRE) **Mrs R. Dobbin**
31 VINNY GAMBINI (IRE), 9, b g Vinnie Roe (IRE)—Red Velvet **Mr & Mrs Duncan Davidson**
32 WICKED GAMES (IRE), 5, br m Flemensfirth (USA)—Tariana (IRE) **Mr & Mrs Duncan Davidson**

Other Owners: Mrs S. K. Davidson, D. H. Davidson, Mr R. T. De Plumpton Hunter, Mr L. Dimsdale, Mr A. G. Dobbin, Mrs M. R. Edwardson, J. M. Edwardson, Mr Nagy El Azar, Mr J. A. F. Filmer-Wilson, Mr R. P. Gilbert, Mrs K. E. Gilbert, Mrs A. Green, R. A. Green, Mr A. Houghton, Mrs A. M. Houghton, Mr R. Houghton, J. R. Jeffreys, Sir Chippendale Keswick, Miss J. G. K. Matterson, Mrs C. Rooney, Mr P. A. Rooney, Mr D. A. C. Spencer-Churchill.

Assistant Trainer: Tony Dobbin (07775) 680894

Jockey (NH): Craig Nichol, Wilson Renwick. **Conditional:** Lorcan Murtagh.

156 MR MICHAEL DODS, Darlington

Postal: **Denton Hall Farm, Piercebridge, Darlington, Co. Durham, DL2 3TY**
Contacts: PHONE **(01325) 374270** FAX **(01325) 374020**
MOBILE **(07860) 411590/ (07773) 290830 C** Dods
E-MAIL dods@michaeldodsracing.co.uk WEBSITE www.michaeldodsracing.co.uk

1 **ALANS PRIDE (IRE)**, 4, ch g Footstepsinthesand—True Crystal (IRE) **Alan Henderson & Alan Bolton**
2 **APROVADO (IRE)**, 4, b g Approve (IRE)—Aldburgh **Hanson, McKiver, Percival**
3 **BARNEY MCGREW (IRE)**, 13, b g Mark of Esteem (IRE)—Success Story **N. A. Riddell**
4 **BUCCANEERS VAULT (IRE)**, 4, gr g Aussie Rules (USA)—Heaven's Vault (IRE) **D. Neale**
5 **DENTON CARNIVAL (IRE)**, 4, ch g Captain Rio—Be My Lover **Denton Hall Racing Ltd**
6 **DESERT ACE (IRE)**, 5, ch g Kheleyf (USA)—Champion Place **Excelsior Racing Ltd**
7 **DRAGON KING (IRE)**, 4, ch g Dylan Thomas (IRE)—Alexander Queen (IRE) **Cosy Seal Racing Limited**
8 **FINN CLASS (IRE)**, 5, b g Exceed And Excel (AUS)—Finnmark **Mr M. D. Pearson**
9 **GET KNOTTED (IRE)**, 4, ch g Windsor Knot (IRE)—Genuinely (IRE) **D. Neale**
10 **GLEN MOSS (IRE)**, 7, b h Moss Vale (IRE)—Sail With The Wind **Mr R. S. Fiddes**
11 **GOLDEN SPUN (IRE)**, 4, b g Hard Spun (USA)—Scarlet's Tara (USA) **Mr R. S. Fiddes**
12 **GOWANHARRY (IRE)**, 7, ch m Choisir (AUS)—Aahgowangowan (IRE) **L. Waugh**
13 **HERNANDOSHIDEAWAY**, 4, b g Hernando (FR)—Alba Stella **Mr D C Batey & Mr Foster Watson**
14 **KIWI BAY**, 11, b g Mujahid (USA)—Bay of Plenty (FR) **Kiwi Racing**
15 **LE CHAT D'OR**, 8, b g One Cool Cat (USA)—Oh So Well (IRE) **Dr A. J. F. Gillespie**
16 **LORD OF THE ROCK (IRE)**, 4, b g Rock of Gibraltar (IRE)—La Sylphide **Mr & Mrs G. Turnbull**
17 **MASS RALLY (IRE)**, 9, b g Kheleyf (USA)—Reunion (IRE) **Ritchie Fiddes & John Cockcroft**
18 **MECCA'S ANGEL (IRE)**, 5, gr m Dark Angel (IRE)—Folga **D. T. J. Metcalfe**
19 **MUSTAQBAL (IRE)**, 4, b g Invincible Spirit (IRE)—Alshamatry (USA) **M. J. K. Dods**
20 **OCEAN SHERIDAN (IRE)**, 4, b g Starspangledbanner (AUS)—
Endless Night (GER) **Mr J Blackburn & Mr A Turton**
21 **POMME DE TERRE (IRE)**, 4, ch g Sakhee's Secret—Suzie Quw
22 **REFLATION**, 4, b g Stimulation (IRE)—Miss Poppy **Mrs C. E. Dods**
23 **ROCKTHERUNWAY (IRE)**, 7, ch g Nayef (USA)—Femme Fatale **Sedgewick,Dods,Sunley Racing Partnership**
24 **SEA WOLF (IRE)**, 4, b g Amadeus Wolf—Rose de France (IRE) **Cosy Seal Racing Limited**
25 **TRINITY STAR (IRE)**, 5, gr g Kheleyf (USA)—Zamiyla (IRE) **Trinity Racing**
26 **WHAT COULD SHE BE (IRE)**, 4, b f Dark Angel (IRE)—Halliwell House **Mr R. S. Fiddes**

THREE-YEAR-OLDS

27 **BALTIC RAIDER (IRE)**, b g Baltic King—Frippet (IRE) **Pearson & Lowthian**
28 **BRADLEYSINTOWN (IRE)**, ch g Thousand Words—Anazah (USA) **Sekura Trade Frames Ltd**
29 **CAPE CRUSADER (IRE)**, br g Kheleyf (USA)—Naddwah **Denton Hall Racing Ltd**
30 **CAUSEY ARCH (IRE)**, b g Jeremy (USA)—Coill Cri (IRE) **J A Wynn-Williams & D Neale**
31 **CHEEKY ANGEL (IRE)**, gr f Dark Angel (IRE)—Cheeky Weeky **Ritchie Fiddes & Simon Chappell**
32 **CROFT RANGER (IRE)**, b g Bushranger (IRE)—Alexander Duchess (IRE) **Mr Ron Davison & Mr Hugh Linsley**
33 **DARK COMMAND**, b g Kheleyf (USA)—Desert Liaison **Mr Ron Davison & Mr Geoff Thompson**
34 **DUSKY RAIDER (IRE)**, gr g Clodovil (IRE)—Rahila (IRE) **Mr A Wynn Williams & Mr D Graham**
35 **EASTON ANGEL (IRE)**, gr f Dark Angel (IRE)—Staceymac (IRE) **Al Shaqab Racing & Mr Ritchie Fiddes**
36 **GOWANLESS (IRE)**, b g Monsieur Bond (IRE)—Aahgowangowan (IRE) **L. Waugh**
37 **KINGS GOLD (IRE)**, ch g Excellent Art—Party Feet (IRE) **Mr P. Appleton**
38 **KRAFTWORK (IRE)**, gr c Mastercraftsman (IRE)—Paraphernalia (IRE) **Cosy Seal Racing Limited**
39 **LADY MCGUFFY (IRE)**, b f Holy Roman Emperor (IRE)—Fountain of Honour (IRE) **Mr John Sagar & Mr Ian Hill 1**
40 **LAWMAN'S JUSTICE (IRE)**, b c Lawman (FR)—Brazilian Bride (IRE) **Excelsior Racing Ltd**
41 **MARKET CHOICE (IRE)**, b g Majestic Missile (IRE)—Ron's Secret **Wensleydale Bacon Ltd and Mr Rod Rider**
42 **REINFORCED**, ch g Equiano (FR)—Fonnie (IRE) **Mr M J K Dods & Mr W G McHarg**
43 **RICHTER SCALE (IRE)**, gr f Lilbourne Lad (IRE)—Danamight (IRE) **Cosy Seal Racing Limited**
44 **RUN RIO RUN (IRE)**, ch g Captain Rio—Anklesocks (IRE) **Mrs Suzanne Kirkup Mr Michael Dods**
45 **SABRINA BRAZZO**, br f Showcasing—Sabrina Brown **Mr D. O'Callaghan**
46 **STORMY ART (IRE)**, b g Excellent Art—Maybe Grace (IRE) **The Better Together Partnership**
47 **TRANSPENNINE STAR**, ch g Mount Nelson—Brave Mave **Transpennine Partnership**
48 **WAYSIDE MAGIC**, b g Thewayyouare (USA)—Poppy's Rose **Mrs C. M. Hewitson**

TWO-YEAR-OLDS

49 B g 10/4 Archipenko (USA)—Baharah (USA) (Elusive Quality (USA)) (17000)
50 B f 19/2 Tamayuz—Bosphorus Queen (IRE) (Sri Pekan (USA)) (25101) **Mrs A. E. Elliott**
51 **DREAM ON DREAMER (IRE)**, b f 18/2 Dream Ahead (USA)—
Marula (IRE) (Sadler's Wells (USA)) (14765) **Mr R. S. Fiddes**
52 B f 15/4 Acclamation—Fathoming (USA) (Gulch (USA)) (35437) **Mr & Mrs G. Turnbull**
53 B c 15/4 Elnadim (USA)—Fire Line (Firebreak) (12000) **J. N. Blackburn**

MR MICHAEL DODS - Continued

54 FOXY BOY, ch c 19/4 Foxwedge (AUS)—Suzy Wong (Auction House (USA)) (29531) **Sekura Trade Frames Ltd**
55 HELM REEF (IRE), ch f 10/1 Helmet (AUS)—Ekhraaj (USA) (El Prado (IRE)) (34285) **Sekura Trade Frames Ltd**
56 INTENSE ROMANCE (IRE), b f 13/2 Intense Focus (USA)—
                                                   Hedera (USA) (Woodman (USA)) (15503) **Mr H. M. Linsley**
57 B c 5/4 Equiano (FR)—Joyeaux (Mark of Esteem (IRE)) (26000) **Doug Graham & Ron Davison**
58 B c 3/1 Dark Angel (IRE)—Kermana (IRE) (Selkirk (USA)) (47619) **Mr R. S. Fiddes**
59 B f 7/2 Footstepsinthesand—Lake Wanaka (IRE) (Fasliyev (USA)) (20952) **M. J. K. Dods**
60 B g 23/4 Casamento (IRE)—Mausin (IRE) (Monsun (GER)) (15238) **M. J. K. Dods**
61 B c 2/4 Captain Gerrard (IRE)—Mimi Mouse (Diktat) (7500) **Denton Hall Racing Ltd**
62 MOONLIGHT BLUE (IRE), b g 22/3 Approve (IRE)—
                                  Nouvelle Reve (GER) (Acatenango (GER)) (14765) **I.Galletley, S.Lowthian, R.Bell**
63 MY ANGEL, gr f 5/3 Dark Angel (IRE)—Tanda Tula (IRE) (Alhaarth (IRE)) (47619) **Mr M. D. Pearson**
64 B f 27/2 Harbour Watch (IRE)—Sans Reward (IRE) (Barathea) (11000)
65 Gr f 19/2 Hellvelyn—Toy Top (USA) (Tactical Cat (USA))

Other Owners: Al Shaqab Racing UK Limited, D. C. Batey, Mr R. A. Bell, Mr I. Bennett, Mr A. Bolton, Mr S. E. Chappell, Mr S. Cockcroft, Mr R. Cockcroft, Mr J. Cockcroft, Mr W. Cockcroft, R. Davison, Mr I. Galletley, D. R. Graham, Mr K. Hanson, Mrs J. Hanson, A. J. Henderson, Mr I. Hill, K. Kirkup, Mrs S. Kirkup, W. S. D. Lamb, S. R. Lowthian, Mr W. G. McHarg, M. L. Mogg, Mr R. Rider, N. Ridgway, Mr J. Sagar, Mr M. J. Sedgewick, Mr G. C. Thompson, Mr G. Turnbull, Mrs S. E. Turnbull, Mr A. Turton, F. Watson, D. Watts, Wensleydale Bacon Limited, J. A. Wynn-Williams.

Assistant Trainers: Carole Dods, Steve Alderson (07533) 401887

Jockey (flat): Connor Beasley, Paul Mulrennan. **Apprentice:** Philip Dennis. **Amateur:** Miss Chloe Dods, Miss Sophie Dods.

---

157 MR DESMOND DONOVAN, Newmarket

Postal: Flat 2, Brickfields Stud, Cemetery Hill, Exning, Newmarket, Suffolk, CB8 7JH
Contacts: PHONE (01638) 578494 FAX (01638) 578494 MOBILE (07761) 841285
E-MAIL hareparkbloodstock@yahoo.co.uk WEBSITE www.desdonovan.co.uk

1 BALER BOY, 4, b g Sakhee (USA)—Olindera (GER) **W. P. Flynn**
2 CHAMPAGNE CHARLEY, 5, b m Myboycharlie (IRE)—Crossed Wire **The Wednesday Club**
3 DALAKI (IRE), 5, b g Dalakhani (IRE)—Lunda (IRE) **W. P. Flynn**
4 FEELTHERHYTHM (IRE), 5, b m Yeats (IRE)—Queen Althea (IRE) **River Racing**
5 GIANT SEQUOIA, 12, ch g Giant's Causeway (USA)—Beware of The Cat (USA) **River Racing**
6 KING OF MILAN (IRE), 6, b g Milan—Opera Mask (IRE) **The Wednesday Club**
7 MENELIK (IRE), 7, b g Oasis Dream—Chica Roca (USA) **River Racing**
8 RECWAY STRIKER, 7, b g Auction House (USA)—Persistent Memory (USA)
9 STATE TROOPER (IRE), 5, b g Lawman (FR)—Anthyllis (IRE) **W. P. Flynn**
10 STEUBEN (GER), 10, ch g Monsun (GER)—Schwarzach (GER) **Mr B. J. Lewis**
11 STRAWBERRYFIELDS, 4, ch f Three Valleys (USA)—Crossed Wire **C. E. Giblett**
12 TEVEZ, 11, b g Sakhee (USA)—Sosumi **River Racing**
13 WEARDIDITALLGORONG, 4, b f Fast Company (IRE)—Little Oz (IRE) **The Wednesday Club**

TWO-YEAR-OLDS

14 Ch c 23/3 Paco Boy (IRE)—Miss Excel (Exceed And Excel (AUS))
15 Ch f 8/2 Fast Company (IRE)—Olindera (GER) (Lomitas)
16 B c 19/3 Dick Turpin (IRE)—Sciantusa (Barathea (IRE))

Other Owners: Mr J. D. Donovan, Mr B. Drogman, P. P. Mclaughlin, Mr L. R. Pearce.

---

158 MR CONOR DORE, Frampton Fen

Postal: Barford Farm, Swineshead Road, Frampton Fen, Boston, Lincolnshire, PE20 1SG
Contacts: PHONE (01775) 822747 MOBILE (07984) 609170
E-MAIL dores@supanet.com

1 A LITTLE BIT DUSTY, 8, ch g Needwood Blade—Dusty Dazzler (IRE) **Mr David Baldwin & Mr Chris Marsh**
2 AMENABLE (IRE), 9, b g Bertolini (USA)—Graceful Air (IRE) **Mrs J. R. Marsh**
3 CLOCKMAKER (IRE), 10, b g Danetime (IRE)—Lady Ingabelle (IRE) **CHP Consulting Limited**
4 DESERT STRIKE, 10, b g Bertolini (USA)—Mary Jane **A. N. Page**
5 ELUSIVITY (IRE), 8, b g Elusive City (USA)—Tough Chic (IRE) **Mrs L. J. Marsh**
6 EXCELLING OSCAR (IRE), 4, b g Excellent Art—Three Pennies **Mrs J. R. Marsh**

MR CONOR DORE - Continued

7 **FLECKERL (IRE)**, 6, b g Danehill Dancer (IRE)—Spinola (FR) **A. N. Page**
8 **GUD DAY (IRE)**, 8, gr g Aussie Rules (USA)—Queen Al Andalous (IRE) **Mr C. R. Dore**
9 **HERCULLIAN PRINCE**, 4, b g Royal Applause—Thara'a (IRE) **Mrs J. R. Marsh**
10 **HOLLAND PARK**, 4, b c More Than Ready (USA)—B Berry Brandy (USA) **Mr C. R. Dore**
11 **JAARIH (IRE)**, 4, ch g Starspangledbanner (AUS)—Bridge Note (USA) **C. D. Marsh**
12 **MEGAMUNCH (IRE)**, 6, b g Camacho—Liscoa (IRE) **Mrs L. J. Marsh**
13 **ORLANDO ROGUE (IRE)**, 4, b g Bushranger (IRE)—Boston Ivy (USA) **Mr C. R. Dore**
14 **SACRED SQUARE (GER)**, 6, ch g Peintre Celebre (USA)—Square The Circle **C. D. Marsh**
15 **TANCRED (IRE)**, 5, b g Oratorio (IRE)—Mythologie (FR) **Mrs J. R. Marsh**
16 **YUL FINEGOLD (IRE)**, 6, b g Invincible Spirit (IRE)—Mascara **Mrs L. J. Marsh**

THREE-YEAR-OLDS

17 **BUNNIE OSCAR (USA)**, b g Hard Spun (USA)—Shimmer (USA) **Mrs J. R. Marsh**
18 **COMPROMISE**, ch g Compton Place—Palinisa (FR) **Mr J. Gray**

Other Owners: Mr D. N. Baldwin.

---

159 **MR FRANCOIS DOUMEN, Bouce**
Postal: Le Gue, 61570 Bouce, France
Contacts: **PHONE (0033) 2 33 67 11 59 FAX (0033) 2 33 67 82 37 MOBILE (0033) 6 07 42 33 58**
E-MAIL doumenecouves@orange.fr WEBSITE www.francoisdoumenracing.com

1 **BAMBOUZLE (FR)**, 5, b m Forestier (FR)—Quibble (FR)
2 **BRASS BELL (IRE)**, 4, gr g Footstepsinthesand—Cheyrac (FR)
3 **CAPITAL FLIGHT (FR)**, 4, ch f Motivator—Dauphine (SAF)
4 **CHIGARELLUM (FR)**, 4, b g Le Fou (IRE)—Quibble (FR)
5 **DAUPHINE DOREE**, 5, b m Archange d'or (IRE)—Dauphine (SAF)
6 **DROIT D'AUTEUR (FR)**, 4, b g Authorized (IRE)—Margot Mine (IRE)
7 **ECHO MAKER (FR)**, 4, b c Siyouni (FR)—Heaven's Help (USA)
8 **INTELLINGENCIA (FR)**, 5, b m Slickly (FR)—Solosole (USA)
9 **KINGDOM COME (FR)**, 4, b f King's Best (USA)—Topka (FR)
10 **MAKWETI**, 4, b f Makfi—Hometown
11 **SILVER BULLET (FR)**, 4, gr f Silver Frost (IRE)—Folle Dingue (FR)
12 **SLEEKFONTEINE (FR)**, 4, b f Slickly (FR)—Turfontein (FR)
13 **SOIESAUVAGE (FR)**, 5, b m Lauro (GER)—Taffetas (FR)
14 **SWING STATE (FR)**, 4, b g Siyouni (FR)—Fast Lane Lili

THREE-YEAR-OLDS

15 **ACERBO (GER)**, ch c Peintre Celebre (USA)—Acerba (GER)
16 **AIM TO PLEASE (FR)**, b f Excellent Art—Midnight Flash (IRE)
17 **ANOTHER DAY**, b f Monsieur Bond (IRE)—Madam President
18 **BAILEYS PARISIENNE (FR)**, b f Makfi—Eternal Beauty (USA)
19 **BIEN NOMMEE (FR)**, b f Whipper (USA)—Another Name (USA)
20 **CONTE FLEURETTE (FR)**, b f Slickly (FR)—Pretty As Can Be
21 **DONT HESITATE (FR)**, b f Diamond Boy (FR)—Quibble (FR)
22 **GOCRAZYPRINCE (FR)**, b g Chichi Creasy (FR)—Queenofnerverland (IRE)
23 **HIGH TOWER (FR)**, b f Dark Angel (IRE)—Heavenly Music (IRE)
24 **I'LL BE BACK (FR)**, b f Footstepsinthesand—Nude (FR)
25 **KOOK (FR)**, ch g Kheleyf (USA)—Folle Dingue (FR)
26 **OSKARIA (FR)**, b f Chichi Creasy (FR)—Miss Nikita (FR)
27 **PROMPTO (FR)**, gr g Timos (GER)—La Rogerais (FR)
28 **ROIDOR (FR)**, b g Creachadoir (IRE)—Dauphine (SAF)
29 **SENATOR FROST (FR)**, b g Lord of England (GER)—La Biriquina (USA)
30 **TIMOCITA (FR)**, b f Timos (GER)—Solosole (USA)
31 **VAPORETTO CAPRI (IRE)**, ch c Manduro (GER)—Anacapri (FR)
32 **WINK AND WAVE (IRE)**, b f Rip Van Winkle (IRE)—Sea Sex Sun

TWO-YEAR-OLDS

33 B f 16/4 Youmzain (IRE)—Angie Eria (FR) (Galileo (IRE)) (8121)
34 **EBATS ET DEBATS (FR)**, b c 15/5 Whipper (USA)—Folle Dingue (FR) (Golan (IRE))
35 **ENDURING BLISS (FR)**, b f 17/4 Manduro (GER)—Marital Bliss (Double Bed (FR))
36 **ENRICHISSANT (FR)**, b c 20/4 Speedmaster (GER)—Quibble (FR) (Jimble (FR))
37 **ETINCELLANTE (FR)**, b f 28/2 Diamond Boy (FR)—Ukissdawinna (FR) (Bedawin (FR))

MR FRANCOIS DOUMEN - Continued

38 Ch f 5/2 Medicean—Khelwa (FR) (Traditionally (USA))
39 B c 14/3 Lawman (FR)—Kirkinola (Selkirk (USA)) (49464)
40 MARGOTEUR (FR), b c 1/3 Nayef (USA)—Margot Mine (IRE) (Choisir (AUS))
41 MIRIFLOR (FR), b f 5/3 Rajsaman (FR)—Turfontein (FR) (Kahyasi)
42 PETARD (FR), b c 26/4 Kentucky Dynamite (USA)—Pretty As Can Be (Giant's Causeway (USA))
43 Ch f 7/3 Makfi—Shamalana (IRE) (Sinndar (IRE)) (26578)
44 SO PLEASING (FR), b c 24/2 Naaqoos—Midnight Flash (IRE) (Anabaa Blue)
45 XYLAPHONE (FR), b g 18/4 Soldier of Fortune (IRE)—Xanadu Bliss (FR) (Xaar)

Owners: Mr Charles Bonnier, Mr Dermot Cantillon, Mr Stephane Delame, Forenaghts Stud, Ecurie Noel Forgeard, G R Baileys Ltd, Genesis Green Stud, Haras D'Ecouves, Marquise de Moratalla, Conte Henri de Pracomtal, Mr Eric Puerari, Mr Anthony Smurfit, Mrs Doreen Swinburn, Mr Joerg Vasicek, Mr Hans Peter Vogt.

---

160 MR SIMON DOW, Epsom

Postal: **Thirty Acre Barn, Shepherds' Walk, Ashtead, Epsom, Surrey, KT18 6BX**
Contacts: PHONE **(01372) 721490** MOBILE **(07860) 800109**
E-MAIL **simon@simondow.co.uk** Office: **mary@simondow.co.uk** WEBSITE **www.simondow.co.uk**
Twitter: **@SimonDowRacing**

1 AUTUMN TONIC (IRE), 4, b g Approve (IRE)—Trempjane **K. F. Butler**
2 BIG TOMS GIRL, 4, ch f Shirocco (GER)—Plaisterer **David Andrews Plastering**
3 BROCKLEBANK (IRE), 7, b g Diamond Green (FR)—La Stellina (IRE) **C. G. J. Chua**
4 DIAMOND CHARLIE (IRE), 8, br g Diamond Green (FR)—Rosy Lydgate **David & Stanley Adams**
5 DUTIFUL SON (IRE), 6, b g Invincible Spirit (IRE)—Grecian Dancer **Will Salthouse & Jimmy Chua**
6 EL CAMPEON, 4, b br g Multiplex—Villabella (FR) **Mr R. J. Moss**
7 FORCEFUL APPEAL (USA), 8, b br g Successful Appeal (USA)—Kinetic Force (USA) **Mr M. McAllister**
8 GALINTHIAS, 4, b g Sixties Icon—Tidie France (USA) **Taylor, Meadows, Snell, Taylor, Dow**
9 LE TORRENT, 4, ch g Sir Percy—Cinnas Ransom **P. G. Jacobs**
10 NONNO GIULIO (IRE), 5, ch g Halling (USA)—Contrary (IRE) **S. L. Dow**
11 OCCULT, 4, b g Oasis Dream—Trojan Queen (USA) **Six Mile Hill Racing**
12 PRESUMIDO (IRE), 6, b g Iffraaj—Miss Megs (IRE) **Mr R. J. Moss**
13 SIXTIES LOVE, 5, b m Sixties Icon—Love Always **T. Staplehurst**
14 SWOT, 4, b g Exceed And Excel (AUS)—House Point **The Big Cat Partnership**

THREE-YEAR-OLDS

15 BREVET, b c Zamindar (USA)—Prove **Jacobs, Meadows, Parker, Taylor**
16 BUSTA NELLIE, ch f Pastoral Pursuits—Vezere (USA) **Mr R. J. Moss**
17 DREAM LOVE, b f Rail Link—Love Always **T. Staplehurst**
18 HOMBRE ROJO (IRE), b c Intikhab (USA)—Sidney Girl **Mr R. J. Moss**
19 HURRICANE ROCK, ch g Rock of Gibraltar (IRE)—Seasonal Cross **Aldis & Hayes**
20 B g Dick Turpin (IRE)—Plaisterer
21 REGAL GAIT (IRE), b g Tagula (IRE)—Babylonian **P. G. Jacobs**
22 TRUST THE MAN (IRE), br c Manduro (GER)—Saree **A. J. Morton**

TWO-YEAR-OLDS

23 CHICA DE LA NOCHE, b f 8/4 Teofilo (IRE)—Welsh Cake (Fantastic Light (USA)) (62000) **Mr R. J. Moss**
24 COMPTON ABBEY, b f 15/3 Compton Place—Bolsena (Red Ransom (USA)) (11428) **H. Hunt**
25 CORREDORDEL VIENTO (USA), b br c 13/4 Lonhro (AUS)—
                                        Asheville (USA) (Clever Trick (USA)) (82000) **Mr R. J. Moss**
26 DAMO, ch c 24/4 New Approach (IRE)—Umliilo (Mtoto) (25000) **Mr R. J. Moss**
27 Ch f 12/5 Mayson—Grand Lucre (Grand Slam (USA)) **S. L. Dow**
28 HARBOUR SANCTUARY, b f 15/3 Harbour Watch (IRE)—
                                        Cefira (USA) (Distant View (USA)) (5714) **The Sandbaggers Club**

Other Owners: Mr D. Adams, Mr S. J. Adams, Mrs A. Aldis, Mrs E. Curley, Miss S. J. Hayes, Mr G. P. Hayes, M. G. Mackenzie, Mrs S. P. Meadows, T. G. Parker, Mrs R. Pott, Mr W. J. Salthouse, Ms S. A. Snell, Mr W. J. Taylor, Miss J. E. Taylor, Vogue Development Company (Kent) Ltd, D. P. Walsh, Mr M. S. Wynn.

Assistant Trainer: Daniel Hutchison

161 MR CHRIS DOWN, Cullompton
Postal: **Upton, Cullompton, Devon, EX15 1RA**
Contacts: **PHONE (01884) 33097 FAX (01884) 33097 MOBILE (07828) 021232**
E-MAIL cjdownracing@gmail.com

1 **AROSEFOROSCAR**, 7, b m Oscar (IRE)—Made For A King **The Red White & Blue Partnership**
2 **BILLY DUTTON**, 10, ch g Sir Harry Lewis (USA)—Tinoforty (FR) **W. A. Bromley**
3 **BILLY MY BOY**, 7, b g Volochine (IRE)—Key West (FR) **Mr J. B. Radford**
4 **CRAIGANEE (IRE)**, 9, b g Craigsteel—Hows She Going (IRE) **P Holland,JT Measures,MA Kerr,V Holland**
5 **CULM COUNSELLOR**, 7, ch g Erhaab (USA)—Miss Counsel **Culm Valley Racing**
6 **DRAGON'S DEN (IRE)**, 9, b g Antonius Pius (USA)—Tallassee **G. R. Waterman**
7 **FOXY ACT**, 5, ch m Act One—Brown Fox **C. J. Down**
8 **FROZEN OVER**, 8, b g Iceman—Pearly River **O'Neill, Capps, Di Vincenzo**
9 **GRUMPY JACKIE**, 4, ch f Grape Tree Road—Hayley's Flower (IRE) **G. D. Thompson**
10 **HOT PEPPER**, 8, gr g Tikkanen (USA)—Copper Valley **Mrs G. H. Leeves**
11 **ICE TRES**, 7, br m Iceman—Tup Tim **Mrs W. Atkins**
12 **KEY TO MILAN**, 10, b g Milan—Key West (FR) **C. J. Down**
13 **LADIES DANCING**, 10, b g Royal Applause—Queen of Dance (IRE) **Upton Racing**
14 **LEGION D'HONNEUR (UAE)**, 11, b g Halling (USA)—Renowned (IRE) **Mrs M. Trueman**
15 **LOYAUTE (FR)**, 9, ch m Green Tune (USA)—Iles Marquises (FR) **Upton Racing 2**
16 **MAX FORTE (IRE)**, 6, br g Indian River (FR)—Brook Forte **P Holland,JT Measures,MA Kerr,V Holland**
17 **MOTTS CROSS (IRE)**, 5, b g Scorpion (IRE)—Rainy Season (IRE) **Mrs S. M. Trump**
18 **ORDENSRITTER (GER)**, 8, ch g Samum (GER)—Dramraire Mist **Red Baron Racing**
19 **STARLIT NIGHT**, 4, b f Nayef (USA)—Perfect Night **Quarter Past Three**
20 **THE LITTLE RED FOX**, 6, ch m Volochine (IRE)—Brown Fox **C. J. Down**
21 **TRIPLE CHIEF (IRE)**, 5, b g High Chaparral (IRE)—Trebles (IRE) **G. D. Thompson**
22 **UPTON WOOD**, 10, ch g Fleetwood (IRE)—Miss Counsel **C. J. Down & C. B. Stevens**

Other Owners: Mr A. Boylan, Mr M. G. Capps, Mrs S. J. Cork, Mr M. Di-Vincenzo, Dr M. J. Dixon, Mrs L. M. Edwards, Mrs G. H. Hancock, Mr A. D. Hill, P. D. Holland, Mrs V. Holland, Ms M. A. Kerr, Mr J. T. Measures, Mr A. G. O'Neill, Mr B. Stamp, Mr C. B. Stevens, K. W. Tyrrell.

Jockey (NH): James Davies, Richard Johnson, Tom Scudamore. **Conditional:** Giles Hawkins.

162 MISS SAM DRAKE, Guiseley
Postal: **Manor Farm, Old Hollings Hill, Guiseley, Leeds, West Yorkshire, LS20 8EW**
Contacts: **MOBILE (07921) 003155**

1 **ATTIMO (GER)**, 7, ch g Nayef (USA)—Alanda (GER) **Mrs J. E. Drake**
2 **BOURBON PRINCE**, 5, ch g Aqlaam—Good Enough (FR) **Mrs J. E. Drake**
3 **CROCODILE DANCER**, 6, b g Croco Rouge (IRE)—She Likes To Boogy (IRE) **Mrs J. E. Drake**
4 Ch g Ask—Dalzenia (FR) **Mrs J. E. Drake**
5 **DISTIME (IRE)**, 10, b g Flemensfirth (USA)—Technohead (IRE) **Mrs J. E. Drake**
6 **HOLLINS HILL**, 6, b g Lucarno (USA)—Bonnie Buttons **Mrs J. E. Drake**
7 **NICKI'S NIPPER**, 8, b m Denounce—Mistress Star **Mrs J. E. Drake**
8 **RAKTIMAN (IRE)**, 9, ch g Rakti—Wish List (IRE) **Mrs J. E. Drake**
9 **STAR PRESENTER (IRE)**, 8, b g Presenting—Star Councel (IRE) **Mrs J. E. Drake**
10 **VIOLONISTE (FR)**, 7, b g Epalo (GER)—Parade (FR) **Mrs J. E. Drake**

163 MR CLIVE DREW, Rampton
Postal: **Fox End Stables, 83 King Street, Rampton, Cambridgeshire, CB24 8QD**
Contacts: **PHONE/FAX (01954) 250772 MOBILE (07917) 718127**
E-MAIL polly.drew@googlemail.com

1 **DAINTY DAISEY (IRE)**, 4, b br f Pastoral Pursuits—Nursling (IRE) **C. Drew**
2 **HALLO SEXY**, 4, br f Halling (USA)—Maziona **C. Drew**
3 **MAISON BRILLET (IRE)**, 9, b g Pyrus (USA)—Stormchaser (IRE) **C. Drew**
4 **MONSIEUR ROYALE**, 6, ch g Monsieur Bond (IRE)—Bond Royale **C. Drew**

Assistant Trainer: Miss Polly Drew

164 **MISS JACKIE DU PLESSIS, Saltash**
Postal: **Burell Farm, Longlands, Saltash, Cornwall, PL12 4QH**
Contacts: **PHONE (01752) 842362 MOBILE (07970) 871505**
E-MAIL ziggerson@aol.com

1 ABSOLUTELY BYGONES (IRE), 8, b g Alderbrook—Majella (IRE) **Miss J. M. du Plessis**
2 ARTHUR BURRELL, 7, ch g With The Flow (USA)—Kingsmill Quay **Miss J. M. du Plessis**
3 CAILLEACH ANNIE (IRE), 7, b m Blueprint (IRE)—Graineuaile (IRE) **Miss J. M. du Plessis**
4 COOL GEORGE, 8, b g Pastoral Pursuits—Magic Valentine **R. J. Reip, M. Stevenson**
5 DIDDYPURPTOON, 10, b m Lucky Story (USA)—Dafne **Miss J. M. du Plessis**
6 DORIS DE SILVER, 7, gr m Silver Patriarch (IRE)—Magic Valentine **Mr R. J. Reip**
7 FEAR GLIC (IRE), 10, b g Dr Massini (IRE)—Graineuaile (IRE) **Miss J Du Plessis & Mr G Waterman**
8 LONG JOHN, 9, gr g Silver Patriarch (IRE)—Magic Valentine **R. J. Reip, M. Stevenson**
9 RAY DIAMOND, 11, ch g Medicean—Musical Twist (USA) **Miss J. M. du Plessis**
10 ST DOMINICK (IRE), 9, b g Oscar (IRE)—Kilcrea Breeze (IRE) **Miss J. M. du Plessis**
11 TREHAN CROSS, 7, b m Bandmaster (USA)—Halton Quay **Miss J. M. du Plessis**
12 WINNING SPARK (USA), 9, b g Theatrical—Spark Sept (FR) **Miss J. M. du Plessis**
13 ZIGGERSON HILL, 9, ch m Kadastrof (FR)—Tregale **Miss J. M. du Plessis**

Other Owners: Mr M. F. Stevenson, G. R. Waterman.

165 **MRS ANN DUFFIELD, Leyburn**
Postal: **Sun Hill Racing Stables, Sun Hill Farm, Constable Burton, Leyburn, North Yorkshire, DL8 5RL**
Contacts: **PHONE (01677) 450303 FAX (01677) 450993 MOBILE (07802) 496332**
E-MAIL ann@annduffield.co.uk WEBSITE www.annduffield.co.uk

1 CASILA (IRE), 4, b f High Chaparral (IRE)—Miletrian (IRE) **M. Wormald**
2 CHANT (IRE), 6, b g Oratorio (IRE)—Akarita (IRE) **Mrs Ann Starkie & Mrs I. Starkie**
3 GEORGE DRYDEN (IRE), 4, gr g Zebedee—Key To Fortune (GER) **Mr S. Bradley**
4 LANDING NIGHT (IRE), 4, b g Kodiac—Night Delight (IRE) **Mr J. Dance**
5 MARSH PRIDE, 4, b f Stimulation (IRE)—Peneia (USA) **Mr J. Dance**
6 RED CHARMER (IRE), 6, b g Red Clubs (IRE)—Golden Charm (IRE) **Mr I Farrington & Mr R Chapman**
7 SHOW BOAT, 4, b g Showcasing—Bluegrass Gal (USA) **The Duchess of Sutherland**
8 TOBOGGAN'S GIFT, 4, b f Major Cadeaux—Toboggan Lady **Mr T. P. McMahon & Mr D. McMahon**

THREE-YEAR-OLDS

9 BIRRAFUN (IRE), b f Zebedee—Flower Bowl (IRE) **Middleham Park Racing CXIX**
10 BRONTE FLYER, ch f Nayef (USA)—Shohrah (USA) **Yorkshire Rose Partnership**
11 DANZEB (IRE), gr g Zebedee—Daneville (IRE) **Mr Stephen Bradley & Mr Alan Court**
12 DEMPSEY ROLL, b g Bushranger (IRE)—Suzie Quw **Mr Douglas McMahon & Partner**
13 ENCANTAR, b f Equiano (FR)—Enrapture (USA) **Mr D J & Mrs S A Shewring & Partner**
14 HARMONIC WAVE (IRE), b f Zebedee—Pure Folly (IRE) **Mr J. Dance**
15 HEAVEN SCENT, ch f Phoenix Reach (IRE)—Hel's Angel (IRE) **Mrs H. L. Baines**
16 HILARY J, b f Mount Nelson—The Terrier **E & R Stott**
17 JUST A GROOVE (IRE), b g Kodiac—Callanish **J Dance, J Cullinan, R Marley**
18 LADY CHARA, b f Stimulation (IRE)—Noble Nova **The Duchess of Sutherland**
19 LADY NAHEMA (IRE), b f Zoffany (IRE)—Jamary (IRE) **Mr D Barker, Mr D McMahon & Mr M Twells**
20 LETBYGONESBEICONS, b g Sixties Icon—Composing (IRE) **Birrafun Partnership & Partner**
21 MY AMIGO, gr c Stimulation (IRE)—Blue Crest (FR) **J Dance, D J & S A Shewring, M Tanner**
22 MY TWO SCOOPS, ch g Showcasing—Miss Beaudacious (IRE) **Mr J. Dance**
23 NINETTA (IRE), b f New Approach (IRE)—Pine Chip (USA) **Ms J. F. Bianco**
24 PASSIONATEPRINCESS (IRE), b f Elnadim (USA)—Romany Princess (IRE) **The Passionate Partnership**
25 ROSINA, b f Showcasing—Mondovi **Ms J. F. Bianco**
26 ROUNDABOUT TIME (IRE), gr c Zebedee—Brosna Time (IRE) **The Duchess of Sutherland**
27 SILHUETTE (IRE), b f Canford Cliffs (IRE)—Lisfannon **Mr J. Dance**
28 SILVER STREAK (IRE), gr g Dark Angel (IRE)—Happy Talk (IRE) **Punchbowl Racing**
29 SOUTHERN SEAS, ch f Archipenko (USA)—Verecunda **Miss K. Rausing**
30 TALLULAH FLEUR, b f Royal Applause—Topflightcoolracer **P. Bamford**
31 TOBOGGAN'S FIRE, b f Firebreak—Toboggan Lady **Grange Park Racing,Mr T P & D McMahon**
32 WHISPERING SOUL (IRE), b f Majestic Missile (IRE)—
                            Belle of The Blues (IRE) **Mr John Dance & Mr John Gatenby**
33 YOUNG WINDSOR (IRE), ch g Windsor Knot (IRE)—Invincible Woman (IRE) **Punchbowl Racing**

MRS ANN DUFFIELD - Continued

TWO-YEAR-OLDS

34 **ARNOLD**, b c 31/3 Equiano (FR)—Azurinta (IRE) (Azamour (IRE)) (20671)
35 Gr f 6/4 Dark Angel (IRE)—
　　　　　Belle of The Blues (IRE) (Blues Traveller (IRE)) (16980) **Middleham Park Racing LXXV & Partner**
36 **BENIDICTION (IRE)**, b f 25/3 Pastoral Pursuits—Centenerola (USA) (Century City (IRE)) (33333)
37 B c 15/3 Intense Focus (USA)—Breedj (IRE) (Acclamation) (14765)
38 B f 17/3 Sir Prancealot (IRE)—Bronze Queen (IRE) (Invincible Spirit (IRE)) (22147) **Mr J. Dance**
39 **COLLINGHAM PARK (IRE)**, ch c 26/4 Dream Ahead (USA)—
　　　　　Pine Chip (USA) (Nureyev (USA)) (16000) **Ingham Racing Syndicate**
40 **DAVINCI DAWN**, b f 20/2 Poet's Voice—Bonnie Brae (Mujahid (USA)) (28571) **Mrs A. Duffield**
41 **DECREES OF MOTION (IRE)**, b f 4/4 Lawman (FR)—Barring Decree (IRE) (Dalakhani (IRE)) (11073) **Mr J. Dance**
42 B c 1/4 Sir Prancealot (IRE)—Dubai Princess (IRE) (Dubai Destination (USA)) (20952)
43 Ch f 19/4 Zebedee—Elizabelle (IRE) (Westerner) (26577)
44 B f 10/3 Intense Focus (USA)—Folcungi (IRE) (Mukaddamah (USA)) (13289) **The Duchess of Sutherland**
45 B f 17/3 Equiano (FR)—Fontegiusta (IRE) (Desert Prince (IRE))
46 B g 13/4 Harbour Watch (IRE)—Gentle Guru (Ishiguru (USA)) (5714)
47 **HARBOUR LIGHTNING**, ch f 23/4 Harbour Watch (IRE)—Divine Power (Kyllachy) (11428) **M. Wormald**
48 **HIGH SHAW**, b c 24/2 Paco Boy (IRE)—Mondovi (Kyllachy) (15238)
49 **HOT NATURED (IRE)**, b f 29/4 Canford Cliffs (IRE)—Teddy Bears Picnic (Oasis Dream) (61904) **Mr J. Dance**
50 **LADOFASH**, b c 5/2 Canford Cliffs (IRE)—Curras Spirit (Invincible Spirit (IRE)) (34285) **Mr J. Dance**
51 **MISS BATES**, b f 19/4 Holy Roman Emperor (IRE)—Jane Austen (IRE) (Galileo (IRE)) **The Duchess of Sutherland**
52 **NIFTY NIECE (IRE)**, gr f 6/4 Zebedee—Hasty Harriet (IRE) (Choisir (AUS)) (14764) **The Duchess of Sutherland**
53 **PANTHER IN PINK (IRE)**, b gr f 21/4 Zebedee—
　　　　　Annus Iucundus (IRE) (Desert King (IRE)) (28571) **Mrs A. Duffield**
54 **PEACH PAVLOVA (IRE)**, b f 6/4 Elzaam (AUS)—Zvezda (USA) (Nureyev (USA)) **E & R Stott**
55 B f 25/3 Equiano (FR)—Quixada (GER) (Konigstiger (GER))
56 **RAINBOW MIST (IRE)**, b c 9/4 Lilbourne Lad (IRE)—
　　　　　Misty Night (IRE) (Galileo (IRE)) (11428) **Mr C. Buckingham**
57 **ROYAL BLUE CARAVEL (IRE)**, b f 16/1 Henrythenavigator (USA)—
　　　　　Holly Blue (Bluebird (USA)) (50203) **ICM Racing**
58 B f 27/3 Tamayuz—Silver Kestrel (USA) (Silver Hawk (USA)) (25714) **Mr J. Dance**
59 **TWIZZELL**, b f 10/3 Equiano (FR)—Greensand (Green Desert (USA)) (36913) **Mr J. Dance**
60 B c 8/4 Vale of York (IRE)—Velvet Kiss (IRE) (Danehill Dancer (IRE)) (7619) **Mrs A. Duffield**

Other Owners: D. K. Barker, Mr R. P. Chapman, Mr D. G. Colledge, Mr B. J. Connolly, Mr A. Court, A. D. Crombie, J. Cullinan, Mr I. J. Farrington, Mr J. Gatenby, Mr M. Gornall, Mr I. Harle, M. T. S. Ingham, Mr R. J. Marley, Mr T. P. McMahon, Mr D. S. McMahon, Mr D. McMahon, J. R. Owen, T. S. Palin, Mr M. D. Parker, Mr D. B. Plows, M. Prince, Mr A. Richmond, Mrs B. M. Richmond, Mrs S. A. Shewring, Mr D. J. Shewring, Mrs A. Starkie, Mrs I. L. A. Starkie, Miss E. Stott, Miss R. Stott, Mr M. C. P. Suddards, Mr E. Surr, Mr M. R. Tanner, Mr M. J. Twells.

Assistant Trainer: Julie Wilson

Jockey (flat): P. J. McDonald. **Conditional:** Colm McCormack. **Apprentice:** Rowan Scott.

---

166 MR BRENDAN W. DUKE, The Curragh
Postal: **Fenway House, Pollardstown, Curragh, Co. Kildare, Ireland**
Contacts: **MOBILE (00353) 85 8189724**

1 **EMPRESS SCORPION (IRE)**, 6, b m Scorpion (IRE)—Square Up (IRE) **Mr Joseph Duke**
2 **FIONN'S LADY (IRE)**, 4, b f Cape Cross (IRE)—Fashion Trade **Mr Christopher Leonard**
3 **FOCAS MOR (IRE)**, 5, ch m Intense Focus (USA)—Intriguing Humor (CAN) **Mrs Jackie Bolger**
4 **LAKE MARIA (IRE)**, 7, b m Kheleyf (USA)—Tamariyya (IRE) **Brendan W Duke Racing Syndicate**
5 **LAMH IN AIRDE (USA)**, 4, ch f Macho Uno—Fardus (USA) **Mrs Jackie Bolger**
6 **MOUNTMELLICK GIRL (IRE)**, 4, b f Beneficial—Dream Witness (FR) **Martin Hayes & Peter Slezak**
7 **PUNCH BAG (IRE)**, 5, ch g Teofilo (IRE)—Heir Today (IRE) **Martin Hayes & Peter Slezak**
8 **QUI BONO (IRE)**, 5, gr g Beneficial—Dream Witness (FR) **Mr Joseph Duke**
9 **UNO VOCE (IRE)**, 4, b g Vocalised (USA)—Derpat (IRE) **Brendan W Duke Racing Syndicate**
10 **VOCAL HEIR (IRE)**, 4, b f Vocalised (USA)—Heir Today (IRE) **Mr Christopher Leonard**
11 **VOCAL VELOCITY (IRE)**, 4, b g Vocalised (USA)—Voronova (IRE) **Mrs Jackie Bolger**

THREE-YEAR-OLDS

12 **ALLINONE (IRE)**, b f Bushranger (IRE)—Ambika (IRE) **Mrs Jackie Bolger**
13 **ATHASACH (IRE)**, b f Manduro (GER)—Fashion Trade **Mrs Jackie Bolger**
14 **LEATH NA HOIBRE (IRE)**, b c Vocalised (USA)—Tus Maith (IRE) **Mrs Jackie Bolger**

MR BRENDAN W. DUKE - Continued

15 **MURMURATION (IRE)**, b f Vocalised (USA)—Lily Marette (IRE) **Mrs Jackie Bolger**
16 **ODISHA (USA)**, ch f Drosselmeyer (USA)—Mocha d'oro (USA) **Mrs Jackie Bolger**
17 **SILVERCUPS (IRE)**, b f Roderic O'Connor (USA)—Klang (IRE) **Mrs Marguerite Joyce**
18 **THE MOUSE DOCTOR (IRE)**, b c Lord Shanakill (USA)—Afilla **Mr Joseph Duke**
19 **VOCAL DEFENSE (IRE)**, br c Vocalised (USA)—Redrightreturning **Mrs Jackie Bolger, Mr John Corcoran**
20 **VOCAL PERFECTION (IRE)**, b f Vocalised (USA)—Darina (IRE) **Mrs Jackie Bolger**

TWO-YEAR-OLDS

21 B c 3/4 Vocalised (USA)—Aeraiocht (IRE) (Tenby) **Mrs Jackie Bolger**
22 B f 12/5 Footstepsinthesand—Carakiysa (IRE) (Docksider (USA)) **Gary and Sharon Davis**
23 B f 19/4 Famous Name—
Dathuil (IRE) (Royal Academy (USA)) (11074) **Mrs Jackie Bolger, Martin Hayes, James Moir, Peter Slezak
Partnership**
24 B c 1/4 Vocalised (USA)—Heir Today (IRE) (Princely Heir (IRE)) **Mrs Jackie Bolger**
25 **LANDLINE (IRE)**, b c 28/4 Vocalised (USA)—Bipasha (IRE) (Rock of Gibraltar (IRE)) **Mrs Jackie Bolger**
26 B f 27/3 Fast Company (IRE)—Nellie Nolan (USA) (Storm Cat (USA)) (2214) **Mr Joseph Duke**
27 **ROUNDING (IRE)**, b c 3/5 Vocalised (USA)—Derpat (IRE) (Invincible Spirit (IRE)) **Mrs Jackie Bolger**

Jockey (flat): Rory Cleary, Kevin Manning, Ronan Whelan. **Jockey (NH):** Andrew Lynch. **Apprentice:** Daniel Redmond.

---

167 MR IAN DUNCAN, Coylton
Postal: **Sandhill Farm, Coylton, Ayr, Ayrshire, KA6 6HE**
Contacts: **PHONE (01292) 571118 FAX (01292) 571118 MOBILE (07731) 473668**
E-MAIL jennyclose86@googlemail.com

1 **FINAGHY AYR (IRE)**, 8, ch g Lahib (USA)—Ali Ankah (IRE) **Mr A. J. R. Lilley**
2 **GOLDEN SPARKLE (IRE)**, 10, ch m Samraan (USA)—Bye For Now **Miss H. A. Cross**
3 **KING OF FASHION (IRE)**, 6, ch g Desert King (IRE)—French Fashion (IRE) **Great Northern Partnership 2**
4 **LOCHNELL (IRE)**, 7, br m Winged Love (IRE)—Nothing For Ever (IRE) **Alan & Barry Macdonald**
5 **MAURA LILY (IRE)**, 7, br m Lahib (USA)—Ali Ankah (IRE) **Mr A. J. R. Lilley**
6 **MILBOROUGH (IRE)**, 10, b g Milan—Fox Burrow (IRE) **Miss H. A. Cross**
7 **PERSIAN FASHION (IRE)**, 7, b m Lahib (USA)—Kiera's Gale (IRE) **I. A. Duncan**
8 **SEPTEMBER SON (IRE)**, 6, b g September Storm (GER)—Regal Pageant (IRE) **Mr A. J. R. Lilley**
9 **SPRING OVER (IRE)**, 10, ch m Samraan (USA)—Superswap (IRE) **I. A. Duncan**
10 **WHY BUT WHY (USA)**, 8, b g Whywhywhy (USA)—Miss Orah **I. A. Duncan**

Other Owners: Mr A. L. Gregg, J. K. S. Law, Mr B. N. MacDonald, Mr A. G. MacDonald.

---

168 MR ED DUNLOP, Newmarket
Postal: **La Grange Stables, Fordham Road, Newmarket, Suffolk, CB8 7AA**
Contacts: **PHONE (01638) 661998 FAX (01638) 667394 MOBILE (07785) 328537**
E-MAIL edunlop@eddunloppracing.co.uk WEBSITE www.edunlop.com

1 **DARK RED (IRE)**, 4, gr g Dark Angel (IRE)—Essexford (IRE) **R. J. Arculli**
2 **DUTCH UNCLE**, 4, b g Dutch Art—Evasive Quality (FR) **R. J. Arculli**
3 **HARLESTONE HOPES**, 4, b g Olden Times—Harlestone Lady **J. L. Dunlop**
4 **INNISCASTLE LAD**, 4, b g Kyllachy—Glencal **E. A. L. Dunlop**
5 **JUSTICE FIRST**, 4, b g Zebedee—Nelly's Glen **Mr R. Ng**
6 **OASIS FANTASY (IRE)**, 5, br g Oasis Dream—Cara Fantasy (IRE) **Windflower Overseas & J L Dunlop OBE**
7 **SAGACIOUSLY (IRE)**, 4, b f Lawman (FR)—Saga Celebre (FR) **The Sagacious Lot**
8 **SCRUTINISE**, 4, b g Intense Focus (USA)—Tetravella (IRE) **Thurloe Thoroughbreds XXXIV**
9 **SHINGWEDZI (SAF)**, 4, b m Trippi (USA)—Buffalo Dance (IRE)
10 **TRIP TO PARIS (IRE)**, 5, b g Champs Elysees—La Grande Zoa (IRE) **La Grange Partnership**
11 **VERISMO**, 4, b g Hurricane Run (IRE)—Cross Current **B. Andersson**

THREE-YEAR-OLDS

12 **AHDAATH (IRE)**, b f Kodiac—Sonny Sunshine **Hamdan bin Rashid Al Maktoum**
13 **AL HAMD (IRE)**, b g Intikhab (USA)—Bakoura **Hamdan bin Rashid Al Maktoum**
14 **ALFAHAD (IRE)**, b c New Approach (IRE)—Al Tamooh (IRE) **Hamdan bin Rashid Al Maktoum**
15 **ALQUBBAH (IRE)**, b f Arcano (IRE)—Musharakaat (IRE) **Hamdan bin Rashid Al Maktoum**
16 **AMAZING RED (IRE)**, b c Teofilo (IRE)—Artisia (IRE) **R. J. Arculli**
17 **ARCHIMENTO**, ch c Archipenko (USA)—Caribana **The Optimistic Lot**

MR ED DUNLOP - Continued

18 **BLUSHES (FR),** b f Siyouni (FR)—Pink And Red (USA) **The Sagacious Lot**
19 **CAFOO (IRE),** ch c Makfi—Kournikova (SAF) **M. Alharbi**
20 **CAPRICIOUS CANTOR (IRE),** b f Cape Cross (IRE)—Alleluia **Mr Alec Leopold & Ms Leanne Norman**
21 **CHARIOTEER,** b g Champs Elysees—Skyrider (IRE) **Bluehills Racing Limited**
22 **CHESTNUT STORM (IRE),** ch f Rip Van Winkle (IRE)—Always Attractive (IRE) **J. Strauss & Sir A. Page Wood**
23 **CLIFF FACE (IRE),** b f Canford Cliffs (IRE)—Kotdiji **Bluehills Racing Limited**
24 **DORA'S FIELD (IRE),** b f Rip Van Winkle (IRE)—Rydal Mount (IRE) **R. S. E. Gifford**
25 **FLINTY FELL (IRE),** b f Rock of Gibraltar (IRE)—Manoeuvre (IRE) **St Albans Bloodstock Limited**
26 **FUN MONEY,** b f Authorized (IRE)—Grand Lucre **The EDR Partnership**
27 **GABRIELLE,** b f Paco Boy (IRE)—Bounty Box **The Belfour Partnership**
28 **GIRL WITH A PEARL (IRE),** ch f Dutch Art—Pointed Arch (IRE) **Racing Fillies**
29 **GLOBAL AVENGER (IRE),** b c Kodiac—Silent Serenade **Dr J. Hon**
30 **GLORYETTE,** b f Raven's Pass (USA)—Cara Fantasy (IRE) **Windflower Overseas Holdings Inc**
31 **KAFOO,** b g Dansili—Nidhaal (IRE) **Hamdan bin Rashid Al Maktoum**
32 **MANJAAM (IRE),** ch c Tamayuz—Priory Rock (IRE) **M. Alharbi**
33 **MICHAEL'S MOUNT,** ch g Mount Nelson—Dumnoni **Miltil Consortium**
34 **MUJAMALA (IRE),** b f Exceed And Excel (AUS)—Habaayib **Hamdan bin Rashid Al Maktoum**
35 **NORDENFELT (IRE),** b c Lilbourne Lad (IRE)—There With Me (USA) **W. Cox**
36 **ON THE BILL (IRE),** b g Kyllachy—Secret Flame **The Old Etonian Racing Syndicate**
37 **OPPOSITION,** gr g Dalakhani (IRE)—Censored **Highclere Thoroughbred Racing(Melbourne)**
38 **PIMPERNELLA (IRE),** b f Elusive Pimpernel (USA)—Soviet Belle (IRE) **Windflower Overseas Holdings Inc**
39 **QEYAADAH (IRE),** b g Acclamation—Effervesce (IRE) **Hamdan bin Rashid Al Maktoum**
40 **RAASMAAL,** b g Poet's Voice—Luminda (IRE) **Hamdan bin Rashid Al Maktoum**
41 **RAS AL MAL (IRE),** ch c Tamayuz—Midnight Glimmer (IRE) **M. Alharbi**
42 **RED VERDON (USA),** ch c Lemon Drop Kid (USA)—Porto Marmay (IRE) **R. J. Arculli**
43 **ROCK 'N RED (IRE),** b f Fastnet Rock (AUS)—Red Fantasy (IRE) **R. J. Arculli**
44 **ROCKERY (IRE),** b f Fastnet Rock (AUS)—Rain Flower (IRE) **Sir Peter Vela & Hon Mrs Peter Stanley**
45 **SAGELY (IRE),** b f Frozen Power (IRE)—Saga Celebre (FR) **Dr J. Hon**
46 **SHAFAFYA,** b f Shamardal (USA)—Tanaghum **Hamdan bin Rashid Al Maktoum**
47 **SHARAAKAH (IRE),** b f Roderic O'Connor (IRE)—Lanark Belle **M. Alharbi**
48 **SNOW PIXIE (USA),** br f Flower Alley (USA)—Woodland Dream (IRE) **Anamoine Ltd**
49 **SOCIAL MEDIA,** b f New Approach (IRE)—Mischief Making (USA) **Cliveden Stud Ltd**
50 **SWIFTEE (IRE),** ch g Camacho—Algaira (USA) **Bluehills Racing Limited**
51 **TIMIA,** b f Cape Cross (IRE)—Cinerama (IRE) **Mr A. Alharbi**
52 **TOFFEE APPLE (IRE),** b f Zoffany (IRE)—Myrtle Beach (IRE) **P. G. Goulandris**
53 **VIVRE POUR VIVRE (IRE),** b c Pour Moi (IRE)—Miss Quality (USA) **Mrs S. M. Roy**
54 **WARRIOR PRINCE,** ch g Sakhee (USA)—Queen of Iceni **Mrs I. H. Stewart-Brown & Mr M. J. Meacock**
55 **WEALTH TAX,** gr g Canford Cliffs (IRE)—Firoza (FR) **W. J. and T. C. O. Gredley**
56 **ZAUFFALY (FR),** ch g Zoffany (IRE)—Lady Sadowa **The Octopus Partnership**

TWO-YEAR-OLDS

57 **AL EMARATALYOUM (IRE),** ch c 30/4 Lope de Vega (IRE)—Heart of Ice (IRE) (Montjeu (IRE)) (85000) **M. Alharbi**
58 **AL NAFOORAH,** b f 17/1 Bated Breath—Cat O' Nine Tails (Motivator) (66445) **M. Alharbi**
59 B c 10/3 Born To Sea (IRE)—Alkhawarah (USA) (Intidab (USA)) (61904) **Thurloe Thoroughbreds XXXVII**
60 **ALNIYAT,** ch f 7/5 Sepoy (AUS)—Agata Laguna (IRE) (Elnadim (USA)) **Hamdan bin Rashid Al Maktoum**
61 **ALQUWWA (IRE),** b c 23/2 Teofilo (IRE)—Al Tamooh (IRE) (Dalakhani (IRE)) **Hamdan bin Rashid Al Maktoum**
62 B c 6/4 Holy Roman Emperor (IRE)—Annalina (USA) (Cozzene (USA)) (32000) **E. A. L. Dunlop**
63 **BOOSHBASH (IRE),** gr f 15/3 Dark Angel (IRE)—Surrey Storm (Montjeu (IRE)) (43000) **M. Alharbi**
64 **CAROL (IRE),** b f 5/4 Acclamation—Miss Topsy Turvy (IRE) (Mr Greeley (USA))
65 **CHOCOLATE ACCOUNT (USA),** gr ro f 12/3 Exchange Rate (USA)—
                                    Western Vision (USA) (Gone West (USA)) (52000) **M. Alharbi**
66 B c 26/4 Exceed And Excel (AUS)—Cloud's End (Dubawi (IRE)) (110000) **Mr A. S. Al Naboodah**
67 **CONDENSED,** b f 19/1 Dansili—Cut Short (USA) (Diesis) **Cliveden Stud Ltd**
68 B c 11/2 Mayson—Crown (IRE) (Royal Applause) (78000) **Dr J. Hon**
69 B c 6/5 Dansili—Crystal Maze (Gone West (USA)) (140000) **Mrs Emma Capon & Lord Lloyd Webber**
70 **FAIR HEAD (IRE),** b f 17/2 Iffraaj—Dawaama (IRE) (Dansili) (25714) **J L Stitt,J G Stitt,Sir A Page-Wood**
71 B f 12/5 Excelebration (IRE)—Gems of Araby (Zafonic (USA)) (25839) **Bluehills Racing Limited**
72 B f 16/4 War Front (USA)—Gilt (USA) (Bernardini (USA)) (259462) **Mr A. S. Al Naboodah**
73 **INSTIGATION,** b f 25/4 Bated Breath—Rainbow's Edge (Rainbow Quest (USA)) **Mr W. P. Wyatt**
74 B c 7/4 The Factor (USA)—Jive Talk (Kingmambo (USA)) (59061) **Mr G. B. Bolton**
75 B f 26/3 Lawman (FR)—Kelowna (IRE) (Pivotal) (8500) **J Brown, A Bengough & E Dunlop**
76 **KHITAAMY (IRE),** b c 25/4 Approve (IRE)—
                                    Halliwell House (Selkirk (USA)) (50000) **Hamdan bin Rashid Al Maktoum**
77 B c 23/3 Invincible Spirit (IRE)—Lixirova (FR) (Slickly (FR)) (380000) **Mr A. S. Al Naboodah**
78 **MAKMAN (IRE),** b c 24/3 Kodiac—Sheila Blige (Zamindar (USA)) (130000) **Hamdan bin Rashid Al Maktoum**

MR ED DUNLOP - Continued

79 Ch c 24/4 Foxwedge (AUS)—Malelane (IRE) (Prince Sabo) (27000)
80 **MULZIM**, b c 5/2 Exceed And Excel (AUS)—Samaah (IRE) (Cape Cross (IRE)) **Hamdan bin Rashid Al Maktoum**
81 **MUSHAREEFA (IRE)**, b f 2/2 Makfi—Winesong (IRE) (Giant's Causeway (USA)) (66445) **M. Alharbi**
82 **MUTAMAYEL (IRE)**, b c 25/2 Mawatheeq (USA)—Musharakaat (IRE) (Iffraaj) **Hamdan bin Rashid Al Maktoum**
83 **OUD METHA BRIDGE (IRE)**, ch c 7/4 Helmet (AUS)—Central Force (Pivotal) **M. Alharbi**
84 Ch c 25/2 Sepoy (AUS)—Palitana (USA) (Giant's Causeway (USA)) (300000) **Mr A. S. Al Naboodah**
85 **PANTERA NEGRA (IRE)**, b f 27/3 Champs Elysees—Penchee (Grand Lodge (USA)) (22148)
86 Ch c 6/3 Lope de Vega (IRE)—Pietra Dura (Cadeaux Genereux) (160000) **Mr A. S. Al Naboodah**
87 B f 15/2 Frankel—Platonic (Zafonic (USA)) (849021) **Mr A. S. Al Naboodah**
88 Ch c 14/3 Sir Percy—Queen of Iceni (Erhaab (USA))
89 B c 1/2 Henrythenavigator (USA)—Red Fantasy (IRE) (High Chaparral (IRE)) **R. J. Arculli**
90 **RIPPER STREET (IRE)**, b c 22/2 Big Bad Bob (IRE)—
                               Caster Sugar (USA) (Cozzene (USA)) (43000) **The MHSL Racing Partnership**
91 Ch c 24/2 Sepoy (AUS)—See You Later (Emarati (USA)) (31000)
92 B c 30/4 Oasis Dream—Seta (Pivotal) (420000) **Mr A. S. Al Naboodah**
93 B c 1/3 Kyllachy—Soliza (IRE) (Intikhab (USA)) (26000) **Dr J. Hon**
94 **SOQRAT**, b c 26/1 Paco Boy (IRE)—Tamara Moon (IRE) (Acclamation) (95238) **Hamdan bin Rashid Al Maktoum**
95 B br c 30/1 Distorted Humor (USA)—Spare Change (Bernardini (USA)) (152625) **Mr A. S. Al Naboodah**
96 **SPARKLE**, b f 27/2 Oasis Dream—Gemstone (IRE) (Galileo (IRE)) (190000) **Old Road Securities Plc**
97 **SUKOOT (IRE)**, ch c 26/3 Sir Prancealot (IRE)—
                               Yandina (Danehill (USA)) (57142) **Hamdan bin Rashid Al Maktoum**
98 B f 4/5 Invincible Spirit (IRE)—Sweet Stream (ITY) (Shantou (USA)) (97000)
99 **THE LACEMAKER**, b f 27/1 Dutch Art—Sospel (Kendor (FR)) (90000) **Mrs G. A. Rupert**
100 B f 22/4 Bated Breath—Time Will Show (FR) (Exit To Nowhere (USA)) **Weatherby, Hambury, Allison, Milmo**
101 **TITAN**, b c 19/4 Lawman (FR)—Dragonera (Doyen (IRE)) **Preston Lodge Stud, Champneys**
102 Ch c 29/3 Mastercraftsman (IRE)—Yaqootah (USA) (Gone West (USA)) (110000) **R. J. Arculli**

Other Owners: S. A. Allison, Mr A. N. C. Bengough, J. M. Brown, Mrs E. Capon, Mr P. A. Deal, The Countess Of Derby, Mrs R. S. Dunlop, R. P. Foden, Mr J. J. Gompertz, T. C. O. Gredley, W. J. Gredley, Mr R. I. Hambury, B. G. Hellyer, The Hon H. M. Herbert, Highclere Thoroughbred Racing Ltd, Mr J. Johnson, Mr A. Leopold, Mr C. P. Linney, Lord A. Lloyd-Webber, M. J. Meacock, P. H. Milmo, Mr T. Milner, A. M. V. Nicoll, Ms L. C. Norman, Sir Anthony Page-Wood, Mr O. J. W. Pawle, Mr R. A. Pilkington, S. J. Purdew, Mrs F. Schwarzenbach, Mr J. A. B. Stafford, The Hon Mrs Frances Stanley, Mr N. J. Statham, Mrs J. Stewart-Brown, Mr J. G. Stitt, Mr J. L. Stitt, Mr J. E. A. Strauss, Sir P. J. Vela, Sir Reddy Watt, J. R. Weatherby.

---

169 MR HARRY DUNLOP, Lambourn

Postal: **Windsor House Stables, Crowle Road, Lambourn, Hungerford, Berkshire, RG17 8NR**
Contacts: PHONE (01488) 73584 FAX (01488) 674172 MOBILE (07880) 791895
E-MAIL info@harrydunlopracing.com WEBSITE www.harrydunlopracing.com

1 **A MONTMARTRE (FR)**, 4, b f Montmartre (FR)—Stefania (IRE) **Glanvilles Stud Partners**
2 **BRITTLETON**, 4, b g Aqlaam—Fairy Dance (IRE) **Sir Philip Wroughton & Mrs James Blyth Currie**
3 **EARLY MORNING (IRE)**, 5, gr g New Approach (IRE)—Summer's Eve **The Early Risers**
4 **FLAMBEUSE**, 5, b m Cape Cross (IRE)—Flamenba (USA) **Glanvilles Stud Partners**
5 **LULANI (IRE)**, 4, b f Royal Applause (IRE)—Louverissa (IRE) **Mr & Mrs James Blyth Currie**
6 **MEMORIES GALORE (IRE)**, 4, b g Invincible Spirit (IRE)—
                               Persian Memories (IRE) **Windflower Overseas Holdings Inc**
7 **ROBINS PEARL (FR)**, 4, ch f Linngari (IRE)—Fire Sale (ARG) **The Blue Bar Partnership**
8 **RUM SWIZZLE**, 4, b f Mawatheeq (USA)—Port Providence **The Nigel Bennett Partnership**
9 **SEEBEEDEE**, 4, b f Multiplex—Border Ballet (IRE) **Glanvilles Stud Partners**
10 **STORM ROCK**, 4, b c Rock of Gibraltar (IRE)—Seasonal Cross **Malcolm & Alicia Aldis**
11 **SUNDAY ROYAL (FR)**, 4, b g Sunday Break (JPN)—Princess d'orange (IRE) **Mr & Mrs T O'Donohoe**

THREE-YEAR-OLDS

12 **BRETONCELLES (FR)**, b f Le Havre (IRE)—Carolles (FR) **Daniel MacAuliffe & Anoj Don**
13 **CALIFORNIA LAD**, b g Aussie Rules (USA)—Medaille d'or (USA) **Daniel MacAuliffe & Anoj Don**
14 **D'NIRO (IRE)**, b c Big Bad Bob (IRE)—Causeway Charm (USA) **Weston Brook Farm Bromfield & Whitaker**
15 **DYLANTELLE**, b f Dylan Thomas (IRE)—Bay Swallow (IRE) **Glanvilles Stud Partners**
16 **EMBROIDERY (IRE)**, gr f Mastercraftsman (IRE)—Joyful (USA) **Glanvilles Stud Partners**
17 **EVIDENCE (IRE)**, b f Excellent Art—Peachmelba (USA) **Glanvilles Stud Partners**
18 **FINELCITY (GER)**, b f g Elusive City (USA)—Finity (USA) **The Blue Bar**
19 **HERMARNA (IRE)**, br f Heliostatic (IRE)—Louverissa (IRE) **Mr & Mrs James Blyth Currie**
20 **INVIGORATE**, b c Stimulation (IRE)—Pesse (IRE) **Woodley, Gehring, Drake, Craig-Wood**

MR HARRY DUNLOP - Continued

21 **KASHTAN**, ch f Sakhee's Secret—Gitane (FR) **Whitaker, Gehring & Partners**
22 **LINGUIST (FR)**, ch g Linngari (IRE)—Western Bowl (USA) **Janet Weston Carolyn Whitaker Sue Johnson**
23 **MEROULA (FR)**, b f Vision d'etat (FR)—Laureldean Desert **Mr & Mrs James Blyth Currie**
24 **POULICHE**, b f Monsieur Bond (IRE)—Tarneem (USA) **Bissettdown Racing**
25 **QUICK WITTED**, b f Poet's Voice—Fastback (IRE) **Brightwalton Bloodstock Limited**
26 **ROBIN OF NAVAN (FR)**, ch c American Post—Cloghran (FR) **Cross, Deal, Foden, Sieff**
27 **SUND CITY (FR)**, b f Turtle Bowl (IRE)—Calithea (IRE) **Windsor House Racing**
28 **THREE BROTHERS (FR)**, gr c Slickly (FR)—Vivartic (FR) **Mr N. Pascall**
29 **TORQUAY**, b f Aqlaam—Torcross **Mr R. J. McCreery**

TWO-YEAR-OLDS

30 **ASSANILKA (FR)**, b f 16/3 Diamond Green (FR)—Regal Step (Royal Applause) (25839) **The Three Musketeers**
31 **ATLANTIC BEAUTY**, ch f 2/2 Archipenko (USA)—
　　　　　Medaille d'or (With Approval (CAN)) (24362) **Daniel MacAuliffe & Anoj Don**
32 B f 19/2 Danehill Dancer (IRE)—Bay Swallow (IRE) (Daylami (IRE)) **Glanvilles Stud Partners**
33 **COASTAL CYCLONE**, b c 12/3 Canford Cliffs (IRE)—
　　　　　Seasonal Cross (Cape Cross (IRE)) **Malcolm Aldis & Susan Abbott Racing**
34 Ch c 19/3 Harbour Watch (IRE)—Dress Code (IRE) (Barathea (IRE)) (11000) **Mrs Susan Roy**
35 B c 22/3 Lord Shanakill (USA)—Elouges (IRE) (Dalakhani (IRE)) (11000) **Mrs M. A. Parker**
36 B f 19/3 Sakhee's Secret—Green Room (In The Wings) **Windsor House Stables Partnership & C & N Elwes**
37 **HARROWBY STREET (FR)**, ch c 22/4 Nathaniel (IRE)—
　　　　　Aquarelliste (FR) (Danehill (USA)) (66445) **Brook Farm Bloodstock**
38 B f 1/4 Nathaniel (IRE)—Luminda (IRE) (Danehill (USA)) (38000) **Mr Peter Deal**
39 **NETLEY ABBEY**, b c 13/2 Myboycharlie (IRE)—
　　　　　Ana Style (FR) (Anabaa Blue) (22148) **Woodley, Bromfield, Cross, Whitaker**
40 Ch f 6/4 Dream Ahead (USA)—Party Appeal (USA) (Mr Greeley (USA)) (7000) **Mr Khalifa Dasmal**
41 **ROCK ON DANDY**, gr c 27/4 Rajsaman (FR)—
　　　　　Minnie's Mystery (FR) (Highest Honor (FR)) (31746) **Daniel MacAuliffe & Anoj Don**
42 B c 5/5 Kheleyf (USA)—Shimoni (Mark of Esteem (IRE)) **Mr Derek Thrower**
43 **VIKING HOARD (IRE)**, b c 22/3 Vale of York (IRE)—
　　　　　Tibouchina (IRE) (Daylami (IRE)) (23000) **Be Hopeful Partnership**
44 B c 9/2 Zamindar (USA)—Waitingonacloud (In The Wings) (18000) **Mr David Hearson**
45 **WINNING BID**, b c 16/4 Captain Gerrard (IRE)—Best Bidder (USA) (Mr Greeley (USA)) (9047) **Mr Khalifa Dasmal**

Assistant Trainer: Tom Frost

170　**MRS ALEXANDRA DUNN, Wellington**
Postal: **The Gallops, West Buckland, Wellington, Somerset, TA21 9LE**
Contacts: **MOBILE (07738) 512924**
WEBSITE www.alexandradunnracing.com

1 **BEAU KNIGHT**, 4, b g Sir Percy—Nicola Bella (IRE) **West Buckland Bloodstock Ltd**
2 **BLACK NARCISSUS (IRE)**, 7, b m Westerner—Arcanum (IRE) **Team Dunn**
3 **BLU CAVALIER**, 6, b g Kayf Tara—Blue Ride (IRE) **Mrs Angela Tincknell & Mr W. Tincknell**
4 4, Ch g Presenting—Blue Ride (IRE) **W. C. Tincknell**
5 **CHASING FAIRIES**, 5, gr m Fair Mix (IRE)—Trial Tiger **Mrs C. J. Banks**
6 **ENTRY TO EVRYWHERE (IRE)**, 8, b g Exit To Nowhere (USA)—
　　　　　Killowen Pam (IRE) **G. Butler & West Buckland Bloodstock**
7 **GOONJIM (IRE)**, 5, ch g Beneficial—Clogga Native (IRE) **The Profile Partnership**
8 **GUARACHA**, 5, ch g Halling (USA)—Pachanga **West Buckland Bloodstock Ltd**
9 **HELIUM (FR)**, 11, b g Dream Well (FR)—Sure Harbour (SWI) **West Buckland Bloodstock Ltd**
10 **HONOURABLE EXIT (IRE)**, 9, b g Exit To Nowhere (USA)—Honor Love (FR) **The Honourables**
11 **JASLAMOUR (FR)**, 5, ch g Valanour (IRE)—Jasla (FR) **Mr W. A. Thomas**
12 **LOUGH DERG ISLAND (IRE)**, 8, b g Court Cave (IRE)—Clondalee Fred (IRE) **Miss R. J. Smith-Maxwell**
13 **MYSTERY DRAMA**, 6, b m Hernando (FR)—Mystery Lot (IRE) **West Buckland Bloodstock Ltd**
14 **NEW REACTION**, 5, b g New Approach (IRE)—Intaaj (IRE) **The Game Birds**
15 **ROYAL CHARM (FR)**, 11, bl g Cadoudal (FR)—Victoria Royale (FR) **W. C. Tincknell**
16 **ROYAL CHIEF (IRE)**, 7, gr g Royal Anthem (USA)—Help Yourself (IRE) **The Game Birds**
17 **SLIDECHECK (IRE)**, 9, b g Dushyantor (USA)—Stormey Tune (IRE) **West Buckland Bloodstock Ltd**
18 **SPRING STEEL (IRE)**, 7, b g Dushyantor (USA)—Fieldtown (IRE) **N Berbillion & West Buckland Bloodstock**
19 **TACTICAL MANOEUVRE (IRE)**, 5, b g Marienbard (USA)—Pride O'fleet (IRE) **West Buckland Bloodstock Ltd**
20 **TEACHMETOBOUGGIE**, 6, ch g Tobougg (IRE)—Teachmetotango **Staplegrove Racing & R. P. B. Michaelson**
21 **TRAPPER PEAK (IRE)**, 7, b g Westerner—Banningham Blaze **West Buckland Bloodstock Ltd**

MRS ALEXANDRA DUNN - Continued

22 **VANISHING**, 4, b f Sir Percy—Valoria **West Buckland Bloodstock Ltd**
23 **WALLAWALLABINGBANG**, 7, b m Midnight Legend—Suzie Cream Cheese (IRE) **Mrs T. Knaggs**
24 **WINGED EXPRESS (IRE)**, 7, b g Winged Love (IRE)—Zaffaran Express (IRE) **Mr J. Burley & The Bucklanders**
25 **WORLDOR (FR)**, 10, b g Lost World (IRE)—Karenzed (FR) **West Buckland Bloodstock Ltd**
26 **ZERO VISIBILITY (IRE)**, 9, b g Classic Cliche (IRE)—
                                                   Jessica's Pet (IRE) **West Buckland Bloodstock & D Fitzgerald**

Other Owners: Mr D. R. Arthur, Mrs Y. Bennett, Mr N. Berbillion, J. Burley, Mr F. Clothier, Mr D. J. Fitzgerald, Mr J. Fowler, R. P. B. Michaelson, Mrs K. R. Smith-Maxwell, Mr S. J. Studley, Mrs A. Tincknell, Mrs C. M. Wheatley, Mr T. Wheatley, Mrs G. White.

---

171 MRS CHRISTINE DUNNETT, Norwich
Postal: **College Farm, Hingham, Norwich, Norfolk, NR9 4PP**
Contacts: **PHONE (01953) 850596 FAX (01953) 851364 MOBILE (07775) 793523**
E-MAIL christine@christinedunnett.com WEBSITE www.christinedunnett.com

1 **ARRYZONA**, 5, b g Phoenix Reach (IRE)—Southwarknewsflash **Christine Dunnett Racing (Arryzona)**
2 **BAILEYS PURSUIT**, 4, ch f Pastoral Pursuits—Royal Mistress **Mrs M. A. Benjafield**
3 **BONGO BELLE**, 5, ch m Phoenix Reach (IRE)—Bongoali
4 **BORN TO FLY (IRE)**, 5, b m Kodiac—Cayambe (IRE) **Mr P. D. West**
5 **COLLEGE DOLL**, 7, ch m Piccolo—Southwarknewsflash
6 **DANZOE (IRE)**, 9, b g Kheleyf (USA)—Fiaba **One For All**
7 **DELYSDREAM**, 4, br c Dutch Art—Goodbye Cash (IRE) **Mr C. R. Moore**
8 **ELLINGHAM (IRE)**, 5, b m Bushranger (IRE)—No Way (IRE)
9 **FLAMINGO BEAT**, 6, ch g Beat Hollow—Flamingo Flower (USA) **Mr P. D. West**
10 **GIVE IT A WHIRL**, 5, br m Pastoral Pursuits—Life's A Whirl **Mr A. Machin & Mrs C. Dunnett**
11 **GIVE US A BELLE (IRE)**, 7, b g Kheleyf (USA)—Bajan Belle (IRE) **Mr F Butler & Mrs C Dunnett**
12 **HAPPYDOINGNOTHING**, 5, b g Avonbridge—Neferura **Mr P. D. West**
13 **HUMOUR (IRE)**, 5, b g Invincible Spirit (IRE)—Hucking Hot **The Humourites**
14 **PERSEVERENT PETE (USA)**, 6, b br g Johannesburg (USA)—Indian Halloween (USA) **Mr P. D. West**
15 **SATIN WATERS**, 5, b m Halling (USA)—Velvet Waters **Ron Spore & P D West**
16 **SINEMA**, 4, gr g Compton Place—Dictatrix **Mr P. D. West**

THREE-YEAR-OLDS

17 **SAKHASTIC**, b g Sakhee's Secret—Rutland Water (IRE) **Annwell Inn Syndicate**

TWO-YEAR-OLDS

18 **PROUD KATE**, b f 14/4 Proud Citizen (USA)—Oceans Apart (Desert Prince (IRE)) **Mr & Mrs Alan Barnard**

Other Owners: Mr P. Amey, Mrs K. M. Barnard, Mr A. Barnard, G. Bromley, Mr D. G. Burt, F. Butler, Mrs C. A. Dunnett, Mr A. S. Machin, Mr T. Milner, Mr J. Riches, Mr M. Skellett, Mr E. N. Sparkes, R. C. Spore.

---

172 MR SEAMUS DURACK, Upper Lambourn
Postal: **The Croft Stables, Upper Lambourn, Hungerford, Berkshire, RG17 8QH**
Contacts: **PHONE (01488) 71941 MOBILE (07770) 537971**
E-MAIL sd.111@btinternet.com

1 **ALL TALK N NO DO (IRE)**, 5, b g Kodiac—Woodren (USA) **Mrs A. Cowley**
2 4, Gr g Stowaway—Annilogs Palm (IRE)
3 **BAY SLY (IRE)**, 9, b g Stowaway—On A Mission (IRE) **Mr G. Tardi**
4 4, Ch g Mr Dinos (IRE)—Daly Lady (IRE)
5 **GOODBY INHERITENCE**, 4, b c Medicean—Chili Dip **Mrs A. Cowley**
6 **HAHNENKAM (IRE)**, 6, b g Stowaway—Bahnasa (IRE) **Mr G. Tardi**
7 **IFTIRAAQ (IRE)**, 5, b g Muhtathir—Alzaroof (USA) **The Acorn Partnership**
8 **JUST JOELLIOTT (IRE)**, 6, b g Great Exhibition—Solara (GER)
9 **KELPIE BLAZE (IRE)**, 5, gr g Aussie Rules (USA)—Woodsia **Mrs A. Cowley**
10 **LINGUINE (FR)**, 6, ch g Linngari (IRE)—Amerissage (USA) **Mrs A. Cowley**
11 **NICELY INDEED (IRE)**, 6, b g Marienbard—Rare Dollar (IRE) **Mr Gary Tardi & ownaracehorse.co.uk**
12 **RON HEGARTY (IRE)**, 5, b g Gamut (IRE)—Financial Heiress (IRE) **Egan Waste Services Ltd**
13 **STRONG CONTENDER**, 4, b c Rail Link—Morzine
14 **SYNODIC (USA)**, 4, br c Henrythenavigator (USA)—Seven Moons (JPN)
15 **THE RECTIFIER (USA)**, 9, b br g Langfuhr (CAN)—Western Vision (USA) **Mrs A. Cowley**

MR SEAMUS DURACK - Continued

16 **TOUR DE VILLE (IRE)**, 6, b g Beneficial—Galant Tour (IRE) **Hey Ho Let's Go**
17 **TOURNAMENT**, 5, b h Oasis Dream—Concentric **S. P. Tucker**

THREE-YEAR-OLDS
18 **HELLS BABE**, gr f Hellvelyn—Blues In Cee (IRE) **Mrs L. White**
19 **VALITOP**, b c Pivotal—Songerie **S. P. Tucker**

TWO-YEAR-OLDS
20 B c 2/4 High Chaparral (IRE)—Valencha (Domedriver (IRE)) (28000) **Ownaracehorse & Stephen Tucker**

Other Owners: J. J. Hathorn, Mrs F. K. Hathorn, Mr S. J. Hopkins, Ownaracehorse Ltd, Mr A. P. D. Wyke.

Assistant Trainer: Faye Bramley

Jockey (flat): George Baker, Oisin Murphy, Timmy Murphy. **Jockey (NH):** Conor O'Farrell.
Amateur: Miss Faye Bramley.

---

173 MR CHRIS DWYER, Newmarket
Postal: **Grooms Cottage, Brickfield Stud, Exning Road, Newmarket, Suffolk, CB8 7JH**
Contacts: **PHONE (01638) 578651 FAX (01638) 578651 MOBILE (07831) 579844**
E-MAIL getadwyer@aol.com

1 **BAILEYS EN PREMIER (FR)**, 5, b g Exceed And Excel (AUS)—
Numberonedance (USA) **G. R. Bailey Ltd (Baileys Horse Feeds)**
2 **BASIL BERRY**, 5, b g Tobougg (IRE)—Dolly Coughdrop (IRE) **Strawberry Fields Stud**
3 **BINT DANDY (IRE)**, 5, b m Dandy Man (IRE)—Ceol Loch Aoidh (IRE) **M. M. Foulger**
4 **DARK SIDE DREAM**, 4, b g Equiano (FR)—Dream Day **M. M. Foulger**
5 **FOIE GRAS**, 6, b g Kyllachy—Bint Zamayem (IRE) **Mrs S. Dwyer**
6 **NOGUCHI (IRE)**, 11, ch g Pivotal—Tuscania (USA) **Mr D. McGrath**
7 **PATRIOTIC (IRE)**, 8, b g Pivotal—Pescara (IRE) **M. M. Foulger**
8 **SAVED MY BACON (IRE)**, 5, b m Camacho—Sally Green (IRE) **Mrs J. Hughes & Mrs C. Kemp**
9 **YOUR LUCKY DAY**, 4, b g Cockney Rebel (IRE)—Fontaine House **Mrs I. L. Sneath**

THREE-YEAR-OLDS
10 **DARK SIDE PRINCESS**, b f Strategic Prince—Brazilian Breeze (IRE) **M. M. Foulger**
11 **LOURDES LADY**, b f Arabian Gleam—Wenden Belle (IRE) **Mr D. Devereux**
12 **SUQOOR**, b g Equiano (FR)—Ukraine (IRE) **G. R. Bailey Ltd (Baileys Horse Feeds)**
13 **TEVERSHAM**, b g Kheleyf (USA)—Snow Shoes **Strawberry Fields Stud**

TWO-YEAR-OLDS
14 Ch c 26/2 Excelebration (IRE)—Lady's Art (FR) (Verglas (IRE)) **G. R. Bailey Ltd (Baileys Horse Feeds)**
15 **LILY VIOLET**, ch f 4/4 Avonbridge—Gretel (Hansel (USA)) **Mrs S. Dwyer**
16 **PRECIOUS PLUM**, b f 13/4 Equiano (FR)—Miss Polly Plum (Doyen (IRE)) **Mrs J. Hughes & Mrs C. Kemp**
17 B c 1/1 Holy Roman Emperor (IRE)—Tegan (Cape Cross (IRE)) (6644) **Mr P. Venner**

Other Owners: Mr J. P. Bushe, Mrs Shelley Dwyer, Mrs Julia Hughes, Mrs Carrie Kemp, Mr G. F. L. Robinson, Mr Basil White.

Assistant Trainer: Shelley Dwyer (07949) 612256

Apprentice: Josh Crane.

---

174 MISS CLAIRE DYSON, Evesham
Postal: **Froglands Stud Farm, Froglands Lane, Cleeve Prior, Evesham, Worcestershire, WR11 8LB**
Contacts: **PHONE (07803) 720183 (01789) 774000 FAX (01789) 774000**
E-MAIL cdyson@live.co.uk WEBSITE www.clairedysonracing.co.uk

1 **ADADREAM**, 7, b g Abzu—Madam Ross **C. R. Green**
2 **BOOMTOWN**, 11, b g Fantastic Light (USA)—Ville d'amore (USA) **FSF Racing**
3 **CHEAT THE CHEATER (IRE)**, 9, b g Flemensfirth (USA)—Ballyclough Gale **Pink Fizz Fillies**
4 **CLASSIC TUNE**, 6, b g Scorpion (IRE)—Classic Fantasy **D. J. Dyson**
5 **CRESSWELL PRINCE (IRE)**, 6, b g Bienamado (USA)—Faraday Lady (IRE) **B & S Vaughan**
6 **EL INDIO (IRE)**, 9, b g Flemensfirth (USA)—Final Bond (IRE) **D J Pardy & D J Dyson**

MISS CLAIRE DYSON - Continued

7 **GIVEITACHANCE (IRE)**, 9, b g Clerkenwell (USA)—Native Lisa (IRE) **Miss R. J. Rowland**
8 **ICANMOTOR**, 9, b m Midnight Legend—Lochnagold **Mr K. Elvins**
9 **LEAGUE OF HIS OWN (IRE)**, 7, ch g Beneficial—Miss Eastwood (IRE) **FSF Racing**
10 **MEMORY OF LIGHT (IRE)**, 7, gr g Westerner—Be Thankfull (IRE) **Mr G. T. Sainsbury**
11 **MIDNIGHT OWLE**, 6, ch g Midnight Legend—Owlesbury Dream (IRE) **D. J. Dyson**
12 **NELTARA**, 12, b g Kayf Tara—Lucia Forte **D. J. Dyson**
13 **OVER MY HEAD**, 8, gr g Overbury (IRE)—Altesse de Sou (FR) **Ms I. Heritage**
14 **TERRA FIRMA**, 6, b g Lucarno (USA)—Solid Land (FR) **Miss C. Dyson**
15 **TOAST AND JAM (IRE)**, 7, b g Clerkenwell (USA)—Summittotalkabout (IRE) **Miss C. Dyson**

Other Owners: Miss C. Dyson, Mr D. J. Dyson, Mr D. J. Pardy, Miss L. Rogers, Miss Becky Rowland, Mrs S. Vaughan, Mr B. Vaughan.

Assistant Trainer: Becky Rowland

Jockey (NH): Brendan Powell, Nick Scholfield. **Conditional:** Conor Shoemark. **Amateur:** Mr G. S. Quinn.

---

175 MR SIMON EARLE, Warminster
Postal: **Little Croft, Tytherington, Warminster, Wiltshire, BA12 7AD**
Contacts: **PHONE** (01985) 840450 **FAX** (01985) 840450 **MOBILE** (07850) 350116
E-MAIL simon@simonearleracing.com **WEBSITE** www.simonearleracing.com

1 **GET BACK TO ME (IRE)**, 9, b g Presenting—My Name's Not Bin (IRE) **Mr R. L. Dacombe**
2 **GUSTAV (IRE)**, 6, b g Mahler—Pakaradyssa (FR) **The Plum Merchants**
3 **HEADLY'S BRIDGE (IRE)**, 10, b g Tillerman—Brockton Flame **Mrs P. L. Bridel**
4 **KAVANAGHS CORNER (IRE)**, 7, b g Coroner (IRE)—Annacarney (IRE) **Mrs B. O'Flynn**
5 **LAPALALA (IRE)**, 5, b m Oscar (IRE)—Lala Nova (IRE) **Dr V. M. G. Ferguson**
6 **WATER RAIL**, 7, b g Manipulator (IRE)—Madame Mozaik (USA) **Mr S. A. Earle**

Other Owners: Mr A. C. Clift, Mr T. M. Santry.

Jockey (flat): George Baker. **Jockey (NH):** Paddy Brennan, Andrew Thornton. **Conditional:** Alice Mills.

---

176 MR MICHAEL EASTERBY, Sheriff Hutton
Postal: **New House Farm, Sheriff Hutton, York, North Yorkshire, YO60 6TN**
Contacts: **PHONE** (01347) 878368 **FAX** (01347) 878204 **MOBILE** (07831) 347481
E-MAIL enquiries@mickeasterby-racing.co.uk **WEBSITE** www.mickeasterby-racing.co.uk

1 **ALDRETH**, 5, b g Champs Elysees—Rowan Flower (IRE) **Mr A Morse, Mr M Cox & Mr E Grant**
2 **ANIERES BOY**, 4, b g Kheleyf (USA)—Place Morny (IRE) **Mr B. Padgett**
3 **ARROWTOWN**, 4, b f Rail Link—Protectress **S. Hull, S. Hollings, L. Folwell, M. J. R. Bannister**
4 **ATREUS**, 4, b g Indesatchel (IRE)—Devassa
5 **BAJAN REBEL**, 5, ch m Bahamian Bounty—Silca Key **Julian Rooney & Steve Hull**
6 **BANNY'S LAD**, 7, ch g Osorio (GER)—Skytrial (USA) **Mr M. J. R. Bannister**
7 **BIONIC INDIAN**, 4, b g Acclamation—Strawberry Moon (IRE) **Mr A. Saha**
8 **BOSHAM**, 6, b g Shamardal (USA)—Awwal Malika (USA) **P. Easterby**
9 **BOWSON FEAR**, 4, b g Monsieur Bond (IRE)—Bow Bridge **Mrs A. Jarvis**
10 **CACTUS VALLEY (IRE)**, 7, b g Lawman (FR)—Beech Gardens **D Fielding, S Hollings & S Hull**
11 **CHASMA**, 6, b m Kayf Tara—Luneray (FR) **Mr B Padgett & Lord Daresbury**
12 **CITY GROUND (USA)**, 9, b br g Orientate (USA)—Magnet (USA) **Miss S. Brotherton**
13 **CLASSINAGLASS**, 9, b g Grape Tree Road—Sounds Familiar (IRE) **The Coniston Hotel Racing Club**
14 **CURZON LINE**, 7, b g Dubawi (IRE)—Polska (USA) **M. W. Easterby**
15 **DAY OF THE EAGLE (IRE)**, 10, b g Danehill Dancer (USA)—Puck's Castle **S Hull, S Hollings & D Fielding**
16 **DAYLIGHT**, 6, ch g Firebreak—Dayville (USA) **Mr B. Burdett**
17 **FELIX DE VEGA (IRE)**, 4, b g Lope de Vega (IRE)—Lafite **A Simpson, D Fielding & S Hull**
18 **GANBEI**, 10, ch g Lomitas—Native Ring (FR) **N. W. A. Bannister**
19 **HANSEATIC**, 7, b g Galileo (IRE)—Insinuate (USA) **Blunt, Brook, Hull, Chandler & Westwood**
20 **HEART LOCKET**, 4, b f Champs Elysees—Zante **Mr A. Chandler & Mr L. Westwood**
21 **HERNANDO TORRES**, 9, b g Iffraaj—Espana **David Scott & Co (Pattern Makers) Ltd**
22 **HOOF IT**, 9, b g Monsieur Bond (IRE)—Forever Bond **Mr A. Chandler & Mr L. Westwood**
23 **HOOFALONG**, 6, b g Pastoral Pursuits—Baymist **A Chandler, L Westwood, D & Y Blunt**
24 **HOT SPICE**, 8, b g Kodiac—Harlestone Lady **S Hull, D Swales, A Turton & J Blackburn**

MR MICHAEL EASTERBY - Continued

25 **IGGY**, 6, ch g Lucarno (USA)—Fujakka (IRE)
26 **KALK BAY (IRE)**, 9, b g Hawk Wing (USA)—Politesse (USA) **Linda Folwell, Steve Hull & David Swales**
27 **LIGHTENING ROD**, 11, b g Storming Home—Bolero **Mr N W A Bannister & Mr S Hull**
28 **MAGIC CITY (IRE)**, 7, b g Elusive City (USA)—
                                             Annmarie's Magic **D. Swales, A. Turton, L. Folwell, J. Blackburn**
29 **MOUNTAIN MAN**, 4, b g Hellvelyn—Jane Jubilee (IRE) **E. A. Brook**
30 **MUSAAID (IRE)**, 4, br g Lawman (FR)—Fonda (USA)
31 **NARCISSIST (IRE)**, 7, b g Dylan Thomas (IRE)—Gabare (FR) **D. Scott**
32 **OIL STRIKE**, 9, b g Lucky Story (USA)—Willisa **M. W. Easterby**
33 **PERFECT PASTURE**, 6, b g Pastoral Pursuits—Word Perfect **S Hull, S Hollings & D Swales**
34 **PERFECT PEAK**, 4, ch f Distant Peak (IRE)—Word Perfect **Wildcard Racing & Mr J Burton**
35 **PIVOTMAN**, 8, ch g Pivotal—Grandalea **K. Wreglesworth**
36 **PURPLE ROCK (IRE)**, 4, b g Fastnet Rock (AUS)—Amethyst (IRE) **M. Blades, D. Swales, S. Hull, S. Hollings**
37 **QAFFAAL (USA)**, 5, b g Street Cry (IRE)—Wasseema (USA) **Calam & Holdsworth & Mr M Burrows**
38 **RAENNAVICH**, 4, b f Black Sam Bellamy (IRE)—Lady Wright (IRE) **J. Douglas**
39 **REAR ADMIRAL (IRE)**, 10, b g Dushyantor (USA)—Ciaras Charm (IRE) **S Hollings, S Hull, A Turton, D Fielding**
40 **ROYCANO**, 6, ch g Lucarno (USA)—Royal Distant (USA) **Mr M. J. R. Bannister**
41 **SAINTS AND SINNERS (IRE)**, 8, b g Gold Well—How Provincial (IRE) **Mr N Wrigley & Mrs J Lukas**
42 **SCARLETT PEAK (IRE)**, 5, b g Scorpion (IRE)—Tabita (IRE) **B Padgett, Lord Daresbury & E Brook**
43 **SHADOWS LENGTHEN**, 10, b g Dansili—Bay Shade (USA) **T. A. F. Frost**
44 **SLINGSBY**, 5, b g Dutch Art—Ballet Fame (USA) **Mr S Hull, Mr B Hoggarth & Mrs C Mason**
45 **SPACE WAR**, 9, b g Elusive City (USA)—Princess Luna (GER) **M. W. Easterby**
46 **STRONG MAN**, 8, b g Gentleman's Deal (IRE)—Strong Hand **Mr S Hollings & Mr P Easterby**
47 **TAFAHOM (IRE)**, 4, b g Acclamation—Dance Set **P. Easterby, W. H. & Mrs J. A. Tinning**
48 **TAMAYUZ MAGIC (IRE)**, 5, b g Tamayuz—Anne Tudor **W. H. & Mrs J. A. Tinning**
49 **TAPIS LIBRE**, 8, b g Librettist (USA)—Stella Manuela (FR) **Mrs S. E. Mason**
50 **TORRID**, 5, ch g Three Valleys (USA)—Western Appeal (USA) **J. Blackburn, S. Hull, D. Fielding**
51 **UP TEN DOWN TWO (IRE)**, 7, b g Hurricane Run (IRE)—Darabela (IRE)
52 **YOOHOOF**, 4, b f Black Sam Bellamy (IRE)—Piece of Magic

THREE-YEAR-OLDS

53 **ARREST WARRANT**, b c Acclamation—Dream Day **W. J. and T. C. O. Gredley 1**
54 **BLACK GRASS**, b g Monsieur Bond (IRE)—Alustar **T Dewhirst, L Folwell, S Hull & D Swales**
55 **BLACK IS BLACK (IRE)**, b g Big Bad Bob (IRE)—Dazzling Dancer **A R Legal Collections Limited**
56 **CONTENDIT**, b g Indesatchel (IRE)—Hope Chest **Mr B. Padgett**
57 **FIRST WHEAT**, b g Monsieur Bond (IRE)—Ballet Fame (USA) **Mrs C. E. Mason**
58 **INGLEBY ERIN**, b f Medicean—Mistress Twister **Ingleby Bloodstock Limited**
59 **KINGTHISTLE**, ch g Monsieur Bond (IRE)—Chez Cherie **E A Brook & D Scott**
60 **MARY ANNING**, b f Dutch Art—Grasshoppergreen (IRE) **Arno's Partnership**
61 **MELGATE MELODY**, b g Royal Applause—Maeander (FR) **Mr B. Hoggarth**
62 **TAKE IN TIME**, b g Hellvelyn—Barnacla (IRE) **M. W. Easterby**

TWO-YEAR-OLDS

63 B f 8/5 Camacho—Alustar (Emarati (USA))
64 B f 29/5 Notnowcato—El Molino Blanco (Royal Applause) **Mr D. Scott**
65 B c 7/3 American Post—Golden Gleam (IRE) (Acclamation) (5500)
66 B c 20/3 Poet's Voice—Grand Slam Maria (FR) (Anabaa (USA)) (5000)
67 B c 2/3 Mount Nelson—Holamo (IRE) (Montjeu (IRE))
68 Ch f 9/4 Doncaster Rover (USA)—Lawless Bridget (Alnasr Alwasheek) (1714)
69 Br f 7/5 Camacho—Martha's Way (Tiger Hill (IRE)) (4761)
70 B c 30/4 Champs Elysees—Neath (Rainbow Quest (USA)) (6500)
71 B f 24/2 Sakhee (USA)—Peace Lily (Dansili) (3000) **Mr A. Stott**
72 B f 6/5 Monsieur Bond (IRE)—Prices Lane (Gentleman's Deal (IRE)) **Mr M. Burrows**
73 B f 17/3 Dream Ahead (USA)—Snowtime (IRE) (Galileo (IRE)) (12500)
74 **STUBYTUESDAY**, b c 25/2 Dick Turpin (IRE)—Just Dreams (Salse (USA)) (4761) **Mr S. Daynes**
75 Br f 1/3 Lilbourne Lad (IRE)—Sues Surprise (IRE) (Montjeu (IRE)) (9523)
76 Ch c 14/4 Zoffany—Sycamores (FR) (Gold Away (IRE)) (7500) **Mr D. Scott**
77 Ch c 19/3 Sepoy (AUS)—Syvilla (Nayef (USA))
78 B f 10/2 Equiano (FR)—Valiant Runner (Haafhd) (12000)
79 B f 23/5 Camacho—Whitby (IRE) (Dubawi (IRE)) (3809) **Arno's Partnership**

MR MICHAEL EASTERBY - Continued

Other Owners: A R Legal Collections Limited, Mr N. Agran, Mr Peter Baker, Mr N. W. A. Bannister, Mr M. J. R. Bannister, Mr A. G. Black, Mr J. N. Blackburn, Mrs Y. Blunt, Mr David Blunt, Mr N. J. Bonarius, Mr Andy Bonarius, Mr E. A. Brook, Mr Michael Burrows, Mr Jeff Burton, Mr T. Calam, Mr Andrew Chandler, Mr M. Cox, Lord Daresbury, Mr T. C. Dewhirst, Mr Peter Easterby, Mr M. W. Easterby, Mr Dean Fielding, Mrs L. S. Folwell, Mr P Gilleard, Mr E. Grant, Mr T. C. O. Gredley, Mr W. J. Gredley, Mr C. M. Hills, Mr Bernard Hoggarth, Mr P. Holdsworth, Mr S. A. Hollings, Mr Steve Hull, Ingleby Bloodstock Limited, Mrs Julia Lukas, Mrs C. E. Mason, Mr A. Morse, Mr B. Padgett, Mr Julian Rooney, Mr David Scott, Mr M. J. Silver, Mr Andrew Simpson, Stittenham Racing, Mr A. F. Stott, Mr D. Swales, Mr W. H. Tinning, Mrs J. A. Tinning, Mr Andrew Turton, Mr Lee Westwood, Mr N. H. T. Wrigley.

Assistant Trainer: D. M. Easterby

Jockey (flat): Graham Gibbons, Paul Mulrennan, James Sullivan. **Jockey (NH):** Jake Greenall.
Conditional: Harry Bannister. **Apprentice:** Nathan Evans, Danielle Mooney.
Amateur: Miss S. Brotherton, Miss J. Coward, Miss Joanna Mason.

---

177 MR TIM EASTERBY, Malton
Postal: **Habton Grange, Great Habton, Malton, North Yorkshire, YO17 6TY**
Contacts: **PHONE (01653) 668566 FAX (01653) 668621**
E-MAIL easterby@btconnect.com WEBSITE www.timeasterby.co.uk

1 AGENTLEMAN (IRE), 6, b g Trans Island—Silvine (IRE) **A. R. Turnbull**
2 ARDLUI (IRE), 8, b g Galileo (IRE)—Epping **C. H. Stevens**
3 ATTENTION SEAKER, 6, b m Bollin Eric—Pay Attention **Ryedale Partners No 6**
4 AZAGAL (IRE), 5, b m Azamour (IRE)—Brave Madam (IRE) **R. Sidebottom**
5 AZERELLE (IRE), 4, ch f Arcano (IRE)—Simply Topping (IRE) **D. G. Iceton**
6 BOLLIN ACE, 9, b g Bollin Eric—Bollin Annabel **Ryedale Partners No 3**
7 BREAKABLE, 5, ch m Firebreak—Magic Myth (IRE) **Ryedale Partners No 9**
8 CADEAUX POWER, 5, b m Major Cadeaux—Right Answer **Bearstone Stud Limited**
9 CAPTAIN DUNNE (IRE), 11, b g Captain Rio—Queen Bodicea (IRE) **Middleham Park Racing XV & Partners**
10 COLOUR OF THE WIND, 5, gr m Dylan Thomas (IRE)—Makhsusah (IRE) **S. A. Heley**
11 DANCE AND ROMANCE, 4, b f Kayf Tara—Sweetheart **Reality Partnerships II**
12 DANCE KING, 6, ch g Danehill Dancer (IRE)—One So Wonderful **A. R. Turnbull**
13 DARK DUNE (IRE), 8, b g Diamond Green (FR)—Panpipes (IRE) **Ryedale Partners No 5**
14 DEW POND, 4, b g Motivator—Rutland Water (IRE) **Ashfield Caravan Park**
15 DUKE OF YORKSHIRE, 6, b g Duke of Marmalade (IRE)—Dame Edith (FR) **Habton Farms**
16 DUTCH BREEZE, 5, ch g Dutch Art—Oasis Breeze **Mr & Mrs J. D. Cotton**
17 FAST SHOT, 8, b g Fasliyev (USA)—Final Pursuit **Ontoawinner 10 & Partner**
18 FATHER BERTIE, 4, b g Firebreak—Magical Music **Mr J. R. Saville**
19 GRAN CANARIA QUEEN, 7, b br m Compton Place—Ex Mill Lady **The Senators**
20 GRISSOM (IRE), 10, b g Desert Prince (IRE)—Misty Peak (IRE) **J. F. Bowers**
21 HAWK HIGH (IRE), 6, b g High Chaparral (IRE)—Septembers Hawk (IRE) **T. J. Hemmings**
22 HONEYSUCKLE LIL (IRE), 4, b f Alfred Nobel (IRE)—Twinberry (IRE) **A. R. Turnbull**
23 IFANDBUTWHYNOT (IRE), 10, b g Raise A Grand (IRE)—Cockney Ground (IRE) **Claire Hollowood & Henry Dean**
24 INSPECTOR NORSE, 5, b g Norse Dancer (IRE)—Indiana Blues **Habton Farms**
25 JANAAB (IRE), 6, ch g Nayef (USA)—Mood Indigo (IRE) **Numac Engineering Ltd**
26 KENNY THE CAPTAIN (IRE), 5, ch g Captain Rio—Kelso Magic (USA) **Reality Partnerships V**
27 KING OF THE CELTS (IRE), 8, b g Celtic Swing—Flamands (IRE) **Mrs B. Oughtred**
28 LEN'S LEGACY (IRE), 4, ch g Fruits of Love (USA)—Manucrin **The Mount Fawcus Partnership 1**
29 MAPPIN TIME (IRE), 8, b g Orientate (USA)—Different Story (USA) **P. Baillie**
30 MATTMU, 4, b c Indesatchel—Katie Boo (IRE) **J. F. Bowers**
31 MIDNIGHT MOJITO, 4, b f Azamour (IRE)—Shaken And Stirred **Habton Farms**
32 MILLY BALOO, 5, b m Desideratum—Tarabaloo **R. W. Metcalfe**
33 MIN ALEMARAT (IRE), 5, ch g Galileo (IRE)—Baraka (IRE) **Habton Farms**
34 MOCKINGBIRD HILL, 4, b g Cockney Rebel (IRE)—Claws **N. A. Jackson**
35 MUKHAYYAM, 4, b g Dark Angel (IRE)—Caster Sugar (USA) **Hamdan bin Rashid Al Maktoum**
36 MULTELLIE, 4, b g Multiplex—Bollin Nellie **D. Scott**
37 MY REWARD, 4, b g Rail Link—Tarot Card **Mr M. J. Macleod**
38 MYSTIC MIRAAJ, 4, ch g Iffraaj—Salsa Brava (IRE) **R. Taylor & Mr P. Hebdon**
39 OFF ART, 6, ch g Dutch Art—Off Camera **Mr D B & Mrs C Lamplough**
40 ON A PAR, 4, b g Major Cadeaux—Dancing Loma (FR) **Habton Farms**
41 ONE WORD MORE (IRE), 6, b g Thousand Words—Somoushe (IRE) **Mr M. J. Macleod**
42 OUR THOMAS (IRE), 4, b g Dylan Thomas (IRE)—Sinamay (USA) **T. J. Hemmings**
43 PACNGO, 4, b f Paco Boy (IRE)—Orange Pip **Mr D B Lamplough & Mrs C Lamplough & Ptnr**

MR TIM EASTERBY - Continued

44 **PAROLE (IRE)**, 4, ch g Mastercraftsman (IRE)—Leniency (IRE) **The Mount Fawcus Partnership**
45 **PENNY ROYALE**, 4, b f Monsieur Bond (IRE)—Royal Punch **C. H. Stevens**
46 **PIXEY PUNK**, 4, gr f Mount Nelson—Mosquera (GER) **Mr J. R. Saville**
47 **POET MARK**, 4, b g Vale of York (IRE)—Attanagh (IRE) **Reality Partnerships I**
48 **RELIGHT MY FIRE**, 6, ch g Firebreak—Making Music **J. Gill**
49 **RIVER BOLLIN**, 6, b g Bollin Eric—Bollin Roberta **C. H. Stevens**
50 **RIVER RHYTHM**, 7, b m Bollin Eric—Cumbrian Rhapsody **Habton Farms**
51 **RUN RUCTIONS RUN (IRE)**, 7, b m Westerner—Perfect Prospect (IRE) **T. E. Ford**
52 **SAKHEE'S RETURN**, 4, b g Sakhee's Secret—Sofia Royale **Ontoawinner, M Hulin & Partner**
53 **SALMON SUSHI**, 5, ch g Dalakhani (IRE)—Salsa Steps (USA) **Habton Farms**
54 **SEE THE SUN**, 5, ch g Assertive—Cocabana **C. H. Stevens**
55 **SILVERY MOON**, 9, gr g Verglas—Starry Night **C. H. Stevens**
56 **SMART BOY (IRE)**, 5, b g Mahler—Supreme Style **T. J. Hemmings**
57 **SNOANO**, 4, b g Nayef (USA)—White Dress (IRE) **Mr M. J. Macleod**
58 **SOUL BROTHER (IRE)**, 5, b g Captain Rio—Goodwood March **C. H. Stevens**
59 **SOUTHERN STRIFE**, 5, b g Dubawi (IRE)—Savannah Belle **Habton Farms**
60 **STORMIN TOM (IRE)**, 4, b g Dylan Thomas (IRE)—She Storm (IRE) **Three Jolly Farmers**
61 **SURROUND SOUND**, 6, b g Multiplex—Tintera (IRE) **Mr C. Wilson**
62 **TARA THE TIGER**, 5, b m Kayf Tara—El Tigress (GER) **Reality Partnerships**
63 **TIMONEER (USA)**, 6, b br g Elusive Quality (USA)—Gentle Gale (USA) **David Scott & Co Ltd & Mr E A Brook**
64 **TWO B'S**, 5, b g Bollin Eric—Bollin Nellie **Habton Farms**
65 **VERY FIRST TIME**, 4, b g Champs Elysees—Like A Virgin (USA) **Habton Farms**
66 **WHAT A GAME (IRE)**, 5, ch g Milan—Moscow Mo Chuisle (IRE) **Dubelem (Racing) Limited**
67 **WHITE FLAG**, 5, b m Sakhee's Secret—Rainbow Spectrum (FR) **Mr W. A. Robinson**

THREE-YEAR-OLDS

68 B g Aussie Rules (USA)—Ailincala (IRE) **Langham Hall Stud Three**
69 **BAZULA (IRE)**, b g Tagula (IRE)—Lilly Be (IRE) **G. Horsford**
70 **BEAUTIFUL FIRTH**, b f Poet's Voice—Roslea Lady (IRE) **R. Sidebottom**
71 **BOBBY'S BABE**, b f Big Bad Bob (IRE)—Express Logic **Rosemary's Racing & Partner**
72 **BOSSIPOP**, ch g Assertive—Opopmil (IRE) **A. R. Turnbull**
73 **CROMBAY (IRE)**, b f Approve (IRE)—Ms Cromby (IRE) **R. Taylor & Mr P. Hebdon**
74 **EAST STREET REVUE**, ch g Pastoral Pursuits—Revue Princess (IRE) **S. A. Heley**
75 **EXCESSABLE**, ch c Sakhee's Secret—Kummel Excess (IRE) **Mr B Guerin & Habton Farms**
76 **FLYING PURSUIT**, ch g Pastoral Pursuits—Choisette **Ontoawinner, M Hulin & Partner**
77 **HIGH ON LIGHT**, b f Makfi—Estephe (IRE) **Habton Farms**
78 **ICEFALL (IRE)**, b g Frozen Power (IRE)—Silvertine (IRE) **Ryedale Partners No. 10**
79 **JUST HISS**, b g Lawman (FR)—Feather Boa (IRE) **The Sandmoor Partnership**
80 **LILOZZA (IRE)**, ro f Lilbourne Lad (IRE)—Vanozza (FR) **Habton Farms**
81 B g Frozen Power (IRE)—Liscoa (IRE)
82 **MIDNIGHT MALIBU (IRE)**, b f Poet's Voice—Midnight Martini **D. A. West**
83 **MININGGOLD**, b f Piccolo—Rosein **Middleham Park Racing XII**
84 B g Sakhee's Secret—Montjeu's Melody (IRE) **Habton Farms**
85 **MY LUCILLE (IRE)**, b f Lawman (FR)—Stroke of Six (IRE) **Mr M. J. Macleod**
86 **OH JAMES**, b c Monsieur Bond (IRE)—Sea Flower (IRE) **Gremot Racing**
87 **PONTY ROYALE (IRE)**, b f Royal Applause—Sodashy (IRE) **Calvert, O'Neill & Partner**
88 **POPSIES JOY (IRE)**, b f Alfred Nobel (IRE)—Senzate **Reality Partnerships IV**
89 **QUICK N QUIRKY (IRE)**, b f Lilbourne Lad (IRE)—Beseech (IRE) **Mr N. F. Arton**
90 **ROKERBY HALL**, b f Dutch Art—Royal Punch **C. H. Stevens**
91 **ROSE ECLAIR**, b f Major Cadeaux—Katie Boo (IRE) **J. F. Bowers**
92 **RYEDALE RIO (IRE)**, b g Captain Rio—Hallucination (IRE) **Ryedale Partners No 4**
93 **SILENT DIVA**, gr f Sakhee's Secret—Silent Waters **R. Taylor & Mr P. Hebdon**
94 **SILVER SANDS (IRE)**, gr g Zebedee—Eloquent Rose (IRE) **C. H. Stevens**
95 **STILL ON TOP**, b c Royal Applause—Poulaine Bleue **CDM Developments (North West) Limited**
96 **TARNEND LASS**, b f Equiano (FR)—Valjarv (IRE) **Reality Partnerships I**
97 B c Art Connoisseur (IRE)—Tarziyma (IRE) **Habton Farms**

TWO-YEAR-OLDS

98 Ch f 4/4 Bated Breath—Affability (IRE) (Dalakhani (IRE)) (6500) **Habton Farms**
99 **AQLAAMATION (IRE)**, ch c 1/3 Aqlaam—Alzaroof (USA) (Kingmambo (USA)) (14765) **Ryedale Partners No 7**
100 B c 22/4 Lilbourne Lad (IRE)—Aqualina (IRE) (King's Theatre (IRE)) (20952) **Reality Partnerships III**
101 **BABALUGATS (IRE)**, br f 15/4 Elzaam (AUS)—Ellanova (Kyllachy) (3691) **Mr M. J. Macleod**
102 **BLAME THE TRAINER**, ch f 26/2 Kyllachy—
Fabine (Danehill Dancer (IRE)) (9523) **Lamplough, Powell & Partner**
103 **BROTHER MCGONAGALL**, b c 4/5 Equiano (FR)—Anatase (Danehill (USA)) **Reality Partnerships VI**

MR TIM EASTERBY - Continued

104 **COCO LA BELLE (IRE)**, b f 12/4 Sir Prancealot (IRE)—
Dry Lightning (Shareef Dancer (USA)) (11812) **Mr C. Wilson**
105 **COMPUTABLE**, ch c 20/1 Compton Place—
Kummel Excess (IRE) (Exceed And Excel (AUS)) (71428) **Mr B Guerin Mrs E J Wills & Habton Farms**
106 **DREAMORCHID (IRE)**, br f 16/2 Dream Ahead (USA)—Dark Orchid (Shamardal (USA)) (23809) **Mrs J. P. Connew**
107 B f 4/4 Harbour Watch (IRE)—Foolish Lady (Exceed And Excel (AUS)) (19047) **Reality Partnerships VII**
108 B f 3/3 Zoffany (IRE)—Gleaming Silver (IRE) (Dalakhani (IRE)) (22886) **Miss B. C. Duxbury**
109 Ch c 24/2 Harbour Watch (IRE)—Golden Dirham (Kheleyf (USA)) (22857) **Ontoawinner 10 & Partner 2**
110 **GREY MIST**, gr c 29/3 Mastercraftsman (IRE)—Kekova (Montjeu (IRE)) (11000) **Mr G. C. Vibert**
111 B f 22/2 Compton Place—Heliograph (Ishiguru (USA)) (4285) **Reality Partnerships VIII**
112 **HUGGING THE RAILS (IRE)**, b c 4/2 Royal Applause—
Aqraan (In The Wings) (32380) **CDM Developments (North West) Limited**
113 **KICK KING KATIE (IRE)**, br f 17/3 Showcasing—
Provence (Averti (IRE)) (27316) **Ontoawinner, SDH Project Services Ltd**
114 **MY CHERRY BLOSSOM**, b f 21/2 Kyllachy—Echo River (IRE) (Irish River (FR)) (23809) **Mrs J. E. Pallister**
115 **MYLLACHY**, b f 18/3 Kyllachy—Enchanted Princess (Royal Applause) (10000) **R. Sidebottom**
116 **NOBILITY (IRE)**, b c 30/4 Alfred Nobel (IRE)—
Structura (USA) (Stormin Fever (USA)) (7142) **Ontoawinner,J.Pak,Trojan Horse & Partner**
117 **OREGON POINT (USA)**, b c 26/1 Cape Blanco (IRE)—
Dream The Blues (IRE) (Oasis Dream) (14000) **A. R. Turnbull**
118 **OUR CHARLIE BROWN**, b c 18/4 American Post—
Cordoba (Oasis Dream) (11428) **Ontoawinner, SDH Project Services Ltd**
119 **POWERCELL (IRE)**, b f 21/3 Power—Celtic Heroine (IRE) (Hernando (FR)) (3000) **Grange Park Racing VI**
120 Br c 7/4 Dandy Man (IRE)—Prevarication (IRE) (In The Wings) (13333) **Habton Farms**
121 Ch c 19/4 Piccolo—Rioliina (IRE) (Captain Rio) (6666) **Habton Farms**
122 B f 12/4 Dick Turpin (IRE)—Sheppard's Watch (Night Shift (USA)) (24761) **Habton Farms**
123 **SUITED (IRE)**, b f 27/3 Paco Boy (IRE)—Birthday Suit (IRE) (Daylami (IRE)) (20952) **Ontoawinner 10 & Partner 1**
124 B c 26/4 Lilbourne Lad (IRE)—Tiltili (IRE) (Spectrum (IRE)) (10476) **Mr C. Buckingham**
125 **YORKSHIRE PUDDING**, b f 3/4 Sleeping Indian—Cadeau Speciale (Cadeaux Genereux) **Mr N. A. Rhodes**

Other Owners: P. J. W. Botham, Mr S. Bridge, E. A. Brook, Mr S. N. Bulmer, J. D. Cotton, Mrs B. Cotton, A. D. Crombie, David Scott & Co (Pattern Makers) Ltd, Mr H. T. H. Dean, Miss Lynn Douglas, M. H. Easterby, T. D. Easterby, Mr D. S. Fawcus, Mrs M. W. Fawcus, Mr G. Fox, Mr J. H. Green, Mr R. P. Guerin, Mr P. F. Hebdon, Mrs C. Hollowood, Mr M. A. S. Hulin, Mrs D. Lamplough, D. B. Lamplough, Mrs J. Magnier, Mr J. J. Morley, Mrs J. Morley, Mr J. E. Mott, Mr J. Mounsey, Mr P. E. Nodding, Mr N. J. O'Brien, Mr M. O'Neill, Mr J. Pak, T. S. Palin, Mr M. Pearson, D. F. Powell, Mr J. Preston, M. Prince, A. H. Raby, Mr E. Surr, R. Taylor, Miss S. J. Turner, Mr G. Walker, The Hon Mrs E. J. Wills.

Apprentice: Rachel Richardson. **Amateur:** Mr W. Easterby.

---

178 **MR BRIAN ECKLEY, Brecon**
Postal: **Closcedi Farm, Llanspyddid, Brecon, Powys, LD3 8NS**
Contacts: **PHONE (01874) 622422 MOBILE (07891) 445409**
E-MAIL brian.eckley@live.co.uk

1 **JAUNTY INFLIGHT**, 7, b g Busy Flight—Jaunty Walk **B. J. Eckley**
2 **JAUNTY JET**, 4, b f Lucarno (USA)—Jaunty Spirit **B. J. Eckley**
3 4, B g Sulamani (IRE)—Jaunty June **B. J. Eckley**
4 **JAUNTY THOR**, 6, b g Norse Dancer (USA)—Jaunty Walk **B. J. Eckley**
5 4, B g Lucarno (USA)—Jaunty Walk **B. J. Eckley**
6 4, Ch f Sulamani (IRE)—Poppy Smith **B. J. Eckley**
7 **REVOQUE DOKEY**, 5, b m Revoque (IRE)—Somethingaboutmary (IRE) **B. J. Eckley**

---

179 **MR ROBERT EDDERY, Newmarket**
Postal: **Robert Eddery Racing, Heyward Place Stables, Hamilton Road, Newmarket, Suffolk, CB8 7JQ**
Contacts: **PHONE (01638) 428001 MOBILE (07938) 898455**
E-MAIL info@robertedderyracing.com WEBSITE www.robertedderyracing.com

1 **CORNELIOUS (IRE)**, 4, b g Cape Cross (IRE)—Fantastic Spring (USA) **Mr D. Bannon**
2 **CRAFTSMANSHIP (FR)**, 5, ch h Mastercraftsman (IRE)—Jennie Jerome (IRE) **Trisha Keane & Julia Rayment**

MR ROBERT EDDERY - Continued

3 **DONNCHA (IRE)**, 5, br h Captain Marvelous (IRE)—Seasonal Style (IRE) **Mr David Bannon**
4 **FEELING EASY (IRE)**, 4, b f Bushranger (IRE)—Easy Feeling (IRE) **Mr E. Phillips & Mrs P. Aitken**
5 **MISTER MUSIC**, 7, b g Singspiel (IRE)—Sierra **Longview Stud & Bloodstock Ltd**
6 **POWER UP**, 5, b m Rail Link—Melpomene **Ms D. Harding**
7 **RUDI FIVE ONE (FR)**, 5, b g American Post—Dansia (GER) **Anderson, Mathews & Kerve**

THREE-YEAR-OLDS

8 **ADMIRALS CHOICE**, b g Mount Nelson—Admirable Spirit **Longview Stud & Bloodstock Ltd**
9 **CONNIE O'MEARA (IRE)**, b f Roderic O'Connor (IRE)—Korabushka **Mr D. Bannon**
10 **DIVINE TOUCH**, b f Kheleyf (USA)—Easy To Love (USA) **E. S. Phillips**
11 **FALSE ID**, b c Aqlaam—Miss Dutee **Mr E. Phillips & Mrs P. Aitken**
12 **GRACEFUL LADY**, b f Sixties Icon—Leitzu (IRE) **Graham & Lynn Knight**
13 **HEPPLEWHITE**, b c Rail Link—Millistar **Mr David Bannon & Mr Owen O'Brien**

TWO-YEAR-OLDS

14 B f 24/3 Mullionmileanhour (IRE)—Alectrona (FR) (Invincible Spirit (IRE))
15 B c 10/1 Lope de Vega (IRE)—Campina (Oasis Dream) (20671) **Mr D. Bannon**
16 Ch f 23/3 Equiano (FR)—Culture Queen (King's Best (USA)) **Mr E. Phillips**
17 **DEMI'S QUEST**, b f 13/4 Roderic O'Connor (IRE)—Demi Voix (Halling (USA)) **Longview Stud & Bloodstock Ltd**
18 B f 16/1 Mastercraftsman (IRE)—Fascination Street (IRE) (Mujadil (USA)) (1619)
19 B f 27/3 Royal Applause—Inflammable (Montjeu (IRE)) **Mr E. Phillips**
20 **SEVENTII**, b f 30/1 Medicean—Lowndes (Rail Link) (19047) **Graham & Lynn Knight**
21 **WAGONER**, b c 14/5 Bushranger (IRE)—Artistry (Night Shift (USA)) **Longview Stud & Bloodstock Ltd**

Other Owners: Mrs P. Aitken, Mr Ian Anderson (Edinburgh), Ms T. Keane, Mr M. Kerve, Mrs L. C. Knight, Mr G. Knight, Mrs Millicent Mathews, Mr O. O'Brien, Mrs J. M. Rayment.

Jockey (flat): Andrea Atzeni.

---

180 **MR STUART EDMUNDS, Newport Pagnell**
Postal: **6 Fences Farm, Tyringham, Newport Pagnell, Buckinghamshire, MK16 9EN**
Contacts: **PHONE** (01908) 611406 Office (01908) 611369 **FAX** (01908) 611255
MOBILE (07778) 782591
E-MAIL Trishandstu@aol.com

1 **BOLD CONQUEST (IRE)**, 8, b g Oscar (IRE)—Massappeal Supreme (IRE) **Nick Brown Racing**
2 **CHARMAYNE**, 4, b f Sirocco (GER)—Ancora **G. C. Hartigan**
3 **CHRISTMAS TWENTY (IRE)**, 6, br g Zagreb (USA)—Celestial Gale (IRE) **The Chicheley Partnership**
4 **CLOONACOOL (IRE)**, 7, b g Beneficial—Newhall (IRE) **Nick Brown Racing**
5 **EREYNA**, 7, gr m Erhaab (USA)—Tereyna **Exors of the Late Mrs R. L. M. Robeson**
6 **FOCUSING**, 6, ch m Central Park (IRE)—Spot The Dot **G. C. Hartigan**
7 **GREY WARBLER**, 4, gr f Notnowcato—Cetti's Warbler **Exors of the Late Mrs R. L. M. Robeson**
8 **KAYLA**, 6, b m Kayf Tara—Palila **Exors of the Late Mrs R. L. M. Robeson**
9 **NATIVE PRINCESS**, 6, b m Tobougg (IRE)—Forest Pride (IRE) **The Oakley Partnership**
10 **PADDY THE DEEJAY (IRE)**, 7, b g Fruits of Love (USA)—Sue Pickering (IRE) **KTDA Consultancy Limited**
11 **PETETHEPEAR (IRE)**, 6, br g Pierre—Rockababy (IRE) **KTDA Consultancy Limited**
12 **PINE WARBLER**, 7, b g Pilsudski (IRE)—Cetti's Warbler **Exors of the Late Mrs R. L. M. Robeson**
13 **PIQUERO**, 4, ch g Pasternak—Daurica **Exors of the Late Mrs R. L. M. Robeson**
14 **REYNO**, 8, b g Sleeping Indian—Tereyna **Exors of the Late Mrs R. L. M. Robeson**
15 **SAN TELM (IRE)**, 11, b g Oscar (IRE)—Magical Mist (IRE) **The Tyringham Partnership**
16 **SAVINGFORVEGAS (IRE)**, 6, ch m Beneficial—Peggy Cullen (IRE) **Mr B. H. Turner**
17 **SMART EXIT (IRE)**, 9, b g Exit To Nowhere (USA)—Navaro (IRE) **The Ravenstone Partnership**
18 **SNEAKING BUDGE**, 4, b g Nayef—Ikat (IRE) **Nick Brown Racing**
19 5, Ch h Midnight Legend—Time For A Glass
20 **WOLF OF WINDLESHAM (IRE)**, 4, ch g Mastercraftsman (IRE)—Al Amlah (USA) **M. W. Lawrence**

Other Owners: Mr N. J. Brown, D. Yates.

181 MR GORDON EDWARDS, Minehead
Postal: **Summering, Wheddon Cross, Minehead, Somerset, TA24 7AT**
Contacts: PHONE **(01643) 831549** FAX **(01643) 831549** MOBILE **(07970) 059297**
E-MAIL **angela@edwards3212.fsnet.co.uk**

1 SHANANN STAR (IRE), 10, br m Anshan—Baile An Droichid (IRE) **G. F. Edwards**
2 SUPREME DANEHILL (IRE), 8, b g Indian Danehill (IRE)—Monte Rosa (IRE) **G. F. Edwards**

Amateur: Mr D. Edwards.

182 MISS LUCINDA EGERTON, Malton
Postal: **Birdsall Grange, Birdsall, Malton, North Yorkshire, YO17 9NP**
Contacts: PHONE **(01944) 768233** MOBILE **(07900) 458666**
E-MAIL **lucy@legertonracing.co.uk** WEBSITE **www.legertonracing.co.uk**

1 BOLLIN LINE, 9, b g Bollin Eric—Leading Line **Miss L. Egerton**
2 CATCH THE MAGIC (IRE), 7, b m Catcher In The Rye (IRE)—That's Magic (IRE) **Miss L. Egerton**
3 DRAGONFLI, 4, b g Revoque (IRE)—Chiddingfold Chick **P. Robinson, D. Woodhead & L. Egerton**
4 HI BOB, 8, b g Bollin Eric—Leading Line **P. Robinson, D. Woodhead & L. Egerton**
5 LADY RA (IRE), 7, br m Beneficial—Thethirstyscholars (IRE) **Miss L. Egerton**
6 ODDS ON DAN (IRE), 10, b g Oscar (IRE)—Grange Classic (IRE) **Panther Racing Limited**
7 QUITE SPARKY, 9, b g Lucky Story (USA)—Imperialistic (IRE) **Reassuringly Racy Club**
8 SAFARI JOURNEY (USA), 12, ch g Johannesburg (USA)—Alvernia (USA) **Reassuringly Racy Club**
9 SMOOTHIE PRESS ON (IRE), 8, b g Fruits of Love (USA)—Haven Island (IRE) **E. R. Lebbon & L. Egerton**
10 STOW, 11, ch g Selkirk (USA)—Spry **Reassuringly Racy Club**
11 SUNSHINE QUEST, 4, b f Bahamian Bounty—Intermission (IRE) **Keep The Faith Partnership**

Other Owners: Mrs C. M. Egerton, Mr E. R. Lebbon, Mr P. Robinson, Mrs G. M. Swinglehurst, J. M. Swinglehurst, Mr D. A. Woodhead.

183 MISS CLARE ELLAM, Atlow
Postal: **Turlow Cottage, Turlow Fields Lane, Hognaston, Derbyshire, DE6 1PW**
Contacts: MOBILE **(07974) 075042**

1 5, Gr m Proclamation (IRE)—A Mothers Love **Bob Borsley**
2 AN CAPALL MOR (IRE), 10, b g Flemensfirth (USA)—Corravilla (IRE) **Miss C. L. Ellam, Bob Borsley**
3 BALLINALACKEN (IRE), 8, b g Fruits of Love (USA)—Miss Daisy **Chrissy's Passion Racing**
4 CANDELITA, 9, b m Trade Fair—Gramada (IRE) **Mr M. Watkinson**
5 CHESTERTERN, 9, ch g Karinga Bay—My Tern (IRE) **Mr Phil Dutton**
6 DETOUR AHEAD, 8, ch m Needwood Blade—My Tern (IRE) **Mr Phil Dutton**
7 DUKE OF HANOVER, 5, b g Duke of Marmalade (IRE)—Caro George (USA) **Miss Clare L. Ellam**
8 MULLIGAN'S MAN (IRE), 9, b g Morozov (USA)—Rashmulligan (IRE) **Harpers Brook Racing**
9 5, B m Multiplex—My Tern (IRE) **Mr Phil Dutton**
10 4, B f Beat All (USA)—My Tern (IRE) **Mr Phil Dutton**
11 WELLFORTH (IRE), 12, b g New Frontier (IRE)—Faitch's Lady (IRE) **Miss Clare L. Ellam**

Other Owners: Mr R. J. Borsley, Mr W. R. Chudley, Mr Philip Dutton, Mr Tim Foster, Mr Thomas R. Vaughan.

Jockey (NH): David England.

183a MR GORDON ELLIOTT, Co. Meath
Postal: **Cullentra House, Longwood, Co. Meath, Ireland**
Contacts: PHONE **(00353) 46 9555051** MOBILE **(00353) 86 2495453**
E-MAIL **zoe@gordonelliottracing.com** WEBSITE **www.gordonelliottracing.com**

1 AINSLIE (IRE), 4, gr ro g Mastercraftsman (IRE)—Capriole **Mr N. O'Keefe**
2 ALTIEPIX (FR), 6, ch g Fragrant Mix (USA)—Naltiepy (FR) **Gigginstown House Stud**
3 ANNIHILATE (IRE), 5, b g Westerner—Bollin Jasmine **Gigginstown House Stud**
4 AUTHORIZED CADEAUX (IRE), 4, b g Authorized (IRE)—Nord's Cadeaux **Gigginstown House Stud**
5 AZORIAN (IRE), 8, b g Westerner—Eliane di Rupette **L. M. Power**

MR GORDON ELLIOTT - Continued

6 **BALL D'ARC (FR)**, 5, b g Network (GER)—Pretty Moon (FR) **Gigginstown House Stud**
7 **BALLELA BOY (IRE)**, 5, b g Golan (IRE)—Oscar Road (IRE) **Gigginstown House Stud**
8 **BALNASLOW (IRE)**, 9, b g Presenting—Noble Choice **Gigginstown House Stud**
9 **BALTAZAR D'ALLIER (FR)**, 5, b br g Malinas (GER)—Kinoise d'allier (FR) **Mr John P. McManus**
10 **BAROQUE STYLE (IRE)**, 10, b br g Old Vic—Chasing The Blues (IRE) **T Howley Jnr/Oliver Jack Murphy**
11 **BAYAN (IRE)**, 7, b g Danehill Dancer (IRE)—Kindling **Core Syndicate**
12 **BE THE HERO (IRE)**, 5, b g Oscar (IRE)—Pearly Princess (IRE) **Gigginstown House Stud**
13 **BINGO CONTI (FR)**, 5, b g Coastal Path—Regina Conti (FR) **Mr John Doyle**
14 **BLESS THE WINGS (IRE)**, 11, b g Winged Love (IRE)—Silva Venture (IRE) **Adrian Butler/S P O'Connor**
15 **BLESSED KING (IRE)**, 6, b g Desert King (IRE)—Lady Max (IRE) **T. J. Doran**
16 **BLOOD CRAZED TIGER (IRE)**, 5, b g King's Theatre (IRE)—Mardi Roberta (IRE) **Gigginstown House Stud**
17 **BRELADE**, 4, b g Presenting—Polivalente (FR) **Mr D. Sharkey**
18 **BRIGHT NEW DAWN (IRE)**, 9, br g Presenting—Shuil Dorcha (IRE) **Gigginstown House Stud**
19 **BROKEN SOUL (IRE)**, 5, b g Beneficial—Alicia's Charm (IRE) **Gigginstown House Stud**
20 **BULL RIDE (IRE)**, 5, ch g Marienbard (IRE)—Kilbarry Demon (IRE) **Gigginstown House Stud**
21 **BUONAROTTI BOY (IRE)**, 4, b g Galileo (IRE)—Funsie (FR) **G. Elliott**
22 **CALIN DES ONGRAIS (FR)**, 4, br g Elasos (FR)—Nympheas (FR) **Gigginstown House Stud**
23 **CAMPEADOR (FR)**, 4, gr g Gris de Gris (FR)—Royale Video (FR) **Mr John P. McManus**
24 **CANOVA (IRE)**, 5, ch g Art Connoisseur (IRE)—Rain Dancer (IRE) **Cullentra Racing Syndicate**
25 **CAPTAIN VON TRAPPE (IRE)**, 7, b g Germany (USA)—Culmore Native (IRE) **Gigginstown House Stud**
26 **CARRIG CATHAL**, 5, b g Fair Mix (IRE)—Blackwater Bay (IRE) **Mr Tom Doran**
27 **CASUAL APPROACH (IRE)**, 7, b g Scorpion (IRE)—Lead'er Inn (IRE) **Mr N. M. Earls**
28 **CAUSE OF CAUSES (USA)**, 8, b g Dynaformer (USA)—Angel In My Heart (FR) **Mr John P. McManus**
29 **CHATHAM HOUSE RULE**, 5, gr g Authorized (IRE)—Cozy Maria (USA) **Gigginstown House Stud**
30 **CLARCAM (FR)**, 6, b g Califet (FR)—Rose Beryl (FR) **Gigginstown House Stud**
31 **COGRYHILL (IRE)**, 6, b g Presenting—Rare Gesture (IRE) **Gigginstown House Stud**
32 **CURRENT EXCHANGE (IRE)**, 11, ch g Beneficial—Musical Millie (IRE) **Kaniz Bloodstock Investments Ltd**
33 **DALLAS COWBOY (IRE)**, 6, b g Beneficial—Watson River (IRE) **Gigginstown House Stud**
34 **DANCING MEADOWS (IRE)**, 6, ch m Alhaarth (IRE)—Kylebeg Dancer (IRE) **D. A. Charlesworth**
35 **DE PLOTTING SHED (IRE)**, 6, b g Beneficial—Lady Willmurt (IRE) **Ives/Ashley/Vasey Partnership**
36 **DEADPAN (IRE)**, 5, b g Yeats (IRE)—Midnight Flirt (IRE) **Gigginstown House Stud**
37 **DEATH DUTY (IRE)**, 5, b g Shantou (USA)—Midnight Gift (IRE) **Gigginstown House Stud**
38 **DELEGATE**, 6, ch g Robin des Champs (FR)—As You Leave (FR) **Gigginstown House Stud**
39 **DESERTMORE STREAM (IRE)**, 8, b g Celtic Swing—Another Cross (FR) **Gigginstown House Stud**
40 **DESOTO COUNTY**, 7, gr g Hernando (FR)—Kaldounya **Mr & Mrs Paul & Clare Rooney**
41 **DIAMOND KING (IRE)**, 8, b g King's Theatre (IRE)—Georgia On My Mind (FR) **Mrs D. L. Whateley**
42 **DOLDRUM BAY (IRE)**, 5, b br g Presenting—Victoria Theatre (IRE) **Mr Chris Jones**
43 **DON COSSACK (GER)**, 9, br g Sholokhov (IRE)—Depeche Toi (GER) **Gigginstown House Stud**
44 **DOUBLE SCORES (IRE)**, 7, br g Kalanisi (IRE)—Izntitgreat (IRE) **Gigginstown House Stud**
45 **DOVE MOUNTAIN (IRE)**, 5, b g Danehill Dancer (IRE)—Virginia Waters (USA) **Gordon Elliott Racing Club**
46 **EMDALE RUBY (IRE)**, 6, ch m Generous—Bonny Rathlin (IRE) **Mr T. D. A. McCrum**
47 **END OF LINE**, 5, b g Pastoral Pursuits—Just Devine (IRE) **Mr W. J. Salthouse**
48 **EVERYDAY EVERYHOUR**, 5, b g Presenting—Candello **Gigginstown House Stud**
49 **FAGAN**, 6, ro g Fair Mix (IRE)—Northwood May **R. A. Bartlett**
50 **FARAWAY MOUNTAIN (IRE)**, 8, ch g Indian Haven—Muschana **Gordon Elliott Racing Club**
51 **FIELD OF LIGHT**, 4, b g Pastoral Pursuits—Luminda (IRE) **Mr V. Caldwell**
52 **FIGURATIVE (IRE)**, 6, ch g Alhaarth (IRE)—Thegoodwans Sister (IRE) **Gigginstown House Stud**
53 **FREE EXPRESSION (IRE)**, 7, b g Germany (USA)—Create A Storm (IRE) **Mr John P. McManus**
54 **GENERAL PRINCIPLE (IRE)**, 7, b g Gold Well—How Provincial (IRE) **Gigginstown House Stud**
55 **GEORGES CONN (IRE)**, 8, b g Whitmore's Conn (USA)—Georges Girl (IRE) **Don't Tell The Woman Syndicate**
56 **GLENLOE (IRE)**, 5, br g Kayf Tara—Mandys Native (IRE) **Mr John P. McManus**
57 **HARDEN (IRE)**, 5, b g Gold Well—Jenny's Bond (IRE) **Gigginstown House Stud**
58 **HOSTILE FIRE (IRE)**, 5, b g Iffraaj—Royal Esteem **Mrs P. Sloan**
59 **ISABELLA LIBERTY (FR)**, 5, b m Soldier of Fortune (IRE)—Samsa (FR) **Twenty Syndicate**
60 **ISODON (FR)**, 4, b g Martaline—Between You And Me (FR) **Gigginstown House Stud**
61 **JETSTREAM JACK (IRE)**, 6, b g Beneficial—Westgrove Berry (IRE) **Mrs Diana L. Whateley**
62 **JURY DUTY (IRE)**, 5, b g Well Chosen—Swan Heart (IRE) **Sideway Syndicate**
63 **JUST WILLIAM (IRE)**, 8, b g Bandari (IRE)—Dark Horizon (IRE) **Mrs Jayne McConnell**
64 **KASHMIRI SUNSET, (IRE)**, 5, b g Tiger Hill (IRE)—Sagamartha **Mr & Mrs Paul & Clare Rooney**
65 **KILLER CROW (IRE)**, 7, ch g Presenting—Rivervail (IRE) **Gigginstown House Stud**
66 **KINGS LINE (IRE)**, 5, b g King's Theatre (IRE)—Line Apple (FR) **Gigginstown House Stud**
67 **LADY FANDANGO (IRE)**, 4, b f Holy Roman Emperor (IRE)—Alifandango (IRE) **Cullentra Racing Syndicate**
68 **LORD SCOUNDREL (IRE)**, 7, b g Presenting—Noble Choice **Gigginstown House Stud**
69 **LUNAR LOGIC**, 4, b g Motivator—Moonmaiden **Mr O. J. Murphy**
70 **MAIL DE BIEVRE (FR)**, 11, b br g Cadoudal (FR)—Coyote Davis (IRE) **Patrick E. Atkinson**

MR GORDON ELLIOTT - Continued

71 **MALA BEACH (IRE)**, 8, b g Beneficial—Peppardstown (IRE) **Mr Chris Jones**
72 **MESAIMEER (IRE)**, 5, ch h Camacho—Najaaba (USA) **G. Elliott**
73 **MISS DINAMIC (IRE)**, 7, b m Kutub (IRE)—Royal Molly (IRE) **C. Flattery**
74 **MISSY TATA (FR)**, 4, b f Astarabad (USA)—Queen Running (FR) **Mr Simon Munir/Mr Isaac Souede**
75 **MISTAMEL (IRE)**, 4, b g Rip Van Winkle (IRE)—Without Precedent (FR) **Let It Rip Syndicate**
76 **MONBEG NOTORIOUS (IRE)**, 5, b g Milan—Borleagh Princess (IRE) **Gigginstown House Stud**
77 **MUNSTEAD PRIDE**, 4, ch g Sir Percy—Memsahib **E. A. Collins**
78 **MYZTIQUE (IRE)**, 6, b m High Chaparral (IRE)—Lady Rene (IRE) **Ms. M. McKenna**
79 **NATIONAL SERVICE (USA)**, 5, b g War Chant (USA)—Cotton Club Ballet (USA) **Mr Tom Howley**
80 **NICKNAME EXIT (FR)**, 6, b g Nickname (FR)—Exit To Fire (FR) **Gigginstown House Stud**
81 **NO MORE HEROES (IRE)**, 7, br g Presenting—What A Breeze (IRE) **Gigginstown House Stud**
82 **NOBLE ENDEAVOR (IRE)**, 7, b g Flemensfirth (USA)—Old Moon (IRE) **Mr Chris Jones**
83 **OFFICER SYDNEY (IRE)**, 4, b g Lawman (FR)—Morena Park **Mr & Mrs P Rooney Partnership**
84 **OPERATING (IRE)**, 9, b g Milan—Seymourswift **Mr & Mrs Paul & Clare Rooney**
85 **OR JAUNE DE SOMOZA (FR)**, 4, ch g Bernebeau (FR)—Planete d'o (FR) **Gigginstown House Stud**
86 **OSCAR BARTON (IRE)**, 11, b g Oscar (IRE)—I Can Imagine (IRE) **Kaniz Bloodstock Investments Ltd**
87 **OVERTURES**, 4, b g New Approach (IRE)—Most Charming (FR) **Gigginstown House Stud**
88 **PADRE TITO (IRE)**, 8, b g Milan—Augusta Brook (IRE) **Twenty Times Three Syndicate**
89 **PERSIFLAGE**, 4, b f Sir Percy—Emirates First (IRE) **G Elliott/T Cromwell/Mrs B Mcconnell**
90 **POLYMATH (IRE)**, 5, ch g Stowaway—Godlylady (IRE) **Gigginstown House Stud**
91 **PRINCE OF SCARS (IRE)**, 6, b g Flemensfirth (USA)—Spirit Leader (IRE) **Gigginstown House Stud**
92 **RACING'S DREAM**, 5, b g Iffraaj—There's Two (IRE) **Mr W. J. Salthouse**
93 **RIVERSIDE CITY (IRE)**, 7, ch g Presenting—Blazing Sky (IRE) **Mr John P. McManus**
94 **ROBIN THYME (IRE)**, 6, b g Robin des Champs (FR)—
                          Boragh Thyme (IRE) **M. M. Sammon, M. A. Sammon, B. K. Fitzpatrick & R. Crean**
95 **ROCK LOBSTER**, 4, ch g Bahamian Bounty—Reeling N' Rocking (IRE) **Bodhran Makers Syndicate**
96 **ROCKET PUNCH (IRE)**, 4, b g Makfi—Crystal Reef **Gigginstown House Stud**
97 **ROI DU MEE (FR)**, 11, b g Lavirco (GER)—British Nellerie (FR) **Gigginstown House Stud**
98 **ROLL IT OUT (IRE)**, 7, b g Kayf Tara—Liss A Chroi (IRE) **Mr John P. McManus**
99 **ROMAN GOLD (IRE)**, 6, ch g Beneficial—Another Burden **Gigginstown House Stud**
100 **SENIOR COUNSEL (IRE)**, 5, b g Galileo (IRE)—Discreet Brief (IRE) **Ten Men Syndicate**
101 **SHADOW CATCHER (IRE)**, 8, ch g Haafhd—Unchain My Heart **Mrs P. Sloan**
102 **SHAN DUN NA NGALL (IRE)**, 5, b g Shantou (USA)—Omanah (USA) **Twenty Times Two Syndicate**
103 **SHATTERED LOVE (IRE)**, 5, b m Yeats (IRE)—Tracker **Gigginstown House Stud**
104 **SONIC RAINBOW (GR)**, 4, ch f Harmonic Way—Rainbow Way **Mr O. J. Murphy**
105 **SOUL KALIBER (IRE)**, 6, b g Marienbard (IRE)—Rosie Bee (IRE) **Gigginstown House Stud**
106 **SPACE CADET (IRE)**, 6, b g Flemensfirth (USA)—Shuil A Hocht (IRE) **Mr C. Jones**
107 **SQUOUATEUR (IRE)**, 5, gr g Martaline—Samansonnienne (FR) **Mr John P. McManus**
108 **STEADY MAJOR (IRE)**, 4, b g Invincible Spirit (IRE)—Combust (USA) **Gordon Elliott Racing Club**
109 **STEAMBOAT BILL (IRE)**, 5, b g Kalanisi (IRE)—Freemantle Doctor (IRE) **T. B. McKnight**
110 **STEAMBOAT QUAY (IRE)**, 5, b g Milan—Sunny Native (IRE) **Mr John P. McManus**
111 **SUTTON PLACE (IRE)**, 5, b g Mahler—Glebe Beauty (IRE) **Mr John P. McManus**
112 **SWORDFIGHT (IRE)**, 4, ch g Mastercraftsman (IRE)—Dundel (IRE) **Gigginstown House Stud**
113 **TAGLIETELLE**, 7, b g Tagula (IRE)—Averami **Olduvai Syndicate**
114 **THE STORYTELLER (IRE)**, 5, ch g Shantou (USA)—Bally Bolshoi (IRE) **Mrs P. Sloan**
115 **TIGER ROLL (IRE)**, 6, b g Authorized (IRE)—Swiss Roll (IRE) **Gigginstown House Stud**
116 **TOCORORO (IRE)**, 4, b f Teofilo (IRE)—Firecrest (IRE) **Gigginstown House Stud**
117 **TOMBSTONE (IRE)**, 6, ch g Robin des Champs (FR)—Connaught Hall (IRE) **Gigginstown House Stud**
118 **TYCOON PRINCE (IRE)**, 6, b g Trans Island—Downtown Train (IRE) **Gigginstown House Stud**
119 **UCELLO CONTI (FR)**, 8, b g Martaline—Gazelle Lulu (FR) **Mr S. Munir**
120 **UNIC DE BERSY (FR)**, 8, b g Nononito (FR)—Caliostra de Bersy (FR) **Gigginstown House Stud**
121 **VERCINGETORIX (IRE)**, 5, b g Dylan Thomas (IRE)—Great Artist (FR) **Mr S. Munir & Mr I. Souede**
122 **VICTORY MILL (IRE)**, 6, b br g King's Theatre (IRE)—Full of Surprises (IRE) **Gigginstown House Stud**
123 **VOTE OF CONFIDENCE (USA)**, 6, ch g Pleasantly Perfect (USA)—Sogna di Me **Confidence Partnership**
124 **VUKOVAR (FR)**, 7, b g Voix du Nord (FR)—Noraland (FR) **Mr D. Charlesworth**
125 **WATER SPRITE (IRE)**, 5, b m Papal Bull—Wish Upon A Star (IRE) **Five Men Syndicate**
126 **WESTEND STAR (IRE)**, 7, b g Old Vic—Camlin Rose (IRE) **Mr & Mrs Paul & Clare Rooney**
127 **WHISTLE DIXIE (IRE)**, 6, b m Kayf Tara—Fairy Blaze (IRE) **Gigginstown House Stud**
128 **WOLFSLAIR (IRE)**, 5, b g Yeats (IRE)—Hidden Reserve (IRE) **Gigginstown House Stud**

Assistant Trainer: Oliver Murphy

184 MISS JOEY ELLIS, Newmarket
Postal: **Georgia House Stud, Bradley Road, Burrough Green, Newmarket, Suffolk, CB8 9NH**
Contacts: PHONE **(07827) 316360**
E-MAIL **georgiahousestud@live.co.uk** WEBSITE **www.joeyellisracing.co.uk**

1 **BEAT THE BLUES**, 4, b f Aqlaam—Beat As One **Mr B. S. F. Edwards**
2 **CAPELENA**, 5, br m Cape Cross (IRE)—Roslea Lady (IRE) **Mr H. Foster, Mr K. Rogers, Mr J. Rogers**
3 **CELESTIAL VISION (USA)**, 4, b g Henrythenavigator (USA)—Damini (USA) **Mrs A. B. Ellis**
4 **COUNTY WEXFORD (IRE)**, 5, b g Teofilo (IRE)—Tiffed (USA) **Mr B. S. F. Edwards**
5 **DESAFINADO (IRE)**, 4, ch f Dutch Art—Sweetsformysweet (USA) **Mrs A. B. Ellis**
6 **ERTIKAAN**, 9, b g Oasis Dream—Aunty Mary **Mrs A. B. Ellis**
7 **INTIMIDATOR (IRE)**, 5, b g Intikhab (USA)—Zither **Mrs A. B. Ellis**
8 **ROYAL CAPER**, 6, b g Royal Applause—Ukraine (IRE) **Mrs A. B. Ellis**
9 **SILVER SECRET**, 5, gr g Moss Vale (IRE)—Alphilda **Mrs A. B. Ellis**

TWO-YEAR-OLDS
10 **AUTUMN GLOW**, b f 4/4 Sir Percy—Steady Rain (Zafonic (USA)) (800) **Mrs A. B. Ellis**
11 B f 20/3 Lord Shanakill (USA)—Lola Rosa (IRE) (Peintre Celebre (USA)) (7000) **Mr L. J. Doolan**

Assistant Trainer: Johnny Dekeyser

Jockey (flat): Stevie Donohoe. **Apprentice:** Shelley Birkett. **Amateur:** Miss Joey Ellis.

185 MR BRIAN ELLISON, Malton
Postal: **Spring Cottage Stables, Langton Road, Norton, Malton, North Yorkshire, YO17 9PY**
Contacts: OFFICE **(01653) 690004** FAX **(01653) 690008** MOBILE **(07785) 747426**
E-MAIL **office@brianellisonracing.co.uk** WEBSITE **www.brianellisonracing.co.uk**

1 **ALWAYS RESOLUTE**, 5, b g Refuse To Bend (IRE)—Mad Annie (USA) **Market Avenue Racing Club Ltd**
2 **AMERICAN HUSTLE (IRE)**, 4, b f Jeremy (USA)—Love In May (IRE) **Market Avenue Racing Club Ltd**
3 **APTERIX (FR)**, 6, b g Day Flight—Ohe Les Aulmes (FR) **P. J. Martin**
4 **AWJAB (IRE)**, 4, b g Bahamian Bounty—Applause (IRE) **Mr A. J. Bonarius**
5 **BALLYCRYSTAL (IRE)**, 5, b g Oscar (IRE)—Musical Madam (IRE) **P. J. Martin**
6 **BALTY BOYS (IRE)**, 7, b g Cape Cross (IRE)—Chatham Islands (IRE) **Koo's Racing Club, Carr & Jacobs**
7 **BAR DE LIGNE (FR)**, 10, b g Martaline—Treekle Toffee (FR) **P. J. Martin**
8 **BARAWEEZ (IRE)**, 6, b g Cape Cross (IRE)—Aquarelle Bleue **A. R. Barnes**
9 **BEN CEE PEE M (IRE)**, 11, ch g Beneficial—Supreme Magical **CPM Group Limited**
10 **BOOLASS (IRE)**, 4, b f Bushranger (IRE)—Silent Secret (IRE) **Mrs J. A. Martin**
11 **BURNING BLAZE**, 6, b g Danroad (AUS)—Demeter (USA) **Mere Civilians**
12 **BUTHELEZI (USA)**, 8, b g Dynaformer (USA)—Ntombi (USA) **Westbourne Racing Club 1 & Brian Ellison**
13 **CANNY KOOL**, 4, b g Kheleyf (USA)—Kool Acclaim **Market Avenue Racing Club Ltd**
14 **CARTHAGE (IRE)**, 5, b g Mastercraftsman (IRE)—Pitrizzia **J Gilbert, M Lawrence, A Bruce**
15 **CRACKDELOUST (FR)**, 4, b g Daramsar (FR)—Magic Rose (FR) **P. J. Martin**
16 **DEFINITLY RED (IRE)**, 7, ch g Definite Article—The Red Wench (IRE) **P. J. Martin**
17 **DOMINADA (IRE)**, 4, b g Mastercraftsman (IRE)—Red Blossom (USA) **Julie & Keith Hanson**
18 **DOWN TIME (USA)**, 6, b g Harlan's Holiday (USA)—Frappay (USA) **Brian Ellison**
19 **DREAM WALKER (FR)**, 7, gr g Gold Away (IRE)—Minnie's Mystery (FR) **Mr K. Brown**
20 **DUSKY BOB (IRE)**, 11, br g Bob Back (USA)—Sunsets Girl (USA) **Mr D. R. Gilbert**
21 **EASTERN RACER (IRE)**, 4, b g Bushranger (IRE)—Queen Cobra (IRE) **Mrs J. A. Martin**
22 **EBAZAN (IRE)**, 7, ch g Lemon Drop Kid (USA)—Ebaza (IRE) **Mrs C. L. Ellison**
23 **ECHO OF LIGHTNING**, 6, b g Echo of Light—Classic Lass **Victoria Greetham & Emily Beasley**
24 **EYES OF A TIGER (IRE)**, 5, b g Golan (IRE)—Backtothekingsnest (IRE) **P. J. Martin**
25 **FAIR LOCH**, 8, gr g Fair Mix (IRE)—Ardentinny **Mrs J. A. Martin**
26 **FILM DIRECTOR (IRE)**, 8, b g Tiger Hill (IRE)—Stage Manner **P. J. Martin**
27 **FIVE IN A ROW (IRE)**, 8, ch g Blueprint (IRE)—Ela Plaisir (FR) **P. J. Martin**
28 **FLIGHT PLAN (IRE)**, 6, ch g Strategic Prince—Nans Lady (IRE) **D Gilbert, M Lawrence, A Bruce**
29 **FOREST BIHAN (FR)**, 5, ch g Forestier (FR)—Katell Bihan (FR) **P. J. Martin**
30 **FULL DAY**, 5, ch m Champs Elysees—Capistrano Day (USA) **Mr D. R. Gilbert**
31 **GENERAL MAHLER (IRE)**, 6, b g Mahler—High Dough (IRE) **P. J. Martin**
32 **GERRY THE GLOVER (IRE)**, 4, b g Approve—Umlani (IRE) **Mrs J. A. Martin**
33 **GRANDEST**, 5, b g Dansili—Angara **Five Grand**
34 **HARTFORD STARTS (IRE)**, 6, b g Chineur (FR)—Desert Design **Mr K. Brown**
35 **HELLO BEAUTIFUL (IRE)**, 5, ch m Captain Rio—Tekhania (IRE) **Brian Ellison**
36 **IMPERIAL PALACE (IRE)**, 4, b g Montjeu (IRE)—First Breeze (USA) **Brian Ellison**

MR BRIAN ELLISON - Continued

37 **IT'S A MANS WORLD**, 10, b g Kyllachy—Exhibitor (USA) **David Foster & Brian Ellison**
38 **JAC THE LEGEND**, 7, b g Midnight Legend—Sky Burst **P. J. Martin**
39 **JETHRO (IRE)**, 5, b g Craigsteel—Wee Mo (IRE) **P. J. Martin**
40 4, B f Tikkanen (USA)—La Fille d'or (IRE) **P. J. Martin**
41 **LEGAL ART**, 4, ch f Dutch Art—Sosumi **Mr K. J. Strangeway**
42 **LETHEGOODTIMESROLL (IRE)**, 5, ch m Mahler—Little Pearl (IRE) **Mrs J. A. Martin**
43 **MAHLERDRAMATIC (IRE)**, 6, br g Mahler—Image of Vermont (IRE) **P. J. Martin**
44 **MANHATTAN SWING (IRE)**, 6, b g Invincible Spirit (IRE)—Bluebell Park (USA) **Mrs J. A. Martin**
45 **MASHAARI (IRE)**, 7, b g Monsun (GER)—Thakafaat (IRE) **P. J. Martin**
46 **MISS RANGER (IRE)**, 4, gr f Bushranger (IRE)—Remiss (IRE) **Jane Greetham & Victoria Greetham**
47 **MON BRAV**, 9, b g Sampower Star—Danehill Princess (IRE) **Brian Ellison**
48 **MOUNT MIZOOKA**, 5, b m Mount Nelson—Mizooka **Mrs J A Martin & Mrs C L Ellison**
49 **MOYODE WOOD**, 11, b g Overbury (IRE)—Country Choice (IRE) **Mr D. Foster**
50 **NORTHGATE LAD (IRE)**, 4, gr g Dark Angel (IRE)—Canosa (IRE) **Mrs J. A. Martin**
51 **OREGON GIFT**, 4, b g Major Cadeaux—Dayville (USA) **Mrs S. P. B. Frosell**
52 **OSCAR BLUE (IRE)**, 6, gr g Oscar (IRE)—Blossom Rose (IRE) **P. J. Martin**
53 **PEA SHOOTER**, 7, b g Piccolo—Sparkling Eyes **Mr A. H. L. Zheng**
54 **PERCY'S LASS**, 4, gr f Sir Percy—Brave Mave **CPM Group Limited**
55 **PERSIAN STEEL (IRE)**, 4, ch g Lucarno—Persian Walk (FR) **Mrs J. A. Martin**
56 **POINT THE WAY (IRE)**, 5, br g Brian Boru—Caslain Og (IRE) **P. J. Martin**
57 **PUSS MOTH**, 4, b f Paco Boy (IRE)—Seeking Dubai **Market Avenue Racing Club Ltd**
58 **RACING EUROPE (IRE)**, 7, b g Kayf Tara—Titanic Quarter (IRE) **P. J. Martin**
59 **REGAL WAYS (IRE)**, 4, b f r Royal Applause—Step This Way (USA) **CPM Group Ltd & Brian Ellison**
60 **ROCCO'S CHOICE (IRE)**, 4, b g Multiplex—No Page (IRE) **Mrs J. A. Martin**
61 **ROCK ON BOLLINSKI**, 6, b g Bollin Eric—Bred For Pleasure **Mr E. J. Worrell**
62 **SAM'S ADVENTURE**, 4, b g Black Sam Bellamy (IRE)—My Adventure (IRE) **Mrs J. A. Martin**
63 **SAND BLAST**, 5, b g Oasis Dream—New Orchid (USA) **Standring, Nichol, Brook & WRS**
64 **SEAMOUR (IRE)**, 5, b g Azamour (IRE)—Chifney Rush (IRE) **P. J. Martin**
65 **SERENITY NOW (IRE)**, 8, b g Key of Luck (USA)—Imdina (IRE) **Mr J. M. Basquill**
66 **SIKANDAR (IRE)**, 4, ch g Medicean—Siniyya (IRE) **Mrs J. A. Martin**
67 **SILVER GLAZE (IRE)**, 4, gr g Verglas (IRE)—Tullawadgeen (IRE) **Mrs J. A. Martin**
68 **SMART TALK (IRE)**, 6, b m Hubbly Bubbly (USA)—Belon Breeze (IRE) **Mrs J. A. Martin**
69 **SOUL INTENT (IRE)**, 6, b h Galileo (IRE)—Flamingo Guitar (USA) **The Soul Intentions**
70 **STIPULATE**, 7, b g Dansili—Indication **Mrs C. L. Ellison**
71 **SUITOR**, 4, ch g Dutch Art—Entreat **A. R. Barnes**
72 **TEENAGE DREAM**, 8, b g Antonius Pius (USA)—Lucayan Star (IRE) **Market Avenue Racing Club Ltd**
73 **THE GREY TAYLOR (IRE)**, 7, gr g Royal Anthem (USA)—Penny Tan (IRE) **P. J. Martin**
74 **THE LINKSMAN (IRE)**, 4, b g Westerner—Lost Link (IRE) **P. J. Martin**
75 **TOMNGERRY (IRE)**, 6, b g Craigsteel—Lady Vic (IRE) **Mrs J. A. Martin**
76 **TOP OF THE GLAS (IRE)**, 5, gr g Verglas (IRE)—Fury Dance (USA) **Market Avenue Racing Club Ltd**
77 **TOTALIZE**, 7, b g Authorized (IRE)—You Too **D Gilbert, M Lawrence, A Bruce**
78 **VIENS CHERCHER (IRE)**, 5, b g Milan—La Zingarella (IRE) **P. J. Martin**
79 **ZAIDIYN (FR)**, 6, b g Zamindar (USA)—Zainta (IRE) **P. J. Martin**
80 **ZELDINA**, 6, ch m Mount Nelson—Tetravella (IRE) **Mr S. L. Catchpole & Mr K. Hanson**

THREE-YEAR-OLDS

81 **AMELIA GRACE (IRE)**, ch f Starspangledbanner (AUS)—Esuvia (IRE) **Brian Ellison**
82 Ch f Haafhd—Ananda Kanda (USA) **Koo's Racing Club & Brian Ellison**
83 **ANDYS GIRL (IRE)**, gr f Clodovil (IRE)—Fishy **Mr Andrew Dawson & Mr Andrew Wainwright**
84 **ANGEL IN THE SNOW**, ch g Haafhd—Chilly Filly (IRE) **Mr D. R. Gilbert**
85 **BABY BALLERINA**, b f Kheleyf (USA)—Markova's Dance **Julie & Keith Hanson**
86 **BAD GIRL CAOIMHE (IRE)**, br f Big Bad Bob (IRE)—Sumostars (IRE) **Mr S. Pegley**
87 **BE KOOL (IRE)**, b g Approve (IRE)—Accounting **Market Avenue Racing Club Ltd**
88 B f Approve (IRE)—Bokhara Silk (IRE) **Andy Farrell & Brian Ellison**
89 **CRANBERRY PARK (IRE)**, b f Acclamation—Queen Padme (IRE) **J. James**
90 **FROZON**, b g Kheleyf (USA)—Crozon **A. R. Barnes**
91 **G'DAY AUSSIE**, b g Aussie Rules (USA)—Moi Aussi (USA) **Mrs J. A. Martin**
92 **GENERAL ALEXANDER (IRE)**, gr g Zebedee—Alexander Express (IRE) **Mrs J. A. Martin**
93 **HARLY FOREST**, b g Holy Roman Emperor (IRE)—Goslar **Brian Ellison**
94 **JORDAN JAMES (IRE)**, b g Equiano (FR)—Deira (USA) **Market Avenue Racing Club Ltd**
95 **LADY MEDUSA (IRE)**, b f Zoffany (IRE)—Lovegood (IRE) **Market Avenue Racing Club Ltd**
96 **LUCA HERE**, b g Misu Bond (IRE)—Striking Cat **Mrs C. L. Ellison**
97 **MARY E**, b f Monsieur Bond (IRE)—Lily Lenor (IRE) **Brian Ellison**
98 **MIKRO POLEMISTIS (IRE)**, b f Big Bad Bob (IRE)—Kristal Xenia (IRE) **D Gilbert, M Lawrence, A Bruce**
99 **MR MORSE**, ro g Hellvelyn—Songsheet **Mrs J. A. Martin**

MR BRIAN ELLISON - Continued

100 **NIETZSCHE**, ch g Poet's Voice—Ganga (IRE) **D Gilbert, M Lawrence, A Bruce, G Wills**
101 **OUR RILEY**, b g Equiano (FR)—Irtahal (USA) **Brian Ellison**
102 **SPECIALV (IRE)**, br f Big Bad Bob (IRE)—Montbretia **D Gilbert, M Lawrence, A Bruce**
103 **SUPERABUNDANCE (IRE)**, ch f Zoffany (IRE)—Pivotalia (IRE) **J Basquill, K Strangeway, M Jenkins**
104 **THE DOHA EXPRESS (IRE)**, b c Canford Cliffs (IRE)—Chatham Islands (USA) **Koo's Racing Club**
105 **TOTAL POWER**, b g Sleeping Indian—House of Frills **D Gilbert, M Lawrence, A Bruce**
106 **WHITECLIFF PARK (IRE)**, b c Canford Cliffs (IRE)—Venetian Rhapsody (IRE) **D Gilbert, M Lawrence, A Bruce**
107 **WILSONS RUBY (IRE)**, b g Lilbourne Lad (IRE)—Atlas Silk **A. R. Barnes**
108 **YORK ROSE**, b f Vale of York (IRE)—Desertion **Mrs J. A. Martin**
109 **ZEBEDAIOS (IRE)**, b g Zebedee—Refuse To Give Up (IRE) **Mrs J. A. Martin**

TWO-YEAR-OLDS

110 B c 22/2 Bated Breath—Capistrano Day (USA) (Diesis) (72380) **Mrs J. A. Martin**
111 B c 19/3 Haafhd—Chilly Filly (IRE) (Montjeu (IRE)) (952) **Mr D. R. Gilbert**
112 B c 28/3 Tagula (IRE)—Memphis Belle (Linamix (FR)) (13289) **Mr A. H. L. Zheng**
113 **MISS MONRO (IRE)**, br f 4/4 Intense Focus (USA)—Runway Girl (IRE) (Dansili) (5167) **Mr K. Brown**
114 Ch c 7/2 Camacho—Obsessive Secret (IRE) (Grand Lodge (USA)) (66666) **Mrs J. A. Martin**
115 **OREWA (IRE)**, ch c 8/2 Helmet (AUS)—Lucky (IRE) (Sadler's Wells (USA)) (13289) **Mr K. Brown**
116 **SUMNER BEACH**, ch c 24/4 Aqlaam—Cosmic Song (Cosmonaut) (4060) **Mr K. Brown**
117 **TALLINSKI (IRE)**, ch c 1/2 Mayson—Estonia (Exceed And Excel (AUS)) (47619) **Mrs J. A. Martin**

Other Owners: Mrs E. Beasley, Mr N. J. Bonarius, E. A. Brook, A. Carr, Mr S. L. Catchpole, Mr C. W. Cheesman, Mr A. Dawson, Mr M. N. Dennis, Mr A. S. Farrell, Miss V. Greetham, Mrs J. Greetham, Mr D. J. Haddrell, Mr K. Hanson, Mrs J. Hanson, Mr W. D. Hawkes, Mrs M. C. Jacobs, Mr M. J. Jenkins, Mr A. Killarney, Mr M. Lawrence, Mrs F. Murphy, Mr A. Nichol, Mr D. M. Standring, Mr A. Wainwright, Mr K. S. Ward, Mrs J. Ward, Westbourne Consultants Ltd, Mr G. Wills.

Assistant Trainer: Jessica Bell, Mobile (07939) 480860

Jockey (flat): Ben Curtis. **Jockey (NH):** Danny Cook. **Conditional:** Craig Gallagher, Megan Carberry, Garry Lavery. **Apprentice:** Megan Carberry, David Fitzpatrick, Garry Lavery, Ben Robinson, Callum Shepherd. **Amateur:** Mr Matthew Brown, Mr John Wiley, Miss Laura Wilson.

---

186 MR DAVID ELSWORTH, Newmarket
Postal: **Kings Yard**, Egerton House Stables, Cambridge Road, Newmarket, Suffolk, CB8 0TH
Contacts: PHONE (01638) 665511 FAX (01638) 665310 MOBILE (07771) 804828
E-MAIL david.elsworth@virgin.net

1 **ARABIAN QUEEN (IRE)**, 4, b f Dubawi (IRE)—Barshiba (IRE) **J. C. Smith**
2 **BASTILLE DAY**, 4, ch g Champs Elysees—Vivianna **Lordship Stud & David Elsworth**
3 **BURNING THREAD (IRE)**, 9, b g Captain Rio—Desert Rose **The Muro Partnership**
4 **HIGHLAND CASTLE**, 8, b g Halling (USA)—Reciprocal (IRE) **D. R. C. Elsworth**
5 **JUSTICE GOOD (IRE)**, 4, b c Acclamation—Qui Moi (CAN) **Mr R. Ng**
6 **JUSTICE WELL**, 4, b g Halling (USA)—Porthcawl **Mr R. Ng**
7 **LA SUPERBA (IRE)**, 4, ch f Medicean—La Spezia (IRE) **Mr Mark Dixon & Luke Lillingston**
8 **MARK HOPKINS**, 4, b g Mount Nelson—Halska **Mr R. J. McCreery**
9 **MASTER THE WORLD (IRE)**, 5, gr g Mastercraftsman (IRE)—Zadalla **Quinn & Benham**
10 **MELODIOUS**, 4, b f Cape Cross—Gower Song **Mrs Doreen Tabor**
11 **SOMETHINGTHRILLING**, 4, b f Makfi—Something Exciting **Trebles Holford Thoroughbreds**
12 **SPECULATIVE BID (IRE)**, 5, b g Excellent Art—Barzah (IRE) **Quinn & Benham**
13 **TOUCH THE SKY**, 5, ch g Sea The Stars (IRE)—Love Divine **Lordship Stud**

THREE-YEAR-OLDS

14 **AUSTRALIAN QUEEN**, b f Fastnet Rock (AUS)—Barshiba (IRE) **J. C. Smith**
15 **BILLET DOUX (IRE)**, br f Dark Angel (IRE)—Tullawadgeen (IRE) **Hot To Trot Racing Club**
16 **DASHING APPROACH**, ch f New Approach (IRE)—Dashiba **J. C. Smith**
17 **DAYLIGHT ROBBERY**, br g Dick Turpin (IRE)—Imperialistic (IRE) **The National Stud 1**
18 **JUSTICE ANGEL (IRE)**, gr f Dark Angel (IRE)—Malaica (IRE) **Mr R. Ng**
19 **JUSTICE BOLD (IRE)**, br gr g Zebedee—Chantilly Beauty (FR) **Mr R. Ng**
20 **JUSTICE EARS (IRE)**, b c Dylan Thomas (IRE)—Shanghai Visit (IRE) **Mr R. Ng**
21 **JUSTICE FOCUSED (IRE)**, b g Intense Focus (USA)—Moon Shine (FR) **Mr R. Ng**
22 **JUSTICE LADY (IRE)**, br f Dream Ahead (USA)—Celestial Dream (IRE) **Mr R. Ng**
23 **JUSTICE LASS (IRE)**, b f Canford Cliffs (IRE)—Dibiya (USA) **Mr R. Ng**
24 **JUSTICE LAW (IRE)**, gr c Acclamation—Inishtearaght (IRE) **Mr R. Ng**
25 **JUSTICE LUCKY (USA)**, b g Scat Daddy (USA)—Lucky Be Me (CAN) **Mr R. Ng**

MR DAVID ELSWORTH - Continued

26 **JUSTICE PLEASING,** b c Kodiac—Spangle **Mr R. Ng**
27 **JUSTICE ROCK,** b g Acclamation—Fashion Rocks (IRE) **Mr R. Ng**
28 **JUSTICE SUPER (IRE),** b g Jeremy (USA)—Supercat (USA) **Mr R. Ng**
29 **MON PETITE ETOILE (FR),** b f What A Caper (IRE)—Arundhati (IRE) **Mr John Duffy**
30 **NORSE CASTLE,** b c Norse Dancer (IRE)—Hursley Hope (IRE) **J. C. Smith**
31 **PAX AETERNA (USA),** b f War Front (USA)—Gold Collection (USA) **GB Partnership**
32 **SEA OF FLAMES,** ch g Aqlaam—Hidden Fire **J. C. Smith**
33 **THE NEW MASTER,** br c New Approach (IRE)—Maziona **J. C. Smith**

TWO-YEAR-OLDS

34 B f 10/4 Fastnet Rock (AUS)—Ardbrae Lady (Overbury (IRE)) (70000) **D. Elsworth**
35 B c 23/5 Rip Van Winkle (IRE)—Barzah (IRE) (Darshaan) (50000) **Quinn & Benham & D. Elsworth**
36 B f 16/2 Cape Blanco (IRE)—Carini (Vettori (IRE)) (12000) **D. Elsworth**
37 B c 2/2 Pour Moi (IRE)—Chatline (IRE) (One Cool Cat (USA)) (150000) **Mrs Doreen Tabor**
38 Ch f 26/3 Dream Ahead (USA)—Choose Me (IRE) (Choisir (AUS)) (73827) **D. Elsworth**
39 Br c 18/4 Teofilo (IRE)—Dashiba (Dashing Blade) **J. C. Smith**
40 Ch c 27/4 Tamayuz—
        Diamond Tango (FR) (Acatenango (GER)) (29531) **Quinn & Benham & L. Quinn & D. Whitford**
41 Ch f 4/4 Zebedee—Fantasy Princess (USA) (Johannesburg (USA)) (5906) **Ivor Perry & D. Elsworth**
42 B f 6/4 Pour Moi (IRE)—Haretha (IRE) (Alhaarth (IRE)) (25101) **D. Elsworth**
43 B f 5/5 Intikhab (USA)—Lady Gabrielle (IRE) (Dansili) **Luke Lillingston, Julian Nettlefold & David Elsworth**
44 Cc 9/3 Casamento (IRE)—Makheelah (Dansili) (17718) **Quinn & Benham & L. Quinn & D. Whitford**
45 B f 23/2 Lawman (FR)—Marika (Marju (IRE)) (90000) **GB Partnership**
46 B f 15/2 Bahamian Bounty—Paradise Place (Compton Place) (20000) **D. R. C. Elsworth**
47 B f 1/3 Motivator—Premier Prize (Selkirk (USA)) **J. C. Smith**
48 Ch f 26/4 Zebedee—Rinneen (IRE) (Bien Bien (USA)) (9597) **Ivor Perry & D. Elsworth**
49 Ch f 13/2 Shamardal (USA)—Seattle Ribbon (USA) (Seattle Dancer (USA)) **J. C. Smith**
50 Ch f 4/3 Excelebration (IRE)—Snoqualmie Girl (IRE) (Montjeu (IRE)) **J. C. Smith**
51 B c 6/3 Frankel—Swiss Lake (USA) (Indian Ridge) (235000) **Lordship Stud & D. Elsworth**

Other Owners: Mr D. R. C. Elsworth, Mr R. S. Hoskins, Mr Luke Lillingston, Mr Brian O'Rourke.

Assistant Trainer: Mr Paul Holley

Apprentice: Adam Maclean.

---

187 **MISS SARA ENDER, Malton**
Postal: 57 Park Road, Norton, Malton, North Yorkshire, YO17 9EA
Contacts: **PHONE** (01653) 228758 **MOBILE** (07983) 462314
E-MAIL seequineservices@hotmail.com **WEBSITE** www.nevilleender.wix.com/enderracing

1 **BOLD PRINCE RUPERT (IRE),** 6, br g Royal Anthem (USA)—Fortune And Favour (IRE) **N. P. Ender**
2 **CASTLEY LANE,** 10, b g Dapper—Holly **N. P. Ender**
3 **EASTER HUNT (IRE),** 7, br g Kalanisi (IRE)—Easter Day (IRE) **N. P. Ender**
4 **FARANG BER SONG,** 5, b g Selkirk (USA)—Dazzle **N. P. Ender**
5 **GREY MONK (IRE),** 8, gr g Alderbrook—Thats The Bother (IRE) **N. P. Ender**
6 **JUST TALKING (IRE),** 14, br g Windsor Castle—Fam-E Fam-E (IRE) **N. P. Ender**
7 **STITCHED IN TIME (IRE),** 9, b g Needle Gun (IRE)—Broken Pockets (IRE) **N. P. Ender**

---

188 **MR TIM ETHERINGTON, Malton**
Postal: Wold House Stables, Langton Road, Norton, Malton, North Yorkshire, YO17 9QG
Contacts: **OFFICE** (01653) 692842 **HOME** (01653) 693049

1 **BECOME AWARE,** 4, b g Sakhee (USA)—Sainte Gig (FR) **C. J. Clark**
2 **PURA VIDA,** 4, b f Stimulation (IRE)—Coffee Ice **T. J. Etherington**

189 **MR JAMES EUSTACE, Newmarket**
Postal: Park Lodge Stables, Park Lane, Newmarket, Suffolk, CB8 8AX
Contacts: PHONE (01638) 664277 FAX (01638) 664156 MOBILE (07802) 243764
E-MAIL jameseustace@tiscali.co.uk WEBSITE www.jameseustace.com

1 AVIATOR (GER), 8, br g Motivator—Amore (GER) **The MacDougall Two**
2 CHIEF SPIRIT, 4, b g Norse Dancer (IRE)—Indian Angel **J. C. Smith**
3 ICE SLICE (IRE), 5, b g Dark Angel (IRE)—Ice Rock (IRE) **The MacDougall Two**
4 LONGSIDE, 4, b g Oasis Dream—Hypoteneuse (IRE) **Park Lodge Racing**
5 MAJOR CRISPIES, 5, b g Pastoral Pursuits—Nellie Melba **G. N. Carstairs**
6 NUFOOTH (IRE), 4, b f Elnadim (USA)—Sahaayeb (IRE) **The MacDougall Two**
7 PERCEUS, 4, b g Sir Percy—Lady Hestia (USA) **Mr T. H. Barma**
8 SANDY COVE, 5, br g Oasis Dream—Maganda (IRE) **Blue Peter Racing 12**
9 SIR NOTE (FR), 6, gr g Victory Note (USA)—Niangara (FR) **G. F. Chesneaux**
10 SPA'S DANCER (IRE), 9, b g Danehill Dancer (IRE)—Spa **The MacDougall Two**
11 WILY FOX, 9, ch g Observatory (USA)—Kamkova (USA) **Blue Peter Racing 10**
12 WIND PLACE AND SHO, 4, br g Shirocco (GER)—Coh Sho No **H. D. Nass**

THREE-YEAR-OLDS

13 APACHE MYTH, ch f Sakhee's Secret—Indian Angel **J. C. Smith**
14 FOLLY BERGERE (IRE), ch f Champs Elysees—Rainbow Queen (FR) **Mr & Mrs R Scott & Mrs James Eustace**
15 GLITTERING, ch f Firebreak—Razzle (IRE) **Sherin Lloyd & Friends**
16 NEXT TRAIN'S GONE, b g Rail Link—Coh Sho No **H. D. Nass**
17 NORSE CUSTOM, b f Norse Dancer (IRE)—Accustomed **J. C. Smith**
18 PENNERLEY, b f Aqlaam—Penelewey **Major M. G. Wyatt**
19 POCKET, b f Paco Boy (IRE)—Take The Plunge **Mr Peter Charter & Blue Peter Racing 13**
20 POPPY TIME, b f Pour Moi (IRE)—Shamandar (FR) **Mr & Mrs R. Scott**
21 PRESS GANG, b g Mount Nelson—Rutba **Blue Peter Racing 14**
22 SHADOW SPIRIT, b f Makfi—Highland Shot **J. C. Smith**
23 TORIANO, ch c Equiano (FR)—Ticki Tori (IRE) **Chesneaux, Hassiakos & Littmoden**

TWO-YEAR-OLDS

24 B c 14/2 Henrythenavigator (USA)—Danehill Music (IRE) (Danehill Dancer (IRE)) **J. C. Smith**
25 ENVOY, gr c 26/3 Delegator—La Gessa (Largesse) (16190) **H. R. Moszkowicz**
26 B f 3/4 Excebelration (IRE)—Hidden Fire (Alhaarth) (IRE) **J. C. Smith**
27 Br c 3/4 So You Think (NZ)—Highland Shot (Selkirk (USA)) **J. C. Smith**
28 PENNY GREEN, b f 6/3 Halling (USA)—Penelewey (Groom Dancer (USA)) **Major M. G. Wyatt**
29 B f 26/2 High Chaparral (IRE)—Rainbow Queen (FR) (Spectrum (IRE)) **Mr & Mrs R. Scott**
30 VOICE OVER, b f 8/4 Poet's Voice—Goslar (In The Wings) **Major M. G. Wyatt**
31 VOTE, b f 27/2 Aqlaam—Bidding Time (Rock of Gibraltar (IRE)) (8000) **Rushby, Hagen, McCreery & Eustace**

Other Owners: Mr R. P. Abel, Mr D. F. Ballheimer, T. H. Barma, Mrs B. J. Carter, P. F. Charter, Mr B. M. Cimmering, C. Z. Curtis, Mr T. E. Dyke, Mrs G. R. Eustace, Mr A. C. Frost, Mr S. J. Gibson, Mrs A. Gibson, Mr R. J. Hagen, S. Hassiakos, Mrs L. R. Lawson, N. P Littmoden, Mrs S. A. Lloyd, R. E. Lloyd, R. J. McCreery, Mrs K. A. McGladdery, Mr I. L. Rushby, Mrs P. M. Scott, R. Scott, Mrs K. J. Smith, Mr R. J. Uzupris.

190 **MR DAVID EVANS, Abergavenny**
Postal: Ty Derlwyn Farm, Pandy, Abergavenny, Monmouthshire, NP7 8DR
Contacts: PHONE (01873) 890837 (07834) 834775 E. Evans FAX (01873) 890837
MOBILE (07860) 668499
E-MAIL info@pdevansracing.co.uk / pdevansracing@btinternet.com
WEBSITE www.pdevansracing.co.uk

1 AIR OF YORK (IRE), 4, b g Vale of York (IRE)—State Secret **Anthony Cooke & Lynn Cullimore**
2 AL'S MEMORY (IRE), 7, b g Red Clubs (IRE)—Consensus (IRE) **Mrs R. L. Barnes**
3 ANONYMOUS JOHN (IRE), 4, gr g Baltic King—Helibel (IRE) **Mrs R. L. Barnes**
4 ARCHIE STEVENS, 6, b g Pastoral Pursuits—Miss Wells (IRE) **P & K Swinnerton**
5 BLACK DAVE (IRE), 6, b g Excellent Art—Miss Latina (IRE) **Mrs E Evans & Mr J Smith**
6 CABUCHON (GER), 9, b g Fantastic Light (USA)—Catella (GER) **Mrs E. Evans**
7 CARTOGRAPHIC (USA), 4, b g Henrythenavigator (USA)—Good Student (ARG) **Mrs I. M. Folkes**
8 DOUGAN, 4, b g Dutch Art—Vive Les Rouges **Shropshire Wolves**
9 ESHTYAAQ, 9, b g Mark of Esteem (IRE)—Fleet Hill (IRE) **T. H. Gallienne**
10 FLOWERS ON VENUS (IRE), 4, ch g Raven's Pass (USA)—Chelsea Rose (IRE) **Shropshire Wolves**
11 FOUNDRY SQUARE (IRE), 10, br g Oscar (IRE)—Moon Approach (IRE) **Mr B. J. Mould**

MR DAVID EVANS - Continued

12 **IN YOUR FACE**, 4, ch g Winker Watson—Zambezi (USA)
13 **MOOJANED (IRE)**, 5, b g Raven's Pass (USA)—Mufradat (IRE) **Mr R. Emmanuel**
14 **PADDYS MOTORBIKE (IRE)**, 4, ch g Fast Company (IRE)—
Saffa Garden (IRE) **Walters Plant Hire Ltd Egan Waste Ltd**
15 **REBEL COLLINS (IRE)**, 5, gr g Jeremy (USA)—Million All Day (IRE) **Star Contractors Ltd**
16 **SAYEURI, (IRE)**, 4, b f Siyouni (FR)—Nalear (FR) **A. Stennett**
17 **SMUGGLERS LANE (IRE)**, 4, b g Bushranger (IRE)—Finty (IRE) **Mrs I. M. Folkes**
18 **SWIFT CEDAR (IRE)**, 6, ch g Excellent Art—Ravish **J. E. Abbey**

THREE-YEAR-OLDS

19 **BEST NEW SHOW (IRE)**, gr f Clodovil (IRE)—Serious Delight **Mr P. F. O'Callaghan**
20 **BROUGHTONS FANCY**, b f Pastoral Pursuits—Lifetime Romance (IRE) **Mrs Lynn Cullimore & Mrs E Evans**
21 **CLIVE CLIFTON (IRE)**, b g Wootton Bassett—Dearest Daisy **P Clifton,Twenty Four Seven Recruitment**
22 **ENGLISHWOMAN**, b f Acclamation—Tesary **R. Kent**
23 **ESSENAITCH (IRE)**, b c Zoffany (IRE)—Karlisse (IRE) **Walters Plant Hire Spiers & Hartwell**
24 **FRIVOLOUS LADY (IRE)**, b f Bushranger (IRE)—Ufallya (IRE) **Mr B Drew & Mr W Clifford**
25 **FRIVOLOUS PRINCE (IRE)**, b g Baltic King—Sweet Reflection (IRE) **Prof Caroline Tisdall & Wayne Clifford**
26 **GRACIOUS JOHN (IRE)**, b g Baltic King—Dorn Hill **T. Reffell**
27 **INGEN BRAVE**, gr f Mastercraftsman (IRE)—Antrim Rose **Houghton Bloodstock**
28 **LILBOURNE PRINCE (IRE)**, b g Lilbourne Lad (IRE)—Defensive Boast (USA) **Wayne Clifford & Bryan Drew**
29 B f Hat Trick (JPN)—Lotus Sutra (USA)
30 **OUTBACK BLUE**, gr c Aussie Rules (USA)—Beautiful Lady (IRE) **Mrs R. L. Barnes**
31 **PEAK HILL**, ch g Bahamian Bounty—River Naiad **Walters Plant Hire, Egan Waste, R Davies**
32 **PROVOKING (USA)**, b br g Any Given Saturday (USA)—Fair and Lively (USA) **N. Shutts**
33 **PUTEMINTHEBOOT (IRE)**, b f Medicean—Tiger Royale **Mrs I. M. Folkes**
34 **RIP VAN SUZY (IRE)**, b f Rip Van Winkle (IRE)—Suzy Bliss **Mrs E. Evans**
35 **SACRAMENT (IRE)**, b f Acclamation—Alstemeria (IRE) **Mr P. F. O'Callaghan**
36 B f Zoffany (IRE)—Breezeway (IRE) **T. H. Gallienne**
37 **SILVER SPRINGS (IRE)**, gr f Zebedee—Charming Vista **Dukes Head Racing**
38 **TASTEOFEXCELLENCE (IRE)**, b f Excellent Art—Scrumptious **J. L. Collins**
39 **THATSALLIMSAYING (IRE)**, br f Dandy Man (IRE)—Model Looks (IRE) **John Abbey & Mike Nolan**
40 **ZEBEDEE'S GIRL (IRE)**, b f Zebedee—Rafelite **D. E. Edwards**
41 **ZEEONEANDONLY (IRE)**, b f Zebedee—Subtle Shimmer **E. R. Griffiths**

TWO-YEAR-OLDS

42 Ch c 27/2 Captain Gerrard (IRE)—Aquasulis (IRE) (Titus Livius (FR)) **P. D. Evans**
43 B f 4/4 Compton Place—Aswaaq (IRE) (Peintre Celebre (USA)) (9047) **Mr R. W. Prince**
44 **BARA BRITH**, b f 1/3 Hellvelyn—Crazy Chris (Ishiguru (USA)) **E. R. Griffiths**
45 B f 18/3 Sir Prancealot (IRE)—Delia (IRE) (Darshaan) (12550)
46 B f 12/2 Pour Moi (IRE)—Distant Symphony (FR) (Dalakhani (IRE)) (20000)
47 B f 3/5 Sir Prancealot (IRE)—Dolphin Stamp (IRE) (Dolphin Street (FR)) (7751)
48 Ch c 20/4 Dragon Pulse (IRE)—Global Tour (USA) (Tour d'or (USA)) (21904) **Mrs E. Evans**
49 B f 1/3 Rip Van Winkle (IRE)—How High The Sky (IRE) (Danehill Dancer (USA)) (4000) **E. R. Griffiths**
50 Ch f 19/4 Arcano (IRE)—Kindest (Cadeaux Genereux) **M. F. Nolan**
51 **LETMESTOPYOUTHERE (IRE)**, b c 17/4 Sir Prancealot (IRE)—
Romanylei (IRE) (Blues Traveller (IRE)) (25839) **M. F. Nolan**
52 **LITTLE NOSEGAY (IRE)**, gr f 8/4 Clodovil (IRE)—
Bank On Black (IRE) (Big Bad Bob (IRE)) (3026) **Mrs I. M. Folkes**
53 B f 13/4 Fastnet Rock (AUS)—Lucky Spin (Pivotal) (25839) **J. L. Collins**
54 Ch c 4/3 Kyllachy—Ma Paloma (FR) (Highest Honor (FR)) (41904) **P. D. Evans**
55 **MAKEMERICHJOHN (IRE)**, b c 18/4 Baltic King—Golden Strands (Primo Dominie) (12181) **Mr T. H. Earle**
56 B f 13/4 Big Bad Bob (IRE)—Mudalalah (IRE) (Singspiel (IRE)) (11812) **Shropshire Wolves**
57 B f 19/4 Dandy Man (IRE)—On My Kness (FR) (Fasliyev (USA)) (8121) **Mr A. L. Al Zeer**
58 **PRINCESS WAY (IRE)**, gr f 28/4 Zebedee—Stef's Girl (IRE) (Petardia) (7013) **Mrs E. Evans**
59 B c 28/2 Delegator—Rockburst (Xaar) (8500) **Mr N. Buresli**
60 B f 28/3 Arcano (IRE)—Sablonne (USA) (Silver Hawk (USA)) (800) **M. J. Benton**
61 B c 8/4 Bushranger (IRE)—School Holidays (IRE) (Harlan's Holiday (USA)) (12550) **T. H. Gallienne**
62 B f 22/2 Showcasing—Shared Moment (IRE) (Tagula (IRE)) (16000) **M. J. Benton**
63 B c 29/4 Dandy Man (IRE)—Umlani (IRE) (Great Commotion (USA)) (90000) **Mr N. I. O'Callaghan**
64 B f 16/3 Royal Applause—Welsh Anthem (Singspiel (IRE))

MR DAVID EVANS - Continued

Other Owners: Mr J. Babb, M. Bryson, H. M. W. Clifford, Mr P. Clifton, Mr A. D. Cooke, Mrs Lynn Cullimore, Mr P. G. Dalton, Mr R. J. Davies, Mr B. J. C. Drew, Egan Waste Services Ltd, R. W. Sharp, R. Simpson, Mr J. E. Smith, Spiers & Hartwell Ltd, Mr P. B. Swinnerton, Mr K. F. Swinnerton, Prof C. Tisdall, Twenty Four Seven Recruitment Services Ltd, Walters Plant Hire Ltd.

Assistant Trainer: Mrs Emma Evans

Jockey (flat): John Egan. **Apprentice:** Harry Burns, Hollie Doyle. **Amateur:** Miss K. F. Begley.

---

191 | MR HYWEL EVANS, Kidwelly
Postal: **Llwynpiod Farm, Llangyndeyrn, Kidwelly, Carmarthenshire, SA17 5HD**
Contacts: **PHONE (01267) 231501 MOBILE (07970) 718989**

1 NORMALLY, 12, b g Tobougg (IRE)—Constant Delight **Mr H. G. Evans**
2 TOM BACH (IRE), 12, ch g Bach (IRE)—Fiovefontaine (IRE) **Mr H. G. Evans**

---

192 | MR JAMES EVANS, Upton On Severn
Postal: **Holdfast Stables, Upton On Severn, Worcester, WR8 0RA**
Contacts: **MOBILE (07813) 166430**
E-MAIL **herbie_evans@hotmail.com** WEBSITE **www.hjamesevans.co.uk**

1 AMIRAL COLLONGES (FR), 6, ch g Dom Alco (FR)—Idole Collonges (FR) **Mr S. D. Faiers**
2 BUCKONTUPENCE (IRE), 8, b g Brian Boru—Miss Od (IRE) **The Prince Of Darkness Partnership**
3 CALL ME BEN (IRE), 6, ch g Beneficial—Good Foundation (IRE) **Mr S. D. Faiers**
4 DESILVANO, 7, b g Desideratum—Cruz Santa **International Plywood (Importers) Ltd**
5 FRIENDSHIP BAY, 12, b g Midnight Legend—Friendly Fairy **Mrs J. Evans**
6 GOODOLDHONKYTONK (IRE), 8, b m Oscar (IRE)—Pharfetched **Running Dragon Racing 2**
7 IT'S OSCAR (IRE), 9, b g Oscar (IRE)—Lady Bramble (IRE) **Mrs J. Evans**
8 MIDNIGHT BROWNIE, 5, b g Midnight Legend—Friendly Fairy **Mrs J. Evans**
9 MINELLA BLISS (IRE), 11, gr g Old Vic—Carraigrose (IRE) **Running Dragon Racing 2**
10 MIXOLOGIST, 9, gr g Fair Mix (IRE)—Matchboard Again (IRE) **Miss S. Troughton**
11 MUHTARIS (IRE), 6, b g Teofilo (IRE)—Fann (USA) **The Cheltenham Boys Racing Club 1**
12 NIGHTSWIFT, 4, b g Midnight Legend—Sharbasia (IRE) **Mr S. D. Faiers**
13 NOBEL LEADER (IRE), 6, b g Alflora (IRE)—Ben Roseler (IRE) **Mr S. D. Faiers**
14 PHOENIX FLIGHT (IRE), 11, b g Hawk Wing (USA)—Firecrest (IRE) **Mrs J. Evans**
15 PRINCE OF STEAL (IRE), 6, b g Craigsteel—Princess Gloria (IRE) **The Cheltenham Flyers**
16 RIZAL PARK (IRE), 5, b g Milan—Carlingford Lough (USA) **T. & J. Porter & Harlequin Racing**
17 ROC DE GUYE (FR), 11, b g Video Rock (FR)—Kasibelle de Guye (FR) **S. Crawley, T. Crawley**
18 SANDS COVE (IRE), 9, b g Flemensfirth (USA)—Lillies Bordello (IRE) **James Evans Racing**
19 TANNER HILL (IRE), 8, b g Milan—Carlingford Lough (IRE) **P Wright-Bevans S Matner P Smith & A Pidgeon**
20 TRACKMATE, 10, b g Muhtarram (USA)—Cruz Santa **Preece Hamilton Porter Deni**
21 VENT NIVERNAIS (FR), 7, ch g Shaanmer (IRE)—Lobella (FR) **Elegant Clutter Ltd**

Other Owners: Mrs S. Crawley, Mr T. P. M. Crawley, Mr James Evans, Mrs J. Evans, Mr Toby Fowler, Mr Martin Hamilton, Miss Deni Harper-Adams, International Plywood (Importers) Ltd, Mrs Helen Llewelyn, Mr Martin Llewelyn, Mr Steve Matner, Mr A. J. Pidgeon, Miss Tina Porter, Mr B. Preece, Mr Paul M. Smith, Mr Andrew Staines, Mr Paul Wright-Bevans.

Assistant Trainer: Mrs Jane Evans

Jockey (NH): Mark Quinlan, Liam Treadwell.

---

193 | MRS MARY EVANS, Haverfordwest
Postal: **Hengoed, Clarbeston Road, Haverfordwest, Pembrokeshire, SA63 4QL**
Contacts: **PHONE (01437) 731336**

1 MAIZY MISSILE (IRE), 14, b m Executive Perk—Landsker Missile **Mary & Billy Evans**
2 MOUNTAIN OF ANGELS, 7, b m Midnight Legend—Landsker Missile **Mary & Billy Evans**
3 SUPERMAN DE LA RUE (FR), 10, b g Akhdari (USA)—Impala de La Rue (FR) **Mary & Billy Evans**

Other Owners: W. J. Evans, Mrs M. Evans.

Assistant Trainer: W J Evans

194 MRS NIKKI EVANS, Abergavenny
Postal: **Penbiddle Farm, Penbidwal, Pandy, Abergavenny, Gwent, NP7 8EA**
Contacts: **(01873) 890957 FAX (01873) 890957 MOBILE (07977) 753437**
E-MAIL **nikki@penbiddle.fsnet.co.uk** WEBSITE **www.nikki-evans-racing.co.uk**

1 AGREEMENT (IRE), 6, b g Galileo (IRE)—Cozzene's Angel (USA) **N Bougourd, J Berry, S Hellens**
2 AKINSPIRIT (IRE), 12, b g Invincible Spirit (IRE)—Akebia (USA) **Sussex Racing**
3 AS A DREAM (IRE), 4, b f Azamour (IRE)—Wedding Dream **Hanford's Chemists Ltd/ John Berry**
4 6, Ch g Dreams End—Atlantic Lady (GER) **Mrs N. S. Evans**
5 JUST LEWIS, 9, ch g Sir Harry Lewis (USA)—McMahon's River **Mrs N. S. Evans**
6 LATE SHIPMENT, 5, b g Authorized (IRE)—Time Over **Mrs M. E. Gittings-Watts**
7 LORD ADARE (IRE), 8, b g Moscow Society (USA)—Gonearethedays (IRE) **Sussex Racing**
8 MARI ME OSCAR (IRE), 6, b m Oscar (IRE)—Nostra (FR) **Hanford's Chemist Ltd**
9 MY SCAT DADDY (USA), 7, b g Scat Daddy (USA)—Will Be A Bates **Mr W. Smith**
10 MY SON MAX, 8, b g Avonbridge—Pendulum **Mrs M. E. Gittings-Watts**
11 PREMIER JACK'S, 5, b g Tobougg (IRE)—Arabellas Homer **Nikki Evans Racing**
12 SEACON BEG (IRE), 7, b g Generous (IRE)—Moon Storm **Mrs M. E. Gittings-Watts**
13 STEEL RAIN, 8, b g Striking Ambition—Concentration (IRE) **Mr J. Berry**
14 SUE BE IT (IRE), 5, b m Presenting—Runaround Sue (IRE) **Hanford's Chemist Ltd**
15 THE SNEEZER (IRE), 13, br g Topanoora—Bel Azur (IRE) **Sussex Racing**
16 THRTYPOINTSTOTHREE (IRE), 5, b g Kodiac—Miss Taken (IRE) **Hanford's Chemists Ltd/ John Berry**
17 WELSH REBEL, 4, ch g Cockney Rebel (IRE)—Lasting Image **Welsh Connections Racing**
18 ZEBS LAD (IRE), 4, ro g Zebedee—Dubai Princess (IRE) **Sussex Racing**

THREE-YEAR-OLDS
19 B f Multiplex—Bella Bambina **Mr J. Berry**
20 DONTTOUCHTHECHIPS (IRE), b g Lilbourne Lad (IRE)—Trim (IRE) **Mr J. Berry**
21 FLASH N SMART, b f Sakhee's Secret—Lady Trish **P. T. Evans**
22 JUNO MONETA (IRE), b f Holy Roman Emperor (IRE)—Alarme Belle **Mr J. Berry**
23 B f Jeremy (USA)—Right Reason (IRE) **Mrs N. S. Evans**

Other Owners: Mr N. Bougourd, Lady J. Hayward, Mr S. J. Hellens, Mr J. Schwartz, A. N. Waters.

Assistant Trainer: Mr P. T. Evans

195 MR JAMES EWART, Langholm
Postal: **James Ewart Racing Limited, Craig Farm, Westerkirk, Langholm, Dumfriesshire, DG13 0NZ**
Contacts: PHONE **(01387) 370707 MOBILE (07786) 995073**
E-MAIL **office@jeracing.co.uk** WEBSITE **www.jamesewarttracing.com**

1 ANGE DES MALBERAUX (FR), 6, b g Michel Georges—Petite Baie (FR) **Mrs Hugh Fraser**
2 ARISTO DU PLESSIS (FR), 6, b g Voix du Nord (FR)—J'aime (FR) **Mrs J. E. Dodd**
3 ASCOT DE BRUYERE (FR), 6, b br g Kapgarde (FR)—
Quid de Neuville (FR) **Daresbury, Humbert, Ewart, Kesson, Ogilvie, Percy, Cookson**
4 AVIDITY, 7, b g Passing Glance—Epicurean **Leeds Plywood & Doors Ltd**
5 5, B br g Great Palm (USA)—Azturk (FR) **N. M. L. Ewart**
6 4, B br f Tikkanen (USA)—Azturk (FR)
7 BERING UPSUN, 5, b g And Beyond (IRE)—Bering Up (IRE) **The South Hayrigg Partnership**
8 BILL D'ARON (FR), 5, ch g Dom Alco (FR)—Nobless d'aron (FR) **Mrs Hugh Fraser**
9 CA LE FERRA (FR), 6, b g Turgeon (USA)—Branceilles (FR) **Southhayrigg, Friel, Wilson, Humbert**
10 CALACH (FR), 4, gr g Fragrant Mix (IRE)—Nobless d'aron (FR) **K Wilson J Harris P Daresbury J Westoll**
11 CALIX DELAFAYETTE (FR), 4, b g Caballo Raptor (CAN)—Obepinedelafayette (FR) **Mrs J. E. Dodd**
12 CATCHING SHADOWS (IRE), 7, b g Catcher In The Rye (IRE)—
Castletown Girl **Mr N & Mrs J Sperling Mr T Reid**
13 CIVIL UNREST (IRE), 10, ch g Blueprint (IRE)—Yore (IRE) **Ancrum Pointer 1 & Craig Farm Syndicate**
14 LEADING SCORE (IRE), 6, b g Scorpion (IRE)—Leading Rank (IRE) **Drew, Palmer, Carruthers & Graham**
15 LORD WISHES (IRE), 9, b g Milan—Strong Wishes (IRE) **Leeds Plywood & Doors Ltd**
16 LYBOWLEN, 6, b g Lyphento (USA)—Bowling On **Mr Lord Daresbury & Wilson Graham**
17 LYCIDAS (GER), 7, b g Zamindar (USA)—La Felicita **J. D. Gordon**
18 MULTIPEDE, 10, b g Multiplex—Playful Lady **Mrs Hugh Fraser**
19 PREMIER GRAND CRU (FR), 10, b g Kaldounevees (FR)—Last Harvest (FR) **Leeds Plywood & Doors Ltd**
20 RAIL DITCH (IRE), 4, b g Yeats (IRE)—Tasmani (FR) **Mrs Ray Calder**
21 ROC DE PRINCE, 7, b g Shirocco (GER)—Louella (USA) **Humbert, Kesson, Wilson & Craig Farm**

MR JAMES EWART - Continued

22 **ROCKLIM (FR)**, 6, b g Laverock (IRE)—Stille Baroque (FR) **Craig Farm Syndicate, D Down & R Palmer**
23 **SA SUFFIT (FR)**, 13, b g Dolpour—Branceilles (FR) **Friel Humbert Kesson Wilson Craig Farm**
24 **SCORPIONS STING (IRE)**, 7, b g Scorpion (IRE)—Strong Wishes (IRE) **DoddCarruthersKessonMurrillsPalmer**
25 **SKY FULL OF STARS (IRE)**, 6, b g Mahler—Gold Flo (IRE) **J. D. Gordon**
26 **SLEEP IN FIRST (FR)**, 10, b br g Sleeping Car (FR)—First Union (FR) **First Sleepers Union & Craig Syndicate**
27 **SNUKER**, 9, b g Snurge—Briar Rose (IRE) **J Percy,D Down,R Boyd,CraigFarmSyndicate**
28 **STONE OF FOLCA**, 8, b g Kodiac—Soyalang (FR)
29 **TOUCH OF STEEL (IRE)**, 7, b g Craigsteel—Tourmaline Girl (IRE) **Mrs Hugh Fraser**
30 **UEUETEOTL (FR)**, 8, gr g Tikkanen (USA)—Azturk (FR) **Dodd, Graham & Sperling**
31 **UN GUET APENS (FR)**, 8, b g Enrique—Belisama (FR) **Drew, Sperling, Graham, Carruthers**
32 **ZARU (FR)**, 10, b br g Laveron—Zianini (FR) **Mrs Humbert, Drew**

THREE-YEAR-OLDS

33 **DUNLY (FR)**, b g Gris de Gris (IRE)—Octavine du Meix (FR) **Mark James**
34 **GREEN TIKKANA**, b f Tikkanen (USA)—Think Green
35 **MAROCCHINO**, gr b g Tikkanen (USA)—Mocha (FR)
36 **PORTO DU SUD (FR)**, b g Lord du Sud (FR)—Queen du Vallon (FR) **Steve Murrills**
37 **SAO MAXENCE (FR)**, b g Saint des Saints (FR)—Primadona (FR) **Mrs Jill Dodd**

TWO-YEAR-OLDS

38 B g 26/4 Arabian Gleam—High Meadow Girl (Pursuit of Love)
39 B gr g 18/4 Arabian Gleam—High Meadow Jo (Silver Patriarch (IRE))

Other Owners: Mr James D. Allen, Mr Robert Boyd, Mr R. Carruthers, Mr Allan Cartner, Mr G. Chamberlain, Lord Daresbury, Mrs J. M. Dodd, Mr D. Down, Mrs Lavinia Drew, Mr N. M. L. Ewart, Mr Maurice Friel, Mr R. P. Galashan, Mr D. Graham, Mrs Ann Graham, Mr W. Graham, Mr John Harris, Mrs A. G. Humbert, Dr Colin Kesson, Mr M. M. Matthews, Mr Peter Ogilvie, Dr Roy Palmer, Mr J. D. Percy, Mr C. T. Reid, Mr Robert Smith, Mrs J. E. Sperling, Mr N. A. Sperling, Mr B. Tait, Mr G. Taitt, Mr Iain Todd, Ms Heather K. Walker, Mr James Westoll, Mr Kirk A. Wilson, Mr S. Wood.

Assistant Trainer: Briony Ewart

Jockey (NH): Lucy Alexander. **Conditional:** Dale Irving.

---

196 **MR LES EYRE, Beverley**
Postal: **Ivy House Stables, Main Street, Catwick, Beverley, North Humberside, HU17 5PJ**
Contacts: **MOBILE (07864) 677444**

1 **BOXING SHADOWS**, 6, b g Camacho—Prima Ballerina **Mr B. Parker**
2 **COMPTON PARK**, 9, ch h Compton Place—Corps de Ballet (USA) **Mr B. Parker**
3 **DISCLOSURE**, 5, b g Indesatchel (IRE)—Gemini Gold (IRE) **Les Eyre Racing Partnership I**
4 **FAIRY POOLS**, 5, ch m Halling (USA)—Maring **Mrs D. W. Davenport**
5 **INTENSE STYLE (IRE)**, 4, ch g Intense Focus (USA)—Style Queen (IRE) **RP Racing Ltd**
6 **MAKE ON MADAM (IRE)**, 4, b f Captain Rio—Rye (IRE) **Mr G Parkinson & Baz Gibson**
7 **MARMION**, 4, b g Cape Cross (IRE)—Margarula (IRE) **RP Racing Ltd**
8 **QIBTEE (IRE)**, 6, b g Antonius Pius (USA)—Embers of Fame (IRE) **Mr N. C. White & Mrs C. E. White**

THREE-YEAR-OLDS

9 **BEVERLEY BULLET**, b g Makfi—Don't Tell Mary (IRE) **Mr M. J. Rozenbroek**
10 **COMPTON MEWS**, ch f Compton Place—Dhuyoof (IRE) **Mr B. Parker**
11 **EL PRINCIPE**, b g Strategic Prince—Shamrock Lady (IRE) **Mr M. J. Rozenbroek**
12 **ESCAPADE**, b f Monsieur Bond (IRE)—Heart of Svetlana (IRE) **Just A F.E.W. Of Us**
13 **SANDRA'S SECRET (IRE)**, gr f Zebedee—Good For Her **Sunpak Potatoes**
14 **VAN GERWEN**, ch g Bahamian Bounty—Disco Ball **Sunpak Potatoes**

Other Owners: Mr T. S. Ely, Mr A D Eyre, Mrs K. E. Fletcher, Mr B. W. Gibson, Mr G. Parkinson, Mrs C. H. Watson, Mr P. J. Watson, Mr N. C. White, Mrs C. E. White, Mrs S. J. Yates, Mr A. Yates.

197 MR RICHARD FAHEY, Malton
Postal: RF Racing Ltd, Mews House, Musley Bank, Malton, North Yorkshire, YO17 6TD
Contacts: **PHONE** (01653) 698915 **FAX** (01653) 699735 **MOBILE** (07713) 478079
E-MAIL enquiries@richardfahey.com **WEBSITE** www.richardfahey.com

1 **ABBEY ANGEL (IRE)**, 4, b f Arcano (IRE)—Sanna Bay (IRE) **Mrs H. Steel**
2 **ALBEN STAR (IRE)**, 8, b g Clodovil (IRE)—Secret Circle **Mr J. K. Shannon & Mr M. A. Scaife**
3 **ARCTIC FEELING (IRE)**, 8, ch g Camacho—Polar Lady **Percy / Green Racing 2**
4 **BAHAMIAN C**, 5, b g Bahamian Bounty—Amandian (IRE) **S & G Clayton**
5 **BALLESTEROS**, 7, ch g Tomba—Flamenco Dancer **Dr M. B. Q. S. Koukash**
6 **BALLYMORE CASTLE (IRE)**, 4, br g Invincible Spirit (IRE)—
Ballymore Lady (USA) **Middleham Park Racing XXVI**
7 **BAYAN KASIRGA (IRE)**, 6, b m Aussie Rules (USA)—Gwyllion (USA) **Mr S. Humphreys**
8 **BEARDWOOD**, 4, ch g Dutch Art—Valentina Guest (IRE) **D. W. Armstrong**
9 **BILLY BOND**, 4, b g Monsieur Bond (IRE)—Princess Cocoa (IRE) **Mr & Mrs P. Ashton**
10 **BIRKDALE BOY (IRE)**, 4, br g Alfred Nobel (IRE)—
Yaky Romani (IRE) **Middleham Park Racing LXXXII & C. Tasker**
11 **CANYARI (IRE)**, 5, b g Dandy Man—Morna's Fan (FR) **M. A. Leatham**
12 **CHARACTER ONESIE (IRE)**, 4, b g Dark Angel (IRE)—Flame Keeper (IRE) **Aykroyd & Sons Limited**
13 **CHISWICK BEY (IRE)**, 8, b g Elusive City (USA)—Victoria Lodge (IRE) **Mr M. J. Macleod**
14 **CLOUDS REST**, 4, b f Showcasing—Ahwahnee
15 **COSMIC HALO**, 7, ch m Halling (USA)—Cosmic Case **The Cosmic Cases**
16 **COSMIC STATESMAN**, 4, ch g Halling (USA)—Cosmic Case **Hazel Tattersall, Mr G. Hyde & Partner**
17 **DAWN MIRAGE**, 4, b g Oasis Dream—Prima Luce (IRE) **Merchants and Missionaries**
18 **DESIRE**, 4, ch f Kyllachy—Colonel's Daughter **R. A. Fahey**
19 **DEVIOUS SPIRIT (IRE)**, 4, br g Intikhab (USA)—Unintentional **Percy/Green Racing**
20 **EL VIENTO (FR)**, 8, ch g Compton Place—Blue Sirocco **John Nicholls Ltd/David Kilburn**
21 **ENGLISH SUMMER**, 9, b g Montjeu (IRE)—Hunt The Sun **Dr M. B. Q. S. Koukash**
22 **FARHAM (USA)**, 4, b g Smart Strike (CAN)—Diamondrella **Al Shaqab Racing UK Limited**
23 **FARLOW (IRE)**, 8, ch g Exceed And Excel (AUS)—Emly Express (IRE) **Red Sky Partnership 1**
24 **FULLON CLARETS**, 4, ch g Equiano (FR)—Palinisa (IRE) **The Matthewman Partnership**
25 **FURIOUSLY FAST (IRE)**, 4, b g Fast Company (IRE)—Agouti **Merchants and Missionaries**
26 **GABRIAL (IRE)**, 7, b g Dark Angel (IRE)—Guajira (IRE) **Dr M. B. Q. S. Koukash**
27 **GABRIAL THE HERO (USA)**, 7, b g War Front (USA)—Ball Gown (USA) **Dr M. B. Q. S. Koukash**
28 **GABRIAL THE TERROR (IRE)**, 6, b g Kheleyf (USA)—Simla Bibi **Dr M. B. Q. S. Koukash**
29 **GABRIAL THE THUG (FR)**, 6, b g Azamour (IRE)—Baliyna (USA) **Dr M. B. Q. S. Koukash**
30 **GEORGE BOWEN (IRE)**, 4, gr g Dark Angel (IRE)—Midnight Oasis **M. A. Scaife**
31 **GLEESE THE DEVIL (IRE)**, 5, br g Manduro (GER)—Causeway Song (USA) **Dr M. B. Q. S. Koukash**
32 **GRANDAD'S WORLD (IRE)**, 4, b g Kodiac—Nose One's Way (IRE) **Mr D. Hardman & Mrs S. Hardman**
33 **HIGH BAROQUE (USA)**, 4, b g Lookin At Lucky (USA)—Yesterday (IRE) **R. A. Fahey**
34 **HOME CUMMINS (IRE)**, 4, b f Rip Van Winkle (IRE)—Alava (IRE) **Mrs H. Steel**
35 **IMSHIVALLA (IRE)**, 5, b m Acclamation—Subtle Affair (IRE) **Pow Partnership**
36 **INGLEBY SPRING (IRE)**, 4, br f Zebedee—Jouel (IRE) **Percy Green Racing 3**
37 **INNOCENT TOUCH (IRE)**, 5, bl g Intense Focus (USA)—Guajira (IRE) **Nicholas Wrigley & Kevin Hart**
38 **INTIWIN (IRE)**, 4, b g Intikhab (USA)—Muluk (USA) **Mrs H. Steel**
39 **IXELLES DIAMOND (IRE)**, 5, br m Diamond Green (FR)—Silk Point (IRE) **Miss L. Tillett**
40 **JAN VAN HOOF (IRE)**, 5, b g Dutch Art—Cosenza **M. A. Leatham**
41 **JOHNNY B GOODE (IRE)**, 4, b g Approve (IRE)—Musica E Magia (IRE) **J. Gill**
42 **KHELMAN (IRE)**, 6, b g Kheleyf (USA)—Mandolin (IRE) **S & G Clayton**
43 **LUIS VAZ DE TORRES (IRE)**, 4, b g Tagula (IRE)—Tekhania (IRE) **Lets Go Racing 1**
44 **MAIDEN APPROACH**, 5, b m New Approach (IRE)—Ivowen (USA) **Middleham Park Racing LXVII**
45 **MAJESTIC MYLES (IRE)**, 4, b g Majestic Missile—Gala Style (IRE) **Richard Fahey Ebor Racing Club Ltd**
46 **MANCHESTAR**, 6, b g Elusive City (USA)—Grande Terre (IRE) **Mr & Mrs D. Calder**
47 **MFIFTYTHREEDOTCOM (IRE)**, 5, ch g Tamayuz—Pearl Trader (IRE) **M53 Motors Ltd T/A M53 Ford**
48 **MICA MIKA (IRE)**, 8, ch g Needwood Blade—Happy Talk (IRE) **Mrs U. Towell**
49 **MITRE PEAK**, 4, CH F Shamardal (USA)—Milford Sound
50 **MODERNISM**, 7, b g Monsun (GER)—La Nuit Rose (FR) **Dr M. B. Q. S. Koukash**
51 **MUSTIQUE DANCER (IRE)**, 4, b f Rip Van Winkle (IRE)—Cilium (IRE) **Middleham Park Racing XCI & Partner**
52 **NORMANDY KNIGHT**, 4, b g Acclamation—Prayer (IRE) **Mrs H. Steel**
53 **NUNO TRISTAN (USA)**, 4, b g Henrythenavigator (USA)—Saintly Speech (USA) **R. A. Fahey**
54 **OAK BLUFFS (IRE)**, 4, b g Royal Applause—Key Stage (IRE) **Mrs U. Towell**
55 **ONE BOY (IRE)**, 5, ch g Captain Gerrard (IRE)—Paris Song (IRE) **Sekura Trade Frames Ltd**
56 **ORTAC ROCK (IRE)**, 7, b g Aussie Rules (USA)—Fashion Guide (IRE) **Wildcard Racing Syndicate X2**
57 **OUR BOY JACK (IRE)**, 7, b g Camacho—Jina (IRE) **Middleham Park Racing XXXVI**
58 **PATRICK (IRE)**, 4, b g Acclamation—Red Liason (IRE) **Mrs A. M. Riney**
59 **PICCADILLY JIM (IRE)**, 5, gr g Royal Applause—Silver Dip **Frank Lenny Financial Services Limited**

MR RICHARD FAHEY - Continued

60 **QUEST OF COLOUR (IRE)**, 5, b m Iffraaj—With Colour **Havelock Racing 2**
61 **QUILL ART**, 4, b g Excellent Art—Featherweight (IRE) **P. S. Cresswell & Mrs P. A. Morrison**
62 **ROYAL CONNOISSEUR (IRE)**, 5, b g Art Connoisseur (IRE)—Valferno (IRE) **S & G Clayton, Mr A. Blower**
63 **SCARLET BOUNTY (IRE)**, 4, b f Bahamian Bounty—Red Kyte **R. A. Fahey**
64 **SHALABINA**, 4, b f Nayef (USA)—Shibina (IRE) **Middleham Park Racing XCVI**
65 **SIMPLY SHINING (IRE)**, 6, ch m Rock of Gibraltar (IRE)—Bright Smile **Mrs H. Steel**
66 **SIREN'S COVE**, 4, b f Sir Percy—Siren Sound **Merchants and Missionaries**
67 **SPIRIT OF ZEB (IRE)**, 4, ch g Zebedee—Miss Glitters (IRE) **IMEJ Racing**
68 **SPRING OFFENSIVE (IRE)**, 4, b g Iffraaj—Night Sphere **A. Rhodes Haulage & Mr P. Timmins**
69 **STARDRIFTER**, 4, b g Rock of Gibraltar (IRE)—Alchemilla **Mrs H. Steel**
70 **SUEGIOO (FR)**, 7, ch g Manduro (GER)—Mantesera (IRE) **Dr M. B. Q. S. Koukash**
71 **SUPER QUICK (IRE)**, 4, b f Rip Van Winkle (IRE)—Public Ransom (IRE) **Mr & Mrs J. D. Cotton**
72 **THIRD TIME LUCKY (IRE)**, 4, gr g Clodovil (IRE)—Speckled Hen (IRE) **The Musley Bank Partnership & Partner**
73 **WITHERNSEA (IRE)**, 5, b g Dark Angel (IRE)—Charlene Lacy (IRE) **City Vaults Racing 1**

THREE-YEAR-OLDS

74 **ABU KHADRA (IRE)**, b c Oasis Dream—Flashy Wings **J. Alharbi**
75 **ALL THAT JAS (IRE)**, gr f Jeremy (USA)—Anice Stellato (IRE) **Richard Fahey Ebor Racing Club Ltd**
76 **ANOTHER TOUCH**, b g Arcano (IRE)—Alsalwa (IRE) **Nicholas Wrigley & Kevin Hart**
77 **APPLETON**, ch c Showcasing—Valentina Guest (IRE) **D. W. Armstrong**
78 **BACK TO BOND**, ch g Monsieur Bond (IRE)—Nicola's Dream **P. D. Smith Holdings Ltd**
79 **BAHAMIAN SUNSHINE**, ch c Bahamian Bounty—Tagula Sunrise (IRE) **The Fairweather Foursome**
80 **BALANCE**, ch f Pivotal—Danella (FR) **Mr W. A. Tinkler**
81 **BIRCHWOOD (IRE)**, b c Dark Angel—Layla Jamil (IRE) **Godolphin Management Company Ltd**
82 **BLACK MAGIC (IRE)**, gr g Poet's Voice—Centifolia (FR) **Mrs H. Steel**
83 **CARNAGEO (FR)**, b g Pivotal—Sudarynya (IRE) **The Up For Anything Syndicate**
84 **CHAMPAGNE DUCHESS (IRE)**, ch f Zebedee—Zafaraya (IRE) **Ms A. Canham-White**
85 **COTTON CAMERA (IRE)**, b f Lilbourne Lad (IRE)—Dffra (IRE) **Mrs H. Steel**
86 **DOLPHIN VISTA (IRE)**, b c Zoffany (IRE)—Fiordiligi (IRE) **Mr Y. M. Nasib**
87 **DONJUAN TRIUMPHANT (IRE)**, b c Dream Ahead (USA)—Mathuna (IRE) **Middleham Park Racing LXXXVII**
88 **DOSE**, b f Teofilo (IRE)—Prescription **Cheveley Park Stud Limited**
89 **DRIFTING SPIRIT (IRE)**, b f Clodovil (IRE)—Laureldean Spirit (IRE) **Sheikh R. D. Al Maktoum**
90 **ESKENDASH (USA)**, ch c Eskendereya (USA)—Daffaash (USA) **Richard Fahey Ebor Racing Club Ltd**
91 **ESPOIR**, b f Cockney Rebel (IRE)—Quiquillo (USA) **Diamond Racing Ltd**
92 **FLOWING CLARETS**, ch f Pastoral Pursuits—Flying Clarets (IRE) **The Matthewman One Partnership**
93 **FOOTLIGHT**, b f Showcasing—Wood Fairy **Mrs P. B. E. P. Farr**
94 **FULL OF PROMISE**, b f Kyllachy—Arculinge **Richard Fahey Ebor Racing Club Ltd**
95 **GARCIA**, b g Paco Boy (IRE)—Birdie **Highclere Thoroughbred Racing (Pelham)**
96 **GIN IN THE INN (IRE)**, b c Alfred Nobel (IRE)—Nose One's Way (IRE) **Mr D. H. Hardman & Mrs S. Hardman**
97 **GLENEVE (IRE)**, b c Intikhab (USA)—Dalannda (IRE) **S & G Clayton**
98 **HIDDEN TREASURES**, ch f Zoffany (IRE)—Swynford Pleasure **Mr W. A. Tinkler**
99 **HOLD ON MAGNOLIA**, ch c Monsieur Bond (IRE)—Mawjoodah **Mr D. R. Gilbert**
100 **HOLIDAY HENRY (USA)**, b g Lookin At Lucky (USA)—Lady Ilsley (USA) **R. A. Fahey**
101 **HUTTON (IRE)**, b g Lawman (FR)—Moynsha Lady **D. W. Armstrong**
102 **HYLAND HEATHER (IRE)**, b f Lilbourne Lad (IRE)—Maidservant (USA) **Mrs H. Steel**
103 **I'M READY (IRE)**, ch f Iffraaj—Ready When You Are (IRE) **R. A. Fahey**
104 **IMPRESSIVE SPIRIT (IRE)**, b f Sakhee's Secret—Kondakova (IRE) **The Matthewman One Partnership**
105 **IN MY PLACE**, b g Compton Place—Luxuria (IRE) **A. Rhodes Haulage & Mr P. Timmins**
106 **INAAM (IRE)**, b c Camacho—Duckmore Bay (IRE) **Yorkshire Connections Ltd**
107 **INVERMERE**, b f Kyllachy—Kootenay (IRE) **Mcculloch Bloodstock Ltd**
108 **ISLAND FLAME (IRE)**, b f Kodiac—Noble Flame (IRE) **Northumbria Leisure Ltd**
109 **JADELLA WILLFIN**, b f Tobougg (IRE)—Daysiwaay (IRE) **Middleham Park Racing CII & Partner**
110 **JEANIE'S PLACE**, ch f Compton Place—Good Again **Crown Select**
111 **JERSEY ROY**, b g Major Cadeaux—Charlie Girl **Middleham Park Racing LIII & Partner**
112 **JORDAN SPORT**, b c Dubawi (IRE)—Wonder Why (GER) **J. Alharbi**
113 **L'APOGEE**, ch g Rip Van Winkle (IRE)—Pappas Ruby (USA) **Mrs J. E. Newett**
114 **LADY TURPIN (IRE)**, gr f Arakan (USA)—Proficiency **UK Racing Syndicate**
115 **LINE SPORT (IRE)**, ch c Exceed And Excel (AUS)—Majestic Dubai **J. Alharbi**
116 **LUNA MARE (IRE)**, b f Galileo (IRE)—Pale Moon Rising (IRE) **Mr W. A. Tinkler**
117 **LYDIATE (IRE)**, b f Acclamation—Maid To Order (IRE) **D. W. Armstrong**
118 **MATRON OF HONOUR (IRE)**, b f Teofilo (IRE)—Wedding Gift (FR) **Mr W. A. Tinkler**
119 **MAYFAIR LADY**, b f Holy Roman Emperor (IRE)—Lady Luachmhar (IRE) **Mrs H. Steel**
120 **MISS GOLDSMITH (IRE)**, gr f Mastercraftsman (IRE)—Golden Legacy (IRE) **R. A. Fahey**
121 **MONACO ROSE**, b f Sir Percy—Pallas **Dr M. B. Q. S. Koukash**
122 **NOVINOPHOBIA**, ch g Showcasing—Malelane (IRE) **P. Timmins & A. Rhodes Haulage**

MR RICHARD FAHEY - Continued

123 ORMSKIRK, gr g Hellvelyn—River Song (USA) **D. W. Armstrong**
124 PARISIANNA, b f Champs Elysees—Simianna **Bearstone Stud Limited & Jack Berry**
125 PENWORTHAM (IRE), b g Dandy Man (IRE)—Portofino Bay (IRE) **D. W. Armstrong**
126 PERCEYSVIVACE, b f Sir Percy—Calico Moon (USA) **Mr D. A. Bardsley**
127 PICCARDO, ch c Piccolo—Billiard **Percy Green Racing 4**
128 POWERALLIED (IRE), b c Camacho—Kaplinsky **Dr M. B. Q. S. Koukash**
129 PRYING PANDORA (FR), b f Dark Angel (IRE)—Leniency (IRE) **Middleham Park Racing X**
130 RETURN OF THE MAK, b c Makfi—Tell The Wind (IRE) **Mr P. F. O'Callaghan**
131 RIBCHESTER (IRE), b c Iffraaj—Mujarah (IRE) **Godolphin Management Company Ltd**
132 RING OF ART, b c Dutch Art—Katimont (IRE) **Mr & Mrs J. D. Cotton**
133 ROSE MARMARA, ch f Exceed And Excel (AUS)—Show Rainbow **J. Alharbi**
134 RUBIS, ch f Monsieur Bond (IRE)—Princess Cocoa (IRE) **Mr & Mrs P. Ashton**
135 SADIE BABES (IRE), b f Iffraaj—Daffodil Walk (IRE) **Mr P. Hyland**
136 SANAADH, ch c Exceed And Excel (AUS)—Queen's Logic (IRE) **J. Alharbi**
137 SHOWBIZZY, ch f Showcasing—Nellie Ellis **Racegoers Club Owners Group**
138 SKIPTON (IRE), b f Dark Angel (IRE)—Emirates Hills **D. W. Armstrong**
139 SUNNUA (IRE), gr f Dark Angel (IRE)—Island Sunset (IRE) **Middleham Park Racing II & Partner**
140 SUPERIOR LABOR, b f Mastercraftsman (IRE)—Wing Diva (IRE) **Merchants and Missionaries**
141 THEOS LOLLY (IRE), b c Kodiac—Aluana (IRE) **Mr M. J. Macleod**
142 THRAYA QUEEN, ch f Shamardal (USA)—Samira Gold (FR) **J. Alharbi**
143 TURPIN STAR, b g Dick Turpin (IRE)—Classic Lass **CBWS Partnership**
144 WINTER HEY LANE (USA), ch f Speightstown (USA)—Clambake (IRE) **D. W. Armstrong**
145 WOOTTON VALE (IRE), b g Wootton Bassett—Shining Vale (USA) **John Nicholls (Trading) Ltd**
146 YA JAMMEEL, b c Dubawi (IRE)—Silver Touch (IRE) **J. Alharbi**
147 YOSEMITE, gr f Makfi—Dansa Queen **Merchants and Missionaries**
148 YOU DARE TO DREAM (IRE), b f Royal Applause—Sanna Bay (IRE) **Mr P. Hyland**
149 YOUNG JOHN (IRE), b g Acclamation—Carpet Lady (IRE) **Mrs A. M. Riney**
150 ZAHRAT NARJIS, b f Exceed And Excel (AUS)—Nijoom Dubai **J. Alharbi**
151 ZAINA RIZEENA, ch f Shamardal (USA)—Sweet Lilly **J. Alharbi**

Trainer did not wish details of his two-year-olds to appear

Other Owners: A. Rhodes Haulage Ltd, Mr Terence Alderson, Mrs P. Ashton, Mr P. Ashton, Bearstone Stud Limited, Mr J. Berry, Mr A. Blower, Mr Andy Bonarius, Mr M. Bradley, Mr Andrew Brown, Mr E. Bruce, Mr I. T. Buchanan, Mrs J. Calder, Mr G. Calder, Mr J. P. Carr, Mr A. Clark, Mr Steven Clayton, Mrs G. A. Clayton, Mr James Clayton, Mr Arthur Collins, Mr S. C. Corbett, Mr A. E. Corbett, Mr J. D. Cotton, Mrs B. Cotton, Mr Mel Cressey, Mr P. S. Cresswell, Mr Garry Cuthbert, Mr K. A. Dean, Mr M. J. K. Dods, Mr Sam Ellis, Facility Solutions Management Limited, Mr R. A. Fahey, Mr K. J. Farrer, Mr M. Feneron, Mr Brian W. Goodall, Mr J. D. Gordon, Mr David A. Green, Mrs Stella Hardman, Mr Dean Hardman, Mr P. L. Harrison, Mr Kevin Hart, Mr Roger Hart, The Hon H. Herbert, Highclere Thoroughbred Racing Ltd, Mr D. Holgate, Mr Christopher A. Hood, Mr K. Hubery, Mr G. R. Hunnam, Mr G. Hyde, Mr D. R. John, John Nicholls (Trading) Ltd, Mr R. F. Johnson, Mr D. Kilburn, Mr D. M. Knaggs, Mrs Christine Lally, Mr P. Longstaff, Mr P. D. Macintosh, Mr Michael Mackay, Mrs J Malcolmson, Mr Robert McAlpine, Mrs P. A. Morrison, Mrs Margaret Nelson, Mr John R. Owen, Mr T. S. Palin, Mr G. J. Paver, Mr M. Prince, Mr Mel Roberts, Mr Michael Ryan (Bradford), Mr M. A. Scaife, Mr J. K. Shannon, Mr Jim Struth, Mr A. Tattersall, Mrs Hazel Tattersall, Mr D. M. Tempest, Mr Peter Timmins, Mr Andrew Tinkler, Mr P. M. Watson, Mr G. Weaver, Mr David Westerman, Mr John Wicks, Mr David Wild, Mr S. Wood, Mr Martin Wood, Mr N. H. T. Wrigley.

Assistant Trainer: Robin O'Ryan

Jockey (flat): Tony Hamilton, Paul Hanagan, George Chaloner. **Jockey (NH):** Brian Hughes. **Apprentice:** Samantha Bell, Jack Garritty, Natalie Hambling, Hayley Irvine, Adam McNamara. **Amateur:** Miss Alyson Deniel.

---

198 MR CHRIS FAIRHURST, Middleham
Postal: **Glasgow House, Middleham, Leyburn, North Yorkshire, DL8 4QG**
Contacts: **PHONE/FAX (01969) 622039 MOBILE (07889) 410840**
E-MAIL cfairhurst@tiscali.co.uk WEBSITE www.chrisfairhurstracing.com

1 CROWN AND GLORY (IRE), 9, b g Turtle Island (IRE)—Monteleena (IRE) **Mr & Mrs W. H. Woods**
2 DANZELLA, 4, b f Desideratum—Danzatrice **980 Racing**
3 DISTRICT ATTORNEY (IRE), 7, b g Lawman (FR)—Mood Indigo (IRE) **The PQD Partnership**
4 ELLERINA, 4, b f Stimulation (IRE)—Dream Quest **Mr A. Davies**
5 HIGHFIELD LASS, 5, b m Cayman Kai (IRE)—Jendorcet **Mrs P. J. Taylor-Garthwaite**
6 MOOTABAR (IRE), 9, gr g Verglas (IRE)—Melanzane **Mrs A. M. Leggett**
7 SHIRLS SON SAM, 8, b g Rambling Bear—Shirl **Mrs C. Arnold**

MR CHRIS FAIRHURST - Continued

8 THACKERAY, 9, b g Fasliyev (USA)—Chinon (IRE) **Mrs C. Arnold**
9 WHO'S SHIRL, 10, b m Shinko Forest (IRE)—Shirl **Mrs S. France**

THREE-YEAR-OLDS

10 EMILIE BRONTE, b f Mullionmileanhour (IRE)—Yorke's Folly (USA) **Mrs A. M. Leggett**
11 FLORENZA, b g Haafhd—Danzatrice **980 Racing**
12 KAZOEY, b f Stimulation (IRE)—Dubawi's Spirit (IRE) **Mr A. Davies**
13 THE ARMED MAN, b g Misu Bond (IRE)—Accamelia **Mrs C. Arnold**

Other Owners: Mr T. Bryson, Mr M. D. Tozer, Mr J. M. Tozer, Mrs G. H. Woods, Mr W. H. Woods.

---

199 | **MR JAMES FANSHAWE, Newmarket**
Postal: **Pegasus Stables, Snailwell Road, Newmarket, Suffolk, CB8 7DJ**
Contacts: **PHONE (01638) 664525 FAX (01638) 664523**
E-MAIL james@jamesfanshawe.com WEBSITE www.jamesfanshawe.com / www.fredarcher.com

1 ARTHENUS, 4, b g Dutch Art—Lady Hen **A. Coombs & J. W. Rowley**
2 ESTEEMABLE, 4, ch f Nayef (USA)—Ring of Esteem **Mrs C. R. Philipson**
3 FLORISS, 4, b f Medicean—Joshua's Princess **The Ridgewood Syndicate**
4 FLY, 4, ch f Pastoral Pursuits—Hannda (IRE) **Mr T. R. G. Vestey**
5 HALLELUJAH, 8, b m Avonbridge—My Golly **CLS (Chippenham) Limited**
6 HE'S MY BOY (IRE), 5, gr g Dark Angel (IRE)—Rose of Battle **Mr P. S. Ryan**
7 HIGH JINX (IRE), 8, b g High Chaparral (IRE)—Leonara (GER) **Mr & Mrs W. J. Williams**
8 HIGHER POWER, 4, b g Rip Van Winkle (IRE)—Lady Stardust **Mrs Martin Armstrong**
9 HORS DE COMBAT, 5, ch g Mount Nelson—Maid For Winning (USA) **Chris van Hoorn Racing**
10 KNIGHT OWL, 6, b g Rock of Gibraltar (IRE)—Miss Ivanhoe (IRE) **Miss Annabelle Condon**
11 LANDWADE LAD, 9, b g Dansili—Sell Out **Mr Simon Gibson**
12 MISSED CALL (IRE), 6, b m Authorized (IRE)—Incoming Call (USA) **Mr Malcolm C. Denmark**
13 MODERAH, 4, b f Makfi—Meetyouthere (IRE) **Mr Salem Bel Obaida**
14 MR PICKWICK, 4, b g Mount Nelson—Never Lose **Johnstone Partnership**
15 PECKING ORDER (IRE), 4, b f Fastnet Rock (AUS)—Shemaya (IRE) **Merry Fox Stud Limited**
16 RETURN ACE, 4, b f Zamindar (USA)—Match Point **Helena Springfield Ltd**
17 SAAB ALMANAL, 5, b g Dubawi (IRE)—Caribbean Pearl (USA) **Mr Mohamed Obaida**
18 SPEEDY BOARDING, 4, b f Shamardal (USA)—Dash To The Front **Helena Springfield Ltd**
19 SPIRIT RAISER (IRE), 5, b m Invincible Spirit (IRE)—Macadamia (USA) **Lord Vestey**
20 STAR STORM (IRE), 4, b c Sea The Stars (IRE)—Sayyedati Storm (USA) **Mr Mohamed Obaida**
21 THAI NOON (IRE), 4, b g Dansili—Alsace Lorraine (IRE) **Merry Fox Stud Limited**
22 THE TIN MAN, 4, b g Equiano (FR)—Persario **Fred Archer Racing - Ormonde**
23 UP IN LIGHTS (IRE), 4, ch f Makfi—Spotlight **Mr Mohamed Obaida**

THREE-YEAR-OLDS

24 ALWAYS SUMMER, b f Flatter (USA)—Air Kiss **Dr Catherine Wills**
25 ALZEBARH (IRE), ch f Poet's Voice—Dubai Pearl (IRE) **Mr Mohamed Obaida**
26 BATTAILES, b g Acclamation—Ada River **Mr Simon Gibson**
27 BLUES SISTER, b f Compton Place—Persario **Mr & Mrs M Morris, Mr & Mrs P Hopper**
28 COLUMN, b c Mount Nelson—Tottie **Mr J. H. Richmond-Watson**
29 EMPRESS ROCK (IRE), b f Fastnet Rock (AUS)—Roman Empress (IRE) **Apple Tree Stud**
30 ENMESHING, ch g Mastercraftsman (IRE)—Yacht Club (USA) **Mr Ben C. M. Wong**
31 FILUMENA, ch f Pivotal—Phillipina **Cheveley Park Stud**
32 INDULGED, b f Teofilo (IRE)—Fondled **Cheveley Park Stud**
33 ISSUE, b f Nayef (USA)—Isis (USA) **Dr Catherine Wills**
34 KING OF NAPLES, b g Excellent Art—Avon Lady **Mr P. S. Ryan**
35 LORD GEORGE (IRE), gr c Sir Percy—Mahima (FR) **Fred Archer Racing - Bend Or**
36 MAZZINI, ch c Exceed And Excel (AUS)—Firenze **Mr & Mrs P Hopper, Mr & Mrs M Morris**
37 NOBLE STAR (IRE), b c Acclamation—Wrong Answer **Mr Tang Wai Bun Tony**
38 PERMISSION, b f Authorized (IRE)—Continua (USA) **Mrs J Scott, J F Dean & Lady Trenchard**
39 POINTEL (FR), b c Le Havre (IRE)—Polysheba (FR) **Mrs A. M. Swinburn**
40 PRINCESSE EVA (FR), b f Manduro (GER)—Wing Stealth (USA) **Normandie Stud Ltd**
41 B f Fastnet Rock (AUS)—Quiet Protest **Mr John P. McManus**
42 REGICIDE (IRE), b g Archipenko (USA)—Armoise **Chris van Hoorn Racing**
43 REPLENISH (FR), ch c Le Havre (IRE)—Brambleberry **Mac & Friends**
44 SAM MISSILE (IRE), b c Smart Strike (CAN)—Kitty Matcham (IRE) **Apple Tree Stud**
45 SILCA WINGS, b f Multiplex—Silca Destination **Apple Tree Stud**

MR JAMES FANSHAWE - Continued

46 **SLEEPLESSINSEATTLE**, b f Rip Van Winkle (IRE)—Caught On Camera **Helena Springfield Ltd**
47 **STONEY BROKE**, b f Dansili—Alvee (IRE) **Merry Fox Stud Limited**
48 **TEGARA**, ch f Hard Spun (USA)—Damaniyat Girl (USA) **Mr Mohamed Obaida**
49 **ZEST (IRE)**, b f Duke of Marmalade (IRE)—Affinity **Elite Racing Club**

TWO-YEAR-OLDS

50 **AIRWAY**, b g 3/5 Poet's Voice—Air Kiss (Red Ransom (USA)) **Dr Catherine Wills**
51 B f 29/4 Acclamation—Double Fantasy (GER) (Indian Ridge) (40604) **Fred Archer Racing - Ladylove**
52 B f 20/2 Sepoy (AUS)—Dubai Sea (Street Sense (USA)) (20000) **Mr Mohamed Obaida**
53 **ENFOLDING (IRE)**, b c 6/5 Fastnet Rock (AUS)—
                   Althea Rose (Green Desert (USA)) (110000) **Mr Ben C. M. Wong**
54 **ENVISAGING (IRE)**, b c 8/4 Zoffany (IRE)—Star of Stars (IRE) (Soviet Star (USA)) (81210) **Mr Ben C. M. Wong**
55 Ch f 15/3 New Approach (IRE)—Fann (USA) (Diesis) (100000) **Mrs A. M. Swinburn**
56 Ch f 8/4 Sepoy (AUS)—Firenze (Efisio) **Jan and Peter Hopper**
57 **FLAMING MARVEL (IRE)**, b c 4/4 Redoute's Choice (AUS)—
                   Flame of Hestia (Giant's Causeway (USA)) (50000) **Merry Fox Stud Limited**
58 Ch c 25/2 Sepoy (AUS)—Hannda (IRE) (Dr Devious (IRE)) **Mr T. R. G. Vestey**
59 **INCANDESCENT**, b f 15/2 Pivotal—Bedazzled (Authorized) (70000) **Cheveley Park Stud**
60 Br gr f 25/2 Dalakhani (IRE)—Inchiri (Sadler's Wells (USA)) (70000) **Mrs Olivia Hoare**
61 B c 20/2 Kyllachy—Joshua's Princess (Danehill (USA)) (62000) **Fred Archer Racing - Energy**
62 Gr c 31/3 Mastercraftsman (IRE)—Kinigi (Verglas (IRE)) (62753) **Fred Archer Racing - Atlantic**
63 **LIGHTER**, b f 27/4 Nathaniel (IRE)—Floodlit (Fantastic Light (USA)) **Cheveley Park Stud**
64 **MAC'S KYLLACHY**, ch c 23/4 Kyllachy—Folly Lodge (Grand Lodge (USA)) (65000) **Michael McDonnell**
65 Gr f 11/2 Mastercraftsman (IRE)—Mahima (FR) (Linamix (FR)) (33222) **Andrew & Julia Turner**
66 B f 29/4 Sixties Icon—Panna (Polish Precedent (USA)) **Lord Halifax**
67 B f 20/3 Kodiac—Pearl Mountain (IRE) (Pearl of Love (IRE)) (125000) **Mrs A. M. Swinburn**
68 **PHILANDERER**, b c 16/3 Pivotal—Fondled (Selkirk (USA)) (30000) **Cheveley Park Stud**
69 **POSEUR**, b c 20/4 Pivotal—Tottie (Fantastic Light (USA)) **Mr J. H. Richmond-Watson**
70 **ROUBLES (USA)**, b c 9/2 Speightstown (USA)—Soviet Song (USA) (Marju (IRE)) **Elite Racing Club**
71 B c 12/3 Sea The Stars (IRE)—Sayyedati Symphony (USA) (Gone West (USA)) **Mr Mohamed Obaida**
72 B f 4/4 Aqlaam—Soundwave (Prince Sabo) **Manor Farm Stud (Rutland)**
73 **SYMBOL**, ch f 6/2 Nathaniel (IRE)—Succinct (Hector Protector (USA)) (15000) **Dr Catherine Wills**
74 **TRIBUTE ACT**, b f 26/1 Exceed And Excel (AUS)—Sister Act (Marju (USA)) **Elite Racing Club**
75 Gr f 11/4 Le Havre (IRE)—Trip To Fame (FR) (Lordmare (FR)) (44296) **Mr Malcolm C. Denmark**

Other Owners: Mr Geoffrey Baber, Mrs Denise Beetles, Mr Graham Beetles, Mr John E. Bodie, The Hon Mrs Penny Butler, Mr Isidore Carivalis, Mrs Denise Dunkley, Mr P. J. Dunkley, Mr Roy Eady, Mrs H. S. Ellingsen, Nigel and Carolyn Elwes, Mrs Libby Fanshawe, Mr Brian Fanshawe, Mrs Georgie Fanshawe, Mr Patrick Forward, Mr Colin Gilbert, Mrs Gillian Godfrey, Mr Guy A. A. C. Gredley, Mr Tony Hill, Mr Harry Johnstone, Mr John Johnstone, Mrs Zara Johnstone, Mrs Sarah King, Mr Arne Korsbakken, Mr and Mrs Tim Law, Mr Niall Lynch, Mr Gary Marney, Mrs Lorraine Marney, Mr T. Mohan, Mr K. Mohan, Miss M. Noden, Miss Olivia Palmer, Mr Gordon Papworth, Mrs Pat Rowley, Mr William Russell, Mr David I. Russell, Mr Ulf Ryden, Ms Hermione Scrope, Mr Nigel Smith, Mr Rob Stevens, Miss A. D. Swift, Mr David Tarrant, Mr Peter Tarrant, Mrs Tam Murray Thriepland, Mrs Jan Trew-Smith, Mr M. Weinfeld.

---

200   **MR JOHNNY FARRELLY, Bridgwater**
Postal: **Smocombe Racing Stables, Enmore, Bridgwater, Somerset, TA5 2EB**
Contacts: **PHONE (01278) 671782 MOBILE (07811) 113363**

1 **ABLAZING (IRE)**, 5, b g Mastercraftsman (IRE)—Moore's Melody (IRE) **Hanford's Chemist Ltd**
2 **ALL TOGETHER (FR)**, 5, ch g Zambezi Sun—Mareha (IRE) **Mrs Z. Wentworth**
3 **AMITIE WALTZ (FR)**, 4, b g Sinndar (IRE)—Lia Waltz (FR) **Third Time Lucky**
4 **AMORE ALATO**, 7, b g Winged Love (IRE)—Sardagna (FR) **Mrs S. J. Faulks**
5 **ASCENDANT**, 10, ch g Medicean—Ascendancy **F. A. Clegg**
6 **BLACKWATER KING (IRE)**, 8, b br g Beneficial—Accordian Lady (IRE) **Mr & Mrs Paul & Clare Rooney**
7 **DEGOOCH (IRE)**, 7, ch g Gamut (IRE)—Blonde Ambition (IRE) **Mr & Mrs Paul & Clare Rooney**
8 **EXEMPLARY**, 9, b g Sulamani—Epitome **Monday Boys Partnership**
9 **FINISH THE STORY (IRE)**, 10, b g Court Cave (IRE)—Lady of Grange (IRE) **Mr A. Knowles**
10 **HIGHRIDGE PRINCESS (IRE)**, 8, b m Lord Americo—End of The Rainbow (IRE) **The Lansdowners**
11 **KAZLIAN (FR)**, 8, b g Sinndar (IRE)—Quiet Splendor (USA) **Twelve Pipers Piping**
12 **LOVE THE LEADER (IRE)**, 8, b g Fruits of Love (USA)—Suelena (IRE) **Mr J. Farrelly**
13 **MARKAMI (FR)**, 6, ch g Medicean—Marque Royale **P. M. Tosh**
14 **MARVELLOUS MONTY (IRE)**, 6, br m Oscar (IRE)—Montys Miss (IRE) **Hanford's Chemist Ltd**
15 **MOLLY OSCAR (IRE)**, 10, b m Oscar (IRE)—Bishop's Folly **Mr J. Farrelly**

MR JOHNNY FARRELLY - Continued

16 **MOVING WAVES (IRE)**, 5, b m Intense Focus (USA)—Kimola (IRE) **Mrs Z. Wentworth**
17 **OSCAR JANE (IRE)**, 9, b m Oscar (IRE)—Turrill House **P. M. Tosh**
18 **PENZILO (IRE)**, 10, b m Luso—Penzita (IRE) **P. M. Tosh**
19 **QULINTON (FR)**, 12, b g Bulington (FR)—Klef du Bonheur (FR) **Mr R. M. Whitby**
20 **RIVERSBRIDGE**, 7, b g Desert King (IRE)—Kinsford Water **Faulks, Sutton & Toller**
21 **RODERICK RANDOM**, 6, b g Kayf Tara—Clotted Cream (USA) **Mrs S. J. Faulks**
22 **SANDFORD CASTLE (IRE)**, 6, b g Norwich—Pegs Polly (IRE) **Mr J. Farrelly**
23 **SHOUTING HILL (IRE)**, 6, br g Golan (IRE)—Brook Queen (IRE) **Hanford's Chemist Ltd**
24 **SPORTING BOY (IRE)**, 8, b g Barathea (IRE)—Sportsticketing (IRE) **H. M. W. Clifford**
25 **WAR SINGER (USA)**, 9, b g War Chant (USA)—Sister Marilyn (USA) **The War Cabinet**
26 **WESTERN SUNRISE (IRE)**, 7, b m Westerner—Presenting Gayle (IRE) **Mr D. J. Adams**
27 **ZERO GRAND (IRE)**, 5, b g Thousand Words—Ellistown Lady (IRE) **H. M. W. Clifford**

Other Owners: J. F. Baldwin, Mr M. J. Fitzpatrick, Mr J. Gwyther, Mr G. R. Heapy, T. Neill, Palatinate Thoroughbred Racing Limited, Mr C. G. Paletta, Mr P. A. Rooney, Mrs C. Rooney, Mr T. Rowsell, Mr R. A. C. Toller, R. T. Wilkins.

---

201 **MISS JULIA FEILDEN**, Newmarket
Postal: **Harraton Stud, Laceys Lane, Exning, Newmarket, Suffolk, CB8 7HW**
Contacts: **PHONE (01638) 577040 FAX (01638) 577040 MOBILE (07974) 817694**
E-MAIL juliafeilden@aol.com WEBSITE www.juliafeildenracing.com

1 **ARTBEAT (IRE)**, 4, b f Dutch Art—Easy Beat (IRE) **Mrs J. E. Lambert**
2 **ATTAIN**, 7, b g Dansili—Achieve **Newmarket Equine Tours Racing Club**
3 **AUTOMOTIVE**, 8, b g Beat Hollow—Bina Ridge **Stowstowquickquickstow Partnership**
4 **CANDESTA (USA)**, 6, b g First Defence (USA)—Wandesta **Mr & Mrs George Bhatti & Partner**
5 **DAKOTA CITY**, 5, b g Three Valleys (USA)—West Dakota **Good Company Partnership**
6 **DARK DIAMOND (IRE)**, 6, b g Dark Angel (IRE)—Moon Diamond **R. J. Creese**
7 **DISSERTATION**, 4, b f Champs Elysees—Reel Style **R. J. Creese**
8 **DUKE OF DIAMONDS**, 4, gr g Duke of Marmalade (IRE)—Diamond Line (FR) **Carol Bushnell & Partners**
9 **HANDHELD**, 9, ch g Observatory (USA)—Kid Gloves **Newmarket Equine Tours Racing Club**
10 **HARRY BOSCH**, 6, b g Kyllachy—Fen Guest **Mr Steve Brown**
11 **LIMERICK LORD (IRE)**, 4, b g Lord Shanakill (USA)—Hollow Green (IRE) **Steve Clarke & Partners**
12 **MOMENT TO DREAM**, 4, b f Halling (USA)—Pretty Majestic (IRE) **Steve Clarke & Partners**
13 **SABRE ROCK**, 6, b g Dubawi (IRE)—Retainage (USA) **The Pink Rabbits**
14 **SILVER ALLIANCE**, 8, gr g Proclamation (IRE)—Aimee Vibert **In It To Win Partnership**
15 **STAR OF THE STAGE**, 4, b g Invincible Spirit (IRE)—Enact **Mr & Mrs George Bhatti & Partners 2**
16 **TEPUTINA**, 4, ch f Teofilo (IRE)—West Lorne (USA) **Newmarket Equine Tours Racing Club**
17 **THE DUCKING STOOL**, 9, ch m Where Or When (IRE)—Dance Sequel **Newmarket Equine Tours Racing Club**
18 **VASTLY (USA)**, 7, gr ro g Mizzen Mast (USA)—Valentine Band (USA) **The Sultans of Speed**
19 **VEERAYA**, 6, b g Rail Link—Follow Flanders **Mr A. R. Farook**

THREE-YEAR-OLDS

20 **ARCHIE TECT**, ch g Archipenko (USA)—Sovereign Seal **Miss J. Feilden**
21 **BIG BANG**, b g Observatory (USA)—Bavarica **Newmarket Equine Tours Racing Club**
22 **GO ON GAL (IRE)**, b f Approve—Jeritza **Go On Gal Partnership**
23 **KEMSING**, ch g Footstepsinthesand—St Edith (IRE) **Miss J. Feilden**
24 **LITTLE ORCHID**, b f Observatory (USA)—Bushy Dell (IRE) **Mr R. J. Creese**
25 **SERENDIB'S GLORY (IRE)**, b f Holy Roman Emperor (IRE)—Rose of Mooncoin (IRE) **Mr A. R. Farook**

TWO-YEAR-OLDS

26 **CHAMPAGNE REEF**, gr f 8/4 Literato (FR)—Kritzia (Daylami (IRE)) (5500) **Mrs Carol Bushnell**
27 **MUNGO MADNESS**, gr g 3/4 Sir Percy—Emma's Gift (IRE) (Aussie Rules (USA)) **Mrs Emma Raffan**
28 **MY NAME IS JEFF**, b c 2/3 Mount Nelson—Vale of Belvoir (IRE) (Mull of Kintyre (USA)) **Miss J. Feilden**
29 **OUR CILLA**, gr f 29/3 Sixties Icon—Kinetix (Linamix (FR)) (10000) **Mrs Carol Bushnell**
30 **SECRET BALLERINA**, ch f 27/2 Sakhee's Secret—
Ballyea (IRE) (Acclamation) (4500) **Good Company Partnership**

MISS JULIA FEILDEN - Continued

31 SUNSET BOUNTY, b f 4/2 Bahamian Bounty—
Sunset Kitty (USA) (Gone West (USA)) (3000) **Steve Clarke & Partners**

Other Owners: Mr J. M. Basquill, Mrs Caroline Bhatti, Mr George Bhatti, Mr J. Birkett, Mr S. Brown, Mr S. J. Clarke, Mr E. H. M. Frost, Mr David Haddrell, Mr Andrew Mitchell, Mr Chris Page, Mr R. E. Partridge, Ms Hannah Ranner, Mr K. J. Strangeway, Mrs A. S. Styles, Mr O. A. Wideson, Mr R. Wright.

Assistant Trainer: Ross Birkett

Jockey (flat): Adam Beschizza. **Apprentice:** Shelley Birkett. **Amateur:** Mr R. Birkett.

---

202 **MR CHARLIE FELLOWES, Newmarket**
Postal: **St. Gatien Cottage, Vicarage Road, Newmarket, Suffolk, CB8 8HP**
Contacts: **PHONE (01638) 666948 MOBILE (07968) 499596**
E-MAIL **charlie@charliefellowesracing.co.uk** WEBSITE **www.charliefellowesracing.co.uk**

1 **ACCESSION (IRE),** 7, b g Acclamation—Pivotal's Princess (IRE) **Lady De Ramsey**
2 **BUCKLAND BEAU,** 5, b g Rock of Gibraltar (IRE)—Heavenly Whisper (IRE) **Mr P. S. McNally**
3 **CAROLINAE,** 4, ch f Makfi—You Too **Mr S. M. bel Obaida**
4 **CLASSICAL ROSE,** 4, b f Amadeus Wolf—Monaazalah (IRE) **Mr F. J. Perry**
5 **HEIBA (IRE),** 4, ch c Starspangledbanner (AUS)—Pina Colada **Saleh Al Homaizi & Imad Al Sagar**
6 **QUEEN ZAIN (IRE),** 4, b f Lawman (FR)—Tropical Lady (IRE) **Mr A. Al Banwan**
7 **TWIN POINT,** 5, br g Invincible Spirit (IRE)—Gemini Joan **Mr F. J. Perry**
8 **ZAIN ART (IRE),** 4, b f Excellent Art—Zigarra **Mr A. Al Banwan**

THREE-YEAR-OLDS

9 **DREAM ROLE,** b f Acclamation—Maid To Dream **Emma Capon & Mrs Simon Marsh**
10 **ENDLESS ACRES (IRE),** b g Champs Elysees—Eternity Ring **Saffron House Stables Partnership**
11 **HIJRAN (IRE),** ch f Mastercraftsman (IRE)—Sunny Slope **Saleh Al Homaizi & Imad Al Sagar**
12 **PRINCE OF ARRAN,** b c Shirocco (GER)—Storming Sioux **Mr S. M. bel Obaida**
13 **RIP IT UP,** b c Rip Van Winkle (IRE)—Monaazalah (IRE) **T. M. Jennings**
14 **SALVO,** b f Acclamation—Passe Passe **A. E. Oppenheimer**
15 **THE BURNING MAN,** b c Desert Party (USA)—Ras Shaikh (USA) **Mr S. M. bel Obaida**
16 **VROOM (IRE),** ch c Poet's Voice—Shivaree **Emma Capon & Mrs Simon Marsh**

TWO-YEAR-OLDS

17 B c 19/3 Dark Angel (IRE)—And Again (USA) (In The Wings) (180000) **Mr C. H. Fellowes**
18 B c 10/3 Canford Cliffs (IRE)—Beyond Belief (IRE) (Sadler's Wells (USA)) (31007) **Mr C. H. Fellowes**
19 Br f 20/3 Requinto (IRE)—Cant Hurry Love (Desert Prince (IRE)) (31007) **Equine Enthusiasts**
20 B c 28/2 Poet's Voice—Clear Impression (IRE) (Danehill (USA)) (12000) **Mr C. H. Fellowes**
21 **CRYPTONITE (IRE),** br c 26/4 Dark Angel (IRE)—Bowness (Efisio) (88593) **Mr C. Bacon**
22 B c 21/2 Invincible Spirit (IRE)—Doula (USA) (Gone West (USA)) (250000) **Mr C. H. Fellowes**
23 B c 16/4 Vale of York (IRE)—Dubai Pearl (IRE) (Refuse To Bend (IRE)) (21000) **M. Obaida**
24 B f 11/3 Lawman (FR)—Ellbeedee (IRE) (Dalakhani (IRE)) **Saleh Al Homaizi & Imad Al Sagar**
25 **EYESIGHT,** ch g 16/4 Medicean—Look So (Efisio) **J. H. Richmond-Watson**
26 B c 26/2 Holy Roman Emperor (IRE)—Flambeau (Oasis Dream) (200000) **Mr C. H. Fellowes**
27 **GENTLE WHISPER,** b f 18/4 Lawman (FR)—Speak Softly To Me (USA) (Ogygian (USA)) (42000) **Mrs E. Capon**
28 **JUPITER ASCENDING,** b c 3/2 Excelebration (IRE)—Habita (IRE) (Montjeu (USA)) (80000) **Mr C. Bacon**
29 B f 23/3 Mizzen Mast (USA)—Pearl In The Sand (IRE) (Footstepsinthesand) (20000) **W. McAlpin**
30 **SENTINEL,** b c 15/3 Sepoy (AUS)—Baralinka (IRE) (Barathea (IRE)) **Elite Racing Club**
31 B c 18/4 Mawatheeq (USA)—Tasheyaat (Sakhee (USA)) (8859) **Mr S. Bin Khalifa Al Kuwari**
32 **ZAIN STAR (IRE),** b c 12/2 Shamardal (USA)—
Astrologie (FR) (Polish Precedent (USA)) (115000) **Mr A. Al Banwan**

Other Owners: I. J. Al-Sagar, Mr R. Cooper, Mr A. J. Hill, Saleh Al Homaizi, Mr J. Isherwood, Mrs J. F. Marsh, Miss M. Noden.

---

203 **MR JOHN FERGUSON, Cowlinge**
Trainer is to hand in his licence in April and did not wish details of his string to appear

204 MR DOMINIC FFRENCH DAVIS, Lambourn

Postal: **College House, 3 Oxford Street, Lambourn, Hungerford, Berkshire, RG17 8XP**
Contacts: **YARD** (01488) 73675 **Home** (01488) 72342 **FAX** (01488) 73675 **MOBILE** (07831) 118764
E-MAIL ffrenchdavis@btinternet.com WEBSITE www.ffrenchdavis.com

1 **CHILL IN THE WOOD**, 7, br m Desert King (IRE)—Zaffaranni (IRE) **Mr D. G. Cramm**
2 **COSTANTE VIA (IRE)**, 5, b m Milan—Spirit Rock (IRE) **D. J. S. Ffrench Davis**
3 **IF I WERE A BOY (IRE)**, 9, b m Invincible Spirit (IRE)—Attymon Lill (IRE) **Mr R. F. Haynes**
4 **JELLY MONGER (IRE)**, 4, b f Strategic Prince—Royal Jelly **Gary Black & Mark Duthie**
5 **KNOCKALONGI**, 10, b g Fair Mix (IRE)—Understudy **D. J. S. Ffrench Davis**
6 **ROLLING DICE**, 5, b g Rail Link—Breathing Space (USA) **Miss Alison Jones**
7 **SURF IN SEPTEMBER (IRE)**, 7, b m September Storm (GER)—Juno Beach **Mr D. G. Cramm**
8 **VAN HUYSEN (IRE)**, 4, br g Excellent Art—Tara Too (IRE) **Prof C. D. Green**
9 **WHATTHEBUTLERSAW (IRE)**, 7, br g Arcadio (GER)—Phar From Men (IRE) **D. J. S. Ffrench Davis**

THREE-YEAR-OLDS

10 **BELLE OF SEVILLE**, b f Duke of Marmalade (IRE)—Kekova **Mr R. F. Haynes**
11 **CHARLIE PARKER (IRE)**, b g Mybeycharlie (IRE)—Solaria (IRE) **D. J. S. Ffrench Davis**
12 **MANSON**, ch c Equiano (FR)—Swain's Gold (USA) **The Agincourt Partnership**
13 **MIDNIGHT MOOD**, b f Aqlaam—Inflammable **Miss Alison Jones**
14 **MONDAY CLUB**, ch g Strategic Prince—Support Fund (IRE) **Faber, Ffrench Davis, Head & Taylor**

TWO-YEAR-OLDS

15 B f 25/2 Sir Prancealot (IRE)—Hi Katriona (IRE) (Second Empire (IRE)) (30000) **N. Pickett**

Other Owners: G. H. Black, Mr J. O. Chapman, M. Duthie, Mr E. S. G. Faber, Mr N. A. Fenn, Mrs P. Ffrench Davis, Mr G. J. Head, Mr T. G. Holroyd, Mrs J. E. Taylor.

Assistant Trainer: Avery Ffrench Davis

Jockey (flat): James Doyle. **Jockey (NH):** Mark Grant.

205 MR GUISEPPE FIERRO, Hednesford

Postal: **Bentley Brook House, Rawnsley Road, Hednesford, Cannock, Staffordshire, WS12 1RB**
Contacts: **HOME/YARD** (01543) 879611 **MOBILE** (07976) 321468

1 **JUST LIKE BETH**, 8, b m Proclamation (IRE)—Just Beth **G. Fierro**
2 **LITTLE DOTTY**, 7, br m Erhaab (USA)—Marsh Marigold **G. Fierro**
3 **RED HOTT ROBBIE**, 7, b g Revoque (IRE)—Abbiejo (IRE) **G. Fierro**
4 **SUNDANCE BOY**, 7, gr g Proclamation (IRE)—Just Beth **G. Fierro**

Assistant Trainer: M Fierro

206 MRS MARJORIE FIFE, Stillington

Postal: **White Thorn Farm, Stillington, Easingwold, York, YO61 1LT**
Contacts: **PHONE** (01347) 822012 **MOBILE** (07890) 075217
E-MAIL wfife10416@aol.com

1 **BEST TRIP (IRE)**, 9, b g Whipper (USA)—Tereed Elhawa **Mrs J. Mchugh**
2 **CLASSIC SENIORITY**, 4, b g Kyllachy—Dramatic Solo **Mr D. & Mr S. Woodall**
3 **DREESE (IRE)**, 5, b g Dandy Man (IRE)—Lucky Flirt (USA) **HuggyMac Racing**
4 **FLY WITH EMIRATES (IRE)**, 4, b g Lawman (FR)—Keriyka (IRE)
5 **INEXES**, 4, gr g Exceed And Excel (AUS)—Likeable **21st Century Racing**
6 **INTENSE STARLET (IRE)**, 5, ch m Intense Focus (USA)—Glady Starlet (GER) **Mrs E. M. Burke**
7 **PERFECT WORDS (IRE)**, 6, ch g Thousand Words—Zilayah (USA) **Green Lane**
8 **POLITICO**, 4, ch f Medicean—Tatawut **Mr & Mrs D. C. Coates**
9 **ROYAL HOLIDAY (IRE)**, 9, ch g Captain Rio—Sunny Slope **Mrs M. Turner**
10 **SALTARELLO (IRE)**, 4, b g Fast Company (IRE)—Step Dancing **Mrs M. Turner**
11 **SARTORI**, 5, b g Elnadim (USA)—Little Caroline (IRE) **R. W. Fife**

MRS MARJORIE FIFE - Continued

12 **SAVANNAH BEAU**, 4, b f Major Cadeaux—Mancunian Way **Market Avenue Racing Club Ltd**
13 **SHERMAN MCCOY**, 10, ch g Reset (AUS)—Naomi Wildman (USA) **Mr T. W. Fife**
14 **SIMMPLY SAM**, 9, b m Nomadic Way (USA)—Priceless Sam **Mrs S. M. Barker**
15 **SIRPERTAN**, 5, b g Sir Percy—Tanwir **Mr G. Smith**
16 5, B g Notnowcato—Special Beat
17 **WEE HOLIO (IRE)**, 5, b g Tikkanen (USA)—Eskimo Kiss (IRE) **Mr C. Buckingham**

THREE-YEAR-OLDS

18 **TRIBESMAN**, ch g Equiano (FR)—Millsini **Mr T. W. Fife**

TWO-YEAR-OLDS

19 B c 27/1 Major Cadeaux—Mancunian Way (Green Desert (USA)) (28571)

Other Owners: Mrs B. Catterall, A. W. Catterall, Mrs A. Coates, Mr D. C. Coates, Mr A. Huggins, Mr J. Mcalpine, Mr C. R. Piercy, Mr D. Woodall, Mr S. Woodall.

---

207 MR TIM FITZGERALD, Malton
Postal: **Norton Grange, Norton, Malton, North Yorkshire, YO17 9EA**
Contacts: **OFFICE** (01653) 692718 **FAX** (01653) 600214 **MOBILE** (07950) 356437
E-MAIL fitzgeraldracing@hotmail.com

1 **KASTELA STARI**, 9, b m Beat Hollow—Campaspe **T. J. Fitzgerald**
2 **OBBOORR**, 7, b g Cape Cross (IRE)—Felawnah (USA) **Dukes Racing 1**
3 **RAINFORD GLORY (IRE)**, 6, ch g Rock of Gibraltar (IRE)—My Dolly Madison **Dukes Racing 1**
4 **SKYWARDS MILES (IRE)**, 4, b f New Approach (IRE)—Park Twilight (IRE) **Dukes Racing 1**
5 **WARFARE**, 7, b g Soviet Star (USA)—Fluffy **Dukes Racing 1**

Other Owners: Mrs K. Dukes, O. R. Dukes.

---

208 MR JOHN FLINT, Bridgend
Postal: **Cherry Tree, 71 Woodlands Park, Kenfig Hill, Bridgend, Mid-Glamorgan, CF33 6EB**
Contacts: **PHONE** (01656) 744347 **FAX** (01656) 744347 **MOBILE** (07581) 428173
E-MAIL john@johnflintracing.com **WEBSITE** www.johnflintracing.com

1 **ARIAN (IRE)**, 4, b f King's Theatre (IRE)—Brave Betsy (IRE) **Mr D. M. Mathias**
2 **AYLA'S EMPEROR**, 7, b m Holy Roman Emperor (IRE)—Ayla (IRE) **Mr L. H. & Mrs T. Evans**
3 **BERNISDALE**, 8, ch m Bertolini (USA)—Carradale **Mr R. M. James**
4 **BOB WILL (IRE)**, 11, b g Bob's Return (IRE)—Mini Moo Min **J. L. Flint**
5 **EDDIEMAURICE (IRE)**, 5, ch g Captain Rio—Annals **Mr D. M. Mathias**
6 **GENTLE NATURE**, 5, b g Dr Massini (IRE)—Eagle's Landing **Palms Landscaping Limited**
7 **KAYF MOSS**, 8, b g Kayf Tara—Madam Mosso **Mr L. H. & Mrs T. Evans**
8 **LAC SACRE (FR)**, 7, b g Bering—Lady Glorieuse (FR) **Mr L. H. & Mrs T. Evans**
9 **MERCHANT OF MILAN**, 8, b g Milan—Repunzel **Mr & Mrs A. J. Mutch**
10 **MOSS STREET**, 6, b g Moss Vale (IRE)—Street Style (IRE) **Burnham Plastering & Drylining Ltd**
11 **RUN BOB RUN**, 5, b g Beat All (USA)—Rash-Gale (IRE) **Katchar Racing**
12 **TAROUM (IRE)**, 9, b g Refuse To Bend (IRE)—Taraza (IRE) **J. L. Flint**
13 **TOE TO TOE (IRE)**, 8, br g Presenting—Tavildara (IRE) **Palms Landscaping Limited**
14 **TRAVIS BICKLE (IRE)**, 5, b g Sky Mesa (USA)—Out of Woods (USA) **Mr D. M. Mathias**
15 **URBAN SPACE**, 10, ch g Sulamani (IRE)—Rasmalai **Mr J. Tucker**

THREE-YEAR-OLDS

16 **BAZ'S BOY**, b g Compton Place—Spunger **Mr B. M. Jones**

Other Owners: Mr L. H. Evans, Mrs T. Evans, Mrs S. Mutch, Mr A. J. Mutch, Mrs T. J. Raymond, Mr S. A. Raymond.

Assistant Trainer: Mrs Martine Louise Flint (07968) 044487

Jockey (NH): Rhys Flint.

209 **MR DAVID FLOOD, Swindon**
Postal: **15 High Street, Chiseldon, Swindon, Wiltshire, SN4 0NG**
Contacts: **PHONE (07919) 340619**
E-MAIL **davidflood1@hotmail.co.uk**

1 BAZOOKA (IRE), 5, b g Camacho—Janadam (IRE) **Mr N. Ahmad**
2 JIM THE DANGER, 6, b g Lucarno (USA)—Kompete

TWO-YEAR-OLDS

3 B f 3/2 Sir Percy—Bruma (IRE) (Footstepsinthesand)
4 Ch f 13/2 Piccolo—Crochet (IRE) (Mark of Esteem (IRE))
5 B c 17/3 Piccolo—Dilli Dancer (Dansili)

210 **MR STEVE FLOOK, Leominster**
Postal: **The Granary Stables, Downwood Farm, Shobdon, Leominster, Herefordshire, HR6 9NH**
Contacts: **MOBILE (07811) 511566**
E-MAIL **lwallace@btinternet.com**

1 AL FATIH (IRE), 5, b g Montjeu (IRE)—Sky High Flyer **G. Byard**
2 BLACK JACK JAXON, 4, gr g Fair Mix (IRE)—No Virtue **S. M. Flook**
3 FAST SCAT (IRE), 4, ch f Scat Daddy (USA)—Furusato (USA) **Chasing Charlie Syndicate**
4 GOLD HUNTER (IRE), 6, b g Invincible Spirit (IRE)—Goldthroat (IRE) **G. Byard**
5 GRANDIOSO (IRE), 9, b g Westerner—Champagne Warrior (IRE) **Foxhunters In Mind**
6 MISS TILLY OSCAR (IRE), 10, b m Oscar (IRE)—Whisky Chaser **Mrs S. E. Vaughan**
7 MON GARCON FRANKIE, 4, ch g Sulamani (IRE)—Rhetorique (FR) **Chasing Charlie Syndicate**
8 OVER THE BRIDGE, 6, b g Multiplex—Do It On Dani **The Ever Hopeful Partnership**
9 ROCK OF AGES, 7, ch g Pivotal—Magic Peak (IRE) **Chasing Charlie Syndicate**
10 STEADY EDDIE, 6, b g Zafeen (FR)—Indian Girl **Mr E. C. Everall**

Other Owners: Mr A. Morris, Mr R. T. R. Price, Miss L. Wallace.

Assistant Trainer: Lynn Wallace

211 **MR TONY FORBES, Uttoxeter**
Postal: **Hill House Farm, Poppits Lane, Stramshall, Uttoxeter, Staffordshire, ST14 5EX**
Contacts: **PHONE (01889) 562722 MOBILE (07967) 246571**
E-MAIL **tony@thimble.net**

1 MADRASA (IRE), 8, b g High Chaparral (IRE)—Shir Dar (FR) **Mr A. L. Forbes**
2 MEDIEVAL BISHOP (IRE), 7, b g Bachelor Duke (USA)—On The Backfoot (IRE) **Mr A. L. Forbes**
3 NOLECCE, 9, ch g Reset (AUS)—Ghassanah **Mr A. L. Forbes**

Assistant Trainer: Mr Tim Eley

212 **MRS PAM FORD, Hereford**
Postal: **Stone House Stables, Preston Wynne, Hereford, Herefordshire, HR1 3PB**
Contacts: **HOME/FAX (01432) 820604 MOBILE (07733) 152051**
E-MAIL **pam_ford@hotmail.co.uk**

1 APACHE CHIEF, 8, b g Tikkanen (USA)—Dara's Course (IRE) **K. R. Ford**
2 CAPTAIN OATS (IRE), 13, b g Bahhare (USA)—Adarika **Miss V. A. M. Davies**
3 FREDDIE BEAR, 8, b g Grape Tree Road—Zajira (IRE) **Miss V. A. M. Davies**
4 RUNNING SQUAW, 8, ch m Denounce—Georgie McTaggart **K. R. Ford**
5 SAMTHEMAN, 11, b g Dancing Spree (USA)—Sisterly **K. R. Ford**

Assistant Trainer: Mr K Ford

Jockey (flat): Royston Ffrench. **Jockey (NH):** James Davies.

213 MR RICHARD FORD, Garstang
Postal: **The Paddocks, Strickens Lane, Barnacre, Garstang, Preston, Lancashire, PR3 1UD**
Contacts: **PHONE (01995) 605790 (07802) 764094 MOBILE (07976) 522768**
E-MAIL clarksonhorses@barnacre.fsbusiness.co.uk
WEBSITE www.lancashireracingstables.co.uk

1 **AN FEAR CIUIN (IRE)**, 5, b g Galileo (IRE)—Potion **D. M. Proos**
2 **AUTHENTICITY**, 5, b g Authorized (IRE)—Jubilee **Mrs S. E. Barclay**
3 **CABBIES LOU**, 4, b f Sakhee's Secret—Regal Run (USA) **Mr G. Budden**
4 **DEBT TO SOCIETY (IRE)**, 9, ch g Moscow Society (USA)—Nobody's Darling (IRE) **Mr & Mrs G. E. Pickering**
5 **DERRYFADDA (IRE)**, 7, b g Scorpion (IRE)—San Diego (IRE) **Mr & Mrs G. E. Pickering**
6 **DOLPHIN ROCK**, 9, b g Mark of Esteem (IRE)—Lark In The Park (IRE) **MIA Racing**
7 **DR BEAUJOLAIS (IRE)**, 10, b g Dr Massini (IRE)—Satlin (IRE) **Winks Racing**
8 4, B g Black Sam Bellamy (IRE)—Empress of Light **The Four Aces**
9 **INSOLENCEOFOFFICE (IRE)**, 8, b g Kodiac—Sharp Diversion (USA) **CCCNLP**
10 **LATE FOR SUPPER (IRE)**, 7, ch g Kahtan—Tillery (IRE) **The Coz Syndicate**
11 **MISSESGEEJAY**, 6, br m Beat All (USA)—Riverbank Rainbow **Brandsby Racing**
12 4, B g Bertolini (USA)—Monica Geller **Mrs S. E. Barclay**
13 **MOONBI CREEK (IRE)**, 9, b g Fasliyev (USA)—Moonbi Range (IRE) **Mrs S. E. Barclay**
14 **MOUNT CHEIRON (USA)**, 5, b g Henrythenavigator (USA)—Chalamont (IRE) **The Style Council**
15 **ONDA DISTRICT (IRE)**, 4, b g Oasis Dream—Leocorno (IRE) **Messrs Chrimes, Winn & Wilson**
16 **PRESENT TREND (IRE)**, 7, br m Presenting—Trendy Attire (IRE) **Network Racing**
17 **PRINCE OF TIME**, 4, ch g Bahamian Bounty—Touching (IRE) **Mr B. Hartley**
18 **RAINBOW BEAUTY**, 6, ch m Manduro—Just Like A Woman **Messrs Chrimes, Winn & Wilson**
19 **ROB ROYAL (IRE)**, 8, b g Royal Anthem (USA)—Shamble Street (IRE) **Mrs S. E. Barclay**
20 **SAN PIETRO (FR)**, 8, b g Poliglote—Sainte Berinne (FR) **Mrs C. P. Lees-Jones**
21 **SWALEDALE LAD (IRE)**, 9, b g Arakan (USA)—Tadjnama (USA) **Mr W. D. Challoner**
22 **TOWN ORATOR**, 4, gr g Proclamation (IRE)—Town House **J. H. Chrimes**
23 **UNIDEXTER (IRE)**, 6, br g Footstepsinthesand—Run To Jane (IRE) **Winks Racing**

THREE-YEAR-OLDS

24 B g Arcano (IRE)—Mystic Smile (IRE) **Winks Racing**
25 **THE ROOF HUB**, b c Dick Turpin (IRE)—Glen Molly (IRE) **D. M. Proos**

TWO-YEAR-OLDS

26 B g 2/4 Sleeping Indian—Dulally (Dubawi (IRE)) **The Bounty Hunters**

Other Owners: Mr Leo Aspinall, Mr Alan Ayres, Mr John Ball, Mr Tony Ball, Mr Edd Briscoe, Mrs Leslie Buckley, Mr Paul Bushell, Mr Andrew Calderbank, Mr John Calderbank, Mr Andy Clarke, Mr Paul Clarkson, Mr John Jackson, Mr Hugh Logan, Mr Richard Mattinson, Mr Geoff Metcalfe, Mr Dion Penston, Mr Brian Postlethwaite, Mr David Price, Mr Paul Steadman, Mr Phillip Thompson, Mr Alan Tickle, Mr Matthew Tickle, Mrs Irene Tickle, Mr Matt Watkinson, Mr Trevor Willis, Mr Clive Wilson.

Assistant Trainer: Stella Barclay

Jockey (flat): Graham Lee. **Jockey (NH):** Harry Challoner. **Apprentice:** Callum Rodriguez.

214 MRS RICHENDA FORD, Blandford Forum
Postal: **Garlands Farm, The Common, Okeford Fitzpaine, Blandford Forum, Dorset, DT11 0RT**
Contacts: **MOBILE (07800) 634846**
E-MAIL richendasnook@hotmail.co.uk

1 **BALL HOPPER (IRE)**, 12, ch g Rock Hopper—Lady Vic (IRE) **Mr & Mrs K. B. Snook**
2 5, B m Pasternak—Coolers Quest
3 **DAYS AHEAD (IRE)**, 9, ch g Kheleyf (USA)—Hushaby (IRE) **Mr & Mrs K. B. Snook**
4 **MADDOXTOWN (IRE)**, 10, b g Luso—Augusta Victoria **Mr & Mrs K. B. Snook**
5 **SOMERBY (IRE)**, 13, b g Sadler's Wells (USA)—Oriental Mystique **Mr & Mrs K. B. Snook**
6 **THE CAT'S AWAY (IRE)**, 8, ch g Alderbrook—Mrs Jack Russell (IRE) **Mr & Mrs K. B. Snook**
7 **THEATRE MILL (IRE)**, 8, b g King's Theatre (IRE)—River Mill (IRE) **Mr & Mrs K. B. Snook**

Other Owners: Mrs M. Snook, K. B. Snook.

215 MR BRIAN FORSEY, Taunton
Postal: **Three Oaks, Ash Priors, Taunton, Somerset, TA4 3NQ**
Contacts: **PHONE (01823) 433914 MOBILE (07747) 392760**
E-MAIL forsey2001@yahoo.com

1 **AUREATE**, 12, ch g Jade Robbery (USA)—Anne d'autriche (IRE) **B. Forsey**
2 **BARISTA (IRE)**, 8, b g Titus Livius (FR)—Cappuccino (IRE) **Three Oaks Racing & Mrs P Bosley**
3 **DROPZONE (USA)**, 7, b g Smart Strike (CAN)—Dalisay (IRE) **Mr Alan Stevens & Mr Brian Forsey**
4 **FOLLOW THE MASTER**, 10, b g Alflora (IRE)—Daisy May **Mrs P. M. Bosley**

THREE-YEAR-OLDS
5 Ch f Winker Watson—Quaker Parrot **B. Forsey**

Other Owners: A. G. Stevens.

Assistant Trainer: Susan Forsey

216 MISS SANDY FORSTER, Kirk Yetholm
Postal: **Halterburn Head, Yetholm, Kelso, Roxburghshire, TD5 8PP**
Contacts: **PHONE/FAX (01573) 420615 FAX (01573) 420615**
MOBILE (07880) 727877 or (07976) 587315
E-MAIL clivestorey@btinternet.com

1 **CHARMING MINSTREL**, 7, b g Needwood Blade—Madam Bijou **Miss S. E. Forster**
2 4, B g Overbury (IRE)—Dusky Dante (IRE)
3 **HIGH FAIR**, 10, b m Grape Tree Road—Miss Tango **D. Simpson**
4 **LOWANBEHOLD (IRE)**, 9, gr g Cloudings (IRE)—Marble Quest (IRE) **C. Storey**
5 **NO SUCH NUMBER**, 8, b g King's Best (USA)—Return (USA) **J M & H M Crichton & Dave Skeldon**
6 **SEE THE LEGEND**, 11, b m Midnight Legend—Amys Delight **The Border Racers**
7 **TRIONA BEY**, 6, b m And Beyond (IRE)—Catriona **C. Storey**
8 **WINTER LINK**, 6, b m Rail Link—Winter Bloom (USA) **D. Simpson**

Other Owners: J. M. Crichton, Miss H. M. Crichton, D. A. Skeldon.

Assistant Trainer: C. Storey

Jockey (NH): Adrian Lane.

217 MISS JOANNE FOSTER, Ilkley
Postal: **Brookleigh Farm, Burley Road, Menston, Ilkley, West Yorkshire, LS29 6NS**
Contacts: **PHONE (07980) 301808 MOBILE (07980) 301808**
E-MAIL info@jofosterracing.co.uk WEBSITE www.jofosterracing.co.uk

1 **ALLTHEDOLLARS (IRE)**, 6, ch g Stowaway—Pamsy Wamsy (IRE) **Mad For Fun & Partners (2)**
2 **CAMACHOICE (IRE)**, 6, b g Camacho—Nouvelle Reve (GER) **Mad 4 Fun & Partners**
3 **CARA COURT (IRE)**, 10, b g Court Cave (IRE)—Tarasandy (IRE) **Eshwin & Golden Racing Partnership**
4 **CELTIC ABBEY**, 9, br g Overbury (IRE)—Celtic Native (IRE) **The Golden Syndicate**
5 **CHASE THE WIND (IRE)**, 7, ch g Spadoun (FR)—Astreeasthewind (IRE) **J. Nixon**
6 **HOUNDSCOURT (IRE)**, 9, b g Court Cave (IRE)—Broken Rein (IRE) **The Berry Syndicate**
7 **OUR PHYLLI VERA (IRE)**, 7, b m Motivator—With Colour **Golden Syndicate & Mrs L Pearson**
8 **OUTTILALLHOURS (IRE)**, 8, br g Dr Massini (IRE)—Cherry Vale (IRE) **Eshwin Racing & Partners**
9 **PINEROLO**, 10, b g Milan—Hollybush (IRE) **Golden Syndicate & Partner**
10 **RAKNRUIN (IRE)**, 6, ch g Rakti—Barrell Rose (IRE) **Miss J. E. Foster**
11 **URBAN GALE (IRE)**, 11, b g City Honours (USA)—Margale (IRE) **P. Foster**

Other Owners: Mr J. Batty, J. Berry, Mr N. J. Curtin, Mrs L. E. Pearson, Mr K. Quigley, Mr J. A. Saxby, Mr D. Taylor.

Assistant Trainer: P. Foster

218 **MR JIMMY FOX, Marlborough**
Postal: **Highlands Farm Stables, Herridge, Collingbourne Ducis, Marlborough, Wiltshire, SN8 3EG**
Contacts: **PHONE** (01264) 850218 **(07931)** 724358 **MOBILE** (07702) 880010
E-MAIL jcfoxtrainer@aol.com

1 DREAMING AGAIN, 6, b g Young Ern—Maedance **The Dancing Partners**
2 FRANKIE, 5, gr g Firebreak—Winterbourne **R. E. Kavanagh**
3 GRACIOUS GEORGE (IRE), 6, b g Oratorio (IRE)—Little Miss Gracie **Mrs B. A. Fuller**
4 HEDGE END (IRE), 5, gr m Verglas (IRE)—Trilemma **The Lads & Lasses**
5 HENRY GRACE (IRE), 5, b h Oratorio (IRE)—Little Miss Gracie **Barbara Fuller & Claire Underwood**
6 NEWTOWN CROSS (IRE), 6, ch g Kheleyf (USA)—Sacred Pearl (IRE) **Mutton & Lamb**
7 STAR PURSUITS, 4, b f Pastoral Pursuits—Garter Star **Mrs S. J. Fox**
8 THE WEE CHIEF (IRE), 10, ch g King Charlemagne (USA)—La Belle Clare (IRE) **R. E. Kavanagh**
9 WILD FLOWER (IRE), 4, b f Approve (IRE)—Midsummernitedream (GER) **Mrs S. J. Fox**

THREE-YEAR-OLDS

10 FACE YOUR DEMONS, b f Stimulation (IRE)—Psychic's Dream **Mrs S. J. Fox**
11 GRACEFUL JAMES (IRE), ch c Rock of Gibraltar (IRE)—Little Miss Gracie **Abacus Employment Services Ltd**
12 PURPLE BELLE, br f Assertive—Stunning In Purple (IRE) **Mrs B. A. Fuller**

Other Owners: Mrs E. Estall, Mr D. S. Estall, Mr C. Fiford, Mrs C. C. Underwood.

Assistant Trainer: Sarah-Jane Fox

Jockey (flat): Pat Dobbs.

---

219 **MISS SUZZANNE FRANCE, Norton**
Postal: **Cheesecake Hill House, Cheesecake Hill, Norton, Malton, North Yorkshire, YO17 9PJ**
Contacts: **PHONE** (01653) 691947 **FAX** (01653) 691947 **MOBILE** (07904) 117531
E-MAIL suzzannemunchie@talk21.com
WEBSITE www.suzzannefranceracing.com / www.newstartracing.co.uk

1 AD VITAM (IRE), 8, ch g Ad Valorem (USA)—Love Sonnet **Newstart Partnership**
2 GEORGE BAILEY (IRE), 4, b g Zebedee—Zuzu (IRE) **Newstart Partnership**
3 STAMP DUTY (IRE), 8, b g Ad Valorem (USA)—Lothian Lass (IRE) **Newstart Partnership**

THREE-YEAR-OLDS

4 WHISPERING WOLF, b f Amadeus Wolf—Ashover Amber **Newstart Partnership**

Other Owners: Mrs P. France, Mr P. France, Newstart Partnership.

Assistant Trainer: Mr Aaron James

Amateur: Mr Aaron James.

---

220 **MR DEREK FRANKLAND, Brackley**
Postal: **Springfields, Mixbury, Brackley, Northamptonshire, NN13 5RR**
Contacts: **FAX** (01280) 847334 **MOBILE** (07763) 020406
E-MAIL dsfrankland@aol.com

1 REBEL HIGH (IRE), 12, ch g Hymns On High—Celia's Fountain (IRE) **D. S. Frankland & D. J. Trott**
2 TOO HOT TO BOUGGIE, 5, b m Tobougg (IRE)—Princess Hotpot (IRE) **D. S. Frankland & D. J. Trott**
3 WALKABOUT CREEK (IRE), 9, b g Alderbrook—La Mouette (USA) **D. S. Frankland & D. J. Trott**

Other Owners: D. S. Frankland, Mr D. J. Trott.

Jockey (NH): David Bass, Harry Skelton, Liam Treadwell.

221   MR JAMES FROST, Buckfastleigh
Postal: Hawson Stables, Buckfastleigh, Devon, TQ11 0HP
Contacts: YARD (01364) 642267 HOME (01364) 642332 FAX (01364) 643182
MOBILE (07860) 220229

1 **ALEFOU D'AIRY (FR)**, 6, b g Anzillero (GER)—Lafolie d'airy (FR) **Share My Dream**
2 **ARCHIE RICE (USA)**, 10, b g Arch (USA)—Gold Bowl (USA) **Frost Racing Club**
3 **ARTY BELLA**, 5, b m Overbury (IRE)—Gertrude Webb **Approved Air Ltd**
4 **BOGOSS DU PERRET (FR)**, 5, b br g Malinas (GER)—Lady Paques (FR) **N. W. Lake**
5 **HURRICANE RIDGE (IRE)**, 7, b g Hurricane Run (IRE)—Warrior Wings **Mrs J F Bury & Mrs K Morgan**
6 **ICE KONIG (FR)**, 7, gr g Epalo (GER)—Isarwelle (GER) **Mr T. J. G. Martin**
7 **LA VOIX (FR)**, 4, b f Voix du Nord (FR)—Loupaline (FR) **Richards Racing**
8 **MISS SISKIN**, 7, b m Morpeth—Miss Grace **J. D. Frost**
9 **MONET MOOR**, 7, b m Morpeth—Miracle Monarch **Frost Racing Club**
10 **RAILWAY STORM (IRE)**, 11, ch g Snurge—Stormy Bee (IRE) **Mr C. Coward**
11 **RAILWAY VIC (IRE)**, 9, b g Old Vic—Penny Apples (IRE) **Frost Racing Club**
12 **RUSTY NAIL (IRE)**, 11, b g Tikkanen (USA)—Aoki (IRE) **Frost Racing Club**
13 **SANGRAM (IRE)**, 9, b g Blueprint (IRE)—Margeno's Fountain (IRE) **Mr T. Saye**
14 **SCHOOL FOR SCANDAL (IRE)**, 8, b g Pivotal—Sensation **Mr C. Unwin**
15 **THEGREENDALEROCKET (IRE)**, 7, b g Oscar (IRE)—Classy Society (IRE) **Approved Air Ltd**
16 **UNION SAINT (FR)**, 8, b g Saint des Saints (FR)—Us Et Coutumes (FR) **P. M. Tosh**

Other Owners: Mrs J. F. Bury, Mr Geoff Easson, Mr J. D. Frost, Mr M. Kay, Mr R. H. G. Michelmore, Mrs K. Morgan, Mr B. A. Robarts, Ms H. Vernon-Jones.

Assistant Trainer: G. Frost. **Amateur:** Miss Bryony Frost.

222   MR KEVIN FROST, Market Drayton
Postal: Helshaw Grange, Warrant Road, Stoke Heath, Market Drayton, Shropshire, TF9 2JP
Contacts: PHONE (01630) 638855 (07748) 873092 MOBILE (07919) 370081
E-MAIL info@kevinfrostracing.co.uk WEBSITE www.kevinfrostracing.co.uk

1 **BROADSWORD (IRE)**, 4, ch f Dandy Man (IRE)—Petticoat Hill (UAE) **Mr David Slater**
2 **CHIEFTAIN'S CHOICE (IRE)**, 7, b g King's Theatre (IRE)—Fairy Native (IRE) **Mr C. S. Hinchy**
3 **CLANCY'S CROSS (IRE)**, 7, b g Oscar (IRE)—Murphy's Lady (IRE) **Mr K. Frost**
4 **DRUMLANG (IRE)**, 10, b g Soviet Star (USA)—Sherekiya (IRE) **Mr M. Roberts & Mr P. E. Roberts**
5 5, B m Multiplex—Evelith Abbey (IRE) **Playboy Kennels**
6 **GREAT HALL**, 6, b g Halling (USA)—L'affaire Monique **Mr C. S. Hinchy**
7 **HARDY BLACK (IRE)**, 5, b g Pastoral Pursuits—Wondrous Story (USA) **Wildcard Racing Syndicate X1**
8 5, B m Shantou (USA)—Morning Calm
9 **MOULIN ROUGE (DEN)**, 5, ch m Zambezi Sun—Embattle (FR)
10 **RACING KNIGHT (IRE)**, 4, b g Sir Percy—Salydora (FR) **Mr C. S. Hinchy**
11 **RACING SPIRIT**, 4, ch g Sir Percy—Suertuda **Mr K. Frost**
12 **ROYAL ROMAN**, 4, b f Holy Roman Emperor (IRE)—Noble Penny **Mr David Slater**
13 4, B f Black Sam Bellamy (IRE)—Samrana (FR) **Playboy Kennels**
14 4, B f Milan—Santia **Playboy Kennels**
15 **SEVERAL (USA)**, 4, b g Rock Hard Ten (USA)—Proud Fact (USA) **Mr K. Frost**
16 **SHAMLAN (IRE)**, 4, br g Shamardal (USA)—Atamana (IRE) **Mr K. Frost**
17 **SINGULAR QUEST**, 4, ch g Dalakhani (IRE)—Singuliere (IRE) **Mr K. Frost**
18 **SURF AND TURF (IRE)**, 10, ch g Beneficial—Clear Top Waltz (IRE) **Mr C. S. Hinchy**
19 **SWNYMOR (IRE)**, 7, b g Dylan Thomas (IRE)—Propaganda (IRE) **Mr K. Frost**
20 **TAHIRA (GER)**, 6, ch m Doyen (IRE)—Tennessee Queen (GER) **Mr C. S. Hinchy**
21 **THE CLONLISK BUG (IRE)**, 6, b g Scorpion (IRE)—Apollo Lady **Smokey & The Bandits**
22 **TOGA TIGER (IRE)**, 9, b g Antonius Pius (USA)—Minerwa (GER) **Jan Mead Kelly Gould**

THREE-YEAR-OLDS

23 B g Kheleyf (USA)—Lady Darayna **Mr K. Frost**
24 B g Bushranger (IRE)—Little Doll **Mr Phil Slater**
25 **MURDANOVA (IRE)**, gr c Zebedee—Agnista (IRE) **Mr Phil Slater**

Other Owners: Mr S. W. Deakin, Mr Carl Hinchy, Mrs Jan Mead, Mr D. Mead, Playboy Kennels, Mr M. Roberts, Mr P. E. Roberts, Mr P. Slater, Mr D. Slator, Wildcard Racing Syndicate.

Jockey (NH): Brian Hughes. **Conditional:** Jake Hodson.

223 **MR HUGO FROUD, Bruton**
Postal: **Redlynch Farm, Redlynch, Nr Bruton, Somerset, BA10 0NH**
Contacts: **MOBILE (07590) 413550**
E-MAIL hugo.froud@hugofroudracing.com WEBSITE www.hugofroudracing.com

1 **BEAUCHAMP VIKING**, 12, b g Compton Admiral—Beauchamp Jade **Mrs M. S. Emery**
2 **COEUR TANTRE (IRE)**, 5, ch g Fruits of Love (USA)—Ding Dong Belle **The Aeolus Syndicate**
3 **DARDANELLA**, 9, b m Alflora (IRE)—Ella Falls (IRE) **Mr P. K. J. Langdown**
4 **DEFINING YEAR (IRE)**, 8, b g Hawk Wing (USA)—Tajaathub (USA) **Mr D. Haggerty**
5 **MARKY BOB (IRE)**, 4, b g Turtle Island (IRE)—Bobomy (IRE) **The Marky Bob Syndicate**
6 **OUR ISLAND (IRE)**, 11, b g Turtle Island (IRE)—Linda's Leader (IRE) **Mr P. K. J. Langdown**
7 **WHAT LARKS (IRE)**, 8, b g Pierre—Bint Rosie **Mrs H. A. Heal**

Other Owners: Mr H. C. Froud, Ms G. S. Langford, Mr C. Vaughan-Fowler.

224 **MR HARRY FRY, Seaborough**
Postal: **Flat 1, Manor Farm, Seaborough, Beaminster, Dorset, DT8 3QY**
Contacts: **PHONE (01308) 868192 FAX (01308) 867512**
E-MAIL info@harryfryracing.com WEBSITE www.harryfryracing.com

1 **A PLEIN TEMPS (FR)**, 6, b g Alberto Giacometti (IRE)—
Flower des Champs (FR) **R P B Michaelson & E M Thornton**
2 **ACTING LASS (IRE)**, 5, b g King's Theatre (IRE)—Darrens Lass (IRE) **Nigel & Barbara Collison**
3 **ACTIVIAL (FR)**, 6, gr g Lord du Sud (FR)—Kissmirial (FR) **Potensis Bloodstock Limited**
4 **AIR HORSE ONE**, 5, gr g Mountain High (IRE)—Whisky Rose (IRE) **The Dons**
5 **AMERICAN (FR)**, 6, b g Malinas (GER)—Grande Sultane (FR) **The Jago Family Partnership**
6 **AYALOR (FR)**, 6, b g Khalkevi (IRE)—Physicienne (FR) **Potensis Bloodstock Ltd & Chris Giles**
7 **BABY SLEEP (FR)**, 5, b g Al Namix (FR)—Sleeping Doll (FR) **GDM Partnership**
8 **BAGS GROOVE (IRE)**, 5, b g Oscar (IRE)—Golden Moment (IRE) **M. Pescod**
9 **BEHIND TIME (IRE)**, 5, b g Stowaway—She's Got To Go (IRE) **J. P. McManus**
10 **BILLY MERRIOTT (IRE)**, 10, b g Dr Massini (IRE)—Hurricane Bella (IRE) **G. D. Taylor**
11 **BIM BAM BOUM (FR)**, 5, b g Crossharbour—Quoball (FR) **The Boomers**
12 **BIRETTA**, 5, ch m Kirkwall—Burqa **Potensis Bloodstock Limited**
13 **BITOFAPUZZLE**, 8, b m Tamure (IRE)—Gaelic Gold (IRE) **Potensis Bloodstock Ltd & Chris Giles**
14 **BLACK MISCHIEF**, 4, b g Black Sam Bellamy (IRE)—Miss Mitch (IRE) **Tom Chadney and Friends**
15 **BLUE BUTTONS (IRE)**, 8, b m King's Theatre (IRE)—Babet (IRE) **Harry Fry Racing Club**
16 **BROTHERLY COMPANY (IRE)**, 4, b g Fast Company (IRE)—Good Lady (IRE) **Brian & Sandy Lambert**
17 **CALLING DES BLINS (IRE)**, 4, b f Konig Turf (GER)—Quelye des Blins (FR) **Potensis Bloodstock Limited**
18 **CHALONNIAL (FR)**, 4, ch g Protektor (GER)—Kissmirial (FR) **Mr Chris Giles & Potensis Bloodstock Ltd**
19 **CHARMIX (FR)**, 6, b g Laveron—Open Up (FR) **N. G. Cooper**
20 **DASHING OSCAR (IRE)**, 6, b g Oscar (IRE)—Be My Leader (IRE) **Andy & Sharon Measham**
21 4, B g Milan—Derravaragh Sayra (IRE) **Mr & Mrs P Rooney Partnership**
22 **DESERT QUEEN**, 8, b m Desert King (IRE)—Priscilla **The Jago Family Partnership**
23 **DRUMCLIFF (IRE)**, 5, b g Presenting—Dusty Too **J. P. McManus**
24 **DUBH DES CHAMPS (IRE)**, 4, br g Robin des Champs (FR)—Aneda Dubh (IRE) **Mad Racing Partnership**
25 **FLETCHERS FLYER (IRE)**, 8, b g Winged Love (IRE)—Crystal Chord (IRE) **Masterson Holdings Limited**
26 **GENERAL GINGER**, 6, ch g Generous (IRE)—Nuzzle **Hazard Chase Racing**
27 **GOLDEN BIRTHDAY (FR)**, 5, b g Poliglote—Gold Or Silver (FR) **G. C. Stevens**
28 **GUNNER FIFTEEN (IRE)**, 8, b g Westerner—Grandy Hall (IRE) **Masterson Holdings Limited**
29 **HE'S A CHARMER (IRE)**, 6, gr g Mahler—Sunny South East (IRE) **Andy & Sharon Measham**
30 **HELL'S KITCHEN**, 5, b g Robin des Champs (FR)—Mille Et Une (FR) **J. P. McManus**
31 **HENRYVILLE**, 8, b g Generous (IRE)—Aquavita **R P B Michaelson & E M Thornton**
32 **INSTINGTIVE (IRE)**, 5, b g Scorpion (IRE)—Fully Focused (IRE) **Tom Taylor Racing**
33 **IVOR'S QUEEN (IRE)**, 7, b m King's Theatre (IRE)—Sonnerschien (IRE) **Ivor Perry & Ashton Selway**
34 **JESSBER'S DREAM (IRE)**, 6, b m Milan—Maddy's Supreme (IRE) **Mr Chris Giles & Potensis Bloodstock Ltd**
35 **JOLLY'S CRACKED IT (FR)**, 7, b g Astarabad (USA)—Jolly Harbour **GDM Partnership**
36 **JOLLY'S LEGACY (FR)**, 5, gr g Al Namix (FR)—Jolly Harbour **GDM Partnership**
37 **KARINGA DANCER**, 10, b g Karinga Bay—Miss Flora **H. B. Geddes**
38 5, Br g Kayf Tara—Labelthou (FR)
39 **LADY OF LAMANVER**, 6, b m Lucarno (USA)—Lamanver Homerun **Dr D. Christensen**
40 **LITTLE ACORN**, 5, b m Presenting—Whiteoak (IRE) **Andy & Sharon Measham**
41 **MEME'S HORSE (IRE)**, 6, b g Scorpion (IRE)—Alittlebitofheaven **Masterson Holdings Limited**
42 **MERIBEL MILLIE**, 5, b m Kayf Tara—Ede'iff **Mr A. D. Polson**

MR HARRY FRY - Continued

43 **MICK JAZZ (FR)**, 5, b g Blue Bresil (FR)—Mick Maya (FR) **Potensis Bloodstock Limited**
44 4, B g Milan—Miss Baden (IRE)
45 **MISTERTON**, 5, gr g Sagamix (FR)—Mighty Splash **Wilkin, Orr, Boileau and Sim**
46 **MOUNTAIN EAGLE (IRE)**, 7, b g Mountain High (IRE)—Ceart Go Leor (IRE) **Mahon Racing**
47 **MR KITE**, 5, b g Sixties Icon—Mar Blue (FR) **N. G. Cooper**
48 **NEW VENNTURE (FR)**, 4, b f Kapgarde (FR)—Polyandry (IRE) **The King's Men**
49 **NITROGEN (IRE)**, 9, b g Old Vic—Katday (FR) **C. G. Roach**
50 **NOBLE NED**, 7, b g Kayf Tara—Leachbrook Lady **Westbourne Racing Club & Partners**
51 **OPENING BATSMAN (IRE)**, 10, b g Morozov (USA)—Jolly Signal (IRE) **The Twelfth Man Partnership**
52 **OVERTOWN EXPRESS (IRE)**, 8, br g Overbury (IRE)—Black Secret **Mrs Lorna Squire & Mr Richard Metherell**
53 **PAMPANINI**, 5, b m Milan—Loxhill Lady **Harry Fry Racing Club**
54 **POLAMCO (IRE)**, 7, b g Old Vic—Shanesia (IRE) **Mr A. D. Polson**
55 **POLLYOGAN (IRE)**, 6, br m Oscar (IRE)—Marlogan (IRE) **Somerset Racing**
56 **PRESENTING ARMS (IRE)**, 9, b g Presenting—Banningham Blaze **Mr J. M. Dare**
57 **QUEEN ODESSA (IRE)**, 5, b m King's Theatre (IRE)—Ma Furie (FR) **Mr J. K. Whymark**
58 **RIDGEWAY FLYER**, 5, b g Tobougg (IRE)—Running For Annie **A. J. Norman**
59 **ROMASSOR (FR)**, 8, b g Assessor (IRE)—Baba Roma (FR) **P. E. Atkinson**
60 **ROYALZARO (FR)**, 6, gr g Laveron—Royale Wheeler (FR) **P. M. Warren**
61 **SAINTINGRID (FR)**, 4, b g Saint des Saints (FR)—Pollypink (FR)
62 **SECRET DOOR (IRE)**, 5, b m Stowaway—Cellar Door (IRE) **Mr Simon Munir & Mr Isaac Souede**
63 **SHUIL ROYALE (IRE)**, 11, b g King's Theatre (IRE)—Shuil Na Lee (IRE) **R. P. Fry**
64 **SIR IVAN**, 6, b g Midnight Legend—Tisho **The Eyre Family**
65 **SOLON GLORY (FR)**, 5, b m Solon (GER)—Stille Baroque (FR) **Mrs D. J. White-Hamilton**
66 **SPACE ODDITY (FR)**, 5, b br g Al Namix (FR)—Schoune (FR)
67 **TEMPLATE (IRE)**, 5, ch g Iffraaj—Sagaing **Coral Champions Club**
68 **THOMAS BROWN**, 7, b g Sir Harry Lewis (USA)—Tentsmuir **The Corse Lawners**
69 **TONGANUI (IRE)**, 5, ch g Stowaway—Murrosie (IRE) **The Eyre Family**
70 **UNOWHATIMEANHARRY**, 8, b g Sir Harry Lewis (USA)—Red Nose Lady **Harry Fry Racing Club**
71 **VIVANT POEME (FR)**, 7, b g Early March—Hasta Manana (FR) **Andy & Sharon Measham**
72 **VOIX D'EAU (FR)**, 6, b g Voix du Nord (FR)—Eau de Chesne (FR) **Harry Fry Racing Club**
73 **WATER WILLOW**, 4, b f Tobougg (IRE)—Water Flower **Avalon Surfacing & Construction Co Ltd**
74 **WHATAKNIGHT**, 7, b g Midnight Legend—What A Mover **J. M. Dare, T. Hamlin, J. W. Snook**
75 **ZULU OSCAR**, 7, b g Oscar (IRE)—Loxhill Lady **Caroline Fry & Susie Dilhorne**

THREE-YEAR-OLDS

76 **SAM I (FR)**, gr g Lord du Sud (FR)—Blue Girl Star (FR) **Seuss Racing**

Other Owners: Mr C. Blackburn, P. H. Boss, Mrs J. Calder, G. Calder, Mrs S. Cameron, Mr D. E. Campbell, A. Carr, T. H. Chadney, G. Charlesworth, D. Charlesworth, S. J. Clare, Mr M. F. Cohen, Mrs B. Collison, Mr N. Collison, Mr S. Cullum, R. B. Denny, Viscountess S. J. Dilhorne, Mrs P. E. Dolan-Abrahams, E. J. Dolan-Abrahams, Mr J. N. I. Edwards, Mrs C. A. Eyre, Mr C. G. S. Eyre, Miss R. E. Eyre, Mr H. Eyre, Dr C. E. Fry, R. A. Fry, Mr C. M. Giles, T. Hamlin, Mr T. Hanrahan, Mr W. D. Hawkes, Miss M. L. A. Jago, Mr F. C. A. Jago, Mrs J. L. Jago, Mr P. J. A. Jago, Mr B. Lambert, Mr R. F. Magrath, Mr D. J. Mahon, Mr T. F. McGowan, Mrs S. M. Measham, Mr A. R. Measham, R. J. Metherell, R. P. B. Michaelson, S. E. Munir, Mrs S. Orr, Mr H. T. Pelham, W. I. M. Perry, Mr M. Powell, E. J. Saunders, A. G. Selway, Mr M. Smith, J. W. Snook, Mr I. Souede, Mrs L. Squire, Mr D. J. Stevens, Mr L. A. Taylor, Mr M. J. Taylor, G. M. Thornton, E. M. Thornton, Mr J. P. G. Turner, Mr A. Ward, Westbourne Consultants Ltd, Mr J. C. Whiting, Mr R. C. Wilkin, A. S. Williamson.

Assistant Trainer: Ciara Fry

Jockey (NH): Ryan Mahon, Nick Scholfield, Noel Fehily. **Conditional:** Liam McKenna.
Amateur: Mr Will Biddick, Mr M. Legg.

---

225 **MISS CAROLINE FRYER, Wymondham**
Postal: **Browick Hall Cottage, Browick Road, Wymondham, Norfolk, NR18 9RB**
Contacts: **PHONE** (01953) 601257 **MOBILE** (07768) 056076
E-MAIL caroline@carolinefryerracing.co.uk / c.fryer528@btinternet.com
WEBSITE www.carolinefryerracing.co.uk

1 **BALLOCHMYLE (IRE)**, 6, b g Milan—Not So Green (IRE) **Rosemary Lady Hughes & John Harrison**
2 **MISS EXCELLENCE**, 4, b f Exceed and Excel (AUS)—Hunter's Fortune (USA) **Mr J. D. Ward**
3 **NEW HORIZONS (IRE)**, 6, b g Presenting—Namloc (IRE) **Mr A. & Mrs P. Hurn**
4 **RIDDLESTOWN (IRE)**, 9, b g Cloudings (IRE)—Gandi's Dream (IRE) **Mr J. D. Ward**

Other Owners: Mr J. Harrison, Lady Rosemary Hughes.

226 MR IVAN FURTADO, Wiseton

Postal: **Flat 2, Wiseton Stables, Wiseton, Doncaster, South Yorkshire, DN10 5AE**
Contacts: MOBILE **(07783) 520746**
E-MAIL ivanfurtado@hotmail.co.uk

1 **AFKAR (IRE)**, 8, b g Invincible Spirit (IRE)—Indienne (IRE) **Dallas Racing**
2 **BRIDEY'S LETTUCE (IRE)**, 4, b g Iffraaj—Its On The Air (IRE) **Mr G. M. Copp**
3 **BUSHEPHALUS (IRE)**, 4, gr g Dark Angel (IRE)—White Daffodil (IRE) **Mr S. Laffan**
4 **CASCADIA (IRE)**, 5, b m Mujadil (USA)—Tucum (IRE) **Dallas Racing**
5 **EDDY MERCS**, 4, bl g Striking Ambition—Bella Tutrice (IRE)
6 **EXPOSE**, 8, ch g Compton Place—Show Off **The Giggle Factor Partnership**
7 **GLORIOUS ASSET**, 4, b g Aqlaam—Regal Asset (USA) **The Giggle Factor Partnership**
8 **INTENSICAL (IRE)**, 5, b g Intense Focus (USA)—Christinas Letter (IRE) **The Giggle Factor Partnership**
9 **JUST BE LUCKY (IRE)**, 4, ch g Intense Focus (USA)—Anda **C. V. Wentworth**
10 **KACHOU**, 4, b f Excellent Art—Milwaukee (FR) **Dallas Racing**
11 **MONOPOLI**, 7, ch m Cadeaux Genereux—Jump Ship **The Giggle Factor Partnership**
12 **MYBOYDANIEL**, 4, b g Myboycharlie—Priti Fabulous (IRE) **Dallas Racing**
13 **READY (IRE)**, 6, ch g Elnadim (USA)—Fusili (IRE) **Mr R. Hull**
14 **ROYAL ACQUISITION**, 6, b g Royal Applause—Flavian **Dallas Racing**
15 **SKI BLAST**, 5, ch g Three Valleys (USA)—Chasing Stars **The Giggle Factor Partnership**
16 **SOBER UP**, 4, b f Kheleyf (USA)—Morning After **The Giggle Factor Partnership**
17 **ZAEEM**, 7, b g Echo of Light—Across (ARG) **The Giggle Factor Partnership**

THREE-YEAR-OLDS

18 **EMERALD BAY**, b f Kyllachy—Bahia Emerald (IRE) **Mrs J. Bownes**
19 **IMSHI'S LITTLE BRO (IRE)**, b g Lilbourne Lad (IRE)—Subtle Affair (IRE) **Dallas Racing**
20 **MUSTN'T GRUMBLE (IRE)**, ch g Intense Focus (USA)—Lough Mist (IRE) **From The Front Racing**
21 **NOUVELLI DANCER (IRE)**, b f Lilbourne Lad (IRE)—Kiralik **Mr S. Laffan**
22 B f Haathd—Royal Nashkova **The Giggle Factor Partnership**
23 **SUZU**, ch f Monsieur Bond (IRE)—Moorhouse Girl **Mr R. Hull**

TWO-YEAR-OLDS

24 B c 30/3 Mawatheeq (USA)—Hallingdal (UAE) (Halling (USA)) (2000)
25 B f 4/4 Elnadim (USA)—Jackline (Diktat) (800)
26 Gr c 5/4 Hellvelyn—Phoenix Rising (Dr Fong (USA)) (3500)

Other Owners: Mr S. Franks, Mr A. N. Gargan, Mr M. A. Glassett, Mr J. R. Holt, Mr S. G. Morris, N. P. Sennett.

227 MR JOHN GALLAGHER, Moreton-In-Marsh

Postal: **Grove Farm, Chastleton, Moreton-In-Marsh, Gloucestershire, GL56 0SZ**
Contacts: PHONE/FAX **(01608) 674492 MOBILE (07780) 972663**
E-MAIL gallagherracing@phonecoop.coop WEBSITE www.gallagherracing.com

1 **ADA LOVELACE**, 6, b m Byron—Satin Braid **Mr D. A. Clark**
2 **ANGEL WAY (IRE)**, 7, br m Trans Island—Zilayah (USA) **Mr D. J. Ellis**
3 **HEARTSONG (IRE)**, 7, b m Kheleyf (USA)—Semiquaver (IRE) **John Gallagher**
4 **ISEEMIST (IRE)**, 5, gr m Verglas (IRE)—Krasivaya (IRE) **K. Marsden**
5 **JEANS LADY**, 7, b m Milan—Indian Miss **D. G. Robinson**
6 **LADWEB**, 6, ch g Bertolini (USA)—Adweb **The Juniper Racing Club & Andrew Bell**
7 **LUNGARNO PALACE (USA)**, 5, b g Henrythenavigator (USA)—
Good Time Sally (USA) **Caveat Emptor Partnership**
8 **MAJESTIC MOON (IRE)**, 6, b g Majestic Missile (IRE)—Gala Style (IRE) **Caveat Emptor Partnership**
9 **MAJOR PUSEY**, 4, ch g Major Cadeaux—Pusey Street Lady **C. R. Marks (Banbury)**
10 **OOLOGIST**, 5, gr g Proclamation (IRE)—Orchid's Silver **Mr Charles Stone & Mr Trevor Beeches**
11 **PORT LAIRGE**, 6, b g Pastoral Pursuits—Stylish Clare (IRE) **Quench Racing Partnership**
12 6, B m Arcadio (GER)—Sovana (FR)

MR JOHN GALLAGHER - Continued

THREE-YEAR-OLDS

13 **OUR YOUNG UN**, b g Native Ruler—Dani (IRE)
14 **PUSEY'S SECRET**, b f Sakhee's Secret—Pusey Street Lady **C. R. Marks (Banbury)**

TWO-YEAR-OLDS

15 **GALA CELEBRATION (IRE)**, b c 21/4 Excelebration (IRE)—
Elusive Galaxy (IRE) (Elusive City (USA)) (35437) **Caveat Emptor Partnership**
16 **ILEY BOY**, b c 11/5 Delegator—Menha (Dubawi (IRE)) (2857) **C. R. Marks (Banbury)**
17 **JUNOESQUE**, b f 13/3 Virtual—Snake Skin (Golden Snake (USA)) (1142) **The Juniper Racing Club Ltd**

Other Owners: Mr T. A. Beeches, Mr A. Bell, Mr B. Downard, Mr M. W. Goodall, Mr J. N. Greenley, Mrs B. A. Long, J. F. Long, Mr M. Preedy, Mr C. Stone.

Assistant Trainer: Mrs R. Gallagher

Jockey (flat): Neil Callan, Martin Lane, Chris Catlin, Jamie Spencer.

---

228   MRS ILKA GANSERA-LÉVÊQUE, Newmarket
Postal: **St Wendred's, Hamilton Road, Newmarket, Suffolk, CB8 7JQ**
Contacts: **PHONE (07981) 772715 MOBILE (07855) 532072**
E-MAIL ilkagansera@gmail.com WEBSITE www.gansera-leveque.com

1 **FORCE OF DESTINY (GER)**, 4, b c Galileo (IRE)—Four Roses (IRE) **Graf P. Von Stauffenberg**
2 **SHIROCCO CLOUD**, 4, b f Shirocco (GER)—Cloud Hill **Strawberry Fields Stud**

THREE-YEAR-OLDS

3 **ANNOUSHKA**, b f Proclamation (IRE)—Anapola (GER)
4 **EINSTEIN**, b c Aqlaam—Park Crystal (IRE)
5 **MYLITTLESANCTUM**, b f Mawatheeq (USA)—Sanctum **F. B. B. White**
6 **STAPLEHURST (IRE)**, b f Beat Hollow—Kelpie (IRE) **S. K. McPhee**

TWO-YEAR-OLDS

7 **CAMBRIDGE FAVORITE**, b f 18/3 Aussie Rules (USA)—Sanctum (Medicean) **Strawberry Fields Stud**
8 Ch f 14/3 Native Ruler—Lady Author (Authorized (IRE))
9 **SEPRANI**, b f 17/2 Sepoy (AUS)—King's Guest (IRE) (King's Best (USA)) (20000) **Book 3 Partnership**

Other Owners: Mr S. J. Brown, Mr M. Grant, G. F. L. Robinson.

Assistant Trainer: Stephane Lévêque

Jockey (flat): Raul Da Silva, Lemos De Sousa. **Apprentice:** Tim Clark. **Amateur:** Mr Matt Johnson.

---

229   MRS SUSAN GARDNER, Longdown
Postal: **Woodhayes Farm, Longdown, Exeter, Devon, EX6 7SB**
Contacts: **PHONE/FAX (01392) 811213 MOBILE (07936) 380492**
E-MAIL woodhayesstudfarm@btinternet.com WEBSITE www.suegardnerracing.co.uk

1   **BREDON HILL LAD**, 9, ch g Kirkwall—Persian Clover **Mr & Mrs R W & Mrs J M Mitchell**
2   **BREDON HILL POPPY**, 7, b m Kayf Tara—Persian Clover **R. W. Mitchell**
3   **BREEZE ALONG**, 6, ch g Denounce—Briery Breeze (IRE) **D. V. Gardner**
4   4, B f Indian Danehill (IRE)—Briery Breeze (IRE) **D. V. Gardner**
5   **COEUR BLIMEY (IRE)**, 5, b br g Winged Love (IRE)—Eastender **Mr K. T. Harris**
6   4, Ch g Schiaparelli (GER)—Darjeeling (IRE) **D. V. Gardner**
7   **DOCTOR LOOK HERE (IRE)**, 6, b g Dr Massini (IRE)—Eye Vision (IRE) **G. N. Noye**
8   **FLYING AWARD (IRE)**, 12, br g Oscar (IRE)—Kates Machine (IRE) **Mrs B. Russell**
9   **HERE'S HERBIE**, 8, b g Classic Cliche (IRE)—Tyre Hill Lilly **G. N. Noye**
10 **ONLY GORGEOUS (IRE)**, 7, b g Vertical Speed (FR)—Pure Beautiful (IRE) **D. V. Gardner**
11 **RAFAFIE**, 8, b g Kayf Tara—Florie **D. V. Gardner**
12 **SIROP DE MENTHE (FR)**, 6, ch g Discover d'auteuil (FR)—Jolie Menthe (FR) **Clear Racing & Partner**

MRS SUSAN GARDNER - Continued

13 **STORM ALERT**, 9, ch g Karinga Bay—Rash-Gale (IRE) **D. V. Gardner**
14 **TEA TIME FRED**, 7, b g Kayf Tara—Darjeeling (IRE) **D. V. Gardner**
15 **TRANS EXPRESS (IRE)**, 6, br g Trans Island—Hazel Fastrack **D. V. Gardner**
16 5, B m Kayf Tara—Tyre Hill Lilly **D. V. Gardner**
17 4, B f Sulamani (IRE)—Tyre Hill Lilly **D. V. Gardner**

Other Owners: Mr D. V. Gardner, Tom Gardner, Mrs M. M. Greening, Mr B. Greening, Mr R. W. Mitchell, Mrs J. M. Mitchell.

Assistant Trainer: D. V. Gardner

Jockey (NH): Aidan Coleman, Lucy Gardner, Micheal Nolan.

---

230 **MR JEREMY GASK, Stockbridge**
Postal: Danebury Racing Stables, Nether Wallop, Stockbridge, Hampshire, SO20 6JX
Contacts: **MOBILE (07507) 555303**
E-MAIL info@horsesfirstracing.com WEBSITE www.horsesfirstracing.com

1 **CAMINEL (IRE)**, 5, b m Kyllachy—Jalissa **Mr M. Allen**
2 **DOMINIUM (USA)**, 9, b g E Dubai (USA)—Sudenlylastsummer (USA) **Horses First Racing Ltd**
3 **EQUELUS**, 4, b g Equiano (FR)—Merle **The Rock & Rollers**
4 **FIRE AND PASSION**, 4, b g Dutch Art—Mary Goodnight **Mr V. C. Y. Tan**
5 **FLYING BEAR (IRE)**, 5, b g Kodiac—Marinebird (IRE) **Flying Bear Partnership**
6 **GOLLY MISS MOLLY**, 5, b m Exceed And Excel (AUS)—Amicable Terms **Amelco UK Ltd**
7 **JAMHOORI**, 8, b h Tiger Hill (IRE)—Tanasie **Guy Carstairs & Horses First Racing**
8 **LIGHT ROSE (IRE)**, 6, b m Cape Cross (IRE)—Laureldean Lady (IRE) **Jamie & Lucy Hart**
9 **MEDICEAN MAN**, 10, ch g Medicean—Kalindi **Mr Stuart Dobb & Miss Kate Dobb**
10 **NELSON QUAY (IRE)**, 6, b g Holy Roman Emperor (IRE)—Frippet (IRE) **Brankin & Hawk Racing**
11 **NEW LEYF (IRE)**, 10, b br g Kheleyf (USA)—Society Fair (FR) **Guy Carstairs & Horses First Racing**
12 **OASIS ROSE (FR)**, 4, b f Naaqoos—Dream Rose (IRE) **P. Webb**
13 **PUTARINGONIT (IRE)**, 4, ch f Peintre Celebre (USA)—Virginias Best **Amelco UK Ltd**
14 **SUTTON SIOUX**, 5, b m Sleeping Indian—Once Removed **Horses First Racing Ltd**
15 **TRENDING (IRE)**, 7, gr g Dark Angel (IRE)—Call Later (USA) **The Twitterati**

THREE-YEAR-OLDS

16 **BORN TO FINISH (IRE)**, b g Dark Angel (IRE)—Music Pearl (IRE) **Crowd Racing Partnership**
17 **CUBAN QUEEN (USA)**, ro f Elusive Quality (USA)—One Smokin' Lady (USA) **Mr M Moss & Mr P Bamford**
18 **DUTCH ARCHER**, b g Dutch Art—Cecily **Mr A J Edwards & Mr S Dobb**
19 B g Mastercraftsman (IRE)—Fairest of All (IRE) **Anglo Australian Racing**
20 **FANDANGO (GER)**, b c Lord of England (GER)—Fitness (IRE) **Anglo Australian Racing**
21 **FLY TRUE**, b f Raven's Pass (USA)—Have Faith (IRE)
22 **GEOFF POTTS (IRE)**, ch g Zebedee—Our Sheila **Jamie & Lucy Hart**
23 **HAMISH MCGONAGAIN**, b c Kyllachy—Inya Lake **Jamie & Lucy Hart**
24 **HODGKINS TRUST (IRE)**, b g Key of Luck (USA)—Rumuz (IRE) **The Hodgkins Trust Partnership**
25 **K'GARI SPIRIT**, b f Major Cadeaux—Ivory Silk **Miss K. M. Dobb**
26 **KEYMAN (IRE)**, ch g Manduro (GER)—Kesh Kumay (IRE) **Anglo Australian Racing**
27 **LIGHTFEET (USA)**, b c Lonhro (AUS)—Southern Protocol (USA) **Mr V. C. Y. Tan**
28 B c Duke of Marmalade (IRE)—Miracolia (IRE) **Anglo Australian Racing**
29 **PORTLAND BELLE (IRE)**, b f Fastnet Rock (AUS)—
    Square Pants (USA) **Joanne Walsh,Carrie Rogers,James Knight**
30 Br c Big Bad Bob (IRE)—Rejuvenation (IRE) **Anglo Australian Racing**
31 **ROSEALEE (IRE)**, gr f Zebedee—Why Now **The Sutton Veny Syndicate**
32 **SEA OF HOPE (IRE)**, b f Rock of Gibraltar (IRE)—Labrusca **The Pillars of Hercules Partnership**
33 **STORMY ANGEL (FR)**, ro gr c Stormy River (FR)—Angel's Camp (USA) **P. Webb**
34 **THE DETAINEE**, b g Aqlaam—Jakarta Jade **Crowd Horse Bell Ltd**
35 **TRIPARTITE (IRE)**, b g Zebedee—Baltic Belle (IRE) **The Salt House Syndicate**
36 B c Teofilo (IRE)—Whos Mindin Who (IRE) **Anglo Australian Racing**
37 **WINDMILLS GIRL**, b f Sir Percy—Cosmic Countess (IRE) **Gracelands Stud Partnership**
38 **ZOPHILLY (IRE)**, b f Zoffany (IRE)—Extreme Pleasure (IRE) **Horses First Partners**

Other Owners: P. Bamford, Mr A. G. Bloom, S. T. Brankin, G. N. Carstairs, Mr S. Dobb, Mr A. J. Edwards, Mr M. Eves, Mr J. Hart, Mrs L. Hart, Mrs Noel Harwerth, J. A. Knight, Mr M. J. Moss, Mrs C. B. Rogers, Mrs J. C. Walsh, E. Wilmott, Mrs O. J. Wilmott, R. V. Young, Mrs K. M. Young.

Apprentice: David Parkes.

231 MRS ROSEMARY GASSON, Banbury
Postal: Alkerton Grounds, Balscote, Banbury, Oxfordshire, OX15 6JS
Contacts: PHONE (01295) 730248 MOBILE (07769) 798430
E-MAIL arb@aqf.myzen.co.uk

1 ADIOS ALONSO (IRE), 10, b g Saffron Walden (FR)—Rosy Rockford (IRE) **Mrs R. Gasson**
2 CROCO MISTER (IRE), 9, ch g Croco Rouge (IRE)—Nimrods Dream (IRE) **Mrs R. Gasson**
3 IRISH OCTAVE (IRE), 6, b g Gamut (IRE)—Fairytaleofnewyork (IRE) **Mrs R. Gasson**
4 IRISH RANGER (IRE), 5, b g Gamut (IRE)—Erins Emblem (IRE) **Mrs R. Gasson**
5 JOLLY BOYS OUTING (IRE), 13, b g Glacial Storm (USA)—St Carol (IRE) **Mrs R. Gasson**
6 KILCASCAN, 12, b g Alflora (IRE)—Peasedown Tofana **Mrs R. Gasson**
7 MR MCGUINESS (IRE), 6, b g Kalanisi (IRE)—Maig Mandy (IRE) **Mrs R. Gasson**
8 SCARTARE (IRE), 5, br g Trans Island—La Speziana (IRE) **Mrs R. Gasson**

Conditional: Ben Poste.

232 MR MICHAEL GATES, Stratford-Upon-Avon
Postal: Comfort Park Stud, Campden Road, Clifford Chambers, Stratford-Upon-Avon, CV37 8LW
Contacts: MOBILE (07581) 246070
E-MAIL comfortparkstud@hotmail.co.uk

1 CARN ROCK, 8, b g Tamure (IRE)—Solent Sunbeam **M. Gates**
2 HANDSOME BUDDY (IRE), 9, br g Presenting—Moya's Magic (IRE) **M. Gates**

233 MR JONATHAN GEAKE, Marlborough
Postal: Harestone House, East Kennett, Marlborough, Wiltshire, SN8 4EY
Contacts: PHONE (01672) 861784 MOBILE (07768) 350738
E-MAIL jageake@yahoo.co.uk

1 A LASTING JOY, 5, b m Refuse To Bend (IRE)—Sir Kyffin's Folly **Mrs A. Leftley**
2 BONDI MIST (IRE), 7, gr m Aussie Rules (USA)—Akoya (IRE) **Double Kings Partnership**
3 DANCE WITH ME (IRE), 7, b g Danehill Dancer (IRE)—Perpetual Time **A. J. Geake**
4 FIDELITY, 4, b g Halling (USA)—Sir Kyffin's Folly **Mrs A. Leftley**
5 GLENS WOBBLY, 8, ch g Kier Park (IRE)—Wobbly **Mr R. G. Symes**
6 HEEZARARITY, 8, b g Librettist (USA)—Extremely Rare (IRE) **Miss E. Tanner**
7 LOUKHAAR (IRE), 8, b g Westerner—Gold Air **Mrs S. A. Geake**
8 MICQUUS (IRE), 7, b g High Chaparral (IRE)—My Potters (USA) **Mrs A. Leftley**
9 PRINCE OF CARDAMOM (IRE), 4, b g Nayef (USA)—Tiger Spice **Mrs P. D. Gulliver**
10 SACRAMENTO KING (IRE), 7, gr g Desert King (IRE)—Kindle Ball (FR) **Mrs P. D. Gulliver**
11 SHOT IN THE DARK (IRE), 7, ch g Dr Fong (USA)—Highland Shot **Mrs P. D. Gulliver**

Other Owners: Mrs Margaret Geake, Mrs S. A. Geake.

Assistant Trainer: Mrs S. A. Geake Pupil Assistant: Mr Sam Geake

Jockey (NH): Mark Grant. Apprentice: Ryan Tate. Amateur: Miss K. Lyons.

234 MR TOM GEORGE, Slad
Postal: Down Farm, Slad, Stroud, Gloucestershire, GL6 7QE
Contacts: PHONE (01452) 814267 MOBILE (07850) 793483
E-MAIL tom@trgeorge.com WEBSITE www.tomgeorgeracing.co.uk

1 A GOOD SKIN (IRE), 7, b g Presenting—Trixskin (IRE) **Power Panels Electrical Systems Ltd**
2 ALWAYS ON THE RUN (IRE), 6, b g Robin des Pres (FR)—Kerrys Cottage (IRE) **Mr & Mrs Paul & Clare Rooney**
3 ARCTIC LADY (IRE), 5, b m Milan—Arctic Rose (IRE) **Mr S. W. Clarke**
4 BABY KING (IRE), 7, b g Ivan Denisovich (IRE)—Burn Baby Burn (IRE) **About Two Weeks**
5 BALLINVARRIG (IRE), 9, b g Beneficial—Leos Holiday (IRE) **Lady Hilda Clarke & Simon W Clarke**
6 BARAZA (FR), 5, gr g Smadoun (FR)—Gerbora (FR) **Mr S. W. Clarke**
7 BATTLE OF SHILOH (IRE), 7, b g Shantou (USA)—Realt Na Ruise (IRE) **Mr & Mrs Paul & Clare Rooney**
8 BEHIND THE WIRE (IRE), 5, b g Mahler—Mujavail (IRE) **Crossed Fingers Partnership**
9 BENI LIGHT (FR), 5, b g Crossharbour—Or Light (FR) **Crossed Fingers Partnership**
10 BIG BAD DUDE (IRE), 7, ch g Blueprint (IRE)—Cathedral Ave (IRE) **Mr & Mrs Paul & Clare Rooney**

MR TOM GEORGE - Continued

11 **BIG FELLA THANKS,** 14, b g Primitive Rising (USA)—Nunsdream **T. George**
12 **BIG WINDMILL (IRE),** 5, b g Stowaway—Neighbours Wager (IRE) **Mr D. W. Brookes**
13 **BOMBER COMMAND (FR),** 4, gr g Al Namix (FR)—Ballade Nordique (FR) **Mr S. W. Clarke**
14 **BOYHOOD (IRE),** 5, b g Oscar (IRE)—Glen Dubh (IRE) **H Stephen Smith & The Gabbertas Family**
15 **BUN DORAN (IRE),** 5, b g Shantou (USA)—Village Queen (IRE) **Crossed Fingers Partnership**
16 **CALL ME VIC (IRE),** 9, b g Old Vic—Call Me Dara (IRE) **C. B. Compton**
17 **CERNUNNOS (FR),** 6, b g Della Francesca (USA)—Jackette (USA) **J. P. McManus**
18 **COEUR DE FOU (FR),** 11, ch g Limnos (JPN)—Folly Lady (FR) **T. George**
19 **DANDY DUKE (IRE),** 5, b g Duke of Marmalade (IRE)—
                                         Quest For Eternity (IRE) **Dermot O'Donohoe & Sharon C Nelson**
20 **DEFINITELY BETTER (IRE),** 8, ch m Definite Article—Chevet Girl (IRE) **Mrs E. A. Fletcher**
21 **DEXCITE (FR),** 5, b br g Authorized (IRE)—Belle Alicia (FR) **Crossed Fingers Partnership**
22 **DOUBLE SHUFFLE (IRE),** 6, b g Milan—Fiddlers Bar (IRE) **Crossed Fingers Partnership**
23 **DRILL BABY DRILL,** 5, b m Black Sam Bellamy (IRE)—Tulipa (POL) **Sharon C. Nelson & Dermot O'Donohoe**
24 **FINAL PASS (IRE),** 8, b g Gamut (IRE)—Final Peace (IRE) **Mr & Mrs Paul & Clare Rooney**
25 **FIT THE BRIEF,** 6, b m Kayf Tara—Tulipa (POL) **Sharon C. Nelson & Dermot O'Donohoe**
26 **FLORIDA CALLING (IRE),** 7, ch g Presenting—Nighty Nights (GER) **Vicki Robinson & James Williams**
27 **FORGOTTEN GOLD (IRE),** 10, b g Dr Massini (IRE)—Ardnataggle (IRE) **Mr & Mrs R. Cornock**
28 **FROSTY STEEL (IRE),** 6, b g Craigsteel—Smiths Lady (IRE) **Dermot O'Donohoe & Sharon C Nelson**
29 **GET RHYTHM (IRE),** 6, b g Kayf Tara—Ninna Nanna (FR) **Miss J. A. Hoskins**
30 **GOD'S OWN (IRE),** 8, b g Oscar (IRE)—Dantes Term (IRE) **Crossed Fingers Partnership**
31 **GORSKY ISLAND,** 8, b g Turtle Island (IRE)—Belle Magello (FR) **Silkword Racing Partnership**
32 **GRAND ENTERPRISE,** 6, b g Fair Mix (IRE)—Miss Chinchilla **J B Property Developments (Midlands) Ltd**
33 **HARDROCK DAVIS (FR),** 5, b br g Saint des Saints (FR)—Trumpet Davis (FR) **Mr S. W. Clarke**
34 **JUST BEFORE DAWN (IRE),** 7, b g Millenary—Knocka Beauty (IRE) **Mr S. W. Clarke**
35 **KILBREE KID (IRE),** 9, b g Cloudings (IRE)—Bustingoutallover (USA) **Five Valleys Racing Partnership**
36 **KK LEXION (IRE),** 5, b g Flemensfirth (USA)—Kiloradante (IRE) **C. Perry, J. Lawson, A. Waller, D. Rea**
37 **MAJALA (FR),** 10, b g Lavirco (GER)—Majae (FR) **Sharon Nelson Jeremy & Darren Taylor**
38 **MODULE (FR),** 9, b g Panoramic—Before Royale (FR) **Mr Simon Clarke**
39 **MOSS ON THE MILL,** 8, br g Overbury (IRE)—Mimis Bonnet (FR) **Mr & Mrs R. Cornock**
40 **NO DUFFER,** 9, ch g Karinga Bay—Dolly Duff **Mr D. C. Robey**
41 **NOCHE DE REYES (FR),** 7, b br g Early March—Cochinchine (IRE) **David Rea & Express Contract Drying Ltd**
42 **O MAONLAI (IRE),** 8, b g Oscar (IRE)—Another Gaye (IRE) **Power Panels Electrical Systems Ltd**
43 **OLOFI (FR),** 10, gr g Slickly (FR)—Dona Bella (FR) **McNeill Family Ltd**
44 **ON THE CASE,** 6, ch g Generous (IRE)—Tulipa (POL) **Sharon C. Nelson & Dermot O'Donohoe**
45 **PARSNIP PETE,** 10, b g Pasternak—Bella Coola **The Parsnips**
46 **RABUNDA (IRE),** 6, b g Milan—Cush Ramani (IRE) **Mr & Mrs M C Houghton**
47 **RISING BREEZE (FR),** 5, b g Shirocco (GER)—Moon Tree (FR) **Mr D. W. Brookes**
48 **ROC D'APSIS (FR),** 7, gr g Apsis—Rocapina (FR) **Mr David Rea & Miss Diane Fudge**
49 **SAINT ARE (FR),** 10, b br g Network (GER)—Fortanea (FR) **Mr D. W. Fox**
50 **SIR VALENTINO (FR),** 7, b g Early March—Valentine (FR) **Doone Hulse Susie Saunders & Lady Cobham**
51 **SMOKING JACKET (IRE),** 6, b g Beneficial—Unalaska (IRE) **Vicki Robinson & James Williams**
52 **SOME ARE LUCKY (IRE),** 5, b g Gold Well—Foreign Estates (IRE) **Power Panels Electrical Systems Ltd**
53 **SONG SAA,** 6, b m Midnight Legend—Mystere (IRE) **Sharon C. Nelson & Georgie McGrath**
54 **STAMP YOUR FEET (IRE),** 4, b g Galileo (IRE)—Nausicaa (USA) **Mr T. W. Morley**
55 **STORMING STRUMPET,** 6, b m Kayf Tara—Rosita Bay **PJL Racing**
56 **THE WORLDS END (IRE),** 5, b g Stowaway—Bright Sprite (IRE) **McNeill Family Ltd**
57 4, Ch f Midnight Legend—Tulipa (POL) **Sharon C. Nelson**
58 **UNTIL WINNING (FR),** 8, b g Kapgarde (FR)—Fripperie (FR) **Thoroughbred Ladies**
59 **VALSEUR DU GRANVAL (FR),** 7, b g Della Francesca (USA)—La Grande Vallee (FR) **Mr S. W. Clarke**
60 **WHATS HAPPENING (IRE),** 9, b g Lahib (USA)—
                                         Rebeccas Star (IRE) **David Rea & Express Contract Drying Ltd**
61 **WILD WEST WIND (IRE),** 7, b g Westerner—Mhuire Na Gale (IRE) **Mr S. W. Clarke**

Other Owners: Mrs C. D. Chamberlain, Exors of the Late Lady Clarke, Lady Cobham, Mrs Michele Cornock, Mr R. Cornock, Express Contract Drying Ltd, Mr J. M. Fawbert, Ms Diane M. Fudge, Mr R. K. Gabbertas, Mr Mark Gabbertas, Mrs S. Gabbertas, Mrs C. M. George, Capt. A. G. George, Mr T. R. George, Mrs S. P. George, Mrs Doone Hulse, Mr John B. Lawson, Mrs Georgie McGrath, Mrs Sharon C. Nelson, Mr D. J. O'Donohoe, Mr David Rea, Mr Nick Rieger, Ms Vicki Robinson, Mrs C. Rollings, Mrs C. Rooney, Mr P.A. Rooney, Mrs Susie Saunders, Mr H. Stephen Smith, A. E. Smith & Co, Mr Jeremy Taylor, Mr Darren Taylor, Mr R. F. Tromans, Mr James S. Williams, Mr Nicholas Williamson.

Assistant Trainer: John Cullinan

Jockey (NH): Paddy Brennan. **Conditional:** Jamie Bargary. **Amateur:** Mr Noel George.

235 MR NICK GIFFORD, Findon
Postal: **The Downs, Stable Lane, Findon, West Sussex, BN14 0RT**
Contacts: OFFICE **(01903) 872226** MOBILE **(07940) 518077**
E-MAIL **downs.stables@btconnect.com** WEBSITE **www.nickgiffordracing.co.uk**

1 **ARROYEAU (FR)**, 6, ch g Nidor (FR)—Miss Lamour (FR) **P. H. Betts**
2 5, B h Proclamation (IRE)—Ashleys Petale (IRE) **Mrs T. J. Stone-Brown**
3 5, Gr h Proclamation (IRE)—Ballerina Girl **Mrs T. J. Stone-Brown**
4 **BROWN BEAR (IRE)**, 5, b g Yeats (IRE)—Moray Firth (UAE) **J. P. McManus**
5 **CASHANOVA (IRE)**, 5, b g Arcadio (GER)—Starshade (IRE) **C.Mehta J.Brooks Mr&Mrs Lovell C.Bray**
6 **DEXTER BENJAMIN (IRE)**, 7, b g Milan—Just Stunning (IRE) **D. G. Trangmar**
7 **DOLLAR BILL**, 7, ch g Medicean—Jardin **Ruth Gifford & Friends**
8 **FAIRY RATH (IRE)**, 10, ch g Accordion—Killoughey Fairy (IRE) **Mrs C. L. Kyle**
9 4, Ch g Shantou (USA)—Flying Answer (IRE)
10 **GENEROUS RANSOM (IRE)**, 8, ch g Generous (IRE)—Penneyrose Bay **Sir Christopher & Lady Wates**
11 **GIVE HIM TIME**, 5, b g Kalanisi (IRE)—Delayed (FR) **Mrs T. J. Stone-Brown**
12 **IDLE TALKER (IRE)**, 4, b g Dandy Man (IRE)—Special Pearl **Coldunell Limited**
13 **JEBS GAMBLE (IRE)**, 5, b g Dubai Destination (USA)—
Gentle Caribou (IRE) **Mrs C Gamble, JEB & Mrs R Gifford**
14 **KARENS LAD (IRE)**, 6, b g Kalanisi (IRE)—Aremebooksready (IRE) **Ham Manor Farms Ltd**
15 **LOYAL COUP (IRE)**, 4, b g Westerner—Dr Bernish Lass (IRE) **J. R. Hulme**
16 **MARKET COURT (IRE)**, 5, b g Court Cave (IRE)—Piepowder **B. Noakes & Baroness S. Noakes**
17 4, B g Presenting—Molly Massini (IRE) **Project Mars Racing Partnership**
18 **NOTRE AMI (IRE)**, 5, br g Kalanisi (IRE)—Shuilan (IRE) **The Morpheus Partnership**
19 **PARTY ROYAL**, 6, b g Royal Applause—Voliere **Coldunell Limited**
20 **PEGGIES VENTURE**, 5, b m Presenting—Peggies Run **Sir Christopher Wates**
21 **PROUTS PUB (IRE)**, 7, b g Catcher In The Rye (IRE)—A Woman In Love **Nick Gifford Racing Club**
22 4, Ch g Black Sam Bellamy (IRE)—Rakajack
23 **STARS ROYALE (IRE)**, 7, b g King's Best (USA)—Open Your Heart (IRE) **Jeremy Kyle & Friends**
24 **THEO'S CHARM (IRE)**, 6, b g Presenting—Kates Charm (IRE) **Mr M. K. O'Shea**
25 **TOOHIGHFORME (IRE)**, 7, b g Mountain High (USA)—Summertime Girl (IRE) **Nick Gifford Racing Club**

Other Owners: Mr J. P. M. Bowtell, Mr J. R. Brooks, Mr J. E. Burrows, Mr M. T. Forbes-Wood, Mrs C. Gamble, Mrs R. E. Gifford, Mr J. Kyle, Mr C. F. Mehta, Baroness S. Noakes, C. B. Noakes, Mr N. M. Roddis, Mr M. A. C. Rudd, Mr M. J. Tracey, Mr P. R. Tymms, Lady G. F. Wates.

Jockey (NH): Leighton Aspell, Tom Cannon, Liam Treadwell. **Amateur:** Mr David Dunsdon.

---

236 MR MARK GILLARD, Sherborne
Postal: **Elm Tree Stud, Holwell, Sherborne, Dorset, DT9 5LL**
Contacts: PHONE **(01963) 23026 (01258) 881111** FAX **(01963) 23297** MOBILE **(07970) 700605**
E-MAIL **Mark@thegillards.co.uk** WEBSITE **markgillardracing.com**

1 **BLACKADDER**, 4, b g Myboycharlie (IRE)—Famcred **R. C. Hambleton**
2 **BYRON BLUE (IRE)**, 7, br g Dylan Thomas (IRE)—
High Society (IRE) **John Singh-Dil Singh Rathore-Tammy Conner**
3 **COMICAL RED**, 8, ch g Sulamani (IRE)—Sellette (IRE) **N. J. McMullan**
4 **DINKY CHALLENGER**, 8, gr br g Midnight Legend—Crusty Lily **Mr P. Isaac**
5 **DONT CALL ME OSCAR (IRE)**, 9, b g Oscar (IRE)—Coolrua (IRE) **N. J. McMullan**
6 **ENCHANTING SMILE (FR)**, 9, b m Rakti—A Thousand Smiles (IRE) **Kay Russell**
7 **HANIBAL LECTOR (IRE)**, 9, b g Dr Massini (IRE)—Pure Indulgence (IRE) **Pippa Grace**
8 **KARL MARX (IRE)**, 6, b g Red Clubs (IRE)—Brillano (FR) **Mr S. Bartlett**
9 **KINGSTON MIMOSA**, 4, b g Kheleyf (USA)—Derartu (AUS) **Mrs D. H. Potter**
10 **LAMB'S CROSS**, 10, b g Rainbow High—Angie Marinie **N. Budden, S. Hosie, R. Jeanes & I. Cahill**
11 **PETITE FANTASIE**, 7, b m Flemensfirth (USA)—Rowlands Dream (IRE) **T. L. Morshead**
12 **REVAADER**, 8, b m Revoque (IRE)—Wave Rider **Miss Kay Russell**
13 **SAINT HELENA (IRE)**, 8, b m Holy Roman Emperor (IRE)—Tafseer (IRE) **Mr A. K. Hosie**
14 **SURPRISE US**, 9, b g Indian Ridge—Pingus **Mr S. J. Garnett**
15 **TENBY JEWEL (IRE)**, 11, b g Pilsudski (IRE)—Supreme Delight (IRE) **McMullan, Rudman & Out Of Bounds**
16 **VEAUCE DE SIVOLA (FR)**, 7, b g Assessor (IRE)—Eva de Chalamont (FR) **Mr G. J. Singh**
17 **WICKLEWOOD**, 10, b g Mujahid (USA)—Pinini **Mr B. R. Rudman**

MR MARK GILLARD - Continued

THREE-YEAR-OLDS

18 FLAMING FYNN, ch g Paco Boy (IRE)—La Polka **Mr D. Hunt**

Other Owners: Mr Neil Budden, Mr I. Cahill, Ms Tammy Conner, Mr Michael Harris, Mr Steven Hosie, Mr R. Jeanes, Mr Michael Kilsby, Mr N. J. McMullan, Mr Brian Rudman, Mr G. J. Singh, Mr Dil Singh Rathore.

Assistant Trainer: Pippa Grace

Jockey (NH): Tommy Phelan.

---

237 MR JAMES GIVEN, Willoughton
Postal: **Mount House Stables, Long Lane, Willoughton, Gainsborough, Lincolnshire, DN21 5SQ**
Contacts: **PHONE (01427) 667618 FAX (01427) 667734 MOBILE (07801) 100496**
E-MAIL james@jamesgivenracing.com WEBSITE www.jamesgivenracing.com

1 ARMS AROUND ME (IRE), 4, ch g Lope de Vega (IRE)—Mexican Milly (IRE) **Suzanne & Nigel Williams**
2 ARTFUL PRINCE, 6, ch g Dutch Art—Royal Nashkova **Ingram Racing**
3 BUSHEL (USA), 6, b g Street Cry (IRE)—Melhor Ainda (USA) **The Cool Silk Partnership**
4 GOLDMADCHEN (GER), 8, b m Ivan Denisovich (IRE)—Goldkatze (GER) **Mr A. Clarke**
5 GROSMONT, 4, br g Hellvelyn—Aimee's Delight **The Cool Silk Partnership**
6 KUNG HEI FAT CHOY (USA), 7, b g Elusive Quality (USA)—Lady Succeed (JPN) **The Cool Silk Partnership**
7 LA FRITILLAIRE, 4, b f Champs Elysees—Generous Diana **Ingram Racing**
8 LEWIS VALENTINE (IRE), 4, b c Rip Van Winkle (IRE)—Full of Love (IRE) **Suzanne & Nigel Williams**
9 MISS BUCKAROO (IRE), 4, b f Acclamation—Pearl Trader (IRE) **Buckhurst Chevaliers**
10 MONSIEUR CHEVALIER (IRE), 9, b g Chevalier (IRE)—Blue Holly (IRE) **The Cool Silk Partnership**
11 ODEON, 5, b g Galileo (IRE)—Kite Mark **Mr A. Owen**
12 ORIENTAL RELATION (IRE), 5, gr g Tagula (IRE)—Rofan (USA) **The Cool Silk Partnership**
13 SANDS CHORUS, 4, b g Footstepsinthesand—Wood Chorus **The Cool Silk Partnership**
14 SHOW ME BAILEYS (FR), 4, b g Naaqoos—Exhibitor (USA) **G. R. Bailey Ltd (Baileys Horse Feeds)**
15 THE DUKKERER (IRE), 5, b br m Footstepsinthesand—Saffron Crocus **Mr A. Clarke**
16 YOU'RE COOL, 4, b g Exceed And Excel (AUS)—Ja One (IRE) **The Cool Silk Partnership**

THREE-YEAR-OLDS

17 CHARAMBA, b f Sir Percy—Rahcak (IRE)
18 COOL SILK BOY (IRE), b c Big Bad Bob (IRE)—Kheleyf's Silver (IRE) **The Cool Silk Partnership**
19 COOL SILK GIRL, br f Motivator—Captain's Paradise (IRE) **The Cool Silk Partnership**
20 FEELIN DICKY, b g Dick Turpin (IRE)—Feelin Foxy **The Cool Silk Partnership**
21 JAZZ LEGEND (USA), b c Scat Daddy (USA)—Champion Ride (USA) **The Cool Silk Partnership**
22 KING OF SWING, b c Dutch Art—Mystic Spirit (IRE) **The Cool Silk Partnership**
23 MEN UNITED (FR), b c Acclamation—Moore's Melody (IRE) **The Cool Silk Partnership**
24 MY JAMAICAN GUY (IRE), b g Duke of Marmalade (IRE)—Mustique Dream **Suzanne & Nigel Williams**
25 SIGN OF THE KODIAC (IRE), b c Kodiac—Summer Magic (IRE) **The Cool Silk Partnership**
26 SILK BOW, b f Elusive City (USA)—Ishraaqat **The Cool Silk Partnership**
27 SIR DUDLEY (IRE), b c Arcano (IRE)—Rosy Dudley (IRE) **The Cool Silk Partnership**
28 STONE QUERCUS (IRE), b g Rock of Gibraltar (IRE)—Redglow (IRE) **The Cool Silk Partnership**
29 STRANDS OF SILK, b f Kodiac—Saldenaera (GER) **The Cool Silk Partnership**

TWO-YEAR-OLDS

30 ALFONSO MANANA (IRE), ch c 16/4 Dutch Art—Chance For Romance (Entrepreneur) (16190) **Mrs S. Oliver**
31 B f 13/2 Bated Breath—Cesseras (IRE) (Cape Cross (IRE)) (6000) **James Given**
32 B f 26/1 Rock of Gibraltar (IRE)—Confusion (FR) (Anabaa (USA))
33 DUSKY MAID (IRE), b f 21/2 Dark Angel (IRE)—Dream Scape (Oasis Dream) (59047) **The Cool Silk Partnership**
34 B f 6/2 Elnadim (USA)—Intishaar (IRE) (Dubai Millennium) (6000) **T. P. Bostwick**
35 B f 27/4 Dandy Man—Labba (Tiger Hill (USA)) (2380)
36 B f 25/4 Zoffany (IRE)—Lara Amelia (IRE) (Ishiguru (USA)) (29523)
37 LITTLE MISS LUCKY (IRE), b f 6/2 Clodovil (IRE)—Lucky Leigh (Piccolo) (19000) **P. Foster & Friends**
38 MIA TIA, ch f 28/2 Equiano (FR)—Tia Mia (Dr Fong (USA)) (19047) **The Cool Silk Partnership**
39 PAQUITA BAILARINA, ch f 16/2 Paco Boy (IRE)—Prima Ballerina (Pivotal) (3333) **R. C. Spore**
40 B f 31/3 Kheleyf (USA)—Saratoga Slew (Footstepsinthesand) **Unregistered Partnership**
41 STREET JAZZ, b c 28/1 Acclamation—Wake Up Call (Noverre (USA)) (71428) **The Cool Silk Partnership**
42 TAWNY PORT, ch c 3/2 Arcano (IRE)—Tawaasul (Haafhd)
43 TRUE ROMANCE (IRE), gr c 12/5 Mastercraftsman (IRE)—
  Full of Love (IRE) (Hawk Wing (USA)) **Suzanne & Nigel Williams**

MR JAMES GIVEN - Continued

44 WARM OASIS, gr c 29/1 Oasis Dream—Warling (IRE) (Montjeu (IRE)) (200000) **The Cool Silk Partnership**
45 YES YOU (IRE), ch f 20/4 Choisir (AUS)—Mexican Milly (IRE) (Noverre (USA)) **Suzanne & Nigel Williams**

Other Owners: Mr M. P. Coleman, Mr P. Foster, T. Hirschfeld, Mr P. A. Horton, S. J. Piper, P. Swann, Mrs B. E. Wilkinson, Mrs S. E. Williams, N. Williams.

238

MR J. L. GLEDSON, Hexham
Postal: **Buteland Farm, Bellingham, Hexham, Northumberland, NE48 2EX**
Contacts: **PHONE (01434) 220911 MOBILE (07790) 977801**
E-MAIL helengledson@yahoo.co.uk

  1 5, Ch g Central Park (IRE)—Lady Fleur **J. L. Gledson**
  2 **NEVILLE WOODS**, 9, b g Alflora (IRE)—Angie Marinie **J. L. Gledson**

Assistant Trainer: Mrs Helen Gledson

Jockey (NH): Jan Faltejsek

239

MR JIM GOLDIE, Glasgow
Postal: **Libo Hill Farm, Uplawmoor, Glasgow, Lanarkshire, G78 4BA**
Contacts: **PHONE (01505) 850212 MOBILE (07778) 241522**
WEBSITE www.jimgoldieracing.com

  1 **ARCTIC COURT (IRE)**, 12, b g Arctic Lord—Polls Joy **Mr & Mrs Raymond Anderson Green**
  2 **BRAES OF LOCHALSH**, 5, b g Tiger Hill (IRE)—Gargoyle Girl **Johnnie Delta Racing**
  3 **CALEDONIA**, 9, b g Sulamani (IRE)—Vanessa Bell (IRE) **F J Connor & J S Goldie**
  4 **CELTIC POWER**, 4, b g Rail Link—Biloxi **Zen Racing & Mr J S Goldie**
  5 **CHEENI**, 4, ch f Orientor—Class Wan **Mrs V. C. Macdonald**
  6 **CLASSY ANNE**, 6, ch m Orientor—Class Wan **Johnnie Delta Racing**
  7 **DHAULAR DHAR**, 14, b g Indian Ridge—Pescara (IRE) **Johnnie Delta Racing**
  8 **FRAY**, 5, b m Champs Elysees—Short Dance (USA) **F. Brady**
  9 **FUNDING DEFICIT (IRE)**, 6, ch g Rakti—Bukat Timah **D. G. Pryde**
 10 **GO GO GREEN (IRE)**, 10, b g Acclamation—Preponderance (IRE) **Johnnie Delta Racing**
 11 **GONINODAETHAT**, 8, b g Proclamation (IRE)—Big Mystery (IRE) **Mr G E Adams & Mr J S Goldie**
 12 **HAIDEES REFLECTION**, 6, b m Byron—Exchanging Glances **Johnnie Delta Racing**
 13 **HAWKEYETHENOO (IRE)**, 10, b g Hawk Wing (USA)—Stardance (USA) **F J Connor & J S Goldie**
 14 **HERO'S STORY**, 6, b g Mount Nelson—Red Roses Story (FR) **J. S. Morrison**
 15 **HIGGS BOSON**, 11, b g Overbury (IRE)—Evening Splash (IRE) **Johnnie Delta Racing**
 16 **JACK DEXTER**, 7, b br g Orientor—Glenhurich (IRE) **F J Connor & J S Goldie**
 17 **JESSIE ALLAN (IRE)**, 5, b m Bushranger (IRE)—Ishimagic **Mr R. W. C. McLachlan**
 18 **JONNY DELTA**, 9, ch g Sulamani (IRE)—Send Me An Angel (IRE) **F J Connor & J S Goldie**
 19 **LATIN REBEL (IRE)**, 9, b g Spartacus (IRE)—Dance To The Beat **Mr R. W. C. McLachlan**
 20 **MERCHANT OF DUBAI**, 11, b g Dubai Destination (USA)—Chameleon **Highland Racing 2**
 21 **MOLLY MILAN**, 8, b m Milan—Dolly Sparks (IRE) **Barraston Racing**
 22 **PIPER BILL**, 5, b g Halling (USA)—Murielle **Mrs J. M. MacPherson**
 23 **PLUS JAMAIS (FR)**, 9, b g Caballo Raptor (CAN)—Branceilles (FR) **Alba-Eire Syndicate**
 24 **RASAMAN (IRE)**, 12, b g Namid—Rasana **J. S. Goldie**
 25 **RIOJA DAY (IRE)**, 6, b g Red Clubs (IRE)—Dai E Dai (USA) **Ayrshire Racing & Partner**
 26 **RONALD GEE (IRE)**, 9, ch g Garuda—Panache Lady (USA) **Whitestonecliffe Racing Partnership**
 27 **ROTHESAY CHANCER**, 8, ch g Monsieur Bond (IRE)—Rhinefield Beauty (IRE)
 28 **SEA OF GREEN**, 4, b f Iffraaj—Sea of Leaves (USA) **J. R. Callow**
 29 **SILVER DUKE**, 5, gr g Papal Bull—Dumaani's Dream (USA) **Mrs M. Craig**
 30 **SIR CHAUVELIN**, 4, b g Authorized (IRE)—Jabbara (IRE) **Mr J. Fyffe**
 31 **STAR CRACKER (IRE)**, 4, ch g Starspangledbanner (AUS)—Champagne Cracker **J. S. Goldie**
 32 **TESTA ROSSA (IRE)**, 6, b g Oratorio (IRE)—Red Rita (IRE) **Mr & Mrs Gordon Grant**
 33 **THE MINCH (IRE)**, 5, b g Flemensfirth (USA)—Akayid **Pryde, Van Der Hoeven & Beaumont**
 34 4, B g Rail Link—Thorntoun Piccolo **W. M. Johnstone**
 35 **TIGER JIM**, 6, b g Tiger Hill (IRE)—Quintrell **Johnnie Delta Racing**
 36 **TITUS BOLT (IRE)**, 7, b g Titus Livius (FR)—Megan's Bay **I. G. M. Dalgleish**
 37 **TOO COOL TO FOOL (IRE)**, 13, b g Bob Back (USA)—Mandysway (IRE) **Johnnie Delta Racing**
 38 **TURTLE WATCH**, 8, b g Where Or When (IRE)—Cita Verda (FR) **Mr & Mrs Raymond Anderson Green**

MR JIM GOLDIE - Continued

THREE-YEAR-OLDS

39 B g Bushranger (IRE)—Emly Express (IRE)
40 ETERNALIST, ch f Equiano (FR)—Eternal Instinct **Zen Racing & Mr J S Goldie**
41 FINAL SPRING (IRE), b f Zebedee—Baileys Cream **Sceptre**
42 B f Shirocco (GER)—Gargoyle Girl
43 B g Elnadim (USA)—My
44 NUOVA SCUOLA, b f Mount Nelson—La Vecchia Scuola (IRE) **Zen Racing & Mr J S Goldie**
45 PICTURE PAINTER (IRE), gr g Zoffany (IRE)—Sisceal **Mr D van der Hoeven & Mr D Pryde**
46 Ch g Makfi—Primo Heights

Other Owners: Mr G. Adams, Mrs S. Armstrong, Mr E. N. Barber, J. J. Beaumont, Mr N. Boyle, Mr T. Cobain, Mr F. J. Connor, Mr G. Davidson, Mr J. Doherty, Mr C. J. Edwards, Mr J. Frew, Mr M. Friel, Mrs D. I. Goldie, Mrs C. H. Grant, Mr G. R. Grant, Mrs A. Green, R. A. Green, P. Hampshire, Mr A. Manson, Mrs W. McGrandles, Mr D. W. McIntyre, A. McManus, W. A. Powrie, Mr R. A. Sankey, A. H. Slone, L. G. Straszewski, G. M. Thomson, Mr D. P. van der Hoeven.

Assistant Trainers: James Goldie, George Goldie.

Jockey (flat): Graham Lee. **Jockey (NH):** Lucy Alexander, Henry Brooke, Denis O'Regan. **Amateur:** Mrs Carol Bartley, Mrs I. Goldie.

---

240 **MR ROBERT GOLDIE, Kilmarnock**
Postal: **Harpercroft, Old Loans Road, Dundonald, Kilmarnock, Ayrshire, KA2 9DD**
Contacts: **PHONE (01292) 317222 FAX (01292) 313585 MOBILE (07801) 922552**

1 ALEXANDER OATS, 13, b g Insan (USA)—Easter Oats **R. H. Goldie**
2 ALFRED OATS, 12, b g Alflora (IRE)—Easter Oats **R. H. Goldie**
3 LAST OF THE OATS, 8, b g Luso—Easter Oats **R. H. Goldie**
4 VICTORIA OATS, 10, b m Old Vic—Easter Oats **R. H. Goldie**

Assistant Trainer: Mrs R H Goldie

---

241 **MR STEVE GOLLINGS, Louth**
Postal: **Highfield House, Scamblesby, Louth, Lincolnshire, LN11 9XT**
Contacts: **YARD (01507) 343204 HOME/FAX (01507) 343213 MOBILE (07860) 218910**
E-MAIL stevegollings@aol.com WEBSITE www.stevegollings.com

1 CAGED LIGHTNING (IRE), 6, b g Haatef (USA)—Rainbow Melody (IRE) **Four Men & A Little Lady**
2 HANDIWORK, 6, ch g Motivator—Spinning Top **Mr C. A. Johnstone**
3 MAKE ME A FORTUNE (IRE), 8, b br g Heron Island (IRE)—Biora Queen (IRE) **Mr P W Baxter & Mr R C Key**
4 SNOW PRINCE, 5, gr g Royal Applause—Snowdrops **Mr C. A. Johnstone**
5 SUBLIMATION (IRE), 6, ch g Manduro (GER)—Meon Mix **Northern Bloodstock Racing**
6 TROOPINGTHECOLOUR, 10, b g Nayef (USA)—Hyperspectra **Mrs Jayne M. Gollings**
7 WITH HINDSIGHT (IRE), 8, b g Ad Valorem (USA)—Lady From Limerick (IRE) **Northern Bloodstock Racing**

Other Owners: Mr P. W. Baxter, Mr S. Chapman, S. Gollings, Mr R. C. Key, Mr S. Stockdale, Mr P. G. Taiano.

Assistant Trainer: Mrs J M Gollings

Jockey (flat): Jamie Spencer. **Jockey (NH):** Keith Mercer, Brian Hughes, Tom Scudamore. **Conditional:** Paul Bohan.

---

242 **MR CHRIS GORDON, Winchester**
Postal: **Morestead Farm Stables, Morestead, Winchester, Hampshire, SO21 1JD**
Contacts: **PHONE (01962) 712774 FAX (01962) 712774 MOBILE (07713) 082392**
E-MAIL chrisgordon68@hotmail.co.uk WEBSITE www.chrisgordonracing.com

1 ALBAHAR (FR), 5, gr g Dark Angel (IRE)—Downland (USA) **Mrs K. Digweed**
2 4, B f Midnight Legend—Annie Greenlaw **B. J. Champion**
3 ATLANTIC ROLLER (IRE), 9, b g Old Vic—Tourist Attraction (IRE) **D. S. Dennis**
4 BALLYCOE, 7, b g Norse Dancer (IRE)—Lizzy Lamb **D. S. Dennis**
5 BALLYHEIGUE BAY (IRE), 9, b g Rudimentary (USA)—Terinka (IRE) **E. J. Farrant**

MR CHRIS GORDON - Continued

6 **BLACK COW (IRE)**, 8, br g Presenting—Back Market Lass (IRE) **Gordon Racing**
7 **COMEONGINGER (IRE)**, 9, b g King's Theatre (IRE)—Miss Poutine (FR) **Mr & Mrs Michael Coates**
8 **COOLKING**, 9, b g King's Theatre (IRE)—Osocool **Sir Peter & Lady Forwood**
9 **COWARDS CLOSE (IRE)**, 9, br g Presenting—Parsee (IRE) **Mr D. F. Henery**
10 **DISPUTED (IRE)**, 6, b g Westerner—Pearly Princess (IRE) **Gilbert & Gamble**
11 **DO WE LIKE HIM (IRE)**, 6, b g Beneficial—Pattern Queen (IRE) **Mr Roger Alwen Mrs Heather Alwen**
12 **FOR TWO (FR)**, 7, gr g Act One—Forcat (FR) **C. E. Gordon**
13 **FULL BLAST (FR)**, 5, b g Khalkevi (IRE)—La Troussardiere (FR) **Mr D. F. Henery**
14 **HALLINGHAM**, 6, b g Halling (USA)—In Luck **Mr D. F. Henery**
15 **JEBRIL (FR)**, 6, b g Astronomer Royal (USA)—Happy Clapper **Mr D. F. Henery**
16 **KING UTHER**, 6, b g Master Blade—Cadbury Castle **A. C. Ward-Thomas**
17 **LADY A**, 6, ch m Apple Tree (FR)—Lady Kay **L. Gilbert**
18 **LIGHTENTERTAINMENT (IRE)**, 8, b g King's Theatre (IRE)—
Dochas Supreme (IRE) **The Not Over Big Partnership**
19 **LOVES DESTINATION**, 5, b m Dubai Destination (USA)—Bijou Love (IRE) **Chris Gordon Racing Club**
20 **MALIBU ROCK**, 8, b g Tiger Hill (IRE)—High Straits **Chris Gordon Racing Club**
21 **MONTECITO (FR)**, 6, b br g Falco (USA)—Bealli (IRE) **RJH Partnership**
22 **MORESTEAD SCREAMER**, 7, b m Imperial Dancer—The Screamer (IRE) **Chris Gordon Racing Club**
23 **NOBLE FRIEND (IRE)**, 8, b g Presenting—Laragh (IRE) **Mrs K. Digweed**
24 **NORSE LEGEND**, 5, b g Norse Dancer (IRE)—Methodical **Woodhaven Racing Syndicate**
25 **ONWITHTHEPARTY**, 7, b g Sir Harry Lewis (USA)—Kentford Fern **Party People**
26 **OUR NIPPER**, 4, ch g Grape Tree Road—Lady Kay **L. Gilbert**
27 **PIPES AT MIDNIGHT**, 4, b g Midnight Legend—Pipes A'calling **Mrs J. M. Butler**
28 **REMILUC (FR)**, 7, b g Mister Sacha (FR)—Markene de Durtal (FR) **Gilbert & Gamble**
29 **ROCKNROBIN (IRE)**, 5, br g Robin des Pres (FR)—Our Presenting (IRE) **Mrs K. Digweed**
30 **RUDE AND CRUDE (IRE)**, 7, b g Rudimentary (USA)—Sorry Sarah (IRE) **Sir Peter & Lady Forwood**
31 **SEA WALL (IRE)**, 8, b g Turgeon (USA)—Si Parfaite (FR) **Draper Edmonds Draper**
32 **SUNLEY SPIRIT**, 6, b m Lucarno (USA)—Sunley Shines **Mr J. B. Sunley**
33 **SUNSHINE MOUNTAIN (FR)**, 4, b g Librettist (USA)—Highest Price (FR) **Mrs I. D. Colderick**
34 **SUPERCILIARY**, 7, b g Dansili—Supereva (IRE) **C. E. Gordon**
35 **TARA BRIDGE**, 8, b g Kayf Tara—Annie Greenlaw **B. J. Champion**
36 **THE CHUCKMEISTER (IRE)**, 7, b g Germany (IRE)—Lady Florian **Mrs C. M. Poland**
37 **TIGRE D'ARON (FR)**, 8, gr g Dom Alco (FR)—Fleche Noir II (FR) **Mrs K. Digweed**
38 **VERY NOBLE (FR)**, 7, b g Martaline—Isati's (FR) **A. C. Ward-Thomas**

Other Owners: Mrs H. J. Alwen, Mr R. N. Alwen, M. O. Coates, Mrs F. A. Coates, J. Draper, Mr M. J. Draper, T. W. Edmonds, Sir P N. Forwood, Lady H. R. Forwood, Mr J. M. Gamble, Mrs J. L. Gordon, Mr P. A. Herbert, Mr J. Hinds, Mr S. C. Hobbs, C. A. Leafe, Miss J. E. Reed, P. J. H. Rowe, R. M. Venn, Mr M. C. Waddingham, Mr S. E. Windsor.

Assistant Trainer: Jenny Gordon

Conditional: Tom Cannon. **Amateur:** Miss M. R. Trainor.

---

243 **MR J. T. GORMAN, Curragh**
Postal: **Maddenstown Lodge Stables, Maddenstown, Curragh, Co. Kildare, Ireland**
Contacts: **PHONE (00353) 45 441404 MOBILE (00353) 872 599603**
E-MAIL jtgorman1@hotmail.com

1 **ATHENRY BOY (IRE)**, 4, br g Excellent Art—Dancing With Stars (IRE) **P. Reilly**
2 **BUSY BUSH (IRE)**, 4, b f Bushranger (IRE)—Candela Bay (IRE) **The Andrews Syndicate**
3 **ITS HARRYS GIRL (IRE)**, 4, b f Kodiac—Ufallya (IRE) **The Andrews Syndicate**
4 **KILLDUNNE (IRE)**, 9, b g Hawk Wing (USA)—Trigger Happy (IRE) **Miss M. McWey**
5 **LETHAL LEGACY (IRE)**, 4, b g Alfred Nobel (IRE)—Cafe Creme (IRE) **The Andrews Syndicate**
6 **SNAP CLICK (IRE)**, 5, b g Kodiac—Happy Hour (GER) **P. Reilly**
7 **TOM KETTLE (IRE)**, 5, ch g Indian Haven—Dakota Two (IRE) **Miss M. McWey**
8 **VOCIFEROUSLY (IRE)**, 4, b f Vocalised (USA)—Azra (IRE) **Mrs J. S. Bolger**

THREE-YEAR-OLDS

9 **DONT QUIT (IRE)**, b g Bushranger (IRE)—Elitista (FR) **The Andrews Syndicate**
10 **EDGY (IRE)**, b f Intikhab (USA)—Numerus Clausus (FR) **The Andrews Syndicate**
11 **VERBOSITY (IRE)**, b f Vocalised (USA)—Stitch Night (IRE) **Mrs J. S. Bolger**

MR J. T. GORMAN - Continued

TWO-YEAR-OLDS

12 B f 1/4 Bushranger (IRE)—Callanish (Inchinor) (2361) **J. T. Gorman**

---

244 **MR JOHN GOSDEN, Newmarket**
Postal: **Clarehaven Stables, Bury Road, Newmarket, Suffolk, CB8 7BY**
Contacts: **PHONE (01638) 565400 FAX (01638) 565401**
E-MAIL jhmg@johngosden.com

1 **BREDEN (IRE)**, 6, b g Shamardal (USA)—Perfect Touch (USA)
2 **CALIFORNIA (IRE)**, 4, b f Azamour (IRE)—Maskaya (USA)
3 **EAGLE TOP**, 5, ch h Pivotal—Gull Wing (IRE)
4 **FAYDHAN (USA)**, 4, br c War Front (USA)—Agreeable Miss (USA)
5 **FLYING OFFICER (USA)**, 6, b g Dynaformer (USA)—Vignette (USA)
6 **FURIA CRUZADA (CHI)**, 5, b m Newfoundland (USA)—Nuestra Machi (CHI)
7 **GM HOPKINS**, 5, b g Dubawi (IRE)—Varsity
8 **JACK HOBBS**, 4, b c Halling (USA)—Swain's Gold (USA)
9 **JAZZI TOP**, 4, b f Danehill Dancer (IRE)—Zee Zee Top
10 **JOHNNY BARNES (IRE)**, 4, b c Acclamation—Mahalia (IRE)
11 **JOURNEY**, 4, b f Dubawi (IRE)—Montare (IRE)
12 **MAHSOOB**, 5, b h Dansili—Mooakada (IRE)
13 **MILL SPRINGS**, 4, b f Shirocco (GER)—Mezzogiorno
14 **MR SINGH**, 4, b c High Chaparral (IRE)—Sundari (IRE)
15 **RICHARD PANKHURST**, 4, ch c Raven's Pass (USA)—Mainstay
16 **SWISS AFFAIR**, 4, b f Pivotal—Swiss Lake (USA)
17 **WAADY (IRE)**, 4, b g Approve (IRE)—Anne Bonney
18 **WESTERN HYMN**, 5, b g High Chaparral (IRE)—Blue Rhapsody

THREE-YEAR-OLDS

19 **AL EGDA**, b f Poet's Voice—Perfect Spirit (IRE)
20 **ALWAYS WELCOME (USA)**, ch g Elusive Quality (USA)—No Matter What (USA)
21 **AMANAAT (AUS)**, b c Exceed And Excel (AUS)—Pietra Dura
22 **AQUALIS**, b f Sea The Stars (IRE)—Rosamixa (FR)
23 **AUNTINET**, b f Invincible Spirit (IRE)—Cozy Maria (USA)
24 **BLUE GERANIUM (IRE)**, b f Dansili—Super Sleuth (IRE)
25 **CAMPOSANTO**, b f Pivotal—Field of Miracles (IRE)
26 **CAPE COVA (IRE)**, b c Cape Cross (IRE)—Sina Cova (USA)
27 **CARTAGO**, b c Dansili—Kilo Alpha
28 **CASTLE HARBOUR**, b c Kyllachy—Gypsy Carnival
29 **CHASTUSHKA (IRE)**, b f Poet's Voice—Sesmen
30 **CITY OF IDEAS**, ch c Dansili—Gertrude Bell
31 **COLONIAL CLASSIC (FR)**, b f Dansili—Flame of Hestia (IRE)
32 **CRAZY HORSE**, b c Sleeping Indian—Mainstay
33 **CYMRIC (USA)**, b c Kitten's Joy—Fastbridled (USA)
34 **DAILY BULLETIN (USA)**, b c Medaglia d'oro (USA)—Life At Ten (USA)
35 **DANGEROUS THOUGHT (USA)**, ch c Super Saver (USA)—Trepidation (USA)
36 **DHAROOS (IRE)**, ch c New Approach (IRE)—Cailiocht (USA)
37 **DOMMERSEN (IRE)**, ch c Dutch Art—Kelowna (IRE)
38 **EAST INDIES**, b g Authorized (IRE)—Elan
39 **ETERNALLY**, b f Dutch Art—Ardent
40 **EXIST**, b f Exceed And Excel (AUS)—Harryana
41 **EYESHINE**, b f Dubawi (IRE)—Casual Look (USA)
42 **FOIBLE**, b c Fastnet Rock (AUS)—Nyarhini
43 **FOUNDATION (IRE)**, ch c Zoffany (IRE)—Roystonea
44 **GALA**, gr f Galileo (IRE)—Misk (FR)
45 **GENERALSHIP (IRE)**, b c New Approach (IRE)—Ahla Wasahl
46 **HAYADH**, b g Oasis Dream—Warling (IRE)
47 **HENRY CROFT**, b c Dubawi (IRE)—Karen's Caper (USA)
48 **HERMITAGE BAY (USA)**, b c War Front (USA)—City Sister (USA)
49 **I AM (IRE)**, b f Galileo (IRE)—Nausicaa (USA)
50 **JATHAB (IRE)**, ch c Shamardal (USA)—Nightime (IRE)
51 **KHOR AL UDAID**, b g Invincible Spirit (IRE)—Brusca (USA)
52 **LA MORTOLA**, b f Dubawi (IRE)—Claba di San Jore (IRE)

MR JOHN GOSDEN - Continued

53 **LAUGH ALOUD,** ch f Dubawi (IRE)—Opera Comique (FR)
54 **LEE BAY,** b c Cacique (IRE)—Bantu
55 **LINGUISTIC (IRE),** b c Lope de Vega (IRE)—Dazzle Dancer (IRE)
56 **LORD NAPIER (IRE),** b c Galileo (IRE)—Jacqueline (IND)
57 **MAZAZ (IRE),** b c Galileo (IRE)—Ice Point (USA)
58 **MOQLA,** b f Teofilo (IRE)—Mooakada (IRE)
59 **MUAITHER (IRE),** b c Poet's Voice—Past The Post (USA)
60 **MUNTAHAA (IRE),** gr c Dansili—Qertaas (IRE)
61 **NATHRA (IRE),** b f Iffraaj—Rada (IRE)
62 **NATURAL BEAUTY,** b f Oasis Dream—Maskunah (IRE)
63 **NAZZAA (IRE),** b c Shamardal (USA)—Multicolour Wave (IRE)
64 **PERIGEE,** b c Cacique (IRE)—Purissima (IRE)
65 **PERSUASIVE (IRE),** b f Dark Angel (IRE)—Choose Me (IRE)
66 **PREDILECTION (USA),** b c First Defence (USA)—Summer Shower
67 **PREQUEL (IRE),** b f Dark Angel (IRE)—Miss Indigo
68 **PRINCELY SUM (USA),** b f Lemon Drop Kid (USA)—Honoria (IRE)
69 **PURSUITOFTHESTARS (IRE),** b f Sea The Stars (IRE)—Pursuit of Life
70 **RATIONALITY (USA),** b f Dansili—Real Sense (IRE)
71 **REMARKABLE,** b c Pivotal—Irresistible
72 **REX BELL (IRE),** b c Dubawi (IRE)—Clara Bow (IRE)
73 **RIMRAAM,** b f Dutch Art—Sinduda
74 **ROYAL ARTILLERY (USA),** b br c War Front (USA)—Masseuse (USA)
75 **SARMADY (USA),** b br c Street Cry (IRE)—Maqaasid
76 **SATISH,** b c Dansili—Maycocks Bay
77 **SHALAA (IRE),** b c Invincible Spirit (IRE)—Ghurra (USA)
78 **SHALDANA,** b f Danehill Dancer (IRE)—Shaleela (IRE)
79 **SIDE HILL (USA),** b f Speightstown (USA)—Hidden Face (USA)
80 **SMAISMA (IRE),** b f Galileo (IRE)—Shadow Song (IRE)
81 **SNOW MOON,** b f Oasis Dream—Sariska
82 **SO MI DAR,** b f Dubawi (IRE)—Dar Re Mi
83 **SOUTHERN STARS,** b f Smart Strike (CAN)—Stacelita (FR)
84 **SOVEREIGN PARADE (IRE),** b f Galileo (IRE)—Dialafara (FR)
85 **STRATUM,** b c Dansili—Lunar Phase (IRE)
86 **SWISS RANGE,** b f Zamindar (USA)—Spanish Sun (USA)
87 **SYMBOLIC,** b c Shamardal (USA)—Resort
88 **TAQAAREED (IRE),** ch f Sea The Stars (IRE)—Ezima (IRE)
89 **TAQDEER (IRE),** ch c Fast Company (IRE)—Brigantia
90 **TAQDEES (IRE),** ch f Sea The Stars (IRE)—Aquarelle Bleue
91 **TASHWEEQ (IRE),** b c Big Bad Bob (IRE)—Dance Hall Girl (IRE)
92 **TATHQEEF (USA),** b c Tapit (USA)—Foxy Danseur (USA)
93 **THE BLACK PRINCESS (FR),** b br f Iffraaj—Larceny (IRE)
94 **TO ETERNITY,** b f Galileo (USA)—All's Forgotten (USA)
95 **UMM BAB (IRE),** b f Sea The Stars (IRE)—Something Mon (USA)
96 **UP TO YOU (USA),** ch f Giant's Causeway (USA)—Vignette (USA)
97 **VERMEULEN,** b g Fastnet Rock (AUS)—Crystal Maze
98 **VINCENT'S FOREVER,** b c Pour Moi (IRE)—Glen Rosie (IRE)
99 **VON BLUCHER (IRE),** ch c Zoffany (IRE)—Tropical Lady (IRE)
100 **WAJEEZ (IRE),** ch c Lope de Vega (IRE)—Chanter
101 **WESTERN PRINCE,** b c Cape Cross (IRE)—Vigee Le Brun (USA)
102 **WHITE HOT (IRE),** b f Galileo (IRE)—Gwynn (IRE)
103 **WINGS OF DESIRE,** ch c Pivotal—Gull Wing (IRE)

TWO-YEAR-OLDS

104 B c 10/4 Galileo (IRE)—Adoration (USA) (Honor Grades (USA))
105 **ALMUKALA (IRE),** b c 7/2 Invincible Spirit (IRE)—Vedela (FR) (Selkirk (USA)) (1033591)
106 **ALNAAS,** b f 24/2 Dansili—Hedaaya (IRE) (Indian Ridge)
107 **ASKING PRICE (USA),** b f 27/3 First Defence (USA)—Price Tag (Dansili)
108 **ASTERION,** b c 7/2 Pivotal—Minoan Dancer (IRE) (Galileo (IRE))
109 **AURORA GOLD,** b f 19/4 Frankel—Midsummer (Kingmambo (USA))
110 B c 14/3 Nathaniel (IRE)—Bahama Spirit (IRE) (Invincible Spirit (IRE)) (140273)
111 B c 31/1 War Front (USA)—Bel Air Beauty (USA) (Smart Strike (CAN)) (320512)
112 B c 17/2 Hard Spun (USA)—Belenkaya (USA) (Giant's Causeway (USA))
113 Br c 25/2 High Chaparral (IRE)—Bezique (Cape Cross (IRE)) (170000)
114 **BIZZARRIA,** ch f 16/5 Lemon Drop Kid (USA)—Lynnwood Chase (USA) (Horse Chestnut (SAF))
115 B f 8/3 Dubawi (IRE)—Brigitta (IRE) (Sadler's Wells (USA)) (425000)

MR JOHN GOSDEN - Continued

116 B f 13/3 Invincible Spirit (IRE)—Concordia (Pivotal)
117 CORONET, gr f 24/2 Dubawi (IRE)—Approach (Darshaan)
118 CRACKSMAN, b c 9/4 Frankel—Rhadegunda (Pivotal)
119 Ch c 30/1 Choisir (AUS)—Damhsa Le Cheile (IRE) (Teofilo (IRE)) (115000)
120 DAMOCLES (GER), b c 24/2 Siyouni (FR)—Duty And Destiny (IRE) (Montjeu (IRE)) (130000)
121 B f 6/4 Galileo (IRE)—Danehurst (Danehill (USA))
122 B c 19/3 Frankel—Dar Re Mi (Singspiel (IRE)) (750000)
123 B c 12/3 Nathaniel (IRE)—Dash To The Front (Diktat) (115000)
124 DEFENCE COUNSEL (USA), ch c 23/2 Afleet Alex (USA)—Faraway Flower (USA) (Distant View (USA))
125 B c 6/3 Oasis Dream—Deliberate (King's Best (USA))
126 B c 31/3 Holy Roman Emperor (IRE)—Disco Volante (Sadler's Wells (USA)) (120000)
127 Ch c 27/4 New Approach (IRE)—Do The Honours (IRE) (Highest Honor (FR)) (110741)
128 B f 27/1 Raven's Pass (USA)—Elas Diamond (Danehill Dancer (IRE)) (160000)
129 ENABLE, b f 12/2 Nathaniel (IRE)—Concentric (Sadler's Wells (USA))
130 Gr f 27/4 Mastercraftsman (IRE)—Flanders (IRE) (Common Grounds) (300000)
131 B f 9/5 Acclamation—Fleche d'or (Dubai Destination (USA))
132 Ch f 1/4 Foxwedge (AUS)—Generous Diana (Generous (IRE)) (65000)
133 B c 27/1 Dansili—Giants Play (USA) (Giant's Causeway (USA)) (260000)
134 GLENCADAM GLORY, b c 4/2 Nathaniel (IRE)—Lady Grace (IRE) (Orpen (USA)) (90000)
135 GREAT SOUND (IRE), b c 12/4 Galileo (IRE)—Wanna (IRE) (Danehill Dancer (IRE)) (320000)
136 GYMNASTE (IRE), b f 14/3 Shamardal (USA)—Galipette (Green Desert (USA)) (191952)
137 B c 2/5 Dark Angel (IRE)—Henties Bay (IRE) (Cape Cross (IRE)) (75000)
138 B c 8/4 Distorted Humor (USA)—Honest Lady (Seattle Slew (USA))
139 Gr c 26/2 Oasis Dream—Honorlina (FR) (Linamix (FR)) (400000)
140 ILLAUNMORE (USA), br f 30/3 Shamardal (USA)—Illaunglass (IRE) (Red Clubs (IRE))
141 B c 30/1 Oasis Dream—Izzi Top (Pivotal) (1100000)
142 B c 28/4 Galileo (IRE)—Jacqueline (IND) (King Charlemagne (USA))
143 B c 11/3 Fastnet Rock (AUS)—Kahyasi Moll (IRE) (Brief Truce (USA))
144 KESWICK, b c 15/1 Dansili—Marywell (Selkirk (USA))
145 B f 22/4 Exceed And Excel (AUS)—Lady Hawkfield (IRE) (Hawk Wing (USA)) (180000)
146 B c 11/2 Holy Roman Emperor (IRE)—Larceny (IRE) (Cape Cross (IRE)) (155038)
147 B f 26/3 Fastnet Rock (AUS)—Lauren Louise (Tagula (IRE)) (320000)
148 LEAPT, b c 12/1 Nathaniel (IRE)—Liel (Pivotal)
149 LOUJAIN (IRE), ch c 9/3 Dubawi (IRE)—Eshaadeh (USA) (Storm Cat (USA))
150 LUQYAA, b f 23/1 Smart Strike (CAN)—Maqaasid (Green Desert (USA))
151 B c 24/4 Invincible Spirit (IRE)—Maakrah (Dubai Destination (USA))
152 MADEENATY (IRE), b f 26/4 Dansili—Mooakada (IRE) (Montjeu (IRE))
153 B f 11/5 Galileo (IRE)—Milanova (AUS) (Danehill (USA))
154 B c 28/2 Dubawi (IRE)—Mont Etoile (IRE) (Montjeu (IRE))
155 MURAAQEB, b c 18/3 Nathaniel (IRE)—Tesary (Danehill (USA)) (180952)
156 B f 26/4 Redoute's Choice (AUS)—My Branch (Distant Relative) (400000)
157 NASEEM (IRE), br c 17/2 Sea The Stars (IRE)—Chiosina (IRE) (Danehill Dancer (IRE))
158 NATURE'S ORDER (IRE), b c 11/2 Dansili—Nature Spirits (Beat Hollow)
159 B c 24/1 Redoute's Choice (AUS)—Nitya (FR) (Indian Ridge) (240000)
160 NOBLY BORN, ch c 15/4 Mayson—Noble One (Primo Dominie)
161 Ch c 30/1 Casamento (IRE)—Ohiyesa (IRE) (Noverre (USA)) (133333)
162 Ch c 25/1 Archipenko (USA)—Oshiponga (Barathea (IRE)) (60000)
163 B c 2/5 Sepoy (AUS)—Our Faye (College Chapel) (55000)
164 PEACEFUL PASSAGE (USA), b f 31/3 War Front (USA)—Flying Passage (USA) (A P Indy (USA))
165 B c 29/1 High Chaparral (IRE)—Pearl City (IRE) (Zamindar (USA)) (50000)
166 B c 13/3 Campanologist (USA)—Praia (GER) (Big Shuffle (USA)) (140000)
167 PRECIOUS RAMOTSWE, b f 17/2 Nathaniel (IRE)—Miss Pinkerton (Danehill (USA))
168 PRESENT TENSE, b f 30/1 Bated Breath—Zenda (Zamindar (USA))
169 PRIVATE ADVISOR, b f 2/4 Pivotal—Confidential Lady (Singspiel (IRE))
170 B c 29/1 Lope de Vega (IRE)—Promesse de L'aube (FR) (Galileo (IRE)) (383905)
171 B f 19/3 Bernardini (USA)—Questing (Hard Spun (USA))
172 Br c 3/3 Cape Cross (IRE)—Quiet Dream (USA) (Seattle Slew (USA)) (425000)
173 Ch f 19/5 Galileo (IRE)—Rags To Riches (USA) (A P Indy (USA))
174 B f 21/1 Galileo (IRE)—Red Avis (Exceed And Excel (AUS)) (200000)
175 REEH (IRE), gr ro f 5/4 Invincible Spirit (IRE)—Vanishing Grey (IRE) (Verglas (IRE))
176 B f 19/5 Galileo (IRE)—Regal Rose (Danehill (USA))
177 REGAL SPLENDOUR, b f 7/2 Pivotal—Regal Realm (Medicean)
178 B c 28/3 Invincible Spirit (IRE)—Riotous Applause (Royal Applause)
179 B f 3/3 Fastnet Rock (AUS)—Rose Blossom (Pastoral Pursuits) (220000)
180 B f 2/4 Sea The Stars (IRE)—Royale Danehill (IRE) (Danehill (USA)) (200000)

MR JOHN GOSDEN - Continued

181 B f 14/2 Sepoy (AUS)—Samdaniya (Machiavellian (USA)) (100000)
182 Ch c 16/5 Lope de Vega (IRE)—Savignano (Polish Precedent (USA)) (225000)
183 B f 4/5 So You Think (NZ)—Sense of Style (USA) (Thunder Gulch (USA))
184 **SEVEN HEAVENS**, b c 21/5 Frankel—Heaven Sent (Pivotal) (620000)
185 **SHUTTER SPEED**, br f 6/3 Dansili—Photographic (Oasis Dream)
186 **SILVERLIGHT**, b c 1/4 Dubawi (IRE)—Arizona Jewel (Dansili)
187 B f 24/3 War Front (USA)—Tare Green (USA) (Giant's Causeway (USA)) (213675)
188 Ch f 31/1 Foxwedge (AUS)—Tebee (Selkirk (USA))
189 Ch f 4/4 New Approach (IRE)—Utrecht (Rock of Gibraltar (IRE))
190 B c 1/3 Redoute's Choice (AUS)—Vadawina (IRE) (Unfuwain (USA)) (701365)
191 **WEEKENDER**, b c 25/1 Frankel—Very Good News (USA) (Empire Maker (USA))
192 B f 1/2 Kodiac—Windy Lane (Dubai Destination (USA)) (125000)
193 B c 18/2 Teofilo (IRE)—Wonderfilly (FR) (Invincible Spirit (IRE)) (95000)
194 B c 11/3 Halling (USA)—Woven Lace (Hard Spun (USA))

Jockey (flat): L. Dettori, Robert Tart, Nicky Mackay, Robert Havlin.

---

245   **MRS HARRIET GRAHAM, Jedburgh**
Postal: **Strip End, Jedburgh, Roxburghshire, TD8 6NE**
Contacts: **PHONE (01835) 840354 MOBILE (07843) 380401**
E-MAIL hgrahamracing@aol.com

1 AZERODEGREE (IRE), 7, b g Azamour (IRE)—Fairy (USA) Mr M. J. McGovern
2 BLUESIDE BOY (IRE), 8, b g Blueprint (IRE)—Asidewager (IRE) Mr G. F. Adam
3 MAGGIE BLUE (IRE), 8, b m Beneficial—Top Ar Aghaidh (IRE) Mr M. J. McGovern
4 RHYMERS HA', 9, br g Kasakov—Salu Mr G. F. Adam
5 RHYMERS STONE, 8, b g Desideratum—Salu Mr G. F. Adam
6 SCOTSWELL, 10, b g Endoli (USA)—Tofino Swell H G Racing
7 TOQUICKLY, 4, b f Tobougg (IRE)—Miss Quickly (IRE) Miss G. Joughin

Other Owners: R. D. Graham, Mrs H. O. Graham.

Assistant Trainer: R D Graham

Jockey (NH): Lucy Alexander, James Reveley. **Conditional:** Calum Bewley.

---

246   **MR CHRIS GRANT, Billingham**
Postal: **Low Burntoft Farm, Wolviston, Billingham, Cleveland, TS22 5PD**
Contacts: **PHONE (01740) 644054 MOBILE (07860) 577998**
E-MAIL chrisgrantracing@gmail.com WEBSITE www.chrisgrantracing.co.uk

1 ACDC (IRE), 6, b g King's Theatre (IRE)—Always Alert (IRE) D&D Armstrong Limited
2 4, Ch f Golan (IRE)—Almost Trumps M. R. Johnson
3 BAFANA BLUE, 5, b g Blueprint (IRE)—Anniejo G. F. White
4 BEAUMONT'S PARTY (IRE), 9, b g High Chaparral (IRE)—Miss Champagne (FR) Elliott Brothers And Peacock
5 BEYOND THE GLEN, 6, b m And Beyond (IRE)—Calabria G. F. White
6 BROADWAY BELLE, 6, b m Lucarno (USA)—Theatre Belle Division Bell Partnership
7 BROKETHEGATE, 11, b g Presenting—Briery Ann C. Grant
8 CLENAGH CASTLE (IRE), 6, b g King's Theatre (IRE)—Orwell's Marble (IRE) D&D Armstrong Limited
9 COUNTDOWN (GER), 8, b g Monsun (GER)—Catella (GER) C. Grant
10 DONNA'S DELIGHT (IRE), 5, b g Portrait Gallery (IRE)—Hot Lips (IRE) D&D Armstrong Limited
11 DONNA'S DIAMOND (IRE), 7, gr g Cloudings (IRE)—Inish Bofin (IRE) D&D Armstrong Limited
12 DRUMS OF WAR (IRE), 4, b g Youmzain (IRE)—Min Asl Wafi (IRE) J. Wade
13 EMERALD THIEF (IRE), 5, b g Kalanisi (IRE)—Nevinch C. Grant
14 FOOLISH MISTRESS, 6, b m Josr Algarhoud (IRE)—Rosie Mist Mr J. Eubank
15 HA'PENNY WOODS (IRE), 6, b g Wareed (IRE)—Muriel's Pride (IRE) D&D Armstrong Limited
16 HEY BOB (IRE), 4, br g Big Bad Bob (IRE)—Bounty Star (IRE) C. Grant
17 JACKS LAST HOPE, 7, b g King's Theatre (IRE)—Ninna Nanna (FR) Mr J. Kenny
18 KALANITI (IRE), 5, b m Kalanisi (IRE)—Miss Twinkletoes (IRE) Mrs S. Sunter
19 KNYSNA BAY, 5, b m Millkom—Knysna Belle G. F. White
20 LUCEMATIC, 10, b m Systematic—Soldier's Song Mrs P. C. Stirling
21 MILAN LADY (IRE), 5, b m Milan—Terre d'orient (FR) D&D Armstrong Limited
22 MINI FRANK, 4, b g Josr Algarhoud (IRE)—Micklow Magic W. Raw

MR CHRIS GRANT - Continued

23 **MISTER KIT**, 8, gr g Tikkanen (USA)—Rosie Mist **Mrs H. N. Eubank**
24 **MR SYNTAX (IRE)**, 12, b g King's Theatre (IRE)—Smile Awhile (USA) **Pinnacle N.H Partnership**
25 **NOTONEBUTTWO (IRE)**, 9, b g Dushyantor (USA)—Daiquiri (IRE) **D&D Armstrong Limited**
26 **OLLIE G**, 8, b g Denounce—Silver Rosa **D&D Armstrong Limited**
27 **PIKES PEAK (IRE)**, 7, br g Kutub (IRE)—Accordionline (IRE) **Miss A. P. Lee**
28 **PLATT LANE (IRE)**, 5, b g Mahler—Ellesmere (IRE) **T. J. Hemmings**
29 **RAYMOND REDDINGTON (IRE)**, 5, b g Spadoun (FR)—Martovic (IRE) **D&D Armstrong Limited**
30 **RIDE THE RANGE (IRE)**, 7, br g High Chaparral (IRE)—Jade River (IRE) **D&D Armstrong Limited**
31 **ROCK RELIEF (IRE)**, 10, gr g Daylami (IRE)—Sheer Bliss (IRE) **D&D Armstrong Limited**
32 **TEARS FROM HEAVEN (USA)**, 10, b br g Street Cry (IRE)—Heavenly Aura (USA) **Mrs S. Sunter**
33 **THE CONN (IRE)**, 6, b g Milan—Grandy Invader (IRE) **T. J. Hemmings**
34 **THEATRE ACT**, 5, ch m Act One—Theatre Belle **Division Bell Partnership**
35 **THEATRE ROYALE**, 4, ch f Sulamani (IRE)—Theatre Belle
36 **TICKANRUN (IRE)**, 6, gr g Tikkanen (USA)—Dusty Lane (IRE) **D&D Armstrong Limited**
37 **TINY DANCER (IRE)**, 8, b g Darsi (FR)—Taipans Girl (IRE) **Mrs A. J. Mccubbin**
38 **TOP CAT DJ (IRE)**, 8, ch g St Jovite (USA)—Lady Coldunell **Miss A. P. Lee**
39 **WHATATUB (IRE)**, 5, b g Kutub (IRE)—County Classic **C. Grant**
40 **WILLIAM MONEY (IRE)**, 9, b g Cloudings (IRE)—All of A Kind (IRE) **D&D Armstrong Limited**

TWO-YEAR-OLDS

41 B g 16/1 Bushranger (IRE)—Honour And Obey (IRE) (Hurricane Run (IRE)) (6275) **C. Grant**
42 B c 21/4 Baltic King—Lady of Knock (IRE) (Indian Ridge) (7013) **C. Grant**

Other Owners: T. Cunningham, J. M. Elliott, C. R. Elliott, Ms S. V. Hattersley, Mr J. Henderson, A. Meale, B. Morton, Mr R. Poole, A. D. Wright.

Assistant Trainer: Mrs S. Grant

Jockey (NH): Brian Hughes, Denis O'Regan. **Conditional:** Diarmuid O'Regan.

247
MR JAMES GRASSICK, Cheltenham
Postal: **4 The Wharf, Coombe Hill, Gloucester, Gloucestershire, GL19 4BB**

1 **ARMEMENT (FR)**, 5, b g Smadoun (FR)—Apparrement (IRE) **Mr G. Brookhouse**
2 **FARRAH'S CHOICE**, 4, b f Equiano (FR)—Esplanade **James Grassick Racing Club**
3 **JUST MARION (IRE)**, 4, b f Bushranger (IRE)—Dolphin Stamp (IRE) **Kernow Loans Ltd**
4 **POETIC LICENSE (IRE)**, 4, b g Dylan Thomas (IRE)—Bright Bank (IRE) **James Grassick Racing Club**

Other Owners: Mrs N. Grassick, J. R. Grassick.

248
MR LIAM GRASSICK, Cheltenham
Postal: **Postlip Racing Stables, Winchcombe, Cheltenham, Gloucestershire, GL54 5AQ**
Contacts: **PHONE** (01242) 603124 **YARD** (01242) 603919 **MOBILE** (07816) 930423
E-MAIL mark.grassick@btopenworld.com

1 **FATHER PAT**, 13, br g Chaddleworth (IRE)—Lady Crusty **L. P. Grassick**
2 **WALTZING TORNADO (IRE)**, 12, ch g Golden Tornado (IRE)—Lady Dante (IRE) **L. P. Grassick**

Assistant Trainer: Mark Grassick

249
MR M. C. GRASSICK, Curragh
Postal: **Fenpark House, Pollardstown, Curragh, Co. Kildare, Ireland**
Contacts: **MOBILE** (00353) 86 3648829
E-MAIL mcgrassick@hotmail.com **WEBSITE** www.michaelcgrassick.com

1 **ELUSIVE IN PARIS (IRE)**, 7, b g Elusive City (USA)—Bradwell (IRE) **Mr Patrick McKeon**
2 **KING OF ARAN (IRE)**, 9, b br g Val Royal (FR)—Innishmore (IRE) **Dont Tell The Missus Syndicate**
3 **LAUREL CREEK (IRE)**, 11, b g Sakura Laurel (JPN)—Eastern Sky (AUS) **Roisin Walshe**
4 **TAPERING (USA)**, 4, gr g Invasor (ARG)—Unbridled Treasure (USA) **Paul Grimes**
5 **TEXAS ROCK (IRE)**, 5, b g Rock of Gibraltar (IRE)—Vestavia (IRE) **Joe Keeling**

MR M. C. GRASSICK - Continued

THREE-YEAR-OLDS
6 TEXAS RADIO (IRE), b g Kyllachy—Miss Rochester (IRE) **Tadhg Geary**

TWO-YEAR-OLDS
7 B f 5/4 Bushranger (IRE)—Apple Blossom Time (IRE) (Invincible Spirit (IRE)) **Joe Keeling**
8 MALIBU MAGIC (IRE), b f 30/1 Rip Van Winkle (IRE)—Awjila (Oasis Dream) (39867) **Tadhg Geary**

Assistant Trainer: David Flynn

MR CARROLL GRAY, Bridgwater
Postal: The Little Glen, Peartwater Road, Spaxton, Bridgwater, Somerset, TA5 1DG
Contacts: MOBILE (07989) 768163

1 ALL BUT GREY, 10, gr g Baryshnikov (AUS)—Butleigh Rose **Mr R. J. Napper and Mr N. P. Searle**
2 ARTHUR'S QUEEN (FR), 5, b m Soldier of Fortune (IRE)—Tintagel **Riverdance Consortium 3**
3 CAUTIOUS KATE (IRE), 9, b m Witness Box (USA)—Cautious Leader **Mr L & Mrs J Waring**
4 GREEN DU CIEL (FR), 11, gr g Smadoun (FR)—Sucre Blanc (FR) **Tim & Liz Heal**
5 KEMICALLIE, 4, b f Passing Glance—Jenny From Brean **Unity Farm**
6 MISTER UNO (IRE), 5, b h Tamayuz—Starlight Smile (USA) **Dr D. Gadian**
7 SAINT BREIZ (FR), 10, b br g Saint des Saints (FR)—Balladina (FR) **Riverdance Consortium 2**
8 VERING (FR), 10, b g Bering—Forcia (FR) **Mr L & Mrs J Waring**

Other Owners: Mr M. J. Colenutt, Mr Richard Flenk, Mrs Elizabeth Heal, Mr T. Heal, Mr R. Napper, Mr N. P. Searle, Mrs J. Waring, Mr L. Waring.

Assistant Trainer: Mrs C. M. L. Gray

Jockey (NH): Micheal Nolan. **Amateur:** Mr R. Hawker.

---

251 **MR PETER GRAYSON, Formby**
Postal: Apartment 7, The Sandwarren, 21 Victoria Road, Formby
Contacts: PHONE (01704) 830668 FAX (01704) 830668
E-MAIL info@pgr.uk.com WEBSITE www.pgr.uk.com

1 RAJEH (IRE), 13, b g Key of Luck (USA)—Saramacca (IRE) **Mr E. Grayson**
2 RIGHTCAR, 9, b g Bertolini (USA)—Loblolly Bay **Mr E. Grayson**
3 SENATOR BONG, 6, ch g Dutch Art—Sunley Gift **Mr E. Grayson**
4 STONEACRE OSKAR, 7, b m Echo of Light—Keidas (FR) **Mr E. Grayson**

Assistant Trainer: Mrs S. Grayson

---

252 **MR WARREN GREATREX, Upper Lambourn**
Postal: Uplands, Upper Lambourn, Hungerford, Berkshire, RG17 8QH
Contacts: PHONE (01488) 670279 FAX (01488) 72193 MOBILE (07920) 039114
E-MAIL info@wgreatrexracing.com WEBSITE www.wgreatrexracing.com

1 ACT OF SUPREMACY (IRE), 6, b g Presenting—Supreme Touch (IRE) **Equis (B) Partnership**
2 ALOOMOMO (FR), 6, b g Tirwanako (FR)—Kayola (FR) **The Large G & T Partnership**
3 ALWAYS MANAGING, 7, b m Oscar (IRE)—Sunshine Rays **H. Redknapp**
4 ALZAMMAAR (USA), 5, b g Birdstone (USA)—Alma Mater **Riverdee Stable & ROA Arkle Partnership**
5 ANOTHER SUNSHINE, 5, b m Kayf Tara—Sunshine Rays **H. Redknapp**
6 APACHE PEARL (IRE), 5, br g Indian Danehill (IRE)—Pearl Buttons **The Glazeley Partnership 3**
7 APRIL DUSK (IRE), 7, b g Turtle Island (IRE)—Rabble Run **R. C. Tooth**
8 BALLYCULLA (IRE), 9, b g Westerner—Someone Told Me (IRE) **No Dramas & Robert Aplin**
9 BELLS 'N' BANJOS (IRE), 6, b g Indian River (FR)—Beechill Dancer (IRE) **The Maple Hurst Partnership**
10 BIGBURY BAY (IRE), 5, b m Stowaway—Clamper (IRE) **J.N.G-M Racing**
11 BILKO'S BACK (IRE), 4, b g Big Bad Bob (IRE)—Chica Roca (USA) **Middleham Park Racing CI**
12 BON ENFANT (FR), 5, gr g Saint des Saints (FR)—Montanara Paris (FR) **Swanee River Partnership**

MR WARREN GREATREX - Continued

13 **BOUDRY (FR)**, 5, b g Crossharbour—Lavande (FR) **Power Geneva Ltd**
14 **BURLINGTON BERT (FR)**, 5, b g Califet (FR)—Melhi Sun (FR) **Martin St. Quinton & Tim Syder**
15 **CAITYS JOY (GER)**, 6, b m Malinas (GER)—Cassilera (GER) **Diamond Club**
16 5, Ch g Nomadic Way (USA)—Captivating Tyna (IRE)
17 **CEANN SIBHEAL (IRE)**, 7, b g Flemensfirth (USA)—Imperial Award (IRE) **The High Kites**
18 **CHEF D'OEUVRE (FR)**, 5, b g Martaline—Kostroma (FR) **McNeill Family Ltd**
19 **COLE HARDEN (IRE)**, 7, b g Westerner—Nosie Betty (IRE) **Mrs Jill Eynon & Mr Robin Eynon**
20 4, B g Mahler—Cooladurragh (IRE) **Bolingbroke, Bunch, Howard & Sutton**
21 **COYOACAN (FR)**, 4, b g Al Namix (FR)—Jetty Dancer (FR) **Potensis Bloodstock Ltd**
22 **DOLATULO (FR)**, 9, ch g Le Fou (IRE)—La Perspective (FR) **Chasemore Farm LLP**
23 **EXTREME APPEAL (IRE)**, 4, b g Excellent Art—Silk Mascara (IRE) **Equis**
24 **FLY DU CHARMIL (FR)**, 5, b g Saint des Saints (FR)—Famous Member (FR) **McNeill Family Ltd**
25 **FLYING SHADOW (GER)**, 4, b g Sholokhov (IRE)—Fitness (USA)
26 **FOR GOODNESS SAKE (IRE)**, 4, b f Yeats (IRE)—Muschana **The Hippy Hippy Shakes Partnership**
27 **GROUNDUNDERREPAIR (IRE)**, 5, b g Milan—Discerning Air **No Dramas Partnership 1**
28 **HANNAH'S PRINCESS (IRE)**, 7, b m Kalanisi (IRE)—Donna's Princess (IRE) **Swanee River Partnership**
29 **HORSTED VALLEY**, 6, gr g Fair Mix (IRE)—Kullu Valley **The Broadwell Fox Partnership**
30 5, B m King's Theatre (IRE)—Isabello (IRE)
31 **KAYSERSBERG (FR)**, 9, b g Khalkevi (IRE)—Alliance Royale (FR) **Mrs Julien Turner & Mr Andrew Merriam**
32 4, B g Winged Love (IRE)—Kiora Lady (IRE) **Urban Cookie Collective**
33 **KNIGHT BACHELOR**, 6, ch g Midnight Legend—Fenney Spring **A. W. K. Merriam**
34 **LA BAGUE AU ROI (FR)**, 5, b m Doctor Dino (FR)—
           Alliance Royale (FR) **Mrs Julien Turner & Mr Andrew Merriam**
35 **MA DU FOU (FR)**, 6, b br g Le Fou (IRE)—Belle du Ma (FR) **Walters Plant Hire & James & Jean Potter**
36 **MAJOR DAVIS (FR)**, 4, b g Vision d'etat (FR)—Majorica Sancta (FR) **Mr W. J. Greatrex**
37 **MASQUERADE (FR)**, 7, b g Fruits of Love (USA)—Beechill Dancer (IRE) **Mrs S. Griffiths**
38 **MILANESE QUEEN**, 5, b m Milan—Kaydee Queen (IRE) **Hockham Lodge Stud**
39 **MISSED APPROACH (IRE)**, 6, b g Golan (IRE)—Polly's Dream (IRE) **Alan & Andrew Turner**
40 **MORNING SYMPHONY (IRE)**, 7, b g Vinnie Roe (IRE)—Heart N Hope (IRE) **Mr W. J. Greatrex**
41 4, B g Flemensfirth (USA)—Nivalf **Middleham Park Racing CI**
42 **NOBLE QUEST**, 4, b g Kalanisi (IRE)—Katalina **Mrs R. I. Vaughan**
43 **ONE TRACK MIND (IRE)**, 6, b g Flemensfirth (USA)—Lady Petit (IRE) **Mr A. J. Weller**
44 **OSCAR PRAIRIE (IRE)**, 11, b g Oscar (IRE)—Silver Prairie (IRE) **Mr W. J. Greatrex**
45 **OUT SAM**, 7, b g Multiplex—Tintera (IRE) **Swanee River Partnership**
46 **PAINT THE CLOUDS**, 11, b g Muhtarram (USA)—Preening **Peter Deal & Jill & Robin Eynon**
47 **PENN LANE (IRE)**, 5, b g Scorpion (IRE)—Belsalsa (FR) **Alan & Andrew Turner**
48 **PENNYWELL (IRE)**, 6, b m Gold Well—Boyne Bridge (IRE) **The Silo Syndicate**
49 **POGGY'S STAR (FR)**, 4, b f Stowaway—Pamsy Wamsy (IRE) **Fitorfat Racing**
50 **POSTBRIDGE (IRE)**, 5, br m Robin des Pres (FR)—Dartmeet (IRE) **Mr P. T. Mott**
51 **PROFESSEUR EMERY (FR)**, 9, b g Officiel (FR)—Karmadeine (FR) **GDM Partnership**
52 **REILLY'S MINOR (IRE)**, 5, b g Westerner—Ringzar (IRE) **Mrs Jill Eynon & Mr Robin Eynon**
53 **RITUAL OF SENSES (IRE)**, 6, b g Milan—Nonnetia (IRE) **Equis & Lady Lloyd Webber**
54 **SAME DIFFERENCE (IRE)**, 10, b g Mr Combustible—Sarahs Reprive (IRE) **Mrs R. I. Vaughan**
55 **SANDHURST LAD (IRE)**, 5, b g Presenting—Off She Goes (IRE) **Nigel & Barbara Collison**
56 **SAVOY COURT (IRE)**, 5, b g Robin des Champs (FR)—North Star Poly (IRE) **Mrs T. J. Stone-Brown**
57 4, B g Westerner—Seesea (IRE) **Mr W. J. Greatrex**
58 **SHAH OF PERSIA**, 9, b g Fair Mix (IRE)—Queen Soraya **Mr A. M. Gibbons**
59 **SHANTOU BOB (IRE)**, 8, b g Shantou (USA)—Bobset Leader (IRE) **Fallon, Shipp & Bolingbroke**
60 **STICKEE FINGERS**, 5, b m Fair Mix (IRE)—Sticky Money **Shade Oak Stud & D Jenks**
61 **THE CALLER**, 5, b g Yeats (IRE)—Wyldello **E.O.D Racing**
62 4, B g Gold Well—The Dark One (IRE) **Mr Darren Flatt**
63 **THE MISSUS**, 5, b m Presenting—Violet Express (FR) **R. B. Waley-Cohen**
64 **THE NIPPER (IRE)**, 5, b m Scorpion (IRE)—Sharp Single (IRE) **Smith, Ratcliffe & Bowring**
65 **THREE COLOURS RED (IRE)**, 4, b g Camacho—Colour's Red (IRE) **Little Roberts Dowley & Turner**
66 **TOP DANCER (IRE)**, 9, b g Dark Moondancer—Latitude (IRE) **The Lone Star Partnership**
67 **TSAR ALEXANDRE (FR)**, 9, b g Robin des Champs (FR)—Bertrange (FR) **The Pantechnicons III**
68 **VIA VOLUPTA**, 6, b m Kayf Tara—Via Ferrata (FR) **Equis**
69 4, B g Shantou (USA)—Village Queen (IRE) **McNeill Family Ltd**
70 **VINCIAETTIS (FR)**, 5, b g Enrique—Over The Sea (FR) **Mrs J & Miss C Shipp**
71 **WARRANTOR (IRE)**, 7, b g Turtle Island (IRE)—Pixie Dust (IRE) **Mrs S. M. Drysdale**
72 **WESTWARD POINT**, 9, ch g Karinga Bay—Hottentot **Mr J. F. F. White**

MR WARREN GREATREX - Continued

Other Owners: Mr Robert Aplin, Mr A. Black, Mrs J. E. Black, Mr Lee Bolingbroke, Mr D. Bowring, Mr T. Boylan, Mr A. R. Bromley, Mrs P. Bunch, Mr Connor Burrowes, Mr J. Cavanagh, Mr Nigel Chamberlain, Mr Gregory Charlesworth, Mr Daniel Charlesworth, Mr Sean Clancy, Mrs Barbara Collison, Mr N. Collison, Mr Jonny Cooke, Mr C K Crossley Cooke, Mr P. A. Deal, Mr Keith Dowley, Mr Charles Egerton, Mrs Judy England, Mr Duncan England, Mrs Sadie Evans, Mrs J. M. Eynon, Mr R. A. F. Eynon, Mrs Padraic Fallon, Mr S. Fisher, Mr Nicholas Gifford-Mead, Mr Warren Greatrex, Mr Raymond Anderson Green, Mr Mark Grier, Mr R. Gurney, Mrs Emma Hockenhull, Mr P. D. Hockenhull, Mr John Horgan, Mr Graeme Howard, Mr W. Jenks, Mr David Jenks, Mr Darren Johns, Mr Robert Levitt, Mr S. M. Little, Mr Charles Liverton, Lady Lloyd-Webber, Mr Richard Mapp, Mr A. W. K. Merriam, Mr S. Munir, Mrs Hugh Murphy, Mr T. S. Palin, Mr Bernard Panton, Mr S. J. Piper, Mr Nick Pogmore, Mr B. G. Pomford, Mr J. E. Potter, Mrs J. E. Potter, Mr M. Prince, Mr J. Ratcliffe, Mr David Roberts, Mr Aidan Robertson, Mr Kieran P. Ryan, Mr S. W. Salkeld, Miss C. Shipp, Mrs Jean Shipp, Mr Michael Smith, Mr W. L. Smith, Mr Isaac Souede, Mr M. G. St Quinton, Mr Charles Sutton, Tim Syder, Mrs Julien Turner, Mr D. A. Turner, Mr Andrew Turner, Mr Alan R. Turner, Mrs Jessica Vaughan-Fowler, Walters Plant Hire Ltd, Mrs R. M. Wilson, Major R. G. Wilson, Mr William Wood.

Assistant Trainer: Trigger Plunkett **Head Lad:** Graham Baines, **Racing Secretary:** Oriana-Jane Baines

Jockey (NH): Gavin Sheehan. **Conditional:** Conor Walsh. **Amateur:** Mr Dominic Sutton.

---

253 MR PAUL GREEN, Lydiate
Postal: **Oak Lea, Southport Road, Lydiate, Liverpool, Merseyside, L31 4HH**
Contacts: **PHONE (0151) 526 0093 FAX (0151) 520 0299 MOBILE (07748) 630685**
E-MAIL paulgreen@mitchell-james.com

1 **ANNEANI (IRE)**, 4, b f Bushranger (IRE)—Hazium (IRE) **M. F. Nolan**
2 **FERDY (IRE)**, 7, b h Antonius Pius (USA)—Trinity Fair **The Winsor Not Group**
3 **LYDIATE LADY**, 4, b f Piccolo—Hiraeth **The Scotch Piper (Lydiate)**
4 **MASTER CHOICE (IRE)**, 4, b g Mastercraftsman (IRE)—No Quest (IRE) **Dr S. Lane**
5 **RUSTY ROCKET (IRE)**, 7, ch h Majestic Missile (IRE)—Sweet Compliance **Seven Stars Racing**
6 4, B g Royal Applause—Sudden Impact (IRE) **P. Green**

THREE-YEAR-OLDS

7 **JABBAROCKIE**, b g Showcasing—Canina
8 B f Equiano (FR)—Sudden Impact (IRE) **P. Green**

Other Owners: Mr G. Barton, Mr S. Clarke, Mr C. J. Dingwall, I. P. Mason.

Assistant Trainer: Fiona Ford

---

254 MR TOM GRETTON, Inkberrow
Postal: **C/o Gretton & Co Ltd, Middle Bouts Farm, Bouts Lane, Inkberrow, Worcester**
Contacts: **PHONE (01386) 792240 FAX (01386) 792472 MOBILE (07866) 116928**
E-MAIL tomgretton@hotmail.co.uk WEBSITE www.tomgrettonracing.com

1 **APPLETREE LANE**, 6, b m Croco Rouge (IRE)—Emmasflora **T. R. Gretton**
2 **ARMEDANDDANGEROUS (IRE)**, 11, b g Kris Kin (USA)—Lucky Fountain (IRE) **Not The Peloton Partnership**
3 **CLARA PEGGOTTY**, 9, b m Beat All (USA)—Clair Valley **Geoffrey Price & Edward Gretton**
4 **CRAZY JANE (IRE)**, 7, br m Definite Article—Blue Romance (IRE) **T. R. Gretton**
5 **DOVER THE MOON (IRE)**, 5, b g Bushranger (IRE)—Gold Script (FR) **G1 Racing Club Ltd**
6 **FINE JEWELLERY**, 7, b g Epalo (GER)—Lola Lolita (FR) **Ms A. S. Potze**
7 5, B m Kayf Tara—Golden Buck **Mrs Z. J. Trembecka-Ross**
8 5, B g Westerner—Ifuseehersayhello
9 **JACKTHEJOURNEYMAN (IRE)**, 7, b g Beneficial—Maslam (IRE) **Mr E. B. O'Reilly Hyland**
10 **KAUTO RIKO (FR)**, 5, b g Ballingarry (IRE)—Kauto Relstar (FR) **Mr & Mrs J Dale & Kauto Riko Partnership**
11 **LITTLE JIMMY**, 9, br g Passing Glance—Sementina (USA) **Tom Gretton Racing & Ownaracehorse Ltd**
12 **PRIMO ROSSI**, 7, b g Primo Valentino (IRE)—Flaming Rose (IRE) **Ownaracehorse Ltd**
13 **RAINBOW LOLLIPOP**, 5, b m Dubawi (IRE)—Cross Section (USA) **T. R. Gretton**
14 **THATS BEN (IRE)**, 11, b g Beneficial—Classy Dancer (IRE) **G1 Racing Club Ltd**
15 **YOUR TURN (IRE)**, 5, b m Milan—Pop Princess **Mrs J. Green**

Other Owners: Mrs J. S. Dale, Mr J. W. Dale, Mr E. P. Gretton, Mrs L. Gretton, Mr J. R. Hynes, Mr G. H. E. Price.

Assistant Trainer: Laura Gretton (07789) 754806

255 MR PATRICK GRIFFIN, Co Dublin
Postal: **Killeen House, Oldtown, Co. Dublin, Ireland**
Contacts: **MOBILE (00353) 871301719**
E-MAIL pggriffin@live.ie

1 4, B f Beneficial—African Keys (IRE) **Mr M. Deren**
2 **BERT LEAF**, 4, b f Kheleyf (USA)—Poppy's Rose **Marie Davis**
3 **CAPTAIN HOX (IRE)**, 7, b g Danehill Dancer (IRE)—Shangri La (IRE) **Mrs S. Ryan**
4 **GRAND TOUR**, 5, b m Rail Link—Cordoba **Mr M. Deren**
5 **HEIST (IRE)**, 6, b g Galileo (IRE)—Matikanehanafubuki (IRE) **Mr M. Deren**
6 **HERE COMES LOVE (IRE)**, 6, b g Winged Love (IRE)—Heres McGoogan (IRE) **R. J. Claydon**
7 **LISBON (IRE)**, 8, b g Cape Cross (IRE)—Caraiyma (IRE) **Mr M. Deren**
8 **MAGGIO (FR)**, 11, b g Trempolino (USA)—La Musardiere (FR) **D. G. Pryde**
9 **PORTRAIT KING (IRE)**, 11, gr g Portrait Gallery (IRE)—Storm Queen (IRE) **J. Beaumont**
10 **SORROW (FR)**, 6, b g Early March—Cochinchine (IRE) **Mr M. Deren**

Other Owners: J. Cox, R. T. Griffin, Mrs P. Griffin, S. B. Hughes, J. Lawless, J. P. Mangan, P. McEntee, D. F. O'Rourke, P. Scholes, Swordlestown Stud.

Assistant Trainer: James Griffin

Jockey (NH): James Reveley, J. J. Burke, Brian Hughes. **Conditional:** D. R. Fox.

256 MR DAVID C. GRIFFITHS, Bawtry
Postal: **Martin Hall, Martin Common, Bawtry, Doncaster, South Yorkshire, DN10 6DA**
Contacts: **PHONE (01302) 714247 MOBILE (07816) 924621**
E-MAIL davidgriffiths250@hotmail.com WEBSITE www.dcgracing.co.uk

1 **ANOTHER (IRE)**, 4, b f Lawman (FR)—Enchanting Muse (USA) **Eros Bloodstock**
2 **BIG STORM COMING**, 6, b g Indesatchel (IRE)—Amber Valley **Fishlake Commercial Motors Ltd**
3 **BROTHER TIGER**, 7, b g Singspiel (IRE)—Three Secrets (IRE) **Norcroft Park Stud**
4 **CYFLYMDER (IRE)**, 10, b g Mujadil (USA)—Nashwan Star (IRE) **Eros Bloodstock**
5 **DECLINED**, 4, b g Authorized (IRE)—Three Secrets (IRE) **Norcroft Park Stud**
6 **DUKE OF FIRENZE**, 7, ch g Pivotal—Nannina **Cheveley Park Stud Limited**
7 **LOPITO DE VEGA (IRE)**, 4, ch g Lope de Vega (IRE)—Athenian Way (IRE) **Mr D Poulton & Mr N Hildred**
8 **MAMBO FEVER**, 5, b m Footstepsinthesand—Mambo's Melody **Norcroft Park Stud**
9 **SINGZAK**, 8, ch g Singspiel (IRE)—Zakuska **Clark Industrial Services Partnership**
10 **STORM KING**, 7, b g Shamardal (USA)—Tarandot (IRE) **Norcroft Park Stud**
11 **TAKE COVER**, 9, b g Singspiel (IRE)—Enchanted **Norcroft Park Stud**
12 **TIN PAN ALLEY**, 8, b g Singspiel (IRE)—Tazmeen **Jason Adlam & Eros Bloodstock**
13 **WILD HILL BOY**, 6, b g Tiger Hill (IRE)—Kalamansi **Eros Bloodstock**
14 **YUNGABURRA (IRE)**, 12, b g Fath (USA)—Nordic Living (IRE) **Mrs S. Griffiths**

THREE-YEAR-OLDS
15 **L C SALOON**, ch g Equiano (FR)—Aberdovey **Clark Industrial Services Partnership**
16 **MIRAMONTE DANCER (IRE)**, b f Fast Company (IRE)—Bonne **Keeping Fast Company Partnership**

TWO-YEAR-OLDS
17 Ro f 15/2 Mastercraftsman (IRE)—Mango Groove (IRE) (Unfuwain (USA)) (14000) **Norcroft Park Stud**
18 B c 29/4 Frozen Power (IRE)—Niamh's Pet (IRE) (Petong) (6644)
19 B c 21/3 Helmet (AUS)—Ready When You Are (IRE) (Royal Applause) (9000)
20 B f 26/4 Big Bad Bob (IRE)—Spinning Gold (Spinning World (USA)) (6644)

Other Owners: Mr J. P. Adlam, Mr A. W. Clark, J. D. Clark, D. C. Griffiths, Mrs S. Hibbert, Mr N. R. Hildred, Mr D. M. Hollis, A. J. Hollis, R. P. B. Michaelson, Mr D. J. Poulton.

Assistant Trainer: Mrs S. E. Griffiths

Apprentice: Alistair Rawlinson.

257   MR SIRRELL GRIFFITHS, Carmarthen
Postal: **Rwyth Farm, Nantgaredig, Carmarthen, Dyfed, SA32 7LG**
Contacts: PHONE **(01267) 290321/290120**

1 BRACKEN HILL, 7, b g Darnay—Tirikumba **S. G. Griffiths**
2 Y O ME, 9, ch m Alflora (IRE)—Yo Kiri-B **S. G. Griffiths**

Assistant Trainer: Martyn Roger Griffiths

258   MRS DIANA GRISSELL, Robertsbridge
Postal: **Brightling Park, Robertsbridge, East Sussex, TN32 5HH**
Contacts: PHONE **(01424) 838241** MOBILE **(07950) 312610**
E-MAIL **digrissell@aol.com** WEBSITE **www.grissellracing.co.uk**

1 ARBEO (IRE), 10, b g Brian Boru—Don't Waste It (IRE) **Nigel & Barbara Collison**
2 BLUE BEAR (IRE), 7, b g Blueprint (IRE)—In For It (IRE) **Mr C. Parker**
3 BORN TO BE FREE, 7, b m Phoenix Reach—Charlie's Angel **C. Cheesman**
4 GRAYHAWK (IRE), 6, gr g Kalanisi (IRE)—Saddler Regal (IRE) **Mrs C. V. Wedmore**
5 HERE I AM (IRE), 9, br g Presenting—The Last Bank (IRE) **Nigel & Barbara Collison**
6 HOUSEPARTY, 8, b g Invincible Spirit (IRE)—Amusing Time (IRE) **Ms G. P. C. Howell**
7 NELSON'S VICTORY, 6, b g Green Horizon—First Class Girl
8 ROLLING DOUGH (IRE), 8, b m Indian Danehill (IRE)—High Dough (IRE) **Mr M. Park**
9 ROPARTA AVENUE, 9, b g Nomadic Way (USA)—Miss Fizz **Mrs D. M. Grissell**

Other Owners: Mr N. Collison, Mrs Barbara Collison, Mrs D. M. Grissell.

Jockey (NH): Marc Goldstein. **Amateur:** Mr O. Wedmore.

259   MR JOHN GROUCOTT, Much Wenlock
Postal: **11 Bourton, Much Wenlock, Shropshire, TF13 6QF**
Contacts: PHONE **(01746) 785603** FAX **(01746) 785603** MOBILE **(07866) 480830**
E-MAIL **lisajmwillis@aol.com**

1 BIG SMILE (IRE), 8, b g Zagreb (USA)—Pretty Buckskin (IRE) **G. D. Kendrick**
2 MIDNIGHT JADE (IRE), 7, b m King's Theatre (IRE)—Hurricane Dawn (IRE) **Mrs Robin Birley**
3 MIDNIGHT TARGET, 6, b m Midnight Legend—Right On Target (IRE) **Mr E. P. Parkes**
4 PRET A THOU (FR), 13, ch g Funny Baby (FR)—Va Thou Line (FR) **C. J. Tipton**
5 TRUCKERS HIGHWAY (IRE), 7, b g Rudimentary (USA)—Countessdee (IRE) **C. J. Tipton**

260   MR RAE GUEST, Newmarket
Postal: **Chestnut Tree Stables, Hamilton Road, Newmarket, Suffolk, CB8 0NY**
Contacts: PHONE **(01638) 661508** FAX **(01638) 667317** MOBILE **(07711) 301095**
E-MAIL **raeguest@raeguest.com** WEBSITE **www.raeguest.com**

1 JANE'S MEMORY (IRE), 4, ch f Captain Rio—Dancing Jest (IRE) **Exors of the Late Mr O. T. Lury**
2 MIRZA, 9, b g Oasis Dream—Millyant **C. J. Mills**

THREE-YEAR-OLDS

3 A LOVE STORY, gr f Archipenko (USA)—Albacocca **Miss K. Rausing**
4 DANCE REBEL, b g Cockney Rebel (IRE)—Slave To The Rythm (IRE) **Ms J. Fenton**
5 DOMINANCE, b f Lilbourne Lad (IRE)—Christmas Tart (IRE) **The Storm Again Syndicate**
6 EARLY SUNSET (IRE), gr f Dark Angel (IRE)—Dear Gracie (IRE) **Barry Stewart & Sakal,Davies & Jennings**
7 FANCI THAT (IRE), b f Elnadim (USA)—Featherlight **Miss V. Markowiak**
8 GOING UP (IRE), ch c Duke of Marmalade (IRE)—Guilia **The Hornets**
9 GOMEZ, b g Multiplex—Elfine (IRE) **Purple & Yellow**
10 KHISMET, b f Kheleyf (USA)—Bisaat (USA) **R. Guest**
11 LASTMANLASTROUND (IRE), b c Azamour (IRE)—Lastroseofsummer (IRE) **The Boot Sarratt Racing Syndicate**
12 NOBLE ACT, b f Kyllachy—Noble Desert (FR) **Pantile Stud**
13 B c Roderic O'Connor (IRE)—Queen Margrethe
14 SHOW STEALER, ch f Showcasing—Winifred Jo **Mr C. S. Joseph**
15 SKYLARK LADY (IRE), ch f Tamayuz—Allegrissimo (IRE) **Pantile Stud**

MR RAE GUEST - Continued

16 TUDOR ICON, b g Sixties Icon—Boleyna (USA) **Mr P. J. Smith**
17 VALE OF FLIGHT (IRE), b f Vale of York (IRE)—Barbera (GER) **Guy Carstairs & Sakal, Davies & Jennings**
18 ZUARI, b f Rock of Gibraltar (IRE)—Takegawa

TWO-YEAR-OLDS

19 B f 18/3 Dandy Man (IRE)—Carrauntoohil (IRE) (Marju (IRE)) (5000) **RGRL Syndicate 2**
20 CHAMPAGNE QUEEN, ch f 2/4 Showcasing—Night Haven (Night Shift (USA)) (19000) **The Reprobates**
21 CHICONOMIC (IRE), gr f 30/4 Clodovil (IRE)—Ashdali (IRE) (Grand Lodge (USA)) (5000) **The Reprobates**
22 B f 30/3 Power—Gaselee (USA) (Toccet (USA)) (29531) **Paul Smith & Rae Guest**
23 B f 23/4 Excelebration (IRE)—Ja One (IRE) (Acclamation)
24 MISS OSIER, ch f 5/4 Mastercraftsman (IRE)—
                                    Lacy Sunday (USA) (King's Best (USA)) (5000) **Peter Saunders & Rae Guest**
25 NOSTALGIE, gr f 23/3 Archipenko (USA)—Neige d'antan (Aussie Rules (USA)) **Miss K. Rausing**
26 ODE TO GLORY, b f 17/2 Poet's Voice—Blue Lyric (Refuse To Bend (IRE)) (20000) **The Reprobates**
27 B c 31/3 Royal Applause—Quantum (IRE) (Alhaarth (IRE)) (33000)
28 B f 19/4 Canford Cliffs (IRE)—Quiet Waters (USA) (Quiet American (USA)) (10000) **RGRL Syndicate 2**
29 Ch f 22/2 Kyllachy—Solfilia (Teofilo (IRE)) (10000) **RGRL Syndicate 2**
30 B f 4/2 Excelebration (IRE)—Velvet Star (IRE) (Galileo (IRE)) (18000)

Other Owners: G. N. Carstairs, Mr A. P. Davies, Mr M. K. Duggan, E. P. Duggan, B. J. Flahive, J. W. Fullick, R. T. Goodes, Mr R. H. Jennings, Mrs L. M. Lambert, D. G. Raffel, Mr P. A. Sakal, P. W. Saunders, Mr J. Shannon, Mrs P. Smith, Mr B. Stewart, D. J. Willis.

Assistant Trainer: Paul Eddery

---

261 **MR RICHARD GUEST, Ingmanthorpe**
Postal: **Ingmanthorpe Racing Stables, Ingmanthorpe Grange Farm, Ingmanthorpe, Wetherby, West Yorkshire, LS22 5HL**
Contacts: **PHONE (07715) 516072 (07713) 132577 MOBILE (07715) 516071**
E-MAIL enquiries@richardguestracing.co.uk WEBSITE www.richardguestracing.co.uk

1 AMBITIOUS ICARUS, 7, b g Striking Ambition—Nesting Box **ABS Metals & Waste**
2 BOLLIHOPE, 4, ch g Medicean—Hazy Dancer **Mrs A. L. Guest**
3 CAPTAIN SCOOBY, 10, b g Captain Rio—Scooby Dooby Do **Mrs A. L. Guest**
4 CHAUVELIN, 5, b g Sir Percy—Enforce (USA) **Mrs A. L. Guest**
5 DINNERATMIDNIGHT, 5, b g Kyllachy—The Terrier **Mrs A. L. Guest**
6 HYDRANT, 10, b g Haafhd—Spring **Mrs A. L. Guest**
7 ISNTSHESOMETHING, 4, br f Assertive—Princess Almora **Mr C. J. Penney**
8 LAST WISH (IRE), 5, b g Raven's Pass (USA)—Quiet Dream (USA) **Mr L. B. Donnelly**
9 MR COOL CASH, 4, b g Firebreak—Cashleen (USA) **Mr I. Lawson**
10 OUTLAW TORN (IRE), 7, ch g Iffraaj—Touch And Love (IRE) **J. S. Kennerley**
11 POLAR FOREST, 6, br g Kyllachy—Woodbeck **Maze Rattan Limited**
12 SAKHALIN STAR (IRE), 5, ch g Footstepsinthesand—Quela (GER) **Bamboozelem**
13 TED'S BROTHER (IRE), 8, b g Fath—Estertide (IRE) **Ontoawinner & Guest**
14 TELLOVOI (IRE), 8, b g Indian Haven—Kloonlara (IRE) **Mrs A. L. Guest**

THREE-YEAR-OLDS

15 BERTIE BUOY, b g Bertolini (USA)—Tide of Love **ColinWing,MichaelCook&StephenHodgkinson**
16 BILLY ROBERTS (IRE), b g Multiplex—Mi Amor (IRE) **The Sensible Drinks Company Limited**
17 BLAGGER, ch g Major Cadeaux—Brogue Lanterns (IRE) **Bamboozelem**
18 DALALAH, b f Exceed And Excel (AUS)—Bashasha (USA) **Bamboozelem**
19 DARK CONFIDANT (IRE), b g Royal Applause—Sleek Gold **D. I. Perry**
20 LADY BACCHUS, b f Compton Place—Beauty (IRE) **Mrs A. L. Guest**
21 LADY JOANNA VASSA (IRE), ch f Equiano (FR)—Lady Natilda **Mrs A. L. Guest**
22 LYDIA'S PLACE, ch f Equiano (FR)—Peace And Love (IRE) **Mr L. B. Donnelly**
23 MR POTTER, ch g Assertive—Enclave (USA) **A Turton, J Blackburn & Partner**
24 UDONTDODOU, b g Fastnet Rock (AUS)—Forever Times **Mrs A. L. Guest**

TWO-YEAR-OLDS

25 Gr g 22/3 Kendargent (FR)—Damoiselle (USA) (Sky Classic (CAN)) (10000) **Mrs A. L. Guest**
26 Ch f 23/4 Harbour Watch (IRE)—Fantastic Santanyi (Fantastic Light (USA)) (7500) **Mrs A. L. Guest**
27 B f 22/2 Equiano (FR)—High Tan (High Chaparral (IRE)) (14285) **Mrs A. L. Guest**
28 B f 20/3 Fast Company (IRE)—Queen Al Andalous (IRE) (King's Best (USA)) (28571) **Mrs A. L. Guest**

MR RICHARD GUEST - Continued

29 B g 13/3 Bated Breath—Stormy Weather (Nashwan (USA)) (16190) **Mrs A. L. Guest**
30 B c 25/4 Equiano (FR)—Vodka Shot (USA) (Holy Bull (USA)) (14000) **Mrs A. L. Guest**

Other Owners: J. N. Blackburn, Mr A. Bullock-Smith, M. J. Mahony, Mr N. J. O'Brien, Mr A. Turton, Mr C. Wing.

Jockey (flat): Connor Beasley, Jason Hart.

---

262 | **MS POLLY GUNDRY, Ottery St Mary**
Postal: Holcombe Brook, Holcombe Lane, Ottery St. Mary, Devon, EX11 1PH
Contacts: **PHONE (01404) 811181 MOBILE (07932) 780621**
E-MAIL pollygundrytraining@live.co.uk

1 ALDERLEY HEIGHTS, 7, b m Windsor Heights—Alderley Girl **Mrs E. D. Shepherd**
2 BERTIE MOON, 6, b g Bertolini (USA)—Fleeting Moon **G. N. Carstairs**
3 DAWSON CITY, 7, b g Midnight Legend—Running For Annie **Ian Payne & Kim Franklin**
4 EDEIFF'S LAD, 9, ch g Loup Sauvage (USA)—Ede'iff **Hawks & Doves Racing Syndicate**
5 FIVEFORTYFIVE, 8, ch g Erhaab (USA)—Golden Mile (IRE) **Mr J. P. Selby**
6 HARRY'S FAREWELL, 9, b g Sir Harry Lewis (USA)—Golden Mile (IRE) **Mr J. P. Selby**
7 PICCOMORE, 6, b m Morpeth—Ivorsagoodun **P. G. Gibbins**
8 RESTLESS REBEL, 7, b g Rocamadour—Restless Native (IRE) **Mr & Mrs R. G. Kelvin-Hughes**
9 SIR DYLAN, 7, b g Dylan Thomas (IRE)—Monteleone (IRE) **M James & S Jarrett**
10 4, B g Milan—Tinagoodnight (FR) **Mr & Mrs R. G. Kelvin-Hughes**

TWO-YEAR-OLDS

11 Ch c 23/4 Bahamian Bounty—Repetischa (IRE) (Peintre Celebre (USA)) **Mrs D. du Feu**

Other Owners: Miss K. M. Franklin, Mr M. James, Mr S. H. Jarrett, R. G. Kelvin-Hughes, Mrs E. A. Kelvin-Hughes, Mr I. T. Payne, J. P. Rawlins, J. L. Sunnucks.

Assistant Trainer: Edward Walker

Jockey (flat): Liam Keniry. **Jockey (NH):** James Best, Tom O'Brien. **Amateur:** Mr Robbie Henderson.

---

263 | **MR WILLIAM HAGGAS, Newmarket**
Postal: Somerville Lodge, Fordham Road, Newmarket, Suffolk, CB8 7AA
Contacts: **PHONE (01638) 667013 FAX (01638) 660534 MOBILE (07860) 282281**
E-MAIL william@somerville-lodge.co.uk WEBSITE www.somerville-lodge.co.uk

1 ADAAY (IRE), 4, b c Kodiac—Lady Lucia (IRE) **Mr Hamdan Al Maktoum**
2 BATTALION (IRE), 6, b g Authorized (IRE)—Zigarra **Sheikh Juma Dalmook Al Maktoum**
3 COLD AS ICE (SAF), 5, b m Western Winter (USA)—Viva (SAF) **Mrs K. Finch & Mrs B. Kieswetter**
4 DAWN MISSILE, 4, b g Nayef (USA)—Ommadawn (IRE) **Options O Syndicate**
5 FOREVER POPULAR (USA), 4, b f Dynaformer (USA)—Pussycat Doll (USA) **Lael Stable**
6 MITRAAD (IRE), 5, ch g Aqlaam—Badweia (USA) **Mr Hamdan Al Maktoum**
7 MUFFRI'HA (IRE), 4, b f Iffraaj—Grecian Dancer **Sheikh Juma Dalmook Al Maktoum**
8 MUTAKAYYEF, 5, ch g Sea The Stars (IRE)—Infallible **Mr Hamdan Al Maktoum**
9 MUTHMIR (IRE), 6, b g Invincible Spirit (IRE)—Fairy of The Night (IRE) **Mr Hamdan Al Maktoum**
10 OUR CHANNEL (IRE), 5, ch g English Channel (USA)—Raw Gold (USA) **Abdulla Al Mansoori**
11 PICK YOUR CHOICE, 4, gr g Elusive Quality (USA)—Enticement **Her Majesty The Queen**
12 PREDOMINANCE (IRE), 4, b g Danehill Dancer (IRE)—Gilded Vanity (IRE) **Highclere Thoroughbred Racing**
13 SEALIFE (IRE), 4, b f Sea The Stars (IRE)—Bitooh **Sheikh Juma Dalmook Al Maktoum**
14 SQUATS (IRE), 4, b g Dandy Man (IRE)—Light Sea (IRE) **Sheikh Rashid Dalmook Al Maktoum**
15 VALLEY OF FIRE, 4, b g Firebreak—Charlie Girl **Sheikh Juma Dalmook Al Maktoum**
16 WONDER LAISH, 4, b c Halling (USA)—Wonder Why (GER) **Jaber Abdullah**
17 YORKER (SAF), 7, b g Jet Master (SAF)—Little Indian (SAF) **Mr B. Kantor**

THREE-YEAR-OLDS

18 AJAYA, b c Invincible Spirit (IRE)—Nessina (USA) **Saleh Al Homaizi & Imad Al Sagar**
19 AL HAWRAA, b f Iffraaj—Kashoof **Mr Hamdan Al Maktoum**
20 ALAADEL, ch c Dubawi (IRE)—Infallible **Mr Hamdan Al Maktoum**
21 AREYAAM ROSE (IRE), b f Teofilo (IRE)—Easy Lover **Saeed Jaber**
22 ASAMA BLUE (IRE), b f Fastnet Rock (AUS)—Butterfly Blue (IRE) **Sir Peter Vela/D Nagle/J Magnier**
23 BARGAIN BUY, ch f Tamayuz—Peace Summit **Sheikh Rashid Dalmook Al Maktoum**

MR WILLIAM HAGGAS - Continued

24 **BARJEEL (USA)**, br c Speightstown (USA)—Listen To My Song (USA) **Mr Hamdan Al Maktoum**
25 **BEAUTY SLEEP (IRE)**, b f Rip Van Winkle (IRE)—Rasana **Mr L. Sheridan**
26 **BEDROCK**, b g Fastnet Rock (AUS)—Gemstone (IRE) **Highclere Thoroughbred Racing**
27 **BESHARAH (IRE)**, b f Kodiac—Dixieland Kiss (USA) **Sheikh Rashid Dalmook Al Maktoum**
28 **BREDA CASTLE**, ch f Dutch Art—Ice Palace **Cheveley Park Stud**
29 **CARENOT (IRE)**, b f Iffraaj—Sahara Sky (IRE) **Mr Paul Makin**
30 **CATOTONIC**, ch g Notnowcato—Rumooz **Mr & Mrs Ian Beard**
31 **COHERENT (IRE)**, b c Rip Van Winkle (IRE)—Hold Off (IRE) **W. J. and T. C. O. Gredley**
32 **CURRICULUM**, b g New Approach (IRE)—Superstar Leo (IRE) **Lael Stable**
33 **DAL HARRAILD**, ch g Champs Elysees—Dalvina **St Albans Bloodstock Ltd**
34 **DAPHNE**, b f Duke of Marmalade (IRE)—Daring Aim **Her Majesty The Queen**
35 **DREAM OF TARA (IRE)**, b f Invincible Spirit (IRE)—Spirit of Tara (IRE) **Miss Pat O'Kelly**
36 **DUBAI EMPRESS (IRE)**, b f Dubawi (IRE)—The World **Abdulla Al Mansoori**
37 **DUTCH DESTINY**, b br f Dutch Art—Danehill Destiny **Cheveley Park Stud**
38 **DWIGHT D**, b c Duke of Marmalade (IRE)—Almatinka (IRE) **W. J. and T. C. O. Gredley**
39 **EASY CODE**, b c Bahamian Bounty—Skirrid **Sheikh Rashid Dalmook Al Maktoum**
40 **ELJEEMI (IRE)**, b c Shamardal (USA)—Arthur's Girl **Sheikh Ahmed Al Maktoum**
41 **EMTIDAAD (IRE)**, ch g Kyllachy—Hana Dee **Ahmed Al Naboodah**
42 **ENTSAR (IRE)**, b f Fastnet Rock (AUS)—Starfish (IRE) **Al Shaqab Racing**
43 **FADILLAH (IRE)**, b f Monsun (GER)—Sasuela (GER) **Saleh Al Homaizi & Imad Al Sagar**
44 **FASTNET TEMPEST (IRE)**, b g Fastnet Rock (AUS)—Dame Blanche (IRE) **O.T.I. Racing /J. Magnier**
45 **FIELD OF STARS**, b f Acclamation—Map of Heaven **Lael Stable**
46 **FLEETING DREAM (IRE)**, b f Dream Ahead (USA)—Flanders (IRE) **Lordship Stud**
47 **FOL O'YASMINE**, b f Dubawi (IRE)—Sewards Folly **Saleh Al Homaizi & Imad Al Sagar**
48 **GOLDEN REIGN (IRE)**, ch f Champs Elysees—Fleche d'or **Clipper Logistics**
49 **GRAVITY FLOW (IRE)**, ch f Exceed And Excel (AUS)—Landela **Sheikh Juma Dalmook Al Maktoum**
50 **GUY FAWKES**, b c Big Bad Bob (IRE)—Flight of Fancy **Her Majesty The Queen**
51 **HIGHLAND DRAGON**, ch c Dutch Art—Tiger Mist (IRE) **M S Bloodstock Ltd**
52 **IN THE CITY**, ch c Exceed And Excel (AUS)—Soft Morning **Simon Munir & Isaac Souede**
53 **INTILAAQAH**, b f Oasis Dream—Quan Yin (IRE) **Sheikh Juma Dalmook Al Maktoum**
54 **ISTANBUL BEY**, ro g Exceed And Excel (AUS)—Starfala **Simon Munir & Isaac Souede**
55 **IZMIR (IRE)**, b f Sir Percy—Limit (IRE) **Mohammed Saeed Al Shahi**
56 **JULIA DREAM**, b f Montjeu (IRE)—Winds of Time (IRE) **Mr & Mrs R. Scott**
57 **KULLU (IRE)**, b f Oasis Dream—Mussoorie (FR) **Mr A. E. Oppenheimer**
58 **LAPILLI**, b g Bahamian Bounty—Blue Lyric **Sheikh Ahmed Al Maktoum**
59 **LIGHT MUSIC**, b f Elusive Quality (USA)—Medley **Her Majesty The Queen**
60 **LOS OLIVOS (USA)**, b c Lemon Drop Kid (USA)—Lynnwood Chase (USA) **Mr A. E. Oppenheimer**
61 **MABROKAH**, b f Lonhro (AUS)—Dubai Sea (USA) **Salem Bel Obaida**
62 **MANSHOOD (IRE)**, b c Iffraaj—Thawrah (IRE) **Mr Hamdan Al Maktoum**
63 **MELABI (IRE)**, b g Oasis Dream—Briolette (USA) **Al Shaqab Racing**
64 **MUJAAMIL**, b c Dansili—Muwakleh **Mr Hamdan Al Maktoum**
65 **MUSAANADA**, b f Sea The Stars (IRE)—Gaze **Mr Hamdan Al Maktoum**
66 **MUTAYYAM**, ch g Aqlaam—Sant Elena **Mr Hamdan Al Maktoum**
67 **MUZDAWAJ**, b c Dansili—Shabiba (USA) **Mr Hamdan Al Maktoum**
68 **NAQDY**, b g Aqlaam—Shuhra (USA) **Mr Hamdan Al Maktoum**
69 **NOBEL DUKE (IRE)**, ch c Duke of Marmalade (IRE)—Dowager **Roberts/Green/Savidge/Whittall-Williams**
70 **NOVALINA (IRE)**, b f Galileo (IRE)—Baraka (IRE) **B. Kantor & M. Jooste**
71 **OLYMPIC RUNNER**, ch f Exceed And Excel (AUS)—Lochridge **Mr J. Smith**
72 **ORIENTAL CROSS (IRE)**, b f Cape Cross (IRE)—Orion Girl (GER) **Her Majesty The Queen**
73 **ORNATE**, b c Bahamian Bounty—Adorn **Cheveley Park Stud**
74 **OUT AND ABOUT (IRE)**, b g Fastnet Rock (AUS)—Starship (IRE) **The Starship Partnership**
75 **QORTAAJ**, b g Kyllachy—Cardrona **Sheikh Ahmed Al Maktoum**
76 **RASMIYA (IRE)**, b f Galileo (IRE)—Crystal Valkyrie (IRE) **Al Shaqab Racing**
77 **RAUCOUS**, b c Dream Ahead (USA)—Shyrl **Highclere Thoroughbred Racing**
78 **RELATIONSHIP**, ch f Pivotal—Courting **Cheveley Park Stud**
79 **RUSSIAN FINALE**, b f Dansili—Russian Rhythm (USA) **Cheveley Park Stud**
80 **SAINTED**, ch f Dutch Art—Blithe **Cheveley Park Stud**
81 **SEHAYLI (IRE)**, b c Iffraaj—Quaich **Sheikh Ahmed Al Maktoum**
82 **SELECTION (FR)**, ch c Siyouni (FR)—Perspective (FR) **Highclere Thoroughbred Racing**
83 **SHUFOOG**, b f Mawatheeq (USA)—Hamloola **Mr Hamdan Al Maktoum**
84 **SILK GEM (IRE)**, b c Roderic O'Connor (IRE)—Fine Silk (USA) **Saeed Manana**
85 **SKY KINGDOM (IRE)**, b c Montjeu (IRE)—We Can Say It Now (AUS) **Mr Paul Makin**
86 **SMASHED**, b g Beat Hollow—Sel **Mr B. Haggas**
87 **SOUNDSTRINGS**, b f Oasis Dream—Straight Lass (IRE) **Lael Stable**
88 **SPECIAL SEASON**, ch c Lope de Vega (IRE)—Keep Dancing (IRE) **Sheikh Rashid Dalmook Al Maktoum**

MR WILLIAM HAGGAS - Continued

89 **STRAW HAT (IRE)**, b f Galileo (IRE)—Velouette **The Old Harrovian Racing Club**
90 **SYMPOSIUM**, ch f Exceed And Excel (AUS)—Soodad **The Royal Ascot Racing Club**
91 **TASLEET**, b c Showcasing—Bird Key **Mr Hamdan Al Maktoum**
92 **TRAINNAH**, b f Pivotal—Whazzat **Al Shaqab Racing**
93 **TUTU NGURU (USA)**, b f Blame (USA)—Haka Girl (USA) **Sheikh Juma Dalmook Al Maktoum**
94 **VICTORY BOND**, b c Medicean—Antebellum (FR) **Duke Of Bedfordshire**
95 **WAVE REVIEWS**, b c Fastnet Rock (AUS)—Critical Acclaim **Mr Nicolas Jones**
96 **WISHPOINT (USA)**, b c Street Cry (IRE)—Key Point (IRE) **Her Majesty The Queen**
97 **WRAPPED**, ch f Iffraaj—Muffled (USA) **Cheveley Park Stud**
98 **ZWAYYAN**, ch c Pivotal—Mail The Desert (IRE) **Al Shaqab Racing**

TWO-YEAR-OLDS

99 **AFDEEK**, b c 25/3 Bated Breath—Soviet Terms (Soviet Star (USA)) (200000) **Mr Hamdan Al Maktoum**
100 B c 3/4 High Chaparral (IRE)—Alamouna (IRE) (Indian Ridge) (300000) **Coolmore & Jooste**
101 **ALFARRIS (FR)**, b c 5/2 Shamardal (USA)—Rose Et Noire (IRE) (Dansili) (339608) **Mr Hamdan Al Maktoum**
102 **ALFOLK (IRE)**, b c 14/2 Invincible Spirit (IRE)—Elmaam (Nayef (USA)) **Mr Hamdan Al Maktoum**
103 **ALROOM (IRE)**, b c 27/2 Kodiac—Beverley Macca (Piccolo) (87619) **Mr Hamdan Al Maktoum**
104 **ALSHIBAA (IRE)**, b c 14/4 New Approach (IRE)—Amjaad (Dansili) **Mr Hamdan Al Maktoum**
105 **ALWAHSH (IRE)**, b c 10/4 Dubawi (IRE)—Gile Na Greine (IRE) (Galileo (IRE)) **Mr Hamdan Al Maktoum**
106 **BATTERED**, b c 26/2 Foxwedge (AUS)—Swan Wings (Bahamian Bounty) (45000) **Mr B. Haggas**
107 B c 11/4 Holy Roman Emperor (IRE)—Bayalika (IRE) (Selkirk (USA)) (105000) **Highclere Thoroughbred Racing**
108 B c 1/3 Harbour Watch (IRE)—Bendis (GER) (Danehill (USA)) **Qatar Racing**
109 Ch f 24/1 Pivotal—Best Terms (Exceed And Excel (AUS)) (330000) **Appletree Stud**
110 B f 14/3 Frankel—Beyond Desire (Invincible Spirit (IRE)) **Qatar Racing & Steve Parkin**
111 **BIOLOGIST (IRE)**, b f 25/3 Sir Prancealot (IRE)—
                    Miss Rosie (Librettist (USA)) (20000) **Mr C Humber & Somerville Lodge Ltd**
112 B c 10/5 Kodiac—Bobby Jane (Diktat) (70000) **Mr L. Sheridan**
113 B f 7/3 Dark Angel (IRE)—Box of Frogs (One Cool Cat (IRE)) (65000) **Sheikh Rashid Dalmook Al Maktoum**
114 **BULDAAN (USA)**, b f 28/2 Tamayuz—Soohaad (USA) (Hard Spun (USA)) **Mr Hamdan Al Maktoum**
115 **CALL TO MIND**, b c 5/2 Galileo (IRE)—Memory (IRE) (Danehill Dancer (IRE)) **Her Majesty The Queen**
116 B f 6/4 Sea The Stars (IRE)—Cap Coz (IRE) (Indian Ridge) (200000) **Mr M. Jooste**
117 B f 10/4 Cacique (IRE)—Cartimandua (Medicean) (160000) **Highclere Thoroughbred Racing**
118 Ch f 18/4 Dubawi (IRE)—Check the Label (USA) (Stormin Fever (USA)) **Lael Stable**
119 **CIRCULATE**, b f 6/2 Dutch Art—Royal Whisper (Royal Applause) (64761) **Cheveley Park Stud**
120 B c 13/2 Mastercraftsman (IRE)—City of Cities (IRE) (In The Wings) (120000) **Mr M. Jooste**
121 C c 12/3 Dragon Pulse (IRE)—City Vaults Girl (IRE) (Oratorio (IRE)) (72000) **Sheikh Ahmed Al Maktoum**
122 Ch gr c 24/1 Exceed And Excel (AUS)—Clinical (Motivator) (450000) **China Horse Club**
123 B f 8/4 Teofilo (IRE)—Coquette Rouge (IRE) (Croco Rouge (IRE)) (80000) **Highclere Thoroughbred Racing**
124 B c 24/4 Fastnet Rock (AUS)—Crazy Volume (IRE) (Machiavellian (USA)) **O.T.I.Partnership & J. Magnier**
125 **CRISTAL FIZZ (IRE)**, ch f 27/2 Power—
                    Effervesce (IRE) (Galileo (IRE)) (45000) **Roberts/Green/Savidge/Whittal-Williams**
126 **DIAGNOSTIC**, gr f 6/3 Dutch Art—Holistic (Pivotal) **Cheveley Park Stud**
127 B f 23/1 Foxwedge (AUS)—Domitia (Pivotal) (32000) **Sheikh Juma Dalmook Al Maktoum**
128 B c 25/2 Sea The Stars—Dream of The Hill (IRE) (Tiger Hill (USA)) (200000) **Messrs B Kantor & MJ Jooste**
129 B c 5/2 Sepoy (AUS)—Electra Star (Shamardal (USA)) (36000) **Mohammed Obaida**
130 B f 1/4 Fastnet Rock (AUS)—Enticing (IRE) (Pivotal) **Lael Stable**
131 **FAIENCE**, b f 10/2 Holy Roman Emperor (IRE)—Delft (Dutch Art) **Cheveley Park Stud**
132 **FAREEQ**, b gr c 14/2 Dark Angel (IRE)—Spate (IRE) (Danehill Dancer (IRE)) (180000) **Mr Hamdan Al Maktoum**
133 **GLITTER GIRL**, b f 22/4 Invincible Spirit (IRE)—Glitterball (IRE) (Smart Strike (CAN)) **Cheveley Park Stud**
134 **HAKEEM**, b c 14/3 Exceed And Excel (AUS)—Khazeena (Oasis Dream) **Mr Hamdan Al Maktoum**
135 **HOLY ROMA**, b f 6/2 Holy Roman Emperor (IRE)—
                    Tamalain (USA) (Royal Academy (USA)) (15000) **A R Legal Partnership**
136 Ch f 26/3 Kyllachy—Ice Palace (Polar Falcon (USA)) **Cheveley Park Stud**
137 Ch c 17/5 Teofilo (IRE)—Juno Marlowe (IRE) (Danehill (USA)) (110000) **Al Shaqab Racing**
138 Ch f 1/3 Frankel—Kirinda (IRE) (Tiger Hill (USA)) (300000) **Al Shaqab Racing**
139 **LABHAY (IRE)**, b f 7/3 New Approach (IRE)—Sooraah (Dubawi (IRE)) **Mohammed Jaber**
140 Gr f 22/2 Sea The Stars (IRE)—Lady Springbank (IRE) (Choisir (AUS)) **David & Yvonne Blunt**
141 B br c 25/3 More Than Ready (USA)—
                    Laura's Pleasure (USA) (Cactus Ridge (USA)) (106837) **Sheikh Juma Dalmook Al Maktoum**
142 B c 30/3 Nathaniel (IRE)—Light Impact (Fantastic Light (USA)) (50000) **Mr B. Kantor**
143 B f 4/2 Dark Angel (IRE)—Lisa's Strong (IRE) (Kalanisi (IRE)) (110000) **Al Shaqab Racing**
144 **LOVING**, b f 6/5 Mayson—Courting (Pursuit of Love) **Cheveley Park Stud**
145 Ch f 26/2 Galileo (IRE)—Majestic Sakeena (IRE) (King's Best (USA)) **Saleh Al Homaizi & Imad Al Sagar**
146 **MATHIX (FR)**, b c 4/3 Kendargent (FR)—Matwan (FR) (Indian Rocket) (29531) **Mr Guy Pariente**
147 B c 28/3 Sepoy (AUS)—Mazuna (IRE) (Cape Cross (IRE)) (200000) **Mr M. Jooste**

MR WILLIAM HAGGAS - Continued

148 MEYRICK, b c 19/4 Helmet (AUS)—Esteemed Lady (IRE) (Mark of Esteem (IRE)) (110000) **John & Julia Aisbit**
149 MOJITO (IRE), b c 2/2 Requinto (IRE)—
    Narva (USA) (Grand Slam (USA)) (236249) **Fiona Carmichael & Ian Jennings**
150 NAAFER, b f 8/4 Oasis Dream—Shabiba (USA) (Seeking The Gold (USA)) **Mr Hamdan Al Maktoum**
151 B c 13/4 Oasis Dream—Nessina (USA) (Hennessy (USA)) **Saleh Al Homaizi & Imad Al Sagar**
152 ON HER TOES (IRE), b f 31/3 Kodiac—Dancing Jest (IRE) (Averti (IRE)) (114433) **Cheveley Park Stud**
153 ORIGINAL CHOICE (IRE), ch c 11/4 Dragon Pulse (IRE)—
    Belle Watling (IRE) (Street Cry (IRE)) (100000) **Mr Albert Goodman**
154 B f 7/2 Oasis Dream—Parisi (Rahy (USA)) (90000) **Qatar Racing**
155 Ch f 13/4 Harbour Watch (IRE)—
    Peace Signal (USA) (Time For A Change (USA)) (30000) **Biddestone Racing Club**
156 B c 31/1 Harbour Watch (IRE)—Perfect Story (IRE) (Desert Story (IRE)) (72000) **Sheikh Ahmed Al Maktoum**
157 B c 12/3 Frankel—Piping (IRE) (Montjeu (IRE)) (553709) **Saleh Al Homaizi & Imad Al Sagar**
158 Ch f 15/4 New Approach (IRE)—Punita (USA) (Distorted Humor (USA)) (90000) **Abdulla Al Mansoori**
159 QUINQUEREME, b f 24/1 Elusive Quality (USA)—
    Finding Neverland (FR) (Green Desert (USA)) **Her Majesty The Queen**
160 RED GUNNER, b c 26/1 Oasis Dream—Blue Maiden (Medicean) (115000) **Simon Munir & Isaac Souede**
161 Ch f 24/2 Dutch Art—Requejada (USA) (First Samurai (USA)) (147655) **Spanish Artist Syndicate**
162 RIVET (IRE), b c 3/4 Fastnet Rock (AUS)—Starship (IRE) (Galileo (IRE)) **The Starship Partnership**
163 B f 14/4 Acclamation—Roo (Rudimentary (USA)) (206718) **China Horse Club**
164 B f 17/3 Iffraaj—Rose of Battle (Averti (IRE)) (40000) **Sheikh Juma Dalmook Al Maktoum**
165 B f 30/3 Invincible Spirit (IRE)—Salonblue (IRE) (Bluebird (USA)) (310000) **China Horse Club**
166 SEED CORN, b f 15/1 Exceed And Excel (AUS)—Scarlet Runner (Night Shift (USA)) **Mr N. Jones**
167 B c 20/5 Galileo (IRE)—Sent From Heaven (IRE) (Footstepsinthesand) (885935) **Qatar Racing & Steven Parkin**
168 B f 31/1 Equiano (FR)—Senta's Dream (Danehill (USA)) (67921) **Sheikh Juma Dalmook Al Maktoum**
169 B c 1/5 Sepoy (AUS)—Sewards Folly (Rudimentary (USA)) **Saleh Al Homaizi & Imad Al Sagar**
170 B f 2/2 Elusive Quality (USA)—Sharnberry (Shamardal (USA)) **St Albans Bloodstock Ltd**
171 B f 18/1 Cape Cross (IRE)—Signella (Selkirk (USA)) (82000) **Sheikh Juma Dalmook Al Maktoum**
172 SMARTDARGENT (FR), b c 10/3 Kendargent (FR)—
    Little Stone (FR) (One Cool Cat (USA)) (150000) **Mr Hamdan Al Maktoum**
173 B c 11/4 Arcano (IRE)—Start The Music (IRE) (King's Best (USA)) (38000) **Sheikh Rashid Dalmook Al Maktoum**
174 STELLENBOSCH (IRE), b c 9/3 High Chaparral (IRE)—
    Serisia (FR) (Exit To Nowhere (USA)) (310077) **Messrs B. Kantor & M. J. Jooste**
175 Ch c 3/3 Sepoy (AUS)—Strings (Unfuwain (USA)) (82000) **Sheikh Ahmed Al Maktoum**
176 B f 4/4 Frankel—Superstar Leo (IRE) (College Chapel) **Lael Stable**
177 TADKHIRAH, b f 15/4 Acclamation—Pin Cushion (Pivotal) (47619) **Mr Hamdan Al Maktoum**
178 TIRANIA, b f 22/4 Pivotal—Tiriana (Common Grounds) (273163) **Yvonne Jacques**
179 UNDER CONTROL (IRE), b c 20/3 Power—High Figurine (IRE) (High Chaparral (IRE)) **Mr D. I. Scott**
180 VIBRANT, b f 22/4 Pivotal—Light Hearted (Green Desert (USA)) **Cheveley Park Stud**
181 B f 26/2 Dubawi (IRE)—Wonder Why (GER) (Tiger Hill (IRE)) **Jaber Abdullah**
182 WUROOD, gr f 26/4 Dark Angel (IRE)—Key Rose (IRE) (Key of Luck (USA)) (119047) **Mr Hamdan Al Maktoum**
183 YAAMEN (USA), b c 21/2 Nayef (USA)—Haamaat (IRE) (Shamardal (USA)) **Mr Hamdan Al Maktoum**

Other Owners: A R Legal Collections Limited, N. N. Agran, Mr Imad Al-Sagar, Mrs C. Beard, Mr I. Beard, Mrs Y. Blunt, Mr David Blunt, Mrs F. J. Carmichael, Mrs Kathleen Finch, Mr Miles Fisher, Mr J. Flannery, Mr M. P. Gibbens, Mr W. J. Gredley, Mr T. C. O. Gredley, F. M. Green, Mr W. J. Haggas, Mrs E. A. Harris, T. F. Harris, Mr M. Heffernan, Mr T. Henderson, The Hon H. Herbert, Highclere Nominated Partner Limited, Highclere Thoroughbred Racing Ltd, Mr Saleh Al Homaizi, Mr C. M. Humber, Mrs G. S. Jackson, Mr R. Jackson, Mr I. Jennings, Mr M. J. Jooste, Mrs B. Kieswetter, L. K. Piggott, Mrs John Magnier, Mr S. Munir, Mrs David Nagle, Mr S. O'Donnell, Mr M. Quirke, G. A. Roberts, A. P. Rogers, Mr S. E. Sangster, Mr G. Savidge, Mrs Audrey Scotney, Mrs P.M. Scott, R. Scott, Mr Isaac Souede, Mr A. Symonds, Mr M. Tabor, Sir Peter Vela, Mr E. B. Whittal-Williams, Mr S. G. Wignall.

Assistant Trainers: Archie Watson, Jason Favell

Apprentice: Nathan Allison, Georgia Cox.

---

264 **MR ALEX HALES, Edgecote**
Postal: **Trafford Bridge Stables, Edgecote, Banbury, Oxfordshire, OX17 1AG**
Contacts: **PHONE** (01295) 660131 **FAX** (01295) 660128 **MOBILE** (07771) 511652
E-MAIL alex@alexhalesracing.co.uk **WEBSITE** www.alexhalesracing.co.uk

1 ALLNECESSARYFORCE (FR), 6, gr g Verglas (IRE)—Kosmic View (USA) **Mr S. Brown**
2 BARENICE (FR), 5, b g Denham Red (FR)—Delice du Soleil (FR) **The Barenice Racing Partnership**
3 BIG JIM, 7, b g Revoque (IRE)—Chilly Squaw (IRE) **Gumbrills Racing Partnership**

MR ALEX HALES - Continued

4 **BIG TIME FRANK (IRE)**, 5, b g Bienamado (USA)—Pure Spirit (IRE) **N Allen & P Bowler**
5 **COCO FLOWER (FR)**, 4, ch f Born King (JPN)—La Fleur du Roy (FR) **The Of-Ten Racing Partnership**
6 **CRAFTY ROBERTO**, 8, ch g Intikhab (USA)—Mowazana (USA) **S Brown H Steele D Fitzgerald**
7 **DUEL AT DAWN (IRE)**, 6, b g Presenting—Phillis Hill **The Duel At Dawn Partnership**
8 **GILZEAN (IRE)**, 10, b g Flemensfirth (USA)—Sheknowso **Edging Ahead**
9 **ISAAC BELL (IRE)**, 8, b g Fruits of Love (USA)—Oso Well (IRE) **A. E. Frost**
10 **KRISTAL STAR**, 4, b f Midnight Legend—Royal Musical **Mr N. Rodway**
11 **MAYBELL**, 5, b m Black Sam Bellamy (IRE)—Chilly Squaw (IRE) **Gumbrills Racing Partnership**
12 **MIDNIGHT CHORISTER**, 8, b g Midnight Legend—Royal Musical **The Choristers**
13 **MINELLAFORLEISURE (IRE)**, 8, br g King's Theatre (IRE)—Dame Foraine (FR) **The Patient Partnership**
14 **OGARITMO**, 7, ch m Manduro (GER)—Querida **Edging Ahead**
15 **PERIQUEST**, 7, b g Overbury (IRE)—Rippling Brook **The Fortune Hunters**
16 **RUNNING WOLF (IRE)**, 5, b g Amadeus Wolf—Monet's Lady (IRE) **The Wolfgangers**
17 **SALUT HONORE (FR)**, 10, b g Lost World (IRE)—Kadalkote (FR) **The Hexagon Racing Partnership**
18 **SAMALARR (IRE)**, 4, gr f Ask—Sika Trix (IRE)
19 **SCOOTER BOY**, 7, b g Revoque (IRE)—Always Forgiving **The Scooter Boy Partnership**
20 **SEAMOOR SECRET**, 4, b f Sakhee's Secret—Labaqa (USA) **Mr R. H. Harrison**
21 **SHINOOKI (IRE)**, 9, br g Blueprint (IRE)—Rapid Response (IRE) **Exors of the Late Mr D. C. R. Allen**
22 **STEPOVER**, 5, b m Midnight Legend—Ring Back (IRE) **Exors of the Late Mr D. C. R. Allen**
23 **TAKE TWO**, 7, b g Act One—Lac Marmot (FR) **Edging Ahead**
24 **ULTIMATUM DU ROY (FR)**, 8, b g Brier Creek (USA)—La Fleur du Roy (FR) **Exors of the Late Mr D. C. R. Allen**
25 **VAILLANT CREEK (FR)**, 7, b g Brier Creek (USA)—Ker Marie (FR) **Exors of the Late Mr D. C. R. Allen**

THREE-YEAR-OLDS

26 **CLIFFMEENA (IRE)**, b f Canford Cliffs (IRE)—Yasmeena (USA) **A. E. Frost**

Other Owners: Mr N. G. Allen, Miss S. A. Baxter, Mr P. O. Bowler, Miss S. Burnell, Mrs K. A. Fry, J. S. C. Fry, A. M. Hales, Ms L. Langford, R. E. Morris-Adams, Mr R. E. Partridge, Mrs H. Steele, Mrs C. Taylor, Mrs J. Way, Mrs J. Wood.

---

265 **MR MICHAEL HALFORD**, Kildare
Postal: **Copper Beech Stables, Doneaney, Kildangan Road, Kildare Town, Co. Kildare, Ireland**
Contacts: **PHONE (00 353) 45 526119 FAX (00 353) 45 526157 MOBILE (00 353) 87 2579204**
E-MAIL info@michaelhalford.com WEBSITE www.michaelhalford.com

1 **ALAMGIYR (IRE)**, 4, b g Desert Style (IRE)—Alaiyma (IRE) **H. H. Aga Khan**
2 **BELEZZA OSCURA (IRE)**, 4, br f Pastoral Pursuits—Flashing Blade **Tay Hu Chor**
3 **CAILIN MOR (IRE)**, 4, b f Lope de Vega (IRE)—Capall An Ibre (IRE) **Donal Breen, David Brennan, J. Morgan**
4 **CASTLE GUEST (IRE)**, 7, b g Rock of Gibraltar (IRE)—Castelletto **Mr Paul Rooney**
5 **CERTERACH (IRE)**, 8, b g Halling (USA)—Chartres (IRE) **Mr Paul Rooney**
6 **CHESTNUT FIRE**, 4, ch g Showcasing—Music In Exile (USA) **Mrs R. Redmond**
7 **DARK ALLIANCE (IRE)**, 5, b g Dark Angel (IRE)—Alinda (IRE) **Jonathan Mullin**
8 **DUCHESSOFFLORENCE**, 4, b f Pivotal—Portal **Mr Michael Enright**
9 **EASTERN RULES (IRE)**, 8, b g Golden Snake (USA)—Eastern Ember **Simon Hales**
10 **EBASANI (IRE)**, 5, ch g Manduro (GER)—Ebatana (IRE) **Mr Paul Rooney**
11 **EBAYYA (IRE)**, 4, b f Azamour (IRE)—Ebalista (IRE) **H. H. Aga Khan**
12 **GOLDEN RAVEN (IRE)**, 4, b br g Raven's Pass (USA)—Superfonic (IRE) **Godolphin Management**
13 **HARCIMC (IRE)**, 4, b g Excellent Art—Love In The Mist (USA) **Mr Richard McNally**
14 **HASANOUR (USA)**, 6, b g Giant's Causeway (USA)—Hasanka (IRE) **Mr R. McNally**
15 **HAT ALNASAR (IRE)**, 4, b c Moss Vale (IRE)—Dream State (IRE) **Mr Fathi Egziama**
16 **KATIYMANN (IRE)**, 4, b g Shamardal (USA)—Katiyra (IRE) **Mrs L. Halford**
17 **MAPLE HILL (IRE)**, 4, b g Rock of Gibraltar (IRE)—Manda Hill (GER) **Tay Hu Chor**
18 **PADDY THE CELEB (IRE)**, 10, ch g Peintre Celebre (USA)—On The Razz (USA) **Mr Paul McMahon**
19 **PORTAGE (IRE)**, 4, b c Teofilo (IRE)—Galley **Godolphin Management**
20 **REDDOT EXPRESS**, 4, ch g Iffraaj—Applauded (IRE) **Tay Hu Chor**
21 **RUMMAGING (IRE)**, 8, ch g Chineur (FR)—Roundabout Girl (IRE) **P. E. I. Newell**
22 **RUSSIAN SOUL (IRE)**, 8, b g Invincible Spirit (IRE)—Russian Hill **Mrs A. Kavanagh**
23 **SEA THE LION (IRE)**, 5, b g Sea The Stars (IRE)—Ramona **John Connaughton**
24 **SHADAGANN (IRE)**, 6, b g Invincible Spirit (IRE)—Shamadara (IRE) **Mr Paul Rooney**
25 **SHANNON SOUL (IRE)**, 4, b g Shamardal (USA)—Paimpolaise (IRE) **Mr Michael Enright**
26 **SKERRAY RULES (IRE)**, 4, b f Aussie Rules (USA)—Skerray **Mr Michael Enright**
27 **TEMASEK STAR (IRE)**, 5, b g Soviet Star (USA)—Crazy About You (IRE) **Tay Hu Chor**
28 **TOSCANINI (IRE)**, 4, b c Shamardal (USA)—Tuzla (FR) **Godolphin Management**
29 **VENEZIA (IRE)**, 5, gr g Galileo (IRE)—St Roch (IRE) **Paul Hickman**

MR MICHAEL HALFORD - Continued

THREE-YEAR-OLDS
30 **AL QAHWA (IRE)**, b c Fast Company (IRE)—Cappuccino (IRE) **Godolphin Management**
31 **ANAMBA**, b f Shamardal (USA)—Anamato (AUS) **Godolphin Management**
32 **AZURE (IRE)**, ch c Thewayyouare (USA)—Morena Park **Mr Kashif Sheikh**
33 **CRAZY TORNADO (IRE)**, b g Big Bad Bob (IRE)—All Day (CHI) **Mr Shrahram Nabil**
34 **DARKYILA (IRE)**, br f Medicean—Daravika (IRE) **H. H. Aga Khan**
35 **DOVER VISION (IRE)**, b f Footstepsinthesand—Deauville Vision (IRE) **Mr Takaya Kimura**
36 **EBADAN (IRE)**, b c Holy Roman Emperor (IRE)—Ebareva (IRE) **H. H. Aga Khan**
37 **EMBIYRA (IRE)**, b f Tamayuz—Elbasana (IRE) **H. H. Aga Khan**
38 **ESHAAN (IRE)**, ch c Tamayuz—Ebalista (IRE) **H. H. Aga Khan**
39 **GABARDINE**, b f Pivotal—Fine Threads **Godolphin Management**
40 **GIFT WRAP (IRE)**, b f Raven's Pass (USA)—Intapeace (IRE) **Godolphin Management**
41 **GOLD CHASER (IRE)**, b c Canford Cliffs (IRE)—Snippets (IRE) **Mr Shahram Nabili**
42 **GOLDEN PEARL**, b f Oasis Dream—Pearl Banks **Mr Michael Enright**
43 **HAZANAMA (IRE)**, ch f Pivotal—Hazarista (IRE) **H. H. Aga Khan**
44 **HOUSEMAID (IRE)**, b f Invincible Spirit (IRE)—Lady Catherine **Godolphin Management**
45 **INDRAHAR (IRE)**, b f Raven's Pass (USA)—Viz (IRE) **Godolphin Management**
46 **KADRA (IRE)**, b f Holy Roman Emperor (IRE)—Kadayna (IRE) **H. H. Aga Khan**
47 **KALASADI (IRE)**, ch c Exceed And Excel (AUS)—Kalidaha (IRE) **H. H. Aga Khan**
48 **KARADENIZA (IRE)**, b f Makfi—Karawana (IRE) **H. H. Aga Khan**
49 **KING TOUT**, b c Medicean—Natalisa (IRE) **Mohmed El Circy**
50 **LADY LAMBERT (IRE)**, b f Holy Roman Emperor (IRE)—Mamacita (IRE) **Mr Michael Enright**
51 **MIGHTY LEGEND (IRE)**, b c Shamardal (USA)—Angels Story (IRE) **John Connaughton**
52 **PEARLITAS SPIRIT (IRE)**, b f Iffraaj—Pearlitas Passion (IRE) **Mr Michael Enright**
53 **PIRQUET (IRE)**, b f Sea The Stars (IRE)—Pleasantry **Godolphin Management**
54 **PROTOCOL (IRE)**, b g Kodiac—Deportment **Godolphin Management**
55 **RAYISA (IRE)**, br f Holy Roman Emperor (IRE)—Rayka (IRE) **H. H. Aga Khan**
56 **REDDOT DANCER (IRE)**, b g Danehill Dancer (IRE)—Roselyn **Tay Hu Chor**
57 **REDDOT ROMAN (IRE)**, br g Holy Roman Emperor (IRE)—Zoumie (IRE) **Tay Hu Chor**
58 **REDSTAROVERCHINA (IRE)**, b f Starspangledbanner (AUS)—Fragrant Air (CAN) **Dr Tan Kai Chah**
59 **REZEKI (IRE)**, b g Multiplex—Skerries (IRE) **Tay Hu Chor**
60 **ROBE OF HONOUR (USA)**, b c Shamardal (USA)—Queen of Denmark (USA) **Godolphin Management**
61 **ROMAN IMPERO (IRE)**, br g Holy Roman Emperor (IRE)—Diksie Dancer **Mr Eric Koh and Tay Hu Chor**
62 **SHALAMANKA (IRE)**, ch f Iffraaj—Shalama (IRE) **H. H. Aga Khan**
63 **SHANNON STORM (IRE)**, b f Teofilo (IRE)—Paimpolaise (IRE) **Mr Michael Enright**
64 **SPIRIT GLANCE (IRE)**, b f Invincible Spirit (IRE)—Gonfilia (GER) **Godolphin Management**
65 **TONKINESE**, b g Authorized (IRE)—Honky Tonk Sally **Godolphin Management**
66 **VITELLO**, b f Raven's Pass (USA)—Vitoria (IRE) **Godolphin Management**
67 **ZILBIYR (FR)**, gr c Holy Roman Emperor (IRE)—Zaziyra (IRE) **H. H. Aga Khan**

TWO-YEAR-OLDS
68 B f 5/4 Oasis Dream—All For Laura (Cadeaux Genereux) (120000) **Mr Michael Enright**
69 B c 23/2 Invincible Spirit (IRE)—Alshahbaa (Alhaarth (IRE)) **Mr Michael Enright**
70 Ch c 27/4 Iffraaj—Anamarka (Mark of Esteem (IRE)) (95976) **Godolphin Management**
71 B f 7/5 New Approach (IRE)—Anamato (AUS) (Redoute's Choice (AUS)) **Godolphin Management**
72 Ch f 27/3 Pivotal—Antique (IRE) (Dubai Millennium) **Godolphin Management**
73 B c 11/4 Street Cry (IRE)—Betwixt (USA) (Empire Maker (USA)) **Godolphin Management**
74 Ch f 29/1 Choisir (AUS)—Bless You (Bahamian Bounty) (9597) **Zhang Yuesheng**
75 B c 29/3 Dream Ahead (USA)—Bora Blues (Peintre Celebre (USA)) (16980) **Tay Hu Chor**
76 B f 14/3 Helmet (AUS)—Bright Morning (Dubai Millennium) **Godolphin Management**
77 B c 3/2 Invincible Spirit (IRE)—Cabaret (IRE) (Galileo (IRE)) (84902) **Tay Hu Chor and E. Koh**
78 **CARA MARK (IRE)**, b c 28/1 Inuvik (AUS)—Lady Mandy (Teofilo (IRE)) **Tay Hu Chor**
79 Ch f 24/4 Raven's Pass (USA)—Causeway Lass (AUS) (Giant's Causeway (USA)) **Godolphin Management**
80 C f 29/1 Distorted Humor (USA)—Crazy Party (USA) (A P Indy (USA)) (164835) **Godolphin Management**
81 B f 28/2 Exceed And Excel (AUS)—Danse Arabe (IRE) (Seeking The Gold (USA)) **Godolphin Management**
82 B f 25/3 Rip Van Winkle (IRE)—Dawera (IRE) (Spinning World (USA)) **H. H. Aga Khan**
83 B br c 12/3 Congrats (USA)—Diva Delite (USA) (Repent (USA)) (97680) **Godolphin Management**
84 B f 28/3 Helmet (AUS)—Eaton Street (Discreet Cat (USA)) **John Heffernan / Paddy Hyland**
85 B f 27/3 Casamento (IRE)—Erreur (IRE) (Desert King (IRE)) **J. Osborne**
86 B f 8/4 Pivotal—Etive (USA) (Elusive Quality (USA)) **Godolphin Management**
87 C f 11/5 Girolamo (USA)—Forty Greeta (ARG) (Roar (USA)) **Godolphin Management**
88 B f 29/1 Tamayuz—Hanakiyya (IRE) (Danehill Dancer (IRE)) **H. H. Aga Khan**
89 Ch c 20/3 Lope de Vega (IRE)—Hazarista (IRE) (Barathea (IRE)) **H. H. Aga Khan**
90 Gr c 24/1 Dark Angel (IRE)—Heeby Jeeby (Lawman (FR)) (104761) **Godolphin Management**

MR MICHAEL HALFORD - Continued

91 B f 20/3 Teofilo (IRE)—Hikma (USA) (Street Cry (IRE)) **Godolphin Management**
92 B c 14/4 Elzaam (AUS)—Instant Memories (IRE) (Ad Valorem (USA)) (14765) **M. Halford**
93 **KHANISARI (IRE),** gr c 15/4 Dark Angel (IRE)—Kadayna (IRE) (Dalakhani (IRE)) **H. H. Aga Khan**
94 B c 9/4 Bernardini (USA)—Looking Glass (USA) (Seeking The Gold (USA)) **Godolphin Management**
95 Ch c 12/2 Pivotal—Macleya (GER) (Winged Love (IRE)) (88593) **Godolphin Management**
96 Br c 29/3 Footstepsinthesand—Mamacita (IRE) (High Chaparral (IRE)) **Mr Michael Enright**
97 B c 2/3 Casamento (IRE)—Marhaba (Nayef (USA)) (29531) **Godolphin Management**
98 Ch c 21/4 Proud Citizen (USA)—Maria's Storm (USA) (Maria's Mon (USA)) (25641) **E. Koh**
99 B f 9/2 Cape Cross (IRE)—Minidress (Street Cry (IRE)) **Godolphin Management**
100 Ch c 5/3 Raven's Pass (USA)—Mowazana (IRE) (Galileo (IRE)) (45773) **Zhang Yuesheng**
101 B f 2/3 Dunkirk (USA)—Mycatcandance (USA) (Storm Cat (USA)) (33222) **Tay Hu Chor and E. Koh**
102 Ch f 2/3 Shamardal (USA)—Nadia (Nashwan (USA)) **Godolphin Management**
103 B f 3/4 Street Cry (IRE)—Northern Melody (IRE) (Singspiel (IRE)) **Godolphin Management**
104 B c 12/5 Footstepsinthesand—Pearlitas Passion (IRE) (High Chaparral (IRE)) **Mr Michael Enright**
105 Ch c 15/4 Pure Prize (USA)—
                  Perils of Pauline (USA) (Stravinsky (USA)) (26578) **Tay Hu Chor, E. Koh, D. Cantillon**
106 B f 16/4 Pivotal—Persinette (USA) (Kingmambo (USA)) **Godolphin Management**
107 B c 4/3 Raven's Pass (USA)—Picture Hat (USA) (El Prado (IRE)) **Godolphin Management**
108 Ch c 3/3 Helmet (AUS)—Pina Colada (Sabrehill (USA)) **Godolphin Management**
109 Ch c 9/3 Dutch Art—Providencia (Oasis Dream) **Godolphin Management**
110 **REHANA (IRE),** b f 15/4 Dark Angel (IRE)—Rayka (IRE) (Selkirk (USA)) **H. H. Aga Khan**
111 B f 11/3 So You Think (USA)—Roselyn (Efisio) (19933) **Tay Hu Chor**
112 B f 3/5 Raven's Pass (USA)—Russian Society (Darshaan) **Godolphin Management**
113 B c 28/4 Elusive Quality (USA)—Tactfully (IRE) (Discreet Cat (USA)) **Godolphin Management**
114 Ch c 1/5 Casamento (IRE)—Tempete (Dubai Millennium) **Godolphin Management**
115 B c 26/5 Azamour (IRE)—Virana (IRE) (King's Best (USA)) **H. H. Aga Khan**
116 B f 10/3 Holy Roman Emperor (IRE)—Zariziyna (IRE) (Dalakhani (IRE)) **H. H. Aga Khan**

Assistant Trainer: Fabian Burke

Jockey (flat): Shane Foley. **Apprentice:** Conor Hoban, Sean Corby, Jamie Joyce, Conor McGovern, Robbie Smithers.
Amateur: Mr Evan Halford.

---

266 **MISS SALLY HALL, Middleham**
Postal: **Brecongill, Coverham, Leyburn, North Yorkshire, DL8 4TJ**
Contacts: **PHONE (01969) 640223 FAX (0800) 066 4274**
E-MAIL sally@brecongill.co.uk

1 **ALTHAROOS (IRE),** 6, br g Sakhee (USA)—Thamara (USA) **Colin Platts**
2 **AMERICAN GIGOLO,** 4, b g Azamour (IRE)—Sadie Thompson (IRE) **G. B. Turnbull Ltd**
3 **JACK LAMB,** 4, gr g Sulamani (IRE)—Charlotte Lamb **Miss S. E. Hall**
4 4, Ch f Monsieur Bond (IRE)—Pigment **Miss S. E. Hall**
5 **ROCK A DOODLE DOO (IRE),** 9, b g Oratorio (IRE)—Nousaiyra (IRE) **Colin Platts**
6 4, B f Sakhee (USA)—Turn Back **Miss S. E. Hall**

Other Owners: W. Jarvis.

Assistant Trainer: Colin Platts

Jockey (NH): Richard Johnson. **Amateur:** Mrs D.S. Wilkinson.

---

267 **MRS MARY HAMBRO, Cheltenham**
Postal: **Cotswold Stud, Sezincote, Moreton-In-Marsh, Gloucestershire, GL56 9TB**
Contacts: **PHONE (01386) 700700 FAX (01386) 700701 MOBILE (07860) 632990**
E-MAIL maryhambro@mac.com

1 **BADGER BANK,** 4, gr g Zamindar (USA)—Rose Row **Mrs M. C. Hambro**
2 **FROZEN LAKE (USA),** 4, b g Elusive Quality (USA)—Creative Design (USA) **Mrs M. C. Hambro**
3 **PRIMOGENITURE (IRE),** 5, b g Glory of Dancer—Jacqueline (IND) **Mrs M. C. Hambro**
4 **TOAD CORNER,** 4, b g Shirocco (GER)—Didbrook **Mrs M. C. Hambro**

MRS MARY HAMBRO - Continued

THREE-YEAR-OLDS

5 BUCKLE STREET, br g Cacique (IRE)—Rose Row **Mrs M. C. Hambro**

TWO-YEAR-OLDS

6 B c 30/4 Cacique (IRE)—Rose Row (Act One) **Mrs M. C. Hambro**

268
MRS DEBRA HAMER, Carmarthen
Postal: **Bryngors Uchaf, Nantycaws, Carmarthen, Dyfed, SA32 8EY**
Contacts: **HOME (01267) 234585 MOBILE (07980) 665274**
E-MAIL hamerracing@hotmail.co.uk

1 BRONWYDD, 6, br m Needle Gun (IRE)—Talkingstick (IRE) **A. T. Bailey**
2 CELTIC FELLA (IRE), 9, gr b g Kahtan—Mens Business (IRE) **Mr T. M. Morse**
3 LAYERTHORPE (IRE), 4, b bl g Vale of York (IRE)—Strobinia (IRE) **Mr C. A. Hanbury**
4 LOOKS LIKE POWER (IRE), 6, ch g Spadoun (FR)—Martovic (IRE) **Mr C. A. Hanbury**
5 MAGICAL MAN, 9, b br g Lahib (USA)—Majestic Di (IRE) **Mr C. A. Hanbury**
6 MICHIGAN ASSASSIN (IRE), 14, b g King's Theatre (IRE)—Shuil Ar Aghaidh **Mr C. A. Hanbury**
7 PENNANT DANCER, 9, b g Grape Tree Road—Pennant Princess **Mr P. J. Woolley**
8 PENNANT LADY, 6, b br m Black Sam Bellamy (IRE)—Pennant Princess **Mr P. J. Woolley**
9 SLICE OF LEMON, 4, b f Dr Massini (IRE)—Lady Maranzi **Mrs D. A. Hamer**
10 SUPER SCORPION (IRE), 6, b g Scorpion (IRE)—Nolagh Supreme (IRE) **Mrs J. M. Edmonds**
11 SUPREME BOB (IRE), 10, b g Bob's Return (IRE)—Supremememories (IRE) **Mrs J. M. Edmonds**
12 TOBEFAIR, 6, b br g Central Park (IRE)—Nan **Down The Quay Club**

Other Owners: Mr M. J. Cole, Mr A. G. Pannell.

Assistant Trainer: Mr M. P. Hamer

269
MRS ALISON HAMILTON, Denholm
Postal: **Dykes Farm House, Hawick, Roxburghshire, TD9 8TB**
Contacts: **PHONE (01450) 870323 MOBILE (07885) 477349**
E-MAIL Alisonhamilton53@yahoo.com

1 PAINTERS LAD (IRE), 5, b g Fruits of Love (USA)—Great Cullen (IRE) **J. P. G. Hamilton**
2 PARKIE BOY, 5, b g Central Park (IRE)—Parlour Game **Mr & Mrs D. S. Byers**
3 SOME LAD (IRE), 11, b g Beneficial—Some News (IRE) **J. P. G. Hamilton**
4 TAMBOUR MAJOR (FR), 9, b g Myrakalu (FR)—Joaillere (FR) **Hamilton Racing**
5 THE ICE FACTOR, 8, b g Iceman—Kiruna **J. P. G. Hamilton**
6 THE LAST LEG (IRE), 7, b g Old Vic—Raphuca (IRE) **J. P. G. Hamilton**
7 TOWERBURN (IRE), 7, b g Cloudings (IRE)—Lady Newmill (IRE) **J. P. G. Hamilton**
8 WHAT A DREAM, 10, ch g Supreme Sound—Ben Roseler (IRE) **R. J. Kyle, D. & J. Byers**

Other Owners: Mrs M. A. Bowie, D. S. Byers, Mrs M. J. Byers, Mrs A. C. Hamilton, Exors of the Late Mr R. J. Kyle.

Assistant Trainer: Mr G. Hamilton

270
MR ANDREW HAMILTON, Carluke
Postal: **Nellfield House, Braidwood, Carluke, South Lanarkshire, ML8 4PP**
Contacts: **MOBILE (07974) 744421**
E-MAIL andrewhamiltoncoach@btinternet.com

1 BAYFIRTH (IRE), 13, b g Flemensfirth (USA)—Baylough Lady (IRE) **Mr A. B. Hamilton**
2 RED PIANO, 7, ch g Flemensfirth (USA)—Gavotte du Cochet (FR) **Mr A. B. Hamilton**

271 MRS ANN HAMILTON, Newcastle Upon Tyne
Postal: **Claywalls Farm, Capheaton, Newcastle Upon Tyne, Tyne and Wear, NE19 2BP**
Contacts: **PHONE (01830) 530219 MOBILE (07704) 670704**
E-MAIL **annhamilton1952@hotmail.com**

1 **EDMUND (IRE)**, 9, b g Indian River (FR)—Awomansdream (IRE) **I. Hamilton**
2 **NINE ALTARS (IRE)**, 7, b g Heron Island (IRE)—Tawny Owl (IRE) **I. Hamilton**
3 **NUTS WELL**, 5, b g Dylan Thomas (IRE)—Renada **I. Hamilton**
4 **OAK VINTAGE (IRE)**, 6, b g Fruits of Love (USA)—Brandam Supreme (IRE) **I. Hamilton**
5 **RUNSWICK ROYAL (IRE)**, 7, ch g Excellent Art—Renada **I. Hamilton**
6 **TRUST THOMAS**, 8, ch g Erhaab (USA)—Yota (FR) **I. Hamilton**

THREE-YEAR-OLDS

7 B g Great Palm (USA)—Miss Royello **I. Hamilton**

Assistant Trainer: Ian Hamilton

272 MR B. R. HAMILTON, Co. Down
Postal: **100 Ballynoe Road, Downpatrick, Co. Down, Northern Ireland**
Contacts: **MOBILE (07779) 591970**
E-MAIL **brianhamilton70@yahoo.co.uk**

1 **ILLUMINATI (FR)**, 6, b g Solon (GER)—Viva Moranbon (FR) **Sean Macklin**
2 **JIMMY TWO TIMES (IRE)**, 7, b g Shantou (USA)—Shedan (IRE) **Sean Graham**
3 **MARKET ROAD (IRE)**, 6, gr g Tikkanen (USA)—Clydeside (IRE) **B. A. Hamilton**
4 **ONE TICK (IRE)**, 6, b g Tikkanen (USA)—Garvey Lough (IRE) **Joe Tumelty**
5 **SOME CHAOS (IRE)**, 5, b g Brian Boru—Iruna Iris (IRE) **Some Syndicate**
6 **SOVEREIGN PRINCESS (IRE)**, 6, b m Ramonti (FR)—Sovereign Magic **Paul Trainor**
7 **TWILIGHT SHADOW (IRE)**, 5, b m Tikkanen (USA)—Trinity Belle (FR) **Stone Circle Syndicate**

Assistant Trainer: B. A. Hamilton

Amateur: Mr D. G. Lavery.

273 MR MICKY HAMMOND, Middleham
Postal: **Oakwood Stables, East Witton Road, Middleham, Leyburn, North Yorkshire, DL8 4PT**
Contacts: **PHONE (01969) 625223 MOBILE (07808) 572777**
E-MAIL **mickyhammondracing@hotmail.com WEBSITE www.mickyhammondracing.co.uk**

1 **ABBEY STORM (IRE)**, 10, br g Presenting—Bobbies Storm (IRE) **Mr & Mrs Paul & Clare Rooney**
2 **ALCHIMIX (FR)**, 6, b g Al Namix (FR)—Julie Noire (FR) **I. J. Barran**
3 **ALDERBROOK LAD (IRE)**, 10, ch g Alderbrook—Alone Tabankulu (IRE) **Masters Of The Hall**
4 **APPLAUS (GER)**, 4, b g Tiger Hill (IRE)—All About Love (GER) **J. Buzzeo**
5 **AULDTHUNDER (IRE)**, 9, b g Oscar (IRE)—Jill's Girl (IRE) **The Rat Pack Racing Club**
6 **BEER GOGGLES (IRE)**, 5, br g Oscar (IRE)—Tynelucy (IRE) **Richard & Katherine Gilbert**
7 **BESPOKE LADY (IRE)**, 7, ch m Presenting—Coole Alainn (IRE) **Mr & Mrs Paul & Clare Rooney**
8 **BIG THUNDER**, 6, gr g Dalakhani (IRE)—Charlotte O Fraise (IRE) **Richard & Katherine Gilbert**
9 **BLUE HUSSAR (IRE)**, 5, b g Montjeu (IRE)—Metaphor (USA) **Mr R. M. Howard**
10 **BOLDBOB (IRE)**, 4, gr g Verglas (IRE)—Special Park (USA) **M.H.O.G. 2**
11 **CADMIUM**, 5, b m Major Cadeaux—Miss Mirasol **Oakwood Rainbow**
12 **CARALINE (FR)**, 5, b m Martaline—Vie Ta Vie (FR) **Give Every Man His Due**
13 **CELTIC AGENT**, 8, b g Kayf Tara—Poor Celt **Mrs Susan Johnson**
14 **CHAMPAGNE RANSOM (FR)**, 4, gr ro f Mastercraftsman (IRE)—Linorova (USA) **Oakwood Minions**
15 **CORREGGIO**, 6, ch g Bertolini (USA)—Arian Da **Forty Forty Twenty**
16 **DAKOTA GREY**, 5, gr g Fair Mix (IRE)—Miss Sassi **Still Game Associates**
17 **DUE EAST**, 6, b m Bollin Eric—Poor Celt **Mrs S. Johnson**
18 **ENDLESS CREDIT (IRE)**, 6, b br g High Chaparral (IRE)—Pay The Bank **Mike and Eileen Newbould**
19 **FAISEUR DE MIRACLE**, 4, b g Makfi—Flawly **The Three M's**
20 **FREDERIC**, 5, b g Zamindar (USA)—Frangy **Mr & Mrs Paul & Clare Rooney**
21 **GEORGE FERNBECK**, 8, ch g Java Gold (USA)—Burmese Days **R M & T Holdings Limited**
22 **GRAN PARADISO (IRE)**, 4, ch c Galileo (IRE)—Looking Lovely (IRE) **Mike and Eileen Newbould**
23 **INCHCOLM (IRE)**, 6, br g Presenting—Rose of Inchiquin (IRE) **M.H.O.G.**
24 **INVICTUS (GER)**, 4, b g Exceed And Excel (AUS)—Ivowen (USA) **Mike and Eileen Newbould**

MR MICKY HAMMOND - Continued

25 **IT'S ALL ABOUT ME (IRE)**, 4, b f King's Theatre (IRE)—Annie Spectrim (IRE) **Richard & Katherine Gilbert**
26 **JUMPANDTRAVEL (IRE)**, 7, b m Millenary—Youbetido (IRE) **V. Kelly**
27 **JUST CAMERON**, 9, b g Kayf Tara—Miss Fencote **Mr & Mrs P. Chapman**
28 **KISUMU**, 4, b g High Chaparral (IRE)—Arum Lily (USA) **2 esses, 2 bees, 2 ems & a tee**
29 **LIBBY MAE (IRE)**, 6, b m High Chaparral (IRE)—Empty Pocket **Mr & Mrs P. Chapman**
30 **LONGUEVILLE FLIER (IRE)**, 7, b g Definite Article—Talk The Talk **Red & Whites**
31 **LOWCARR MOTION**, 6, b g Rainbow High—Royalty (IRE) **Irv's Gang**
32 **LUVLYLYNNTHOMAS**, 4, gr f Equiano (FR)—Dansa Queen **Bendery Properties Holdings Ltd**
33 **MASIRANN (IRE)**, 8, b g Tiger Hill (IRE)—Masilia (IRE) **Mike and Eileen Newbould**
34 **MAXIE T**, 5, b g Dalakhani (IRE)—Ballet Ballon (USA) **Newroc & Co**
35 **MERCHANT OF MEDICI**, 9, b g Medicean—Regal Rose **JFW Properties Limited**
36 **MINELLA HERO (IRE)**, 8, b g Old Vic—Shannon Rose (IRE) **Ball & Lees**
37 **MULTI GRAIN**, 4, b f Sir Percy—Grain Only **Mike and Eileen Newbould**
38 **ONLY ORSENFOOLSIES**, 7, b g Trade Fair—Desert Gold (IRE) **Foolsies**
39 **ONLYFOOLSOWNHORSES (IRE)**, 5, br g Presenting—Lizzy Langtry (IRE) **Richard & Katherine Gilbert**
40 **OSCAR O'SCAR (IRE)**, 8, b g Oscar (IRE)—Shining Lights (IRE) **Newroc 1**
41 **PABUSAR**, 8, b g Oasis Dream—Autumn Pearl **Maybe The Last Time**
42 **PADDLING (FR)**, 5, b g Walk In The Park (IRE)—Sea Mamaille (FR) **Masters Of The Hall 2**
43 **PAY THE KING (IRE)**, 9, b g King's Theatre (IRE)—Knocktartan (IRE) **Mr S. Paley**
44 **PERTUIS (IRE)**, 10, gr g Verglas (IRE)—Lady Killeen (IRE) **M.H.O.G.**
45 **POLITBUREAU**, 9, b g Red Ransom (USA)—Tereshkova (USA) **Maybe The Last Time**
46 **RATHLIN**, 11, b g Kayf Tara—Princess Timon **Masters Of The Hall 2**
47 **RAYADOUR (IRE)**, 7, b g Azamour (IRE)—Rayyana (IRE) **Jimmy Mac**
48 **RETURN FLIGHT**, 5, b g Kayf Tara—Molly Flight (IRE) **Mike and Eileen Newbould**
49 **RHYTHM OF SOUND (IRE)**, 6, ch g Mahler—Oscarvail (IRE) **The Fanciers**
50 **ROSAIRLIE (IRE)**, 8, ch m Halling (USA)—Mrs Mason (IRE) **The Late Night Drinkers & Wishful Thinkers**
51 **ROXYFET (FR)**, 6, b g Califet (FR)—Roxalamour (FR) **Mr R. J. Ball**
52 **RUSSIAN ROYALE**, 6, b m Royal Applause—Russian Ruby (FR) **M.H.O.G.**
53 **SHALAMZAR (FR)**, 7, ch g Selkirk (USA)—Shamalana (IRE) **Maybe The Last Time**
54 **SHERRY**, 5, b m Tobougg (IRE)—Vino **Guy Reed Racing**
55 **SILVER TASSIE (IRE)**, 8, b g Shantou (USA)—Silver Castor (IRE) **Mr R. M. Howard**
56 **STHENIC (FR)**, 4, b g Fastnet Rock (AUS)—Ela's Giant **Oakwood Outlaws**
57 **STICKLEBACK**, 7, ch m Manduro (GER)—The Stick **The Rat Pack Racing Club**
58 **STRAIT RUN (IRE)**, 5, ch g Rock of Gibraltar (IRE)—Gentlemen's Guest (USA) **Littlethorpe Park Racing**
59 **SUMMERLEA (IRE)**, 10, ch g Alhaarth (IRE)—Verbania (IRE) **Oakwood Minions**
60 **TAYLOR (IRE)**, 7, b m Presenting—Britway Lady (IRE) **D H Lees & Sons Limited**
61 **THE RAMBLIN KID**, 8, b g Westerner—Disallowed (IRE) **J. Buzzeo**
62 **TRIANGULATE**, 4, b g Zamindar (USA)—Heart of Hearts **Mr R. A. Beattie**
63 **TRIUMPH DAVIS (IRE)**, 7, b m Flemensfirth (USA)—Bodhran Davis (IRE) **M.H.O.G.**
64 **TULLAMORE DEW (IRE)**, 14, ch g Pistolet Bleu (IRE)—Heather Point **Give Every Man His Due**
65 **TUSCAN GOLD**, 9, ch g Medicean—Louella (USA) **M.H.O.G.**
66 **VAYLAND**, 7, ch g Generous (IRE)—Dotandadash (IRE) **Richard & Katherine Gilbert**
67 **VECHEKA (IRE)**, 5, b g Lawman (FR)—Lidanski (IRE) **R M & T Holdings Limited**
68 **VERKO (FR)**, 7, br g Lavirco (GER)—Lady Vernizy (FR) **Mr D. Green**
69 **VODKA WELLS (FR)**, 6, b g Irish Wells (FR)—Kahipiroska (FR) **Mike and Eileen Newbould**
70 **WATERCLOCK (IRE)**, 7, ch g Notnowcato—Waterfall One **The Young Ones**
71 **WAYWARD SUN (IRE)**, 5, b g Double Eclipse (IRE)—Mahonrun (IRE) **The Wayward Lads**
72 **WISHING WELL**, 4, b f Bahri (USA)—Amourallis (IRE) **The Pennies Dropped Partnership**
73 **YORKIST (IRE)**, 8, ch g Urban Ocean (FR)—Kilbarry Demon (IRE) **Mike and Eileen Newbould**

THREE-YEAR-OLDS

74 **ALLFREDANDNOBELL (IRE)**, b g Alfred Nobel (IRE)—Its In The Air (IRE) **The Oakwood Nobels**
75 **BECKY THE THATCHER**, b f Mastercraftsman (IRE)—Fairmont (IRE) **McGoldrick Racing Syndicate 4**
76 **CALYPSO DELEGATOR (IRE)**, b g Lilbourne Lad (IRE)—Amber Nectar (IRE) **Bendery Properties Holdings Ltd**
77 **QUOTELINE DIRECT**, ch g Sir Percy—Queen's Pudding (USA) **JFW Properties Limited**

Other Owners: Mr A. Bradley, S. T. Brankin, Mr J. Carthy, Mrs J. Chapman, Mr P. W. Chapman, Mrs J. Cobb, Mr S. J. M. Cobb, Mr M. Dixon, Mr R. P. Gilbert, Mrs K. E. Gilbert, Mr R. Green, M. D. Hammond, Mr D. A. Harrison, Mr D. Hartley, Mr J. A. Hill, Mrs G. Hogg, Mr L. Horvath, J. M. Hughes, Mr D. Hymas, Mrs A. Kane, M. Kelly, R. J. Longley, I. M. Lynch, Mr R. Manners, Mr S. Martin, Mr J. McAllister, Mrs N. McGrath, J. M. Newbould, Mrs E. E. Newbould, Mr G. Newton, G. R. Orchard, Mr J. Pettit, Mr A. M. Phillips, Mr E. Price, Mr T. Rodney, Mr P. A. Rooney, Mrs C. Rooney, N. J. Rust, Mr C. M. Sharpe, Mr A. Stainton, J. B. Stead, Mr J. E. Tennant, Mr M. J. Waite, Mr K. Ward, M. White.

MR MICKY HAMMOND - Continued

Assistant Trainer: Mrs. G. Hogg (07809) 428117

Conditional: Joe Colliver, Finian O'Toole, Hugo Thompson-Brown. **Amateur:** Miss R. Smith, Miss Catherine Walton, Mr Joe Wright.

---

274 **MR MIKE HAMMOND, Abberley**
Postal: **Cherry Ash, Bank Lane, Abberley, Worcester, Worcestershire, WR6 6BQ**
Contacts: **PHONE (01299) 896057 MOBILE 07894 050183**
E-MAIL mphatwellcottage@aol.com WEBSITE www.hammondracing.co.uk

1 ISABELLESPRINCESS (IRE), 8, b m Westerner—Perkaway (IRE) **D Pain & Sons**
2 MILLED (IRE), 9, b g Millenary—Miss Culfadda (IRE) **Mrs Z. R. Hammond**
3 MISS U PEANUTS, 7, b m Norse Dancer (IRE)—Rock N Role VII **Mr R. M. Evans**

Other Owners: Mr P. R. Pain, Mr A. Pain, Mrs S. Pain, Mrs P. R. Pain, Mrs A. S. Taylor.

Assistant Trainer: Zoe Hammond

---

275 **MR GARY HANMER, Tattenhall**
Postal: **Church Farm, Harthill Lane, Harthill, Tattenhall, Chester, Cheshire, CH3 9LQ**
Contacts: **MOBILE (07737) 181165**

1 CRUISING BYE, 10, b g Alflora (IRE)—Althrey Flame (IRE) **F. Lloyd**
2 DON'T HANG ABOUT, 11, ch g Alflora (IRE)—Althrey Flame (IRE) **F. Lloyd**
3 DONTTELLTHEMISSIS (IRE), 5, b m Flemensfirth (USA)—Blue Gale (IRE) **Mr P Burke & Mrs N Burke**
4 FAIR ASK, 8, gr m Fair Mix (IRE)—Ask Me Not (IRE) **F. Lloyd**
5 FUSIONFORCE (IRE), 9, b g Overbury (IRE)—Seviot **Mr S. P. Edkins**
6 HIGH COUNSEL (IRE), 7, br g Presenting—The Bench **Herongate Racers**
7 LOCH GARMAN ARIS (IRE), 6, b g Jammaal—See Em Aime (IRE) **George Brookes & Family**
8 POINT OF DEPARTURE (IRE), 5, b g Mahler—Miranda's Lace (IRE) **F. Lloyd**
9 SQUEEZE ME, 9, b m Grape Tree Road—Ask Me Not (IRE) **F. Lloyd**
10 THE ROAD AHEAD, 9, b m Grape Tree Road—Althrey Flame (IRE) **F. Lloyd**
11 VINNIEWHITEFOOT, 9, ch g Grape Tree Road—Mistress Return **P. S. Burke**
12 WHAT A LAUGH, 11, b g Kayf Tara—Just For A Laugh **Mr & Mrs R. Davies-Cooke**

Other Owners: Mrs S. Archdale, G. E. Brookes, Mrs N. Burke, Mr R. P. Davies-Cooke, Mrs S. Davies-Cooke, Mr L. Felstead.

---

276 **MR RICHARD HANNON, Marlborough**
Postal: **R. Hannon Limited, Herridge House, Collingbourne Ducis, Marlborough, Wiltshire, SN8 3EG**
Contacts: **PHONE (01264) 850254 FAX (01264) 850076**
E-MAIL kevin@richardhannonracing.co.uk WEBSITE www.richardhannonracing.co.uk

1 AZMAAM (IRE), 4, gr c Dark Angel (IRE)—Miss Indigo
2 BLACK CHERRY, 4, b f Mount Nelson—Arctic Char
3 BURNT SUGAR (IRE), 4, b c Lope de Vega (IRE)—Lady Livius (IRE)
4 COULSTY (IRE), 5, b h Kodiac—Hazium (IRE)
5 DESERT FORCE, 4, b c Equiano (FR)—Mail The Desert (IRE)
6 EMELL, 6, ch g Medicean—Londonnetdotcom (IRE)
7 ESTIDHKAAR (IRE), 4, b c Dark Angel (IRE)—Danetime Out (IRE)
8 FRANCISCO, 4, b g Paco Boy (IRE)—Blue Goddess (IRE)
9 GIBEON (IRE), 4, b c Cape Cross (IRE)—Gravitation
10 LEXINGTON TIMES (IRE), 4, b c Paco Boy (IRE)—Fuaigh Mor (IRE)
11 MOHEET (IRE), 4, b c High Chaparral (IRE)—Abunai
12 MYSTIC JADE, 4, ch f Raven's Pass (USA)—Mauri Moon
13 NAYEL (IRE), 4, b c Acclamation—Soliza (IRE)
14 ROYAL TOAST (IRE), 4, b g Duke of Marmalade (IRE)—Ripalong (IRE)
15 SHELL BAY (USA), 4, b g Hard Spun (USA)—Rebel Account (USA)
16 SHIFTING POWER, 5, ch h Compton Place—Profit Alert (IRE)
17 SILVER QUAY (IRE), 4, gr c Dark Angel (IRE)—She Runs (FR)
18 TASHAAR (IRE), 4, b c Sea The Stars (IRE)—Three Moons (IRE)

MR RICHARD HANNON - Continued

19 TOORMORE (IRE), 5, b h Arakan (USA)—Danetime Out (IRE)
20 TUPI (IRE), 4, b c Tamayuz—Carioca (IRE)
21 WINDSHEAR, 5, b g Hurricane Run (IRE)—Portal

THREE-YEAR-OLDS

22 AGUEROOO (IRE), b g Monsieur Bond (IRE)—Vision of Peace (IRE)
23 AL HAFFANAH (IRE), b f Acclamation—Street Style (IRE)
24 AL KIRANA (IRE), b f Exceed And Excel (AUS)—Ripalong (IRE)
25 AL MARKHIYA (IRE), b f Arcano (IRE)—Danetime Out (IRE)
26 ALDAIR, b c Pastoral Pursuits—Tremelo Pointe (IRE)
27 ALKHOR, b c Exceed And Excel (AUS)—Ruse
28 ALSAADEN, b f Acclamation—Bahia Breeze
29 ALTARSHEED (IRE), b g Lilbourne Lad (IRE)—Lilakiya (IRE)
30 ANCIENT TRADE (USA), ch c Speightstown (USA)—Nafisah (IRE)
31 ANDREYEV, b c Dutch Art—Balalaika
32 ATLANTIC SUN, br c Roderic O'Connor (IRE)—Robema
33 BAHAARAH (IRE), b f Iffraaj—Love Intrigue (IRE)
34 BAY OF ST MALO (IRE), b f Canford Cliffs (IRE)—Distant Skies
35 BIGGER AND BETTER, b c Fastnet Rock (AUS)—Interlace
36 BLACKOUT (FR), b c Dream Ahead (USA)—Belle Masquee (IRE)
37 BOYCIE, b c Paco Boy (IRE)—Eve
38 CACICA, b f Cacique (IRE)—Moonlight Mystery
39 CANFORD CROSSING (IRE), b c Canford Cliffs (IRE)—Smartest (IRE)
40 CHIEF WHIP (USA), ch c Giant's Causeway (USA)—Canterbury Lace (USA)
41 DANEHILL KODIAC (IRE), b c Kodiac—Meadow
42 DHEBAN (IRE), gr g Exceed And Excel (AUS)—Comeback Queen
43 DUBAI MISSION (IRE), b c New Approach (IRE)—Al Joza
44 DUBAI'S SECRET, ch c Paco Boy (IRE)—Lilli Marlane
45 DUTCH TREATY, ch f Dutch Art—Entreat
46 EJAAZAH (IRE), b f Acclamation—English Ballet (IRE)
47 ELTEZAM (IRE), b c Kodiac—Tymora (USA)
48 B f Canford Cliffs (IRE)—Elusive Galaxy (USA)
49 FASHAAK (IRE), b c Starspangledbanner (AUS)—Szabo (IRE)
50 FEED THE GOATER (FR), b g Fastnet Rock (AUS)—Lumiere Astrale (FR)
51 GOLD ELIZA (IRE), ch f Pivotal—Srda (USA)
52 GREAT PAGE (IRE), b f Roderic O'Connor (IRE)—Areeda (IRE)
53 HERMANN, b c Authorized (IRE)—Alamanni (USA)
54 HOWARDIAN HILLS (IRE), b c Vale of York (IRE)—Handsome Anna (IRE)
55 HUMPHREY BOGART (IRE), b c Tagula (IRE)—Hazarama (IRE)
56 ILLUMINATE (IRE), b f Zoffany (IRE)—Queen of Stars (USA)
57 IN THE RED (IRE), b c Elusive Pimpernel (USA)—Roses From Ridey (IRE)
58 INLAND SEA (USA), b c Scat Daddy (USA)—Cat's Eye Witness (USA)
59 JAYJINSKI (IRE), gr c Zebedee—Prime Time Girl
60 KESSELRING, ch c New Approach (IRE)—Anna Oleanda (IRE)
61 KING OF ROOKS, b c Acclamation—Slap Shot (IRE)
62 KISMET HARDY, ch c Mount Nelson—Quinzey's Best (IRE)
63 KYLEA (IRE), b f Iffraaj—Pitrizza (IRE)
64 LEAP, ch f Pounced (USA)—Liel
65 LEXINGTON LAW (IRE), b c Lawman (FR)—Tus Nua (IRE)
66 LIGHT UP OUR WORLD (IRE), b f Zoffany (IRE)—Shine Like A Star
67 LOADING (IRE), b c Arcano (IRE)—Sally Wood (CAN)
68 LOG OUT ISLAND (IRE), b c Dark Angel (IRE)—White Daffodil (IRE)
69 MADRINHO (IRE), ch c Frozen Power (IRE)—Perfectly Clear (USA)
70 MANSOOB, ch c Paco Boy (IRE)—Descriptive (IRE)
71 MAQAM (IRE), br f Dansili—Thai Haku (IRE)
72 MARENKO, b f Exceed And Excel (AUS)—Safina
73 MELFIT (IRE), b c Sea The Stars (IRE)—Alshahbaa (IRE)
74 MUSDAM (USA), b c Exchange Rate (USA)—Valid Lilly (USA)
75 NAJD, b c Dick Turpin (IRE)—Mookhlesa
76 NATURAL WONDER, ro f Paco Boy (IRE)—Galapagar (USA)
77 NOT TOUCH, ch c Dream Ahead (USA)—Umlilo
78 OH THIS IS US (IRE), b c Acclamation—Shamwari Lodge (IRE)
79 OUT OF THE DARK (IRE), b f Kyllachy—Assumption (IRE)
80 PACO PAT, b c Paco Boy (IRE)—Tanwir
81 PALAWAN, b c Mount Nelson—Apple Sauce

MR RICHARD HANNON - Continued

82 **PARIS PROTOCOL**, b c Champs Elysees—Island Vista
83 **PATENT**, b g Paco Boy (IRE)—Film Script
84 **PERFORMER**, b f New Approach (IRE)—Annalina (USA)
85 **PHANTOM FLIPPER**, ch c Bahamian Bounty—Artistic License (IRE)
86 **RACQUET**, br c Pastoral Pursuits—Billie Jean
87 **RISING SUNSHINE (IRE)**, b c Dark Angel (IRE)—Little Audio (IRE)
88 **RITASUN (FR)**, b br g Monsun (GER)—Baselga (GER)
89 **ROCCOR**, b f Rock of Gibraltar (IRE)—Corinium (IRE)
90 **SEE YOU WHEN (IRE)**, b c Acclamation—Lighthouse
91 **SHAAN (IRE)**, b f Iffraaj—Evening Time (IRE)
92 **SHAWAAHID (IRE)**, b c Elnadim (USA)—Vexatious (IRE)
93 **SHWAIMSA (IRE)**, b f Canford Cliffs (IRE)—Sharp Point (IRE)
94 **SKEAPING**, b c Excellent Art—Gale Green
95 **SNAN (IRE)**, b c High Chaparral (IRE)—Slow Sand (USA)
96 **STEEL OF MADRID (IRE)**, b c Lope de Vega (IRE)—Bibury
97 **STORM RISING (IRE)**, b c Canford Cliffs (IRE)—Before The Storm
98 **TABARRAK (IRE)**, b c Acclamation—Bahati (IRE)
99 **TAQWAA (IRE)**, ch c Iffraaj—Hallowed Park (IRE)
100 **TARAABUT (IRE)**, b c Lilbourne Lad (IRE)—Cuilaphuca (IRE)
101 **TASKEEN (IRE)**, b c Lilbourne Lad (IRE)—Lola Rosa (IRE)
102 **TELEGRAM**, b c Dream Ahead (USA)—Miss Chaussini (IRE)
103 **THE INVISIBLE DOG (IRE)**, b c Canford Cliffs (IRE)—Aljumar (IRE)
104 **TONY CURTIS**, b c Rock of Gibraltar (IRE)—Strawberry Lolly
105 **TORCH**, b c Paco Boy (IRE)—Singed
106 **VENTURA FALCON (IRE)**, b f Excellent Art—Danish Gem
107 **VENTURA STORM (IRE)**, b c Zoffany (IRE)—Sarawati (IRE)
108 **VIREN'S ARMY (IRE)**, b c Twirling Candy (USA)—Blue Angel (IRE)
109 **VISION OF BEAUTY (FR)**, b f Vision d'etat (FR)—Belle Dame (GER)
110 **WALKING IN RHYTHM (IRE)**, b f Lord Shanakill (USA)—So Sweet (IRE)
111 **WAR GLORY (IRE)**, b c Canford Cliffs (IRE)—Attracted To You (IRE)
112 **WAR WHISPER (IRE)**, b c Royal Applause—Featherweight (IRE)
113 **WILEY POST**, b c Kyllachy—Orange Pip
114 **WINTER ROSE (IRE)**, b f Dark Angel (IRE)—Rose of Battle
115 **ZABDI**, b c Zebedee—Musical Moonlight

TWO-YEAR-OLDS

116 B c 7/2 Zebedee—African Moonlight (UAE) (Halling (USA)) (80000)
117 B f 16/3 Sir Prancealot (IRE)—Ajla (IRE) (Exceed And Excel (AUS)) (14000)
118 **AKAMANTO (IRE)**, b c 15/3 Cape Cross (IRE)—Allofus (IRE) (Celtic Swing) (85000)
119 B c 22/2 Power—Al Ihtithar (IRE) (Barathea (IRE)) (160000)
120 B f 7/4 Kodiac—Alexander Wonder (IRE) (Redback) (57142)
121 Ch c 14/2 Harbour Watch (IRE)—Almatinka (IRE) (Indian Ridge) (30000)
122 **ALMOREB (IRE)**, b c 9/3 Raven's Pass (USA)—Macadamia (IRE) (Classic Cliche (IRE)) (180000)
123 B c 7/3 Pastoral Pursuits—Amalfi (IRE) (Acclamation) (49523)
124 B f 5/3 Requinto (IRE)—Amour Fou (IRE) (Piccolo) (30476)
125 **ANZASI (IRE)**, b c 4/2 Sir Prancealot (IRE)—Throne (Royal Applause) (85000)
126 Ch c 16/2 Tamayuz—Aphorism (Halling (USA)) (18000)
127 B c 11/4 Medicean—Apple Dumpling (Haafhd) (24000)
128 B c 20/4 Dark Angel (IRE)—Appleblossom Pearl (IRE) (Peintre Celebre (USA)) (80000)
129 B f 11/1 Lonhro (AUS)—Aquarius Star (Danehill Dancer (IRE)) (184569)
130 **AURIC GOLDFINGER (IRE)**, b c 15/3 Kyllachy—Ghenwah (FR) (Selkirk (USA)) (60000)
131 B c 19/3 Shamardal (USA)—Ballybacka Lady (IRE) (Hurricane Run (IRE)) (525000)
132 B f 8/3 Archipenko (USA)—Barnezet (GR) (Invincible Spirit (IRE))
133 **BLACK BOLT (IRE)**, br c 23/4 Cape Cross (IRE)—Safiya Song (IRE) (Intikhab (USA)) (30000)
134 Ch c 10/2 Sepoy (AUS)—Blaugrana (IRE) (Exceed And Excel (AUS)) (147655)
135 Gr c 11/4 Clodovil (IRE)—Boucheron (Galileo (IRE)) (44296)
136 B f 9/4 Canford Cliffs (IRE)—Briery (IRE) (Salse (USA)) (51428)
137 **BRISTOL MISSILE (USA)**, b br c 27/3 Kitten's Joy (USA)—Dearest Girl (IRE) (Galileo (IRE)) (107050)
138 Gr f 21/3 Dark Angel (IRE)—Bun Penny (Bertolini (USA)) (171428)
139 **BUSKIN RIVER (IRE)**, b c 13/4 Kodiac—Miss Smilla (Red Ransom (USA)) (68571)
140 B c 16/1 Canford Cliffs (IRE)—Cake (IRE) (Acclamation)
141 **CARAMURU (IRE)**, b c 9/3 Casamento (IRE)—Zaynaba (IRE) (Traditionally (USA)) (76190)
142 **CASTELLATED**, b f 1/5 Teofilo (IRE)—Portal (Hernando (FR))
143 B f 1/2 Zoffany (IRE)—Caterina di Cesi (Cape Town (IRE)) (119047)
144 B c 12/2 Helmet (AUS)—Causeway Song (USA) (Giant's Causeway (USA)) (100000)

MR RICHARD HANNON - Continued

145 B c 12/4 High Chaparral (IRE)—Ceedwell (Exceed And Excel (AUS)) (20671)
146 B f 28/4 Kodiac—Clockwise (Pivotal)
147 COMPANY, ch f 9/3 Pivotal—Invitee (Medicean)
148 CONTROL CENTRE (IRE), b c 23/3 Dragon Pulse (IRE)—Margaux Magique (IRE) (Xaar) (33333)
149 B f 5/2 Invincible Spirit (IRE)—Countess Ferrama (Authorized (IRE)) (260000)
150 B f 4/2 Acclamation—Decorative (IRE) (Danehill Dancer (IRE)) (80000)
151 Gr c 21/3 Dark Angel (IRE)—Delira (IRE) (Namid) (150000)
152 B f 18/3 Sepoy (AUS)—Desert Sunrise (Green Desert (USA)) (80000)
153 DEVIL'S BRIDGE (IRE), b c 16/2 Casamento (IRE)—Cantaloupe (Priolo (USA)) (55238)
154 B c 3/4 Wootton Bassett—Diamond Star (IRE) (Daylami (IRE)) (59062)
155 DICK TRACY (IRE), b c 2/2 Lawman (FR)—Modeeroch (IRE) (Mozart (IRE)) (84902)
156 B f 30/3 Canford Cliffs (IRE)—Divine Grace (IRE) (Definite Article) (180000)
157 B c 26/4 Choisir (AUS)—Eternity Ring (Alzao (USA))
158 B c 17/4 Kodiac—Feet of Flame (USA) (Theatrical) (75000)
159 Gr c 9/4 Zebedee—Fig Digliani (IRE) (Fasliyev (USA))
160 Ch f 8/3 Sepoy (AUS)—Fleeting Image (Sir Percy) (125000)
161 FLYING NORTH, b f 3/3 Raven's Pass (USA)—Round The Cape (Cape Cross (IRE))
162 B f 28/2 Invincible Spirit (IRE)—Forgotten Me (IRE) (Holy Roman Emperor (IRE)) (150000)
163 B c 27/2 Lawman (FR)—French Fern (IRE) (Royal Applause) (59047)
164 Gr f 19/1 Dark Angel (IRE)—Fruit O'the Forest (IRE) (Shinko Forest (IRE)) (80000)
165 B f 15/4 Dandy Man (IRE)—Gala Style (IRE) (Elnadim (USA)) (80952)
166 B f 10/2 Poet's Voice—Gee Kel (IRE) (Danehill Dancer (IRE)) (28000)
167 GIOVANNI ACUTO, gr c 6/2 Redoute's Choice (AUS)—Alla Speranza (Sir Percy) (103359)
168 HEAVENLY ANGEL, gr f 2/4 Dark Angel (IRE)—Ballyalla (Mind Games) (48000)
169 B f 17/3 Kodiac—High Dasher (IRE) (High Chaparral (IRE))
170 B f 13/3 Zebedee—High Society Girl (IRE) (Key of Luck (USA))
171 HIPPOCAMPUS (IRE), b c 27/4 Born To Sea (IRE)—Tolzey (USA) (Rahy (USA)) (66666)
172 HUSHOOD (IRE), b c 21/3 Champs Elysees—Cochin (USA) (Swain (IRE)) (160000)
173 Ch c 10/3 Dutch Art—Israar (Machiavellian (USA)) (100000)
174 JERSEY HEARTBEAT, b f 8/3 Bated Breath—Selkirk Sky (Selkirk (USA)) (40000)
175 JUAN HORSEPOWER, b c 17/3 Foxwedge (AUS)—Elysee (IRE) (Fantastic Light (USA)) (47619)
176 KITSEY (IRE), b f 28/2 High Chaparral (IRE)—Thistlestar (USA) (Lion Heart (USA)) (36190)
177 KREB'S CYCLE (IRE), ch c 12/4 Helmet (AUS)—La Noe (Nayef (USA)) (62753)
178 B f 14/2 Artie Schiller (USA)—Ladue (IRE) (Demons Begone (USA)) (50000)
179 B f 24/2 Iffraaj—Lady Pitrizza (IRE) (Night Shift (USA)) (50000)
180 LARCHMONT LAD (IRE), b c 15/3 Footstepsinthesand—Fotini (IRE) (King's Best (USA)) (81210)
181 B c 29/3 Frankel—Latin Love (IRE) (Danehill Dancer (USA)) (130000)
182 LEGENDARY LUNCH (IRE), ch c 20/3 Dragon Pulse (IRE)—Taalluf (USA) (Hansel (USA)) (74285)
183 B c 17/2 Nayef (USA)—Lemon Rock (Green Desert (USA)) (55000)
184 B f 16/3 Invincible Spirit (IRE)—Lethal Quality (USA) (Elusive Quality (USA)) (258397)
185 LEXINGTON SKY (IRE), b f 16/4 Iffraaj—Hurricane Lily (IRE) (Ali-Royal (IRE)) (55000)
186 LIMELITE (IRE), b f 23/3 Dark Angel (IRE)—Light It Up (IRE) (Elusive City (USA)) (50000)
187 B c 20/1 Requinto (IRE)—Livia's Wake (IRE) (Galileo (IRE)) (34285)
188 LUCIOLE, b f 10/2 High Chaparral (IRE)—Marmoom Flower (IRE) (Cape Cross (IRE)) (95976)
189 B c 18/3 Canford Cliffs (IRE)—Lulawin (Kyllachy) (120000)
190 MAJESTE, b c 27/1 Acclamation—Winged Valkyrie (IRE) (Hawk Wing (USA)) (47619)
191 MALCOLM THE PUG (IRE), b c 24/3 Acclamation—La Zona (IRE) (Singspiel (IRE)) (48000)
192 MAMDOOD (IRE), gr c 2/3 Clodovil (IRE)—Fact (American Post) (45000)
193 B f 2/2 Acclamation—Marvada (IRE) (Elusive City (USA)) (55238)
194 MAYAN GOLD, b f 23/3 Paco Boy (IRE)—Flash of Gold (Darshaan)
195 B c 17/2 Roderic O'Connor (IRE)—Meon Mix (Kayf Tara) (55370)
196 B c 21/3 Acclamation—Miss Hawai (FR) (Peintre Celebre (USA)) (100000)
197 MONEY IN MY POCKET (IRE), b f 4/4 Acclamation—Azabara (Pivotal) (66445)
198 MONOSHKA (IRE), b c 27/1 Kodiac—Coastal Waters (Halling (USA)) (71428)
199 B f 23/3 Nathaniel (IRE)—Mosqueras Romance (Rock of Gibraltar (IRE)) (125507)
200 MR SCARAMANGA, b c 16/3 Sir Percy—Lula (Oasis Dream) (57585)
201 MR TYRRELL (IRE), b c 19/3 Helmet (AUS)—Rocking (Oasis Dream) (62000)
202 MUMS THE WORD, b f 4/4 Mayson—Tell Mum (Marju (IRE)) (52000)
203 B f 13/4 Kyllachy—Mundus Novus (USA) (Unbridled's Song (USA))
204 MUQAATIL (USA), b br c 3/4 Lonhro (AUS)—Lightning Lydia (USA) (Broad Brush (USA)) (160000)
205 MUSCIKA, bc 13/4 Kyllachy—Miss Villefranche (Danehill Dancer (IRE))
206 MUSTARRID (IRE), br c 23/2 Elzaam (AUS)—Symbol of Peace (IRE) (Desert Sun) (103359)
207 MUTAHAADY (IRE), b c 17/2 Elzaam (AUS)—Midnight Oasis (Oasis Dream) (120000)
208 MUTAWATHEB (IRE), gr c 1/3 Dark Angel (IRE)—Queen Myrine (IRE) (Oratorio (IRE)) (180000)
209 B c 2/4 Kodiac—Novel Fun (IRE) (Noverre (USA)) (360000)

MR RICHARD HANNON - Continued

210 Gr c 29/3 Zebedee—Novelina (IRE) (Fusaichi Pegasus (USA))
211 Ch c 28/3 Bahamian Bounty—Oh Sedulous (IRE) (Lawman (FR)) (52000)
212 **OPENING TIME**, b c 19/1 Harbour Watch (IRE)—Dozy (IRE) (Exceed And Excel (AUS)) (52000)
213 **PACO PUNCH (IRE)**, b c 30/1 Paco Boy (IRE)—Trilemma (Slip Anchor) (62753)
214 Gr f 9/3 Dark Angel (IRE)—Party Whip (IRE) (Whipper (USA)) (50000)
215 B c 28/2 High Chaparral (IRE)—Paulaya (GER) (Peintre Celebre (USA)) (95976)
216 **PEAK PRINCESS (IRE)**, b f 7/2 Foxwedge (AUS)—Foot of Pride (IRE) (Footstepsinthesand) (90000)
217 Gr c 15/4 Dark Angel (IRE)—Penicuik (Hernando (FR)) (50000)
218 **PEPITA (IRE)**, ch f 4/3 Sir Prancealot (IRE)—Esterlina (IRE) (Highest Honor (FR))
219 Ch f 20/1 Nathaniel (IRE)—Petite Nymphe (Golan (IRE)) (30000)
220 Ch c 11/1 Tamayuz—Place de Moscou (IRE) (Rock of Gibraltar (IRE)) (35000)
221 **PLANT POT POWER (IRE)**, b c 23/2 Lawman (FR)—Featherweight (IRE) (Fantastic Light (USA)) (41000)
222 B f 3/2 Bated Breath—Pretty Primo (IRE) (Kyllachy) (55000)
223 **PRIMROSE PLACE**, ch f 16/4 Compton Place—Pretty Girl (IRE) (Polish Precedent (USA))
224 **PUSSY GALORE (IRE)**, b f 20/2 Harbour Watch (IRE)—Green Chorus (IRE) (Oratorio (IRE)) (43809)
225 **RESTORE (IRE)**, b c 22/4 Dark Angel (IRE)—Attracted To You (IRE) (Hurricane Run (IRE)) (55000)
226 B f 6/3 Bated Breath—Salmon Rose (IRE) (Iffraaj) (64761)
227 **SAWLAAT (IRE)**, gr c 16/4 Clodovil (IRE)—Jaywick (UAE) (Jade Robbery (USA)) (176190)
228 **SECOND PAGE**, b c 12/3 Harbour Watch (IRE)—Almunia (IRE) (Mujadil (USA)) (60000)
229 **SEE THE SEA (IRE)**, b f 15/4 Born To Sea (IRE)—Shahmina (IRE) (Danehill (USA)) (59047)
230 **SHERBERT**, b f 25/3 Power—Original (Caerleon (USA)) (70136)
231 B f 24/2 Requinto (IRE)—Shoooz (IRE) (Soviet Star (USA))
232 B f 2/2 Sir Prancealot (IRE)—Singingintherain (IRE) (Kyllachy) (22857)
233 B c 24/3 Dark Angel (IRE)—Skehana (IRE) (Mukaddamah (USA)) (130000)
234 B f 28/1 Tamayuz—Society Gal (IRE) (Galileo (IRE)) (30476)
235 B c 11/2 Roderic O'Connor (IRE)—Specific (IRE) (Dubawi (IRE))
236 B c 13/4 Elusive Pimpernel (USA)—Spiritville (IRE) (Invincible Spirit (IRE)) (88593)
237 **SPONGIE CAKE (IRE)**, b f 22/4 Lawman (FR)—Belgique (IRE) (Compton Place) (55370)
238 B c 13/2 Fastnet Rock (AUS)—Starstone (Diktat) (155000)
239 **STERLING SILVA (IRE)**, ch c 25/3 Sakhee's Secret—Silicon Star (FR) (Starborough)) (51679)
240 B f 14/3 Lilbourne Lad (IRE)—Stoney Cove (IRE) (Needwood Blade) (14765)
241 B c 8/3 Azamour (IRE)—Strela (GER) (Lomitas) (29531)
242 **SUFFRAGETTE CITY (IRE)**, b f 14/3 Dragon Pulse (IRE)—Queen of Stars (USA) (Green Desert (USA)) (76190)
243 **SWELL HILL**, b f 12/4 Foxwedge (AUS)—Sea Fret (Nayef (USA))
244 **TADWEEN (IRE)**, b c 13/2 Tagula (IRE)—Stained Glass (Dansili) (85714)
245 **TAFAAKHOR (IRE)**, gr c 29/4 Dark Angel (IRE)—Tellelle (IRE) (Trans Island) (190000)
246 B c 17/2 Bahamian Bounty—Tahtheeb (IRE) (Muhtarram (USA)) (119047)
247 **TAI HANG DRAGON (IRE)**, b f 22/1 Tamayuz—Give A Whistle (IRE) (Mujadil (USA)) (147655)
248 B c 10/3 Rock of Gibraltar (IRE)—Tedarshana (Darshaan) (114433)
249 **TESKO FELLA (IRE)**, b c 28/2 Myboycharlie (IRE)—Foundation Filly (Lando (GER)) (73827)
250 **TIGGALISCIOUS (IRE)**, b f 10/2 Acclamation—Mea Parvitas (Oasis Dream) (47619)
251 B f 13/3 Motivator—Turning Leaf (IRE) (Last Tycoon) (300000)
252 **WARRIOR'S SPIRIT (IRE)**, b c 16/2 Requinto (IRE)—Sandbox Two (IRE) (Foxhound (USA)) (100000)
253 **WEFAIT (IRE)**, b c 9/5 Harbour Watch (IRE)—Night Club (Mozart (IRE)) (30476)
254 **WHIP NAE NAE (IRE)**, ch c 2/3 Dragon Pulse (IRE)—Love In May (IRE) (City On A Hill (USA)) (60000)
255 **WHITE MISCHIEF (IRE)**, gr f 5/3 Dark Angel (IRE)—Galileo's Star (IRE) (Galileo (IRE)) (147655)
256 **WITH ONE ACCORD**, b f 15/3 Acclamation—Raymi Coya (CAN) (Van Nistelrooy (USA))
257 B c 17/2 Fame And Glory—Wood Sprite (Mister Baileys) (65000)
258 Br f 17/1 Sepoy (AUS)—Wosaita (Generous (IRE)) (250000)
259 **YOUDIRTYRAT (IRE)**, gr c 29/1 Excelebration (IRE)—Alina (IRE) (Galileo (IRE)) (66666)
260 **ZEBBY SIZZ (IRE)**, gr c 14/1 Zebedee—Derval (IRE) (One Cool Cat (USA)) (47619)

Assistant Trainer: Tom Ward

Jockey (flat): Pat Dobbs, Cam Hardie, Kieran O'Neill, Sean Levey. **Apprentice:** Tom Marquand, Gary Mahon, Hollie Doyle, Tina Smith, Mitch Godwin, Megan Nicholls.

---

277 MR GEOFFREY HARKER, Thirsk
Postal: **Stockhill Green, York Rd, Thirkleby, Thirsk, North Yorkshire, YO7 3AS**
Contacts: **PHONE (01845) 501117 FAX (01845) 501614 MOBILE (07803) 116412/(07930) 125544**
E-MAIL gandjhome@aol.com WEBSITE www.geoffharkerracing.com

1 **ARISTOCRATIC DUTY**, 5, b m Zamindar (USA)—Duty Paid (IRE) **P. I. Harker**
2 **BLING KING**, 7, b g Haafhd—Bling Bling (IRE) **P. I. Harker**

MR GEOFFREY HARKER - Continued

3 **CABAL**, 9, br m Kyllachy—Secret Flame **Phil Harker & Dave Buist**
4 **CHARM PARK**, 6, b g Desideratum—Queen's Lodge (IRE) **Mr W Bavill & Mr D. Bavill**
5 **FAIR FOR ALL**, 5, b g Fair Mix (IRE)—Falcons Theatre (IRE) **Mr B. Turner**
6 **JUDICIOUS**, 9, ch g Pivotal—Virtuous **Mr M. Reay**
7 **MOCCASIN (FR)**, 7, b g Green Tune (USA)—Museum Piece **The Crazy Gang**
8 **MUMFORD**, 4, b g Stimulation (IRE)—Noble Nova **P. I. Harker**
9 **SHAMAHEART (IRE)**, 6, b g Shamardal (USA)—Encouragement **A. S. Ward**

TWO-YEAR-OLDS

10 B f 8/5 Doncaster Rover (USA)—Ykikamoocow (Cape Town (IRE))

Other Owners: Mr D. Bavill, Mr Wayne Bavill, Mr Dave Buist, Mr Neil Burns, Mr John Clydesdale, Mr Mark Fowler, Mr P. I. Harker, Mr Steven Taylor.

Assistant Trainer: Jenny Harker

Jockey (NH): W. T. Kennedy.

---

278 **MR RICHARD HARPER, Kings Sutton**
Postal: **Home Farm, Kings Sutton, Banbury, Oxfordshire, OX17 3RS**
Contacts: **PHONE (01295) 810997 FAX (01295) 812787 MOBILE (07970) 223481**
E-MAIL rharper@freeuk.com

1 **JUST SKITTLES**, 8, b g Storming Home—Miss Roberto (IRE) **R. C. Harper**
2 **PANTOLONI**, 5, b g Dansili—Short Skirt **R. C. Harper**
3 **TOP BENEFIT (IRE)**, 14, gr g Beneficial—Cottage Lass (IRE) **R. C. Harper**

Assistant Trainer: C. Harper

---

279 **MRS JESSICA HARRINGTON, Kildare**
Postal: **Commonstown Stud, Moone, Co. Kildare, Ireland**
Contacts: **PHONE (00353) 5986 24153 FAX (00353) 5986 24292 MOBILE (00353) 8725 66129**
E-MAIL jessica@jessicaharringtonracing.com WEBSITE www.jessicaharringtonracing.com

1 **ALE AMBROSIO (IRE)**, 4, br f Big Bad Bob (IRE)—Memorys of Madness (IRE) **Robcour**
2 **ASHES OF LOVE (IRE)**, 6, b m Fruits of Love (USA)—Brave Thistle (IRE) **Mr Joe Doyle**
3 **AZURE SKY (IRE)**, 4, b g Azamour (IRE)—Venturi **Charlotte Musgrave & Mr Trevor Stewart**
4 **BARNACLE BILL (IRE)**, 4, gr g Big Bad Bob (IRE)—Katch Me Katie **Millhouse LLC**
5 **BESTOW (IRE)**, 5, b m Presenting—Seymourswift **Mr George Hartigan**
6 **BILLY'S HOPE (IRE)**, 5, b m King's Theatre (IRE)—Lady Bellingham (IRE) **The Flyers Syndicate**
7 **BOCCA BACIATA (IRE)**, 4, b br f Big Bad Bob (IRE)—Sovana (FR) **Flaxman Stables Ireland Ltd**
8 **BOLD BID (IRE)**, 4, b g Big Bad Bob (IRE)—Magpie (USA) **Mr Geoffrey Ruddock**
9 **BOOM BOX (IRE)**, 4, b g Big Bad Bob (IRE)—Dona Alba (IRE) **A Blessing In Disguise Partnership**
10 **BRIGHT TOMORROW (IRE)**, 5, b g Robin des Pres (FR)—Gweedara (IRE) **Mr Michael Buckley**
11 **CANDLESTICK (IRE)**, 5, b g Scorpion (IRE)—Pescetto Lady (IRE) **Robcour**
12 **CLONKEEN LAD**, 4, b g Rail Link—Moon Search **Mr David Bobbett**
13 **CLOSE SHAVE**, 5, b g Presenting—Knock Down (IRE) **Mr J. P. McManus**
14 **DON'T TOUCH IT (IRE)**, 6, b g Scorpion (IRE)—Shandora (IRE) **Mr J. P. McManus**
15 **FLAVIANA (IRE)**, 6, b m Flemensfirth (USA)—Saddlers Green (IRE) **Mr Roberto Rea**
16 4, B c Oscar (IRE)—Folidalways (FR) **Mrs Jessica Harrington**
17 **FORGE MEADOW (IRE)**, 4, b f Beneficial—Ballys Baby (IRE) **Mr Joe Doyle**
18 **HIGH STRATOS**, 7, b g Montjeu (IRE)—Hyabella **Westerwood Global Ltd**
19 **HOLD YOUR NERVE (IRE)**, 5, b g Robin des Champs (FR)—Katie's Cracker **Mrs Jessica Harrington**
20 **JACK BLUE (IRE)**, 4, b g Duke of Marmalade (IRE)—Key Secure **Miss Kate Harrington**
21 **JACK NAYLOR**, 4, b f Champs Elysees—Fashionable **Mr Gerry Byrne**
22 **JELAN (IRE)**, 4, b f Milan—La Noire (IRE) **Mr Gerard McGrath**
23 **JETT (IRE)**, 5, b g Flemensfirth (USA)—La Noire (IRE) **Mr Gerard McGrath**
24 **KABJOY (IRE)**, 5, b m Intikhab (USA)—Lunar Love (IRE) **Favourites Racing Ltd**
25 **KALINITE (IRE)**, 4, b br g Kalanisi (IRE)—Gerarda (IRE) **Mr Geoffrey Ruddock**
26 **KATY P**, 4, b f Ask—Kingara **Mr P. Atkinson**
27 **KEPPOLS QUEEN (IRE)**, 8, br m Indian River (FR)—Keppols Princess (IRE) **Mrs Mona O'Loughlin**
28 **LAKE CHAMPLAIN (IRE)**, 4, b g Manduro (GER)—Fantasy Girl (IRE) **A Blessing In Disguise Partnership**
29 4, B g Milan—Last of Many (IRE) **Mr Howard Spooner & Mr Ian Weaver**

MRS JESSICA HARRINGTON - Continued

30 **LOUPGAROU (FR)**, 4, gr g Martaline—Jasminday Doree (FR) **Diarmuid Horgan**
31 **MACNICHOLSON (IRE)**, 7, b g Definite Article—Heroic Performer (IRE) **Mr Joe O'Flaherty**
32 **MARSHALL JENNINGS (IRE)**, 4, b g Lawman (FR)—Zuniga's Date (USA) **Carmichael Jennings**
33 4, B g Oscar (IRE)—Meelick Flyer (IRE) **Howard Spooner, Conor Carney & Brian Kearney**
34 **MODEM**, 6, b g Motivator—Alashaan **Mr Turlough Blessing**
35 **MOONE DANCER (IRE)**, 4, b f Rip Van Winkle (IRE)—Celeste (FR) **Mrs Jessica Harrington**
36 **NEVERUSHACON (IRE)**, 5, b g Echo of Light—Lily Beth (IRE) **David Reid Scott**
37 **NEW TO THIS TOWN (IRE)**, 5, b g Milan—
Jade River (FR) **Lynch Bages, Mr Justin Carthy, Orpendale & Others**
38 **NEWBERRY NEW (IRE)**, 4, br g Kodiac—Sunblush (UAE) **Rathmoyle Exports**
39 **OSCAR SAM (IRE)**, 7, b g Oscar (IRE)—Good Thyne Jenny (IRE) **Mr Billy Cooper**
40 **OUR DUKE (IRE)**, 6, b g Oscar (IRE)—Good Thyne Jenny (IRE) **Mr Billy Cooper**
41 **OUT OF CONTEXT (IRE)**, 4, b f Intikhab (USA)—Context **Mr Dermot Cantillon & Mrs P. K. Cooper**
42 **PLAYBOOK (IRE)**, 5, b g Milan—Majorite Bleue (FR) **Robcour**
43 4, B f Beneficial—Prairie Bell (IRE) **The Flyers Syndicate**
44 **PRINCESS ALOOF (IRE)**, 5, b m Big Bad Bob (IRE)—Little Miss Diva (IRE) **Commonstown Racing Stables**
45 **PRIVATE PARTY (IRE)**, 4, b g Big Bad Bob (IRE)—Meduse Bleu **Commonstown Racing Stables**
46 **RAISE A TAIL (IRE)**, 6, ch g Definite Article—
Fillmein (IRE) **Mr Ian Wheeler, Mr Howard Spooner & Mr Matt Wheeler**
47 **ROCK ON THE MOOR (IRE)**, 8, b m Flemensfirth—Home At Last (IRE) **Exors of the Late Mr S. Hemstock**
48 **ROCK THE WORLD (IRE)**, 8, b g Orpen (USA)—Sue N Win (IRE) **Mr Michael Buckley & Mr Justin Carthy**
49 **SANDYMOUNT DUKE (IRE)**, 7, b g Hernando (FR)—Joleah (IRE) **Mr Ron Wood**
50 **ST BRELADES BAY (IRE)**, 4, b g Camacho—Tides **Carmichael Jennings**
51 **SUNNI MAY (IRE)**, 5, b g Presenting—Northwood May **Favourites Racing Ltd**
52 **TEN THEATRE (IRE)**, 4, b f King's Theatre (IRE)—Carrigmorna Flyer (IRE) **Diarmuid Horgan**
53 **THERE YOU GO (IRE)**, 5, b g Milan—Cuiloge Lady (IRE) **Mr J. P. McManus**
54 **THIRSTY WORK (IRE)**, 5, b g Robin des Champs (FR)—Koko Rose (IRE) **Mr J. P. McManus**
55 **TTEBBOB (IRE)**, 7, b g Milan—Our Dream (IRE) **Mr David Bobbett**
56 **TWINKLETOES (IRE)**, 5, gr m Daylami (USA)—Cool N Calm **Miss Kate Harrington**
57 **UNYIELDING**, 4, b c Oasis Dream—Victoria Cross (IRE) **Millhouse LLC**
58 **WALK TO FREEDOM (IRE)**, 6, br g Arcadio (GER)—Carryonharriet (IRE) **Whole Of The Moone Syndicate**
59 **WEATHER WATCH (IRE)**, 6, b g Hurricane Run (IRE)—Caravan of Dreams (IRE) **Mrs Jessica Harrington**
60 4, Br g f Kalanisi (IRE)—West Hill Rose (IRE) **Lakeside**
61 **WOODLAND OPERA (IRE)**, 6, br g Robin des Champs (FR)—
Opera Hat (IRE) **Mrs Diana Cooper, Mrs Valerie Cooper & Mrs Carolyn Waters**
62 **YOUNG BIDDER (IRE)**, 4, ch g Presenting—Zarinava (IRE) **Mr David Bobbett**

THREE-YEAR-OLDS

63 **BOBABOUT (IRE)**, b g Big Bad Bob (IRE)—Chaperoned (IRE) **Howard Spooner**
64 **BRAVER THE BULL (IRE)**, b c Big Bad Bob (IRE)—Danzelline **Anamoine Ltd**
65 **CAMILE (IRE)**, b f Captain Rio—Heroic Performer (IRE) **GBLOGBD Ltd**
66 B f Cockney Rebel (IRE)—Compose **Mr P. Atkinson**
67 **EAST COKER (IRE)**, b g Pour Moi (IRE)—Bounce (FR) **Favourites Racing Ltd**
68 **EAST OF PERSIA (IRE)**, b c Elusive Pimpernel (USA)—Shinko Dancer (IRE) **Anamoine Ltd**
69 **EASY PASS (IRE)**, br g Elusive Pimpernel (USA)—Shady Nook (IRE) **Anamoine Ltd**
70 **ENDLESS RIVER**, b f Tobougg (IRE)—Blaeberry **Lady Jennie Bland**
71 **ENGLISH PALE (IRE)**, b g Elusive Pimpernel (USA)—Terme Cay (USA) **Anamoine Ltd**
72 **ESCAPE PARADISE (IRE)**, b f Elusive Pimpernel (USA)—Daniysha (IRE) **Anamoine Ltd**
73 **FINAL FRONTIER (IRE)**, b c Dream Ahead (USA)—Polly Perkins (IRE) **Mrs P.K.Cooper & Vimal Khosla**
74 **FRANK WILDE (IRE)**, b g Danehill Dancer (IRE)—
Kiss My Tiara (IRE) **Mrs Jessica Harrington & Barronstown Stud**
75 **GLENMAYNE (IRE)**, ch f Duke of Marmalade (IRE)—Green Castle (IRE) **Stonethorn Stud Farm Ltd**
76 **HAMLEY (FR)**, b f Fastnet Rock (AUS)—Mary Arnold (IRE) **Niarchos Family**
77 **HINT OF FROST (IRE)**, ch g Excellent Art—Glamorous (GER) **Mrs Jessica Harrington**
78 **MADRUGADA (IRE)**, b f Canford Cliffs (IRE)—Renashaan (IRE) **Sir Peter Vela**
79 **MISS MONTANA (IRE)**, b f High Chaparral (IRE)—Miletrian (IRE) **Mr Richard Kelvin Hughes & Triermore Stud**
80 **MS BRINKLEYS (IRE)**, b f Arcano (IRE)—Follow My Lead **Mr Justin Carthy, Mr R. Galway & Others**
81 **MULLIGATAWNY (IRE)**, b c Lope de Vega (IRE)—Wild Whim (IRE) **Millhouse LLC**
82 **NEARLY FAMOUS (IRE)**, b f Rip Van Winkle (IRE)—Ermena **Mrs Jessica Harrington**
83 **PALAVICINI RUN (IRE)**, ch f Palavicini (USA)—Dawn's Sharp Shot (IRE) **Anamoine Ltd**
84 **ROCKNROLLBABY (IRE)**, b f Fastnet Rock (AUS)—
Jazz Baby (IRE) **Mrs Gina Galvin, Mrs Yvonne Nicoll, David Reid Scott & Others**
85 **STRIKING GOLD**, b c Stimulation (IRE)—Dream Quest **Mrs Harriet Jellett & Miss Philippa Mains**

MRS JESSICA HARRINGTON - Continued

TWO-YEAR-OLDS

86 B c 6/5 Fastnet Rock (AUS)—Arosa (IRE) (Sadler's Wells (USA)) **Mrs Jessica Harrington**
87 **AWARENESS (USA),** b f 23/4 Distorted Humor (USA)—
Visions of Clarity (IRE) (Sadler's Wells (USA)) **Flaxman Stables Ireland Ltd**
88 Ch c 30/4 Artie Schiller (USA)—Bragadocious (USA) (Salem Drive (USA)) (13431) **McElroy Racing Syndicate**
89 B c 16/3 Lope de Vega (IRE)—Caravan of Dreams (IRE) (Anabaa (USA)) (110000) **Millhouse LLC**
90 Ch f 29/3 Dragon Pulse (IRE)—Dancing Duchess (IRE) (Danehill Dancer (IRE)) (16242) **Mrs Jessica Harrington**
91 B f 3/2 Rip Van Winkle (IRE)—Dansable (IRE) (Dansili) **Mrs Jessica Harrington**
92 Ch c 26/4 Mastercraftsman (IRE)—Dromod Mour (IRE) (Azamour (IRE)) (31746) **Vimal Khosla**
93 B f 11/5 Mount Nelson—Eccentricity (USA) (Kingmambo (USA)) (25839)
Mr Russell Jones, Mrs Patrick Cooper, Ms Suzi Prichard Jones & others
94 B f 20/2 Arcano (IRE)—Heart's Desire (IRE) (Royal Applause) (28054) **Mr John Hussey**
95 **LITTLE PRINCESS (GER),** b f 29/4 Kamsin (GER)—Little Wonder (GER) (Desert Prince (IRE)) **Mr Max Plapp**
96 B f 24/1 Acclamation—Manieree (IRE) (Medicean) (200000) **Stonethorn Stud Farm Ltd**
97 B f 30/3 Big Bad Bob (IRE)—Meduse Bleu (Medicean) **Mrs Jessica Harrington**
98 Gr f 30/1 Clodovil (IRE)—
Namibia (GER) (Galileo (IRE)) (47988) **Mrs Patrick Cooper, Mr Russell Jones & Ms Suzi Prichard-Jones**
99 **ONE LINER,** b c 22/4 Delegator—Quip (Green Desert (USA)) (33960) **Carmichael Jennings**
100 Gr f 15/3 Fast Company (IRE)—
Platinum Darling (IRE) (Iffraaj) (19195) **Mrs Patrick Cooper, Mr Russell Jones & Ms Suzi Prichard-Jones**
101 B f 29/4 Lope de Vega (IRE)—Queen Bodicea (IRE) (Revoque (IRE)) (20000)
Mrs Jessica Harrington, Hayley O'Connor & Mr Brian Acheson
102 Br f 27/3 Sir Percy—Rubileo (Galileo (IRE)) **Richie Galway**
103 B f 24/4 Excelebration (IRE)—Scotch Bonnet (IRE) (Montjeu (IRE)) (18000)
Richie Galway, Margaret Davin, Jason Morris, Dick O'Sullivan
104 B f 9/1 Nayef (USA)—Set Dreams (FR) (Galileo (IRE)) **Niarchos Family**
105 Gr c 14/4 Dark Angel (IRE)—Trinity Scholar (IRE) (Invincible Spirit (IRE)) (120000) **Millhouse LLC**

Assistant Trainer: Mrs Emma Galway

Jockey (flat): Fran Berry, Shane Foley. **Jockey (NH):** Mark Bolger, Robert Power. **Conditional:** Paddy Kennedy.
Amateur: Miss Kate Harrington, Mr Mark Fahey.

---

280 | **MISS GRACE HARRIS, Shirenewton**
Postal: **White House, Shirenewton, Chepstow, Gwent, NP16 6AQ**

1 **ASPENS SHADOW,** 4, ch f Captain Gerrard (IRE)—Aspen Ridge (IRE) **Wood Bank Racing**
2 **CAI SHEN (IRE),** 8, ch g Iffraaj—Collada (IRE) **Mr R. C. Williams**
3 **CHIEF BRODY,** 5, b g Phoenix Reach (IRE)—Cherry Plum **Jaws I Syndicate**
4 **DIMINUTIVE (IRE),** 4, ch f Fast Company (IRE)—Take It Easee (IRE) **Ms M. Harris**
5 **DIRTY DEXTER,** 5, b g Beat All (USA)—Redlands Charm **Wood Bank Racing**
6 **FAINT HOPE,** 4, ch g Midnight Legend—Rhinestone Ruby
7 **FIRGROVE BRIDGE (IRE),** 4, ch g Dandy Man (IRE)—Over Rating **Mr J. Rocke**
8 **GRAMS AND OUNCES,** 9, b g Royal Applause—Ashdown Princess (IRE) **Mr R. C. Williams**
9 **LA CAPE CONCORDE,** 4, b g Cape Cross (IRE)—La Concorde (FR) **Grace Harris Racing**
10 **LIVING LEADER,** 7, b g Oasis Dream—Royal Jade **Michelle Harris & Mrs Vicki Davies**
11 **ORBIT THE MOON (IRE),** 8, b g Oratorio (IRE)—Catch The Moon (IRE) **Mr G. L. Williams**
12 **ORTHODOX LAD,** 8, ch g Monsieur Bond (IRE)—Ashantiana **Ms M. Harris**
13 **PADDY THE OSCAR (IRE),** 13, b g Oscar (IRE)—Parsonage **Michelle Harris & Deberah Lawton**
14 **TEIDE PEAK (IRE),** 7, b g Cape Cross (IRE)—Teide Lady **Grace Harris Racing**

THREE-YEAR-OLDS

15 **TALLY'S SONG,** b f Piccolo—Talamahana **Paul & Ann de Weck**

Other Owners: Mrs V. M. Davies, Mrs A. De Weck, Miss G. Harris, Mrs D. L. S. Lawton, Mr T. J. Maund-Powell, Mrs J. Maund-Powell, R. B. Phillips, Miss L. J. Sandford, P. L. de Weck.

281 MR RONALD HARRIS, Chepstow

Postal: **Ridge House Stables, Earlswood, Chepstow, Monmouthshire, NP16 6AN**
Contacts: **PHONE (01291) 641689 FAX (01291) 641258 MOBILE (07831) 770899**
E-MAIL ridgehousestables.ltd@btinternet.com WEBSITE www.ronharrisracing.co.uk

1 **AGERZAM**, 6, b g Holy Roman Emperor (IRE)—Epiphany **Mrs R. M. Serrell**
2 **ARIZONA SNOW**, 4, b g Phoenix Reach (IRE)—Calgary **Ridge House Stables Ltd**
3 **BALLIOL**, 4, b g Exceed And Excel (AUS)—Cinerama (IRE) **Mr Robert & Mrs Nina Bailey**
4 **CASTANEA**, 4, ch g Pivotal—Invitee **Ridge House Stables Ltd**
5 **CLASSIC PURSUIT**, 5, b h Pastoral Pursuits—Snake's Head **Ridge House Stables Ltd**
6 **CORPORAL MADDOX**, 9, b g Royal Applause—Noble View (USA) **S & A Mares & Ridge House Stables Ltd**
7 **DANDYS PERIER (IRE)**, 5, br g Dandy Man (IRE)—Casual Remark (IRE) **Ridge House Stables Ltd**
8 **DIAMOND VINE (IRE)**, 8, b g Diamond Green (FR)—Glasnas Giant **Ridge House Stables Ltd**
9 **FANTASY JUSTIFIER (IRE)**, 5, b g Arakan (USA)—Grandel **Farley, Fantasy Fellowship B & RHS**
10 **GOWER PRINCESS**, 5, ch m Footstepsinthesand—Hollow Quaill (IRE) **Ridge House Stables Ltd**
11 **IMAGERY (IRE)**, 4, ch g Pivotal—Fantasize **Ridge House Stables Ltd**
12 **JUDGE 'N JURY**, 12, ch g Pivotal—Cyclone Connie **Ridge House Stables Ltd**
13 **LIGHT FROM MARS**, 11, gr g Fantastic Light (USA)—Hylandra (USA) **Mrs N. J. Macauley**
14 **MAJESTIC HERO (IRE)**, 4, b g Majestic Missile (IRE)—Xena (IRE) **Mrs Jackie Jarrett & Ridge House Stables**
15 **NOCTURN**, 7, b g Oasis Dream—Pizzicato **Mrs R. M. Serrell**
16 **NOVERRE TO GO (IRE)**, 10, ch g Noverre (USA)—Ukraine Venture **Robert & Nina Bailey**
17 **PEACE SEEKER**, 8, b g Oasis Dream—Mina **Ridge House Stables Ltd**
18 **PENSAX LAD (IRE)**, 5, gr g Verglas (IRE)—Betelgeuse **S. & A. Mares**
19 **RAIN WIND AND FIRE (USA)**, 4, ch c Eskendereya (USA)—Call Mariah (USA) **Ridge House Stables Ltd**
20 **SECRET WITNESS**, 10, ch g Pivotal—It's A Secret **Ridge House Stables Ltd**
21 **TOP COP**, 7, b g Acclamation—Speed Cop **Ridge House Stables Ltd**
22 **TRIGGER PARK (IRE)**, 5, ch g Tagula (IRE)—Raazi **Mr John & Margaret Hatherell & RHS Ltd**
23 **UNION ROSE**, 4, b c Stimulation (IRE)—Dot Hill **Mr D. A. Evans**
24 **VINCENTTI (IRE)**, 6, b g Invincible Spirit (IRE)—Bint Al Balad (IRE) **Robert & Nina Bailey**
25 **YEATS MAGIC (IRE)**, 4, b c Yeats (IRE)—Orinoco (IRE) **Robert & Nina Bailey**

THREE-YEAR-OLDS

26 **CANFORD STAR (IRE)**, b f Canford Cliffs (IRE)—Alexander Alliance (IRE) **S. & A. Mares**
27 **JUST GLAMOROUS (IRE)**, ch c Arcano (IRE)—Glamorous Air (IRE) **Robert & Nina Bailey**
28 **NORTHERN BEAU (IRE)**, b f Canford Cliffs (IRE)—View (IRE) **Northern Marking Ltd**
29 **POWERFUL DREAM (IRE)**, b f Frozen Power (IRE)—Noble View (USA) **Ridge House Stables Ltd**
30 **TOPSOIL**, b c Kheleyf (USA)—Edge of Gold **Robert & Nina Bailey**
31 **UNDER THE COVERS**, b f Stimulation (IRE)—Sakha **Ridge House Stables Ltd**
32 **VALIANT FAITH**, b f Aussie Rules—Special Destiny **Mr D. M. Joseph**

TWO-YEAR-OLDS

33 B c 27/2 Stimulation (IRE)—Baldemosa (FR) (Lead On Time (USA)) (2571) **Ridge House Stables Ltd**
34 **CANIZAY (IRE)**, ch c 8/3 Tagula (IRE)—Baltic Dip (IRE) (Benny The Dip (USA)) (16000) **Northern Marking Ltd**
35 B c 17/3 Stimulation (IRE)—Fiancee (IRE) (Pivotal) (1904) **Ridge House Stables Ltd**
36 Ch c 19/2 Stimulation (IRE)—Immortelle (Arazi (USA)) (3428) **Ridge House Stables Ltd**
37 B c 2/2 Aqlaam—Violette (Observatory (USA)) (5047) **Ridge House Stables Ltd**

Other Owners: Mr Robert Bailey, Mrs Nina Bailey, Mr P Charter, Mr I. Farley, Mr R. Fox, Mrs Margaret Hatherell, Mr John Hatherell, Mrs Jackie Jarrett, Mr S. Mares, Mrs A. Mares, Monmouthshire Racing Club, Ridge House Stables Ltd, South Wales Argus & Chepstow Racing Club, Paul & Anne de Weck.

Jockey (flat): Luke Morris, William Twiston-Davies. **Apprentice:** George Downing.

282 MR SHAUN HARRIS, Worksop

Postal: **Pinewood Stables, Carburton, Worksop, Nottinghamshire, S80 3BT**
Contacts: **PHONE (01909) 470936 FAX (01909) 470936 MOBILE (07768) 950460**
E-MAIL shaunharris.racing@hotmail.co.uk WEBSITE www.shaunharrisracing.co.uk

1 **AZA RUN (IRE)**, 6, b g Hurricane Run (IRE)—Aza Wish (IRE) **Miss G. H. Ward**
2 **BETTY BOO (IRE)**, 6, ch m Thousand Words—Poker Dice **Mr A. K. Elton**
3 **CASSANDANE (IRE)**, 4, br f Jeremy (USA)—Princess Atoosa (USA) **Nottinghamshire Racing**
4 **CULLODEN**, 4, b c Kyllachy—Mamounia (IRE) **Burflex (Scaffolding) Ltd**
5 **ERSHAAD (IRE)**, 4, b g Acclamation—Emerald Peace (IRE) **Vision Bloodstock**
6 **FIRST SUMMER**, 4, b g Cockney Rebel (IRE)—Silken Dalliance **Vision Bloodstock**

MR SHAUN HARRIS - Continued

7 **FUJIN,** 5, b g Oasis Dream—Phantom Wind (USA) **Mrs S. L. Robinson**
8 **GAME MASCOT,** 6, ch g Kheleyf (USA)—Tolzey (USA) **Mr W. Hobson**
9 **HEAR THE CHIMES,** 7, b g Midnight Legend—Severn Air **Miss G. H. Ward**
10 **HOOKS LANE,** 4, ch g Bertolini (USA)—Zaville **J. Morris**
11 **MAJOR MUSCARI (IRE),** 8, ch g Exceed And Excel (AUS)—Muscari **J. Morris**
12 **MUSIC HALL (FR),** 6, gr g Stormy River (FR)—Aaliyah (GER) **Vision Bloodstock**
13 **NOTTS SO BLUE,** 5, b m Pastoral Pursuits—Blue Nile (IRE) **www.nottinghamshireracing.co.uk (2)**
14 **ORDER OF SERVICE,** 6, ch g Medicean—Choir Gallery **Burflex (Scaffolding) Ltd**
15 **RAZZLE DAZZLE 'EM,** 7, b g Phoenix Reach (IRE)—Rasmani **Shaun Harris Racing Club**
16 **ROCKWEILLER,** 9, b g Rock of Gibraltar (IRE)—Ballerina Suprema (IRE) **S. A. Harris**
17 **ROSIE CROWE (IRE),** 4, b f Approve (IRE)—Tolzey (USA) **R. L. Crowe**
18 **ROY'S LEGACY,** 7, b h Phoenix Reach (IRE)—Chocolada **S Mohammed, S Rowley & S Harris**
19 **SECRET MILLIONAIRE (IRE),** 9, b g Kyllachy—Mithl Al Hawa **Mr W. Hobson**
20 **SO STROPPY POPPY,** 4, ch f Phoenix Reach (IRE)—Toy Girl (IRE) **Miss G. H. Ward**
21 **THAT BE GRAND,** 5, b m Firebreak—Manila Selection (USA) **C A Harris & Peter Dawson**
22 **THOU SWELL (IRE),** 4, b g Tiznow (USA)—Kamarinskaya (USA) **All Weather Bloodstock**
23 **VODKA TIME (IRE),** 5, b g Indian Haven—Cappuccino (IRE) **Shaun Harris Racing Club**
24 **WHATSUPJACK (IRE),** 9, b g Catcher In The Rye (IRE)—
Riverstown Girl (IRE) **Paula Ward & Shaun Harris Racing**

THREE-YEAR-OLDS

25 Ch f Compton Place—Here To Me **Miss G. H. Ward**
26 **KYLLA,** b f Kyllachy—Mamounia (IRE) **Burton Agnes Bloodstock**
27 **ROB'S LEGACY,** ch g Phoenix Reach (IRE)—Clumber Pursuits **www.nottinghamshireracing.co.uk (2)**

TWO-YEAR-OLDS

28 B f 3/3 Elzaam (AUS)—Kodiac Island (Kodiac) (13000) **Nick Blencowe, John Guest, David Botterill**
29 B f 30/4 Elzaam (AUS)—Princess Nicole (IRE) (Alhaarth (IRE)) (1476) **Mr A. Fenn**
30 B f 27/1 Frozen Power (IRE)—Sophie'jo (Agnes World (USA)) (4761)
31 B c 14/4 Sir Prancealot (IRE)—Vampire Queen (IRE) (General Monash (USA)) (14765)
32 B f 23/4 Trans Island—Vanilla Delight (IRE) (Orpen (USA)) (2285) **Mr C. Harris**

Other Owners: Mr N. J. Blencowe, D. R. Botterill, Mrs M. C. Coltman, The Hon Mrs E. S. Cunliffe-Lister, P. G. Dawson, Mr J. J. Guest, Mr R. Hawke, Mr S. Mohammed, Mr S. Rowley, Miss Paula Ward.

283	**MISS LISA HARRISON, Wigton** Postal: **Cobble Hall, Aldoth, Nr Silloth, Cumbria, CA7 4NE** Contacts: **PHONE (01697) 361753 FAX (01697) 342250 MOBILE (07725) 535554** E-MAIL lisa@daharrison.co.uk

1 **GREEN ZONE (IRE),** 5, b g Bushranger (IRE)—Incense **Exors of the Late Mr David A. Harrison**
2 **INDEPUB,** 9, b g Indesatchel (IRE)—Champenoise **Abbadis Racing Club**
3 **JOHNNY GO,** 6, b g Bollin Eric—Waverbeck (IRE) **Mr J. B. Harrison**
4 **KASHSTAREE,** 5, b m Sakhee (USA)—Celestial Welcome **Abbadis Racing Club & Partner**
5 **LADY VIVONA,** 8, gr m Overbury (IRE)—Ladylliat (FR) **Mrs F. H. Crone**
6 **MURTYS DELIGHT (IRE),** 9, b g Bach (IRE)—Valley Supreme (IRE) **Exors of the Late Mr David A. Harrison**
7 **MUWALLA,** 9, b g Bahri (USA)—Easy Sunshine (IRE) **Bell Bridge Racing**
8 **PRESENTED (IRE),** 9, ch g Presenting—Rustic Court (IRE) **Abbadis Racing Club & Partner**
9 **SOLWAY BAY,** 14, b g Cloudings (IRE)—No Problem Jac **Exors of the Late Mr David A. Harrison**
10 **SOLWAY BERRY,** 5, b m Overbury (IRE)—Solway Rose **Exors of the Late Mr David A. Harrison**
11 **SOLWAY LARK,** 5, b g Beat All (USA)—Solway Larkin (IRE) **Exors of the Late Mr David A. Harrison**
12 **SOLWAY LEGEND,** 9, ch g And Beyond (IRE)—Spicey Cut **Mr & Mrs Batey**
13 **SOLWAY PRINCE,** 7, ch g Double Trigger (IRE)—Solway Rose **Exors of the Late Mr David A. Harrison**
14 **SOLWAY SAM,** 13, b g Double Trigger (IRE)—Some Gale **Exors of the Late Mr David A. Harrison**
15 **SOLWAY STORM (IRE),** 6, gr g Indian River (FR)—The Grey Lady (IRE) **Exors of the Late Mr David A. Harrison**
16 **SOLWAY SUNRISE,** 5, b m Overbury (IRE)—Solway Sunset **Exors of the Late Mr David A. Harrison**
17 **SOLWAY TRIGGER,** 7, b g Double Trigger (IRE)—Double Flight **Exors of the Late Mr David A. Harrison**
18 **WILLIE HALL,** 12, b g Alflora (IRE)—G'ime A Buzz **R. H. Hall**

Other Owners: Mr K. D. Batey, Mrs A. E. Batey, Mr D. Gillespie, Mr J. D. Graves, Mr N. Haughan, R. E. Jackson, Mr J. H. Monkhouse, Mrs L. Monkhouse.

284 MR EDWARD P. HARTY, Curragh
Postal: Mulgrave Lodge, Pollardstown, Curragh, Co Kildare, Ireland
Contacts: **PHONE (00353) 86 2255336 (00353) 45 531116**
E-MAIL epharty@eircom.net **WEBSITE** www.eddieharty.com

1 BUCK DANCING (IRE), 7, b g King's Theatre (IRE)—Polly Anthus
2 CONEY ISLAND (IRE), 5, b g Flemensfirth (USA)—Millys Gesture (IRE)
3 COPPERS AND COINS, 5, b g Presenting—Daprika (FR)
4 COPY THAT (IRE), 5, b g Milan—Ben's Pride
5 DALMATIA (IRE), 5, gr m Cape Cross (IRE)—Dalataya (IRE)
6 DANDY BRIDGE (IRE), 5, b m Milan—Banbury Cross (IRE)
7 DASAATEER (IRE), 4, b g Mount Nelson—Trishuli
8 DONNELLAN (IRE), 7, ch g Germany (USA)—Classic Difference (IRE)
9 DRESSEDTOTHENINES (IRE), 9, b m Oscar (IRE)—Regal Holly
10 EQUAL STATUS (IRE), 5, b g Flemensfirth (USA)—Tricky Present (IRE)
11 HALF MOON STREET (IRE), 4, b g Westerner—Lusos Wonder (IRE)
12 4, B f Beneficial (IRE)—Hester Hall (IRE)
13 IF NOT FOR YOU (IRE), 8, b g Celtic Swing—Ker Lani (FR)
14 JACK DILLINGER (IRE), 5, b g Westerner—Peppardstown (IRE)
15 JOSHUA LANE (IRE), 7, b g Gamut (IRE)—Teffia Native (IRE)
16 KALAWAR (USA), 4, b g More Than Ready (USA)—Kaloura (IRE)
17 KLINNSMAN (IRE), 7, b g Germany (USA)—Killooley (IRE)
18 4, B br g Yeats (IRE)—Lightstorm (IRE)
19 MINELLA FORU (IRE), 7, b g King's Theatre (IRE)—Shannon Rose (IRE)
20 MOON OVER GERMANY (IRE), 5, ch g Germany (USA)—Elea Moon (IRE)
21 MORE THAN EVER (IRE), 6, b m Robin des Champs (FR)—Raichu (IRE)
22 MUY BONITA (IRE), 5, b m Flemensfirth (USA)—Vincenta (IRE)
23 QUEENS WILD (IRE), 6, b m Westerner—Pepsi Starlet (IRE)
24 SABRAGE (IRE), 4, b c Fastnet Rock (AUS)—Champagne Toni (IRE)
25 SORT IT OUT (IRE), 7, b br g Milan—Snowbelle (IRE)
26 SPRING FORWARD (IRE), 5, b g Oscar (IRE)—My Twist (IRE)
27 ST MARTIN'S LANE (IRE), 5, b g Milan—A Stroke of Luck (IRE)
28 STATE OF ORIGIN (IRE), 7, b g Germany (USA)—Romeos Juliet (IRE)
29 UAINTSEENOTHINGYET, 5, b g Yeats (IRE)—Highland Ceilidh (IRE)
30 WILLIAM B (IRE), 5, b b g Yeats (IRE)—Gallic Approach (IRE)

Owners: N. O. Flaherty, Robert Guiry, Derek Jordan, L. Kinsella, M. McHale, J. P. McManus, Mrs K. Quinn, Philip Reynolds, Robert Sinclair, Stanley Watson.

Assistant Trainer: Patrick Harty

Jockey (flat): Fran Berry. **Jockey (NH):** Barry Geraghty, Adrian Heskin, Mark Walsh. **Amateur:** Miss Carolyn Harty.

285 MR BEN HASLAM, Middleham
Postal: Castle Hill Stables, Castle Hill, Middleham, Leyburn, North Yorkshire, DL8 4QW
Contacts: **PHONE (01969) 624351 MOBILE (07764) 411660**
E-MAIL office@benhaslamracing.com **WEBSITE** www.benhaslamracing.com

1 CAMANCHE GREY (IRE), 5, gr g Camacho—Sense of Greeting (IRE) **Mr L. Ashmore**
2 CHARLIE'S APPROVAL (IRE), 4, b f Approve (IRE)—Authenticate **Mr L. Ashmore**
3 EVER SO MUCH (IRE), 7, b g Westerner—Beautiful World (IRE) **J. P. McManus**
4 HI DANCER, 13, b g Medicean—Sea Music **Mr R. A. Tocher**
5 LADY LEKKI (IRE), 4, b f Champs Elysees—One Zero (USA) **Go Alfresco Racing**
6 MOON OVER RIO (IRE), 5, b m Captain Rio—Moonchild (GER) **Blue Lion Racing IX**
7 OPERATEUR (IRE), 8, b g Oratorio (IRE)—Kassariya (IRE) **Mrs C Barclay & M T Buckley**
8 RIVERLYNX (IRE), 4, b f Holy Roman Emperor (IRE)—Banba (IRE) **Go Alfresco Racing**
9 ROSE OF THE MOON (IRE), 11, gr g Moonax (IRE)—
Little Rose (IRE) **Middleham Park Racing XXXIII & Partners**
10 SHESNOTFORTURNING (IRE), 6, b m Refuse To Bend (IRE)—Diplomats Daughter **Mr B. M. R. Haslam**
11 WHISKY MARMALADE (IRE), 4, b f Duke of Marmalade (IRE)—
Nashatara (USA) **Middleham Park Racing LXX & Partner**

THREE-YEAR-OLDS

12 ANY JOY (IRE), b f Zoffany (IRE)—For Joy **Milner & Partner**
13 EPEIUS (IRE), b c Arakan (USA)—Gilda Lilly (USA) **The Trojan Horse Partnership & Partner**

MR BEN HASLAM - Continued

14 **FREEZE A CROWD (IRE)**, b f Frozen Power (IRE)—Skies Are Blue **Middleham Park Racing I**
15 **LORD BOPPER (IRE)**, b g Frozen Power (IRE)—Lady Bracknell (IRE) **Mrs Carol Aldridge & Mrs C Barclay**
16 **MAN OF LA MANCHA (IRE)**, b c Zoffany (IRE)—Sarella Loren (USA) **Mrs C. Barclay**
17 **MRS MAGS**, b f Sleeping Indian—Esteraad (IRE) **Mrs C. Barclay**

TWO-YEAR-OLDS

18 B c 4/3 Lope de Vega (IRE)—Al Basar (USA) (Sahm (USA)) (20000) **Mr B. M. R. Haslam**
19 B c 7/4 Arakan (USA)—Ambonnay (Ashkalani (IRE)) (14000) **James Pak Racing**
20 B f 21/4 Hellvelyn—Ball Burst (IRE) (Imperial Ballet (IRE)) (3809) **Mr B. M. R. Haslam**
21 B c 10/2 Sir Prancealot (IRE)—Beguiler (Refuse To Bend (IRE)) (28571) **Middleham Park Racing**
22 **CASTLE HILL CASSIE (IRE)**, ch f 7/3 Casamento (IRE)—
                                         Angel Bright (IRE) (Dark Angel (IRE)) (35000) **Ontoawinner**
23 B f 5/4 Zoffany (IRE)—Dame Rochelle (Danehill Dancer (IRE)) (5000) **The Trojan Horse Partnership**
24 B c 1/4 Sir Prancealot (IRE)—Greenflash (Green Desert (USA)) (30000) **Mr B. M. R. Haslam**
25 Ch c 1/4 Stimulation (IRE)—Psychic's Dream (Oasis Dream) (8571) **Mr B. M. R. Haslam**
26 B c 3/2 Pivotal—Respondez (Oasis Dream) **Madams Farm Ltd & Mr J. Instone**

Other Owners: Mrs C. Barclay, Mr M. T. Buckley, Lord Daresbury, Miss Lynn Douglas, Mr B. M. R. Haslam, Mrs S. Milner, Mr D. Morland, Mr T. S. Palin, Mr M. Prince, Mr G. Walker, Mrs N. Wellingham, Mr R. Young.

---

286   MR NIGEL HAWKE, Tiverton
Postal: **Thorne Farm, Stoodleigh, Tiverton, Devon, EX16 9QG**
Contacts: **PHONE (01884) 881666 MOBILE (07769) 295839**
E-MAIL nigel@thornefarmracingltd.co.uk WEBSITE www.nigelhawkethornefarmracing.co.uk

1 **ACADIAN (FR)**, 6, b g Sulamani (IRE)—Acarina (IRE) **Mead & Vowles**
2 **ALL KINGS (IRE)**, 7, b g Milan—Rilmount (IRE) **Avalon Surfacing & Construction Co Ltd**
3 **ANAY TURGE (FR)**, 11, gr g Turgeon (USA)—Anayette (FR) **Mrs K. Hawke**
4 **ANIS DES MALBERAUX (FR)**, 6, b g Reste Tranquille (FR)—Scavenger (FR) **Mrs K. Hawke**
5 **AVEL VOR (IRE)**, 5, ch g Green Tune (USA)—High Perfection (IRE) **N J McMullan, S H Bryant & Partner**
6 **BELLINI DUBREAU (FR)**, 5, ch g Anzillero (GER)—Lonita d'airy (FR) **Air Cdre Hallam & Mrs Martin Hallam**
7 **BERRY DE CARJAC (FR)**, 5, ch g Epalo (GER)—Miria Galanda (FR) **Pearce Bros Partnership**
8 **BUFFALO SABRE (FR)**, 4, b g Turgeon (USA)—Kerry Rose (FR) **Mrs K. Hawke**
9 **CALIN DU BRIZAIS (FR)**, 5, b g Loup Solitaire (USA)—Caline du Brizais (FR) **Pearce Bros Partnership**
10 **CAMRON DE CHAILLAC (FR)**, 4, bl g Laverock (IRE)—Hadeel **Mrs K. Hawke**
11 **DECKERS DELIGHT**, 5, b m Tobougg (IRE)—Oleana (IRE) **Mead & Vowles**
12 **FASHION ICON (FR)**, 5, b m Arvico (FR)—Royale Sulawesie (FR) **The Why Not Partnership & Partner**
13 **FLINTS LEGACY**, 4, gr f Sagamix (FR)—Luneray (FR)
14 **FLORA AURORA**, 8, ch g Afflora (IRE)—Dawn Spinner **D. R. Mead**
15 **GREYBOUGG**, 7, gr g Tobougg (IRE)—Kildee Lass **Mead, Di Vincenzo, Capps**
16 **JACK IN A BOX**, 6, b g Kayf Tara—La Dame Brune (FR) **Mr M. J. Phillips**
17 **JOHANOS (FR)**, 5, ch g Limnos (JPN)—Madame Johann (FR) **D. R. Mead**
18 **KADALKIN (FR)**, 10, b g Robin des Champs (FR)—Kadalma (FR) **D. R. Mead**
19 **KIPUKA**, 4, b f Authorized (IRE)—Rakata (USA) **Thorne Farm Racing Limited**
20 **LE PERGOLESE (FR)**, 10, b g Sagacity (FR)—Rasinixa (FR) **Thorne Farm Racing Partnership**
21 **LOCH GARMAN (FR)**, 5, gr g Maresca Sorrento (FR)—Ballade Nordique (FR) **D. R. Mead**
22 **LORD BALLIM (FR)**, 6, ch g Balko (FR)—Lady Pauline (FR) **Mr J. W. Hall**
23 **MASTER NEO (FR)**, 10, gr g Turgeon (USA)—Really Royale (FR) **Mr W E Donohue & Pearce Bros**
24 **MIDNIGHT REQUEST**, 7, b g Midnight Legend—Friendly Request **W E Donohue J M Donohue**
25 **NAIL 'M (IRE)**, 8, b g Milan—Honor Kicks (FR) **D. R. Mead**
26 **PEARL ROYALE (IRE)**, 4, b f Robin des Champs (FR)—Dartmeet (IRE) **Air Cdre Hallam & Mrs Martin Hallam**
27 **PETERGATE**, 5, b g Alhaarth (IRE)—Shamayel **Air Cdre Hallam & Mrs Martin Hallam**
28 **POINT N SHOOT (IRE)**, 5, b g Broadway Flyer (USA)—Ali's Dipper (IRE) **Mead & Vowles**
29 **POMME**, 5, b m Observatory (USA)—Mirthful (USA) **Mrs K Hawke & Mr M Phillips**
30 **QUEEN OF EPIRUS**, 8, ch m Kirkwall—Andromache **Thorne Farm Racing Limited**
31 4, B g Fruits of Love (USA)—Rathturtin Brief (IRE)
32 **RED RED ROVER (IRE)**, 6, ch g Royal Anthem—Ithastobedone (IRE) **M. J. Rowe**
33 **REJAAH**, 4, b f Authorized (IRE)—Dhan Dhana (IRE) **Mrs K. Hawke & Mr W. Simms**
34 **ROBIN WHY NOT (IRE)**, 4, b g Robin des Pres (FR)—Lady Mariah **Thorne Farm Racing Limited**
35 **SAMINGARRY (FR)**, 9, ch g Ballingarry (IRE)—Samansonnienne (FR) **D. R. Mead**
36 **SPEREDEK (FR)**, 5, b br g Kapgarde (FR)—Sendamagic (FR) **Kapinhand & Partner**
37 **TAKE A BREAK (FR)**, 5, b br g Sunday Break (JPN)—Popee (FR) **Pearce Bros Partnership**
38 **TELEX (USA)**, 5, gr g Empire Maker (USA)—Kinetic Force (USA) **Thorne Farm Racing Limited**

MR NIGEL HAWKE - Continued

39 **THEUNNAMEDSOLDIER**, 8, b g Revoque (IRE)—Miss Tango **D. R. Mead**
40 **TOKYO JAVILEX (FR)**, 9, b g Sleeping Car (FR)—Etoile du Lion (FR) **D. R. Mead**
41 **WHIMSICAL NOTION**, 6, b g Midnight Legend—Friendly Request **W. E. Donohue**

THREE-YEAR-OLDS

42 **OURO BRANCO (FR)**, b g Kapgarde (FR)—Dolce Vita Yug **Unregistered Partnership**

Other Owners: Mrs K. M. Brain, S. H. Bryant, Mr M. G. Capps, Mr M. Di-Vincenzo, Mrs J. M. Donohue, Air Commodore M. R. Hallam, Mrs M. Hallam, Mr T. B. James, Mrs H. M. Jefferies, Mr H. J. Jefferies, N. J. McMullan, Mr D. Mitchell, Mr D. A. Pearce, Mr S. R. Pearce, Mr W. J. Simms, Mrs D. E. Smith, Mr J. A. Vowles.

Assistant Trainers: Joe Tickle, Katherine Hawke

Jockey (NH): Dave Crosse, Tom Scudamore. Conditional: James Best. Amateur: Mr Lee Drowne.

287
MR RICHARD HAWKER, Frome
Postal: Rode Farm, Rode, Bath, Somerset, BA11 6QQ
Contacts: PHONE (01373) 831479

1 5, Gr bl m Dr Massini (IRE)—Charliebob **R. G. B. Hawker**
2 4, B c Dr Massini (IRE)—Charliebob **R. G. B. Hawker**
3 **FAUVE (IRE)**, 5, b g Montjeu (IRE)—Simaat (USA) **Ms E. J. Southall**
4 **SKATING HOME (IRE)**, 10, b g Luso—Wintry Day (IRE) **Winning Edge Racing**

Other Owners: Mrs S. E. Hawker.

288
MR JONATHAN HAYNES, Brampton
Postal: Cleugh Head, Low Row, Brampton, Cumbria, CA8 2JB
Contacts: PHONE (01697) 746253 MOBILE (07771) 511471

1 **BERTIELICIOUS**, 8, b g And Beyond (IRE)—Pennepoint **J. C. Haynes**
2 **BEYONDTEMPTATION**, 8, ch m And Beyond (IRE)—Tempted (IRE) **J. C. Haynes**
3 **BEYONDTHEFLAME**, 6, b m And Beyond (IRE)—Flame of Zara **J. C. Haynes**
4 **GETONSAM**, 4, ch g Black Sam Bellamy (IRE)—Pennepoint **J. C. Haynes**
5 **MRS GRASS**, 9, ch m And Beyond (IRE)—Tempted (IRE) **J. C. Haynes**
6 **NEXT HIGHT (IRE)**, 9, b g High Chaparral (IRE)—Night Petticoat (GER) **J. C. Haynes**

289
MISS GAIL HAYWOOD, Moretonhampstead
Postal: Stacombe Farm, Doccombe, Moretonhampstead, Newton Abbot, Devon, TQ13 8SS
Contacts: PHONE (01647) 440826
E-MAIL gail@gghracing.com WEBSITE www.gghracing.com

1 **CHICA RAPIDA**, 4, ch f Paco Boy (IRE)—Tora Bora **Mrs Jo Ann Bland**
2 **FLEUR DU WELD**, 8, ch m Weld—Midnight Walker **Mrs J. B. Floyd-Walker**
3 **HIJA**, 5, b m Avonbridge—Pantita **Haywood's Heroes**
4 **MAGNUS ROMEO**, 5, b g Manduro (GER)—Chili Dip **Mr R. E. Stuart-Jervis**
5 **MILBURN**, 10, ch g First Trump—Baroness Rose **Mr R. E. Stuart-Jervis & Miss G. G. Haywood**
6 **RICHARDOFDOCCOMBE (IRE)**, 10, b g Heron Island (IRE)—Strike Again (IRE) **Mr R. E. Stuart-Jervis**
7 **RUSSIAN'S LEGACY**, 6, b m Kayf Tara—Ruby Star (IRE) **Mr I. F. Gosden & Miss G. G. Haywood**
8 **SECRET PALACE**, 4, ch f Pastoral Pursuits—Some Sunny Day **Mrs Mary Tutton Creese & Miss G. G. Haywood**

Other Owners: Mr Martin John Haywood, Mr Malcolm Joseph Haywood, Gp Capt M. W. Haywood MBE, Mrs Suzie Haywood.

Assistant Trainer: William McColl

Conditional: Alice Mills.

290 **MRS C. HEAD-MAAREK, Chantilly**
Postal: **32 Avenue du General Leclerc, 60500 Chantilly, France**
Contacts: **PHONE (0033) 3445 70101 FAX (0033) 3445 85333 MOBILE (0033) 6073 10505**
E-MAIL christiane.head@wanadoo.fr

1 **BE MY LADY,** 4, b f Duke of Marmalade (IRE)—Za Za Zoom (IRE)
2 **EPICURIS,** 4, b g Rail Link—Argumentative
3 **GALLICE (IRE),** 4, b f Fuisse (FR)—Gout de Terroir (USA)
4 **GREENSTREET (FR),** 5, b g Mr Sidney (USA)—Treasure Queen (USA)
5 **LYDIANE (IRE),** 4, b f Dunkerque (FR)—Cartama
6 **RED CROWN (AUT),** 4, b f Youmzain (IRE)—Red Pearl (FR)
7 **TROIS POINTS (FR),** 4, b g Motivator—Trading (FR)

THREE-YEAR-OLDS

8 **AVOCET (USA),** b f Artie Schiller (USA)—Striking Example (USA)
9 **BRIGANTES,** b f Oasis Dream—Arizona Jewel
10 **CALINA (FR),** b f Dunkerque (FR)—Cable Beach (USA)
11 **CYCLETTA (USA),** b f First Defence (USA)—Classy Touch (USA)
12 **DETACHMENT,** b c Motivator—Argumentative
13 **EXTINGUISH (FR),** b c Dansili—Silver Fame (USA)
14 **FALCON'S VISION (FR),** ch g Pivotal—Visualize
15 **FLAG FEN,** b c Oasis Dream—Kid Gloves
16 **FUNDING,** b c Zamindar (USA)—Acquisition
17 **LOANNE (FR),** b f Pour Moi (IRE)—Drosia (IRE)
18 **MADENCIA (FR),** b f Hurricane Cat (USA)—Manadouna (FR)
19 **MAGELAN (FR),** b c Fuisse (FR)—Mytographie (FR)
20 **MATERIAL,** b c Cacique (IRE)—Talkative
21 **MIDWEEK,** b f Motivator—Contiguous (USA)
22 **MIGHT IS RIGHT (IRE),** b f Lawman (FR)—Perse
23 **MNEERAH (FR),** ch f Giant's Causeway (USA)—Gointobegone (USA)
24 **MONDELINO (FR),** b g Youmzain (IRE)—Mishina (FR)
25 **MONETISE (USA),** b g Medaglia d'oro (USA)—Aviate
26 **NAPOLEON (IRE),** b c Jeremy (USA)—Desert Drama (IRE)
27 **PRESIDENCY,** b c Oasis Dream—Quest To Peak (USA)
28 **PYRETOS (IRE),** B C Holy Roman Emperor (IRE)—Galaktea (IRE)
29 **SANDSTONE,** b f Dansili—Helleborine
30 **SEMINI (FR),** b f Fuisse (FR)—Spirale d'or (FR)
31 **SIR ALEC (FR),** b g Mr Sidney (USA)—Rose Rose (USA)
32 **STEP IN LATE (FR),** b f Footstepsinthesand—Titillate (IRE)
33 **TEXADA,** b f Cacique (IRE)—Spacecraft (USA)
34 **TYRANA (FR),** b f Motivator—Treasure (FR)

TWO-YEAR-OLDS

35 B f 21/4 American Post—Acquisition (Dansili)
36 B f 8/4 Oasis Dream—Argumentative (Observatory (USA))
37 **BEAT THE CROWD (IRE),** b c 4/4 Cape Cross (IRE)—Dubai Flower (Manduro (GER)) (50000)
38 Ch f 22/1 Rip Van Winkle (IRE)—Candicans (Dansili)
39 **CASCADE (FR),** ch f 15/4 Motivator—Cable Beach (USA) (Langfuhr (CAN))
40 **FATIMA (FR),** b f 31/1 Mr Sidney (USA)—Funny Feerie (FR) (Sillery (USA))
41 **FLAUTIST (USA),** b br f 2/3 First Defence (USA)—Flute (USA) (Seattle Slew (USA))
42 B f 15/3 Holy Roman Emperor (IRE)—Gagarina (IRE) (Galileo (IRE)) (25839)
43 **GOLDY (FR),** b f 8/2 Youmzain (IRE)—Golden Life (USA) (Coronado's Quest (USA))
44 **HIGH LIVE (FR),** b f 6/4 Dunkerque (FR)—Highborne (FR) (Anabaa (USA))
45 **LOYAL JUSTICE,** ch c 2/5 Teofilo (IRE)—Sentimental Value (USA) (Diesis) (180000)
46 B c 10/3 Mastercraftsman (IRE)—Mi Dica (Green Desert (USA))
47 **NATIONAL DEFENSE,** b c 16/1 Invincible Spirit (USA)—Angel Falls (Kingmambo (USA)) (206718)
48 B c 3/5 Oasis Dream—Quenched (Dansili)
49 **REVE,** b c 10/3 Nathaniel (IRE)—Rouge (FR) (Red Ransom (USA)) (22148)
50 **ROSE BLANCHE (FR),** ch f 12/2 Motivator—Rose Rose (USA) (Cozzene (USA))
51 **SILVER RING (FR),** b c 6/4 Motivator—Silver Fame (USA) (Quest For Fame (USA)) (36913)
52 **SORTIE (FR),** b f 5/3 Mr Sidney (USA)—Silverware (FR) (Polish Precedent (USA))
53 **STRATONIKA (FR),** b f 20/3 Mr Sidney (USA)—Smyrnes (FR) (Anabaa (USA))
54 **TERRE (FR),** b f 3/4 Motivator—Trevise (FR) (Anabaa (USA)) (885935)
55 **TRESORIER,** b c 25/2 Dunkerque (FR)—Treasure (FR) (Anabaa (USA))
56 **UNPRECEDENTED (FR),** b c 22/3 Fastnet Rock (AUS)—Nans Joy (IRE) (In The Wings) (60000)

MRS C. HEAD-MAAREK - Continued

57 B c 8/4 Zamindar (USA)—Valentine Girl (Alzao (USA))
58 WINNING PURSUIT (IRE), b c 14/4 Sea The Stars (IRE)—Kandalek (Hawk Wing (USA)) (110741)
59 B f 6/2 Holy Roman Emperor (IRE)—Ysandre (Zamindar (USA))

Assistant Trainer: Christopher Head

Conditional: Claudic Jerome.

 291

MR PETER HEDGER, Hook
Postal: **P C F Racing, Chalky Lane, Dogmersfield, Hook, Hampshire, RG27 8TG**
Contacts: **PHONE (01243) 543863 FAX (01243) 543913 MOBILE (07860) 209448**
E-MAIL hedgerlaura@hotmail.com

1 AFRO, 6, b m Araafa (IRE)—Largo (IRE) **P C F Racing Ltd**
2 BARNMORE, 8, b g Royal Applause—Veronica Franco **P C F Racing Ltd**
3 BRIDGE BUILDER, 6, b g Avonbridge—Amazing Dream (IRE) **P C F Racing Ltd**
4 CONTINUUM, 7, b br g Dansili—Clepsydra **P C F Racing Ltd**
5 FRANCO'S SECRET, 5, b g Sakhee's Secret—Veronica Franco **P C F Racing Ltd**
6 JOHN JOINER, 4, b g Captain Gerrard (IRE)—Nigella **Mrs Susan Lynch & Mr Andy Lomax**
7 LUCKY DI, 6, br m Araafa (IRE)—Lucky Date (IRE) **P C F Racing Ltd**
8 PEARLY PRINCE, 4, b g Cockney Rebel (IRE)—Princess Raya **Mrs V. Keen**
9 RUN FOUR YOUR LIFE, 5, ch g Bertolini (USA)—Pick A Nice Name **Mrs V. Keen**
10 RUZEIZ (USA), 7, b g Muhtathir—Saraama (USA) **P C F Racing Ltd**
11 SHACKLED N DRAWN (USA), 4, b g Candy Ride (ARG)—
　　　　　　　　　　　　　　　　　Cajun Flash (USA) **Ron Smith Recycling Ltd & P. R. Hedger**
12 SILVER DIXIE (USA), 6, br g Dixie Union (USA)—More Silver (USA) **P C F Racing Ltd**
13 WHIPCRACKAWAY (IRE), 7, b g Whipper—Former Drama (USA) **P. R. Hedger**

THREE-YEAR-OLDS

14 MY SHOOTIN STAR, gr f Winker Watson—Miss Venice (IRE) **P. R. Hedger**
15 PACABAG, b f Paco Boy (IRE)—Veronica Franco **P C F Racing Ltd**

TWO-YEAR-OLDS

16 B c 14/4 Makfi—Veronica Franco (Darshaan) **P C F Racing Ltd**

Other Owners: Arun Green, Mr P. R. Hedger, Mr Simon Holt, Andy Lomax, Mrs Susan Lynch, Wendy Mole, P C F Racing Ltd, Prof D. B. A. Silk.

Assistant Trainer: Mr Shaun Keightley (01252) 850016

Jockey (flat): Charles Bishop. **Jockey (NH):** Leighton Aspell.

 292

MR NICKY HENDERSON, Lambourn
Postal: **Seven Barrows, Lambourn, Hungerford, Berkshire, RG17 8UH**
Contacts: **PHONE (01488) 72259 MOBILE (07774) 608168**
E-MAIL nj.henderson@virgin.net

1 A TAIL OF INTRIGUE (IRE), 8, b g Tillerman—
　　　　　　　　　　　　　　Princess Commanche (IRE) **Mr Oscar Singh & Miss Priya Purewal**
2 ACT ALONE, 7, b g Act One—Figlette **S W Group Logistics Limited**
3 AIGLE DE LA SEE (FR), 6, gr g Al Namix (FR)—Janita de La See (FR) **Mr Simon Munir & Mr Isaac Souede**
4 ALPHA MALE (FR), 5, b g Poliglote—Arzuaga **M. A. C. Buckley**
5 ALTIOR (IRE), 6, b g High Chaparral (IRE)—Monte Solaro (IRE) **Mrs P. J. Pugh**
6 ARGANTE (FR), 7, b br g Singspiel (IRE)—Abyaan (IRE) **Mr R. P. A. Spiller**
7 ARGOCAT (IRE), 8, b g Montjeu (IRE)—Spirit of South (AUS) **Mrs F. H. Hay**
8 ARMAANS WISH (IRE), 5, ch g Presenting—Pretty Puttens (IRE) **Middleham Park Racing LXIII**
9 BADEN (FR), 5, gr g Martaline—Ma Sonate (USA) **Triermore Stud**
10 BALLINURE (IRE), 6, b g Alkaadhem—Christy's Pride (IRE) **Mrs M. Parker**
11 BARDD (IRE), 4, b g Dylan Thomas (IRE)—Zarawa (IRE) **Elite Racing Club**
12 BARMAN (FR), 5, b g Racinger (FR)—Koscina (FR) **The Bartenders**
13 BEAR'S AFFAIR (IRE), 10, br g Presenting—Gladtogetit **G. B. Barlow**
14 BEAT THAT (IRE), 8, b g Milan—Knotted Midge (IRE) **M. A. C. Buckley**
15 BELLATOR (FR), 5, b h Network (GER)—Onysia (FR) **The Shillelagh Partnership**

MR NICKY HENDERSON - Continued

16 **BERCE (FR)**, 5, b g Peer Gynt (JPN)—Fauconnerie (FR) **Potensis Bloodstock Limited**
17 **BEWARE THE BEAR (IRE)**, 6, b g Shantou (USA)—Native Bid (IRE) **G. B. Barlow**
18 **BIRCH HILL (IRE)**, 6, b g Kalanisi (IRE)—Miss Compliance (IRE) **R. A. Bartlett**
19 **BIVOUAC (FR)**, 5, b g Califet (FR)—Pazadena (FR) **Mr Chris Giles & Potensis Bloodstock Ltd**
20 **BLACK N BLUE**, 4, ch g Galileo (IRE)—Coyote **Mr Alan Spence**
21 **BLOODY MARY (FR)**, 5, gr m Fragrant Mix (FR)—Sacade (FR) **J. P. McManus**
22 **BLUE FASHION (IRE)**, 7, b g Scorpion (IRE)—Moon Glow (FR) **Mr & Mrs J. D. Cotton**
23 **BOBS WORTH (IRE)**, 11, b g Bob Back (USA)—Fashionista (IRE) **The Not Afraid Partnership**
24 **BRAIN POWER (IRE)**, 5, b g Kalanisi (IRE)—Blonde Ambition (IRE) **M. A. C. Buckley**
25 **BRIGHT EYES**, 5, b m Hernando (FR)—Chomba Womba (IRE) **Mr & Mrs R. G. Kelvin-Hughes**
26 **BROXBOURNE (IRE)**, 7, b m Refuse To Bend (IRE)—Rafting (FR) **The Gleneagles Partnership**
27 **BUVEUR D'AIR (FR)**, 5, b g Crillon (FR)—History (FR) **Potensis Bloodstock Ltd & Chris Giles**
28 **CALL THE COPS (IRE)**, 7, b g Presenting—Ballygill Heights (IRE) **J. P. McManus**
29 **CAPTAIN CONAN (FR)**, 9, b g Kingsalsa (USA)—Lavandou **Triermore Stud**
30 **CARACCI APACHE (IRE)**, 6, b g High Chaparral (IRE)—Campanella (GER) **W. H. Ponsonby**
31 **CARDINAL WALTER (IRE)**, 7, br b g Cape Cross (IRE)—Sheer Spirit (IRE) **Mrs F. H. Hay**
32 **CHAMPAGNE EXPRESS**, 6, b g Kalanisi (IRE)—Marvellous Dream (FR) **Owners Group 008**
33 **CHAPEL HALL (IRE)**, 6, b g Arcadio (GER)—Auction Hall **R. M. Kirkland**
34 **CHOCCA WOCCA**, 6, b m Kayf Tara—Chomba Womba (IRE) **Mr & Mrs R. G. Kelvin-Hughes**
35 **CHRISTMAS IN APRIL (FR)**, 4, b g Crillon (FR)—
                               Similaresisoldofa (FR) **Potensis Bloodstock Ltd & J Palmer Brown**
36 **CLEAN SHEET (IRE)**, 7, b g Oscar (IRE)—High Park Lady (IRE) **J. P. McManus**
37 **CLEMENCY**, 5, b m Halling (USA)—China Tea (USA) **Elite Racing Club**
38 **CLONDAW BANKER (IRE)**, 7, b g Court Cave (IRE)—Freya Alex **Mr Alan Spence**
39 **CLOSE ESCAPE (IRE)**, 5, b g Robin des Pres (FR)—Music School (IRE) **Middleham Park Racing CXXI**
40 **CLOSE TOUCH**, 8, b g Generous (IRE)—Romantic Dream **Her Majesty The Queen**
41 **COCKTAILS AT DAWN**, 8, b g Fair Mix (FR)—Fond Farewell (IRE) **R J H Geffen & Sir John Ritblat**
42 **COLONIAL DREAMS (IRE)**, 4, b g Westerner—Dochas Supreme (IRE) **C. N. Barnes**
43 **COMELY**, 4, b f Midnight Legend—Belle Magello (FR) **Her Majesty The Queen**
44 **CONSUL DE THAIX (FR)**, 4, b g Loxias (FR)—Mange de Thaix (FR) **J. P. McManus**
45 **COOL MACAVITY (IRE)**, 8, b g One Cool Cat (USA)—Cause Celebre (IRE) **Triermore Stud**
46 **COOLE CHARMER (IRE)**, 7, ch g Flemensfirth (USA)—Ericas Charm **Mr Chris Giles & Potensis Bloodstock Ltd**
47 **CULTIVATOR**, 5, b g Alflora (IRE)—Angie Marinie **Kimmins Family & Friends**
48 **CUP FINAL (IRE)**, 7, ch g Presenting—Asian Maze (IRE) **J. P. McManus**
49 **DAYS OF HEAVEN (FR)**, 6, b br g Saint des Saints (FR)—Daramour (FR) **M. A. C. Buckley**
50 **DERKSEN (IRE)**, 6, b g Robin des Champs (FR)—Anns Present (IRE) **T. J. Hemmings**
51 **DIFFERENT GRAVEY (IRE)**, 6, b g High Chaparral (IRE)—Newtown Dancer (IRE) **Mr & Mrs R. G. Kelvin-Hughes**
52 **DIVINE SPEAR (IRE)**, 5, b g Oscar (IRE)—Testaway (IRE) **Middleham Park Racing LXII**
53 **DUKE DEBARRY (IRE)**, 5, b g Presenting—Blue Dante (IRE) **Middleham Park Racing CIX**
54 **ERICHT (IRE)**, 10, b g Alderbrook—Lady Orla (IRE) **Mrs B. A. Hanbury**
55 **FAIRLEE GREY**, 7, gr g Fair Mix (IRE)—Halo Flora **J. L. Gledson**
56 **FELL RUNNER**, 5, b g High Chaparral (IRE)—Firoza (FR) **Anthony Speelman**
57 **FIXE LE KAP (FR)**, 4, gr g Kapgarde (FR)—Lady Fix (FR) **Mr Simon Munir & Mr Isaac Souede**
58 **FLY CAMP (FR)**, 6, gr g Westerner—Pearlsforthegirls **Mrs M. Parker**
59 **FOREVER FIELD (IRE)**, 6, b g Beneficial—Sarahs Reprive (IRE) **R. M. Kirkland**
60 **FRENCH OPERA**, 13, b g Bering—On Fair Stage (IRE) **Mrs Judy Wilson & Martin Landau**
61 **FULL SHIFT (FR)**, 7, b g Ballingarry (IRE)—Dansia (GER) **J. P. McManus**
62 **GAITWAY**, 6, b g Medicean—Milliegait **Mrs J. K. Powell**
63 **GOLD PRESENT (IRE)**, 6, br g Presenting—Ouro Preto **Mr & Mrs J. D. Cotton**
64 **GOLDEN HOOF (IRE)**, 8, b g Oscar (IRE)—Nuovo Style (IRE) **The Hoof Partnership**
65 **GOOD IDEA (IRE)**, 5, b g Arcadio (GER)—Aunt Annie (IRE) **Mrs F. H. Hay**
66 **GRANIT (IRE)**, 6, b g Arcadio (GER)—Can't Stop (GER) **Mrs J. K. Powell**
67 **HADRIAN'S APPROACH (IRE)**, 9, b g High Chaparral (IRE)—
                               Gifted Approach (IRE) **Mr & Mrs R. G. Kelvin-Hughes**
68 **HAMMERSLY LAKE (FR)**, 8, b g Kapgarde (FR)—Loin de Moi (FR) **M. A. C. Buckley**
69 **HARGAM (FR)**, 5, gr g Sinndar (IRE)—Horasana (FR) **J. P. McManus**
70 **HIGHWAY STAR (FR)**, 4, br g Vision d'etat (FR)—Lyli Rose (FR) **Michael Buckley & Lord Vestey**
71 **HUNTERS HOOF (IRE)**, 7, b g Flemensfirth (USA)—Madgehill (IRE) **London Bridge Racing Partnership**
72 **HURRICANE HIGGINS (IRE)**, 8, br g Hurricane Run (IRE)—Mare Aux Fees **Mr Alan Spence**
73 **JENKINS (IRE)**, 4, b g Azamour (IRE)—Aladiyna (IRE) **Pump & Plant Services Ltd**
74 **JOSSES HILL (IRE)**, 8, b g Winged Love (IRE)—Credora Storm (IRE) **Mr Alan Spence**
75 **KAYF GRACE**, 6, b m Kayf Tara—Potter's Gale (IRE) **James & Jean Potter**
76 **KHEZERABAD (FR)**, 4, ch g Dalakhani (IRE)—Khelwa (FR) **Mr Simon Munir & Mr Isaac Souede**
77 **KILCREA VALE (IRE)**, 6, b g Beneficial—Inflation (FR) **Mr Alan Spence**
78 **KNOCK CASTLE (IRE)**, 4, b g Kayf Tara—Bella Macrae **Her Majesty The Queen**

MR NICKY HENDERSON - Continued

79 **L'AMI SERGE (IRE)**, 6, b g King's Theatre (IRE)—La Zingarella (IRE) **Mr Simon Munir & Mr Isaac Souede**
80 **LAUDATORY**, 10, b g Royal Applause—Copy-Cat **Mr E. R. Newnham**
81 **LAURIUM**, 6, ch g Gold Away (IRE)—Silver Peak (FR) **The Ten From Seven**
82 **LE DAUPHIN (IRE)**, 5, b g Robin des Champs (FR)—Miss Denman (IRE) **Lady Tennant**
83 **LEADEROFTHEDANCE**, 7, b m Norse Dancer (IRE)—Glenda Lough (IRE) **T. J. Whitley**
84 **LESSONS IN MILAN (IRE)**, 8, b g Milan—Lessons Lass (IRE) **T. J. Hemmings**
85 **LIEUTENANT MILLER**, 10, b g Beat All (USA)—Still Runs Deep **W. H. Ponsonby**
86 **LOUGH KENT**, 7, b g Barathea (IRE)—King's Doll (IRE) **Mrs C. M. Mould**
87 **LYVIUS**, 8, b g Paolini (GER)—Lysuna (GER) **T. J. Hemmings**
88 **MA FILLEULE (FR)**, 8, gr m Turgeon (USA)—Kadaina (FR) **Mr Simon Munir & Mr Isaac Souede**
89 **MAESTRO ROYAL**, 7, b g Doyen (IRE)—Close Harmony **Mrs R. H. Brown**
90 **MAGIC BULLET (IRE)**, 5, b g Flemensfirth (USA)—Some Bob Back (IRE) **C. N. Barnes**
91 **MALTON ROSE (IRE)**, 5, b g Milan—Pharney Fox (IRE) **Mr G. M. Copp**
92 **MELANGERIE**, 4, b f Fair Mix (IRE)—Angie Marinie **The Barrow Boys**
93 **MIGHT BITE (IRE)**, 7, b g Scorpion (IRE)—Knotted Midge (IRE) **The Knot Again Partnership**
94 **MINELLA AWARDS (IRE)**, 5, b g Oscar (IRE)—Montys Miss (IRE) **Potensis Bloodstock Ltd & Chris Giles**
95 **MINSTREL ROYAL**, 6, b g Kayf Tara—Close Harmony **Mrs R. H. Brown**
96 **MONBEG LEGEND**, 6, b g Midnight Legend—Reverse Swing **Mr G. M. Copp**
97 **MY TENT OR YOURS (IRE)**, 9, b g Desert Prince (IRE)—Spartan Girl (IRE) **J. P. McManus**
98 **MY WIGWAM OR YOURS (IRE)**, 7, b g Beneficial—Midnight Pond (IRE) **The Happy Campers**
99 **NATIVE DISPLAY (IRE)**, 6, b g Presenting—Native Shore (IRE) **J. Palmer-Brown**
100 **NESTERENKO (GER)**, 7, b g Doyen (IRE)—Nordwahl (GER) **Mr J. Meyer**
101 **NEUMOND (GER)**, 5, b g Sholokhov (IRE)—Natalis (GER) **Mrs J. Wilson**
102 **NEW MEMBER (IRE)**, 5, b g Alhaarth (IRE)—Sincere (IRE) **Mrs F. H. Hay**
103 **NEWSWORTHY**, 6, br g Presenting—Cousin Jen (IRE) **Michael Buckley & Mrs Susannah Ricci**
104 **NICOLAS CHAUVIN (IRE)**, 8, b g Saffron Walden (FR)—Kenzie (IRE) **The Gleneagles Partnership**
105 **NO HERETIC**, 8, b g Galileo (IRE)—Intrigued **Mrs F. H. Hay**
106 **O O SEVEN (IRE)**, 6, b g Flemensfirth (USA)—Kestral Heights (IRE) **Triermore Stud**
107 **OH SO GIGOLO (IRE)**, 6, b g Milan—Oh So Breezy (IRE) **Seven Barrows Limited**
108 **OK CORRAL (IRE)**, 6, b g Mahler—Acoola (IRE) **J. P. McManus**
109 **OMESSA HAS (FR)**, 4, gr f Martaline—Ombre Folle **Mr Simon Munir & Mr Isaac Souede**
110 **ONE FOR THE GUV'NR (IRE)**, 7, b g Oscar (IRE)—Wintry Day (IRE) **Bradley Partnership**
111 **ONLY FOR LOVE**, 5, br m Kalanisi (IRE)—Sardagna (FR) **W. H. Ponsonby**
112 **ORBIT LIGHT (IRE)**, 5, b m Echo of Light—Niobe **Orbit Performance**
113 **OSCAR HOOF (IRE)**, 8, b g Oscar (IRE)—New Legislation (IRE) **The Hoof Partnership**
114 **PEACE AND CO (FR)**, 5, b g Falco (USA)—Peace Lina (FR) **Mr Simon Munir & Mr Isaac Souede**
115 **PEPPAY LE PUGH (IRE)**, 5, b g Arakan (USA)—Pinaflore (FR) **Potensis Bloodstock Limited**
116 **PERLESQUE (FR)**, 4, gr f Martaline—Anazeem (IRE) **Lady Tennant**
117 **PHOBIAPHILIAC (IRE)**, 5, b g Beneficial—Denys Eyre (IRE) **Bradley Partnership**
118 **POETRY EMOTION (IRE)**, 5, b g Gamut (IRE)—Vivre Aimer Rire (FR) **Eventmasters Racing**
119 **POKORA DU LYS (FR)**, 5, b g Saint des Saints (FR)—Shailann (FR) **Million in Mind Partnership**
120 **POLLY PEACHUM (IRE)**, 8, b m Shantou (USA)—Miss Denman (IRE) **Lady Tennant & Robert Waley-Cohen**
121 **POST WAR**, 5, b g Nayef (USA)—Antebellum (FR) **Andrew Bedford**
122 **POUGNE BOBBI (FR)**, 5, b br g Protektor (GER)—Amicus **Mr J. Meyer**
123 **PREMIER BOND**, 6, b g Kayf Tara—Celtic Native (IRE) **Middleham Park Racing XI**
124 **PRIORY LAD (IRE)**, 5, b g Arcadio (GER)—Auction Hall **R. M. Kirkland**
125 **PROTEK DES FLOS (FR)**, 4, b g Protektor (GER)—Flore de Chantenay (FR) **Potensis Bloodstock Limited**
126 **QUIET CANDID (IRE)**, 7, b m Beneficial—Lady of Appeal (IRE) **Middleham Park Racing XXXIV**
127 **RATHER BE (IRE)**, 5, b g Oscar (IRE)—Irish Wedding (IRE) **Matt & Lauren Morgan**
128 **RED HAMMER**, 4, b g Falco (USA)—Voie de Printemps (FR) **Mr Simon Munir & Mr Isaac Souede**
129 **REIGNING SUPREME (IRE)**, 5, b g Presenting—Gli Gli (IRE) **M. A. C. Buckley**
130 **RIVER OF INTRIGUE (IRE)**, 6, b g Indian River (FR)—
　　　　　　　　　　　　　　　　　　　　Molly Hussey (IRE) **Mr Oscar Singh & Miss Priya Purewal**
131 **RIVER WYLDE (IRE)**, 5, b g Oscar (IRE)—Clarin River (IRE) **Grech & Parkin**
132 **ROBINS REEF (IRE)**, 6, br m Robin des Champs (FR)—Tropical Ocean (IRE) **Kelvin-Hughes & Bartlett**
133 **ROYAL IRISH HUSSAR (IRE)**, 6, b g Galileo (IRE)—Adjalisa (IRE) **Triermore Stud**
134 **SAINT CHARLES (FR)**, 6, b g Manduro (GER)—Tropical Barth (IRE) **J. P. McManus**
135 **SANAIJA**, 5, ch m Pivotal—Sanjida (IRE) **Mr Simon Munir & Mr Isaac Souede**
136 **SCORPIO QUEEN (IRE)**, 4, b f Scorpion (IRE)—Frankly Native (IRE) **Mrs E. C. Roberts**
137 **SIGN OF A VICTORY (IRE)**, 7, b g Kayf Tara—Irish Wedding (IRE) **Matt & Lauren Morgan**
138 **SILVERHOW (IRE)**, 5, br g Yeats (IRE)—Monte Solaro (IRE) **Mrs P. J. Pugh**
139 **SIMONSIG**, 10, gr g Fair Mix (IRE)—Dusty Too **R. A. Bartlett**
140 **SNAKE EYES (IRE)**, 8, b g Oscar (IRE)—Be My Belle (IRE) **J. P. McManus**
141 **SPECIAL AGENT**, 7, b g Invincible Spirit (USA)—Flight of Fancy **Her Majesty The Queen**
142 **SPRINTER SACRE (FR)**, 10, b br g Network (GER)—Fatima III (FR) **Mrs C. M. Mould**

MR NICKY HENDERSON - Continued

143 **STOWAWAY MAGIC (IRE)**, 5, b g Stowaway—Irish Mystics (IRE) **Grech & Parkin**
144 **SUGAR BARON (IRE)**, 6, b g Presenting—Shuil Oilean (IRE) **Anthony Speelman**
145 **SWOOP TO CONQUER (IRE)**, 4, br g Presenting—One Swoop (IRE) **W. H. Ponsonby**
146 **TAKE TO HEART**, 4, b g Sakhee (USA)—Romantic Dream **Her Majesty The Queen**
147 **TALES OF THE TWEED (IRE)**, 4, b g Robin des Champs (FR)—
　　　　　　　　　　　Dancer Privado (IRE) **Hodgkiss @ Kelvin-Hughes's**
148 **THEATRE TERRITORY (IRE)**, 6, b m King's Theatre (IRE)—Specifiedrisk (IRE) **R. B. Waley-Cohen**
149 **THEINVAL (FR)**, 6, b g Smadoun (FR)—Kinevees (FR) **Mr & Mrs Sandy Orr**
150 **THOMAS CAMPBELL**, 4, b g Yeats (IRE)—Hora **Mr & Mrs R. G. Kelvin-Hughes**
151 **TOP NOTCH (FR)**, 5, b g Poliglote—Topira (FR) **Mr Simon Munir & Mr Isaac Souede**
152 **TOWER OF ALLEN (IRE)**, 5, b g Beneficial—
　　　　　　　　　　　Baile An Droichid (IRE) **Highclere Thoroughbred Racing-Beneficial**
153 **TOWERING (IRE)**, 7, b g Catcher In The Rye—Bobs Article (IRE) **Middleham Park Racing LIX**
154 **TRIOLO D'ALENE (FR)**, 9, ch g Epalo (GER)—Joliette d'alene (FR) **Mr & Mrs Sandy Orr**
155 **VAILLANT NONANTAIS (FR)**, 5, b g My Risk (FR)—Sweet Life (FR) **Mrs J. K. Powell**
156 **VANITEUX (FR)**, 7, br g Voix du Nord (FR)—Expoville (FR) **Mr & Mrs R. G. Kelvin-Hughes**
157 **VODKA 'N TONIC (IRE)**, 7, b g Presenting—Ballagh Dawn (IRE) **Bradley Partnership**
158 **VOLNAY DE THAIX (FR)**, 7, ch g Secret Singer (FR)—Mange de Thaix (FR) **Mrs J. Wilson**
159 **VYTA DU ROC (FR)**, 7, gr g Lion Noir—Dolce Vyta (FR) **Mr Simon Munir & Mr Isaac Souede**
160 **WALT (IRE)**, 5, b g King's Theatre (IRE)—Allee Sarthoise (FR) **Potensis Bloodstock Limited**
161 **WHAT'S THE SCOOP (IRE)**, 6, ch g Presenting—Dame d'harvard (USA) **M. A. C. Buckley**
162 **WHISPER (FR)**, 8, b g Astarabad (USA)—Belle Yepa (FR) **Walters Plant Hire Ltd**
163 **WHOSHOTWHO (IRE)**, 5, br g Beneficial—Inishbeg House (IRE) **The Blue Bar Partnership**
164 **WILLIAM DU BERLAIS (FR)**, 5, b g Trempolino (USA)—Harpyes (FR) **J. P. McManus**
165 **WILLIAM HENRY (IRE)**, 6, b g King's Theatre (IRE)—Cincuenta (IRE) **Walters Plant Hire Ltd**
166 **WISHING WIND**, 6, b m Kayf Tara—Romantic Dream **Her Majesty The Queen**

THREE-YEAR-OLDS

167 **THYMIAN GIRL (GER)**, ch f Sholokhov (IRE)—Tres Passing (FR) **Mr J. Meyer**

Other Owners: Mrs F. Bartlett, Mr M. J. Bell, Mrs D. C. Broad, A. R. Bromley, B. G. Brown, E. Burke, Mr M. J. Butt, Mr A. Chandler, Mr P. R. Clinton, Mr G. Cooper, P. J. Cornell, Mrs B. Cotton, J. D. Cotton, Mr J. P. Craft, Mr C. T. Cromwell, G. M. Davies, Mr D. Downie, A. T. Eggleton, Mrs B. D. M. Fenton, Mr L. Garside-Beattie, Mr R. J. H. Geffen, Mr C. M. Giles, G. F. Goode, Mr C. M. Grech, C. O. P. Hanbury, R. V. Harding, Ms N. C. Heath, N. J. Henderson, Highclere Nominated Partner Limited, Highclere Thoroughbred Racing Ltd, Mr C. J. Hill, Mr A. J. Hill, Mr B. M. Hillier, J. Hornsey, Mr J. L. Housden, D. Humphreys, J. F. Jarvis, Mr J. Jenner, Lady J. A. Kay, Mrs E. A. Kelvin-Hughes, Mr C. Kimmins, Mr M. B. J. Kimmins, Mrs A. M. Kirk, M. R. Landau, Mr R. Lewis, K. F. J. Loads, Mr J. Lomas, Miss N. Martin, Mr I. D. Miller, P. J. Mills, W. D. C. Minton, Mr J. Monaghan, Mrs L. K. Morgan, M. Morgan, S. E. Munir, Mrs D. C. Nicholson, Miss M. Noden, Mr L. D. Nunn, Mr J. Olliffe, Mrs C. R. Orr, Mr J. A. M. Orr, M. A. Osborne, Mrs G. E. D. Ospedale, T. S. Palin, Mr C. M. Parker, Mr S. J. Parkin, Mr D. E. Perchard, S. R. C. Philip, Mrs J. Plumptre, Mrs M. J. Potter, J. E. Potter, Brig C. K. Price, M. Prince, Miss P. Purewal, Mrs B. Reid, Mrs S. Ricci, Sir J. H. Ritblat, Miss P. A. Ross, Mr H. S. Sharpstone, Mr E. J. N. Sheasby, Mrs D. Sheasby, Mr G. A. Sheppard, Mr J. Simpson, Mr A. Singh, Mr I. Souede, D. F. Sumpter, Lord Vestey, Mr L. J. Westwood, Mr T. N. White, Miss S. Wilde, Mr M. J. F. T. Wilson.

Jockey (NH): Barry Geraghty, Andrew Tinkler, Nico De Boinville, Peter Carberry, David Bass.
Conditional: Jeremiah McGrath, Freddie Mitchell.

---

293 | **MR PAUL HENDERSON, Whitsbury**
Postal: **1 Manor Farm Cottage, Whitsbury, Fordingbridge, Hampshire, SP6 3QP**
Contacts: PHONE (01725) 518113 FAX (01725) 518113 MOBILE (07958) 482213
E-MAIL phendersonracing@gmail.com

1 **ALRIGHT BENNY (IRE)**, 13, ch g Beneficial—Flashey Thyne (IRE) **The Ray Of Hope Partnership**
2 **APPROPRIATE (FR)**, 6, b m Kapgarde (FR)—Oreli (FR) **The Ray Of Hope Partnership**
3 **CHARGING INDIAN (IRE)**, 10, b g Chevalier (IRE)—Kathy Tolfa (IRE) **Miss J. Patten**
4 **DANCING DIK**, 11, b g Diktat—Maureena (IRE) **The Ray Of Hope Partnership**
5 **DOITFORTHEVILLAGE (IRE)**, 7, b g Turtle Island (IRE)—Last Chance Lady (IRE) **The Rockbourne Partnership**
6 **ENNISNAG (IRE)**, 11, b m Bach (IRE)—Ask Mother (IRE) **The Ray Of Hope Partnership**
7 **GARDE FOU (FR)**, 10, b g Kapgarde (FR)—Harpyes (FR) **John Finch & Mareilder Racing Part 1**
8 **LIFE OF A LUSO (IRE)**, 12, b g Luso—Life of A Lady (IRE) **Mareildar Racing Part 1**
9 **MERRY MAST (USA)**, 7, b g Mizzen Mast (USA)—Dancing Shoes (IRE) **Mrs J. L. Chappell**
10 **MISS OSCAROSE (IRE)**, 9, b m Oscar (IRE)—Private Rose (IRE) **Sarah Habib & Ed Hawkings**
11 **MOUNT VESUVIUS (IRE)**, 8, b g Spartacus (IRE)—Parker's Cove (USA) **The Ray Of Hope Partnership**
12 **PADDY THE STOUT (IRE)**, 11, b g Oscar Schindler (IRE)—Misty Silks **John Finch & Mareilder Racing Part 1**

MR PAUL HENDERSON - Continued

13 **RIOR (IRE)**, 9, b g King's Theatre (IRE)—Sara's Gold (IRE) **The Ray Of Hope Partnership**
14 **SIZING SAHARA**, 8, gr g Shirocco (GER)—Aristocratique **Mrs J. L. Chappell**
15 **STARKIE**, 9, b g Putra Sandhurst (IRE)—Lysways **D. S. Dennis**
16 **TALK OF THE SOUTH (IRE)**, 7, b g Milan—Smalltowntalk (IRE) **The Rockbourne Partnership**
17 **THEPARTYSOVER**, 11, gr g Cloudings (IRE)—Just A Tipple (IRE) **The Ray Of Hope Partnership**
18 **TREACY HOTELS BOY (IRE)**, 9, br g Overbury (IRE)—Bridgehotel Rose (IRE) **The Rockbourne Partnership**
19 **UN BEAU ROMAN (FR)**, 8, bl g Roman Saddle (IRE)—Koukie (FR) **John H. W. Finch & The Romans**

THREE-YEAR-OLDS

20 **MEDBURN DREAM**, b c Showcasing—Tiegs (IRE) **Mr E. L. Evans**

Other Owners: J. H. W. Finch, Mr R. J. Galpin, Mrs S. J. Habib, Mr E. J. Hawkings, P. F. Henderson, J. F. R. Stainer.

---

294 MR MICHAEL HERRINGTON, Thirsk
Postal: Garbutt Farm, Cold Kirby, Thirsk, North Yorkshire, YO7 2HJ
Contacts: PHONE (01845) 597793 MOBILE (07855) 396858 / (07554) 558217
E-MAIL info@michaelherringtonracing.co.uk WEBSITE www.michaelherringtonracing.co.uk

1 **ANOTHER LINCOLNDAY**, 5, ch g Desideratum—Another Paris **Mr J. D. Spensley & Mrs M. A. Spensley**
2 **DUKE COSIMO**, 6, ch g Pivotal—Nannina **Mr Stuart Herrington**
3 **HADAJ**, 7, b g Green Desert (USA)—My Amalie (IRE) **Mr J. S. Herrington**
4 **INDASTAR**, 6, b g Indesatchel (IRE)—Charcoal **Mr K. Blackstone**
5 **INSHAA**, 4, b c Dansili—Hidden Brief **Sprint Thoroughbred Racing Ltd**
6 **MACHIAVELIAN STORM (IRE)**, 4, gr f Dark Angel (IRE)—Terri's Charmer (USA) **Mrs H. Lloyd-Herrington**
7 **MERCERS ROW**, 9, b g Bahamian Bounty—Invincible **Mr K. Fitzsimons**
8 **MISHAAL (IRE)**, 6, ch g Kheleyf (USA)—My Dubai (IRE) **Kelvyn Gracie & Lawrence McCaughey**
9 **PRYERS PRINCESS**, 4, ch f Medicean—Opening Ceremony (USA) **Mr H. Hurst**
10 **TICKS THE BOXES (IRE)**, 4, ch g Fast Company (IRE)—Swan Sea **Mr & Mrs D. Yates**

THREE-YEAR-OLDS

11 **BAHRIKATE**, b f Bahri (USA)—Dispol Katie **Mr K. Fitzsimons**
12 **BETTERCALLPHOENIX**, b g Motivator—Opening Ceremony (USA) **Mr H. Hurst**
13 **DAZEEKHA**, b f Captain Gerrard (IRE)—Dazakhee **Mr & Mrs D. Yates**
14 **INTALZA (IRE)**, br f Intikhab (USA)—Talzaqueen (SWI) **Mr K. Fitzsimons**
15 B g Dutch Art—Miss Respect **Mr H. Hurst**

Other Owners: Mr Kelvyn Gracie, Mr Lawrence McCaughey, Mr D. Silversides, Mrs Annaley Yates, Mr D. Yates.

Assistant Trainer: Helen Lloyd-Herrington

---

295 MR PETER HIATT, Banbury
Postal: Six Ash Farm, Hook Norton, Banbury, Oxfordshire, OX15 5DB
Contacts: PHONE (01608) 737255 FAX (01608) 730641 MOBILE (07973) 751115

1 **COCONELL**, 6, b m Rock of Gibraltar (IRE)—Marula (IRE) **Mr C. Demczak**
2 **FLAG OF GLORY**, 9, b g Trade Fair—Rainbow Sky **N. D. Edden**
3 **GEEAITCH**, 7, ch g Cockney Rebel (IRE)—Grand Rebecca (IRE) **P. J. R. Gardner**
4 **KIRKMAN (IRE)**, 5, ch g Virtual—Validate **P. W. Hiatt**
5 **MEXICAN JIM**, 4, ch g Dubai Destination (USA)—Artic Bliss **First Chance Racing**
6 **MEXICAN MICK**, 7, ch g Atraf—Artic Bliss **First Chance Racing**
7 **MONARCH MAID**, 5, b m Captain Gerrard (IRE)—Orange Lily **Mr C. Demczak**
8 **PHILHARMONIC HALL**, 8, b g Victory Note (USA)—Lambast **P. Porter**
9 **ROXY LANE**, 7, b m Byron—Comme Ca **Mr R G Robinson & Mr R D Robinson**
10 **SHIRATAKI (IRE)**, 8, b g Cape Cross (IRE)—Noodle Soup (USA) **P. W. Hiatt**
11 **TARAKKOM (FR)**, 4, ch g Naaqoos—Sahabah (USA) **P. Kelly**
12 **TATAWU (IRE)**, 4, b g Mawatheeq (USA)—Mooteeah (IRE) **R. N. Coles**
13 **WILDOMAR**, 7, b g Kyllachy—Murrieta **P. W. Hiatt**

THREE-YEAR-OLDS

14 **ALLEN'S FOLLY**, b f Captain Gerrard (IRE)—Rabarama **P. W. Hiatt**
15 **OLYMPIC DUEL (IRE)**, b g Acclamation—Olympic Medal **R. G. & R. D. Robinson**
16 **RED TEA**, ch f Sakhee (USA)—Maimoona (IRE) **P. W. Hiatt**

MR PETER HIATT - Continued

Other Owners: Mr T. J. Boniface, Mr A. Bruton, Mr R. Robinson, Mr R. D. Robinson, Mr Mark J. Savage.

Assistant Trainer: Mrs E. Hiatt

Jockey (flat): William Carson, Chris Catlin. **Apprentice:** Ciaran McKee. **Amateur:** Miss M. Edden, Miss M. King.

---

296 **MR PHILIP HIDE, Findon**
Postal: **7 Nepfield Close, Findon, Worthing, West Sussex, BN14 0SS**
Contacts: **MOBILE (07768) 233324**

1 AYR OF ELEGANCE, 4, b f Motivator—Gaelic Swan (IRE) **Mr W. F. N. Davis**
2 BALLROOM ANGEL, 4, gr f Dark Angel (IRE)—Ballroom Dancer (IRE) **Mr P. E. Hide**
3 BLACK CAESAR (IRE), 5, b g Bushranger (IRE)—Evictress (IRE) **The Long Furlong**
4 COUGAR KID (IRE), 5, b g Yeats (IRE)—Western Skylark (IRE) **Mr H J O'Reilly & Mr E Tynan**
5 GOTASINGGOTADANCE, 4, b f Royal Applause—Water Gipsy **Mrs S. R. Wadman**
6 LUCKY LEYF, 4, b f Kheleyf (USA)—Lucky Dice **Heart Of The South Racing**
7 SNOW CONDITIONS, 5, b m Aussie Rules (USA)—Snow Gonal (FR) **P. Turner, J. Davies & The Hides**
8 ZAMBEASY, 5, b g Zamindar (USA)—Hanella (IRE) **Heart Of The South Racing**

THREE-YEAR-OLDS

9 BERGHOLT (IRE), b c Sir Percy—Sularina (IRE) **Dick Hine & Nigel Thomas**
10 B c Fastnet Rock (AUS)—Cozzene's Angel (USA)
11 B c Fastnet Rock (AUS)—Dance Parade (USA)
12 MONTYCRISTO, b c Motivator—Water Gipsy **Priesthawes Partnership**
13 ONEHELLUVATOUCH, gr f Hellvelyn—Soft Touch (IRE) **Heart Of The South Racing**
14 SUPER SEER, b g Pivotal—Entre Nous (IRE) **Horace Cheng & Brook Stud Bloodstock**
15 TILLY'S BRIDGE, b f Avonbridge—Ivory Lace **The Bridget Partnership**

TWO-YEAR-OLDS

16 B g 21/4 Equiano (FR)—Akhira (Emperor Jones (USA)) (4761) **Mr P. E. Hide**
17 B c 8/2 Poet's Voice—China (Royal Academy (USA)) (32000)
18 B f 14/2 Lando (GER)—Teresa Balbi (Master Willie)
19 Br c 9/1 Pivotal—Vassaria (IRE) (Rock of Gibraltar (IRE)) **Hide & Seekers**
20 B c 2/4 Poet's Voice—Zuleika Dobson (Cadeaux Genereux) (17000) **Mr Y. O. Wong**

Other Owners: Mrs E. Adamski, Mr M. H. Bunting, Mr H. L. D. Cheng, J. Davies, Mr T. Francis, Mr A. G. Hide, Mr R. Hine, Mr S. H. Hughes, Mrs P. A. Miles, Mr H. J. O'Reilly, J. R. Penny, Mr G. Reeves, Mr N. A. D. Thomas, Mr P. Turner, Mrs P. M. Tyler, Mr E. D. Tynan, D. G. A. E. Woods, Mr E. W. J. Woods.

---

297 **MRS LAWNEY HILL, Aston Rowant**
Postal: **Woodway Farm, Aston Rowant, Watlington, Oxford, OX49 5SJ**
Contacts: **PHONE (01844) 353051 FAX (01844) 354751 MOBILE (07769) 862648**
E-MAIL lawney@lawneyhill.co.uk WEBSITE www.lawneyhill.co.uk

1 BERTENBAR, 12, b g Bertolini (USA)—Ardenbar **Mrs C. A. Wyatt**
2 BILLY TWYFORD (IRE), 9, b g Brian Boru—The Distaff Spy **Mr A. J. Weller**
3 CHANGEOFLUCK (IRE), 8, b g Gold Well—Sotattie **For Fun Partnership**
4 CROSSHARE, 5, b g Crosspeace (IRE)—Perecapa (IRE) **Dr P. Stutchbury**
5 DOUBLE HANDFUL (GER), 10, bl g Pentire—Durania (GER) **A. Hill**
6 MISS MAYFAIR (IRE), 9, b m Indian Danehill (IRE)—Cocktail Party (USA) **Mr R Carmichael & Alan Hill**
7 OLIVER'S HILL (IRE), 7, b g Shantou (USA)—River Rouge (IRE) **Mrs D. M. Caudwell**
8 QUINZ (FR), 12, b g Robin des Champs (FR)—Altesse du Mou (FR) **A. L. Cohen**
9 ROYAL ETIQUETTE (IRE), 9, b g Royal Applause—Alpine Gold (IRE) **A. Hill**
10 SECURE CLOUD (IRE), 5, b g High Chaparral (IRE)—Cabo (FR) **Prolinx Limited**
11 SHIMBA HILLS, 5, b g Sixties Icon—Search Party **Shimba Hills/Fortnum Racing Partnership**
12 TAKE A BOW, 7, b g Norse Dancer (IRE)—Madame Illusion (FR) **Take A Bow Partnership**

Other Owners: Mr R. J. Carmichael, Mrs D. Clark, Ms G. H. Hedley, Mr B. L. Hiskey, Mr B. P. Jessup, D. F. Sumpter.

Jockey (flat): George Baker. **Jockey (NH):** Aidan Coleman, Nick Scholfield. **Apprentice:** Megan Nicholls. **Amateur:** Mr Joe Hill.

298 MR MARTIN HILL, Totnes
Postal: **The Barn, Knaves Ash Stables, Nr Redpost, Littlehempston, Totnes, Devon, TQ9 6NG**
Contacts: PHONE **(01803) 813102** MOBILE **(07980) 490220**
E-MAIL **info@martinhillracing.co.uk** WEBSITE **www.martinhillracing.co.uk**

1 **BADILOU (FR)**, 5, b br g Ballingarry (IRE)—Doumia (FR) **The French Connection**
2 **CARRE NOIR (FR)**, 7, b br g Clety (FR)—Luella (FR) **The Pi Eyed Squared**
3 **ELLA'S PROMISE**, 7, ch m Doyen (IRE)—Sweet N' Twenty **2014 EP**
4 **LADYBIRD BLUE**, 5, b m Captain Gerrard (IRE)—Pacifiste (IRE) **Kittymore Racing**
5 **MEXICAN BORDER (GER)**, 7, b g Sholokhov (IRE)—Moricana (GER) **The Detroit Reds**
6 **MIXELLE DAYS**, 5, gr m Sagamix (FR)—One of Those Days **Merv Leach & Jon Hearne**
7 **MONSIEUR DARSI (IRE)**, 6, b g Darsi (FR)—Durgams Delight (IRE) **Mrs S. A. White**
8 **RYDON PYNES**, 8, b g Beat All (USA)—Persian Smoke **The Rydon Pynes Partnership**

Other Owners: Mr J. L. Coombs, Mr Jon Hearne, Mr Martin Hill, Mrs Amanda Hutchings, Mr David Luscombe, Mrs Hilda M. Luscombe, Mrs Elizabeth Mogford, Mr R. Thomasson.

Assistant Trainer: Rachel Williams

Jockey (flat): Luke Morris. **Jockey (NH):** Jeremiah McGrath. **Conditional:** Alice Mills. **Amateur:** Miss Bryony Frost.

299 MR CHARLES HILLS, Lambourn
Postal: **Wetherdown House, Lambourn, Hungerford, Berkshire, RG17 8UB**
Contacts: PHONE **(01488) 71548** FAX **(01488) 72823**
E-MAIL **info@charleshills.co.uk** WEBSITE **www.charleshills.com**

1 **ALNASHAMA**, 4, b g Dubawi (IRE)—Ghanaati (USA) **Mr Hamdan Al Maktoum**
2 **B FIFTY TWO (IRE)**, 7, br g Dark Angel (IRE)—Petite Maxine **Gary and Linnet Woodward**
3 **COMMEMORATIVE**, 4, ch c Zamindar (USA)—Revered **Mr K. Abdullah**
4 **COTAI GLORY**, 4, ch c Exceed And Excel (AUS)—Continua (USA) **Kangyu Int. Racing (HK) Ltd & Mr F Ma**
5 **DUTCH CONNECTION**, 4, ch c Dutch Art—Endless Love (IRE) **Mrs Susan Roy and Cheveley Park Stud**
6 **FREE TO LOVE**, 4, br f Equiano (FR)—All Quiet **Lady Whent**
7 **HAKAM (USA)**, 4, b c War Front (USA)—Lauren Byrd (USA) **Mr Hamdan Al Maktoum**
8 **HEATSTROKE**, 4, b c Galileo (IRE)—Walklikeanegyptian (IRE) **Mrs Fitri Hay**
9 **JALLOTA**, 5, b g Rock of Gibraltar (IRE)—Lady Lahar **Mrs Fitri Hay**
10 **KILL OR CURE (IRE)**, 4, b g Acclamation—Welsh Mist **Mr Hamdan Al Maktoum**
11 **LUCKY BEGGAR (IRE)**, 6, gr g Verglas (IRE)—Lucky Clio (IRE) **Hon Mrs Corbett, C Wright, Mrs B W Hills**
12 **MAGICAL MEMORY (IRE)**, 4, gr g Zebedee—Marasem **Kennet Valley Thoroughbreds I**
13 **OGBOURNE DOWNS**, 6, b g Royal Applause—Helen Sharp **S W Group Logistics Limited**
14 **OPITO BAY (IRE)**, 4, ch f Bahamian Bounty—Reveuse de Jour (IRE) **Sir Peter Vela**
15 **PASSING STAR**, 5, b h Royal Applause—Passing Hour (USA) **Mr John C. Grant**
16 **STRATH BURN**, 4, b c Equiano (FR)—Irish Light (USA) **Qatar Racing Limited & R A Bartlett**
17 **TANZEEL (IRE)**, 5, b g Elusive City (USA)—Royal Fizz (IRE) **Mr Hamdan Al Maktoum**

THREE-YEAR-OLDS

18 **A MOMENTOFMADNESS**, b c Elnadim (USA)—Royal Blush **Tony Wechsler & Ann Plummer**
19 **ALEEF (IRE)**, b c Kodiac—Okba (USA) **Mr Hamdan Al Maktoum**
20 **AMAANY**, br f Teofilo (IRE)—Almass (IRE) **Mr Hamdan Al Maktoum**
21 **ANCIENT WORLD (USA)**, ch c Giant's Causeway (USA)—Satulagi (USA) **Mrs Fitri Hay**
22 **ARCAMIST**, gr f Arcano (IRE)—Good Enough (FR) **Mrs Julie Martin and David R. Martin**
23 **ARITHMETIC (IRE)**, b g Invincible Spirit (IRE)—Multiplication **Morecombe,Anderson,Sangster,Farquhar**
24 **BEAULY**, ch f Sea The Stars (IRE)—Pickle **Mr R. A. Bartlett**
25 **BIG SHOES (IRE)**, br g Big Bad Bob (IRE)—Caro Mio (IRE) **Gary and Linnet Woodward & Partner**
26 **BURMA ROAD**, b f Poet's Voice—Strawberry Moon (IRE) **Mr Dan Hall & Mrs Julie & David R Martin**
27 **CAPTAIN JOEY (IRE)**, b g Kodiac—Archetypal (IRE) **Mr A. L. R. Morton**
28 **CARRY ME HOME**, b c Dark Angel (IRE)—Toffee Vodka (IRE) **Gary and Linnet Woodward**
29 **CASE KEY**, gr c Showcasing—Fluttering Rose **Sheikh Juma Dalmook Al Maktoum**
30 **CLIFFS OF DOVER**, b g Canford Cliffs—Basanti (USA) **Mr and Mrs J. D. Cotton**
31 **DARK CRESCENT (IRE)**, b c Elnadim (USA)—Zenella **Mr Chi Un Fred Ma**
32 **DOUBLY MOTIVATED (IRE)**, ch f Iffraaj—Chicane **Jim & Susan Hill**
33 **DREAM JOURNEY (IRE)**, ch f Dream Ahead (USA)—Khibraat **Sheikh Juma Dalmook Al Maktoum**
34 **ELRONAQ**, b g Invincible Spirit (IRE)—Cartimandua **Mr Hamdan Al Maktoum**
35 **EXOTERIC**, b c Champs Elysees—Short Dance (USA) **Mr K. Abdullah**
36 **FASHION PARADE**, b f Fastnet Rock (AUS)—Festivale (IRE) **Mr Abdulla Al Khalifa**
37 **FINISHINGTHEHAT**, b f Sixties Icon—Endless Love (IRE) **Mrs Susan Roy**

MR CHARLES HILLS - Continued

38 **FORCE (IRE)**, ch c Raven's Pass (USA)—Holly's Kid (USA) **Highclere Thoroughbred Racing**
39 **FRENCHMAN (FR)**, b c Le Havre (IRE)—Como (USA) **Kennet Valley Thoroughbreds V**
40 **GARTER (IRE)**, b f Fastnet Rock (AUS)—Princess Iris (IRE) **Highclere Thoroughbred Racing (Walpole)**
41 **GRAPEVINE (IRE)**, b c Lilbourne Lad (IRE)—High Vintage (IRE) **Mrs J. K. Powell**
42 **GUNMETAL (IRE)**, gr c Clodovil (IRE)—March Star (IRE) **Mrs J. K. Powell**
43 **GYPSY EYES (IRE)**, b f High Chaparral (IRE)—Brown Eyes **Mrs B. V. Sangster & Mrs Paul Shanahan**
44 **HARIKIRI (IRE)**, ch f Teofilo (IRE)—Queen of Lyons (USA) **Plantation Stud**
45 **HEARTSTONE (IRE)**, b f Fastnet Rock (AUS)—Eva's Request (IRE) **Lady Bamford**
46 **HENSHAW**, b g Archipenko (USA)—Memory Lane **Mr Edwin Cheung**
47 **HIGH GROUNDS (IRE)**, b c High Chaparral (IRE)—Civility Cat (USA) **A M Shead, Cavendish Inv. Ltd, J Hanson**
48 **IBN MALIK (IRE)**, ch c Raven's Pass (USA)—Moon's Whisper (USA) **Mr Hamdan Al Maktoum**
49 **INITIALLY**, b f Dansili—Emplane (USA) **Mr K. Abdullah**
50 **IONA ISLAND**, b f Dutch Art—Still Small Voice **Mr John C. Grant**
51 **IRISH ECLARE (IRE)**, b c Equiano (FR)—Delitme (IRE) **Mrs Clare Kelvin & Mrs B W Hills**
52 **JADAAYIL**, b f Oasis Dream—Muthabara (IRE) **Mr Hamdan Al Maktoum**
53 **LAKE PLACID**, b c Champs Elysees—Phantom Wind (USA) **Mr K. Abdullah**
54 **LITTLE VOICE (USA)**, b f Scat Daddy (USA)—Excelente (IRE) **Mr & Mrs T O'Donohoe**
55 **LORD KELVIN (IRE)**, br g Iffraaj—Eastern Appeal (IRE) **Mrs Fitri Hay**
56 **LORD TOPPER**, b c Sir Percy—Fugnina **Hillwood Racing, Mick & Janice Mariscotti**
57 **LOVE ON THE ROCKS (IRE)**, ch f Exceed And Excel (AUS)—My Love Thomas (IRE) **The Chriselliam Partnership**
58 **MAHFOOZ (IRE)**, b c Teofilo (IRE)—Itqaan (USA) **Mr Hamdan Al Maktoum**
59 **MARBOOH (IRE)**, b c Dark Angel (IRE)—Muluk (IRE) **Mr Hamdan Al Maktoum**
60 **MENAI (IRE)**, b c Dark Angel (IRE)—Glisten **Julie Martin & David R. Martin & Partner**
61 **MISHWAAR**, b g Arcano (IRE)—Misdaqeya **Mr Hamdan Al Maktoum**
62 **MONDRIAN JONES**, b c Dutch Art—Akhira **Jim & Susan Hill**
63 **MOORSIDE**, b f Champs Elysees—Marching West (USA) **Mr K. Abdullah**
64 **MOOTAHARER (IRE)**, b c Dubawi (IRE)—Tahrir (IRE) **Mr Hamdan Al Maktoum**
65 **MUSTALLIB (IRE)**, b c Iffraaj—Rocking **Mr Hamdan Al Maktoum**
66 **PEPPARD (IRE)**, b f Dansili—Arum Lily (USA) **Mr K. Abdullah**
67 **PRIVATE JET**, b c Paco Boy (IRE)—Sheer Indulgence (FR) **Mr Lee Tze Bun Marces**
68 **QUEEN'S CODE (IRE)**, b f Shamardal (USA)—Dehbanu (IRE) **Sheikh Rashid Dalmook Al Maktoum**
69 **RAVELIN (USA)**, ch f Congrats (USA)—Rouwaki (USA) **Mr K. Abdullah**
70 **SAHREEJ (IRE)**, gr c Zebedee—Petite Boulangere (IRE) **Mr Hamdan Al Maktoum**
71 **SANTE (IRE)**, b f Dream Ahead (USA)—Zeiting (IRE) **Mr & Mrs R. Kelvin-Hughes**
72 **SEPAL (USA)**, b f Afleet Alex (USA)—Faraway Flower (USA) **Mr K. Abdullah**
73 **SERRADURA (IRE)**, b f Acclamation—Days of Summer (IRE) **Kangyu Int. Racing (HK) Ltd & Mr F Ma**
74 **SHANGHAI GLORY (IRE)**, ch g Exceed And Excel (AUS)—Hecuba **Kangyu Int. Racing (HK) Ltd & Mr F Ma**
75 **SHOREDITCH**, ch c Dubawi (IRE)—Revered **Mr K. Abdullah**
76 **SKARA MAE (IRE)**, b f Canford Cliffs (IRE)—Winged Valkyrie (IRE) **Marston Stud & Mrs B W Hills**
77 **SONNET (IRE)**, b f Kyllachy—Poetical (IRE) **Mr & Mrs R. Kelvin-Hughes**
78 **SUMMER COLLECTION (IRE)**, b f Teofilo (IRE)—Towards (USA) **Sheikh Juma Dalmook Al Maktoum**
79 **SWILLY SUNSET**, b g Kyllachy—Spanish Springs (IRE) **Mr John C. Grant**
80 **TAKATUL (USA)**, b c Smart Strike (CAN)—Torrestrella (IRE) **Mr Hamdan Al Maktoum**
81 **WINK AND WIN (IRE)**, b f Rip Van Winkle (IRE)—Windmill **Jim & Susan Hill**
82 **WITHHOLD**, b c Champs Elysees—Coming Back **Mr K. Abdullah**
83 **ZAAKHIR (IRE)**, b f Raven's Pass (USA)—Zahoo (IRE) **Mr Hamdan Al Maktoum**
84 **ZZORO (IRE)**, b c Manduro (GER)—Krynica (USA) **Sheikh Juma Dalmook Al Maktoum**

TWO-YEAR-OLDS

85 **AFAAK**, b c 3/3 Oasis Dream—Ghanaati (USA) (Giant's Causeway (USA))
86 Ch f 15/3 Sepoy (AUS)—Ainia (Alhaarth (IRE)) (46511)
87 **ANIF (IRE)**, br c 2/5 Cape Cross (IRE)—Cadenza (FR) (Dansili)
88 B f 5/5 Holy Roman Emperor (IRE)—Another Storm (USA) (Gone West (USA)) (265780)
89 Ch c 30/3 Power—Arpege (IRE) (Sadler's Wells (USA)) (77519)
90 **BALESTRA**, b c 15/2 Bated Breath—Nimble Thimble (USA) (Mizzen Mast (USA))
91 **BATTAASH (IRE)**, b c 10/2 Dark Angel (IRE)—Anna Law (IRE) (Lawman (FR)) (200000)
92 B c 30/1 Bated Breath—Bimini (Sadler's Wells (USA)) (47988)
93 **BODY ARMOUR (USA)**, b c 18/5 First Defence (USA)—Willstar (USA) (Nureyev (USA))
94 **BORTHWEN (IRE)**, b f 10/4 Lawman (FR)—Apticanti (USA) (Aptitude (USA)) (103359)
95 **CAPTAIN HAWK**, b c 23/4 Acclamation—Vintage Gardenia (Selkirk (USA)) (103359)
96 B f 6/4 Dark Angel (IRE)—Chelsea Morning (USA) (Giant's Causeway (USA)) (49523)
97 B c 13/2 Exceed And Excel (AUS)—Cherry Orchard (IRE) (King's Best (USA)) (240000)
98 **CORAL SEA**, gr f 4/3 Excelebration (IRE)—Tropical Paradise (IRE) (Verglas (IRE)) (100000)
99 **DAWAALEEB (USA)**, b c 2/5 Invincible Spirit (IRE)—Plaza (USA) (Chester House (USA)) (198412)

MR CHARLES HILLS - Continued

100 Ch c 27/4 Sir Percy—Dayrose (Daylami (IRE)) (55000)
101 Br f 12/2 Bated Breath—Dixey (Diktat) (66666)
102 DR GOODHEAD (FR), b f 19/4 Zoffany (IRE)—Whoosh (FR) (Muhtathir) (47619)
103 Ch f 23/2 Intikhab (USA)—Esloob (USA) (Diesis) (30000)
104 B f 16/3 Fastnet Rock (AUS)—Eva's Request (IRE) (Soviet Star (USA))
105 B f 30/4 Blame (USA)—Excelente (IRE) (Exceed And Excel (AUS)) (106837)
106 FAROOK (IRE), b c 26/2 Raven's Pass (USA)—Wrong Answer (Verglas (IRE)) (420000)
107 B c 28/3 Choisir (AUS)—Grandel (Owington) (71428)
108 B c 30/1 Galileo (IRE)—Half Queen (USA) (Deputy Minister (CAN))
109 B c 24/3 Born To Sea (IRE)—Hallowed Park (IRE) (Barathea (IRE)) (84902)
110 B f 25/3 Fastnet Rock (AUS)—Ho Hi The Moon (IRE) (Be My Guest (USA))
111 Ch c 2/5 Poet's Voice—Hora (Hernando (FR))
112 Ch f 23/1 City Zip (USA)—Imperial Pippin (USA) (Empire Maker (USA))
113 Ch c 25/3 Kendargent (FR)—Ispanka (Invincible Spirit (IRE)) (120000)
114 IT'S HOW WE ROLL (IRE), b c 20/4 Fastnet Rock (AUS)—Clodora (FR) (Linamix (FR))
115 B f 22/3 Cacique (IRE)—Jolie Etoile (Diesis)
116 KENDARARA (FR), b f 31/1 Kendargent (FR)—Damdam Freeze (FR) (Indian Rocket) (73827) .
117 KHITAAMY (USA), b c 21/1 Raven's Pass (USA)—Safarjal (IRE) (Marju (IRE))
118 MAGILLEN (IRE), ch c 12/4 Lope de Vega (IRE)—Lady Natilda (First Trump) (88593)
119 MALMAS (USA), gr c 6/1 Street Cry (IRE)—Wid (USA) (Elusive Quality (USA))
120 MANAAHIL, b f 25/2 Dubawi (IRE)—Mudaaraah (Cape Cross (IRE))
121 B c 11/5 High Chaparral (IRE)—Meiosis (USA) (Danzig (USA)) (50000)
122 B c 23/3 Casamento (IRE)—Mia Divina (Exceed And Excel (AUS)) (60000)
123 Ch c 24/2 Exceed And Excel (AUS)—Miss Queen (USA) (Miswaki (USA))
124 B c 12/4 Kodiac—Mistress Marina (AUS) (Galileo (IRE)) (92284)
125 MUDAJAJ (USA), b c 26/4 Arch (USA)—Checkered Flag (USA) (A P Indy (USA)) (259462)
126 MULHIMATTY, b f 6/2 Invincible Spirit (IRE)—Raasekha (Pivotal)
127 MUSAWAAT, b c 15/3 Equiano (FR)—Starry Sky (Oasis Dream) (95000)
128 NAFAAYES (IRE), ch f 19/4 Sea The Stars (IRE)—Shamtari (IRE) (Alhaarth (IRE))
129 NESHMEYA, b f 23/3 Lawman (FR)—High Heeled (IRE) (High Chaparral (IRE))
130 B f 1/5 Excelebration (IRE)—Never A Doubt (Night Shift (USA))
131 B c 2/2 Lope de Vega (IRE)—Olympic Medal (Nayef (USA)) (100000)
132 B c 29/3 Sir Prancealot (IRE)—Operissimo (Singspiel (IRE)) (40000)
133 Ch c 17/4 Helmet (AUS)—Park Approach (IRE) (Indian Ridge) (10000)
134 PARYS MOUNTAIN (IRE), gr c 25/2 Dark Angel (IRE)—Muzdaan (IRE) (Exceed And Excel (AUS)) (73827)
135 B c 27/3 Sepoy (AUS)—Persario (Bishop of Cashel) (152380)
136 B f 3/2 Acclamation—Poppets Sweetlove (Foxhound (USA)) (52000)
137 B c 2/2 Zoffany (IRE)—Queenie Keen (IRE) (Refuse To Bend (IRE)) (60000)
138 B c 10/4 Harbour Watch (IRE)—Renowned (IRE) (Darshaan) (59062)
139 B c 1/3 Raven's Pass (USA)—Ripalong (IRE) (Revoque (IRE)) (95000)
140 B c 20/2 Lope de Vega (IRE)—Rivabella (FR) (Iron Mask (USA)) (82000)
141 ROBIN'S PURSE, b f 10/2 Sir Percy—Morant Bay (IRE) (Montjeu (IRE))
142 B c 20/2 Myboycharlie (IRE)—Royal Confidence (Royal Applause)
143 B gr f 16/3 Dutch Art—Royal Fortune (IRE) (Invincible Spirit (IRE)) (155038)
144 Ch c 17/3 Bahamian Bounty—Royal Punch (Royal Applause) (66666)
145 RUBENS DREAM, ch c 6/3 Dutch Art—Apace (IRE) (Oasis Dream) (133333)
146 B f 27/2 Exceed And Excel (AUS)—Ruby Rocket (IRE) (Indian Rocket)
147 RUZMA (IRE), ch f 10/3 Exceed And Excel (AUS)—Laqataat (IRE) (Alhaarth (IRE))
148 B f 18/2 Oasis Dream—Short Dance (USA) (Hennessy (USA))
149 Ch f 28/3 Tamayuz—Solar Event (Galileo (IRE)) (40000)
150 SUKIWARRIOR (IRE), ch f 3/2 Power—Umniya (IRE) (Bluebird (USA)) (43809)
151 SUN BEAR, b c 8/3 Dansili—Great Heavens (Galileo (IRE))
152 SWILLY BAY (IRE), gr c 17/3 Mastercraftsman (IRE)—Eastern Appeal (IRE) (Shinko Forest (IRE)) (73827)
153 B f 24/4 Elusive Quality (USA)—Tawaarud (USA) (Gulch (USA))
154 THAAQIB, gr c 5/3 Invincible Spirit (IRE)—Light Shine (Dansili) (450000)
155 THAFEERA (USA), b f 12/2 War Front (USA)—Aqsaam (USA) (Dynaformer (USA))
156 B f 6/2 Dutch Art—Through The Forest (USA) (Forestry (USA)) (103359)
157 B f 13/4 Paco Boy (IRE)—Toffee Vodka (IRE) (Danehill Dancer (USA))
158 USTUDIO, ch c 15/3 Dutch Art—Rotunda (Pivotal) (100000)
159 B c 5/4 Lawman (FR)—Viz (IRE) (Darshaan) (66445)
160 WAQAAS, b c 2/3 Showcasing—Red Mischief (IRE) (Red Clubs (IRE)) (161904)
161 B f 10/2 Lawman (FR)—Whisp (GER) (Rainbow Quest (USA)) (65000)
162 B c 1/2 Helmet (AUS)—Without Precedent (FR) (Polish Precedent (USA)) (60000)

MR CHARLES HILLS - Continued

Other Owners: Mr W. H. Carson, Chelsea Thoroughbreds - Raker, Mr Alastair Donald, Mr M. P. Gibbens, Mrs Christopher Hanbury, Major Christopher Hanbury, The Helmet Club, 5 Hertford Street, Mr C. B. Hills, Mr B. W. Hills, Mrs Philippa Hills, Saleh Al Homaizi & Imad Al Sagar, Mr D. M. James, Mr Steve Jenkins, Mrs John Magnier, Mr N. Martin, Andy Smith & Friends, The Hon Mrs P. Stanley, Mr P. Winkworth.

Assistant Trainers: Kevin Mooney, Joe Herbert

Jockey (flat): Darryll Holland.

MR MARK HOAD, Lewes
Postal: **Windmill Lodge Stables, Spital Road, Lewes, East Sussex, BN7 1LS**
Contacts: **PHONE (01273) 477124/(01273) 480691 FAX (01273) 477124 MOBILE (07742) 446168**
E-MAIL markhoad@aol.com

1 **AL GUWAIR (IRE)**, 6, b g Shirocco (GER)—Katariya (IRE) **G. C. Brice**
2 **GLIMMER OF HOPE**, 5, b g Tiger Hill (IRE)—Fontaine House **Mrs I. L. Sneath**
3 **HIGHSALVIA COSMOS**, 5, b g High Chaparral (IRE)—Salvia **J. Baden White**
4 **MOVIE MAGIC**, 5, b m Multiplex—Alucica **Mr B Pay**
5 **RAGDOLLIANNA**, 12, b m Kayf Tara—Jupiters Princess **Mr D. M. & Mrs M. A. Newland**
6 **SANTADELACRUZE**, 7, b g Pastoral Pursuits—Jupiters Princess **R Hoad & I Headington**
7 **SEBS SENSEI (IRE)**, 5, ch g Art Connoisseur—Capetown Girl **Mr M. L. Waters**
8 **STAFF SERGEANT**, 9, b g Dubawi (IRE)—Miss Particular (IRE) **Mr M. L. Waters**
9 **TATTING**, 7, ch g Street Cry (IRE)—Needlecraft (IRE) **Mrs I. L. Sneath**

TWO-YEAR-OLDS

10 B c 31/1 Mayson—Roshina (IRE) (Chevalier (IRE)) (4285)

Other Owners: I.R. Headington, R. P. C. Hoad, D. M. Newland, Mrs M. A. Newland.

MR PHILIP HOBBS, Minehead
Postal: **Sandhill, Bilbrook, Minehead, Somerset, TA24 6HA**
Contacts: PHONE (01984) 640366 FAX (01984) 641124 MOBILE (07860) 729795
E-MAIL pjhobbs@pjhobbs.com WEBSITE www.pjhobbs.com

1 **ACCORDING TO HARRY (IRE)**, 7, b g Old Vic—Cassilis (IRE) **Bradley Partnership**
2 **AL ALFA**, 9, ch g Alflora (IRE)—Two For Joy (IRE) **The Hon J. R. Drummond**
3 **ALLEE BLEUE (IRE)**, 6, ch g Mount Nelson—Murrieta **A. L. Cohen**
4 **ANTIPHONY (IRE)**, 5, b g Royal Anthem (USA)—Hazel's Glory (IRE) **Mr M. C. Sargent**
5 **ASTON CANTLOW**, 8, b g Hurricane Run (IRE)—Princess Caraboo (IRE) **Mr A. R. E. Ash**
6 **ATIRELARIGO (FR)**, 6, b g Puit d'or (GER)—Ouchka (FR) **Mrs K. V. Vann**
7 **BACCHANEL (FR)**, 5, b g Vendangeur—Pardielle (FR) **Gold & Blue Limited**
8 **BALTHAZAR KING (IRE)**, 12, b g King's Theatre (IRE)—Afdala (IRE) **The Brushmakers**
9 **BANYU (FR)**, 5, b g Dylan Thomas (IRE)—Banyu Dewi (GER) **David Maxwell Racing & Barber Wadlow Ltd**
10 4, B f Winged Love (IRE)—Battle Over (FR) **Bradley Partnership**
11 **BEAU DU BRIZAIS (FR)**, 4, gr g Kapgarde (FR)—Belle du Brizais (FR) **Mrs C. Skan**
12 **BERTIE BORU (IRE)**, 9, b g Brian Boru—Sleeven Lady **Unity Farm Holiday Centre Ltd**
13 **BILBROOK BLAZE**, 6, b g Kayf Tara—Za Beau (IRE) **Owners For Owners: Bilbrook Blaze**
14 **BINCOMBE**, 8, gr g Indian Danehill (IRE)—Siroyalta (IRE) **M. Short**
15 **BOLD HENRY**, 10, b g Kayf Tara—Madam Min **J. P. McManus**
16 **BRAAVOS**, 5, br g Presenting—Tatanka (IRE) **Mrs D. L. Whateley**
17 **BRADFORD BRIDGE (IRE)**, 4, b g Milan—Isis Du Berlais (FR) **Brocade Racing**
18 **BRISE VENDEENNE (FR)**, 5, gr m Dom Alco (FR)—Naiade Mag (FR) **D. J. Burke**
19 **BROTHER TEDD**, 7, gr g Kayf Tara—Neltina **Scrase Farms**
20 **CAPTAIN BOCELLI (IRE)**, 7, b g Kayf Tara—Beautiful Tune (FR) **Mrs D. L. Whateley**
21 **CARRIGMORNA KING (IRE)**, 10, b g King's Theatre (IRE)—Carrigmorna Flyer (IRE) **R. & Mrs J. E. Gibbs**
22 **CASPER KING (IRE)**, 5, b g Scorpion (IRE)—Princess Supreme (IRE) **The Brushmakers**
23 **CATHERINES WELL**, 7, b m Kayf Tara—Dudeen (IRE) **Mr M. Pendarves**
24 **CHAMPAGNE WEST (IRE)**, 8, b g Westerner—Wyndham Sweetmarie (IRE) **R. S. Brookhouse**
25 **CHELTENIAN (FR)**, 10, b g Astarabad (USA)—Salamaite (FR) **R. S. Brookhouse**
26 **COPPER KAY**, 6, b m Kayf Tara—Presenting Copper (IRE) **Aiden Murphy & Alan Peterson**
27 **CORRIE LOCH**, 4, b f King's Theatre (IRE)—Penneyrose Bay **Sir Christopher & Lady Wates**

MR PHILIP HOBBS - Continued

28 4, B g Robin des Champs (FR)—Crystal Stream (IRE) **T. D. J. Syder**
29 **DALIA POUR MOI (FR)**, 7, gr g Daliapour (IRE)—Khariyada (FR) **Highclere Thoroughbred Racing - Dalia**
30 **DESERT RETREAT (IRE)**, 5, b g Sandmason—Suny House **Louisville Syndicate III**
31 **DRAYTONIAN (IRE)**, 6, b g King's Theatre (IRE)—Full of Birds (FR) **Mrs D. L. Whateley**
32 4, B g Arcadio (GER)—Drinadaly (IRE) **Mr & Mrs Paul & Clare Rooney**
33 **DRUMLEE SUNSET (IRE)**, 6, br g Royal Anthem (USA)—Be My Sunset (IRE) **R. S. Brookhouse**
34 **DUKE DES CHAMPS (IRE)**, 6, b g Robin des Champs (FR)—
Ballycowan Lady (IRE) **Diana Whateley & Tim Syder**
35 **DUNRAVEN STORM (IRE)**, 11, br g Presenting—Foxfire **Mrs K. V. Vann**
36 **EARDISLAND**, 6, b m Kayf Tara—Aranga (IRE) **Unity Farm Holiday Centre Ltd**
37 **FILBERT (IRE)**, 10, b g Oscar (IRE)—Coca's Well (IRE) **R Triple H**
38 **FINGAL BAY (IRE)**, 10, b g King's Theatre (IRE)—Lady Marguerrite **Mrs C. Skan**
39 **FOR GOOD MEASURE (IRE)**, 5, b g King's Theatre (IRE)—Afdala (IRE) **J. P. McManus**
40 **GALA BALL (IRE)**, 6, b g Flemensfirth (USA)—Nuit des Chartreux (FR) **R. & Mrs J. E. Gibbs**
41 **GARDE LA VICTOIRE (FR)**, 7, b g Kapgarde (FR)—Next Victory (FR) **Mrs D. L. Whateley**
42 **GEORGIE LAD (IRE)**, 8, b g Gold Well—Top Step (IRE) **D R Peppiatt & Partners (Georgie Lad)**
43 **GOLDEN DOYEN (IRE)**, 5, b g Doyen (IRE)—Goldsamt (GER) **Merry Old Souls**
44 **ICONIC STAR**, 6, b m Sixties Icon—Cullen Bay (IRE) **C Bothway & R Boyce**
45 **IF IN DOUBT (IRE)**, 8, b g Heron Island (IRE)—Catchers Day (IRE) **J. P. McManus**
46 **IMPERIAL PRESENCE (IRE)**, 5, ch g Presenting—Penneyrose Bay **Sir Christopher & Lady Wates**
47 **INK MASTER (IRE)**, 6, b g Whitmore's Conn (USA)—Welsh Connection (IRE) **A. E. Peterson**
48 **JABOLTISKI (SPA)**, 4, b g Delfos (IRE)—Sonic Sea (IRE) **Mrs S. J. Lanz**
49 **KAHALEESI**, 4, b f Shirocco (GER)—Maiden Voyage **Valda Burke & Diana L Whateley**
50 **KAYF ADVENTURE**, 5, b g Kayf Tara—My Adventure (IRE) **Mrs K. V. Vann**
51 **KAYF WILLOW**, 7, b m Kayf Tara—Mrs Philip **Newton Abbot Racing Syndicate**
52 **KRUZHLININ (GER)**, 9, ch g Sholokhov (IRE)—Karuma (GER) **Mr & Mrs Paul & Clare Rooney**
53 **KUBLAI (FR)**, 6, b g Laveron—Java Dawn (IRE) **Mr D. W. Hill**
54 **LAPALALA (IRE)**, 5, b m Oscar (IRE)—Lala Nova (IRE) **Dr V. M. G. Ferguson**
55 **LITTLE MISS POET**, 4, b f Yeats (IRE)—R de Rien Sivola (FR) **M. J. Tuckey**
56 **LOUIS' VAC POUCH (IRE)**, 4, b g Oscar (IRE)—Coming Home (FR) **The Vacuum Pouch Company Limited**
57 **MENDIP EXPRESS (IRE)**, 10, b br g King's Theatre (IRE)—Mulberry (IRE) **David Maxwell Racing Limited**
58 **MIDNIGHT GLORY**, 4, b f Midnight Legend—Land of Glory **Mrs L. R. Lovell**
59 **MIDNIGHT VELVET**, 6, b m Midnight Legend—Tamergale (IRE) **Mrs Caren Walsh & Mrs Lesley Field**
60 **MILES TO MILAN (IRE)**, 6, b g Milan—Princesse Rooney (FR) **Mrs Lesley Field & Mrs Caren Walsh**
61 **MISS MOBOT**, 6, b m Midnight Legend—Fleur de Nikos (IRE) **Mrs J. C. P. Walter**
62 **MOTHER BROWN (IRE)**, 5, b m Scorpion (IRE)—Luck of The Deise (IRE) **Mr M. Pendarves**
63 **MOUNTAIN KING**, 7, b g Definite Article—Belle Magello (FR) **Mrs D. L. Whateley**
64 **NO COMMENT**, 5, br g Kayf Tara—Dizzy Frizzy **J. P. McManus**
65 **ONE COOL SCORPION (IRE)**, 5, b g Scorpion (IRE)—One Cool Kate (IRE) **Louisville Syndicate II**
66 **ONEFITZALL (IRE)**, 6, b g Indian Danehill (IRE)—Company Credit (IRE) **Mick Fitzgerald Racing Club**
67 **ONENIGHTINVIENNA (IRE)**, 7, b g Oscar (IRE)—Be My Granny **Mrs J. A. S. Luff**
68 **OZZIE THE OSCAR (IRE)**, 5, b g Oscar (IRE)—Private Official (IRE) **Bradley Partnership**
69 **PERFORM (IRE)**, 7, b g King's Theatre (IRE)—Famous Lady (IRE) **Merry Old Souls**
70 **PERSIAN SNOW (IRE)**, 10, b g Anshan—Alpine Message **David Maxwell Racing Limited**
71 **POPPY KAY**, 6, b m Kayf Tara—Double Kay (IRE) **Aiden Murphy & Alan Peterson**
72 **PULL THE CHORD (IRE)**, 6, b g St Jovite (USA)—Gold Chord (IRE) **Brocade Racing**
73 **QUADRILLER (FR)**, 9, b g Lando (GER)—Tabachines (FR) **P. J. Hobbs**
74 **QUE SERA (IRE)**, 6, b g Rakti—Mitsina **Miss I. D. Du Pre**
75 **RETURN SPRING (IRE)**, 9, b g Vinnie Roe (IRE)—Bettys Daughter (IRE) **D. J. Jones**
76 **ROCK THE KASBAH (IRE)**, 6, ch g Shirocco (GER)—Impudent (IRE) **Mrs D. L. Whateley**
77 **ROLLING DYLAN (IRE)**, 5, ch g Indian River (FR)—Easter Saturday (FR) **Miss I. D. Du Pre**
78 **ROYAL MILAN (IRE)**, 6, b g Milan—Aimees Princess (IRE) **The Mount Fawcus Partnership**
79 **ROYAL REGATTA (IRE)**, 8, b g King's Theatre (IRE)—
Friendly Craic (IRE) **Mrs Lesley Field & Mrs Eileen Murphy**
80 **SADDLERS ENCORE (IRE)**, 7, br g Presenting—Saddlers Leader (IRE) **R. & Mrs J. E. Gibbs**
81 **SANDYGATE (IRE)**, 6, b g Golan (IRE)—Wet And Windy **T. J. Hemmings**
82 **SAUSALITO SUNRISE (IRE)**, 8, b g Gold Well—Villaflor (IRE) **Mrs D. L. Whateley**
83 **SCOOP THE POT (IRE)**, 6, b g Mahler—Miss Brecknell (IRE) **J. P. McManus**
84 **SCORESHEET (IRE)**, 5, br g Scorpion (IRE)—Tocane (FR) **Mr B K Peppiatt & Mr D R Peppiatt**
85 **SHAMBOUGG**, 5, b g Tobougg (IRE)—More Likely **M. G. St Quinton**
86 **SHOW ON THE ROAD**, 5, b g Flemensfirth (USA)—Roses of Picardy (FR) **R. M. Penny**
87 **SO FINE (IRE)**, 10, b g Definite Article—Not So Green (IRE) **Mrs L. R. Lovell**
88 **ST SAVIOUR**, 4, b g Danehill Dancer (USA)—Titivation **Highclere Thoroughbred Racing-St Saviour**
89 **STAR TROUPER (IRE)**, 6, b g King's Theatre (IRE)—Wyndham Sweetmarie (IRE) **Diana Whateley & Tim Syder**
90 **STERNRUBIN (GER)**, 5, b g Authorized (IRE)—Sworn Mum (GER) **J. T. Warner**

MR PHILIP HOBBS - Continued

91 **STRONG PURSUIT (IRE)**, 6, ch g Flemensfirth (USA)—Loughaderra (IRE) **T. D. J. Syder**
92 **SYKES (IRE)**, 7, b g Mountain High (IRE)—Our Trick (IRE) **Bradley Partnership**
93 **TAPACULO**, 5, b g Kayf Tara—Aniston (IRE) **Mrs C. Skan**
94 **TEARSOFCLEWBAY**, 5, b m Kayf Tara—Fenney Spring **Mrs Caren Walsh & Mrs Kathleen Quinn**
95 **TEN SIXTY (IRE)**, 6, br g Presenting—Senora Snoopy (IRE) **A. L. Cohen**
96 **THE SKYFARMER (IRE)**, 8, br g Presenting—Koral Bay (FR) **Mrs J. J. Peppiatt**
97 **THEATRE ROUGE (IRE)**, 4, b f King's Theatre (IRE)—Toulon Rouge (IRE) **Racegoers Club Owners Group**
98 **THREE FACES WEST (IRE)**, 8, b g Dr Massini (IRE)—Ardnataggle (IRE) **Mr & Mrs Paul & Clare Rooney**
99 **TOOWOOMBA (IRE)**, 8, b g Milan—Lillies Bordello (IRE) **Taylormaid**
100 **TRICKAWAY (IRE)**, 8, b g Stowaway—Rosie's Trix (IRE) **The Mount Fawcus Partnership**
101 **TRICKY (IRE)**, 7, br g Indian Danehill (IRE)—Amelia Island (IRE) **P. J. Hobbs**
102 **VERNI (FR)**, 7, ch g Sabrehill (USA)—Nobless d'aron (FR) **Mr & Mrs Paul & Clare Rooney**
103 **VIEUX LILLE (FR)**, 6, b g Robin des Champs (FR)—Park Athlete (IRE) **Louisville Syndicate III**
104 **VILLAGE VIC (IRE)**, 9, b g Old Vic—Etoile Margot (FR) **A. E. Peterson**
105 **WAIT FOR ME (FR)**, 6, b g Saint des Saints (FR)—Aulne River (FR) **A. L. Cohen**
106 **WALTER WHITE (IRE)**, 6, b g Dark Angel—Fun Time **Govier & Brown**
107 **WAR SOUND**, 7, b g Kayf Tara—Come The Dawn **The Englands and Heywoods**
108 **WESTEND STORY (IRE)**, 5, b g Westerner—Sarahall (IRE) **Mick Fitzgerald Racing Club**
109 **WISHFUL THINKING**, 13, ch g Alflora (IRE)—Poussetiere Deux (FR) **Mrs D. L. Whateley**
110 **WOODFORD COUNTY**, 9, b g Sonus—Moylena **The Englands and Heywoods**

Other Owners: Barber Wadlow Ltd, Mr C. H. Bothway, Mr R. Boyce, Mrs A. E. M. Broom, Mr G. R. Broom, G. S. Brown, Mrs V. F. Burke, C. J. Butler, Mr A. J. Chapman, Mr T. J. Dykes, Mr A. D England, Mrs E. England, Mr D. V. Erskine Crum, Mr D. S. Fawcus, Mrs M. W. Fawcus, Mrs L. H. Field, H. R. Gibbs, Mrs J. E. Gibbs, Mrs C. F. Godsall, Mr P. Govier, Mr P. F. Govier, Mr T. M. Hailstone, J. R. Hall, C. G. Hellyer, The Hon H. M. Herbert, Mr A. H. Heywood, Mr A. S. Heywood, Highclere Nominated Partner Limited, Highclere Thoroughbred Racing Ltd, Mr J. R. Holmes, Mrs J. Hughes, Mr R. B. Ingram, A. Loze, Miss N. Martin, Mrs R. Mason, Mr P. Masterson, Mrs E. Murphy, H. A. Murphy, R. A. S. Offer, B. K. Peppiatt, D. R. Peppiatt, Mr N. D. Peppiatt, Mrs K. Quinn, D. A. Rees, Mrs C. Rooney, Mr P. A. Rooney, Exors of the Late Mrs J. E. Scrase, Mr N. D. Scrase, Mr J. M. Scrase, Mr J. Simpson, M. C. Stoddart, Mrs T. J. Swift, Mrs Ann Taylor, Mrs C. J. Walsh, Sir Christopher Wates, Lady G. F. Wates, Mr R. M. E. Wright.

Assistant Trainer: Richard White

Jockey (NH): James Best, Richard Johnson, Micheal Nolan, Tom O'Brien. **Conditional:** Tom Cheesman, Ciaran Gethings, Conor Smith. **Amateur:** Mr Sean Houlihan, Mr Nick Lawton.

---

302 MISS CLARE HOBSON, Royston
Postal: **The Woolpack, London Road, Reed, Royston, Hertfordshire, SG8 8BB**

1 **BANKSANDDITCHES (IRE)**, 10, b g Dilshaan—Ardbess **Mr H. R. Hobson**
2 **HUSTLE (IRE)**, 11, ch g Choisir (AUS)—Granny Kelly (USA) **Mr H. R. Hobson**
3 **IRISH REBEL (IRE)**, 12, b g Tel Quel (FR)—Never On Sunday (IRE) **Mrs R. E. Hobson**
4 **ISHUSHARELLA**, 7, b m Doyen (IRE)—Emily-Mou (IRE) **Mr H. R. Hobson**
5 **JUMP TO THE BEAT**, 6, b m Beat All (USA)—Binny Bay **Mr H. R. Hobson**
6 **LOTTA SCARES**, 8, b g Primitive Proposal—Scare McClare **Mr H. R. Hobson**
7 **MAYPOLE LASS**, 6, ch m Halling (USA)—Maigold Lass **Mr H. R. Hobson**
8 **RANDS HILL**, 6, b m Fair Mix (IRE)—Proper Posh **Mrs R. E. Hobson**

---

303 MR RICHARD HOBSON, Stow-On-The-Wold
Postal: **Park House, Wyck Beacon, Wyck Rissington, Cheltenham, Gloucestershire, GL54 2NE**

1 **ALLYSSON MONTERG (FR)**, 6, b g Network (GER)—Mellyssa (FR) **Mr D. W. Fox**
2 **ATHOU DU NORD (FR)**, 6, b g Voix du Nord (FR)—Orathou du Plaid (FR) **Mr R. H. Hobson**
3 **ATOMIK D'OLIVATE (FR)**, 6, gr g Martaline—Lady Easter (FR) **Mr R. H. Hobson**
4 **BUENO RICA (FR)**, 5, bl g Califet (FR)—Infante de Rica (FR) **Mr R. H. Hobson**
5 **CHIC NAME (FR)**, 4, b g Nickname (FR)—Vuelta Al Ruedo (FR) **D. A. Thorpe**
6 **COBALT MARTHEN (FR)**, 4, b br g Balko (FR)—Hellen Marthen (FR) **D. A. Thorpe**
7 **FULGUS (FR)**, 4, gr c Visionary (FR)—Rapsody In Love (FR) **Mr R. H. Hobson**
8 **NEWORLD (FR)**, 7, gr g Lost World (IRE)—Crusch Alva (FR) **Mr R. H. Hobson**
9 **VAL D'ARC (FR)**, 7, b g Le Balafre (FR)—Lextrienne (FR) **Thurloe 54**
10 **VALADOM (FR)**, 7, gr g Dadarissime (FR)—Laurana (FR) **Mr R. H. Hobson**

MR RICHARD HOBSON - Continued

THREE-YEAR-OLDS

11 B f Midnight Legend—Won More Night **D. A. Thorpe**

Other Owners: Mr O. J. W. Pawle, Mr J. A. B. Stafford.

---

304 | **MR JOHN HODGE, Cumnock**
Postal: **Corbie Lodge, Muirdyke Farm, Cumnock, Ayrshire, KA18 2SG**

1 FLAMING THISTLE (IRE), 12, b g Flemensfirth (USA)—Native Thistle (IRE) **J. M. C. Hodge**
2 LUCTOR EMERGO (IRE), 7, b g Amadeus Wolf—Batilde (IRE) **J. M. C. Hodge**

---

305 | **MR RON HODGES, Somerton**
Postal: **Little Orchard, George Street, Charlton Adam, Somerton, Somerset, TA11 7AS**
Contacts: **PHONE (01458) 223922 MOBILE (07770) 625846**
E-MAIL mandyhodges@btconnect.com

1 ACTONETAKETWO, 6, b m Act One—Temple Dancer **The Gardens Entertainments Ltd**
2 DREAMS OF GLORY, 8, ch g Resplendent Glory (IRE)—Pip's Dream **P. E. Axon**
3 MILES OF SUNSHINE, 11, b g Thowra (FR)—Rainbow Nation **The Gardens Entertainments Ltd**
4 MISS TENACIOUS, 9, b m Refuse To Bend (IRE)—Very Speed (USA) **John Frampton & Paul Frampton**
5 MISTER MUSICMASTER, 7, b g Amadeus Wolf—Misty Eyed (IRE) **Mrs L. Sharpe & Mrs S. G. Clapp**
6 ONE LAST DREAM, 7, ch g Resplendent Glory (IRE)—Pip's Dream **A. M. Midgley**
7 POPESWOOD (IRE), 4, b g Haatef (USA)—Binfield (IRE) **Mrs A. R. Hart**
8 QUARRYMAN, 5, ch g Act One—Bluebell Path **P. L. Hart**

THREE-YEAR-OLDS

9 EVENING STARLIGHT, gr ro f Kyllachy—Night Haven **Miss R. J. Dobson**
10 HERE'S TWO, b f Hellvelyn—There's Two (IRE) **K. J. Corcoran**
11 WILSPA'S MAGIC (IRE), gr f Zebedee—Triple Zero (IRE) **The Gardens Entertainments Ltd**

Other Owners: Mrs S. G. Clapp, J. L. Frampton, Mr P. S. Frampton, R. J. Hodges, Mrs L. Sharpe, D. R. Tucker.

---

306 | **MR SIMON HODGSON, Yeovil**
Postal: **Queen Camel House, High Street, Queen Camel, Yeovil, Somerset, BA22 7NF**
Contacts: **PHONE (01935) 851152**

1 AVITHOS, 6, b m Kayf Tara—Digyourheelsin (IRE) **Mrs L. M. Clarke**
2 BLACK ART, 4, ch c Black Sam Bellamy (IRE)—Art Series **Mrs L. M. Clarke**
3 BROTHER NORPHIN, 4, b g Norse Dancer (IRE)—Orphina (IRE) **Mr J. A. Mould**
4 DEBIT, 5, b g Pivotal—Silver Kestrel (USA) **Mr C. E. Weare**
5 FINAL SAY, 6, b m Alflora (IRE)—En Vacances (IRE) **Miss Juliet E Reed & Mr Michael Truan**
6 HOMERS ODYSSEY, 6, b g Overbury (IRE)—Aikaterine **Miss J. E. Reed**
7 KYLIES WILD CARD, 4, b f Aussie Rules (USA)—Jemiliah **N. J. Stafford**
8 MILDMAY ARMS, 4, b g Kheleyf (USA)—Akathea **Simon Hodgson Racing Partnership 1**
9 MOUNT HOLLOW, 11, b g Beat Hollow—Lady Lindsay (IRE) **Mrs L. M. Clarke**
10 NORPHIN, 6, b g Norse Dancer (IRE)—Orphina (IRE) **Mr J. A. Mould**
11 ON DEMAND, 5, ch m Teofilo (IRE)—Mimisel **Ms Christine Thomas & Mr Jim Hoyland**
12 QUALITY ART (USA), 8, b g Elusive Quality (USA)—Katherine Seymour **Mrs L. M. Clarke**
13 SENOR GEORGE (IRE), 9, b g Traditionally (USA)—Mrs St George (IRE) **Mr C. E. Weare**
14 TRAKEUR (FR), 9, b g Myrakalu (FR)—Nataly (FR) **Mrs Julie Whatley & Mrs Sandra Boggon**

THREE-YEAR-OLDS

15 Ch f Compton Place—Oriental Girl **Mrs S. A. Grant**

TWO-YEAR-OLDS

16 Ch c 13/4 Sakhee's Secret—La Palma (Sinndar (IRE)) **L. R. Turland**
17 B f 6/5 Approve (IRE)—Mataji (IRE) (Desert Prince (IRE)) (4000) **Mr C. E. Weare**

MR SIMON HODGSON - Continued

18 B c 3/4 Born To Sea (IRE)—Next To The Top (Hurricane Run (IRE)) **Mrs L. M. Clarke**
19 B f 28/4 Poet's Voice—Palais Polaire (Polar Falcon (USA)) (10000) **M. C. Humby**

Other Owners: Mrs S. B. Boggon, Mr J. S. Hoyland, Mr M. A. Muddiman, Ms C. Thomas, Mr M. R. Truan, Mrs J. Whatley.

---

307 MR EAMONN M. HOGAN, Roscam
Postal: **Rosshill, Roscam, Galway, Co. Galway, Ireland**
Contacts: **PHONE (00353) 91756899 MOBILE (00353) 879175175**
E-MAIL rosshillfarm@eircom.net WEBSITE www.rosshillfarm.com

1 ASTEROID BELT (IRE), 7, ch g Heliostatic (IRE)—Affaire Royale (IRE) **BIMA Partnership**
2 4, B g Robin des Pres (FR)—Crack The Kicker (IRE) **E. M. Hogan**
3 5, B g Brian Boru—Curahard Again (IRE) **Rusty Partnership**
4 GREY ROSS (IRE), 6, gr g Pilsudski (IRE)—Slieve League (IRE) **D. Greally**
5 4, B g Curtain Time (IRE)—Triptodicks (IRE) **Rosshill Farm**
6 VAULKIE, 7, b g Revoque (IRE)—Cromarty **D. Greally**

THREE-YEAR-OLDS

7 B g Winged Love (IRE)—Bibi's Pearl (IRE)

TWO-YEAR-OLDS

8 Gr f 21/4 Winged Love (IRE)—Dees Rock (IRE) (Arzanni) **Deidre Greally**
9 B f 19/4 Gamut (IRE)—Keep Thinking (IRE) (Turtle Island (IRE)) **E. M. Hogan**

Other Owners: S. Cannon, I. Grealy, Mary Hogan, A. Neary, Rossa Bloodstock, D. R. Ryan.

Jockey (flat): F. M. Berry. **Amateur:** Mr P.J. O'Neill.

---

308 MR HENRY HOGARTH, Stillington
Postal: **New Grange Farm, Stillington, York, YO61 1LR**
Contacts: **PHONE (01347) 811168 FAX (01347) 811168 MOBILE (07788) 777044**
E-MAIL harryhogarth@ymail.com

1 ALTO DES MOTTES (FR), 6, b g Dream Well (FR)—Omance (FR) **Hogarth Racing**
2 DENY, 8, ch g Mr Greeley (USA)—Sulk (IRE) **Hogarth Racing**
3 DUNDEE BLUE (IRE), 8, gr g Cloudings (IRE)—Eurolucy (IRE) **Hogarth Racing**
4 FIGHTING BACK, 5, b g Galileo (IRE)—Maroochydore (IRE) **Hogarth Racing**
5 HATTONS HILL (IRE), 7, b g Pierre—Cluain Chaoin (IRE) **Hogarth Racing**
6 HERITAGE WAY, 7, b g Tamayaz (CAN)—Morning Caller (IRE) **Hogarth Racing**
7 KILCULLEN LADY (IRE), 6, b m Scorpion (IRE)—Glittering Star (IRE) **Hogarth Racing**
8 OVER AND ABOVE (IRE), 10, b g Overbury (IRE)—Rose Gold (IRE) **Hogarth Racing**
9 PAMAK D'AIRY (FR), 13, b g Cadoubel (FR)—Gamaska d'airy (FR) **Hogarth Racing**
10 PIERRERS BOUNTY (IRE), 9, b g Pierre—Willow Stream (IRE) **Hogarth Racing**
11 ROJO VIVO, 10, b g Deploy—Shareef Walk **Hogarth Racing**
12 SUPER LUNAR (IRE), 7, b g Super Celebre (FR)—Kapricia Speed (FR) **Hogarth Racing**

Other Owners: Mr H. P. Hogarth, Mr J. L. Hogarth, Mr J. Hogarth, Mr P. H. Hogarth.

Assistant Trainer: Claire Nelson

Conditional: Tony Kelly.

---

309 MR ALAN HOLLINGSWORTH, Feckenham
Postal: **Lanket House, Crofts Lane, Feckenham, Redditch, Worcestershire, B96 6PU**
Contacts: **PHONE (01527) 68644/892054 FAX (01527) 60310 MOBILE (07775) 670644**
E-MAIL kombined@btconnect.com

1 AGITATION, 12, b g Cloudings (IRE)—Shadowgraff **A. F. Hollingsworth**
2 BEAU BROOK, 7, b m Kayf Tara—An Bothar Dubh **Kombined Motor Services Ltd**
3 BOARDWALK, 7, br m Alflora (IRE)—Indyana Run **Kombined Motor Services Ltd**
4 BRAGABOUT, 9, b g Alflora (IRE)—Gemmabel **A. F. Hollingsworth**
5 CHECKETS, 8, b m Alflora (IRE)—Emmabella **Kombined Motor Services Ltd**

MR ALAN HOLLINGSWORTH - Continued

6 **CLEETONS TURN**, 9, b g Alflora (IRE)—Indyana Run **Kombined Motor Services Ltd**
7 **I CANCAN**, 8, b g Alflora (IRE)—Shadowgraff **Kombined Motor Services Ltd**
8 **PACKAGE DEAL**, 8, b g Alflora (IRE)—Gemmabel **Kombined Motor Services Ltd**

Assistant Trainer: Sharon Smith

Jockey (NH): James Davies, Nick Scholfield. **Amateur:** Mr James Martin.

---

310 **MR ANDREW HOLLINSHEAD, Lamorlaye**
Postal: **11 Voie de la Grange des Pres, 60260 Lamorlaye, France**
Contacts: **MOBILE (07968) 733080**
E-MAIL hollinsheadracing@gmail.com WEBSITE www.hollinsheadracing.com

1 **ESSANAR**, 5, br g Notnowcato—Spirito Libro (USA) **Mr Paul Shaw & Mr Mark Round**
2 **FINAL ATTACK (IRE)**, 5, b g Cape Cross (IRE)—Northern Melody (IRE) **Neville Chapman /A. N. Hollinshead**
3 **FLYING CAPE (IRE)**, 5, b g Cape Cross (IRE)—Reine Zao (FR) **J. L. Marriott**
4 **KING OF ROCK (FR)**, 7, ch g Rock of Gibraltar—Sunburst **Geoff Lucas/Helen Marsh**
5 **TREE OF GRACE (FR)**, 5, ch g Gold Away (IRE)—Three Times (SWE) **Neville Chapman /A. N. Hollinshead**
6 **VESKING (FR)**, 4, ch g Vespone (IRE)—Shaking **A. N. Hollinshead/Paul Shaw**

THREE-YEAR-OLDS

7 **CALAJANI (FR)**, b c Azamour (IRE)—Clarinda (FR) **Neville Chapman/A. N. Hollinshead**

Assistant Trainer: Debbie Hollinshead (07977) 934638

---

311 **MISS SARAH HOLLINSHEAD, Upper Longdon**
Postal: **Lodge Farm, Upper Longdon, Rugely, Staffordshire, WS15 1QF**
Contacts: **PHONE (01543) 490298**

1 **AMBITIOUS BOY**, 7, bl g Striking Ambition—Cherished Love (IRE) **Mr C. W. Wardle & Mrs J. E. Wardle**
2 **BILASH**, 9, gr g Choisir (AUS)—Goldeva **Pyle & Hollinshead**
3 **BLUE VALENTINO**, 7, b g Primo Valentino (IRE)—Blue Water **Mr G. Else**
4 **DHA CHARA (IRE)**, 6, b g Ramonti (FR)—Campiglia (IRE) **Mr N. S. Sweeney**
5 **EASTERN MAGIC**, 9, b g Observatory (USA)—Inchtina **Mrs C. A. Stevenson**
6 **HANDSOME DAN (IRE)**, 10, b g Busy Flight—Beautiful City (IRE) **Graham Brothers Racing Partnership**
7 **LACEY**, 7, b g Rail Link—Shamana (USA) **Mr N. S. Sweeney**
8 **LINEMAN**, 6, b g Rail Link—Shamana (USA)
9 5, Ch g Kyllachy—Look Here's Carol (IRE) **S. L. Edwards**
10 **NATALIA**, 7, ch m Dutch Art—Pintle **Miss S. A. Hollinshead**
11 **NOMADIC LAD**, 6, b g Nomadic Way (USA)—Lysways **R. Robinson**
12 **RIGHT MADAM (IRE)**, 4, b f Jeremy—Mawaared **J. L. Marriott**
13 **SMART DAISY K**, 6, b m Pastoral Pursuits—Katy-Q (IRE) **Mr & Mrs D. J. Smart**
14 **SMART DJ**, 5, ch g Major Cadeaux—Katy-Q (IRE) **Mr & Mrs D. J. Smart**
15 **SPIRIT RAPPING (IRE)**, 4, b g Azamour (IRE)—Snowpalm **J. L. Marriott**
16 **THIMAAR (USA)**, 8, b br g Dynaformer (USA)—Jinaan (USA) **David Lockwood & Fred Lockwood**
17 **UNCLE BERNIE (IRE)**, 6, gr g Aussie Rules (USA)—Alwiyda (USA) **Graham Brothers Racing Partnership**
18 **WELL OWD MON**, 6, b g Vitus—Farina (IRE) **The Giddy Gang**
19 **ZENAFIRE**, 7, b g Firebreak—Zen Garden **Mr R. J. R. Moseley**

THREE-YEAR-OLDS

20 **CASTLEREA TESS**, ch f Pastoral Pursuits—Zartwyda (IRE) **Graham Brothers Racing Partnership**
21 B f Sir Percy—Wulfrida (IRE) **The Three R's**

TWO-YEAR-OLDS

22 **STRIKING FOR GOLD**, b c 22/4 Equiano (FR)—Crossbow (Mount Nelson) (9523) **M. A. N. Johnson**
23 **TESS GRAHAM**, b f 11/4 Pastoral Pursuits—Zartwyda (IRE) (Mozart (IRE))

Other Owners: Mr A. M. Graham, Mr M. P. Graham, D. R. Horne, Mr A. Lawrence, Mr E. T. D. Leadbeater, D. J. Lockwood, Mr F. M. Lockwood, A. L. Marriott, Mrs T. P. Pyle, M. J. F. Pyle, D. J. Smart, Mrs K. D. Smart, C. W. Wardle, Mrs J. E. Wardle.

312 **MRS STEPH HOLLINSHEAD, Rugeley**
Postal: **Deva House, Bardy Lane, Longdon, Rugeley, Staffordshire, WS15 4LJ**
Contacts: PHONE **(01543) 493656** MOBILE **(07791) 385335**
E-MAIL **Steph_hollinshead@hotmail.co.uk** WEBSITE **www.stephhollinsheadracing.com**

1 CAHAR FAD (IRE), 4, b g Bushranger (IRE)—Tarbiyah **D Hodson, K Meredith, N Sweeney**
2 CERISE FIRTH, 4, b f Pastoral Pursuits—Vermilion Creek **Mr M. Johnson & Mrs L. A. Hollinshead**
3 FRANK THE BARBER (IRE), 4, gr g Zebedee—Red Rosanna **Mrs D. A. Hodson**
4 HAZEL'S SONG, 4, b f Orpen (USA)—Songbook
5 LITTLE, 4, b f Paco Boy (IRE)—Wafeira **Magg Group & Steph Hollinshead**
6 MIDNIGHT MEMORIES, 6, ch m Midnight Legend—Bajan Blue **Mrs S. C. Hawkins**
7 MISSANDEI, 4, b f Red Rocks (IRE)—Onda Chiara (ITY) **Mrs V. C. Gilbert**
8 PRECIEUX, 5, b m Indian Danehill (IRE)—Miss Holly **Mrs L. A. Hollinshead**
9 SNOWY DAWN, 6, gr g Notnowcato—Tereyna **Mrs C. A. Stevenson**
10 SPIRIT OF ROSANNA, 4, gr f Hellvelyn—Tharwa (IRE) **Mrs D. A. Hodson**

THREE-YEAR-OLDS

11 BELLEDESERT, b f Pastoral Pursuits—Ocean Blaze **K Meredith, D Hodson, The Ocean Four**
12 GOLDEN ROSANNA, b f Equiano (FR)—Goldeva **Mrs D. A. Hodson**
13 KARENS STAR, b f Piccolo—Maarees **Beaudesert Racing**
14 LADY EMMA, b f Mount Nelson—Songbook **Hazeldine Partnership**
15 VIRTUAL SONG, b f Virtual—Song of The Desert **D. Sutherland**

TWO-YEAR-OLDS

16 B c 28/1 Royal Applause—Dream In Waiting (Oasis Dream) **Mr & Mrs I. H. Bendelow**
17 B c 21/2 Bushranger (IRE)—Peace Talks (Pivotal) (7000) **Ocean Four**
18 B f 8/4 Poet's Voice—She Storm (IRE) (Rainbow Quest (USA)) (5500) **Mrs D. A. Hodson**
19 B f 15/4 Pastoral Pursuits—Vermilion Creek (Makbul) **Mr M. Johnson & Mrs L. A. Hollinshead**

Other Owners: I. H. Bendelow, Mrs P. Bendelow, Mr D. J. Carter, Mr M. Gibbons, Mr G. Hancock, Mr D. Hodson, Mrs J. E. Howlett, M. A. N. Johnson, K. S. Meredith, Mrs J. A. Naccache, Mr G. T. Rowley, Mr N. S. Sweeney.

Assistant Trainer: Adam Hawkins

313 **MR PATRICK HOLMES, Middleham**
Postal: **Little Spigot, Coverham, Middleham, Leyburn, North Yorkshire, DL8 4TL**
Contacts: PHONE **(01969) 624880** MOBILE **(07740) 589857**
E-MAIL **patrick@foulriceparkracing.com** WEBSITE **www.foulriceparkracing.com**

1 BOGARDUS (IRE), 5, b g Dalakhani (IRE)—Sugar Mint (IRE) **Foulrice Park Racing Limited**
2 CHARAVA (IRE), 4, br g Captain Marvelous (IRE)—Sweet Compliance **Oakfield Racing**
3 COOKIE RING (IRE), 5, b g Moss Vale (IRE)—Talah **Mrs A. M. Stirling**
4 FILLYDELPHIA (IRE), 5, b m Strategic Prince—Lady Fonic **Foulrice Park Racing Limited, Mrs Ailsa Stirling**
5 FOOT THE BILL, 11, b g Generous (IRE)—Proudfoot (IRE) **Mr C. R. Stirling**
6 FRAMLEY GARTH (IRE), 4, b g Clodovil (IRE)—
   Two Marks (USA) **Foulrice Park Racing Limited, Mr Colin Stirling, FPR Yorkshire Syndicate**
7 GRENADE (IRE), 4, b g Paco Boy (IRE)—Amira **Foulrice Park Racing Limited, Mr Colin Stirling**
8 LIFE KNOWLEDGE (IRE), 4, ch g Thewayyouare (USA)—
   Rosa Bellini (IRE) **Mrs C. M. Clarke, Foulrice Park Racing Ltd**
9 LIL SOPHELLA (IRE), 7, ch m Indian Haven—Discotheque (USA) **Mrs S. Porteous**
10 LORD ARATAN (GER), 9, b g Tiger Hill (IRE)—Luce (IRE) **Mrs Kim Jackson, Foulrice Park Racing Limited**
11 MAPLE STIRRUP (IRE), 4, b f Duke of Marmalade (IRE)—
   Street Shaana (FR) **Mr Colin Stirling, Foulrice Park Racing Limited**
12 MARINERS MOON (IRE), 5, ch g Mount Nelson—Dusty Moon **Mr Colin Stirling, Foulrice Park Racing Limited**
13 MUNJALLY, 5, b g Acclamation—Parabola **Foulrice Park Racing Limited**
14 OPTIMA PETAMUS, 4, gr g Mastercraftsman (IRE)—
   In A Silent Way (IRE) **Mrs C. M. Clarke, Foulrice Park Racing Ltd**
15 PATRON OF EXPLORES (USA), 5, b g Henrythenavigator (USA)—
   India Halo (ARG) **Mrs Ailsa Stirling, Foulrice Park Racing Limited, FPR Yorkshire Syndicate**
16 PROSTATE AWARENESS (IRE), 5, b g Camacho—Genuinely (IRE) **Foulrice Park Racing Limited**
17 SWISS LAIT, 5, b m Milk It Mick—Matilda Peace **Foulrice Park Racing Limited, Mr Colin Stirling**
18 TIME OF MY LIFE (GER), 5, ch h Nayef (USA)—Tamaja (GER) **Mrs C. M. Clarke, Foulrice Park Racing Limited**
19 VOICE FROM ABOVE (IRE), 7, b m Strategic Prince—Basin Street Blues (IRE) **Mrs A. M. Stirling**

MR PATRICK HOLMES - Continued

20 **YOURHOLIDAYISOVER (IRE)**, 9, ch g Sulamani (IRE)—Whitehaven **Foulrice Park Racing Limited**
21 **ZUBOON (IRE)**, 4, b g Dansili—Tabassum (IRE) **Foulrice Park Racing Limited**

THREE-YEAR-OLDS

22 **AUXILIARY**, b g Fast Company (IRE)—Lady Xara (IRE) **Mrs C. M. Clarke, Foulrice Park Racing Ltd**
23 **DIAMOND AVALANCHE (IRE)**, b g Alfred Nobel (IRE)—
Queens Flight **Mrs C. M. Clarke, Foulrice Park Racing Ltd**
24 **FOULRICE FLYER**, b g Winker Watson—Big Old Unit **Foulrice Park Racing Limited**
25 **MISSION MARS**, b g Kyllachy—Ashraakat (USA) **Mrs C. M. Clarke, Foulrice Park Racing Ltd**

Other Owners: Foulrice Park Racing Limited, Mrs Ailsa Stirling, Mr Colin Stirling.

Assistant Trainer: Russ Garritty

Conditional: John Kington.

---

314 MR JOHN HOLT, Peckleton
Postal: **Hall Farm, Church Road, Peckleton, Leicester**
Contacts: **PHONE/FAX (01455) 821972 MOBILE (07850) 321059**
E-MAIL hallfarmracing@btconnect.com WEBSITE www.hallfarmracing.co.uk

1 **CANTON MASSINI**, 5, b g Dr Massini (IRE)—Mandarin Star **Mr A. C. Cook**
2 **DREAM BOUNTY**, b f Bahamian Bounty—Dream In Waiting **Mr A. C. Cook**
3 **GOADBY**, 5, gr m Kodiac—Gone Sailing **Cleartherm Glass Sealed Units Ltd**
4 **MINI'S DESTINATION**, 8, b m Dubai Destination (USA)—Heather Mix **J. R. Holt**
5 **NOMADRUSH**, 6, b m Nomadic Way (USA)—Tanguero (IRE) **Mrs C. M. Tyler**
6 **NUMBER THEORY**, 8, b g Halling (USA)—Numanthia (IRE) **Mr M. S. Fonseka**
7 4, Ch g Denounce—Sharabosky **Mr T. M. Dorman**
8 **SHARABOSKY**, 12, ch m Shahrastani (USA)—Bosky **Mr T. M. Dorman**
9 **SWEET MIDNIGHT**, 4, b f Mawatheeq (USA)—Sweet Reply **Mrs P. Y. Page**

THREE-YEAR-OLDS

10 **BARNSDALE**, b g Stimulation (IRE)—Seren Teg **J. R. Holt**
11 **CLON ROCKET (IRE)**, b g Lilbourne Lad (IRE)—Ryalahna (IRE) **Planters (Leicester) Limited**
12 **ICEAXE**, b f Stimulation (IRE)—Laser Crystal (IRE) **J. R. Holt**

TWO-YEAR-OLDS

13 B f 1/3 Camacho—Blades Princess (Needwood Blade) (2095)

Assistant Trainer: Jessica Holt

---

315 MR ANTHONY HONEYBALL, Beaminster
Postal: **Potwell Farm, Mosterton, Beaminster, Dorset, DT8 3HG**
Contacts: PHONE **(01308) 867452** MOBILE **(07815) 898569**
E-MAIL anthony@ajhoneyballracing.co.uk WEBSITE www.ajhoneyballracing.co.uk

1 **ACAJOU DES BIEFFES (FR)**, 6, b br g Millennium Bio (JPN)—Pietragella (FR) **The 4 Samurai**
2 **ACT NOW**, 7, br m Act One—Lady Turk (FR) **Barrow Hill**
3 **AMBER ALERT**, 6, b m Vitus—Imperial Amber **Worsdall, Tolley & Honeyball**
4 **ANDA DE GRISSAY (FR)**, 6, b m Network (GER)—Karima II (FR) **The Deauville Connection**
5 **AS DE FER (FR)**, 10, b g Passing Sale (FR)—Miss Hollywood (FR) **Midd Shire Racing**
6 **CHILL FACTOR (IRE)**, 7, b g Oscar (IRE)—Glacial Princess (IRE) **Potwell Partners**
7 **CITY SUPREME (IRE)**, 6, b g Milan—Run Supreme (IRE) **San Siro Six**
8 **CRESSWELL BREEZE**, b m Midnight Legend—Cresswell Willow (IRE) **Bright N Breezy**
9 **DOUBLE ACCORD**, 6, ch m Double Trigger (IRE)—Got Tune (FR) **R. W. Huggins & Atlantic Racing**
10 **DRAGOON GUARD (IRE)**, 5, b g Jeremy (USA)—Elouges (IRE) **Geegeez.co.uk PA**
11 **EAST WING (IRE)**, 4, b g Winged Love (IRE)—Eastender **Geegeez.co.uk PA**
12 4, B f Black Sam Bellamy (IRE)—Fact Not Fiction **D. McCullough & A. Honeyball**
13 **FOUNTAINS BLOSSOM**, 7, b m Passing Glance—Fountain Crumble **Anthony Honeyball Racing Club Ltd**
14 **FOUNTAINS FLYPAST**, 12, b g Broadway Flyer (USA)—Miss Flower Girl **Anthony Honeyball Racing Club Ltd**
15 **FOUNTAINS WINDFALL**, 6, b g Passing Glance—Fountain Crumble **The Fountains Partnership**
16 **LE COEUR NET (FR)**, 4, ch g Network (GER)—Silverwood (FR) **Potwell Optimists**

MR ANTHONY HONEYBALL - Continued

17 **LILY WAUGH (IRE)**, 9, b m King's Theatre (IRE)—Killultagh Dawn (IRE) **Go To War**
18 **MIDNIGHT TUNE**, 5, b m Midnight Legend—Harmonic Motion (IRE) **The Park Homes Syndicate**
19 **NEVER SAYS NEVER**, 8, b g Tamure (IRE)—Quick Exit **Mr R. Hall**
20 **PRINCE OF THIEVES (IRE)**, 6, b g Robin des Pres (FR)—Sly Empress (IRE) **Sherwood Rangers**
21 **PURE VISION (IRE)**, 5, b g Milan—Distillery Lane (IRE) **J. P. McManus**
22 **REGAL ENCORE (IRE)**, 8, b g King's Theatre (IRE)—Go On Eileen (IRE) **J. P. McManus**
23 **ROUQUINE SAUVAGE**, 8, ch m Loup Sauvage (USA)—No Need For Alarm **J. P. McManus**
24 **ROYAL NATIVE (IRE)**, 8, b g King's Theatre (IRE)—Hollygrove Native (IRE) **Michael & Angela Bone**
25 **ROYAL SALUTE**, 6, br g Flemensfirth (USA)—Loxhill Lady **Anthony Honeyball Racing Club Ltd**
26 **SOLSTICE SON**, 7, b g Haafhd—Karasta (USA) **The Summer Solstice**
27 **SOULSAVER**, 4, ch g Recharge (IRE)—Lapina (IRE) **R. J. Matthews**
28 **TARADREWE**, 9, b m Kayf Tara—Kaream **Frosties Friends II**
29 **THE GEEGEEZ GEEGEE (IRE)**, 7, b g Beneficial—Shanann Lady (IRE) **Geegeez.co.uk PA**
30 **VICTORS SERENADE (IRE)**, 11, b g Old Vic—Dantes Serenade (IRE) **Michael & Angela Bone**

Other Owners: Atlantic Racing Limited, Mr George T. Birks, Mr M. Bisogno, Mrs A. P. Bone, Mr Michael Bone, Mrs Marion Bowden, Mr David Briers, Mr James Burley, Mr Jim Cannon, Mr Graham Craig, Mr Ian Dickson, Mrs George Eyre, Mr J. P. Fairrie, Mr T. C. Frost, Mr M. S. Green, Mr A. Honeyball, Mr R. W. Huggins, Mr Eric Jones, Mr N. J. McMullan, Mr B. G. Middleton, Mr Lloyd Moody, Mr J. P. Romans, Mr Mike Rowe, Mr A. J. Shire, Mr Andy Smith, Mr R. G. Tizzard, Mrs Sarah Tizzard, Mr Chris Vowles, Mrs Shirley Worsdall.

Assistant Trainer: Rachael Honeyball (07813) 984418

Jockey (NH): Aidan Coleman, Ryan Mahon. **Conditional:** David Noonan.

---

316 **MR STUART HOWE, Tiverton**
Postal: **Ringstone Stables, Oakford, Tiverton, Devon, EX16 9EU**
Contacts: **PHONE (01398) 351224 MOBILE (07802) 506344**
E-MAIL hshowe@stuarthoweracing.co.uk

1 9, B g Chineur (FR)—Bali Royal
2 7, Br m Lahib (USA)—Clifton Mist
3 **ETOILE DE VIE**, 6, ch m Lucarno (USA)—Spark of Life
4 **MY LEGAL LADY**, 11, b m Sir Harry Lewis (USA)—Clifton Mist **H. S. Howe**
5 **PARTY PALACE**, 12, b m Auction House (USA)—Lady-Love **B. P. Jones**
6 **TRESOR DE LA VIE (FR)**, 9, gr g Epalo (GER)—Joie de La Vie (FR) **Ms C. Carter**

Other Owners: Mrs V. W. Jones.

Jockey (NH): Tom Scudamore. **Conditional:** Giles Hawkins.

---

317 **MR JAMES HUGHES, Gilfach Goch**
Postal: **4 Pontrhondda Road, Tonypandy, Mid-Glamorgan, CF40 2SZ**

1 **MAGGIE ARON**, 10, gr m Generous (IRE)—Pems Gift **J. S. Hughes**
2 **ONE COOL WESTERNER (IRE)**, 6, b g Westerner—Over The Grand (IRE) **J. S. Hughes**

---

318 **MRS JO HUGHES, Lambourn**
Postal: **Hill House Stables, Folly Road, Lambourn, Hungerford, Berkshire, RG17 8QE**
Contacts: **PHONE (01488) 71444 FAX (01488) 71103 MOBILE (07900) 680189**
E-MAIL johughes3@aol.co.uk WEBSITE www.johughesracing.co.uk

1 **ANTONIO JOLI (IRE)**, 4, b g Arcano (IRE)—Snowtime (IRE) **Mrs C. C. Regalado-Gonzalez**
2 **CALEDONIA LAIRD**, 5, b g Firebreak—Granuaile O'malley (IRE) **Isla & Colin Cage**
3 **LADY GEMINI**, 4, b f Myboycharlie (IRE)—Gemini Gold (IRE) **James Henderson & Pat Hanly**
4 **SHOW ME THE BAR**, 4, b g Showcasing—Barbough **L Ormsby, M West & J Hughes**
5 **SILVER MAN**, 9, gr g Silver Patriarch (IRE)—Another Mans Cause (FR) **T. J. Wardle**

MRS JO HUGHES - Continued

THREE-YEAR-OLDS

6 **COMPTON SKY (USA)**, b g Sky Mesa (USA)—See How She Runs (USA) **D Bird, J Hearne, J Smith & J Hughes**
7 **DAYBREAK LADY**, ch f Firebreak—Musical Day **Isla & Colin Cage**
8 **HENRY THE EXPLORER (CAN)**, b c Henrythenavigator (USA)—Game (FR) **Isla & Colin Cage & James Hearn**
9 **LEFORTOVO (FR)**, b c Arcano (IRE)—Lorientaise (IRE) **L Ormsby, H Downs, R Bedford & J Hughes**
10 **MISTAKEN LADY**, b f Multiplex—Sharoura **Joseph Hearne & Jo Hughes**
11 **MUMBLES MAGIC (IRE)**, b f Thousand Words—Chaguaramas (IRE) **John Wardle & Jo Hughes**
12 B f Showcasing—Nelly's Glen
13 **NO EDUCATION**, b c Showcasing—Ceilidh Band **Joe Smith, Jimmy Smith, Jo Hughes**
14 **POWERED (IRE)**, b g Frozen Power (IRE)—Confirm (IRE) **James Hearne & Jo Hughes**
15 **WICKED WOO**, b f Multiplex—Icky Woo **James Hearne & Jo Hughes**

Other Owners: Mr R. J. Bedford, D. G. Bird, Mrs I. Cage, C. J. Cage, B. H. Downs, Mr P. J. Hanly, Mr J. M. H. Hearne, Mr J. Hearne, Mr J. Henderson, Mrs J. F. Hughes, Miss L. Ormsby, Mr J. D. A. Smith, J. Smith, Mr M. West.

Assistant Trainer: Paul Blockley (07778 318295)

Jockey (flat): Paul Hanagan. **Jockey (NH):** Mark Grant. **Apprentice:** Harry Burns, Josephine Gordon.
Amateur: Mr James Hughes.

---

319 | MR RICHARD HUGHES, Upper Lambourn
Postal: **Weathercock House, Upper Lambourn, Hungerford, Berkshire, RG17 8QT**
Contacts: **PHONE** (01488) 71198 **MOBILE** (07768) 894828
E-MAIL office@richardhughesracing.co.uk **WEBSITE** www.richardhughesracing.co.uk

1 **BANK OF GIBRALTAR**, 4, ch g Rock of Gibraltar (IRE)—Banksia **Mr Richard Hughes**
2 **BARYE**, 5, b g Archipenko (USA)—Oblige **A. G. D. Hogarth**
3 **BELIEVE IT (IRE)**, 4, b c Rip Van Winkle (IRE)—Have Faith (IRE) **Mr Richard Hughes**
4 **BUNBURY**, 4, b c Dansili—Ithaca (USA) **The Villains**
5 **BURNING DESIRE (IRE)**, 5, b g Galileo (IRE)—Flames **Mr David Leon & James Devine**
6 **CAPE DISCOVERY**, 4, ch g Shamardal (USA)—Kotsi (IRE) **Thames Boys**
7 **CASTLE TALBOT (IRE)**, 4, b c Rock of Gibraltar (IRE)—Louve Sacree (USA) **Mr G. Dolan**
8 **DUCHESS OF MARMITE (IRE)**, 4, b f Duke of Marmalade (IRE)—Reprise **Rathordan Partnership**
9 **DYNAMO (IRE)**, 5, b g Galileo (IRE)—Trading Places **Foxtrot NH Racing Partnership X**
10 **ELYSIAN FLYER (IRE)**, 4, b g Majestic Missile (IRE)—Starisa (IRE) **The Low Flyers**
11 **PRESTO BOY**, 4, b g Compton Place—Presto Levanter **Mr Richard Hughes**
12 **QUALITY SONG (USA)**, 4, b g Elusive Quality (USA)—Run In (USA) **Mr H. A. Lootah**
13 **RUSSIAN REALM**, 6, b g Dansili—Russian Rhythm (USA) **Mr Richard Hughes**
14 **SHAMAHAN**, 7, b g Shamardal (USA)—Hanella (IRE) **Forever Hopeful**
15 **THE BIG LAD**, 4, ch g Kheleyf (USA)—Cultured Pride (IRE) **Mr Don Churston & Mr Ray Greatorex**
16 **WAHAAB (IRE)**, 5, ch g Tamayuz—Indian Ink (IRE) **Mr M. Clarke**

THREE-YEAR-OLDS

17 B f Aqlaam—Bint Doyen **M. Al Nabouda**
18 **CULTURED KNIGHT**, ch c Compton Place—Cultured Pride (IRE) **Mr Don Churston & Mr Ray Greatorex**
19 **POLLY'S SERENADE**, b f Kyllachy—Flamenco Dancer **M. R. Flitton**

TWO-YEAR-OLDS

20 B c 28/1 Harbour Watch (IRE)—Al Hawa (USA) (Gulch (USA)) (18000) **The Heffer Syndicate**
21 B c 15/3 Harbour Watch (IRE)—Anneliina (Cadeaux Genereux) (33333) **Mr Richard Hughes**
22 B c 7/5 Myboycharlie (IRE)—Art of Dance (Medicean) (15000) **Mr Richard Hughes**
23 Gr c 5/3 Pour Moi (IRE)—Balandra (Medicean) (75000) **Mr J. E. Lund**
24 B gr f 15/1 Mastercraftsman (IRE)—Bright Sapphire (IRE) (Galileo (IRE)) (85000) **Mr J. E. Lund**
25 **CASPIAN GOLD (IRE)**, ch c 20/2 Born To Sea (IRE)—
    Eminence Gift (Cadeaux Genereux) (120000) **M Hughes & M Kerr-Dineen**
26 **CINQUE PORT**, ch c 9/2 Compton Place—Jump Ship (Night Shift (USA)) **M. H. Dixon**
27 B f 20/3 Mastercraftsman (IRE)—Corrozal (GER) (Cape Cross (IRE)) (23000)
28 **FLANAGAN (GER)**, b c 29/3 Cacique (IRE)—
    Flames To Dust (GER) (Oasis Dream) (75000) **HighclereThoroughbredRacing-Oscar Wilde**
29 **GOLDEN WOLF (IRE)**, b br c 26/4 Big Bad Bob (IRE)—
    Jeunesse Doree (IRE) (Rock of Gibraltar (IRE)) (35437) **Aristotle's Elements**
30 B f 9/4 Quality Road (USA)—I'm From Dixie (USA) (Dixieland Band (USA)) **Danny Waters & Adrian Regan**
31 B c 20/3 Zebedee—Irish Design (IRE) (Alhaarth (IRE)) (72000) **Mr D. S. Waters**

MR RICHARD HUGHES - Continued

32 JASHMA (IRE), b c 23/5 Power—
Daganya (IRE) (Danehill Dancer (IRE)) (81210) **M Clarke, S Geraghty, J Jeffries**
33 KING OF PARIS, b c 11/2 Exceed And Excel (AUS)—
Dubai Queen (USA) (Kingmambo (USA)) **Sheikh Mohammed Obaid Al Maktoum**
34 B c 5/2 Myboycharlie (IRE)—Lady Oriande (Makbul) (66445) **Macdonald,Wright,Creed,Jiggins & Miller**
35 B c 31/3 So You Think (NZ)—Lukrecia (IRE) (Exceed And Excel (AUS)) (12000) **Mr Richard Hughes**
36 LUZIA, b f 17/2 Cape Cross (IRE)—Bint Almukhtar (IRE) (Halling (USA)) **Sheikh Mohammed Obaid Al Maktoum**
37 B f 6/2 Exceed And Excel (AUS)—Naruko (USA) (Street Cry (IRE)) (100000) **Mr Richard Hughes**
38 NATHANIA, ch f 14/2 Nathaniel (IRE)—Glen Rosie (IRE) (Mujtahid (USA)) (105000) **Mr Richard Hughes**
39 Gr f 24/1 Dark Angel (IRE)—Nepali Princess (IRE) (Mr Greeley (USA)) (191952) **Al Shaqab Racing UK Limited**
40 B c 25/1 Sir Prancealot (IRE)—Pale Orchid (IRE) (Invincible Spirit (IRE)) (44000) **Mr Richard Hughes**
41 B f 2/2 Paco Boy (IRE)—Papabile (USA) (Chief's Crown (USA))
42 PATCHWORK, ch c 29/4 Paco Boy (IRE)—Medley (Danehill Dancer (IRE)) **Her Majesty The Queen**
43 B c 16/4 Sir Prancealot (IRE)—Peyto Princess (Bold Arrangement) (35000) **Sir David Seale**
44 B f 28/2 Lawman (FR)—Red Boots (IRE) (Verglas (IRE)) (40000) **The Saints**
45 ROCK N ROLL GLOBAL (IRE), ch c 27/2 Power—
Laughter (IRE) (Sadler's Wells (USA)) (45773) **Jed Gaffney and Frank McGrath**
46 B c 15/3 Requinto (IRE)—Royal Esteem (Mark of Esteem (IRE)) (61904) **Carmichael Jennings**
47 B c 7/3 Sir Prancealot (IRE)—She's A Character (Invincible Spirit (IRE)) (33333) **Mr D. S. Waters**
48 B c 20/2 More Than Ready (USA)—Silimiss (Dansili) (60000) **Mr D. S. Waters**
49 B f 23/2 Dark Angel (IRE)—Sister Red (IRE) (Diamond Green (FR)) (47619) **Saleh Al Homaizi & Imad Al Sagar**
50 B c 4/4 Canford Cliffs (IRE)—
Street Style (IRE) (Rock of Gibraltar (IRE)) (240000) **Saleh Al Homaizi & Imad Al Sagar**
51 TANNI GREY (IRE), br gr f 5/4 Zebedee—Xarzee (IRE) (Xaar) (9523) **Mr & Mrs J Harris**
52 TWENTY TIMES (IRE), b f 5/5 Dream Ahead (USA)—Mad Existence (IRE) (Val Royal (FR)) (73827) **True Reds**
53 VIOLET'S LADS (IRE), b f 24/2 Myboycharlie (IRE)—Cape Violet (IRE) (Cape Cross (IRE)) (14765) **J. Daniels**
54 WATERVILLE DANCER (IRE), b c 12/2 Nathaniel (IRE)—
Tobiano (USA) (Mt Livermore (USA)) (36913) **Mr M. Clarke**
55 B c 8/3 Sepoy (AUS)—Zanzibar (IRE) (In The Wings) (100000) **Malih L. Al Basti**
56 ZAVIKON, b c 30/1 Compton Place—
Hakuraa (IRE) (Elnadim (USA)) (71428) **Embleton, Galloway, Hanley & Lawrence**

Other Owners: Mrs J. Abraham, Mr D. Abraham, I. J. Al-Sagar, Mr D. Barrett, Mrs F. J. Carmichael, D. G. Churston, J. T. Devine, Mr M. A. Embleton, Sir A. Ferguson, Mr J. Gaffney, Mr B. S. Galloway, Mr S. A. Geraghty, R. E. Greatorex, Mr D. Hajiantoni, Mr S. A. Hanley, Mrs P. A. Harris, Mr J. E. Harris, Mr H. R. Heffer, Mr R. P. Heffer, Mr M. Heffernan, Highclere Nominated Partner Limited, Highclere Thoroughbred Racing Ltd, Saleh Al Homaizi, Mr M. B. Hughes, Mr J. Jeffries, Mr I. Jennings, Mr Kerr-Dineen, Mr K. Lawrence, D. Leon, Mr A. T. Macdonald, Mr E. Malone, G. A. Mason, Mr F. McGrath, Mr M. J. Mitchell, Mr G. O'Sullivan, Dr L. F. Parks, Mr S. A. J. Penny, Mr M. Quirke, Mr A. Regan, Mr R. H. Seward, Mr G. P. Triefus, L. R. Turland, C. N. Wright, Mrs F. P. Young.

Apprentice: Stephen Cummins, Steph Joannides, Chris Kelly.

320
MRS SANDRA HUGHES, Kildare
Postal: **Osborne Lodge, Kildare, Co. Kildare, Ireland**
Contacts: **PHONE (00353) 4552 1490 FAX (00353) 4552 1643 MOBILE (00353) 87 3781739**
E-MAIL sandrahughes1970@hotmail.com

1 ACAPELLA BOURGEOIS (FR), 6, ch g Network (GER)—Jasmine (FR) **Slaneyville Syndicate**
2 ALL HELL LET LOOSE (IRE), 7, b g Shantou (USA)—Gan Ainm (IRE) **Gigginstown House Stud**
3 APACHE JACK (IRE), 8, b br g Oscar (IRE)—Cailin Supreme (IRE) **Mrs P. Sloane**
4 ART OF LOGISTICS (IRE), 8, b g Exit To Nowhere (USA)—Sanadja (IRE) **Munnelly Support Services**
5 ART OF PAYROLL (GER), 7, b g Shirocco (GER)—Anna Maria (GER) **Bishopsgate Syndicate**
6 ART OF SECURITY (IRE), 6, b g High Chaparral (USA)—Irish Wedding (IRE) **Munnelly Support Services**
7 ART OF SYNERGY (IRE), 5, b g Yeats (IRE)—Elizabeth Tudor (IRE) **Munnelly Support Services**
8 BACK BEFORE DAWN (IRE), 7, b m Oscar (IRE)—Back To Bavaria (IRE) **U S of Pieland Syndicate**
9 BAKMAJ (FR), 4, b g Balko (FR)—Myralienne (FR) **T. O'Driscoll**
10 BELLE LAKE BOY (IRE), 5, gr g Acambaro (GER)—Ezilana (IRE) **Lyreen Syndicate**
11 BUYER BEWARE (IRE), 4, br g Big Bad Bob (IRE)—Adoring (IRE) **T. O'Driscoll**
12 CANALY (IRE), 11, b g Bob Back (USA)—Starry Lady (IRE) **Michael B. Moore**
13 CARLITOS BAY (IRE), 5, b g Definite Article—Avitta (IRE) **Seven To Eleven Syndicate**
14 CLAREN LAD (IRE), 4, ch g Duke of Marmalade (IRE)—Zapping (IRE) **Mrs Mary Roche**
15 COEUR JOYEUX (IRE), 5, ch g Beneficial—Hayabusa (IRE) **J. P. McManus**
16 EMPEROR OF EXMOOR (IRE), 9, b g Montjeu (IRE)—Shamriyna (IRE) **Francis G. Kenny**
17 ESHAYKO (GER), 5, br g Sholokhov (IRE)—Eshaya (GER) **Mrs Margaret M. Dunne**

MRS SANDRA HUGHES - Continued

18 4, B g Ask—Flora May **Ms S. Hughes**
19 **GIANT SPIRIT (USA)**, 4, ch g Giant's Causeway (USA)—Saintlike (USA) **Miss Michelle Doyle**
20 **GOLDEN WONDER (IRE)**, 10, b g Goldmark (USA)—Polyploid (IRE) **P. M. Cooney**
21 **GUITAR PETE (IRE)**, 6, br g Dark Angel (IRE)—Innishmore (IRE) **Mrs P. Sloane**
22 **HERBIEGOESBANANAS (IRE)**, 6, br g Presenting—Current Liability **Neville Eager**
23 **HUNTING HARRY**, 5, b g Kyllachy—Celestial Princess **Mrs D. T. Hughes**
24 4, B g Oscar (IRE)—Irish Wedding (IRE) **Munnelly Support Services**
25 **JONJOELA (IRE)**, 5, b m Great Exhibition (IRE)—Yorkshire Blade (IRE) **Philip J. Burke**
26 **KNOCKANARRIGAN (IRE)**, 8, b g Shantou (USA)—Ruby Thewes (IRE) **Neville Eager**
27 4, B g Mahler—Kuwalla (IRE) **Ms S. Hughes**
28 **LIEUTENANT COLONEL**, 7, br g Kayf Tara—Agnese **Gigginstown House Stud**
29 4, B f Presenting—Lola d'haguenet (FR) **Ms S. Hughes**
30 **LOUIE THE SECOND (IRE)**, 5, ch g Trans Island—Shaylejon (IRE) **James F. Dunne**
31 **LYREEN LEGEND**, 9, b g Saint des Saints (FR)—Bint Bladi (FR) **Lyreen Syndicate**
32 **NEARLY NAMA'D (IRE)**, 8, b g Millenary—Coca's Well (IRE) **J. P. McManus**
33 **OFF THE CHARTS (IRE)**, 7, b g Beneficial—Coppenagh Lady (IRE) **J. P. McManus**
34 **OR DE VASSY (FR)**, 4, b br g Assessor (IRE)—Mona Vassy (FR) **T. O'Driscoll**
35 4, B g Flemensfirth (USA)—Pandorama Lady (IRE) **Ms S. Hughes**
36 **PAUPLEWEL (FR)**, 9, ch g Kaldounevees (FR)—Miss Irish (FR) **T. O'Driscoll**
37 **PHIL'S MAGIC (IRE)**, 6, b br g Fruits of Love (USA)—Inch Rose (IRE) **Lyreen Syndicate**
38 **PINK COAT**, 9, gr g Alhaarth (IRE)—In The Pink (IRE) **Mrs D. T. Hughes**
39 4, B g Wolfe Tone (IRE)—Raquel (IRE) **P. J. Murphy**
40 **RAZ DE MAREE (FR)**, 11, ch g Shaanmer (IRE)—Diyala III (FR) **James J. Swan**
41 4, B f Stowaway—Running Wild (IRE) **Ms S. Hughes**
42 4, B g Robin des Champs (FR)—Sarah Massini (IRE) **T. O'Driscoll**
43 **SHEAMUS (IRE)**, 7, ch g Definite Article—She's A Venture (IRE) **Slaneyville Syndicate**
44 **SIDE SADDLE (IRE)**, 6, b m King's Theatre—Steel Grey Lady (IRE) **Slaneyville Syndicate**
45 **SILKEN THOMAS (IRE)**, 5, gr g Dark Angel (IRE)—Innishmore (IRE) **Munnelly Support Services**
46 **SMALL WORLD (IRE)**, 5, b g Shantou (USA)—Bodhran Davis (FR) **Three Locks Syndicate**
47 **SMOKING BIG CIGARS**, 6, b g Kayf Tara—Coldabri (IRE) **Tanqueray Ten Syndicate**
48 **SOME TIKKET (IRE)**, 9, b g Tikkanen (USA)—Ally Rose (IRE) **Mr K. Jones**
49 **SPORTS BARROW (IRE)**, 4, b g Windsor Knot (IRE)—Liberty Grace (IRE) **Malih Lahej Al Basti**
50 **SUB LIEUTENANT (IRE)**, 7, b g Brian Boru—Satellite Dancer (IRE) **Gigginstown House Stud**
51 **THE GRANSON (IRE)**, 4, b g Jeremy (USA)—Kimberely Bay (IRE) **Padraig Coffee**
52 **THUNDER AND ROSES (IRE)**, 8, b br g Presenting—Glen Empress (IRE) **Gigginstown House Stud**
53 **TOTAL RECALL (IRE)**, 7, b g Westerner—Augest Weekend (IRE) **Slaneyville Syndicate**
54 4, B g Presenting—Water Rock **Ms S. Hughes**
55 **WEST BRIDGE**, 5, b m Yeats (IRE)—Starello **Daniel Corry**
56 **WINGOLDANDWEARIT (IRE)**, 5, b br g Definite Article—Connemara Rose (IRE) **Miss A. Lalor**
57 **WRATH OF TITANS (IRE)**, 7, b g Oscar (IRE)—Glen Empress (IRE) **Gigginstown House Stud**

Other Owners: Gerry Bell, J. Keeling, Patrick Monaghan, P. J. Murphy, Sabrina Power.

Jockey (NH): J. J. Burke, Roger Loughran. **Conditional:** Cian Collins.

---

321   MS N. M. HUGO, Newmarket
Postal: **36 King George Avenue, Exning, Newmarket, Suffolk, CB8 7ES**
Contacts: **MOBILE (07736) 360550**
E-MAIL nickyhugo1@gmail.com

1 **CLASSIC ROSES**, 4, b f Youmzain (IRE)—Masque Rose
2 **MAREY (IRE)**, 7, b m Fruits of Love (USA)—Mill Thyme **Ms N. M. Hugo**
3 **PURANA**, 5, ch m Pastoral Pursuits—Arruhan (IRE) **Ms N. M. Hugo**
4 **SIGNORE MOMENTO (IRE)**, 10, b g Captain Rio—Gitchee Gumee Rose (IRE)

---

322   MRS SARAH HUMPHREY, West Wratting
Postal: **Yen Hall Farm, West Wratting, Cambridge, Cambridgeshire, CB21 5LP**
Contacts: **PHONE (01223) 291445 FAX (01223) 291451 MOBILE (07798) 702484**
E-MAIL sarah@yenhallfarm.com WEBSITE www.sarahhumphrey.co.uk

1 **BIG MIKE (IRE)**, 8, b g Flemensfirth (USA)—Minoras Return (IRE)
2 **CALL AT MIDNIGHT**, 11, b m Midnight Legend—Second Call **Mrs S. Humphrey**

MRS SARAH HUMPHREY - Continued

3 **CALL ME KAL (IRE)**, 5, b g Kalanisi (IRE)—Miss Compliance (IRE) **The Old Eatonians**
4 **CHAMBORD DU LOIR (FR)**, 6, b g Ange Gabriel (FR)—Etoile de Loir (FR) **Mrs S. Humphrey**
5 **FARE THEE WELL (IRE)**, 6, b g Duke of Marmalade (IRE)—Bowstring (IRE)
6 **FLEMI TWO TOES (IRE)**, 10, b g Flemensfirth (USA)—Silva Venture (IRE) **Entente Cordiale**
7 **INDIAN DAUDAIE (FR)**, 9, ch g Nicobar—Aldounia (FR) **Entente Cordiale**
8 **KNIGHT'S PARADE (IRE)**, 6, b g Dark Angel (IRE)—Toy Show (IRE)
9 **LARTETA (FR)**, 7, b g Enrique—Ariel (IRE) **Yen Hall Farm Racing**
10 **LE SAUMON (IRE)**, 6, b g Milan—Super Size (IRE) **Yen Hall Farm Racing**
11 **MAHLERS SPIRIT (IRE)**, 6, ch g Mahler—Belle Dame (IRE) **Come Up Trumps**
12 **MESUT (FR)**, 5, bl g Early March—Alicesprings (FR) **A Whyte, D Nott & S Greenlees**
13 **PARK STEEL (IRE)**, 6, b g Craigsteel—Orient Star (IRE)
14 **RED SEVENTY**, 7, b g Sakhee (USA)—Dimakya (USA) **Yen Hall Farm Racing**
15 **THE SCOURGE (IRE)**, 5, b g Whipper (USA)—House Rebel (IRE) **Yen Hall Farm Racing**
16 **TOP MAN MARTY (IRE)**, 7, b g Westerner—Tribal Princess **Dr R. C. Britton**
17 **UNKNOWN LEGEND (IRE)**, 9, b g Heron Island (IRE)—Late Call (IRE) **Yen Hall Farm Racing**
18 **WHO YOU FOR (IRE)**, 6, b g Craigsteel—Knappogue Honey (IRE) **The Doc Partnership**

Other Owners: Dr R. Britton, Miss J. M. Custerson, Mr Arnold Eaton, Mr R. N. Fuller, Mrs L. Greenlees, Mrs S. J. Humphrey, Mr A. R. Humphrey, Mr D. F. Nott, Mr A. A. Whyte, Yen Hall Farm Racing.

Assistant Trainer: Mr A. R. Humphrey

Jockey (NH): Jack Quinlan. **Conditional:** Romain Clavreul. **Amateur:** Mr B. Clark.

---

323 MR KEVIN HUNTER, Natland
Postal: **Larkrigg, Natland, Cumbria, LA9 7QS**
Contacts: **PHONE (01539) 560245**

1 **ALLIED ANSWER**, 8, gr g Danehill Dancer (IRE)—Hotelgenie Dot Com **K. Hunter**
2 **CATACLYSM (IRE)**, 6, b g Captain Rio—Marilaya (IRE) **K. Hunter**
3 **GLENWOOD PRINCE (IRE)**, 10, b g King's Theatre (IRE)—Moll Bawn (IRE) **K. Hunter**

---

324 MISS LAURA HURLEY, Kineton
Postal: **Kineton Grange Farm, Kineton, Warwick, Warwickshire, CV35 0EE**
Contacts: **PHONE (01926) 640380**

1 **BARRA ROTHA (IRE)**, 9, ch g Perugino (USA)—That's Magic (IRE) **Mrs R. Hurley**
2 **BIG NIGHT OUT**, 10, b m Midnight Legend—Big Decision **Mrs R. Hurley**
3 **CATCHIN TIME (IRE)**, 8, b g Chineur (FR)—Lady Dane (IRE) **Mrs R. Hurley**
4 **GWILI SPAR**, 8, ch g Generosity—Lady of Mine **Mrs R. Hurley**

---

325 MISS ALISON HUTCHINSON, Exning
Postal: **116 Parkers Walk, Studlands, Newmarket, Suffolk, CB8 7AP**
Contacts: **PHONE (01638) 482180 MOBILE (07960) 630204**
E-MAIL alison.hutchinson1@hotmail.co.uk
WEBSITE www.alisonhutchinsonhorseracing.weebly.com

1 **SAFIRA MENINA**, 4, b f Paco Boy (IRE)—Isla Azul (IRE) **Miss A. L. Hutchinson**
2 **STRIKE FORCE**, 12, b g Dansili—Miswaki Belle (USA) **Miss A. L. Hutchinson**

Jockey (flat): Tom Eaves, Robert Havlin, Oisin Murphy, James Sullivan. **Amateur:** Miss A. L. Hutchinson.

326 **MRS CAROLE IKIN, Sutton In The Elms**
Postal: Walton Lodge Farm, Sutton In The Elms, Leicestershire, LE9 6RB
Contacts: PHONE (01455) 282321 MOBILE (07850) 278491
E-MAIL nevagree@yahoo.co.uk WEBSITE www.equinespa.co.uk

1 ART LOOKER (IRE), 4, b g Excellent Art—Looker **Mrs C. J. Ikin**
2 RIME AVEC GENTIL (FR), 11, b g Kapgarde (FR)—Quenice (FR) **Mrs C. J. Ikin**

Assistant Trainer: Mr P. J. Ikin

327 **MR ROGER INGRAM, Epsom**
Postal: Wendover Stables, Burgh Heath Road, Epsom, Surrey, KT17 4LX
Contacts: PHONE (01372) 748505 or (01372) 749157 FAX (01372) 748505
MOBILE (07773) 665980 / (07715) 993911
E-MAIL roger.ingram.racing@virgin.net WEBSITE www.rogeringramracing.com

1 ARU CHA CHA, 5, b g Myboycharlie (IRE)—Royal Arruhan **Mr S. J. Appleyard**
2 AWESOME ROCK (IRE), 7, ch g Rock of Gibraltar (IRE)—Dangerous Diva (IRE) **Mr M. F. Cruse**
3 BICKERSHAW, 4, b g Equiano (FR)—Ring of Love **Mr Peter Burton**
4 BRIDGE THAT GAP, 8, b h Avonbridge—Figura **Mr R. Ingram**
5 DUKES MEADOW, 5, b g Pastoral Pursuits—Figura **The Stargazers**
6 ENCAPSULATED, 6, b g Zamindar (USA)—Star Cluster **Mrs E. N. Nield**
7 5, B m Morpeth—Miracle Monarch **Mr K. Tollick**
8 NELSON'S PRIDE, 5, b m Mount Nelson—Bandanna **Mrs C. E. Hallam**
9 PRINCE OF PARIS, 4, b c Champs Elysees—Cool Kitten (IRE) **Mr G. E. Ley**
10 TRIPLE CHOCOLATE, 6, b g Danehill Dancer (IRE)—Enticing (IRE) **Dukes Head Racing**

THREE-YEAR-OLDS

11 FASTNET PRINCE (IRE), b g Fastnet Rock (AUS)—Lucky Spin **John Leo Collins**
12 SILVER WINGS (IRE), gr g Zebedee—Daisy Hill **Collins & Reilly**

Other Owners: Mr Pat Dalton, Mr John Leo Collins, Mr Michael Joy, Mr D. Ross-Watt.

Assistant Trainer: Sharon Ingram

Apprentice: Rhiain Ingram.

328 **MR DEAN IVORY, Radlett**
Postal: Harper Lodge Farm, Harper Lane, Radlett, Hertfordshire, WD7 7HU
Contacts: PHONE (01923) 855337 FAX (01923) 852470 MOBILE (07785) 118658
E-MAIL deanivoryracing@gmail.com WEBSITE www.deanivoryracing.co.uk

1 CASPIAN PRINCE (IRE), 7, ch g Dylan Thomas (IRE)—Crystal Gaze (IRE) **Mr S. Louch**
2 CATHARINA, 4, ch f Dutch Art—Lambadora **K. T. Ivory**
3 ELJADDAAF (IRE), 5, b g Shamardal (USA)—Almansoora (USA) **Wentdale Ltd & Mrs L A Ivory**
4 FIRMDECISIONS (IRE), 6, b g Captain Rio—Luna Crescente (IRE) **White Bear Racing**
5 GOLDEN AMBER (IRE), 5, b m Holy Roman Emperor (IRE)—Time of Gold (USA) **Heather & Michael Yarrow**
6 GOLDSLINGER (FR), 4, b g Gold Away (IRE)—Singaporette (FR) **Heather & Michael Yarrow**
7 HARLEQUIN STRIKER (IRE), 4, b g Bahamian Bounty—Air Maze **Harlequin Direct Ltd**
8 LANCELOT DU LAC (ITY), 6, b g Shamardal (USA)—Dodie Mae (USA) **Michael & Heather Yarrow**
9 LIBRISA BREEZE, 4, gr g Mount Nelson—Bruxcalina (FR) **Mr A. G. Bloom**
10 LINKS DRIVE LADY, 8, br m Striking Ambition—Miskina **It's Your Lucky Day**
11 O DEE, 4, ch g Iffraaj—Queen's Grace **Radlett Racing**
12 RAVENS HEART (IRE), 4, b g Dansili—Hymn of Love (IRE) **Harlequin Direct Ltd & Dean Ivory**
13 ROSIE'S PREMIERE (IRE), 4, b f Showcasing—Golden Rosie (IRE) **Mrs H. Yarrow**
14 SAN QUENTIN (IRE), 5, gr g Lawman (FR)—In The Soup (USA) **Mr S. Louch**
15 SEA SILK, 4, b g Shamardal (USA)—Ocean Silk (USA) **Cynthia Smith & Lesley Ivory**
16 SECRET BIRD (IRE), 4, br g Arcano (IRE)—Asfurah (USA) **Marchwood Aggregates**
17 SHANTI, 6, b g Dansili—Maycocks Bay **D. K. Ivory**
18 SIRIUS PROSPECT (USA), 8, b br g Gone West—Stella Blue (FR) **Miss N. I. Yarrow**
19 SOARING SPIRITS (IRE), 6, ch g Tamayuz—Follow My Lead **Mrs D. A. Carter**
20 SPINNING ROSE, 4, ch f Pivotal—Aqua Rose (USA) **John Waterfall, Richard & Ian R Gethin**
21 STAKE ACCLAIM (IRE), 4, b g Acclamation—Golden Legacy (IRE) **Mr M. J. Yarrow**

MR DEAN IVORY - Continued

22 **TAGULA NIGHT (IRE)**, 10, ch g Tagula (IRE)—Carpet Lady (IRE) **Gordon Papworth & John Fishpool**
23 **TANGRAMM**, 4, b br g Sakhee's Secret—Tripti (IRE) **Mr J. L. Marsden**
24 **TROPICS (USA)**, 8, ch g Speightstown (USA)—Taj Aire (USA) **D. K. Ivory**
25 **VARSOVIAN**, 6, ch g Refuse To Bend (IRE)—Queen of Poland **Geoff Copp & Radlett Racing**

THREE-YEAR-OLDS

26 **ARCTIC ANGEL (IRE)**, b g Dark Angel (IRE)—Charlene Lacy (IRE) **The Macaroni Beach Society**
27 **BLAZE OF HEARTS (IRE)**, b c Canford Cliffs (IRE)—Shesthebiscuit **Miss N. I. Yarrow**
28 **BRUNTINGTHORPE (IRE)**, b g Thousand Words—Cooke's Bar (IRE) **Mr S. Louch**
29 **DOR'S LAW**, b f Lawman (FR)—Law of Chance **Mrs D. A. Carter**
30 **FIGHTING TEMERAIRE (IRE)**, b c Invincible Spirit (IRE)—Hot Ticket (IRE) **Michael & Heather Yarrow**
31 **FOREVER YOURS (IRE)**, b g Canford Cliffs (IRE)—Gilded (IRE) **Mr A. Chapman**
32 **JACK THE LAIRD (IRE)**, b g Acclamation—Pretty Demanding (IRE) **Michael & Heather Yarrow**
33 **JUSTICE (IRE)**, b f Lawman (FR)—Sheboygan (IRE) **K T Ivory & Mrs Valerie Hubbard**
34 **KADRIZZI (IRE)**, ch g Hurricane Cat (USA)—Kadiania (FR) **Mr A Chapman & Wentdale Limited**
35 **LUCYMAI**, b f Multiplex—Miss Lesley **Mr R. Beadle**
36 **OJAI (IRE)**, br f Big Bad Bob (IRE)—Femme Fatale **Wood Hall Stud Limited**
37 **PACOHONTAS**, b br f Paco Boy (IRE)—Balliasta (IRE) **Downlands Racing**
38 **PALMINA**, ch f Bahamian Bounty—Starfleet **Wood Hall Stud Limited**
39 **PEARLY QUEEN**, b f Dutch Art—Surprise (IRE) **Heather & Michael Yarrow**
40 **R BAR OPEN (FR)**, b br g Orpen (USA)—Bahama Love (USA) **The Macaroni Beach Society**
41 **RED RUFFIAN (IRE)**, ch g Tamayuz—Hatria (IRE) **Mrs Gwen Thomas & Radlett Racing**
42 **TESORO (IRE)**, b f Galileo (IRE)—Theann **Heather & Michael Yarrow**
43 **TWIN SAILS**, b c Sir Percy—Atwirl **Mr H.Robin Heffer and K T Ivory**

TWO-YEAR-OLDS

44 B br g 3/2 Exchange Rate (USA)—Bema (USA) (Pulpit (USA)) (45000) **Mr H. R. Heffer**
45 **BOBBY VEE**, ch f 16/5 Camacho—Miss Lesley (Needwood Blade) (9523) **Mr Roger S Beadle & Radlett Racing**
46 **CAPPANANTY CON**, gr c 8/3 Zebedee—
  Fairmont (IRE) (Kingmambo (USA)) (22000) **Mr J Biggane & Radlett Racing**
47 Ch f 10/2 Bated Breath—Gretna (Groom Dancer (USA)) (15238) **Wood Hall Stud Limited**
48 **HARLEQUIN STORM**, b c 29/3 Clodovil (IRE)—
  Convidada (IRE) (Trans Island) (42000) **Harlequin Direct Ltd**
49 B c 6/3 Holy Roman Emperor (IRE)—Kibini (Galileo (IRE)) (13000) **Solario Racing**
50 **LOTHARIO**, gr c 11/2 Dark Angel (IRE)—
  Kisses For Me (IRE) (Sadler's Wells (USA)) (142857) **Heather & Michael Yarrow**
51 **POET'S QUEST**, b f 15/4 Poet's Voice—Quest For Freedom (Falbrav (IRE)) **Leon Vaessen**
52 **SEAVIEW**, b f 4/4 Harbour Watch (IRE)—Welanga (Dansili) (22000) **Mr H.Robin Heffer and K T Ivory**
53 B f 21/2 Compton Place—Sonko (IRE) (Red Clubs (IRE)) **J. A. Khan**
54 **SURFINA**, b f 9/2 Acclamation—Drift And Dream (Exceed And Excel (AUS)) (20000) **K T Ivory & H Robin Heffer**
55 **SWEET SIENNA**, ch f 3/2 Harbour Watch (IRE)—
  Look Busy (IRE) (Danetime (IRE)) (57142) **Michael & Heather Yarrow**
56 **EIRENE**, b f 28/3 Declaration of War (USA)—Za Za Zoom (IRE) (Le Vie Dei Colori) (85000) **Mr M. J. Yarrow**

Other Owners: Mr J. Biggane, Mr G. M. Copp, J. E. Fishpool, Mr I. R. Gethin, Mr R. Gethin, Mrs V. Hubbard, Mrs L. A. Ivory, Miss E. Morgan, D. Morgan, G. Papworth, Mrs C. Smith, Mr R. W. Sturges, Mrs A. M. Sturges, Mrs G. Thomas, Mr J. B. Waterfall, Wentdale Limited.

Assistant Trainer: Chris Scally

Apprentice: Paul Booth.

---

329 **MISS TINA JACKSON, Loftus**
Postal: **Tick Hill Farm, Liverton, Loftus, Saltburn, Cleveland, TS13 4TG**
Contacts: **PHONE (01287) 644952 MOBILE (07774) 106906**

1 **ARDESIA (IRE)**, 12, b g Red Sunset—Lowtown **A. Jackson**
2 **FLEDERMAUS (IRE)**, 6, br g Jeremy (USA)—Khayrat (IRE) **H. L. Thompson**
3 **IVORS INVOLVEMENT (IRE)**, 4, b g Amadeus Wolf—Summer Spice (IRE) **H. L. Thompson**
4 **JAN DE HEEM**, 6, ch g Dutch Art—Shasta **H L Thompson & D Tucker**
5 **JOSEPH MERCER (IRE)**, 9, b g Court Cave (IRE)—Vikki's Dream (IRE) **H. L. Thompson**
6 **KING'S REALM (IRE)**, 9, ch g King's Best (USA)—Sweet Home Alabama (IRE) **H. L. Thompson**
7 **PURPLE HARRY**, 8, gr g Sir Harry Lewis (USA)—Ellfiedick **H. L. Thompson**
8 **REBEL ROGER**, 7, b g Revoque (IRE)—Sally Scally **H. L. Thompson**

MISS TINA JACKSON - Continued

9 **ROSY RYAN (IRE)**, 6, b m Tagula (IRE)—Khaydariya (IRE) **H. L. Thompson**
10 **SORY**, 9, b g Sakhee (USA)—Rule Britannia **H. L. Thompson**
11 **TAKAATUF (IRE)**, 10, b g Dubai Destination (USA)—Karlaka (IRE) **H. L. Thompson**
12 **WILLIAM WILD**, 8, b g Bollin Eric—Winnie Wild **H. L. Thompson**

Other Owners: Mr D. Tucker.

---

330 **MRS VALERIE JACKSON, Newcastle Upon Tyne**
Postal: Edge House, Belsay, Newcastle Upon Tyne, Tyne and Wear, NE20 0HH
Contacts: **PHONE (01830) 530218 MOBILE (07808) 812213**

1 **KNICK KNACK (IRE)**, 6, b g Kalanisi (IRE)—Full Imperatrice (FR) **Mrs V. S. Jackson**
2 **PADDY'S YARN (IRE)**, 6, ch g Houmayoun (FR)—Deidamia (USA) **Mrs V. S. Jackson**

---

331 **MR LEE JAMES, Malton**
Postal: Cheesecake Hill Stables, Beverley Road, Norton, Malton, North Yorkshire, YO17 9PJ
Contacts: **PHONE (01653) 699466 FAX (01653) 699581 MOBILE (07732) 556322**

1 **EXCELLENT ADDITION (IRE)**, 6, ch g Excellent Art—Race The Wild Wind (USA) **Mr Ian Johnson**
2 **MA PETIT LUMIER**, 6, b g Echo of Light—Alisdanza **L. R. James**
3 6, B m Dubai Destination (USA)—Palisandra (USA) **Mrs C. Lloyd-James**
4 **SHADOW OF THE DAY**, 9, b g Sugarfoot—She Who Dares Wins **Mrs C. Lloyd James**
5 **STRIKEMASTER (IRE)**, 10, b g Xaar—Mas A Fuera (IRE) **L. R. James**

Assistant Trainer: Carol James

Jockey (NH): Kyle James.

---

332 **MR IAIN JARDINE, Carrutherstown**
Postal: Paddock House, Hetlandhill Farm, Carrutherstown, Dumfriesshire, DG1 4JX
Contacts: **PHONE (01450) 860718 MOBILE (07738) 351232**
E-MAIL iainjardineracing@hotmail.co.uk

1 **ARCHIPELIGO**, 5, b g Archipenko (USA)—Red Slew **Tapas Partnership**
2 **BRUICHLADDICH**, 4, b g Westerner—Highland Cherry **Distillery Racing Club**
3 **CALCULATED RISK**, 7, ch g Motivator—Glen Rosie (IRE) **Mr S. R. Middleton**
4 **CALL ME CROCKETT (IRE)**, 4, ch g Intense Focus (USA)—Forest Storm (USA) **Mr Kirk Wilson & Maurice Friel**
5 **CYMRAEG BOUNTY**, 4, ch g Bahamian Bounty—Croeso Cusan **Mr M. Andrews**
6 **DOUBLE WHAMMY**, 10, b g Systematic—Honor Rouge (IRE) **Alex & Janet Card**
7 **HEART O ANNANDALE (IRE)**, 9, b g Winged Love (IRE)—She's All Heart **K. Milligan Partnership**
8 **LA BACOUETTEUSE (FR)**, 11, b g Miesque's Son (USA)—Toryka **Miss S. A. Booth**
9 **LOUD AND CLEAR**, 5, b g Dalakhani (IRE)—Whispering Blues (IRE) **Tapas Partnership**
10 7, B m Fair Mix (IRE)—Miss Nel **R. H. Goldie**
11 **MY LITTLE CRACKER (IRE)**, 6, b m Scorpion (IRE)—Cailin Gruaig Dubh (IRE) **Mr & Mrs Paul & Clare Rooney**
12 **NAKEETA**, 5, b g Sixties Icon—Easy Red (IRE) **Alex & Janet Card**
13 **NEVER NEVER (IRE)**, 6, b g Jeremy (USA)—Argus Gal (IRE) **Mr & Mrs Paul & Clare Rooney**
14 **NEWMARKET WARRIOR (IRE)**, 5, b g Dalakhani (IRE)—Heavens Peak **Mr I. Jardine**
15 **PUSH ME (IRE)**, 9, gr m Verglas (IRE)—Gilda Lilly (USA) **Alex & Janet Card**
16 4, B f Sixties Icon—River Alder **Mr M Friel, Mr T Reid & Mr K Wilson**
17 6, Bl gr h Fair Mix (IRE)—See My Girl
18 **SEVENBALLS OF FIRE (IRE)**, 7, b g Milan—Ladamurraydance (IRE) **Mr A. M. Russell**
19 **SHREWD**, 6, b g Street Sense (USA)—Cala (FR) **Tapas Partnership**
20 **SPES NOSTRA**, 8, b g Ad Valorem (USA)—Millagros (IRE) **J. A. Cringan**
21 **SPIRIT OF THE SEA (IRE)**, 4, b f Invincible Spirit (IRE)—Cedar Sea (IRE) **W. M. Johnstone**
22 **STAR OF SPRING (IRE)**, 4, b f Iffraaj—Gift of Spring (USA) **Mr I. Jardine**
23 **STONEHAM**, 5, b m Sixties Icon—Cibenze **The Dregs Of Humanity & Partner**
24 **SUPREME GAEL**, 5, br m Supreme Sound—Italstar (IRE) **Linden Lads**
25 **TIGER'S HOME**, 6, b m Tiger Hill (IRE)—Homeward (IRE) **Miss S. A. Booth and Mr J. Kyle**
26 **TOKARAMORE**, 4, b f Sulamani (IRE)—More Likely (IRE) **Mrs A. F. Tullie**

MR IAIN JARDINE - Continued

THREE-YEAR-OLDS

27 **BASSETT BLEU,** b c Wootton Bassett—Lafontaine Bleu **The Cosmic Cases**
28 B c Sakhee (USA)—Folly Bridge **Mr I. E. Ives**
29 **SOPHISTICA (IRE),** b f Thousand Words—Texas Queen **Alex & Janet Card**

TWO-YEAR-OLDS

30 B c 11/2 Zebedee—Kitty Softpaws (IRE) (Royal Applause) (19047) **Mr & Mrs Paul & Clare Rooney**
31 B f 27/3 Tagula (IRE)—Leglen Wood (IRE) (High Chaparral (IRE)) (5000)
32 B c 9/3 Sixties Icon—Sailing Days (Kris) (5000)
33 **TAEL O' GOLD,** ch f 7/3 Zoffany (IRE)—Wedding Dream (Oasis Dream) (13000) **Alasdair and Eliza Ross**
34 Ch c 20/3 Dragon Pulse (IRE)—
Toberanthawn (IRE) (Danehill Dancer (IRE)) (19047) **Mr & Mrs Paul & Clare Rooney**

Other Owners: R. M. S. Allison, I. T. Buchanan, Mr A. J. Butler, Mr A. M. Card, Mrs J. A. Card, Mr M. Friel, E. Graham, T. D. Griffiths, A. G. Guthrie, Mr J. Kyle, K. J. Milligan, Mr A. T. Murphy, Mrs M. S. Nelson, Mr C. T. Reid, R. Robinson, Mrs C. Rooney, Mr P. A. Rooney, Mrs E. M. Y. Ross, Mr A. Ross, A. Walmsley, Mr K. A. Wilson.

Jockey (flat): David Allan. **Jockey (NH):** Adrian Lane.

---

333 MR WILLIAM JARVIS, Newmarket
Postal: **Phantom House, Fordham Road, Newmarket, Suffolk, CB8 7AA**
Contacts: **OFFICE (01638) 669873 HOME (01638) 662677 FAX (01638) 667328**
E-MAIL mail@williamjarvis.com WEBSITE www.williamjarvis.com

1 **CLERK'S CHOICE (IRE),** 10, b g Bachelor Duke (USA)—Credit Crunch (IRE) **M. C. Banks**
2 **DEMONSTRATION (IRE),** 4, b g Cape Cross (IRE)—Quiet Protest (USA) **P. C. J. Dalby & R. D. Schuster**
3 **DIXIE'S DREAM (IRE),** 7, b g Hawk Wing (USA)—Hams (USA) **W. Jarvis**
4 **JODIES JEM,** 6, br g Kheleyf (USA)—First Approval **Mrs R. L. Banks**
5 **PEARL EARING (IRE),** 5, b m Excellent Art—Triple Axel (IRE) **Raceology Partnership**
6 **SHWAIMAN (IRE),** 6, br g Authorized (IRE)—Blue Lightning **M. C. Banks**
7 **SILK KNIGHT,** 4, ch c Sir Percy—Tussah **Mr & Mrs A. E. Pakenham**

THREE-YEAR-OLDS

8 **COLD SNAP (IRE),** b c Medicean—Shivering **P. C. J. Dalby & R. D. Schuster**
9 **HIGHWAYMAN,** b g Dick Turpin (IRE)—Right Rave (IRE) **Easterwood Equestrian**
10 **LADY LLOYD,** b f Paco Boy (IRE)—Carafe **Peter Pan Partnership**
11 **LULWORTH (IRE),** b g Canford Cliffs (IRE)—Aitch (IRE) **P. C. J. Dalby & R. D. Schuster**
12 **ONWARDSANDUPWARDS,** b g Multiplex—Turn Back **The Willie Robertson Partnership**
13 Ch g Haathd—Pigment **Miss S. E. Hall**
14 **PORT PARADISE,** gr g Paco Boy (IRE)—Yacht Woman (USA) **A. N. Verrier**
15 **PSYCHOTIC,** b c Nayef (USA)—Palatial **Mr C. A. Washbourn**
16 **QUICK LOOK,** b g Kheleyf (USA)—Weqaar (USA) **M. C. Banks**
17 **WIMPOLE HALL,** b c Canford Cliffs (IRE)—Sparkling Eyes **Ms E. L. Banks**

TWO-YEAR-OLDS

18 B c 5/4 Mayson—Authora (IRE) (Authorized (IRE)) (45000) **Ms E. L. Banks**
19 **DOLLY DIMPLES,** ch grf 27/3 Sir Percy—Brave Mave (Daylami (IRE)) **Mr James Munroe**
20 B f 4/4 Pour Moi (IRE)—Double Green (IRE) (Green Tune (USA)) (55370) **Mr K. J. Hickman**
21 B c 26/3 Born To Sea (IRE)—Drombeg Dawn (IRE) (Orpen (USA)) (5000) **Partnership**
22 **FLAMETREESOFTHIKA,** b f 21/4 Frozen Power (IRE)—
Nairobi (FR) (Anabaa (USA)) (5500) **Raceology Partnership**
23 **GIRL SQUAD,** b f 22/2 Intikhab (USA)—Foxtrot Alpha (IRE) (Desert Prince (IRE)) (7000) **Raceology Partnership**
24 **JUANITO CHICO (IRE),** br c 15/2 Pour Moi (IRE)—Miss Kittyhawk (IRE) (Hawk Wing (USA)) (36913) **A. N. Verrier**
25 Ch f 21/4 Bated Breath—Ocean View (USA) (Gone West (USA)) (44296) **Mr K. J. Hickman**
26 **OFF TO BOND STREET,** b c 24/3 Paco Boy (IRE)—Woodbeck (Terimon) (22000) **Mr R. L. Banks**
27 Ch c 2/5 Sepoy (AUS)—One Giant Leap (IRE) (Pivotal) (20000)
28 **RED GUANA (IRE),** ch f 29/3 Famous Name—Guana (IRE) (Dark Angel (IRE)) (9000) **G. B. Turnbull Ltd**
29 **ROMAN ERA,** b g 18/4 Mount Nelson—Darcique (Cacique (IRE)) (1800) **Raceology Partnership**
30 B c 2/3 Aqlaam—Shersha (IRE) (Priolo (USA)) (11000) **Partnership**
31 Ch c 22/4 Casamento (IRE)—Two Marks (USA) (Woodman (USA)) **Dr Jim Walker**
32 B f 28/2 Lawman (FR)—Wizz Kid (IRE) (Whipper (USA)) (118124) **Mr K. J. Hickman**

MR WILLIAM JARVIS - Continued

Other Owners: Mr James Bowditch, Ms S. A. Cheshire, Mr P. C. J. Dalby, Mr R. Lloyd, Mrs V. H. Pakenham, A. E. Pakenham, Mr Richard Schuster, Ms Mary Rose Woodham.

Assistant Trainer: James Toller

---

334 MR MALCOLM JEFFERSON, Malton
Postal: Newstead Cottage Stables, Norton, Malton, North Yorkshire, YO17 9PJ
Contacts: **PHONE** (01653) 697225 **MOBILE** (07710) 502044
E-MAIL newsteadracing@btconnect.com **WEBSITE** www.malcolmjefferson.co.uk

 1 **ANNE'S VALENTINO**, 6, b m Primo Valentino (IRE)—Annie's Gift (IRE) **The Magic Circle**
 2 **BOY NAMED SIOUX**, 5, b g Indian Danehill (IRE)—Annie's Gift (IRE) **The Corse Lawners**
 3 **CAPTAIN SAM**, 4, b g Black Sam Bellamy (IRE)—Grande Terre (IRE) **Mr & Mrs G. Calder**
 4 **CARD GAME (IRE)**, 7, b m Scorpion (IRE)—Cardona **Messrs Hales Dodd Wood & Dickinson**
 5 **CHILLY MISS**, 7, b m Iceman—Fairlie **Racegoers Club Owners Group**
 6 **CLOUDY DREAM (IRE)**, 6, gr g Cloudings (IRE)—Run Away Dream (IRE) **T. J. Hemmings**
 7 **COOZAN GEORGE**, 7, b g Bollin Eric—Pasja (IRE) **A. N. Barrett**
 8 **CYRUS DARIUS**, 7, b g Overbury (IRE)—Barton Belle **Mr & Mrs G Calder & Mr P M Warren**
 9 **DANTE'S WAY (IRE)**, 7, b g Scorpion (IRE)—Benedicta Rose (IRE) **T. J. Hemmings**
10 **DOUBLE W'S (IRE)**, 6, ch g Fruits of Love (USA)—Zaffre (IRE) **Wharton & Wilson**
11 **DUBAI ANGEL (IRE)**, 5, b g Dubai Destination (USA)—Just Another Penny (IRE) **Mrs D. W. Davenport**
12 **ETHELWYN**, 6, ch m Alflora (IRE)—Our Ethel **J. M. Jefferson**
13 **FIRTH OF THE CLYDE**, 11, b g Flemensfirth (USA)—Miss Nel **R. H. Goldie**
14 **FROBISHER BAY (IRE)**, 5, b g Touch of Land (FR)—Ballybeg Katie (IRE) **Mrs K. M. Richardson**
15 **GREY LIFE**, 10, gr g Terimon—More To Life **Exors of the Late Mr D. T. Todd**
16 **GULLY'S EDGE**, 6, b g Kayf Tara—Shuildante (IRE) **Mrs K S Gaffney & Mrs Louie Stevenson**
17 **HELMSLEY LAD**, 5, gr g Fair Mix (IRE)—Wuchowsen (IRE) **Derek Gennard & Gillian Gennard**
18 **HI GEORGE**, 8, b g Doyen (IRE)—Our Ethel **Forever Young Racing Partnership**
19 **HIGH HOPPER (IRE)**, 6, b g Mountain High (IRE)—Stormy Moment (IRE) **Mr M. C. Thuey**
20 **JURBY**, 6, b g Motivator—Darariyna (IRE) **T. J. Hemmings**
21 **KING OF THE WOLDS (IRE)**, 9, b g Presenting—Azaban (IRE) **Mr & Mrs G. Calder**
22 **LA DAMA DE HIERRO**, 6, br m Proclamation (IRE)—Altogether Now (IRE) **J. M. Jefferson**
23 **MAJOR IVAN (IRE)**, 7, b g Fruits of Love (USA)—Martinstown Queen (IRE) **Mrs I C Straker & Steven Key**
24 **MCGREGOR'S COTTAGE (IRE)**, 5, b m Brian Boru—Dewasentah (IRE) **Mrs D. W. Davenport**
25 **MOUNT MEWS (IRE)**, 5, b g Presenting—Kneeland Lass **T. J. Hemmings**
26 **MR MONOCHROME**, 5, b g Indian Danehill (IRE)—Our Ethel **Mr & Mrs G. Calder & P M Warren**
27 **NAUTICAL TWILIGHT**, 6, gr m Proclamation (IRE)—Anabranch **Capt M. S. Bagley**
28 **ONLY ORVIETO (IRE)**, 5, b m Kayf Tara—Vigna Maggio (FR) **Mr D. M. Gibbons**
29 **OSCAR ROCK (IRE)**, 8, b g Oscar (IRE)—Cash And New (IRE) **Mr & Mrs G. Calder**
30 **PAIR OF JACKS (IRE)**, 8, ch g Presenting—Halona **Mrs Rita Williams**
31 **PETAPENKO**, 5, b g Archipenko (USA)—Tricoteuse **R. Collins**
32 **RENOYR (FR)**, 11, b g Kalmoss (FR)—Idee de Valeur (FR) **J. M. Jefferson**
33 **RETRIEVE THE STICK**, 7, b m Revoque (IRE)—Anabranch **Newstead Racing Partnership**
34 **RYEDALE RACER**, 5, b g Indian Danehill (IRE)—Jontys'lass **Derek Gennard & Gillian Gennard**
35 **SECRETE STREAM (IRE)**, 7, ch g Fruits of Love (USA)—Bonny River (IRE) **Mrs M. E. Dixon**
36 **SHARPASAKNIFE (IRE)**, 6, b g Flemensfirth (USA)—Omas Lady (IRE) **The Mount Fawcus Partnership**
37 **STORM FORECAST (IRE)**, 5, b g September Storm (GER)—Katie Kelly (IRE) **J. M. Jefferson**
38 **STOUT CORTEZ**, 5, b g Hernando (FR)—Zooming (IRE) **J. D. Abell**
39 **SUN CLOUD (IRE)**, 9, b g Cloudings (IRE)—Miss Melrose **Boundary Garage (Bury) Limited**
40 **TIGER MOUNTAIN (IRE)**, 5, b g Mountain High (IRE)—Our Trick (IRE) **Mrs M. M. Jagger**
41 **URBAN HYMN (FR)**, 8, b g Robin des Champs (FR)—Betty Brune (FR) **Mr & Mrs G. Calder**
42 **VIRTUALLY OURS (IRE)**, 4, ch f Virtual—Our Ethel **Racegoers Club Owners Group**

Other Owners: Mr G. Calder, Mrs J. Calder, Mrs E. J. Dolan-Abrahams, Mr E. J. Dolan-Abrahams, Mrs M. W. Fawcus, Mr D. S. Fawcus, Mrs K. S. Gaffney, Mr Derek Gennard, Mrs Gillian Gennard, Mrs S. Jefferson, Mr S. Key, Mrs Alix Stevenson, Mrs I. C. Straker, Mr N. J. Taylor, Mr P. M. Warren, Mr R. Wharton, Mr J. H. Wilson.

Assistant Trainer: Ruth Jefferson

Jockey (NH): Brian Hughes. **Conditional:** Harry Russell.

335 MR J. R. JENKINS, Royston

Postal: **Kings Ride, Therfield Heath, Royston, Hertfordshire, SG8 9NN**
Contacts: **PHONE (01763) 241141 (01763) 246611 FAX (01763) 248223 MOBILE (07802) 750855**
E-MAIL john@johnjenkinsracing.co.uk WEBSITE www.johnjenkinsracing.co.uk

1 **ALSHAN FAJER,** 6, ch g Lemon Drop Kid (USA)—Illuminise (IRE) **Glynn Linder & Wendy Jenkins**
2 **ARCHIPENTURA,** 4, b f Archipenko (USA)—Bookieslass Girl (IRE)
3 **AUDEN (USA),** 8, b g Librettist (USA)—Moyesii (USA) **Miss Caroline A. Jenkins**
4 4, B g What A Caper (IRE)—Barlin Bay **Vinny Cooke**
5 **BELROG,** 5, ch g New Approach (IRE)—Millennium Dash **Mrs C. Goddard**
6 **BILLY RED,** 12, ch g Dr Fong (USA)—Liberty Bound **Mrs I. C. Hampson**
7 **BLACKWOOD ROVER (IRE),** 8, b g Turtle Island (IRE)—Lady of Fleet (IRE) **B. S. P. Dowling**
8 **BRAVE RICHARD (IRE),** 5, b g Jeremy (USA)—Certainly Brave **D.Waters.A.Finn.R.Paterson.K.MacRowan**
9 **BUBBLY BAILEY,** 6, b g Byron—Night Gypsy **Mrs S. Bowmer**
10 **DALKADAM (FR),** 5, gr g Martaline—Cadoudame (FR) **Miss A. Finn**
11 **DO IT TOMORROW (IRE),** 4, b f Daylami (IRE)—Seminova **Tower Bloodstock**
12 **DORKAS,** 7, b m Doyen (IRE)—Jawwala (USA) **P. J. Kirkpatrick**
13 **FINE 'N DANDY (IRE),** 5, ch g Dandy Man (IRE)—Pearly Brooks **Miss A. Finn**
14 **GALUPPI,** 5, b g Galileo (IRE)—La Leuze (IRE) **Miss A. Finn**
15 **GET PRANCER,** 4, ch g Archipenko (USA)—Clever Omneya (USA) **Mrs I. C. Hampson**
16 **GREAT EXPECTATIONS,** 8, b g Storming Home—Fresh Fruit Daily **The Great Expectations Partnership**
17 **HI TIDE (IRE),** 12, br g Idris (IRE)—High Glider **Mrs W. A. Jenkins**
18 **KARAM ALBAARI (IRE),** 8, b h King's Best (USA)—Lilakiya (IRE) **Mr M. D. Goldstein**
19 **LEWISHAM,** 6, b g Sleeping Indian—Almunia (IRE) **Mr Mark Benton**
20 **LITTLE INDIAN,** 6, b g Sleeping Indian—Once Removed **Two Little Indians**
21 **LOLITA,** 4, ch f Sir Percy—Miss Ippolita **Robert Ellis & Guy Montgomery**
22 **MEEBO (IRE),** 5, b m Captain Rio—Abbeyleix Lady (IRE) **Mr B. L. Polkey**
23 **MISHRIF (USA),** 10, b br g Arch (USA)—Peppy Priscilla (USA) **Mrs W. A. Jenkins**
24 **MONSIEUR JAMIE,** 8, b g Monsieur Bond (IRE)—Primula Bairn **Mr M. D. Goldstein**
25 **ONLY TEN PER CENT (IRE),** 8, b g Kheleyf (USA)—Cory Everson (IRE) **Mrs W. A. Jenkins**
26 **OSCARS JOURNEY,** 6, ch g Dubai Destination (USA)—Fruit of Glory **Mrs Theresa McCoubrey**
27 **OUR SAVANNAH (IRE),** 4, b f High Chaparral (IRE)—Alinea (USA) **Tower Bloodstock**
28 **PARISIAN STAR,** 4, ch f Champs Elysees—Cavallo da Corsa **Miss Caroline A. Jenkins**
29 **PRETTY BUBBLES,** 7, b m Sleeping Indian—Willmar **Mr M. D. Goldstein**
30 **PURPLE SPECTRUM,** 5, gr g Verglas (IRE)—Rainbow's Edge **Roldvale Ltd G Pascoe Barry Silkman**
31 **SAWWALA,** 6, b m Sakhee (USA)—Jawwala (USA) **P. J. Kirkpatrick**
32 **SIGN OF THE TIMES,** 4, b f Medicean—Still Small Voice **J. Shack**
33 **SILVER MOUNTAIN,** 5, gr g Sir Percy—Pearl Bright (FR) **Ms A. Juskaite**
34 **SINGLE SUMMIT,** 4, b c Hellvelyn—Once Removed **Mrs C. Goddard**
35 **SPITFIRE,** 11, b g Mujahid (USA)—Fresh Fruit Daily **Mrs W. A. Jenkins**
36 **ST PATRICK'S DAY (IRE),** 4, b c Fastnet Rock (AUS)—Race For The Stars (USA) **Miss A. Finn**
37 **TILSWORTH MICKY,** 4, b g Kheleyf (USA)—Tilsworth Charlie **Michael Ng**
38 **TIRADIA (FR),** 9, b br g Without Connexion (IRE)—Jimanji (FR) **B. S. P. Dowling**
39 **U S NAVY SEAL (USA),** 4, b br c War Front (USA)—Questress (USA) **Miss A. Finn**
40 **WHALEWEIGH STATION,** 5, b g Zamindar (USA)—Looby Loo **Mr J. Melo**

THREE-YEAR-OLDS

41 B f Archipenko (USA)—Ashwell Rose
42 **CLEVER DIVYA,** b f Archipenko (USA)—Clever Omneya (USA) **Miss A. Finn**
43 **FOXINTHEHENHOUSE,** ch f Bahamian Bounty—Pants **Dr D. S. Myers & Mr A. S. Reid**
44 B c Champs Elysees—Pnyka (IRE) **R. Stevens**
45 B f Cockney Rebel (IRE)—Sakhacity
46 B f Mullionmileahour (IRE)—United Passion

TWO-YEAR-OLDS

47 B f 31/3 Mount Nelson—Ellcon (IRE) (Royal Applause) **Mr Michael Turner**
48 B c 7/5 Pastoral Pursuits—Miss Ippolita (Diktat) **VSN Ltd**
49 B f 2/4 Mullionmileahour (IRE)—Numanthia (IRE) (Barathea (IRE))
50 B f 1/1 Dick Turpin (IRE)—Sakhacity (Sakhee (USA))

Other Owners: Mr G. Barnard, Mr Matt Bartram, Mr Mark Benton, Mrs S. Bowmer, Mr Stephen Bullock, Mr G. J. Burchell, Mr I. J. Callaway, Mr Vinny Cooke, Mr Paul Cousins, Mr B. S. P. Dowling, Mr Robert M. Ellis, Miss A. Finn, Mr P. J. Finn, Mrs Irene Hampson, Miss Caroline A. Jenkins, Mrs W. A. Jenkins, Mr G. D. J. Linder, Mr K. Macrowan, Mrs Theresa McCoubrey, Mr Jefferson Melo, Mr Guy Montgomery, Dr D. S. Myers, Mr Michael Ng, Mr G. J. Pascoe, Mr R. Paterson, Mr Barry Polkey, Mr A. Reid, Roldvale Limited, Mr Jonathan Shack, Mr B. Silkman, Mr Robin Stevens, Mr D. J. Tattersall, Mr P. J. Trotter, Mr Michael Turner, Mr Danny Waters, Mr Peter Watson, Mr C. P. Watson.

336 MR ALAN JESSOP, Chelmsford
Postal: **Flemings Farm, Warren Road, South Hanningfield, Chelmsford, Essex, CM3 8HU**
Contacts: **PHONE (01268) 710210 MOBILE (07718) 736482**

1 **BLAZING GLEN (IRE)**, 8, ch g Beneficial—Kofiyah's Rose (IRE) **Mrs G. Jessop**
2 **CHORAL BEE**, 7, b m Oratorio (IRE)—Chief Bee **Mrs G. Jessop**
3 **MAX MILANO (IRE)**, 11, b g Milan—Stellissima (IRE) **Mrs G. Jessop**
4 **STEEPLEOFCOPPER (IRE)**, 10, ch g Classic Cliche (IRE)—Tanya Thyne (IRE) **Mrs G. Jessop**
5 **STICKERS**, 9, b g Generous (IRE)—Dunsfold Duchess (IRE) **Mrs G. Jessop**

337 MRS LINDA JEWELL, Maidstone
Postal: **Southfield Stables, South Lane, Sutton Valence, Maidstone, Kent, ME17 3AZ**
Contacts: **PHONE (01622) 842788 MOBILE (07856) 686657**
E-MAIL lindajewell@hotmail.com WEBSITE www.lindajewellracing.co.uk

1 **CLAUDE GREENWOOD**, 6, b g Lucky Story (USA)—Greenmeadow **Valence Racing**
2 **CLONUSKER (IRE)**, 8, b g Fasliyev (USA)—Tamburello (IRE) **Mr D. N. Yeadon**
3 **DUE SOUTH (IRE)**, 5, b g City Honours (USA)—Lady Shackleton (IRE) **Valence Racing III**
4 **EASYONTHEEYE (IRE)**, 5, br m Kalanisi (IRE)—Lady Bernie (IRE) **P. A. Oppenheimer**
5 **FIFI L'AMOUR (IRE)**, 10, ch m Flemensfirth (USA)—Supreme Adventure (IRE) **Valence Racing**
6 **FINE TUNE (IRE)**, 5, b g Medicean—Phillippa (IRE) **Mrs R. V. Watson**
7 **GOOD BOND**, 4, b g Monsieur Bond (IRE)—Seminole Sun (IRE) **Mrs F. J. Dean**
8 **HAB SAB (IRE)**, 4, b g Papal Bull—Tamburello (IRE) **Mr T. Betteridge**
9 **HECTON BAY (IRE)**, 5, b g Trans Island—Reserve The Right (IRE) **Mr H J Jarvis & Mrs P Jarvis**
10 **INDISPENSABELLE**, 7, b m Passing Glance—Belle Largesse **Mr R. Churcher**
11 **ITOLDYOU (IRE)**, 10, ch g Salford Express (IRE)—Adisadel (IRE) **Valence Racing Too**
12 **KAFEEL (USA)**, 5, b g First Samurai (USA)—Ishraak (USA) **K. Johnson, K. Jessup**
13 **KAYFLIN (FR)**, 8, b m Kayf Tara—Flinders **Valence Racing**
14 **KINGSCOMBE (USA)**, 7, gr o g Mizzen Mast (USA)—Gombeen (USA) **P. A. Oppenheimer**
15 **MAB DAB (IRE)**, 5, b g Papal Bull—Pret A Porter (UAE) **Mr T. Betteridge**
16 **MACCABEES**, 7, b g Motivator—Takarna (IRE) **K. Johnson, K. Jessup 1**
17 **RED ANCHOR (IRE)**, 12, ch g Snurge—Clonartic (IRE) **Mrs S. M. Stanier**

THREE-YEAR-OLDS

18 **ITS A SHEILA THING**, ch f Sir Percy—Sefemm **Mrs F. J. Dean**

Other Owners: H. J. Jarvis, Mrs P. Jarvis, Mr K. P. Jessup, Mrs L. C. Jewell, Mr K. W. Johnson, R. I. B. Young.

Assistant Trainer: Karen Jewell

Jockey (flat): Robert Havlin. **Jockey (NH):** Tom Cannon, Tom Garner.

338 MR BRETT JOHNSON, Epsom
Postal: **The Durdans Stables, Chalk Lane, Epsom, Surrey, KT18 7AX**
Contacts: **MOBILE (07768) 697141**
E-MAIL thedurdansstables@googlemail.com WEBSITE www.brjohnsonracing.co.uk

1 **BRAVE DECISION**, 9, gr g With Approval (CAN)—Brave Vanessa (USA) **Mr R. I. Knight**
2 **CAYUGA**, 7, b g Montjeu (IRE)—Ithaca (USA) **B. R. Johnson**
3 **GUITARIST**, 4, ch g Raven's Pass (USA)—Strings **Mr C. Westley**
4 **O MALLEY'S OSCAR (IRE)**, 11, b g Oscar (IRE)—Notre Dame (IRE) **Mr R. I. Knight**
5 **OAKBANK (USA)**, 5, b g Empire Maker (USA)—Summer Shower (USA) **Mr C. Westley**
6 **SATCHVILLE FLYER**, 5, ch g Compton Place—Palinisa (FR) **Mr N Jarvis, Mr T Broke-Smith, Mr G Tann**
7 **SENOR FIRECRACKER (IRE)**, 4, b g Acclamation—Miss Eze **Tann Racing**

THREE-YEAR-OLDS

8 **CHEAPO**, ch g Aqlaam—Shy Appeal (IRE) **Mr A. Chapman**
9 **CLANDON**, b g Sakhee's Secret—Whassup (FR) **Mrs A. M. Upsdell**
10 **ROMAN URN**, ch g Major Cadeaux—Symphonic Dancer (USA) **Mr A. Chapman**

MR BRETT JOHNSON - Continued

TWO-YEAR-OLDS

11 **GINGER TRUFFLE**, ch f 11/4 Sixties Icon—Whassup (FR) (Midyan (USA)) **Mrs A. M. Upsdell**
12 B f 23/3 Delegator—No Song (Zamindar (USA)) (8571) **Mr C. Westley**
13 B f 1/3 Compton Place—Private Means (Dansili) (1500)
14 Ch g 3/2 Pivotal—Regal Velvet (Halling (USA)) (20952) **Mr C. Westley**

Other Owners: Mr T. W. Broke-Smith, J. Daniels, Mr N. A. Jarvis, Omni Colour Presentations Ltd, G. Tann, Mrs E. Tann.

Assistant Trainer: Vanessa Johnson

---

339 **MISS EVE JOHNSON HOUGHTON, Blewbury**
Postal: **Woodway, Blewbury, Didcot, Oxfordshire, OX11 9EZ**
Contacts: PHONE **(01235) 850480 (01235) 850500 (Home)** FAX **(01235) 851045**
MOBILE **(07721) 622700**
E-MAIL **Eve@JohnsonHoughton.com** WEBSITE **www.JohnsonHoughton.com**

1 **AJIG**, 5, ch m Bahamian Bounty—Atwirl **Eden Racing Club**
2 **CHARLIE WELLS (IRE)**, 5, b g High Chaparral (IRE)—Numbers Game **Eden Racing**
3 **COOL BAHAMIAN (IRE)**, 5, b g Bahamian Bounty—Keritana (FR) **Mr L R Godfrey & Mr R F Johnson Houghton**
4 **FIELDMOUSE**, 4, b f Champs Elysees—Intervene **Mrs V. D. Neale**
5 **GANYMEDE**, 5, b g Oasis Dream—Gaze **Ganymede Partnership**
6 **GOLDEN WEDDING (IRE)**, 4, b g Archipenko (USA)—Peace Lily **Mrs F. M. Johnson Houghton**
7 **GORING (GER)**, 4, b g Areion (GER)—Globuli (GER) **G. C. Stevens**
8 **MISS INGA SOCK (IRE)**, 4, ch f Tagula (IRE)—Support Fund (IRE) **The Ascot Colts & Fillies Club**
9 **NEW RICH**, 5, b g Bahamian Bounty—Bling Bling (IRE) **Eden Racing Club**
10 **PANTHER PATROL (IRE)**, 6, b g Tagula (IRE)—Quivala (USA) **G. C. Stevens**
11 **PLYMOUTH SOUND**, 4, b g Fastnet Rock (AUS)—Shardette (IRE) **T Keane, M Page, D Smith & R Whichelow**
12 **ROOM KEY**, 4, ch g Mount Nelson—Saturday Girl **The Picnic Partnership**
13 **STARCROSSED**, 4, b g Cape Cross—Gretna **The Picnic Partnership**
14 **STARLIT CANTATA**, 5, b m Oratorio (IRE)—Starlit Sky **Mrs H. B. Raw**
15 **WHAT ABOUT CARLO (FR)**, 5, b g Creachadoir (IRE)—Boccatenera (GER) **A. J. Pye-Jeary**

THREE-YEAR-OLDS

16 **BECCA CAMPBELL (IRE)**, b f Roderic O'Connor (IRE)—Scottendale **Miss E. A. Johnson Houghton**
17 **CANFORD LILLI (IRE)**, b f Canford Cliffs (IRE)—Aine (IRE) **Peter Wollaston & Peter Johnson**
18 **COARSE CUT (IRE)**, b g Duke of Marmalade (IRE)—Keladora (USA) **Equi ex Incertis Partners**
19 **CUDDLE**, b f Intikhab (USA)—Karlovy **Mrs V. D. Neale**
20 **FANTASY QUEEN**, b f Aqlaam—Regal Curtsy **Mrs Z. C. Campbell-Harris**
21 **FLEETING VISIT**, b g Manduro (GER)—Short Affair **The Pantechnicons V**
22 **ICE AGE (IRE)**, b g Frozen Power (IRE)—Incendio **Eden Racing III**
23 **IN HASTE (IRE)**, gr g Clodovil (IRE)—Hasty Katie (IRE) **Mrs Rice, Mrs Johnson Houghton, Mr Blake**
24 **PATANJALI (IRE)**, b f Poet's Voice—Penang (IRE) **Mrs K. C. Pye-Jeary**
25 **REAVER (IRE)**, b c Sabiango (GER)—Mattinata **A. J. Pye-Jeary**
26 **SCARLET DRAGON**, b g Sir Percy—Welsh Angel **W. H. Ponsonby**
27 **SOIREE**, b f Piccolo—Nightunderthestars **Lt Cdr P. S. Emmet**
28 **SPINNING PEARL (IRE)**, b f Dylan Thomas (IRE)—Spinning Gold **Miss E. A. Johnson Houghton**
29 **SUNBAKED (IRE)**, b f Kodiac—Bronze Baby (USA) **Miss E. A. Johnson Houghton**
30 **SUNLIT WATERS**, ch f New Approach (IRE)—Faraway Waters **Mr R Crutchley & Mr S Posford**
31 **TOULSON**, b c Champs Elysees—Flower Market **Mrs V. D. Neale**

TWO-YEAR-OLDS

32 B c 19/3 Exceed And Excel (AUS)—Anadolu (IRE) (Statue of Liberty (USA)) (18000) **R. F. Johnson Houghton**
33 C c 17/4 Equiano (FR)—Australia Fair (Pivotal) (18456) **Eden Racing IV**
34 **BAHAMADAM**, b f 4/5 Bahamian Bounty—Pelagia (IRE) (Lycius (USA)) **J. P. Repard**
35 **BE BE KING (IRE)**, b c 27/2 Bated Breath—Champion Place (Compton Place) (55370) **G. C. Stevens**
36 C c 28/3 Henrythenavigator (USA)—Bee Eater (Green Desert (USA)) (25000) **The Pantechnicons VI**
37 Gr c 26/2 Clodovil (IRE)—Caherassdotcom (Compton Place) (11812) **Astor, Baring, Brown & Cochrane**
38 **DIXIE PEACH**, b f 10/4 Avonbridge—Support Fund (Intikhab (USA)) (571) **Miss E. A. Johnson Houghton**
39 **DUSTY BERRY**, ch f 21/3 Sixties Icon—Hazelberry (Bertolini (USA)) **J. H. Widdows**
40 B f 16/2 Broken Vow (USA)—European Union (USA) (Successful Appeal (USA)) (30000) **Mrs H. B. Raw**
41 B f 22/4 Iffraaj—Fairy Moss (IRE) (Amadeus Wolf) **Overbury Racing Club**
42 **FAVOURITE ROYAL (IRE)**, b f 22/4 Acclamation—
Affirmative (Pivotal) **J Cross, M Duckham, L Godfrey, P Wollaston**

MISS EVE JOHNSON HOUGHTON - Continued

43 Ch f 10/4 Footstepsinthesand—Felin Gruvy (IRE) (Tagula (IRE)) (2214) **Mrs J. E. O'Halloran**
44 B c 22/4 Mount Nelson—Flower Market (Cadeaux Genereux) **Mrs V. D. Neale**
45 B f 28/2 Lawman (FR)—Fontley (Sadler's Wells (USA)) (47000) **Mrs V. D. Neale**
46 **HO'OPONOPONO (FR)**, b c 24/1 Rajsaman (FR)—Nostalchia (FR) (Genereux Genie) (15503)
47 B f 7/4 Born To Sea (IRE)—Johannesburg Cat (USA) (Johannesburg (USA)) (16980)
48 Br f 5/4 So You Think (NZ)—Lebenstanz (Singspiel (IRE)) (5000)
49 **ON TO VICTORY**, b c 2/4 Rock of Gibraltar (IRE)—
                         Clouds of Magellan (USA) (Dynaformer (USA)) (18000) **W. H. Ponsonby**
50 Gr c 27/4 Mastercraftsman (IRE)—Privet (IRE) (Cape Cross (IRE)) (8500) **The Picnic Partnership**
51 Ch c 23/2 Le Havre (IRE)—Raving Monsun (Monsun (GER)) (8000) **The Picnic Partnership**
52 B c 8/4 Delegator—Roodle (Xaar) (8000) **Mrs F. M. Johnson Houghton**
53 **SHELTERED WATERS**, b f 19/3 Aqlaam—Velvet Waters (Unfuwain (USA)) **Mr R. E. Crutchley**
54 **SUPER JULIUS**, ch c 27/4 Bated Breath—Paradise Isle (Bahamian Bounty) (35000) **Mr B. Miller**
55 B c 10/3 Zamindar (USA)—Veiled Beauty (USA) (Royal Academy (USA))

Other Owners: Viscount Astor, Mr D. S. Blake, Miss A. L. Bossom, Mr P. Bowden, Mr A. H. Cowan, Mr J. C. Cross, J. M. Curtis, Mr M. R. Duckham, Mr D. G. Fussey, Mr L. R. A. Godfrey, Mr L. A. Harvey, Mr P. J. Johnson, Lady J. A. Kay, Ms T. Keane, Mr R. Lewis, Mr C. O. A. Liverton, Sir I. Magee, Fiona Marner, Mrs J. A. McWilliam, Mr I. D. Miller, Mr M. E. Page, Mr S. J. D. Posford, Mrs E. R. Rice, Mr H. S. Sharpstone, Mr John Smith, D. M. Smith, Mr S. J. N. Sweeting, J. R. Wallis, Mr R. S. Weigl, Mr R. Whichelow, Mr N. White, Mr F. Wintle, Mr P. R. Wollaston.

Assistant Trainer: R. F. Johnson Houghton

---

340 MR KENNY JOHNSON, Newcastle Upon Tyne
Postal: **Grange Farm, Newburn, Newcastle Upon Tyne, Tyne and Wear, NE15 8QA**
Contacts: **PHONE (01912) 674464**

1 **BYGONES FOR COINS (IRE)**, 8, ch m Danroad (AUS)—Reservation (IRE) **R. W. Johnson**
2 **CAPTAIN SHARPE**, 8, ch g Tobougg (IRE)—Helen Sharp **Mr A. V. W. Kidd**
3 **COOLANURE (IRE)**, 7, b m Portrait Gallery (IRE)—Aiguille (IRE) **R. W. Johnson**
4 **POLITELYSED**, 10, ch m Courteous—Allegedly Red
5 **ROSQUERO (IRE)**, 11, ch g Blushing Flame (USA)—Kingsgirl (IRE) **Alan Kidd Dave Bamlet Racing R Johnson**
6 **SOLID JUSTICE (IRE)**, 5, b g Rock of Gibraltar (IRE)—Burnin' Memories (USA) **R. Naylor**
7 **SUNRISE DANCE**, 7, ch m Monsieur Bond (IRE)—Wachiwi (IRE) **J. L. Armstrong**
8 **UNDER THE RED SKY (IRE)**, 9, ch g Insatiable (IRE)—Official Secret **R. C. Whitelock**
9 **VALNAMIXE DU MEE (FR)**, 7, b g Al Namix (FR)—Kateline du Mee (FR) **TLA & RA Robson & Mrs L Gander**
10 **VODKA RED (IRE)**, 8, b g Ivan Denisovich (IRE)—Begine (IRE) **Ontoawinner,R Johnson,Carter Thompson**

Other Owners: Mr D. Bamlet, Mr I. M. Blacklock, Mr A. Carter, Mrs L. R. Gander, Mr N. J. O'Brien, Mrs R. A. Robson, T. L. A. Robson, Mr S. Thompson.

---

341 MRS SUSAN JOHNSON, Madley
Postal: **Carwardine Farm, Madley, Hereford**
Contacts: **PHONE (01981) 250214 FAX (01981) 251538**

1 **THE LAST BRIDGE**, 9, b g Milan—Celtic Bridge **I. K. Johnson**

Jockey (NH): Richard Johnson.

---

342 MR MARK JOHNSTON, Middleham
Postal: **Kingsley Park, Park Lane, Middleham, North Yorkshire, DL8 4QZ**
Contacts: **PHONE (01969) 622237 FAX (01969) 622484**
E-MAIL mark@markjohnstonracing.com WEBSITE www.markjohnstonracing.com

1 **DONNA GRACIOSA (GER)**, 4, b f Samum (GER)—Donna Alicia (GER) **Mr Abdullah Al Mansoori**
2 **ENLACE**, 4, b f Shamardal (USA)—Crossover **Sheikh Hamdan Bin Mohammed Al Maktoum**
3 **FINAL**, 4, b g Arabian Gleam—Caysue **C. H. Greensit & W. A. Greensit**
4 **FIRE FIGHTING (IRE)**, 5, b g Soldier of Fortune (IRE)—Savoie (FR) **A. D. Spence**
5 **FREIGHT TRAIN (IRE)**, 4, b g Manduro—Sigonella (IRE) **Michael Spence**
6 **MALVESI**, 7, b g Iceman—Madam Valentine **Wadacre Stud**
7 **MAMBO PARADISE**, 4, b f Makfi—Mambo Halo (USA) **Around The World Partnership**

MR MARK JOHNSTON - Continued

8 **MAMBO RHYTHM**, 5, b m Authorized (IRE)—Mambo Halo (USA) **Around The World Partnership**
9 **MASTER OF FINANCE (IRE)**, 5, ch g Mastercraftsman (IRE)—Cheal Rose (IRE) **J. D. Abell**
10 **MISTER UNIVERSE**, 4, br c Cape Cross (IRE)—Miss Ivanhoe (IRE) **Mr Abdullah Al Mansoori**
11 **NOTARISED**, 5, b g Authorized (IRE)—Caribbean Dancer (USA) **Mr H. C. Hart**
12 **PUBLILIA**, 4, b f Makfi—Terentia **Mr Abdullah Al Mansoori**
13 **REVOLUTIONIST (IRE)**, 4, b c Pivotal—Mysterial (USA) **Sheikh Hamdan Bin Mohammed Al Maktoum**
14 **RHYTHMICAL**, 4, b f Halling (USA)—Caribbean Dancer (USA) **Mr H. C. Hart**
15 **SEA THE SKIES**, 5, b g Sea The Stars (IRE)—Model Queen (USA) **A. D. Spence**
16 **SENNOCKIAN STAR**, 6, ch g Rock of Gibraltar (IRE)—Chorist **The Vine Accord**
17 **STETCHWORTH (IRE)**, 5, ch g New Approach (IRE)—Hallowed Park (IRE) **Kingsley Park 4**
18 **SUREWECAN**, 4, b g Royal Applause—Edge of Light **D. C. Livingston**
19 **THINK SNOW (USA)**, 4, ch f Giant's Causeway—
Snow Forest (USA) **Mr Christopher Wright & Vicky Snook**
20 **THREE MERRY LADS**, 4, b g Danehill Dancer (IRE)—Obsessive (USA) **Mrs J. E. Newett**
21 **TOGETHERWECAN (IRE)**, 4, b f Danehill Dancer (IRE)—Crystal Bull (USA) **D. C. Livingston**
22 **VIVE MA FILLE (GER)**, 4, b f Doyen (IRE)—Vive Madame (GER) **R W Huggins & Atlantic Racing**
23 **WATERSMEET**, 5, gr g Dansili—Under The Rainbow **Mr J. A. Barson**
24 **YORKIDDING**, 4, b f Dalakhani (IRE)—Claxon **Mr P. R. York**
25 **YORKINDRED SPIRIT**, 4, b f Sea The Stars (IRE)—Paracel (USA) **Mr P. R. York**
26 **ZAND (IRE)**, 6, b g Zamindar (USA)—Zanara (IRE) **M. W. Graff**

THREE-YEAR-OLDS

27 **ABAREEQ**, ch c Haafet (USA)—Hafawa (IRE) **Hamdan Al Maktoum**
28 **ADVENTUROUS (IRE)**, b c Invincible Spirit (IRE)—Rosia (IRE) **Sheikh Hamdan Bin Mohammed Al Maktoum**
29 **AHDAF**, ch c Pastoral Pursuits—Bayja (IRE) **Mr Abdullah Al Mansoori**
30 **ALEKO**, b c Cape Cross (IRE)—Monnavanna (IRE) **Sheikh Hamdan Bin Mohammed Al Maktoum**
31 **ALLAMERICANBLAZE**, ch c Giant's Causeway—Junia Tepzia (IRE) **Target Category Solutions Ltd**
32 **AUTUMN BLOSSOM (USA)**, b f Bernardini (USA)—
Late Romance **Sheikh Hamdan Bin Mohammed Al Maktoum**
33 **BAILEYS ESQUIRE**, b c Halling (USA)—Silversword (FR) **G. R. Bailey Ltd (Baileys Horse Feeds)**
34 **BATHOS (IRE)**, b c Poet's Voice—Santolina (USA) **Sheikh Hamdan Bin Mohammed Al Maktoum**
35 **BEAVERBROOK**, b c Cape Cross (IRE)—Bint Almatar (USA) **Sheikh Hamdan Bin Mohammed Al Maktoum**
36 **BEMUSEMENT**, b f Exceed And Excel (AUS)—Sweet Folly (IRE) **Sheikh Hamdan Bin Mohammed Al Maktoum**
37 **BRANDBERG (IRE)**, ch c Cape Cross (IRE)—Eaton Street **Sheikh Hamdan Bin Mohammed Al Maktoum**
38 **BURATINO (IRE)**, ch c Exceed And Excel (AUS)—Bergamask (USA) **Godolphin Management Company Ltd**
39 **BUTTERMERE (USA)**, ch f Street Cry (IRE)—Belenkaya (USA) **Sheikh Hamdan Bin Mohammed Al Maktoum**
40 **CAPE SPEED (FR)**, b c Cape Cross (IRE)—At A Great Rate (USA) **Kingsley Park 3 - Originals**
41 B g Bahamian Bounty—Caribbean Dancer (USA) **Mr H. C. Hart**
42 **CHICAGO SCHOOL (IRE)**, ch c Approve (IRE)—Ms Sasha Malia (IRE) **The Acorn Partnership & Dr J Walker**
43 **COLOUR PLAY (USA)**, b f Medaglia d'oro (USA)—
Blue Duster (USA) **Sheikh Hamdan Bin Mohammed Al Maktoum**
44 **DALEELAK (IRE)**, b c Arcano (IRE)—Alshamatry (USA) **Hamdan Al Maktoum**
45 **DAWAA**, ch f Tamayuz—Athreyaa **Hamdan Al Maktoum**
46 **DEODORO (USA)**, b f Medaglia d'oro (USA)—
Anna Wi'yaak (JPN) **Sheikh Hamdan Bin Mohammed Al Maktoum**
47 **DESSERTOFLIFE (IRE)**, gr f Mastercraftsman (IRE)—Cranky Spanky (IRE) **T T Bloodstocks**
48 **EQLEEM**, b c Acclamation—Blessing **Hamdan Al Maktoum**
49 **FIREGLOW**, b f Teofilo (IRE)—Fading Light **Sheikh Hamdan Bin Mohammed Al Maktoum**
50 **FIRST PARTY**, gr f Royal Applause—Third Party **Mezzone Family**
51 **FLYING LESSON (IRE)**, ch c Roderic O'Connor (IRE)—
Acushladear (IRE) **Mr Salem Rashid & Mr Abdullah Al Mansoori**
52 **FONDIE (IRE)**, b f Oasis Dream—Prima Luce (IRE) **Mr Abdullah Al Mansoori**
53 **FOUR MILE BEACH**, br c Dalakhani (IRE)—Rappel **J. D. Abell**
54 **FURIANT**, b g Invincible Spirit (IRE)—Save Me The Waltz (FR) **Sheikh Hamdan Bin Mohammed Al Maktoum**
55 **GALESBURG (IRE)**, b c Shamardal (USA)—Calista **Sheikh Hamdan Bin Mohammed Al Maktoum**
56 **GOLD MERLION (IRE)**, b f Alhaarth (IRE)—Sea of Time (USA) **N. S. Yong**
57 **HALEY BOP (IRE)**, ch f Dream Ahead (USA)—Hallie's Comet (IRE) **Mr Abdullah Al Mansoori**
58 **HAWATIF (IRE)**, b f Royal Applause—Excellerator (USA) **Mr Abdullah Al Mansoori**
59 B c Danehill Dancer (IRE)—Heavenly Bay (IRE) **Mark Johnston Racing Ltd**
60 **HERALDIC (USA)**, b br c Discreet Cat (USA)—
Chilukki's Song (USA) **Sheikh Hamdan Bin Mohammed Al Maktoum**
61 **HIGHBURGH ROAD (IRE)**, b f Pour Moi (IRE)—Alta Lena (FR) **Mark Johnston Racing Ltd**
62 **HIGHLY SPRUNG (IRE)**, b g Zebedee—Miss Donovan **D. C. Livingston**
63 **HUNTLAW**, b g Oasis Dream—Attraction **The Duke Of Roxburghe**
64 **INTRODUCTORY (IRE)**, b f Roderic O'Connor (IRE)—Pleasure Place (IRE) **Mr Abdullah Al Mansoori**

MR MARK JOHNSTON - Continued

65 **JAAMEH (IRE)**, b c Iffraaj—Miss Gibraltar **Hamdan Al Maktoum**
66 **JESSICA JO (IRE)**, ch f Mastercraftsman (IRE)—Naomh Geileis (USA) **Mrs C. E. Budden**
67 **JINTNI**, b c Poet's Voice—Ivory Gala (FR) **Sheikh Hamdan Bin Mohammed Al Maktoum**
68 **JUSTE POUR NOUS**, b c Pour Moi (IRE)—Steam Cuisine **Holleyhead, Ross, White & Johnston**
69 **KELVIN HALL**, ch f Halling (USA)—Barawin (IRE) **Kingsley Park 4**
70 **KING'S PAVILION (IRE)**, b c King's Best (USA)—Embassy **Sheikh Hamdan Bin Mohammed Al Maktoum**
71 **KINGSLEY KLARION (IRE)**, b c Arcano (IRE)—May Day Queen (IRE) **P. Dean**
72 **LA SALESSE (FR)**, b f Manduro (GER)—Ailette **J. D. Abell**
73 **LEYBURN**, ch f Shamardal (USA)—Lurina (IRE) **Sheikh Hamdan Bin Mohammed Al Maktoum**
74 **LIDO LADY (IRE)**, b f Danehill Dancer (IRE)—Showbiz (IRE) **Kingsley Park 3 - Originals**
75 **LORD OF THE VALLEY**, b c Sir Percy—Marakabei **Kingsley Park 3 - Originals**
76 **LOUVENCOURT (FR)**, b br c Halling (USA)—Lungwa (IRE) **Mr Abdullah Al Mansoori**
77 **LUMIERE**, gr f Shamardal (USA)—Screen Star (IRE) **Sheikh Hamdan Bin Mohammed Al Maktoum**
78 **MARIEE**, b f Archipenko (USA)—Maria di Scozia **Miss K. Rausing**
79 **MARY BEALE (FR)**, ch f Shamardal (USA)—What A Picture (FR) **Sheikh Hamdan Bin Mohammed Al Maktoum**
80 B c Kitten's Joy (USA)—Menekineko (USA) **Mr Abdullah Al Mansoori**
81 **MINIATURIST (IRE)**, b c Shamardal (USA)—Herboriste **Sheikh Hamdan Bin Mohammed Al Maktoum**
82 **MONTSARRAT (IRE)**, br c Poet's Voice—Flying Flag (IRE) **Sheikh Hamdan Bin Mohammed Al Maktoum**
83 **MUHADATHAT**, b f Showcasing—Cavallo da Corsa **Mr Abdullah Al Mansoori**
84 **NEW CALEDONIA (IRE)**, b c Cape Cross (IRE)—Tessa Reef (IRE) **Sheikh Hamdan Bin Mohammed Al Maktoum**
85 **ODE TO EVENING**, ch c Poet's Voice—Ever Love (BRZ) **Sheikh Hamdan Bin Mohammed Al Maktoum**
86 **OPERA BUFFA (IRE)**, b f Exceed And Excel (AUS)—
                                        Dubai Opera (USA) **Sheikh Hamdan Bin Mohammed Al Maktoum**
87 **ORDINAL**, b c Shamardal (USA)—Mille **Sheikh Hamdan Bin Mohammed Al Maktoum**
88 **OUTRANK**, ch c Exceed And Excel (AUS)—Lane County (USA) **Sheikh Hamdan Bin Mohammed Al Maktoum**
89 **PLAGIARISM (USA)**, b f Lonhro (AUS)—Journalist (IRE) **Sheikh Hamdan Bin Mohammed Al Maktoum**
90 **POWDERHORN (IRE)**, b c Raven's Pass (USA)—Innclassic (IRE) **Sheikh Hamdan Bin Mohammed Al Maktoum**
91 **RAH RAH**, b f Lonhro (AUS)—Rahiyah (USA) **Godolphin Management Company Ltd**
92 **RAVENHOE (IRE)**, ch g Bahamian Bounty—Breathless Kiss (USA) **J. D. Abell**
93 **RENFREW STREET**, br f Iffraaj—Malpas Missile (IRE) **D. C. Livingston**
94 **RICHIE MCCAW**, b c Zamindar (USA)—Cochin (USA) **M. H. Watt**
95 **RIFLESCOPE (IRE)**, b c Raven's Pass (USA)—Red Intrigue (IRE) **Sheikh Hamdan Bin Mohammed Al Maktoum**
96 **RIVER THAMES**, b c Bernardini (USA)—River Street **Sheikh Hamdan Bin Mohammed Al Maktoum**
97 **ROSY MORNING (IRE)**, b f Exceed And Excel (AUS)—
                                        Bright Morning **Sheikh Hamdan Bin Mohammed Al Maktoum**
98 B br f Intikhab (USA)—Salamanque (FR) **Mr Abdullah Al Mansoori**
99 **SCARPETA (FR)**, b c Soldier of Fortune (IRE)—Sanada (IRE) **Mr B. Yeardley**
100 **SECOND SERVE (IRE)**, b c Cape Cross (IRE)—Aguinaga (IRE) **Mr S Richards,Mr N Browne,Mrs R Frosell**
101 **SENNOCKIAN SONG**, ch c New Approach (IRE)—Chorist **The Vine Accord**
102 **SHADOW GAME**, b c Shamardal (USA)—Victoria Star (IRE) **Sheikh Hamdan Bin Mohammed Al Maktoum**
103 B f Shamardal (USA)—Shemissa (IRE) **C. N. Wright**
104 **SIGNED AND SEALED**, b g Authorized (IRE)—Broken Peace (USA) **R. S. Brookhouse**
105 **SILENT DREAMER**, b f Dream Ahead (USA)—In A Silent Way (IRE) **A. Saeed**
106 **SIXTH SENSE (IRE)**, ch c Shamardal (USA)—
                                        Shinko Hermes (IRE) **Sheikh Hamdan Bin Mohammed Al Maktoum**
107 **SOGNO D'AMORE (USA)**, b c Bernardini (USA)—
                                        Love Dancing (ARG) **Sheikh Hamdan Bin Mohammed Al Maktoum**
108 **SOLDIER IN ACTION (FR)**, b c Soldier of Fortune (IRE)—Ripley (GER) **A. D. Spence**
109 **SPACE MOUNTAIN**, b c Sea The Stars (IRE)—Ripples Maid **J. M. Brown**
110 **STADIUS (IRE)**, b c Cape Cross (IRE)—Sherifa (GER) **Sheikh Hamdan Bin Mohammed Al Maktoum**
111 **STAR FOCUS (IRE)**, b f Intense Focus (USA)—Star of Siligo (USA) **Kingsley Park 2 - Fairyhouse**
112 **STAR OF LOMBARDY (IRE)**, b f Cape Cross (IRE)—Million Waves (IRE) **P. Dean**
113 **STREET DUEL (USA)**, b c Street Cry (IRE)—Fifth Avenue Doll (USA) **S. Ali**
114 **TARTAN BUTE**, b c Azamour (IRE)—On A Soapbox (USA) **Mr F. Bird**
115 **TAWAKKOL**, b c Firebreak—Dayville (USA) **Hamdan Al Maktoum**
116 **TEMPLIER (IRE)**, b c Mastercraftsman (IRE)—Tigertail (FR) **Mr Gerry Ryan**
117 **THOLEN (USA)**, b f Lonhro (AUS)—Zelanda (IRE) **Sheikh Hamdan Bin Mohammed Al Maktoum**
118 **TRIASSIC (IRE)**, b g Vale of York (IRE)—Livadiya (IRE) **Kingsley Park 2 - Fairyhouse**
119 **TURBINE (IRE)**, b c Cape Cross (IRE)—Chiquita Linda (IRE) **Sheikh Hamdan Bin Mohammed Al Maktoum**
120 **TWISTING HAY**, b c Cape Cross (IRE)—Blaugrana (IRE) **Sheikh Hamdan Bin Mohammed Al Maktoum**
121 **TWOBEELUCKY**, b c Tobougg (IRE)—She's The Lady **R. S. Brookhouse**
122 **WAHQA**, b g Intikhab (USA)—Max One Two Three (IRE) **Hamdan Al Maktoum**
123 **WELFORD**, b c Dubawi (IRE)—Avongrove **Sheikh Hamdan Bin Mohammed Al Maktoum**
124 **WHITMAN**, b br c Poet's Voice—Sundrop (JPN) **Sheikh Hamdan Bin Mohammed Al Maktoum**

MR MARK JOHNSTON - Continued

125 YORKEE MO SABEE (IRE), ch c Teofilo (IRE)—Pivotal's Princess (IRE) **Mr P. R. York**
126 ZAMINDO, ch g Zamindar (USA)—Mosqueras Romance **M. W. Graff**

TWO-YEAR-OLDS

127 ALEXANDER M (IRE), ch c 4/4 Mastercraftsman (IRE)—
    Naomh Geileis (USA) (Grand Slam (USA)) **Christine Budden**
128 B c 23/3 Acclamation—Alexander Youth (IRE) (Exceed And Excel (AUS)) (50000) **Mr J. A. Barson**
129 B br f 17/3 Lonhro (AUS)—Alizes (NZ) (Rory's Jester (AUS)) **Sheikh Hamdan Bin Mohammed Al Maktoum**
130 Ch f 14/3 Pivotal—Angel's Tears (Seeking The Gold (USA)) **Sheikh Hamdan Bin Mohammed Al Maktoum**
131 B f 15/3 Teofilo (IRE)—Belle Josephine (Dubawi (IRE)) **Sheikh Hamdan Bin Mohammed Al Maktoum**
132 B c 3/2 Raven's Pass (USA)—Beneventa (Most Welcome) (85000) **Hamdan Al Maktoum**
133 B c 1/4 New Approach (IRE)—Beta (Selkirk (USA)) **Sheikh Hamdan Bin Mohammed Al Maktoum**
134 Gr ro f 10/3 Street Boss (USA)—Blue Dress (Danzig (USA)) **Sheikh Hamdan Bin Mohammed Al Maktoum**
135 B f 15/2 Acclamation—Blue Rocket (IRE) (Rock of Gibraltar (IRE)) (27000) **R. C. Tooth**
136 B c 4/5 Pivotal—Camlet (Green Desert (USA)) **Sheikh Hamdan Bin Mohammed Al Maktoum**
137 B c 23/4 Mastercraftsman (IRE)—Catch The Blues (IRE) (Bluebird (USA)) (22148) **H J W Partnership**
138 B c 1/3 Lawman (FR)—Cedar Sea (IRE) (Persian Bold) (31007) **Mr Abdullah Al Mansoori**
139 B c 14/2 Cape Cross (IRE)—
    Chantilly Pearl (USA) (Smart Strike (CAN)) (66445) **Sheikh Hamdan Bin Mohammed Al Maktoum**
140 B f 22/4 Invincible Spirit (IRE)—
    Chaquiras (USA) (Seeking The Gold (USA)) **Sheikh Hamdan Bin Mohammed Al Maktoum**
141 B f 23/4 Casamento (IRE)—Cool Tarifa (IRE) (One Cool Cat (USA)) (9523) **Kingsley Park 5**
142 B f 7/5 Pivotal—Copperbeech (IRE) (Red Ransom (USA)) **Sheikh Hamdan Bin Mohammed Al Maktoum**
143 B f 11/4 Excelebration (IRE)—Coventina (IRE) (Daylami (IRE)) (13000) **Kingsley Park 5**
144 B c 22/2 Lawman (FR)—Croisiere (USA) (Capote (USA)) (51679) **3 Batterhams and a Reay**
145 Ch f 9/3 Sepoy (AUS)—Crossover (Cape Cross (IRE)) **Sheikh Hamdan Bin Mohammed Al Maktoum**
146 Gr c 13/3 Dark Angel (IRE)—Dance Club (IRE) (Fasliyev (USA)) (110000) **Hamdan Al Maktoum**
147 B c 8/5 Elusive Quality (USA)—
    Dear Bela (ARG) (Indygo Shiner (USA)) **Sheikh Hamdan Bin Mohammed Al Maktoum**
148 B br c 24/3 Cape Cross (IRE)—
    Desert Gazelle (USA) (Smart Strike (CAN)) **Sheikh Hamdan Bin Mohammed Al Maktoum**
149 Br f 10/5 Raven's Pass (USA)—
    Dinka Raja (USA) (Woodman (USA)) (35000) **Hussain Lootah**
150 Gr c 18/4 Frankel—Dookus (IRE) (Linamix (FR)) (95976) **Hussain Lootah**
151 B f 29/4 Shamardal (USA)—
    Double Vie (IRE) (Tagula (IRE)) (29531) **Sheikh Hamdan Bin Mohammed Al Maktoum**
152 B f 9/3 Yorgunnabelucky (USA)—Dream Esteem (Mark of Esteem (IRE)) **R. S. Brookhouse**
153 B f 5/3 Casamento (IRE)—Dubai Opera (USA) (Dubai Millennium) **Sheikh Hamdan Bin Mohammed Al Maktoum**
154 B f 7/4 Helmet (AUS)—
    Dubai Sunrise (USA) (Seeking The Gold (USA)) **Sheikh Hamdan Bin Mohammed Al Maktoum**
155 B c 19/1 Poet's Voice—Duniatty (Green Desert (USA)) (118124) **Sheikh Hamdan Bin Mohammed Al Maktoum**
156 B f 5/4 Teofilo (IRE)—Dusty Answer (Zafonic (USA)) (10000) **Kingsley Park 5**
157 B f 25/4 Sepoy (AUS)—
    Emotion Parade (ARG) (Parade Marshal (USA)) **Sheikh Hamdan Bin Mohammed Al Maktoum**
158 B f 3/3 Harbour Watch (IRE)—Endorsement (Warning) (12000) **Mr Markus Graff**
159 B f 19/4 Casamento (IRE)—Epic Similie (Lomitas) **Sheikh Hamdan Bin Mohammed Al Maktoum**
160 Ch f 17/4 Casamento (IRE)—Exultate Jubilate (USA) (With Approval (CAN)) (10000) **Chris Buckley**
161 B c 23/5 Cape Cross (IRE)—Famusa (Medicean) (16000) **Ali Saeed**
162 Ch f 27/2 Mastercraftsman (IRE)—Fig Tree Drive (USA) (Miswaki (USA)) (25101) **Mr R. S. Brookhouse**
163 B f 27/3 Dark Angel (IRE)—Hope of An Angel (IRE) (Intikhab (USA)) (22148) **Thurloe Thoroughbreds**
164 IL SICARIO (IRE), b c 20/4 Zebedee—Starring (FR) (Ashkalani (IRE)) (51679) **Mr Peter Savill**
165 B c 17/1 Shamardal (USA)—Illandrane (IRE) (Cape Cross (IRE)) **Sheikh Hamdan Bin Mohammed Al Maktoum**
166 Ch c 9/5 Street Cry (IRE)—Ishitaki (ARG) (Interprete (ARG)) **Sheikh Hamdan Bin Mohammed Al Maktoum**
167 B gr f 29/3 Mastercraftsman (IRE)—Jalissa (Mister Baileys) **G. R. Bailey Ltd (Baileys Horse Feeds)**
168 Ch f 3/4 Power—Jallaissine (IRE) (College Chapel) (22148) **Mr D. Livingston**
169 Ch f 6/3 Kitten's Joy (USA)—
    La Coruna (USA) (Thunder Gulch (USA)) (36913) **N Browne,M Bradford,S Frosell,S Richards**
170 LA VIE EN ROSE, b f 17/2 Henrythenavigator (USA)—Lady Jane Digby (Oasis Dream) **Miss K. Rausing**
171 B c 19/3 Exceed And Excel (AUS)—
    Lacily (USA) (Elusive Quality (USA)) **Sheikh Hamdan Bin Mohammed Al Maktoum**
172 B f 20/1 Henrythenavigator (USA)—Lady Eclair (IRE) (Danehill Dancer (IRE)) (22148) **Netherfield House Stud**
173 LAUREATE, b f 7/2 Poet's Voice—Step This Way (USA) (Giant's Causeway (USA)) **S. R. Counsell**
174 LOVE DREAMS (IRE), b c 22/1 Dream Ahead (USA)—
    Kimola (IRE) (King's Theatre (IRE)) (42000) **Crone Stud Farms Ltd**
175 LOVE OASIS, b f 31/3 Oasis Dream—Pickle (Piccolo) (33222) **Crone Stud Farms Ltd**

MR MARK JOHNSTON - Continued

176 LOVE POWER (IRE), b c 25/4 Power—Royal Fizz (IRE) (Royal Academy (USA)) (36913) **Crone Stud Farms Ltd**
177 B c 8/4 So You Think (NZ)—
    Mambo Halo (USA) (Southern Halo (USA)) (42000) **J S Morrison & Around The World Partnership**
178 B f 20/3 Shamardal (USA)—Melhor Ainda (USA) (Pulpit (USA)) **Sheikh Hamdan Bin Mohammed Al Maktoum**
179 B c 23/4 Raven's Pass (USA)—Mid Mon Lady (IRE) (Danetime (IRE)) (35000) **Mr Abdullah Al Mansoori**
180 B c 25/2 Shamardal (USA)—
    Miss Jean Brodie (USA) (Maria's Mon (USA)) **Sheikh Hamdan Bin Mohammed Al Maktoum**
181 MLLE GEORGES, ch f 16/4 Archipenko (USA)—Mme de Stael (Selkirk (USA)) **Miss K. Rausing**
182 B f 25/3 Rock of Gibraltar (IRE)—Muravka (IRE) (High Chaparral (IRE)) (76190) **Mr & Mrs Newett**
183 B c 3/4 Mastercraftsman (IRE)—My Lass (Elmaamul (USA)) (19195) **The Goodmove Syndicate**
184 B f 4/2 Dream Ahead (USA)—Nellie Melba (Hurricane Sky (AUS)) **Countess of Lonsdale**
185 Ch c 26/4 Hard Spun (USA)—Newsreel (IRE) (A P Indy (USA)) **Sheikh Hamdan Bin Mohammed Al Maktoum**
186 B c 28/2 Poet's Voice—Oasis Jade (Oasis Dream) **Sheikh Hamdan Bin Mohammed Al Maktoum**
187 Ch c 26/4 Helmet (AUS)—Pearl Grey (Gone West (USA)) **Sheikh Hamdan Bin Mohammed Al Maktoum**
188 B f 31/1 Sepoy (AUS)—Perfect Star (Act One) (32000) **Mr Abdullah Al Mansori**
189 B f 16/2 Excelebration (IRE)—Pioneer Bride (USA) (Gone West (USA)) (22857) **Mr P. Dean & Mr R. Priestley**
190 POWERFUL LOVE (IRE), b c 22/5 Clodovil (IRE)—
    Ruby Ridge (IRE) (Acatenango (GER)) (45000) **Crone Stud Farms Ltd**
191 Ch c 17/4 Bahamian Bounty—Prianca (GER) (Diktat) (19047) **J. D. Abell**
192 B gr f 6/5 Exceed And Excel (AUS)—
    Princess Taise (USA) (Cozzene (USA)) **Sheikh Hamdan Bin Mohammed Al Maktoum**
193 B c 24/5 Poet's Voice—Pryka (ARG) (Southern Halo (USA)) **Sheikh Hamdan Bin Mohammed Al Maktoum**
194 B f 22/3 Lonhro (AUS)—Puppet Queen (USA) (Kingmambo (USA)) **Sheikh Hamdan Bin Mohammed Al Maktoum**
195 Ch c 29/3 Poet's Voice—Rahiyah (USA) (Rahy (USA)) **Sheikh Hamdan Bin Mohammed Al Maktoum**
196 B c 13/2 Invincible Spirit (IRE)—
    Rio Osa (AUS) (Canny Lad (AUS)) **Sheikh Hamdan Bin Mohammed Al Maktoum**
197 RUSUMAAT (IRE), b c 7/3 Arcano (IRE)—Queen Wasp (IRE) (Shamardal (USA)) (42857) **Hamdan Al Maktoum**
198 B br f 24/4 Lonhro (AUS)—
    Secret Charm (IRE) (Green Desert (USA)) **Sheikh Hamdan Bin Mohammed Al Maktoum**
199 B c 17/2 Cape Cross (IRE)—Serenity Star (Monsun (GER)) **Sheikh Hamdan Bin Mohammed Al Maktoum**
200 B c 23/3 Manduro (GER)—Shane (GER) (Kornado) **Sheikh Hamdan Bin Mohammed Al Maktoum**
201 B f 12/3 Dark Angel (IRE)—She Basic (IRE) (Desert Prince (IRE)) (25389) **J. D. Abell**
202 SOFIA'S ROCK (FR), b c 24/2 Rock of Gibraltar (IRE)—
    Princess Sofia (UAE) (Pennekamp (USA)) (73827) **Mr Graham Mezzone**
203 Ch f 12/2 Dutch Art—Spiralling (Pivotal) (40000) **Trevor Stewart**
204 B c 30/3 Cape Cross (IRE)—
    Star Blossom (USA) (Good Reward (USA)) **Sheikh Hamdan Bin Mohammed Al Maktoum**
205 Ch f 1/2 Tamayuz—Storm Lily (USA) (Storm Cat (USA)) **Sheikh Hamdan Bin Mohammed Al Maktoum**
206 Gr ro c 22/2 Lonhro (AUS)—Summer Fete (IRE) (Pivotal) **Sheikh Hamdan Bin Mohammed Al Maktoum**
207 B c 1/5 Teofilo (IRE)—Tessa Reef (IRE) (Mark of Esteem (IRE)) **Sheikh Hamdan Bin Mohammed Al Maktoum**
208 THE LAST LION (IRE), b c 12/2 Choisir (AUS)—
    Mala Mala (IRE) (Brief Truce (USA)) (60538) **John Brown & Megan Dennis**
209 THINK SO (IRE), b c 31/3 So You Think (NZ)—
    Mabalane (IRE) (Danehill (USA)) (30000) **Holleyhead, Ross, White & Johnston**
210 B f 28/1 Makfi—Titivation (Montjeu (IRE)) (47619) **Mr P. Rooney**
211 B f 29/1 Shamardal (USA)—Tizdubai (USA) (Cee's Tizzy (USA)) **Sheikh Hamdan Bin Mohammed Al Maktoum**
212 B br c 16/3 Cape Cross (IRE)—
    What A Charm (IRE) (Key of Luck (USA)) **Sheikh Hamdan Bin Mohammed Al Maktoum**
213 B f 30/1 Acclamation—Wiltshire Life (IRE) (Camacho) (36190) **Lowther Racing**
214 Ch c 19/3 Foxwedge (AUS)—Zubova (Dubawi (IRE)) (19000) **Mr Jim Duggan & Mr Scott Brown**

Other Owners: Mr Abdulla Al Mansoori, Atlantic Racing Limited, Mrs R. F. Batterham, Mr C. M. Batterham, Mr Martin Bradford, Mr E. Brierley, Mr N. N. Browne, Mr M. Budden, Mr Matthew Budden, Mr Alan J. Burke, Mr Paul Dean, Mr Dan Downie, Mrs Lisa Fellows, Mrs Robert Frosell, Mr A. Greenhalgh, Mr W. A. Greensit, Mr C. H. Greensit, Mr Jason Hathorn, Mrs Fiona Hathorn, Mr Tony Hill, Mr B. M. Hillier, Robin Holleyhead, Mr Richard B. Huckerby, Mr R. W. Huggins, Mr M. R. Lonsdorfer, Manor Farm Stud (Rutland), Mr Graham Mezzone, Mr Colin J. Norton, Mr Salem Rashid, Mr Stevie Richards, Mrs Stevie Richards, Mrs Victoria Snook, Mr Geoffrey Turnbull, Mrs S. E. Turnbull, Mr C. Wachter, Mr J. Wachter, Dr J. Walker, Mr David F. White, Mr Christopher Wright.

Assistant Trainers: Deirdre Johnston & Jock Bennett

343 MR ALAN JONES, Minehead
Postal: **East Harwood Farm, Timberscombe, Minehead, Somerset, TA24 7UE**
Contacts: **FAX 01633 680232 MOBILE (07901) 505064**
E-MAIL heritageracing@btconnect.com WEBSITE www.alanjonesracing.co.uk

1 **BEAU BAY (FR)**, 5, b g Bernebeau (FR)—Slew Bay (FR) **Burnham Plastering & Drylining Ltd**
2 **BOBBITS WAY**, 11, b g Overbury (IRE)—Bit of A Chick **Mr T. S. M. S. Riley-Smith**
3 **MA'IRE RUA (IRE)**, 9, ch g Presenting—Long Acre **Mr T. S. M. S. Riley-Smith**
4 **MISSMEBUTLETMEGO**, 6, b g With The Flow (USA)—Bay Bianca (IRE) **Mr T. S. M. S. Riley-Smith**
5 **NORISAN**, 12, ch g Inchinor—Dream On Deya (IRE) **Burnham Plastering & Drylining Ltd**
6 **POKARI (FR)**, 4, ch g Bonbon Rose (FR)—Pokara (FR)
7 **QUINCY DES PICTONS (FR)**, 12, b g Kadalko (FR)—
Izabel des Pictons (FR) **Burnham Plastering & Drylining Ltd**
8 **REST AND BE (IRE)**, 9, b br m Vinnie Roe (IRE)—Bobs Star (IRE) **Mr T. S. M. S. Riley-Smith**
9 **SPIN CAST**, 8, b g Marju (IRE)—Some Diva **F. A. Clegg**
10 **STAND BY ME (IRE)**, 6, b g Dream Well (FR)—In Love New (FR) **Mr T. S. M. S. Riley-Smith**
11 **SUPERNOVERRE (IRE)**, 10, b g Noverre (USA)—Caviare **Mr T. S. M. S. Riley-Smith**
12 **TIQUER (FR)**, 8, b g Equerry (USA)—Tirenna (FR) **Burnham Plastering & Drylining Ltd**

Assistant Trainer: Miss A. Bartelink

Jockey (NH): Richard Johnson, Paddy Brennan, Tom O' Brien. **Amateur:** Mr O. Greenall.

344 MR MALCOLM JONES, Treharris
Postal: **Pant-Y-Ffynnon House, Bedlinog, Treharris, Mid Glamorgan**

1 **ASHTOWN (IRE)**, 9, b g Westerner—Christmas River (IRE) **M. G. Jones**
2 **GLENKEAL (IRE)**, 10, ch g Marignan (USA)—Conna Dodger (IRE) **M. G. Jones**
3 **TA HA (IRE)**, 8, br g Posidonas—Euro Dancer (IRE) **M. G. Jones**
4 **VALLEYOFTHEFOX**, 6, b g Petrovich (USA)—Ruby Dante (IRE) **M. G. Jones**

345 MRS VIOLET M. JORDAN, Moreton Morrell
Postal: **Sanbrook Farm, Back Lane, Shrewley, Warwick, Warwickshire, CV35 7BD**
Contacts: **MOBILE (07831) 101632**
E-MAIL jordyracer29@hotmail.co.uk

1 **BOOKTHEBAND (IRE)**, 6, ch g Dubawi (IRE)—Songbook **Farmers & Cricketers Partnership**
2 **KILLFINNAN CASTLE (IRE)**, 13, br g Arctic Lord—Golden Seekers **Farmers & Cricketers Partnership**
3 **MEESON**, 5, gr g Fair Mix (IRE)—Premiere Foulee (FR) **Mrs Violet M. Jordan**

Other Owners: Mr D. J. Pearson, Mr T. Powell.

Assistant Trainer: Gaye Williams

346 MRS CAROLINE KEEVIL, Motcombe
Postal: **Larkinglass Farm, Motcombe, Shaftesbury, Dorset, SP7 9HY**
Contacts: **PHONE (01747) 854141 FAX (01747) 854141 MOBILE (07768) 867424**
E-MAIL keevilracing@gmail.com WEBSITE www.keevilracing.com

1 **AN TARBH OG (IRE)**, 8, b g Fruits of Love (USA)—Finnuala Supreme (IRE) **The Jago Family Partnership**
2 **BALLYANTICS (IRE)**, 5, b g Marienbard (IRE)—Ballindante (IRE) **Mrs C. Keevil**
3 **DARKESTBEFOREDAWN (IRE)**, 9, br g Dr Massini (IRE)—Camden Dolphin (IRE) **The Jago Family Partnership**
4 **DENNY KERRELL**, 5, b g Midnight Legend—Tilla **Mrs C. Keevil**
5 **JACK BY THE HEDGE**, 7, b g Overbury (IRE)—Bluebell Path **Mrs Sara Biggins & Mrs Celia Djivanovic**
6 **JAJAMCOOL (IRE)**, 6, b g Marienbard (IRE)—Scarlete (FR) **Lady Sutton**
7 **KNIGHT OFTHE REALM**, 7, b g Kayf Tara—Flow **Mrs H. R. Dunn**
8 **LET'S TANGO (IRE)**, 5, ch g Mahler—Miss Ogan (IRE) **Mrs L. R. Lovell**
9 **PALMARIA**, 6, b m Kayf Tara—Ollejess **Lady Sutton**

MRS CAROLINE KEEVIL - Continued

10 **PRINCE MAHLER (IRE)**, 6, b g Mahler—Strokestown Queen (IRE) **Mr S. C. C. Stacey**
11 **REGAL FLOW**, 9, b g Erhaab (USA)—Flow **Mrs H. R. Dunn**
12 **STRAWBERRY HILL (IRE)**, 10, b g Winged Love (IRE)—Icydora (FR) **K S B Bloodstock**

Other Owners: Mrs S. J. Biggins, Mr K. W. Biggins, Mrs C. J. Djivanovic, Mr F. C. A. Jago, Miss M. L. A. Jago, Mr P. J. A. Jago, Mrs J. L. Jago.

Jockey (NH): James Best, Tom O'Brien, Ian Popham. **Conditional:** Will Featherstone. **Amateur:** Mr Lee Drowne.

---

347 **MR MARTIN KEIGHLEY, Cheltenham**
Postal: **Condicote Stables, Luckley, Moreton-In-Marsh, Gloucestershire, GL56 0RD**
Contacts: **MOBILE (07767) 472547**
E-MAIL keighleyracing@btinternet.com WEBSITE www.martinkeighleyracing.com

1 **ALTESSE DE GUYE (FR)**, 6, ch m Dom Alco (FR)—Mascotte de Guye (FR) **Daydream Believers**
2 **ANY CURRENCY (IRE)**, 13, b g Moscow Society (USA)—Native Bavard (IRE) **Cash Is King**
3 **AS JUSSINIERE (FR)**, 6, b br g Network (GER)—Indian Sun (FR) **Martin Keighley Racing Partnership**
4 **BALLYMOUNTAIN BOY (IRE)**, 5, b g Mountain High (IRE)—Minoras Return (IRE)
5 **BOBBLE EMERALD (IRE)**, 8, ch g Rudimentary (USA)—Aunt Emeralds (IRE)
6 6, B g Kayf Tara—Born To Dream (IRE)
7 **CLASSIC COLORI (IRE)**, 9, b g Le Vie Dei Colori—Beryl **Mrs B. Keighley**
8 **COTTERSROCK (IRE)**, 6, b g Robin des Pres—Toasted Oats (IRE) **Mr S. Baikie**
9 **CREEPY (IRE)**, 8, b g Westerner—Prowler (IRE) **Mrs B. Keighley**
10 **DARNITNEV**, 6, b g Darnay—Lavender Della (IRE) **Mrs R. E. Nelmes**
11 **DOUBLE CHOCOLATE**, 13, b g Doubletour (USA)—Matching Green **Red & Black Racing**
12 **FLEMENTIME (IRE)**, 8, ch m Flemensfirth (USA)—Funny Times **Figjam II**
13 **FORECAST**, 4, ch c Observatory (USA)—New Orchid (USA) **Mr K. Davies & Mr S. Baikie**
14 **GEORGIAN KING**, 13, b g Overbury (IRE)—Roslin **R. Allsop**
15 **JEANS LADY**, 7, b m Milan—Indian Miss **D. G. Robinson**
16 **JOHNNY OG**, 7, b g Flemensfirth (USA)—Mrs Roberts **T.Hanlon M.Boothright S.Hanlon N.Martin**
17 **LAUGHINGALLTHEWAY**, 5, b g Darnay—Smilingatstrangers **Mrs Sarah Hamilton & Mr M Jenkins**
18 **MARLEY JOE (IRE)**, 5, b g Arcadio (GER)—Tuscarora (IRE) **Mr O. F. Ryan**
19 **MERLIN'S WISH**, 11, gr g Terimon—Sendai **Miss R. Toppin**
20 **MIDNIGHT THOMAS**, 7, b g Midnight Legend—Vivacious Lass (IRE) **Close Partnership**
21 **MONTY'S REVENGE (IRE)**, 11, b g Bob's Return (IRE)—
                                Native Bavard (IRE) **The Red Socks & Mrs Belinda Keighley**
22 **MORNING HERALD**, 5, br m Lucky Story (USA)—Wakeful **Mr C. G. M. Lloyd-Baker**
23 **MORTLESTOWN (IRE)**, 8, b g Milan—Pima (IRE) **M. Boothright**
24 **REAL GONE KID**, 5, b g Kalanisi (IRE)—Karmest **Mr R Davies & Mr S Baikie**
25 **SEYMOUR ERIC**, 11, b g Bollin Eric—Seymour Chance **Mrs C J Black & Ten Out Of Ten Racing**
26 **SOLSTICE STAR**, 6, b g Kayf Tara—Clover Green (IRE) **E&G Racing Ltd**
27 **SUGAR MIX**, 5, gr g Sagamix (FR)—Bruley **Mrs Anne Lee-Warner**
28 **THADY QUIL (IRE)**, 6, ch g Stowaway—Aunt Sue (IRE) **Owners For Owners: Thady Quil**
29 **THE WEXFORDIAN (IRE)**, 7, b g Shantou (USA)—Going My Way **M Boothright, T Hanlon & G Duncan**
30 **TOFFEE HOLLAND**, 5, b g Overbury (IRE)—Roslin **Mr R. Allsop**
31 **VIKING MISTRESS**, 8, b m Bollin Eric—Mistress Caramore (IRE) **Mrs B. Keighley**
32 **WEYBURN (IRE)**, 5, gr g September Storm (GER)—Saffron Pride (IRE) **M. Boothright**

THREE-YEAR-OLDS

33 **JAZZY (IRE)**, b c Roderic O'Connor (IRE)—Lucayan Beauty (IRE) **Jazz Summers Racing**

Other Owners: Mr Stuart Baikie, Mr Neil Bannister, Mr Shaun Bannister, Mrs C. J. Black, Mr M. Boothright, Mr R. Davies, Mr P.K. Davis, Mr G. K. Duncan, Mr P. Egan, Mr Geoff Godsall, Mrs Sarah Hamilton, Mr Tyrone Hanlon, Mr S. R. Harman, Mrs Lottie Hayman-Joyce, Mr Simon Hayman-Joyce, Mr James Hayman-Joyce, Mr Stefan Hibbett, Mr J. Huckle, Mrs E. A. Huckle, Mrs Jacqueline Hughes, Miss A. Humes, Mr M. Jenkins, Mrs Angela Lear, Mr W. P. Ledward, Miss C. Lees-Jones, Dr M. M. Ogilvy, Mr Peter R. Thomas, Mr G. M. Thornton, Mr H. Watts, Mr N. Whittle.

Assistant Trainer: Mr Jamie Goldstein

348 MR CHRISTOPHER KELLETT, Swadlincote
Postal: **Jubilee Racing Stables, Snareston Road, Appleby Magna, Swadlincote,**
Derbyshire, DE12 7AJ
Contacts: **PHONE** (01530) 515595 **FAX** (01530) 515595 **MOBILE** (07966) 097989
E-MAIL christopherkellett@btinternet.com **WEBSITE** www.chriskellettracing.co.uk

1 A SWELL LYE, 5, ch g Resplendent Glory (IRE)—Bahhmirage (IRE) **Miss S. L. Walley**
2 DOT DASH DOT, 4, b f Rainbow High—Never Lost **J. E. Titley**
3 DOUNYA'S BOY, 7, ch g Sakhee (USA)—Dounya (USA) **Miss S. L. Bailey**
4 MASTER SQUIRREL, 5, gr g Great Palm (USA)—Overthrow **D. H. Muir & Exors of the Late Mrs R. E. Muir**
5 MR SQUIRREL (IRE), 9, gr g Great Palm (USA)—
                                           Patsy Donnellan (IRE) **D. H. Muir & Exors of the Late Mrs R. E. Muir**
6 SIR LUKE ARNO, 5, b g Lucarno (USA)—Never Lost **J. E. Titley**
7 UPPER LAMBOURN (IRE), 8, b g Exceed And Excel (AUS)—In The Fashion (IRE) **Miss S. L. Bailey**

Other Owners: Exors of the Late Mrs R. E. Muir, D. H. Muir.

349 MISS GAY KELLEWAY, Newmarket
Postal: **Queen Alexandra Stables, 2 Chapel Street, Exning, Newmarket, Suffolk, CB8 7HA**
Contacts: **PHONE** (01638) 577778 **MOBILE** (07974) 948768
E-MAIL gaykellewayracing@hotmail.co.uk **WEBSITE** www.gaykellewayracing.com

1 CALTRA COLLEEN, 4, b f Sixties Icon—Mistic Magic (IRE) **G Kerr & G Kelleway**
2 CAPTAIN FELIX, 4, b g Captain Gerrard (IRE)—Sweet Applause (IRE) **Mr M. Bartram**
3 DOMINANDROS (FR), 5, b g Teofilo (IRE)—Afya **Winterbeck Manor Stud & Partners**
4 JE T'AIME ENCORE, 4, b g Acclamation—Mimisel **La Belle Femme Syndicate**
5 LIGHTSCAMERACTION (IRE), 4, ch g Pastoral Pursuits—Silca Boo **LCA Lights Camera Action Ltd**
6 OAKLEY STAR, 4, b f Multiplex—Star Welcome **B. C. Oakley**
7 ROYAL MARSKELL, 7, b g Multiplex—Socialise **Miss C. Y. Wootten**
8 SAILOR MALAN, 4, b g Mount Nelson—Flying Hi **S. Bailey**
9 SHOWTIME STAR, 6, b g Byron—Piddies Pride (IRE) **Mortlock, Countrywide Classics & Nigel Skandett**
10 4, B c Myboycharlie (IRE)—Silver Elite **A. P. Griffin**
11 STOSUR (IRE), 5, b m Mount Nelson—Jules (IRE) **B. C. Oakley**
12 WHAT A PARTY (IRE), 4, ch f Windsor Knot (IRE)—Tarziyma (IRE) **M. M. Foulger**

THREE-YEAR-OLDS
13 COLOR FORCE (IRE), gr f Dark Angel (IRE)—Amistad (GER) **A.C. Entertainment Technologies Limited**
14 FIFTYTINTSOFSILVER (IRE), gr f Clodovil (IRE)—
                                    Marju Guest (IRE) **Shane Buy, Lynne Stanbrook, Gay Kelleway**
15 IRVINE LADY (IRE), ch f Footstepsinthesand—Ascot Lady (IRE) **Mr G. Kerr**
16 LET THERE BE LIGHT, ch g Phoenix Reach—Pink Supreme **G Kerr T Newman N Shapley M Watt**
17 MASQUERADED (USA), ch c Drosselmeyer (USA)—Maudie May (USA) **Bubbly Racing**
18 NEW ABBEY ANGEL (IRE), gr g Dark Angel (IRE)—Alinda (IRE) **Mr A. G. MacLennan**
19 PHOENIX BEAT, b f Phoenix Reach (IRE)—Beat Seven **Winterbeck Manor Stud Ltd**
20 PRISOM (IRE), b f Zebedee—Crystal Theatre (IRE) **Oakley, Smith & Buy**
21 SAKHEE'S JEM, ch f Sakhee's Secret—Amandian (IRE) **M. M. Foulger**
22 SEPTEMBER ISSUE, b c Dutch Art—Alexander Ballet **Gay Kelleway/Buy/Kerr**
23 YEAH BABY YEAH (IRE), b f Art Connoisseur (IRE)—Royal Interlude (IRE) **Bailey & Winterbeck Manor Stud**

TWO-YEAR-OLDS
24 B c 3/2 Phoenix Reach (IRE)—Chocolada (Namid) (43809) **Kelleway / Winterbeck**
25 B c 1/3 Mawatheeq (USA)—Silver Elite (Forzando) **A. P. Griffin**

Other Owners: Mr N. Bailey, Mrs S. Bailey, Mr Matt Bartram, Mr Shane Buy, Countrywide Classics Limited, Miss Patricia Crook, Mr P. Durnin, Miss Jemma Foulger, Miss Gay Kelleway, Mr Graham Kerr, Mr Ralph Mortlock, Mrs Y. Mullin, Mr Toby Newman, Mr Brian C. Oakley, Panther Racing Ltd, Mr A. B. Parr, Mr Nigel S. Scandrett, Mr R. Sedgley, Mr. N. Shapley, Mr Bob W. Smith, Mr Ian J. Sparham, Mrs Lynne Stanbrook, Mr Peter Wales, Mr Michael Watt, Winterbeck Manor Stud.

Assistant Trainer: Anne-Sophie Crombez **Head Girl:** Liz Mullin

Jockey (flat): Adam Kirby, Luke Morris. **Jockey (NH):** Jamie Moore. **Amateur:** Mr Ross Birkett, Miss Hayley Moore.

350 **MISS LYNSEY KENDALL, Carlisle**
Postal: **The Stables, Lambley Bank, Scotby, Carlisle, Cumbria, CA4 8BX**
Contacts: **PHONE (01228) 513069 MOBILE (07818) 487227**
E-MAIL lynseykendall@hotmail.co.uk

1 GREAT ANTICIPATION (IRE), 7, b g Ashkalani (IRE)—La Bekkah (FR) **Mr & Mrs R. S. Kendall**

Other Owners: Mrs M. E. Kendall, Mr R. S. Kendall.

351 **MR NICK KENT, Brigg**
Postal: **Newstead House, Newstead Priory, Cadney Road, Brigg, Lincolnshire, DN20 9HP**
Contacts: **PHONE (01652) 650628 MOBILE (07710) 644428**
E-MAIL nick@nickkent.co.uk WEBSITE www.nickkent.co.uk

1 BOWIE (IRE), 9, br g Pelder (IRE)—La Fenice (IRE) **Cynthia Commons, Marina Kent, Nick Kent**
2 CELTIC SIXPENCE (IRE), 8, b m Celtic Swing—Penny Ha'penny **Cynthia Commons, Nick Kent**
3 COMBUSTIBLE KATE (IRE), 10, b m Mr Combustible (IRE)—Aussie Hope **Nick Kent Racing Club II**
4 4, B g Mahler—Ellesmere (IRE) **Mr A. R. P. Parkin**
5 ELLUSIVANCE (IRE), 6, b g Elusive Quality (USA)—Germance (USA) **Mr W. H. Eastwood**
6 4, B g Sulamani (IRE)—Eva's Edge (IRE) **Mr A. R. P. Parkin**
7 GONALSTON CLOUD (IRE), 9, gr g Cloudings (IRE)—Roseoengus (IRE) **R. J. Jackson**
8 HILLVIEW LAD (IRE), 8, b g Vinnie Roe (IRE)—Kabale (IRE) **Newstead Priory Racing Club**
9 IVANS BACK (IRE), 11, b g Soviet Star (USA)—Better Back Off (IRE) **Ms V. M. Cottingham**
10 LORD GOLAN, 8, b g Singspiel (IRE)—Lady Golan (IRE) **R. J. Jackson**
11 LOST IN NEWYORK (IRE), 9, b g Arakan (USA)—Lace Flower **Timbercare Racing Partnership**
12 MUSTANG ON, 6, b g Croco Rouge (IRE)—More To Life **Nick Kent**
13 ROBBING THE PREY (IRE), 5, b g Robin des Pres (FR)—Derravarra Lady (IRE) **The Bells Steakhouse Ltd**
14 SKYFIRE, 9, ch g Storm Cat (USA)—Sunray Superstar **Cynthia Commons, Nick Kent**
15 SPENDAJENNIE (IRE), 7, b m Old Vic—American Jennie (IRE) **Nick Kent Racing Club**
16 THE WHITE DUKE (IRE), 7, ch r Pelder (IRE)—Concinna (FR) **Cynthia Commons, Marina Kent, Nick Kent**

THREE-YEAR-OLDS

17 SAVANNAH STAR, b f Haafhd—Mitsuki **Nick Kent**

Other Owners: Mr Ken Boot, Mr Ray Boot, Miss C. Commons, Mr Nick Kent, Mr J. Kent, Mrs Marina Kent, Mr Andy Parkin, Mrs Wendy Wesley.

Assistant Trainer: Mrs Jane Kent

Jockey (NH): Adam Wedge. **Conditional:** Charlie Deutsch. **Amateur:** Mr Tom Broughton.

352 **MR ALAN KING, Barbury Castle**
Postal: **Barbury Castle Stables, Wroughton, Wiltshire, SN4 0QZ**
Contacts: **PHONE (01793) 815009 FAX (01793) 845080 MOBILE (07973) 461233**
E-MAIL alanking.racing@virgin.net WEBSITE www.alankingracing.co.uk

1 ADA MAY, 5, b m Black Sam Bellamy (IRE)—Sienna Sunset (IRE) **R. Bailey**
2 ALASKAN POET, 4, b g Yeats (IRE)—Takotna (IRE) **Ian Payne & Kim Franklin**
3 ANGEL FACE, 5, b m Kayf Tara—Safari Run (IRE) **Walters Plant Hire Ltd**
4 ANNACOTTY (IRE), 8, b g Beneficial—Mini Moo Min **Mrs E. A. Prowting**
5 ARALDUR (FR), 12, ch g Spadoun (FR)—Aimessa **Mr D. J. S. Sewell**
6 ARDAMIR (FR), 4, b g Deportivo—Kiss And Cry (FR) **The Dunkley & Reilly Partnership**
7 AVISPA, 7, b m Kayf Tara—Ladylliat (FR) **The Wasp Partnership**
8 AWESOME ROSIE, 5, b m Midnight Legend—
Awesome Aunt (IRE) **Mrs Meacham, Withyslade & Mrs A L Davies**
9 AZZERTI (FR), 4, b g Voix du Nord—Zalagarry (FR) **Alan King**
10 BASTIEN (FR), 5, b br g Panoramic—Que du Charmil (FR) **Alan King**
11 BETTATOGETHER, 7, b g Fair Mix (IRE)—Ella Falls (IRE) **R. Bailey**
12 BIG CHIEF BENNY (IRE), 5, ch g Beneficial—Be Airlie **Oitavos Partnership**
13 BILLY BISCUIT (IRE), 8, b g Presenting—Native Vixen (IRE) **Miss J. M. Bodycote**
14 BLACK SAM, 6, ch m Black Sam Bellamy (IRE)—Amaretto Rose **Ray Bailey, Dibbie Hues & Alan King**
15 BOARD OF TRADE, 5, ch g Black Sam Bellamy (IRE)—Realms of Gold (USA) **Ian Payne & Kim Franklin**
16 BROD NA HEIREANN (IRE), 7, b g Westerner—Diaconate (IRE) **Mr D. J. S. Sewell**

MR ALAN KING - Continued

17 **BULFIN ISLAND (IRE)**, 7, b g Milan—Tournore Court (IRE) **Alan King**
18 **BULL AND BUSH (IRE)**, 7, br m Presenting—Sound of The Crowd (IRE) **W. A. Harrison-Allan**
19 **CAHILL (IRE)**, 4, b g Lawman (FR)—Malaspina (IRE) **McNeill Family Ltd**
20 **CAJUN FIDDLE (IRE)**, 5, b m Robin des Champs (FR)—Silk Style **Mickleton Racing Club**
21 4, B c Midnight Legend—Calamintha **Mrs K. Holmes**
22 **CARRAIG MÓR (IRE)**, 8, b g Old Vic—Lynrick Lady (IRE) **Masterson Holdings Limited**
23 **CHATEZ (IRE)**, 5, b g Dandy Man (IRE)—Glory Days (GER) **Mrs P. Andrews**
24 **CHATO (FR)**, 4, ch g Malinas (GER)—Queen Bruere (FR) **Mr Richard Webb & Mr Alan King**
25 **CHOCALA (IRE)**, 6, b g Rock of Gibraltar (IRE)—Arbella **High 5**
26 **CHOSEN WELL (IRE)**, 7, b g Well Chosen—Killmaleary Cross (IRE) **Keirle, Love, Sullivan & Holmes**
27 **CLONDAW FONZ (IRE)**, 5, b g Court Cave (IRE)—Sweetasanu (IRE) **N Farrell, J Murray, J Wright & A King**
28 **COGBURN**, 4, ch g Black Sam Bellamy (IRE)—Realms of Gold (USA) **Mrs Sue Welch & Alan King**
29 **COUNTRY MADAM (IRE)**, 4, b f Medaglia d'oro (USA)—Rajeem **Mr A. R. W. Marsh**
30 **CRIQ ROCK (FR)**, 5, ch g Kap Rock (FR)—Criquetot (FR) **The Trouble Partnership**
31 **CYBELLE COLOMBE (FR)**, 4, b f Network (GER)—Sismaelle (FR) **Alan King**
32 **DAVID CRICKET**, 4, b g Shirocco (GER)—Lady Cricket (FR) **Normandie Stud Ltd**
33 **DESERT JOE (IRE)**, 10, b g Anshan—Wide Country (IRE) **Mrs E. A. Prowting**
34 **DEVIL TO PAY**, 10, b g Red Ransom (USA)—My Way (IRE) **Horace 5**
35 **DUKE OF SONNING**, 4, ch g Duke of Marmalade (IRE)—Moonshadow **McNeill Family Ltd**
36 **DUN BAY CREEK**, 5, b g Dubai Destination (USA)—Over It **Mr J. J. Murray**
37 **DUNDEE**, 8, ch g Definite Article—Gardana (FR) **T. J. Hemmings**
38 **DUSKY LEGEND**, 6, b m Midnight Legend—Tinagoodnight (FR) **Mr & Mrs R. G. Kelvin-Hughes**
39 **ELGIN**, 4, b g Duke of Marmalade (IRE)—China Tea (USA) **Elite Racing Club**
40 **ELKSTONE**, 5, b g Midnight Legend—Samandara (FR) **Miss J M Bodycote & Alan King**
41 **FIRST MOHICAN**, 8, ch g Tobougg (IRE)—Mohican Girl **W. H. Ponsonby**
42 **FORGIVING GLANCE**, 4, gr f Passing Glance—Forgiving **Mrs K. Holmes**
43 **FRED LE MACON (FR)**, 7, b g Passing Sale (FR)—Princess Leyla **Alan King & Niall Farrell**
44 **GABRIELLA ROSE**, 6, b m Kayf Tara—Elaine Tully (IRE) **The Godparents**
45 **GENSTONE TRAIL**, 10, b m Generous (USA)—Stoney Path **Mrs S. C. Welch**
46 **GIBRALFARO (IRE)**, 4, b c Dalakhani (IRE)—Ronda **McNeill Family Ltd**
47 **GILD MASTER**, 4, b g Excellent Art—Nirvana **McNeill Family Ltd**
48 **GIVE HIM A GLANCE**, 5, bl gr g Passing Glance—Giving **Mrs K. Holmes**
49 **GONE TOO FAR**, 8, b g Kayf Tara—Major Hoolihan **J. P. McManus**
50 **GRUMETI**, 8, b g Sakhee (USA)—Tetravella (IRE) **McNeill Family Ltd**
51 **HANDSOME SAM**, 5, ch g Black Sam Bellamy (IRE)—Rose Marine **Andrew Gemmell & Ron Sullivan**
52 **HEREWEGO HEREWEGO (IRE)**, 5, b g Kalanisi (IRE)—Downtown Train (IRE) **J. P. McManus**
53 **HIDDEN CARGO (IRE)**, 4, b g Stowaway—All Heart **T. D. J. Syder**
54 **HINDON ROAD (IRE)**, 9, b g Antonius Pius (USA)—Filoli Gardens **A. J. Viall**
55 **HOLLOW PENNY**, 8, b g Beat Hollow—Lomapamar **Mr D. J. S. Sewell**
56 **HURRICANE VIC**, 6, b g Mount Nelson—Fountains Abbey (USA) **The Trouble Partnership**
57 **INFORMATIONISKING (IRE)**, 5, b g Flemensfirth (USA)—Leading Lady **J. P. McManus**
58 **INNER DRIVE (IRE)**, 8, b g Heron Island (IRE)—Hingis (IRE) **McNeill Family Ltd**
59 **KAREZAK (IRE)**, 5, b g Azamour (IRE)—Karawana (IRE) **McNeill Family Ltd**
60 **KATIE TOO (IRE)**, 5, b m King's Theatre (IRE)—Shivermetimber (IRE) **Mr & Mrs C. Harris**
61 **KERROW (IRE)**, 6, b g Mahler—Olives Hall (IRE) **T. J. Hemmings**
62 **KINGS BAYONET**, 9, ch g Needwood Blade—Retaliator **W. H. Ponsonby**
63 **KIR ROYAL**, 5, ch m Lucarno (USA)—Priscilla **Jamie & Judy Magee**
64 **L'AMIRAL DAVID (FR)**, 6, b g My Risk (FR)—Mme La Vicomtesse (FR) **Mr D. J. S. Sewell**
65 **L'UNIQUE (FR)**, 7, b m Reefscape—Sans Tune (FR) **D. J. Barry**
66 **LABEL DES OBEAUX (FR)**, 5, b g Saddler Maker (IRE)—La Bessiere (FR) **David Sewell & Terry Warner**
67 **LADY PERSEPHONE (FR)**, 5, br m Sir Percy—Acenanga (GER) **All The Kings Ladies**
68 **LASER BLAZER**, 8, b g Zafeen (FR)—Sashay **Calne Engineering Ltd**
69 **LASER LIGHT**, 5, b g Kutub (IRE)—Sioux Falls (IRE) **Mr Simon Munir & Mr Isaac Souede**
70 **LETSBY AVENUE**, 8, b g Tikkanen (USA)—Peel Me A Grape **Mrs E. A. Prowting**
71 **MAGIC MUSIC MAN**, 5, b g Authorized (IRE)—Magic Music (IRE) **R. Bailey**
72 **MALAK DES MOTTES (FR)**, 6, gr g Ange Gabriel (FR)—Anareta des Mottes (FR) **J. P. McManus**
73 **MARTHA MCCANDLES**, 5, b m Tobougg (IRE)—Tabulate **Alan King**
74 **MCCABE CREEK (IRE)**, 6, b g Robin des Pres (FR)—Kick And Run (IRE) **Ian Payne & Kim Franklin**
75 **MEDINAS (FR)**, 9, b br g Malinas (GER)—Medicis (FR) **Mr & Mrs F. D. Bell**
76 **MESSIRE DES OBEAUX (FR)**, 4, b g Saddler Maker (IRE)—Madame Lys (FR) **Potensis Bloodstock Limited**
77 **MIA'S STORM (IRE)**, 6, b m September Storm (GER)—Letitia's Gain (IRE) **The Maple Street Partnership**
78 **MIDNIGHT COWBOY**, 5, gr g Midnight Legend—Kali **Mr & Mrs C. Harris**
79 **MIDNIGHT PRAYER**, 11, b g Midnight Legend—Onawing Andaprayer **The Legends Partnership**
80 **MILES TO MEMPHIS (IRE)**, 7, b g Old Vic—Phillis Hill **Mrs Lesley Field & Mr Jules Sigler**
81 **MILLE NAUTIQUE (FR)**, 5, b g Panis (USA)—Anoush (USA) **Mrs J. A. Watts**

MR ALAN KING - Continued

82 MINELLA CHARMER (IRE), 5, b g King's Theatre (IRE)—Kim Hong (IRE) **Mr D. J. S. Sewell**
83 MINELLA TREASURE (IRE), 6, b g King's Theatre (IRE)—Ringzar (IRE) **Mr D. J. S. Sewell**
84 MIRKAT, 6, b g Kalanisi (IRE)—Miracle **Bellamy, Burke, Hannigan & Harding**
85 MISS CRICK, 5, b m Midnight Legend—Kwaheri **Mr D. J. S. Sewell**
86 MISS MINX, 5, b m Tobougg (IRE)—Victory Flip (IRE) **Mr E. T. D. Leadbeater**
87 MONTBAZON (FR), 9, b br g Alberto Giacometti (IRE)—Duchesse Pierji (FR) **Mr D. J. S. Sewell**
88 MY KHALEESI, 5, b m Kayf Tara—Katess (IRE) **Mrs M. C. Sweeney**
89 MYSTERY CODE, 4, b f Tobougg (IRE)—Mystery Lot (IRE) **The Barbury Lions**
90 NED STARK (IRE), 8, b g Wolfe Tone (IRE)—Last Moon (IRE) **The Dunkley & Reilly Partnership**
91 OCEANE (FR), 4, b g Kentucky Dynamite (USA)—Zahrana (FR) **McNeill Family Ltd**
92 ORDO AB CHAO (IRE), 7, b g Heron Island (IRE)—Houldyurwhist (IRE) **Mr A. R. W. Marsh**
93 PADDYS RUNNER, 4, gr g Sir Percy—Frosty Welcome (USA) **Let's Live Racing**
94 PANTXOA (FR), 9, b g Daliapour (IRE)—Palmeria (IRE) **Mrs J. A. Watts**
95 PASSMORE, 4, b f Passing Glance—Call Me A Legend **J. P. McManus**
96 PEMBA (FR), 4, ch f Zanzibari (USA)—Ayaam (IRE) **Million in Mind Partnership**
97 PHANTOM RIVER, 4, b f Observatory (USA)—Madam'x **Alan King**
98 PRECISION FIVE, 7, b m Proclamation (IRE)—Sashay **Calne Engineering Ltd**
99 PRESENTING LISA (IRE), 7, b m Presenting—Miss Esther (GER) **Mrs E. A. Prowting**
100 RENKO, 4, b g Archipenko (USA)—Park Law (IRE) **Mondial Racing & Robert Haim**
101 RIDGEWAY STORM (IRE), 6, b g Hurricane Run (IRE)—Hesperia **W. H. Ponsonby**
102 ROBERTO PEGASUS (USA), 10, b br g Fusaichi Pegasus (USA)—
  Louju (USA) **Mrs P Andrews, I Payne & Ms K Franklin**
103 ROYAL PLAZA, 5, b g King's Theatre (IRE)—Friendly Craic (IRE) **Mrs Lesley Field & Mr Jules Sigler**
104 SALMANAZAR, 8, b g Classic Cliche (IRE)—Leroy's Sister (FR) **Top Brass Partnership**
105 SCEAU ROYAL (FR), 4, b g Doctor Dino (FR)—Sandside (FR) **Mr Simon Munir & Mr Isaac Souede**
106 SEGO SUCCESS (IRE), 8, b g Beneficial—The West Road (IRE) **Mr E. T. D. Leadbeater**
107 SHADARPOUR (IRE), 7, b g Dr Fong (USA)—Shamadara (IRE) **ARC Racing Syndicates**
108 SIMPLY A LEGEND, 7, b g Midnight Legend—Disco Danehill (USA) **Mrs E. A. Prowting**
109 SIR ANTONY BROWNE, 4, ch g Black Sam Bellamy (IRE)—Shayaza **Incipe Partnership**
110 SKELETON BOB (IRE), 4, b c Getaway (GER)—Bay Rebel (IRE) **S. M. Smith**
111 SMAD PLACE (FR), 9, gr g Smadoun (FR)—Bienna Star (FR) **Mrs P. Andrews**
112 SMART MOTIVE, 6, b g Motivator—Santana Lady (IRE) **Mrs C. Skan**
113 SPELLBOUND, 7, b m Doyen (IRE)—Kasamba **Withyslade**
114 STONEY'S TREASURE, 12, ch g Silver Patriarch (IRE)—Stoney Path **Mrs Sue Welch & Alan King**
115 TANGLEY, 4, b f Black Sam Bellamy (IRE)—All Rise (GER) **Alan King**
116 TARA VIEW, 5, b m Kayf Tara—Temptation (FR) **D. J. Barry**
117 TED'S LAD, 6, b g Kayf Tara—Stravsea **Mr E. T. D. Leadbeater**
118 THE BARBURY QUEEN, 6, br m Milan—Royal Shares (IRE) **W. H. Ponsonby**
119 THE MUMPER (IRE), 9, b g Craigsteel—Na Moilltear (IRE) **The Weighed In Partnership**
120 THE TOURAD MAN (IRE), 10, b g Shantou (USA)—Small Iron **Mr & Mrs F Bell,N Farrell, A Marsh**
121 THE UNIT (IRE), 5, b g Gold Well—Sovana (FR) **International Plywood (Importers) Ltd**
122 THOMAS SHELBY (IRE), 5, b g Witness Box (USA)—Deemiss (IRE) **McNeill Family & A King**
123 TICKITY BLEUE, 8, gr m Tikkanen (USA)—Cerise Bleue (FR) **Let's Live Racing**
124 TOO FAR GONE (IRE), 5, br g Jeremy (USA)—Rockahoolababy (IRE) **N. S. G. Bunter**
125 TRAVERTINE (IRE), 6, b g Danehill Dancer (IRE)—Mer de Corail (IRE) **J. P. McManus**
126 TURN OVER SIVOLA (FR), 9, b g Assessor (IRE)—Notting Hill (FR) **International Plywood (Importers) Ltd**
127 ULZANA'S RAID (IRE), 7, ch g Bach (IRE)—Peace Time Beauty (IRE) **T. Barr**
128 UXIZANDRE (FR), 8, ch g Fragrant Mix (IRE)—Jolisandre (FR) **J. P. McManus**
129 VALDEZ, 9, ch g Doyen (IRE)—Skew **Riverdee Stable**
130 4, Ch g Kier Park (IRE)—Waheeba **Withyslade**
131 WHO DARES WINS (IRE), 4, b g Jeremy (USA)—Savignano **W. H. Ponsonby**
132 WILDE BLUE YONDER (IRE), 7, b g Oscar (IRE)—Blue Gallery (IRE) **Maybe Only Fools Have Horses**
133 WILLIAM H BONNEY, 5, b g Midnight Legend—Calamintha (IRE) **Mr & Mrs R. Scott**
134 WILLIAM HUNTER, 4, b g Mawatheeq (USA)—Cosmea **Incipe Partnership**
135 WILLOUGHBY HEDGE, 9, b g King's Theatre (IRE)—Mini Mandy **T. J. Hemmings**
136 WINNER MASSAGOT (FR), 5, ch g Muhaymin (USA)—Winnor (FR) **Masterson Holdings Limited**
137 WINTER ESCAPE (IRE), 5, b g Robin des Pres (FR)—Saddleeruppat (IRE) **J. P. McManus**
138 WISHING AND HOPING (IRE), 6, b g Beneficial—Desperately Hoping (IRE) **Mrs P. Andrews**
139 YANWORTH, 6, ch g Norse Dancer (USA)—Yota (FR) **J. P. McManus**
140 ZIGA BOY (FR), 7, gr g Califet (FR)—Our Ziga (FR) **Axom Li**
141 ZIPPLE BACK (IRE), 4, b g Sendawar (IRE)—With Conviction (IRE) **Potensis Bloodstock Limited**

THREE-YEAR-OLDS

142 BURGUILLOS, ch c Lope de Vega (IRE)—Hazy Dancer **Hunscote Stud**
143 CELESTRA, b f Doyen (IRE)—Triple Cee (IRE) **Barbury Castle Stud**

MR ALAN KING - Continued

144 **COSMEAPOLITAN,** b g Mawatheeq (USA)—Cosmea **Barbury Castle Stud**
145 **EASY EASY,** ch g Rip Van Winkle (IRE)—Nizza (GER) **McNeill Family Ltd**
146 **GIVEAWAY GLANCE,** br f Passing Glance—Giving **Mrs K. Holmes**
147 **HARDINGTON,** b c Fastnet Rock (AUS)—La Cucina (IRE) **The Fastnet Partnership**
148 **INN THE BULL (GER),** ch g Lope de Vega (IRE)—Ile Rousse **McNeill Family Ltd**
149 **INVOCATION (FR),** b or c Intense Focus (USA)—Fabiola (GER) **Mr Simon Munir & Mr Isaac Souede**
150 **JIM DANDY,** ch g Dandy Man (IRE)—Noctilucent (JPN) **The Barbury Lions**
151 **MASTER BLUEYES (IRE),** gr g Mastercraftsman (IRE)—Miss Blueyes (IRE) **The Barbury Lions**
152 **PRIMITIVO,** b g Excellent Art—Dolcetto (IRE) **Farrell, Field, King & Mellor**
153 **RAINBOW DREAMER,** b c Aqlaam—Zamhrear **The Maple Street Partnership**
154 **SIR VALENTINE (GER),** b c Cacique (IRE)—Singuna (GER) **Walters Plant Hire & James & Jean Potter**
155 **THE OTMOOR POET,** b g Yeats (IRE)—Kristalette (IRE) **M. J. Tuckey**
156 **TYRELL (IRE),** b g Teofilo (IRE)—Sleeveless (USA) **Apple Tree Stud**

Other Owners: Mr D. J. Anderson, Ms C. S. Antell, Axom Ltd, M. Ball, Mrs H. L. Bell, Mr F. D. Bell, D. Bellamy, Mr R. J. Benton, J. Bernstein, Mr R. A. Bevan, Mr R. G. Beville, Mr D. Bickerton, Mark A. Blackwell, Mr David Bond, A. R. Bromley, D. J. Burke, Miss A. J. Burr, Mr R. J. Caddick, Ms C. L. Calver, Mrs D. C. Casey-McCarthy, Mr J. H. Chester, Mr S. Clancy, J. L. Clarke, Mr N. Clyne, Mr J. B. Cohen, Mr P. G. Cooke, R. Cressey, Mrs A. L. Davies, Mr D. Downie, Mrs D. Dunkley, P. J. Dunkley, A. T. Eggleton, N. Farrell, Mrs L. H. Field, Mr A. J. Fletcher, L. R. Frampton, R. B. Francis, Miss K. M. Franklin, S. G. Friend, M. A. Gemmell, Miss S. Gill, Mr P. M. Goldsmith, G. F. Goode, Miss C. A. Green, Mr M. Grier, Mr J. S. Gutkin, R. Haim, Mr A. J. Hannigan, P. R. Harding, R. V. Harding, Mrs C. A. Harris, Mr C. I. K. Harris, Mr D. A. Heffer, Mr A. J. Hill, D. F. Hill, Mr S. C. Hillman, J. Holmes, Mr A. Horne, Mrs D. J. Hues, D. Humphreys, Mr A. Humphreys, Mr J. Jenner, Mr J. Johnson, G. F. Keirle, R. G. Kelvin-Hughes, Mrs E. A. Kelvin-Hughes, Mrs R. J. King, Miss E. A. Lake, Mr W. P. Ledward, R. M. Levitt, S. Love, Mrs J Magee, Mr J. Magee, Mrs S. M. Maine, Mrs G. Meacham, Mr T. K. Mellor, Mr I. D. Miller, W. D. C. Minton, S. E. Munir, Mrs D. C. Nicholson, Miss M. Noden, Mr P. Patel, Mr I. T. Payne, Miss H. Pease, Mrs J. Plumptre, Mrs M. J. Potter, Mr R. M. Potter, J. E. Potter, Mrs J. Prince, Mrs G. E. Purkiss-Miles, D. F. Reilly, J. P. L. Reynolds, Mr S. J. Rogers, Mrs P. M. Scott, R. Scott, J. Sigler, Mrs L. A. Smith, Mr I. Souede, Mrs K. Stephens, Mr R. T. Sullivan, Mr J. A. Tabet, Mrs M. G. Thomas, Mrs C. Townroe, Mrs K. J. Tudor, Mr J. Turner, Mr D. Underwood, J. T. Warner, Mr R. A. Webb, Mr J. J. Webster, Mr T. M. Welsh, Mr T. N. White, Mr T. Withers, Mr F. R. Woodward, J. Wright.

Assistant Trainers: Oliver Wardle, Dan Horsford

Jockey (NH): Wayne Hutchinson. **Conditional:** Tom Bellamy, Jamie Insole. **Amateur:** Mr Danny Burton, Mr Lewis Ferguson, Mr Harry Teal.

353

MR NEIL KING, Wroughton
Postal: Ridgeway Racing Ltd, Upperherdswick Farm, Barbury Castle, Wroughton, Wiltshire, SN4 0QH
Contacts: PHONE (01793) 845011 FAX (01793) 845011 MOBILE (07880) 702325
E-MAIL neil@neil-king.co.uk WEBSITE www.neil-king.co.uk

1 **ASHBRITTLE,** 9, b g Rainbow Quest (USA)—Caesarea (GER) **J. L. Rowsell**
2 **BIG MEADOW (IRE),** 5, br g Marienbard (IRE)—Lakyle Lady (IRE) **Mr P. M. H. Beadles**
3 **CICERON (IRE),** 10, b g Pivotal—Aiglonne (USA) **Mr M. Secretan**
4 **CONSORTIUM (IRE),** 4, b g Teofilo (IRE)—Wish List (IRE) **Govier & Brown & Neil King**
5 **DELGANY DEMON,** 8, b g Kayf Tara—Little Twig (IRE) **C. M. Wilson**
6 **ELYSIAN PRINCE,** 5, b g Champs Elysees—Trinkila (USA) **Mr D. S. Lee**
7 **EPIC ETHEL,** 5, b m Midnight Legend—Violet Elizabeth **Mark&Tracy Harrod, T Brown,Doug,James,Gaz**
8 **EXMOOR CHALLENGE,** 7, b g Thank Heavens—Bullys Maid **Mrs D. Bullard**
9 **GOLDEN THREAD,** 6, ch g Singspiel (IRE)—Alpenrot (IRE) **Mrs V. D. Neale**
10 **HERDSWICK HOLLOA (IRE),** 5, ch g Marienbard (IRE)—Cash A Lawn (IRE) **Mr Ken Lawrence & Mr Neil King**
11 **HOLBROOK PARK,** 6, b g Midnight Legend—Viciana **Mrs B. M. Chamberlain**
12 **INFINITYANDBEYOND (IRE),** 5, gr g Medaaly—Ten Dollar Bill (IRE) **Mrs H. M. Buckle**
13 **KELTIC RHYTHM (IRE),** 9, b g Milan—Ballinaroone Girl (IRE) **Stephen Lower Insurance Services Limited**
14 **LIL ROCKERFELLER (USA),** 5, ch g Hard Spun (USA)—Layounne (USA) **Davies Smith Govier & Brown**
15 **LITTLE WINDMILL (IRE),** 6, ch g Mahler—Ennismore Queen (IRE) **Barry Williams & Donald Caldwell**
16 **MASTER RAJEEM (USA),** 7, b br g Street Cry (IRE)—Rajeem **Barry Williams & Donald Caldwell**
17 **MERCERS COURT (IRE),** 8, b g Court Cave (IRE)—
Vikki's Dream (IRE) **David Nott, Ken Lawrence, Tim Messom**
18 **MILANSBAR (IRE),** 9, b g Milan—Ardenbar **Mr R. N. Bothway**
19 **MINNIE MILAN (IRE),** 7, b m Milan—Shiminnie (IRE) **Mark & Tracy Harrod,P Branigan,T Messom**
20 **OH LAND ABLOOM (IRE),** 6, b g King's Theatre (IRE)—Talinas Rose (IRE) **Reefer Distribution Services Ltd**
21 **OLD FASHION,** 4, b f Shirocco (GER)—Oriental Dance **B Smith, K Lawrence, P Branigan & J Davies**
22 **PRINCETON ROYALE (IRE),** 7, br g Royal Anthem (USA)—Shelikesitsstraight (IRE) **D Nott, P Beadles, R Clarke**
23 **QUINCY MAGOO (IRE),** 7, ch g Mountain High (IRE)—Vicky's Lodge (IRE) **Mark & Tracy Harrod**

MR NEIL KING - Continued

24 **RAVENS BROOK (IRE)**, 10, br g Alderbrook—Triple Triumph (IRE) **The Ridgeway Racing For Fun Partnership**
25 **REGULATION (IRE)**, 7, br g Danehill Dancer (IRE)—Source of Life (IRE) **Amber Road Partnership**
26 **ROMANEE VIVANT**, 6, b m Multiplex—Mrs Oh (IRE) **Ms R. L. Fradley**
27 **SAFFRON WELLS (IRE)**, 8, b g Saffron Walden (FR)—Angel's Folly **Mark Harrod & Peter Beadles**
28 **STEELING DOLLARS (IRE)**, 4, b f Craigsteel—Ten Dollar Bill (IRE) **JeeVeePee**
29 **THE BOSS'S DREAM (IRE)**, 8, b g Luso—Mrs Kick (IRE) **SLIS Ltd, Mr M Gibbons & Mr D Nott**
30 **TOM HALL**, 6, b g Pastoral Pursuits—Villarosi (IRE) **Hunter Racing**
31 **TOWN MOUSE**, 6, ch g Sakhee (USA)—Megdale (IRE) **Mr Brian Bell & Mr John Smith**
32 **UNBUCKLED (IRE)**, 6, b m Presenting—Una Kasala (GER) **Mrs H. M. Buckle**
33 **YOU SAY WHAT (IRE)**, 6, b g Milan—Wave Rack (IRE) **Turner Webb**
34 **ZEROESHADESOFGREY (IRE)**, 7, gr g Portrait Gallery—Hazy Rose (IRE) **Mrs H. M. Buckle**

Other Owners: Mr B. Bell, Mr P. A. Branigan, G. S. Brown, Mr T. Brown, Mr D. R. Caldwell, Mr N. J. Catterwell, Mr R. Clarke, Mr J. A. B. Currie, J. Davies, Mr A. Douglas, Mr M. H. Gibbons, Mr P. F. Govier, Mr P. Govier, Mrs T. Harrod, Mr M. Harrod, Mr R. Hunter, Mrs K. Hunter, Mr D. Jee, N. King, Mr K. Lawrence, Mr G. Loughlin, Mr T. J. Messom, Mr G. P. Milburn, D. F. Nott, Mr J. W. Preuninger, Mr J. H. Smith, R. W. Smith, Mr A. J. Smith, Mr P. Turner, Mrs L. Webb, Mr B. M. V. Williams.

Head Lad: Mark Rowlands. **Racing Secretary:** Amy Clapham

Jockey (flat): Martin Lane, Liam Jones, Adam Kirby, Tom Queally. **Jockey (NH):** Trevor Whelan, Mark Grant, Richard Johnson, Jamie Moore, Jack Quinlan, Harry Skelton. **Conditional:** Bridget Andrews, Lizzie Kelly. **Amateur:** Miss Kate Gowing.

---

354 MR WILLIAM KINSEY, Ashton
Postal: **R Kinsey Partnership, Peel Hall, Gongar Lane, Ashton, Chester**
Contacts: PHONE (01829) 751230 MOBILE (07803) 753719
E-MAIL will@kinseyracing.co.uk WEBSITE www.kinseyracing.co.uk

1 **ALLBARNONE**, 8, b g Alflora (IRE)—What A Gem **Girls Are Loud**
2 **ALPHA VICTOR (IRE)**, 11, b g Old Vic—Harvest View (IRE) **Denton,Kinsey,Osborne Hse,Wesley-Yates**
3 **DUNCOMPLAINING (IRE)**, 7, b g Milan—Notcomplainingbut (IRE) **D. Wesley-Yates**
4 **FUTURE SECURITY (IRE)**, 7, ch g Dalakhani (IRE)—Schust Madame (IRE) **Nobaj & John Naylor**
5 **LEAVING LAS VEGAS**, 5, b g Layman (USA)—Woven Silk (USA) **The Gentlemen Farmers**
6 **PREMIER SAGAS (FR)**, 12, b g Sagacity (FR)—Estampe (FR) **Mrs T R Kinsey & Mr P Jones**
7 **ROAD TO ROME (IRE)**, 6, b g Choisir (AUS)—Tibbie **The Missing Link**
8 **SHOULDAVBOUGHTGOLD (IRE)**, 9, b g Classic Cliche (IRE)—Sancta Miria (IRE) **The Missing Link**
9 **WHENSKIESAREBLUE (IRE)**, 5, b m Presenting—Blue Gallery (IRE) **The Steam Powered Syndicate**

Other Owners: Mr C. B. Denton, Mr T. B. Denton, Mr P. A. Jones, Mrs J. Kinsey, Mr W. R. Kinsey, Mr J. P. Naylor, Nobaj Ltd, Osborne House Ltd.

---

355 MR PHILIP KIRBY, Richmond
Postal: **Green Oaks Farm, East Appleton, Richmond, North Yorkshire, DL10 7QE**
Contacts: MOBILE (07984) 403558
E-MAIL sharphillowners@gmail.com WEBSITE www.philipkirbyracing.co.uk

1 **AGGLESTONE ROCK**, 11, b g Josr Algarhoud (IRE)—Royalty (IRE) **Geoff & Pam Kirby**
2 **ANIKNAM (FR)**, 6, b g Nickname (FR)—Kelle Home (FR) **Nobaj Ltd**
3 **ARCO (IRE)**, 5, b m Flemensfirth (USA)—Babygotback (IRE) **K. L. Foster**
4 **BIRTHDAY GUEST (GER)**, 7, ch g Areion (GER)—Birthday Spectrum (GER) **Nobaj Ltd**
5 **BITUMEN BELLE (IRE)**, 4, b f Oscar (IRE)—Midnight Pond (IRE) **Well Oiled Partnership**
6 **BOLD HENMIE (IRE)**, 5, b g Henrythenavigator (USA)—Seminole Lass (USA) **Faye Stephenson & Ben Lapham**
7 **BRUCE ALMIGHTY (IRE)**, 5, b g Yeats (IRE)—Lady Rolfe (IRE) **Mr A. D. Bradshaw**
8 **CALL IT ON (IRE)**, 10, ch g Raise A Grand (IRE)—Birthday Present **The Green Oaks Partnership**
9 **CAVALIERI (IRE)**, 6, b g Oratorio (IRE)—Always Attractive (IRE) **The Cavalieri Partnership**
10 **CHLOE'S IMAGE**, 6, b m Lucky Story (USA)—Iwunder (IRE) **Mrs Philippa Kirby**
11 **CITY DREAMS (IRE)**, 6, b m Rakti—Attymon Lill (IRE) **B. Dunn**
12 **CLEVE COTTAGE**, 8, ch g Presenting—Reverse Swing **Mr D. J. Phillips**
13 **COURTOWN OSCAR (IRE)**, 7, b g Oscar (IRE)—Courtown Bowe Vll **Nobaj Ltd**
14 **EASTVIEW BOY**, 5, ch g Iktibas—Eastview Princess **Eastview Thoroughbreds**
15 **EPISODE**, 5, b g Lucky Story (USA)—Epicurean **Ontoawinner & Friends**
16 **FACTOR FIFTY (IRE)**, 7, b g Definite Article—Sun Screen **TopSpec Partnership**

MR PHILIP KIRBY - Continued

17 **FULL SPEED (GER)**, 11, b g Sholokhov (IRE)—Flagny (FR) **L & D Interiors Ltd**
18 **GOLDAN JESS (IRE)**, 12, b g Golan (IRE)—Bendis (GER) **The Jessies,Colin Fletcher,Brian Cobbett**
19 **HUGH'S SECRET (IRE)**, 4, b g Yeats (IRE)—Walkyrie (FR) **Mr A. D. Bradshaw**
20 **IFTIKAAR (IRE)**, 6, b g Cape Cross (IRE)—Anbella (FR) **Mrs J. Sivills**
21 **IMPROVED (IRE)**, 6, ch g Rainwatch—Show Potential (IRE) **John Birtles & P Kirby**
22 **KEEP UP (GER)**, 4, b g Monsun (GER)—Katy Carr **Colin Fletcher & P Kirby**
23 **KINGS GREY (IRE)**, 12, gr g King's Theatre (IRE)—Grey Mo (IRE) **Kings Grey Partnership**
24 **KIWAYU**, 7, b g Medicean—Kibara **Mrs Jayne Sivills**
25 **LADY BUTTONS**, 6, b m Beneficial—Lady Chapp (IRE) **Mrs Jayne Sivills**
26 **LADY WESTERNER**, 4, b f Westerner—Lady Chapp (IRE) **Mrs Jayne Sivills**
27 **LEXINGTON BAY (IRE)**, 8, b g High Chaparral (IRE)—Schust Madame (IRE) **The Gathering & The Gathered**
28 **LITTLE BRUCE (IRE)**, 4, b g Yeats (IRE)—Lady Rolfe (IRE) **Mr A. D. Bradshaw**
29 **MAC TIERNAN (IRE)**, 9, b g Minashki (IRE)—Softly Softly (IRE) **Faye Stephenson & Ben Lapham**
30 **MAN IN BLACK (FR)**, 7, gr g Turgeon (USA)—Mimosa de Wasa (FR) **Nobaj Ltd**
31 **MOSCOW PRESENTS (IRE)**, 8, b g Presenting—Moscow Madame (IRE) **Nobaj & Tony Sadler**
32 **MOSHE (IRE)**, 5, b g Dansili—Rosinka (IRE) **Mr & Mrs G. Capstick**
33 **NAUTICAL NITWIT (IRE)**, 7, b g Let The Lion Roar—Mrs Pugwash (IRE) **The Birrafun Partnership I**
34 **NEXT EDITION (IRE)**, 8, b g Antonius Pius (USA)—Starfish (IRE) **The Dibble Bridge Partnership**
35 **PASS MUSTER (IRE)**, 9, b g Theatrical—Morning Pride (IRE) **Mr P. Kirby**
36 **PERENNIAL**, 7, ch g Motivator—Arum Lily (USA) **Ace Bloodstock & The Gathered**
37 **PLATINUM (IRE)**, 9, b g Azamour (IRE)—Dazzling Park (IRE) **Mrs Philippa Kirby**
38 **QUADRIGA (IRE)**, 6, b g Acclamation—Turning Light (GER) **The Batham Boys**
39 **ROCKY TWO (IRE)**, 6, ch g Rock of Gibraltar (IRE)—Toorah Laura La (USA) **Mr A. S. Taylor**
40 **RUMBLE OF THUNDER (IRE)**, 10, b g Fath (USA)—Honey Storm (IRE) **The Well Oiled Partnership**
41 **SAKHEE'S CITY (FR)**, 5, b g Sakhee (USA)—A Lulu Ofa Menifee (USA) **Mrs J. Sivills**
42 **SPLASH OF VERVE (IRE)**, 4, b g Fast Company (IRE)—Ellistown Lady (IRE) **Faye Stephenson & Ben Lapham**
43 **SUGGESTION**, 4, gr g Dansili—Jibboom (USA) **Ian Nicol**
44 **TARA TIME**, 5, b m Kayf Tara—Prophets Honor (FR) **The Philip Kirby Racing Partnership**
45 **TRANSIENT BAY (IRE)**, 6, b g Trans Island—Boarding Pass (IRE) **The Waking Ned Partnership**
46 **TRIPLE EIGHT (IRE)**, 8, b g Royal Applause—Hidden Charm (IRE) **RedHotGardogs**
47 **ULLSWATER (IRE)**, 8, b g Singspiel (IRE)—Uluwatu (IRE) **Mrs C. Orton**
48 **UP THE BEES**, 6, b g Kayf Tara—West River (USA) **Colin German**
49 **WEMYSS POINT**, 4, b g Champs Elysees—Wemyss Bay **Mr P. Kirby**
50 **WHITCHURCH**, 4, b g Mawatheeq (USA)—Silvereine (FR) **The Turf N' Surf Racing Partnership**

THREE-YEAR-OLDS

51 B f Flying Legend (USA)—Lady Chapp (IRE) **Mrs Jayne Sivills**
52 **MR CHUCKLES (IRE)**, b c Arcano (IRE)—Caribbean Escape **Brian Dunn & Judith Darling**
53 **RAJAPUR**, gr g Dalakhani (IRE)—A Beautiful Mind (GER) **Faye Stephenson & Ben Lapham**
54 **REGAL MONARCH**, b g Notnowcato—Regal Fairy (IRE) **East Layton Stud**
55 B f Native Ruler—Royalty (IRE) **Mr P. Kirby**
56 B c Archipenko (USA)—Sparkling Clear **Castleton Bloodstock**

TWO-YEAR-OLDS

57 **DARES TO DREAM (IRE)**, br f 15/3 Beneficial—
Miss McGoldrick (IRE) (Kasakov) (6643) **Ashley & Sue Clark & Malcolm Long**
58 **ENLIGHTEN ME (IRE)**, b f 3/3 Sir Prancealot (IRE)—Tea Chest (IRE) (In The Wings) **Shades of Grey Partnership**
59 B f 7/5 Equiano (FR)—Hula Ballew (Weldnaas (USA)) **The Jessies**
60 B f 5/3 Aqlaam—Rosewood Belle (USA) (Woodman (USA)) (5000) **Mr P. Kirby**
61 Ch f 25/4 Arcano (IRE)—Seminole Lass (USA) (Indian Charlie (USA)) **Castleton Bloodstock**
62 B f 3/3 Equiano (FR)—Still Small Voice (Polish Precedent (USA)) **Castleton Bloodstock**

Other Owners: Ace Bloodstock Ltd, Mr J. Bell, Mr John Birtles, Mr Steve Bocking, Mr R. G. Capstick, Mr Ashley Clark, Mrs Sue Clark, Mr Brian Connolly, Mr K. J. Corcoran, Mr Alan Davies, Mr B. Dunn, Mr C. Fletcher, Mr R. Hamilton, Mr John Hanson, Mr W. Hayler, Mr P. A. Kilpatrick, Mrs Philippa Kirby, Mr B. Lapham, Mr Mick Mahon, Mr David Marshall, Mr A. Pierce, Mr Hugh T. Redhead, Mr Andrew J. Roberts, Mr Tony Sadler, Mr J. Stent, Miss Faye Stephenson, Mr M. C. P. Suddards, Mr Les Waugh, Mr C. E. Weare, Mr Simon J. Wyatt.

Assistant Trainer: Simon Olley

Jockey (NH): Adam Nicol, James Reveley. **Apprentice:** Ross Turner. **Amateur:** Miss Julie Heneghan.

356 MR SYLVESTER KIRK, Upper Lambourn

Postal: Cedar Lodge Stables, Upper Lambourn, Hungerford, Berkshire, RG17 8QT
Contacts: **PHONE (01488) 73215 FAX (01488) 670012 MOBILE (07768) 855261**
E-MAIL info@sylvesterkirkracing.co.uk WEBSITE www.sylvesterkirkracing.co.uk

1 **CELESTIAL BAY**, 7, b m Septieme Ciel (USA)—Snowy Mantle **Homebred Racing**
2 **CHARLES CAMOIN (IRE)**, 8, b g Peintre Celebre (USA)—Birthday (IRE) **Mr C Wright, Hon Mrs J M Corbett**
3 **CRITICAL SPEED**, 4, ch f Pivotal—Speed Cop **Mr J. C. Smith**
4 **DELAGOA BAY (IRE)**, 8, b m Encosta de Lago (AUS)—Amory (GER) **Homebred Racing**
5 **DIAMOND SAM**, 4, ch g Compton Place—Kurtanella **Mrs Philip Snow & Partners**
6 **GOLD PRINCE (IRE)**, 4, b c Nayef (USA)—Premier Prize **Mr J. C. Smith**
7 **JOLIE DE VIVRE (IRE)**, 4, b f Thewayyouare (USA)—Jolie Clara (FR) **Dr B. Matalon & Mr I. Wight**
8 **MAGICAL DAZE**, 4, b f Showcasing—Poulaine Bleue **Mr T. Pearson**
9 **MAYMYO (IRE)**, 5, b b Invincible Spirit (IRE)—Lady Windermere (IRE) **Mr H. Balasuriya**
10 **MOUNTAIN MUSIC**, 4, b f Three Valleys (USA)—Meadow Floss **Mr D. J. Huelin**
11 **PACOLITA (IRE)**, 4, ch f Paco Boy (IRE)—Clara (IRE) **Mr G Dolan & Mr P Wheatley**
12 **PERCY VEER**, 4, ch g Sir Percy—Fandangerina **Mr M Crow**
13 **PINK RIBBON (IRE)**, 4, gr c Dark Angel (IRE)—My Funny Valentine (IRE) **Mrs M. Cousins**
14 **SEE AND BE SEEN**, 6, b g Sakhee's Secret—Anthea **Mr T. Pearson**

THREE-YEAR-OLDS

15 **CALYPSO CHOIR**, ch f Bahamian Bounty—Heavenly Song (IRE) **Mr J. C. Smith**
16 **DREAM DESTINATION (IRE)**, b c Showcasing—Never Let You Down (IRE) **Malih L. Al Basti**
17 **DREAM DUBAI**, b c Kyllachy—Welsh Anthem **Malih L. Al Basti**
18 **GAWDAWPALIN (IRE)**, b c Holy Roman Emperor (IRE)—Dirtybirdie **Mr H. Balasuriya**
19 **HARMONY BAY (IRE)**, b f Fast Company (IRE)—Consensus (IRE) **Mr M Nicolson & Mr A Wilson**
20 **HEREWARD THE WAKE**, gr c Fastnet Rock (AUS)—
                              Miss Universe (IRE) **The Hon Mrs J. M. Corbett & Mr C. Wright**
21 **ICE CRISTAL (IRE)**, ch f Frozen Power (IRE)—Cristalita (IRE) **Mrs J. Challen & Partner**
22 **INDIE MUSIC**, ch f Sakhee's Secret—Indiana Blues **Mr J. C. Smith**
23 **MR MARCHWOOD**, gr c Medicean—Crocus Rose **Marchwood Aggregates**
24 **NORSE MAGIC**, b f Norse Dancer (IRE)—Gift of Love (IRE) **Mr J. C. Smith**
25 **PROTEST (IRE)**, b c Fastnet Rock (AUS)—Phrase **Mr N. Pickett**
26 **RIPOLL (IRE)**, b c Alfred Nobel (IRE)—Lahu Lady **Mr D Harding and Mr C Conroy**
27 **SPINNERS BALL (IRE)**, b c Excellent Art—Meek Appeal (USA) **Mr E. McCay**
28 **TESSELLATE (IRE)**, b f Acclamation—Sterope (FR) **Mr N. Simpson**
29 **WINGED DANCER**, b c Norse Dancer (IRE)—Winged Diva (IRE) **Mr J. C. Smith**

TWO-YEAR-OLDS

30 Ch c 22/4 Paco Boy (IRE)—Barawin (IRE) (Hawk Wing (USA)) (18000) **Mr Richard Hannon**
31 B f 20/3 Mastercraftsman (IRE)—Corrozal (GER) (Cape Cross (IRE)) (23000) **Mrs B Facchino**
32 Br c 5/3 Dark Angel (IRE)—Cross Section (USA) (Cape Cross (IRE)) (40000) **Malih L. Al Basti**
33 B f 16/5 Holy Roman Emperor (IRE)—Daraliya (IRE) (Kahyasi) (14765) **Mrs B Facchino**
34 B f 18/2 High Chaparral (IRE)—Dimelight (Fantastic Light (USA)) **Mr J. C. Smith**
35 B c 23/4 Kyllachy—Fly Free (Halling (USA)) (30000) **Malih L. Al Basti**
36 B c 27/4 Canford Cliffs (IRE)—Gali Gal (IRE) (Galileo (IRE)) (62753) **Mr H. Balasuriya**
37 B f 16/4 Holy Roman Emperor (IRE)—Interchange (IRE) (Montjeu (IRE)) (48000) **Mr Fergus Anstock**
38 B c 26/3 Bahamian Bounty—Kampai (Sakhee (USA)) (12380) **Mr T Lock**
39 **LATEST QUEST (IRE)**, b c 8/4 Zebedee—Fancy Theory (USA) (Quest For Fame) (18000) **Mr & Mrs R Gander**
40 Ch c 11/4 Sakhee's Secret—Lochangel (Night Shift (USA)) **Mr J. C. Smith**
41 Gr c 6/3 Royal Applause—Mujdeya (Linamix (FR)) (20671)
42 Ch c 9/5 Zamindar (USA)—Opera Dancer (Norse Dancer (IRE)) **Mr J. C. Smith**
43 **PEACE TRAIN**, b f 23/4 Bahamian Bounty—Tamara (Marju (IRE)) **Malih L. Al Basti**
44 B c 25/4 Rip Van Winkle (IRE)—Phrase (Royal Anthem (USA)) (20000) **Deauville Daze**
45 B c 17/4 Power—Pitrizzia (Lando (GER)) (20671)
46 Gr c 12/2 Dark Angel (IRE)—Ride For Roses (IRE) (Barathea (IRE)) (60000) **Malih L. Al Basti**
47 B f 24/4 Delegator—Rock Candy (IRE) (Rock of Gibraltar (IRE)) (4761) **Mr T Hayes & Partner**
48 **SIMMIE (IRE)**, b f 22/4 Fast Company (IRE)—Kathy Sun (IRE) (Intikhab (USA)) (3500) **Mr N. Simpson**
49 Ch c 7/3 Mastercraftsman (IRE)—Snoqualmie Star (Galileo (IRE)) **Mr J. C. Smith**
50 **SPRINGBOURNE**, b g 12/3 Hellvelyn—Musical Key (Key of Luck (USA)) (3809) **Mr B. Ansell**
51 B c 14/2 Acclamation—Starlight Smile (USA) (Green Desert (USA)) (80000) **Alison Jones**
52 B c 10/4 Harbour Watch (IRE)—Stoneacre Sarah (Cadeaux Genereux) (19047) **Mrs C. Murphy**
53 B g 10/2 Kheleyf (USA)—Wood Chorus (Singspiel (IRE)) (3000) **Lady O'Brien**

Assistant Trainer: Fanny Kirk

357 MR STUART KITTOW, Cullompton

Postal: **Haynefield Farm, Blackborough, Cullompton, Devon, EX15 2JD**
Contacts: HOME (01823) 680183 FAX (01823) 680601 MOBILE (07714) 218921
E-MAIL stuartkittowracing@hotmail.com WEBSITE www.stuartkittowracing.com

1 BAKHT A RAWAN (IRE), 4, b g Rip Van Winkle (IRE)—Foolish Ambition (GER) **Chris & David Stam**
2 BOB LEWIS, 10, b g Sir Harry Lewis (USA)—Teelyna **Mrs P. J. Pengelly**
3 CARTMELL CLEAVE, 4, br g Pastoral Pursuits—There's Two (IRE) **Mr G. D. C. Jewell**
4 DAGHASH, 7, b g Tiger Hill (IRE)—Zibet **Mrs P. E. Hawkings**
5 DILGURA, 6, b m Ishiguru (USA)—Dilys **R Ingham, S Kittow & R Perry**
6 DIZZEY HEIGHTS (IRE), 4, b f Halling (USA)—Extreme Pleasure (IRE) **Black Type Partnership IV**
7 KLEITOMACHOS (IRE), 8, b g Barathea (IRE)—Theben (GER) **E. J. S. Gadsden**
8 LALOR (GER), 4, b g It's Gino (GER)—Laviola (GER)
9 4, B br g Areion (GER)—Laren (GER)
10 MACDILLON, 10, b g Acclamation—Dilys **W. S. Kittow**
11 MAD ENDEAVOUR, 5, b g Muhtathir—Capefly **R. S. E. Gifford**
12 MAY BE SOME TIME, 8, ch g Iceman—Let Alone **Dr G. S. Plastow**
13 OUR FOLLY, 8, b g Sakhee (USA)—Regent's Folly (IRE) **Midd Shire Racing**
14 PLAUSEABELLA, 5, b m Royal Applause—Ellablue (IRE) **Mrs G. R. Shire**
15 TOBOUGGALOO, 5, ch m Tobougg (IRE)—Let Alone **Dr G. S. Plastow**

THREE-YEAR-OLDS

16 GUILDED ROCK, gr g Hellvelyn—Once Removed **The Racing Guild**
17 NANNY MAKFI, b f Makfi—Pan Galactic **The Nanny Makfi Partnership**
18 NIGHTINGALE VALLEY, ch f Compton Place—Dancing Storm **M. E. Harris**
19 PROCTOR, b g Makfi—Super Motiva **Qatar Racing Limited**
20 ROSIE LEA (FR), b f Manduro (GER)—Saralea (FR) **Mr J. R. Urquhart**
21 RUSSIAN RASCAL, b g Kyllachy—Russian Ruby (FR) **P. A. & M. J. Reditt**
22 SIR COMPTON, b g Compton Place—Dilys **Cushing, Jewell, Harvey & Kittow**

TWO-YEAR-OLDS

23 B f 26/3 Malinas (GER)—Arctic Magic (IRE) (Saddlers' Hall (IRE))
24 DILINGER, b c 27/4 Equiano (FR)—Dilys (Efisio) **Cushing,Ingham,Boswell,Urquhart&Wilson**
25 B f 27/4 Harbour Watch (IRE)—Doliouchka (Saumarez) (16000) **R. S. E. Gifford**
26 INCENTIVE, b f 15/4 Stimulation (IRE)—Folly Drove (Bahri (USA))
27 SKILFUL LORD (IRE), ch c 30/1 Lord Shanakill (USA)—Monsusu (IRE) (Montjeu (IRE)) (20952)
28 B c 17/2 Sir Percy—Strictly Lambada (Red Ransom (USA)) (70000) **E. J. S. Gadsden**
29 TROTTER, b c 14/3 Piccolo—Vintage Steps (IRE) (Bahamian Bounty) (26666) **Mr K. B. Hodges**

Other Owners: D. W. Arnesen, Mrs S. G. Arnesen, John Boswell, Mrs A. Bull, Andrew Bull, H. A. Cushing, Mr N. Harvey, Mr A. R. Ingham, B. G. Middleton, Mrs R. J. M. Perry, Mrs P. A. Reditt, M. J. Reditt, A. J. Shire, Mr D. B. Stam, Dr C. Stam, Ms W. A. Stoker, R. A. Stoker, Mr T. P. Wilson.

Assistant Trainer: Mrs Judy Kittow

Jockey (NH): Paddy Brennan, Tom Scudamore.

358 MR WILLIAM KNIGHT, Angmering

Postal: **Lower Coombe Racing Stables, Angmering Park, Littlehampton, West Sussex, BN16 4EX**
Contacts: PHONE (01903) 871188 FAX (01903) 871184 MOBILE (07770) 720828
E-MAIL william@wknightracing.co.uk WEBSITE www.wknightracing.co.uk

1 ALHELLA, 4, b f Kyllachy—Maid In The Shade **Sheikh A. H. F. M. A. Al Sabah**
2 BLOODSWEATANDTEARS, 8, b g Barathea (IRE)—Celestial Princess **Canisbay Bloodstock**
3 CHINA GIRL (IND), 4, b f Dancing Forever (USA)—Oriental Lady (IRE) **Chasemore Farm LLP**
4 CLOTILDE, 4, br f Dubawi (IRE)—Mary Boleyn (IRE) **Chasemore Farm LLP**
5 COLORADA, 4, ch f Lope de Vega (IRE)—Isabella Glyn (IRE) **Mr T. G. Roddick**
6 EXALTED (IRE), 5, b g Acclamation—Eman's Joy **N. J. Roach**
7 FIRE SHIP, 7, b g Firebreak—Mays Dream **IGP Partnership & P. Winkworth**
8 GAVLAR, 5, b g Gentlewave (IRE)—Shawhill **Canisbay Bloodstock**
9 JACOB CATS, 7, b g Dutch Art—Ballet **Canisbay Bloodstock**
10 NOBLE GIFT, 6, ch g Cadeaux Genereux—Noble Penny **Canisbay Bloodstock**
11 ROWAN RIDGE, 8, ch g Compton Place—Lemon Tree (USA) **Mr & Mrs N. Welby**
12 ROYAL REEF (IRE), 4, b g Duke of Marmalade (IRE)—Bintalreef (USA) **W. J. Knight**
13 RUSSIAN APPROVAL, 4, b f Authorized (IRE)—Russian Rhapsody **The Cromhall Stud**

MR WILLIAM KNIGHT - Continued

14 **SAOI (USA)**, 9, ch g Wiseman's Ferry (USA)—Careyes (IRE) **Mr D. A. Docherty**
15 **SEASIDE SIZZLER**, 9, ch g Rahy (USA)—Via Borghese (USA) **I. J. Heseltine**
16 **SECRET ART (IRE)**, 6, ch g Excellent Art—Ivy Queen (IRE) **Art of Racing**
17 **SOLAR FLAIR**, 4, b g Equiano (FR)—Air Biscuit (IRE) **Art Of Racing & The Kimber Family**

THREE-YEAR-OLDS

18 **ARTISANDRA (FR)**, ch f Mastercraftsman (IRE)—Kezia (FR) **Wardley Bloodstock**
19 **AUTHOR'S DREAM**, gr g Authorized (IRE)—Spring Dream (IRE) **Heseltine & Conroy**
20 **BALLARD DOWN (IRE)**, b g Canford Cliffs (IRE)—Mackenzie's Friend **Angmering Park Thoroughbreds I**
21 **CAPTAIN PEACOCK**, b g Champs Elysees—Blast Furnace (IRE) **Chasemore Farm LLP**
22 **COLONEL BOSSINGTON (IRE)**, b c Azamour (IRE)—Ros The Boss (IRE) **The Expendables**
23 **DARK AVENUE**, b f Champs Elysees—Dark Quest **Hot To Trot Racing Club 6**
24 **DNANEER (IRE)**, b f Invincible Spirit (IRE)—Lulua (USA) **Sheikh A. H. F. M. A. Al Sabah**
25 **EASTERN LADY (IND)**, ch f Dancing Forever (USA)—Oriental Lady (IRE) **Chasemore Farm LLP**
26 **ENGLISH HERO**, b g Royal Applause—Merton Matriarch **P. Winkworth**
27 **EQUAL POINT**, b g Equiano (FR)—Point Perfect **Angmering Park Thoroughbreds III et al**
28 **GOODWOOD ZODIAC (IRE)**, b g Kodiac—Insieme (IRE) **Goodwood Racehorse Owners Group (22) Ltd**
29 **KIRINGA**, ch f Kyllachy—Good Health **Jon & Julia Aisbitt**
30 **KNIGHT COMMANDER**, br g Sir Percy—Jardin **Angmering Park Thoroughbreds II**
31 **LADY MACAPA**, b f Equiano (FR)—Brazilian Style **Fromthestables.com Racing V**
32 **NICEONECENTURION**, ch g Teofilo (IRE)—Turn of A Century **The Expendables**
33 **ROBANNE**, b f Paco Boy (IRE)—Arctic Song **Mrs E. C. Roberts**
34 **SKY OF STARS (IRE)**, b c Frozen Power (IRE)—So So Lucky (IRE) **Elaine Chivers & Merlin Racing**
35 **SOUTHDOWN LAD (IRE)**, b c Lilbourne Lad (IRE)—Elizabelle (IRE) **Mr T. G. Roddick**
36 **SWEET SWAGGER**, ch f Showcasing—Strawberry Leaf **The Oil Men Partnership**
37 **THE JUGGLER**, b g Archipenko (USA)—Oblige **Mrs Susie Hartley & The Kimber Family**
38 **ZARA'S PRINCE (IRE)**, b g Zebedee—Czars Princess (IRE) **Mr N. J. Roach**

TWO-YEAR-OLDS

39 B c 11/4 Elnadim (USA)—Albeed (Tiger Hill (IRE)) (16980) **Angmering Park Thoroughbreds IV**
40 B c 5/5 Footstepsinthesand—
All Night Dancer (IRE) (Danehill Dancer (IRE)) (40605) **Willis & Angmering Park Thoroughbreds V**
41 B c 26/4 Paco Boy (IRE)—Amanda Carter (Tobougg (IRE)) (25000) **Sheikh A. H. F. M. A. Al Sabah**
42 **ANY QUESTIONS**, ch c 15/2 Poet's Voice—Funday (Daylami (IRE)) (32000) **S. Ali**
43 B c 15/5 Thewayyouare (USA)—Ask Annie (IRE) (Danehill (USA)) (17718)
44 B f 15/2 Royal Applause—Brazilian Style (Exit To Nowhere (USA)) **P. Winkworth**
45 B c 20/4 Sixties Icon—Cyclone Connie (Dr Devious (IRE)) (24000)
46 **EOLIAN**, b c 20/2 Poet's Voice—Charlecote (IRE) (Caerleon (USA)) (45000) **Mr & Mrs Mark Tracey**
47 **ETERNAL DREAM**, ch c 6/2 Dream Ahead (USA)—
Get Happy (IRE) (Zamindar (USA)) (20952) **Mrs Susie Hartley & Ms Elaine Chivers**
48 B c 29/1 Equiano (FR)—Folly Bridge (Avonbridge) (30000)
49 B c 8/4 Lawman (FR)—Gimasha (Cadeaux Genereux) **P. Winkworth**
50 Ch f 21/3 Helmet (AUS)—Giveupyeraulsins (IRE) (Mark of Esteem) (42500)
51 **JINKIE PINK (IRE)**, b f 8/4 Teofilo (IRE)—
Hurricane Havoc (IRE) (Hurricane Run (IRE)) (17000) **Elaine Chivers & Merlin Racing**
52 Ch f 5/4 Dutch Art—La Adelita (IRE) (Anabaa (USA)) **Mrs M. Bryce**
53 B gr f 29/1 Campanologist (USA)—Nolas Lolly (IRE) (Lomitas) (9000) **Angmering Park Thoroughbreds VI**
54 B c 31/3 Delegator—Purest (Shamardal (USA)) (8000) **Mr & Mrs N. Welby & Fromthestables.com**
55 **UNIT OF ASSESSMENT (IRE)**, b c 10/3 Dragon Pulse (IRE)—
Before The Storm (Sadler's Wells (USA)) (38095) **Mr A. Hetherton**
56 B c 22/2 Lawman (FR)—Western Pearl (High Chaparral (IRE)) (20000) **Mr & Mrs N. Welby**

Other Owners: Mr Jon Aisbitt, Mrs Julia Aisbitt, Mrs J. E. Black, Mr A. Black, Mr J. A. Bryan, Mr Richard Bryan, Ms Lauren Chivers, Miss Charlotte Chivers, Ms Elaine Chivers, Mr Carl Conroy, Mr N. A. Coster, Mr D. A. Docherty, Mr P. J. Gregg, Mrs E. Gregson-Williams, Mr Rupert Gregson-Williams, Mrs Susie Hartley, Mr I. J. Heseltine, Mr R. F. Kilby, Dr Scott Kimber, Mrs Carol Kimber, Mrs Emily Knight, Mr W. J. Knight, Mr I. G. Martin, Miss Lesley McGrath, Mrs Wendy J. Price, Mr Derek R. Price, Mr N. J. Roach, Mr Mike Rudd, Miss Maureen Stopher, Mrs I. M. Tracey, Mr Mark Tracey, Mrs N. Welby, Mr N. Welby, P. Winkworth.

Assistant Trainer: Matthew Darling

Apprentice: Callum Shepherd.

359 MR DANIEL KUBLER, Lambourn
Postal: **High View Stables, Folly Road, Lambourn, Hungerford, Berkshire, RG17 8QE**
Contacts: **MOBILE (07984) 287254**
E-MAIL **daniel@kublerracing.com** WEBSITE **www.kublerracing.com**

1 BAILIWICK, 5, b g Oratorio (IRE)—Imperial Bailiwick (IRE) **Mr & Mrs G. Middlebrook**
2 FIREBACK, 9, b g Firebreak—So Discreet
3 KARNAGE (IRE), 4, b g Lawman (FR)—Kazinoki (UAE) **Keep Racing**
4 MANDRIA (IRE), 4, b f Duke of Marmalade (IRE)—Albertine Rose **Mr & Mrs G. Middlebrook**
5 OUTRAGE, 4, ch g Exceed And Excel (AUS)—Ludynosa (USA) **D Blunt & G Middlebrook**
6 TRIMOULET, 7, b g Teofilo (IRE)—Riberac **Mr & Mrs G. Middlebrook**
7 WHO'STHEDADDY, 4, br g Avonbridge—Lisathedaddy **Mrs P Wilson & Mr C Wilson**
8 YOU'RE MY CRACKER, 4, ch f Captain Gerrard (IRE)—Dalmunzie (IRE) **Mr & Mrs Paul & Clare Rooney**

THREE-YEAR-OLDS
9 AMOR INVICTO (IRE), b g Holy Roman Emperor (IRE)—Love In The Mist (USA) **Capture The Breeze**
10 BOOTY FULL (IRE), b f Intikhab (USA)—Explore **Mrs M. O'Sullivan**
11 HILLTOP RANGER (IRE), b f Bushranger (IRE)—Beatrix Potter (IRE) **Diskovery Partnership III**
12 SILHOUETTE (IRE), ch g Frozen Power (IRE)—Missalonghi (IRE) **Titan Assets**
13 SONNENTANZ (IRE), b f Vale of York (IRE)—Irish Fountain (USA) **Mr M. Wichser**
14 UNFORESEEN, b f Sky Mesa (USA)—Distinctive **Mr & Mrs G. Middlebrook**
15 VIRTUOUS BELLE, b f Virtual—Petong's Pet **Denarius Consulting Ltd**
16 ZIPPY, b f Hellvelyn—Ziggy Zaggy **Selwood Bloodstock**

TWO-YEAR-OLDS
17 AV A WORD, b c 26/2 Aussie Rules (USA)—Real Me (Mark of Esteem (IRE))
18 DIXIE'S DOUBLE, b f 7/3 Multiplex—Dress Design (IRE) (Brief Truce (USA))
19 FLOODED, ch c 7/2 Archipenko (USA)—Spate Rise (Speightstown (USA)) (4000)
20 JACK BLANE, b c 16/4 Kheleyf (USA)—Blane Water (USA) (Lomond (USA)) **Mr P. J. H. Whitten**
21 B c 1/3 Invincible Spirit (IRE)—Love Everlasting (Pursuit of Love) (220000) **Mr & Mrs G. Middlebrook**
22 B f 22/3 Big Bad Bob (IRE)—Miracle Steps (CAN) (Theatrical) (29531)
23 SNIPER VIPER, ch f 8/4 Paco Boy (IRE)—Brilliance (Cadeaux Genereux) (571)
24 SOCRATES, b c 24/3 Dick Turpin (IRE)—Lisathedaddy (Darnay) **Wilbart Racing**
25 SOLENT MEADS (IRE), ch c 21/3 Intense Focus (USA)—No Trimmings (IRE) (Medecis) (19195) **Mr P. Britton**
26 Ch c 29/3 Sepoy (AUS)—Violet (IRE) (Mukaddamah (USA)) (40000)
27 B c 15/3 High Chaparral (IRE)—Witch of Fife (USA) (Lear Fan (USA)) (31746) **London City Bloodstock**

Other Owners: Mr S. Barter, Mrs Y. Blunt, Mr D. Blunt, Mr K. A. Cosby, Mrs C. E. Kubler, Mr D. Kubler, Kubler Racing Ltd, Mr S. G. Lake, Mr C. McHale, G. Middlebrook, Mrs L. A. Middlebrook, Mrs M. O'Sullivan, Mrs C. Rooney, Mr P. A. Rooney, Mr A. Watson, Mr C. C. Wilson, Mrs P. S. Wilson.

Assistant Trainer: Claire Kubler

360 MR TOM LACEY, Woolhope
Trainer did not wish details of his string to appear

361 MR CARLOS LAFFON-PARIAS, Chantilly
Postal: **38, Avenue du General Leclerc, 60500 Chantilly, France**
E-MAIL **ecuries.laffon.parias@wanadoo.fr**

1 ARVIOS, 4, ch c Medecean—Akrivi (IRE) **Stilvi Compani**
2 COLDSTONE (FR), 4, ch g Gold Away (USA)—Vraona **Stilvi Compani**
3 MADERNIA (IRE), 4, ch f Duke of Marmalade (IRE)—Gali Gal (IRE) **Bering SL**
4 NO MOOD, 5, ch h Monsun (GER)—Impressionnante **Wertheimer et Frere**
5 OLANTHIA (IRE), 4, b f Zamindar (USA)—Olivia (IRE) **Stilvi Compani**
6 SPIRIT OF QATAR (FR), 4, b g Monsun (GER)—Sandy Girl (FR) **Al Shahania Stud**
7 SPIRITUEUX (IRE), 5, b h Invincible Spirit (IRE)—Stormina (USA) **Wertheimer et Frere**

MR CARLOS LAFFON-PARIAS - Continued

THREE-YEAR-OLDS

8 **AERIE**, b f High Chaparral (IRE)—Wingspan (USA) **Wertheimer et Frere**
9 **AKANTHA (FR)**, b f Excellent Art—Alfreda **Stilvi Compani**
10 **AKTORIA (FR)**, b f Canford Cliffs (IRE)—Granadilla **Stilvi Compani**
11 **ALIGNEMENT**, b c Pivotal—Soldata (USA) **Wertheimer et Frere**
12 **ARIVIA (FR)**, b f Medicean—Arrivee (FR) **Wertheimer et Frere**
13 **ATTENDU (FR)**, b c Acclamation—Gwenseb (FR) **Wertheimer et Frere**
14 **AYAMONTE (FR)**, b c Whipper (USA)—Benalmadena (FR) **Sarl Darpat FR**
15 **BIENTEVEO (IRE)**, b g Pivotal—Kirkinola **Jupisa Tres**
16 **BIG SUR (FR)**, b c Cape Cross (IRE)—Kylia (USA) **Wertheimer et Frere**
17 **CONIL (FR)**, b g Orpen (USA)—Trylko (USA) **Sarl Darpat FR**
18 **DISTINGO (IRE)**, b c Smart Strike (CAN)—Distinctive Look (IRE) **Wertheimer et Frere**
19 **EMOTICON (FR)**, b g Dansili—Flash Dance (IRE) **Wertheimer et Frere**
20 **ENJOY THE SILENCE (FR)**, b c Elusive City (USA)—Cerita (IRE) **Stilvi Compani**
21 **EXTENTION (USA)**, b f Hat Trick (JPN)—Quiet Royal (USA) **Wertheimer et Frere**
22 **IONI (FR)**, b f Ialysos (GR)—Mazea (IRE) **Stilvi Compani**
23 **KALVOS (FR)**, ch c Dutch Art—Loxandra **Stilvi Compani**
24 **KARYNIA (FR)**, ch f Footstepsinthesand—Keisha (FR) **Stilvi Compani**
25 **KORINNA (FR)**, b f Muhtathir—Betwixt (IRE) **Stilvi Compani**
26 **KRYFI (FR)**, b f Mr Sidney (USA)—Kresna (FR) **Stilvi Compani**
27 **LEFT HAND**, ch f Dubawi (IRE)—Balladeuse (FR) **Wertheimer et Frere**
28 **NIMPHEAS (USA)**, b f Smart Strike (CAN)—Underwater (USA) **Wertheimer et Frere**
29 **NISEA (FR)**, b f Danehill Dancer (IRE)—Skia (FR) **Stilvi Compani**
30 **NOT READY (USA)**, gr ro f More Than Ready (USA)—Zaftig (USA) **Wertheimer et Frere**
31 **OKANA**, b f Zamindar (USA)—Oceanique (USA) **Wertheimer et Frere**
32 **ORFEAS (FR)**, b c Galileo (IRE)—Light Quest (USA) **Stilvi Compani**
33 **PETUNIA (FR)**, b f Pivotal—Esneh (IRE) **Wertheimer et Frere**
34 **READY TO SMILE (USA)**, b f Distorted Humor (USA)—Buster's Ready (USA) **Wertheimer et Frere**
35 **REDCOL (FR)**, b f Nayef (USA)—Russiana (IRE) **Wertheimer et Frere**
36 **SASPARELLA (FR)**, b f Shamardal (USA)—Desertiste **Wertheimer et Frere**
37 **SINABOY (FR)**, b c Evasive—Sina (GER) **Montojo**
38 **SPARTAKISTE (IRE)**, b c Dansili—Occupandiste (IRE) **Wertheimer et Frere**
39 **TAX HEAVEN (IRE)**, b f Rock of Gibraltar (IRE)—Futurista (USA) **Wertheimer et Frere**
40 **TOLOMEO (IRE)**, b c Dalakhani (IRE)—Tiyi (FR) **Wertheimer et Frere**
41 **URBAN HILL**, b f Galileo (IRE)—Sea Hill (USA) **Wertheimer et Frere**

TWO-YEAR-OLDS

42 **ACROBATE**, b c 6/4 Oasis Dream—Balladeuse (FR) (Singspiel (IRE)) **Wertheimer et Frere**
43 **AFRICAN RIDE**, b c 8/5 Candy Ride (ARG)—Palota Falls (USA) (Kris S (USA)) **Wertheimer et Frere**
44 **ATOMIQUE (IRE)**, ch f 10/2 Galileo (IRE)—Impressionnante (Danehill (USA)) **Wertheimer et Frere**
45 **AVOCATE**, b f 22/2 Lawman (FR)—Merville (FR) (Montjeu (IRE)) **Wertheimer et Frere**
46 **DALAKANIA (IRE)**, b gr f 10/2 Dalakhani (IRE)—Arme Ancienne (Sillery (USA)) **Wertheimer et Frere**
47 **DISCREET MOON**, b f 23/4 Malibu Moon (USA)—
                           Discreetly Awesome (USA) (Awesome Again (CAN)) **Wertheimer et Frere**
48 **EMBAJADORES (IRE)**, ch c 10/2 Pivotal—Freedom Flashing (USA) (Proud Citizen (USA)) **Sarl Darpat FR**
49 **ESPACE**, b c 5/2 Galileo (IRE)—Evaporation (FR) (Red Ransom (USA)) **Wertheimer et Frere**
50 **GRANDE BLEUE (IRE)**, b f 20/4 Oasis Dream—Oceanique (USA) (Forest Wildcat (USA)) **Wertheimer et Frere**
51 **GUERRIERE (IRE)**, b f 2/3 Invincible Spirit (IRE)—Mathematicienne (IRE) (Galileo (IRE)) **Wertheimer et Frere**
52 **HARD DRINK (USA)**, b c 2/3 Lemon Drop Kid (USA)—
                           Toppisme (USA) (Saint Ballado (CAN)) **Wertheimer et Frere**
53 **HILARANT (FR)**, b c 31/1 Azamour (IRE)—Comique (USA) (Distorted Humor (USA)) **Wertheimer et Frere**
54 **INDISCRETE (FR)**, b f 1/1 Siyouni (FR)—Ecoute (USA) (Manila (USA)) **Wertheimer et Frere**
55 **MILK MAN (USA)**, ch c 13/3 Kitten's Joy (USA)—Meteor Miracle (USA) (Twining (USA)) **Wertheimer et Frere**
56 **MY SOUL**, b f 5/4 Elusive City (USA)—Tia Kia (IRE) (Montjeu (IRE)) (21410) **Stilvi Compani**
57 B f 1/1 So You Think (NZ)—Nymfia (IRE) (Invincible Spirit (IRE)) (44296) **Stilvi Compani**
58 **ORIENTAL (JPN)**, b c 4/4 Smart Strike (CAN)—Iron Lips (Iron Mask (USA)) **Wertheimer et Frere**
59 **SANJITA (IRE)**, ch f 5/3 Zamindar (USA)—Barbayam (Stormy River (FR)) **Wertheimer et Frere**
60 **SILIGREEN**, b f 30/3 Dansili—Polygreen (FR) (Green Tune (USA)) **Wertheimer et Frere**
61 **VAGABONDE (IRE)**, b f 4/4 Acclamation—Desertiste (Green Desert (USA)) **Wertheimer et Frere**
62 **WESTIT**, gr f 11/4 Tapit (USA)—West Ocean (USA) (Elusive Quality (USA)) **Wertheimer et Frere**

362 **MR NICK LAMPARD, Marlborough**
Postal: **South Cottage, 2 The Crossroads, Clatford, Marlborough, Wiltshire, SN8 4EA**
Contacts: **PHONE (01672) 861420**

1 JUST SATISFACTION, 7, b m Trade Fair—Bathwick Fancy (IRE) **The Outside Chance Racing Club**
2 MINMORE GREY (IRE), 7, gr g Primary (USA)—Hopeful Memory (IRE) **The Outside Chance Racing Club**
3 RUBY TAYLOR, 4, b f Passing Glance—Bold Rose **The Outside Chance Racing Club**
4 SADMA, 7, gr g Street Cry (IRE)—Blue Dress (USA) **Just A Bit Of Fun**
5 WITCH FROM ROME, 5, b g Holy Roman Emperor (IRE)—Spangle **The Outside Chance Racing Club**

Other Owners: Ms C. J. Gaisford, Miss C. D. Roberts, Miss A. E. A. Solomon, Mr H. Spooner.

363 **MR DAVID LANIGAN, Upper Lambourn**
Postal: **Kingsdown Stables, Upper Lambourn, Hungerford, Berkshire, RG17 8QX**
Contacts: **PHONE (01488) 71786 FAX (01488) 674148 MOBILE (07803) 257864**
E-MAIL david@laniganracing.co.uk WEBSITE www.laniganracing.co.uk

1 ALMODOVAR (IRE), 4, b g Sea The Stars (IRE)—Melodramatic (IRE)
2 ANZHELIKA (IRE), 4, ch f Galileo (IRE)—Ange Bleu (USA)
3 DAWN SKY, 12, b g Fantastic Light (USA)—Zacheta
4 FOR WHAT (USA), 8, ch h Mingun (USA)—Cuanto Es (USA)
5 INTERCEPTION (IRE), 6, ch m Raven's Pass (USA)—Badee'a (IRE)
6 MITCHUM SWAGGER, 4, b g Paco Boy (IRE)—Dont Dili Dali
7 POLYBIUS, 5, b g Oasis Dream—Freedonia
8 REAL SMART (CAN), 4, gr f Smart Strike (CAN)—Rose Diamond (IRE)
9 TREVISANI (IRE), 4, b g Dubawi (IRE)—Geminiani
10 WARRIOR OF LIGHT (IRE), 5, b g High Chaparral (IRE)—Strawberry Fledge (USA)

THREE-YEAR-OLDS

11 ACRUX, b c Dansili—Ikat (IRE)
12 ARMED AND READY (FR), gr c Kendargent (FR)—San Sicharia (IRE)
13 ATHLON (IRE), b g Arakan (USA)—Alexander Divine
14 CENERENTOLA (IRE), b f Shamardal (USA)—Geminiani
15 CLAYMORE (IRE), gr c Kodiac—Krasotka (IRE)
16 CRYSTALLOGRAPHER (IRE), br f Big Bad Bob (IRE)—Desert Alchemy (IRE)
17 DANILOVNA (IRE), br f Dansili—Hoity Toity
18 DOSTOYEVSKY (IRE), b c Galileo (IRE)—My Branch
19 DREAM FREE, b g Oasis Dream—Freedonia
20 DUNE DANCER (IRE), b c Footstepsinthesand—Leonica
21 GERSHWIN, b c Shamardal (USA)—Gradara
22 GOLD RETURN (IRE), b f Gold Away (IRE)—Ourika (IRE)
23 INTERCEPTED (IRE), b c Raven's Pass (USA)—Cape Rocker
24 KING OF CORNWALL (IRE), b g Duke of Marmalade (IRE)—Course de Diamante (IRE)
25 MIND SHIFT (USA), b c Arch (USA)—Light Blow (USA)
26 PALMAROLA (IRE), b f Sea The Stars (IRE)—Palmeraie (USA)
27 QUEEN CORDELIA (IRE), b f Acclamation—Rebelline (IRE)
28 TETRADRACHM, b c Holy Roman Emperor (IRE)—Dahlia's Krissy (USA)
29 THRILLED (IRE), b f Kodiac—Fuerta Ventura (IRE)
30 WAPPING (USA), b c Smart Strike (CAN)—Exciting Times (FR)

TWO-YEAR-OLDS

31 B c 29/3 Paco Boy (IRE)—Hazita (Singspiel (IRE)) (22000)
32 B c 12/4 Excelebration (IRE)—Hip (Pivotal) (20000)
33 B c 14/3 The Factor (USA)—I Am Iron Woman (Any Given Saturday (USA)) (33222)
34 B c 19/2 Kitten's Joy (USA)—Imagistic (USA) (Deputy Minister (CAN)) (40000)
35 B f 18/4 Bated Breath—Intermission (IRE) (Royal Applause) (22000)
36 B c 13/3 Kitten's Joy (USA)—Iteration (USA) (Wild Again (USA)) (100000)
37 B c 31/3 Archipenko (USA)—Jardin (Sinndar (IRE)) (30000)
38 KUIPER BELT (USA), b c 14/2 Elusive Quality (USA)—Youre So Sweet (USA) (Storm Cat (USA))
39 LIGHT OF JOY (USA), ch f 27/2 Kitten's Joy (USA)—Light Blow (USA) (Kingmambo (USA))
40 B f 10/2 Kitten's Joy (USA)—Manda Bay (USA) (Empire Maker (USA)) (60000)
41 B c 11/4 Kitten's Joy (USA)—Mayakoba (USA) (War Chant (USA)) (10000)
42 Ch f 8/2 Exceed And Excel (AUS)—Paramita (FR) (Galileo (IRE))
43 Ch c 17/1 Rip Van Winkle (IRE)—Portentous (Selkirk (USA)) (30000)

MR DAVID LANIGAN - Continued

44 B c 3/2 Henrythenavigator (USA)—Satwa Pearl (Rock of Gibraltar (IRE))
45 **SPUTNIK PLANUM (USA),** b c 19/4 Quality Road (USA)—Shiva (JPN) (Hector Protector (USA))
46 B c 29/3 Cacique (IRE)—Star Cluster (Observatory (USA)) (50000)
47 B f 11/3 Exceed And Excel (AUS)—Sunset Avenue (USA) (Street Cry (IRE)) (70000)
48 B c 24/2 Iffraaj—The Giving Tree (IRE) (Rock of Gibraltar (IRE)) (30000)

Owners: Mr Saif Ali, Mr Richard Bateman, Mr Oliver Bell, Mr George Bolton, Mr Paul Brosnan, Mrs Emma Capon, Cheveley Park Stud, Course Investment Corporation, Mr Paul Dean, Ms Madeleine Delaney, Mr Andrew Dick, Mr B. Dunn, Mr Matt FitzGerald, Miss Jane Keir, Mr Stephen Lamprell, Mr Bob Lanigan, Lord Lloyd-Webber, Mrs John Magnier, Mr Mick Mariscotti, Mrs Janice Mariscotti, Mr Stephen D. Martus, Mr C. A. McMillan, Niarchos Family, Mr B. E. Nielsen, Mr Eamonn O'Connor, Orpendale, Mr A. Payne, Mr & Mrs Kenneth and Sarah Ramsey, Mr Kevin Scott, Mr Craig Scott, Mr Jeffrey Stephens, Mr M. Tyson, Woodford Racing X LLC.

---

364 | **MISS EMMA LAVELLE, Andover**
Postal: **Cottage Stables, Hatherden, Andover, Hampshire, SP11 0HY**
Contacts: PHONE **(01264) 735509** OFFICE **(01264) 735412** FAX **(01264) 735529**
MOBILE **(07774) 993998**
E-MAIL **emma@elavelle.freeserve.co.uk** WEBSITE **www.emmalavelle.com**

1 **AKA DOUN (FR),** 5, b g Smadoun (FR)—Akar Baby **Mr A. Gemmell**
2 **ANDY KELLY (IRE),** 7, ch g Flemensfirth (USA)—Fae Taylor (IRE) **The Optimists**
3 4, B f King's Theatre (IRE)—Artist's Muse (IRE) **Mustoe & Lavelle**
4 **BALIBOUR (FR),** 4, b g Policy Maker (IRE)—Saintheze (FR) **The High Altitude Partnership**
5 **BELLE EMPRESS,** 5, b m Black Sam Bellamy (IRE)—Empress of Light **Mighty Acorn Stables**
6 **BLOWN COVER,** 7, b g Kayf Tara—Cullen Bay (IRE) **Roger Hetherington & Colin Bothway**
7 **CASINO MARKETS (IRE),** 8, b g Fruits of Love (USA)—Vals Dream (IRE) **Mighty Acorn Stables**
8 **CAULFIELDS VENTURE (IRE),** 10, b g Catcher In The Rye (IRE)—Saddlers' Venture (IRE) **C. F. Colquhoun**
9 **CHAPEL GARDEN (IRE),** 7, br g Heron Island (IRE)—Grape Love (FR) **Tim Syder & N. Mustoe**
10 **CHELSEA FLYER (IRE),** 5, b g Westerner—Aktress (IRE) **Mrs Rosemary Luck & Mrs Deirdre Walker**
11 **CLARET CLOAK (IRE),** 9, b g Vinnie Roe (IRE)—Bewildered (USA) **Hawksmoor Partnership**
12 **CLOSING CEREMONY (IRE),** 7, b g Flemensfirth (USA)—
Supreme Von Pres (IRE) **The High Altitude Partnership**
13 **COURT BY SURPRISE (IRE),** 11, b g Beneficial—Garryduff Princess (IRE) **N. Mustoe**
14 **CRACK ON MAISIE,** 5, ch m Gold Away (IRE)—Maisie Daisie (FR) **GDM Partnership**
15 **CRACK ON TOM (IRE),** 7, ch g Great Exhibition (USA)—Nordic Cloud (IRE)
16 **CRIMSON ARK (IRE),** 6, b g Arcadio (GER)—Crimson Flower (IRE) **Gemmell, Langton, Ryan & Sieff**
17 **DEMOGRAPHIC (USA),** 7, b g Aptitude (USA)—Private Line (USA) **Mrs A. C. Lavelle**
18 **DIAMOND DUST,** 5, gr m Bandmaster (USA)—Absalom's Lady **Swanbridge Bloodstock Limited**
19 **FORTUNATE GEORGE (IRE),** 6, b g Oscar (IRE)—Fine Fortune (IRE) **The George Inn Racing Syndicate**
20 **FOX APPEAL (IRE),** 9, b g Brian Boru—Lady Appeal (IRE) **The Hawk Inn Syndicate 3**
21 **FULL IRISH (IRE),** 8, b g Flemensfirth (USA)—Miss Kettlewell (IRE) **N. Mustoe**
22 4, B g Kayf Tara—Gaye Sophie **N. Mustoe & Tim Syder**
23 **GULLINBURSTI (IRE),** 10, b g Milan—D'ygrande (IRE) **N. Mustoe**
24 **HARD AS A ROCK (FR),** 5, b g Network (GER)—Fany Noune (FR) **GDM Partnership**
25 **HATTON BANK,** 7, ch m Flemensfirth (USA)—Persian Walk (FR) **Mr G. P. MacIntosh**
26 **HIGH NOON (IRE),** 4, b g Westerner—Seymourswift **N. Mustoe**
27 **IRISH MUSTARD,** 6, b g Kayf Tara—French Spice **N. Mustoe**
28 **JAVERT (IRE),** 7, b g Kayf Tara—Royalrova (IRE) **Axom LII**
29 **JOYRIDER (IRE),** 4, b g Stowaway—Aileen Supreme (IRE) **N. Mustoe**
30 **JUNCTION FOURTEEN (IRE),** 7, b g King's Theatre (IRE)—Chevet Girl (IRE) **Martin St. Quinton & Tim Syder**
31 **LA PREMIERE DAME (FR),** 5, b m Poliglote—Sentosa (FR) **The Pick 'N' Mix Partnership**
32 **LADY MARKBY (IRE),** 5, b m Oscar (IRE)—Leitrim Bridge (IRE) **Mrs S. Metcalfe**
33 **LE BEC (FR),** 8, ch g Smadoun (FR)—La Pelode (FR) **T. D. J. Syder**
34 **LETS HOPE SO,** 6, b m Generous (IRE)—Baily Mist (IRE) **Cottage Stables Racing Club**
35 **LORINER'S DANCER,** 8, b m Carnival Dancer—Loriner's Lass **Mr J. Small**
36 **MOSSPARK (IRE),** 8, b g Flemensfirth (USA)—Patio Rose **N. Mustoe & Tim Syder**
37 **MR FENTON (IRE),** 5, b g Trans Island—Carnagh Girl (IRE) **The Hawk Inn Syndicate**
38 **MR MOUNTAIN (IRE),** 6, b g Mountain High (IRE)—Not Mine (IRE) **N. Mustoe**
39 **MRSROBIN (IRE),** 6, b m Robin des Pres (FR)—Regents Dancer (IRE) **T. D. J. Syder**
40 **MYTHICAL LEGEND,** 5, ch m Midnight Legend—Materiality **Swanbridge Bloodstock Limited**
41 **ONDERUN (IRE),** 7, b g Flemensfirth (USA)—Warts And All (IRE) **Lavelle Foster Metcalfe Copland**
42 **OUT OF THE MIST (IRE),** 7, b m Flemensfirth (USA)—Mistinguett (IRE) **Swanbridge Bloodstock Limited**
43 **PARISH BUSINESS (IRE),** 8, b br g Fruits of Love (USA)—Parkality (IRE) **N. Mustoe**
44 **PAWN STAR (IRE),** 6, b g Beneficial—Missindependence (IRE) **Hawk Inn Syndicate 5**

MISS EMMA LAVELLE - Continued

45 4, B g Oscar (IRE)—Presenting Shares (IRE) **Mr A. Gemmell**
46 **PRIVATE MALONE (IRE)**, 7, b g Darsi (FR)—Native Artist (IRE) **Mrs Sarah Stevens & Mr P. Mitford-Slade**
47 **SEE THE WORLD**, 6, b g Kayf Tara—My World (IRE) **Mrs N. Turner, Mrs P. Tozer & Miss C. Schicht**
48 **SET LIST (IRE)**, 7, b g Heron Island (IRE)—Copper Magic (IRE) **T. D. J. Syder**
49 **SHOTGUN PADDY (IRE)**, 9, b g Brian Boru—Awesome Miracle (IRE) **Axom (XXXVI)**
50 **SUBORDINATE (GER)**, 7, b g Echo of Light—Suborneuse (USA) **The Jumping Stars**
51 **THE SWEENEY (IRE)**, 4, b g Oscar (IRE)—Banningham Blaze **N. Mustoe**
52 **TIME IS MONEY**, 7, b m Presenting—No More Money **Cottage Stables Racing Club**
53 **VAGRANT EMPEROR (IRE)**, 13, b g Oscar (IRE)—Dragonmist (IRE) **Mrs A. C. Lavelle**
54 **VENDREDI TROIS (FR)**, 7, b g Shaanmer (IRE)—Legende Sacree (FR) **Awdry, Gemmell, Pomford & Williams**
55 **WATER WAGTAIL**, 9, b g Kahyasi—Kentford Grebe **D. I. Bare**
56 **WELL REGARDED (IRE)**, 11, b g Dr Massini (IRE)—Glenelly Valley (IRE)
57 **WELL REWARDED (IRE)**, 6, b g Beneficial—Lady Fancy (IRE) **Andy & The Frisky Fillies**
58 **WOODLAND WALK**, 8, ch m Generous (IRE)—Duchess of Kinsale (IRE) **Cottage Stables Racing Club**
59 **YABADABADOO**, 8, b g Doyen (IRE)—Kabayil **Elite Racing Club**

Other Owners: Mr C. V. Awdry, Axom Ltd, Mr C. H. Bothway, G. Charlesworth, D. Charlesworth, Mrs J. Copland, Mr D. Downie, Mrs A. M. Dunne, Mr L. P. Dunne, Mr C. N. H. Foster, Mr R. J. Fowler, Mrs N. J. Haigh, Mr S. Halpern, Mrs C. D. Halpern, Mrs S. C. Hepworth, Mr R. R. Hetherington, Mr A. J. Hill, Mr L. G. Kimber, Miss I. G. Langton, R. J. Lavelle, Mrs R. A. Luck, Mr J. J. P. McNeile, Mr S. T. Merry, Mrs D. J. Merry, P. B. Mitford-Slade, Mrs C. A. Moysey, Mr P. Nicholls, Miss M. Noden, B. G. Pomford, K. P. Ryan, Miss C. Schicht, Mrs V. Scott, Sir David Sieff, Mr M. Smith, M. G. St Quinton, Mrs S. V. M. Stevens, Mrs M. R. Taylor, Mrs K. M. Taylor, Mrs P. Tozer, Mrs N. C. Turner, Mrs J. C. Verity, Mrs D. Walker, Mr A. G. Weston, Mr P. R. Weston, Mrs P. H. Williams.

Assistant Trainer: Barry Fenton

---

365 MR BARRY LEAVY, Stoke-on-Trent
Postal: **Cash Heath Farm, Cash Heath, Forsbrook, Stoke-on-Trent, ST11 9DE**
Contacts: **HOME/FAX (01782) 398591 MOBILE (07540) 806915**
E-MAIL lauraleavy@hotmail.co.uk WEBSITE www.leavyracing.co.uk

1 **AKULA (IRE)**, 9, ch g Soviet Star (USA)—Danielli (IRE) **B. Leavy**
2 **FLOBURY**, 8, b m Overbury (IRE)—Miss Flora **Mr J. K. S. Cresswell**
3 **GEORGIAN FIREBIRD**, 6, b m Firebreak—Skovshoved (IRE) **Mrs E. A. Wilson**
4 **HELAMIS**, 6, b m Shirocco (GER)—Alnoor (USA) **N. Heath**
5 **LEAN BURN (USA)**, 10, b g Johannesburg (USA)—Anthelion (USA) **N. Heath**
6 **MINISTEROFINTERIOR**, 11, b g Nayef (USA)—Maureen's Hope (USA) **Mrs L. M. Leavy**
7 **ON THE RIGHT PATH**, 9, b g Pursuit of Love—Glen Falls **Deborah Hart & Alan Jackson**
8 **SCENT OF POWER**, 4, b f Authorized (IRE)—Aromatherapy **Cops & Robbers**
9 **SOLIDAGO (IRE)**, 9, b g Vinnie Roe (IRE)—Native Belle (IRE) **Mrs S D Ashford & Mr D B Holmes**

Other Owners: F. W. Dronzek, Mrs D. J. Hart, D. B. Holmes, Mr F. A. Jackson, Mr C. N. Nightingale, Mr D. Rowlinson, Mrs S. D. Williams-Ashford.

Assistant Trainer: Mrs L Leavy

Conditional: Harry Challoner. **Apprentice:** Ryan Holmes.

---

366 MISS KERRY LEE, Presteigne
Postal: **Bell House, Byton, Powys, LD8 2HS**
Contacts: **PHONE (01544) 267672 MOBILE (07968) 242663**
E-MAIL kerry@kerrylee.co.uk WEBSITE www.kerrylee.co.uk

1 **ACES OVER EIGHTS (IRE)**, 7, b m Old Vic—Conjure Up (IRE) **Sam Thorp & R L Baker**
2 **ALFIE SPINNER (IRE)**, 11, b g Alflora (IRE)—Little Red Spider **A. Beard & B. Beard**
3 **BISHOPS ROAD (IRE)**, 8, b g Heron Island (IRE)—Nice Resemblance (IRE) **D. A. Halsall**
4 **DEFINITE FUTURE (IRE)**, 7, b g Definite Article—Miss Marilyn (IRE) **Mr R. L Baker**
5 **EATON HILL (IRE)**, 4, b g Yeats (IRE)—Guilt Less (FR) **Mr & Mrs J. H. Watson**
6 **GASSIN GOLF**, 9, b g Montjeu (IRE)—Miss Riviera Golf **W. Roseff**
7 **GOLDRAY**, 10, ch m Central Park (IRE)—Go Mary **Miss C. E. Phillips**
8 **GOODTOKNOW**, 8, b g Presenting—Atlantic Jane **Burling Daresbury MacEchern Nolan Potter**
9 **GREY GOLD (IRE)**, 11, gr g Strategic Choice (USA)—Grouse-N-Heather **Mrs M. A. Boden**
10 **HAPPY DIVA (IRE)**, 5, b m King's Theatre (IRE)—Megans Joy (IRE) **W. Roseff**
11 **HEREFORDSHIRE**, 8, b g Beneficial—Handmemy Moneydown (IRE) **R. A. Lee**

MISS KERRY LEE - Continued

12 **HIGHWAY CODE (USA)**, 10, b g Street Cry (IRE)—Fairy Heights (IRE) **D. E. Edwards**
13 **INCENTIVISE (IRE)**, 13, ch g Snurge—Festive Isle (IRE) **R Bartlett J Hulston & Mrs B M Ayres**
14 **ITSHARD TO NO (IRE)**, 7, b g Helissio (FR)—Miniballist (IRE) **D. E. Edwards**
15 **JAYO TIME (IRE)**, 7, b g Morozov (USA)—Billythefilly (IRE) **Mr S R Holt & Mrs B M Ayres**
16 **KNOCK A HAND (IRE)**, 11, br g Lend A Hand—Knockcross (IRE) **D. A. Halsall**
17 **KRIS SPIN (IRE)**, 8, br g Kris Kin (USA)—Auditing Empress (IRE) **Six To Five Against**
18 **KYLEMORE LOUGH (IRE)**, 7, b g Revoque (IRE)—One of The Last **M J McMahon & Denis Gallagher**
19 **MAGHERAL EXPRESS (IRE)**, 7, b g Gold Well—Patzanni (IRE) **Christopher W. T. Johnston**
20 **MATCHAWAY (IRE)**, 7, b g Milan—Hatch Away (IRE) **Mr & Mrs C R Elliott & Mr Will Roseff**
21 **MOUNTAINOUS (IRE)**, 11, b g Milan—Mullaghcloga (IRE) **Hartley Phillips Roseff Shields**
22 **MR BACHSTER (IRE)**, 11, b g Bach (IRE)—Warrior Princess (IRE) **R. A. Lee**
23 **NICHOLASCOPERNICUS (IRE)**, 7, ch g Medicean—Ascendancy **D. A. Halsall**
24 **RUSSE BLANC (FR)**, 9, wh g Machiavellian Tsar (FR)—Fleur de Mad (FR) **Mr M. R. H. Jackson**
25 **SCALES (IRE)**, 10, b g Bob Back (USA)—Mrs Avery (IRE) **A Beard B Beard S Ripley**
26 **SIMPLY WINGS (IRE)**, 12, b g Winged Love (IRE)—Simply Deep (IRE) **Sam Thorp & Kerry Lee**
27 **SIR WILL (IRE)**, 5, b g Yeats (IRE)—Tinopasa (FR) **West Coast Haulage**
28 **TOP GAMBLE (IRE)**, 8, ch g Presenting—Zeferina (IRE) **Walters Plant Hire & James & Jean Potter**
29 **TRESOR DE BONTEE (FR)**, 9, b g Grand Seigneur (FR)—Bontee (FR) **Glass Half Full**

Other Owners: Mrs B. M. Ayres, Mr R. L. Baker, R. Bartlett, A. C. Beard, B. M. Beard, Mrs R. L. Burling, Mr P. R. Burling, Lord Daresbury, Mrs J. A. Elliott, C. R. Elliott, Mr Denis Gallagher, Mr G. T. Gilbert, R. L. Hartley, Mr S. R. Holt, J. P. Hulston, Miss K. Lee, Mr Richard Lee, G. M. MacEchern, Mr M. J. McMahon, Mr P. Nolan, Mr P. T. G. Phillips, Mrs M. J. Potter, J. E. Potter, Lady Susan Ripley, Mr Will Roseff, Mr T. M. Shields, Mr S. Thorp, Walters Plant Hire Ltd, J. H. Watson, Mrs H. Watson.

Assistant Trainer: Richard Lee

Jockey (NH): Jake Greenall, Richard Johnson, Jamie Moore, Charlie Poste. **Conditional:** Ciaran Gethings.
Amateur: Mr Tom Marret, Mr Stan Sheppard, Miss Tabitha Worsley.

---

367 MRS SOPHIE LEECH, Westbury-on-Severn
Postal: T/A Leech Racing Limited, Tudor Racing Stables, Elton Road, Elton, Newnham, Gloucestershire, GL14 1JN
Contacts: **PHONE (01452) 760691 MOBILE (07775) 874630**
E-MAIL info@leechracing.co.uk WEBSITE www.leechracing.co.uk

1 **AMERICAN LIFE (FR)**, 9, b br g American Post—Poplife (FR) **American Life Partnership**
2 **AN POC AR BUILE (IRE)**, 7, ch g Mountain High (IRE)—Miniconjou (IRE) **Leech Racing Platinum Club**
3 **ANTEROS (IRE)**, 8, b g Milan—Sovereign Star (IRE) **K. W. Bell**
4 **BALLYMACAHILLCROSS (IRE)**, 8, br g Presenting—Topanberry (IRE)
5 **BANDIT COUNTRY (IRE)**, 7, b g Flemensfirth (USA)—Calomeria
6 **CHAMPAGNE N CAVIAR (IRE)**, 8, b g Tiger Hill (IRE)—Leukippids (IRE) **N. W. A. Bannister**
7 **CRY FURY**, 8, b g Beat Hollow—Cantanta **C. J. Leech**
8 **CULWORTH BOY (IRE)**, 6, b g Tajraasi (USA)—Cadre Idris (IRE) **Mrs S. E. Brown**
9 **DOTHRAKI RAIDER**, 5, b g Kayf Tara—French Spice **E O Haddock & M Gorman**
10 **DUN SCAITH (IRE)**, 8, b g Vinnie Roe (IRE)—Scathach (IRE)
11 **FLANS O MAN (IRE)**, 6, b g Milan—Boro Supreme (IRE)
12 **IMAN (IRE)**, 6, b g Dansili—Ioannina **Iman Partnership**
13 **KAPRICORNE (FR)**, 9, b g Kapgarde (FR)—Colombe Royale (FR) **Cheltenham Racing Club**
14 **LOOKSLIKERAINTED (IRE)**, 9, b g Milan—Kilcrea Gale (IRE) **J Cocks, R S Liddington & C J Leech**
15 **LOVCEN (GER)**, 11, b g Tiger Hill (IRE)—Lady Hawk (GER) **J. O'Brien & C. J. Leech**
16 **MAN OF PLENTY**, 7, ch g Manduro (GER)—Credit-A-Plenty **G. D. Thompson**
17 **MART LANE (IRE)**, 11, br g Stowaway—Western Whisper (IRE) **G. D. Thompson**
18 5, Br m Kalanisi (IRE)—Maxis Girl (IRE)
19 **MIDNIGHT APPEAL**, 11, b g Midnight Legend—Lac Marmot (FR) **GD Building Ltd,RS Liddington,CJ Leech**
20 **MOSTLY BOB (IRE)**, 13, b g Bob Back (USA)—Town Gossip (IRE) **Mr C. R. Leech**
21 4, B g Court Cave (IRE)—Native Success (IRE) **C. J. Leech**
22 **OLD MAGIC (IRE)**, 11, b g Old Vic—Maeve's Magic (IRE) **Cheltenham Racing Club**
23 **OLYMPIAN BOY (IRE)**, 12, b g Flemensfirth (USA)—Notanissue (IRE) **J. Cocks & C. J. Leech**
24 **OWEN GLENDOWER (IRE)**, 11, br g Anshan—Native Success (IRE) **O'Brien,Mitchell,Frame,Lawton & Leech**
25 **PADDLES LOUNGE (IRE)**, 9, b g Oscar (IRE)—Sister Rosza (IRE) **Mrs L. Winrow-Campbell**
26 **PECKHAMECHO (IRE)**, 10, b g Beneficial—Nolans Pride (IRE) **G. D. Thompson**
27 **RADMORES REVENGE**, 13, b g Overbury (IRE)—Harvey's Sister
28 **RIVER D'OR (FR)**, 11, b g Saint Preuil (FR)—Une Pomme d'or (FR)
29 **RIVER MAIGUE (IRE)**, 9, b g Zagreb (USA)—Minor Tantrum (IRE) **C. J. Leech**

MRS SOPHIE LEECH - Continued

30 **ROCKY ELSOM (USA)**, 9, b g Rock of Gibraltar (IRE)—Bowstring (IRE) **The Montpellier Friends**
31 **RUPERRA TOM**, 8, b g Kayf Tara—Cathy's Dream (IRE) **Mr T. J. Rees**
32 **SEVEN SUMMITS (IRE)**, 9, b g Danehill Dancer (IRE)—Mandavilla (IRE) **C. J. Leech**
33 **SILMI**, 12, gr g Daylami (IRE)—Intimaa (IRE) **J. O'Brien & C. J. Leech**
34 **SPANISH TREASURE (GER)**, 10, b g Black Sam Bellamy (IRE)—Santa Zinaada (GER) **Mr C. R. Leech**
35 **SWANAGE BAY (IRE)**, 9, b g Dilshaan—Special Mention (IRE) **Dr J. D. Dalton**
36 **TAMARILLO GROVE (IRE)**, 9, b g Cape Cross (IRE)—Tamarillo **G Doel, RS Liddington & C J Leech**
37 **WHITSTABLE NATIVE**, 8, b g Bertolini (USA)—Break of Dawn (USA) **Mr B. Woodward**
38 **WINSTON CHURCHILL (IRE)**, 10, b g Presenting—Star Councel (IRE) **G. D. Thompson**
39 **YASIR (USA)**, 8, b g Dynaformer (USA)—Khazayin (USA) **Mike Harris Racing Club**

Other Owners: Mr J. J. Cocks, Lord Daresbury, G. Doel, Mr K. A. Frame, GD Building & Roofing Contractors Ltd, Mr M. J. Gorman, Mr E. O. Haddock, A. D. I. Harris, Mr M. E. Harris, Mr M. D. Kilsby, Mr D. W. Lawton, Mr R. S. Liddington, Mr D. Mitchell, Mr J. P. Naylor, J. O'Brien, Mr C. Parkin, Mr J. T. Watts.

Assistant Trainer: Christian Leech (07880) 788464

Jockey (NH): Paul Moloney.

---

368 MRS SHEILA LEWIS, Brecon
Postal: Mill Cottage, Three Cocks, Brecon, Powys, LD3 0SL
Contacts: **PHONE** (01497) 847081
E-MAIL sheilalewisracing1@gmail.com

1 **CARHUE (IRE)**, 9, b g Luso—Awtaar (USA) **W. B. R. Davies**
2 **CASTLETOWN (IRE)**, 8, b g Oscar (IRE)—Closing Thyne (IRE) **W. B. R. Davies**
3 **FIRST IN THE QUEUE (IRE)**, 9, b g Azamour (IRE)—Irina (IRE) **W. B. R. Davies**
4 **TRY IT SOMETIME (IRE)**, 8, b g Milan—Lead'er Inn (IRE) **W. B. R. Davies**

---

369 MR CLIFFORD LINES, Exning
Postal: Hethersett House, Church House, Exning, Newmarket, Suffolk, CB8 7EH
Contacts: **PHONE** (01638) 608016 **FAX** (01638) 608016 **MOBILE** (07980) 120157
E-MAIL hethersetthouse@gmail.com

1 **TYRSAL (IRE)**, 5, b g Jeremy (USA)—Blanchelande (IRE) **Prima Racing Partnership**

THREE-YEAR-OLDS

2 **MISUE**, b f Hellvelyn—Milly-M

Other Owners: Ms S. Cawthorn, C. V. Lines.

---

370 MR BERNARD LLEWELLYN, Bargoed
Postal: Ffynonau Duon Farm, Pentwyn, Fochriw, Bargoed, Mid-Glamorgan, CF81 9NP
Contacts: **PHONE** (01685) 841259 **FAX** (01685) 843838 **MOBILE** (07971) 233473/(07960) 151083
E-MAIL bernard.llewellyn@btopenworld.com

1 **AAMAN (IRE)**, 10, gr g Dubai Destination (USA)—Amelinaa (IRE) **Mr A. James**
2 **ARTY CAMPBELL (IRE)**, 6, b g Dylan Thomas (IRE)—Kincob (USA) **Mr A. James**
3 **BOBBY DOVE**, 9, b g Fraam—Flakey Dove **B. J. Llewellyn**
4 **BORAK (IRE)**, 4, b g Kodiac—Right After Moyne (IRE) **Mr D. A. Smerdon**
5 **COSETTE (IRE)**, 5, b m Champs Elysees—Luanas Pearl (IRE) **Mr D. A. Smerdon**
6 **EDGE (IRE)**, 5, b g Acclamation—Chanter **Mr D. P. Maddocks**
7 **FILATORE (IRE)**, 7, ch g Teofilo (IRE)—Dragnet (IRE) **B. J. Llewellyn**
8 **FLANAGANS FIELD (IRE)**, 8, b g Araafa (IRE)—Zvezda (USA) **Mrs E. A. Llewellyn**
9 **FUZZY LOGIC (IRE)**, 7, b g Dylan Thomas (IRE)—Gates of Eden (USA) **G. Mills**
10 **GLOBAL THRILL**, 7, b g Big Shuffle (USA)—Goonda **Mr A. James**
11 **GOING NOWHERE FAST (IRE)**, 11, b g Exit To Nowhere (USA)—Sister Gabrielle (IRE) **A. J. Williams**
12 **HANSUPFORDETROIT (IRE)**, 11, b g Zagreb (USA)—Golden Needle (IRE) **Mr A. James**
13 **KASHGAR**, 7, b g Hernando (FR)—Miss Katmandu (IRE) **Mr A. James**
14 **KOZMINA BAY**, 7, b m Notnowcato—Kozmina (IRE) **Mr G. Anstee**
15 **L FRANK BAUM (IRE)**, 9, b g Sinndar (IRE)—Rainbow City (IRE) **B. J. Llewellyn**

MR BERNARD LLEWELLYN - Continued

16 LET ME IN (IRE), 6, ch g Pivotal—I Hearyou Knocking (IRE) **B. J. Llewellyn**
17 LIGHTS OF BROADWAY (IRE), 10, b m Broadway Flyer (USA)—Supreme Call (IRE) **B. W. Parren**
18 MARENGO, 5, gr g Verglas (IRE)—Cloudchaser (IRE) **Mrs Beth Williams**
19 NABHAN, 4, b g Youmzain (IRE)—Danidh Dubai (IRE) **Gethyn Mills & Alex James**
20 NEVER EQUALLED (IRE), 7, br g Brian Boru—Broken Thought (IRE) **Miss I. G. Tompsett**
21 NORAB (GER), 5, b g Galileo (IRE)—Night Woman (GER) **J. T. Warner**
22 PANDORICA, 8, b m Indesatchel (IRE)—Hope Chest **B. J. Llewellyn**
23 PETRIFY, 6, b g Rock of Gibraltar (IRE)—Frigid **Wesbry Racing**
24 SWEET WORLD, 12, b g Agnes World (USA)—Douce Maison (IRE) **B. J. Llewellyn**
25 TASTE THE WINE (IRE), 10, gr g Verglas (IRE)—Azia (IRE) **A. J. Williams**
26 TIJORI (IRE), 8, b g Kyllachy—Polish Belle **Mr M. V. Edwards**
27 TORETTO (IRE), 8, ch g Peintre Celebre (USA)—Petite-D-Argent **B. J. Llewellyn**

Other Owners: Mr R. Jasper.

Assistant Trainer: J L Llewellyn

Jockey (flat): Daniel Muscutt, David Probert. **Jockey (NH):** Mark Quinlan. **Conditional:** Jordan Williams, Robert Williams. **Apprentice:** Jordan Williams.

---

371 MISS NATALIE LLOYD-BEAVIS, East Garston
Postal: **Parsonage Racing Stables, Newbury Road, East Garston, Hungerford, Berkshire, RG17 7ER**
Contacts: **PHONE (01488) 648347 MOBILE (07768) 117656**
E-MAIL nlbracing@gmail.com

1 ANGELITO, 7, ch g Primo Valentino (IRE)—Supreme Angel **Parsonage Racing Partnership**
2 9, B g Singspiel (IRE)—Baileys Honour **G. B. Watts**
3 BOND MYSTERY, 4, b g Monsieur Bond (IRE)—Scooby Dooby Do **Miss N. A. Lloyd-Beavis**
4 8, Ch m Monsieur Bond (IRE)—Dangermouse **G. B. Watts**
5 FISHERMAN FRANK, 5, b g Rail Link—Ribbons And Bows (IRE) **Mr T. Suttle**
6 HIGHEST RED, 7, ch g Byron—Honor Rouge (IRE) **Miss N. A. Lloyd-Beavis**
7 HURRICANE ALERT, 4, b g Showcasing—Raggle Taggle (IRE) **Mr M. R. Baldry**
8 MEYREM ANA, 6, b m Beat All (USA)—Champagne Lou Lou **Miss N. A. Lloyd-Beavis**
9 5, B m Overbury (IRE)—Miss O'grady (IRE)
10 MUNICH (IRE), 12, b g Noverre (USA)—Mayara (IRE) **Miss N. A. Lloyd-Beavis**
11 ROLY TRICKS, 5, b m Pastoral Pursuits—Freya Tricks **R. Eagle**
12 TAX REFORM (IRE), 6, b g Namid—Happy Flight (IRE) **Mr M. R. Baldry**
13 WICKED TARA, 6, b m Assertive—Tara King **Mr K. Walters**

THREE-YEAR-OLDS

14 DYNAMITE SAMMY, ch f Black Sam Bellamy (IRE)—Darcique **Miss N. A. Lloyd-Beavis**
15 ISHIANICON, b f Sixties Icon—Ishibee (IRE) **G. B. Watts**
16 JOULES, b c Oasis Dream—Frappe (IRE) **Parsonage Racing Partnership**
17 TIM THE TAXI, b g Compton Place—Polar Dawn **Mr T. Suttle**
18 TWILIGHT PURSUITS, b f Pastoral Pursuits—Exexel **Mr M. R. Baldry**

Jockey (NH): David Bass. **Apprentice:** Charlie Bennett.

---

372 MR ALAN LOCKWOOD, Malton
Postal: **Fleet Cross Farm, Brawby, Malton, North Yorkshire, YO17 6QA**
Contacts: **PHONE (01751) 431796 MOBILE (07747) 002535**

1 AUTHENTICATION, 7, b g Authorized (IRE)—Valley of Gold (FR) **A. J. Lockwood**
2 BELLE PEINTURE (FR), 5, ch m Peintre Celebre (USA)—Grosgrain (USA) **Highgreen Partnership**
3 CHRISTMAS LIGHT, 9, b m Zafeen (FR)—Arabian Dancer **A. J. Lockwood**
4 PORT VIEW (IRE), 10, b g Classic Cliche (IRE)—Francie's Treble **A. J. Lockwood**

Other Owners: T. Crawford, D. J. Lumley, Mr J. Richardson, J. Stubbs, Mr Derek Wilson.

373 MR DAVID LODER, Bishops Castle
Postal: **David Loder Racing Ltd, Newton Farm House, Bishops Castle, Shropshire, SY9 5DS**
Contacts: PHONE **(01588) 630279**
E-MAIL office@davidloder.co.uk

1 BOSTON DE LA ROCHE (FR), 5, b g Malinas (GER)—
            Quesland de La Roche (FR) **Highclere Thoroughbred Racing - Boston I**
2 4, B g Kalanisi (IRE)—Dancing Hill **Glencoe Investments**
3 FRANCOPHILE (FR), 4, ch g Sea The Stars (IRE)—Empress of France (USA) **Glencoe Investments**
4 HI VIC (IRE), 11, ch g Old Vic—Tully Bridge (IRE) **Mrs W. D. Sykes**
5 KATERNER (FR), 4, b g Westerner—Kaprissima (FR) **Quartet**
6 MIDAS GOLD (IRE), 4, b g Rip Van Winkle (IRE)—Hespera **Glencoe Investments 2**
7 MIDNIGHT TOUR, 6, b m Midnight Legend—Uppermost **James & Jean Potter**
8 MISS FLEMING, 4, b f Flemensfirth (USA)—Uppermost **Quartet**
9 NANCY'S TRIX (IRE), 7, br m Presenting—Murrurundi (IRE) **OE Racing NH Partnership**
10 OLD PRIDE (IRE), 8, ch g Old Vic—Feel The Pride (IRE) **Mrs F. H. Hay**
11 RECENTLY ACQUIRED, 4, b g Beat Hollow—Acquisition **Quartet**
12 4, Ch f Schiaparelli (GER)—Royal Keel **Glencoe Investments**
13 SHABRAQUE (IRE), 4, b g Azamour (IRE)—Teide Lady
14 VAN WILDER (IRE), 4, b g Rip Van Winkle (IRE)—Zelding (IRE) **Glencoe Investments**

Other Owners: Mr J. G. D. Brocklehurst, Highclere Nominated Partner Limited, Highclere Thoroughbred Racing Ltd, D. R. Loder, Mrs A. J. Loder, C. Longsdon, Mrs I. Peter-Hoblyn, J. E. Potter, Mrs M. J. Potter, Mr R. C. Wilkin.

374 MR JOHN E. LONG, Royston
Postal: **Lower Yard, Kings Ride Stables, Baldock Road, Royston, Hertfordshire, SG8 9NN**
Contacts: MOBILE **(07958) 296945/(07815) 186085**
E-MAIL winalot@aol.com

1 BERMACHA, 11, ch m Bertolini (USA)—Machaera **M. J. Gibbs**
2 CHANDRAYAAN, 9, ch g Bertolini (USA)—Muffled (USA) **R. D. John**
3 ESPRESSO ROMANO, 5, b m Pastoral Pursuits—Canterloupe (IRE) **Mr J. S. Muscat**
4 MULTI QUEST, 4, b f Multiplex—Ryan's Quest (IRE) **M. J. Gibbs**
5 MYBROTHERJOHNNY, 5, b g Tiger Hill (IRE)—Montjeu's Melody (IRE) **Mr J. S. Muscat**
6 ROBERO, 4, b c Piccolo—Ceilidh Band **Ms M. Todd**
7 TRUST ME BOY, 8, gr g Avonbridge—Eastern Lyric **R. Pearson & J. Pearson**
8 WILLOW JUBILEE, 4, b f Champs Elysees—Opera Belle **Mrs S. Bambridge**

Other Owners: Miss J. L. Pearson, Mr R. J. Pearson.

Assistant Trainer: Miss S Cassidy

375 MR CHARLIE LONGSDON, Chipping Norton
Postal: **Hull Farm Stables, Stratford Road, Chipping Norton, Oxfordshire, OX7 5QF**
Contacts: PHONE **(08450) 525264 FAX (08450) 525265 MOBILE (07775) 993263**
E-MAIL charlie@charlielongsdonracing.com WEBSITE www.charlielongsdonracing.com

1 A VOS GARDES (FR), 6, br g Kapgarde (FR)—Miscia Nera (FR) **The Rollright Stones**
2 APPLE OF OUR EYE, 6, b g Passing Glance—Apple Anthem **The Tweed Clad Fossils**
3 ARGOT, 5, b g Three Valleys (USA)—Tarot Card **Westbourne Racing Club**
4 ATLANTIC GOLD (IRE), 6, b g Robin des Pres (FR)—Marys Isle (IRE) **C W Booth & Mark E Smith**
5 AZURE FLY (IRE), 8, br g Blueprint (IRE)—Lady Delight (IRE) **Girls Allowed**
6 BALLYDINE (IRE), 6, ch g Stowaway—Bealaha Essie (IRE) **D. A. Halsall**
7 BESTWORK (FR), 5, bl g Network (GER)—Harmony (FR) **CLS Bloodstock**
8 BOB TUCKER (IRE), 9, b g Brian Boru—Acumen (IRE) **Mr N. Davies**
9 BRANDENBURG GATE (IRE), 5, b g Germany (USA)—Miss Anchor (IRE) **Swanee River Partnership**
10 CADOUDOFF (FR), 6, gr g Davidoff (GER)—Hera du Berlais (FR) **The Four Kings**
11 COOLOGUE (IRE), 7, b g Helissio (FR)—Scolboa (IRE) **The New Club Partnership**
12 COOPER'S FRIEND (IRE), 7, b g Kayf Tara—Graphic Lady (IRE) **The Stewkley Shindiggers Partnership**

MR CHARLIE LONGSDON - Continued

13 **CRACK OF THUNDER (IRE)**, 7, b g September Storm (GER)—Keep Hunting (IRE) **Crack Of Thunder Partnership**
14 **CRAZY PENGUIN (IRE)**, 5, b g Milan—Lady Appeal (IRE) **Swanee River Partnership**
15 **CRICKEL WOOD (FR)**, 6, b g Muhtathir—Tanguista (FR) **Mr R. J. Aplin**
16 **DEFINITLY GREY (IRE)**, 5, gr g Daylami (IRE)—Caroline Fontenail (IRE) **Jeromes Partnership**
17 **DROP OUT JOE**, 8, ch g Generous (IRE)—La Feuillarde (FR) **The Jesters**
18 **EN PASSE (IRE)**, 7, b m Flemensfirth (USA)—Asklynn **Mr P. J. Curtin**
19 **FRAMPTON (IRE)**, 7, b g Presenting—Drumavish Lass (IRE) **Mr R. D. H. Brindle**
20 **GERMANY CALLING (IRE)**, 7, b g Germany (USA)—Markir (GER) **Mr T. Hanlon**
21 **GRANDADS HORSE**, 10, b br g Bollin Eric—Solid Land (FR) **Whites of Coventry Limited**
22 **HANNIBAL THE GREAT (IRE)**, 8, b g Milan—Town Gossip (IRE) **The Pantechnicons**
23 **HARRISTOWN**, 6, ch g Bering—New Abbey **Kyuna Memories**
24 **KALANE (IRE)**, 7, b m Kalanisi (IRE)—Fairy Lane (IRE) **P. Murphy**
25 **KILCOOLEY (IRE)**, 7, b g Stowaway—Bealaha Essie (IRE) **J. H. & S. M. Wall**
26 **KILLALA QUAY**, 9, b g Karinga Bay—Madam Bijou **Mr Richard & Mrs Susan Perkins**
27 **LEITH HILL LAD**, 6, b g Kayf Tara—Leith Hill Star **Mrs J. Maltby**
28 **LEITH HILL LEGASI**, 7, b m Kahyasi—Leith Hill Star **Mr & Mrs N. F. Maltby**
29 **LONG LUNCH**, 7, b g Kayf Tara—Royal Keel **Battersby, Birchall, Halsall & Vestey**
30 **LOOSE CHIPS**, 10, b g Sir Harry Lewis (USA)—Worlaby Rose **Barrels Of Courage**
31 **MAGIC MUSTARD (IRE)**, 5, ch g Stowaway—Honey Mustard (IRE) **Magic Mustard Partnership**
32 **MASTERPLAN (IRE)**, 6, b g Spadoun (FR)—Eurolucy (IRE) **G. M. MacEchern**
33 **MIDNIGHT GEM**, 6, b m Midnight Legend—Barton Flower **Ms G. E. Morgan**
34 **MIDNIGHT SHOT**, 6, b g Midnight Legend—Suave Shot **D. A. Halsall**
35 **MOLO**, 6, b m Kalanisi (IRE)—Belle Magello (FR) **The Encore Syndicate**
36 **MONBEG CHARMER (IRE)**, 5, br g Daylami (IRE)—Charming Present (IRE) **Lady Dulverton**
37 **NIGHTFLY**, 5, b m Midnight Legend—Whichway Girl **Mrs D. P. G. Flory**
38 **NIGHTLINE**, 6, b g Midnight Legend—Whichway Girl **Mrs D. P. G. Flory**
39 **NO NO JOLIE (FR)**, 4, gr f Martaline—Virgata (FR) **R. Jenner & J. Green**
40 **NO NO MAC (IRE)**, 7, b g Oscar (IRE)—Whatdoyouthinkmac (IRE) **R. Jenner & J. Green**
41 **OFF THE GROUND**, 10, b g Oscar (IRE)—Kaysel (IRE) **Off The Ground**
42 **ORANGE NASSAU (FR)**, 10, gr g Martaline—Vilaya (FR) **The Ferandlin Peaches**
43 **OUR KAEMPFER (IRE)**, 7, b g Oscar (IRE)—Gra-Bri (IRE) **Swanee River Partnership**
44 **PENDRA (IRE)**, 8, ch g Old Vic—Mariah Rollins (IRE) **J. P. McManus**
45 **PETE THE FEAT (IRE)**, 12, b g King's Theatre (IRE)—Tourist Attraction (IRE) **Don Sebastiao Partnership**
46 **PIED DU ROI (IRE)**, 6, b g Robin des Pres (FR)—Long Acre **The Pantechnicons II**
47 **PROMANCO**, 7, b m Kayf Tara—Shelayly (IRE) **Mrs S. I. Tainton**
48 **QUIETO SOL (FR)**, 5, ch g Loup Solitaire (USA)—First Wonder (FR) **Mrs S. Longsdon**
49 **READY TOKEN (IRE)**, 8, gr g Flemensfirth (USA)—Ceol Tire (IRE) **Foxtrot Racing: Ready Token**
50 **REPEAT THE FEAT (FR)**, 5, br g Kingsalsa (USA)—Sharon du Berlais (FR) **Don Sebastiao Partnership**
51 **SAINT CAJETON (FR)**, 4, b g Saint des Saints (FR)—Erivieve (FR) **Five Saints Racing**
52 **SARPECH (IRE)**, 5, b g Sea The Stars (IRE)—Sadima (IRE) **Mr Richard & Mrs Susan Perkins**
53 **SCORPION PRINCESS (IRE)**, 5, b m Scorpion (IRE)—Cailin's Princess (IRE) **Mr J. N. Greenley**
54 **SHANTOU MAGIC (IRE)**, 9, b g Shantou (USA)—Supreme Magical **Owners For Owners: Shantou Magic**
55 **SHE'S SOME FLOWER**, 4, b f Midnight Legend—Samandara (FR) **Mr P. J. Curtin**
56 **SHEAR ROCK (IRE)**, 6, b g Spadoun (FR)—Sleeping Diva (FR) **Jones, Smith & Walsh**
57 **SILENT WARRIOR**, 4, br g Yeats (IRE)—Zariyka (IRE) **Cheltenham Amigos**
58 **SIMPLY THE WEST (IRE)**, 7, b g Westerner—Back To Stay (IRE) **Biddestone Racing Partnership XI**
59 **SNOW LEOPARDESS**, 4, gr f Martaline—Queen Soraya **Mrs M. M. Fox-Pitt**
60 **SONG OF THE NIGHT (IRE)**, 5, b g Mahler—Pollys Attic (IRE) **Neysauteur Partnership & Robert Aplin**
61 **SPIRIT OF SHANKLY**, 8, ch g Sulamani (IRE)—Lago d'oro (IRE) **D. A. Halsall**
62 **SPORTS DAY**, 4, b f Beat Hollow—Midsummer Magic **Her Majesty The Queen**
63 **ST JOHNS POINT (IRE)**, 8, b g Darsi (FR)—Dunsford Belle (IRE) **No Boys Allowed**
64 **THE FUGITIVE (IRE)**, 5, b g Flemensfirth (USA)—Alleygrove Lass (IRE) **Owners For Owners: The Fugitive**
65 **TINTED ROSE**, 4, ch f Black Sam Bellamy (IRE)—Miniature Rose **Jones, Broughtons, Wilson, Weaver**
66 **TJONGEJONGE (FR)**, 5, b g Blue Bresil (FR)—Vavea (FR) **The Halsall Family**
67 **TULLOW TONIC (IRE)**, 5, b m Beneficial—Annalecky (IRE) **Hamer, Hawkes & Hellin**
68 **VIVAS (IRE)**, 5, b br g Davidoff (GER)—Lavircas (FR) **Mr N. Davies**
69 **VIVE LE ROI (IRE)**, 5, b g Robin des Pres (FR)—Cappard View (IRE) **Mr T. Richens**
70 **WELLS DE LUNE (FR)**, 5, b g Irish Wells (FR)—Pepite de Lune (FR) **Swanee River Partnership**
71 **WESTERN MILLER (IRE)**, 5, b g Westerner—Definite Miller (IRE) **The Pantechnicons IV**
72 **WILBERDRAGON**, 6, b g Kayf Tara—Swaythe (USA) **R. Jenner & J. Green**
73 **ZARA HOPE (IRE)**, 5, b m Stowaway—Agua Caliente (IRE) **Mr M. E. Smith**

MR CHARLIE LONGSDON - Continued

Other Owners: Mr D. Abraham, Mr Tareq Al-Mazeedi, Mr Robert Aplin, Mr William Armitage, Mr Hugh Arthur, Mr George Bailey, Mr Nigel Birch, Mr C. W. Booth, Mr Tim Bostwick, Mr T. Boylan, Mr Richard Brindle, Mr Ian M. Brown, Mr James Burley, Mr John Cantrill, Mr Ashley Carr, Mr Steve Corcoran, Mr C K Crossley Cooke, Mrs R. Doel, Mrs Cax du Pon, Mr F. S. W. Dudley, Mr Ian Dunbar, Mr Tim Dykes, Mr Peter Erskine, Mr William Esdaile, Mr H. Fentum, Mr H. Gallacher, Mr Ivan Howard Goldsmith, Mrs J. Green, Mr M. W. Gregory, Mr Jonathan Halsall, Mr B. R. Halsall, Mr Alan Halsall, Mr C. M. Hamer, Mrs R. J. Harris, Mr P. V. Harris, Mr M. Hawkes, Mr M. R. Hawkins, Mrs Louise Hellin, Mr W. John Henderson, Mr Dev Hill, Mrs H. J. Hoffman, Mr Jon Hughes, Ms R. Jenner, Mr Colin Jones, Mr Chris Jordan, Mrs Louise King, Mr S. Lambert, Mr G. J. Larby, Mrs Sarah Jane Lavan, Mr O. Lee, Mr Charles Liverton, Mr J. K. Llewellyn, Mrs S. Longsdon, Mr Charlie Longsdon, Mrs N. F. Maltby, Mr N. F. Maltby, Mr C. Marriott, Mr David Mason, Mrs Sue Morley, Mr John Motson, Dr M. M. Ogilvy, Mrs H. Pauling, Miss Nicola Pearson, Mr R. A. H. Perkins, Mrs R. S. Perkins, Mr B. P. Roberts, Mr John Roddan, Mr Hugh Shapter, Mr W. G. Shaw, Mr Peter J. Smith, Mr Mark E. Smith, Mrs S. Spencer-Jones, Mr S. Spencer-Jones, Mrs John Steel, Mrs S. M. Wall, Mr J. H. Wall, Mrs Caren Walsh, Westbourne Consultants Ltd, Mr Jim White, Mr F. Wintle, Mr James D. G. Wright.

Assistant Trainer: David John Jeffreys

Jockey (NH): Noel Fehily. **Conditional:** Charlie Deutsch. **Amateur:** Miss Claire Hart.

---

376 **MR DANIEL MARK LOUGHNANE, Butterton**
Postal: **Butterton Racing Stables, Park Road, Butterton, Newcastle, Staffordshire, ST5 4DZ**
Contacts: **MOBILE (07805) 531021**

1 **ALMANACK**, 6, b g Haatef (USA)—Openness **Mr P. Slater**
2 **APACHE GLORY (USA)**, 8, b br m Cherokee Run (USA)—Jumeirah Glory (USA) **Mr J. Stimpson**
3 **AUSSIE RULER (IRE)**, 4, br g Aussie Rules (USA)—Experiment (IRE) **S. & A. Mares**
4 **BASINGSTOKE (IRE)**, 7, b g Elusive City (USA)—Ryninch (IRE) **The Batham Boys**
5 **BINKY BLUE (IRE)**, 4, b f Approve (IRE)—Sabander Bay (USA) **Mrs C. M. Loughnane**
6 **CANTANKEROUS**, 5, b g Myboycharlie (IRE)—Akhira **Ian O'Connor & Clare Loughnane**
7 **CHARLIE LAD**, 4, b g Myboycharlie (IRE)—Night Owl **S & A Mares & C Loughnane**
8 **COILLTE CAILIN (IRE)**, 6, b m Oratorio (IRE)—Forest Walk (IRE) **Mr P. Moran**
9 **COSMIC RAY**, 4, b g Phoenix Reach (IRE)—Beat Seven **Over The Moon Racing III**
10 **DILETTA TOMMASA (IRE)**, 6, ch m Dylan Thomas (IRE)—Chronicle **Mr J. Stimpson**
11 **FOR SHIA AND LULA (IRE)**, 7, b g Majestic Missile (IRE)—Jack-N-Jilly (IRE) **Over The Moon Racing IV**
12 **JOLLY RED JEANZ (IRE)**, 5, ch m Intense Focus (USA)—Sovienne (USA) **MMIMM Racing**
13 **JUMBO PRADO (USA)**, 7, gr ro g El Prado (IRE)—Sant Elena **Mr J. Stimpson**
14 **KHAJAALY (IRE)**, 9, b g Kheleyf (USA)—Joyfullness (USA) **Amazing Racing**
15 **LES GAR GAN (IRE)**, 5, b m Iffraaj—Story **Mr J. P. Evitt**
16 **LOGANS LAD (IRE)**, 6, b g Baltic King—Lulu Island **Mr Ian O'Connor**
17 **MATRAASH (USA)**, 10, b h Elusive Quality (USA)—Min Alhawa (USA) **Over The Moon Racing**
18 **MR DANDY MAN (IRE)**, 5, ch g Dandy Man (IRE)—Boudica (IRE) **S. & A. Mares**
19 **ON A WHIM**, 4, b f Tamayuz—Love Me Tender **Mr R. M. Brilley**
20 **ROSSMORE'S PRIDE (IRE)**, 8, br g Heron Island (IRE)—Parsons Supreme (IRE) **Mr D. H. Slater**
21 **THE FIRM (IRE)**, 7, b g Acclamation—Aspen Falls (USA) **Amazing Racing**
22 **VERUS DELICIA (IRE)**, 7, b m Chineur (FR)—Ribbon Glade (UAE) **Mr R. M. Brilley**
23 **VIVA VERGLAS (IRE)**, 5, gr g Verglas (IRE)—Yellow Trumpet **The Batham Boys**
24 **YOURINTHEWILL (USA)**, 8, ch g Aragorn (IRE)—Lenarue (USA)
25 **ZED CANDY GIRL**, 6, ch m Sakhee's Secret—Musical Twist (USA) **Mr J. Stimpson**

THREE-YEAR-OLDS

26 **AFRICAN TRADER (USA)**, b br c Lonhro (AUS)—Nasaieb (IRE) **Mr D. H. Slater**
27 **ALWAYS ENDEAVOUR**, b f Amadeus Wolf—Anaya **Mr Ian O'Connor**
28 **ANGELICAL (IRE)**, b f Dark Angel (IRE)—Ladylishandra (IRE) **Ms A. Quinn**
29 **INWITHACHANCE (IRE)**, b g Thousand Words—Sombreffe **Live In Hope Partnership**
30 **LITTLE MISS KODI (IRE)**, b f Kodiac—Sensasse (IRE) **S. & A. Mares**
31 **ORMANUMPS (IRE)**, b g Elnadim (USA)—Tawjeeh **Mr R. M. Brilley**
32 **PENSAX LADY (IRE)**, b f Fast Company (IRE)—Aljafliyah **S. & A. Mares**
33 **PORCUPINE CREEK (IRE)**, b g Zebedee—Daanaat (IRE) **Mr P. Slater**
34 **SOMEPINK (IRE)**, b f Lilbourne Lad (IRE)—Cloonkeary **Mr R. M. Brilley**
35 **STREET OUTLAW (IRE)**, b g Haatef (USA)—Helen Wells (IRE) **Mr P. Slater**
36 **SUNSHINEANDBUBBLES**, b f Multiplex—Dockside Strike **Amazing Racing**
37 B c Holy Roman Emperor (IRE)—Tralanza (IRE)
38 **WHACKING BULLOCK (IRE)**, b c Lovelace—Carracove (IRE) **Mr P. Slater**

MR DANIEL MARK LOUGHNANE - Continued

TWO-YEAR-OLDS
39 AFFORDABILITY, b c 6/3 Bushranger (IRE)—Munaa's Dream (Oasis Dream) (4761) **Mr Ian O'Connor**
40 B f 19/4 Lilbourne Lad (IRE)—Cape Sydney (IRE) (Cape Cross (IRE))
41 B f 22/4 Stimulation (IRE)—Lambadora (Suave Dancer (USA))
42 B c 19/4 Thewayyouare (USA)—Margaux Dancer (IRE) (Danehill Dancer (IRE)) (7382) **The Batham Boys**
43 B c 1/4 Nayef (USA)—Pooka's Daughter (IRE) (Eagle Eyed (USA)) (9966) **The Batham Boys**

Other Owners: Mr D. S. Allan, K. J. Corcoran, B. Dunn, S. P. Hackney, Mr R. M. Hough, Mr M. O. Hough, Mr S. Mares, Mrs A. Mares, Mr A. T. Pierce, Mrs P. A. Smith, Mr C. E. Weare.

377

MR DAVID LOUGHNANE, Nawton
Postal: **Arthington Barn Stables, Highfield Lane, Nawton, York, YO62 7TU**
Contacts: PHONE **(01439) 770184** MOBILE **(07527) 173197**
E-MAIL **info@daveloughnaneracing.com** WEBSITE **www.daveloughnaneracing.com**

1 **AGE OF ELEGANCE (IRE)**, 4, b f Makfi—Elegant Pride **Nawton Bloodstock**
2 **BALDUCCI**, 9, b g Dansili—Miss Meltemi (IRE) **Roger Fell**
3 **BRITISH EMBASSY (IRE)**, 4, b g Clodovil (IRE)—Embassy Belle (IRE) **Nawton Bloodstock**
4 **CAMCHICA (IRE)**, 4, b f Camacho—Varnay **Nawton Bloodstock**
5 **EARTH DRUMMER (IRE)**, 6, b g Dylan Thomas (IRE)—In Dubai (USA) **Nawton Bloodstock**
6 **ELLE DORADO**, 4, ch f Paco Boy (IRE)—Clever Millie (USA) **Nawton Bloodstock**
7 **FUWAIRT (IRE)**, 4, b g Arcano (IRE)—Safiya Song (IRE) **Roses Partnership & Roger Fell**
8 **HAZEL BLUE (IRE)**, 5, b m Kodiac—Pure Folly (IRE) **Roger Fell**
9 **MONT RAS (IRE)**, 9, ch g Indian Ridge—Khayrat (IRE) **Colne Valley Racing**
10 **MUNTADAB (IRE)**, 4, b g Invincible Spirit (IRE)—Chibola (ARG) **Roger Fell & High Hopes Partnership**
11 **MUQARRED (USA)**, 4, b g Speightstown (USA)—Bawaara (FR) **Nawton Bloodstock**
12 **SHERIFF OF NAWTON (IRE)**, 5, b g Lawman (FR)—Pivotal Role **Roger Fell**
13 **SOPHISTICATED HEIR (IRE)**, 6, b g New Approach (IRE)—
My Girl Sophie (USA) **Colne Valley Racing & Roger Fell**
14 **THANKSTOMONTY**, 4, b g Dylan Thomas (IRE)—Beldarian **Colne Valley Racing**
15 **TWO FOR TWO (IRE)**, 8, b g Danehill Dancer (IRE)—D'articleshore (IRE) **Nawton Bloodstock**

THREE-YEAR-OLDS
16 **DON'T TELL NIK (IRE)**, b f Lawman (FR)—Karliysha (IRE) **Roger Fell**
17 **HIGHTIME GIRL**, ch f Pivotal—Hightime Heroine (IRE) **Middleham Park**
18 **LOZAH**, b f Lawman (FR)—Princess Luna (GER) **Nawton Bloodstock**
19 Ch f Frozen Power (IRE)—Pivotal Role **Roger Fell**

TWO-YEAR-OLDS
20 B f 13/2 Tagula (IRE)—Celtic Lynn (IRE) (Celtic Swing) (12550) **Roger Fell**
21 Ch c 24/4 Bahamian Bounty—Clytha (Mark of Esteem (IRE)) (14765) **Roger Fell**

378

MR SHAUN LYCETT, Cheltenham
Postal: **Church Farm, Little Rissington, Cheltenham, Gloucestershire, GL54 2ND**
Contacts: PHONE **(01451) 824143** MOBILE **(07788) 100894**
E-MAIL **trainer@bourtonhillracing.co.uk** WEBSITE **www.bourtonhillracing.co.uk**

1 **ALL THE WINDS (GER)**, 11, ch g Samum (GER)—All Our Luck (GER) **Nicholls Family**
2 **AUMERLE**, 4, b g Authorized (IRE)—Succinct **D. Teevan**
3 **BALMORAL PRINCE**, 5, b g Multiplex—Balmoral Princess **Mr H. S. Maan**
4 **BARE NECESSITIES (IRE)**, 6, b g Sandmason—Marquante (IRE) **D Gilbert, M Lawrence, A Bruce**
5 **EXCELLENT PUCK (IRE)**, 6, b g Excellent Art—Puck's Castle **Davis Phelps Nicholls Atkins**
6 **MALAYSIAN BOLEH**, 6, ch g Compton Place—Orlena (USA) **D Gilbert, M Lawrence, A Bruce, G Wills**
7 **MARMALAD (IRE)**, 4, b g Duke of Marmalade (IRE)—Primissima (USA) **D. Teevan**
8 **MIKEYS DREAM (IRE)**, 7, b g Vinnie Roe (IRE)—Missallusion (IRE) **S. Lycett**
9 **MONSART (IRE)**, 4, b g Echo of Light—Monet's Lady (IRE) **L & M Atkins**
10 **NUTCRACKER PRINCE**, 5, b g Rail Link—Plum Fairy **D Gilbert, M Lawrence, A Bruce**
11 **OUR GOLDEN GIRL**, 6, ch m Dutch Art—Nemorosa **The Golden Boys Partnership**
12 **OVERRIDER**, 6, b g Cockney Rebel—Fustaan (IRE) **L & M Atkins**
13 **PRIMROSE COURT (IRE)**, 6, ch m Golan (IRE)—Sugar Kane Kowa (IRE) **S. Lycett**
14 **TIDAL WAY (IRE)**, 7, gr g Red Clubs (IRE)—Taatof (IRE) **Mr H. E. Peachey**

MR SHAUN LYCETT - Continued

15 **VICARAGE GOLD,** 4, b f Kheleyf (USA)—Kyleene **The Golden Boys Partnership**
16 **WINDY WRITER (IRE),** 6, b br g Rudimentary (USA)—Hardabout (IRE) **Worcester Racing Club**

Other Owners: Mr L. Atkins, Mrs M. Atkins, Mr D. R. Gilbert, M. P. Hill, Mr M. Lawrence, Mr M. Lovett, Mr P. Nicholls, Mr R. Nicholls, Mrs E. Nicholls, Mr M. White, Mr G. Wills.

---

379 MR JOHN MACKIE, Church Broughton
Postal: **The Bungalow, Barton Blount, Church Broughton, Derby**
Contacts: PHONE **(01283) 585604/585603** FAX **(01283) 585603** MOBILE **(07799) 145283**
E-MAIL **jmackie@bartonblount.freeserve.co.uk**

1 **AVAILABLE (IRE),** 7, b m Moss Vale (IRE)—Divert (IRE) **Derbyshire Racing V**
2 **CAPTAIN SWIFT (IRE),** 5, br g Captain Rio—Grannys Reluctance (IRE) **Mrs S. P. Adams**
3 **DUNQUIN (IRE),** 4, b g Cape Cross (IRE)—Last Resort **Mrs C. Seymour**
4 **FIGHTER JET,** 8, b g Oasis Dream—Totality **Ladas**
5 **HALLSTATT (IRE),** 10, ch g Halling (USA)—Last Resort **NSU Leisure & Mrs Carolyn Seymour**
6 **HURRY HOME POPPA (IRE),** 6, b g Holy Roman Emperor (IRE)—My Renee (USA) **Mr D. Ward**
7 **IMPECCABILITY,** 6, b m Lucky Story (USA)—Impeccable Guest (IRE) **Derbyshire Racing IV**
8 **INFLEXIBALL,** 4, b f Refuse To Bend (IRE)—Sphere (IRE) **Derbyshire Racing II**
9 **INNISH MAN (IRE),** 4, b g Fastnet Rock (AUS)—Super Gift (IRE) **Derbyshire Racing VII**
10 **KANTARA CASTLE (IRE),** 5, b g Baltic King—Arbitration (IRE) **Derbyshire Racing III**
11 **KEEP CALM,** 6, b g War Chant (USA)—Mayaar (USA) **Derbyshire Racing VI**
12 **L'INGANNO FELICE (FR),** 6, br g Librettist (USA)—Final Overture (FR) **Mr A. Dawson & Mrs K. Campbell**
13 **MARMAS,** 7, ch g Sir Percy—Kitabaat (IRE) **Mr G. R. Shelton**
14 **MOON JET (IRE),** 4, b g Ask—Playwaki (USA) **Ladas**
15 **OFF THE PULSE,** 6, b g Araafa (IRE)—Off By Heart **Mr G. B. Maher**
16 **OFFBEAT SAFARIS (IRE),** 8, b g Le Vie Dei Colori—Baywood **Mrs E. M. Mackie**
17 **RIVER PURPLE,** 9, b g Bollin Eric—Cerise Bleue (FR) **Sotby Farming Company Limited**
18 **ROBBEN,** 4, b g Dutch Art—Little Greenbird **Sotby Farming Company Limited**
19 **ROCK SONG,** 7, b g Rock of Gibraltar (IRE)—Jackie's Opera (FR) **Mr G. R. Shelton**

THREE-YEAR-OLDS

20 **FIRE JET (IRE),** ch f Ask—Lightning Jet **Ladas**

TWO-YEAR-OLDS

21 **LUNAR JET,** ch c 10/4 Ask—Lightning Jet (Dutch Art) **Ladas**

Other Owners: Mr S. P. Adams, Mrs Kate Campbell, Mr A. Dawson, Mrs J. Mackie, Mr Christopher Mullin, Mrs May Mullin, NSU Leisure Ltd, Mr David Penman, Mrs Carolyn Seymour, Mr A. J. Wall, Mr C. J. Wall.

---

380 MR BRUCE MACTAGGART, Hawick
Postal: **Greendale, Hawick, Roxburghshire, TD9 7LH**
Contacts: PHONE/FAX **(01450) 372086** MOBILE **(07764) 159852/(07718) 920072**
E-MAIL **brucemact@btinternet.com**

1 4, B f Robin des Champs (FR)—Buffy **K. Rennie**
2 4, B f King's Theatre (IRE)—Daisies Adventure (IRE) **Mrs H. A. M. Mactaggart**
3 **FLOWALONG (IRE),** 6, b m Flemensfirth (USA)—Water Stratford (IRE) **Greendale Racing Syndicate**
4 **RED TANBER (IRE),** 13, ch g Karinga Bay—Dreamy Desire **Hugh T. Redhead**
5 4, B f King's Theatre (IRE)—Water Stratford (IRE)

Other Owners: Mrs F. M. Godson.

Assistant Trainer: Mrs H. Mactaggart

---

381 MR PETER MADDISON, Skewsby
Postal: **5 West End Cottages, Skewsby, York, YO61 4SG**
Contacts: PHONE **(01347) 888385**

1 **BATTLEDANCER,** 10, b g Baryshnikov (AUS)—Cede Nullis **P. Maddison**
2 **MINDEN DAWN,** 10, gr m Baryshnikov (AUS)—Minden Rose **P. Maddison**

MR PETER MADDISON - Continued

3 **MINDEN MARCH**, 11, b m Baryshnikov (AUS)—Minden Rose **P. Maddison**
4 **SGT BULL BERRY**, 9, b g Alflora (IRE)—Cede Nullis **P. Maddison**

Conditional: Jamie Hamilton.

---

382 MR MICHAEL MADGWICK, Denmead
Postal: Forest Farm, Forest Road, Denmead, Waterlooville, Hampshire, PO7 6UA
Contacts: **PHONE/FAX** (02392) 258313 **MOBILE** (07835) 964969

1 **COMEDY HOUSE**, 8, b g Auction House (USA)—Kyle Akin **Los Leader**
2 **JERSEY BULL (IRE)**, 4, b g Clodovil (IRE)—Chaguaramas (IRE) **Mrs S. G. Bunney**
3 **MANHATTAN MEAD**, 6, ch g Central Park (IRE)—Honey Nut **Mrs L N Harmes, K McCormack & M Madgwick**
4 **MONEY TALKS**, 6, br g Motivator—Movie Mogul **Recycled Products Limited**
5 **MULTITASK**, 6, b g Multiplex—Attlongglast **Mrs L. N. Harmes**
6 **SHANTOU BREEZE (IRE)**, 9, b m Shantou (USA)—Homersmare (IRE) **M. J. Madgwick**
7 **TOMMYS GEAL**, 4, b f Halling (USA)—Steel Free (IRE) **Recycled Products Limited**
8 **TOP POCKET**, 4, b g Royal Applause—Movie Mogul **Recycled Products Limited**

THREE-YEAR-OLDS

9 **MULTIGIFTED**, b f Multiplex—Attlongglast **Mrs L. N. Harmes**
10 **NO BODY'S FOOL**, ch f Sixties Icon—Leleyf (IRE) **P. Taplin**
11 **ROD OF IRON**, br g Alkaased (USA)—Leading Star **Recycled Products Limited**
12 **RON'S BALLAD**, ch g Sakhee's Secret—Nom de La Rosa (IRE) **Saloop**

TWO-YEAR-OLDS

13 B c 20/5 Captain Gerrard (IRE)—Dockside Strike (Docksider (USA)) (5000) **Mrs L. Harmes & Mr M. Madgwick**

Other Owners: Mrs L. N. Harmes, Mr M. Madgwick, Mr K. McCormack, Mrs C. S. Muddle, Mr R. A. Muddle, Mr Robert Oliver, Mr T. Smith, Mr Peter Taplin.

Assistant Trainer: David Madgwick

Jockey (flat): George Baker, Adam Kirby. **Jockey (NH):** Marc Goldstein. **Amateur:** Mr Lance Madgwick.

---

383 MRS HEATHER MAIN, Wantage
Postal: Kingston Common Farm, Kingston Lisle, Wantage, Oxfordshire, OX12 9QT
Contacts: **PHONE** (01367) 820124 **FAX** (01367) 820125
E-MAIL heather.main@hotmail.com **WEBSITE** www.heathermainracing.com

1 **CHILDESPLAY**, 5, ch m Byron—Parting Gift **Wetumpka Racing & Andrew Knott**
2 **EMERALD PETRINA (IRE)**, 4, b f Byron—Oshauna (IRE) **Marcus Scott Russell & Sam Thomasson**
3 **HANNAH JUST HANNAH**, 7, gr m Proclamation (IRE)—Evaporate **The New Kennet Connection**

THREE-YEAR-OLDS

4 **ARAGON KNIGHT**, b g Kheleyf (USA)—Midnight Allure **Mr & Mrs D. R. Guest**
5 Ch f Mount Nelson—Follow My Dream
6 **ROCK ICON**, b g Sixties Icon—Monashee Rock (IRE) **Matt Salaman & M J Black**

TWO-YEAR-OLDS

7 **ISLAND CLOUD**, b f 12/3 Harbour Watch (IRE)—Cloud Illusions (USA) (Smarty Jones (USA)) (21000) **D. M. Kerr**
8 B f 5/2 Equiano (FR)—Jane Jubilee (IRE) (Mister Baileys)
9 **RAKE'S PROGRESS**, b c 21/1 Sir Percy—Cartoon (Danehill Dancer (IRE)) (4500) **Coxwell Partnership**
10 **ROYAL MELODY**, b f 7/3 Royal Applause—Wannabe Free (Red Ransom (USA)) **Mr & Mrs D. R. Guest**

Other Owners: Mr M. Black, Mr J. M. Duncan, Mr D. R. Guest, Mr A. Knott, Mrs H. S. Main, J. P. M. Main, Mr M. Salaman, Mr M. Scott Russell, Miss A. E. A. Solomon, Mr M. R. Telfer, Mr S. Thomasson.

384 MRS JANE MAKIN, South Milford
Postal: Fryston Lodge Farm, Off A63, South Milford, Leeds, North Yorkshire, LS25 5JE

1 **I'M OKAY (IRE)**, 5, b m Oscar (IRE)—Supreme Stroke (IRE) **Mr R. G. Makin**
2 **MARY OSCAR (IRE)**, 6, b m Oscar (IRE)—Quinnsboro Native (IRE) **Mr R. G. Makin**
3 **VICKY JANE**, 5, b m Kayf Tara—Annie's Answer (IRE) **Mr R. G. Makin**

Assistant Trainer: Mr R. G. Makin

385 MRS ALYSON MALZARD, Jersey
Postal: Les Etabl'yes, Grosnez Farm, St Ouen, Jersey, JE3 2AD
Contacts: MOBILE (07797) 738128
E-MAIL malzardracing@gmail.com

1 **ALBECQ**, 4, b g Paco Boy (IRE)—Helen Sharp **Trevor & Pat Gallienne**
2 **BROWN VELVET**, 4, b f Kodiac—Silkenveil (IRE) **La Vallette Ltd**
3 **CARRERA**, 6, b g Sixties Icon—Aileen's Gift (IRE) **Malzard Racing**
4 **COUNTRY BLUE (FR)**, 7, bl g Country Reel (USA)—Exica (FR) **Mrs E. A. Bass**
5 **DARK DAYS**, 5, b g Black Sam Bellamy (IRE)—Darwinia (GER) **Mrs E. A. Bass**
6 **FOURNI (FR)**, 7, ch m Rakti—Eckbeag (USA) **Ms Joan Lowery**
7 **KERSIVAY**, 10, gr g Royal Applause—Lochmaddy **Malzard Racing**
8 **LARCH (IRE)**, 4, b f Acclamation—Shady Nook (IRE) **Mr A. Taylor**
9 **OCEAN CRYSTAL**, 4, gr f Stimulation (IRE)—Crystal Gale (IRE) **Channel Highland Racing**
10 **PAS D'ACTION**, 8, ch g Noverre (USA)—Bright Vision **Jim Jamouneau**
11 **PASSIONATE AFFAIR (IRE)**, 5, ch g Broken Vow (USA)—Charmgoer (USA) **Mr A. Taylor**
12 **REVE DE GOSSE (FR)**, 6, b g Green Desert (USA)—The Best Girl (FR) **Malzard Racing**
13 **ROSSETTI**, 8, gr g Dansili—Snowdrops **Sheikh A'Leg Racing**
14 **SPANISH BOUNTY**, 11, b g Bahamian Bounty—Spanish Gold **Malzard Racing**
15 **SPEEDY WRITER**, 6, b g Byron—Merch Rhyd-Y-Grug **La Vallette Ltd**
16 **SPRING DIXIE (IRE)**, 4, gr f Zebedee—Dixie Jazz **Sheikh A'Leg Racing**

Other Owners: Mrs H. M. Bonney, Mr R. Bonney, Mr W. McLuskey, Mr J. B. Ryan.

Assistant Trainer: Vicki Perchard

Jockey (flat): Jemma Marshall. **Jockey (NH):** Mattie Batchelor. **Amateur:** Miss Michelle Hooper.

386 MR JAMES JOSEPH MANGAN, Mallow
Postal: Curraheen, Conna, Mallow, Co. Cork, Ireland
Contacts: FAX (00353) 585 9116 MOBILE (00353) 8726 84611
E-MAIL marymangan14@gmail.com

1 **CONNA CROSS (IRE)**, 5, b g Lecroix (GER)—Country Time (IRE) **Hanford's Chemist Ltd**
2 **FIDDLERS BOW (IRE)**, 7, b g Whitmore's Conn (USA)—Soraleda (IRE) **Mr Brenden Ferris**
3 **KILCREA (IRE)**, 9, b g Definite Article—Lightly Dreaming (FR) **Mr Michael O'Driscoll**
4 **LETTER OF CREDIT (IRE)**, 11, br g Bob Back (USA)—Common Verse (IRE) **No Credit Syndicate**
5 **MONTYS MEADOW (IRE)**, 8, b g Oscar (IRE)—Montys Miss (IRE) **Hanford's Chemist Ltd**
6 **PERFECT PROMISE (IRE)**, 8, b m Presenting—Snape (IRE) **Ms Janet Reader**
7 **SOCKSY (IRE)**, 5, ch m Flemensfirth (USA)—Bachello (IRE) **Mr Cedric Brooks**
8 **WINTER MAGIC (IRE)**, 8, b g Cloudings (IRE)—
Mr K's Winterblues (IRE) **Mrs T. C. Kouwenberg & Mrs Nicola Kent**

Assistant Trainer: Mary Mangan

387 MR CHARLIE MANN, Upper Lambourn
Postal: Neardown, Upper Lambourn, Hungerford, Berkshire, RG17 8QP
Contacts: PHONE (01488) 71717 / 73118 FAX (01488) 73223 MOBILE (07721) 888333
E-MAIL charlie@charliemann.info WEBSITE www.charliemannracing.com

1 **AGNES B**, 6, gr m Great Palm (USA)—Say Sadie **Charlie Mann Racing Club**
2 **AIRPUR DESBOIS (FR)**, 6, b g Canyon Creek (IRE)—Hero's Dancer (FR) **Mr P. T. Mott**

MR CHARLIE MANN - Continued

3 **BALTIC STORM (IRE)**, 5, b g Kandahar Run—Born Wild (GER) **Mr J. Heron**
4 **BRIDAL SUITE (IRE)**, 7, b g Craigsteel—Selinda Spectrum (IRE) **Charlie Mann Racing Club II**
5 **CAPATOSTA (USA)**, 4, ch g Flashy Bull (USA)—Da River Hoss (USA) **The Neardowners**
6 **CODY WYOMING**, 10, b g Passing Glance—Tenderfoot **Charlie Mann Racing Club I**
7 **DRAGON CITY**, 6, b g Elusive City (USA)—Oulianovsk (IRE) **Earth Wind and Fire**
8 **DUKES DEN**, 5, b g Duke of Marmalade (IRE)—Green Room (FR) **The Neardowners**
9 **ELMORE BACK (IRE)**, 7, b g Wareed (IRE)—Katie Buckers (IRE) **Mr A Stone, Mr B Brindle & Mrs C Hill**
10 **EPHRAIM**, 5, b g Rail Link—Enrica **Power Panels Electrical Systems Ltd**
11 **EXPEDITE (IRE)**, 5, b g Brian Boru—Angelica Garnett **Mr S. Kimber**
12 **FINE PARCHMENT (IRE)**, 13, b g Presenting—Run For Cover (IRE) **N. W. A. Bannister**
13 **GOWANAUTHAT (IRE)**, 8, ch g Golan (IRE)—Coolrua (IRE) **Mr B Beacham & Mrs J M Mayo**
14 **LE LEGRO (IRE)**, 6, b g Mountain High (IRE)—Good To Travel (IRE) **The Neardowners**
15 **LIBECCIO (FR)**, 5, b g Shirocco (GER)—Francais **Mr J. Heron**
16 **MAID OF MILAN (IRE)**, 5, br m Milan—Joes Lady (IRE) **The Neardowners**
17 **MORNEY WING (IRE)**, 7, b g Antonius Pius (USA)—Tillan Fuwain (FR) **The Steeple Chasers**
18 **MR BIG (IRE)**, 15, ch g Eurobus—All A Struggle (IRE) **C. J. Mann**
19 **MURRAY MOUNT (IRE)**, 6, b g Trans Island—Ash **Mr M. S. Hitchcroft**
20 **MY ANCHOR**, 5, b g Mount Nelson—War Shanty **Mr P. T. Mott**
21 **NIMBUS GALE (IRE)**, 7, b g Cloudings (IRE)—Barton Gale (IRE) **Mr A. Pountney**
22 **QUEBEC**, 5, b g Dansili—Milford Sound **The Steeple Chasers**
23 **ROYAL REDEMPTION (IRE)**, 7, b g Milan—Royale Laguna (FR) **L Kimber, J Thorneloe & T Swerling**
24 **SEVENTH SKY (GER)**, 9, b g King's Best (USA)—Sacarina **Mr J. Heron**
25 **SOME KINDA LAMA (IRE)**, 5, gr g Daylami (IRE)—Last Sunrise (IRE) **The Steeple Chasers**
26 **SURENESS (IRE)**, 6, ch m Hurricane Run (IRE)—Silk Dress (IRE) **Mr P. T. Mott**
27 **TANGO UNCHAINED (IRE)**, 9, b g Golan (IRE)—Crimson Bow (GER) **N. W. A. Bannister**
28 **TO BEGIN**, 5, b g Tobougg (IRE)—Sagina **Mr J. Heron**
29 **VICTOR LEUDORUM (IRE)**, 9, b g Wareed (IRE)—Rock Garden (IRE) **R. J. Tompkins**

Other Owners: Mr B. Beacham, W. A. Brindle, Mr E. S. G. Faber, Mrs C. J. Hill, Mr L. G. Kimber, Mrs J. M. Mayo, Mrs K. T. Pilkington, Mr A. Stone, Mr T. A. Swerling, Major J. G. Thorneloe.

Assistant Trainer: Matthew Fox **Secretary:** Rose Osborn

Jockey (NH): Noel Fehily. **Conditional:** Thomas Dowling.

---

388 MR GEORGE MARGARSON, Newmarket
Postal: Graham Lodge, Birdcage Walk, Newmarket, Suffolk, CB8 0NE
Contacts: **HOME/FAX** (01638) 668043 **MOBILE** (07860) 198303
E-MAIL george@georgemargarson.co.uk **WEBSITE** www.georgemargason.co.uk

1 **ELUSIVE GUEST (FR)**, 5, b g Elusive City (USA)—Mansoura (IRE) **John Guest Racing Ltd**
2 **EXCELLENT AIM**, 9, b g Exceed And Excel (AUS)—Snugfit Annie **Graham Lodge Partnership II**
3 **EXCELLENT GUEST**, 9, b g Exceed And Excel (AUS)—Princess Speedfit (FR) **John Guest Racing Ltd**
4 **ILLUSTRATION (IRE)**, 8, b g Pivotal—In Anticipation (IRE) **Mrs W. McLaughlin**
5 **JAMMY GUEST (IRE)**, 6, b g Duke of Marmalade (IRE)—Ardbrae Lady **John Guest Racing Ltd**
6 **LADY KYLLAR**, 4, b f Kyllachy—Miss Otis **Mangiacapra, Hill, Hook Partnership**
7 **LMNTRIX**, 4, b g Mount Nelson—Big Mystery (IRE)
8 **MAGICAL SPEEDFIT (IRE)**, 11, ch g Bold Fact (USA)—Magical Peace (IRE) **Graham Lodge Partnership II**
9 **PRINCESS GUEST (IRE)**, 4, b f Iffraaj—Princess Speedfit (FR) **John Guest Racing Ltd**
10 **REBELLIOUS GUEST**, 7, b g Cockney Rebel (IRE)—Marisa (GER) **John Guest Racing Ltd**
11 **SHYRON**, 5, b g Byron—Coconut Shy **Mr F Butler & Mrs Connie Taylor**
12 **SNAPPY GUEST**, 4, b g Kodiac—Golden Shadow (IRE) **John Guest Racing Ltd**
13 **STORM RUNNER (IRE)**, 8, b g Rakti—Saibhreas (IRE) **Graham Lodge Partnership II**
14 **YOUNG JACKIE**, 8, b m Doyen (IRE)—Just Warning **Graham Lodge Partnership II**

THREE-YEAR-OLDS

15 **ANY GUEST (IRE)**, b c Zoffany (IRE)—Princess Speedfit (FR) **John Guest Racing Ltd**
16 **CARIBBEAN SPRING (IRE)**, b g Dark Angel (IRE)—Bogini (IRE) **Mr A. J. Bonarius**
17 **GATILLO**, gr c Showcasing—Crystal Gale (IRE) **Jakes Family**
18 **LADY KHELEYF**, bl f Kheleyf (USA)—Mosa Mine **Graham Lodge Partnership**
19 **POETIC GUEST**, ch c Poet's Voice—Diamond Run **John Guest Racing Ltd**
20 **SHYPEN**, b f Archipenko (USA)—Coconut Shy **F. Butler**

MR GEORGE MARGARSON - Continued

TWO-YEAR-OLDS

21 B c 22/4 Fast Company (IRE)—Balm (Oasis Dream) (25000) **John Guest Racing Ltd**
22 CINDERELLA QUEEN (IRE), b f 8/5 Makfi—Spring Star (FR) (Danehill (USA)) (22000) **J. Alharbi**
23 B c 5/3 Archipenko (USA)—Coconut Shy (Bahamian Bounty) **F. Butler**
24 B f 8/2 Sayif (IRE)—Delma (IRE) (Authorized (IRE)) **Saleh Al Homaizi**
25 LADY KAVIAR (IRE), b f 20/3 Lope de Vega (IRE)—
　　　　　　　　　　　Maoin Dor (IRE) (Manduro (GER)) (40000) **Graham Lodge Partnership**
26 B f 5/2 Sayif (IRE)—Manaaber (USA) (Medicean) **Saleh Al Homaizi**
27 POET'S WISH, b c 13/2 Poet's Voice—Winner's Wish (Clodovil (IRE)) **Mr A. Al Mansoori**
28 Ch f 31/1 Mayson—Rhal (IRE) (Rahy (USA)) (18000) **J. Alharbi**
29 Ch c 23/2 Bated Breath—Si Belle (IRE) (Dalakhani (IRE)) (28000) **John Guest Racing Ltd**

Other Owners: Mr S. Hill, Mrs E. L. Hook, Mr J. C. Jakes, Mrs T. M. A. Jakes, Mr J. G. Mangiacapra, Mrs C. D. Taylor.

Assistant Trainer: Katie Margarson

Apprentice: Lulu Stanford.

---

389 **MR A. J. MARTIN, Summerhill**
Postal: **Arodstown, Moynalvey, Summerhill, Co. Meath, Ireland**
Contacts: **PHONE (00353) 46 955 8633 FAX (00353) 46 955 8632 MOBILE (00353) 86 276 0835**
E-MAIL arodstown@eircom.net

1 ANIBALE FLY (FR), 6, b g Assessor (IRE)—Nouba Fly (FR) **J. P. McManus**
2 BLACKWATER BRIDGE (IRE), 6, b g Westerner—Gale Johnston (IRE) **Neighbours Racing Club**
3 BLAIR PERRONE (IRE), 7, b g Rudimentary (USA)—Stonehallqueen (IRE) **John Breslin**
4 BOBBIE'S DIAMOND (IRE), 6, b g Vinnie Roe (IRE)—Betty's The Best (IRE) **Deborah Breslin**
5 BOMBA STICK (FR), 5, b br g Early March—Inchala **John Breslin**
6 CLONALIG HOUSE (IRE), 6, b g Rakti—Balakera (FR) **Glen Devlin**
7 CLONARD STREET, 4, b c Archipenko (USA)—Moi Aussi (USA) **John P. McManus**
8 CORNELIUS (FR), 4, b g Country Reel (USA)—Dinaha (FR) **Greg Bryce**
9 CORRI LINDO (FR), 6, br g Corri Piano (FR)—Daresta (FR) **Timothy Fitzgerald**
10 DELVIN ROAD (IRE), 8, b br g Beneficial—Susans Glory **Lily Lawlor**
11 DOLLAR AND A DREAM (IRE), 7, b g Fruits of Love (USA)—Gorgeous Georgina (IRE) **Aidan Shiels**
12 DOUNIKOS (FR), 5, b g Smadoun (FR)—Baby Sitter (FR) **Gigginstown House Stud**
13 FILL YOUR HANDS (IRE), 7, b g Milan—Cailin's Perk (IRE) **Gigginstown House Stud**
14 FIRE IN HIS EYES (IRE), 5, b g Stowaway—Carrigeen Kohleria (IRE) **Gigginstown House Stud**
15 FIVE O'CLOCK TEA (FR), 9, b g Martillo (GER)—Sally's Cry (FR) **City Gunners Syndicate**
16 GALLANT OSCAR (IRE), 10, b g Oscar (IRE)—Park Wave (IRE) **John P. McManus**
17 GLADIATOR KING (IRE), 7, b g Dylan Thomas (IRE)—Sheer Bliss (IRE) **John P. McManus**
18 HEATHFIELD (IRE), 9, ch g Definite Article—Famous Lady (IRE) **John P. McManus**
19 IMPROVER (IRE), 5, b g Ad Valorem (USA)—Titus Wonder (IRE) **Ronnie Jordan**
20 JEREMY'S JET (IRE), 5, b g Jeremy—Double Vie (IRE) **P. Reilly**
21 KINNITTY CASTLE (IRE), 6, b g Beneficial—Jendam (IRE) **Aidan Shiels**
22 LEONARDO (GER), 4, ch g Areion (GER)—Lolli Pop (GER) **Malcolm C. Denmark**
23 LIFT THE LATCH (IRE), 6, b g Beneficial—Queen Astrid (IRE) **John P. McManus**
24 LIP SERVICE (IRE), 7, ch g Presenting—Top Her Up (IRE) **Malcolm C. Denmark**
25 LIVING NEXT DOOR (IRE), 10, b g Beneficial—Except Alice (IRE) **John Breslin**
26 LORD DE BEAUFAI (FR), 8, b g Epalo (GER)—Perle de Beaufai (FR) **Rainbow Gems Syndicate**
27 MARINERO (IRE), 7, b g Presenting—Peggy Maddock (IRE) **Gigginstown House Stud**
28 MINELLA SCAMP (IRE), 7, b g King's Theatre (IRE)—Forgotten Star (IRE) **Malcolm C. Denmark**
29 MYDOR (FR), 6, ch g Stormy River (FR)—Fabulousday (USA) **Mulvany's Bar Syndicate**
30 NO DICE (IRE), 7, ch g Presenting—Roxbury **Malcolm C. Denmark**
31 NO SECRETS (IRE), 12, b g King's Theatre (IRE)—Happy Native (IRE) **Malcolm C. Denmark**
32 NOBLE EMPEROR (IRE), 8, b g Spadoun (FR)—Cherry Tops (IRE) **John P. McManus**
33 OIGHEAR DUBH (IRE), 5, gr g Verglas (IRE)—Silly Goose (IRE) **Newtown Anner Stud Farms**
34 OKOTOKS (IRE), 6, b g Gamut (IRE)—Whats Another One (IRE) **Malcolm C. Denmark**
35 OUR RACHAEL (IRE), 4, b f Haatef (USA)—Maigh Nuad (IRE) **Donal Houlihan**
36 PETIT CHEF (IRE), 5, br g Sunday Break (JPN)—Luarca **Adrian Collins**
37 PIRES, 12, br g Generous (IRE)—Kaydee Queen (IRE) **Lily Lawlor**
38 REDERA (IRE), 10, b g Chevalier (IRE)—Lady Redera (IRE) **Peter William Partnership**
39 RIVAGE D'OR (IRE), 11, b g Visionary (FR)—Deesse d'allier (FR) **Gigginstown House Stud**
40 SARWISTAN (IRE), 6, b g Nayef (USA)—Seraya (FR) **John Breslin**
41 SMOOTH OPERATOR, 4, b g Azamour (IRE)—Teggiano (IRE) **Malcolm C. Denmark**

MR A. J. MARTIN - Continued

42 **SPACIOUS SKY (USA)**, 7, b g North Light (IRE)—Ratings (USA) **P. Reilly**
43 **STATEN ISLAND (IRE)**, 6, ch g Trans Island—Clover Pearl (IRE) **Gareth Coen**
44 **TAYTO PARK (FR)**, 7, ch g Balko (FR)—Moonlight Shadows (FR) **Mr Tayto Partnership**
45 **THE PLAN MAN (IRE)**, 6, b g Jeremy (USA)—Sanfrancullinan (IRE) **Gigginstown House Stud**
46 **TUDOR CITY (IRE)**, 4, b g Yeats (IRE)—She's Our Mare (IRE) **John Breslin**
47 **USURP (IRE)**, 5, b g Flemensfirth (USA)—Gypsy Mo Chara (IRE) **Gigginstown House Stud**
48 **WHATSFORUWONTGOBYU (IRE)**, 6, b g Well Chosen—Meadstown Miss (IRE) **John P. McManus**
49 **WHITE ARM (FR)**, 7, b g Turgeon (USA)—White Consel (FR) **John P. McManus**

THREE-YEAR-OLDS
50 **AN DROICHEAD (IRE)**, b f Zebedee—Special Return (IRE) **Glen Devlin/D. Murnaghan**

---

390 **MR ANDREW J. MARTIN, Chipping Norton**
Postal: **Yew Tree Barn, Hook Norton Road, Swerford, Chipping Norton, Oxfordshire, OX7 4BF**
Contacts: **PHONE (01608) 737288**

1 **FITZ VOLONTE**, 9, br g Passing Glance—Swordella **A. J. Martin**
2 **GONEINAGLANCE**, 7, b m Passing Glance—It's Missy Imp **A. J. Martin**
3 **MIDNIGHT MUSTANG**, 9, b g Midnight Legend—Mustang Molly **A. J. Martin**
4 **MIGHTY MUSTANG**, 6, b g Passing Glance—Mustang Molly **A. J. Martin**
5 **MILITARIAN**, 6, b g Kayf Tara—Mille Et Une (FR) **Lady Jane Grosvenor**
6 **ORANGER (FR)**, 14, b g Antarctique (IRE)—True Beauty **A. J. Martin**
7 **SUNNY LEDGEND**, 11, b g Midnight Legend—Swordella **A. J. Martin**
8 **TRACKING TIME**, 9, b g Central Park (IRE)—E Minor (IRE) **A. J. Martin**

---

391 **MR CHRISTOPHER MASON, Caerwent**
Postal: **Whitehall Barn, Five Lanes, Caerwent, Monmouthshire**
Contacts: **PHONE (01291) 422172 FAX (01633) 666690 MOBILE (07767) 808082**
E-MAIL cjmason@tiscali.co.uk

1 **BEYOND THE EDGE**, 4, ch f Compton Place—Edge of Gold **Mr & Mrs C. J. Mason**
2 **EDGED OUT**, 6, b m Piccolo—Edge of Light **Mr & Mrs C. J. Mason**

Other Owners: Mrs A. L. Mason, C. J. Mason.

Assistant Trainer: Annabelle Mason

---

392 **MRS JENNIFER MASON, Cirencester**
Postal: **Manor Farm, Ablington, Bibury, Cirencester, Gloucestershire, GL7 5NY**
Contacts: **PHONE (01285) 740445 MOBILE (07974) 262438**
E-MAIL pwmason2002@yahoo.co.uk WEBSITE www.jennifermasonracing.com

1 **HOOGHLY RIVER (IRE)**, 6, b g Indian River (FR)—Mrs Woman (IRE) **Mason Racing Club**
2 **OSKAR DENARIUS (IRE)**, 5, b g Authorized (IRE)—
                                        Elizabethan Age (FR) **Hon David Howard & Mr Bruce Johnson**
3 **SARUNI (IRE)**, 5, b g September Storm (GER)—Bathsheba **Mrs J. S. Mason**

Other Owners: Mrs R. D. Greenwood, The Hon David F. Howard, Mr B. S. Johnson, Mrs M. E. Slocock.

Assistant Trainer: Mr Peter W. Mason

Jockey (NH): Felix De Giles. **Amateur:** Mr Peter Mason.

---

393 **MISS JANE MATHIAS, Llancarfan**
Postal: **Crosstown, Llancarfan, Vale of Glamorgan, CF62 3AJ**
Contacts: **MOBILE (07779) 382727**

1 **DEFINATELY VINNIE**, 6, ch g Vinnie Roe (IRE)—Sohapara **Mrs S. E. Mathias**
2 **SOVINNIE (IRE)**, 7, ch g Vinnie Roe (IRE)—Sohapara **Mrs S. E. Mathias**

394 MR G. C. MAUNDRELL, Marlborough
Postal: **Ogbourne Down, Ogbourne St Andrew, Marlborough, Wilts**
Contacts: **PHONE (01672) 841202**

1 **DELINEATE (IRE)**, 7, b m Definite Article—New Line (IRE) **G. C. Maundrell**
2 **DREAM PERFORMANCE (IRE)**, 11, b m Oscar (IRE)—Pharlen's Dream (IRE)
3 **MINOR CHORD**, 10, b m Alflora (IRE)—Minimum **G. C. Maundrell**
4 **TAMBURA**, 6, b m Tamure (IRE)—Singing Cottage **G. C. Maundrell**

Amateur: Mr Z. Baker.

395 MR GRAHAM MAYS, Littlehampton
Postal: **Woodleighs House, Warningcamp, Arundel, West Sussex, BN18 9QZ**
Contacts: **MOBILE (07889) 041228**

1 **BEAUFORT TWELVE**, 7, b g Hurricane Run (IRE)—Violette **Angmering Park**
2 **COTTON KING**, 9, ch g Dubawi (IRE)—Spinning The Yarn **Lady Mary Mumford**
3 **LAUGHARNE**, 5, b g Authorized (IRE)—Corsican Sunset (USA) **Angmering Park Farms LLP**
4 **PURPLE LANE (IRE)**, 5, ch g Danehill Dancer (IRE)—Big Heart **Angmering Park Farms LLP**
5 **SWIFT BLADE (IRE)**, 8, ch g Exceed And Excel (AUS)—Gold Strike (IRE) **Angmering Park**

Other Owners: Exors of the Late Lady S. Clutton, Exors of the Late Lady Herries.

396 MR PHILIP MCBRIDE, Newmarket
Postal: **Exeter House Stables, 33 Exeter Road, Newmarket, Suffolk, CB8 0NY**
Contacts: **PHONE/FAX (01638) 667841 MOBILE (07929) 265711**

1 **ANTON CHIGURH**, 7, b g Oasis Dream—Barathiki **Black Star Racing**
2 **BRIGLIADORO (IRE)**, 5, ch g Excellent Art—Milady's Pride **Mr S. Agodino**
3 **MR SHEKELLS**, 4, b g Three Valleys (USA)—Quip **Mr Nigel Davies & Mr P. J. McBride**
4 **OLD TOWN BOY**, 5, b h Myboycharlie (IRE)—Native Ring (FR) **Mr R. Wilson**

THREE-YEAR-OLDS

5 **CHAPESS**, b f Pastoral Pursuits—Inchcoonan **Black Star Racing**
6 **FREE BOUNTY**, b c Dick Turpin (IRE)—Native Ring (FR) **Four Winds Racing & Serafino Agodino**
7 **FREE TO ROAM (IRE)**, gr f Bushranger (IRE)—Operissimo **P. J. McBride**
8 **LIME AND LEMON (IRE)**, b f Makfi—Nimboo (USA) **Qatar Racing Limited**
9 **PARADISE PALM**, ch f Sakhee's Secret—Akathea **Miss C. M. McBride**
10 **PRINCESS COOKIE**, b f Sakhee's Secret—Rouge Dancer **Mr H. J. Cooke**
11 **QUATRIEME AMI**, b c Equiano (FR)—Hundred Year Flood (USA) **Ten Fools & A Horse & Partner**
12 **RIVERS OF ASIA**, ch c Medicean—Aliena (IRE) **Four Winds Racing Partnership**

TWO-YEAR-OLDS

13 **MISTER RAFFLES**, b c 3/3 Cockney Rebel (IRE)—Shrewd Decision (Motivator) **D. P. Fremel**

Other Owners: Mr J. W. Blake, C. M. Budgett, Mr G. P. Chapman, N. L. Davies, J. Gunnell, Mrs E. A. Mear, Mr R. J. Mear, Mr N. A. Rooney, Mrs A. M. Wilson.

397 MR DONALD MCCAIN JNR, Cholmondeley
Postal: **D McCain Racing Ltd, Bankhouse, Cholmondeley, Malpas, Cheshire, SY14 8AL**
Contacts: **PHONE (01829) 720352/720351 FAX (01829) 720475 MOBILE (07903) 066194**
E-MAIL info@donaldmccain.co.uk WEBSITE www.donaldmccain.co.uk

1 **ACROSS THE BAY (IRE)**, 12, b g Bob's Return (IRE)—The Southern (IRE) **Scotch Piper Syndicate**
2 4, B g Getaway (GER)—Arrive In Style (IRE)
3 **ASKAMORE DARSI (IRE)**, 7, b g Darsi (FR)—Galamear **Deva Racing Darsi Partnership**
4 **ASTRUM**, 6, gr g Haafhd—Vax Star **Sarah & Wayne Dale**
5 **BEATU (IRE)**, 7, b g Beat All (USA)—Auntie Bob **T. G. Leslie**
6 **BENZANNO (IRE)**, 7, b g Refuse To Bend (IRE)—Crossanza (IRE) **T. G. Leslie**
7 **BIG HANDS HARRY**, 7, b g Multiplex—Harristown Lady **Richard & Katherine Gilbert**

MR DONALD MCCAIN JNR - Continued

8 **BILLFROMTHEBAR (IRE)**, 9, b g Morozov (USA)—Eden Breeze (IRE) **Mr M. W. Sanders**
9 **BLACK JACK ROVER (IRE)**, 7, b g Vinnie Roe (IRE)—Kilgefin Tina (IRE) **Deva Racing Black Jack Partnership**
10 **BOURNE**, 10, gr g Linamix (FR)—L'affaire Monique **Mr M. J. Taylor**
11 **BREEZEMOUNT (IRE)**, 6, b g Flemensfirth (USA)—Hep To The Jive (FR) **Mrs S. K. McCain**
12 **BROAD SPECTRUM (IRE)**, 5, b g Gamut (IRE)—Knock Na Brona (IRE) **T. J. Hemmings**
13 **CAUTIOUS MAN (IRE)**, 4, b g Golan (IRE)—Hackler Poitin (IRE) **Mr J. M. Glews**
14 **CLONDAW DRAFT (IRE)**, 8, b g Shantou (USA)—Glen Ten (IRE) **T. G. Leslie**
15 **CLONDAW KAEMPFER (IRE)**, 8, b g Oscar (IRE)—Gra-Bri (IRE) **T Leslie & D Gorton**
16 **CLOUDY JOKER (IRE)**, 8, gr g Cloudings (IRE)—Rosa View (IRE) **On Cloud Eight Syndicate**
17 **CORRIN WOOD (IRE)**, 9, gr g Garuda (IRE)—Allstar Rose (IRE) **Dermot Hanafin Robert Rose Ian Whitfield**
18 **COURT DISMISSED (IRE)**, 6, b g Court Cave (IRE)—Carramanagh Lady (IRE) **Special Piping Materials Ltd**
19 **COURT OF LAW (IRE)**, 8, b g Court Cave (IRE)—Divine Dancer (IRE) **D. R. McCain**
20 4, B g Oscar (IRE)—Courtain (USA)
21 **CULMINATION**, 4, b g Beat Hollow—Apogee **Tim & Miranda Johnson**
22 **DANCEINTOTHELIGHT**, 9, gr g Dansili—Kali **Mrs S. K. McCain**
23 **DESERT CRY (IRE)**, 10, b br g Desert Prince (IRE)—Hataana (USA) **N.Y.P.D Racing**
24 **EXACTLY WHAT**, 7, b g Multiplex—Heathyards Tipple (IRE) **Mr G. Fitzpatrick**
25 **FEATHER LANE (IRE)**, 6, b g Court Cave (IRE)—Laffan's Bridge (IRE) **T. G. Leslie**
26 **FIRE AND SMOKE**, 6, b g Overbury (IRE)—Camelia Walk **Mr G. Fitzpatrick**
27 **FIVE FOR FIFTEEN (IRE)**, 7, b g Craigsteel—Gentle Eyre (IRE) **Let's Live Racing**
28 **FRANCISCAN**, 8, b g Medicean—Frangy **T. G. Leslie**
29 **FREDDIES PORTRAIT (IRE)**, 7, gr g Portrait Gallery (IRE)—Phara (IRE) **T. G. Leslie**
30 **GATACRE STREET**, 4, b g Lucarno (USA)—Sherry Darling (IRE) **Mr J. M. Glews**
31 **GOLDEN BANNER (IRE)**, 5, b g Gold Well—Banner Buzz (IRE) **D. R. McCain**
32 **GOLDEN INVESTMENT (IRE)**, 7, b g Gold Well—Mangan Pet (IRE) **T. G. Leslie**
33 **GRAY DAY (IRE)**, 5, gr g Daylami (IRE)—Carrigeen Diamond (IRE) **Dr G. M. Thelwall Jones**
34 5, B h Multiplex—Heathyards Tipple (IRE)
35 **HELLORBOSTON (IRE)**, 8, b g Court Cave (IRE)—Helorhiwater (IRE) **Arctic Drunkies**
36 **HILLS OF DUBAI (IRE)**, 7, ch g Dubai Destination (USA)—Mowazana (IRE) **T. G. Leslie**
37 4, B f King's Theatre (IRE)—Holme Rose **T. G. Leslie**
38 **I NEED GOLD (IRE)**, 8, b g Gold Well—Coola Cross (IRE) **Deva Racing Golden Partnership**
39 **IRISH HAWKE (IRE)**, 4, b g Montjeu (IRE)—Ahdaab (USA) **Sarah & Wayne Dale**
40 **JELLIED EEL JACK (IRE)**, 7, b g Scorpion (IRE)—Melodic Tune (IRE) **A. J. Perkins**
41 **KATACHENKO (IRE)**, 7, b g Kutub (IRE)—Karalee (IRE) **T. J. Hemmings**
42 **KILRONAN CASTLE**, 5, ch g Indian River (FR)—Greatest Friend (IRE) **Mrs B. McCain**
43 **KOUP DE KANON (FR)**, 10, b g Robin des Pres (FR)—Coup de Sabre (FR) **Mr M. J. Taylor**
44 **LASTBUTNOTLEAST (IRE)**, 6, ch m Flemensfirth (USA)—Lakil Princess (IRE) **D. R. McCain**
45 **LEXI'S BOY (IRE)**, 8, gr g Verglas (IRE)—Jazan (IRE) **T. G. Leslie**
46 **LIFE AND SOUL (IRE)**, 9, b g Azamour (IRE)—Way For Life (GER) **Mr M. J. Taylor**
47 **LOUGH DERG WALK (IRE)**, 7, b g Turtle Island (IRE)—Whispers In Moscow (IRE) **T. G. Leslie**
48 **LYME PARK**, 5, bl gr m Multiplex—So Cloudy **Tim & Miranda Johnson**
49 **LYRIC STREET (IRE)**, 8, b g Hurricane Run (IRE)—Elle Danzig (GER) **Mr M. J. Taylor**
50 **MAHLER LAD (IRE)**, 6, b g Mahler—Sister Merenda (IRE) **T. G. Leslie**
51 **MANSONIEN L'AS (FR)**, 10, b g Mansonnien (FR)—Star des As (FR) **Let's Live Racing**
52 4, B g Yeats (IRE)—Midnight Flirt (IRE) **Jon Glews & Brendan Richardson**
53 4, B g Oscar (IRE)—Miss Cilla (IRE) **T. G. Leslie**
54 **MO CHAILIN (IRE)**, 5, b m Milan—Consultation (IRE) **Mrs S. C. Leslie**
55 **MOVE TO THE GROOVE (IRE)**, 6, b g Catcher In The Rye (USA)—Valley of Love (IRE) **D. R. McCain**
56 **MYRTLE DRIVE (IRE)**, 5, b m Kalanisi (IRE)—Miss Fara (FR) **Mr B. J. Richardson**
57 **NAFAATH (IRE)**, 10, ch g Nayef (USA)—Alshakr **D. R. McCain**
58 **NEFYN BAY**, 7, b g Overbury (IRE)—So Cloudy **Tim & Miranda Johnson**
59 **OSCATARA (IRE)**, 9, b br g Oscar (IRE)—Nethertara (USA) **T. G. Leslie**
60 **PALERMO DON**, 6, b g Beat Hollow—Kristal Bridge **T. G. Leslie**
61 **PARIYAN (FR)**, 4, ch c Sinndar (IRE)—Pink And Red (USA) **D. R. McCain**
62 **PERFECT POISON (IRE)**, 8, b g Vinnie Roe (IRE)—Noddys Confusion (IRE) **Mr R. J. Gwynne**
63 **PRINCE KHURRAM**, 6, b g Nayef (USA)—Saree **T. G. Leslie**
64 **QATEA (IRE)**, 4, ch g Duke of Marmalade (IRE)—Taking Liberties (IRE) **D. R. McCain**
65 **RAISE A SPARK**, 6, b g Multiplex—Reem Two **Mr R. Pattison & Mr R. Kent**
66 **ROCKALZARO (FR)**, 4, gr g Balko (FR)—Royale Wheeler (FR) **D. R. McCain**
67 **ROCKY STONE (IRE)**, 8, b g Cloudings (IRE)—Crandon Park **Penketh & Sankey Jech Racing Club**
68 **ROLLING THUNDER (IRE)**, 6, gr g Cloudings (IRE)—Peazar (IRE) **T. J. Hemmings**
69 **SCIALFA (IRE)**, 5, b m Westerner—Whispers In Moscow (IRE) **Mr J. M. Glews**
70 **SEALOUS SCOUT (IRE)**, 8, b g Old Vic—Hirayna **T. G. Leslie**
71 **SEAN BAN (IRE)**, 6, b g Flemensfirth (USA)—Galingale (IRE) **Mr M. J. Taylor**
72 **SHANTOU TIGER (IRE)**, 7, b g Shantou (USA)—Opus One **Deva Racing Shantou Partnership**

MR DONALD MCCAIN JNR - Continued

73 **SIGN MANUAL,** 7, b g Motivator—New Assembly (IRE) **Graham & Carole Worsley**
74 **SILVER GENT (IRE),** 8, gr g Milan—All's Rosey (IRE) **Deva Racing Milan Partnership**
75 **STAR IN FLIGHT,** 9, b g Mtoto—Star Entry **D. R. McCain**
76 **STONEBROOK (IRE),** 8, b g Flemensfirth (USA)—Boberelle (IRE) **J. P. McManus**
77 **SUBTLE GREY (IRE),** 7, gr g Subtle Power (IRE)—Milltown Rose (IRE) **Deva Racing Subtle Grey Partnership**
78 **SUPERFECTION (IRE),** 7, b m Shantou (USA)—Sarah's Cottage (IRE) **Chasing Gold Limited**
79 **SUPREME ASSET (IRE),** 8, b g Beneficial—Hollygrove Supreme (IRE) **Lucky Bin Racing**
80 **SWATOW TYPHOON (IRE),** 9, b g Shantou (USA)—Oscar Leader (IRE) **Mr G. Fitzpatrick**
81 **SWIFT ARROW (IRE),** 10, b g Overbury (IRE)—Clover Run (IRE) **Mrs A. E. Strang Steel**
82 4, B g Arcadio (GER)—Swiftur **Clwydian Connections**
83 **TAKE THE CASH (IRE),** 7, b g Cloudings (IRE)—Taking My Time (IRE) **T. J. Hemmings**
84 **THE BACKUP PLAN (IRE),** 7, ch g Presenting—Jay Lo (IRE) **N.Y.P.D Racing**
85 **THE PIERRE LARK (IRE),** 6, b g Pierre—Kyle Lark **D. R. McCain**
86 **THEATRICAL STYLE (IRE),** 7, b g Alhaarth (IRE)—Little Theatre (IRE) **Deva Racing Palladium Partnership**
87 **THYNE FOR GOLD (IRE),** 5, b g Robin des Pres (FR)—My Name's Not Bin (IRE) **Livvys Racing Group**
88 **UBALTIQUE (FR),** 8, b g Balko (FR)—Ode Antique (FR) **T. G. Leslie**
89 **UNCLE MONTY (IRE),** 7, b g Milan—She's A Gamble (IRE) **Clwydian International**
90 **UP AND GO (FR),** 8, ch g Martaline—Santoria (FR) **T. G. Leslie**
91 **VALLEYOFMILAN (IRE),** 9, b g Milan—Ikdam Valley (IRE) **Tim & Miranda Johnson**
92 **VENUE,** 6, b g Beat Hollow—Shirley Valentine **David Lockwood & Peter Spencer**
93 **VOLCANIC (FR),** 7, b g Al Namix (FR)—Queen of Rock (FR) **Elite Racing Club**
94 **WAZOWSKI,** 7, b g Overbury (IRE)—Malay
95 **WELSH BARD (IRE),** 7, ch g Dylan Thomas (IRE)—Delphinium (IRE) **George Tobitt & Richard Gurney**
96 **WHAT HAPPENS NOW (IRE),** 7, b g Dr Massini (IRE)—Euro Burden (IRE) **Deva Racing Dr Massini Partnership**
97 **WHATDOESTHEFOXSAY (IRE),** 7, ch m Vinnie Roe (IRE)—She's The One (IRE) **Mrs Sarah Leslie**
98 **WHISKEY CHASER (IRE),** 8, br g Flemensfirth (USA)—

   Cregane Lass (IRE) **Deva Racing Flemensfirth Partnership**
99 **WHITSUNDAYS (IRE),** 7, b g Kutub (IRE)—Urdite's Vic (IRE) **Deva Racing Whitsundays Partnership**
100 **WILLIAM OF ORANGE,** 5, b g Duke of Marmalade (IRE)—Critical Acclaim **T. W. Johnson & G. Maxwell**
101 **WITNESS IN COURT (IRE),** 9, b g Witness Box (USA)—Inter Alia (USA) **T. G. Leslie**
102 **ZE KING,** 7, b g Manduro (GER)—Top Flight Queen **D. R. McCain**
103 **ZIP WIRE (IRE),** 7, b g Oratorio (IRE)—Jaya (USA) **Mr M. J. Taylor**

THREE-YEAR-OLDS

104 Ch g Beat Hollow—Hesperia **Katherine & Richard Gilbert 1**

Other Owners: Mr M. Ball, Mr Michael J. Campbell, Mr Anthony Coyne, Mr K. Coyne, Mr James Currie, Mr Wayne Dale, Mrs S. J. Dale, Mr A. Douglas, Mr W. A. Eastup, Elite Racing, Mrs J. Foster, Mr M. Foster, Mr L. R. Frampton, Mr Richard Gilbert, Mrs Katherine Gilbert, Mr D. Gorton, Mr R. Gurney, Mr Dermot Hanafin, Mr Tony Hill, Mrs Miranda Johnson, Mr Tim Johnson, Mr G. L. Joynson, Mr R. Kent, Mr Steve Kent, Mrs Kay Kent, Mr Paul Landrum, Mr Will Lazar, Mrs Sarah Leslie, Mr Fred Lockwood, Mr D. J. Lockwood, Mr George Maxwell, Mr D. Moyes, Miss M. Noden, Mr Ray Pattison, Mr Brendan Richardson, Mr B. Robbins, Mr Robert Rose, Scotch Piper Syndicate, Mr Peter J. Spencer, Mr Alex Steedman, Mr George Tobitt, Mr Neil Watt, Mr I. Whitfield, Mrs Carole Worsley, Mr Graham Worsley.

Assistant Trainer: Adrian Lane

Jockey (NH): Adrian Lane, Wilson Renwick. **Conditional:** James Cowley, Ronan Short, Cai Williams. **Amateur:** Mr Theo Gillard, Miss Abbie McCain, Mr Harry Stock.

---

398 **MR TIM MCCARTHY, Godstone**
Postal: **Nags Hall Farm, Oxted Road, Godstone, Surrey, RH9 8DB**
Contacts: **PHONE (01883) 740379 FAX (01883) 740381 MOBILE (07887) 763062**

1 **DUTCHARTCOLLECTOR,** 5, b g Dutch Art—Censored **Surrey Racing Club**
2 **FIFTY FIFTY,** 4, br g Kheleyf (USA)—Dodona **Mr Alan Spence**
3 **GHOST TRAIN (IRE),** 7, b g Holy Roman Emperor (IRE)—

   Adrastea (IRE) **Homecroft Wealth Racing & T D McCarthy**
4 **UNDERSTORY (USA),** 9, b g Forestry (USA)—Sha Tha (USA) **Homecroft Wealth Racing & T D McCarthy**
5 **WATER THIEF (USA),** 4, b g Bellamy Road (USA)—Sometime (IRE) **Surrey Racing Club**

Other Owners: Mrs C. V. McCarthy, T. D. McCarthy, S. J. Piper, Mr N. Pogmore.

Assistant Trainer: Mrs C.V. McCarthy

399 MISS DANIELLE MCCORMICK, Lathom

Postal: Blythe Hall, Blythe Lane, Lathom, Ormskirk, Lancashire, L40 5TY
Contacts: **PHONE (01695) 572358 MOBILE (07590) 513752**
E-MAIL danielle-mccormick@hotmail.co.uk

1 BLYTHE STAR (IRE), 4, b g Thewayyouare (USA)—Run To Jane (IRE) **Blythe Stables LLP**
2 ECHO SPRINGS, 6, b g Kayf Tara—Mrs Malt (IRE) **Blythe Stables LLP**
3 MOXEY, 5, ch g Nayef (USA)—Emily Blake (IRE) **Blythe Stables LLP**

THREE-YEAR-OLDS

4 CARLOVIAN, b g Acclamation—Mimisel **Fergus & Caroline Lyons**
5 KODIMOOR (IRE), b c Kodiac—Victoria Lodge (IRE) **Blythe Stables LLP**

Other Owners: Mrs T. Bell, Mr A. J. Bell, Mr F. Lyons, Mrs C. Lyons.

Amateur: Miss A. McCormick.

400 MR PHIL MCENTEE, Newmarket

Postal: Racefield Stables, Carriageway, Hamilton Road, Newmarket, Suffolk, CB8 7JQ
Contacts: **PHONE (01638) 662092 FAX (01638) 662092 MOBILE (07802) 663256**

1 BLACK VALE (IRE), 5, b g Moss Vale (IRE)—Limit (IRE) **Mrs R. L. Baker**
2 COME ON DAVE (IRE), 7, b g Red Clubs (IRE)—Desert Sprite (IRE) **Wildcard Racing Syndicate**
3 CORNTON ROAD, 4, b g Bertolini (USA)—Sister Rose (FR) **Mr R. W. Carson**
4 GENTLEMEN, 5, ch g Ad Valorem (USA)—Stoney Cove (IRE) **Eventmaker Racehorses**
5 GLASGOW CENTRAL, 5, b g Rail Link—Musical Key **Mrs R. L. McEntee**
6 HONITON LACE, 5, ch m Tobougg (IRE)—Mellifluous (IRE) **Eventmaker Racehorses**
7 JONNIE SKULL (IRE), 10, b g Pyrus (USA)—Sovereign Touch (IRE) **R McEntee & The Guernsey Boys**
8 KINGSTON SASSAFRAS, 4, b g Halling (USA)—Kingston Acacia **Miss R. B. McEntee**
9 MARY ANN BUGG (IRE), 4, b f Bushranger (IRE)—Shobobb **Mr S. Jakes**
10 MOONDAY SUN (USA), 7, gr g Mizzen Mast (USA)—Storm Dove (USA) **Power Geneva Ltd**
11 MY MISTRESS (IRE), 4, ch f Mastercraftsman (IRE)—Majestic Eviction (IRE) **Mr H. R. Nothhaft**
12 NIFTY KIER, 7, b g Kier Park (IRE)—Yeldham Lady **Mrs R. L. McEntee**
13 NOVABRIDGE, 8, ch g Avonbridge—Petrovna (IRE) **Power Geneva Ltd**
14 SWISS CROSS, 9, b g Cape Cross (IRE)—Swiss Lake (USA) **Mr S. Jakes**
15 TASAABOQ, 5, b g Aqlaam—Seldemosa **Mrs R. L. Baker**
16 TORREON (IRE), 5, b g High Chaparral—Teide Lady
17 TOWER POWER, 5, b g Nayef (USA)—Voile (IRE) **Miss M. Bishop-Peck**
18 TOYMAKER (IRE), 5, b g Starcraft (NZ)—Eurolink Raindance (IRE) **Eventmaker Racehorses**

THREE-YEAR-OLDS

19 EMILY GOLDFINCH, ch f Prime Defender—Lakelands Lady (IRE) **McHugh & Paxton**
20 ROMAN MAGIC (IRE), b f Holy Roman Emperor (IRE)—Folle Blanche (USA) **Mr S. Jakes**
21 STILL KICKING (IRE), b g Bahamian Bounty—Sister Clement (IRE) **Mr S. Jakes**

TWO-YEAR-OLDS

22 ELEMENTO, ch g 27/2 Assertive—Black Baccara (Superior Premium) (5238) **Eventmaker Racehorses**
23 RED MOHICAN, ch f 14/2 Harbour Watch (IRE)—
                              Magical Cliche (USA) (Affirmed (USA)) (12000) **Eventmaker Racehorses**
24 SWISS VINNARE, b c 24/1 Arabian Gleam—Matilda Peace (Namaqualand (USA)) **Mr S. Jakes**

Other Owners: Mr A. J. Bonarius, Mr N. J. Bonarius, Mr M. A. Humphris, T. D. Johnson, Ms J. McHugh, Mr J. M. Paxton, Mr M. D. Queripel.

401 MR MURTY MCGRATH, Maidstone

Postal: Spicketts House, Kiln Barn Road, East Malling, Kent, ME19 6BG
Contacts: **PHONE (01732) 840173 MOBILE (07818) 098073**
E-MAIL mjmcgrath@hotmail.com

1 FREEMASON, 5, b g Cape Cross (IRE)—Candy Mountain **Gallagher Equine Ltd**
2 REZWAAN, 9, b g Alhaarth (IRE)—Nasij (USA) **Gallagher Equine Ltd**

MR MURTY MCGRATH - Continued

3 **SYDNEY RUFFDIAMOND**, 4, b g Equiano (FR)—Pirouetting **Gallagher Equine Ltd**
4 **ZARRINA BLUE**, 5, b m Helissio (FR)—Zaffre Bleu (IRE) **M. McGrath**

THREE-YEAR-OLDS
5 **KEIBA (IRE)**, br c Dark Angel (IRE)—True Magic **Gallagher Equine Ltd**
6 **LEE'S HALL (IRE)**, b g Invincible Spirit (IRE)—Russian Roubles (IRE) **Gallagher Equine Ltd**

TWO-YEAR-OLDS
7 Ch c 23/2 Poet's Voice—River Song (USA) (Siphon (BRZ)) (18000) **Mr R. P. Gallagher**

Assistant Trainer: Heidi McGrath (07795) 178178

Jockey (flat): Shane Kelly.

---

402 **MRS JEAN MCGREGOR, Milnathort**
Postal: **Wester Tillyrie Steading, Milnathort, Kinross, KY13 0RW**
Contacts: **PHONE (01577) 861792 MOBILE (07764) 464299**
E-MAIL purebred68@hotmail.co.uk

1 7, B g Beat Hollow—Boutique **Mrs D. Thomson**
2 **CROOKOFDEVON**, 7, b g Desideratum—Blue Morning **J. Thomson**
3 5, B m Rob Roy (USA)—Ginger Brandy **Mrs D. Thomson**
4 **JACKOFHEARTS**, 8, b g Beat Hollow—Boutique **Mr S. Taylor**
5 4, B f Supreme Sound—Lingham Bridesmaid
6 **SLANEY STAR (IRE)**, 8, b g Cloudings (IRE)—Slaney Rose (IRE) **Miss A. McGregor**
7 **SPRINGSTRIDE**, 4, b f Jeremy (USA)—Stoney Cove (IRE) **Mr R. C. Davison**
8 **THEHOODLUM**, 9, b g Fraam—Trilby **Tillyrie Racing Club**

Other Owner: Mr Scott Burnett.

Jockey (flat): Andrew Mullen. **Jockey (NH):** Henry Brooke, Sean Quinlan. **Conditional:** Jonathan England, John Kington. **Amateur:** Miss A.L. McGregor.

---

403 **MS KAREN MCLINTOCK, Newcastle-Upon-Tyne**
Postal: **The Byerley Stud, Ingoe, Newcastle-Upon-Tyne, NE20 0SZ**
Contacts: **PHONE (01661) 886356 MOBILE (07966) 776710**
E-MAIL karen.mclintock@equiname.co.uk WEBSITE www.karenmclintock.co.uk

1 **AUSTRALASIA (IRE)**, 6, b g Zerpour (IRE)—Leachestown (IRE) **06 Zoo Ltd**
2 **BANKS O' HOUXTY**, 6, b g Generous (IRE)—Border Mist (IRE) **W. M. Aitchison**
3 5, B g Multiplex—Barichara (FR) **Richard Kent & Equiname Ltd**
4 **DERRYDOON**, 6, b g Multiplex—Wahiba Reason (IRE) **Mrs A. M. O'Sullivan**
5 **EMPEROR SAKHEE**, 6, ch g Sakhee (USA)—Pochard **06 Zoo Ltd**
6 **GURKHA BRAVE (IRE)**, 8, b g Old Vic—Honeyed (IRE) **Mr A. C. Lamont**
7 **GURKHA FRIEND**, 4, b c Showcasing—Parabola **Mr D. Eddy**
8 **OFFICER CADET**, 7, b g Kayf Tara—Miss Invincible **06 Zoo Ltd**
9 **ROCKWOOD**, 5, b g Rock of Gibraltar (IRE)—Hannah Frank (IRE) **Mr I. R. Clements & Dr L. G. Parry**
10 **SENATUS (FR)**, 4, b g Early March—Winter Brook (FR) **06 Zoo Ltd**
11 **TAOPIX**, 4, b br g Rip Van Winkle (IRE)—Sinister Ruckus (USA) **Mr G. R. Stockdale**

THREE-YEAR-OLDS
12 **AVENUE OF STARS**, b c Makfi—Clifton Dancer **Mr A. C. Lamont**

Other Owners: Mr I. R. Clements, Equiname Ltd, R. Kent, Dr L. G. Parry.

Assistant Trainer: Donald Eddy

404 MR ED MCMAHON, Lichfield

Postal: **Horsley Brook Farm, Tamworth Road, Lichfield, Staffordshire, WS14 9PT**
Contacts: **PHONE** (01543) 481224 **FAX** (01543) 651100 **MOBILE** (07787) 951630
E-MAIL comeracing@horsleybrook.fsnet.co.uk **WEBSITE** www.edmcmahonracing.co.uk

1 **COLOUR MY WORLD**, 6, gr g With Approval (CAN)—Nadeszhda **Mr P. A. Wilkins**
2 **EMJAYEM**, 6, ch g Needwood Blade—Distant Stars (IRE) **Mrs J. McMahon**
3 **EXPRESS HIMSELF (IRE)**, 5, b g Dylan Thomas (IRE)—Lightwood Lady (IRE) **Milton Express Limited**
4 **GOLD CLUB**, 5, b g Multiplex—Oceana Blue **The C H F Partnership**
5 **NOBLE STORM (USA)**, 10, b g Yankee Gentleman (USA)—Changed Tune (USA)
6 **ROCKET RONNIE (IRE)**, 6, b g Antonius Pius (USA)—
Ctesiphon (USA) **Mr C A Mills,Mr A Fallon,Mr G Purchase**
7 **SAKHEE'S ROSE**, 6, b m Sakhee's Secret—Isobel Rose (IRE) **Mr J. R. Dwyer**
8 **SECRET LOOK**, 6, ch g Sakhee's Secret—Look Here's Carol (IRE) **S. L. Edwards**
9 **VENUTIUS**, 9, b g Doyen (IRE)—Boadicea's Chariot **Mrs F. S. Williams**

THREE-YEAR-OLDS

10 **ANDALUSITE**, br f Equiano (FR)—Kammaan **The LAM Partnership**
11 B f Passing Glance—Fireburst **Mrs P. J. Toye**
12 **MOI AUSSIE**, gr f Aussie Rules (USA)—Oceana Blue **The C H F Partnership**
13 **MYSTERIOUS GLANCE**, b f Cacique (IRE)—Largo (IRE) **S. L. Edwards**
14 **MYSTERIOUS LOOK**, ch f Sakhee's Secret—Look Here's Carol (IRE) **S. L. Edwards**
15 **RENEGE**, ch f Firebreak—Today's The Day **Mr C. G. Conway**
16 **SOCIETY ANGEL (IRE)**, gr f Dark Angel (IRE)—Gooseberry Pie **The W.H.O. Society**

TWO-YEAR-OLDS

17 B f 27/1 Harbour Watch (IRE)—Honeymead (IRE) (Pivotal) (18000) **E. S. A. McMahon**
18 **LESANTI**, b c 6/4 Royal Applause—Kammaan (Diktat) **The LAM Partnership**
19 **LUDWIGSBURG**, br gr c 27/3 Mount Nelson—Cheerfully (Sadler's Wells (USA)) (7000) **The LAM Partnership**
20 B c 15/4 Delegator—Muara (Wolfhound (USA)) (571) **Mr W. R. Arblaster**
21 **SUETONIUS**, b c 4/3 Royal Applause—Vespasia (Medicean) (5500) **Mrs F. S. Williams**
22 **THE DALEY EXPRESS (IRE)**, b c 9/5 Elzaam (AUS)—
Seraphina (IRE) (Pips Pride) (28571) **Milton Express Limited**

Other Owners: Mr A. Fallon, C. H. Fischer, K. H. Fischer, Dr M. F. Ford, Mr C. Mills, Ms L. M. Mulcahy, Mr G. Purchase, Mr D. Thomas.

Assistant Trainer: Bryan Arthur McMahon

405 MR BRIAN MCMATH, Newmarket

Postal: **26 The Street, Snailwell, Newmarket, Suffolk, CB8 7LU**
Contacts: **PHONE** (01638) 578841 **MOBILE** (07734) 564923
E-MAIL brian.mcmath@hotmail.com

1 **GIANTSTEPSAHEAD (IRE)**, 7, br g Footstepsinthesand—Salty Air (IRE) **Mr K. R. Hills**
2 4, B c Myboycharlie (IRE)—Razor Sharp **Mr C. Sheen, Mr P. Cromwell, Miss C. Bishop**
3 **SHERRYS SWEETPEA**, 8, b m Needwood Blade—Compendium **Miss C. Rowe**
4 **WERONAWINNERSHERRY**, 7, b m Needwood Blade—Wizby **Mr R. C. Ames**

THREE-YEAR-OLDS

5 **ICONS IMAGE**, ch g Sixties Icon—Marrimeclaire (IRE) **Mr K. R. Hills**

Assistant Trainer: Claire Bishop

Jockey (flat): Tom Queally. **Apprentice:** Daniel Muscutt. **Amateur:** Miss Claire Bishop.

406 MR GRAEME MCPHERSON, Stow-On-The-Wold

Postal: **Martins Hill, Bledington Road, Stow-on-the-wold, Gloucestershire, GL54 1JH**
Contacts: **PHONE** (01451) 830769 **MOBILE** (07815) 887360
WEBSITE www.mcphersonracing.co.uk

1 **ACHIMOTA (IRE)**, 10, b g Double Eclipse (IRE)—Tullyfoyle (IRE) **W. J. Odell**
2 **ALEXANDER THE GREY**, 5, gr g Fair Mix (IRE)—Cadourova (FR) **Mr H. Burdett**

MR GRAEME MCPHERSON - Continued

3 **AMI DESBOIS (FR)**, 6, b g Dream Well (FR)—Baroya (FR) **EPDS Racing Partnership 12**
4 **BACH TO BEFORE (IRE)**, 8, b g Bach (IRE)—Fairfield Mist (IRE) **Mr R. D. Potter**
5 4, B g Flemensfirth (USA)—Ballerina Laura (IRE) **G. McPherson**
6 **BENEFICIAL JOE (IRE)**, 6, b br g Beneficial—Joleen (IRE) **Mr & Mrs Paul & Clare Rooney**
7 **BIBI D'EOLE (FR)**, 5, ch g Storm Trooper (GER)—Bibi Star (FR) **Mr & Mrs Paul & Clare Rooney**
8 **CHARLIE COOK (IRE)**, 7, b g Royal Anthem (USA)—Supreme Baloo (IRE) **Graham & Carole Worsley**
9 **DELIRIOUS LOVE (IRE)**, 4, b g Definite Article—Grangeclare Lark (IRE) **Wildcat Syndicate**
10 **DOLLY DIAMOND**, 7, b m Erhaab (USA)—Solid Land (FR) **EPDS Racing 16 & Partner**
11 **EVERVESCENT (IRE)**, 7, b g Elnadim (USA)—Purepleasureseeker (IRE) **Ever Equine**
12 **EXTREME IMPACT**, 10, b g Rock of Gibraltar (IRE)—Soviet Moon (IRE) **Extreme Racing Fans**
13 **FLYING LIGHT (IRE)**, 10, b g Chevalier (IRE)—Light-Flight (IRE) **The McPherson Racing Partnership**
14 **GABRIEL OATS**, 7, ch g Grape Tree Road—Winnow **The Self Preservation Society & Partner**
15 4, B g Oscar (IRE)—Garryduff Princess (IRE) **G. McPherson**
16 **GREAT VALUE (IRE)**, 11, b g Revoque (IRE)—Dame de L'oise (USA) **The McPherson Racing Partnership**
17 **HARRY HUNT**, 9, b g Bertolini (USA)—Qasirah (IRE) **The Reserved Judgment Partnership**
18 **HEY BILL (IRE)**, 6, b g Indian Danehill (IRE)—Grange More (IRE) **H. S. Smith**
19 **HOLLY BUSH HENRY (IRE)**, 5, b g Yeats (IRE)—Maslam (IRE) **Lady Bamford & Alice Bamford**
20 **HOLLYWOOD ALL STAR (IRE)**, 7, b g Kheleyf (USA)—Camassina (IRE) **The McPherson Racing Partnership**
21 **IKORODU ROAD**, 13, b g Double Trigger (IRE)—Cerisier (IRE) **W. J. Odell**
22 **KAYF BLANCO**, 7, b g Kayf Tara—Land of Glory **L.Day, Mr H.Burdett & Mr G.McPherson**
23 **LONDONIA**, 4, gr g Paco Boy (IRE)—Snowdrops **EPDS Racing 16 & Partner**
24 **MONEY MAID (IRE)**, 8, ch m Blueprint (IRE)—Maid of Music (IRE) **EPDS Racing Partnership 5**
25 **OCEAN VENTURE (IRE)**, 8, ch g Urban Ocean (FR)—Starventure (IRE) **Mr J. Chamberlain**
26 **PANDY WELLS**, 7, b m Kayf Tara—Alina Rheinberg (GER) **Mike & Linda Paul**
27 **POLO SPRINGS**, 9, gr m Baryshnikov (AUS)—Cristal Springs **Denarius Consulting Ltd**
28 **PYRSHAN (IRE)**, 7, b g Pyrus (USA)—Runshangale (IRE) **Mr K. J. N. Meek**
29 **RED ADMIRABLE (IRE)**, 10, b g Shantou (USA)—Eimears Pet (IRE) **Wildcat Syndicate**
30 **RUBY WILDE (IRE)**, 5, b m Oscar (IRE)—Hazel Grove (IRE) **Mrs L. Day**
31 **SAMOSET**, 6, b g Sir Percy—Great Quest (IRE) **Mr & Mrs A. Mews**
32 **SCOOBY (IRE)**, 5, b g Dubai Destination (USA)—Maggie Howard (IRE) **The Ladies Of Martins Hill**
33 **SHADY GLEN (IRE)**, 7, br g Dr Massini (IRE)—Poppins (IRE) **The McPherson Racing Partnership**
34 **SKIPTHECUDDLES (IRE)**, 5, b g Westerner—Autumn Sky (IRE) **Mr R. Cunningham**
35 **THE RACING DUKE (IRE)**, 4, b g Duke of Marmalade (IRE)—
     Wrong Key (IRE) **Mrs L.Day, Mr H.Burdett & Mr G.McPherson**
36 **TITANS APPROACH (IRE)**, 7, b g High Chaparral (IRE)—Armelles Approach (IRE) **Four Lawyers and a Banker**
37 **TRILLERIN MINELLA (IRE)**, 8, b g King's Theatre (IRE)—Eva Fay (IRE) **Mrs L. Day**
38 **UMBRA D'ANJOU (IRE)**, 5, b g Double Eclipse (IRE)—Belle d'anjou (FR)
39 **ZABEEL STAR (IRE)**, 4, ch g Arcano (IRE)—Deep Winter **The Self Preservation Society & Partner**

Other Owners: Lady Bamford, Miss A. C. Bamford, Mrs M. E. Barton, K. R. Elliott, Mr R. J. P. Gilmore, Mr I. J. B. Gray, Mrs S. M. McPherson, Mrs S. Mews, Mr A. Mews, Mr M. R. Paul, Mrs L. C. Paul, Mr J. R. Powell, Mr P. A. Rooney, Mrs C. Rooney, Miss T. Sloan, Mr T. J. Whiting, Mr A. Woollard, Mr G. W. Worsley, Mrs C. P. Worsley.

Assistant Trainers: Mick Finn, Jodie Mogford.

Jockey (NH): Wayne Hutchinson. **Conditional:** Ollie Garner, Killian Moore.

---

407 MR MARTYN MEADE, Newmarket
Postal: **Sefton Lodge, 8 Bury Road, Newmarket, Suffolk, CB8 7BT**
Contacts: **PHONE** (01638) 666100 **MOBILE** (07879) 891811
E-MAIL mmeade@martynmeaderacing.com **WEBSITE** www.martynmeaderacing.com

1 **DARMA (IRE)**, 4, b f Acclamation—Dark Dancer (FR)
2 **FOREVER NOW**, 5, b h Galileo (IRE)—All's Forgotten (USA)
3 **IRISH ROOKIE (IRE)**, 4, b f Azamour (IRE)—Bold Assumption
4 **MIDNIGHT WHISTLER (USA)**, 4, b c Henrythenavigator (USA)—Ball Gown (USA)
5 **MYSTICAL SPIRIT (FR)**, 4, ch c Spirit One (FR)—Miss Maguilove (FR)
6 **NAVIGATE (IRE)**, 4, b c Iffraaj—Dorothy Dene
7 **SOLO HUNTER**, 5, b g Sleeping Indian—Night Owl

THREE-YEAR-OLDS

8 **ACLAIM (IRE)**, b c Acclamation—Aris (IRE)
9 **ANNIE SALTS**, b f Zebedee—Dazzling View (USA)
10 **C NOTE (IRE)**, b c Iffraaj—Alexander Queen (IRE)

MR MARTYN MEADE - Continued

11 **CHELSEA LAD (IRE)**, b c Clodovil (IRE)—Yali (IRE)
12 **CONSULTING**, ch c Kyllachy—Doctor's Note
13 **DE VEER CLIFFS (IRE)**, b f Canford Cliffs (IRE)—Mill Guineas (USA)
14 **EDIFICATION**, b c Dream Ahead (USA)—Elegant Pride
15 **GUANABARA BAY (IRE)**, b c Clodovil (IRE)—Sakaka
16 **KURLAND (IRE)**, gr f Kheleyf (USA)—Bunditten (IRE)
17 **LANGHAM**, b f Royal Applause—Three Ducks
18 **LENIENCE (IRE)**, b f Oasis Dream—Acts of Grace (USA)
19 **MILROW (IRE)**, b c Tamayuz—Cannikin (IRE)
20 **MYWAYISTHEONLYWAY (IRE)**, b c Tamayuz—Soul Custody (CAN)
21 **PHILEAS FOGG (IRE)**, b c Arcano (IRE)—Ava's World (IRE)
22 B f Royal Applause—Pink Stone (FR)
23 **PRAY FOR PARIS**, ch f Champs Elysees—Port Providence
24 **REUBEN JAMES**, b c Cape Cross (IRE)—Privalova (IRE)
25 **RIO'S CLIFFS**, b f Canford Cliffs (IRE)—What's Up Pussycat (IRE)
26 **SHOOFLY (IRE)**, b f Azamour (IRE)—Natural Flair (USA)
27 **ST JAMES'S PARK (IRE)**, br c Invincible Spirit (IRE)—Rakiza (IRE)
28 **THE PLOUGH (IRE)**, gr c Sea The Stars (IRE)—Chinese White (IRE)
29 **WHISTLE (IRE)**, b f Holy Roman Emperor (IRE)—Multaka (USA)
30 **WILAMINA (IRE)**, b f Zoffany (IRE)—Tropical Lake (IRE)

TWO-YEAR-OLDS

31 Gr f 25/4 Canford Cliffs (IRE)—Beautiful Hill (IRE) (Danehill (USA)) (16242)
32 B f 30/4 Fastnet Rock (AUS)—Brazilian Samba (IRE) (Sadler's Wells (USA)) (45714)
33 **BREAKFAST (IRE)**, ch f 11/3 Arcano (IRE)—Croque Madame (IRE) (Galileo (IRE))
34 Ch f 20/4 Helmet (AUS)—Bunditten (IRE) (Soviet Star (USA)) (38095)
35 B c 6/2 Excelebration (IRE)—Dance Troupe (Rainbow Quest (USA)) (38000)
36 B f 31/1 Rip Van Winkle (IRE)—Dhamma (USA) (Broad Brush (USA)) (17718)
37 B c 6/4 Foxwedge (AUS)—Elegant Pride (Beat Hollow)
38 **ERNSTSTAVROBLOFELD (USA)**, ch c 28/3 Elusive Quality (USA)—Minute Limit (IRE) (Pivotal) (45773)
39 B f 6/3 Pastoral Pursuits—Jasmick (IRE) (Definite Article) (5000)
40 B c 17/2 Cape Cross (IRE)—Kinetica (Stormy Atlantic (USA)) (35437)
41 B f 19/4 Authorized (IRE)—Let's Dance (IRE) (Danehill Dancer (IRE))
42 Br f 8/3 Paco Boy (IRE)—Miliana (IRE) (Polar Falcon (USA)) (29531)
43 B f 24/2 Rip Van Winkle (IRE)—Necklace (Darshaan) (62753)
44 B f 24/2 Henrythenavigator (USA)—Right Answer (Lujain (USA)) (28571)
45 Ch f 15/2 Casamento (IRE)—Silver Grey (IRE) (Chineur (FR))
46 B f 10/3 Azamour (IRE)—Simkana (IRE) (Kalanisi (IRE)) (45000)
47 Ch c 7/4 Intense Focus (USA)—Star of The West (Galileo (IRE))
48 B f 20/5 Shamardal (USA)—Sugarhoneybaby (IRE) (Docksider (USA)) (50000)
49 B f 5/4 Dark Angel (IRE)—Vistaria (USA) (Distant View (USA))
50 B c 4/3 Frankel—You'll Be Mine (USA) (Kingmambo (USA)) (150000)

Owners: Sheikh Khalifa Al Maktoum, Hamdan Al Maktoum, Mr J. Anderson, R. F. Barnes, Mr John Barnes, Mr D. H. A. C. Caddy, Calypso Bloodstock, Canning Downs, Chelsea Thoroughbreds, Mrs L. Coffey, Essafinaat, Mr P. Fitzsimons, Mrs D. E. Glading, Ladyswood Stud, Mrs Joy Mackay, Mrs Karen Marshall, McPeake Investments (NI) Ltd, Mr A. P. Mithen, R. H. W. Morecombe, Mrs Jane Newett, Rosemont Stud Syndicate, Mr W. J. Salthouse, Sefton Syndicate, Mr H. Sherborne, Mr J. Spence.

Assistant Trainer: Freddie Meade (Fmeade@Martynmeaderacing.com)

Jockey (flat): Fergus Sweeney.

---

408 **MR NOEL MEADE, Navan**
Postal: Tu Va Stables, Castletown-Kilpatrick, Navan, Co. Meath, Ireland
Contacts: **PHONE (00 353) 46 905 4197 FAX (00 353) 46 905 4459 MOBILE (00 353) 87 256 6039**
WEBSITE www.noelmeade.com

1 **A GENIE IN ABOTTLE (IRE)**, 5, b g Beneficial—Erkindale Miss (IRE)
2 **AENGUS (IRE)**, 6, b g Robin des Champs (FR)—Which Thistle (IRE)
3 **APACHE STRONGHOLD (IRE)**, 8, b g Milan—First Battle (IRE)
4 4, B f Brian Boru—Ardent Love (IRE)
5 6, B g Tikkanen (USA)—Ballooley (IRE)
6 4, B g Beneficial—Ballyoscar (IRE)

MR NOEL MEADE - Continued

7 **BAROSSA PEARL (IRE)**, 6, b m Milan—What An Answer (IRE)
8 **BEL AMI DE SIVOLA (FR)**, 5, b g Network (GER)—Notting Hill (FR)
9 **BENEMEADE (IRE)**, 8, b g Beneficial—Millicent Bridge (IRE)
10 **BLACK ACE (IRE)**, 5, b g Yeats (IRE)—All Our Blessings (IRE)
11 **BLACKBERRY LASS (IRE)**, 5, b m King's Theatre (IRE)—Market Lass (IRE)
12 **BONNY KATE (IRE)**, 6, ch m Beneficial—Peppardstown (IRE)
13 7, B br g Winged Love (IRE)—Brescia (FR)
14 **BRIGHTEST FLAME (IRE)**, 5, b g Shantou (USA)—Sparkling Sword
15 8, Ch g Royal Anthem (USA)—Butchies Girl (IRE)
16 **CHAMPOLEON (IRE)**, 6, gr g Turtle Bowl (IRE)—Trasimene
17 **CHEROKEE BILL**, 5, b g Robin des Champs (FR)—Daizinni
18 **CLARA SORRENTO (FR)**, 5, gr g Maresca Sorrento (FR)—Call Me Clara (FR)
19 **CLAY ALLISON (IRE)**, 5, b g Primary (USA)—Cockpit Lady (IRE)
20 **DE NAME ESCAPES ME (IRE)**, 6, ch g Vinnie Roe (IRE)—Heartlight (IRE)
21 **DISKO (FR)**, 5, gr g Martaline—Nikos Royale (FR)
22 **EXECUTIVE DECISION (IRE)**, 8, ch g Turgeon (USA)—Thalie Eria (FR)
23 **FAIR RETURN**, 6, b g Presenting—Polivalente (FR)
24 **GETAWAY KID (IRE)**, 4, ch g Getaway (GER)—Bambootcha (IRE)
25 **GETTYSBURG ADDRESS (IRE)**, 5, b g Milan—Cat Burglar (IRE)
26 **GRECO ROMAIN (IRE)**, 5, b g Martaline—De Haute Lutte (USA)
27 **GUNNERY SERGEANT (IRE)**, 5, b br g Presenting—Dame Foraine (FR)
28 **HARVEY LOGAN (IRE)**, 7, b g Saffron Walden (FR)—Baie Barbara (IRE)
29 **HECK THOMAS (IRE)**, 8, b g Oscar (IRE)—Good Heighway (IRE)
30 **HOODOO BROWN**, 5, ch g Refuse To Bend (IRE)—Paradise Dancer (IRE)
31 **ICE COLD SOUL (IRE)**, 6, b g Stowaway—Western Whisper (IRE)
32 **JACK SLADE (IRE)**, 6, ch g Stowaway—Sharps Express (IRE)
33 **JOSEPHINE MARCUS (USA)**, 6, b m Flemensfirth (USA)—Tart of Tipp (IRE)
34 **KAGNEY (IRE)**, 5, br g Kalanisi (IRE)—Clondalee (IRE)
35 **KILLER MILLER (IRE)**, 7, b g Flemensfirth (USA)—Miss Brandywell (IRE)
36 5, B g Scorpion (IRE)—Kilmington Breeze (IRE)
37 **LA GALONDRINA (IRE)**, 4, ch f Thewayyouare (USA)—Myloveportofino (IRE)
38 **LADYSINGSTHEBLUES (IRE)**, 4, b f Robin des Champs (FR)—Ghillie's Bay (IRE)
39 **LAVERTEEN (FR)**, 5, b g Laveron—Manson Teene (FR)
40 **LEOPARDS LEAP (IRE)**, 5, b g Arcadio (GER)—Talk of Rain (FR)
41 **LORD IN RED (GER)**, 4, ch g Noroit (GER)—Lady In Red (GER)
42 **MAD CAREW (IRE)**, 4, b g Getaway (GER)—Babygotback (IRE)
43 **MAHLER TEN (IRE)**, 4, b g Mahler—Native Mo (IRE)
44 4, B g Milan—Marble Desire (IRE)
45 5, B g Flemensfirth (USA)—Merry Batim (IRE)
46 **MINELLA FAIR (IRE)**, 5, b g Flemensfirth (USA)—Bell Walks Run (IRE)
47 **MONKSLAND (IRE)**, 9, b g Beneficial—Cush Jewel (IRE)
48 **MOULIN A VENT**, 4, gr g Sagamix (FR)—Bahia Blanca (FR)
49 5, Ch g Presenting—Niamh's Dream (IRE)
50 **NIGHT GENERATION (GER)**, 4, ch g Sholokhov (IRE)—Night Woman (GER)
51 4, Ch g Jeremy (USA)—Noctilucent (JPN)
52 **OFFICIEUX (FR)**, 5, ch g Discover d'auteuil (FR)—Souri des Champs (FR)
53 **PERSHING MISSILE (IRE)**, 4, b g Milan—Banbury Cross (IRE)
54 **PRINCESS LARA (IRE)**, 4, b f Alhaarth (IRE)—First Battle (IRE)
55 **RATHNURE REBEL (IRE)**, 6, b g Beneficial—Euro Magic (IRE)
56 **RED GIANT (IRE)**, 5, ch g Beneficial—Barrack Star (IRE)
57 **RISE OF AN EMPIRE (IRE)**, 6, b g Stowaway—Kymin (IRE)
58 **ROAD TO RICHES (IRE)**, 9, b g Gamut (IRE)—Bellora (IRE)
59 **RUNFORBOB (IRE)**, 4, b g Shantou (USA)—What An Answer (IRE)
60 **RUSSIAN BILL (IRE)**, 6, b g Kalanisi (IRE)—Littleton Liberty
61 5, B g Hurricane Run (IRE)—Saratogane (FR)
62 **SHE'S A STAR (IRE)**, 4, b f Well Chosen—Lobinstown Girl (IRE)
63 **SHOWEM SILVER (IRE)**, 5, b g Winged Love (IRE)—Swap Shop (IRE)
64 **SILVER TURTLE (FR)**, 5, gr g Turtle Bowl (IRE)—Trasimene
65 **SNOW FALCON (IRE)**, 6, b g Presenting—Flocon de Neige (IRE)
66 4, B g Curtain Time (IRE)—Southcoast Gale (IRE)
67 **STONEFORD (IRE)**, 5, b g Beneficial—Hester Hall (IRE)
68 **STRETCHINGTHETRUTH (IRE)**, 5, b g Gold Well—Maryanndoyle (IRE)
69 7, B g Winged Love (IRE)—Swap Shop (IRE)
70 **TAMLOUGH BOY**, 5, b g Central Park (IRE)—Zamyatina (IRE)
71 **TEXAS JACK (IRE)**, 10, b g Curtain Time (IRE)—Sailors Run (IRE)

MR NOEL MEADE - Continued

72 **THE HERDS GARDEN**, 7, b g Multiplex—Eternal Legacy (IRE)
73 **THE RORY STORY (IRE)**, 5, b g Flemensfirth (USA)—Phardester (IRE)
74 **THOMOND (IRE)**, 8, b g Definite Article—Hushaby (IRE)
75 4, B g Milan—Thousand Wings (GER)
76 **TICONDEROGA (IRE)**, 5, b g Robin des Champs (FR)—Wayward Star (IRE)
77 **TULSA JACK (IRE)**, 7, b g Urban Ocean (FR)—Jessica's Pet (IRE)
78 **TURFMANS DAUGHTER (IRE)**, 6, b m Flemensfirth (USA)—Atomic Winner (IRE)
79 **UNE LAVANDIERE (FR)**, 5, b m Laveron—Nouvelle Donne (FR)
80 **UP THE TOWN (IRE)**, 4, b g Windsor Knot (IRE)—Tara Tara (IRE)
81 **WAXIES DARGLE**, 7, b g Sakhee—Cup of Love (USA)
82 **WES HARDIN (IRE)**, 7, b g Beneficial—Luas Luso (IRE)
83 **WOUNDED WARRIOR (IRE)**, 7, b g Shantou (USA)—Sparkling Sword
84 **ZIP WYATT (IRE)**, 7, ch g Flemensfirth (USA)—Tricky Present (IRE)

THREE-YEAR-OLDS

85 **DODGYBINGO (IRE)**, b g Roderic O'Connor (IRE)—Happy Flight (IRE)
86 **KITTY LEROY (IRE)**, b f Lend A Hand—Lush Sister (IRE)

Assistant Trainer: Damien McGillick

Jockey (NH): Sean Flanagan, Paul Carberry. **Conditional:** Ger Fox, Jonathan Moore, Barry Reynolds.
Amateur: Miss Nina Carberry.

---

409 | **MR BRIAN MEEHAN, Manton**
Trainer did not wish details of his string to appear

---

410 | **MR DAVID MENUISIER, Pulborough**
Postal: **To Agori House, Coombelands Lane, Pulborough, West Sussex, RH20 1BP**
Contacts: **MOBILE 07876 674095**
E-MAIL david@dmhorseracing.com WEBSITE www.dmhorseracing.com

1 **HAVRE DE PAIX (FR)**, 4, b br f Le Havre (IRE)—Bridge of Peace **Mr C. A. Washbourn**
2 **HIER ENCORE (FR)**, 4, ch g Kentucky Dynamite (USA)—Hierarchie (FR) **Shinco Racing Limited**
3 **JETHOU ISLAND**, 5, ch m Virtual—Lihou Island **Mrs F. A. Veasey & Partners**
4 **SINFONIETTA (FR)**, 4, b g Sinndar (IRE)—Final Whistle (IRE) **Mr C. A. Washbourn**
5 **SLUNOVRAT (FR)**, 5, b g Astronomer Royal (USA)—Slewmamba (FR) **Shinco Racing Limited**
6 **SPECULATOR**, 4, gr c Bahamian Bounty—Swift Dispersal **Gail Brown Racing (VI)**

THREE-YEAR-OLDS

7 **ANGEL GRACE (IRE)**, gr f Dark Angel (IRE)—Light Sea (IRE) **Mr C. A. Washbourn**
8 **ASPEN AGAIN (IRE)**, b f Intikhab (USA)—Deira Dubai **Mr C. A. Washbourn**
9 **BIGMOUTH STRIKES (IRE)**, ch g Raven's Pass (USA)—Chiosina (IRE) **Mr C. A. Washbourn**
10 **CORPUS CHORISTER (FR)**, b f Soldier of Fortune (IRE)—Bridge of Peace **Mr C. A. Washbourn**
11 **KAATSKILL NAP (FR)**, ch g Rip Van Winkle (IRE)—Last Cast (FR) **Mr C. A. Washbourn**
12 **NAZIBA (IRE)**, gr f Zebedee—Nashaat **Skinfaxi Racing (I)**
13 **RED ROSE RIOT (IRE)**, b f Tamayuz—Red Bandanna (IRE) **Mr C. A. Washbourn**
14 **RODERIC'S SECRET (IRE)**, ch g Roderic O'Connor (IRE)—Midris (IRE) **Clive Washbourn & Robert Wasey**
15 **SAUNTER (FR)**, gr g Myboycharlie (IRE)—Marie des Fleurs (FR) **M. H. Watt**
16 **THE BLACK CYGNET**, br f Pastoral Pursuits—The Dark Eider **The Felicity Veasey Partnership**
17 **THUNDERING BLUE (USA)**, gr c Exchange Rate (USA)—Relampago Azul (USA) **Mr C. A. Washbourn**

TWO-YEAR-OLDS

18 **BIANCA MINOLA (FR)**, ch f 1/2 Shakespearean (IRE)—Transylvania (FR) (Motivator) (7382) **Mr C. A. Washbourn**
19 **CONTRAPPOSTO (IRE)**, b c 1/3 Cacique (IRE)—
                         Interim Payment (USA) (Red Ransom (USA)) (44000) **Mr C. A. Washbourn**
20 **KNOCKONHEAVENSDOOR (FR)**, ch f 23/4 Pirateer (IRE)—
                         Krasavitsa (FR) (Dancing Spree (USA)) **Shinco Racing Limited**
21 **MAKE TIME (IRE)**, ch c 13/3 Makfi—Poppet's Lovein (Lomitas) (60000) **Gail Brown Racing (VII)**

MR DAVID MENUISIER - Continued

22 **PRECIOUS EQUITY (FR),** b f 11/3 Equiano (FR)—
Anasy (USA) (Gone West (USA)) (5906) **Skinfaxi Racing (II) & Partner**
23 **RAINBOW RISING (FR),** b f 8/5 Henrythenavigator (USA)—
Rainbow Goddess (Rainbow Quest (USA)) (23624) **Mr C. A. Washbourn**

Other Owners: Mrs H. G. Clinch, Mr N. E. Gosset, Mr Derek Rogers, Mr F. C. Taylor, Mrs F. A. Veasey, Mr Robert Wasey, Mr R. H. Wright.

---

411 **MISS REBECCA MENZIES, Brandsby**
Postal: **Rebecca Menzies Racing, Foulrice Farm, Brandsby, York, North Yorkshire, YO61 4SB**
Contacts: PHONE (01347) 889652 MOBILE (07843) 169217
E-MAIL rebecca@rebeccamenzies.com WEBSITE www.rebeccamenzies.com

1 **ASUNCION (FR),** 6, b m Antarctique (IRE)—Liesse de Marbeuf (FR) **EPDS Racing Partnership 6**
2 **BALDING BANKER (IRE),** 10, b g Accordion—What A Breeze (IRE) **Club Racing Banker Partnership**
3 **BISHOP LIGHTFOOT (IRE),** 7, b g Helissio (FR)—Dawn Bid (IRE) **EPDS Racing Partnership 9**
4 **CALYPSO STORM (IRE),** 5, b g Trans Island—Valin Thyne (IRE) **John Dance & Partner**
5 **CAPTAIN MOWBRAY,** 5, ch g Shami—Some Like It Hot **Premier Racing Partnerships**
6 **CELTIC ARTISAN (IRE),** 5, ch g Dylan Thomas (IRE)—Perfectly Clear (USA) **EPDS Racing Partnership 11**
7 **CHAVOY (FR),** 11, br g Saint des Saints (FR)—Dictania (FR) **Mr Ian Shaw & Partner**
8 **HADA MEN (USA),** 11, b g Dynaformer (USA)—Catchy (USA) **Gay & Peter Hartley**
9 **HALCYON DAYS,** 7, b g Generous (IRE)—Indian Empress **ICM Racing**
10 **LADY CLITICO (IRE),** 5, b m Bushranger (IRE)—Villa Nova (IRE) **ICM Racing & Mr John Dance**
11 **MOTION TO STRIKE (IRE),** 6, b g Beneficial—Comeragh Girl (IRE) **Mr J. Dance**
12 **POPPIES MILAN (IRE),** 7, b g Milan—Second Best (IRE) **Poppies Europe Limited**
13 **ROYAL MACNAB (IRE),** 8, b g Beneficial—Tina McBride (IRE) **The Extra Time Partnership**
14 **SAMSON COLLONGES (FR),** 10, gr g Fragrant Mix (FR)—
Idole Collonges (FR) **Premier Racing Partnerships & ICM Racing**
15 4, B g Scorpion (IRE)—Skatey Kate (IRE) **Ms D. Fields**
16 **SUMMER STORM,** 6, b g Lucarno (USA)—Midsummer Magic **The Mount Racing Club & Duncan Horton**
17 **TOMKEVI (FR),** 5, b g Khalkevi (IRE)—Tamsna (FR) **Mr P J Howe & Mr R G Oliver**
18 **WATER GARDEN (FR),** 10, gr g Turgeon (USA)—Queenstown (FR) **Love To Race Partnership**
19 **ZAKATAL,** 10, gr g Kalanisi (IRE)—Zankara (FR) **David Furman & John Sugarman**

THREE-YEAR-OLDS

20 Gr f Zebedee—Alexander Ridge (IRE) **Mr J. Dance**
21 **COOL CRESCENDO,** b f Royal Applause—Cool Catena **Mr J. Dance**
22 **HASHTAG FRENZY,** ch g Compton Place—One Night In May (IRE) **ICM Racing**

TWO-YEAR-OLDS

23 Br c 1/3 Intense Focus (USA)—Aussie Opera (IRE) (Aussie Rules (USA)) (4798) **Mr J. Dance**
24 **BERTORIZZIA (FR),** ch f 1/4 Bertolini (USA)—Kadiania (FR) (Indian Rocket) (11812) **Mr J. Dance**
25 B c 3/3 Frozen Power (IRE)—New Blossom (IRE) (Shirocco (GER)) (9597) **Mr J. Dance**
26 B f 9/4 Dragon Pulse (IRE)—Safqa (Singspiel (IRE)) (9597) **Mr J. Dance**

Other Owners: J. Berry, Mr A. N. Eaton, Mrs M. Feely, Mr D. E. Furman, Mr M. Gornall, Mr I. Harle, P. A. H. Hartley, Mrs R. C. Hartley, Mr G. W. Holden, Mr D. C. Horton, Mr P. J. Howe, Miss R. E. A. Menzies, Mr R. G. Oliver, Mr G. W. Peacock, Mr J. R. Powell, Mr I. Shaw, Miss T. Sloan, Major P. H. K. Steveney, Mr J. B. Sugarman.

Assistant Trainer: Carly Dixon

---

412 **MR PHIL MIDDLETON, Aylesbury**
Postal: **Dorton Place, Dorton Park Farm, Dorton, Aylesbury, Buckinghamshire, HP18 9NR**
Contacts: PHONE (01844) 237503 FAX (01844) 237503 MOBILE (07860) 426607

1 **CHURCH FIELD (IRE),** 8, b g Heron Island (IRE)—Dante's Thatch (IRE) **Mr P. W. Middleton**
2 **CON FORZA (IRE),** 7, b g Milan—Classic Track **Mr P. W. Middleton**
3 **EXITAS (IRE),** 8, b g Exit To Nowhere (USA)—Suntas (IRE) **Mr P. W. Middleton**
4 **SATANIC BEAT (IRE),** 7, br g Dark Angel (IRE)—Slow Jazz (USA) **Mr P. W. Middleton**
5 **TALES OF MILAN (IRE),** 9, b g Milan—The Millers Tale (IRE) **Mr P. W. Middleton**

Assistant Trainer: Helen Day

413 MR PAUL MIDGLEY, Westow
Postal: Sandfield Farm, Westow, York, YO60 7LS
Contacts: **Office** (01653) 658790 **FAX** (01653) 658790 **MOBILE** (07976) 965220
E-MAIL ptmidgley@aol.com WEBSITE www.ptmidgley.com

1 ANOTHER WISE KID (IRE), 8, b g Whipper (USA)—Romancing **M. Ng**
2 DESERT LAW (IRE), 8, b g Oasis Dream—Speed Cop **Taylor's Bloodstock Ltd**
3 FUEL INJECTION, 5, gr g Pastoral Pursuits—Smart Hostess **Mrs M. Verity**
4 GAMESOME (FR), 5, b g Rock of Gibraltar (IRE)—Hot Coal (USA) **TA & PJ Stephenson,S Wibberley,R Bradley**
5 GIANT SPARK, 4, b g Orientor—Annie Gee **F. Brady**
6 GROUNDWORKER (IRE), 5, b g Tagula (IRE)—Notepad **Blackburn Family**
7 LINE OF REASON (IRE), 6, br g Kheleyf (USA)—Miss Party Line (USA) **Taylor's Bloodstock Ltd**
8 MISSISSIPPI, 7, b g Exceed And Excel (AUS)—Ruby Rocket (IRE) **Glasshoughton Racing**
9 MONSIEUR JOE (IRE), 9, b g Choisir (AUS)—Pascali **Taylor's Bloodstock Ltd**
10 NAGGERS (IRE), 5, ch g Excellent Art—Trika **Taylor's Bloodstock Ltd**
11 NINJAGO, 6, b g Mount Nelson—Fidelio's Miracle (USA) **Taylor's Bloodstock Ltd**
12 OLDJOESAID, 12, b g Royal Applause—Border Minstral (IRE) **Pee Dee Tee Syndicate & T W Midgley**
13 OLIVIA FALLOW (IRE), 4, b f Vale of York (IRE)—Spinning Maid (USA) **A. Bell**
14 ORIENT CLASS, 5, ch g Orientor—Killer Class **F Brady,A Williams,P Lindley,S Wibberley**
15 RELATED, 6, b g Kheleyf (USA)—Balladonia **Taylor's Bloodstock Ltd**
16 RIPON ROSE, 4, br f Ferrule (IRE)—Dispol Isle (IRE) **W. B. Imison**
17 SCARBOROUGH, 5, ch m Dandy Man—Alchimie (IRE) **Taylor's Bloodstock Ltd**
18 SILVANUS (IRE), 11, b g Danehill Dancer (IRE)—Mala Mala (IRE) **C. Alton**
19 SUMMER ISLES, 6, b m Exceed And Excel (AUS)—Summers Lease **Yenilecas Syndicate**
20 SUNRAIDER (IRE), 9, b g Namid—Doctrine **D. Mann**
21 TANGO SKY, 8, b g Namid—Sky Galaxy (USA) **Bartle, Wibberley & Midgley**

THREE-YEAR-OLDS

22 ANNIE T, b f Makfi—Hanella (IRE) **F. Brady**
23 EMERALD ASSET (IRE), b g Frozen Power (IRE)—Balance The Books **Jackson, Johnson & Thwaites**
24 IRISH CAILIN (IRE), b f Desert Millennium (IRE)—Shone Island (IRE) **Banks, Lindsay & Sheard**
25 MISTER MISCHIEF, b g Makfi—Bluebelle Dancer **Mr J. A. Hall**
26 MR ORANGE (IRE), b g Paco Boy (IRE)—Shirley Blake (IRE) **Mr J Blackburn & Mr A Turton**
27 TWENTYSVNTHLANCERS, b g Hellvelyn—Subtle Move (USA) **Sandfield Racing**

TWO-YEAR-OLDS

28 B g 12/3 Monsieur Bond (IRE)—Cool In The Shade (Pastoral Pursuits) (2857) **Mrs M. Verity**
29 EMERALD SECRET (IRE), b f 23/3 Arcano (IRE)—
   Limit (IRE) (Baratthea (IRE)) (19000) **Jackson, Johnson & Thwaites**
30 B f 15/2 Harbour Watch (IRE)—Glittering Prize (UAE) (Cadeaux Genereux) (15238) **Taylor's Bloodstock Ltd**
31 B f 16/4 Casamento (IRE)—Hanella (IRE) (Galileo (IRE)) (18000) **F. Brady**
32 JOLLYDEE (IRE), b f 6/4 Frozen Power (IRE)—Spinning Maid (USA) (Forestry (USA)) (7382) **Mr R. Bradley**
33 B g 8/4 Orientor—Killer Class (Kyllachy) **F. Brady**
34 B f 23/2 Bated Breath—Merry Diva (Bahamian Bounty) (8000) **P. T. Midgley**
35 Ch f 19/3 Helmet (AUS)—Sea of Leaves (USA) (Stormy Atlantic (USA)) (20000) **F. Brady**
36 B f 3/3 Acclamation—Somerset Falls (UAE) (Red Ransom (USA)) (11812) **J. N. Blackburn**
37 B f 9/4 Sir Prancealot (IRE)—Yasmeena (USA) (Mr Greeley (USA)) (11904) **Taylor's Bloodstock Ltd**

Other Owners: Mr R. Banks, Mr D. Bartle, Mr P. Bateson, Mrs G. I. Blackburn, Mr A. B. Blackburn, Mr A. Jackson, Mr R. F. Johnson, Mrs Y. Lavin, Mr P. N. Lindley, Mr M. P. Lindsay, Mrs L. Maher, Mrs N. McDonnell, Mr T. W. Midgley, Ms C. Mulrennan, Ms S. O'Dowd, Mr J. N. Sheard, Mr P. J. Stephenson, T. A. Stephenson, Mr C. Thwaites, Mr A. Turton, Mr A. D. Ward, Mr S. Wibberley, A. Williams.

Assistant Trainer: Mrs W. E. Midgley.

414 MR ROD MILLMAN, Cullompton
Postal: The Paddocks, Kentisbeare, Cullompton, Devon, EX15 2DX
Contacts: **PHONE/FAX** (01884) 266620 **MOBILE** (07885) 168447
E-MAIL rod.millman@ic24.net

1 AZURE AMOUR (IRE), 4, b f Azamour (IRE)—Al Euro (FR) **The Dirham Partnership**
2 BIOTIC, 5, b g Aqlaam—Bramaputra (IRE) **Mrs B. Sumner**
3 COTTON CLUB (IRE), 5, b g Amadeus Wolf—Slow Jazz (USA) **The Links Partnership**

MR ROD MILLMAN - Continued

4 **DANCE**, 7, b m Erhaab (USA)—Shi Shi **Mrs C. Knowles**
5 **EUGENIC**, 5, br g Piccolo—Craic Sa Ceili (IRE) **B. C. Scott**
6 **HAVANA BEAT (IRE)**, 6, b g Teofilo (IRE)—Sweet Home Alabama (IRE) **B. R. Millman**
7 **ICEBUSTER**, 8, ch g Iceman—Radiate **The Links Partnership**
8 **ISIS BLUE**, 6, b g Cockney Rebel (IRE)—Bramaputra (IRE) **Cantay Racing**
9 **MARCANO (IRE)**, 4, b g Arcano (IRE)—Aquatint **The Links Partnership**
10 **MASTER CARPENTER (IRE)**, 5, ch h Mastercraftsman (IRE)—Fringe **The Links Partnership**
11 **MIDNIGHT RIDER (IRE)**, 8, b g Red Ransom (USA)—Foreplay (IRE) **B. R. Millman**
12 **PRESENT ACCEPTED**, 9, b g Presenting—Kwaheri **Mrs P. N. Dutfield**
13 **STARVING MARVIN**, 8, b g Hawk Wing (USA)—Oleana (IRE) **Seasons Holidays**

THREE-YEAR-OLDS

14 **APACHE SONG**, ch f Mount Nelson—Pantita **Titan Assets**
15 **BUKLE (IRE)**, b g Approve (IRE)—Rumline **Mr C. H. Saunders**
16 **CONCUR (IRE)**, ch g Approve (IRE)—Tradmagic (IRE) **Miss G. J. Abbey**
17 **HANDYTALK (IRE)**, b g Lilbourne Lad (IRE)—Dancing With Stars (IRE) **Cantay Racing**
18 **LADY FONTENAIL**, b f Compton Place—Nina Fontenail (FR) **The Links Partnership**
19 **METTE**, b f Virtual—Regal Gallery **Mrs B. Sumner**
20 **O'CONNOR (IRE)**, ch g Roderic O'Connor (IRE)—Fly By Magic (IRE) **The Links Partnership**
21 **PLYMOUTH MO**, b g Hellvelyn—Welcome Home **The Mo Partnership**
22 **PUSHY LADY**, b f Piccolo—Jane's Payoff (IRE) **K. L. Dare**
23 **RAJADAMRI**, gr g Hellvelyn—Crofters Ceilidh **Mustajed Partnership**
24 **SIR RODERIC (IRE)**, b g Roderic O'Connor (IRE)—Begin The Beguine (IRE) **The Links Partnership**
25 **ST JOHN'S**, b g Aqlaam—Diam Queen (GER) **B. R. Millman**

TWO-YEAR-OLDS

26 B c 10/5 Sir Prancealot (IRE)—Dessert Flower (IRE) (Intikhab (USA)) (5714) **B. R. Millman**
27 B c 13/1 Compton Place—Dubai Affair (Dubawi (IRE)) (38095) **The Links Partnership**
28 **ICE PAC**, br f 8/4 Paco Boy (IRE)—Arctic Char (Polar Falcon (USA)) **Miss G. J. Abbey**
29 B c 20/2 Sir Prancealot (IRE)—Paris Glory (USA) (Honour And Glory (USA)) (20952) **The Links Partnership**
30 B c 14/2 Royal Applause—Saint Lucia (IRE) (Whipper (USA)) (19047) **E. J. S. Gadsden**
31 B c 20/1 Famous Name—Sweet Power (Pivotal) (28571) **The Links Partnership**
32 **SWEET PURSUIT**, b f 6/4 Pastoral Pursuits—Sugar Beet (Beat Hollow) **Always Hopeful Partnership**

Other Owners: Mr B. Barrett, P. Bartlam, Mr T. Bennett, R. T. Ferris, Mr R. D. Gamlin, Mr S. J. Kattau, Mr S. G. Lake, Mr M. Leach, V. B. Lewer, D. A. Little, Mr A. M. Nolan, Mrs M. O'Sullivan, S. M. Perry, Mr T. Tompkins.

Assistant Trainer: Louise Millman

Jockey (flat): Andrea Atzeni. **Apprentice:** Pat Millman.

---

415 MR NICK MITCHELL, Dorchester
Postal: **1 Racklands, Piddletrenthide, Dorchester, Dorset, DT2 7QP**
Contacts: PHONE (01300) 348049 MOBILE (07770) 892085
E-MAIL nick.mitch@btinternet.com WEBSITE www.nickmitchellracing.com

1 **DANCE FLOOR KING (IRE)**, 9, b g Generous (IRE)—Strawberry Fool (FR) **N. Elliott**
2 **GET READY FREDDY**, 6, b g Sixties Icon—Summer Shades **Glanvilles Stud Partners**
3 **HINXWORTH (IRE)**, 7, b g Milan—Open Cry (IRE) **N. Elliott**
4 **PRESIDING (IRE)**, 7, b g Flemensfirth (USA)—Maghereareagh Lady (IRE)
5 , B m Alflora (IRE)—She's No Muppet
6 **STEEL A TUNE**, 7, gr g Proclamation (IRE)—Skip 'n' Tune (IRE) **Mr M. S. Rose**

Other Owners: Dr G. W. Guy, Mr W. D. Procter.

Jockey (NH): Daryl Jacob. **Amateur:** Mr R. G. Henderson.

416 **MR PHILIP MITCHELL, Kingston Lisle**
Postal: **Church Cottage, Kingston Lisle, Wantage, Oxfordshire, OX12 9QL**
Contacts: **PHONE (01367) 820299 FAX (01367) 820299 MOBILE (07836) 231462**
E-MAIL philipmitchell48@gmail.com

1 **AL QATARI (USA)**, 7, b br g Dynaformer (USA)—Where's The Church (USA) **Mrs P. A. Mitchell**
2 **CHORAL CLAN (IRE)**, 5, b g Oratorio (IRE)—Campbellite **Bob Harris & Patricia Mitchell**
3 **WYATT (IRE)**, 4, b g Lawman (FR)—Umlilo **Mrs P. A. Mitchell**

Other Owners: Mr Bob Harris, Mrs Patricia Mitchell, Star Pointe Ltd.

Jockey (flat): Jack Mitchell. **Conditional:** Freddie Mitchell.

417 **MR RICHARD MITCHELL, Dorchester**
Postal: **East Hill Stables, Piddletrenthide, Dorchester, Dorset, DT2 7QY**
Contacts: **PHONE/FAX (01300) 348739 MOBILE (07775) 843136**
E-MAIL easthillstables@tiscali.co.uk

1 **BENBECULA**, 7, b g Motivator—Isle of Flame **Mr & Mrs Andrew May**
2 **HENCHARD**, 5, b g Deltic (USA)—Kittenkat **N. R. Mitchell**
3 **LORD WESSEX**, 5, b g Deltic (USA)—Society Night (IRE) **Mrs E. Mitchell**
4 **TAGINE**, 5, b m Deltic (USA)—Panhandle **Mrs E. Mitchell**
5 **THUNDERING HOME**, 9, gr g Storming Home—Citrine Spirit (IRE) **Mrs K. M. Boughey**

Other Owners: Mr Andrew May, Mrs Andrew May.

Assistant Trainer: Mrs E. Mitchell

418 **MR JAMES MOFFATT, Grange-Over-Sands**
Postal: **Pit Farm Racing Stables, Cartmel, Grange-Over-Sands, Cumbria, LA11 6PJ**
Contacts: **PHONE (01539) 536689 FAX (01539) 536236 MOBILE (07767) 367282**
E-MAIL jamesmoffatt@hotmail.co.uk WEBSITE www.jamesmoffatt.co.uk

1 **ALTRUISM (IRE)**, 6, b g Authorized (IRE)—Bold Assumption **Mr V R Vyner-Brooks, Mr K Bowron**
2 **AMUSE ME**, 10, gr g Daylami (IRE)—Have Fun **Vilprano, Bowron & Beaumont**
3 **CAPTAIN BROWN**, 8, b g Lomitas—Nicola Bella (IRE) **K. Bowron**
4 **CAPTAIN RHYRIC**, 7, ch g Dylan Thomas (IRE)—Nuts In May (USA) **Bowes Lodge Stables**
5 **DANNY O'RUAIRC (IRE)**, 4, b c Fast Company (IRE)—Tawoos (FR) **Bowes Lodge Stables**
6 **FANTASY KING**, 10, b g Acclamation—Fantasy Ridge **Mr V. R. Vyner-Brooks**
7 **FREDERIC CHOPIN**, 5, ch g Tamayuz—Eliza Gilbert **Bowes Lodge Stables**
8 **GOLDEN TOWN**, 5, b g Invincible Spirit (IRE)—Princesse Dansante (IRE) **Bowes Lodge Stables**
9 **HIGHLAND LODGE (IRE)**, 10, b g Flemensfirth (USA)—Supreme Von Pres (IRE) **Bowes Lodge Stables**
10 **MAY'S BOY**, 8, gr h Proclamation (IRE)—Sweet Portia (IRE) **K. Bowron**
11 **MAYBE I WONT**, 11, b g Kyllachy—Surprise Surprise **The Sheroot Partnership**
12 **MONDLICHT (USA)**, 6, b g Malibu Moon (USA)—Moonlight Cruise (USA) **Cartmel Priory Partnership**
13 **MORNING ROYALTY (IRE)**, 9, b g King's Theatre (IRE)—Portryan Native (IRE) **Mrs E. M. Milligan**
14 5, B m Josr Algarhoud (IRE)—Only Millie
15 **QUEL ELITE (FR)**, 12, b g Subotica (FR)—Jeenly (FR) **Hadwin, Hall, Moffatt, Chamberlain Bros.**
16 **REDPENDER (IRE)**, 10, gr g Great Palm (USA)—Josie Murphy (IRE) **K. Bowron**
17 **SAM LORD**, 12, ch g Observatory (USA)—My Mariam
18 **SMART RULER (IRE)**, 10, ch g Viking Ruler (AUS)—Celebrated Smile (IRE) **The Vilprano Partnership**
19 **WAY TO FINISH**, 10, b g Oasis Dream—Suedoise **Mr A. Macleod**

TWO-YEAR-OLDS

20 B f 17/2 Mullionmileanhour (IRE)—Speedy Senorita (IRE) (Fayruz)

Other Owners: J. J. Beaumont, Mr S. B. Chamberlain, Mr K. Hadwin, Mr J. W. Hall, A. R. Mills, D. J. Moffatt, Mr S. Wilson, Mrs J. C. Wilson.

MR JAMES MOFFATT - Continued

Assistant Trainer: Nadine Jameson

Jockey (NH): Brian Hughes. **Amateur:** Miss Alexander Wilson.

419
MR ISMAIL MOHAMMED, Newmarket
Postal: **Grange House Stables, Hamilton Road, Newmarket, Suffolk, CB8 0TE**
Contacts: **PHONE (01638) 669074 MOBILE (07766) 570271 / (07747) 191606**
E-MAIL justina.stone@dubairacingclub.com

1 **EDUCATE,** 7, b g Echo of Light—Pasithea (IRE) **S. Ali**
2 **FALCON'S SONG (USA),** 4, b br f U S Ranger (USA)—Saudia (USA) **Sheikh J. D. Al Maktoum**
3 **JAILAWI (IRE),** 5, b g Iffraaj—Tortue (IRE) **S. H. Altayer**
4 **MURAABIT,** 4, ch g Makfi—Ho Hi The Moon (IRE) **S. H. Altayer**
5 **NIBLAWI (IRE),** 4, b g Vale of York (IRE)—Finnmark **S. Ali**
6 **TOUGH CALL (IRE),** 4, b c Iffraaj—Pivotal's Princess **S. Ali**

THREE-YEAR-OLDS

7 **BAN SHOOF,** b c Shirocco (GER)—Pasithea (IRE) **S. Ali**
8 **BEATBYBEATBYBEAT,** ch f Poet's Voice—Beat As One **Saif Ali & Saeed H. Altayer**
9 **BUMPTIOUS,** b f Acclamation—Cast In Gold (USA) **Mr A. Al Mansoori**
10 **COMPTON LADY (IRE),** b f Compton Place—Treble Seven (USA) **S. Ali**
11 **FACE OF GLORY (IRE),** b c Big Bad Bob (IRE)—Interchange (IRE) **Dr A. Ridha**
12 **MOON ARROW (IRE),** b c Authorized (IRE)—Moon Sister (IRE) **Mr A. S. Belhab**
13 **POET'S BEAUTY (IRE),** ch c Poet's Voice—Extreme Beauty (USA) **Dr A. Ridha**
14 **POSSIBLE FUTURE,** b g Compton Place—Lalectra **S. H. Altayer**
15 **PURE SOUL,** b c Iffraaj—Spiritual Healing (IRE) **Mr A. Al Mansoori**
16 **RASHEEQ (IRE),** b c Vale of York (IRE)—Limber Up (IRE) **S. H. Altayer**
17 **ROMANTIC ANGEL (USA),** b f Macho Uno (USA)—Non Sibi (USA) **Mr A. Al Mansoori**
18 **SO MUCH FUN (IRE),** b f Iffraaj—Seminole Lass (USA) **Mr I. Mohammed**
19 **TEOFILO WOLF,** b f Teofilo (IRE)—She Wolf **Dr A. Ridha**
20 **THAHAB IFRAJ (IRE),** ch c Frozen Power (IRE)—Penny Rouge (IRE) **S. H. Altayer**
21 **THERTHAAR,** b c Kyllachy—Red Tiara (USA) **S. Ali**
22 **TOUCHED BY LOVE (USA),** b c Street Sense (USA)—Love of Dubai (USA) **Mr M. Al Shafar**
23 **ZUBEIDA,** b f Authorized (IRE)—Tegwen (USA) **Mr A. S. Belhab**

TWO-YEAR-OLDS

24 B c 13/2 Kyllachy—Forthefirstime (Dr Fong (USA)) (65000)
25 B c 24/2 Dream Ahead (USA)—Libys Dream (IRE) (Invincible Spirit (IRE)) (68000)
26 B f 25/2 Iffraaj—Oratrix (IRE) (Oratorio (IRE)) (55000)
27 B c 26/4 Sir Percy—Pilcomayo (IRE) (Rahy (USA)) (62000)
28 B c 5/4 Kyllachy—Regina (Green Desert (USA)) (40000)
29 B c 7/5 Famous Name—Right Reason (IRE) (Manduro (GER)) (50000)
30 B f 30/4 Kodiac—River Style (IRE) (Desert Style (IRE)) (40000)
31 Br f 1/5 Poet's Voice—Rustam (Dansili) (12000)
32 B f 10/2 Harbour Watch (IRE)—Secret Night (Dansili) (27000)
33 B c 3/4 Kyllachy—Starfly (IRE) (Invincible Spirit (IRE)) (52000)
34 B f 28/2 Acclamation—Titova (Halling (USA)) (80000)

Other Owners: Mr Saif Ali, Mr Saeed H. Altayer.

Assistant Trainer: Mike Marshall

420
MRS LAURA MONGAN, Epsom
Postal: **Condover Stables, Langley Vale Road, Epsom, Surrey, KT18 6AP**
Contacts: **PHONE (01372) 271494 FAX (01372) 271494 MOBILE (07788) 122942**
E-MAIL ljmongan@hotmail.co.uk WEBSITE www.lauramongan.co.uk

1 **ALSADAA (USA),** 13, b g Kingmambo (USA)—Aljawza (USA) **Mrs P. J. Sheen**
2 **BARREN BROOK,** 9, b g Beat Hollow—Carinthia (IRE) **Mrs L. J. Mongan**

MRS LAURA MONGAN - Continued

3 **CHARLIE'S STAR**, 4, b f Hellvelyn—Sweet Sorrow (IRE) **Charlie's Starrs & Laura Mongan**
4 **FIRST AVENUE**, 11, b g Montjeu (IRE)—Marciala (IRE) **Mrs L. J. Mongan**
5 **HARVEY (IRE)**, 5, br m Presenting—One Swoop (IRE) **Mr R. Goodall**
6 **HIPZ (IRE)**, 5, br m Intense Focus (USA)—Radha **Aberdour Racing Club**
7 **KEPPEL ISLE (IRE)**, 7, b g Heron Island (IRE)—Wadi Khaled (FR) **Mrs P. J. Sheen**
8 **LADY LUNCHALOT (USA)**, 6, b m More Than Ready (USA)—Betty Johanne (USA) **Charlie's Starrs**
9 **LEITH HILL (IRE)**, 6, bg Mountain High (IRE)—Ballinacariga Rose (IRE) **Mrs P. J. Sheen**
10 **MADAME DE GUISE (FR)**, 7, b m Le Balafre (FR)—Paradana (FR) **Mrs P. J. Sheen**
11 **MISS YEATS**, 5, b m Yeats (IRE)—Mrs Wallensky (IRE) **Mrs P. J. Sheen**
12 **MORGAN'S BAY**, 11, b g Karinga Bay—Dubai Dolly (IRE) **Mrs L. J. Mongan**
13 **NOOR AL HAYA (IRE)**, 6, b m Tamayuz—Hariya (IRE) **Condover Racing**
14 **ORSM**, 9, b g Erhaab (USA)—Royal Roulette **Mrs P. J. Sheen**
15 **RIVERMOUTH**, 11, ch g Karinga Bay—Rippling Brook **Mrs P. J. Sheen**
16 **SILVER TICKET (IRE)**, 5, gr g Tikkanen (USA)—Windmill View (IRE) **Mrs P. J. Sheen**
17 **SKIDBY MILL (IRE)**, 6, b m Ramonti (FR)—Glasnas Giant **Charlie's Starrs**
18 **TURNBURY**, 5, b g Azamour (IRE)—Scottish Heights (IRE) **Mrs L. J. Mongan**
19 **VOICE CONTROL (IRE)**, 4, gr g Dalakhani (IRE)—Scottish Stage (IRE) **Mrs P. J. Sheen**
20 **WITH APPROVAL (IRE)**, 4, b g Approve (IRE)—Kelsey Rose **Mrs P. J. Sheen**
21 **WOOFIE (IRE)**, 4, b g Duke of Marmalade (IRE)—Violet Ballerina (IRE) **Mrs P. J. Sheen**

Other Owners: Mr S. W. Bain, Mr A. W. Bain, Miss F. Madel.

Assistant Trainer: Ian Mongan

Jockey (flat): Liam Jones. **Jockey (NH):** Tom Cannon.

---

421 MR ARTHUR MOORE, Naas
Postal: Dereens, Caragh, Naas, Co. Kildare, Ireland
Contacts: PHONE (00353) 4587 6292 MOBILE (00353) 8725 52535
E-MAIL arthurlmoore@eircom.net

1 **AUGEST BENEFIT (IRE)**, 8, b g Beneficial—Augest Weekend (IRE) **Mrs K. O'Toole**
2 **BACK OFF MATE (IRE)**, 8, b g Old Vic—Flyhalf (IRE) **M. Beresford**
3 **BALLYCAHANE (IRE)**, 7, b g Flemensfirth (USA)—Laughing Lesa (IRE) **Ballycahane Syndicate**
4 **DANDRIDGE**, 7, ch g Doyen (IRE)—Arantxa **R. Bartlett**
5 4, B g Kalanisi (IRE)—Dinny Kenn (IRE) **Exors of the Late S. Hemstock**
6 **FEVER PITCH (IRE)**, 10, b g Dushyantor (USA)—Stormey Tune (IRE) **Mr J. P. McManus**
7 **GENTLEMAN DUKE (IRE)**, 8, b g Bachelor Duke (USA)—Housekeeping **Mr J. P. McManus**
8 **HOP IN (IRE)**, 9, b g Flemensfirth (USA)—Prowler (IRE) **C. Hanbury**
9 4, b g Fruits of Love (USA)—Kopoosha (IRE) **Dominic Jones**
10 **MITEBEALL FORLUCK**, 8, b g Westerner—Iborga (FR) **C. Hanbury**
11 **ON THE DRY (IRE)**, 5, b g Milan—Cailins Honour (IRE) **Mr J. P. McManus**
12 **ONE COOL POET (IRE)**, 4, b g Urban Poet (USA)—Oasis Star (IRE) **Oliver Bernard Ryan**
13 **ONTOPOFTHEWORLD (IRE)**, 7, ch g Desert King (IRE)—Zaffre (IRE) **Planets In Orbit Syndicate**
14 **PASS THE HAT**, 9, ch g Karinga Bay—Moor Spring **M. Beresford**
15 **SKELLIG ROCKS (FR)**, 5, b g Poliglote—Skellig Mist (FR) **Mrs T. K. Cooper**
16 **THE TRACTOR MAN (IRE)**, 6, ch g Flemensfirth (USA)—Sadie's Pet (IRE) **J. Magnier**
17 4, B g Milan—Time For An Audit **T. Syder**
18 **TREAT YOURSELF (IRE)**, 9, b g Beat Hollow—Cartesian **L. Breslin**
19 **WHATS THE PLOT (IRE)**, 4, b c Alfred Nobel (IRE)—Hazarama (IRE) **Mrs A. L. T. Moore**

THREE-YEAR-OLDS
20 **GOSSIP CENTRAL (IRE)**, ch g Windsor Knot (IRE)—Radio Wave **J. P. Byam & G. King**

Assistant Trainer: John Daniel Moore

Jockey (flat): F. Berry. **Jockey (NH):** D. Russell, J. J. Burke, R. Colgan.

422 **MR GARY MOORE, Horsham**
Postal: Cisswood Racing Stables, Sandygate Lane, Lower Beeding, Horsham,
West Sussex, RH13 6LR
Contacts: HOME (01403) 891997 YARD (01403) 891912 FAX (01403) 891924
MOBILE (07753) 863123
E-MAIL garyjayne.moore@virgin.net WEBSITE www.garymooreracing.com

1 AGINCOURT REEF (IRE), 7, b g Gold Well—Hillside Native (IRE) **Mr A. Head, Mr R. Lockwood & Mr M. Burne**
2 AHIO (FR), 5, b g Chichi Creasy (FR)—Amalhouna (FR) **Mr R E Anderson**
3 ALKETIOS (GR), 5, b g Kavafi (IRE)—Mazea (IRE) **G. A. Jackman**
4 ANTONY (FR), 6, b g Walk In The Park (IRE)—Melanie du Chenet (FR) **The Winning Hand**
5 AR MAD (FR), 6, b g Tiger Groom—Omelia (FR) **Mr A. J. Head**
6 ART LIBRE (FR), 5, b g Librettist (USA)—Peinture Parfaite (FR) **Mr G. L. Moore**
7 ART OF SWING (FR), 4, b g Excellent Art—Shahmina (IRE) **Jacobs Construction (Holdings) Limited**
8 ASPASIUS (GER), 4, b g Desert Prince (IRE)—Aspasia Lunata (GER) **Mr P. T. Mott**
9 BAGGING TURF (IRE), 6, b m Scorpion (IRE)—Monica's Story **Mrs M. Devine**
10 BARON ALCO (FR), 5, ch g Dom Alco (FR)—Paula (FR) **Mr J. K. Stone**
11 BIRDIE QUEEN, 6, b m Pastoral Pursuits—Silver Miss (FR) **The Golf Partnership**
12 BLACK SWAN KAUTO (FR), 5, ch g Byzantium (FR)—Kauto Lorette (FR) **Mrs A. Gloag**
13 BLUE SIRE (FR), 5, b br g Day Flight—Hirlish (FR) **The Preston Family & Friends Ltd**
14 BOLISTER (FR), 5, b g Le Balafre (FR)—Girlish (FR) **Galloping On The South Downs Partnership**
15 BRAVE VIC (IRE), 8, b g Old Vic—Baliya (IRE) **R. Henderson**
16 BRITANIO BELLO (FR), 5, b g Irish Wells (FR)—Tchi Tchi Bang Bang (FR) **Mr A. J. Head**
17 BROCKWELL, 7, b g Singspiel (IRE)—Noble Plum **South Wind Racing 3**
18 CABIMAS, 9, b g King's Best (USA)—Casanga (IRE) **Mr Andrew Bradmore**
19 CAPSIS DESBOIS (FR), 4, b g Apsis—Gesse Parade (FR) **Heart Of The South Racing**
20 CENTREOFEXCELLENCE (IRE), 5, b g Oscar (IRE)—Calm Approach (IRE) **Mr G. L. Moore**
21 CHRIS PEA GREEN, 7, b g Proclamation (IRE)—Another Secret **C Green & Galloping On The South Downs**
22 CIVIL WAR (IRE), 7, b g Scorpion (IRE)—Silvestre (ITY) **Mr A. J. Head**
23 CLAYTON, 7, b g Peintre Celebre (USA)—Blossom **Mr A. J. Head**
24 DABADIYAN (IRE), 6, b g Zamindar (USA)—Dabista (IRE) **Mark Albon, Chris Stedman & G L Moore**
25 DAIDAIDAI (FR), 6, b g Lando (GER)—Noble World (GER) **Mrs Suzie Russell**
26 DAREBIN (GER), 4, ch g It's Gino (GER)—Delightful Sofie (GER) **Chris Stedman & Mark Albon**
27 DE BLACKSMITH (IRE), 8, b g Brian Boru—Gift of The Gab (IRE) **Mrs E. A. Kiernan**
28 5, b g Dr Massini—Dew Drop Inn (IRE)
29 DRACO'S CODE, 5, b g Galileo (IRE)—Lady Karr **The Golf Partnership**
30 DUBAWI LIGHT, 5, b g Dubawi (IRE)—Shesadelight **Mr N. J. Roach**
31 DUDE ALERT (IRE), 6, b g Windsor Knot (USA)—Policy **Mr M. R. Baldry**
32 DUTCH GOLDEN AGE (IRE), 4, b c Kodiac—Magic Melody **R. Green**
33 DUTCH MASTERPIECE, 6, b g Dutch Art—The Terrier **R. Green**
34 DYNAMIC RANGER (USA), 5, b g U S Ranger (USA)—Dynamous (USA) **Mr M. L. Albon**
35 EL FENIX (IRE), 4, b g Lope de Vega (IRE)—Woodmaven (USA) **Patterson Hinds & Curwen**
36 EMPERORS WARRIOR (IRE), 4, ch g Thewayyouare (USA)—World Sprint (GER) **Shark Bay Racing Syndicate**
37 EMPTY MARMALADES (FR), 5, b g Poliglote—Arvicaya **Westbourne Racing Club**
38 ETAAD (USA), 5, b g Intidab (USA)—Red's Lucky Lady (USA) **John Ansell & Ian J Herbert**
39 FELLA, 4, b g Sagamix (FR)—Encore du Cristal (USA) **E. A. Condon**
40 FENNANN, 5, b g Dutch Art—Embraced **Mr M. R. Baldry**
41 FLASHMAN, 7, ch g Doyen—Si Si Si **Mr A. D. Bradmore**
42 FLUTE BOWL, 6, b m Black Sam Bellamy (IRE)—Queen's Dancer **C. E. Stedman**
43 FREDDY WITH A Y (IRE), 6, b g Amadeus Wolf—Mataji (IRE) **double-r-racing.com & Mr M K George**
44 FREEMASON, 5, b g Cape Cross (IRE)—Candy Mountain **Gallagher Equine Limited**
45 FRUITY O'ROONEY, 13, b g Kahyasi—Recipe **Heart Of The South Racing**
46 GAELIC SILVER (FR), 10, b g Lando (GER)—Galatza (FR) **The Winning Hand**
47 GAME SET DASH (USA), 4, b g Arch (USA)—Proudeyes (USA) **Mr G. L. Moore**
48 GENEROUS HELPINGS (IRE), 7, ch g Generous (IRE)—
Saffron Pride (IRE) **Galloping On The South Downs Partnership**
49 GENTLEMAN'S DREAM (IRE), 4, b g Flemensfirth (USA)—Fair And Aisey (IRE) **Dedman Properties Limited**
50 GOLANOVA, 8, b g Golan (IRE)—Larkbarrow **Galloping On The South Downs Partnership**
51 GOLD CARROT, 8, b g Beat All (USA)—Emma-Lyne **A. Head**
52 GOOD LUCK CHARM, 7, b g Doyen (IRE)—Lucky Dice **Heart Of The South Racing**
53 GORES ISLAND (IRE), 10, b g Beneficial—Just Leader (IRE) **Collins, Horsfall, Michael & O'Sullivan**
54 GRAASTEN (GER), 4, ch g Sholokhov (IRE)—Golden Time (GER) **G. L. Moore**
55 GRAND FACILE, 4, b g Henrythenavigator (USA)—Santolina (USA) **Patterson Hinds & Curwen**
56 GUARDS CHAPEL, 8, b g Motivator—Intaaj (IRE) **Mr A. D. Bradmore**
57 GUN SHY (IRE), 8, b g Norwich—Debbies Scud (IRE) **P. R. Chapman**
58 GUNNER MOYNE, 4, b c Excellent Art—Maramkova (IRE) **Mr Danny O'Neil**

MR GARY MOORE - Continued

59 **HALLING'S WISH**, 6, br g Halling (USA)—Fair View (GER) **WBC Partnership**
60 **HERMOSA VAQUERA (IRE)**, 6, b m High Chaparral (IRE)—Sundown **Mr M. R. Baldry**
61 **HURRICANE ALERT**, 4, b g Showcasing—Raggle Taggle (IRE) **Mr M. R. Baldry**
62 **ILEWIN FOR HANNAH**, 9, b g Generous (IRE)—Ilewin Janine (IRE) **T. J. Segrue**
63 **ILEWIN GEEZ**, 6, ch g Generous (IRE)—Ilewin Janine (IRE) **T. J. Segrue**
64 **ILEWINDELILAH**, 8, b m Grape Tree Road—Bridepark Rose (IRE) **T. J. Segrue**
65 **INIESTA (IRE)**, 5, b h Galileo (IRE)—Red Evie (IRE) **Mr A. J. Foreman**
66 **JAY ARE (IRE)**, 7, b g Heron Island (IRE)—Vulpalm (IRE) **Mr G. L. Moore**
67 **JUSTIFICATION**, 8, b g Montjeu (IRE)—Colorspin (FR) **Mrs E. A. Kiernan**
68 **KING COOL**, 5, b g King's Theatre (IRE)—Cool Spice **Mr P. Mott**
69 **KNIGHT OF PLEASURE**, 7, ch g Exit To Nowhere (USA)—Kim Fontenail (FR) **The Knights Of Pleasure**
70 **KNIGHTLY PLEASURE**, 5, b m Kayf Tara—Kim Fontenail (FR) **The Knights Of Pleasure**
71 **KNOCKNANUSS (IRE)**, 6, b g Beneficial—Dato Vic (IRE) **Sargent Evans**
72 **KRUGERMAC (IRE)**, 5, b br g Kalanisi (IRE)—Vindonissa (IRE) **Mr Hinds & Galloping On The South Downs**
73 **KYLLACHY SPIRIT**, 8, b g Kyllachy—Cartuccia (IRE) **Mrs J R Jenrick & Mr R D Jenrick**
74 **LADY MARL**, 5, b m Duke of Marmalade (IRE)—Empress Anna (IRE) **Crimbourne Stud**
75 **LE CAPRICIEUX (FR)**, 5, b g Alberto Giacometti (IRE)—Eria Flore (FR) **Mr A. J. Foreman**
76 **LEO LUNA**, 7, b g Galileo (IRE)—Eva Luna (USA) **Mr P. B. Moorhead**
77 **LIGHT WELL (IRE)**, 8, b g Sadler's Wells (USA)—L'ancresse (IRE) **B. Siddle & B. D. Haynes**
78 **MAJOR MARTIN (IRE)**, 7, b g Flemensfirth (USA)—Miss Emer (IRE) **Ms Adrienne Gross**
79 **MASTER OF SPEED (IRE)**, 4, ch g Mastercraftsman (IRE)—Mango Groove (IRE) **A. Head & G. Dreher**
80 , Ch f Schiaparelli (GER)—Megasue **Galloping on the South Downs Partnership**
81 **MILKY WAY (IRE)**, 4, b g Galileo (IRE)—Beauty Bright (IRE) **Patterson Hinds & Curwen**
82 **MOUNT SHAMSAN**, 6, b g Danehill Dancer (IRE)—Shamaiel (IRE) **G. L. Moore**
83 **MR FICKLE (IRE)**, 7, b g Jeremy (USA)—Mamara Reef **Gary Moore Racing**
84 **NETHERBY**, 10, b g Fair Mix (IRE)—Lissadell (IRE) **R. Green**
85 **OH SO FRUITY**, 6, b g Midnight Legend—Recipe **Heart Of The South Racing**
86 **OSGOOD**, 9, b g Danehill Dancer (IRE)—Sabreon **G. L. Moore**
87 **PANDORA'S PYX**, 4, b f Indesatchel (IRE)—Hope Chest **Mr P. Lear**
88 **PIKE CORNER CROSS (IRE)**, 4, b g Cape Cross (IRE)—Smart Coco (USA) **Mr A. A. Byrne**
89 **PLUTOCRACY (IRE)**, 6, b g Dansili—Private Life (FR) **Power Geneva Ltd**
90 **PROXIMATE**, 6, b g Nayef (USA)—Contiguous (USA) **Mr P. B. Moorhead**
91 **REBLIS (IRE)**, 11, b g Assessor (IRE)—Silbere (FR) **Kingsley, Avery, Farr, Glover, Humphreys**
92 **RED AVENGER (USA)**, 6, b br g War Front (USA)—Emotional Rescue (USA) **The Hon. R. J. Arculli**
93 **REMIND ME LATER (IRE)**, 7, b g Zerpour (IRE)—Two T'three Weeks **Mrs M. Devine**
94 **ROCKFAST**, 4, b g Fastnet Rock (AUS)—Empress Anna (IRE) **Crimbourne Stud**
95 **ROYAL BATTALION**, 5, b g Sea The Stars (IRE)—Yummy Mummy **Heart Of The South Racing**
96 **ROYAL CLASSIC (FR)**, 6, b g Anabaa Blue—Rapid Lomita (GER) **C. E. Stedman**
97 **RYDAN (IRE)**, 5, ch g Intense Focus (USA)—Lough Mewin (IRE) **Jacobs Construction (Holdings) Limited**
98 **RYEOLLIEAN**, 5, ch g Haafhd—Brave Mave **Mr B. Fry**
99 **SEA SERPENT (FR)**, 4, b g Great Journey (JPN)—Serpolette (FR) **Mr Jerry Hinds**
100 **SEARCHING (IRE)**, 4, ro g Mastercraftsman (IRE)—Miracolia (IRE) **P. R. Chapman**
101 **SECRET MISSILE**, 6, b g Sakhee's Secret—Malelane (IRE) **Ms C. L. Salmon**
102 **SHALIANZI (IRE)**, 6, b g Azamour (IRE)—Shalama (IRE) **Mr A. J. Head**
103 **SIRE DE GRUGY (FR)**, 10, ch g My Risk (FR)—Hirlish (FR) **The Preston Family & Friends Ltd**
104 **SONG AND DANCE MAN**, 6, b g Danehill Dancer (IRE)—Song (USA) **Ms Adrienne Gross**
105 **STONEGATE**, 6, b g Kayf Tara—Megalex **Galloping On The South Downs Partnership**
106 **SWEET PERSUASION**, 4, ch f Motivator—Sweet Lemon (IRE) **Heart Of The South Racing**
107 **SWING EASY**, 6, b g Zamindar (USA)—Shahmina (IRE) **Mr T Jacobs, Mr J Harley, Mr A Foreman**
108 **THE GREEN OGRE**, 6, b g Dubai Destination (USA)—Takegawa **Past The Post Racing & G L Moore**
109 **TOP DIKTAT**, 8, b g Diktat—Top Romance (IRE) **Miss T. R. Hale**
110 **TORERO**, 7, b g Hernando (FR)—After You **Mrs Ann Gloag**
111 **TOTHEMOONANDBACK (IRE)**, 8, gr g Dr Massini (IRE)—Mrs Jones (FR) **David & Jane George**
112 **TOXARIS (IRE)**, 4, ch f Teofilo (IRE)—Right Key (USA) **Chegwidden Systems Ltd**
113 **TRAFFIC FLUIDE (FR)**, 6, b g Astarabad (USA)—

               Petale Rouge (FR) **Galloping On The South Downs Partnership**
114 **TRIUMPHANT (IRE)**, 7, b g Danehill Dancer (IRE)—Meek Appeal (USA) **Mark Albon & Chris Stedman**
115 **TWO SUGARS**, 8, b g Val Royal (FR)—Princess Galadriel **Mrs P. Akhurst**
116 **UBAK (FR)**, 8, b g Kapgarde (FR)—Gesse Parade (FR) **Mr N. J. Peacock**
117 **UPTOWNDOWNONE (IRE)**, 7, b g Oscar (IRE)—Lady Meribel **Mr J. K. Stone**
118 **VIKEKHAL (FR)**, 7, b g Khalkevi (IRE)—Gesse Parade (FR) **The Old Brokers**
119 **VINO GRIEGO (FR)**, 11, b g Kahyasi—Vie de Reine (FR) **C. E. Stedman**
120 **VIOLET DANCER (FR)**, 6, b g Bertolini (USA)—Another Secret **D Bessell & Galloping On The South Downs**
121 **VISION DES CHAMPS (FR)**, 7, b g Saint des Saints (FR)—Manita Des Champs (FR) **Polo Racing & Friends**
122 **WHINGING WILLIE**, 7, b g Cape Cross (IRE)—Pacific Grove **Mr P. B. Moorhead**

MR GARY MOORE - Continued

THREE-YEAR-OLDS

123 **ART COLLECTION (FR)**, b g Shakespearean (IRE)—Renascent Rahy **R. Green**
124 **CHANDON ELYSEES**, b f Champs Elysees—Upstream **Mr M. Baldry**
125 **CILAOS GLACE (FR)**, b g Voix du Nord (FR)—Miss Glacee (FR) **Heart Of The South Racing**
126 **CLEVEDON COURT**, b f Royal Applause—Bow River Arch (USA) **Mr M. Anderson**
127 **CONSTABLE CLOUDS (USA)**, b c Blame (USA)—For Spacious Skies (USA) **R. Green**
128 **COOL ANGEL (IRE)**, gr f Zebedee—Malthouse Mistress (IRE) **Mr A. A. Byrne**
129 **DEGAS BRONZE**, b f Showcasing—Local Fancy **R. Green**
130 **GERMAN WHIP**, b c Zoffany—Tan Tan **G. L. Moore**
131 **GOLDENFIELD (IRE)**, b g Footstepsinthesand—Society Gal (IRE) **Mr & Mrs W W Fleming**
132 **GUNS OF LEROS (USA)**, b br c Cape Blanco (IRE)—Zappeuse (USA) **Mr P. Hunt**
133 **HEPWORTH MARBLE (IRE)**, b f Lilbourne Lad (IRE)—Angel Nights (IRE) **R. Green**
134 **IMARI KID (IRE)**, b c Pour Moi (IRE)—Breathe (FR) **Mr P. B. Moorhead**
135 **KEIBA (IRE)**, br c Dark Angel (IRE)—True Magic **Gallagher Equine Ltd**
136 **LEE'S HALL (IRE)**, b g Invincible Spirit (IRE)—Russian Roubles (IRE) **Gallagher Equine Ltd**
137 **LILLY BONBON (IRE)**, ch f Zoffany (IRE)—Simonda **E. A. Condon**
138 B c Green Horizon—Luisa Miller (IRE) **Mr Michael Park**
139 **OUTBACK PRINCESS**, gr f Aussie Rules (USA)—Royal Assent **Heart Of The South Racing**
140 **PERSAVERANCE**, b c Sir Percy—Marliana (USA) **Patricia & Michael Curlewis**
141 **POUR PAVOT (IRE)**, b f Pour Moi (IRE)—Lake Windermere (IRE) **Mrs Mary-Anne Parker**
142 **ROYAL PHOENIX**, b f Royal Applause—Ashes (USA) **Mr M. Baldry**
143 **SEXTON BLAKE (IRE)**, b c Rip Van Winkle (IRE)—Soviet Treat (IRE) **Mr J. E. Harley & Mr T. Jacobs**
144 **SWEET DREAM LADY (IRE)**, b f Rip Van Winkle (IRE)—Visite Royale (IRE) **M. K. George**
145 **TWILIGHT PURSUITS**, b f Pastoral Pursuits—Exexel **Mr M. R. Baldry**
146 **YOU'RE A GOAT**, b f Notnowcato—Three Wrens (IRE) **Power Geneva Ltd**

TWO-YEAR-OLDS

147 Ch c 20/3 Helmet (AUS)—Kalabunga (IRE) (Val Royal (FR)) (3333)
148 **GAIA PRINCESS (IRE)**, gr f 24/2 Dark Angel (IRE)—
                        Mount Eliza (IRE) (Danehill (USA)) (44296) **Shahzadi Naila Misha Fadhlullah**
149 B c 18/5 Teofilo (IRE)—Jessica's Dream (IRE) (Desert Style (IRE)) (70000) **R. Green**
150 Ch f 10/5 Delegator—Saharan Song (IRE) (Singspiel (IRE)) (571) **Mr A. A. Byrne**
151 Gr f 16/4 Dark Angel (IRE)—Selfara (Oasis Dream) (100000) **Mr J E Harley & Mr T Jacobs**
152 B c 26/4 Nathaniel (IRE)—Windy Britain (Mark of Esteem (IRE)) (30000)

Other Owners: Mr D. Adam, Mrs Eloise Adamski, Mr M. Albon, Mr M. Anderson, Mr J. J. Anderson, Mr John Ansell, Mrs E. Avery, Mrs Vanda Baker, Mr A. M. Basing, Mr Laurence A. Bellman, Mr David Bessell, Rev L. M. Brown, Mr R. Brown, Mr M. Burne, A. Carr, Mr J. A. Collins, Mr Victor Coutin, Mr Michael Curlewis, Mrs Patricia Curlewis, Mr S. Curwen, double-r-racing.com, Mr David Evans, Mr Gary Fenlon, Mrs W. W. Fleming, Mr W. W. Fleming, Mr Bryan Fry, Mr J. A. Gent, Mr M. K. George, Mr M. Goodrum, Mr Chris Green, Mr J. E. Harley, Mr B. D. Haynes, Mr Ian J. Herbert, Mr Philip Herbert, Mr J. Hinds, Mr T. Jacobs, Jacobs Construction (Holdings) Limited, Mrs J. R. Jenrick, Mr R. D. Jenrick, Mr Warren Jupp, Mr P Kingsley, Mr John Knight, Mr Richard Lockwood, Mr Steve Michael, Mrs B. B. Mills, Newco 1111 Ltd, Mrs Mary-Anne Parker, Mr Charles Parker, Mr John Penny, Mr M. G. Rogers, Mr Rodger Sargent, Mr R. M. Siddle, Mr C. E. Stedman, Mr D. H. Steel, Mr M. C. Waddingham, Mr Martin Webb, Westbourne Consultants Ltd.

Assistant Trainers: David Wilson, Andrew Glassonbury

Jockey (flat): George Baker, Ryan Moore, Fergus Sweeney. **Jockey (NH):** Andrew Glassonbury, Jamie Moore, Joshua Moore. **Conditional:** George Gorman. **Apprentice:** Hector Crouch, Jason Nuttall. **Amateur:** Miss Becky Butler, Mr Charlie Jewell, Miss Hayley Moore.

423

MR J. S. MOORE, Upper Lambourn
Postal: **Berkeley House Stables, Upper Lambourn, Hungerford, Berkshire, RG17 8QP**
Contacts: **PHONE** (01488) 73887 **FAX** (01488) 73997 **MOBILE** (07860) 811127 / (07900) 402856
E-MAIL jsmoore.racing@btopenworld.com **WEBSITE** www.stanmooreracing.co.uk

1 **CASCADING STARS (IRE)**, 4, b f Tagula (IRE)—Subtle Affair (IRE) **S. & A. Mares**
2 **CHEFCHAOUEN (IRE)**, 4, b f Dylan Thomas (IRE)—Love Thirty **The Well Fleeced Partnership**
3 **HELMSMAN (IRE)**, 4, b g Alhaarth (IRE)—La Cuvee **Mr Matty Williams & J. S. Moore**
4 **INVINCIBLE DIAMOND (IRE)**, 4, ch g Arakan (USA)—Invincible Woman (IRE) **R. J. Styles**
5 **JIMMY'S HALL**, 4, b g Kyllachy—Up At Dawn **J. S. Moore**
6 **LE ROCK (IRE)**, 4, b g Rock of Gibraltar (IRE)—Reine Violette (FR) **Mr G. V. March & J. S. Moore**

MR J. S. MOORE - Continued

7 **MRS BUBBLES (IRE)**, 4, b f Lord Shanakill (USA)—Champagne Blitz (IRE) **Mr Gerard Kennedy & J. S. Moore**
8 **SHEILA'S BUDDY**, 7, ch g Reel Buddy (USA)—Loreto Rose **R. J. Styles**

THREE-YEAR-OLDS

9 **ABBERLEY DANCER (IRE)**, b f Lilbourne Lad (IRE)—Babberina (IRE) **S & A Mares, E. Tidmarsh & J. S. Moore**
10 **BOHEMIAN ORIGIN (IRE)**, ch g Zoffany (IRE)—Rainbow Lyrics (IRE) **Pineapple Stud & J. S. Moore**
11 **FASTER COMPANY (IRE)**, b g Fast Company (IRE)—Lily Rio (IRE) **Nothing Sweeter Partnership & J. S. Moore**
12 **FLEECED AGAIN (IRE)**, b g Bushranger (IRE)—Sightseer (USA) **The Well Fleeced Partnership**
13 **GOLDEN ISLES (IRE)**, ch f Mastercraftsman (IRE)—Aphorism **D. M. Kerr**
14 **HEARMENOW (IRE)**, b g Kodiac—Crystalline Stream (FR) **Mr M. Fitzpatrick & J. S. Moore**
15 **LADY PRESIDENT (IRE)**, b f Fast Company (IRE)—Lovere **The Petticoat Government**
16 **MANHATTAN SKYLINE (IRE)**, gr f Clodovil (IRE)—

Rainbow Above You (IRE) **J. S. Moore & Mrs J. A. Newell-Smyth**
17 B g Dark Angel (IRE)—Manuka Magic (IRE) **J. S. Moore & Partner**
18 **REPEAT OFFENDER (IRE)**, b g Thewayyouare (USA)—Dame Rochelle (IRE) **D. M. Kerr**
19 **ROMANCINGTHESTONE**, b f Bertolini (USA)—

Diamond Vanessa (IRE) **Miss D. L. Wisbey, Mr R. Viney & J. S. Moore**
20 **SKY FERRY**, br g Captain Gerrard (IRE)—Ellovamul **Caroline Instone & J. S. Moore**
21 **SKY ISLAND (IRE)**, b f High Chaparral (IRE)—Nasanice (USA) **Mr Donald Kerr & J. S. Moore**
22 **STRADUFF (IRE)**, b g Kodiac—She's A Minx (IRE) **J. S. Moore & Partner**
23 **THE BURNHAM MARE (IRE)**, b f Kodiac—Courte Paille (IRE) **The Swan Partnership & Mrs Natalie Jones**
24 **THREEBAGSUE (IRE)**, ch f Lord Shanakill (USA)—Feet of Flame (USA) **The Well Fleeced Partnership**

TWO-YEAR-OLDS

25 B f 19/3 Showcasing—Anapola (GER) (Polish Precedent (USA)) (12000) **Mr Kieron Badger & J. S. Moore**
26 **ANGIE BABY**, b f 12/2 Compton Place—

Angie And Liz (IRE) (Spectrum (IRE)) (952) **Tom & Evelyn Yates & J. S. Moore**
27 **CHAMASAY**, ch c 26/4 Sayif (IRE)—Miss Chamanda (IRE) (Choisir (AUS)) (571) **E. A. R. Morgans**
28 Ch f 3/3 Arcano (IRE)—Cheeky Weeky (Cadeaux Genereux) (2953) **Wendy Jarrett, Sara Moore & J. S. Moore**
29 B c 28/2 Lilbourne Lad (IRE)—Do Disturb (Sinndar (IRE))
30 Ch c 18/3 Casamento (IRE)—Fancy Vivid (IRE) (Galileo (IRE)) (10000) **Mr Ray Styles & J. S. Moore**
31 B br c 24/3 Harbour Watch (IRE)—Forest Prize (Charnwood Forest (IRE)) (8000) **Mrs T. Burns & J. S. Moore**
32 **FOREST STEPS (IRE)**, b f 29/3 Footstepsinthesand—

Zeena (Unfuwain (USA)) (3322) **Mr G. V. March & J. S. Moore**
33 B g 29/3 Sayif (IRE)—Glen Molly (IRE) (Danetime (IRE)) (2857)
34 B f 5/4 Helmet (AUS)—Hear My Cry (USA) (Giant's Causeway (USA)) (5000) **Caroline Instone & J. S. Moore**
35 **HOLD ME TIGHT (IRE)**, b c 13/4 Zoffany (IRE)—

All Embracing (IRE) (Night Shift (USA)) (2953) **Wendy Jarrett, Sara Moore & J. S. Moore**
36 B f 10/3 Excelebration (IRE)—La Baracca (IRE) (Hurricane Run (IRE)) **Mr Sean O'Sullivan & J. S. Moore**
37 **LADY PARKER**, gr f 5/5 Zebedee—

Westering Home (IRE) (Mull of Kintyre (USA)) (1844) **Sarah Parker & J. S. Moore**
38 B c 7/4 Mount Nelson—Like A Virgin (IRE) (Iron Mask (USA)) (4000)
39 Ch f 9/4 Sakhee's Secret—Loreto Rose (Lahib (USA)) **R. J. Styles**
40 B c 28/4 Fast Company (IRE)—Mirandassister (IRE) (Titus Livius (FR)) (6666) **The Moore The Merrier**
41 **NUDGE NUDGE**, ch g 27/3 Winker Watson—Silca Key (Inchinor) (2857) **Mr David Klein & J. S. Moore**
42 B f 24/2 Fastnet Rock (AUS)—On The Nile (IRE) (Sadler's Wells (USA)) **Mr Donald Kerr & J. S. Moore**
43 B f 24/1 Elzaam (AUS)—On Thin Ice (IRE) (Verglas (IRE)) (2214) **Wendy Jarrett, Sara Moore & J. S. Moore**
44 **PATROUILLE DE NUIT (IRE)**, b g 27/2 Bushranger (IRE)—

Kyanight (IRE) (Kodiac) (2361) **RJH Limited, Mr J. P. Hames, J. S. Moore**
45 **PAVED IN GOLD (IRE)**, b g 28/2 Bushranger (IRE)—

Sovereign Street (Compton Place) (6275) **Wendy Jarrett, Sara Moore & J. S. Moore**
46 **RADAR LOVE (IRE)**, b f 11/4 Sir Prancealot (IRE)—

Sonic Night (IRE) (Night Shift (USA)) (5714) **Mr David Klein & J. S. Moore**
47 B f 20/1 Tagula (IRE)—Ragsta (IRE) (Key of Luck (USA)) (590)
48 B f 26/4 Casamento (IRE)—Reign of Fire (IRE) (Perugino (USA)) (5167)
49 **RINKY DINK DAWN (IRE)**, ch c 16/3 Born To Sea (IRE)—

Saffa Garden (King's Best (USA)) (1714) **J. S. Moore & Partner**
50 B f 10/4 Mount Nelson—Sahariri (IRE) (Red Ransom (USA)) (800)
51 **SHEILA'S LAD (IRE)**, b g 15/2 Lilbourne Lad (IRE)—

Lady Dottie (IRE) (Motivator) (4000) **Mr Ray Styles & J. S. Moore**
52 B c 14/4 Requinto (IRE)—Silk Point (IRE) (Barathea (IRE)) (16000)
53 B f 4/3 Zoffany (IRE)—Tessa Romana (IRE) (Holy Roman Emperor (IRE)) (5167) **Mr G. V. March & J. S. Moore**
54 **ZORRO**, b g 23/4 Zebedee—Milnagavie (Tobougg (IRE)) (16000) **Pineapple Stud & J. S. Moore**

MR J. S. MOORE - Continued

Other Owners: Mr M. J. Ablett, Mrs R. Ablett, Mr Kieron Badger, Mrs T. Burns, Mr M. Fitzpatrick, J. P. Hames, Ms Caroline Instone, Mrs Wendy Jarrett, Mrs Natalie Jones, Mr G. Kennedy, Mr David Klein, Mr G. V. March, Mr S. Mares, Mrs A. Mares, Mr Kevin McMullen, Mrs Sara Moore, Mr J. S. Moore, Mr P. Mott, Mrs J. A. Newell-Smyth, S. O'Sullivan, R J H Limited, Mr P. V. Smyth, Mr E. Tidmarsh, Mr R. J. Viney, Mr M. Williams, Mr M. Winter, Miss D. L. Wisbey.

Assistant Trainer: Mrs S. Moore

Jockey (flat): Liam Jones. **Apprentice:** Josephine Gordon.

---

424 **MR KEVIN MORGAN, Newmarket**
Postal: **Gazeley Park Stables, 13 - 15 Moulton Road, Gazeley, Newmarket, Suffolk, CB8 8RA**
Contacts: **PHONE (01638) 454830 FAX (01638) 551888 MOBILE (07768) 996103**
E-MAIL kandcracing@hotmail.com

1 BAIHAS, 6, b g Nayef (USA)—Allegretto (IRE) **Blue Grey Chevron Racing & Roemex Ltd**
2 GHAAWY, 5, b g Teofilo (IRE)—Asawer (IRE) **Blue Grey Chevron Racing & Roemex Ltd**
3 HAAMES (IRE), 9, b g Kheleyf (USA)—Jumilla (USA) **Roemex Ltd**
4 HARROGATE FAIR, 6, b g Trade Fair—Starbeck (IRE) **Miss K. L. Squance**
5 ISDAAL, 9, ch m Dubawi (IRE)—Faydah (USA) **Roemex Ltd**
6 KALASKADESEMILLEY, 5, b g Myboycharlie (IRE)—Congressional (IRE) **Mrs C. E. Peck**
7 MAKHFAR (IRE), 5, b g Bushranger (IRE)—Let Me Shine (USA) **Blue Grey Chevron Racing & Roemex Ltd**
8 MEZMAAR, 7, b g Teofilo (IRE)—Bay Tree (IRE) **Roemex Ltd**
9 MUZAAHIM (IRE), 5, ch g Tamayuz—Elizabeth Swann **Mr S. P. Giles**
10 TAARESH (IRE), 11, b g Sakhee (USA)—Tanaghum **Roemex Ltd**

THREE-YEAR-OLDS

11 MUSIC MAJOR, br g Bertolini (USA)—Music Maid (IRE) **Miss K. L. Squance**

Other Owners: Mr A. Flathers, Mr R. Ward.

Head Lad: Catherine Peck

---

425 **MR PAUL MORGAN, Lisvane**
Postal: **The Hollies, Rudry Road, Lisvane, Cardiff, South Glamorgan, CF14 0SN**

1 A BOLD MOVE (IRE), 6, b g Shantou (USA)—Sprint For Gold (USA) **Walters Plant Hire Ltd**
2 CONAS TAOI (IRE), 7, b g Exit To Nowhere (USA)—Zudika (IRE) **All Stars Sports Racing**
3 JOHN REEL (FR), 7, b g Country Reel (USA)—John Quatz (FR) **Walters Plant Hire Ltd**
4 POTTERS CORNER (IRE), 6, b g Indian Danehill (IRE)—
Woodford Beauty (IRE) **Walters Plant, Maule, Davies, Potter**
5 RELKWOOD (IRE), 6, gr g Beneficial—Rose Wood **All Stars Sports Racing 2**
6 VERYGOODVERYGOOD (FR), 5, b g Yeats (IRE)—Rose d'or (IRE) **Walters Plant Hire Ltd**
7 WINNING TICKET (IRE), 5, b g Kalanisi (IRE)—Saddlers' Venture (IRE) **Walters Plant Hire Spiers & Hartwell**

THREE-YEAR-OLDS

8 STONECOLDSOBA, b g Aqlaam—Aswaaq (IRE) **Walters Plant Hire Spiers & Hartwell**

Other Owners: Mr J. J. V. Davies, Mr A. James, Mr E. N. Liddiard, Mr G. C. Maule, J. E. Potter, Mrs M. J. Potter, Spiers & Hartwell Ltd.

---

426 **MR DAVE MORRIS, Newmarket**
Postal: **Albert House Stables, Moulton Road, Newmarket, Suffolk, CB8 8DU**
Contacts: **PHONE (01638) 675780 MOBILE (07711) 010268**
E-MAIL info@rebel-racing.co.uk WEBSITE www.rebel-racing.co.uk

1 GROOVEJET, 5, b m Cockney Rebel (IRE)—Vino Veritas (USA) **Phil Cunningham**
2 NAPOLEON SOLO, 4, b g Cockney Rebel (IRE)—Trump Street **Phil Cunningham**

MR DAVE MORRIS - Continued

THREE-YEAR-OLDS

3 **ACE REBEL**, ch c Bahamian Bounty—Quadrophenia **Rebel Racing III**
4 **BURNING LOVE (IRE)**, b f Kodiac—Think (FR) **Rebel Racing**
5 **LONDON REBEL (IRE)**, ch f Arcano (IRE)—Piccadilly Filly (IRE) **Rebel Racing III**
6 **NUCKY THOMPSON**, b g Cockney Rebel (IRE)—Vino Veritas (USA) **Rebel Racing III**
7 **REBEL CAUSE (IRE)**, b g Cockney Rebel (IRE)—Happy Go Lily **Rebel Racing III**
8 **REBEL LIGHTNING (IRE)**, gr c Zebedee—Bellechance **Rebel Racing III**
9 **REBEL RAISER (IRE)**, b g Kheleyf (USA)—Trump Street **Rebel Racing III**
10 **REBEL STATE (IRE)**, b c Zoffany (IRE)—Stately Princess **Rebel Racing III**
11 **REBEL SURGE (IRE)**, b f Kodiac—Face The Storm (IRE) **Rebel Racing III**
12 **SIR THEODORE (IRE)**, b g Arcano (IRE)—Key Rose (IRE) **Rebel Racing**
13 **WONDERFUL LIFE (IRE)**, b f Canford Cliffs (IRE)—Feeling Wonderful (IRE) **Rebel Racing III**

TWO-YEAR-OLDS

14 **BERNARDO O'REILLY**, b c 25/2 Intikhab—Baldovina (Tale of The Cat (USA)) (9523) **Rebel Racing (2)**
15 **BOOOM**, b c 31/1 Makfi—Fame Is The Spur (Motivator) (40000) **Rebel Racing (2)**
16 **CARELESS WHISPER**, b f 23/4 Cockney Rebel (IRE)—
Vino Veritas (USA) (Chief's Crown (USA)) (44296) **Rebel Racing (2)**
17 **GUSTAVO FRING**, b c 28/2 Kodiac—Maleha (IRE) (Cape Cross (IRE)) (35000) **Rebel Racing (2)**
18 **KEYSER SOZE**, ch c 14/4 Arcano (IRE)—
Causeway Queen (IRE) (Giant's Causeway (USA)) (50000) **Rebel Racing (2)**
19 **LA ISLA BONITA**, b f 9/4 Foxwedge (AUS)—Excello (Exceed And Excel (AUS)) (21000) **Rebel Racing (2)**
20 **OH GENO**, b c 25/3 Paco Boy (IRE)—Key Light (Acclamation) (30476) **Rebel Racing (2)**
21 **SIR HARRY COLLINS**, gr c 22/3 Zebedee—Unreal (Dansili) (45000) **Rebel Racing (2)**
22 **SOLITARY SISTER**, b f 7/2 Cockney Rebel (IRE)—Sweet Afton (IRE) (Mujadil (USA)) (22148) **Rebel Racing (2)**
23 **THISTIMENEXTYEAR**, gr c 25/4 New Approach (IRE)—
Scarlet Empire (IRE) (Red Ransom (USA)) (70000) **Rebel Racing (2)**
24 **TWISTON SHOUT**, b c 26/1 Lawman—Minkova (IRE) (Sadler's Wells (USA)) (41000) **Rebel Racing (2)**

Other Owners: P. Cunningham, Mr Phil Cunningham, Mr Martin Gowing, Rebel Racing, Rebel Racing (2), Rebel Racing III.

Assistant Trainer: Richard Spencer

Jockey (flat): William Twiston-Davies.

---

427   **MR M. F. MORRIS, Fethard**
Postal: Everardsgrange, Fethard, Co. Tipperary, Ireland
Contacts: **PHONE** (00353) 52 6131474 **FAX** (00353) 52 6131654 **MOBILE** (00353) 86 8543010
E-MAIL mouse@eircom.net

1 **ALAMEIN (IRE)**, 6, b g Beneficial—Lady of Appeal (IRE) **Gigginstown House Stud**
2 **ALPHA DES OBEAUX (FR)**, 6, b g Saddler Maker (IRE)—Omega des Obeaux (FR) **Gigginstown House Stud**
3 **BAILY BAY (IRE)**, 6, b g Robin des Pres (FR)—Native Sylph (IRE) **Mr R. A. Scott**
4 **BAILY CLOUD (IRE)**, 6, ch g Touch of Land (FR)—Cap The Rose (IRE) **Mr R. A. Scott**
5 **BAILY FOX (IRE)**, 4, b g Milan—Shed **Mr R. A. Scott**
6 **BAILY GREEN (IRE)**, 10, b g King's Theatre (IRE)—Dream On Boys (IRE) **Mr R. A. Scott**
7 **BAILY MOON (IRE)**, 5, b g Milan—Givehertime (IRE) **Mr R. A. Scott**
8 **BAILY SMILE (IRE)**, 5, b g Coroner (IRE)—Supertime (IRE) **Mr R. A. Scott**
9 **BAILY SUNSET (IRE)**, 5, ch g Presenting—Kon Tiky (FR) **Mr R. A. Scott**
10 **BRUFF (IRE)**, 9, b g Presenting—Aniston (IRE) **Mr J. P. McManus**
11 **CAROLE ROSE (IRE)**, 6, ch m Mahler—Going For Home (IRE)
12 **DROMNEA (IRE)**, 9, b br g Presenting—Fifth Imp (IRE) **Mrs Anne Daly**
13 **FIRST LIEUTENANT (IRE)**, 11, ch g Presenting—Fourstargale (IRE) **Gigginstown House Stud**
14 **FOLSOM BLUE (IRE)**, 9, b g Old Vic—Spirit Leader (IRE) **Gigginstown House Stud**
15 **GROTESQUE**, 5, b g Kayf Tara—Princess Timon **Gigginstown House Stud**
16 **HOGAN'S ALLEY (IRE)**, 5, ch g Presenting—Enniscoffey (IRE) **Mr J. P. McManus**
17 **HORENDUS HULABALOO (IRE)**, 7, b g Beneficial—Renvyle Society (IRE) **Gigginstown House Stud**
18 **JUST CAUSE (IRE)**, 6, b g Court Cave (IRE)—Secret Can't Say (IRE) **Gigginstown House Stud**
19 **MIRADANE (IRE)**, 9, b g Kayf Tara—Coolvawn Lady (IRE) **Mr B. Maloney**
20 **MOVING TARGET (IRE)**, 5, ch g Flemensfirth (USA)—Hazel Sylph (IRE) **Mrs J. Magnier**
21 **RAVISHED (IRE)**, 8, b g Oscar—Fair Present (IRE) **Gigginstown House Stud**
22 **ROGUE ANGEL (IRE)**, 8, b g Presenting—Carrigeen Kohleria (IRE) **Gigginstown House Stud**
23 **ROLLINGONTHERIVER (IRE)**, 6, gr g Scorpion (IRE)—Mondeo Rose (IRE) **Mrs T. Hyde**

MR M. F. MORRIS - Continued

24 **RULE THE WORLD**, 9, b g Sulamani (IRE)—Elaine Tully (IRE) **Gigginstown House Stud**
25 **SCAMALL DUBH (IRE)**, 6, b g Oscar (IRE)—Inchagreine (IRE) **G. Morrissey**
26 **THE DOORMAN (IRE)**, 7, b g King's Theatre (IRE)—Amber Light (IRE) **Mr J. P. McManus**

---

428 | **MR PATRICK MORRIS, Prescot**
Postal: **Avenue House, George Hale Avenue, Knowsley Park, Prescot, Merseyside, L34 4AJ**
Contacts: **MOBILE (07545) 425235**
E-MAIL info@patmorrisracing.co.uk WEBSITE www.patmorrisracing.co.uk

1 **BAHANGO (IRE)**, 4, b g Bahamian Bounty—Last Tango (IRE) **Mrs S. Morris**
2 **BILLY SLATER**, 4, br c Pastoral Pursuits—Procession **Dr M. B. Q. S. Koukash**
3 **ENERGIA FOX (BRZ)**, 6, ch m Agnes Gold (JPN)—Super Eletric (BRZ) **Dr M. B. Q. S. Koukash**
4 **GABRIAL THE TIGER (IRE)**, 4, b g Kodiac—Invincible **Dr M. B. Q. S. Koukash**
5 **GABRIAL'S KAKA (IRE)**, 6, b g Jeremy (USA)—Love In May (IRE) **Dr M. B. Q. S. Koukash**
6 **GABRIAL'S KING (IRE)**, 7, b g Hurricane Run (IRE)—Danella (IRE) **Dr M. B. Q. S. Koukash**
7 **GRAMERCY (IRE)**, 9, b g Whipper (USA)—Topiary (IRE) **Dr M. B. Q. S. Koukash**
8 **GROWL**, 4, b c Oasis Dream—Desert Tigress (USA) **Dr M. B. Q. S. Koukash**
9 **MASAMAH (IRE)**, 10, gr g Exceed And Excel (AUS)—Bethesda **Dr M. B. Q. S. Koukash**
10 **POSTSCRIPT (IRE)**, 8, ch g Pivotal—Persian Secret (FR) **Dr M. B. Q. S. Koukash**
11 **STEVE PRESCOTT**, 4, gr ro g Dutch Art—Toy Top (USA) **Dr M. B. Q. S. Koukash**
12 **TOP OFFER**, 7, b g Dansili—Zante **Mr M. Watkinson**
13 **VERY GOOD DAY (FR)**, 9, b g Sinndar—Picture Princess **Dr M. B. Q. S. Koukash**

THREE-YEAR-OLDS

14 **ANTIOCO (IRE)**, b c Motivator—Haraplata (GER) **Dr M. B. Q. S. Koukash**
15 **BIRDCAGE**, b f Showcasing—Trinny **Dr M. B. Q. S. Koukash**

Other Owners: M. R. Channon.

---

429 | **MR HUGHIE MORRISON, East Ilsley**
Postal: **Summerdown, East Ilsley, Newbury, Berkshire, RG20 7LB**
Contacts: **PHONE (01635) 281678 FAX (01635) 281746 MOBILE (07836) 687799**
E-MAIL hughie@hughiemorrison.co.uk WEBSITE www.hughiemorrison.co.uk

1 **ATALAN**, 4, b c Azamour (IRE)—Capriolla **The Fairy Story Partnership**
2 **BALTIC BRAVE (IRE)**, 5, b g Baltic King—Negria (IRE) **The Brave Partnership**
3 **CANOODLE**, 4, b f Stimulation (IRE)—Flirtatious **Mrs M. D. W. Morrison**
4 **CHIL THE KITE**, 7, b g Notnowcato—Copy-Cat **Mr Graham Doyle & Miss Hazel Lawrence**
5 **COMPTON MILL**, 4, b g Compton Place—
Classic Millennium **Mr M. Bevan, Mrs R. Luard & Mrs M. D. W. Morrison**
6 **COUSIN KHEE**, 9, b g Sakhee (USA)—Cugina **R. C. Tooth**
7 **DUTCH LAW**, 4, b g Dutch Art—Lawyers Choice **R. C. Tooth**
8 **FERN OWL**, 4, ch g Nayef (USA)—Snow Goose **Sir Thomas Pilkington**
9 **FIELD GAME**, 4, b g Pastoral Pursuits—Tarqua (IRE) **Earl of Carnarvon**
10 **FUN MAC (GER)**, 5, ch g Shirocco (GER)—Favorite (GER) **Mrs Angela McAlpine & Partners**
11 **KISSY SUZUKI**, 4, b f Sakhee's Secret—Yonder **Mrs M. D. W. Morrison**
12 **MAJOR MAC**, 4, ch g Shirocco (GER)—Spring Fashion (IRE) **Mr Paul Brocklehurst & Partners**
13 **MANOLITO**, 4, b g High Chaparral—Break Time **Mr Hugh Morrison**
14 **MAX THE MINISTER**, 6, bl g Pastoral Pursuits—
Franciscaine (FR) **Mrs M. D. W. Morrison, Mr D. Cliff and P. Clunes**
15 **NEARLY CAUGHT (IRE)**, 6, b g New Approach (IRE)—Katch Me Katie **Mr A. N. Solomons**
16 **NOT SO SLEEPY**, 4, ch g Beat Hollow—Papillon de Bronze (IRE) **Lady Blyth**
17 **PASTORAL PLAYER**, 9, b g Pastoral Pursuits—Copy-Cat **The Pursuits Partnership**
18 **SAMSON**, 5, ch g Black Sam Bellamy (IRE)—Riverine **Pangfield Racing IV**
19 **SARSTED**, 4, b g Paco Boy (IRE)—Red Blooded Woman (USA)
Miss Annika Murjahn, The Hon Miss M. Morrison, Mr S. de Zoete & Mr A. J. Struthers
20 **SHUJAHA (AUS)**, 4, b f New Approach (IRE)—Umoya **Mr A. Hine & Mr H. Link**
21 **SISTER SIBYL (IRE)**, 4, b m King's Theatre (IRE)—Rose of The Erne (IRE) **The Hill Stud**
22 **STAR RIDER**, 4, gr f Cape Cross (IRE)—Starfala **Ben & Sir Martyn Arbib**
23 **SWEEPING UP**, 5, b m Sea The Stars (IRE)—Farfala (FR) **Ben & Sir Martyn Arbib**
24 **SWEET SELECTION**, 4, b f Stimulation (IRE)—Sweet Coincidence **Mr Paul Brocklehurst**

MR HUGHIE MORRISON - Continued

25 **THE POODLE FAKER**, 5, b g Pastoral Pursuits—Flirtatious **Mrs M. D. W. Morrison**
26 **VENT DE FORCE**, 5, b h Hurricane Run (IRE)—Capriolla **The Fairy Story Partnership**
27 **ZAMSINA**, 4, b f Zamindar (USA)—Bolsena (USA) **Mr M. E. Wates**

THREE-YEAR-OLDS

28 **ADMIRAL'S SUNSET**, b f Mount Nelson—Early Evening **Mr A. N. Solomons**
29 **AMBUSCADE**, b f Dick Turpin (IRE)—Tarqua (IRE) **Earl of Carnarvon**
30 **AURORA GRAY**, gr f Rip Van Winkle (IRE)—Summer's Eve **Wardley Bloodstock**
31 **BAHAMIAN BOY**, ch g Paco Boy (IRE)—
    Bahamian Babe **Mr Paul Brocklehurst, Mr Hugh Scott-Barrett & Mr T. Pickford**
32 **BRAHMA**, b g Mount Nelson—Swan Queen **Sir Thomas Pilkington**
33 **CATALAN (IRE)**, b f Duke of Marmalade (IRE)—Twice The Ease **Mrs Sonia Rogers & Sir Thomas Pilkington**
34 **CHALCOT (IRE)**, b f High Chaparral (IRE)—Law of The Jungle (IRE) **Mrs Carolyn Whitaker**
35 **CINDERS (IRE)**, b f Lilbourne Lad (IRE)—
    The Fairies Did It (USA) **Mr M. Kerr-Dineen, Mr M. Hughes, Mr W. Eason & Mr G. Rothwell**
36 **DESIRABLE**, b f Stimulation (IRE)—Hot Pursuits **Mrs Isabel Eavis**
37 **EXCELLENT SOUNDS**, b f Exceed And Excel (AUS)—Siren Sound **Helena Springfield Ltd**
38 **HELFIRE**, b f Archipenko (USA)—Relkida **Mr M. Watson & Miss D. Collett**
39 **LAST TANGO INPARIS**, ch f Aqlaam—Strictly Lambada **Helena Springfield Ltd**
40 **MACHO MAC**, ch g Pastoral Pursuits—Clarice Orsini **Mr A. McAlpine, Mr H. Scott-Barrett & Mr A. J. Struthers**
41 **MADAME CLAUD**, ch f Champs Elysees—Change Partners (IRE) **Mr Rhydian Morgan-Jones**
42 **MAESTRO MAC (IRE)**, b c Roderic O'Connor (IRE)—
    Union City Blues (IRE) **Mr A. McAlpine, Mr S. de Zoete & Mr C. Hill**
43 **MARMELO**, b c Duke of Marmalade (IRE)—Capriolla **The Fairy Story Partnership**
44 **OUR LITTLE SISTER (IRE)**, b f Big Bad Bob (IRE)—Rehearsed (IRE) **The Summerdown Partnership**
45 **PASSING DREAM**, b f Passing Glance—Violet's Walk **Mr M. E. Wates**
46 **PASTORAL MUSIC**, b g Pastoral Pursuits—Jasmeno **MNC Racing**
47 **PASTORAL STAR**, ch f Pastoral Pursuits—
    Movie Star (IRE) **Mr G. Swire, Mr & Mrs R. Lloyd, Mr Richard Wright**
48 **PIROUETTE**, ch f Pivotal—Passiflora **The End-R-Ways Partnership & Partners**
49 **PROSPECTUS**, b g Sakhee (USA)—Some Sunny Day **The Black Gold Partnership**
50 **RAVENS QUEST**, ch c Raven's Pass (USA)—Seradim **The Fairy Story Partnership**
51 **REMEMBER ME**, b f Acclamation—Forgotten Me (IRE) **Thurloe Thoroughbreds**
52 **SAUCY SPIRIT**, b f Invincible Spirit (IRE)—Salsa Steps (USA) **Ben & Sir Martyn Arbib**
53 **SCARLET PIMPERNEL**, b f Sir Percy—Sweet Pea **Mr Nicholas Jones**
54 **SENZA UNA DONNA**, b g Sir Percy—Sensationally **Castle Down Racing**
55 **SUNSCAPE (IRE)**, ch f Roderic O'Connor (IRE)—
    Opatja **Fiona Trenchard, The Hon Miss M. Morrison, Declan Morrison & Mrs C. Whitaker**
56 **TOP BEAK (IRE)**, b c Lawman (FR)—Tree Tops **Mr Michael Kerr-Dineen & Mr Martin Hughes**
57 **VAN DYKE**, b c Excellent Art—Respectfully **The Fairy Story Partnership**
58 B f Sakhee's Secret—Yonder **Mrs M. D. W. Morrison**

TWO-YEAR-OLDS

59 B br g 1/5 Shirocco (GER)—Act Three (Beat Hollow) **Mouse Hamilton-Fairley**
60 Ch f 10/2 Bahamian Bounty—Amanjena (Beat Hollow) (16000) **Mr M. E. Wates**
61 B c 25/3 Lawman (FR)—Convention (Encosta de Lago (AUS)) (20000) **Mr Andrew Stone**
62 **CURTSY (IRE)**, ch f 14/5 Galileo (IRE)—
    Acts of Grace (USA) (Bahri (USA)) **Mr Michael Kerr-Dineen & Mr Martin Hughes**
63 B c 20/2 Foxwedge (AUS)—Italian Connection (Cadeaux Genereux) (35000) **Mr Simon Malcolm**
64 **MAGIC BEANS**, br c 16/4 Pastoral Pursuits—Jasmeno (Catcher In The Rye (IRE)) (571) **MNC Racing**
65 **MELLOW**, ch f 18/3 Bahamian Bounty—Tarqua (IRE) (King Charlemagne (USA)) **Lord Carnarvon**
66 Gr c 6/2 Stormy River (FR)—Ms Cordelia (USA) (Anabaa (USA)) **R. C. Tooth**
67 **MULSANNE CHASE**, b c 8/4 Sixties Icon—Hot Pursuits (Pastoral Pursuits) **Mrs I. Eavis**
68 **NORDPOL (GER)**, b c 17/3 Lord of England (GER)—
    Naomia (GER) (Monsun (GER)) (31746) **Thurloe Thoroughbreds XXXVII**
69 B f 24/3 Stimulation (IRE)—Patteresa Girl (Auction House (USA)) (571) **Mr Andrew Stone**
70 Ch c 10/2 Exchange Rate (USA)—
    Persistent Penny (USA) (A P Indy (USA)) (45000) **Mr H. Scott-Barrett, Mr S. De Zoete**
71 Ch c 6/4 Sepoy (AUS)—
    Pivotal Drive (IRE) (Pivotal) (75000) **Mr M. Kerr-Dineen, Mr W. Eason, Mr D. Malpas & Mr G. Rothwell**
72 **POET'S PRINCESS**, ch f 28/3 Poet's Voice—Palace Affair (Pursuit of Love) (34000) **Mr Paul Brocklehurst**
73 B f 11/2 Dutch Art—Port Charlotte (Oasis Dream) (11428) **Lord Margadale**
74 **RUMPOLE**, b c 19/2 Lawman (FR)—
    Complexion (Hurricane Run (IRE)) (130000) **Mr Michael Kerr-Dineen, Mr Martin Hughes & Mr W. Eason**

MR HUGHIE MORRISON - Continued

75 B c 5/5 Casamento (IRE)—Sindiyma (IRE) (Kalanisi (IRE)) (30000) **Mr M. Hankin, Mr C. Fenwick & Mr C. Noell**
76 B f 5/4 Fastnet Rock (AUS)—Starfala (Galileo (IRE)) **Ben & Sir Martyn Arbib**
77 B f 18/2 Sakhee's Secret—Supatov (USA) (Johannesburg (USA)) (571)
78 TEMPLE CHURCH (IRE), b c 28/1 Lawman (FR)—
                        All Hollows (IRE) (Dalakhani (IRE)) (27000) **Mr P. C. J. Dalby & R. D. Schuster**
79 Gr c 7/3 Motivator—Tiysha (IRE) (Araafa (IRE)) (9597) **Mr M. Bevan, Mr A. Pickford & Mr R. Angliss**
80 TOWIE (IRE), b br c 10/2 Sea The Stars (IRE)—
                        Epping (Charnwood Forest (IRE)) (90000) **Mr Michael Kerr-Dineen & Mr Martin Hughes**
81 Ch f 11/4 Dutch Art—Triple Sharp (Selkirk (USA)) **Lady Hardy**
82 B c 18/4 Rip Van Winkle (IRE)—Water Fountain (Mark of Esteem (IRE)) (28000) **The Caledonian Racing Society**

Other Owners: Mr R. A. Angliss, M. Arbib, Mr B. G. Arbib, Mr Graham Ball, Mr T. J. Billington, Mrs P. G. Billington, T. M. Bird, Mrs Ann Chapple, D. Cliff, Mrs P. K. Clunes, Miss D. Collett, P. C. J. Dalby, Mr G. J. Doyle, W. D. Eason, Mrs H. S. Ellingsen, Mr M. P. Gibbens, E. R. Goodwin, Mr R. W. Gregson-Williams, Mrs E. J. Gregson-Williams, Mr Harry Hampson, Mr A. Hine, Mr M. B. Hughes, M. Kerr-Dineen, Miss H. M. Lawrence, Mr H. Link, Mr D. S. Little, Mrs R. A. Luard, D. P. Malpas, Mr A. N. R. McAlpine, Mrs A. M. McAlpine, The Hon Miss M. Morrison, Miss A. E. J. Murjahn, Mr B. G. W. Parker, Mr John Parker, Mr O. J. W. Pawle, A. C. Pickford, Mrs S. M. Rogers, Mr G. C. Rothwell, R. D. Schuster, Mrs Angela Scott, Miss C. S. Scott-Balls, Mr H. Y. Scott-Barrett, Mr J. A. B. Stafford, Mr G. D. W. Swire, Mrs G. D. W. Swire, Viscountess Trenchard, Mrs Anne Usher, M. J. Watson, Mr G. Waylen, M. Weinfeld.

Apprentice: Charlie Bennett. **Amateur:** Miss Georgina Ducker, Mr Robert Pooles, Mr George Roberts.

---

 430   **MR GARRY MOSS, Billingham**
Postal: **12 Tilery Wood, Wynyard, Billingham, Cleveland, TS22 5QR**
Contacts: PHONE (01302) 746456 (07872) 993519 MOBILE (07791) 888129

1 ADDICTIVE DREAM (IRE), 9, ch g Kheleyf (USA)—Nottambula (IRE) **Mr B Morton & Northumbria Leisure Ltd**
2 CHAMBERLAIN, 5, b g Indesatchel (IRE)—Citron **Pinnacle Four Partnership**
3 DUTCH COED, 4, b g Dutch Art—Discoed **Ms S. V. Hattersley**
4 EAGLE EMPIRE (IRE), 4, b g Jeremy (USA)—Red Eagle (IRE) **Pinnacle Four Partnership**
5 FREEWHEEL (IRE), 6, br g Galileo (IRE)—La Chunga (USA) **Pinnacle Four Partnership**
6 GINGER JACK, 9, ch g Refuse To Bend (IRE)—Coretta (IRE) **C. H. McGhie**
7 HENRY SMITH, 4, b g Firebreak—So Discreet **Pinnacle Duo Partnership**
8 INDIBEAU, 4, b f Indesatchel (IRE)—Neardown Beauty (IRE) **B. Morton**
9 RODRIGO DE TORRES, 9, ch g Bahamian Bounty—Leonica **Pinnacle Four Partnership**

THREE-YEAR-OLDS

10 FUMBO JUMBO (IRE), b f Zebedee—Baraloti (IRE) **Pinnacle Four Partnership**
11 B f Major Cadeaux—Neardown Beauty (IRE)
12 PLANETARIA (IRE), b g Lilbourne Lad (IRE)—Red Planet **Pinnacle Four Partnership**

Other Owners: Northumbria Leisure Ltd.

---

431   **MR WILLIAM MUIR, Lambourn**
Postal: **Linkslade, Wantage Road, Lambourn, Hungerford, Berkshire, RG17 8UG**
Contacts: OFFICE (01488) 73098 HOME (01488) 73748 FAX (01488) 73490
MOBILE (07831) 457074
E-MAIL william@williammuir.com WEBSITE www.williammuir.com

1 ALWAYS WILL, 4, b g Sleeping Indian—China Beads **Muir Racing Partnership - Beverley**
2 AVALANCHE EXPRESS, 4, ch c Pivotal—Irresistible **Mr S. P. Hussain**
3 BIG BAZ (IRE), 6, b g Pivotal—Gracefully (IRE) **The Big Baz Partnership**
4 CODE RED, 4, ch c Bahamian Bounty—Just Devine (IRE) **Mrs Michelle Morgan**
5 CROWN COMMAND (IRE), 4, ch c Lope de Vega (IRE)—Pivotal Role **Mr Kenny Kok**
6 EAGER BEAVER, 4, b f Duke of Marmalade (IRE)—Kahlua Kiss **Mr M. J. Caddy**
7 EASY TIGER, 4, b g Refuse To Bend (IRE)—Extremely Rare (IRE) **Ms E. J. Tanner**
8 EQUALLY FAST, 4, b g Equiano (FR)—Fabulously Fast (USA) **Muir Racing Partnership - Haydock**
9 HARRY HOLLAND, 4, b g Dutch Art—Common Consent (IRE) **Muir Racing Partnership - Windsor**
10 HOT MUSTARD, 6, b g Pastoral Pursuits—Lihou Island **Mrs G. Rowland-Clark**
11 LORELEI, 4, b f Excellent Art—Light Dreams **Mr J. O'Mulloy**
12 RESTORER, 4, gr c Mastercraftsman (IRE)—Moon Empress (FR) **Mr C. L. A. Edginton**

MR WILLIAM MUIR - Continued

13 **SIOUXPERHERO (IRE)**, 7, b g Sleeping Indian—Tintern **Muir Racing Partnership - Bath**
14 **SIR GARETH**, 4, b g Nayef (USA)—Portmeirion **Usk Valley Stud**
15 **STEPPER POINT**, 7, b g Kyllachy—Sacre Coeur **Mr C. L. A. Edginton**
16 **TRUTH OR DARE**, 5, b g Invincible Spirit (IRE)—Unreachable Star **Carmel Stud**

THREE-YEAR-OLDS

17 **ANGRYWHITEPYJAMAS (IRE)**, b c Manduro (GER)—Ornellaia (IRE) **O'Mulloy, Collenette, Clark**
18 **ARGYLE (IRE)**, gr c Lawman (FR)—All Hallows (IRE) **Mr C. L. A. Edginton**
19 **CALVADOS SPIRIT**, b c Invincible Spirit (IRE)—Putois Peace **Muir Racing Partnership - Deauville**
20 **CAUTIOUS OPTIMISM**, ch g Showcasing—Queen of Havana (USA) **Muir Racing Partnership - Ffos Las**
21 **DESTROYER**, b g Royal Applause—Good Girl (IRE) **Capt J Appoo, Quaintance, Clark, Moore**
22 **ENTERTAINING BEN**, b g Equiano (FR)—Fatal Attraction **Berkeley, Edginton, Niven**
23 **FINE BLEND (IRE)**, br f Sakhee's Secret—Coffee Time (IRE) **Muir Racing Partnership - Windsor**
24 **FLORENCIO**, b c Equiano (FR)—Mary Pekan (IRE) **Excel Racing**
25 B f Fastnet Rock (AUS)—Highwater Dancer (IRE) **Miss Lisa J. Miall**
26 **HITMAN**, b c Canford Cliffs (IRE)—Ballymore Celebre (IRE) **Carmel Stud**
27 **KING OF SPIN**, b c Pivotal—Regina **Muir Racing Partnership - Nottingham**
28 **KITTY FOR ME**, b f Pour Moi (IRE)—Purring (USA) **Edginton, Morgan, Jeffery, Muir**
29 Ch c Major Cadeaux—La Jwaab **Usk Valley Stud**
30 **LOVEISRECKLESS (IRE)**, b f Mount Nelson—Sassari (IRE) **Mr J. O'Mulloy**
31 **MARGOESQUE**, b f Pivotal—Showcall (USA) **Mr Andrew Duffield**
32 **MIKMAK**, b c Makfi—Rakata (USA) **Muir Racing Partnership - Leicester**
33 **MISSY BLUE EYES**, b g Kyllachy—Sapphire Bracelet (IRE) **Mr L A Hill & Mr C L Bacon**
34 **POETIC QUEEN (IRE)**, b f Dylan Thomas (IRE)—Jubilant Lady (USA) **Mr & Mrs G. Middlebrook**
35 **POLISH EMPRESS**, b f Equiano (FR)—Polish Belle **Newsells Park Stud Limited**
36 **ROYAL RESERVE**, b c Duke of Marmalade (IRE)—Lady Hawkfield (IRE) **Muir Racing Partnership - Chester**
37 **SENSE OF SNOW (IRE)**, ch c Kyllachy—Miss Smilla **J. O'Mulloy & J. Collenette**
38 Ch g Rip Van Winkle (IRE)—Starbound (IRE) **Wayfoong Syndicate**
39 **VOICES OF KINGS**, b c Poet's Voice—Khubza **Mr K. Kok**
40 **WELSH ROSE**, b f Exceed And Excel (AUS)—Nantyglo **Usk Valley Stud**
41 **WHITE SHAHEEN**, b c Makfi—Likeable **Mr S. P. Hussain**
42 **WILLYTHECONQUEROR (IRE)**, b g Kodiac—Jazzie (FR) **Perspicacious Punters Racing Club**

TWO-YEAR-OLDS

43 B f 14/3 Choisir (AUS)—Afrodita (IRE) (Montjeu (IRE))
44 Ch c 13/4 Mastercraftsman (IRE)—Billie Jean (Bertolini (USA)) (26000)
45 Ch c 24/2 Nathaniel (IRE)—Castaway Queen (IRE) (Selkirk (USA)) (80000)
46 B c 20/2 Raven's Pass—Crystal Melody (Nureyev (USA)) (33000)
47 Ch f 5/5 Bahamian Bounty—Dame Shirley (Haafhd)
48 B f 21/2 Arabian Gleam—Desert Liaison (Dansili)
49 B f 26/1 Mount Nelson—Don't Stop Me Now (FR) (Zamindar (USA))
50 B c 9/3 Poet's Voice—Electric Feel (Firebreak)
51 B c 18/4 Rip Van Winkle (IRE)—How's She Cuttin' (IRE) (Shinko Forest (IRE)) (50000)
52 Ch c 27/3 New Approach (IRE)—Junia Tepzia (IRE) (Rock of Gibraltar (IRE)) (40000)
53 B f 22/3 Exceed And Excel (AUS)—Kahlua Kiss (Mister Baileys) (52000)
54 B f 5/3 Royal Applause—Miss University (IRE) (Beau Genius (CAN))
55 **MOONLIGHT SILVER**, gr f 18/3 Makfi—Moon Empress (FR) (Rainbow Quest (USA)) (20000)
56 **PHIJEE**, b br c 3/3 Sepoy—Likeable (Dalakhani (IRE)) (30000)
57 Ch c 13/2 Exceed And Excel (AUS)—Putois Peace (Pivotal) (120000)
58 **QUEEN'S LIGHT**, b f 3/2 Fastnet Rock (AUS)—Quesada (IRE) (Peintre Celebre (USA)) (31007)
59 Br c 19/3 Shamardal (USA)—Saphira's Fire (IRE) (Cape Cross (IRE))
60 B f 2/2 Kyllachy—Secret Era (Cape Cross (IRE))
61 B f 17/4 Henrythenavigator (USA)—Shibina (IRE) (Kalanisi (IRE))
62 B f 23/1 Iffraaj—Skirril (Halling (USA)) (20000)
63 B c 17/3 Cacique (IRE)—Snow Crystal (IRE) (Kingmambo (USA)) (68000)
64 B f 8/3 Henrythenavigator (USA)—So Stylish (USA) (Johannesburg (USA)) (20000)
65 **TEXAS WEDGE**, b c 15/5 Foxwedge (AUS)—Sacre Coeur (Compton Place) (32000)
66 Ch c 6/5 Dutch Art—Thrill (Pivotal) (160000)
67 B f 4/4 Mastercraftsman (IRE)—Tintern (Diktat) (5000)
68 B c 1/4 Harbour Watch (IRE)—Valiantly (Anabaa (USA)) (60000)
69 B c 28/2 Equiano (FR)—Varnish (Choisir (AUS))

MR WILLIAM MUIR - Continued

Other Owners: Mr Charlie Austin, Mr G. W. A. Berkeley, Mr Glyn Charles, Mr John Collenette, Mr C. L. A. Edginton, Mr P. Fisher, Mr R. Haim, Mr G. Hope, Mr Ken Jeffery, Mr S. Lamb, Mrs Judith Land, Mr Barry McCabe, Mr K. J. Mercer, Mrs S. Mercer, Mr G. Middlebrook, Mrs L. Middlebrook, Mr Peter Morgan, Mrs Michelle Morgan, Mr Stephen Moss, Mr W. R. Muir, Mr Alasdair Niven, Mr John O'Mulloy, Mr D. L. Quaintance, Mr P. D. Quaintance.

Assistant Trainer: Patrick MacEwan

Jockey (flat): Martin Dwyer.

---

432 MR CLIVE MULHALL, Scarcroft
Postal: **Scarcroft Hall Farm, Thorner Lane, Scarcroft, Leeds, LS14 3AQ**
Contacts: PHONE **(0113) 2893095** FAX **(0113) 2893095** MOBILE **(07979) 527675**
E-MAIL **clive@scarcrofthallracing.co.uk** WEBSITE **www.clivemulhallracing.co.uk**

1 **ANEEDH**, 6, b g Lucky Story (USA)—Seed Al Maha (USA) **Carl Chapman & Mrs Martina Mulhall**
2 **DUBAI MYSTERY (IRE)**, 4, b g Dahjee (USA)—Precious Mystery (IRE) **Carl Chapman & Mrs Martina Mulhall**
3 **LADY LISA JAYNE**, 6, b m Moss Vale (IRE)—Mimic **Carl Chapman & Mrs Martina Mulhall**
4 **LORD SERENDIPITY (IRE)**, 4, gr g Lord Shanakill (USA)—Elitista (FR) **Carl Chapman & Mrs Martina Mulhall**
5 **SEKURAS GIRL (IRE)**, 4, b f Approve (IRE)—Alinda (FR) **Carl Chapman & Mrs Martina Mulhall**
6 **SHARADIYN**, 13, b g Generous (IRE)—Sharadiya (IRE) **Mrs Martina Mulhall**
7 **THINK**, 9, ch g Sulamani (IRE)—Natalie Jay **Mrs C M Mulhall & Carl Chapman**
8 **TUKITINYASOK (IRE)**, 9, b g Fath (USA)—Mevlana (IRE) **Carl Chapman & Mrs Martina Mulhall**
9 **WEIGHT LIMIT (IRE)**, 4, b g Vertical Speed (FR)—Ellie Park (IRE) **Carl Chapman & Mrs Martina Mulhall**

THREE-YEAR-OLDS
10 **BIGBADBOY (IRE)**, b g Big Bad Bob (IRE)—Elegantly (IRE) **Mrs Martina Mulhall & Carl Chapman**
11 **CANDY EXPRESS**, b f Fast Company (IRE)—Sugar Mountain (IRE) **Carl Chapman & Mrs Martina Mulhall**
12 **MRS FROSTY (IRE)**, b f Frozen Power (IRE)—Petticoat Hill (UAE) **Carl Chapman & Mrs Martina Mulhall**

TWO-YEAR-OLDS
13 **FLAME AND FORTUNE (IRE)**, ch g 6/4 Dragon Pulse (IRE)—
Fame And Fortune (IRE) (In The Wings) (19047) **Carl Chapman & Mrs Martina Mulhall**

Other Owners: Mr Carl Chapman, Mrs Yvonne Featherstone, Mrs C. M. Mulhall.

Assistant Trainer: Mrs Martina Mulhall

Jockey (flat): Barry McHugh, James Sullivan. **Jockey (NH):** Brian Harding, Brian Hughes.

---

433 MR NEIL MULHOLLAND, Limpley Stoke
Postal: **Conkwell Grange Stables, Conkwell, Limpley Stoke, Bath, Avon, BA2 7FD**
Contacts: MOBILE **(07739) 258607**
E-MAIL **neil@neilmulhollandracing.com** WEBSITE **www.neilmulhollandracing.com**

1 **ADMIRAL KID (IRE)**, 5, b g Mythical Kid (USA)—English Clover **Equi ex Incertis Partners**
2 **ANGLO PADDY (IRE)**, 7, ch m Mountain High (IRE)—
Hazel Sylph (IRE) **Janet Kirk, Michael Lowry & Keith Adams**
3 **APPLE POPS**, 6, b m Apple Tree (FR)—Rio Pops **Mrs J. M. Abbott**
4 **ASHCOTT BOY**, 8, ch g Lahib (USA)—Last Ambition (IRE) **Mr J. Hobbs**
5 **ATTRACTIVE LIASON (IRE)**, 6, b m Scorpion (IRE)—Sounds Attractive (IRE) **N Webb & P J Proudley**
6 **AUCKLAND DE RE (IRE)**, 6, b br g Network (GER)—Osee de Re (FR) **Mrs D. C. Webb**
7 **BALLYDAGUE LADY (IRE)**, 9, b m Luso—Cottstown Belle (IRE) **Neil Mulholland Racing Club**
8 **BALTIMORE ROCK (IRE)**, 7, b g Tiger Hill (GER)—La Vita E Bella (IRE) **R. S. Brookhouse**
9 4, Ch g Pasternak—Barton Dante **Mrs J. Gerard-Pearse**
10 **BISHOPS COURT**, 6, b g Helissio (FR)—Island of Memories (IRE) **Mr P. C. Tory & Mr P. S. Frampton**
11 **BRIN D'AVOINE (FR)**, 5, b g Califet (FR)—Nemenchka (FR) **Neil Mulholland Racing Club**
12 **BUSBY BURBIDGE**, 5, b g Helissio (FR)—Twin Time **Dajam Ltd**
13 **CAROLE'S DESTRIER**, 8, b g Kayf Tara—Barton May **Mrs C. Skipworth**
14 **CAROLE'S VIGILANTE (IRE)**, 5, ch g Flemensfirth (USA)—Gotta Goa (IRE) **Mrs C. Skipworth**
15 **CHAMPAGNE GEORGE (IRE)**, 6, gr g Acambaro (GER)—Charannah (IRE) **7RUS**
16 **CHANTARA ROSE**, 7, br m Kayf Tara—Fragrant Rose **Steve & Jackie Fleetham**
17 **CHANTECLER**, 5, b g Authorized (IRE)—Snow Goose **Mr J. Hobbs**

MR NEIL MULHOLLAND - Continued

18 **CHICKSGROVE SPRITE (IRE)**, 5, b m Scorpion (IRE)—Homebird (IRE) **Mrs A. R. Hart**
19 **COMMITMENT**, 7, b g Motivator—Courting **Mrs H. R. Cross**
20 **COTTSTOWN FOX (IRE)**, 7, ch g Bandari (IRE)—Cottstown Belle (IRE) **D. J. Bridger**
21 **COURTLANDS PRINCE**, 7, b g Presenting—Bathwick Annie **H. M. W. Clifford**
22 **DEADLY STING (IRE)**, 7, b g Scorpion (IRE)—Gaza Strip (IRE) **Maxilead Limited**
23 **DEJA BOUGG**, 5, b m Tobougg (IRE)—La Riveraine (USA) **H. M. W. Clifford**
24 **DON'TDROPMEIN (IRE)**, 6, b g Stowaway—Real Tempest (IRE) **Hanham Boys Racing Partnership**
25 **EARLS FORT (IRE)**, 6, b g Kalanisi (IRE)—Lillando (IRE) **J. J. Maguire**
26 **EARTH LEGEND**, 5, b g Helissio (FR)—Maori Legend **R. M. Penny**
27 **EBONY EMPRESS (IRE)**, 7, br m Kris Kin (USA)—Auditing Empress (IRE) **Wincanton Race Club**
28 5, B g Tikkanen (USA)—Fields of Barley (IRE) **Mr B. F. Mulholland**
29 **FINGERONTHESWITCH (IRE)**, 6, b g Beneficial—Houseoftherisinsun (IRE) **Cahill, Atwell & Crofts**
30 **FOX NORTON (FR)**, 6, b g Lando (GER)—Natt Musik (FR) **B. Dunn**
31 **GENERAL MONTGOMERY (IRE)**, 7, b g Desert King (IRE)—
Supreme Course (IRE) **Mrs H R Cross & Mrs S A Keys**
32 **GREEK ISLANDS (IRE)**, 8, b g Oasis Dream—Serisia (FR) **Mr D. B. Harris**
33 **HALO MOON**, 8, br g Kayf Tara—Fragrant Rose **Level Par Racing**
34 **HARLEY REBEL**, 4, br g Cockney Rebel (IRE)—Al Kahina **Mrs G. P. Seymour**
35 **HIGHBURY HIGH (IRE)**, 9, gr g Salford Express (IRE)—Betseale (IRE) **The Affordable Partnership**
36 **I'M ASKING (IRE)**, 4, ch f Ask—I'm Maggy (NZ) **Mrs H. R. Cross**
37 **INDIAN BRAVE (IRE)**, 5, b g Definite Article—Fridays Folly (IRE) **D. J. Bridger**
38 **ISTHEREADIFFERENCE (IRE)**, 9, gr g Amilynx (FR)—Jennys Grove (IRE) **Colony Stable Llc**
39 **JOHNS LUCK (IRE)**, 7, b g Turtle Island (IRE)—Jemima Yorke **Mr J. Hobbs**
40 **JUNE FRENCH (FR)**, 8, b m Jimble (FR)—Sunbelt Broker **Brigadier Racing**
41 **KALONDRA (IRE)**, 5, b g Spadoun (FR)—Mystic Vic (IRE) **Mr J. Henderson**
42 4, Gr c Tikkanen (USA)—Kay Theatre (IRE) **Mike, Chris, Stef, Carl, David & Hugh**
43 **KEEP UP KEIRA (IRE)**, 5, b m Scorpion (IRE)—Perspex Queen (IRE) **Mrs D. C. Webb**
44 **KRISTAL HART**, 7, b m Lucky Story (USA)—Moly (FR) **The White Hart Racing Syndicate**
45 **LADY HELISSIO**, 6, b m Helissio (FR)—Barton Dante **David H. Smith**
46 **LEE SIDE LADY**, 6, ch m Mountain High (IRE)—Vicante (IRE) **The Affordable (2) Partnership**
47 **LIFT THE LID (IRE)**, 6, b g Robin des Pres (FR)—Kindly Light (IRE) **Flooring Solutions (NI) Ltd**
48 **LILY MARS (IRE)**, 9, br m Presenting—Tiffany Jazz (IRE) **Strictly Come Racing**
49 **LIONS CHARGE (USA)**, 9, ch g Lion Heart (USA)—Fellwaati (USA) **Neil Mulholland Racing Ltd**
50 **MAID OF TUSCANY (IRE)**, 5, b m Manduro (GER)—Tuscania (USA) **Qdos Racing**
51 **MARSHGATE LANE (USA)**, 7, b g Medaglia d'oro (USA)—Louvain (IRE) **The Affordable Partnership**
52 **MASTER BURBIDGE**, 5, b g Pasternak—Silver Sequel **Dajam Ltd**
53 **MATROW'S LADY (IRE)**, 9, b m Cloudings (IRE)—I'm Maggy (NZ) **Matrow Properties Limited**
54 **MAZOVIAN (USA)**, 8, b g E Dubai (USA)—Polish Style (USA) **Pop Partnership**
55 **MIDNIGHT SEQUEL**, 7, b m Midnight Legend—Silver Sequel **Strictly Come Racing**
56 **MINELLA DEFINITELY (IRE)**, 9, br g Definite Article—West Along **Wellcroomed Ltd**
57 **MINELLA PRESENT (IRE)**, 7, b g Presenting—Dabaya (IRE) **Mrs J. Gerard-Pearse**
58 **MOLLY CAREW**, 4, b f Midnight Legend—Moyliscar **Mrs H R Cross & Mrs S A Keys**
59 **MONSIEUR MURPHY (IRE)**, 6, b g Presenting—Mistress Cara **Mr P. Gray**
60 **MORRIS THE MINER**, 6, b g Apple Tree (FR)—Miner Yours **Mrs D. C. Webb**
61 **MRS BURBIDGE**, 6, b m Pasternak—Twin Time **Dajam Ltd**
62 **OSCARA DARA (IRE)**, 11, b g Oscar (IRE)—Lisa's Storm (IRE) **BG Racing Partnership**
63 **OSCARTEEA (IRE)**, 7, b g Oscar (IRE)—Miss Arteea (IRE) **Steve & Jackie Fleetham**
64 **OWNERS DAY**, 6, gr m Fair Mix (FR)—Charmeille (FR) **The Dickinsons, Clegg, Finch & Lacey**
65 **PASS THE TIME**, 7, b m Passing Glance—Twin Time **Dajam Ltd**
66 5, B m Milan—Peinture Francaise (FR) **Neil Mulholland Racing Ltd**
67 **PERFECT TIMING**, 8, b g Shantou (USA)—Winnetka Gal (IRE) **Hanham Boys Racing Partnership**
68 **PETER THE MAYO MAN (IRE)**, 6, ch g Dylan Thomas (IRE)—Mommkin **Masterson Holdings Limited**
69 **PINK LIPS**, 8, b m Noverre (USA)—Primrose Queen **Mr T. J. Clyne**
70 **PINKIE BROWN (FR)**, 4, gr g Gentlewave (IRE)—Natt Musik (FR) **B. Dunn**
71 **POMME ROUGE**, 6, ch g Apple Tree (FR)—Lavender Dancer **D. V. Stevens**
72 **PROOFREADER**, 7, b g Authorized (IRE)—Blixen (USA) **The Boot Inn Partnership**
73 **PURE POTEEN (IRE)**, 8, ch g Flemensfirth (USA)—Taking My Time (IRE) **Mr N. C. Robinson**
74 **PURSUITOFHAPPINESS (IRE)**, 8, b g Classic Cliche (IRE)—Lake Tour (IRE) **B. A. Derrick**
75 **SAIL BY THE SEA (IRE)**, 8, b g Heron Island (IRE)—Trajectus **R. S. Brookhouse**
76 **SANDGATE**, 4, ch g Compton Place—Jump Ship **Mrs D. C. Webb**
77 **SEVEN CLANS (IRE)**, 4, b g Cape Cross (IRE)—Cherokee Rose (IRE) **The Affordable (2) Partnership**
78 **SHAKY GIFT (IRE)**, 7, b m Milan—Free Lift **Mrs P. L. Bridel**
79 **SHANTOU VILLAGE (IRE)**, 6, b g Shantou (USA)—Village Queen (IRE) **Mrs J. Gerard-Pearse**
80 **SHARP SWORD (IRE)**, 5, ch g King's Best (USA)—Pictavia (IRE) **Mrs H. Dale-Staples**
81 **SI C'ETAIT VRAI (FR)**, 10, b g Robin des Champs (FR)—Bleu Perle (FR) **Mr J. Nicholson**

MR NEIL MULHOLLAND - Continued

82 **SLEEP EASY**, 4, b g Rip Van Winkle (IRE)—Strictly Lambada
83 **SOLOMN GRUNDY (IRE)**, 6, b g Westerner—Marika's King (IRE) **R. S. Brookhouse**
84 **SOUPY SOUPS (IRE)**, 5, ch g Stowaway—Near Dunleer (IRE) **Equi ex Incertis Partners**
85 **SOUTHFIELD ROYALE**, 6, b g Presenting—Chamoss Royale (FR) **Mrs A. B. Yeoman**
86 **SUPREME HOPE (IRE)**, 7, b m Definite Article—Dochas Supreme (IRE) **Mr M. G. Cahill**
87 **THE BAY BANDIT**, 9, b g Highest Honor (FR)—Pescara (IRE) **Neil Mulholland Racing Club**
88 **THE DRUIDS NEPHEW (IRE)**, 9, b g King's Theatre (IRE)—Gifted **The Stonehenge Druids**
89 **THE WAY YOU DANCE (IRE)**, 4, b g Thewayyouare (USA)—Beautiful Dancer (IRE) **BG Racing Partnership**
90 **THE YOUNG MASTER**, 7, b g Echo of Light—Fine Frenzy (IRE) **Dajam & The Old Masters**
91 **VELATOR**, 9, b g Old Vic—Jupiter's Message **Steve & Jackie Fleetham**
92 **VERY EXTRAVAGANT (IRE)**, 7, ch m Touch of Land (FR)—Raveleen Rose (IRE) **B. A. Derrick**
93 **VEXILLUM (IRE)**, 7, br g Mujadil (USA)—Common Cause **J. Heaney**
94 **WADSWICK COURT (IRE)**, 8, b g Court Cave (IRE)—Tarasandy (IRE) **The Chosen Few**
95 **WHATS LEFT (IRE)**, 8, b g Darsi (FR)—Dynamic Venture (IRE) **Mrs A. R. Hart**
96 **WHO'S MICKY BROWN (IRE)**, 6, b g Turtle Island (IRE)—Ginger Crunch (IRE) **Qdos Racing**
97 **ZARLIMAN (IRE)**, 6, ch g Zamindar (USA)—Zarlana (IRE) **Mr M. G. Cahill**

THREE-YEAR-OLDS

98 Br f Kheleyf (USA)—Kryena **Neil Mulholland Racing Ltd**

Other Owners: Mr R. K. Adams, Mrs J. A. V. Allen, Mrs L. S. Atwell, Mr G. J. R. Barry, Mr J. M. Basquill, Mr P. Bowden, Mrs S. L. Boyle, Mr P. Boyle, Mrs W. S. Braithwaite, Sir M. F. Broughton, Mr S. W. Broughton, D. J. Bussell, Mr P. A. Cafferty, Mr S. Clegg, Mrs A. C. Crofts, Mr S. J. Dew, Mrs R. L. J. Dickinson, Mr H. G. Doubtfire, J. H. W. Finch, Mrs J. Fleetham, Mr S. Fleetham, J. L. Frampton, Mr P. S. Frampton, Mr R. T. Greenhill, Mr S. Harbour, M. P. Hill, Mrs S. A. Keys, Mrs J. Kirk, Mr D. L. Lacey, Mrs C. Lewis, Mr M. J. Lowry, Sir I. Magee, B. D. Makepeace, Mr J. G. Mogg, Mr A. J. Moore, R. D. Nicholas, Mr P. J. Proudley, Mr K. J. Strangeway, Mr M. A. Stratford, Mr M. Swallow, Mrs D. J. Symes, Mrs L. G. Thomas, Mr D. Tiernan, P. C. Tory, Mr Simon Trant, Mr J. N. Trueman, Mr R. F. Turner, Mrs R. A. Turner, Mr G. J. Villis, R. B. Waley-Cohen, N. E. Webb, Mr P. Webb.

Conditional: Andrias Guerin.

---

434 MR LAWRENCE MULLANEY, Malton
Postal: **Raikes Farm, Great Habton, Malton, North Yorkshire, YO17 6RX**
Contacts: PHONE **(01653) 668595 MOBILE (07899) 902565**
E-MAIL nicolamullaney@yahoo.co.uk

1 **DENISON FLYER**, 9, b g Tobougg (IRE)—Bollin Victoria **L. A. Mullaney**
2 **FIRST SARGEANT**, 6, gr g Dutch Art—Princess Raya **Rothmere Racing Limited**
3 **JACK LUEY**, 9, b g Danbird (AUS)—Icenaslice (IRE) **The Jack Partnership & Mr S. Rimmer**
4 **KARA TARA**, 6, b m Kayf Tara—Matilda Too (IRE) **C. D. Carr**
5 **KOPASSUS (IRE)**, 4, b g Holy Roman Emperor (IRE)—Couverture (USA) **G.B Racing Club**
6 **NOBLE REACH**, 5, b m Phoenix Reach (IRE)—Comtesse Noire (CAN) **G.B Racing Club**
7 **ZIGGY LEE**, 10, b g Lujain (USA)—Mary O'grady (USA) **Rothmere Racing Limited**

THREE-YEAR-OLDS

8 **ARCANE DANCER (IRE)**, b f Arcano (IRE)—La Reine Mambo (USA) **Mr S. J. Rimmer**
9 **DARK INTENTION (IRE)**, b f High Chaparral (IRE)—Ajiaal **Ian Buckley**

TWO-YEAR-OLDS

10 **ALBIZU CAMPOS**, b c 12/2 Mastercraftsman (IRE)—Lolita Lebron (IRE) (Royal Applause) **Ian Buckley**

Other Owners: Mrs Janie Copley, Mr Keith Drysdale, Mr W. Nason, Mrs Tracy Nason, Mr A. P. Reed, Mr S. Rimmer, Mrs Helen Russell.

---

435 MR MICHAEL MULLINEAUX, Tarporley
Postal: **Southley Farm, Alpraham, Tarporley, Cheshire, CW6 9JD**
Contacts: PHONE **(01829) 261440 FAX (01829) 261440 MOBILE (07753) 650263**
E-MAIL southleyaracing@btinternet.com WEBSITE www.southleyfarm.co.uk

1 **ANTON DOLIN (IRE)**, 8, ch g Danehill Dancer (IRE)—Ski For Gold **C. R. Nugent**
2 **BIG FLOE**, 7, b m Alflora (IRE)—Dominie Breeze **Miss L. S. Young**
3 **BRICBRACSMATE**, 8, b g Revoque (IRE)—Blissphilly **P. J. Lawton**

MR MICHAEL MULLINEAUX - Continued

4 **DEADLINE DAY (IRE)**, 5, b g Montjeu (IRE)—Madame Cerito (USA) **M. Mullineaux**
5 **FEISTY GIRL**, 6, ch m Erhaab (USA)—Dolly Duff **The Weaver Group**
6 **GABRIAL THE BOSS (USA)**, 6, ch g Street Boss (USA)—Bacinella (USA) **H. Clewlow**
7 **HE'S A HAWKER (IRE)**, 11, ch g Fourstars Allstar (USA)—Dromin Deel (IRE) **Mr G. Cornes**
8 **HEY UP ASHEY**, 6, b g Black Sam Bellamy (IRE)—Miss Holly **D. Ashbrook**
9 **JACKSONFIRE**, 4, ch g Firebreak—Fitolini **Mr O. D. Knight**
10 **MANTON BOY**, 7, b g Revoque (IRE)—Got On A Lucky One (IRE) **Mr G. A. Probin**
11 **MC DIAMOND (IRE)**, 4, b g Windsor Knot (IRE)—Vinesgrove (IRE) **Mrs D. Plant**
12 **METHAALY (IRE)**, 13, b g Red Ransom (USA)—Santorini (USA) **S. A. Pritchard**
13 **MINTY JONES**, 7, b h Primo Valentino (IRE)—Reveur **P. Clacher**
14 **MOLKO JACK (FR)**, 12, b br g Lavirco (GER)—Line As (FR) **D. Ashbrook**
15 **MY TIME**, 7, b g Mind Games—Tick Tock **Mr M. Kilner**
16 **OGWEN VALLEY GIRL**, 5, b m Indian Danehill (IRE)—Lucky Find (IRE) **Ogwen Valley Racing**
17 **ORPEN BID (IRE)**, 11, b m Orpen (USA)—Glorious Bid (IRE) **Miss L. S. Young**
18 **OUTLAW KATE (IRE)**, 4, b f Bushranger (IRE)—Diosper (USA) **Mr & Mrs S Ashbrooke & J P Daly**
19 **PEADAR MIGUEL**, 9, b g Danroad (AUS)—La Corujera **Bluestone Partnership**
20 **POOR DUKE (IRE)**, 6, b g Bachelor Duke (USA)—Graze On Too (IRE) **The Weaver Group**
21 **POUND NOTE**, 4, b g Top Line Dancer (IRE)—Avondale Girl (IRE) **M. Mullineaux**
22 **ROMANN ANGEL**, 7, b m Sir Harry Lewis (USA)—Roman Gospel **M. Mullineaux**
23 **ROYAL SEA (IRE)**, 7, b g Refuse To Bend (IRE)—Janayen (USA) **Mr Keith Jones & Mrs Pam Sephton**
24 **SMIRFY'S SILVER**, 12, b g Desert Prince (IRE)—Goodwood Blizzard **Mrs D. Plant**
25 **STANLOW**, 6, b g Invincible Spirit (IRE)—Ghazal (USA) **R Lancaster & J Kelly**
26 **TWO TURTLE DOVES (IRE)**, 10, b m Night Shift (USA)—Purple Rain (IRE) **Mr G. Cornes**
27 **VERY FIRST BLADE**, 7, b g Needwood Blade—Dispol Verity **Ogwen Valley Racing**
28 **WYMESWOLD**, 9, b m Alflora (IRE)—Dominie Breeze **The Hon Mrs S. Pakenham**
29 **YOUNGDOCGALLAGHER (IRE)**, 7, b g Zagreb (USA)—Too Back (IRE) **Mr Denis Gallagher**

THREE-YEAR-OLDS

30 **GOLDEN CAPE**, ch f Native Ruler—Lake Sabina **Mr O. D. Knight**

Other Owners: Mrs M. Ashbrooke, Mr S. Ashbrooke, Mr J. P. Daly, Mr E. A. Griffiths, Mr G. C. Horner, Mr K. Jones, Mr G. Jones, Mr J. Kelly, Mr R. Lancaster, Miss M. Mullineaux, Mr P. Murray, Mr N. Murray-Williams, Mrs P. Sephton.

Assistant Trainers: Stuart Ross, Susan Mullineaux

Amateur: Miss M. J. L. Mullineaux.

---

436 MR SEAMUS MULLINS, Amesbury
Postal: Wilsford Stables, Wilsford-Cum-Lake, Amesbury, Salisbury, Wiltshire, SP4 7BL
Contacts: PHONE/FAX (01980) 626344 MOBILE (07702) 559634
E-MAIL info@jwmullins.co.uk WEBSITE www.seamusmullins.co.uk

1 4, Br g Spadoun (FR)—Accordian Lady (IRE) **Mr M. Adams**
2 **ALDER MAIRI (IRE)**, 9, ch m Alderbrook—Amari Queen **F. G. Matthews**
3 **ALOTTARAIN (IRE)**, 6, b m Zerpour (IRE)—Alottalady (IRE) **S Mullins Racing Club**
4 4, B g Dubai Destination (USA)—Anns Present (IRE) **The Friday Night Club**
5 4, Br g Robin des Pres (FR)—Baby Harriet (IRE) **Andrew Cocks & Tara Johnson**
6 4, B f Flemensfirth (USA)—Blossom Trix (USA) **D. J. Erwin**
7 **BONDS CONQUEST**, 7, ch g Monsieur Bond (IRE)—Another Conquest **F. G. Matthews**
8 **BOSS IN BOOTS (IRE)**, 8, gr g King's Theatre (IRE)—Grey Mo (IRE) **Mr M. Adams**
9 4, B g Kalanisi (IRE)—Chanson du Chenet (FR) **Andrew Cocks & Tara Johnson**
10 **CHATEAU ROBIN (IRE)**, 5, b g Robin des Pres (FR)—Bella With A Zee (IRE) **Andrew Cocks & Tara Johnson**
11 **DOUNEEDAHAND**, 5, b m Royal Applause—Our Sheila **Caloona Racing**
12 **FLUGZEUG**, 8, gr g Silver Patriarch (IRE)—Telmar Flyer **New Forest Racing Partnership**
13 **GHETTO BLASTER (IRE)**, 6, ch g Flemensfirth (USA)—Bachello (IRE) **Mr M. Adams**
14 **GIVEAGIRLACHANCE (IRE)**, 7, b m Iffraaj—Farewell To Love (IRE) **The Five Plus One Partnership**
15 **GLENARIFF**, 7, b m Kayf Tara—Lady Racquet (IRE) **The Up The Glens Partnership & D J Erwin**
16 **GLENARM**, 7, b m Kayf Tara—Rumbled **The Up The Glens Partnership**
17 **GRANDMASTER GEORGE (IRE)**, 7, ch g Generous (IRE)—
Merewood Lodge (IRE) **Andrew Cocks & Tara Johnson**
18 **GREENGAGE SUMMER**, 5, b m Sixties Icon—Linda Green **J. W. Mullins**
19 **HEAD SPIN (IRE)**, 8, b g Beneficial—Who Tells Jan **Mr M. Adams**
20 **HILL FORTS GYPSE (IRE)**, 5, b g Bienamado (USA)—Whistling Gypse (IRE) **Mrs J. C. Scorgie**
21 **JARLATH**, 5, b g Norse Dancer (IRE)—Blue Lullaby (IRE) **Phoenix Bloodstock**

MR SEAMUS MULLINS - Continued

22 **KASTANI BEACH (IRE)**, 10, br g Alderbrook—Atomic View (IRE) **S Mullins Racing Club & Philippa Downing**
23 **KENTFORD HEIRESS**, 6, b m Midnight Legend—Kentford Duchess **D. I. Bare**
24 **KENTFORD MYTH**, 6, b m Midnight Legend—Quistaqua **D. I. Bare**
25 **LILLIAN (IRE)**, 5, b br m Milan—Kay Tully **Andrew Cocks & Tara Johnson**
26 **MANHATTAN SPRING**, 5, b g Central Park (IRE)—Risky May **Woodford Valley Racing**
27 **MISS FORTYWINKS**, 7, gr m Act One—Andromache **J. T. Brown**
28 **MISS SASSYPANTS**, 7, ch m Hernando (FR)—Serraval (FR) **J. T. Brown**
29 **MOGESTIC (IRE)**, 7, b g Morozov (USA)—Crosschild (IRE) **Andrew Cocks & Tara Johnson**
30 **NORMANTON (IRE)**, 6, b br g Norwich—Fly Like A Bird **J. W. Mullins**
31 **REST EASY**, 4, b f Rip Van Winkle (IRE)—Early Evening **Mrs G. Elliott**
32 4, B g Court Cave (IRE)—Rock Money (IRE) **J. W. Mullins**
33 **ROMEO AMERICO (IRE)**, 9, b g Lord Americo—Crazy Falcon (IRE) **S Mullins Racing Club**
34 **RUBY SUSIE**, 5, b m Victory Note (USA)—Ruby Too **Dr R. Jowett**
35 **SAMBA SOUND (IRE)**, 5, ch m Flemensfirth (USA)—Jigs'n Reels (IRE) **S Mullins Racing Club**
36 **SIDBURY HILL**, 8, ch g Midnight Legend—Flora Macdonald **Mrs S. J. Rawlins**
37 4, B g Mister Fotis (USA)—Smilingvalentine (IRE) **J. W. Mullins**
38 **SOMCHINE**, 8, b g Volochine (IRE)—Seem of Gold **Mr C. R. Dunning**
39 **SONG LIGHT**, 6, b g Echo of Light—Blue Lullaby (IRE) **Charles Wilson & A A Goodman**
40 **SPORTSREPORT (IRE)**, 8, b g Coroner (IRE)—Goforthetape (IRE) **Mr C. J. Baldwin**
41 **STING JET (IRE)**, 7, b g Ashkalani (IRE)—Pharrambling (IRE) **J. W. Mullins**
42 **TAKE NOTE (IRE)**, 4, b f Azamour (IRE)—Lolla's Spirit (IRE) **J. W. Mullins**
43 **THE INFORMANT**, 10, gr g Central Park (IRE)—Belle Rose (IRE) **Dr & Mrs John Millar**
44 **WESTERBEE (IRE)**, 5, b m Westerner—Pass The Honey (IRE) **Dr R. Jowett**
45 **WESTERN CAPE (IRE)**, 5, b g Westerner—Simons Girl (IRE) **A. A. Goodman**

THREE-YEAR-OLDS

46 **HARRY'S ENDEAVOUR**, b c Paco Boy (IRE)—Crabapple **Caloona Racing**

Other Owners: Mr Paul Attwater, Mr Andrew Cocks, Mr John Collins, Mr P Collins, Miss Philippa Downing, Mr C. R. Dunning, Mr D. J. Erwin, Mr A. A. Goodman, Mr Alan K. Horsman, Miss Tara Johnson, Dr John Millar, Mrs John Millar, Mr Seamus Mullins, Mr John Pyatt, Mr Stan Reid, Mr Roy Stammers, Mr D. D. Sutherland, Miss R. Toppin, Mr Charles Wilson.

Assistant Trainer: Paul Attwater

Jockey (NH): Kevin Jones, Ryan Mahon, Andrew Thornton. **Conditional:** Jeremiah McGrath.
Apprentice: Lamorna Bardwell. **Amateur:** Mr Daniel Sansom.

---

437 **MR WILLIAM P. MULLINS**, Carlow
Postal: **Closutton, Bagenalstown, Co. Carlow, Ireland**
Contacts: **PHONE (00353) 5997 21786 FAX (00353) 5997 22709 MOBILE (00353) 8725 64940**
E-MAIL wpmullins@eircom.net WEBSITE www.wpmullins.com

1 **A TOI PHIL (FR)**, 6, b g Day Flight—Lucidrile (FR) **Gigginstown House Stud**
2 **ABBYSSIAL (IRE)**, 6, ch g Beneficial—Mega d'estruval (FR) **Mrs Violet O'Leary**
3 **ADMIRAL CHIEF (IRE)**, 5, br g Presenting—Supreme Serenade (IRE) **Gigginstown House Stud**
4 **AINSI VA LA VIE (FR)**, 6, b g wn Lavirco (GER)—Joie de La Vie (FR) **Supreme Horse Racing Club**
5 **AIRLIE BEACH (IRE)**, 6, b m Shantou (USA)—Screaming Witness (USA) **Supreme Horse Racing Club**
6 **AKLAN (IRE)**, 7, gr h Dalakhani (IRE)—Akdara (IRE) **Coach Partnership**
7 **ALELCHI INOIS (FR)**, 8, b g Night Tango (GER)—Witness Gama (FR) **Mrs M. McMahon**
8 **ALLBLAK DES PLACES (FR)**, 4, b br g Full of Gold (FR)—Amiraute (FR) **George Creighton**
9 **AMERICAN TOM (FR)**, 5, b g American Post—Kirkla (FR) **Mrs S. Ricci**
10 **ANALIFET (FR)**, 6, b m Califet (FR)—Viana (FR) **Gigginstown House Stud**
11 **ANNIE O (IRE)**, 7, b m Oscar (IRE)—Rocking Annie (IRE) **B. Fitzpatrick**
12 **ANNIE POWER (IRE)**, 8, ch m Shirocco (GER)—Anno Luce **Mrs S. Ricci**
13 **APPLE'S JADE (FR)**, 4, b f Saddler Maker (IRE)—Apple's For Ever (FR) **Gigginstown House Stud**
14 **ARBOR RUN (IRE)**, 6, ch g Flemensfirth (USA)—Maghanns Pride (IRE) **F. N. Doyle Partnership**
15 **ARBRE DE VIE (FR)**, 6, b g Antarctique (IRE)—Nouvelle Recrue (FR) **Mrs S. Ricci**
16 **ARCTIC FIRE (GER)**, 7, b g Soldier Hollow—Adelma (GER) **Wicklow Bloodstock Limited**
17 **ARE YA RIGHT CHIEF (IRE)**, 11, b g Flemensfirth (USA)—River Clyde (IRE) **Mrs M. McMahon**
18 **ARE YOU BIDDING (IRE)**, 5, ch g Presenting—What A Breeze (IRE) **Mrs J. Donnelly**
19 **ARGENTINO (FR)**, 6, br g Sinndar (IRE)—Syssiss (FR) **Gigginstown House Stud**
20 **ARKWRISHT (FR)**, 6, b g Lavirco (GER)—Latitude (FR) **Gigginstown House Stud**
21 **AS DE FERBET (FR)**, 6, gr g Dom Alco (FR)—Intrigue Deferbet (FR) **Gigginstown House Stud**

MR WILLIAM P. MULLINS - Continued

22 **ASTHURIA (FR)**, 5, b m Sagacity (FR)—Baturia (FR) **George Creighton**
23 **AU QUART DE TOUR (FR)**, 6, b g Robin des Champs (FR)—Qualite Controlee (FR) **Mrs S. Ricci**
24 **AUGUSTA KATE**, 5, b m Yeats (IRE)—Feathard Lady (IRE) **The Masters Syndicate**
25 **AUGUSTIN (FR)**, 6, gr g Martaline—Lili Bleue (FR) **Mrs M. McMahon**
26 **AURKO (FR)**, 6, b br g Balko (FR)—L'auriebatoise (FR) **Mrs S. Ricci**
27 **AVANT TOUT (FR)**, 6, ch g Agent Bleu (FR)—Quiwfty (FR) **Supreme Horse Racing Club**
28 **AVENIR D'UNE VIE (FR)**, 6, gr g Lavirco (GER)—Par Bonheur (FR) **Gigginstown House Stud**
29 **AVICHI (IRE)**, 5, b m Yeats (IRE)—Scandisk (IRE) **Mrs E. M. Motherway**
30 **BABBLING STREAM**, 5, b g Authorized (IRE)—Elasouna (IRE) **John I. O'Byrne**
31 **BABYLONE DES MOTTE (FR)**, 5, b br m Blue Bresil (FR)—Nellyssa Bleu (FR) **Mrs S. Ricci**
32 **BACARDYS (FR)**, 5, b br g Coastal Path—Oasice (FR) **Shanakiel Racing Syndicate**
33 **BACHASSON (FR)**, 5, gr g Voix du Nord (FR)—Belledonne (FR) **Edward O'Connell**
34 **BAKOUGAN (FR)**, 5, b g Antarctique (IRE)—Perle Irlandaise (FR) **Supreme Horse Racing Club**
35 **BALKO DES FLOS (FR)**, 5, ch g Balko (FR)—Royale Marie (FR) **Gigginstown House Stud**
36 **BALLYCASEY (IRE)**, 9, gr g Presenting—Pink Mist (IRE) **Mrs S. Ricci**
37 **BALNASLOW (IRE)**, 9, b g Presenting—Noble Choice **Gigginstown House Stud**
38 **BAMAKO MORIVIERE (FR)**, 5, b g Califet (FR)—Halladine (FR) **Mrs S. Ricci**
39 **BARRA (FR)**, 5, b m Vendangeur (IRE)—Oasaka (FR) **Gigginstown House Stud**
40 **BATTLEFORD**, 5, b g Midnight Legend—Well Maid **Andrea Wylie**
41 **BEAU MOME (FR)**, 5, b g Racinger (FR)—Lamoune (FR) **Mrs S. Ricci**
42 **BEL SAS (FR)**, 5, b g Balko (FR)—Pashka (FR) **Gigginstown House Stud**
43 **BELLO CONTI (FR)**, 5, b g Coastal Path—Posterite (FR) **Gigginstown House Stud**
44 **BELLOW MOME (FR)**, 5, b g Honolulu (IRE)—Oll Mighty Fellow (FR) **Mrs Audrey Turley**
45 **BELLSHILL (IRE)**, 6, b g King's Theatre (IRE)—Fairy Native (IRE) **Andrea & Graham Wylie**
46 **BERRY DES AULMES (FR)**, 5, b g Smadoun (FR)—Opaline des Aulmes (FR) **Gigginstown House Stud**
47 **BLACK HERCULES (IRE)**, 7, b g Heron Island (IRE)—Annalecky (IRE) **Andrea Wylie**
48 **BLACK KEY**, 4, b g Authorized (IRE)—Pentatonic **Gigginstown House Stud**
49 **BLAZER (FR)**, 5, ch g Network (GER)—Juppelongue (FR) **J. P. McManus**
50 **BLEU BERRY (FR)**, 5, b g Special Kaldoun (IRE)—Somosierra (FR) **Mrs M. McMahon**
51 **BLEU ET ROUGE (FR)**, 5, gr g Charming Groom (FR)—Lady du Renom (FR) **J. P. McManus**
52 **BLICK DES OBEAUX (FR)**, 5, gr g Kapgarde (FR)—Quick des Obeaux (FR) **Philip J. Reynolds**
53 **BLOOD COTIL (FR)**, 7, b g Enrique—Move Along (FR) **Mrs S. Ricci**
54 **BLOW BY BLOW (IRE)**, 5, ch g Robin des Champs (FR)—Shean Rose (IRE) **Gigginstown House Stud**
55 **BON PAPA (FR)**, 5, br g Network (GER)—Gibelotte (FR) **J. P. McManus**
56 **BONBON AU MIEL (FR)**, 5, b g Khalkevi (IRE)—Friandise II (FR) **Andrea & Graham Wylie**
57 **BORBOLETA (IRE)**, 6, b m Germany (USA)—Back And Fore (IRE) **J. A. Coleman**
58 **BORDINI (FR)**, 6, b g Martaline—Didinas (FR) **Mrs S. Ricci**
59 **BOSMAN RULE (IRE)**, 8, ch g Gamut (IRE)—Fairy Blaze (IRE) **Philip J. Reynolds**
60 **BOSTON BOB (IRE)**, 11, b g Bob Back (USA)—Bavaway **Andrea & Graham Wylie**
61 **BRAHMA BULL (IRE)**, 5, ch g Presenting—Oligarch Society (IRE) **Mrs S. Ricci**
62 **BRAVISSIMO (FR)**, 5, gr g Al Namix (FR)—Mimi Valley (FR) **Mrs S. Ricci**
63 **BRIAR HILL (IRE)**, 8, b g Shantou (USA)—Backaway (IRE) **Andrea & Graham Wylie**
64 **BUISENESS SIVOLA (FR)**, 5, b g Archange d'or (IRE)—Louve Orientale **Mr Simon Munir & Mr Isaac Souede**
65 **BUNK OFF EARLY (IRE)**, 4, ro g Zebedee—Ctesiphon (USA) **Supreme Horse Racing Club**
66 **BURGAS (FR)**, 5, b br g Protektor (GER)—Tyrolienne Bleue (FR) **Gigginstown House Stud**
67 **BUZZ OFF BARROSO (IRE)**, 4, b f Big Bad Bob (IRE)—Ulanova (IRE) **Ronan P. Fitzpatrick**
68 **CADMIUM (FR)**, 4, b g Early March—Mirquille (FR) **Supreme Horse Racing Club**
69 **CAP D'AUBOIS (FR)**, 4, b g Snow Cap (FR)—Caline Grace (FR) **Mrs S. Ricci**
70 **CASTELLO SFORZA (IRE)**, 5, b g Milan—Young Elodie (FR) **J. P. McManus**
71 **CHAMPAGNE FEVER (IRE)**, 9, gr g Stowaway—Forever Bubbles (FR) **Mrs S. Ricci**
72 **CHILDRENS LIST (IRE)**, 6, b g Presenting—Snipe Hunt (IRE) **Mrs S. Ricci**
73 **CLASSIC PLACE (IRE)**, 6, b g Beneficial—Your Place Or Mine (IRE) **Gigginstown House Stud**
74 **CLINTON HILL (IRE)**, 5, b g Flemensfirth (USA)—Smooching (IRE) **Andrea Wylie**
75 **CLONDAW COURT (IRE)**, 9, br g Court Cave (IRE)—Secret Can't Say (IRE) **Mrs S. Ricci**
76 **CLONDAW WARRIOR (IRE)**, 9, br g Overbury (IRE)—Thespian (IRE) **Act D Wagg Syndicate**
77 **COQUIN MANS (FR)**, 4, b br g Fragrant Mix (IRE)—Quississia Mans (FR) **George Creighton**
78 **COQUINE D'AUNOU (FR)**, 4, gr f Martaline—Jimagine II (FR) **Gigginstown House Stud**
79 **COTE TETE (FR)**, 4, b g Coastal Path—Liste En Tete (FR) **Mrs J. M. Mullins**
80 **CRACK MOME (FR)**, 4, ch g Spanish Moon (USA)—Peche Mome (FR) **Andrea Wylie**
81 **DEVILS BRIDE (IRE)**, 8, b g Helissio (FR)—Rigorous **Gigginstown House Stud**
82 **DIAKALI (FR)**, 7, gr g Sinndar (IRE)—Diasilixa (FR) **Wicklow Bloodstock Limited**
83 **DICOSIMO (FR)**, 5, b g Laveron—Coralisse Royale (FR) **Mrs S. Ricci**
84 **DIGEANTA (IRE)**, 9, b g Helissio (FR)—
　　　　　　　　　　　　　　　　　Scolboa Gold (IRE) **Dr I. M. P. Moran, Colland Sand & Gravel Syndicate**
85 **DJAKADAM (FR)**, 7, b g Saint des Saints (FR)—Rainbow Crest (FR) **Mrs S. Ricci**

MR WILLIAM P. MULLINS - Continued

86 **DON POLI (IRE)**, 7, b g Poliglote—Dalamine (FR) **Gigginstown House Stud**
87 **DOUVAN (FR)**, 6, b g Walk In The Park (IRE)—Star Face (FR) **Mrs S. Ricci**
88 **DREAMBABY (IRE)**, 5, b m Yeats (IRE)—Monumental Gesture **The Hibo Syndicate**
89 **FAUGHEEN (IRE)**, 8, b g Germany (USA)—Miss Pickering (IRE) **Mrs S. Ricci**
90 **FELIX YONGER (IRE)**, 10, b g Oscar (IRE)—Marble Sound (IRE) **Andrea & Graham Wylie**
91 **FIRE IN SOUL (IRE)**, 5, br g Robin des Champs (FR)—Cherry Black (IRE) **Gigginstown House Stud**
92 **FOOTPAD (FR)**, 4, b g Creachadoir (IRE)—Willamina (IRE) **Mr Simon Munir**
93 **FUGI MOUNTAIN (IRE)**, 6, b g Diamond Green (FR)—Sixhills (FR) **Mrs J. M. Mullins**
94 **FULHAM ROAD (IRE)**, 6, b g Shantou (USA)—Bobomy (IRE) **Mrs S. Ricci**
95 **GANGSTER (FR)**, 6, ch g Green Tune (USA)—Dahlia's Krissy (USA) **Gigginstown House Stud**
96 **GITANE DU BERLAIS (FR)**, 6, b m Balko (FR)—Boheme du Berlais (FR) **Mr Simon Munir**
97 **GOOD THYNE TARA**, 6, b br m Kayf Tara—Good Thyne Mary (IRE) **N. G. King**
98 **GREAT FIELD (FR)**, 5, b g Great Pretender (IRE)—Eaton Lass (IRE) **John P. McManus**
99 **HAYMOUNT (IRE)**, 7, ch g Presenting—Ali's Dipper (IRE) **Mrs C. M. Hurley**
100 **HENRY HOWARD (IRE)**, 8, b g Flemensfirth (USA)—Henrietta Howard (IRE) **Mrs M. McMahon**
101 **HERMINATOR (FR)**, 6, br g Night Tango (GER)—Roannaise (FR) **Coldunell Limited**
102 **HERMINIO (FR)**, 4, b c New Approach (IRE)—Histoire Sainte (IRE) **Wicklow Bloodstock (Ireland) Ltd**
103 **HOT ON HER HEELS (IRE)**, 6, b m Stowaway—Orinocco Blue (IRE) **Supreme Horse Racing Club**
104 **INVITATION ONLY (IRE)**, 5, b g Flemensfirth (USA)—Norabelle (IRE) **Andrea Wylie**
105 **ISLEOFHOPENDREAMS**, 9, b g Flemensfirth (USA)—Cool Island (IRE) **Sean Sweeney**
106 **IVAN GROZNY (FR)**, 6, b g Turtle Bowl (IRE)—Behnesa (IRE) **Andrea & Graham Wylie**
107 **JARRY D'HONNEUR (FR)**, 7, b br g Baroud d'honneur (FR)—True Lovely (FR) **J. P. McManus**
108 **KALKIR (FR)**, 5, b g Montmartre (FR)—Kakira (FR) **Mrs S. Ricci**
109 **KARALEE (FR)**, 5, gr m Martaline—Change Partner (FR) **Mrs S. Ricci**
110 **KATE APPLEBY SHOES (IRE)**, 7, b m Flemensfirth (USA)—Gotta Goa (IRE) **Leo McArdle**
111 **KILLULTAGH VIC (IRE)**, 7, b g Old Vic—Killultagh Dawn (IRE) **Mrs Rose Boyd**
112 **KOLUMBUS (IRE)**, 5, b g Robin des Champs (FR)—Saabga (USA) **Sean Sweeney**
113 **LET'S DANCE (FR)**, 4, b f Poliglote—Baraka du Berlais (FR) **Mrs S. Ricci**
114 **LEVMOSS LADY (IRE)**, 7, b m Scorpion (IRE)—Square Up (IRE) **Ms Eleanor Manning**
115 **LIMINI (FR)**, 5, ch m Peintre Celebre (USA)—Her Grace (FR) **Mrs S. Ricci**
116 **LISTEN DEAR (IRE)**, 6, b m Robin des Champs (FR)—Crescendor (FR) **Supreme Horse Racing Club**
117 **LIVELOVELAUGH (IRE)**, 6, b g Beneficial—Another Evening (IRE) **Mrs S. Ricci**
118 **LONG DOG**, 6, b g Notnowcato—Latanazul **Mrs S. Ricci**
119 **LUCKY PASS (FR)**, 5, ch g Ultimately Lucky (IRE)—Fuela Pass (FR) **Gigginstown House Stud**
120 **LYRICAL THEATRE (IRE)**, 7, b m King's Theatre (IRE)—Shuil Dorcha (IRE) **The Hibo Syndicate**
121 **MARASONNIEN (FR)**, 10, b g Mansonnien (FR)—Maracay (FR) **Mrs S. Ricci**
122 **MASTER OF VERSE (IRE)**, 7, b g Milan—Bacchonthebottle (IRE) **Gigginstown House Stud**
123 **MAX DYNAMITE (FR)**, 6, b h Great Journey (JPN)—Mascara (GER) **Mrs S. Ricci**
124 **MCKINLEY**, 6, b g Kheleyf (USA)—Priera Menta (FR) **Gigginstown House Stud**
125 **MEASUREOFMYDREAMS (IRE)**, 8, b g Shantou (USA)—Le Bavellen **Gigginstown House Stud**
126 **MELON**, 4, ch g Medicean—Night Teeny **Mrs J. Donnelly**
127 **MERRY NIGHT (IRE)**, 6, b g Presenting—Our Prima Donna (IRE) **Mrs Violet O'Leary**
128 **MIGUEL ANGEL (FR)**, 6, b g Enrique—Yolaine (FR) **Mrs J. M. Mullins**
129 **MILSEAN (IRE)**, 7, b g Milan—Boro Supreme (IRE) **Gigginstown House Stud**
130 **MIN (FR)**, 5, b g Walk In The Park (IRE)—Phemyka (FR) **Mrs S. Ricci**
131 **MISS ME NOW (IRE)**, 6, b m Presenting—Miss Toulon (IRE) **Blue Blood Racing Club**
132 **MONBEG ROSE (IRE)**, 6, gr m Beneficial—Roses And Wine (IRE) **Gigginstown House Stud**
133 **MORNING RUN (IRE)**, 7, b m King's Theatre (IRE)—Portryan Native (IRE) **Mr H. Murphy**
134 **MOYLE PARK (IRE)**, 8, ch g Flemensfirth (USA)—Lovely Present (IRE) **Mrs S. Ricci**
135 **MOZOLTOV**, 10, b g Kayf Tara—Fairmead Princess **Gigginstown House Stud**
136 **MUTHAZA (FR)**, 4, ch f Muhtathir—John Quatz (FR) **Mrs J. Donnelly**
137 **MYSKA (IRE)**, 6, br m Presenting—Zenaide (IRE) **Supreme Horse Racing Club**
138 **NAMBOUR (GER)**, 6, b g Sholokhov (IRE)—Nanouska (GER) **Gigginstown House Stud**
139 **NET D'ECOSSE (FR)**, 6, ch g Network (GER)—Ecossette (FR) **Gigginstown House Stud**
140 **NEW KID IN TOWN (IRE)**, 7, b g Gamut (IRE)—Echo Queen (IRE) **Simon Wilson**
141 **NICHOLS CANYON (IRE)**, 6, b g Authorized (IRE)—Zam Zoom (IRE) **Andrea & Graham Wylie**
142 **NOBLE INN (FR)**, 6, b g Sinndar (IRE)—Nataliana **M. J. Mulvaney**
143 **ON HIS OWN (IRE)**, 12, b g Presenting—Shuil Na Mhuire (IRE) **Andrea & Graham Wylie**
144 **OPEN EAGLE (IRE)**, 7, b g Montjeu (IRE)—Princesse de Viane (FR) **Supreme Horse Racing Club**
145 **ORATORIANO (FR)**, 5, b g East of Heaven (IRE)—Oratoriane (FR) **Paul Connell**
146 **OUTLANDER (IRE)**, 8, b g Stowaway—Western Whisper (IRE) **Gigginstown House Stud**
147 **PENHILL**, 5, b g Mount Nelson—Serrenia (IRE) **Anthony Bloom**
148 **PETIT MOUCHOIR (FR)**, 5, gr g Al Namix (FR)—Arnette (FR) **Gigginstown House Stud**
149 **PETITE PARISIENNE**, 5, b m Montmartre (FR)—Ejina (FR) **Gigginstown House Stud**
150 **PIQUE SOUS (FR)**, 9, gr g Martaline—Six Fois Sept (FR) **Not Just Any Racing Club**

MR WILLIAM P. MULLINS - Continued

151 **PLEASANT COMPANY (IRE)**, 8, b g Presenting—Katie Flame (IRE) **Malcolm C. Denmark**
152 **POLY ROCK (FR)**, 5, b g Policy Maker (IRE)—Gastinaise (FR) **Supreme House Racing Club**
153 **POND PARK (IRE)**, 5, b g Milan—Lisselton Thatch (IRE) **Mrs M. McMahon**
154 **PONT ALEXANDRE (GER)**, 8, b g Dai Jin—Panzella (FR) **Mrs S. Ricci**
155 **PONT DE ALMA (FR)**, 5, b m Soldier of Fortune (IRE)—Panzella (FR) **Philip J. Reynolds**
156 **POTTERS POINT (IRE)**, 6, b g Robin des Champs (FR)—Tango Lady (IRE) **Gigginstown House Stud**
157 **PRINCE D'AUBRELLE (FR)**, 6, ch g Malinas (GER)—La Star (FR) **Allan McLuckie**
158 **PYLONTHEPRESSURE (IRE)**, 6, b g Darsi (FR)—Minnie O'grady (IRE) **Mrs S. Ricci**
159 **RATHVINDEN (IRE)**, 8, b g Heron Island (IRE)—Peggy Cullen (IRE) **R. A. Bartlett**
160 **RENNETI (FR)**, 7, b g Irish Wells (FR)—Caprice Meill (FR) **Mrs S. Ricci**
161 **RETOUR EN FRANCE (IRE)**, 6, b m Robin des Champs (FR)—Rayane (FR) **Mrs S. Ricci**
162 **RIA D'ETEL (FR)**, 4, b f Martaline—Angesse (FR) **Simon Munir**
163 **RIO TREASURE (IRE)**, 6, b m Captain Rio—Killiney Treasure (IRE) **Mrs M. McMahon**
164 **RIVER RUN (FR)**, 6, gr g Stormy River (FR)—Mixture **Wicklow Bloodstock (Ireland) Ltd**
165 **ROI DES FRANCS (FR)**, 7, b g Poliglote—Grande Souveraine (FR) **Gigginstown House Stud**
166 **ROLLY BABY (FR)**, 11, b g Funny Baby (FR)—Vancia (FR) **Teahon Consulting**
167 **ROUMANIAN (FR)**, 10, b g Kapgarde (FR)—La Grive (FR) **P. W. Mullins**
168 **ROYAL CAVIAR (IRE)**, 8, b g Vinnie Roe (IRE)—Blackwater Babe (IRE) **Mrs S. Ricci**
169 **RUPERT LAMB**, 10, gr g Central Park (IRE)—Charlotte Lamb **Mrs M. McMahon**
170 **SAMBREMONT (FR)**, 6, b g Saint des Saints (FR)—Rainbow Crest (FR) **Shanakiel Racing Syndicate**
171 **SATURNAS (FR)**, 5, b g Davidoff (GER)—Sayuri (GER) **Wicklow Bloodstock (Ireland) Ltd**
172 **SCREAMING ROSE (IRE)**, 5, b m Darsi (FR)—Screaming Witness (IRE) **N. G. King**
173 **SECURITY BREACH (IRE)**, 7, b g Red Clubs (IRE)—Lear's Crown (USA) **Gigginstown House Stud**
174 **SEMPRE MEDICI (FR)**, 6, b h Medicean—Sambala (FR) **Mrs S. Ricci**
175 **SHANESHILL (IRE)**, 7, b g King's Theatre (IRE)—Darabaka (IRE) **Andrea & Graham Wylie**
176 **SHARPS CHOICE**, 5, ch g Montmartre (FR)—Behra (FR) **Supreme Horse Racing Club**
177 **SHUIL A STEFFI (IRE)**, 6, b m Beneficial—Top Ar Aghaidh (IRE) **Kevin E. Doyle**
178 **SIC ET NON (FR)**, 6, b g Forestier (FR)—Limaranta (FR) **Gigginstown House Stud**
179 **SIMENON (IRE)**, 9, b g Marju (IRE)—Epistoliere (IRE) **Wicklow Bloodstock Ltd**
180 **SIR DES CHAMPS (FR)**, 10, b br g Robin des Champs (FR)—Liste En Tete (FR) **Gigginstown House Stud**
181 **SISTER SARAGH (IRE)**, 5, b m Astarabad (USA)—Didinas (FR) **Mrs Margaret M. Dunne**
182 **SNAG LIST (IRE)**, 5, b m Shantou (USA)—Back Log (IRE) **J. P. M. O'Connor**
183 **SO YOUNG (FR)**, 10, b g Lavirco (GER)—Honey (FR) **Mrs M. McMahon**
184 **SOME NECK (FR)**, 5, gr g Yeats (IRE)—Maternelle (FR) **Mrs S. Ricci**
185 **STONE HARD (IRE)**, 6, b g Robin des Champs (FR)—Amber Light (IRE) **Gigginstown House Stud**
186 **SURE REEF (FR)**, 7, ch g Choisir (AUS)—Cutting Reef (IRE) **Andrea & Graham Wylie**
187 **SUTTON MANOR (IRE)**, 5, b g Gold Well—Nighty Bless (IRE) **Gigginstown House Stud**
188 **TARABIYN (IRE)**, 5, gr g Sinndar (IRE)—Timabiyra (IRE) **Supreme Horse Racing Club**
189 **TARARE (FR)**, 7, b g Astarabad (USA)—Targerine (FR) **Mrs S. Ricci**
190 **TELL US MORE (IRE)**, 7, b g Scorpion (IRE)—Zara's Victory (IRE) **Gigginstown House Stud**
191 **TENNIS CAP (FR)**, 9, b g Snow Cap (FR)—Jijie (FR) **Mrs Violet O'Leary**
192 **THE PAPARAZZI KID (IRE)**, 9, b g Milan—Banbury Cross (IRE) **Byerley Thoroughbred Racing**
193 **THOMAS HOBSON**, 6, b g Halling (USA)—La Spezia (IRE) **Mrs S. Ricci**
194 **THOUSAND STARS (FR)**, 12, gr g Grey Risk (FR)—Livaniana (FR) **Hammer & Trowel Syndicate**
195 **TIN SOLDIER (FR)**, 5, b g Soldier of Fortune (IRE)—Everlast (FR) **Philip J. Reynolds**
196 **TORRENT DES MOTTES (FR)**, 5, gr g Montmartre (FR)—Wavy (FR) **Supreme Horse Racing Club**
197 **TOTALLY DOMINANT (USA)**, 7, b g War Chant (USA)—Miss Kilroy (USA) **Mrs S. Ricci**
198 **TOWNSHEND (GER)**, 5, b g Lord of England (GER)—Trikolore (GER) **Mrs S. Ricci**
199 **TURBAN (FR)**, 9, b g Dom Alco (FR)—Indianabelle (FR) **Edward O'Connell**
200 **TURCAGUA (FR)**, 6, gr g Turgeon (USA)—Acancagua (FR) **Mrs S. Ricci**
201 **TWINLIGHT (FR)**, 9, b g Muhtathir—Fairlight (GER) **M L Bloodstock Limited**
202 **UN DE SCEAUX (FR)**, 8, b g Denham Red (FR)—Hotesse de Sceaux (FR) **E. O'Connell**
203 **UNCLE JUNIOR (IRE)**, 15, b g Saddlers' Hall (IRE)—Caslain Nua **Mrs M. McMahon**
204 **UNION DUES (FR)**, 8, b br g Malinas (GER)—Royale Dorothy (FR) **Allan McLuckie**
205 **UP FOR REVIEW (IRE)**, 7, br g Presenting—Coolsilver (IRE) **Andrea & Graham Wylie**
206 **UPAZO (FR)**, 8, b g Enrique—Honey (FR) **Philip J. Reynolds**
207 **URADEL (GER)**, 5, b g Kallisto (GER)—Unavita (GER) **Mrs M. McMahon**
208 **URANNA (FR)**, 8, gr m Panoramic—Irresistible Anna (FR) **Supreme Horse Racing Club**
209 **URANO (FR)**, 8, b g Enrique—Neiland (FR) **Mrs M. Mahon**
210 **VALERIAN BRIDGE (IRE)**, 7, b g Heron Island (IRE)—Screaming Witness (IRE) **Gigginstown House Stud**
211 **VALSEUR LIDO (FR)**, 7, b g Anzillero (GER)—Libido Rock (FR) **Gigginstown House Stud**
212 **VALYSSA MONTERG (FR)**, 7, b br m Network (GER)—Mellyssa (FR) **Mrs S. Ricci**
213 **VAUTOUR (FR)**, 7, b g Robin des Champs (FR)—Gazelle de Mai (FR) **Mrs S. Ricci**
214 **VEDETTARIAT (FR)**, 7, bl g Lavirco (GER)—Platine (FR) **Mrs S. Ricci**
215 **VERAWAL (IRE)**, 5, br g Sinndar (IRE)—Virana (IRE) **Supreme Horse Racing Club**

MR WILLIAM P. MULLINS - Continued

216 **VERY MUCH SO (IRE)**, 6, b g Scorpion (IRE)—Lady Apprentice (IRE) **Supreme Horse Racing Club**
217 **VIGOVILLE (FR)**, 7, b br g Lavirco (GER)—Kadalville (FR) **Mrs S. Ricci**
218 **VILLAGE MYSTIC (FR)**, 5, b br g Saint des Saints (FR)—Mistica (FR) **Gigginstown House Stud**
219 **VINALHAVEN (FR)**, 7, br g Lavirco (GER)—Iconea (FR) **Gigginstown House Stud**
220 **VITALIZED (IRE)**, 4, b f Vocalised (USA)—Astralai (IRE) **Cathal McGuckin**
221 **VROUM VROUM MAG (FR)**, 7, b m Voix du Nord (FR)—Naiade Mag (FR) **Mrs S. Ricci**
222 **WESTERNER LADY (IRE)**, 6, b m Westerner—Cloghoge Lady (IRE) **Anthony P. Butler**
223 **WHERE'S ME (IRE)**, 5, ch m Captain Rio—Josephine Cullen (IRE) **Mrs M. McMahon**
224 **WHITEOUT (GER)**, 5, b m Samum (GER)—Wassiliki (IRE) **D. Lawlor**
225 **WICKLOW BRAVE**, 7, b g Beat Hollow—Moraine **Wicklow Bloodstock Limited**
226 **WISHMOOR (IRE)**, 6, b g Winged Love—Presentingatdawn (IRE) **Gigginstown House Stud**
227 **WOOD BREIZH (FR)**, 6, gr g Stormy River (FR)—Polynevees (FR) **Supreme Horse Racing Club**
228 **YORKHILL (IRE)**, 6, ch g Presenting—Lightning Breeze (IRE) **Andrea Wylie**
229 **YOUNG TURK (FR)**, 5, b g Poliglote—Jasminette Doree (FR) **Gigginstown House Stud**

THREE-YEAR-OLDS

230 **LAWS OF SPIN (IRE)**, b c Lawman (FR)—Spinning Well (IRE) **B. Hourihane**
231 **SUPER BOWL (IRE)**, b c Turtle Bowl (IRE)—Ekadzati (FR) **Supreme Horse Racing Club**

438

MRS ANABEL K. MURPHY, Stratford-on-Avon
Postal: **Warren Chase, Billesley Road, Wilmcote, Stratford-Upon-Avon, Warwickshire, CV37 9XG**
Contacts: **OFFICE (01789) 205087 HOME (01789) 298346 FAX (01789) 263260
MOBILE (07774) 117777**
E-MAIL anabelkmurphyracing@btinternet.com WEBSITE www.anabelkmurphy.co.uk

1 **BOOTED EAGLE (IRE)**, 6, b g Oscar (IRE)—Warmley's Gem (IRE) **Mrs C. Skan**
2 **BUSH WARRIOR (IRE)**, 5, b g Bushranger (IRE)—Lady Corduff (IRE) **Ridgeway Racing Club**
3 **DORMOUSE**, 11, b g Medicean—Black Fighter (USA) **H. A. Murphy**
4 **ELAND ALLY**, 8, b g Striking Ambition—Dream Rose (IRE) **Mrs A. L. M. Murphy**
5 **GENERALYSE**, 7, b g Cadeaux Genereux—Dance To The Blues (IRE) **Aiden Murphy & All The Kings Horses**
6 **INDIAN SCOUT**, 8, b g Indesatchel (IRE)—Manderina **Ridgeway Racing Club & Partner**
7 **KAKAPUKA**, 9, br g Shinko Forest (IRE)—No Rehearsal (FR) **Aiden Murphy & All The Kings Horses**
8 **KING'S ROAD**, 11, ch g King's Best (USA)—Saphire **Mrs A. L. M. Murphy**
9 **KRAZY PAVING**, 4, b g Kyllachy—Critical Path (IRE) **Mr Aiden Murphy & The Hon. Mrs Foster**
10 **RIGOLLETO (IRE)**, 8, b g Ad Valorem (USA)—Jallaissine (IRE) **All The Kings Horses**
11 **TODD**, 6, b g Gentlewave (IRE)—Voice **Touchwood Racing**

Other Owners: Hon S. Foster.

Assistant Trainer: Aiden Murphy

439

MR MIKE MURPHY, Westoning
Postal: **Broadlands, Manor Park Stud, Westoning, Bedfordshire, MK45 5LA**
Contacts: **PHONE (01525) 717305 FAX (01525) 717305 MOBILE (07770) 496103**
E-MAIL mmurphy@globalnet.co.uk WEBSITE www.mikemurphyracing.co.uk

1 **BURN THE BOATS (IRE)**, 7, br g Big Bad Bob (IRE)—Forever Phoenix **Mr D. T. Spratt**
2 **DANDY (GER)**, 7, b g Nayef (USA)—Diacada (GER) **Mr R. E. Tillett**
3 **DISCUSSIONTOFOLLOW (IRE)**, 6, b g Elusive City (USA)—Tranquil Sky **Mr D. T. Spratt**
4 **GRAND PROPOSAL**, 4, gr g Exceed And Excel (AUS)—Si Belle (IRE) **Mr M. Fitzgerald**
5 **KAKATOSI**, 9, br g Pastoral Pursuits—Ladywell Blaise (IRE) **Mr R. E. Tillett**
6 **MUSICAL COMEDY**, 5, b g Royal Applause—Spinning Top
7 **POOL HOUSE**, 5, b g Sakhee's Secret—Gitane (FR) **Ms A. D. Tibbett**
8 **RIO RONALDO (IRE)**, 4, b g Footstepsinthesand—Flanders (USA) **The Castaways**
9 **SCARLET BLAKENEY (IRE)**, 4, ch f Sir Percy—Birdsong (IRE)
10 **STREET ART (IRE)**, 4, ch g Excellent Art—Via Aurelia (IRE) **Ms A. D. Tibbett**
11 **TITAN GODDESS**, 4, b f Equiano (FR)—Phoebe Woodstock (IRE) **Phoebe's Friends**
12 **WELSH GEM**, 4, b f Dylan Thomas (IRE)—Gemini Joan **Mr R. E. Tillett**
13 **ZAMPERINI (IRE)**, 4, ch g Fast Company (IRE)—Lucky Date (IRE) **Mr R. E. Tillett**

MR MIKE MURPHY - Continued

THREE-YEAR-OLDS

14 **ASHFORD ISLAND**, b g Munnings (USA)—Falling Angel **Frank Deely & John McGarry**
15 **LILY ASH (IRE)**, b f Lilbourne Lad (IRE)—Ashdali (IRE) **Ms A. D. Tibbett**
16 **LOTTE LENYA (FR)**, ch f Peintre Celebre (USA)—Tricoteuse **The Kathryn Stud Limited**
17 **MAMOO**, ch c Sir Percy—Meredith **Victoria Taylor & Family**
18 **NUTZMA**, b f Multiplex—Nut (IRE) **Mr D. T. Spratt**
19 **ORANGECHERIE (IRE)**, b f Duke of Marmalade (IRE)—Ochre (IRE) **Llewelyn Runeckles Gautier**
20 **PREMIER CURRENCY (IRE)**, b c Elusive Pimpernel (USA)—Zeena **Mr W. P. Drew**
21 B f Bahamian Bounty—Regal Asset (USA)
22 B f Roderic O'Connor (IRE)—Tartufo Dolce (IRE)
23 **THEE AND ME (IRE)**, b c Canford Cliffs (IRE)—Lake Ladoga **Ms Z. Hatcher**
24 Br c Big Bad Bob (IRE)—Trick (IRE)
25 **WHISPERED KISS**, b f Medicean—Desert Kiss **D.Ellison - B.Olkowicz - P.Speller**

TWO-YEAR-OLDS

26 **DESERT FOX**, b c 8/5 Foxwedge (AUS)—
Snow Moccasin (IRE) (Oasis Dream) (7000) **Rogerson, Lemon, Cooper & Murphy**
27 B c 28/3 Mayson—Phantasmagoria (Fraam) (6000)

Other Owners: Mr F. Deely, Mrs D. Ellison, B. E. Holland, G. I. D. Llewelyn, Mr J. J. McGarry, M. Murphy, Mr B. Olkowicz, Mr B. Rogerson, J. F. Runeckles, Mrs P. S. Speller.

---

440 **MR PAT MURPHY, Hungerford**
Postal: **Glebe House Stables, School Lane, East Garston, Nr Hungerford, Berkshire, RG17 7HR**
Contacts: **OFFICE (01488) 648473 MOBILE (07831) 410409**
E-MAIL pat@mabberleys.freeserve.co.uk WEBSITE www.patmurphyracing.com

1 **BADGER RUN (IRE)**, 5, gr g Acambaro (GER)—Charannah (IRE) **P. G. Murphy**
2 **CATALINAS DIAMOND (IRE)**, 8, b m One Cool Cat (USA)—Diamondiferous (USA) **Briton International**
3 **CLOUDY BOB (IRE)**, 9, gr g Cloudings (IRE)—Keen Supreme (IRE) **Men Of Stone**

Other Owners: B. H. Goldswain, Exors of the Late Mrs J. B. H. Goldswain, Mr R. Guest, Mr P. D. Lloyd.

Jockey (flat): Steve Drowne. **Jockey (NH):** Leighton Aspell.

---

441 **MR BARRY MURTAGH, Carlisle**
Postal: **Hurst Farm, Ivegill, Carlisle, Cumbria, CA4 0NL**
Contacts: **PHONE (01768) 484649 FAX (01768) 484744 MOBILE (07714) 026741**
E-MAIL sue@suemurtagh.wanadoo.co.uk

1 **BARABOY (IRE)**, 6, b g Barathea (IRE)—Irina (IRE) **A. R. White**
2 **CAPE ARROW (IRE)**, 5, b g Cape Cross (IRE)—Aiming **Mr & Mrs A. Trinder**
3 **CENTRE HAAFHD**, 5, b g Haafhd—Deira Dubai **J. R. Callow**
4 **DREAM PLACE**, 5, b m Multiplex—Globe Dream (IRE) **G. & P. Barker Ltd**
5 **JEBULANI**, 6, b g Jelani (IRE)—Susan's Dowry **Mr G. Fell**
6 **JUST LIKE DYLAN (IRE)**, 5, b g Brian Boru—Fainne Oir (IRE) **Mr A. R. White**
7 **KING'S CHORISTER**, 10, ch g King's Best—Chorist **Famous Five Racing**
8 **LAST PICK (IRE)**, 6, b g Gamut (IRE)—Polyzar (IRE) **The Pickled Punters**
9 **PRINCE BLACKTHORN (IRE)**, 10, b g Desert Prince (IRE)—Notable Dear (ITY) **Famous Five Racing**
10 4, B g Beat All (USA)—Sambara (IRE) **Mrs A. Stamper**
11 **SYMBOLIC STAR (IRE)**, 4, b g New Approach (IRE)—Epitome (IRE) **Mrs S. A. Murtagh**
12 **THE LATE SHIFT**, 6, b g Midnight Legend—Ashnaya (FR) **Don't Tell Henry**
13 **TROUBLE IN PARIS (IRE)**, 9, ch g Great Palm (USA)—Ten Dollar Bill (IRE) **Hurst Farm Racing**
14 **UNEX PICASSO**, 8, b g Galileo (IRE)—Ruff Shod (USA) **Mrs S. A. Murtagh**

Other Owners: Mr R. Allen, Mr James Callow, Mr A. J. Markley, Mrs Sue Murtagh, Mr F. P. Murtagh, Mrs A. Trinder, Mr A. Trinder, Mr Derek Wilson.

MR BARRY MURTAGH - Continued

Assistant Trainer: S A Murtagh

Conditional: Lorcan Murtagh.

---

442 **MR WILLIE MUSSON, Newmarket**
Postal: **Saville House, St Mary's Square, Newmarket, Suffolk, CB8 0HZ**
Contacts: PHONE **(01638) 663371 FAX (01638) 667979**
E-MAIL **willie@williemusson.co.uk** WEBSITE **www.williemusson.co.uk**

1 BROUGHTONS BERRY (IRE), 5, b m Bushranger (IRE)—Larrocha (IRE) **Broughton Thermal Insulation**
2 BROUGHTONS HARMONY, 4, ch f Nayef (USA)—Park Melody (IRE) **Broughton Thermal Insulation**
3 BROUGHTONS RHYTHM, 7, b g Araafa (IRE)—Broughton Singer (IRE) **Broughton Thermal Insulation**
4 CANDYMAN CAN (IRE), 6, b g Holy Roman Emperor (IRE)—Palwina (FR) **Miss Alison Jones**
5 COMMON TOUCH (IRE), 8, ch g Compton Place—Flying Finish (FR) **Broughton Thermal Insulation**
6 DONT HAVE IT THEN, 5, b g Myboycharlie (IRE)—Mondovi **Mr L. J. Mann**
7 MAC'S POWER (IRE), 10, b g Exceed And Excel (AUS)—Easter Girl **Broughton Thermal Insulation**
8 ROCKET ROB (IRE), 10, b g Danetime (IRE)—Queen of Fibres (IRE) **Mr P. J. Thompson & W. J. Musson**

THREE-YEAR-OLDS

9 BROUGHTONS MYSTERY, b f Sakhee's Secret—Enchanted Princess **Broughton Thermal Insulation**
10 BROUGHTONS VISION, b g Kheleyf (USA)—Read Federica **Broughton Thermal Insulation**
11 CAMINO, b f Equiano (FR)—Juncea **W. J. Musson**
12 HORATIA THE FLEET, ch f Bahamian Bounty—Countermarch **K. A. Cosby**
13 B g Sakhee's Secret—Inagh River **W. J. Musson**

TWO-YEAR-OLDS

14 BROUGHTONS ADMIRAL, b c 23/3 Born To Sea (IRE)—
                                Chanter (Lomitas) (60000) **Broughton Thermal Insulation**
15 BROUGHTONS KNIGHT, b c 3/5 Foxwedge (AUS)—
                                Disco Ball (Fantastic Light (USA)) (21000) **Broughton Thermal Insulation**
16 BROUGHTONS SPORT, b c 14/2 Showcasing—
                                Ginger Cookie (Bold Edge) (30000) **Broughton Thermal Insulation**
17 BROUGHTONS STORY, b c 9/2 Royal Applause—
                                News Desk (Cape Cross (IRE)) (11000) **Broughton Thermal Insulation**

Other Owners: Mr Patrick Thompson, Mrs N. A. Ward.

---

443 **DR JEREMY NAYLOR, Shrewton**
Postal: **The Cleeve, Elston Lane, Shrewton, Wiltshire, SP3 4HL**
Contacts: PHONE **(01980) 620804 MOBILE (07771) 740126**
E-MAIL **info@jeremynaylor.com** WEBSITE **www.jeremynaylor.com**

1 CROUCHING HARRY (IRE), 7, b g Tiger Hill (IRE)—Catwalk Dreamer (IRE) **Mrs S. P. Elphick**
2 FEARSOME FRED, 7, b g Emperor Fountain—Ryewater Dream **Dr J. R. J. Naylor**
3 JUST ARCHIE (USA), 8, b g Arch (USA)—Copper Rose (USA) **Mrs S. P. Elphick**
4 LADY CARDINAL (IRE), 5, ch m Papal Bull—St Finan's Bay (IRE) **Mrs S. P. Elphick**
5 PADOVA, 10, b g Shahrastani (USA)—My Song of Songs **The Acosta Partnership**
6 5, B m Striking Ambition—Sweet Request **Mrs S. P. Elphick**
7 TOO TRIGGER HAPPY, 7, b m Double Trigger (IRE)—Hilarious (IRE) **The Acosta Partnership**

---

444 **MR JOHN NEEDHAM, Ludlow**
Postal: **Gorsty Farm, Mary Knoll, Ludlow, Shropshire, SY8 2HD**
Contacts: PHONE **(01584) 872112/874826 FAX (01584) 873256 MOBILE (07811) 451137**
E-MAIL **johnlneedham@btconnect.com**

1 9, B m Blueprint (IRE)—Carramore (IRE) **J. L. Needham**
2 DOWNTON FOX, 8, b g Oscar (IRE)—Leinthall Fox **Miss J. C. L. Needham**
3 4, B f Sagamix (FR)—Marlbrook Fox **Miss J. C. L. Needham**
4 RIGHT ROYALS DAY, 7, b m Beneficial—Just For A Laugh **Miss J. C. L. Needham**

MR JOHN NEEDHAM - Continued

Assistant Trainer: P. Hanly

Jockey (NH): Richard Johnson, Paul Moloney. **Amateur:** Mr R Jarrett.

---

445 **MRS HELEN NELMES, Dorchester**
Postal: **Warmwell Stables, 2 Church Cottages, Warmwell, Dorchester, Dorset, DT2 8HQ**
Contacts: **PHONE/FAX (01305) 852254 MOBILE (07977) 510318**
E-MAIL warmwellstud@tiscali.co.uk WEBSITE www.warmwellracing.co.uk

1 GARRYDUFF CROSS (IRE), 6, b g Stowaway—Cooleycall (IRE) **K. A. Nelmes**
2 ITSABOUTIME (IRE), 6, gr g Whitmore's Conn (USA)—Blazing Love (IRE) **All Sorts Dorset Partnership**
3 KALMBEFORETHESTORM, 8, ch g Storming Home—Miss Honeypenny (IRE) **Warmwellcome Partnership**
4 MR TOY BOY, 6, b g Phoenix Reach (IRE)—Toy Girl (IRE) **All Sorts Dorset Partnership**
5 MYLITTLEMOUSE (IRE), 8, b m Turtle Island (IRE)—Ballybeg Rose (IRE) **K. A. Nelmes**
6 NORSE DA, 6, b g Norse Dancer (IRE)—End of An Error **T M W Partnership**
7 THAT WILL DO, 6, ch g Desert King (IRE)—Dusty Shoes **K. A. Nelmes**
8 THE CLYDA ROVER (IRE), 12, ch g Moonax (IRE)—Pampered Molly (IRE) **K. A. Nelmes**
9 THE FINGER POST (IRE), 9, b g Zagreb (USA)—Mystic Madam (IRE) **K. A. Nelmes**

Other Owners: Mrs S. Cobb, Miss V. O. Kardas, Mr M. Miller, Mr C. E. Mundy, Ms A. M. Neville, Mr D. Price.

Assistant Trainer: K Nelmes

---

446 **MR CHRIS NENADICH, Hereford**
Postal: **Lakes Farm, Sutton, Herefordshire, HR1 3NS**
Contacts: **PHONE (01432) 880278 MOBILE (07860) 484400**

1 BOLLIN JUDITH, 10, br m Bollin Eric—Bollin Nellie **Chris & Nick Nenadich**
2 CLOONE SPRINGS (IRE), 10, br g King's Theatre (IRE)—Ceo Draiochta (IRE) **Mr N. A. Price**

Other Owners: Mr N. Nenadich, C. Nenadich.

Assistant Trainer: Marion Collins

---

447 **MR TONY NEWCOMBE, Barnstaple**
Postal: **Lower Delworthy, Yarnscombe, Barnstaple, Devon, EX31 3LT**
Contacts: **PHONE/FAX (01271) 858554 MOBILE (07785) 297210**
E-MAIL huntshawequineforest@talktalk.net

1 ALMOQATEL (IRE), 4, b g Clodovil (IRE)—Majestic Night (IRE) **A. G. Newcombe**
2 8, B g Storming Home—Bogus Penny (IRE) **Mrs S. Wetter**
3 DOVIL'S DUEL (IRE), 5, b g Clodovil (IRE)—Duelling **Mr D. M. J. Gilbert**
4 6, B g Silca Blanka (IRE)—Fiery Angel (IRE) **Mr A. D. Smith**
5 KAY SERA, 8, b g Kayf Tara—Inflation **N. P. Hardy**
6 MAMBO SPIRIT (IRE), 12, b g Invincible Spirit (IRE)—Mambodorga (USA) **N. P. Hardy**
7 MISS MINUTY, 4, gr f Verglas (USA)—Miss Provence **Miss J. S. Dorey**
8 MY METEOR, 9, b g Bahamian Bounty—Emerald Peace (IRE) **Mr P. S. G. Nicholas**
9 8, B br m Monsieur Bond (IRE)—Parisian Lady (IRE) **Mr I. R. Newman**
10 PATAVINUS, 7, ch g Titus Livius (FR)—Bogus Penny (IRE)
11 SPELLMAKER, 7, b g Kheleyf (USA)—Midnight Spell **Joli Racing**

Other Owners: C. J. Buckerfield, A. G. Craig.

Assistant Trainer: John Lovejoy

Jockey (flat): Dane O'Neill, Tom Queally, Fergus Sweeney. **Jockey (NH):** Liam Treadwell, Andrew Thornton.

448 DR RICHARD NEWLAND, Claines
Postal: **Newland Associates Limited, Linacres Farm, Egg Lane, Claines, Worcester, WR3 7SB**
Contacts: **PHONE (07956) 196535**
E-MAIL **richard.newland1@btopenworld.com**

1 BAND OF BLOOD (IRE), 8, b g King's Theatre (IRE)—Cherry Falls (IRE) **J A Provan & C E Stedman**
2 BOLD BACHELOR (IRE), 7, b g Bachelor Duke (USA)—Bold Nora (IRE) **The Berrow Hill Partnership**
3 CLAIRE PET (IRE), 9, b g Pierre—Babs Girld (IRE) **Dr R. D. P. Newland**
4 CUT THE CORNER (IRE), 8, br g Vinnie Roe (IRE)—Snipe Victory (IRE) **Mr P. Drinkwater**
5 DISCAY, 7, b g Distant Music (USA)—Caysue **Foxtrot NH Racing Partnership VIII**
6 DUKE STREET (IRE), 4, b g Duke of Marmalade (IRE)—Act of The Pace (IRE) **Chris Stedman & Mark Albon**
7 EBONY EXPRESS, 7, bl g Superior Premium—Coffee Ice **ValueRacingClub.co.uk**
8 EXPRESS DU BERLAIS (FR), 7, b g Saint des Saints (FR)—Euil Eagle (FR) **Dr R. D. P. Newland**
9 GIOIA DI VITA, 6, b g Sakhee (USA)—Dhuyoof (IRE) **Mark Albon & Chris Stedman**
10 GRAN MAESTRO (USA), 7, ch g Medicean—Red Slippers (USA) **ValueRacingClub.co.uk**
11 HASSLE (IRE), 7, b g Montjeu (IRE)—Canterbury Lace (USA) **Mark Albon & Chris Stedman**
12 MASTEROFDECEPTION (IRE), 8, b g Darsi (IRE)—Sherberry (IRE) **The Berrow Hill Partnership**
13 NO WIN NO FEE, 6, b g Firebreak—Milliscent **Foxtrot Racing**
14 ONE MORE GO (IRE), 5, b g Papal Bull—Enchanted Wood (IRE) **Foxtrot Racing: One More Go**
15 PINEAU DE RE (FR), 13, b g Maresca Sorrento (FR)—Elfe du Perche (FR) **J. A. Provan**
16 ROCK GONE (IRE), 8, b g Winged Love (IRE)—Guillem (USA) **Chris Stedman & Mark Albon**
17 ROYALE KNIGHT, 10, b g King's Theatre (IRE)—Gardana (FR) **C. E. Stedman & R. J. Corsan**
18 SEEFOOD (IRE), 9, b g Kahyasi—Anne Theatre **C E Stedmand & J A Provan**
19 SIOUX CHIEFTAIN (IRE), 6, b g Mount Nelson—Lady Gin (USA) **Ferrybank Properties Limited**
20 THE GOVANESS, 7, b m Kayf Tara—Just Kate **C. B. Brookes**
21 TIGER TREK (IRE), 7, b g Tiger Hill (IRE)—Zayana (IRE)
22 TOP CAT HENRY (IRE), 8, b g Dr Massini (IRE)—Bells Chance (IRE) **Off The Clock Partners & Dr RDP Newland**
23 TRAFALGAR ROCK, 5, b g Mount Nelson—Helter Helter (USA) **Mark Johnston Racing Ltd**
24 VOSNE ROMANEE, 5, ch g Arakan (USA)—Vento Del Oreno (FR) **Foxtrot NH Racing Partnership VI**
25 WESTREN WARRIOR (IRE), 7, b g Westerner—Charming Leader (IRE) **C E Stedman & P Jenkins**
26 YOUNG DILLON (IRE), 5, b g Vinnie Roe (IRE)—Rongai (IRE) **Canard Vert Racing Club**

Other Owners: Mrs J. Abraham, Mr D. Abraham, Mr M. L. Albon, Mr M. P. Ansell, Mr J. R. Couldwell, Mr P. D. Couldwell, Mr A. S. P. Drake, Mr J. M. O. Evans, Foxtrot Racing Management Ltd, Mr P. C. W. Green, Mr P. Jenkins, Mrs L. J. Newland, C. E. Stedman.

Assistant Trainer: Brian Toomey

Amateur: Mr T. Weston.

449 MISS ANNA NEWTON-SMITH, Jevington
Postal: **Bull Pen Cottage, Jevington, Polegate, East Sussex, BN26 5QB**
Contacts: **PHONE (01323) 488354 FAX (01323) 488354 MOBILE (07970) 914124**
E-MAIL **anna_newtonsmith@o2.co.uk WEBSITE www.annanewtonsmith.co.uk**

1 ALBATROS DE GUYE (FR), 6, ch g Maille Pistol (FR)—Balibirds (FR) **Mr G. E. Goring**
2 BURGESS DREAM (IRE), 7, b g Spadoun (FR)—Ennel Lady (FR) **Mr P. Worley**
3 GORING TWO (IRE), 11, br g Needle Gun (IRE)—Kam Slave **Mr G. E. Goring**
4 LITTLE ROXY (IRE), 11, b m Dilshaan—Brunswick **The Ash Tree Inn Racing Club**
5 SHARAKTI (IRE), 9, b g Rakti—Easter Parade
6 THE CHILD (IRE), 7, b g Vertical Speed (FR)—Chancy Hall (IRE) **Miss A. M. Newton-Smith**
7 WALK OF GLEAMS, 7, b m Gleaming (IRE)—Harlequin Walk (IRE) **Mrs J. Brightling**

Other Owners: Mr M. K. Baker, A. K. Walker.

Assistant Trainer: Nicola Worley

Jockey (NH): Marc Goldstein, Andrew Thornton, Adam Wedge. **Amateur:** Miss Megan Spencer.

450 MR DAVID NICHOLLS, Thirsk
Postal: **Tall Trees Racing Ltd, Tall Trees, Sessay, Thirsk, North Yorkshire, YO7 3ND**
Contacts: **PHONE (01845) 501470 FAX (01845) 501666 MOBILE (07971) 555105**
E-MAIL **david.nicholls@btconnect.com WEBSITE www.davidnichollsracing.com**

1 APRICOT SKY, 6, ch g Pastoral Pursuits—Miss Apricot **The Wayward Lads & Partner**

MR DAVID NICHOLLS - Continued

2 **BARNET FAIR**, 8, br g Iceman—Pavement Gates **Mr D. Wheatley**
3 **BIG TIME (IRE)**, 5, br g Kheleyf (USA)—Beguine (USA) **Mrs C. C. Regalado-Gonzalez**
4 **BLAINE**, 6, ch g Avonbridge—Lauren Louise **Lady C. J. O'Reilly**
5 **COMPASS HILL (USA)**, 4, ch g Mizzen Mast (USA)—Zamindarling (USA) **Mrs C. C. Regalado-Gonzalez**
6 **DON'T CALL ME (IRE)**, 9, ch g Haafhd—Just Call Me (NZ) **Matt & Lauren Morgan**
7 **HIT THE LIGHTS (IRE)**, 6, b g Lawman (FR)—Dawn Chorus (IRE) **D. Nicholls**
8 **IMPERIAL LEGEND (IRE)**, 7, b g Mujadil (USA)—Titian Saga (IRE) **Gaga Syndicate**
9 **INDEGO BLUES**, 7, b g Indesatchel (IRE)—Yanomami (USA) **Gaga Syndicate**
10 **INXILE (IRE)**, 11, b g Fayruz—Grandel **D. Nicholls**
11 **KIMBERELLA**, 6, b g Kyllachy—Gleam of Light (IRE) **Mr C. J. Titcomb**
12 **LAYLA'S HERO (IRE)**, 9, b g One Cool Cat (USA)—Capua (USA) **D. Nicholls**
13 **MAJESTIC MANANNAN (IRE)**, 7, b g Majestic Missile (IRE)—Miraculous (IRE) **Dubelem (Racing) Limited**
14 **MANATEE BAY**, 6, b g Royal Applause—Dash of Lime **Alex Nicholls & Partner**
15 **MARMARUS**, 5, b g Duke of Marmalade (IRE)—Polly Perkins (IRE) **Bernard, Mark & Scott Robertson**
16 **MORE BEAU (USA)**, 5, b br g More Than Ready (USA)—Frontier Beauty (USA) **D. Nicholls**
17 **MUJAZIF (IRE)**, 6, br g Shamardal (USA)—Red Bandanna (IRE) **Mr G. D. Taylor**
18 **NEXT STOP**, 5, b m Rail Link—Reaching Ahead (USA) **S. E. Hussey**
19 **ORION'S BOW**, 5, ch g Pivotal—Heavenly Ray (USA) **Mr T. J. Swiers**
20 **PEARL ACCLAIM (IRE)**, 6, b g Acclamation—With Colour **M. A. Scaife**
21 **SIR HENRY RAEBURN (IRE)**, 4, b g Henrythenavigator (USA)—La Traviata (USA) **D. Nicholls**
22 **SOVEREIGN DEBT (IRE)**, 7, gr g Dark Angel (IRE)—Kelsey Rose **Lady C. J. O'Reilly**
23 **STORM RIDER (IRE)**, 5, b g Fastnet Rock (AUS)—On The Nile (IRE) **D. Nicholls**
24 **STORM TROOPER (IRE)**, 5, b g Acclamation—Maid To Order (IRE)
25 **STREET ARTIST (IRE)**, 6, ch g Street Cry (IRE)—Portrayal (USA) **J. A. Rattigan**

THREE-YEAR-OLDS

26 B c Excellent Art—Clinging Vine (USA)
27 **NOAH AMOR (IRE)**, b c Kodiac—Jumbo Romance (IRE) **Middleham Park Racing XIV**
28 **WHO R YA (IRE)**, b c Baltic King—Goose Island (USA) **Mr J Whiting & Ms L Judah**
29 **WISHSONG**, b f Dansili—Princess Janie (USA) **R. F. H. Partnership 1**

TWO-YEAR-OLDS

30 B c 9/2 Pastoral Pursuits—Engaging (Oasis Dream) (24761)
31 B f 25/2 Camacho—Hazelhurst (IRE) (Night Shift (USA)) (6190)
32 **MISCHIEF MANAGED (IRE)**, ch c 21/4 Tagula (IRE)—
Cape Clear (Slip Anchor) (29531) **Dubelem (Racing) Limited**
33 B c 21/2 Famous Name—Regrette Rien (IRE) (Chevalier (IRE)) (23809)

Other Owners: Mr M. Dixon, Mrs C. I. Hesketh, Ms L. Judah, M. Morgan, Mrs L. K. Morgan, Mrs A. A. Nicholls, T. S. Palin, M. Prince, Mr M. A. Robertson, Mr B. A. Robertson, Mr S. B. Robertson, Stittenham Racing, Mrs S. Thomson, Mr M. J. Waite, Mr J. Whiting.

Assistant Trainer: Ben Beasley

Jockey (flat): Paul Quinn, Adrian Nicholls. **Apprentice:** Anna Hesketh. **Amateur:** Mrs Adele Mulrennan.

---

451 **MR PAUL NICHOLLS, Ditcheat**
Postal: Manor Farm Stables, Ditcheat, Shepton Mallet, Somerset, BA4 6RD
Contacts: PHONE (01749) 860656 FAX (01749) 860523 MOBILE (07977) 270706
E-MAIL info@paulnichollsracing.com WEBSITE www.paulnichollsracing.com

1 **ABIDJAN (FR)**, 6, b g Alberto Giacometti (IRE)—Kundera (FR) **Axom L**
2 **ADRIEN DU PONT (FR)**, 4, b g Califet (FR)—Santariyka (FR) **Mrs S. De La Hey**
3 **ALCALA (FR)**, 6, gr g Turgeon (USA)—Pail Mel (FR) **Andrea & Graham Wylie**
4 **ALIBI DE SIVOLA (FR)**, 6, b br g Shaanmer (FR)—Neva de Sivola (FR) **Mr Ian Fogg & Mr Chris Giles**
5 **ALL SET TO GO (IRE)**, 5, gr g Verglas (IRE)—Firecrest **C. G. Roach**
6 **ALL YOURS (FR)**, 5, ch g Halling (USA)—Fontaine Riant (FR) **Mr&MrsP.K.Barber&Potensis Bloodstock Ltd**
7 **AMANTO (GER)**, 6, b g Medicean—Amore (GER) **Miss R. J. Dobson**
8 **ANATOL (FR)**, 6, b g Apsis—Teresa Moriniere (FR) **Mrs S. De La Hey**
9 **AND THE NEW (IRE)**, 5, b g Kalanisi (IRE)—Wheredidthemoneygo (IRE) **Sparkes & Gibson**
10 **ANNALULU (IRE)**, 5, b m Hurricane Run (IRE)—
Louve de Saron (FR) **Highclere Thoroughbred Racing -Anna Lulu**
11 **ANTARTICA DE THAIX (FR)**, 6, gr m Dom Alco (FR)—
Nouca de Thaix (FR) **D.Macdonald, C.Barber, I.Fogg & R.Webb**

MR PAUL NICHOLLS - Continued

12 **ARPEGE D'ALENE (FR)**, 6, gr g Dom Alco (FR)—
Joliette d'alene (FR) **Mr&Mrs P Barber&Potensis Bloodstock Ltd**
13 **ART MAURESQUE (FR)**, 6, b g Policy Maker (IRE)—Modeva (FR) **Mrs S. De La Hey**
14 **AS AND WHEN (IRE)**, 5, br g Presenting—Coole Eile (IRE) **J. P. McManus**
15 **AS DE MEE (FR)**, 6, b br g Kapgarde (FR)—Koeur de Mee (FR) **The Stewart Family & Judi Dench**
16 **AUX PTITS SOINS (FR)**, 6, gr g Saint des Saints (FR)—Reflexion Faite (FR) **Mr J. R. Hales**
17 **BAGAD BIHOUE (FR)**, 5, b g Nickname (FR)—Lann Bihouee (FR) **Owners Group 009**
18 **BAOULET DELAROQUE (FR)**, 5, b g Ungaro (GER)—Opale de La Roque (FR) **Potensis Bloodstock Limited**
19 **BE DARING (FR)**, 5, gr g Dom Alco (FR)—Quinine (FR) **Mr J. R. Hales**
20 **BEAU PHIL (FR)**, 5, ch g Cachet Noir (USA)—Quinine (FR) **Potensis Bloodstock Limited**
21 **BENVOLIO (IRE)**, 9, b g Beneficial—Coumeenoole Lady **Mrs P. Thompson**
22 **BLACK CORTON (FR)**, 5, b g Laverock (IRE)—Pour Le Meilleur (FR) **The Brooks, Kyle & Stewart Families**
23 **BLACK RIVER (FR)**, 7, b g Secret Singer (FR)—Love River (FR) **Andrea & Graham Wylie**
24 **BLACK THUNDER (FR)**, 9, bl g Malinas (GER)—Blackmika (FR) **Donlon, MacDonald, Fulton & Webb**
25 **BOA ISLAND (IRE)**, 6, b g Trans Island—Eskimo Kiss (IRE) **Mrs P. Thompson**
26 **BOL D'AIR (FR)**, 5, b g Blue Bresil—Holding (FR) **Potensis Bloodstock Limited**
27 **BOUVREUIL (FR)**, 5, b g Saddler Maker (IRE)—Madame Lys (FR) **Mr Chris Giles & Potensis Bloodstock Ltd**
28 **BRAVE JAQ (FR)**, 5, ch g Network (GER)—Galaxie (FR) **The Brooks, Kyle & Stewart Families**
29 **BRELAN D'AS (FR)**, 5, b g Crillon (FR)—Las de La Croix (FR) **J. P. McManus**
30 **BRIO CONTI (FR)**, 5, gr g Dom Alco (FR)—Cadoulie Wood (FR) **The Gi Gi Syndicate**
31 **BUGSIE MALONE (IRE)**, 6, b g Mahler—The Irish Whip **C. G. Roach**
32 **CAID DU BERLAIS (FR)**, 7, b g Westerner—Kenza du Berlais (FR) **Donlon, Doyle, MacDonald & C. Barber**
33 **CALIPTO (FR)**, 6, b g Califet (FR)—Peutiot (FR) **Mr Ian Fogg & Mr Chris Giles**
34 **CAPELAND (FR)**, 4, b g Poliglote—Neiland (FR) **Mrs K. A. Stuart**
35 **CAPITAINE (FR)**, 4, gr g Montmartre (FR)—Patte de Velour (FR) **Martin Broughton & Friends 2**
36 **CAPTAIN BUCK'S (FR)**, 4, b g Buck's Boum (FR)—Ombre Jaune (FR) **Donlon & Doyle**
37 **CASH AGAIN (FR)**, 4, bl g Great Pretender (IRE)—Jeu de Lune (FR) **J. P. McManus**
38 **CEASAR MILAN (IRE)**, 8, br g Milan—Standfast (FR) **The Stewart Family**
39 **CHARTBREAKER (FR)**, 5, b g Shirocco (GER)—Caucasienne (FR) **Mrs S. De La Hey**
40 **CHOIX DES ARMES (FR)**, 4, b g Saint des Saints (FR)—Kicka **Mrs S. De La Hey**
41 **CLAN DES OBEAUX (FR)**, 4, b g Kapgarde (FR)—
Nausicaa des Obeaux (FR) **Mr&MrsP.K.Barber&Potensis Bloodstock Ltd**
42 **CLIC WORK (FR)**, 4, b g Network (GER)—Qape Noir (FR) **David Sewell & Terry Warner**
43 **CLO SACRE (FR)**, 4, b g Network (GER)—Legende Sacree (FR) **P. F. Nicholls**
44 **COEUR DE PIGEON (FR)**, 4, gr g Al Namix (FR)—Nouvelle Donne (FR) **The Gi Gi Syndicate**
45 **CONNETABLE (FR)**, 4, b g Saint des Saints (FR)—Montbresia (FR) **Mr C. M. Giles**
46 **COPAIN DE CLASSE (FR)**, 4, b g Enrique—Toque Rouge (FR) **Kyle, Stewart, Vogt & Wylie**
47 **COUP DE PINCEAU (FR)**, 4, b g Buck's Boum (FR)—Castagnette III (FR) **Mr C. A. Donlon**
48 **CRIN AU VENT (FR)**, 4, b g Laveron—Tentative (FR) **Potensis Bloodstock Limited**
49 **DARK INVADER (FR)**, 4, b g Saint des Saints (FR)—Minirose (FR) **Walters Plant Hire Ltd**
50 **DIEGO DU CHARMIL (FR)**, 4, b g Ballingarry (IRE)—Daramour (FR) **Mrs S. De La Hey**
51 **DODGING BULLETS (FR)**, 8, b g Dubawi (IRE)—Nova Cyngi (USA) **Martin Broughton & Friends**
52 **DORMELLO MO (FR)**, 6, b g Conillon (GER)—Neogel (USA) **The Kyle & Stewart Families**
53 **EARTHMOVES (FR)**, 6, b g Antarctique (FR)—Red Rym (FR) **R. M. Penny**
54 **EASTER DAY (FR)**, 8, b g Malinas (GER)—Sainte Lea (FR) **Broughton Thermal Insulation, B Fulton**
55 **EL BANDIT (IRE)**, 5, b br g Milan—Bonnie Parker (IRE) **Colm Donlon, Barry Fulton & Richard Webb**
56 **EMERGING TALENT (IRE)**, 7, b g Golan (IRE)—Elviria (IRE) **Mr & Mrs Paul Barber**
57 **FAGO (FR)**, 8, b br g Balko—Merciki (FR) **Andrea & Graham Wylie**
58 **FAVORITO BUCK'S (FR)**, 4, b g Buck's Boum (FR)—Sangrilla (FR) **Mrs S. De La Hey**
59 **FAZAKERLEY (IRE)**, 5, b g Robin des Pres (FR)—Vita **Woodhouse & Sutton**
60 **FIRSTY (IRE)**, 5, b g Flemensfirth (USA)—Loughaderra Dame (IRE) **Mrs K. A. Stuart**
61 **FRODON (FR)**, 4, b g Nickname (FR)—Miss Country (FR) **Mr Ian Fogg & Potensis Bloodstock Ltd**
62 **GARO DE JUILLEY (FR)**, 4, b br g Ungaro (GER)—Lucy de Juilley (FR) **Mr Ian Fogg & Potensis Bloodstock Ltd**
63 **HAWKHURST (IRE)**, 6, b g Flemensfirth (USA)—Silaoce (FR) **J. P. McManus**
64 **HIGH SECRET (FR)**, 5, b g High Chaparral (IRE)—Secret Question (USA) **Axom LXV**
65 **HOWLONGISAFOOT (IRE)**, 7, b g Beneficial—Miss Vic (IRE) **P. J. Vogt**
66 **IBIS DU RHEU (FR)**, 5, b g Blue Bresil (FR)—Dona du Rheu (FR) **Mr J. R. Hales**
67 **IRISH SAINT (FR)**, 7, b br g Saint des Saints (FR)—Minirose (FR) **Mrs S. De La Hey**
68 **IRVING (FR)**, 8, b g Singspiel (IRE)—Indigo Girl (GER) **Axom XLIX**
69 **JUST A PAR (IRE)**, 9, b g Island House (IRE)—Thebrownhen (IRE) **C G Roach & Paul K Barber**
70 **JUST ACTING (IRE)**, 6, b g Presenting—Azalea (IRE) **J. P. McManus**
71 **KATGARY (FR)**, 6, b g Ballingarry (IRE)—Kotkira (FR) **Andrea & Graham Wylie**
72 **KELTUS (FR)**, 6, gr g Keltos (FR)—Regina d'orthe (FR) **Donlon & MacDonald**
73 **LE MERCUREY (FR)**, 6, b g Nickname (FR)—Feroe (FR) **Colm Donlon & Chris Giles**
74 **LE PREZIEN (FR)**, 5, br g Blue Bresil (FR)—Abu Dhabi (FR) **Million in Mind Partnership**

MR PAUL NICHOLLS - Continued

75 **LIFEBOAT MONA**, 6, b m Kayf Tara—Astar Love (FR) **Axom LV**
76 **LOU VERT (FR)**, 4, b g Vertigineux (FR)—Lourinha (FR) **Brooks,Done,Ferguson,Kyle,Mason&Stewart**
77 **MARRACUDJA (FR)**, 5, b g Martaline—Memorial (FR) **Potensis Bloodstock Limited**
78 **MINELLAHALFCENTURY (IRE)**, 8, b g Westerner—Shanakill River (IRE) **Mr Jeffrey Hordle & Mr Peter Hart**
79 **MOABIT (GER)**, 4, b g Azamour (IRE)—Moonlight Danceuse (IRE) **Owners Group 014**
80 **MODUS**, 6, ch g Motivator—Alessandra **J. P. McManus**
81 **MON PARRAIN (FR)**, 10, b g Trempolino (USA)—Kadaina (FR) **David Maxwell Racing Limited**
82 **MON SUCCESSEUR (FR)**, 5, ch g Forestier (FR)—Sainte Lea (FR) **Mr & Mrs J. D. Cotton**
83 **MONSIEUR GIBRALTAR (FR)**, 5, ch g Spirit One (FR)—Palabras de Amor (FR) **Mrs P. Thompson**
84 **MORE BUCK'S (FR)**, 6, ch g Presenting—Buck's Blue (FR) **The Stewart Family**
85 **MORITO DU BERLAIS (FR)**, 7, b g Turgeon (USA)—Chica du Berlais (FR) **C. G. Roach**
86 **MOVEWITHTHETIMES (IRE)**, 5, ch g Presenting—Dare To Venture (IRE) **J. P. McManus**
87 **MR MIX (FR)**, 5, gr g Al Namix (FR)—Royale Surabaya (FR) **Mr Ian Fogg & Potensis Bloodstock Ltd**
88 **MR MOLE (IRE)**, 8, br g Great Pretender (IRE)—Emmylou du Berlais (FR) **J. P. McManus**
89 **NEXIUS (IRE)**, 7, b g Catcher In The Rye (IRE)—Nicolaia (GER) **Owners Group 012**
90 **NICE N EASY (IRE)**, 6, b g Presenting—Miss Brandywell (IRE) **C. G. Roach**
91 **OLD GUARD**, 5, b g Notnowcato—Dolma (FR) **The Brooks, Kyle & Stewart Families**
92 **ORBASA (FR)**, 5, b g Full of Gold (FR)—Ierbasa de Kerpaul (FR) **Potensis Bloodstock Limited**
93 **PEAK TO PEAK (IRE)**, 4, br g Authorized (IRE)—Bayourida (USA) **Potensis Bloodstock Limited**
94 **PERSIAN DELIGHT**, 6, br g Lucarno (USA)—Persian Walk (FR) **Hypnotised**
95 **PILANSBERG**, 4, b c Rail Link—Posteritas (USA) **Martin Broughton & Friends 3**
96 **POLISKY (FR)**, 9, b g Poliglote—Dusky Royale (FR) **Mrs S. De La Hey**
97 **POLITOLOGUE (FR)**, 5, gr g Poliglote—Scarlet Row (FR) **Mr J. R. Hales**
98 **PORT MELON (IRE)**, 8, br g Presenting—Omyn Supreme (IRE) **C. G. Roach**
99 **PRESENT MAN (IRE)**, 6, b g Presenting—Glen's Gale (IRE) **The Stewart Family & Mr Paul K Barber**
100 **PTIT ZIG (FR)**, 7, b g Great Pretender (IRE)—Red Rym (FR) **Barry Fulton, Chris Giles & Richard Webb**
101 **QUALANDO (FR)**, 5, b g Lando (GER)—Qualite Controlee (FR) **Mrs K. A. Stuart**
102 **RAINY CITY (IRE)**, 6, b g Kalanisi (IRE)—Erintante (IRE) **Sir A Ferguson,G Mason,R Wood & P Done**
103 **RED HANRAHAN (IRE)**, 5, b g Yeats (IRE)—Monty's Sister (IRE) **Mr & Mrs J. D. Cotton**
104 **ROCK ON OSCAR (IRE)**, 6, b g Oscar (IRE)—Brogeen Lady (IRE) **I Fogg,C Barber,D Bennett & D Macdonald**
105 **ROCKY CREEK (IRE)**, 10, b g Dr Massini (IRE)—Kissantell (IRE) **The Johnson & Stewart Families**
106 **ROMAIN DE SENAM (FR)**, 4, b g Saint des Saints (FR)—Salvatrixe (FR) **Mr Chris Giles & Mr Dan Macdonald**
107 **ROTHMAN (FR)**, 6, b g Michel Georges—Bravecentadj (FR) **Mrs J. Hitchings**
108 **ROUGE DEVILS (FR)**, 5, b g Scorpion (FR)—Penny's Dream (FR) **Sir A Ferguson,G Mason,R Wood & P Done**
109 **RUBEN COTTER (IRE)**, 10, b g Beneficial—Bonnie Thynes (IRE) **C. G. Roach**
110 **SAINT ROQUE (FR)**, 10, b g Lavirco (GER)—Moody Cloud (FR) **Mr I. J. Fogg**
111 **SALUBRIOUS (IRE)**, 9, b g Beneficial—Who Tells Jan **The Johnson & Stewart Families**
112 **SAM WINNER (FR)**, 9, b g Okawango (USA)—Noche (IRE) **Mrs A. B. Yeoman**
113 **SAMETEGAL (FR)**, 7, b g Saint des Saints (FR)—Loya Lescribaa (FR) **Mr & Mrs J. D. Cotton**
114 **SAN BENEDETO (FR)**, 5, ch g Layman (USA)—Cinco Baidy (FR) **P. J. Vogt**
115 **SAPHIR DU RHEU (FR)**, 7, gr g Al Namix (FR)—Dona du Rheu (FR) **The Stewart Family**
116 **SELFCONTROL (FR)**, 5, b br g Al Namix (FR)—L'ascension (FR) **The Kyle & Stewart Families**
117 **SEMPER INVICTA (IRE)**, 5, ch g Shantou (USA)—Statim **B.Fulton,C.Giles,Potensis Bloodstock Ltd**
118 **SILSOL (GER)**, 7, b g Soldier Hollow—Silveria (GER) **Michelle And Dan Macdonald**
119 **SILVINIACO CONTI (FR)**, 10, ch g Dom Alco (FR)—Gazelle Lulu (FR) **Potensis Bloodstock Ltd & Chris Giles**
120 **SIMON SQUIRREL (IRE)**, 6, b g Robin des Champs (FR)—Misty Heather (IRE) **Andrea & Graham Wylie**
121 **SIRABAD (FR)**, 6, b g Astarabad (USA)—Maille Sissi (FR) **Brooks, Kyle, Stewart & Webb**
122 **SIRE COLLONGES (FR)**, 10, gr g Dom Alco (FR)—
  Idylle Collonges (FR) **Mrs Angela Tincknell & Mr W. Tincknell**
123 **SOLAR IMPULSE (FR)**, 6, b g Westerner—Moon Glow (FR) **Andrea & Graham Wylie**
124 **SOME BUCKLE (IRE)**, 7, b g Milan—Miss Moppit (IRE) **R. S. Brookhouse**
125 **SOME PLAN (IRE)**, 8, b g Winged Love (IRE)—Lough Hyne **R. S. Brookhouse**
126 **SOUND INVESTMENT (IRE)**, 8, b g Dr Massini (IRE)—Drumcay Polly (IRE) **Owners Group 001**
127 **SOUTHFIELD THEATRE (IRE)**, 8, b g King's Theatre (IRE)—Chamoss Royale (FR) **Mrs A. B. Yeoman**
128 **SOUTHFIELD VIC (IRE)**, 7, ch g Old Vic—Chamoss Royale (FR) **Mrs A. B. Yeoman**
129 **ST DENYS (IRE)**, 7, br g Presenting—Diva Antonia (IRE) **C. G. Roach**
130 **STELLAR NOTION (IRE)**, 8, b br g Presenting—Green Star (FR) **R. S. Brookhouse**
131 **STILLETTO (IRE)**, 7, b g Westerner—Eastertide (IRE) **R. S. Brookhouse**
132 **TAGRITA (IRE)**, 8, b m King's Theatre (IRE)—Double Dream (IRE) **Axom XLVIII**
133 **TARA POINT**, 7, gr m Kayf Tara—Poppet **Mr R. J. H. Geffen**
134 **THE BROCK AGAIN**, 6, ch g Muhtathir—Half Past Twelve (USA) **Axom LIV**
135 **THE EAGLEHASLANDED (IRE)**, 6, b g Milan—Vallee Doree (FR) **Mrs Angela Tincknell & Mr W. Tincknell**
136 **THE OUTLAW (IRE)**, 6, b g Presenting—Bonnie Parker (IRE) **Donlon, MacDonald, Giles & Webb**
137 **TOMMY SILVER (FR)**, 4, b g Silver Cross (FR)—Sainte Mante (FR) **Potensis Bloodstock Limited**
138 **TOUCH KICK (FR)**, 5, b g Presenting—Bay Pearl (FR) **T. J. Hemmings**

MR PAUL NICHOLLS - Continued

139 **ULCK DU LIN (FR)**, 8, b g Sassanian (USA)—Miss Fast (FR) **Mrs S. De La Hey**
140 **UNIONISTE (FR)**, 8, gr g Dom Alco (FR)—Gleep Will (FR) **Mr J. R. Hales**
141 **V NECK (FR)**, 7, b g Sir Harry Lewis (USA)—Swift Settlement **J. P. McManus**
142 **VALCO DE TOUZAINE (FR)**, 7, gr g Dom Alco (FR)—Narcisse de Touzaine (FR) **The Gi Gi Syndicate**
143 **VAROM (FR)**, 7, gr g Charming Groom (FR)—Morava (FR) **Mr John & Jordan Lund**
144 **VESPERAL DREAM (FR)**, 7, bl g Network (GER)—Pampanilla (FR) **The Loving Insurance Partnership**
145 **VIBRATO VALTAT (FR)**, 7, gr g Voix du Nord (FR)—La Tosca Valtat (FR) **Axom XLIII**
146 **VICENTE (FR)**, 7, b g Dom Alco (FR)—Ireland (FR) **Mr Ian Fogg & Mr John Hales**
147 **VICENZO MIO (FR)**, 6, b g Corri Piano (FR)—Sweet Valrose (FR) **Mrs S. De La Hey**
148 **VIRAK (FR)**, 7, b g Bernebeau (FR)—Nosika d'airy (FR) **Hills of Ledbury Ltd**
149 **VIVALDI COLLONGES (FR)**, 7, b g Dom Alco (FR)—Diane Collonges (FR) **The Gi Gi Syndicate**
150 **WARRIORS TALE**, 7, b g Midnight Legend—Samandara (FR) **Michelle And Dan Macdonald**
151 **WHIPCORD (IRE)**, 5, gr g Tikkanen (USA)—Dapples (IRE) **H. M. W. Clifford**
152 **WHISPERING STORM (GER)**, 6, b g Samum (GER)—Wind In Her Hair (GER) **Masterson Holdings Limited**
153 **WINNINGTRY (IRE)**, 5, br g Flemensfirth (USA)—Jeruflo (IRE) **T. J. Hemmings**
154 **WONDERFUL CHARM (FR)**, 8, b g Poliglote—Victoria Royale (FR) **Mr R. J. H. Geffen**
155 **WUFF (IRE)**, 8, b g Beneficial—Dummy Run (IRE) **R. S. Brookhouse**
156 **ZARKANDAR (IRE)**, 9, b g Azamour (IRE)—Zarkasha (IRE) **Potensis Bloodstock Ltd & Chris Giles**
157 **ZUBAYR (IRE)**, 4, b g Authorized (IRE)—Zaziyra (IRE) **P. J. Vogt**

Other Owners: Axom Ltd, P. K. Barber, Mr C. L. Barber, Mrs M. G. Barber, Mr D. Bennett, Mr M. Bower-Dyke, A. R. Bromley, Mr G. F. Brooks, Sir M. F. Broughton, Mr S. W. Broughton, Broughton Thermal Insulations, Mr A. P Brown, D. J. Coles, Mr M. H. Colquhoun, J. D. Cotton, Mrs B. Cotton, Dame J. O. Dench, Mr I. J. Donaldson, Mr P. E. Done, Mr D. Downie, Mr A. Doyle, Mrs L. A. Farquhar, Sir A. Ferguson, B. N. Fulton, Mrs A. K. J. Gibson, G. F. Goode, Miss L. J. Hales, P. L. Hart, The Hon H. M. Herbert, Highclere Thoroughbred Racing Ltd, Mr A. J. Hill, Mr B. M. Hillier, Mr M. J. Holman, J. G. Hordle, Mrs D. A. Johnson, Mr S. D. Johnson, Mr C. L. Keey, Mrs C. L. Kyle, Mr J. E. Lund, Mr J. E. Lund, Mr W. D. Macdonald, Mrs M. Macdonald, Mrs C. Mant, G. A. Mason, Mr B. J. McManus, W. D. C. Minton, Mrs M. E. Moody, Mrs D. C. Nicholson, Mr M. J. O'Shaughnessy, Mrs L. Scott-MacDonald, Mr D. J. S. Sewell, Mrs Claire Simmonds, Mrs A. M. Sparkes, Mr D. D. Stevenson, Mr A. Stewart, Mrs J. A. Stewart, Ms C. Sutton, Mrs A. Tincknell, W. C. Tincknell, J. T. Warner, Mr R. A. Webb, Mr R. J. Wood, Mrs T. A. Woodhouse, M. J. M. Woodhouse, A. W. G. Wylie, Mrs A. Wylie.

Assistant Trainers: Tom Jonason, Andrew Doyle, Harry Derham

Jockey (NH): Sam Twiston-Davies, Sean Bowen, Nick Scholfield. **Conditional:** Harry Cobden, Alice Mills, Jack Sherwood, Jordan Williams. **Apprentice:** Megan Nicholls. **Amateur:** Mr Will Biddick, Mr Lewis Ferguson, Miss Bryony Frost, Mr James King, Mr Stan Sheppard.

---

452 MR PETER NIVEN, Malton

Postal: **Clovafield, Barton-Le-Street, Malton, North Yorkshire, YO17 6PN**
Contacts: **PHONE (01653) 628176 FAX (01653) 627295 MOBILE (07860) 260999**
E-MAIL pruniven@btinternet.com WEBSITE www.peterniven.co.uk

1 **ABSOLUTE ANGEL**, 5, b m Primo Valentino (IRE)—Send Me An Angel (IRE) **P. D. Niven**
2 **ATOMIX (GER)**, 5, b g Doyen (IRE)—Aloe (GER) **Mr G. Wragg**
3 **BEAT THE SHOWER**, 10, b g Beat Hollow—Crimson Shower **Mrs K. J. Young**
4 **BLADES LAD**, 7, ch g Haafhd—Blades Girl **Crown Select**
5 **BRIAN BORANHA (IRE)**, 5, b g Brian Boru—Tapneiram (IRE) **Mrs K. J. Young**
6 **CLEVER COOKIE**, 8, b g Primo Valentino (IRE)—Mystic Memory **P. D. Niven**
7 **HARRY HUSSAR**, 6, b g Primo Valentino (IRE)—Jessie May (IRE) **P. D. Niven**
8 **PINOTAGE**, 8, br g Danbird (AUS)—Keen Melody (USA) **S. J. Bowett**
9 **PIXIEPOT**, 6, b m Alflora (IRE)—Folly Foster **The Rumpole Partnership**
10 **REGENT'S ROCK**, 4, b f Shirocco (GER)—Tiger's Gene (GER) **P. D. Niven**
11 **SAM FLYRYANN**, 5, b g Black Sam Bellamy (IRE)—Folly Foster **The Rumpole Partnership**
12 4, Ch c Sulamani (IRE)—Simply Mystic **Mrs J A Niven & Angus Racing Club**
13 **SIMPLY ROUGE**, 6, b m Croco Rouge (IRE)—Simply Mystic **Mrs J A Niven & Sandy Lodge Racing Club**
14 **SIR SAFIR**, 6, b g Croco Rouge (IRE)—Angela's Ashes **P. D. Niven**

THREE-YEAR-OLDS

15 **A BOY NAMED SUE**, b g Monsieur Bond (IRE)—Elusive Sue (USA) **P. D. Smith Holdings Ltd**
16 **MR LUCAS (IRE)**, b g Le Cadre Noir (IRE)—Maripova (IRE) **Mrs Muriel Ward**

Other Owners: Mr C. Ayris, Mr B. W. Ewart, M. J. Feneron, Miss C. Foster, D. Holgate, Mr A. Needham, Mr M. W. G. Niven, Mrs J. A. Niven, M. A. Scaife.

453 MRS LUCY NORMILE, Glenfarg

Postal: Duncrievie, Glenfarg, Perthshire, PH2 9PD
Contacts: PHONE (01577) 830330 FAX (01577) 830658 MOBILE (07721) 454818
E-MAIL lucy@normileracing.co.uk WEBSITE www.normileracing.co.uk

1 AGRICULTURAL, 10, b g Daylami (IRE)—Rustic (IRE) **Mrs J. Carnaby**
2 BADGED, 7, b g High Chaparral (IRE)—Meshhed (USA) **The Explorers**
3 BERKSHIRE DOWNS, 6, b m Tiger Hill (IRE)—Cut Corn **Riverside Racing**
4 CADORE (IRE), 8, b g Hurricane Run (IRE)—Mansiya **L B N Racing Club**
5 CRUACHAN (IRE), 7, b g Authorized (IRE)—Calico Moon (USA) **P Carnaby & B Thomson**
6 JUST ANNIE, 8, b m Revoque (IRE)—Carbery Spirit (IRE) **Mrs F. M. Whitaker**
7 KARINGO, 9, ch g Karinga Bay—Wild Happening (GER) **Douglas Black,P A Carnaby,P J Carnaby**
8 NEW YOUMZAIN (FR), 7, b g Sinndar (IRE)—Luna Sacra (FR) **The Fiddlers**
9 REMEMBER ROCKY, 7, ch g Haafhd—Flower Market **Byrne Racing**
10 RINNAGREE ROSIE, 10, gr m Silver Patriarch (IRE)—Gretton **The Silver Tops**
11 ROYAL DUCHESS, 6, b m Dutch Art—Royal Citadel (IRE) **Mr S. W. Dick**
12 ROYAL REGENT, 4, b g Urgent Request (IRE)—Royal Citadel (IRE) **Mr S. W. Dick**
13 SILVERTON, 9, gr m Silver Patriarch (IRE)—Gretton **Twentys Plenty**
14 SON OF FEYAN (IRE), 5, ch g Nayef (USA)—Miss Penton **Mrs L. B. Normile**
15 STROBE, 12, ch g Fantastic Light (USA)—Sadaka (USA) **Miss P. A. & Mr P. J. Carnaby**
16 THIS THYNE JUDE, 8, gr m Silver Patriarch (IRE)—This Thyne **L B N Racing Club**
17 WOLF HEART (IRE), 8, b g Dalakhani (IRE)—Lisieux Orchid **Twentys Plenty**

THREE-YEAR-OLDS

18 GRANITE CITY DOC, b g Arabian Gleam—Hansomis (IRE) **Corsby Racing**

Other Owners: Mr D. M. Black, P. Byrne, Mr P. J. Carnaby, Miss P. A. Carnaby, Mr P. Carnaby, Miss F. M. Fletcher, R. N. Ker-Ramsay, Mr A. C. Rodger, B. Thomson, D. A. Whitaker, J. R. Williams.

Assistant Trainer: Libby Brodie (07947) 592438

Jockey (NH): Lucy Alexander. **Amateur:** Mr R. Wilson.

454 MR JOHN NORTON, Barnsley

Postal: Globe Farm, High Hoyland, Barnsley, South Yorkshire, S75 4BE
Contacts: PHONE/FAX (01226) 387633 MOBILE (07970) 212707
E-MAIL johnrnorton@hotmail.com WEBSITE www.johnrnortonracehorsetrainer.co.uk

1 ANNIVERSARIE, 4, ch f Major Cadeaux—Razzle (IRE) **A. R. Middleton**
2 CAPTIVE MOMENT, 10, b m Almaty (IRE)—Captive Heart **J. Norton**
3 DEPORTATION, 9, b g Deportivo—Kyle Rhea **J. R. Norton Ltd**
4 FIDDLER'S FLIGHT (IRE), 10, b g Convinced—Carole's Dove **Fellowship Of The Rose Partnership**
5 FLYING POWER, 8, b g Dubai Destination (USA)—Rah Wa (USA) **Jaffa Racing Syndicate**
6 GOREY LANE (IRE), 10, b g Oscar—Supremely Deep (IRE) **Jaffa Racing Syndicate**
7 KINGSWINFORD (IRE), 10, b g Noverre (USA)—Berenica (USA) **J. R. Norton Ltd**
8 Q TWENTY GIRL (IRE), 4, b f Fast Company (IRE)—Extravagance (IRE) **J. R. Norton Ltd**
9 SYMBOLIST (IRE), 4, b f Yeats (IRE)—Pescia (IRE) **Mr W. M. Brown**

TWO-YEAR-OLDS

10 B f 25/3 Sayif (IRE)—Baby Princess (BRZ) (Crimson Tide (IRE)) (2857) **J. R. Norton Ltd**
11 B f 18/3 Dick Turpin (IRE)—Sindarbella (Sinndar (IRE)) (2095) **J. R. Norton Ltd**
12 B f 10/2 Stimulation (IRE)—Tranquil Flight (Oasis Dream) (3047) **Jaffa Racing Syndicate**

Other Owners: Mr R. M. Firth, Mr P. J. Marshall, Mr J. Norton, Mr P. Woodcock-Jones.

Amateur: Mr P. Hardy.

455 MR JEREMY NOSEDA, Newmarket

Postal: Shalfleet, 17 Bury Road, Newmarket, Suffolk, CB8 7BX
Contacts: PHONE (01638) 664010 FAX (01638) 664100 MOBILE (07710) 294093
E-MAIL jeremy@jeremynoseda.com WEBSITE www.jeremynoseda.com

1 BRAVO ZOLO (IRE), 4, b g Rip Van Winkle (IRE)—Set Fire (IRE)
2 BURCAN (FR), 4, ch g Astronomer Royal (USA)—Sentimental Union (USA)

MR JEREMY NOSEDA - Continued

3 **CERTAIN SMILE (IRE)**, 4, b g Lope de Vega (IRE)—Irish Flower (IRE)
4 **FREE ONE (IRE)**, 4, b g Fast Company (IRE)—Tatamagouche (IRE)
5 **IAN'S MEMORY (USA)**, 5, b br h Smart Strike (CAN)—Rite Moment (USA)
6 **KEYSTROKE**, 4, b c Pivotal—Fondled
7 **LE NOTRE**, 4, b g Champs Elysees—Millistar
8 **MR BOOMER (USA)**, 4, ch g Giant's Causeway (USA)—Element of Truth (USA)
9 **RENOUNCE (IRE)**, 4, b c Elnadim (USA)—Relinquished
10 **SLOANE AVENUE (USA)**, 5, ch h Candy Ride (ARG)—Apt (USA)
11 **WAKEA (USA)**, 5, b br g Cape Cross (IRE)—Imiloa (USA)

THREE-YEAR-OLDS

12 **ABE LINCOLN (USA)**, b c Discreet Cat (USA)—Truly Blushed (USA)
13 **BROADWAY ICON**, b c Sixties Icon—Funny Girl (IRE)
14 **CAP CANAILLE (USA)**, br c Giant's Causeway (USA)—Cassis (USA)
15 **CEE JAY**, ch c Kyllachy—Intermission (IRE)
16 **EGYPTIAN (USA)**, br c Eskendereya (USA)—Street Talk (USA)
17 **ELECTRIFY (IRE)**, b f Invincible Spirit (IRE)—Elopa (GER)
18 **HEARTY (IRE)**, b g Big Bad Bob (IRE)—Ulanova (IRE)
19 **KING JULIEN (IRE)**, b c Canford Cliffs (IRE)—Western Sky
20 **NEMORALIA (USA)**, b br f More Than Ready (USA)—Alina (USA)
21 **PARKOUR (IRE)**, b c Holy Roman Emperor (IRE)—School Holidays (USA)
22 **PIXEL (IRE)**, b f Rip Van Winkle (IRE)—Hadarama (IRE)
23 **PLENARY (USA)**, ch c Kitten's Joy (USA)—Southern Alibi (USA)
24 **ROUGE NOIR**, b f Showcasing—Vive Les Rouges
25 B f Canford Cliffs (IRE)—Sentimental (IRE)
26 **SIXTIES GROOVE (IRE)**, b c Sixties Icon—Gift Dancer

TWO-YEAR-OLDS

27 Br f 2/5 Distorted Humor (USA)—Aldebaran Light (USA) (Seattle Slew (USA))
28 B c 22/4 Dragon Pulse (IRE)—Emsiyah (USA) (Bernardini (USA)) (88593)
29 B c 4/2 Choisir (AUS)—Katherine Lee (IRE) (Azamour (IRE)) (60000)
30 Br c 25/2 Scat Daddy (USA)—Liza Lu (USA) (Menifee (USA)) (170940)
31 B f 22/2 Helmet (AUS)—Paint The Town (IRE) (Sadler's Wells (USA)) (50000)
32 Ch f 23/2 Dutch Art—Parakopi (IRE) (Green Desert (USA)) (36913)
33 B f 12/4 Dutch Art—Passing Stranger (IRE) (Dixie Union) (USA))
34 B c 19/1 More Than Ready (USA)—Return The Jewel (USA) (Broken Vow (USA)) (42735)
35 B f 12/2 Sixties Icon—Spinning Lucy (IRE) (Spinning World (USA))
36 B c 18/3 Medaglia d'oro (USA)—Trepidation (USA) (Seeking The Gold (USA)) (122100)
37 B f 3/4 Lonhro (AUS)—Wear Red (USA) (Henny Hughes (USA))

Assistant Trainer: Dave Bradley

---

456 MR A. P. O'BRIEN, Ballydoyle
Postal: **Ballydoyle Stables, Cashel, Co. Tipperary, Ireland**
Contacts: **PHONE (00353) 6262615**
E-MAIL racingoffice@ballydoyle.com

Older horses and jumpers under the care of Joseph O'Brien at Piltown, Co. Kilkenny are not shown.

1 **BONDI BEACH (IRE)**, 4, b c Galileo (IRE)—One Moment In Time (IRE)
2 **FOUND (IRE)**, 4, b f Galileo (IRE)—Red Evie (IRE)
3 **HIGHLAND REEL (IRE)**, 4, b c Galileo (IRE)—Hveger (AUS)
4 **KINGFISHER (IRE)**, 5, b h Galileo (IRE)—Mystical Lady (IRE)
5 **ORDER OF ST GEORGE (IRE)**, 4, b c Galileo (IRE)—Another Storm (USA)
6 **SIEGE OF ORLEANS (USA)**, 4, b c War Front (USA)—Watch (USA)
7 **VANCOUVER (AUS)**, 4, b c Medaglia d'oro (USA)—Skates (AUS)

THREE-YEAR-OLDS

8 **A YEAR TO REMEMBER (IRE)**, b c Galileo (IRE)—Mubkera (IRE)
9 **ABSOLUTE RULER (IRE)**, b c Oasis Dream—Ideal
10 **AIR FORCE BLUE (USA)**, b br c War Front (USA)—Chatham (USA)
11 **AIR VICE MARSHAL (USA)**, b c War Front (USA)—Gold Vault (USA)
12 **ALICE SPRINGS (IRE)**, ch f Galileo (IRE)—Aleagueoftheirown (USA)
13 **BALLYDOYLE (IRE)**, b f Galileo (IRE)—Butterfly Cove (USA)

MR A. P. O'BRIEN - Continued

14 **BEACON ROCK (IRE)**, ch c Galileo (IRE)—Remember When (IRE)
15 **BEST IN THE WORLD (IRE)**, b f Galileo (IRE)—Red Evie (IRE)
16 **BHUTAN (IRE)**, gr c Galileo (IRE)—Ecology (USA)
17 **BIG BEN**, b c Galileo (IRE)—Flirtation
18 **BLACK HAWK WAR (USA)**, b c War Front (USA)—Lasting Code (USA)
19 **BLACK SEA (IRE)**, b c Galileo (IRE)—Christmas Kid (USA)
20 **BRAVERY (IRE)**, b c Galileo (IRE)—Lady Icarus
21 **CALIFORNIADREAMING (IRE)**, b f Fastnet Rock (AUS)—Descant (USA)
22 **CANDLE ROCKS (IRE)**, b c Fastnet Rock (AUS)—Monevassia (USA)
23 **CELTIC CHIEFTAIN (IRE)**, b c Galileo (IRE)—Sumora (IRE)
24 **CLAUDIO MONTEVERDI (IRE)**, b c Galileo (IRE)—Dance For Fun
25 **COCKATOO ISLAND (USA)**, b c War Front (USA)—Temperence Gift (USA)
26 **COLE PORTER (IRE)**, b c Galileo (IRE)—A Z Warrior (USA)
27 **COOK ISLANDS (IRE)**, b c Fastnet Rock (AUS)—Tree Chopper (USA)
28 **COOLMORE (IRE)**, ch f Galileo (IRE)—You'resothrilling (USA)
29 **CROCODILE SHOES (IRE)**, b c Galileo (IRE)—Mythical Echo (USA)
30 **DEAUVILLE (IRE)**, b c Galileo (IRE)—Walklikeanegyptian (IRE)
31 **DEWDROP (IRE)**, b f Galileo (IRE)—Like A Dame
32 **EARRING (USA)**, br f Dansili—Together (IRE)
33 **ETCHED (IRE)**, b f Dansili—Gagnoa (IRE)
34 **EVEN SONG (IRE)**, b f Mastercraftsman (IRE)—Guantanamera (IRE)
35 **GENERAL MACARTHUR (IRE)**, b c War Front (USA)—Imagine (IRE)
36 **HIBISCUS (IRE)**, b f Galileo (IRE)—Jacqueline Quest (IRE)
37 **HIT IT A BOMB (USA)**, b c War Front (USA)—Liscanna (IRE)
38 **HOUSESOFPARLIAMENT (IRE)**, ch c Galileo (IRE)—Sharp Lisa (USA)
39 **HOW HIGH THE MOON (IRE)**, b f Fastnet Rock (AUS)—Quarter Moon (IRE)
40 **IDAHO (IRE)**, b c Galileo (IRE)—Hveger (AUS)
41 **JOHANNES VERMEER (IRE)**, b c Galileo (IRE)—Inca Princess (IRE)
42 **JONATHAN SWIFT (IRE)**, ch c Galileo (IRE)—Halland Park Lass (IRE)
43 **KELLSTORM (IRE)**, ch c Galileo (IRE)—Another Storm (USA)
44 **KIND OF MAGIC (IRE)**, ch f Galileo (IRE)—Look At Me (IRE)
45 **LAND OF THE FREE (IRE)**, b c Oasis Dream—All For Glory (USA)
46 **LORDOFHOPEANDGLORY (IRE)**, b c High Chaparral (IRE)—Wurflinge (GER)
47 **LIEUTENANT GENERAL (IRE)**, b c Fastnet Rock (AUS)—Lady Lupus (IRE)
48 **LONDON (FR)**, b c Galileo (IRE)—Altana (USA)
49 **LONG ISLAND SOUND (USA)**, b c War Front (USA)—Treasure Trail (USA)
50 **MINDING (IRE)**, b f Galileo (IRE)—Lillie Langtry (IRE)
51 **MONARCH (IRE)**, b c Galileo (IRE)—Secret Garden (IRE)
52 **NEW MILLENNIUM (IRE)**, b c Galileo (IRE)—Banquise (IRE)
53 **PAINTED CLIFFS (IRE)**, b c Canford Cliffs (IRE)—Lulawin
54 **PIETRO TESTA (IRE)**, b c Galileo (IRE)—Penang Pearl (FR)
55 **PORT DOUGLAS (IRE)**, b c Galileo (IRE)—Walzerkoenigin (USA)
56 **PREFER (IRE)**, b f Galileo (IRE)—Pieds de Plume (FR)
57 **PRETTY PERFECT (IRE)**, b f Galileo (IRE)—Milanova (AUS)
58 **QUEEN OF INDIA (IRE)**, b f Fastnet Rock (AUS)—Queen Titi (IRE)
59 **RHINESTONE (IRE)**, b c Montjeu (IRE)—Apticanti (USA)
60 **ROMANESQUE (IRE)**, b c Montjeu (IRE)—Seatone (USA)
61 **SAN FRANCISCO (IRE)**, b c Galileo (IRE)—Rumplestiltskin (IRE)
62 **SANTA ANITA (IRE)**, b c Fastnet Rock (AUS)—Prowess (IRE)
63 **SANTIAGO DE CUBA (IRE)**, b c Pour Moi (IRE)—Marjalina (IRE)
64 **SCHUBERT (USA)**, b c War Front (USA)—Score (IRE)
65 **SEAN O'CASEY (IRE)**, b c Galileo (IRE)—Lahinch (IRE)
66 **SEVENTH HEAVEN (IRE)**, b f Galileo (IRE)—La Traviata (USA)
67 **SHOGUN (IRE)**, b c Fastnet Rock (AUS)—Perihelion (IRE)
68 **SOMEHOW (IRE)**, b f Fastnet Rock (AUS)—Alexandrova (IRE)
69 **STONE MOUNTAIN (IRE)**, b c Fastnet Rock (AUS)—Delphinium (IRE)
70 **SUCCESSOR (IRE)**, b c Galileo (IRE)—Dame Again (AUS)
71 **SWORD FIGHTER (IRE)**, b br c Galileo (IRE)—Tarbela (IRE)
72 **THE GURKHA (IRE)**, b c Galileo (IRE)—Chintz (IRE)
73 **THE MAJOR GENERAL (IRE)**, b c Galileo (IRE)—Scribonia (IRE)
74 **THREE STAR GENERAL (IRE)**, b c Montjeu (IRE)—Honorlina (FR)
75 **TREASURE CHEST (IRE)**, b c Galileo (IRE)—Bonheur (IRE)
76 **TREE OF KNOWLEDGE (IRE)**, b c Oasis Dream—Wonder of Wonders (USA)
77 **TRIPLICATE (IRE)**, b c Galileo (IRE)—Devoted To You (IRE)
78 **UNICORN (IRE)**, b c Galileo (IRE)—One Moment In Time (IRE)

MR A. P. O'BRIEN - Continued

79 US ARMY RANGER (IRE), b c Galileo (IRE)—Moonstone
80 WASHINGTON DC (IRE), b c Zoffany (IRE)—How's She Cuttin' (IRE)
81 WATERLOO BRIDGE (IRE), b c Zoffany (IRE)—Miss Childrey (IRE)
82 WAY TO MY HEART (IRE), ch f Galileo (IRE)—Mystical Lady (IRE)

TWO-YEAR-OLDS

83 B c 8/5 Galileo (IRE)—Airwave (Air Express (IRE))
84 B f 22/2 Fastnet Rock (AUS)—All For Glory (Giant's Causeway (USA))
85 B c 27/1 Galileo (IRE)—Alluring Park (IRE) (Green Desert (USA)) (1250000)
86 B c 14/2 Galileo (IRE)—Alta Anna (FR) (Anabaa (USA))
87 B c 11/2 Invincible Spirit (IRE)—Alta Moda (Sadler's Wells (USA)) (190000)
88 B c 27/3 Power—Amber Nectar (IRE) (Barathea (IRE)) (110741)
89 B c 24/1 Galileo (IRE)—Anatola (GER) (Tiger Hill (IRE))
90 B c 4/5 Galileo (IRE)—Anna Karenina (IRE) (Green Desert (USA))
91 B c 8/3 Fastnet Rock (AUS)—Arabian Mirage (Oasis Dream) (100000)
92 B c 3/5 Invincible Spirit (IRE)—Ashley Hall (USA) (Maria's Mon (USA)) (220000)
93 B c 13/3 Galileo (IRE)—Baraka (IRE) (Danehill (USA))
94 B c 21/4 Scat Daddy (USA)—Barometer (USA) (Point Given (USA)) (183150)
95 B c 2/5 Galileo (IRE)—Blue Symphony (Darshaan)
96 B c 6/4 Galileo (IRE)—Bonheur (IRE) (Royal Academy (USA))
97 B c 15/3 Galileo (IRE)—Breeze Hill (IRE) (Danehill (USA))
98 B c 28/3 Galileo (IRE)—Brightest (Rainbow Quest (USA))
99 Ch c 26/1 Galileo (IRE)—Cape Columbine (Diktat)
100 B c 21/3 Galileo (IRE)—Charlotte Bronte (Danehill Dancer (IRE))
101 B c 7/3 Zoffany (IRE)—Chelsey Jayne (IRE) (Galileo (IRE)) (57142)
102 B c 5/5 Galileo (IRE)—Coachella (Danehill (USA))
103 B c 12/5 Galileo (IRE)—Crystal Valkyrie (IRE) (Danehill (USA)) (600000)
104 B c 25/3 Galileo (IRE)—Danedrop (IRE) (Danehill (USA))
105 Gr c 7/2 Galileo (IRE)—Dialafara (FR) (Anabaa (USA))
106 B f 10/4 Fastnet Rock (AUS)—Dietrich (USA) (Storm Cat (USA))
107 B c 9/5 Galileo (IRE)—Divine Proportions (USA) (Kingmambo (USA))
108 B c 19/1 Galileo (IRE)—Famous (IRE) (Danehill Dancer (IRE))
109 B c 27/2 Galileo (IRE)—Flames (Blushing Flame (USA)) (184569)
110 B c 6/3 Excelebration (IRE)—Four Eleven (CAN) (Arch (USA))
111 B c 21/1 Galileo (IRE)—Hawala (IRE) (Warning)
112 B c 25/4 Galileo (IRE)—Healing Music (FR) (Bering) (191952)
113 B c 14/3 Power—Hoh My Darling (Dansili) (92284)
114 B f 1/5 War Front (USA)—Imagine (IRE) (Sadler's Wells (USA))
115 B c 13/4 Rock of Gibraltar (IRE)—Inchina (Montjeu (IRE)) (250000)
116 B c 18/2 War Front (USA)—Kissed (IRE) (Galileo (IRE))
117 B c 19/3 Galileo (IRE)—Kitty Kiernan (Pivotal)
118 B c 11/2 Fastnet Rock (AUS)—Lady Lupus (IRE) (High Chaparral (IRE))
119 B c 10/2 Excelebration (IRE)—Lady Miletrian (IRE) (Barathea (IRE)) (475000)
120 B f 3/3 War Front (USA)—Liscanna (IRE) (Sadler's Wells (USA))
121 B c 27/4 Galileo (IRE)—Love Me True (USA) (Kingmambo (USA))
122 B c 4/5 War Front (USA)—Magnificent Honour (USA) (A P Indy (USA)) (549450)
123 B f 8/2 Deep Impact (JPN)—Maybe (IRE) (Galileo (IRE))
124 Gr ro c 23/2 Scat Daddy (USA)—Mekko Hokte (USA) (Holy Bull (USA))
125 B c 31/1 Galileo (IRE)—Meow (IRE) (Storm Cat (USA))
126 B c 5/4 Galileo (IRE)—Miarixa (FR) (Linamix (FR))
127 B f 2/2 War Front (USA)—Misty For Me (IRE) (Galileo (IRE))
128 B c 4/5 Galileo (IRE)—Mystical Lady (IRE) (Halling (USA))
129 B c 11/3 Galileo (IRE)—Nell Gwyn (IRE) (Danehill (USA))
130 B br c 18/4 War Front (USA)—Orate (USA) (A P Indy (USA)) (702075)
131 Ch c 25/4 Galileo (IRE)—Pale Moon Rising (IRE) (Kingmambo (USA)) (191952)
132 B c 2/2 Deep Impact (JPN)—Peeping Fawn (USA) (Danehill (USA))
133 B c 13/5 Galileo (IRE)—Penchant (Kyllachy)
134 B c 5/3 Dubawi (IRE)—Pink Symphony (Montjeu (IRE))
135 B c 26/3 Galileo (IRE)—Queen of France (USA) (Danehill (USA))
136 B c 1/2 Galileo (IRE)—Queenscliff (IRE) (Danehill Dancer (IRE))
137 B c 28/4 Galileo (IRE)—Race For The Stars (USA) (Fusaichi Pegasus (USA))
138 B f 10/3 Zoffany (IRE)—Roselita (IRE) (Sadler's Wells (USA))
139 B c 16/4 Frankel—Rosie's Posy (IRE) (Suave Dancer (USA))
140 B c 17/5 Galileo (IRE)—Six Perfections (FR) (Celtic Swing)
141 B c 20/3 Rip Van Winkle (IRE)—Slink (Selkirk (USA))

MR A. P. O'BRIEN - Continued

142 B c 25/2 Excelebration (IRE)—Something Exciting (Halling (USA)) (110741)
143 B c 19/4 Zoffany (IRE)—Swingsky (IRE) (Indian Ridge) (80000)
144 B c 9/5 Galileo (IRE)—Tarbela (IRE) (Grand Lodge (USA))
145 B f 26/1 Power—Tarfshi (Mtoto) (180000)
146 B f 27/1 War Front (USA)—Together (IRE) (Galileo (IRE))
147 B c 5/3 Oasis Dream—Toi Et Moi (IRE) (Galileo (IRE))
148 B c 16/2 Galileo (IRE)—Turbulent Descent (USA) (Congrats (USA))
149 B c 3/4 War Front (USA)—Upperline (USA) (Maria's Mon (USA))
150 Ch c 18/3 Galileo (IRE)—Ventura (IRE) (Spectrum (IRE))
151 B c 12/3 Galileo (IRE)—Wave (IRE) (Dansili)
152 B c 20/2 Galileo (IRE)—Weekend Strike (USA) (Smart Strike (CAN))
153 B c 29/3 War Front (USA)—Wild Poppy (USA) (El Prado (IRE)) (305250)
154 B c 28/1 Galileo (IRE)—You'resothrilling (USA) (Storm Cat (USA))
155 B c 17/3 Pour Moi (IRE)—Ysoldina (FR) (Kendor (FR)) (162421)

---

457 **MR DANIEL O'BRIEN, Tonbridge**
Postal: **Knowles Bank, Capel, Tonbridge, Kent, TN11 0PU**
Contacts: **PHONE (01892) 824072**

1 **BOSTIN (IRE)**, 8, ch g Busy Flight—Bustingoutallover (USA) **D. C. O'Brien**
2 **CANTOR**, 8, b g Iceman—Choir Mistress **D. C. O'Brien**
3 **CHOCOLATE DIAMOND (IRE)**, 5, ch g Intense Focus (USA)—Sagemacca (USA) **D. C. O'Brien**
4 **INTHEJUNGLE (IRE)**, 13, ch g Bob Back (USA)—Whizz **D. C. O'Brien**
5 **IT'S ALL AN ACT (IRE)**, 8, br g Presenting—Royal Lucy (IRE) **Mrs V. O'Brien**
6 **MINORITY INTEREST**, 7, ch g Galileo (IRE)—Minority **D. C. O'Brien**
7 **NOUAILHAS**, 10, b g Mark of Esteem (IRE)—Barachois Princess (USA) **D. C. O'Brien**
8 **SPARTILLA**, 7, b g Teofilo (IRE)—Wunders Dream (IRE) **D. C. O'Brien**
9 **STAGE KING**, 10, b g King's Theatre (IRE)—Blue Dante (IRE) **D. C. O'Brien**

Assistant Trainer: Christopher O'Bryan

Jockey (NH): Mattie Batchelor, Sam Twiston-Davies.

---

458 **MR FERGAL O'BRIEN, Cheltenham**
Postal: **Upper Yard, Grange Hill Farm, Naunton, Cheltenham, Gloucestershire, GL54 3AY**
Contacts: **PHONE (01285) 721150 MOBILE (07771) 702829**
E-MAIL fergaljelly@aol.com

1 **ALLERTON (IRE)**, 9, b g Flemensfirth (USA)—Bonny Hall (IRE) **Mr F. M. O'Brien**
2 **BARNEY DWAN (IRE)**, 6, b g Vinnie Roe (IRE)—Kapricia Speed (FR) **Mr & Mrs Paul & Clare Rooney**
3 **BUACHAILL BEAG**, 5, gr g And Beyond (IRE)—Bon Enfant (IRE) **Mrs P. Duncan**
4 **CHASE THE SPUD**, 8, b g Alflora (IRE)—Trial Trip **Mrs C. J. Banks**
5 **CHILLI ROMANCE (IRE)**, 5, b m Flemensfirth (USA)—Blue Romance (IRE) **Mr I. Slatter**
6 **COLIN'S SISTER**, 5, b m Central Park (USA)—Dd's Glenalla (IRE) **Mrs C. S. C. Beresford-Wylie**
7 **CREEVYTENNANT (IRE)**, 12, b g Bob's Return (IRE)—Northwood May **Mrs P. Duncan**
8 **DIAMOND GESTURE**, 8, ch m Presenting—Rare Gesture (IRE) **M. Fahy**
9 **DOUBLE SILVER**, 9, gr m Silver Patriarch (IRE)—Shadows of Silver **Mr R. C. Mayall**
10 **FARMER MATT (IRE)**, 10, b br g Zagreb (USA)—Ashville Native (IRE) **Mr F. M. O'Brien**
11 **GALLIC WARRIOR (FR)**, 9, b g Nononito (FR)—Rosa Gallica **The Gud Times Partnership**
12 **GALVESTON (IRE)**, 7, ch g Presenting—Rare Gesture (IRE) **M. Fahy**
13 **GRAND INTRODUCTION (IRE)**, 6, b g Robin des Pres (FR)—What A Breeze (IRE) **Geoffrey & Donna Keeys**
14 **IORA GLAS (IRE)**, 7, gr g Court Cave (IRE)—Crossdrumrosie (IRE) **Imperial Racing Partnership**
15 **ISLA FERNANDOS (IRE)**, 6, ch m Flemensfirth (USA)—Kon Tiky (FR) **Graham & Alison Jelley**
16 **JENNYS SURPRISE (IRE)**, 8, b m Hawk Wing (USA)—
Winning Jenny (IRE) **Yes No Wait Sorries & G & P Barker Ltd**
17 **KING MURO**, 6, b g Halling (USA)—Ushindi (IRE) **The General Asphalte Company Ltd**
18 **LILYWHITE GESTURE (IRE)**, 7, b m Presenting—Loyal Gesture (IRE) **M. Fahy**
19 **LORD LANDEN (IRE)**, 11, br g Beneficial—Agua Caliente (IRE) **The B Lucky Partnership**
20 **LOVELY JOB (IRE)**, 6, ch g Touch of Land (FR)—Wyckoff Queen (IRE) **Mr & Mrs Paul & Clare Rooney**
21 **MAN FROM SEVILLE (IRE)**, 6, ch g Duke of Marmalade (IRE)—Basanti (USA) **Mr & Mrs William Rucker**
22 **MISS MAIDEN OVER (IRE)**, 4, b f Carlo Bank (IRE)—Rock Garden (IRE) **The Yes No Wait Sorries**
23 **MORE THAN TWO**, 6, b m Kayf Tara—Sweet Stormy (IRE) **Mr F. M. O'Brien**

MR FERGAL O'BRIEN - Continued

24 **MYSTIFIABLE (IRE)**, 8, gr g Kayf Tara—Royal Keel **Graham & Alison Jelley**
25 **OUR CAT (IRE)**, 8, b m Royal Anthem (USA)—Run Cat (IRE) **The General Asphalte Company Ltd**
26 **OWEN NA VIEW (IRE)**, 8, b br g Presenting—Lady Zephyr (IRE) **The Yes No Wait Sorries**
27 **PERFECT CANDIDATE (IRE)**, 9, b g Winged Love (IRE)—Dansana (IRE) **ISL Recruitment**
28 **POISONED BERRY (IRE)**, 4, b f Scorpion (IRE)—Prunelle (GER) **Mr M. Hampson**
29 **PRIDE OF LECALE**, 5, b g Multiplex—Rock Gossip (IRE) **Mr & Mrs Paul & Clare Rooney**
30 **RIO MILAN (IRE)**, 10, b g Milan—Lady Medina (IRE) **Mrs J. Cumiskey Mr T. Joyce**
31 **SHAKE DEVANEY (IRE)**, 6, b g Rakti—Ediyrna (IRE) **Mr T. Conway & Mrs Conway**
32 **SILVER ROQUE (FR)**, 10, b g Laveron—Bible Gun (FR) **Lord Vestey**
33 **SO OSCAR (IRE)**, 8, b g Oscar (IRE)—So Proper (IRE) **Mrs K. G. Exall**
34 **SON OF SUZIE (IRE)**, 8, gr g Midnight Legend—Suzie Cream Cheese (IRE) **Mrs P. Duncan**
35 **THREE OF A KIND (IRE)**, 7, b g Helissio (FR)—Monadore (IRE) **The Yes No Wait Sorries**
36 **TINELYRA (IRE)**, 10, b g Mr Combustible (IRE)—Ladyogan (IRE) **Mr M. Costello**
37 **TRESPASSERS WILL (IRE)**, 5, b g Scorpion (IRE)—Drum Majorette **Geoffrey & Donna Keeys**
38 **TROIKA STEPPES**, 8, b g Pasternak—Killerton Clover **Mr W. Williamson**
39 **WHERE'S CHERRY (IRE)**, 5, b m King's Theatre (IRE)—I'm Grand (IRE) **Mr F. M. O'Brien**

Other Owners: M. A. Blackford, Mr S. W. Bowers, C. S. J. Coley, Mrs M. Conway, T. Conway, Mrs K. T. Cumiskey, G. & P. Barker Ltd, D. M. Hussey, G. S. Jelley, Mrs A. D. Jelley, T. F. Joyce, G. F. Keeys, Mrs C. M. Keeys, B. M. Mathieson, Mr P. Nurden, I. Robinson, Miss M. R. Robinson, Mr P. A. Rooney, Mrs C. Rooney, Mrs A. Rucker, W. J. Rucker.

459
MR EDWARD J. O'GRADY, Thurles
Postal: **Killeens, Ballynonty, Thurles, Co. Tipperary, Ireland**
Contacts: **PHONE (00353) 529 156 156 FAX (00353) 529 156 466 MOBILE (00353) 86 2590764**
E-MAIL edward@edwardogrady.com

1 **ALL SOULS (IRE)**, 4, b c Cape Cross (IRE)—Altruiste (USA) **Gaticoma Syndicate**
2 **ALLARDYCE**, 4, b g Black Sam Bellamy (IRE)—Woore Lass (IRE) **S. Davis**
3 **BIGGS (IRE)**, 4, b br g Getaway (GER)—California Blue (FR) **J. W. O'Grady**
4 , Ch c Definite Article—Can't Stop (GER) **S. Davis**
5 **CAPBRETON (FR)**, 6, b g Linda's Lad—Noblesse de Robe (FR) **Glebeland Farm Partnership**
6 **EAGLE RIDGE (IRE)**, 5, b g Oscar (IRE)—Azaban (IRE) **John Power**
7 **EARLSHILL (IRE)**, 5, b g Milan—Mrs Marples (IRE) **Mrs E. J. O'Grady, H. Tylor**
8 **GALLANT TIPP (IRE)**, 8, b g Definite Article—Noble Delight (IRE) **John P. McManus**
9 **GETTING LATE (IRE)**, 6, b g Milan—On The Hour (IRE) **John P. McManus**
10 **GREAT KHAN (IRE)**, 5, b g Kalanisi (IRE)—Can't Stop (GER) **Jonathan O'Grady**
11 **ITSNOTHINGPERSONAL (IRE)**, 6, b g Beneficial—Savu Sea (IRE) **John P. McManus**
12 **JUMPTOCONCLUSIONS (IRE)**, 7, b g Scorpion (IRE)—Can't Stop (GER) **John P. McManus**
13 **KITTEN ROCK (FR)**, 6, b g Laverock (IRE)—The Cat Eater (FR) **John P. McManus**
14 **LE VAGABOND (FR)**, 4, b g Footstepsinthesand—Miryale (FR) **Weir Syndicate**
15 4, Br g Portrait Gallery (IRE)—Molly Hussey (IRE) **Glebeland Farm**
16 **MR NICOLLS (IRE)**, 5, b g Milan—Mrs Dempsey (IRE) **Mrs Paul Shanahan, T. Hyde**
17 **MY MATADOR (IRE)**, 5, b g Kandahar Run—My Special (IRE) **Three Jays Partnership**
18 **NERANO (IRE)**, 5, b g Milan—Derriana (IRE) **Louise Fitzgerald (Loumar Partnership)**
19 4, B g Arcadio (GER)—Nylon (GER) **S. Davis**
20 **ORCHESTRAL RUN (IRE)**, 5, b g Mahler—Baunfaun Run (IRE) **Mrs E. J. O'Grady (Loumar)**
21 **PRICKLY (IRE)**, 6, ch g Definite Article—Connemara Rose (IRE) **Simon J. H. Davis**
22 **PRINCE KUP (IRE)**, 5, ch g High Rock (IRE)—Lockup (IRE) **Louise Fitzgerald (Loumar Partnership)**
23 **REFLET AMBRE (FR)**, 6, b g Smadoun (FR)—Glinka Des Aigles (FR) **Ms Louise Fitzgerald**
24 **ROCONGA (IRE)**, 6, b g Rakti—Nafzira (IRE) **Robert Byrne**
25 **SLIPPERY SERPENT (IRE)**, 5, b g Scorpion (IRE)—Tres Chic (IRE) **Mrs E. J. O'Grady**
26 4, B f Kalanisi (IRE)—Soul Mate (IRE) **Mrs E. J. O'Grady**
27 **SOUND MONEY**, 4, b g Zamindar (USA)—Alpensinfonie (IRE) **Out of The Blue Syndicate**
28 **THE WEST'S AWAKE (IRE)**, 5, b g Yeats (IRE)—Bilboa (FR) **Mrs John Magnier**
29 **TOBAR NA GAOISE (IRE)**, 8, b g Whipper (USA)—Starchy **John P. McManus**

THREE-YEAR-OLDS

30 **DUNDRUM DUCHESS (IRE)**, b f Arakan (USA)—Broken Spectre **Mrs E. J. O'Grady**
31 **FAIR GAME (IRE)**, b f Lawman (FR)—Ascendancy **Mrs E. J. O'Grady**

TWO-YEAR-OLDS

32 Ch f 28/3 Rip Van Winkle (IRE)—Chervil (Dansili) (13289) **Mrs E. J. O'Grady**

460 **MR JEDD O'KEEFFE, Leyburn**
Postal: Highbeck, Brecongill, Coverham, Leyburn, North Yorkshire, DL8 4TJ
Contacts: **PHONE (01969) 640330 FAX (01969) 640397 MOBILE (07710) 476705**
E-MAIL jedd@jeddokeefferacing.co.uk WEBSITE www.jeddokeefferacing.co.uk

1 **CHARLES DE MILLE**, 8, b g Tiger Hill (IRE)—Apple Town **Mrs Liz Ingham**
2 **DANOT (IRE)**, 4, ch g Zebedee—Haipipi **United We Stand**
3 **DARK OCEAN (IRE)**, 6, b g Dylan Thomas (IRE)—Neutral **The Fatalists**
4 4, B g Black Sam Bellamy (IRE)—Dawn Spinner **Caron & Paul Chapman**
5 4, B f Oscar (IRE)—Divine Prospect (IRE) **Caron & Paul Chapman**
6 **INSTANT ATTRACTION (IRE)**, 5, b g Tagula (IRE)—Coup de Coeur (IRE) **United We Stand**
7 **LADY POPPY**, 6, b m Kyllachy—Poppets Sweetlove **Ingham Racing Syndicate**
8 **MEDICINE HAT**, 5, b g Multiplex—Blushing Heart **Mrs S. M. Pearson**
9 **MORE MISCHIEF**, 4, b f Azamour (IRE)—Mischief Making (USA) **Caron & Paul Chapman**
10 **SHARED EQUITY**, 5, b g Elnadim (USA)—Pelican Key **Caron & Paul Chapman**
11 **SLEEPING APACHE (IRE)**, 6, ch g Sleeping Indian—Remedy **Mr & Mrs G. Turnbull**
12 **SOVEREIGN BOUNTY**, 4, ch g Bahamian Bounty—Sovereign Abbey (IRE) **Caron & Paul Chapman**
13 **STRUCTURED NOTE (IRE)**, 4, b g Acclamation—Saik (USA) **Caron & Paul Chapman**
14 **TOOLA BOOLA**, 6, b m Tobougg (IRE)—Forsythia **Ingham Racing Syndicate**

THREE-YEAR-OLDS

15 **CANDELISA (IRE)**, br c Dream Ahead (USA)—Vasilia **Paul & Dale Chapman Racing**
16 **DESERT RULER**, b g Kheleyf (USA)—Desert Royalty (IRE) **Highbeck Racing**
17 **INJAM (IRE)**, b g Pour Moi (IRE)—Sniffle (IRE) **Highbeck Racing**
18 **KING'S CURRENCY**, b g Kheleyf (USA)—Mint Royale (USA) **Highbeck Racing**
19 **LAILA HONIWILLOW**, b f Bahamian Bounty—Anatase **Caron & Paul Chapman**
20 **LORD YEATS**, b c Yeats (IRE)—Bogside Theatre (IRE) **Mr & Mrs G. Turnbull**
21 **WHITKIRK**, b g Iffraaj—Bedouin Bride (USA) **T. S. Ingham**

TWO-YEAR-OLDS

22 Ch c 17/4 Notnowcato—Asi (USA) (El Prado (IRE)) (10000) **Arthur Walker**
23 B c 7/4 Fastnet Rock (AUS)—Attasliyah (IRE) (Marju (IRE)) (55000) **Caron & Paul Chapman**
24 B c 9/2 Lilbourne Lad (IRE)—Brunch Bellini (FR) (Peintre Celebre (USA)) (19047) **Paul & Dale Chapman Racing**
25 B c 20/4 Bated Breath—Cresta Gold (Halling (USA)) **Paul & Dale Chapman Racing**
26 Ch c 21/4 Casamento—Mystery Hill (USA) (Danehill (USA)) **Paul & Dale Chapman Racing**
27 B c 8/2 Sayif (IRE)—Noble Nova (Fraam) (20000) **Highbeck Racing**
28 B c 19/2 Royal Applause—Oatcake (Selkirk (USA)) (28571) **Paul & Dale Chapman Racing**
29 B g 4/3 Proclamation (IRE)—Spirit of Ecstacy (Val Royal (FR)) **Mrs S. M. Pearson**

Assistant Trainer: Miss Leanne Kershaw

Jockey (NH): Brian Harding.

461 **MR DAVID O'MEARA, Upper Helmsley**
Postal: Willow Farm, Upper Helmsley, York, YO41 1JX
Contacts: **PHONE (01759) 372427 MOBILE (07747) 825418**
E-MAIL info@davidomeara.co.uk WEBSITE www.davidomeara.co.uk

1 **AFONSO DE SOUSA (USA)**, 6, br g Henrythenavigator (USA)—
Mien (USA) **Middleham Park Racing XCVII & Partners**
2 **ALEJANDRO (IRE)**, 7, b g Dark Angel (IRE)—Carallia (IRE) **Lydonford Ltd**
3 **ALL YOU (IRE)**, 4, b g Siyouni (FR)—Diamond Light (USA) **A Turton, J Blackburn, L Bond & J Kay**
4 **ALPHABETICAL ORDER**, 8, B G Alflora (IRE)—Lady Turk (FR)
5 **AWAKE MY SOUL (IRE)**, 7, ch g Teofilo (IRE)—Field of Hope (IRE) **Zaro Srl**
6 **BERLUSCA (IRE)**, 7, b g Holy Roman Emperor (IRE)—Shemanikha (FR) **Mr P. Ball**
7 **BIRDMAN (IRE)**, 6, b g Danehill Dancer (IRE)—Gilded Vanity (IRE) **Ebor Racing Club IV**
8 **BURANO (IRE)**, 7, ch g Dalakhani (IRE)—Kalimanta (IRE) **The Lawton Bamforth Partnership**
9 **CHANCERY (USA)**, 8, b br g Street Cry (USA)—Follow That Dream **Hollowdean**
10 **CLASSIC FLYER**, 4, b g Stimulation (IRE)—Tranquil Flight **The Classic Strollers Partnership**
11 **CUSTOM CUT (IRE)**, 7, b g Notnowcato—Polished Gem (IRE) **Frank Gillespie & Pat Breslin**
12 **DANDYLEEKIE (IRE)**, 4, B C Dandy Man (IRE)—Cockaleekie (USA)
13 **DUBAI HILLS**, 10, b g Dubai Destination (USA)—Hill Welcome **Mrs F. Denniff**
14 **FATTSOTA**, 8, b g Oasis Dream—Gift of The Night (USA)
15 **FIRMAMENT**, 4, b g Cape Cross (IRE)—Heaven Sent

MR DAVID O'MEARA - Continued

16 **FLYMAN**, 6, b g Pastoral Pursuits—Satin Bell **G. Murray**
17 **FOREIGN DIPLOMAT**, 4, b g Oasis Dream—Longing To Dance **Clipper Group Holdings Ltd**
18 **FORT BASTION (FR)**, 7, b g Lawman (FR)—French Fern (IRE) **Sprint Thoroughbred Racing Ltd**
19 **FREE ZONE**, 7, b g Kyllachy—Aldora **Fromthestables.com Racing** McBride McKay
20 **HARWOODS VOLANTE (IRE)**, 5, ch g Kheleyf (USA)—Semiquaver (IRE) **Great Northern Partnership**
21 **HE'S NO SAINT**, 5, b g Dutch Art—Stellar Brilliant (USA) **Peter R Ball & All About York Partners**
22 **HIGH AND FLIGHTY (IRE)**, 4, b f High Chaparral (IRE)—Missionary Hymn (USA) **Mr W. Hoffman Racing**
23 **HIGHLAND ACCLAIM (IRE)**, 5, b g Acclamation—Emma's Star (ITY) **Mr E.M. Sutherland**
24 **HIT THE JACKPOT (IRE)**, 7, ch g Pivotal—Token Gesture (IRE) **Hambleton Racing Ltd XXX**
25 **INNOCENTLY (IRE)**, 5, ch g Kheleyf (USA)—Innocency (USA) **Mr H. T. H. Dean**
26 **INTISAAB**, 5, b g Elnadim (USA)—Katoom (IRE) **Mr S. Graham**
27 **JEBEDIAH SHINE**, 4, ch f Kyllachy—Ardessie **Sterling Racing**
28 **LORD OF THE LAND (IRE)**, 5, b h Shamardal (USA)—Lady Vettori
29 **LOUIS THE PIOUS**, 8, b br g Holy Roman Emperor (IRE)—Whole Grain **F. Gillespie**
30 **MARAAKIB (IRE)**, 4, b g Dark Angel (IRE)—Mrs Cee (IRE) **Mr E.M. Sutherland**
31 **MIME DANCE**, 5, b g Notnowcato—Encore My Love
32 **MOVE IN TIME**, 8, ch g Monsieur Bond (IRE)—Tibesti **A. Turton, J. Blackburn & R. Bond**
33 **MUSTAQQIL (IRE)**, 4, b g Invincible Spirit (IRE)—Cast In Gold **Mr E.M. Sutherland**
34 **NONCHALANT**, 5, gr g Oasis Dream—Comeback Queen **Mr E.M. Sutherland**
35 **OLIVE MARY**, 4, b f Authorized (IRE)—Jetbeeah (IRE) **Mrs R. J. Mitchell**
36 **OSARUVEETIL (IRE)**, 5, b g Teofilo (IRE)—Caraiyma (IRE)
37 **PANDORA (IRE)**, 4, ch f Galileo (IRE)—Song of My Heart (IRE)
38 **PROVIDENT SPIRIT**, 5, b g Invincible Spirit (IRE)—Port Providence **Will Salthouse, Mick O'Neill, Tina Pardew**
39 **REGAL DAN (IRE)**, 6, b g Dark Angel (IRE)—Charlene Lacy (IRE) **One For The Road & Partner**
40 **REX IMPERATOR**, 7, b g Royal Applause—Elidore **Mr G. D. Turner**
41 **RURAL CELEBRATION**, 5, b m Pastoral Pursuits—Queens Jubilee **Hambleton Racing Ltd - Two Chances**
42 **SALATEEN (IRE)**, 4, ch c Dutch Art—Amanda Carter **Sheikh A. H. F. M. A. Al Sabah**
43 **SAVED BY THE BELL (IRE)**, 6, b g Teofilo (IRE)—Eyrecourt (IRE) **Mr J Blackburn & Mr A Turton**
44 **SEAMSTER**, 9, ch g Pivotal—Needles And Pins (IRE) **P. Bamford**
45 **SINAKAR (IRE)**, 5, b g Manduro (GER)—Siniyya (USA) **Nicholson Baker**
46 **SIR LANCELOTT**, 4, b g Piccolo—Selkirk Rose (IRE) **Mr G. Brogan**
47 **SO BELOVED**, 6, b g Dansili—Valencia **Sprint Thoroughbred Racing Ltd**
48 **STEEL TRAIN (FR)**, 5, b g Zafeen (FR)—Silent Sunday (IRE) **Rasio Cymru I & Dutch Rose Partnerhsip**
49 **SUEDOIS (FR)**, 5, b g Le Havre (IRE)—Cup Cake (IRE)
50 **TAVENER**, 4, b g Exceed And Excel (AUS)—Sea Chorus **Baker, Hensby, Longden, Baker 1**
51 **TERHAAL (IRE)**, 4, b g Raven's Pass (USA)—Silk Trail **Mr J Blackburn & Mr A Turton**
52 **THAT IS THE SPIRIT**, 5, b g Invincible Spirit (IRE)—Fraulein **F. Gillespie**
53 **TREASURY NOTES (IRE)**, 4, b g Lope de Vega (IRE)—Elegant As Well (IRE) **Mr C. T. Proctor**
54 **TRUSTAN TIMES (IRE)**, 10, b g Heron Island (IRE)—
                                          Ballytrustan Maid (IRE) **Mr Ian Armitage & Mr Peter Armitage**

THREE-YEAR-OLDS

55 **ALSVINDER**, b c Footstepsinthesand—Notting Hill (BRZ) **F. Gillespie**
56 **CAPE LOVE (USA)**, ch c Cape Blanco (IRE)—Matroshka (IRE) **Crone Stud Farms Ltd**
57 **COQUINE**, b f Monsieur Bond (IRE)—Stolen Glance **R. S. Cockerill (Farms) Ltd**
58 **CORAL ISLAND**, ch f Equiano (FR)—Windermere Island **Coral Champions Club**
59 **DARK ILLUSTRATOR**, b f Dutch Art—Xtrasensory **Mr L. Bond**
60 **FIRST BOMBARDMENT**, br g Pastoral Pursuits—Magic Myth (IRE) **Northern Hart Racing & Partner**
61 **FLYBOY (IRE)**, b c Zoffany (IRE)—In Dubai (USA) **G. Murray**
62 **HARAZ (IRE)**, b g Acclamation—Hanakiyya (IRE)
63 **HURRICANE HICKS (USA)**, ch g Speightstown (USA)—Specific Dream **Middleham Park Racing CXII & Partner**
64 **ICONIC FIGURE (IRE)**, b g Approve (IRE)—Tough Chic (IRE) **Mr A. Harte**
65 **MON BEAU VISAGE (IRE)**, br g Footstepsinthesand—Hurricane Lily (IRE) **The Pink Pot Partnership LLP**
66 **MUROOR**, ch g Nayef (USA)—Raaya (USA)
67 **NORTH SPIRIT (IRE)**, b g Zebedee—Zara's Girl (IRE) **Mr G. Brogan**
68 Ch f Tagula (IRE)—Santacus (IRE)
69 **TAKALEYF**, b c Kheleyf (USA)—Takarna (IRE) **Hambleton Racing Ltd XXXIX**
70 **TOLSTOY (IRE)**, b c Galileo (IRE)—Song of My Heart (IRE)

TWO-YEAR-OLDS

71 **BLACK ISLE BOY (IRE)**, b c 4/2 Elzaam (AUS)—Shadow Mountain (Selkirk (USA)) (34285) **Mr E.M. Sutherland**
72 B f 22/3 Dutch Art—Eyes (Echo of Light) (110000)
73 B f 7/3 Camacho—Dot Hill (Refuse To Bend) (24000) **Clipper Group Holdings Ltd**
74 **FLEETFOOT JACK (IRE)**, b c 27/3 Kyllachy—Move (Observatory (USA)) (185000)
75 B f 2/4 Nathaniel (IRE)—Impressible (Oasis Dream) (61904) **Clipper Group Holdings Ltd**

MR DAVID O'MEARA - Continued

76 B c 29/4 Kodiac—Jacquelin Jag (IRE) (Fayruz) (32484) **Clipper Group Holdings Ltd**
77 B f 10/5 Dream Ahead (USA)—Kartella (IRE) (Whipper (USA)) (10000) **Nawton Racing Partnership**
78 B c 6/3 Lope de Vega (IRE)—Kate The Great (Xaar) (250000)
79 B c 10/3 Intikhab (USA)—Lady Magdalena (IRE) (Invincible Spirit (IRE)) (36913) **Clipper Group Holdings Ltd**
80 B c 10/4 Cape Cross (IRE)—Lulua (USA) (Bahri (USA)) (85000)
81 B c 10/4 Dandy Man (IRE)—My Funny Valentine (IRE) (Mukaddamah (USA)) (29531) **Clipper Group Holdings Ltd**
82 **NORTHERN ECLIPSE**, b c 21/4 Kyllachy—
                                     Quadrophenia (College Chapel) (42857) **Northern Lads Racing & Partner**
83 B f 1/4 Elzaam (AUS)—Perfectly Clear (USA) (Woodman (USA)) (8121) **Sterling Racing**
84 B f 24/3 Aqlaam—Pizzarra (Shamardal (USA)) (25714) **Clipper Group Holdings Ltd**
85 **RAY DONOVAN (IRE)**, b c 16/2 Acclamation—Always The Lady (Halling (USA)) (22886) **Sterling Racing**
86 **ROYAL HEADLEY (IRE)**, b c 6/3 Nathaniel (IRE)—
                                     Fearless Flyer (IRE) (Brave Act) (90000) **Tiffin Sandwiches Limited**
87 **SHEOAK**, ch f 8/3 Medicean—Pepper Lane (Exceed And Excel (AUS))
88 B c 3/4 Teofilo (IRE)—Twice The Ease (Green Desert (USA)) (100000)
89 B f 14/2 Dark Angel (IRE)—Viola d'amour (IRE) (Teofilo (IRE)) (55000)

Other Owners: Mr S. Allison, Mr I. Armitage, P. Armitage, Mr R. Baker, Mr P. Baker, Mr S. H. Bamforth, Beadle Bloodstock Limited, J. N. Blackburn, R. C. Bond, Mr P. Breslin, S. J. Clare, Mr A. W. Clark, R. J. Cornelius, Mr N. A. Coster, Mr C. Cox, Mr J. Cox, Mr J. W. Cox, Mr A. W. Ellis, Mr A. Fell, S. Franks, A. Franks, Mr A. L. Gregg, Hambleton Racing Ltd, Mr T. Hanrahan, Helmsley Bloodstock Limited, Mr G. D. Hensby, Mr W. Hoffman, Dr J. Hollowood, Mr D. Humphries, Mrs J. Ingham, Mr J. A. Kay, Mr I. Kellett, Mr J. Kelly, Mr P. D. Laidler, Mr M. F. Lawton, Mrs S. Magnier, Mr I. G. Martin, Mr M. McBride, Mr G. McKay, Mr K. Nicholson, D. B. O'Meara, Mr M. O'Neill, Mr G. P. O'Shea, T. S. Palin, Mrs T. F. Pardew, Mr D. J. Pentney, Mr J. D. Pierce, M. Prince, Hugh T. Redhead, Mr W. J. Salthouse, Mr J. F. Simpson, D. Smith, M. Tabor, Mr M. Taylor, S. M. Taylor, Mr K. Thompson, Mr S. R. H. Turner, Mr A. Turton, Mr R. F. Watson.

Jockey (flat): Sam James, Daniel Tudhope. **Apprentice:** Shelley Birkett, Josh Doyle.

---

462 **MR JOHN O'NEILL**, Bicester
Postal: **Hall Farm, Stratton Audley, Nr Bicester, Oxfordshire, OX27 9BT**
Contacts: **PHONE (01869) 277202 MOBILE (07785) 394128**
E-MAIL jgoneill4@gmail.com

1 **BOLLYWOOD BOY**, 5, b g Indian Danehill (IRE)—Little Miss Prim **Ms D. Keane**
2 **ONURBIKE**, 8, b g Exit To Nowhere (USA)—Lay It Off (IRE) **J. G. O'Neill**
3 **SAMIZDAT (FR)**, 13, b g Soviet Star (USA)—Secret Account (FR) **J. G. O'Neill**
4 **SHOWBIZ FLOOZY**, 7, b m Beat All (USA)—Laced Up (IRE) **J. G. O'Neill**

---

463 **MR JONJO O'NEILL**, Cheltenham
Postal: **Jackdaws Castle, Temple Guiting, Cheltenham, Gloucestershire, GL54 5XU**
Contacts: **PHONE (01386) 584209 FAX (01386) 584219**
E-MAIL reception@jonjooneillracing.com WEBSITE www.jonjooneillracing.com

1 **ABOVE BOARD (IRE)**, 5, b g Mahler—Blackwater Babe (IRE) **Mr J. P. McManus**
2 **ALLELU ALLELUIA (GER)**, 5, br g Doyen (IRE)—Anna Spectra (IRE) **Mr J. P. McManus**
3 **ALLOW DALLOW (IRE)**, 9, b g Gold Well—Russland (GER) **Regulatory Finance Solutions Ltd**
4 **AMERICAN LEGEND (IRE)**, 8, b g Presenting—Coole Eile (IRE) **Mr J. P. McManus**
5 **ANOTHER HERO (IRE)**, 7, b g Kalanisi (IRE)—Storm Front (USA) **Mr J. P. McManus**
6 **AUVERGNAT (FR)**, 6, b g Della Francesca (USA)—Hesmeralda (FR) **Mr J. P. McManus**
7 **BEG TO DIFFER (IRE)**, 6, ch g Flemensfirth (USA)—
                                     Blossom Trix (IRE) **Mrs J Magnier, Mr D Smith & Mr M Tabor**
8 **BEGGARS CROSS (IRE)**, 6, b g Presenting—Ballygill Heights (IRE) **Mr T. Hemmings**
9 **BLACKFIRE (FR)**, 4, b g Kingsalsa (USA)—Sister Celestine **The Snowshill Flyers**
10 **BOX OFFICE (FR)**, 5, b g Great Pretender (IRE)—Quelle Mome (FR) **Mr J. P. McManus**
11 **BRONCO BILLY (IRE)**, 6, b g Flemensfirth (USA)—
                                     La Fisarmonica (IRE) **Mrs J Magnier, Mr D Smith & Mr M Tabor**
12 **CAPARD KING (IRE)**, 7, b g Beneficial—Capard Lady (IRE) **Mr J B Gilruth & G & P Barker / Global Engineering**
13 **CATCHING ON (IRE)**, 8, b g Milan—Miracle Lady **Mrs Gay Smith**
14 **CELLDOMFED (IRE)**, 6, b g Beneficial—Eyebright (IRE) **Masterson Holdings Limited**
15 **CELTIC TUNE (FR)**, 5, b g Green Tune (USA)—Kerry Rose (FR) **The Power Mac Partnership**
16 **CHAMPAGNE AT TARA**, 7, gr g Kayf Tara—Champagne Lil **Mr J. P. McManus**
17 **CHAMPAGNE PRESENT (IRE)**, 6, br g Presenting—My Name's Not Bin (IRE) **Mrs Gay Smith**

MR JONJO O'NEILL - Continued

18 **CHINA GREY (FR)**, 4, gr f Slickly (FR)—Dona Bella (FR) **Regulatory Finance Solutions Ltd**
19 **CLOUDY COPPER (IRE)**, 9, gr g Cloudings (IRE)—Copper Supreme (IRE) **Mrs Gay Smith**
20 **COBOLOBO (FR)**, 4, bl g Maresca Sorrento (FR)—Nanou des Brosses (FR) **Anne, Harriet & Lucinda Bond**
21 **COMMANDING SPIRIT (IRE)**, 4, ch g Presenting—Park Athlete (IRE) **Mr Christopher W. T. Johnston**
22 **COMPADRE (IRE)**, 5, b g Yeats (IRE)—Jolivia (FR) **Mrs J Magnier, Mr D Smith & Mr M Tabor**
23 **CONTEUR D'HISTOIRE (FR)**, 4, b g Le Fou (IRE)—Page d'histoire (FR) **Cheval Brun Partnership**
24 **DANCE IN THE DUST (IRE)**, 5, b g Scorpion (IRE)—Samotracia (IRE) **Mrs Gay Smith**
25 **DESTINY'S STAR**, 4, b g Beneficial—Lady Cad (FR) **Mr Jamie Ritblat**
26 **DOESYOURDOGBITE (IRE)**, 4, b g Notnowcato—Gilah (IRE) **DYDB Marketing and Friends of Jackdaws**
27 **DREAM BERRY (FR)**, 5, gr g Dream Well (FR)—Kalberry (FR) **Mr J. P. McManus**
28 **EASTLAKE (IRE)**, 10, b g Beneficial—Guigone (FR) **Mr J. P. McManus**
29 **FESTIVE AFFAIR (IRE)**, 8, b g Presenting—Merry Batim (IRE) **Four The Fun Of It Partnership**
30 **FOR INSTANCE (IRE)**, 6, b g Milan—Justamemory (IRE) **Anne, Harriet & Lucinda Bond**
31 **FORT WORTH (IRE)**, 7, b g Presenting—Victorine (IRE) **Power Panels Electrical Systems**
32 **FORZA MILAN (IRE)**, 4, b g Milan—Nonnetia (FR) **Deep Sea Partnership**
33 **FOUNDATION MAN (IRE)**, 9, b g Presenting—Function Dream (IRE) **Mr P. Hickey**
34 **GO CONQUER (IRE)**, 7, b g Arcadio (GER)—Ballinamona Wish (IRE) **Paul & Clare Rooney**
35 **GOODWOOD MIRAGE (IRE)**, 6, b g Jeremy (USA)—Phantom Waters **Lady Bamford & Alice Bamford**
36 **GRAY HESSION (IRE)**, 9, b g Vinnie Roe (IRE)—Little Paddle (IRE) **Alan D. Gray**
37 **HEDLEY LAMARR (IRE)**, 4, b g Gold Well—Donna's Tarquin (IRE) **J. C. & S. R. Hitchins**
38 **HOLYWELL (IRE)**, 9, b g Gold Well—Hillcrest (IRE) **Mrs Gay Smith**
39 **IN THE ROUGH (IRE)**, 7, b g Scorpion (IRE)—Sounds Charming (IRE) **Mr J. P. McManus**
40 **IT'S A GIMME (IRE)**, 9, b g Beneficial—Sorcera (GER) **Mr J. P. McManus**
41 **IVY GATE (IRE)**, 8, b g Westerner—Key Partner **Jeremy & Germaine Hitchins**
42 **JOHNS SPIRIT (IRE)**, 9, b g Gold Well—Gilt Ridden (IRE) **Mr Christopher W. T. Johnston**
43 **JOIN THE CLAN (IRE)**, 7, b g Milan—Millicent Bridge (IRE) **Mr J. P. McManus**
44 **KAMOOL (GER)**, 6, ch g Mamool (IRE)—Kiss Me Lips (GER) **Lets Live Racing**
45 **KELVINGROVE (IRE)**, 6, b g Hurricane Run (IRE)—Silversword (FR) **The All In Syndicate**
46 **KOVERA (FR)**, 4, b g Antarctique (IRE)—Kesakao (FR) **Anne, Harriet & Lucinda Bond**
47 **LITHIC (IRE)**, 5, b g Westerner—Acoola (IRE) **Jon & Julia Aisbitt**
48 **LOST LEGEND (IRE)**, 9, b g Winged Love (IRE)—Well Orchestrated (IRE) **Mrs Gay Smith**
49 **MAD JACK MYTTON (IRE)**, 6, b g Arcadio (GER)—Gilt Ridden (IRE) **J. C. & S. R. Hitchins**
50 4, B g Getaway (GER)—Madame Martine (IRE) **Penman Bond Partnership**
51 **MANNY OWENS (IRE)**, 4, b br g Manduro (GER)—Arabian Coral (IRE) **Veterinary Immunogenics Ltd**
52 **MATORICO (IRE)**, 5, gr g Mastercraftsman (IRE)—Hashbrown (GER) **Mr J. P. McManus**
53 **MILAN BOUND (IRE)**, 8, b g Milan—Bonnie And Bright (IRE) **Mr J. P. McManus**
54 **MINELLA ROCCO (IRE)**, 6, b g Shirocco (GER)—Petralona (USA) **Mr J. P. McManus**
55 **MISSION COMPLETE (IRE)**, 10, b g Milan—Kilmington Breeze (IRE) **Mr J. P. McManus**
56 **MISTER DICK (FR)**, 4, b g Great Journey (JPN)—Lyric Melody (FR) **Local Parking Security Ltd**
57 **MONBEG GOLD (IRE)**, 6, b g Gold Well—Little Hand (IRE) **Martin Broughton Racing Partners 2**
58 **MONT ROYALE (IRE)**, 8, b g Hurricane Run (IRE)—Wild Academy (IRE) **Phil Tufnell Racing Club**
59 **MONTDRAGON (FR)**, 6, b g Turtle Bowl (IRE)—Bonne Gargotte (FR) **Mr J. P. McManus**
60 **MORE OF THAT (IRE)**, 8, b g Beneficial—Guigone (FR) **Mr J. P. McManus**
61 **MOUNTAIN TUNES (IRE)**, 7, br g Mountain High (IRE)—Art Lover (IRE) **Mr J. P. McManus**
62 **MR SHANTU (IRE)**, 7, b g Shantou (USA)—Close To Shore (IRE) **Local Parking Security Ltd**
63 **MUSTMEETALADY (IRE)**, 6, b g Mustameet (USA)—Ladymcgrath (IRE) **Ms Diane Carr**
64 **ONTHEWESTERNFRONT (IRE)**, 6, b g Robin des Champs (FR)—
     Asian Maze (IRE) **Mrs J Magnier, Mr D Smith & Mr M Tabor**
65 **OPTIMISTIC BIAS (IRE)**, 7, b g Sayarshan (FR)—Dashers Folly (IRE) **Optimistic Four**
66 **OUR ROBIN (IRE)**, 6, b g Robin des Champs (FR)—Palm Lake (IRE) **Paul & Clare Rooney**
67 **PILLARD (FR)**, 4, b g Muhaymin (USA)—Ultime Moment (USA) **Regulatory Finance Solutions Ltd**
68 **POWERFUL SYMBOL (IRE)**, 6, b g Robin des Champs (FR)—Be My Rainbow (IRE) **The Megsons**
69 **PRESENCE FELT (IRE)**, 8, br g Heron Island (IRE)—Faeroe Isle (FR) **Mrs Peter Bond**
70 **PRINCESS TIANA (IRE)**, 5, b m Yeats (IRE)—Ar Muin Na Muice (IRE) **Mrs Gay Smith**
71 **PUDDLE JUMPER (IRE)**, 5, br g Craigsteel—Koko Kabana (IRE) **Brassington Chartering Ltd**
72 **QUARENTA (FR)**, 4, b br g Voix du Nord (FR)—Negresse de Cuta (FR) **Martin, Jocelyn & Steve Broughton**
73 **RAPANUI (IRE)**, 4, ch g Flemensfirth (USA)—Beautiful Night (FR) **Jon & Julia Aisbitt**
74 **REZORBI (FR)**, 5, b g Zafeen (FR)—Reve de nuit (IRE) **Sean O'Driscoll & Michael O'Flynn**
75 **ROCK N RHYTHM (IRE)**, 6, b g Rock of Gibraltar (IRE)—Dark Rosaleen (IRE) **Chanelle Medical Group U.K.**
76 **ROSE REVIVED**, 5, b m Midnight Legend—Miniature Rose **Jones Broughtons Wilson Weaver**
77 **SALOPIEN (IRE)**, 4, b g Gold Well—Musicienne (IRE) **Mr Andrew Bound**
78 **SEBASTIAN BEACH (IRE)**, 5, b g Yeats (IRE)—Night Club **The Megsons**
79 **SEE THE ROCK (IRE)**, 6, b g Shirocco (GER)—Samara (IRE) **Mr J. P. McManus**
80 **SET IN MY WAYS (IRE)**, 5, b g Presenting—Kerry's Girl (IRE) **Mr J. P. McManus**
81 **SHE'S LATE**, 6, ch g Pivotal—Courting **Ms Diane Carr**

MR JONJO O'NEILL - Continued

82 **SHUTTHEFRONTDOOR (IRE)**, 9, b br g Accordion—Hurricane Girl (IRE) **Mr J. P. McManus**
83 **SIMPLE AS THAT (IRE)**, 5, b g Stowaway—Suzy Q (IRE) **Mrs J Magnier, Mr D Smith & Mr M Tabor**
84 **SPOOKYDOOKY (IRE)**, 8, b g Winged Love (IRE)—Kiora Lady (IRE) **The Piranha Partnership**
85 **STEPS AND STAIRS (IRE)**, 6, b g Robin des Pres (FR)—Be Mine Tonight (IRE) **Mr Mark Dunphy**
86 **STRONGLY SUGGESTED**, 9, b g Kayf Tara—Branston Lily **Mr J. P. McManus**
87 **SUPPLY AND DEMAND (IRE)**, 5, br g Scorpion (IRE)—
Nathan Fashion (IRE) **Mrs J Magnier, Mr D Smith & Mr M Tabor**
88 **TAQUIN DU SEUIL (FR)**, 9, b g Voix du Nord (FR)—Sweet Laly (FR) **Martin Broughton & Friends 1**
89 **TERRY THE FISH**, 4, b g Milan—Have More **The Terry The Fishers Partnership**
90 **THE SAINT JAMES (FR)**, 5, b g Saint des Saints (FR)—Aimela (FR) **Mr J. P. McManus**
91 **THE TAILGATER (IRE)**, 5, b g Oscar (IRE)—Zaffaran Express (IRE) **Paul & Clare Rooney**
92 **TOP PRIORITY (FR)**, 5, b g Solon (GER)—Firstote (FR) **Jonjo O'Neill Racing Club**
93 **TUFFATTHETOP (IRE)**, 5, br g Kalanisi (IRE)—Anshabella (IRE) **Tuffatthetop Partners**
94 **TWIRLING MAGNET (IRE)**, 10, b g Imperial Ballet (IRE)—Molly Maguire (IRE) **Mrs Gay Smith**
95 **ULTIMATE DREAM (FR)**, 5, b g Ultimately Lucky (IRE)—Carazia (FR) **The Ultimate Dreamers**
96 **UPSWING (IRE)**, 8, b g Beneficial—Native Country (IRE) **Mr J. P. McManus**
97 **UTILITY (GER)**, 5, b g Yeats (IRE)—Ungarin (GER) **Mrs J Magnier, Mr D Smith & Mr M Tabor**
98 **VISANDI (FR)**, 4, b g Azamour (IRE)—Vadaza (FR) **Michael & John O'Flynn**
99 **WALK WATERFORD**, 5, bl g Fair Mix (IRE)—Woore Lass (IRE) **Alan D. Gray**
100 **WALKAMI (FR)**, 5, b g Walk In The Park (IRE)—Ominneha (FR) **Babbit Racing**
101 **WALTER ONEEIGHTONE (IRE)**, 4, b g Morozov (USA)—Matinee Show (IRE) **Anne, Harriet & Lucinda Bond**
102 **WHICH ONE IS WHICH**, 5, br m King's Theatre (IRE)—Presenting Copper (IRE) **Mr J. P. McManus**
103 **WILL TAKE CHARGE (IRE)**, 5, b g Beneficial—Corraig Lady (IRE) **Mr J. P. McManus**
104 **YEWLANDS (IRE)**, 5, b g Scorpion (IRE)—Calimesa (IRE) **Mr T. Hemmings**

THREE-YEAR-OLDS

105 **CENTURO (USA)**, ch g Cape Blanco (IRE)—Cats Copy (USA) **Mrs Peter Bond**
106 **DESERT CROSS**, b g Arcano (IRE)—Secret Happiness **Mr P. Hickey**
107 **LAD OF LUCK (FR)**, b g Soldier of Fortune (IRE)—Baraka du Berlais (FR) **Stephanie Hoffmann**
108 **PONGO TWISTLETON**, b g Champs Elysees—Pretty Girl (IRE) **The Megsons**
109 **STORM MELODY**, b g Royal Applause—Plume **Mr P. Hickey**

TWO-YEAR-OLDS

110 B c 17/3 Dark Angel (IRE)—Do The Deal (IRE) (Halling (USA)) (35000) **Ms Diane Carr**
111 B c 24/1 Harbour Watch (IRE)—Najmati (Green Desert (USA)) (42000) **Ms Diane Carr**

Other Owners: David Attwood, Mr Ronnie Bartlet, Terry Booth, Mr Les Brewin, Lady Jocelyn Broughton, Sir Martin Broughton, Steve and Jill Broughton, Mike Brown, Mr Michael Burke, Mrs Bridget Byrne, Mr Paul Chaplin, Ms Elaine Chivers, Mrs Berys Connop, Bruce Copp, Brian and Elaine Cosgrove, Paul Delaney, Mrs Susan Farmer, Paul & Jo Farrant, Mr Terry Fitzgerald, Mrs Sarah Hall-Tinker, Mrs Noel Harwerth, Peter Heathcote, Billy Hinshelwood, Mr Martyn Holman, Mr Peter Hopper, Mr Terry Jackson, Marian and Walter James, Mrs Cherry Jones, Paul Lynam, Middleham Park Racing, Mr Tim Milvain, Mr Tom Mohan, Mr Mike Morris, Richard Moxon, Richard Newbold, Mr Chris Pearce, Mr Stephen Perry, Mr Brian Robb, Nick Sercombe, Mr Peter Smith, Mr Robin Stanton Gleaves, Graham & Patricia Stone, Mr Mark Stone, Mr Andrew Turner, Mrs Giles Weaver, Mr Tom Wilson, Mrs Carole Worsley.

---

464 **MR JOHN O'SHEA, Newnham-on-Severn**
Postal: **The Stables, Bell House, Lumbars Lane, Newnham, Gloucestershire, GL14 1LH**
Contacts: **TEL (01452) 760835 FAX (01452) 760233 MOBILE (07917) 124717**
WEBSITE www.johnoshearacing.co.uk

1 **BLACK MINSTREL (IRE)**, 7, b g Dylan Thomas (IRE)—Overlook **Red & Black Racing**
2 **CLEMENT (IRE)**, 6, b g Clodovil (IRE)—Winnifred **K. W. Bell**
3 **COUP DE VENT**, 5, b m Tobougg (IRE)—Pigment **TR Racing Partnership**
4 **DIAMONDS A DANCING**, 6, ch g Delta Dancer—Zing **The Cross Racing Club**
5 **GENERAL BROOK (IRE)**, 6, b g Westerner—Danse Grecque (IRE) **K. W. Bell**
6 **HENRY OLIVER (IRE)**, 8, b g Hasten To Add (USA)—Lisnabrin (IRE) **Miss N. L. Slack**
7 **KINGLANI**, 7, b g Kingsalsa (USA)—Red Japonica **P. Smith**
8 **L STIG**, b g Striking Ambition—Look Here's May **The Sandcroft Partnership**
9 **LOUIS VEE (IRE)**, 8, b br g Captain Rio—Mrs Evans (IRE) **Quality Pipe Supports (Q.P.S.) Ltd**
10 **MAJOR VALENTINE**, 4, b g Major Cadeaux—Under My Spell **Huntbelle Stables**
11 **MEISTER ECKHART (IRE)**, 10, b br g Flemensfirth (USA)—Carrabawn **Atlantic Equine**
12 **NINEPOINTSIXTHREE**, 6, b g Bertolini (USA)—Armada Grove **The Cross Racing Club**
13 **PEAK STORM**, 7, b g Sleeping Indian—Jitterbug (IRE)

MR JOHN O'SHEA - Continued

14 **PORT AND WARD (IRE)**, 7, ch m Captain Rio—Gold Stamp **Mr M. G. Wooldridge**
15 **RED SKIPPER (IRE)**, 11, ch g Captain Rio—Speed To Lead (IRE) **K. W. Bell**
16 **RING EYE (IRE)**, 8, b g Definite Article—Erins Lass (IRE) **Mr G. C. Roberts**
17 **RUN HURRICANE (IRE)**, 8, ch g Hurricane Run (IRE)—Dame's Violet (IRE) **The Cross Racing Club**
18 **SOLIANA**, 4, ch f Dutch Art—Pink Stone (FR) **TR Racing Partnership**
19 **STAFFORD CHARLIE**, 10, ch g Silver Patriarch (IRE)—Miss Roberto (IRE) **N. G. H. Ayliffe**
20 **STAFFORD JO**, 7, ch g Silver Patriarch (IRE)—Miss Roberto (IRE) **N. G. H. Ayliffe**
21 **SWENDAB (IRE)**, 8, b g Trans Island—Lavish Spirit (IRE) **Hunt SB Ltd & The Cross Racing Club**
22 **TRIBAL DANCE (IRE)**, 10, br g Flemensfirth (USA)—Native Sparkle (IRE) **Quality Pipe Supports (Q.P.S.) Ltd**
23 **WHEN IN ROAM (IRE)**, 7, b m Flemensfirth (USA)—Roaming (IRE) **J. R. Salter**

THREE-YEAR-OLDS

24 **DALNESS EXPRESS**, b g Firebreak—Under My Spell **Huntbelle Stables**

Other Owners: Mr N. J. Carter, C. L. Dubois, J. G. Huckle, Mrs E. A. Huckle, Hunt SB Limited, Mr A. G. Hunter, Mr S. P. Jenkins, Merriebelle Irish Farm Limited, Mr V. P. Nolan, Mr S. P. Price, Miss S. F. Willis.

Jockey (flat): Robert Havlin, Luke Morris, Fergus Sweeney.

---

465 MR GEOFFREY OLDROYD, Malton
Postal: **Flint Hall Farm, Morr Lane, Brawby, Malton, North Yorkshire, YO17 6PZ**
Contacts: **PHONE (01653) 668279 MOBILE (07730) 642620**

1 **BOND'S GIFT**, 6, ch m Monsieur Bond (IRE)—Bond Shakira **South Yorkshire Racing**
2 **CROSSLEY**, 7, ch g Monsieur Bond (IRE)—Dispol Diamond **Mr G. R. Oldroyd**
3 **MISS REBERO**, 6, b m Cockney Rebel (IRE)—One Zero (USA) **Lilling Hall Racing**
4 **PRINCESS KHELEYF**, 7, b m Kheleyf (USA)—Jugendliebe (USA) **Mr G. R. Oldroyd**
5 B, g Virtual—Quotation **Mr G. R. Oldroyd**

Other Owners: Mr E. A. Dupont, G. Sanderson, Mr W. N. Standeven, Mr N. Woods.

Assistant Trainer: Craig Lidster

---

466 MR HENRY OLIVER, Abberley
Postal: **Stable End, Worsley Racing Stables, Bank Lane, Abberley, Worcester, Worcestershire, WR6 6BQ**
Contacts: **PHONE (01299) 890143 MOBILE (07701) 068759**
E-MAIL henryoliverracing@hotmail.co.uk WEBSITE www.henryoliverracing.co.uk

1 **ACTIONDANCER (IRE)**, 5, b g Craigsteel—Sudden Action (IRE) **R. G. Whitehead**
2 **AFTER HOURS (IRE)**, 7, b g Milan—Supreme Singer (IRE) **R. G. Whitehead**
3 **BEATABOUT THE BUSH (IRE)**, 5, b br g Bushranger (IRE)—Queen of Fibres (IRE) **Ms S. A. Howell**
4 **BLACK HAWK (IRE)**, 7, b g Craigsteel—Coolharbour Lady (IRE) **Mr Oscar Singh & Miss Priya Purewal**
5 **DAZINSKI**, 10, ch g Sulamani (IRE)—Shuheb **Mr D. M. J. Lloyd**
6 **DESERT RECLUSE (IRE)**, 9, ch g Redback—Desert Design **Mr D. M. J. Lloyd**
7 **DIAMOND ROCK**, 5, b g Kayf Tara—Crystal Princess (IRE) **R. G. Whitehead**
8 **DRESDEN (IRE)**, 8, b g Diamond Green (FR)—So Precious (IRE) **Mr D. M. J. Lloyd**
9 **GRIMLEY GIRL**, 10, b m Sir Harry Lewis (USA)—Grimley Gale (IRE) **R. M. Phillips**
10 **KEEL HAUL (IRE)**, 8, br g Classic Cliche (IRE)—Tara Hall **R. G. Whitehead**
11 **MIGHTY LEADER (IRE)**, 8, b g Milan—Madam Leader (IRE) **Mr Oscar Singh & Miss Priya Purewal**
12 **MINELLAFORLUNCH (IRE)**, 9, b g King's Theatre (IRE)—Loughaderra (IRE) **R. G. Whitehead**
13 **MONDERON (FR)**, 9, b br g Laveron—Lomonde (FR) **Mr Oscar Singh & Miss Priya Purewal**
14 **MOSCOW ME (IRE)**, 9, b g Moscow Society (USA)—Just Trust Me (IRE) **Mr Oscar Singh & Miss Priya Purewal**
15 **OZZY THOMAS (IRE)**, 6, b g Gold Well—Bramble Leader (IRE) **Ms S. A. Howell**
16 **RESTLESS HARRY**, 12, b g Sir Harry Lewis (USA)—Restless Native (IRE) **R. G. Whitehead**
17 **TAKE THE CROWN**, 7, gr g Fair Mix (IRE)—Miss Wizadora **R. G. Whitehead**
18 **THATCHERS GOLD (IRE)**, 8, b g Gold Well—Chesterfield Lady (IRE) **Miss J. M. Green**
19 **WHISPERING HARRY**, 7, b g Sir Harry Lewis (USA)—Welsh Whisper **R. G. Whitehead**

Other Owners: Miss Priya Purewal, Mr Autar Singh.

Assistant Trainer: Heather Oliver

467 **MR JAMIE OSBORNE, Upper Lambourn**
Postal: **The Old Malthouse, Upper Lambourn, Hungerford, Berkshire, RG17 8RG**
Contacts: **PHONE (01488) 73139 FAX (01488) 73084 MOBILE (07860) 533422**
E-MAIL **info@jamieosborne.com** WEBSITE **www.jamieosborne.com**

1 **BOOMERANG BOB (IRE)**, 7, b h Aussie Rules (USA)—Cozzene's Pride (USA) **The Melbourne 10**
2 **CAMDORA (IRE)**, 4, b f Arcano (IRE)—Crimphill (IRE) **Lady Blyth**
3 **CHARLIE BEAR**, 4, b g Myboycharlie (IRE)—Millennium Heiress **M. A. C. Buckley**
4 **DECLAN**, 4, ch g Dylan Thomas (IRE)—Fleurissimo **Normandie Stud Ltd**
5 **DREAM SPIRIT (IRE)**, 5, b g Invincible Spirit (IRE)—Dream Valley (IRE) **J. A. Osborne**
6 **FIELD OF DREAM**, 9, b g Oasis Dream—Field of Hope (IRE) **Middleham Park Racing CXIII & Partner**
7 **FROZEN PRINCESS**, 4, b f Showcasing—Super Midge **Barratt & Johnsons**
8 **LIFE LESS ORDINARY (IRE)**, 4, b g Thewayyouare (USA)—
　　　　　　　　　　　　　　　　　　　　　　　Dont Cross Tina (IRAQ) **Mr Michael Buckley & Mrs Karima Burman**
9 **MISTERIOSO (IRE)**, 4, b c Iffraaj—Roystonea **Ekaterina Solomentseva**
10 **NOBLEST**, 4, ch f Pivotal—Noble One **Mrs L. M. Shanahan**
11 **ORATORIO'S JOY (IRE)**, 6, b m Oratorio (IRE)—Seeking The Fun (USA) **Mr A. F. Tait**
12 **OUTER SPACE**, 5, b g Acclamation—Venoge (IRE) **Tony Taylor & Patrick Gage**
13 **RIALTO MAGIC**, 4, b f Monsieur Bond (IRE)—Discover Home (IRE) **Fromthestables.Com & Partner**
14 **SHAMSHON (IRE)**, 5, b g Invincible Spirit (IRE)—Greenisland (IRE) **M. A. C. Buckley**
15 **SLEIGHT OF HAND (IRE)**, 4, b g Galileo (IRE)—Queen of France (USA) **M. A. C. Buckley**
16 **SMAIH (GER)**, 4, b c Paco Boy (IRE)—Solola (GER) **Mr G. Quintale**
17 **SUMMERSAULT (IRE)**, 5, b g Footstepsinthesand—Sumingasefa **Mrs F Walwyn Mr A Taylor Mr D Christian**

THREE-YEAR-OLDS

18 **CANFORD CHIMES (IRE)**, b c Canford Cliffs (IRE)—Appleblossom Pearl (IRE) **Apple Tree Stud**
19 **DALAVAND (IRE)**, ch g Tamayuz—Kirunavaara (IRE) **Apple Tree Stud**
20 **DAYDREAM (IRE)**, b f Dream Ahead—Intricate Dance (USA) **J. A. Osborne**
21 **DEFROCKED (IRE)**, b g Lope de Vega (IRE)—Portelet **Michael Buckley & Michael Watt**
22 **DR DREY (IRE)**, ch c Bahamian Bounty—Mount Lavinia (IRE) **Mr G. Popov**
23 **DREAM DANA (IRE)**, b f Dream Ahead—Lidanna **Apple Tree Stud**
24 **FIGURANTE (IRE)**, ch f Excellent Art—Savignano **The Hon A. A. Blyth**
25 **HEADS YOU WIN**, ch f Compton Place—Miss Rimex (IRE) **Heads You Win Partnership**
26 **HUNGARIAN RHAPSODY**, b g Showcasing—Rockburst **Mrs S Ricci & Mr Michael Buckley**
27 **ICE ROYAL (IRE)**, b c Frozen Power (IRE)—Salford Princess (IRE) **A. Taylor**
28 **ILLEGALLY BLONDE (IRE)**, b f Lawman (FR)—Kayak **Mr & Mrs I Barratt**
29 **INHERENT VICE (IRE)**, b g Kodiac—Ting A Greeley **Mrs S Ricci & Mr Michael Buckley**
30 **ISRAFEL**, b f Dark Angel (IRE)—Border Minstral (IRE) **Mrs L. Peacock**
31 **LA MANGA (IRE)**, b f Kodiac—Good Shot Noreen (IRE) **Homecroft Wealth Racing VIII**
32 **LEITRIM TRAVELLER (USA)**, b g Henrythenavigator (USA)—Purple (USA) **Chris Watkins & David N. Reynolds**
33 **LETS DO THIS THING (IRE)**, b g Thewayyouare (USA)—Margaux Dancer (IRE) **M. A. C. Buckley**
34 **LITTLE PEBBLES**, ch f Compton Place—Pain Perdu (IRE) **Stephen Short, Adam Signy & Ian Barratt**
35 B c Point Given (USA)—Miss Mockingbird (USA) **Mr G. Quintale**
36 **MONTEVERDI (FR)**, b c Kyllachy—West of Saturn (IRE) **M. A. C. Buckley**
37 **PACKING (IRE)**, b c Lilbourne Lad (IRE)—Elegant Ridge (IRE) **Mr & Mrs I Barratt**
38 **PACKING EMPIRE (IRE)**, b g Holy Roman Emperor (IRE)—
　　　　　　　　　　　　　　　　　　　Ceoil An Aith (IRE) **Mr Ming Ho Lui & Mr Lee Man Bun**
39 **RAMPERS (IRE)**, b g Thewayyouare (USA)—Korresia (IRE) **Fromthestables.Com Racing**
40 **REDMANE**, b c Bahamian Bounty—Miss Villefranche **John Dory Group Ltd**
41 **RUE BALZAC (IRE)**, b g Champs Elysees—Rondo Alla Turca (IRE) **Mr Michael Buckley & Mrs S Ricci**
42 **SCHOOLBOY ERROR (IRE)**, ch g Roderic O'Connor (IRE)—
　　　　　　　　　　　　　　　　　　La Grande Zoa (IRE) **Appletree Stud, M Gumienny & A Signy**
43 **SECRET INTERLUDE (IRE)**, b f Clodovil (IRE)—Elouges (IRE) **The Bo Derek 10 Partnership**
44 **SECRET SINNER (IRE)**, b f Lawman (FR)—Mamela (GER)
45 **TURN ON THE TEARS (USA)**, ch f Cape Blanco (IRE)—Down The Well (IRE) **Mr D. Durkan**
46 **WAYFARING STRANGER (IRE)**, b g Canford Cliffs (IRE)—Billet (IRE) **Mr Michael Buckley & Mrs S Ricci**
47 **ZIO GIANNI (IRE)**, b c Lemon Drop Kid (USA)—August Storm (USA) **Mr G. Quintale**

TWO-YEAR-OLDS

48 Ch g 6/5 Geordieland (FR)—Adees Dancer (Danehill Dancer (IRE)) **Mr A. Taylor**
49 B c 8/3 Casamento (IRE)—Annouska (IRE) (Ad Valorem (USA)) (150000)
50 B f 21/4 Power—Blue Iris (Petong) **Andy Smith & Friends**
51 B c 24/3 Sixties Icon—Brigadiers Bird (IRE) (Mujadil (USA)) (15238)
52 B c 27/1 Holy Roman Emperor (IRE)—Challow Hills (USA) (Woodman (USA)) (70136) **Mr E. Wong**
53 B f 14/3 Approve (IRE)—Coin Box (Dubai Destination (USA)) (20671)

MR JAMIE OSBORNE - Continued

54 Ch c 29/4 Sir Prancealot (IRE)—Fey Rouge (IRE) (Fayruz) (19195)
55 **LONG JOHN SILVER (IRE)**, b c 22/3 Rip Van Winkle (IRE)—
                         Tropical Lady (IRE) (Sri Pekan (USA)) (118124) **M. Buckley & T. Hyde**
56 B c 1/4 Tagula (IRE)—Lupine (IRE) (Lake Coniston (IRE)) (16000)
57 B c 8/2 Elnadim (USA)—Meanwhile (IRE) (Haafhd) (35437) **M. Buckley & C. Noell**
58 Ch c 28/2 Dragon Pulse (IRE)—Mokama (Motivator) (14285)
59 B f 19/2 Poet's Voice—Nawaashi (Green Desert (USA)) (30476)
60 B f 25/4 Elzaam (AUS)—
                         Noble View (USA) (Distant View (USA)) (36913) **Ian Barratt, Stephen Short & Adam Signy**
61 Ch c 27/4 Power—Reveuse de Jour (IRE) (Sadler's Wells (USA)) (36913) **Mr & Mrs I. Barratt**
62 B c 1/2 Kodiac—Roisin's Star (IRE) (Accordion) (55370) **Ian Barratt, Stephen Short & Adam Signy**
63 B c 30/4 Harbour Watch (IRE)—Roodeye (Inchinor) (50000) **M. Buckley & C. Noell**
64 B f 4/4 Acclamation—Semaphore (Zamindar (USA)) (80000) **Rebels With a Cause**
65 B c 14/5 Exceed And Excel (AUS)—Sharp Terms (Kris) (80000) **M. Buckley**
66 Ch c 9/2 Helmet (AUS)—
                         Smoken Rosa (USA) (Smoke Glacken (USA)) (35000) **Ian Barratt, Stephen Short & Adam Signy**
67 B c 19/4 Dutch Art—Sularina (IRE) (Alhaarth (IRE)) (66445) **D. Christian**
68 B f 24/4 Pour Moi (IRE)—Supercharged (IRE) (Iffraaj) (11074) **Islee Risos**
69 B f 24/3 Rip Van Winkle (IRE)—Universe (Cape Cross (IRE)) (14765)
70 B f 7/4 Roderic O'Connor (IRE)—Violet Flame (IRE) (Kalanisi (IRE)) (11812)

Assistant Trainer: Jimmy McCarthy

Apprentice: Lucy Barry. **Amateur:** Mr Peter Raybould.

468

MISS EMMA OWEN, Nether Winchendon
Postal: **Muskhill Farm, Nether Winchendon, Aylesbury, Buckinghamshire, HP18 0EB**
Contacts: **PHONE (01844) 296153 MOBILE (07718) 984799**
E-MAIL emma.l.owen@hotmail.com

1 **ALIDARA (IRE)**, 4, ch f Manduro (GER)—Artisia (IRE) **Mr L. F. Daly**
2 **BARNACLE**, 7, b g Compton Place—Bombalarina (IRE) **Exors of the Late Mr P. J. J. Eddery**
3 **ERTIDAAD (IRE)**, 4, b c Kodiac—Little Scotland **Miss E. L. Owen**
4 **HIGHPLAINS DRIFTER (IRE)**, 5, b g High Chaparral (IRE)—Qhazeenah **Miss E. L. Owen**
5 **HOONOSE**, 7, ch g Cadeaux Genereux—Roodeye **Miss E. L. Owen**
6 **LUTINE CHARLIE (IRE)**, 9, b g Kheleyf (USA)—Silvery Halo (USA) **Miss E. L. Owen**
7 **NASRI**, 10, b g Kyllachy—Triple Sharp **Miss E. L. Owen**
8 **STORM HAWK (IRE)**, 9, b g Hawk Wing (USA)—Stormy Larissa (IRE) **Exors of the Late Mr P. J. J. Eddery**
9 **SUNNY MONDAY**, 4, br c Manduro (GER)—Sunray Superstar **Mr L. F. Daly**

THREE-YEAR-OLDS
10 **AKSUM**, b f Cacique (IRE)—Quiet **K. Abdullah**
11 B c Canford Cliffs (IRE)—April (IRE) **Mr L. F. Daly**
12 **BONCHARD**, b f Champs Elysees—Five Fields (USA) **K. Abdullah**
13 **CROSS CAVE**, b f Rail Link—Valentine Girl **K. Abdullah**

Jockey (flat): Tom Queally, Jamie Spencer.

469

MR HUGO PALMER, Newmarket
Postal: **Kremlin Cottage Stables, Snailwell Road, Newmarket, Suffolk, CB8 7DP**
Contacts: **PHONE (01638) 669880 FAX (01638) 666383 MOBILE (07824) 887886**
E-MAIL info@hugopalmer.com WEBSITE www.hugopalmer.com

1 **AIR OF ASTANA (IRE)**, 4, b g Equiano (FR)—Fairnilee **Air Of Astana Partnership**
2 **ASCRIPTION (IRE)**, 7, b g Dansili—Lady Elgar (IRE) **Mr V. I. Araci**
3 **COVERT LOVE (IRE)**, 4, b f Azamour (IRE)—Wing Stealth (IRE) **FOMO Syndicate**
4 **EXTREMITY (IRE)**, 5, ch g Exceed And Excel (AUS)—Chanterelle (IRE) **Kremlin Cottage II**
5 **HOME OF THE BRAVE (IRE)**, 4, ch c Starspangledbanner (AUS)—
                         Blissful Beat **Flemington Bloodstock Partnership**
6 **NOT NEVER**, 4, ch g Notnowcato—Watchoverme **Mrs E. A. P. Haynes**
7 **SPANISH SQUEEZE (IRE)**, 4, ch g Lope de Vega (IRE)—Appetina **W Duff Gordon, J Bond, Rascals Racing**
8 **STRONG STEPS**, 4, br g Aqlaam—Wunders Dream (IRE) **Al Shaqab Racing UK Limited**

MR HUGO PALMER - Continued

  9 **TAMGA (IRE)**, 4, b c Azamour (IRE)—Miss Beatrix (IRE) **Mr V. I. Araci**
10 **TWITCH (IRE)**, 4, b f Azamour (IRE)—Blinking **The Duke of Roxburghe & The Duke of Devonshire**
11 **WALPOLE (IRE)**, 4, b g Rock of Gibraltar (IRE)—Serena's Storm (IRE) **Roldvale Ltd**

THREE-YEAR-OLDS

12 **AILSA ON MY MIND (IRE)**, br f Dark Angel (IRE)—Embassy Pearl (IRE) **The Albatross Club**
13 **ARCHITECTURE (IRE)**, b f Zoffany (IRE)—Brigayev (ITY) **Mr C. M. Humber**
14 **BANISH (USA)**, b c Smart Strike (CAN)—Beyond Our Reach (IRE) **HighclereThoroughbredRacing-Smart Strike**
15 **BAYDAR**, b c Rock of Gibraltar (IRE)—Splashdown **Mr V. I. Araci**
16 **CHIEFOFCHIEFS**, b c Royal Applause—Danvers **M. L. Ayers**
17 **CORKED (IRE)**, b f Mastercraftsman (IRE)—Dama'a (IRE) **The Corked Partnership**
18 **CRIMEAN TATAR (TUR)**, b c Sea The Stars (IRE)—Unity (IRE) **Mr V. I. Araci**
19 **DRIVE FASTER**, b c Invincible Spirit (IRE)—Fowey (USA) **Mr V. I. Araci**
20 B c Teofilo (IRE)—Eclaircie (IRE) **Sheikh J. D. Al Maktoum**
21 **ECUREUIL (IRE)**, b f Lope de Vega (IRE)—Takizada (IRE) **Al Asayl Bloodstock Ltd**
22 **FABRITIUS (IRE)**, b g Dutch Art—Bay of Pearls (IRE) **Kremlin Cottage VIII**
23 **FEARBUSTER (IRE)**, b f Fastnet Rock (AUS)—Jewel In The Sand (IRE) **Mr M V Magnier & Partners/ T Hyde**
24 **FIFTYSHADESOFPINK (IRE)**, b f Pour Moi (IRE)—Maakrah **Mrs M. Bryce**
25 **GALILEO GOLD**, ch c Paco Boy (IRE)—Galicuix **Al Shaqab Racing UK Limited**
26 **GHOSTWRITER (IRE)**, b c High Chaparral (IRE)—Diara Angel (IRE) **MPH Diara Syndicate**
27 **GIFTED MASTER (IRE)**, b g Kodiac—Shobobb **Dr A. Ridha**
28 **GIMLET**, b g Poet's Voice—Poppo's Song (CAN) **De La Warr Racing**
29 **GOLD TRADE (IRE)**, b c Raven's Pass (USA)—Trading Places **Mr A. Al Mansoori**
30 **HARRY CHAMPION**, b c Cockney Rebel (IRE)—Nine Red **R. C. Tooth**
31 **HAWKSMOOR (IRE)**, b f Azamour (IRE)—Bridal Dance (IRE) **Mr C. M. Humber**
32 **MAGICAL PATH (IRE)**, b gr f Zebedee—Road To Reality (IRE) **Anglia Bloodstock Syndicate VI**
33 **MARSHALL AID (IRE)**, b g Lawman (FR)—Dievotchkina (USA) **W. J. and T. C. O. Gredley**
34 B f Teofilo (IRE)—Mazaaya (USA) **S. Ali**
35 **MENGLI KHAN (IRE)**, b c Lope de Vega (IRE)—Danielli (IRE) **Mr V. I. Araci**
36 B f Cape Blanco (IRE)—Moon Giant (USA) **Mr V. I. Araci**
37 **MURAD KHAN (FR)**, b c Raven's Pass (USA)—Lady Elgar (IRE) **Mr V. I. Araci**
38 **NESSITA**, ch f Shamardal (USA)—Neshla **S. Manana**
39 **PARIS MAGIC**, b c Champs Elysees—Belgooree **Mr A. Al Mansoori**
40 **PERU**, b f Motivator—Bolsena (USA) **W. J. and T. C. O. Gredley**
41 **SACRED TRUST**, b c Acclamation—Paracel (USA) **Mr L. L. Lee**
42 **SALEH (IRE)**, b g Iffraaj—Pellinore (USA) **Mr M. Almutairi**
43 **SECRET INSIDER (USA)**, b f Elusive Quality (USA)—Fashion Insider (USA) **Sheikh J. D. Al Maktoum**
44 Ch g Compton Place—Setting Forth (IRE) **Kremlin Cottage IV**
45 **THEY SEEK HIM HERE (IRE)**, b br c Elusive Pimpernel (USA)—
                                          Spiritville (IRE) **Highclere Thoroughbred Racing-Elusive I**
46 **TO BE WILD (IRE)**, br c Big Bad Bob (IRE)—Fire Up **Carmichael Jennings**
47 **UBLA (IRE)**, ch g Arcano (IRE)—Manuelita Rose (ITY) **MPH Racing - I**
48 **VISITANT**, ch g Pivotal—Invitee **Flemington Bloodstock Partnership II**
49 **WE ARE NINETY (IRE)**, b f Thewayyouare (USA)—Brigids Cross (IRE) **Lady Mary Manton**
50 **ZODIAKOS (IRE)**, b g Kodiac—Zonic **Mr K. W. W. Woo**
51 **ZORLU (IRE)**, b c Invincible Spirit (IRE)—Special Assignment (USA) **Mr V. I. Araci**

TWO-YEAR-OLDS

52 B c 6/3 Exceed And Excel (AUS)—Adonesque (IRE) (Sadler's Wells (USA)) (110000) **Sheikh R. D. Al Maktoum**
53 B c 12/2 Vale of York (IRE)—Al Mahmeyah (Teofilo (IRE)) **Mr H. R. Bin Ghedayer**
54 **AL SULTANAH**, ch f 30/3 Tamayuz—Dubai Media (CAN) (Songandaprayer (USA)) **A. Al Shaikh**
55 B f 31/3 Siyouni (FR)—Amalea (IRE) (Dylan Thomas (IRE)) (45000) **Seventh Lap Racing**
56 Ch c 3/4 Exceed And Excel (AUS)—Anna Amalia (IRE) (In The Wings) (78000) **S. Ali**
57 Ch f 24/4 Raven's Pass (USA)—Artisti (Cape Cross (IRE)) (420000) **Saleh Al Homaizi & Imad Al Sagar**
58 B c 25/3 Azamour (IRE)—Baisse (High Chaparral (IRE)) **Mr G. Schoeningh**
59 **BEE CASE**, br f 3/2 Showcasing—Binabee (Galileo (IRE)) **K. Abdullah**
60 **BETTY GRABLE (IRE)**, b br f 4/3 Delegator—Danella (IRE) (Platini (GER)) (20000) **R. C. Tooth**
61 B c 23/3 Excelebration (IRE)—Blissful Beat (Beat Hollow) (118124) **Mr V. I. Araci**
62 B f 18/2 Holy Roman Emperor (IRE)—Bride Unbridled (IRE) (Hurricane Run (IRE)) **Al Asayl Bloodstock Ltd**
63 B c 25/4 Rip Van Winkle (IRE)—Bright And Clear (Danehill (USA)) (30000) **A. Al Shaikh**
64 **BUSH HOUSE**, b c 6/5 Canford Cliffs (IRE)—
                               Magena (USA) (Kingmambo (USA)) (142857) **W. J. and T. C. O. Gredley**
65 Ch c 12/2 Dutch Art—Cantal (Pivotal) (350000) **Al Shaqab Racing UK Limited**
66 Ch f 21/2 Exceed And Excel (AUS)—Cloud Castle (In The Wings) **S. Manana**
67 B c 10/2 Tamayuz—Coolminx (IRE) (One Cool Cat (USA)) (55000) **Mr L. L. Lee**

MR HUGO PALMER - Continued

68 B c 25/4 Zoffany (IRE)—Corking (IRE) (Montjeu (IRE)) (59062) **MPH Racing - II**
69 B f 30/1 Invincible Spirit (IRE)—Dalasyla (IRE) (Marju (IRE)) (300000) **Al Shaqab Racing UK Limited**
70 B c 10/4 Frankel—Danceabout (Shareef Dancer (USA)) (221483) **Al Shaqab Racing UK Limited**
71 B c 14/2 Frankel—Drops (IRE) (Kingmambo (USA)) **Al Asayl Bloodstock Ltd**
72 ESCOBAR (IRE), b c 7/4 Famous Name—Saying Grace (IRE) (Brief Truce (USA)) (206718) **Carmichael Jennings**
73 EXPRESS LADY (IRE), b f 11/4 Helmet (AUS)—Star Express (Sadler's Wells (USA)) (40000) **Dr A. Ridha**
74 B c 22/3 Kodiac—Fee Eria (FR) (Always Fair (USA)) (95976) **Woodhurst Construction Ltd**
75 B c 28/2 Paco Boy (IRE)—Fine Lady (Selkirk (USA)) (19933) **Seventh Lap Racing**
76 FIRST MOON, b f 18/4 Oasis Dream—Flood Plain (Orpen (USA)) **K. Abdullah**
77 FLEABISCUIT (IRE), b f 18/2 High Chaparral (IRE)—
                                        Bluebelle Dancer (Danehill Dancer (IRE)) (42081) **Lucayan Stud**
78 B f 16/4 Zoffany (IRE)—Flower of Kent (USA) (Diesis) (32000) **Rebels With A Cause**
79 FOR HENRY (IRE), b f 22/3 Galileo (IRE)—Chachamaidee (IRE) (Footstepsinthesand) **R. A. H. Evans**
80 FORTITUDE (IRE), b c 25/1 Oasis Dream—Sweepstake (IRE) (Acclamation) (240000) **Mr I. Al-Khalifa**
81 B f 25/2 Paco Boy (IRE)—Galicuix (Galileo (IRE)) (266666) **Saleh Al Homaizi & Imad Al Sagar**
82 B f 21/2 Power—Growling (IRE) (Celtic Swing) (7000) **Mr H. Palmer**
83 B c 10/4 Frankel—Hazel Lavery (IRE) (Excellent Art) **Al Asayl Bloodstock Ltd**
84 Ch f 17/3 Exceed And Excel (AUS)—Height of Summer (IRE) (Alhaarth (IRE)) **Al Asayl Bloodstock Ltd**
85 HERON (USA), b c 28/1 Quality Road (USA)—Dreamt (Oasis Dream) **K. Abdullah**
86 B c 5/3 Redoute's Choice (AUS)—High Days (IRE) (Hennessy (USA)) **Al Asayl Bloodstock Ltd**
87 B c 3/2 Mayson—Hypnotize (Machiavellian (USA)) (115000) **Al Shaqab Racing UK Limited**
88 IBN ALEMARAT (IRE), b c 29/4 Zoffany (IRE)—Trois Graces (USA) (Alysheba (USA)) (42000) **A. Al Shaikh**
89 INSPECTOR (IRE), b c 7/2 Lawman (FR)—
                                        Helter Helter (USA) (Seeking The Gold (USA)) (95000) **Highclere Thoroughbred Racing- TS Eliot**
90 JEAN HARLOW, b f 2/5 Mount Nelson—Nine Red (Royal Applause) **R. C. Tooth**
91 B br c 11/3 Intense Focus (USA)—Jouel (FR) (Machiavellian (USA)) (40605) **MPH Racing - II**
92 Ch f 1/2 New Approach (IRE)—Jumeirah Palm Star (Invincible Spirit (IRE)) **Mr H. R. Bin Ghedayer**
93 B c 11/2 Danehill Dancer (IRE)—Justly Royal (USA) (Royal Academy (USA)) (44296) **Mr H. A. Lootah**
94 B f 5/2 Shamardal (USA)—Kaabari (USA) (Seeking The Gold (USA)) **S. Manana**
95 Br c 17/4 Dark Angel (IRE)—Karliysha (IRE) (Kalanisi (IRE)) (115000) **Sun Bloodstock Sarl**
96 B f 22/2 Makfi—Katimont (IRE) (Montjeu (IRE)) (110741) **Mr R. W. Hill-Smith**
97 KIND OF BEAUTY (IRE), ch f 23/4 Helmet (AUS)—Extreme Beauty (Rahy (USA)) (16000) **Dr A. Ridha**
98 LEWINSKY (IRE), b f 30/4 Famous Name—
                                        Happy Flight (IRE) (Titus Livius (FR)) (36190) **Anglia Bloodstock Syndicate IX**
99 B c 8/3 Exceed And Excel (AUS)—Lion Forest (USA) (Forestry (USA)) **Mr V. I. Araci**
100 B c 15/3 Zoffany (IRE)—Luminous Gold (Fantastic Light (USA)) (42000) **Seventh Lap Racing**
101 B f 31/3 Rock of Gibraltar (IRE)—Maid For Winning (USA) (Gone West (USA)) (45000) **Mr V. I. Araci**
102 MANCHEGO, b c 26/5 Lope de Vega (IRE)—
                                        Gooseberry Pie (Green Desert (USA)) (52000) **Mr C. Humber / Anglia Bloodstock / Lilburn Estate**
103 B f 18/3 Oasis Dream—Maskunah (IRE) (Sadler's Wells (USA)) **S. Manana**
104 B c 3/5 Kodiac—Mirwara (IRE) (Darshaan) (47987) **Mr H. A. Lootah**
105 B c 9/4 High Chaparral (IRE)—Missionary Hymn (USA) (Giant's Causeway (USA)) (125000) **MPH Racing - II**
106 B f 25/2 High Chaparral (IRE)—Mixed Blessing (Lujain (USA)) (100000) **MPH Racing - II**
107 B c 19/3 Cape Cross (IRE)—Mount Elbrus (Barathea (IRE)) **S. Ali**
108 B c 15/1 Sir Prancealot (IRE)—Mystic Dream (Oasis Dream) (28571) **Anglia Bloodstock Syndicate VIII**
109 B c 25/2 Oasis Dream—Neartica (FR) (Sadler's Wells (USA)) (162421) **Mr V. I. Araci**
110 NILE EMPRESS, b f 16/2 Holy Roman Emperor (IRE)—
                                        Temple of Thebes (IRE) (Bahri (USA)) (20000) **Mr & Mrs A. E. Pakenham**
111 OMEROS, ch c 26/1 Poet's Voice—Caribbean Pearl (USA) (Silver Hawk (USA)) (50000) **Mr C. M. Humber**
112 Ch f 21/4 Medicean—Piano (Azamour (IRE)) (38390) **Seventh Lap Racing**
113 B f 21/3 Invincible Spirit (IRE)—Queen of Tara (IRE) (Sadler's Wells (USA)) (110741) **Carmichael Jennings**
114 ROSELAND (USA), b f 24/1 First Defence (USA)—Aviate (Dansili) **K. Abdullah**
115 B c 14/3 Dream Ahead (USA)—Royal Alchemist (Kingsinger (IRE)) (100000) **Mr A. Al Mansoori**
116 B f 14/4 Poet's Voice—She Wolf (Medicean) (55000) **Dr A. Ridha**
117 SKETCHING, b f 1/3 Nathaniel (IRE)—Prove (Danehill (USA)) **K. Abdullah**
118 B f 12/2 Showcasing—Small Fortune (Anabaa (USA)) (70000) **Mr A. Al Mansoori**
119 Ch f 6/3 Bahamian Bounty—Somersault (Pivotal) (20000) **Mrs P. I. Veenbaas**
120 B f 23/1 Oasis Dream—Soon (IRE) (Galileo (IRE)) **Saleh Al Homaizi & Imad Al Sagar**
121 SPRING JIG (USA), b c 12/2 Spring At Last (USA)—Make A Dance (USA) (Empire Maker (USA)) **K. Abdullah**
122 B c 8/4 Sayif (IRE)—Sweet Coincidence (Mujahid (USA)) (50000) **Saleh Al Homaizi & Imad Al Sagar**
123 Ch c 10/4 Sepoy (AUS)—Sweet Folly (IRE) (Singspiel (IRE)) (50000) **Mr A. Menahi**
124 TAMAYEF (IRE), b c 4/5 Sir Prancealot (IRE)—
                                        Miss Glitters (IRE) (Chevalier (IRE)) (20671) **Commission Air Limited**
125 Br f 19/2 Dark Angel (IRE)—Taraeff (IRE) (Cape Cross (IRE)) (118124) **Mr Noel O'Callaghan**
126 B f 16/4 Canford Cliffs (IRE)—Tencarola (IRE) (Night Shift (USA)) (36000) **Rebels With A Cause**

MR HUGO PALMER - Continued

127 B c 28/2 Redoute's Choice (AUS)—
      Thislillightofmine (USA) (Kingmambo (USA)) **Sheikh Juma Dalmook Al Maktoum**
128 B f 22/4 Cape Cross (IRE)—Turmalin (IRE) (Dalakhani (IRE)) (10000) **Mr A. S. Belhab**
129 **UNFORGETABLE FILLY,** b f 1/3 Sepoy (AUS)—Beautiful Filly (Oasis Dream) (50000) **Dr A. Ridha**
130 Gr f 1/3 Native Khan (FR)—Unity (IRE) (Sadler's Wells (USA)) **Mr V. I. Araci**
131 B f 29/3 Oasis Dream—Virginia Waters (USA) (Kingmambo (USA)) (217792) **Mr V. I. Araci**
132 B f 6/2 Dubawi (IRE)—Vita Nova (IRE) (Galileo (IRE)) **Al Asayl Bloodstock Ltd**
133 **WEDDING BREAKFAST (IRE),** ch f 21/2 Casamento (IRE)—
      Fair Countenance (IRE) (Almutawakel) (24761) **De La Warr Racing**
134 B f 14/3 Nathaniel (IRE)—Whazzat (Daylami (IRE)) (100000) **W. J. and T. C. O. Gredley**
135 **WHITE ROSA (IRE),** b f 11/4 Galileo (IRE)—Dhanyata (IRE) (Danetime (IRE)) (150000) **Highbank Stud**
136 **WORDSEARCH (USA),** b c 5/5 Pleasantly Perfect (USA)—Jibe (USA) (Danzig (USA)) **K. Abdullah**

Other Owners: I. J. Al-Sagar, Mr D. A. Bovington, Mrs A. J. Brudenell, Mr J. A. Bryan, C. Bryce, Mr C. G. A. Budgett, Mrs F. J. Carmichael, Mr C. Chisholm, Countess De La Warr, Lord De La Warr, The Duke of Devonshire, W. A. L. Duff Gordon, W. J. Gredley, T. C. O. Gredley, Mr P. Hernon, Highclere Nominated Partner Limited, Highclere Thoroughbred Racing Ltd, Mr M. P. Hills, Saleh Al Homaizi, T. Hyde, Mr I. Jennings, Mr R. P. Jones, Mr K. MacLennan, Mr M. V. Magnier, Mrs P. E. Mains, Mr M. J. McStay, Mr T. O'Connor, Mrs V. H. Pakenham, A. E. Pakenham, Palatinate Thoroughbred Racing Limited, Mr M. A. Ramsden, The Duke Of Roxburghe, Mrs L. M. Shanahan, Mr M. A. Wainwright, Mrs I. M. Wainwright, Miss V. Webb.

Apprentice: Noel Garbutt.

---

470   MR H. A. PANTALL, Beaupreau
Postal: Le Bois du Coin, Beaupreau 49600, France
Contacts: PHONE (0033) 241 636715 **FAX** (0033) 241 630530 **MOBILE** (0033) 607 450647
E-MAIL hapantall@wanadoo.fr **WEBSITE** www.ecuriepantall.com

Trainer did not supply a list of his older horses

TWO-YEAR-OLDS

1 **ALLELUIA (FR),** f 1/1 Fast Company (IRE)—Annakeen (IRE) (Invincible Spirit (IRE)) (9597)
2 B c 11/5 Redoute's Choice (AUS)—Alpensinfonie (IRE) (Montjeu (IRE)) (73827)
3 **BABYLOVE (FR),** b f 7/3 Zafeen (FR)—Bainorama (FR) (Anabaa (USA)) (40605)
4 **BAR MINA (IRE),** b f 9/4 Falco (USA)—Maisha (GER) (Platini (GER)) (2214)
5 **BARDOUVILLE (FR),** b f 1/1 Linngari (IRE)—Sascilaria (Fasliyev (USA)) (11074)
6 B f 4/4 Redoute's Choice (AUS)—Border Bloom (Selkirk (USA))
7 Br c 29/4 Amico Fritz (GER)—Brangane (IRE) (Anita's Prince) (20671)
8 **CAJAMARCA (FR),** b f 17/4 Amico Fritz (GER)—Centinela (Caerleon (USA)) (14027)
9 **CONSTANTINOPLE (FR),** b c 20/3 Rajsaman (FR)—Green Grass (FR) (Verglas (IRE)) (23624)
10   f 1/1 Kyllachy—Danny's Choice (Compton Place)
11 B c 14/2 Literato (FR)—Dianaba (FR) (Diktat) (25889)
12 **DOUCEUR TOSCANE (FR),** b f 27/4 Silver Frost (IRE)—Douceur Nocturne (FR) (Zieten (USA)) (3691)
13 **ELUSOUDA (FR),** b f 7/4 Soul City (IRE)—Dawaes (FR) (Marchand de Sable (USA))
14 B c 13/3 Multiplex—Elzebieta (IRE) (Monsun (GER)) (5537)
15 **EMIR (FR),** b c 18/3 Alexandros—Enetari (FR) (Antonius Pius (USA))
16 B c 27/2 Pour Moi (IRE)—Emma Knows (FR) (Anabaa (USA)) (33222)
17 B f 12/5 Equiano (FR)—Fabulously Red (Red Ransom (USA)) (7382)
18 Ch c 1/4 Linngari (IRE)—Fire Sale (ARG) (Not For Sale (ARG)) (9597)
19 B f 31/3 Acclamation—Freedom Pass (USA) (Gulch (USA))
20 B c 30/4 Pour Moi (IRE)—Freeing (Dansili)
21 **FUEGO DEL AMOR (FR),** b c 24/3 Dream Ahead (USA)—Femme Fatale (SWI) (Feliciano (SWI)) (33222)
22 **GENTLE MAN (FR),** ch c 3/5 Gentlewave (IRE)—Rain Lily (FR) (Priolo (USA)) (33222)
23 B f 30/4 Fastnet Rock (AUS)—Golden Bottle (Giant's Causeway (USA))
24 **GUANACASTE (IRE),** gr c 18/3 Whipper (USA)—Divine Promesse (FR) (Verglas (IRE)) (27316)
25   c 1/1 Oasis Dream—Hanami (Hernando (FR))
26 B f 30/1 Holy Roman Emperor (IRE)—Hayaku (USA) (Arch (USA))
27 Gr f 16/3 Literato (FR)—High Limits (IRE) (High Chaparral (IRE))
28 B c 5/2 Henrythenavigator (USA)—Hunza Dancer (IRE) (Danehill Dancer (IRE))
29 **ICALO (FR),** b c 14/4 Scalo—Indyca (GER) (Panis (USA)) (22148)
30 **INCAMPO (FR),** b c 19/2 Campanologist (USA)—Indian Cat (IRE) (One Cool Cat (USA))
31 **IYOUNA (FR),** ch f 26/3 Siyouni (FR)—Indianapolis (GER) (Tiger Hill (IRE)) (36913)
32 B f 13/2 Myboycharlie (IRE)—Jules J (USA) (Action This Day (USA))

MR H. A. PANTALL - Continued

33 **KANALETO (FR)**, b c 27/4 Literato (FR)—Fabulatrice (FR) (Turtle Bowl (IRE))
34 **KENACROSS (FR)**, b c 1/1 Kendargent (FR)—Across (ARG) (Roy (USA))
35 Gr c 27/3 Soldier of Fortune (IRE)—Lamarsa (FR) (Chichicastenango (FR)) (6644)
36 **LANDAA (FR)**, f 1/1 Kheleyf (USA)—Tejaara (USA) (Kingmambo (USA)) (73827)
37 **LOOPER (FR)**, b c 20/2 Air Chief Marshal (IRE)—A Ma Yen (ITY) (Doyen (IRE)) (12550)
38 **MAJ OU CHOP (FR)**, ch c 28/4 Deportivo—Sheshmana (FR) (Kendor (FR))
39 **MALKOBOY (FR)**, gr c 4/4 Rajsaman (FR)—Goldy Honor (FR) (Highest Honor (FR))
40 **MASINA CITY (FR)**, b f 3/3 Soul City (IRE)—Toamasina (FR) (Marju (IRE)) (10335)
41 B f 13/2 Excelebration (IRE)—Miss Emma May (IRE) (Hawk Wing (USA))
42 **MISTER O'KEN (FR)**, ro c 3/5 Kendargent (FR)—Miss Sissy (FR) (Sicyos (USA))
43 **MOG EDWARDS (FR)**, b c 16/4 Naaqoos—Fedora (IRE) (Cape Cross (IRE)) (1107)
44 **MY DREAM CHARLIE (FR)**, b c 10/4 Dream Ahead (USA)—My Girl Charlie (IRE) (Kodiac) (8859)
45 **MY LITTLE GIRL (FR)**, b f 24/1 Myboycharlie (IRE)—Gribatune (FR) (Green Tune (USA)) (20671)
46 B f 13/3 Motivator—Nanty (IRE) (Nashwan (USA)) (11074)
47 B c 9/5 Elusive City (USA)—Nice Matin (USA) (Tiznow (USA))
48 **OVER THE CLOUDS (FR)**, b f 18/3 Siyouni (FR)—Olive Green (USA) (Diesis)
49 **PHELPS WIN (FR)**, b c 15/2 Muhtathir—Take Grace (FR) (Take Risks (FR))
50 B f 18/4 Teofilo (IRE)—Pyman's Theory (IRE) (Exceed And Excel (AUS))
51 **QATAR SPIRIT (FR)**, b c 17/5 Elusive City (USA)—Miximaa (Anabaa (USA))
52 **QATAR WEAVE (FR)**, b c 10/3 Soldier of Fortune (IRE)—Mosogna Moon (Boreal (GER))
53 **QUINDIANA (FR)**, ch f 19/2 Linngari (IRE)—Belle Suisse (FR) (Hamas (IRE))
54 B f 1/2 Silver Frost (IRE)—Rampoldina (Montjeu (IRE)) (11812)
55 **RAYON VERT (FR)**, c 1/1 Harbour Watch (IRE)—Mansoura (IRE) (Kalanisi (IRE)) (18456)
56 **RIO GRANDE (FR)**, b c 1/1 Rio de La Plata (USA)—Zomorroda (IRE) (Chineur (FR)) (11074)
57 **RIOTURN (FR)**, ch f 20/2 Rio de La Plata (USA)—Turning For Home (FR) (Spinning World (USA))
58 **RISE HIT (FR)**, b c 30/3 American Post—Rose The One (FR) (Meshaheer (USA))
59 B c 12/2 Dubawi (IRE)—Sabratah (Oasis Dream) (479881)
60 **SLAVA D'ALBEN (FR)**, b f 3/4 Sageburg (IRE)—Nazlia (FR) (Polish Precedent (USA)) (2583)
61 B c 23/2 Youmzain (IRE)—Snow Jasmine (IRE) (Exceed And Excel (AUS)) (16980)
62 c 1/1 Exceed And Excel (AUS)—Soho Star (Smarty Jones (USA))
63 B c 21/3 Authorized (IRE)—Something Strange (IRE) (Holy Roman Emperor (IRE))
64 **SOURYEM (FR)**, gr f 19/5 Soul City (IRE)—Meryem (FR) (Chichicastenango (FR))
65 **STREETS OF RIO (FR)**, b c 1/3 Rio de La Plata (USA)—Snow Lady (SWI) (Vision (USA)) (14765)
66 Ch c 2/5 Rio de La Plata (USA)—Summer Sea (Bahhare (USA)) (22148)
67 **SUNDENE (FR)**, b f 21/2 Zafeen (FR)—Silver Market (FR) (Marchand de Sable (USA))
68 B c 16/1 Linngari (IRE)—Superstition (FR) (Kutub (IRE)) (51679)
69 **TAKE ME HOME (FR)**, b c 19/3 Henrythenavigator (USA)—Trully Belle (IRE) (Bahri (USA)) (11812)
70 **TOUCH OF ART (FR)**, ch f 23/2 Alexandros—Touchee d'amour (GER) (Neshad (USA))
71 B c 4/4 Myboycharlie (IRE)—Vallee Celebre (SWI) (Peintre Celebre (USA))
72 **VELDARGENT (FR)**, b f 27/2 Kendargent (FR)—Velvet Revolver (IRE) (Mujahid (USA)) (47988)
73 **VENEZIA (SWI)**, b f 22/2 Blue Canari (FR)—Vertana (IRE) (Sinndar (IRE)) (16242)

Assistant Trainer: Ludovic Gadbin (0033) 685 070620

Jockey (flat): Fabrice Veron. **Apprentice:** Lukas Delozier.

	MR JOHN PANVERT, Tiverton
471	Postal: **Steart Farm Racing Stables, Stoodleigh, Tiverton, Devon, EX16 9QA** Contacts: **MOBILE (07590) 120314** E-MAIL jemma1881@gmail.com

1 **EDDY**, 7, b g Exit To Nowhere (USA)—Sharway Lady **J. F. Panvert**
2 **SISTERBROOKE (IRE)**, 7, ch m Trans Island—Cool Merenda (IRE) **J. F. Panvert**
3 **TITCH STRIDER (IRE)**, 11, b m Milan—Just Little **J. F. Panvert**
4 **WATCHMETAIL (IRE)**, 10, b br g Amilynx—Ellie Anna (IRE) **J. F. Panvert**
5 **WUN DESTINATION**, 7, b m Dubai Destination (USA)—Mourir d'aimer (USA) **J. F. Panvert**

Jockey (flat): Jim Crowley, Luke Morris. **Jockey (NH):** Conor O'Farrell. **Conditional:** Tom Cheesman.

472 MRS HILARY PARROTT, Redmarley
Postal: **Chapel Farm, Chapel Lane, Redmarley, Gloucester, Gloucestershire, GL19 3JF**
Contacts: **PHONE (01452) 840139 FAX (01452) 840139 MOBILE (07972) 125030**
E-MAIL hkparrott@btinternet.com

1 **DAIZY (IRE)**, 7, ch g Presenting—I Remember It Well (IRE) **Mr T. J. & Mrs H. Parrott**
2 **TINOS TANK (IRE)**, 7, b g Flemensfirth (USA)—Tinopasa (FR) **T. J. Parrott**

Other Owners: Mrs H. Parrott.

473 MR BEN PAULING, Bourton-On-The-Water
Postal: **Bourton Hill Farm, Bourton-On-The-Water, Gloucestershire, GL54 3BJ**
Contacts: **PHONE (01451) 821252 MOBILE (07825) 232888**
E-MAIL ben@benpaulingracing.com WEBSITE www.benpaulingracing.com

1 **A HARE BREATH (IRE)**, 8, b g Alkaadhem—Lady Willmurt (IRE) **Mrs S. N. J. Embiricos**
2 **ALPINE SECRET (IRE)**, 4, br g Stowaway—Squaw Valley (IRE) **Off Piste Partnership**
3 **ALWAYS LION (IRE)**, 6, b g Let The Lion Roar—Addie's Choice (IRE) **Mr & Mrs Paul & Clare Rooney**
4 **BALLYHENRY (IRE)**, 6, br g Presenting—Afarka (IRE) **The Vestey Family Partnership**
5 **BARTERS HILL (IRE)**, 6, b g Kalanisi (IRE)—Circle The Wagons (IRE) **Circle Of Friends**
6 **BURGUNDY BETTY (IRE)**, 6, b m Presenting—Lady Meribel **Mrs B. M. Henley**
7 **CALVA D'HONORE (FR)**, 5, b g Khalkevi (IRE)—Elivette (FR) **Mr & Mrs Paul & Clare Rooney**
8 **CASSIE**, 6, b m Refuse To Bend (IRE)—Strictly Cool (USA) **Pump & Plant Services Ltd**
9 **CASTLE CHEETAH (IRE)**, 8, br g Presenting—Castle Crystal (IRE) **Mr B. Eccles**
10 **CHARLIE BREEKIE (IRE)**, 7, b g Alkaadhem—Highland Breeze (IRE) **The Harefield Racing Club**
11 4, B g Kalanisi (IRE)—Circle The Wagons (IRE)
12 4, B g Tikkanen (USA)—Crimond (IRE) **Mrs S. P. Foran**
13 **CYRIUS MORIVIERE (IRE)**, 6, b g Vendangeur (IRE)—Sagesse Moriviere (FR) **The Pillar P Partnership**
14 **DRUMACOO (IRE)**, 7, b g Oscar (IRE)—My Native (IRE) **Mrs Robin Birley**
15 **ELOPED**, 5, b m Midnight Legend—Southern Exit **Mr L. J. Strangman**
16 **EMPEROR'S HILL (IRE)**, 4, b g Scorpion (IRE)—Watermelon (IRE) **The Bourtoneers**
17 **ITSNOWCATO**, 5, b g Notnowcato—Blaenavon **Genesis Racing Partnership II**
18 **KINGUSSIE**, 8, b g Diktat—Highland Gait **The High T Party**
19 **LE BREUIL (FR)**, 4, ch g Anzillero (GER)—Slew Dancer **Miss E. A. Collins**
20 **LOCAL SHOW (IRE)**, 8, br g Oscar (IRE)—Loughaderra Rose (IRE) **Nicholas Piper & Claire E. Piper**
21 **MALIBU SUN**, 9, ch g Needwood Blade—Lambadora **Easy Going Racing**
22 **MIDNIGHT FOLIE**, 6, b m Midnight Legend—Lady Racquet (IRE) **The Neighbours Partnership**
23 **NEWTON GERONIMO**, 7, b br g Brian Boru—Newton Commanche (IRE) **J. H. & N. J. Foxon**
24 **NEWTON THISTLE**, 9, b g Erhaab (USA)—Newton Venture **J. H. & N. J. Foxon**
25 **PADDY'S FIELD (IRE)**, 6, b br g Flemensfirth (USA)—Kittys Oscar (IRE) **Mr & Mrs Paul & Clare Rooney**
26 **PERFECT PIRATE**, 4, b g Black Sam Bellamy (IRE)—Supreme Gem (IRE) **Mr T. P. Finch**
27 **PITHIVIER (FR)**, 6, b g Poliglote—Kelbelange (FR) **Mr & Mrs Paul & Clare Rooney**
28 **RAVEN'S TOWER (USA)**, 6, b g Raven's Pass (USA)—Tizdubai (USA) **Faithful Friends**
29 **RIDE ON TIME (IRE)**, 6, b g Presenting—Polly Anthus **Whatalot**
30 **SHOWBOATER (IRE)**, 7, b g Milan—Dazala **Mr & Mrs Paul & Clare Rooney**
31 **SILVERGROVE**, 8, b g Old Vic—Classic Gale (USA) **Nicholas Piper & Claire E. Piper**
32 **SMOKING DIXIE (IRE)**, 5, ch g Beneficial—Jacksister (IRE) **Mrs Robin Birley**
33 **SPACE WALKER (IRE)**, 5, b g Astronomer Royal (USA)—Hot Property (USA) **Mr & Mrs Paul & Clare Rooney**
34 **THE HON MACKINLAY (IRE)**, 7, ch g Bold Fact (USA)—Khadija **The Kykie Allsopp Partnership**
35 **TREATY GIRL (IRE)**, 5, b m Milan—Back To Cloghoge (IRE) **The Bourtoneers**
36 **WILLOUGHBY COURT (IRE)**, 5, br g Court Cave (IRE)—Willoughby Sue (IRE) **Mr & Mrs Paul & Clare Rooney**

Other Owners: Mrs C. Belloc Lowndes, Mr G. Bennett, Mr R. J. Claydon, Mrs P. M. Colson, Mr J. Deacon, Mr P. M. Drewett, S. N. Embiricos, Hon S. Foster, Mr R. Foxon, Mr J. H. Foxon, Mrs N. J. Foxon, Mr W. P. Harriman, Mrs C. S. Heber-Percy, Mr B. L. Hiskey, Mr C. N. M. James, Mr R. S. Johnson, Mrs J. E. B. Leigh-Pemberton, Mrs J. Pauling, Mr C. M. Pickard, Miss J. Pimblett, Mr N. Piper, Miss C. E. Piper, Mr T. Robinson-Gamby, Mrs C. Rooney, Mr P. A. Rooney, Mr T. C. Smith, Mrs M. T. Stopford-Sackville, D. F. Sumpter, Lady Vestey, The Hon A. G. Vestey, Lord Vestey, Mr R. W. P. Weeks.

Assistant Trainer: Mary Vestey

Jockey (NH): David Bass, James Davies, Nico De Boinville.

474 MR RAY PEACOCK, Tenbury Wells
Postal: **Elliott House Farm, Vine Lane, Kyre, Tenbury Wells, Worcestershire, WR15 8RL**
Contacts: **PHONE (01885) 410772 MOBILE (07748) 565574/ 07881440135**

1 **BEWDLEY**, 11, b m Best of The Bests (IRE)—Garota De Ipanema (FR) **R. E. Peacock**
2 **GIFTED HEIR (IRE)**, 12, b g Princely Heir (IRE)—Inzar Lady (IRE) **R. E. Peacock**
3 **INTERCHOICE STAR**, 11, b g Josr Algarhoud (IRE)—Blakeshall Girl **Mr J. P. Evitt**
4 **PORTRUSH STORM**, 11, ch m Observatory (USA)—Overcast (IRE) **R. E. Peacock**
5 **RICH HARVEST (USA)**, 11, b br g High Yield (USA)—Mangano (USA) **R. E. Peacock**
6 **SWORDS**, 14, b g Vettori (IRE)—Pomorie (IRE) **R. E. Peacock**

Assistant Trainer: Mrs C Peacock

Jockey (flat): David Probert. Amateur: Miss S. Peacock.

475 MRS LYDIA PEARCE, Newmarket
Postal: **Wroughton House, 37 Old Station Road, Newmarket, Suffolk, CB8 8DT**
Contacts: **PHONE (01638) 664669 MOBILE (07787) 517864**
E-MAIL lsp_8@live.co.uk

1 **BLACK ICEMAN**, 8, gr g Iceman—Slite **A Partnership**
2 **CAPTAIN NAVARRE**, 4, b g Excellent Art—Quantum (IRE) **Lydia Pearce Racing Partnership 1**
3 **COMPARATIVE**, 4, b g Oasis Dream—Indication **Mr A. Watford**
4 **LOUD**, 6, ch g Dutch Art—Applauding (IRE) **Mr Zaheer Chaudhry**
5 **MINSTREL LAD**, 8, ch g Where Or When (IRE)—Teal Flower **P. J. Stephenson**
6 **MON PETIT FLEUR**, 4, b f Arabian Gleam—Mon Petit Diamant **Mr Dick Devereux**
7 **PICTURE DEALER**, 7, b g Royal Applause—Tychy **Killarney Glen**
8 **SEXY SECRET**, 5, b g Sakhee's Secret—Orange Walk (IRE) **R. G. Thurston**

THREE-YEAR-OLDS
9 **CYTRINGAN**, b f Equiano (FR)—Scisciabubu (IRE) **Killarney Glen**
10 **MADDYS DREAM**, b g Arabian Gleam—Group Force (IRE) **Mr Dick Devereux**
11 **STYLISH QUEEN**, b f Arabian Gleam—Stylish Clare (IRE) **Mr Dick Devereux**

TWO-YEAR-OLDS
12 B c 31/3 Intense Focus (USA)—Blandish (USA) (Wild Again (USA)) (2200) **Lydia Pearce**
13 **CAMARADORIE (IRE)**, ch f 30/1 Camacho—Lady Duxyana (Most Welcome) (15238)
14 Ch c 15/2 Fast Company (IRE)—Mana (IRE) (Motivator) (4761) **A Partnership**
15 B f 9/3 Doncaster Rover (USA)—Mon Petit Diamant (Hector Protector (USA)) **Mr Dick Devereux**
16 B c 11/4 Invincible Spirit (IRE)—Snowdrops (Gulch (USA)) (70000) **Killarney Glen**
17 B f 11/4 Equiano (FR)—Tychy (Suave Dancer (USA)) (4500) **Killarney Glen**

Other Owners: S. Andrews, Mr Harry Crothers, N. M. Hanger, Mr Glenn Johnson, Mr Eric Jones, Mrs Louise Marsh, Mrs J. R. Marsh, Mr A. B. Puddick, Mr R. G. Thurston.

Assistant Trainer: Jeff Pearce

Jockey (flat): Simon Pearce.

476 MR OLLIE PEARS, Malton
Postal: **The Office, Old Farmhouse, Beverley Road, Norton, Malton, North Yorkshire, YO17 9PJ**
Contacts: **PHONE (01653) 690746 MOBILE (07760) 197103**
E-MAIL info@olliepearsracing.co.uk WEBSITE www.olliepearsracing.co.uk

1 **EQUILICIOUS**, 4, b f Equiano (FR)—Fabine **Major P. H. K. Steveney**
2 **EXCLUSIVE CONTRACT (IRE)**, 5, br m High Chaparral (IRE)—
                                              Birthday (IRE) **Club Racing Exclusive Partnership**
3 **LEAN ON PETE (IRE)**, 7, b g Oasis Dream—Superfonic (IRE) **K. C. West**
4 **NAOISE (IRE)**, 8, ch g Stormy Atlantic (USA)—Machinale (USA) **T. Elsey**
5 **NOODLES BLUE BOY**, 10, b g Makbul—Dee Dee Girl (IRE) **K. C. West**
6 **SISYPHUS**, 4, b g Halling (USA)—Cape Dancer (IRE) **C. V. Wentworth**
7 **ZEBELINI (IRE)**, 4, gr f Zebedee—Ma Nikitia (IRE) **Mr T. L. Alcock**

MR OLLIE PEARS - Continued

THREE-YEAR-OLDS

8 **ANUSHKA NOO NOO,** b f Makfi—Triple Edition (USA) **Mr A. Caygill**
9 **NORTON WARRIOR,** ch g Elnadim (USA)—Swanky Lady **Ownaracehorse Ltd**
10 **ROARING RORY,** ch g Sakhee's Secret—Barbieri (IRE) **Ownaracehorse Ltd**
11 Ch f Monsieur Bond (IRE)—Valley of The Moon (IRE) **T. Elsey**

TWO-YEAR-OLDS

12 B c 20/2 Holy Roman Emperor (IRE)—Always Attractive (IRE) (King's Best (USA)) (24761) **C. V. Wentworth**
13 **DYNA MIGHT,** b f 26/2 Foxwedge (AUS)—Dyna Bowl (USA) (Dynaformer (USA)) (3500) **Ownaracehorse Ltd**
14 **FIRE ENGINE,** b c 11/5 Compton Place—All The Nines (IRE) (Elusive City (USA)) (2000) **Ownaracehorse Ltd**
15 **I CALL THE SHOTS,** b c 16/2 Delegator—Nellie Ellis (IRE) (Compton Place) (5500) **Ownaracehorse Ltd**
16 **KROY,** b c 10/5 Sleeping Indian—Valley of The Moon (IRE) (Monashee Mountain (USA)) (761) **Mrs S. A. Elsey**
17 B c 15/4 Hellvelyn—Mix It Up (Linamix (FR)) **O. J. Pears**
18 **MR C (IRE),** b c 2/4 Fast Company (IRE)—Vanitycase (IRE) (Editor's Note (USA)) (18095) **Mr A. Caygill**
19 B gr f 10/4 Hellvelyn—Real Diamond (Bertolini (USA)) (761) **J. H. Sissons**
20 **SPANISH BEAUTY,** b f 6/4 Paco Boy (IRE)—Basque Beauty (Nayef (USA)) (1800) **Ownaracehorse Ltd**

Assistant Trainer: Vicky Pears

Jockey (NH): Brian Hughes.

477

MR GEORGE PECKHAM, Newmarket
Postal: **29 Tea Kettle Lane, Stetchworth, Newmarket, Suffolk, CB8 9TP**
Contacts: **MOBILE (07823) 335013**
E-MAIL **george@aislabie.com**

1 **EMPERICAL,** 6, b g Oasis Dream—Kalima **F. Nass**
2 **LOUDLY (USA),** 4, gr f War Front (USA)—T K O Lady (USA) **F. Nass**
3 **MUHAZWARA (IRE),** 4, b f Fastnet Rock (AUS)—Carn Lady (IRE) **F. Nass**

THREE-YEAR-OLDS

4 **ASSISTED,** ch g Motivator—More Sirens (IRE) **F. Nass**
5 **DARING DAY,** b f Acclamation—Silver Kestrel (USA) **F. Nass**
6 **FIREFEET,** b f New Approach (IRE)—Tinaar (USA) **F. Nass**
7 **FLAMING ACE (IRE),** b f Acclamation—Pioneer Bride (USA) **F. Nass**
8 **HEART OF OAK,** b f Oasis Dream—Gakalina (IRE) **Mr Isa Salman & Mr Fawzi Nass**
9 **LISALA (FR),** b f Siyouni (FR)—Lilac Charm (IRE) **F. Nass**
10 B c Giant's Causeway (USA)—Persist (USA) **Mr Abdul Rahman Al Jasmi & Mr Fawzi Nass**
11 B br c Super Saver (USA)—Raise Fee (USA) **Mr Abdul Rahman Al Jasmi & Mr Fawzi Nass**
12 **RUN TO THE HILLS (USA),** b c Quality Road (USA)—Masada (USA) **Fawzi Abdullah Nass & Justin Byrne**
13 B c Unbridled's Song (USA)—The Best Day Ever (USA) **F. Nass**

TWO-YEAR-OLDS

14 B c 11/2 Medicean—Aujiang (GER) (Royal Dragon (USA)) (33222) **F. Nass**
15 B br f 3/2 Holy Roman Emperor (IRE)—Blessed Catch (USA) (Storm Cat (USA)) (55370) **F. Nass**
16 B c 4/2 Aqlaam—Bounty Box (Bahamian Bounty) (31000) **F. Nass**
17 **BROUG (BHR),** b f 23/1 Kloof—Mrs Boss (BRZ) (Wild Event (USA)) **Mr A. M. Al Jasmi**
18 B f 17/2 Dark Angel (IRE)—Folga (Atraf) (825000) **F. Nass**
19 Br c 19/4 Dream Ahead (USA)—Jamary (IRE) (Grand Reward (USA)) (60000) **F. Nass**
20 Gr ro f 18/4 Choisir (AUS)—Light And Airy (Linamix (FR)) (88593) **F. Nass**
21 B c 6/4 Harbour Watch (IRE)—Solstice (Dubawi (IRE)) (55000) **F. Nass**
22 B f 24/3 Galileo (IRE)—Starlit Sands (Oasis Dream) (775193) **F. Nass**
23 B c 8/1 Motivator—Zalia (FR) (Oasis Dream) (103359) **F. Nass**

Other Owners: Mr Abdulrahman M. Al Jasmi, Mr Justin Byrne, Mr Fawzi Abdulla Nass, Mr Khaled A Rahim, Mr Isa Salman.

Jockey (flat): Luke Morris.

478 MISS LINDA PERRATT, East Kilbride

Postal: **North Allerton Farm, East Kilbride, Glasgow, Lanarkshire, G75 8RR**
Contacts: **PHONE (01355) 303425 MOBILE (07931) 306147**
E-MAIL linda.perratt@btinternet.com

1 BANNOCK TOWN, 5, b g Denounce—Miss Pigalle **The Hon Miss H. Galbraith**
2 BLUE SONIC, 6, gr m Proclamation (IRE)—Big Mystery (IRE) **The Jolly Beggars & Mr B Holohan**
3 BUNCE (IRE), 8, b g Good Reward (USA)—Bold Desire **Peter Tsim & Helen Perratt**
4 DARK CRYSTAL, 5, b m Multiplex—Glitz (IRE) **Nil Sine Labore Partnership**
5 DRINKS FOR LOSERS (IRE), 5, b g Mastercraftsman (IRE)—Heart's Desire (IRE) **M. Sawers**
6 IT'S TIME FOR BED, 4, gr f Zebedee—Mystical Ayr (IRE) **Nil Sine Labore Partnership**
7 JINKY, 8, b g Noverre (USA)—Aries (GER) **Mr J. Murphy**
8 LET RIGHT BE DONE, 4, gr g Lawman (FR)—Cheerfully **Mr Peter Tsim &Linda Perratt Racing Club**
9 LITTLE BELTER (IRE), 4, gr g Dandy Man (IRE)—On Thin Ice (IRE) **J. K. McGarrity**
10 MYSTICAL KING, 6, b g Notnowcato—Mystical Ayr (IRE) **Jackton Racing Club**
11 PETERS GREY (IRE), 6, gr g Aussie Rules (USA)—Aliyshan (IRE) **P. Tsim**
12 PITT RIVERS, 7, br g Vital Equine (IRE)—Silca Boo **Mrs H. F. Perratt**
13 ROCK CANYON (IRE), 7, b g Rock of Gibraltar (IRE)—Tuesday Morning **Mrs H. F. Perratt**
14 SAXONETTE, 8, b m Piccolo—Solmorin **Jackton Racing Club**
15 SCHMOOZE (IRE), 7, b m One Cool Cat (USA)—If Dubai (USA) **Jackton Racing Club**
16 SILVER RIME (FR), 11, gr g Verglas (IRE)—Severina **J. K. McGarrity**

THREE-YEAR-OLDS

17 DUTCH DREAM, ch f Dutch Art—Starry Sky **Mr B. A. Jordan**
18 SNEAKIN'PETE, b c Frozen Power (IRE)—Jillolini **John Murphy & Helen Perratt**

Other Owners: Mr Bryan Atkins, Mr B. Holohan, Mr Tom Hughes, Miss Janet Kerr, Mr John Murphy, Miss L. A. Perratt, Mrs Helen Perratt, Mr John J. Sheridan, Mrs Susan Stienlet, Mr Peter Tsim.

Assistant Trainer: Mr Ross Smith

479 MRS AMANDA PERRETT, Pulborough

Postal: **Coombelands Racing Stables, Pulborough, West Sussex, RH20 1BP**
Contacts: **OFFICE (01798) 873011 HOME (01798) 874894 FAX (01798) 875163**
MOBILE (07803) 088713
E-MAIL aperrett@coombelands-stables.com WEBSITE www.amandaperrett.com

1 ARCH VILLAIN (IRE), 7, b g Arch (USA)—Barzah (IRE) **Mr & Mrs F Cotton,Mr & Mrs P Conway**
2 ARCHANGEL RAPHAEL (IRE), 4, b c Montjeu—La Sylvia (IRE) **The Archangel Raphael Partnership**
3 ARTFUL ROGUE (IRE), 5, b g Excellent Art—Szabo (IRE) **Mr & Mrs F Cotton,Mr & Mrs P Conway**
4 ASTRONEREUS (IRE), 5, ch h Sea The Stars (IRE)—Marie Rheinberg (GER) **John Connolly & Odile Griffith**
5 BLUE SURF, 7, ch g Excellent Art—Wavy Up (IRE) **John Connolly And Partners**
6 BRAMSHILL LASS, 7, ch m Notnowcato—Disco Ball **Mrs K. J. L. Hancock**
7 CZECH IT OUT (IRE), 6, b g Oratorio (IRE)—Naval Affair (IRE) **G. D. P. Materna**
8 ELYSIAN FIELDS (GR), 5, ch m Champs Elysees—Second of May **Mrs A. J. Chandris**
9 EXTRASOLAR, 6, b g Exceed And Excel (AUS)—Amicable Terms **Odile Griffith & John Connolly**
10 EYE OF THE STORM (IRE), 6, ch h Galileo (IRE)—Mohican Princess **G. D. P. Materna**
11 FLIGHTY FILIA (IRE), 4, gr f Raven's Pass (USA)—Coventina (IRE) **Cotton, Conway**
12 GLARING, 5, b h Champs Elysees—Brightest **G. D. P. Materna**
13 LIGHTNING CHARLIE, 4, b g Myboycharlie (IRE)—Lighted Way **Lightning Charlie Partnership**
14 OPEN THE RED, 4, b g Lawman (FR)—Acquainted **G. D. P. Materna**
15 PRINCE OF ISLAY (IRE), 5, ch g Nayef (USA)—Feolin **Miss E. J. Mason**
16 SABORIDO (USA), 10, gr g Dixie Union (USA)—Alexine (ARG) **Mrs A. J. Perratt**
17 SAUCY MINX (IRE), 6, b m Dylan Thomas (IRE)—Market Day **Mr & Mrs F Cotton,Mr & Mrs P Conway**
18 THE WARRIOR (IRE), 4, b c Exceed And Excel (AUS)—Aymara **The Warrior Partnership**

THREE-YEAR-OLDS

19 ATTEST, b g Cacique (IRE)—Change Course **K. Abdullah**
20 BALANCING TIME, b g Pivotal—Time On **John Connolly & Odile Griffith**
21 CANFORD BELLE, b f Canford Cliffs (IRE)—Ballyea (IRE) **Canford Belle Partnership**
22 CATCHMENT, b f Oasis Dream—Mirror Lake **K. Abdullah**
23 COMBATIVE, b c Sinndar (IRE)—Intense **K. Abdullah**
24 CONCEPTUAL, b c Nayef (USA)—Half Glance **K. Abdullah**
25 DIVINE PRINCE (GR), ch c Apotheosis (USA)—Pringipessa's Way **Smith, Correale, Cipullo**

MRS AMANDA PERRETT - Continued

26 **ENTRENCH**, b f Oasis Dream—Silent Entrance **K. Abdullah**
27 **EQUINETTE (IRE)**, b f Equiano (FR)—Rougette **D. M. James**
28 **FASHIONABLE SPIRIT (IRE)**, b f Invincible Spirit (IRE)—White And Red (IRE) **Mr Alan Spence**
29 **FROZEN FORCE (IRE)**, ch c Frozen Power (IRE)—La Mere Germaine (IRE) **Mr Alan Spence**
30 **GABSTER (IRE)**, ch f Iffraaj—Mozie Cat (IRE) **Cordage Racing Ltd**
31 **LADY ROCKA**, ch f Rock of Gibraltar (IRE)—Dance Way (IRE) **Coombelands Racing Syndicate**
32 Ch f Reel Buddy (USA)—Leisurely Way **Mrs A. J. Chandris**
33 **MAQUEDA (USA)**, b f Rock Hard Ten (USA)—Proud Fact (USA) **K. Abdullah**
34 **MISCHIEF MAISY (IRE)**, gr f Clodovil (IRE)—Maise and Blue (USA) **Cotton, Conway**
35 **NUTBOURNE LAD (IRE)**, b g Lilbourne Lad (IRE)—Cape Sydney (IRE) **Nutbourne Lad Partnership**
36 Br f Tiantai (USA)—Rainbow Way **Mrs A. J. Chandris**
37 **ROYAL HERO**, b c Royal Applause—Heronetta **Harwoods Racing Club Limited**
38 **SENSIBLE FRIEND (GR)**, ch c Reel Buddy (USA)—
                              Senseansensibility (USA) **Winterfields Farm, Hancock & Pope**
39 **YOU'RE HIRED**, b c Dalakhani (IRE)—Heaven Sent **G. D. P. Materna**
40 **ZHUI FENG (IRE)**, b c Invincible Spirit (IRE)—Es Que **John Connolly & Odile Griffith**

TWO-YEAR-OLDS

41 **CHAPARRACHIK (IRE)**, b c 11/2 High Chaparral (IRE)—
                              Chocolat Chaud (IRE) (Excellent Art) (125507) **John Connolly & Odile Griffith**
42 B c 29/3 Acclamation—Greek Easter (IRE) (Namid) (42000)
43 **LIGHTENING DANCE**, b f 14/4 Nathaniel (IRE)—Dance Lively (USA) (Kingmambo (USA)) **Mrs A. J. Chandris**
44 **MILIUM (USA)**, gr ro f 18/2 First Defence (USA)—Magnifica (USA) (Mizzen Mast (USA)) **K. Abdullah**
45 **MY LADY MARIE**, b f 16/4 Bated Breath—
                              Poppo's Song (CAN) (Polish Navy (USA)) (16000) **Ashley Lewer & Derek James Partnership**
46 **NIMOY (USA)**, b c 11/3 Artie Schiller (USA)—Tolerance (USA) (Seeking The Gold (USA)) **K. Abdullah**
47 B f 13/2 Sinndar (IRE)—Novellara (Sadler's Wells (USA)) **K. Abdullah**
48 **OPEN WIDE (USA)**, b br c 2/4 Invincible Spirit (IRE)—
                              Nunavik (Indian Ridge) (125000) **George Materna & John McInerney**
49 B f 18/1 Poet's Voice—Petit A Petit (IRE) (Holy Roman Emperor (IRE)) (20000)
50 **RED EMPEROR (IRE)**, b c 29/4 Holy Roman Emperor (IRE)—Rougette (Red Ransom (USA)) **D. M. James**
51 **ROC ASTRALE (IRE)**, ch c 25/2 Teofilo (IRE)—
                              Lumiere Astrale (FR) (Trempolino (USA)) (81210) **John Connolly & Odile Griffith**
52 **TAPDANCEALLTHEWAY**, b f 26/3 Nathaniel (IRE)—Tap Dance Way (IRE) (Azamour (IRE)) **Mrs A. J. Chandris**
53 **ZOFFANIST (IRE)**, ch c 8/3 Zoffany (IRE)—
                              Frynia (USA) (Cat Thief (USA)) (44296) **John Connolly & Odile Griffith**

Other Owners: Mr S. W. Barnett, Mr P. Cipullo, J. P. Connolly, Mrs S. M. Conway, Mr J. F. Correale, Mrs S. H. Cotton, F. G. Cotton, Ms O. L. Griffith, Guy Harwood, Mrs B. A. Karn-Smith, Mr A. A. Lewer, Dr J. P. McInerney, Winterfields Farm Ltd.

Assistant Trainer: Mark Perrett

480

MR PAT PHELAN, Epsom
Postal: **Ermyn Lodge, Shepherds Walk, Epsom, Surrey, KT18 6DF**
Contacts: **PHONE (01372) 229014 FAX (01372) 229001 MOBILE (07917) 762781**
E-MAIL **pat.phelan@ermynlodge.com** WEBSITE **www.ermynlodge.com**

1 **ALFIE THE PUG**, 4, b g Pastoral Pursuits—Kapsiliat (IRE) **The HP Partnership**
2 **CELTIC AVA (IRE)**, 4, b f Peintre Celebre (USA)—Denices Desert **Celtic Contractors Limited**
3 **COUP DE GRACE (IRE)**, 7, b g Elusive City (USA)—No Way (IRE) **Mr J. F. Lang**
4 **DEFTERA LAD (IRE)**, 4, b g Fast Company (IRE)—Speedbird (USA) **Mr Y. Mustafa**
5 **DELLBUOY**, 7, b g Acclamation—Ruthie **Timesquare Ltd**
6 **DELUXE**, 4, b g Acclamation—Ainia **Mr P. J. Wheatley**
7 **ENDLESS SEAS**, 6, ch m Refuse To Bend (IRE)—Ocean Ballad **David Gilbert & The Horsetraders**
8 **EPSOM FLYER**, 6, ch g Haafhd—River Cara (USA) **Celtic Contractors Limited**
9 **ERMYN'S EDITH**, 5, b m Fair Mix (IRE)—Ivy Edith **Ermyn Lodge Stud Limited**
10 **ERMYN'S EMERALD**, 4, b br g Alflora (IRE)—Emerald Project (IRE) **Ermyn Lodge Stud Limited**
11 **JAKEY (IRE)**, 6, b g Cape Cross (IRE)—Off Message (IRE) **A. B. Pope**
12 **KEEP TO THE BEAT**, 5, b m Beat Hollow—Cadeau Speciale **Mr Paul Cox & Mr Liam Russell**
13 **LEAH FREYA (IRE)**, 5, b m Aussie Rules—A Woman In Love **Mr E. Gleeson**
14 **LUCKY DOTTIE**, 5, b br m Lucky Story (USA)—Auntie Dot Com **Mr A. J. Smith**
15 **QUEST FOR WONDER**, 4, b f Makfi—Sinndiya (IRE) **Mr W. Bocking**
16 **REPRESENTINGCELTIC (IRE)**, 11, ch g Presenting—Nobull (IRE) **Celtic Contractors Limited**
17 **RIGHT STEP**, 9, b g Xaar—Maid To Dance **A. B. Pope**

MR PAT PHELAN - Continued

18 **RODNEYTHETROTTER,** 4, b g Royal Applause—Ruthie **Tony Smith & Allen Pope**
19 **SAINT HONORE,** 4, b f Champs Elysees—Gwyneth **Mr W. Bocking**

THREE-YEAR-OLDS

20 **EDE'S THE MOVER,** b f Bahamian Bounty—Run For Ede's **Ede's (UK) Ltd**
21 **FENNER HILL NEASA (IRE),** b f Alfred Nobel (IRE)—A Woman In Love **Mr E. Gleeson**
22 **MUSICAL TASTE,** b f Makfi—Blas Ceoil (USA) **Mr W. Bocking**
23 **THOMAS CROMWELL,** b c Sixties Icon—Salim Toto **J. H. Widdows**
24 **YENSIR,** ch c Sir Percy—Yensi **Mr W. Hennessey**

TWO-YEAR-OLDS

25 **DESERT SONG,** b g 22/3 Makfi—Lyra's Daemon (Singspiel (IRE)) (25000) **Epsom Downers**

Other Owners: Mr P. Cox, Mr D. M. J. Gilbert, Mr M. Hess, Ms L. M. Hess, Mrs J. K. Lukas, Mr G. Nutting, Sir D. J. Prosser, Mr L. R. Russell, T. D. J. Syder.

Jockey (flat): J. F. Egan, Shane Kelly. **Jockey (NH):** James Best, Josh Moore. **Conditional:** Paddy Bradley. **Apprentice:** Paddy Bradley. **Amateur:** Miss Laura Dempster.

---

481 **MR ALAN PHILLIPS, Callow End**
Postal: **Jennett Tree Farm, Jennett Tree Lane, Callow End, Worcester, WR2 4UA**
Contacts: **PHONE (01905) 831774 MOBILE (07870) 112235**
E-MAIL alan@alanphillipsracing.com WEBSITE www.alanphillipsracing.com

1 **ANNAMULT (IRE),** 8, ch m Beneficial—Summer Smile (IRE) **Mr A. J. Phillips**
2 4, B g Mahler—Carriacou
3 **ROLL ON RUBY (IRE),** 8, ch m Definite Article—Barichara (FR) **Miss S. B. Munrowd**
4 **SYDNEY OPERA (IRE),** 10, gr g Oscar (IRE)—Hallatte (USA) **B. M. Barrett**
5 **THE MODEL COUNTY (IRE),** 6, b m Robin des Champs (FR)—Ware It Vic (IRE) **Mr D. G. Redfern**
6 **VINTAGE RUBY,** 8, b m Grape Tree Road—Morning Flight (IRE) **B. V. Lund**

THREE-YEAR-OLDS

7 **MR STANDFAST,** b c Mullionmileanhour (IRE)—Phantom Ridge (IRE) **Miss R. L. Edwards**

Jockey (flat): Kieren Fox, Timmy Murphy. **Jockey (NH):** Sean Bowen, Tom Scudamore, Adam Wedge.
Conditional: Ben Poste. **Amateur:** Mr Alex Edwards, Miss Ally Stirling.

---

482 **MR PAUL PHILLIPS, Honiton**
Postal: **Rose Green, Monkton, Honiton, Devon, EX14 9QH**

1 **BOXATRIX,** 8, ch g Arkadian Hero (USA)—Mardereil (IRE) **Mr P. M. Phillips**
2 **HEARTENING,** 8, b m Wace (USA)—Heartleys Quest (IRE) **Mr P. M. Phillips**
3 4, B g Babodana—Lucky Jacasa

---

483 **MR RICHARD PHILLIPS, Moreton-in-Marsh**
Postal: **Adlestrop Stables, Adlestrop, Moreton-in-Marsh, Gloucestershire, GL56 0YN**
Contacts: **PHONE (01608) 658710 FAX (01608) 658713 MOBILE (07774) 832715**
E-MAIL info@richardphillipsracing.com WEBSITE www.richardphillipsracing.com

1 **ARCTIC CHIEF,** 6, b g Sleeping Indian—Neiges Eternelles (FR) **Too Many Chiefs**
2 **BEAUTIFUL PEOPLE (FR),** 5, b br m Early March—Night Fever (FR) **Beautiful People**
3 **BERKELEY BARRON (IRE),** 8, b g Subtle Power (IRE)—Roseabel (IRE) **Mrs E. A. Prowting**
4 **BERTIE BARNES (IRE),** 5, b g Craigsteel—Mahon Rose (IRE) **The Aspirationals**
5 **BLUE COMET,** 5, br g Blueprint (IRE)—Be My Valentine (IRE) **Mrs J. A. Watts**
6 **BRAVE HELIOS,** 6, b g High Chaparral (IRE)—Renowned (IRE) **Mrs J. A. Watts**
7 **CALL ME EMMA (IRE),** 8, b m Beneficial—Clody Girl (IRE) **Upthorpe Racing**
8 **CATKIN COPSE,** 8, b m Alflora (IRE)—Run Tiger (IRE) **The Adlestrop Club**
9 **CELESTIAL MAGIC,** 4, b g Black Sam Bellamy (IRE)—Mighty Merlin **Mrs J. A. Watts**
10 **COSMIC KING (FR),** 4, b g Kingsalsa (USA)—Kikinda (FR) **Mrs J. A. Watts**

MR RICHARD PHILLIPS - Continued

11 **COYABA**, 6, b g Midnight Legend—Peel Me A Grape **Mrs E. A. Prowting**
12 **FLEMENSBAY**, 8, b m Flemensfirth (USA)—Mandys Native (IRE) **Dozen Dreamers Partnership**
13 **GOLDIE LYNCH (IRE)**, 7, b g High-Rise (IRE)—Reapers Present (IRE) **C. Pocock**
14 **HEROD THE GREAT**, 6, ch g Sakhee's Secret—Pella **S. M. Smith**
15 **IRON HORSE**, 5, b g Kayf Tara—What A Vintage (IRE) **The Someday's Here Racing Partnership**
16 5, B m King's Theatre (IRE)—Lerichi (IRE) **The Firebirds**
17 **LISHEEN HILL (IRE)**, 10, b g Witness Box (USA)—Lady Lamb (IRE) **The Aspirationals**
18 **LUCKY THIRTEEN**, 8, b g Passing Glance—Lingua Franca **Mr D. Stockdale**
19 **MR FRANKIE**, 5, b g Sleeping Indian—Shes Minnie **R. T. Phillips**
20 **MUTHABIR (IRE)**, 6, b g Nayef (USA)—Northern Melody (IRE) **The Adlestrop Experience**
21 **MY MISS LUCY**, 10, b m Aflora (IRE)—Corn Lily **Mr W. McLuskey**
22 **NEXT LOT**, 6, b g Mountain High (IRE)—Martha Reilly (IRE) **Upthorpe Racing**
23 **ORGANDI (FR)**, 4, bl f Early March—Creme Pralinee (FR) **Beautiful People**
24 **OUR PROJECT (IRE)**, 5, b g Mountain High (IRE)—House-of-Hearts (IRE) **The Irish Experience**
25 **PALOMA'S PRINCE (IRE)**, 7, ch g Nayef (USA)—Ma Paloma (FR) **Serendipity Syndicate 2006**
26 **POWDERONTHEBONNET (IRE)**, 8, b g Definite Article—Zuhal **Mr W. McLuskey**
27 **SEAVIPER (IRE)**, 7, b g Presenting—Priority Post (IRE) **The Irish Experience**
28 **SHEELBEWHATSHEELBE (IRE)**, 6, b m Oscar (IRE)—Cheerymount (IRE) **B. J. Duckett**
29 **SPEED DEMON (IRE)**, 7, b g Beneficial—Brierfield Lady (IRE) **Mrs S. C. Welch**
30 **SUPER MOON**, 4, b g Black Sam Bellamy (IRE)—Aussie Deal (IRE) **Mrs J. A. Watts**
31 **TEMPLET (IRE)**, 12, b g Desert Prince (IRE)—Bering Down (USA) **Mrs J. A. Watts**
32 **TIME WISE**, 6, b m Kayf Tara—Ceoperk (IRE) **Hopeful Travellers**
33 **TOP SET (IRE)**, 6, ch g Tamayuz—Pray (IRE) **The Adlestrop Club**
34 4, B g Westerner—Torduff Storm (IRE) **R. T. Phillips**
35 **VIVA RAFA (IRE)**, 6, b g Scorpion (IRE)—Back To Stay (IRE) **Ms F. Baxter**
36 **WHAT A SCORE**, 6, gr g Rail Link—Karsiyaka (IRE) **Nut Club Partnership**
37 **WHAT A TEMPEST**, 5, b m Kayf Tara—What A Vintage (IRE) **The Someday's Here Racing Partnership**

Other Owners: Ms K. M. Anderson, Mr M. R. Barnes, J. E. Barnes, Mr J. R. Brown, Mr E. G. Brown, Mr M. P. Chitty, Mr J. E. S. Colling, Mrs H. Colraine, Mrs S. J. Harvey, Mrs H. M. Nixseaman, M. T. Phillips, Dr E. D. Theodore.

Conditional: Daniel Hiskett.

---

484 MISS IMOGEN PICKARD, Leominster
Postal: **The Granary, Sodgeley Farm, Kingsland, Leominster, Herefordshire, HR6 9PY**
Contacts: **MOBILE (07884) 437720**
E-MAIL **bundlepickardracing@yahoo.co.uk**

1 **KEEP 'R LIT**, 4, b f Multiplex—Cashel Dancer **Miss I. H. Pickard**
2 **MISTER FIZZ**, 8, b g Sulamani (IRE)—Court Champagne **Mrs M. J. Wilson**
3 **NINNY NOODLE**, 6, b m Proclamation (IRE)—Court Champagne **Mrs M. J. Wilson**
4 **OURLITTLE SENORITA**, 4, b f Fantastic Spain (USA)—Our Little Missy **Mr P. Pressdee**
5 **PRIVATE JONES**, 7, br g Trade Fair—Dafne **Mr A. P. Rogers**
6 **SHOW ME THE WONDER**, 7, b g Rail Link—Newtown Villa
7 **TEME TRIXIE**, 6, b m Needwood Blade—Castanet **Mr A E & Mr G M Mansell**

Other Owners: Mr G. M. Mansell, A. E. Price.

Assistant Trainer: Jon Flook

---

485 MR DAVID PIPE, Wellington
Postal: **Pond House, Nicholashayne, Wellington, Somerset, TA21 9QY**
Contacts: **PHONE (01884) 840715 FAX (01884) 841343**
E-MAIL **david@davidpipe.com WEBSITE www.davidpipe.com**

1 **ABRACADABRA SIVOLA (FR)**, 6, b g Le Fou (IRE)—Pierrebrune (FR) **The Arthur White Partnership**
2 **ALTERNATIF (FR)**, 6, b g Shaanmer (IRE)—Katerinette (FR) **Prof C. Tisdall**
3 **AMIGO (FR)**, 9, b g Ballingarry (IRE)—Allez Y (FR) **A. L. Cohen & Willsford Racing**
4 **BABY SHERLOCK**, 5, ch g Shirocco (GER)—Lady Cricket (FR) **The Johnson Family**
5 **BALGARRY (FR)**, 9, ch g Ballingarry (IRE)—Marie de Motreff (FR) **Brocade Racing**
6 **BALLYNAGOUR (IRE)**, 10, b g Shantou (USA)—Simply Deep (IRE) **A. Stennett**

MR DAVID PIPE - Continued

7 **BALLYWILLIAM (IRE)**, 6, b g Mahler—Henrietta Howard (IRE) **The Hon Mrs D. Hulse**
8 **BARAKA DE THAIX (FR)**, 5, gr g Dom Alco (FR)—Jaka de Thaix (FR) **Mr Simon Munir & Mr Isaac Souede**
9 **BATAVIR (FR)**, 7, ch g Muhtathir—Elsie (GER) **The Angove Family**
10 **BELLA (FR)**, 5, b br m Johann Quatz (FR)—Hasta Manana (FR) **Prof C. Tisdall**
11 **BIDOUREY (FR)**, 5, b br g Voix du Nord (FR)—Love Wisky (FR) **Brocade Racing**
12 **BIG OCCASION (IRE)**, 9, b g Sadler's Wells (USA)—Asnieres (USA) **The Old Betfairians**
13 **BIRD D'ESTRUVAL (FR)**, 5, ch g Vatori (FR)—Onde d'estruval (FR) **Mr Simon Munir & Mr Isaac Souede**
14 **BLADOUN (FR)**, 8, gr g Smadoun (FR)—Blabliramic (FR) **H. M. W. Clifford**
15 **BORDER BREAKER (IRE)**, 7, b g Indian Danehill (IRE)—Flying Answer (IRE) **Jimmy Hack Racing Partners 1**
16 **BROADWAY BUFFALO (IRE)**, 6, ch g Broadway Flyer (USA)—Benbroadgh Vard (IRE) **Mrs J. Tracey**
17 **BROOK (FR)**, 5, ch g Kandidate—Ninon de Re (FR) **Pipe - Dreaming Ladies**
18 **CARQALIN (FR)**, 4, gr g Martaline—Mica Doree (FR) **Mr M. J. D. Lambert**
19 **CHAMPERS ON ICE (IRE)**, 6, gr g Robin des Champs (FR)—
           Miss Nova **Professor Caroline Tisdall & Bryan Drew**
20 **CHIC THEATRE (IRE)**, 6, gr g King's Theatre (IRE)—La Reine Chic (FR) **Mr B. J. C. Drew**
21 **CLOSER TO HOME (IRE)**, 4, b g Soldier of Fortune (IRE)—
           Maid For Music (IRE) **Mr Andrew Cohen & Mr Alan Kaplan**
22 **CLOUGHERNAGH BOY (IRE)**, 8, ch g Flemensfirth (USA)—
           Windy Bee (IRE) **Stuart & Simon Mercer & Peter Green**
23 **CORK CITIZEN**, 8, b g Overbury (IRE)—Peach of a Citizen (IRE) **Mr A Stennett & Mrs A O'Sullivan**
24 **DELL' ARCA (IRE)**, 7, b g Sholokhov (IRE)—Daisy Belle (GER) **Prof C. Tisdall**
25 **DOCTOR HARPER (IRE)**, 8, b g Presenting—Supreme Dreamer (IRE) **The Johnson Family**
26 **DRAMA KING (IRE)**, 5, b g King's Theatre (IRE)—Miss Arteea (IRE) **M. D. Poland**
27 **DRUMLEE LAD (IRE)**, 6, b g Millenary—Rockport Rosa (IRE) **R. S. Brookhouse**
28 **DUSK TILL DAWN (IRE)**, 7, b g King's Theatre (IRE)—Savu Sea (IRE) **M. D. Poland**
29 **DYNASTE (FR)**, 10, gr g Martaline—Bellissima de Mai (FR) **Mr A. J. White**
30 **EAMON AN CNOIC (IRE)**, 5, b g Westerner—Nutmeg Tune (IRE) **The Angove Family**
31 **EPIC WARRIOR (IRE)**, 7, b g Brian Boru—Deise Dreamer (IRE) **Stuart & Simon Mercer & Peter Green**
32 **FINGERTIPS (FR)**, 4, gr g Martaline—Deesse d'arabie (FR) **Mr Simon Munir & Mr Isaac Souede**
33 **GABRIAL THE GREAT (IRE)**, 7, b g Montjeu (IRE)—Bayourida (USA) **Mr & Mrs Paul & Clare Rooney**
34 **GEVREY CHAMBERTIN (FR)**, 8, gr g Dom Alco (FR)—Fee Magic (FR) **Roger Stanley & Yvonne Reynolds III**
35 **HEATH HUNTER (IRE)**, 9, b g Shantou (USA)—Deep Supreme (IRE) **The Heath Hunter Partnership**
36 **HERBERT PARK (IRE)**, 6, b g Shantou (USA)—Traluide (FR) **Brocade Racing**
37 **HONEYMOON COCKTAIL (FR)**, 5, gr g Martaline—Caipirinia (FR) **Stefanos Stefanou**
38 **HOUSTON DYNIMO (IRE)**, 11, b g Rock of Gibraltar (IRE)—Quiet Mouse (USA) **Miss S. E. Hartnell**
39 **IKRAPOL (FR)**, 4, gr g Poliglote—Ikra (FR) **Mr Simon Munir & Mr Isaac Souede**
40 **IMPULSIVE AMERICAN**, 4, b g American Post—Impulsive Decision (IRE) **Mrs J. Tracey**
41 **INICIAR (GER)**, 6, b g Galileo (IRE)—Iota (GER) **Mr Simon Munir & Mr Isaac Souede**
42 **JUNIOR PACKAGE**, 5, gr g Kayf Tara—Shirley Cricket **M. C. Pipe**
43 **KALIFOURCHON (FR)**, 5, gr g Martaline—Kaly Flight (FR) **CHM Partnership**
44 **KATKEAU (FR)**, 9, b g Kotky Bleu (FR)—Levine (FR) **Prof C Tisdall, Mr J A Gent, Mr R Wilkin**
45 **KIE (IRE)**, 8, b g Old Vic—Asura (GER) **A. Stennett**
46 **KINGS PALACE (IRE)**, 8, b g King's Theatre (IRE)—Sarahs Quay (IRE) **Drew, George & Johnson Family**
47 **KNIGHT CRUSADER (IRE)**, 4, b g Sir Percy—Lac Marmot (FR) **S. P. Bloodstock**
48 **KONIG DAX (GER)**, 6, b g Saddex—Konigin Shuttle (GER) **Mr & Mrs Paul & Clare Rooney**
49 **LA VATICANE (FR)**, 7, gr m Turgeon (USA)—Taking Off (FR) **Ms M. Bukhtoyarova**
50 **LADY OF LONGSTONE (IRE)**, 6, ch m Beneficial—Christdalo (IRE) **Miss S. E. Hartnell**
51 **LOW KEY (IRE)**, 9, b g Pentire—La Capilla **G. D. Thompson**
52 **MAG THE MAN (IRE)**, 6, b m Gamut (IRE)—Derby Hall (IRE) **M. C. Pipe**
53 **MANGO CAP (FR)**, 5, gr g Zambezi Sun—Medjai (FR) **Mr S P Tracey & K Alexander**
54 **MASTER RED (IRE)**, 7, b g Red Clubs (IRE)—Glory Days (GER) **Mr & Mrs Paul & Clare Rooney**
55 **MISS GOTAWAY**, 7, b m Midnight Legend—Strollaway (IRE) **Mrs A. E. R. Goodwin**
56 **MISS WILLIAMS**, 5, b m Kayf Tara—Wee Dinns (IRE) **The Earl Of Donoughmore**
57 **MONETAIRE (FR)**, 10, b br g Anabaa (USA)—Monitrice (FR) **A. Stennett**
58 **MOON RACER (IRE)**, 7, b g Saffron Walden (FR)—Angel's Folly **Professor Caroline Tisdall & Bryan Drew**
59 **MOUNT HAVEN (IRE)**, 6, b g Mountain High (IRE)—Castlehaven (IRE) **The Angove Family**
60 **MOZO**, 5, b m Milan—Haudello (FR) **Mr R. J. H. Geffen**
61 **MR BIG SHOT (IRE)**, 5, br g Flemensfirth (USA)—Une Etoile (IRE) **Prof C. Tisdall**
62 **MY BROTHER SYLVEST**, 10, b g Bach (IRE)—Senna da Silva **Teddington Racing Club**
63 **NAVANMAN (IRE)**, 7, b g Well Chosen—Teamplin (USA) **Mrs Y. Fleet**
64 **NICE THOUGHTS (IRE)**, 4, b g Shamardal (USA)—Zacheta **M. C. Pipe**
65 **OBISTAR (FR)**, 6, b g Astarabad (USA)—Vallee du Luy (FR) **Brocade Racing**
66 **PERSPICACE**, 5, b g Sir Percy—Cassique Lady (IRE) **Mrs Alison Buchanan & Mr William Mackay**
67 **PILGRIMS BAY (IRE)**, 6, b g Turtle Island (IRE)—Lady Ariadna (IRE) **Clifford, Gosden & House**
68 **POOLE MASTER**, 11, ch g Fleetwood (IRE)—Juste Belle (FR) **G. D. Thompson**

MR DAVID PIPE - Continued

69 **PORT NAVAS (IRE)**, 5, b g Court Cave (IRE)—Mrs Quigley (IRE) **John White & Anne Underhill**
70 **PRIDEOFTHECASTLE (IRE)**, 9, b g Waky Nao—Park's Pet (IRE) **Mr B. J. C. Drew**
71 **PRINCE OF POETS**, 5, gr g Byron—Princess Maud (USA) **The Bravo Partnership**
72 **PURPLE 'N GOLD (IRE)**, 7, b g Strategic Prince—Golden Dew (IRE) **Mrs L. Webb**
73 **RATHEALY (IRE)**, 5, b g Baltic King—Baltic Belle (IRE) **The Goodman Partnership**
74 **RED SHERLOCK (IRE)**, 7, ch g Shirocco (GER)—Lady Cricket (FR) **The Johnson Family**
75 **RED SQUARE REVIVAL (IRE)**, 5, b g Presenting—Alder Flower (IRE) **Halewood International Ltd**
76 **SADLER'S GOLD (IRE)**, 6, b g Gold Well—Mrs Quigley (IRE) **G. D. Thompson**
77 **SAINT JOHN HENRY (FR)**, 6, b g Saint des Saints (FR)—Noceane (FR) **Mr B. J. C. Drew**
78 **SHOTAVODKA (IRE)**, 10, ch g Alderbrook—Another Vodka (IRE) **Mrs J. Gerard-Pearse**
79 **SKYLANDER (IRE)**, 7, b g Flemensfirth (USA)—Cat Burglar (IRE) **The Trap Team Partnership**
80 **SMILES FOR MILES (IRE)**, 8, b g Oscar (IRE)—Native Kin (IRE) **Prof C. Tisdall**
81 **SOLL**, 11, ch g Presenting—Montelfolene (IRE) **D. Mossop**
82 **SPENDING TIME**, 7, b g King's Theatre (IRE)—Karello Bay **Brocade Racing**
83 **STANDING OVATION (IRE)**, 9, b g Presenting—Glittering Star (IRE) **The Bravo Partnership**
84 **STARCHITECT (IRE)**, 5, b g Sea The Stars (IRE)—Humilis (IRE) **Mr & Mrs Paul & Clare Rooney**
85 **STARS OVER THE SEA (USA)**, 5, b g Sea The Stars (IRE)—Exciting Times (FR) **R. S. Brookhouse**
86 **STILL TOGETHER (IRE)**, 6, b g Alkaadhem—All-Together **Miss F. Stephenson**
87 **SUSIE SHEEP**, 6, ch m Robin des Champs (FR)—Haudello (FR) **Professor Caroline Tisdall & Bryan Drew**
88 **SWEETTOOTHTOMMY (IRE)**, 6, b g Definite Article—My Linda (FR) **Mrs S. J. Ling**
89 **TAJ BADALANDABAD (IRE)**, 6, ch g Shantou (USA)—Last Chance Lady (IRE) **W. F. Frewen**
90 **THE DRACONIAN (IRE)**, 5, b g Kalanisi (IRE)—Lucky Hand (IRE) **R J H Geffen & P Bennett-Jones**
91 **THE MINKLE (IRE)**, 5, ch g Flemensfirth (USA)—Impudent (IRE) **Mr R. J. H. Geffen**
92 **THUNDER PASS (IRE)**, 5, b g High Chaparral (IRE)—Hadarama (IRE) **Pipe Monkees**
93 **TOP WOOD (FR)**, 9, ch g Kotky Bleu (FR)—Heure Bleu (FR) **Mrs J. Tracey**
94 **TULLYESKER HILL (IRE)**, 7, b g Shantou (USA)—Couture Daisy (IRE) **Mr B. J. C. Drew**
95 **TWENTYTWO'S TAKEN (IRE)**, 8, b m King's Theatre (IRE)—Persian Desert (IRE) **Mr K. Alexander**
96 **UN TEMPS POUR TOUT (IRE)**, 7, b g Robin des Champs (FR)—
　　　　　　　　　　　　　　　　　　　Rougedespoir (FR) **Professor Caroline Tisdall & Bryan Drew**
97 **UNANIMITE (FR)**, 5, ch g Kentucky Dynamite (USA)—
　　　　　　　　　　　　　　　　　　　Dame Blanche (USA) **Mr Simon Munir & Mr Isaac Souede**
98 **UNIQUE DE COTTE (FR)**, 8, b g Voix du Nord (FR)—Kadalka de Cotte (FR) **J. P. McManus**
99 **VAZARO DELAFAYETTE (FR)**, 7, bl g Robin des Champs (FR)—Etoile du Merze (FR) **Mr B. J. C. Drew**
100 **VIEUX LION ROUGE (FR)**, 7, ch g Sabiango (GER)—Indecise (FR) **Prof Caroline Tisdall & Mr John Gent**
101 **WEATHER BABE**, 8, b m Storming Home—Bathwick Babe (IRE) **H. M. W. Clifford**
102 **WESTBROOKE WARRIOR (IRE)**, 5, b g Robin des Champs (FR)—Tango Lady (IRE) **Mr B. J. C. Drew**
103 **WHAT A MOMENT (IRE)**, 6, b g Milan—Cuiloge Lady (IRE) **Bryan Drew & Steve Roper**
104 **WILLEM (FR)**, 6, b g Turtle Bowl (IRE)—Zita Blues (IRE) **W. F. Frewen**

Other Owners: Mr S. J. Angove, Mr D. B. Angove, J. Apiafi, Mr J. Attfield, Mr P. Bennett-Jones, Mrs R. C. V. Brook, Mr G. R. Broom, Mrs A. E. M. Broom, Mrs A. Buchanan, Mr S. W. Buckley, Mr J. T. Chalmers, A. L. Cohen, Mr S. F. Coton, Mrs C. Cruddace, Mr M. J. Cruddace, Mrs H. Danson, J. T. Ennis, Mrs L. A. Farquhar, J. A. Gent, Mr P. George, Mr I. F. Gosden, R. B. Gray, P. J. Green, J. J. Hathorn, Mrs F. K. Hathorn, Mr T. M. Hely-Hutchinson, Mr R. House, Mr K. R. Ives, Mr D. L. Ives, Mrs D. A. Johnson, Mr S. D. Johnson, Mr R. Jones, Alan Kaplan, R. Kent, Mr W. J. Mackay, S. M. Mercer, Mr S. S. Mercer, S. E. Munir, Mrs A. M. O'Sullivan, D. J. Reid, Mrs Y. J. Reynolds, Mr P. A. Rooney, Mrs C. Rooney, Mr S. R. Roper, Mr N. Ryan, Mrs B. P. Siddall, Mr I. Souede, R. K. Stanley, Mr C. J. R. Sweeting, Mr C. R. R. Sweeting, Mr S. P. Tracey, Mrs A. Underhill, Mrs P. S. Wallace, Mr S. T. Wallace, Mr R. C. Wilkin, Willsford Racing Ltd.

Assistant Trainer: Mr M. C. Pipe C.B.E.

Jockey (NH): Conor O'Farrell, Tom Scudamore. **Conditional:** Kieron Edgar, Michael Heard, David Noonan.
Amateur: Mr Tom Greatrex.

---

486 | **MR MARK PITMAN, Upper Lambourn**
Postal: **Weathercock House, Upper Lambourn, Hungerford, Berkshire, RG17 8QT**
Contacts: **PHONE (01488) 73311**

1 **CAPTAINOFINDUSTRY (IRE)**, 7, b g Definite Article—Talk of Rain (FR) **M. C. Denmark**
2 **CONTEMPT OF COURT (IRE)**, 7, b g Milan—Moss Artiste (IRE) **M. C. Denmark**
3 **DIAMOND LIFE**, 10, b g Silver Patriarch (IRE)—Myrrh **M. C. Denmark**
4 **EMILIO LARGO**, 8, b g Cadeaux Genereux—Gloved Hand **M. C. Denmark**
5 **FACE TO FACE**, 7, b g Kayf Tara—Monsignorita (IRE) **M. C. Denmark**

MR MARK PITMAN - Continued

  6 4, B c King's Theatre (IRE)—Get Me Home (IRE) **M. C. Denmark**
  7 **GOLDEN GATE BRIDGE (GER)**, 4, b g Kamsin (GER)—Galla Placidia (GER) **M. C. Denmark**
  8 4, B c Shirocco (GER)—Monsignorita (IRE) **M. C. Denmark**
  9 4, B c Shirocco (GER)—Ryde On **M. C. Denmark**
10 **SPOILT ROTTEN**, 7, b g Kayf Tara—Rosita Bay **M. C. Denmark**
11 **STOP THE PRESS**, 7, b g Halling (USA)—Ryde On **M. C. Denmark**

THREE-YEAR-OLDS

12 B g Paco Boy (IRE)—Buena Notte (IRE) **M. C. Denmark**

---

487 **MR CHARLES POGSON, Newark**
Postal: **Allamoor Farm, Mansfield Road, Farnsfield, Nottinghamshire, NG22 8HZ**
Contacts: **PHONE (01623) 882275 MOBILE (07977) 016155**

  1 4, B g Bach (IRE)—Aphrodisias (FR) **C. T. Pogson**
  2 **BALLYBOGEY (IRE)**, 10, b g Definite Article—Beenaround (IRE) **James Callow, Chris West & Charles Pogson**
  3 **BALLYCAMP (IRE)**, 7, br g Kayf Tara—All Our Blessings (IRE) **Wordingham Plant Hire & Partner**
  4 **COUNTERSIGN**, 7, b g Authorized (IRE)—Circle of Love **C. T. Pogson**
  5 **CUSHEEN BRIDGE (IRE)**, 8, b g Oscar (IRE)—One Hell Ofa Woman (IRE) **Wordingham Plant Hire**
  6 4, B g Multiplex—Gertrude Webb **C. T. Pogson**
  7 **KAYFTON PETE**, 10, b g Kayf Tara—Jonchee (FR) **Wordingham Plant Hire & Partner**
  8 **MINELLA FORFITNESS (IRE)**, 9, b g Westerner—Ring of Water (USA) **Wordingham Plant Hire & Partner**
  9 **MOIDORE**, 7, b g Galileo (IRE)—Flash of Gold **C. T. Pogson**
10 **MONDO CANE (IRE)**, 9, b g Beneficial—La Vita E Bella (FR) **C. T. Pogson**
11 **MR ELEVATOR (IRE)**, 6, br g Sandmason—Greenwood Lady (IRE) **Wordingham Plant Hire & Partner**
12 **NORTHERN OSCAR (IRE)**, 8, b g Oscar (IRE)—Cailin's Princess (IRE) **C. T. Pogson**
13 **SCOPPIO DEL CARRO**, 5, b g Medicean—Sadie Thompson (IRE) **Wordingham Plant Hire & Partner**

Other Owners: J. R. Callow, Mr C. West, P. L. Wordingham, Mrs P. A. Wordingham.

Assistant Trainer: Adam Pogson

Jockey (NH): Adam Pogson.

---

488 **MR KEITH POLLOCK, Carluke**
Postal: **10 Lee Meadow Road, Braidwood, Carluke, Lanarkshire, ML8 5PJ**
Contacts: **PHONE (01555) 772194 FAX (01555) 772194 MOBILE (07714) 293556**
E-MAIL info@mosko.co.uk

  1 **DESTINY AWAITS (IRE)**, 7, b g Dubai Destination (USA)—Mellow Jazz **Mr K. Pollock**
  2 **GIANT HEIGHTS**, 4, b g Velvet Heights (IRE)—Giant Strides (IRE) **Mr K. Pollock**
  3 9, B g Indian Creek—Lady Ward (IRE) **Mr K. Pollock**

---

489 **MR NICHOLAS POMFRET, Tilton-on-the-Hill**
Postal: **Red Lodge Farm, Marefield Lane, Tilton-on-the-Hill, Leicester, Leicestershire, LE7 9LJ**
Contacts: **PHONE (01162) 597537 MOBILE (07885) 598810**

  1 **BETTY BORGIA**, 10, ch m Killer Instinct—Bellefleur **N. J. Pomfret**
  2 5, B g First Trump—Intrepid Gal **N. J. Pomfret**
  3 **LORDS PARK STAR (IRE)**, 7, b br g Presenting—Mary's View (IRE) **Mrs S. McLean**
  4 **SAMARINTA**, 7, ch m Samraan (USA)—Araminta **R. P. Brett**

THREE-YEAR-OLDS

  5 B f Kayf Tara—Tessanoora **Mrs S. McLean**

490 MR JONATHAN PORTMAN, Upper Lambourn

Postal: Whitcoombe House Stables, Upper Lambourn, Hungerford, Berkshire, RG17 8RA
Contacts: PHONE (01488) 73894 FAX (01488) 72952 MOBILE (07798) 824513
E-MAIL jonathan@jonathanportmanracing.com WEBSITE www.jonathanportmanracing.com

1 **ALBERT HERRING**, 4, b g Tobougg (IRE)—Balsamita (FR) **Anthony Boswood**
2 **ALERT**, 4, b f Zamindar (USA)—Tereshkina (IRE) **Whitcoombe Park Racing**
3 **BALMORAL CASTLE**, 7, b g Royal Applause—Mimiteh (USA) **J. G. B. Portman**
4 **BUCKLEBERRY**, 4, ch g Sakhee's Secret—Smart Hostess **J. G. B. Portman**
5 **CLASSIC MISSION**, 5, ch g Bahamian Bounty—Triple Cee (IRE) **J. G. B. Portman**
6 **EDGE OF HEAVEN**, 4, b f Pastoral Pursuits—Halfwaytoparadise **Mascalls Stud**
7 **FASOLT**, 4, b g Tobougg (IRE)—Mighty Splash **Anthony Boswood**
8 **HOUND MUSIC**, 4, ch f Ashkalani (IRE)—Saffron Fox **Mrs E. Edwards-Heathcote**
9 **ICKYMASHO**, 4, b f Multiplex—Icky Woo **C.R. Lambourne, M. Forbes, D. Losse**
10 **JACK BEAR**, 5, b g Joe Bear (IRE)—Colins Lady (FR) **Joe Bear Racing**
11 **JOE PACKET**, 9, ch g Joe Bear (IRE)—Costa Packet (IRE) **J. G. B. Portman**
12 **MADAME LAFITE**, 4, b f Dutch Art—Poppo's Song (CAN) **J. T. Habershon-Butcher**
13 **MAYBELATER**, 4, b f Mount Nelson—Muscovado (USA) **Mrs J. Wigan**
14 **MONSIEUR RIEUSSEC**, 6, bl g Halling (USA)—Muscovado (USA) **J. T. Habershon-Butcher**
15 **NOW WHAT**, 9, ch m Where Or When (IRE)—Vallauris **Mrs S. Portman**
16 **PASAKA BOY**, 6, ch g Haafhd—Shesha Bear **RWH Partnership**
17 **RUSSIAN RADIANCE**, 4, ch f Paco Boy (IRE)—Russian Ruby (FR) **The Traditionalists**
18 **RUSSIAN REMARQUE**, 5, b g Archipenko (USA)—Accede **The Traditionalists**
19 **UNCLE PETTIT (IRE)**, 8, b br g Heron Island (IRE)—Special Ballot (IRE) **Anthony Boswood**

THREE-YEAR-OLDS

20 **ART ECHO**, b g Art Connoisseur (IRE)—Madhaaq (IRE) **Follow The Flag Partnership**
21 **BELLOTTA**, ch f Nayef (USA)—Ela Paparouna **Mr P Afia & Partners**
22 **DESERT TANGO**, ch f Paco Boy (IRE)—Photographie (USA) **Mrs H Maitland Jones**
23 **ELEGANT ANNIE**, b f Lawman (FR)—An Ghalanta (IRE) **Tom Edwards & Partners**
24 **EQUISTAR**, ch c Equiano (FR)—Halfwaytoparadise **Mascalls Stud**
25 **GENUINE APPROVAL (IRE)**, ch f Approve (IRE)—Genuinely (IRE) **The Genuine Partnership**
26 **INTIMATELY**, b g Intense Focus (USA)—Midnight Fling **Whitcoombe Park Racing**
27 **MAGIC GARDEN (IRE)**, b f Zebedee—Sisal (IRE) **J. G. B. Portman**
28 **MISTER SHOWMAN**, b br g Showcasing—Theatre Royal **Runs In The Family**
29 **PAUSE FOR APPLAUSE**, b g Royal Applause—Zarkavean **C.R. Lambourne, M. Forbes, D. Losse**
30 **PERUSAL (IRE)**, b f Sir Percy—Overlook **J. G. B. Portman**
31 **PINCH A KISS**, ch f Sakhee's Secret—Pin Cushion **Follow The Flag Partnership**
32 **PLANET SUITE (FR)**, b f Astronomer Royal (USA)—Happy Clapper **Simon Skinner**
33 **POP CULTURE**, ch f Equiano (FR)—Naizak (IRE) **Mr & Mrs L J Walker**
34 **POSTER GIRL**, b f Excellent Art—Accede **Berkeley Racing**
35 **RAVENSWOOD**, br g Lawman (FR)—Whatami **J. T. Habershon-Butcher**
36 **RUSSIAN RANGER (IRE)**, b g Bushranger (IRE)—Pink Sovietstaia (FR) **The Traditionalists**
37 **SMILE OF APPROVAL (IRE)**, b f Approve (IRE)—Min Asl Wafi (IRE) **Whitcoombe Park Racing**
38 **TIZ HERSELF (IRE)**, gr f Dandy Man—Pitullie (USA) **Berkeley Racing**
39 **YOU'LL DO**, b g Approve (IRE)—Tentears **J. G. B. Portman**

TWO-YEAR-OLDS

40 **A MOMENT OF MAGIC**, b c 27/3 Hellvelyn—Theatre Royal (Royal Applause) **Ann Plummer & Tony Weischler**
41 **ASHAZURI**, b f 3/5 Dick Turpin (IRE)—Shesha Bear (Tobougg (IRE)) **RWH Partnership**
42 **BALGAIR**, ch c 8/3 Foxwedge (AUS)—Glencal (Compton Place) (12000) **J. T. Habershon-Butcher**
43 **BROAD APPEAL**, ch c 11/3 Medicean—Shy Appeal (IRE) (Barathea (IRE)) (17142) **Berkeley Racing**
44 B f 13/4 Sakhee's Secret—Dancing Nelly (Shareef Dancer (USA)) **Lady Hardy**
45 **FRESH FOX**, ch f 6/3 Sakhee's Secret—May Fox (Zilzal (USA)) **The Hon Mrs R. Pease**
46 B f 7/4 Pastoral Pursuits—Halfwaytoparadise (Observatory (USA)) **Mascalls Stud**
47 **HARBOURING**, ch f 17/2 Harbour Watch (IRE)—Juncea (Elnadim (USA)) (5238) **Philip Afia**
48 **MANCINI**, ch c 3/3 Nathaniel (IRE)—Muscovado (USA) (Mr Greeley (USA)) (27000) **Laurence Bellman**
49 B g 3/3 Firebreak—Oak Leaves (Mark of Esteem (IRE))
50 **ORIN SWIFT (IRE)**, b c 26/4 Dragon Pulse (IRE)—
                                          Hollow Green (IRE) (Beat Hollow (IRE)) (28000) **J. T. Habershon-Butcher**
51 **RUSSIAN REGARD (IRE)**, ch g 24/1 Intense Focus (USA)—
                                          Russian Rave (Danehill Dancer (IRE)) (11000) **The Traditionalists**
52 B f 2/3 Intikhab (USA)—Shawaaty (IRE) (Monsun (GER)) (16000) **Unregistered Partnership**

MR JONATHAN PORTMAN - Continued

53 B g 18/4 Piccolo—Spanish Gold (Vettori (IRE)) (4761)
54 **SWAN SERENADE**, b f 5/4 Paco Boy (IRE)—Accede (Acclamation) (11428) **The Hon Mrs D. Joly**
55 **TALLULAH ROCKS**, b f 1/2 Tagula (IRE)—Daunt Rock (Rock of Gibraltar (IRE)) **Daunt Rock Partnership**
56 B f 15/2 Royal Applause—Tease (IRE) (Green Desert (USA)) (14000)

Other Owners: Mr Jim Atkinson, Mr Nigel Austin, Mr Ian Bath, Mr Jeremy Brownlee, Mr G. F. Clark, Mr Steve Dawes, Mr Tom Edwards, Mr Tony Edwards, Mr S. A. Emmett, Mr G. Gash, Mrs B. Hearn, Mr J. Hobson, Mr J. Homan, Mrs L. J. Losse, Mr S. McDonald, Mr A. McWilliam, Mr D. Milton, Mr C. Parnell, Mr D. Popely, Mr R. Popely, Mr David F. Powell, Mr R. Pritchard, Mr S. M. Ransom, Mr M. A. Ransom, Mr H. Symonds, Mr G. Thomas, Mr M. Tye, Mr G. Wickens, Mr D. Willcocks.

Amateur: Mr J. Harding.

491
MR JAMIE POULTON, Lewes
Postal: **Stud Farmhouse, Telscombe, Lewes, East Sussex, BN7 3HZ**
Contacts: **YARD (01273) 300515 HOME (01273) 300127 FAX (01273) 300915**
MOBILE (07980) 596952
E-MAIL **jamie@poulton8.orangehome.co.uk**

1 **BANGKOK PETE (IRE)**, 11, b g Alflora (IRE)—Kinnegads Pride (IRE) **Miss S. Young**
2 **DOUBLE DEALITES**, 6, b m Double Trigger (IRE)—Linden Grace (USA) **Miss V. Markowiak**
3 **FARBREAGA (IRE)**, 10, b g Shernazar—Gleann Alainn **Miss V. Markowiak**
4 **FIX UP LOOK SHARP**, 5, b h Sakhee (USA)—Featherlight **Miss V. Markowiak**
5 **GORHAMS GIFT**, 8, b g Double Trigger (IRE)—Linden Grace (USA) **The Never Dropped Partnership**
6 **LAAHIJ**, 4, b g Arcano (IRE)—Acicula (IRE) **Mr M. D. Ogburn**
7 **NORMAN THE RED**, 6, ch g Tobougg (IRE)—Linden Lime **Mr R. C. Moules**
8 **SEMILLE OBON**, 4, b gr g Royal Applause—Starparty (USA) **Horseheath Lodge Racing**
9 **SOBER SAILOR (IRE)**, 9, b g Hawkeye (IRE)—Ronni Pancake
10 **TANGO TURNER (IRE)**, 4, ch c Excellent Art—Kassyderia (IRE) **Tango Turner Partnership**
11 **UP FOUR IT (IRE)**, 8, b g Luso—Newgate Beauty (IRE) **Miss V. Markowiak**

Other Owners: Mr A. Bayford, Mr O. D. Costello, Mr I. C. Cusselle, Mr K. Farmer.

Assistant Trainer: Mrs C D Poulton

Jockey (NH): Mattie Batchelor.

492
MR BRENDAN POWELL, Upper Lambourn
Postal: **Frenchmans Lodge Stables, Upper Lambourn, Hungerford, Berkshire, RG17 8QW**
Contacts: **PHONE (01488) 73650 FAX (01488) 73650 MOBILE (07785) 390737**
E-MAIL **brendan.powell@btconnect.com WEBSITE www.brendanpowellracing.com**

1 **BEACH BAR (IRE)**, 5, b g Azamour (IRE)—Toasted Special (USA) **Mr J Byrne & Mr P Conway**
2 **COCKLE TOWN BOY**, 4, ch g Cockney Rebel (IRE)—Rare Cross (IRE) **Teamchoochoo & Partners**
3 **DARK AMBER**, 6, b m Sakhee (USA)—Donna Vita **Mr C. McGuckin**
4 **DARK EMERALD (IRE)**, 6, gr g Dark Angel (IRE)—Xema **Mr K. R. E. Rhatigan**
5 **ELEMENT QUARTET (IRE)**, 7, b m Brian Boru—Glendante (IRE) **Wildcard Racing Syndicate X1**
6 **ELUSIVE ELLEN (IRE)**, 6, b m Elusive City (USA)—Ellen's Girl (IRE) **B. G. Powell**
7 **FIRE SHIP**, 7, b g Firebreak—Mays Dream **IGP Partnership & P Winkworth**
8 **GANNICUS**, 5, b g Phoenix Reach (IRE)—Rasmani **Winterbeck Manor Stud Ltd**
9 **GEORGIES PIP**, 5, b m Apple Tree (FR)—Lady Kay **L. Gilbert**
10 **GOLDEN BIRD (IRE)**, 5, b g Sinndar (IRE)—Khamsin (USA) **Teamchoochoo & Partners**
11 **HELL YEAH**, 5, b g Raven's Pass (USA)—Go Between **I. S. Smith**
12 **HOLD HANDS**, 5, b m Lawman (FR)—Tiponi (IRE) **D & J Newell**
13 **LADY FROM GENEVA**, 9, ch m Generous (IRE)—Schizo-Phonic **L. Gilbert**
14 **LETTHERIVERRUNDRY (IRE)**, 6, br g Diamond Green (FR)—Dissitation (IRE) **J. P. McManus**
15 **LITTLE BIG MAN**, 5, b g Sleeping Indian—Doris Souter (IRE) **Teamchoochoo & Partners**
16 **MOOTACADIM**, 4, ch g Galileo (IRE)—Kindling **The Arkle Bar Partnership**
17 **MORESTEAD (IRE)**, 11, ch g Traditionally (USA)—Itsy Bitsy Betsy (USA) **B. G. Powell**
18 **MORTHANALEGEND**, 7, b g Midnight Legend—Morwenna (IRE) **R. H. Kerswell**
19 **ON STAGE**, 7, ch m Act One—In The Stocks **E. J. S. Gadsden**
20 **ONE PURSUIT (IRE)**, 8, b g Pastoral Pursuits—Karinski (USA) **Mr N. J. E. Maher**
21 **RAKAAN (IRE)**, 9, ch g Bahamian Bounty—Petite Spectre **ACC Syndicate**
22 **RENAISSANCE RED**, 4, ch g Medicean—Special Moment (IRE) **Mr & Mrs T O'Donohoe**

MR BRENDAN POWELL - Continued

23 **SMOKETHATTHUNDERS (IRE)**, 6, gr g Elusive City (USA)—Zinstar (IRE) **Northern Line Racing Ltd**
24 **STOCKHILL DIVA**, 6, ch m Haafhd—April Stock **Mrs M. Fairbairn & E. Gadsden**
25 **STONECUTTER (IRE)**, 5, gr g Mastercraftsman (IRE)—Sparkle of Stones (FR) **Northern Line Racing Ltd**
26 4, B g Sulamani (IRE)—Sweet Robinia (IRE) **P. H. Betts**
27 **THE SALMON MAN**, 4, b c Showcasing—Donna Vita **C McGuckin, Mrs M Fairbairn & P Dean**
28 **UNCLE DERMOT (IRE)**, 8, b g Arakan (USA)—Cappadoce (IRE) **Mr K. R. E. Rhatigan**
29 **VIOLETS BOY (IRE)**, 9, br g King's Theatre (IRE)—Sunshine Rays **H. Redknapp**

THREE-YEAR-OLDS

30 B c Dark Angel (IRE)—Headborough Lass (IRE)
31 **ZEBSTAR (IRE)**, b c Zebedee—Zinstar (IRE) **Northern Line Racing Ltd**

TWO-YEAR-OLDS

32 **GARTH ROCKETT**, b c 17/4 Delegator—Leelu (Largesse) **P. Banfield**
33 B c 29/3 Lilbourne Lad (IRE)—Xema (Danehill (USA)) (22148)

Other Owners: Mr A. J. Bonarius, Mr G. J. Burchell, Mr J. A. Byrne, Mr I. J. Callaway, Mr P. Conway, P. Dean, Mrs M. Fairbairn, Mr A. Fellows, Mr M. A. Humphreys, Mr A. Kay, Mr C. McAvoy, Mrs J. Newell, D. J. M. Newell, Mr T. L. O'Donohoe, Mrs E. E. O'Donohoe, P. L. Winkworth.

Jockey (flat): Seb Sanders. **Jockey (NH):** Brendan Powell, Andrew Tinkler. **Apprentice:** Matthew Lawson.
Amateur: Miss Jenny Powell.

493	**MR TED POWELL**, Reigate

Postal: **Nutwood Farm, Gatton Park Road, Reigate, Surrey, RH2 0SX**
Contacts: **PHONE (01737) 765612**

1 **AJJAADD (USA)**, 10, b g Elusive Quality (USA)—Millstream (USA) **Katy & Lol Pratt**
2 **SNOW KING (USA)**, 6, ch g Elusive Quality (USA)—Cloudspin (USA) **Mr D. G. Acomb**

Other Owners: L. C. Pratt, Mrs K. J. Pratt.

494	**SIR MARK PRESCOTT BT**, Newmarket

Postal: **Heath House, Newmarket, Suffolk, CB8 8DU**
Contacts: **PHONE (01638) 662117 FAX (01638) 666572**
E-MAIL mark_prescott@btconnect.com

1 **AMOUR DE NUIT (IRE)**, 4, b g Azamour (IRE)—Umthoulah (IRE) **Mr L. A. Larratt - Osborne House**
2 **CELESTIAL PATH (IRE)**, 4, b c Footstepsinthesand—
                 Miss Kittyhawk (IRE) **Mr Gordon C. Woodall & Prof C. Tisdall**
3 **MERRITT ISLAND**, 4, b f Exceed And Excel (AUS)—Moon Crystal **Mr & Mrs John Kelsey-Fry**
4 **MOSCATO**, 5, gr g Hernando (FR)—Alba Stella **The Green Door Partnership**
5 **PALLASATOR**, 7, b g Motivator—Ela Athena **Qatar Racing Ltd**
6 **RAINBOW PRIDE (IRE)**, 4, gr g Clodovil (IRE)—Rahila (IRE) **Charles C. Walker - Osborne House II**
7 **SEA OF HEAVEN (IRE)**, 4, b g Sea The Stars (IRE)—Maid of Killeen (IRE) **Lady Bamford**
8 **SEA PRIDE (IRE)**, 5, b m Sea The Stars (IRE)—Claxon **Bluehills Racing Ltd**

THREE-YEAR-OLDS

9 **ABBEYLEIX**, gr g Sir Percy—Alvarita **Mr Timothy J. Rooney**
10 **ALINSTANTE**, b f Archipenko (USA)—Algarade **Miss K. Rausing**
11 **ALL THE RAGE**, b f Dubawi (IRE)—Intrigued **Denford Stud**
12 **ALSACIENNE**, gr f Dalakhani (IRE)—Alabastrine **Miss K. Rausing**
13 **BEAR FACED**, b g Intikhab (USA)—Hulcote Rose (IRE) **The Barkers & Chris Jenkins**
14 **CAPE CRYSTAL (IRE)**, b f Cape Cross (IRE)—Lady Rockfield (IRE) **Axom LVII**
15 **CARTWRIGHT**, b g High Chaparral (IRE)—One So Marvellous **Mr J. L. C. Pearce**
16 **COCOA BEACH (IRE)**, b f Acclamation—Smart Coco (USA) **Mr Donald R. Dizney**
17 **COTE D'AZUR**, ch c Champs Elysees—Florentia **Mr N. Greig**
18 **DUSTY RAVEN**, ch g Raven's Pass (USA)—Dust Dancer **Bluehills Racing Ltd**
19 **FLYMETOTHESTARS**, b c Sea The Stars (IRE)—Precious Gem (IRE) **Lady Bamford**

SIR MARK PRESCOTT BT - Continued

20 **LATE SHOW**, br f Authorized (IRE)—Hydro Calido (USA) **Lordship Stud**
21 **LUGANO**, b c Galileo (IRE)—Swiss Lake (USA) **Mr J. L. C. Pearce**
22 **MARSHA (IRE)**, b f Acclamation—Marlinka **Elite Racing**
23 **MEDDLESOME**, b g Medicean—Meddle **Mr N. Greig - Osborne House**
24 **MISS MARINA BAY**, ch f Galileo (IRE)—Miss Corniche **Mr J. L. C. Pearce**
25 **MOCKINBIRD (IRE)**, b f Makfi—Littlefeather **Sir Edmund Loder**
26 **MONJENI**, b g Montjeu (IRE)—Polly's Mark (IRE) **Fergus Anstock & Alice Mills**
27 **MOTIVATE**, b g Motivator—Hispalis (IRE) **Mr P. Bamford - Osborne House**
28 **MYSTIQUE HEIGHTS**, b g High Chaparral (IRE)—Musique Magique (IRE) **Mr G. C. Woodall**
29 **O'CONNOR'S GIRL**, b f Roderic O'Connor (IRE)—Dollar Bird (IRE) **Biddestone Racing Partnership XIV**
30 **OCEAN READY (USA)**, b g More Than Ready (USA)—Tjinouska (USA) **Baxter, Gregson, Jenkins & Warman**
31 **PALISADE**, b g Fastnet Rock (AUS)—Portal **Cheveley Park Stud**
32 **RED BOX**, b f Exceed And Excel (AUS)—Confidential Lady **Cheveley Park Stud**
33 **RIOCA (IRE)**, b f Jeremy (USA)—Rising Wind (IRE) **Lady O'Reilly**
34 **ST MICHEL**, b c Sea The Stars (IRE)—Miss Provence **Mr J. L. C. Pearce**
35 **STATUS QUO (IRE)**, br g Thewayyouare (USA)—Again Royale (IRE) **Mr G. Moore - Osborne House II**
36 **TENZING NORGAY**, gr g Aussie Rules (USA)—Miss Katmandu (IRE) **Mr J. L. C. Pearce**
37 **TIME WARP**, ch g Archipenko (USA)—Here to Eternity (USA) **Mr W. E. Sturt - Osborne House**
38 **TYRANNICAL**, br c Dansili—Queen of Mean **Mr T. Bunting - Osborne House, Sir P. Vela, P. Stanley**

TWO-YEAR-OLDS

39 **ALLEGIANCE**, gr f 14/4 Archipenko (USA)—Alba Stella (Nashwan (USA)) **Miss K. Rausing**
40 **ALTERNATE ROUTE**, b c 4/4 New Approach (IRE)—
    Almamia (Hernando (FR)) (19933) **Mr P. J. McSwiney-Osborne House**
41 Gr c 26/4 Archipenko (USA)—
    Alvarita (Selkirk (USA)) (100000) **Charles C. Walker - Osborne House and Miss K. Rausing**
42 **ANNA MEDICI**, b f 13/4 Sir Percy—Florentia (Medicean) **Mr N. Greig**
43 B f 27/2 Authorized (IRE)—Archina (IRE) (Arch (USA)) (75000) **Mrs Carmen Fruhbeck and Denford Stud**
44 **BOOST**, b f 7/4 Pivotal—Hooray (Invincible Spirit (IRE)) **Cheveley Park Stud**
45 B f 7/4 Fastnet Rock (AUS)—Briolette (IRE) (Sadler's Wells (USA)) **The Old Harrovian Racing Club**
46 **CLIFDEN ARTS (IRE)**, b f 31/3 Acclamation—Aravonian (Night Shift (USA)) **Mrs P. K. O'Rourke**
47 **DIPTYCH (USA)**, br f 12/2 Hat Trick (JPN)—Fork Lightning (USA) (Storm Cat (USA)) **Denford Stud**
48 **EASY WIND**, b f 18/2 Shirocco (GER)—Attainable (Kalanisi (IRE)) **Mr C. Jenkins**
49 **ELYSEES PALACE**, b c 28/3 Champs Elysees—
    Ventura Highway (Machiavellian (USA)) (80000) **Mr J. E. Fishpool - Osborne House**
50 **ESPRESSO FREDDO (IRE)**, b c 19/4 Fast Company (IRE)—
    Spring Bouquet (IRE) (King's Best) (26578) **Middleham Park Racing**
51 Ch f 13/4 Bahamian Bounty—Half Moon Hotel (With Approval (CAN)) **Miss K. Rausing**
52 **IMPASSIONED**, ch f 29/4 Bahamian Bounty—Ardent (Pivotal) **Cheveley Park Stud**
53 **LAW POWER**, b c 16/3 Lawman (FR)—Clarietta (Shamardal (USA)) (150000) **Bluehills Racing Ltd**
54 **MELINOE**, b f 27/3 Sea The Stars (IRE)—Persefona (Montjeu (IRE)) (120000) **Mr Fergus Anstock**
55 **MELODINE**, ch f 16/3 Archipenko (USA)—Monda (USA) (Cozzene (USA)) **Miss K. Rausing**
56 **MISS MIRABEAU**, b f 13/3 Oasis Dream—Miss Corniche (Hernando (FR)) **Mr J. L. C. Pearce**
57 **NEWT**, b f 3/3 Sixties Icon—Froglet (Shaamit (IRE)) **Mr J. B. Haggas**
58 **OXFORD BLU**, b c 27/3 Aqlaam—Blue Zealot (IRE) (Galileo (IRE)) **Mrs Olivia Hoare and Mr J. M. Castle**
59 **PENTITO RAP (USA)**, b c 26/1 Smart Strike (CAN)—
    Sing Like A Bird (USA) (Lawyer Ron (USA)) (73260) **Mr and Mrs John Kelsey-Fry**
60 **PIONEERTOWN (IRE)**, b c 17/2 High Chaparral (IRE)—
    Tempura (GER) (Cape Cross (IRE)) (200000) **Mr J. L. C. Pearce**
61 **REFRESHED (IRE)**, b f 1/3 Rip Van Winkle (IRE)—Elegant Beauty (Olden Times) (50000) **Lady O'Reilly**
62 **SEE YOU AFTER (IRE)**, b c 30/5 Siyouni (FR)—
    Zaziyra (IRE) (Dalakhani (IRE)) (29531) **Mr T. Bunting - Osborne House III**
63 **SINGLE ESTATE**, b c 11/2 Tamayuz—
    Duo de Choc (Manduro (GER)) (45000) **Mr David Howard, Mr Colin Chisholm and Sir Mark Prescott**
64 **STARSHELL (IRE)**, b g 14/3 Sea The Stars (IRE)—
    Aquarelle Bleue (Sadler's Wells (USA)) (88000) **Mr John Brown & Mrs Megan Dennis**
65 **TORONTO SOUND**, b c 3/4 Aussie Rules (USA)—Caribana (Hernando (FR)) (58000) **Mr William Rucker**
66 **TURNING GOLD**, ch c 2/5 Pivotal—
    Illusion (Anabaa (USA)) (47000) **Mrs Helen Jones, Mr W. F. Charnley and Sir Mark Prescott**
67 **VEILED SECRET (IRE)**, b c 13/1 Teofilo (IRE)—
    Seven Veils (IRE) (Danehill Dancer (IRE)) (70000) **Mr T. Bunting - Osborne House II**
68 **WOLFCATCHERJACK (IRE)**, b c 28/4 Lawman (FR)—Alleluia (Caerleon (USA)) (31007) **Ne'er Do Wells V**
69 **XENON**, b f 24/3 Kyllachy—Cool Question (Polar Falcon (USA)) **The Lady Fairhaven and Hon James Broughton**

SIR MARK PRESCOTT BT - Continued

Other Owners: Mr T. Al-Mazeedi, Mr P. Barker, Mrs Z. Barker, Mr E. A. Baxter, Mr Tim Bostwick, Mr G. W. Brickwood, Mr B. D. Burnet, Mrs Elizabeth Coughlin, Mr D. Ellis, Mr K. H. Foster, Mr Phil Fry, Mr P. G. Goulandris, The Hon. Mrs G. Greenwood, Mrs Caroline Gregson, Mr Micheal Jeffery, Mr David Mann, Mr T. S. Palin, Mr M. Prince, Mr M. Rudd, Prince Faisal Salman, Mr B. A. Taylor, Mrs J. Taylor, Mr M. Tracey, The Hon. Lady Troubridge, Mrs S. L. Warman, Mr E. J. Williams.

Assistant Trainer: William Butler, **Pupil Assistant:** Robert McDowall

Jockey (flat): L. Morris, R. Powell. **Apprentice:** M. Fernandes, R. Jessop.

---

495 MISS KATY PRICE, Hay-On-Wye
Postal: **Harewood Farm, Archenfield, Hay-On-Wye, Hereford, Herefordshire, HR3 5TB**

1 IDAMAY (IRE), 5, br m Stowaway—Aguida (FR) **N. Elliott**
2 MINELLACELEBRATION (IRE), 6, b g King's Theatre (IRE)—Knocktartan (IRE) **N. Elliott**
3 PREMIER ROSE (IRE), 7, b m Westerner—Alltoplayfor (IRE) **N. Elliott**

---

496 MR RICHARD PRICE, Hereford
Postal: **Criftage Farm, Ullingswick, Hereford, Herefordshire, HR1 3JG**
Contacts: **PHONE (01432) 820263 FAX (01432) 820785 MOBILE (07929) 200598**

1 BONJOUR STEVE, 5, b g Bahamian Bounty—Anthea **B. Veasey**
2 CHAMPAGNE BOB, 4, gr g Big Bad Bob (IRE)—Exclusive Approval (USA) **Mr M. F. Oseman**
3 DEEBAJ (IRE), 4, br g Authorized (IRE)—Athreyaa **Mr & Mrs K. Reece**
4 DISTANT HIGH, 5, b m High Chaparral (IRE)—Distant Dreamer (USA) **My Left Foot Racing Syndicate**
5 IGUACU, 12, b g Desert Prince (IRE)—Gay Gallanta (USA) **Mr & Mrs D. C. Holder**
6 TAURUS TWINS, 10, b g Deportivo—Intellibet One
7 ZARIA, 5, b m Tomba—Princess Zara **Mrs K. E. Oseman**

THREE-YEAR-OLDS

8 CAPTAIN JACK, b g Mount Nelson—Court Princess **Mr & Mrs D. Holder**
9 KINGSTREET LADY, b f Royal Applause—Intellibet One **Kingstreet Partnership**
10 OCEAN GALE, b f Shirocco (GER)—Ocean Transit (IRE) **The Super Fruit Partnership**

Other Owners: Mr G. E. Amey, Mr G. D. Bailey, Mr Douglas Boddy, Mr P. J. Hoare, Mr Derek C. Holder, Mrs Cheryl Holder, Mrs Marlene Pugh.

Assistant Trainer: Jane Price

---

497 MR PETER PRITCHARD, Shipston-on-Stour
Postal: **The Gate House, Whatcote, Shipston-On-Stour, Warwickshire, CV36 5EF**
Contacts: **PHONE (01295) 680689**

1 ANNIE'SBOYDAVE, 6, b g Passing Glance—Earcomesannie (IRE) **Annie Miller,R W Stowe,David Pritchard**
2 EARCOMESTHEDREAM (IRE), 13, b g Marignan (USA)—Play It By Ear (IRE) **Woodlands (Worcestershire) Ltd**
3 TIKKETORIDE, 8, gr g Tikkanen (USA)—Safe Arrival (USA) **Mrs A. D. Pritchard**
4 TISFREETDREAM (IRE), 15, b g Oscar (IRE)—Gayley Gale (IRE) **Woodlands (Worcestershire) Ltd**

Other Owners: Mrs A. J. Miller, Mr D. Pritchard, Mr R. W. Stowe.

Assistant Trainer: Mrs. E. Gardner

Jockey (NH): Jamie Moore.

498 MR PETER PURDY, Bridgwater
Postal: **Fyne Court Farm, Broomfield, Bridgwater, Somerset, TA5 2EQ**
Contacts: **PHONE (01823) 451632 FAX (01823) 451632 MOBILE (07860) 392786**
E-MAIL purdy844@btinternet.com

1 **MAY COURT**, 9, b g Groomsbridge May I—Tudor Sunset **P. D. Purdy**
2 **THE BLONDE EMPEROR**, 11, ch g Emperor Fountain—Tudor Blonde **P. D. Purdy**
3 **THE TALL BLONDE**, 7, ch m Mutazayid (IRE)—Tudor Blonde **P. D. Purdy**
4 9, B g High Tension (USA)—Tudor Blonde **P. D. Purdy**

499 MR DENIS QUINN, Newmarket
Postal: **Marlborough House Stables, Old Station Road, Newmarket, Suffolk, CB8 8DW**
Contacts: **MOBILE (07435) 340008**

1 **CHERRY STREET**, 7, b g Alhaarth (IRE)—Weqaar (USA) **Mr A. Dal Pos**
2 **CLOCK ON TOM**, 6, b g Trade Fair—Night Owl **Mr J. T. Mangan**
3 **COLONEL ALI**, 5, b g Halling (USA)—Preceder **Mr J. T. Mangan**
4 **CRAFTYBIRD**, 5, ch m Mastercraftsman (IRE)—Tobaranama (IRE) **Mr J. T. Mangan**
5 **DEEP BLUE DIAMOND**, 4, b f Sir Percy—Apple Blossom (IRE)
6 **LITTLEMISSPARTON**, 4, b f Sir Percy—Miss Prism
7 **NORMAN'S STAR**, 5, b g Tiger Hill (IRE)—Canis Star **Mr D. P. Quinn**
8 **RED FLUTE**, 4, ch g Piccolo—Fee Faw Fum (IRE) **Mr T. Al Nisf**
9 **RELIGHT THE FIRE**, 5, ch g Firebreak—Alula **Mr D. P. Quinn**
10 **ROYAL PARTY**, 4, b f Royal Applause—Foxtrot Alpha (IRE) **Mr R. Favarulo**
11 **SAHARA DESERT (IRE)**, 5, b g Montjeu (IRE)—Festoso (IRE) **Mr D. P. Quinn**
12 **SHINING ROMEO**, 4, b g Royal Applause—Silver Pivotal (IRE) **Mr J. T. Mangan**

THREE-YEAR-OLDS
13 **RIAL (IRE)**, b f Dark Angel (IRE)—Coin Box **Mr R Bruni & Partner**
14 **SALT LAKE SOOTY**, gr c Arabian Gleam—Kilmovee
15 **SOMERS LAD (IRE)**, b c Lilbourne Lad (IRE)—Somaggia (IRE) **Mr D. P. Quinn**
16 **SWEEP OF DIAMONDS**, br c Mawatheeq (USA)—Apple Blossom (IRE)

TWO-YEAR-OLDS
17 B c 1/4 Dick Turpin (IRE)—Acclamatory (Royal Applause) **Mr R. Favarulo**

Other Owners: Mrs L. Botti, Mr R. Bruni.

500 MR JOHN QUINN, Malton
Postal: **Bellwood Cottage Stables, Settrington, Malton, North Yorkshire, YO17 8NR**
Contacts: **PHONE (01944) 768370 MOBILE (07899) 873304**
E-MAIL info@johnquinnracing.co.uk WEBSITE www.johnquinnracing.co.uk

1 **ARTHURS SECRET**, 6, ch g Sakhee's Secret—Angry Bark (USA) **David Scott & Co (Pattern Makers) Ltd**
2 **CHEBSEY BEAU**, 6, b g Multiplex—Chebsey Belle (IRE) **Kent, Greaves, Dawson**
3 **COSMIC TIGRESS**, 5, b m Tiger Hill (IRE)—Cosmic Case **The Cosmic Cases**
4 **EL BEAU (IRE)**, 5, ch g Camacho—River Beau (IRE) **Highfield Racing (Camacho)**
5 **EVANESCENT (IRE)**, 7, b g Elusive City (USA)—Itsanothergirl **Mrs S. Quinn**
6 **FINAL COUNTDOWN**, 5, ch g Selkirk (USA)—Culture Queen **Estio Pinnacle Racing**
7 **GRAND MEISTER**, 5, gr g Mastercraftsman (IRE)—Wait It Out (USA) **Highfield Racing 4**
8 **HIDDEN JUSTICE (IRE)**, 7, b g Lawman (FR)—Uncharted Haven **Highfield Racing 2**
9 **HUBERTAS**, 4, b g Lord of England (GER)—Western Eyes (IRE) **The Pro-Claimers**
10 **KASHMIR PEAK (IRE)**, 7, b g Tiger Hill (IRE)—Elhareer (IRE) **Win Only SP Only Partnership**
11 **KILAS GIRL (IRE)**, 6, b m Milenary—Ballybeg Dusty (IRE) **Ross Harmon**
12 **L'AIGLE ROYAL (GER)**, 5, b g Sholokhov (IRE)—Laren (GER) **J. T. Warner**
13 **LADY BEAUFORT**, 5, ch m Shirocco (GER)—Kadassa (IRE) **The Desperados**
14 **MISS LILLIAN**, 6, gr m Rob Roy (USA)—Thorn of The Rose (IRE) **Mr S. McKie**
15 **MISTIROC**, 5, br g Rocamadour—Mistinguett (IRE) **Ailsa Russell**
16 **MOONLIGHTNAVIGATOR**, 4, b br c Henrythenavigator (USA)—Victorica (USA) **Malcolm Walker**
17 **NEZAR (IRE)**, 5, ch g Mastercraftsman (IRE)—Teddy Bears Picnic **Maxilead Limited**
18 **PARK PLACE**, 6, b g Beat Hollow—Blend **Crowe Partnership**
19 **POETIC VERSE**, 6, gr m Byron—Nina Fontenail (FR) **J. N. Blackburn**

MR JOHN QUINN - Continued

20 **QUINTO**, 6, ch g Desideratum—Cruz Santa **Mr S. W. Knowles**
21 **RAISED ON GRAZEON**, 5, ch m Lucky Story (USA)—Graze On And On **Mr J. Rowbottom**
22 4, Ch f Sulamani (IRE)—Sounds Familiar (IRE) **Mrs M. Luck**
23 **THE KID**, 5, b g High Chaparral (IRE)—Shine Like A Star **D. Ward**
24 **THISONETIME (IRE)**, 5, b g Kalanisi (IRE)—Dizzy's Whisper (IRE) **Mr S. McKie**
25 **TRENDSETTER (IRE)**, 5, b g Mastercraftsman (IRE)—Fashion Trade **Maxilead Limited**
26 **ZANETTO**, 6, b g Medicean—Play Bouzouki **Malcolm Walker**

THREE-YEAR-OLDS

27 **AL SHAHANIYA (IRE)**, ch f Zoffany (IRE)—Sweet Kristeen (USA) **Al Shaqab Racing**
28 **AL ZUBARAH**, b f Exceed And Excel (AUS)—Tropical Paradise (IRE) **Al Shaqab Racing**
29 **ANCIENT ASTRONAUT**, b g Kodiac—Tatora **Ross Harmon**
30 **AUMIT HILL**, b c Authorized (IRE)—Eurolinka (IRE) **Mrs S. Quinn**
31 **BAD PENNY (IRE)**, b f Kodiac—Double Fantasy (GER) **Mrs Z. Wentworth**
32 **CATASTROPHE**, b g Intikhab (USA)—Mrs Snaffles (IRE) **J. N. Blackburn**
33 **EL ASTRONAUTE (IRE)**, ch c Approve (IRE)—Drumcliffe Dancer (IRE) **Ross Harmon**
34 **IKERRIN ROAD (IRE)**, b c Iffraaj—Fantastic Spring (USA) **Mrs S. Quinn**
35 **INDIAN PURSUIT (IRE)**, b g Compton Place—Church Melody **Mr M. Walker**
36 **LAGUNA SUNRISE (IRE)**, b f Footstepsinthesand—Alexander Loyalty (IRE) **Charles Wentworth**
37 **MORE KUDOS (USA)**, ch g Exchange Rate (USA)—Marquise Quest (USA) **Mrs S. Quinn**
38 **PROJECT BLUEBOOK (FR)**, bl g Sinndar (IRE)—Apperella **Mr R. Harmon**
39 **REPUTATION (IRE)**, b g Royal Applause—Semaphore **Highclere Thoroughbred Racing (Applause)**
40 **SAFE VOYAGE (IRE)**, b g Fast Company (IRE)—Shishangaan (IRE) **Ross Harmon**
41 **SMART MOVER (IRE)**, b f Fast Company (IRE)—Alltherightmoves (IRE) **Racing Ventures 2014**
42 **SPEED COMPANY (IRE)**, b g Fast Company (IRE)—Trentini (IRE) **Wilson Woo**
43 **SPIRIT OF ZEBEDEE (IRE)**, gr c Zebedee—Sampers (IRE) **Mr M. Walker**
44 **ST DUNSTAN (IRE)**, b c Zoffany (IRE)—Box of Frogs (IRE) **S. A. T. Quinn**
45 **THE LYNCH MAN**, b g Sakhee's Secret—Diliza **Bob McMillan**
46 **TRED SOFTLY (IRE)**, b g Yeats (IRE)—Elayoon (USA) **Ross Harmon**
47 **WORLDS HIS OYSTER**, b c Pivotal—Regal Salute **Ross Harmon**
48 **WOTABREEZE (IRE)**, ch g Excellent Art—Sparkling Crystal (IRE) **The New Century Partnership**
49 **WOWCHA (IRE)**, b f Zoffany (IRE)—Muravka (IRE) **Chasemore Farm**
50 **WRIGHT PATTERSON (IRE)**, b g Dream Ahead (USA)—Anam Allta (IRE) **Harlen Ltd**

TWO-YEAR-OLDS

51 B f 9/5 Requinto (IRE)—A L'aube (IRE) (Selkirk (USA)) (14764)
52 **ACTUALISATION**, b c 25/2 Exceed And Excel (AUS)—Eluding (Street Cry (IRE)) (75000) **Racing Ventures**
53 **BREAKING FREE**, ch c 24/4 Kyllachy—Hill Welcome (Most Welcome) (36190) **Adams, Blades, Bruton, Ellis**
54 **CHEVALIER DU LAC (IRE)**, b c 25/3 Sir Prancealot (IRE)—
　　　　Crimson Sunrise (IRE) (Holy Roman Emperor (IRE)) (12550) **Mr Bill Hobson**
55 B f 14/3 Helmet (AUS)—Dorothy Dene (Red Ransom (USA)) (36190) **Richard Kent**
56 **DOUBLE DUTCH**, ch c 11/4 Dutch Art—Duchess Dora (IRE) (Tagula (IRE)) (31007) **Maxilead Limited**
57 Br c 23/3 Zebedee—Journey's End (IRE) (In The Wings) (15000)
58 **LONDON GRAMMAR (IRE)**, b f 11/4 Sir Prancealot (IRE)—Emmas Princess (USA) (Bahhare (USA)) (19933)
59 B f 28/4 Kodiac—Miznapp (Pennekamp (USA)) (35238) **Harlen Limited**
60 Ch c 27/1 Power—My Sweet Georgia (IRE) (Royal Applause) (33333) **Mr R. L. Houlton**
61 B g 27/3 Famous Name—Nice Wee Girl (IRE) (Clodovil (IRE)) (18456) **Excelsior Racing**
62 **OCEANIC (IRE)**, b c 23/3 Born To Sea (IRE)—
　　　　Shanghai Lily (King's Best (USA)) (25000) **Fletcher, Outhart, Maddison & Moran**
63 **PERFORMING (IRE)**, ch c 27/4 Showcasing—Mansiya (Vettori (IRE)) (55370) **Racing Ventures**
64 Ch c 3/2 Fast Company (IRE)—Princess Banu (Oasis Dream) (41904) **Mr R. Harmon**
65 **SHE'S ZOFF (IRE)**, b f 29/3 Zoffany (IRE)—
　　　　Vindication People (Vindication (USA)) (50000) **Racing Ventures**
66 B f 21/3 Clodovil (IRE)—Trentini (IRE) (Singspiel (IRE)) (20000)

Other Owners: Mr Steve Avery, Mr R. J. Blades, Mr James Bloom, Mr I. T. Buchanan, Mr Mick Burrowes, Mr P. Halkett, Mr S. A. Kaznowski, Mr N. E. F. Luck, Mr I. A. Marmion, Mr Justin Murphy, Mrs Margaret Nelson, Mr G. Oxtoby, Mr S. A. T. Quinn, Mrs S. Quinn, Mr C. G. Simmonds, Mr Mike Thomas, Mr Robert Turner.

Assistant Trainer: Sean Quinn

501 MR MICK QUINN, Newmarket

Postal: **Southgate Barn, Hamilton Road, Newmarket, Suffolk, CB8 0WY**
Contacts: **PHONE (01638) 660017 FAX (01638) 660017 MOBILE (07973) 260054**
E-MAIL mick@quinn2562.fsnet.co.uk

1 **ANFIELD**, 5, b m Captain Gerrard (IRE)—Billie Holiday **M. Quinn**
2 **RACING ANGEL (IRE)**, 4, b f Dark Angel (IRE)—Roclette (USA) **YNWA Partnership**
3 **REFUSE COLETTE (IRE)**, 7, ch m Refuse To Bend (IRE)—Roclette (USA) **YNWA Partnership**
4 **WORLD RECORD (IRE)**, 6, b g Choisir (AUS)—Dancing Debut **J. E. Quorn**

THREE-YEAR-OLDS

5 **HARLEQUIN ROCK**, bl g Rock of Gibraltar (IRE)—Berry Baby (IRE) **A. Viner**

Other Owners: Mr D. Kearns.

Assistant Trainer: Miss Karen Davies

Jockey (flat): William Twiston-Davies.

502 MISS SALLY RANDELL, Swindon

Postal: **White Horse Cottage, Elmcross House, Broad Hinton, Swindon, Wiltshire, SN4 9PF**
Contacts: **PHONE (01793) 731045 MOBILE (07868) 728440**
E-MAIL info@sallyrandellracing.com WEBSITE www.sallyrandellracing.com

1 **ARISTOCRACY**, 5, b g Royal Applause—Pure Speculation **The Not So Privileged**
2 **BEL AMI RICH**, 6, b g Black Sam Bellamy (IRE)—Granny Rich **P. M. Rich**
3 **DRIFTASHORE (IRE)**, 9, b g Jackson's Drift (USA)—Your Cheatin Heart (IRE) **Power Geneva Ltd**
4 **GOAL (IRE)**, 8, b g Mujadil (USA)—Classic Lin (FR) **Mr M. Hampson**
5 **GOOD MAN HUGHIE (IRE)**, 7, ch g Flemensfirth (USA)—Good Dawn (IRE) **Power Geneva Ltd**
6 **LADY KNIGHT (IRE)**, 5, b m Champs Elysees—Knight's Place (IRE) **The Milk Sheiks**
7 **MANDY'S BOY (IRE)**, 6, b g Kyllachy—African Queen (IRE) **The 'Keeping The Dream Alive' Syndicate**
8 **SERGEANT DICK (IRE)**, 11, b g Lord of Appeal—Darawadda (IRE) **Connect Eight**
9 **SIR ALBIE**, 4, b g Sir Percy—Hazel Bank Lass (IRE) **Mr M. J. Tedham**
10 **VERSANT**, 4, b g Authorized (IRE)—Tanzania (USA) **Miss R. L. K. Kavanagh**

Other Owners: Mr V. Askew, Mr Kevin Cook, Mr David Hillier, Mr K. D. Linsley, Mr Paul Mannion, Mr Tony Millett, Mr Rob Parker, Miss S. Pilkington, Mrs Pamela Randell, Mr Peter Ross, Mr Peter Whittaker, Mr A. Wilde, Mr G. A. Windle, Mr A. Windle.

Assistant Trainer: Andy Turnell

Jockey (NH): James Banks. Amateur: Mr Sam Burton, Miss Brodie Hampson.

503 MR W. T. REED, Hexham

Postal: **Moss Kennels, Haydon Bridge, Hexham, Northumberland, NE47 6NL**
Contacts: **PHONE (01434) 344016 MOBILE (07703) 270408 / (07889) 111885**
E-MAIL timreed8@aol.com

1 **DAYDREAM BELIEVER**, 4, b f Acclamation—Idonea (CAN) **Mr & Mrs Philip C. Smith**
2 **INDIAN TEMPLE (IRE)**, 7, b g Indian River (FR)—Ballycraggan (IRE) **Mr J. K. Huddleston**
3 **SIMPLY LUCKY (IRE)**, 7, b g Flemensfirth (USA)—Derrygowna Court (IRE) **Mr & Mrs Philip C. Smith**
4 **VIKING REBEL (IRE)**, 14, b g Taipan (IRE)—Clodagh's Dream **Mr W. T. Reed**

Other Owners: Mrs J. W. Smith, Mr P. C. Smith.

Assistant Trainer: Mrs E. J. Reed

Amateur: Mr W. H. R. Reed.

504 **MR WILLIAM REED, Umberleigh**
Postal: Stowford Farm, East Stowford, Chittlehampton, Umberleigh, Devon, EX37 9RU
Contacts: **PHONE (01769) 540292 MOBILE (07967) 130991**

1 **ALL DOWNHILL (IRE)**, 6, b g Indian Danehill (IRE)—Socialite Girl **W. J. Reed**
2 **J R HAWK (IRE)**, 8, b br g Hawk Wing (USA)—Miss Shivvy (IRE) **W. J. Reed**
3 **WHAT A JOKE (IRE)**, 9, b g Vinnie Roe (IRE)—Shaping **W. J. Reed**

505 **MR DAVID REES, Haverfordwest**
Postal: The Grove Yard, Clarbeston Road, Haverfordwest, Pembrokeshire, SA63 4SP
Contacts: **PHONE (01437) 731308 FAX (01437) 731551 MOBILE (07775) 662463**
E-MAIL davidreesfencing@lineone.net

1 **CAWDOR HOUSE BERT**, 9, b g Kayf Tara—Lady Shanan (IRE) **A. J. & Dai Rees**
2 **DREAM BOLT (IRE)**, 8, ch g Urban Ocean (FR)—Riviera Dream (IRE) **Mr D A Rees & Mr N Adams**
3 **FISHING BRIDGE (IRE)**, 11, ch g Definite Article—Rith Ar Aghaidh (IRE) **D. A. Rees**
4 **GARDINERS HILL (IRE)**, 6, br g Stowaway—Mysterious Lass (IRE) **Mr D A Rees & Mr N Adams**
5 **LIMPOPO TOM (IRE)**, 9, ch g Saffron Walden (FR)—Sharpe (FR) **Eddie & Dai**
6 **LUKES HILL (IRE)**, 8, b g Bandari (IRE)—New Power (IRE) **Mr RJC Lewis/Mr P.A.T. Rice**
7 **MACARTHUR (IRE)**, 12, b g Montjeu (IRE)—Out West (USA) **D. A. Rees**
8 **PAY YOUR WAY (IRE)**, 8, gr g Cloudings (IRE)—Supreme Bond (IRE) **D. A. Rees**
9 **ROMEO IS BLEEDING (IRE)**, 10, b g Carroll House—Ean Eile (IRE) **Mr D L Evans & Mr D A Rees**
10 **SANDEEL BAY (IRE)**, 10, ch g Gulland—Dollar Bay (IRE) **D. A. Rees**
11 **SHANKSFORAMILLION**, 7, b g Needle Gun (IRE)—Cool Connie (IRE) **BW & RE Mansell**
12 **SIR MATTIE (IRE)**, 11, b br g Moscow Society (USA)—Manhattan Catch (IRE) **Mr RJC Lewis / Mr P.A.T. Rice**

Other Owners: Mr N. Adams, Mr D. L. Evans, Mr R. J. C. Lewis, Mrs R. E. Mansell, Mr B. W. Mansell, Mr E. W. Morris, Mr D. Rees, Mr A. J. Rees, Mr P. Rice.

506 **MRS HELEN REES, Dorchester**
Postal: Distant Hills, Chalmington, Dorchester, Dorset, DT2 0HB
Contacts: **PHONE (01300) 320683 MOBILE (07715) 558289**
E-MAIL helen-rees@live.co.uk

1 **KAHDIAN (IRE)**, 6, br g Rock of Gibraltar (IRE)—Katiykha (IRE) **Mrs H. E. Rees**
2 **RESIDENCE AND SPA (IRE)**, 8, b g Dubai Destination (USA)—Toffee Nosed **Mrs H. E. Rees**

Assistant Trainer: Mr Rupert Rees

507 **MR SEAN REGAN, Middleham**
Postal: Low Beck, Coverham, Middleham, Leyburn, North Yorkshire, DL8 4TJ
Contacts: **MOBILE (07866) 437476**
E-MAIL sean@seanreganracing.com WEBSITE www.seanreganracing.com

1 **PTOLOMEOS**, 13, b g Kayf Tara—Lucy Tufty **Mrs C. D. Taylor**
2 **RED LEGACY**, 8, ch m Distant Music (USA)—Emma May **Mrs L. Grasby**
3 **TOM'S ANNA (IRE)**, 6, b m Antonius Pius (USA)—Vanilla Delight (IRE) **Mrs C. D. Taylor**

508 **MR ANDREW REID, Mill Hill, London**
Postal: Highwood Lodge, Highwood Hill, Mill Hill, London, NW7 4HB
Contacts: **PHONE (07836) 214617 (07747) 751603 FAX (0207) 3184445**
E-MAIL cbithell2000@yahoo.co.uk

1 **ATHLETIC**, 7, b g Doyen (IRE)—Gentle Irony **A. S. Reid**
2 **EXIT EUROPE**, 4, ch g Bahamian Bounty—Depressed **A. S. Reid**
3 **IXELLES DIAMOND (IRE)**, 5, br m Diamond Green (FR)—Silk Point (IRE) **A. S. Reid**
4 **PURPLE SURPRISE**, 4, b f Teofilio (IRE)—Manic **A. S. Reid**
5 **SPIRAEA**, 6, ch m Bahamian Bounty—Salvia **A. S. Reid**

MR ANDREW REID - Continued

 6 **TREASURE THE RIDGE (IRE)**, 7, b g Galileo (IRE)—Treasure The Lady (IRE) **A. S. Reid**
 7 **VIF ARGENT (FR)**, 7, b g Dom Alco (FR)—Formosa (FR) **A. S. Reid**

THREE-YEAR-OLDS

 8 Ch f Bahamian Bounty—Depressed **A. S. Reid**
 9 **SHIPSHAPE MYFOOT**, b f Bahamian Bounty—Rise **A. S. Reid**

Assistant Trainer: Josh G. Hamer

Jockey (flat): Jim Crowley. **Apprentice:** Alfie Warwick.

509

MRS JACQUELINE RETTER, Cullompton
Postal: **7 Manor Close, Kentisbeare, Cullompton, Devon, EX15 2BG**
Contacts: **PHONE/FAX (01884) 266078 MOBILE (07912) 889655**

 1 **EXILES RETURN (IRE)**, 14, b g Needle Gun (IRE)—Moores Girl (IRE) **Mrs J. G. Retter**
 2 **ON THE RAZ**, 9, b m Rakaposhi King—Trillow **Mrs J. G. Retter**

510

MR KEITH REVELEY, Saltburn
Postal: **Groundhill Farm, Lingdale, Saltburn-by-the-Sea, Cleveland, TS12 3HD**
Contacts: **OFFICE (01287) 650456 FAX (01287) 653095 MOBILE (07971) 784539**
E-MAIL reveleyracing@yahoo.co.uk

 1 **AFFECTIONATE LADY (IRE)**, 5, b m Dandy Man (IRE)—Agouti **Mr P. Collins**
 2 **BALMUSETTE**, 7, b m Halling (USA)—Tcherina (IRE) **Mr & Mrs W. J. Williams**
 3 **BAMBYS BOY**, 5, b g Lucarno (USA)—Bamby (FR) **Mrs S. P. Granger**
 4 **BOOK AT BEDTIME**, 5, b m Midnight Legend—Northern Native (IRE) **Mrs S. A. Smith**
 5 4, Ch g Midnight Legend—Brackenmoss (IRE) **Reveley Farms**
 6 **BRAVE SPARTACUS (IRE)**, 10, b g Spartacus (IRE)—Peaches Polly **R. Collins**
 7 **BROCTUNE PAPA GIO**, 9, b g Iobougg (IRE)—Fairlie **Thwaites Young Alessi & Reveley Farms**
 8 4, B g Vinnie Roe (IRE)—Chione (IRE) **R. Collins**
 9 **DONNA'S PRIDE**, 7, b m Beat All (USA)—Pennys Pride (IRE) **Sun King Partnership**
10 **FLORAMOSS**, 5, b m Afflora (IRE)—Brackenmoss (IRE) **The Lingdale Optimists & Partner**
11 **HARVEY'S HOPE**, 10, b g Sinndar (IRE)—Ancara **The J.P.B & Partners**
12 **HOOKERGATE GRAMMAR**, 4, b g Yeats (IRE)—Oulianovsk (IRE) **Mr M. W. Joyce**
13 **MIDNIGHT MONTY**, 6, ch g Midnight Legend—Marello **Mr & Mrs W. J. Williams**
14 **NIGHT IN LONDON (IRE)**, 6, b m Vinnie Roe (IRE)—Chione (IRE) **Mrs M B Thwaites & Mr M E Foxton**
15 **NIGHT IN MILAN (IRE)**, 10, b g Milan—Chione (IRE) **R. Collins**
16 **REDKALANI (IRE)**, 8, b g Ashkalani (IRE)—La Femme En Rouge **Cristiana's Crew**
17 **SAMEDI SOIR**, 6, b m Black Sam Bellamy (IRE)—Bonne Anniversaire **Shade Oak Stud**
18 **SPECIAL CATCH (IRE)**, 9, b g Catcher In The Rye (IRE)—Top Quality **Mr Mike Browne & Mr William McKeown**
19 **SPICULAS (IRE)**, 7, ch g Beneficial—Alicia's Charm (IRE) **R. Collins**
20 **SULTANS PRIDE**, 4, b g Sulamani (IRE)—Pennys Pride (IRE) **Reveley Racing I & Reveley Farms**
21 **TEESCOMPONENTS MAX**, 7, b g Grape Tree Road—Our Tees Component (IRE) **Tees Components Ltd**
22 **TEKTHELOT (IRE)**, 10, b g Shantou (USA)—Bryna (IRE) **Mrs A. Trevaskis**
23 **THE NAME'S BOND**, 4, ch g Monsieur Bond (IRE)—Fairlie **The Phoenix Racing C.O.**
24 **VIC'S LAST STAND (IRE)**, 6, b m Old Vic—Misleain (IRE) **Mr R. N. Ellerbeck**
25 **VICTOR HEWGO**, 11, b g Old Vic—Pennys Pride (IRE) **Sir Ian Good**
26 **WAITING PATIENTLY (IRE)**, 5, b g Flemensfirth (USA)—Rossavon (IRE) **R. Collins**
27 **WALTZ DARLING (IRE)**, 8, b g Iffraaj—Aljafliyah **Mrs M B Thwaites & Mr M E Foxton**

THREE-YEAR-OLDS

28 **FLORAL BOUQUET**, bl f Fair Mix (IRE)—Florarossa **Mrs A. Fulton**
29 **GREAT COLACI**, b g Sulamani (IRE)—Fairlie **Rug, Grub & Pub Partnership**
30 **KARCH**, b f Sulamani (IRE)—Let It Be **Mr A. Frame**

TWO-YEAR-OLDS

31 Ch g 17/5 Haafhd—Let It Be (Entrepreneur) **Mr A. Frame**

MR KEITH REVELEY - Continued

Other Owners: Mr T. Alderson, Mr C. Alessi, C. Anderson, Mrs C. M. Baxter, Exors of the Late Mr D. E. Baxter, Mr J. P. Bladen, Mr D. Bowen, M. J. Bradley, M. F. Browne, Mrs M. Clark-Wright, J. W. Coates, E. Coll, Mr A. Collins, A. E. Corbett, Mr M. Cressey, B. D. Drinkall, M. E. Foxton, Mr B. W. Goodall, D. A. Green, Mrs D. E. Greenhalgh, R. J. Hart, Mrs Emma Hockenhull, P.D. Hockenhull, Mr J. D. Lovell, W. J. McKeown, Mr A. J. Rae, D. C. Renton, Exors of the Late Mr J. E. Renton, Reveley Farms, Mrs A. S. Rodgers, R. V. Smith, J. Struth, Mr J. Thoroughgood, Mrs M. B. Thwaites, D. Wild, Mrs M. Williams, W. J. Williams, Mrs C. M. Yates, D. L. Young.

Assistant Trainer: Fiona Reveley

Jockey (NH): James Reveley.

MRS LYDIA RICHARDS, Chichester

511

Postal: **Lynch Farm, Hares Lane, Funtington, Chichester, West Sussex, PO18 9LW**
Contacts: **YARD** (01243) 574379 **HOME** (01243) 574882 **MOBILE** (07803) 199061
E-MAIL lydia.richards@sky.com

1 AALY, 9, b g Milan—Leyaaly **Mrs Lydia Richards**
2 4, B g Avonbridge—Baytown Flyer **Mrs Lydia Richards**
3 FAHEEM, 5, b g Halling (USA)—White Star (IRE) **Mrs E. F. J. Seal**
4 HONG KONG JOE, 6, b g Oasis Dream—Singed **The Demoiselle Bond Partnership**
5 LEYLA'S GIFT, 7, b m Milan—Leyaaly **Mrs Lydia Richards**
6 MAIGH DARA (IRE), 7, br g Cacique (IRE)—Dara Diva (IRE) **The Inner Steel Partnership**
7 MIGHTY THOR, 6, b g Norse Dancer (IRE)—Leyaaly **Mrs Lydia Richards**
8 UP TILL MIDNIGHT, 7, ch m Midnight Legend—Uplift
9 VENETIAN LAD, 11, ro g Midnight Legend—Henrietta Holmes (IRE) **The Venetian Lad Partnership**

Other Owners: Mr Hamish Kinmond, Mr Graeme Musker, Mrs Lydia Richards, Mrs Judy Seal.

MR NICKY RICHARDS, Greystoke

512

Postal: **Rectory Farm, Greystoke, Penrith, Cumbria, CA11 0UJ**
Contacts: **OFFICE** (01768) 483392 **HOME** (01768) 483160 **FAX** (01768) 483933
MOBILE (07771) 906609
E-MAIL n.g.richards@virgin.net WEBSITE www.nickyrichardsracing.com

1 ANOTHER BILL (IRE), 6, ch g Beneficial—Glacier Lilly (IRE) **Langdale Bloodstock**
2 ANYWAYTHEWINDBLOWS, 4, ch g Shirocco (GER)—Welanga **Mrs C. A. Torkington**
3 BALLYBOKER BREEZE (IRE), 8, b g Gold Well—Ballyboker Lady (IRE) **Mr & Mrs Paul & Clare Rooney**
4 BAYSBROWN (IRE), 6, b g Fruits of Love (USA)—Whenever Wherever (IRE) **Langdale Bloodstock**
5 BAYWING (IRE), 7, br g Winged Love (IRE)—Cerise de Totes (FR) **David & Nicky Robinson**
6 BERNARDELLI (IRE), 8, b g Golan (IRE)—Beautiful Blue (IRE) **Henriques & Lloyd-Bakers**
7 BETTER GETALONG (IRE), 5, b g Gold Well—Arequipa (IRE) **D. Wesley-Yates**
8 BLAKERIGG (IRE), 5, b g Presenting—Azalea (IRE) **David & Nicky Robinson**
9 CAIUS MARCIUS (IRE), 5, b g King's Theatre (IRE)—Ain't Misbehavin (IRE) **C. P. Norbury**
10 CARINENA (IRE), 7, b m Shantou (USA)—Dinny Kenn (IRE) **Mrs C. A. Torkington**
11 CHIDSWELL (IRE), 7, b g Gold Well—Manacured (IRE) **David & Nicky Robinson**
12 CONQUER GOLD (IRE), 4, b g Gold Well—Ballinamona Wish (IRE) **Mr & Mrs Paul & Clare Rooney**
13 CRINKLE CRAGS (IRE), 6, ch g Trans Island—Ashanti Dancer (IRE) **Tarzan Bloodstock**
14 CUIL ROGUE (IRE), 8, b g Presenting—Coolshamrock (IRE) **Tarzan Bloodstock**
15 CULTRAM ABBEY (IRE), 8, br g Fair Mix (IRE)—Kansas City (FR) **The Roper Family**
16 DUKE OF NAVAN (IRE), 8, b br g Presenting—Greenfieldflyer (IRE) **David & Nicky Robinson**
17 ECHO EXPRESS (IRE), 4, b g Echo of Light—If Dubai (USA) **Henriques, Lloyd-Baker, Westoll, Wrigley**
18 EDUARD (IRE), 8, b g Morozov (USA)—Dinny Kenn (IRE) **Eddie Melville**
19 FIRE ROCK (IRE), 5, b g Scorpion (IRE)—Cooline Jana (IRE) **Tarzan Bloodstock**
20 GLINGERSIDE (IRE), 5, b g Milan—Kettle 'n Cran (IRE) **James Westoll**
21 GOLD FUTURES (IRE), 7, b g Gold Well—Don't Discount Her (IRE) **Mrs C. A. Torkington**
22 HESTER FLEMEN (IRE), 8, ch m Flemensfirth (USA)—Hester Hall (IRE) **Mr & Mrs Paul & Clare Rooney**
23 IMADA (IRE), 6, br g Arcadio (GER)—Anck Su Namun (IRE) **Kenny Haughey & Laura Sabiani**
24 ISAACSTOWN LAD (IRE), 9, b g Milan—Friends of Friends (IRE) **M S Borders Racing Club & Partners**
25 LAFTERLANDS (IRE), 5, b g Azamour (IRE)—Madam Gaffer **Mrs J. Fortescue**
26 LOOKING WELL (IRE), 7, b g Gold Well—Different Level (IRE) **D. Wesley-Yates**
27 MALIN BAY (IRE), 11, b g Milan—Mirror of Flowers **David & Nicky Robinson**
28 MARDALE (IRE), 6, b m Robin des Champs (FR)—Lizzy Langtry (IRE) **East To West Racing Club**
29 MOSCOW CALLING (IRE), 5, b g Morozov (USA)—Bubble Bann (IRE) **Tarzan Bloodstock**

MR NICKY RICHARDS - Continued

30 **ONE FOR HARRY (IRE)**, 8, b g Generous (IRE)—Strawberry Fool (FR) **The Fife Boys + 1**
31 **ONE FOR HOCKY (IRE)**, 8, b g Brian Boru—Wire Lady (IRE) **Kingdom Taverns Ltd**
32 **PARC DES PRINCES (USA)**, 10, b br g Ten Most Wanted (USA)—Miss Orah **Tarzan Bloodstock**
33 **PROGRESS DRIVE (IRE)**, 5, b g Stowaway—Dolphins View (IRE) **Mr A. Cochrane**
34 **RANDY PIKE (IRE)**, 6, b g Mahler—Niamh's Leader (IRE) **Langdale Bloodstock**
35 **REIVERS LAD**, 5, b g Alflora (IRE)—Reivers Moon **Mr J. M. Stenhouse**
36 **SHOTOFWINE**, 7, b g Grape Tree Road—Icy Gunner **Mr & Mrs Paul & Clare Rooney**
37 **SIMPLY NED (IRE)**, 9, ch g Fruits of Love (USA)—Bishops Lass (IRE) **David & Nicky Robinson**
38 **SIR VINSKI (IRE)**, 7, ch g Vinnie Roe (IRE)—Mill Emerald **The Anne Marie Melville/The Northern Raiders**
39 **ST GREGORY (IRE)**, 8, ch m Presenting—Ardrom **The Grafton Lounge Partnership**
40 **STRAIT OF MAGELLAN (IRE)**, 4, ch g Captain Rio—Golden (FR) **Mrs Pat Sloan**
41 **STREAMS OF WHISKEY (IRE)**, 9, br g Spadoun (FR)—Cherry Tops (IRE) **Mr & Mrs R. G. Kelvin-Hughes**
42 **TAKINGRISKS (IRE)**, 7, b g Golden Tornado (IRE)—Downtown Rosie (IRE) **Mr F. Bird**
43 **TEDDY TEE (IRE)**, 7, b g Mountain High (IRE)—Knocksouna Lady (IRE) **David & Nicky Robinson**
44 **TOP BILLING**, 7, br g Monsun (GER)—La Gandilie (FR) **Doreen McGawn & Stewart Tate**
45 **TUTCHEC (FR)**, 9, gr g Turgeon (USA)—Pocahontas (FR) **Club 4 Racing**
46 **UN NOBLE (FR)**, 6, gr g Near Honor (GER)—Noble Gary (FR) **Mrs C. A. Torkington**
47 **WESTERN RULES (IRE)**, 6, b g Westerner—Ryehill Lady (IRE) **Bob Bennett & Jimmy Dudgeon**
48 **WICKED SPICE (IRE)**, 7, b g Old Vic—Afdala (IRE) **Mrs E. E. R. Sloan**
49 **WINTER ALCHEMY (IRE)**, 11, b g Fruits of Love (USA)—Native Land **The Alchemy Partnership**
50 **WOT A SHOT (IRE)**, 7, b g Refuse To Bend (USA)—Ashdali (IRE) **M S Borders Racing Club & Partners**

Other Owners: Mr A. Clark, Mrs R. L. Elliot, Mr Charlie Fortescue, Mr Nick Fortescue, Mr Guy Henriques, Mrs Rhonda Hill, Mr P. Laverty, Mr P. Renton, Mrs Nicholas Wrigley.

Assistant Trainer: Miss Joey Richards

Jockey (NH): Brian Harding, Craig Nichol. **Conditional:** Ryan Day.

---

513 **MR JOHN DAVID RICHES, Pilling**
Postal: **Moss Side Farm, Off Lancaster Road, Scronkey, Pilling, Lancashire, PR3 6SR**

1 **DE LESSEPS (USA)**, 8, ch g Selkirk (USA)—Suez **J. W. Barrett**
2 **GAMBINO (IRE)**, 6, b g Red Clubs (IRE)—Temptation Island (IRE) **J. D. Riches**
3 **INDIAN GIVER**, 8, b m Indesatchel (IRE)—Bint Baddi (FR) **J. D. Riches**
4 **LADY BROOME**, 5, ch m Erhaab (USA)—Minnesinger **Charles Broome & Partners**
5 **MUBROOK (USA)**, 11, b g Alhaarth (IRE)—Zomaradah **Gold Tooth Racing**
6 **PICKS PINTA**, 5, b g Piccolo—Past 'n' Present **J. D. Riches**
7 **RUTTERKIN (USA)**, 8, gr g Maria's Mon (USA)—Chilukki Cat (USA) **J. W. Barrett**
8 **SPOKEN WORDS**, 7, b m Fruits of Love (USA)—Jerre Jo Glanville (USA) **Mrs L. Wohlers**

THREE-YEAR-OLDS

9 **LOWRIE**, b f Assertive—Miacarla **J. D. Riches**
10 **TRULOVE**, b f Piccolo—Snow Dancer (IRE) **Mrs L. Wohlers**

TWO-YEAR-OLDS

11 **PICCOLINO**, b f 17/4 Piccolo—Miacarla (Forzando) **J. D. Riches**

Other Owners: Mr C. M. Broome, Mr E. Broome, Mr M. W. Ennis, Mr G. J. Vallely.

---

514 **MR MARK RIMELL, Witney**
Postal: **Fairspear Racing Stables, Fairspear Road, Leafield, Witney, Oxfordshire, OX29 9NT**
Contacts: **PHONE (01993) 878551 MOBILE (07778) 648303/(07973) 627054**
E-MAIL rimell@rimellracing.com WEBSITE www.rimellracing.com

1 **BHAKTI (IRE)**, 9, b g Rakti—Royal Bossi (IRE) **M. G. Rimell**
2 **BREATH OF LIFE**, 6, b m Zafeen (FR)—Pretty Lady Rose **Sarah Waring & Woodland Generators**
3 **OVERLORD**, 4, b g Lawman (FR)—Hip **M. G. Rimell**
4 **ROXY BELLE**, 6, b m Black Sam Bellamy (IRE)—Royal Roxy **M. G. Rimell**
5 **ROYAL ROO**, 7, b m Overbury (IRE)—Royal Roxy (IRE) **Mrs A. Rimell**
6 4, B f Kayf Tara—Royal Roxy (IRE)
7 **RUMOUR HAS IT**, 5, b m Beat All (USA)—Top Gale (IRE)

MR MARK RIMELL - Continued

    8 SAIL WITH SULTANA, 5, ch m Black Sam Bellamy (IRE)—Strathtay **Mrs M. R. T. Rimell**
    9 4, Ch g Schiaparelli (GER)—Strathtay **Mrs M. R. T. Rimell**
  10 TOPMAN TED, 5, b g Beat All (USA)—Pretty Lady Rose **Sarah Waring & Woodland Generators**

Other Owners: Ms S. Waring, Woodlands (Worcestershire) Ltd.

Assistant Trainer: Anne Rimell

---

515   MR DAVE ROBERTS, Kenley
Postal: **Leasowes Farm, Kenley, Shrewsbury, Shropshire, SY5 6NY**
Contacts: **PHONE (01746) 785255**

  1 RED TOUCH (USA), 4, b br g Bluegrass Cat (USA)—Touchnow (CAN) **D. B. Roberts**
  2 SCOGLIO, 8, b g Monsieur Bond (IRE)—Ex Mill Lady **D. B. Roberts**
  3 SLEEPY SUNDAY, 6, b m Revoque (IRE)—Cool Spring (IRE) **D. B. Roberts**
  4 SPIRIT RIVER (FR), 11, b g Poliglote—Love River (FR) **D. B. Roberts**
  5 STORYTALE, 4, ch g Rip Van Winkle (IRE)—Night Haven **D. B. Roberts**

THREE-YEAR-OLDS

  6 CHESHAM ROSE (IRE), gr f Mastercraftsman (IRE)—Rose's Destination (IRE) **Mr D. Bradbury**

---

516   MR MIKE ROBERTS, Hailsham
Postal: **Summertree Farm, Bodle Street Green, Hailsham, East Sussex, BN27 4QT**
Contacts: **PHONE (01435) 830231 FAX (01435) 830887 MOBILE (07774) 208040**
E-MAIL **mike@summertree-racing.com**

  1 BETSY BOO BOO, 7, b m King's Theatre (IRE)—Quark Top (FR) **M. J. Roberts**
  2 BLACKJAX, 6, br m Black Sam Bellamy (IRE)—Jaxelle (FR) **M. J. Roberts**
  3 BRAVE CUPID, 6, ch m Black Sam Bellamy (IRE)—Newport (FR) **M. J. Roberts**
  4 I'M A RASCAL, 7, ch g Erhaab (USA)—Mohican Pass **M. J. Roberts**
  5 SAUCYSIOUX, 6, b m Tobougg (IRE)—Mohican Pass **M. J. Roberts**
  6 SNIPPETYDOODAH, 8, b m King's Theatre (IRE)—Kimpour (FR) **M. J. Roberts**
  7 URANOX (FR), 8, b g Special Kaldoun (IRE)—Judelle (FR) **M. J. Roberts**

Assistant Trainer: Marie Martin

---

517   MISS SARAH ROBINSON, Bridgwater
Postal: **Newnham Farm, Shurton, Stogursey, Bridgwater, Somerset, TA5 1QG**
Contacts: **PHONE (01278) 732357 FAX (01278) 732357 MOBILE (07866) 435197 / (07518) 785291**
E-MAIL **info@sarahrobinsonracing.co.uk** WEBSITE **www.sarahrobinsonracing.co.uk**

  1 BERWIN (IRE), 7, b m Lawman (FR)—Topiary (IRE) **Mr B. Robinson**
  2 JOE THE ROGUE (IRE), 9, gr g Amilynx (FR)—Roco-Bridge (IRE) **Mr B. Robinson**
  3 NEWNHAM FLYER (IRE), 14, gr m Exit To Nowhere (USA)—Paper Flight **Mr B. Robinson**

Assistant Trainer: Mr B. Robinson

Jockey (NH): Kevin Jones, Ian Popham. **Amateur:** Mr Luke Kilgarriff, Miss S. Robinson.

---

518   MISS PAULINE ROBSON, Capheaton
Postal: **Kidlaw Farm, Capheaton, Newcastle Upon Tyne, NE19 2AW**
Contacts: **PHONE (01830) 530241 MOBILE (07721) 887489 or (07814) 708725 (David)**
E-MAIL **pauline@prracing.co.uk**

  1 HABBIE SIMPSON, 11, b g Elmaamul (USA)—Hamanaka (USA) **S. Love**
  2 HUMBIE (IRE), 12, b g Karinga Bay—South Queen Lady (IRE) **Mr & Mrs Raymond Anderson Green**
  3 LAC LEMAN (GER), 5, b g Doyen (IRE)—Learned Lady (JPN) **D&D Armstrong Limited**
  4 RIVAL D'ESTRUVAL (FR), 11, b g Khalkevi (IRE)—
                                     Kermesse d'estruval (FR) **Mr & Mrs Raymond Anderson Green**

MISS PAULINE ROBSON - Continued

5 **SHARP RISE (IRE)**, 9, b g Croco Rouge (IRE)—Missusan (IRE) **I Couldn't Switch Club**
6 **TEO VIVO (FR)**, 9, gr g Great Pretender (IRE)—Ifranne (FR) **It's a Bargain Syndicate**
7 **ULUROO (FR)**, 4, b g Centennial (IRE)—Kica (FR) **Mr & Mrs Raymond Anderson Green**
8 **UPSILON BLEU (FR)**, 8, b g Panoramic—Glycine Bleue (FR) **Mr & Mrs Raymond Anderson Green**
9 **VISION DE LA VIE (FR)**, 6, ch g Sin Kiang (FR)—Vidaharmosa (FR) **I Couldn't Switch Club**

Other Owners: Mrs J. E. Dodd, Mrs E. M. Fairbairn, Mrs A. Green, R. A. Green, Mr D. J. A. Green, Mr M. J. Jenkins.

Assistant Trainer: David Parker

---

519 **MR R. A. ROSS, Consett**
Postal: **Rock Cottage Farm, 79 Iveston Lane, Consett, Co. Durham, DH8 7TB**

1 **COLROCKIN**, 5, b g Great Palm (USA)—Suetsu (IRE) **R. A. Ross**
2 **DE BEE KEEPER (IRE)**, 8, b g Milan—Festival Leader (IRE) **R. A. Ross**
3 **ROCKU**, 6, b g Great Palm (USA)—Suetsu (IRE) **R. A. Ross**

---

520 **MR BRIAN ROTHWELL, Malton**
Postal: **Old Post Office, Oswaldkirk, Malton, North Yorkshire, YO62 5XT**
Contacts: **PHONE (01439) 788859 MOBILE (07969) 968241**
E-MAIL brian.rothwell1@googlemail.com

1 **BERTHA BURNETT (IRE)**, 5, gr m Verglas (IRE)—Starsazi **Greta Sparks**
2 **COMPETITION**, 4, b g Multiplex—Compolina **Mickley Stud & Derrick Mossop**
3 **HOMELAND (IRE)**, 4, b g Galileo (IRE)—Withorwithoutyou (IRE) **Paul Moorhouse**
4 **REGAL SWAIN (IRE)**, 8, b g Ivan Denisovich (IRE)—Targhyb (IRE) **Andrew Sparks**
5 **SIRIUS STAR**, 7, b g Beat All (USA)—Miss Sirius **The Sirius Racing Partnership**
6 **TAWAN**, 5, b g Tiger Hill—Lady Netbetsports (IRE) **Brian Rothwell**
7 **TEMPLESHELIN (IRE)**, 7, b g Olden Times—Reasoning **Brian Rothwell**
8 **TIGER TWENTY TWO**, 5, b g Authorized (IRE)—Collette's Choice **Mr A. J. Sparks**
9 **TORNESEL**, 5, b g Teofilo (IRE)—Bezant (IRE) **Brian Rothwell**
10 **YAWAIL**, 5, b br m Medicean—Al Tamooh (IRE) **Brian Rothwell**

TWO-YEAR-OLDS

11 **THORNTON FRANK**, b g 26/5 Misu Bond (IRE)—Byton (Byron) **S. P. Hudson**
12 **THORNTON MARY**, b f 29/4 Mawatheeq (USA)—Bezant (IRE) (Zamindar (USA)) (7500) **S. P. Hudson**

---

521 **MR J. - C. ROUGET, Pau**
Postal: **Chemin de la Foret Bastard, 64000 Pau, France**
Contacts: **PHONE (0033) 5593 32790 FAX (0033) 5593 32930 MOBILE (0033) 6102 70335**
E-MAIL ste.rouget@orange.fr

1 **AIMLESS LADY (FR)**, 4, b f Peer Gynt (JPN)—Poet's Studio (USA) **Ecurie M. Sardou, J.-C. Rouget**
2 **ALCOY (FR)**, 4, b c Aussie Rules (USA)—Breath of Love (USA) **Ecurie A. Caro**
3 **BROADWAY BOOGIE (IRE)**, 4, b c Distorted Humor (USA)—Grande Melody (IRE) **B. Belinguier**
4 **DUKE OF DUNDEE (FR)**, 4, b g Duke of Marmalade (IRE)—Santa Louisia **Ecurie J.-L. Tepper**
5 **ERVEDYA (FR)**, 4, b f Siyouni (FR)—Elva (IRE) **S. A. Aga Khan**
6 **FEE D'ARTOIS (FR)**, 4, b f Palace Episode (USA)—Vallabelle (FR) **O. Carli**
7 **KENCHAROVA (FR)**, 4, b f Kendargent (FR)—Kirona **A. Jathiere**
8 **KENDEMAI (FR)**, 5, gr h Carlotamix (FR)—Kendorya (FR) **B. Belinguier, J.-C. Rouget**
9 **KERMIYAN (FR)**, 9, b g Green Desert (USA)—Kerasha (FR) **S. A. Aga Khan**
10 **L'ARDENT (FR)**, 5, ch h Soldier of Fortune (IRE)—Princesse de Viane (FR) **B. Magrez Horses**
11 **LA CORNICHE (FR)**, 4, b f Naaqoos—Mademoisellechichi (FR) **P. Augier, Ecurie J.-L. Tepper, J.-C. Rouget**
12 **LARVOTTO (FR)**, 4, b c Astronomer Royal (USA)—Senderlea (IRE) **Ecurie des Charmes**
13 **LE DEPUTE (FR)**, 4, bl c Literato (FR)—
     Hamida (USA) **La Valle Martigny, du Buisson, de Courson, Vigier, Dupont**
14 **LORESHO (FR)**, 5, b h Halling (USA)—Luna Gulch (FR) **H. H. Aga Khan**
15 **LUCELLE (IRE)**, 4, b f High Chaparral (IRE)—Larceny (IRE) **Haras de la Morsangliere, Ecurie des Charmes**
16 **MANCORA (FR)**, 4, ch f Iffraaj—Mantadive (FR) **P. Segalot**

MR J. - C. ROUGET - Continued

17 **MOONLIGHT IN PARIS (FR)**, 4, b f Literato (FR)—Isalou (FR) **Ecurie J.-L. Tepper**
18 **QAWAAREB (IRE)**, 4, ch c Teofilo (IRE)—Masaafat **Hamdan Al Maktoum**
19 **SAANE (FR)**, 5, b g Le Havre (IRE)—Salamon **G. Augustin-Normand**
20 **SILAS MARNER (FR)**, 9, b h Muhtathir—Street Kendra (FR) **A. Jathiere**
21 **SPEED ROAD (FR)**, 5, b h King's Best (USA)—Life On The Road (IRE) **L. Dassault**
22 **SUNNY (FR)**, 7, ch g Muhtathir—Vol Sauvage (FR) **B. Magrez Horses, J.-C. Rouget**
23 **TANIYA (FR)**, 4, b f High Chaparral (IRE)—Takaniya (IRE) **S. A. Aga Khan**
24 **WIRELESS (FR)**, 5, ch h Kentucky Dynamite (USA)—Sachet (USA) **Ecurie I. M. Fares**
25 **ZAFIRO (FR)**, 4, b c Sageburg (IRE)—La Romagne (FR) **Ecurie A. Caro**

THREE-YEAR-OLDS

26 **ABOULIE (IRE)**, b f Exceed And Excel (AUS)—Anja (IRE) **Haras d'Etreham, M. Lagasse, Riviera Equine**
27 **ACADEMIC (IRE)**, ch c Zamindar (USA)—Heliocentric (FR) **M. S. Schwartz Racing**
28 **AJOU (FR)**, b f Siyouni (FR)—Azucar (IRE) **G. Augustin-Normand**
29 **AL WATHNA**, b f Nayef (USA)—Lemon Twist (IRE) **Al Shaqab Racing**
30 **ALCYONE (FR)**, b g Air Chief Marshal (IRE)—Golding Star (FR) **G. Augustin-Normand, Mme E. Vidal**
31 **ALDABA (FR)**, b f Loup Breton (GER)—Mille Etoiles (USA) **Ecurie A. Caro**
32 **ALMANZOR (FR)**, b c Wootton Bassett—Darkova (FR) **G. Augustin-Normand, Ecurie A. Caro**
33 **ALNAJMAH**, br f Dansili—Joanna (IRE) **Hamdan Al Maktoum**
34 **AMAZING LADY (GER)**, gr f Lord of England (GER)—Audrey (GER) **P. Beziat, S. Lauray**
35 **AMERICAN WHIPPER (FR)**, b g Whipper (USA)—Abondante (USA) **P. Augier, Ecurie du Loup**
36 **APPLE BETTY (IRE)**, b f Galileo (IRE)—Absolutelyfabulous (IRE) **J. Allen**
37 **ASHTIYNA (FR)**, b f Turtle Bowl (IRE)—Ashalina (FR) **H. H. Aga Khan**
38 **ASSOUFID**, b f Sunday Break (JPN)—Selena (FR) **G. Pierlot, P. Gautier, A. Gautier**
39 **ATLANTIDE (IRE)**, gr c Halling (USA)—Miss Spinamix (IRE) **Boetie Racing II, Ecurie La Boetie**
40 **BAROU (FR)**, b c Le Havre (IRE)—Salamon **G. Augustin-Normand**
41 **BELIEVER**, b f Lawman (FR)—Militante (IRE) **Qatar Racing Ltd**
42 **BEYCHEVELLE (USA)**, b f War Front (USA)—La Conseillante (USA) **J. Allen**
43 **BEYNOSTORM (FR)**, ch c Stormy River (FR)—Beynotown **Ecurie I. M. Fares**
44 **BILLIONNAIRE (IRE)**, gr g Acclamation—Marie Rossa **C. Marzocco, L Marzocco**
45 **BOLCHEVIK (IRE)**, ch c Muhtathir—Cotes d'armor (FR) **A. Jathiere, Ecurie M. Offenstadt**
46 **BONJOUR MAMIE (FR)**, gr f Manbolix (FR)—La Deauvillaise (FR) **Ecurie M. Sardou**
47 **BRULE PARFUM (FR)**, b g Vertigineux (FR)—Land of Life (IRE) **G. Pierlot, P. Gautier, A. Gautier**
48 **CAMP COURAGE (UAE)**, b c War Front (USA)—Storybook (UAE) **J. Allen**
49 **CHELKAR**, b g Azamour (IRE)—Cherryxma (FR) **H. H. Aga Khan**
50 **CLAIRE DE LUNE (IRE)**, ch f Galileo (IRE)—Solo de lune (IRE) **J. Allen**
51 **COEUR DE ROCKEUSE**, b f Lilbourne Lad (IRE)—Tenepia (FR) **Ecurie J.-L. Tepper, F. McNulty**
52 **CROSS TIE WALKER (IRE)**, gr c Cape Cross (IRE)—Netrebko (IRE) **Ecurie J.-L. Tepper, J. C. Rouget**
53 **DARICE (IRE)**, b f Cape Cross (IRE)—Darakiyla (IRE) **Razza Pallorsi SNC**
54 **DAYANA (FR)**, ch f Iffraaj—Decouverte (IRE) **Ecurie J.-L. Tepper**
55 **DIYABAKIYR**, gr g Azamour (IRE)—Diasilixa (FR) **H. H. Aga Khan**
56 **DRAMATURGE (FR)**, b g Muhtathir—Benzolina (FR) **Boetie Racing II, Ecurie La Boetie**
57 **DREAM OF ARC (FR)**, b f Hurricane Cat (USA)—Kunoichi (USA) **Ecurie Gribomont**
58 **DUC DES LOGES (FR)**, ch c Le Havre (IRE)—
                Birdy Namnam (USA) **F. Le Clec'h, Ecurie du Loup, Ec. La Vallee Martigny, R. Prouveur**
59 **ECHAUFFOUR (FR)**, b c Le Havre (IRE)—Langrune (IRE) **G. Augustin-Normand**
60 **ELENNGA (FR)**, ch f Exceed And Excel (AUS)—Elva (IRE) **S. A. Aga Khan**
61 **ELUSIVE MILLION (IRE)**, b f Pour Moi (IRE)—Million Spirits (IRE) **M. S. Schwartz Racing**
62 B f Footstepsinthesand—En Vitesse **Riviera Equine**
63 **FEDERICO**, b g Acclamation—Frangy **Ecurie des Charmes**
64 **FENJAL (FR)**, b c Tale of The Cat (USA)—Gypsy Hollow (USA) **Al Shaqab Racing**
65 **FRANKO FOLIE**, b f Kendargent (FR)—Atlantic Festival (USA) **D.-Y. Treves**
66 **FRESH AIR (IRE)**, b f Montjeu (IRE)—Silver Star **J. Allen**
67 **FRONT PAGE STORY (USA)**, b f War Front (USA)—Tempo West (USA) **J. Allen**
68 **GEORGE PATTON (USA)**, gr ro c War Front (USA)—Photograph (USA) **J. Allen**
69 **GETBACK IN PARIS (IRE)**, ch c Galileo (IRE)—
                Elusive Wave (IRE) **Ecurie J.-L. Tepper, Mrs S. Magnier, D. Smith, M. Tabor**
70 **GHAALY**, b c Tamayuz—Ghizlaan (USA) **Hamdan Al Maktoum**
71 **HIGH SCHOOL DAYS (USA)**, ch f Elusive Quality (USA)—Baroness Richter (IRE) **J. Allen**
72 **HOUSE OF DIXIE (USA)**, b f War Front (USA)—Homebound (USA) **J. Allen**
73 **HURRICANE (FR)**, b g Hurricane Cat (USA)—Monatora (FR) **D.-Y. Treves**
74 **IMAGINE IN PARIS, FR)**, b f Myboycharlie (IRE)—Adamantina (FR) **Ecurie J.-L. Tepper**
75 **INSENSE (FR)**, gr c Slickly (FR)—Insan Mala (IRE) **J.-C. Seroul, J.-C. Rouget**
76 **JADHABA (IRE)**, b f Galileo (IRE)—Naissance Royale (IRE) **Al Shaqab Racing**
77 **JAVA BLUE (FR)**, b f Makfi—Deep And Blue (USA) **Mme G. Forien**

MR J. - C. ROUGET - Continued

78 **JEMAYEL (IRE)**, ch f Lope de Vega (IRE)—Nawal (FR) **Al Shaqab Racing**
79 **JUSTWANTACONTACT (IRE)**, ch c Rock of Gibraltar (IRE)—
Just Little (FR) **Ec., La Vallee Martigny, Ecurie J.-L. Tepper, N. Saltiel**
80 **KAZAROY (FR)**, gr c Kendargent (FR)—Pearl Sky (FR) **A. Jathiere**
81 **KERILA (FR)**, b f Makfi—Kerasha (FR) **S. A. Aga Khan**
82 **KHAMRY (FR)**, b c Poet's Voice—Poppets Sweetlove **Hamdan Al Maktoum**
83 **KINGLIGHT (FR)**, b g Kendargent (FR)—Vespona (FR) **G. Ben Lassin, Ecurie J.-L. Tepper**
84 **KIPANGA**, b f Lawman (FR)—Avventura (USA) **C. Marzocco, L. Marzocco**
85 **KLIMTH (FR)**, b g Peintre Celebre (USA)—Inca Wood (UAE) **D.-Y. Treves**
86 **KOSHKA (FR)**, ch f Siyouni (FR)—Everlast (FR) **A. Jathiere**
87 **KOTAMA (FR)**, b f Siyouni (FR)—Kozaka (FR) **S. A. Aga Khan**
88 **L'ENCHANTEUR (FR)**, b g Caradak (IRE)—Golden Section (USA) **L. Dassault**
89 **LA CRESSONNIERE (FR)**, b f Le Havre (IRE)—Absolute Lady (IRE) **G. Augustin-Normand, Ecurie A. Caro**
90 **LAKALAS (FR)**, b f Turtle Bowl (IRE)—Nazlia (FR) **Ecurie J.-L. Tepper, Ecurie des Charmes**
91 **LET IT BE IN PARIS (FR)**, b g Dark Angel (IRE)—
Guiana (GER) **Ecurie J.-L. Tepper, Ec. La Vallee Martigny, N. Saltiel**
92 **LET'S MISBEHAVE (IRE)**, b f Montjeu (IRE)—Kasora (IRE) **J. Allen**
93 **LITTLE GHETTO BOY (FR)**, b g Lawman (FR)—Ahea (USA) **Ecurie M. Sardou**
94 **LOPE SUPREME**, ch f Lope de Vega (IRE)—Jesting **C. Marzocco**
95 **LOUP ROYAL (IRE)**, b g Astronomer Royal (USA)—
Lia Waltz (FR) **Ecurie du Loup, Ec. La Vallee Martigny, B. Patou, Mme M. Romano**
96 **LOVE STREET (USA)**, ch f Kitten's Joy—Bold World (USA) **D.-Y. Treves**
97 **MAGNOLEA (IRE)**, b f Acclamation—Carcassone (IRE) **F. Salman**
98 **MAIZE AND BLUE (IRE)**, b c Danehill Dancer—Grande Melody (IRE) **J. Allen**
99 **MARMOGAH (FR)**, b f Invincible Spirit (IRE)—Causa Proxima (FR) **Al Shaqab Racing**
100 **MASHKA (IRE)**, ch f Exceed And Excel (AUS)—Mambia **A. Jathiere, G. Laboureau**
101 **MAYYAS (IRE)**, b c Sea The Stars (IRE)—Don't Hurry Me (IRE) **Al Shaqab Racing**
102 **MEKHTAAL (FR)**, ch c Sea The Stars (IRE)—Aiglonne (USA) **Al Shaqab Racing**
103 **MESONERA (FR)**, b f Sunday Break (JPN)—Niska (USA) **Ecurie A. Caro**
104 **MEZIDON (FR)**, gr g Le Havre (IRE)—Belliflore (FR) **G. Augustin-Normand, Mme E. Vidal**
105 **MILLEPASSI (IRE)**, b g Holy Roman Emperor (IRE)—Gaselee (USA) **D.-Y. Treves**
106 **MOISVILLE (FR)**, b f Hat Trick (JPN)—Mixed Intention (USA) **G. Augustin-Normand**
107 **MORE THAN A DREAM (IRE)**, b c Halling (USA)—Chabelle **D.-Y. Treves**
108 **MOURASKA**, b f Include (USA)—Mouraniya (IRE) **S. A. Aga Khan**
109 **MUSHAWWEQ (IRE)**, b br c Dubawi (IRE)—Mudaaraah **Hamdan Al Maktoum**
110 **MUTAMADED (IRE)**, b c Arcano (IRE)—Sahaayeb (IRE) **Hamdan Al Maktoum**
111 **NAWARAT (USA)**, b f Street Sense (USA)—Taseel (USA) **Hamdan Al Maktoum**
112 **OUEZY (IRE)**, b f Le Havre (IRE)—Merville (IRE) **G. Augustin-Normand**
113 **PASSADOBLE (IRE)**, b f Dream Ahead (USA)—Pertinence (IRE) **Riviera Equine, Haras d'Etreham**
114 **PHENICEAN (IRE)**, b c Rock of Gibraltar (IRE)—
Public Ransom (IRE) **E. Puerari, J.-C. Rouget, Mme D. Ades-Hazan, M. Henochsberg**
115 **PLEDGE OF HONOUR (FR)**, ch f Zoffany (IRE)—Out of Honour (IRE) **Qatar Racing Ltd**
116 **POSITIVE VIBRATION (IRE)**, b r f Canford Cliffs (IRE)—Midnight Partner (IRE) **Ecurie M. Sardou**
117 **PRINCESS DUTCH (FR)**, b f Dutch Art—Almahroosa (USA) **S. Boucheron**
118 **QEMAH (IRE)**, b f Danehill Dancer (IRE)—Kartica **Al Shaqab Racing**
119 **RED KITTEN (IRE)**, b c Kitten's Joy (USA)—Red Diadem **Ecurie I. M. Fares**
120 **ROCHENKA (FR)**, b f Rock of Gibraltar (IRE)—Lunashkaya **A. Jathiere**
121 **ROCK OF THE MOON**, b f Rock of Gibraltar (IRE)—Pegase Hurry (USA) **J.-F. Gribomont**
122 **ROMAN RIDGE**, b f Holy Roman Emperor (IRE)—Baino Ridge (FR) **Ecurie I. M. Fares**
123 **ROMAZZINO (FR)**, b g Rip Van Winkle (IRE)—Doctors Nurse (USA) **C. Marzocco, L. Marzocco**
124 **ROSAY (IRE)**, b f Raven's Pass (USA)—Petit Calva (FR) **G. Augustin-Normand, Mme E. Vidal**
125 **SADIA (FR)**, b f Teofilo (USA)—Sadiyna (FR) **H. H. Aga Khan**
126 **SAINT SIMEON (IRE)**, b g Le Havre (IRE)—Sahara Sonnet (USA) **G. Augustin-Normand**
127 **SARYSHAGANN (FR)**, gr c Iffraaj—Serasana **S. A. Aga Khan**
128 **SHAHNAZ**, b f Dark Angel (IRE)—Shamsa (FR) **S. A. Aga Khan**
129 **SHALANI (FR)**, b c High Chaparral (IRE)—Shamalana (IRE) **S. A. Aga Khan**
130 **SOME ROMANCE (IRE)**, b f Galileo (IRE)—Withorwithoutyou (IRE) **J. Allen**
131 **SOTTEVILLE (FR)**, b f Le Havre (IRE)—Sandsnow (IRE) **G. Augustin-Normand**
132 **STYLISH CAT**, ch f Gio Ponti (USA)—Buddha Lady **B. Lynam**
133 **TAAREEF (USA)**, ch c Kitten's Joy (USA)—Sacred Feather (USA) **Hamdan Al Maktoum**
134 **TAKADIYR (FR)**, b c Manduro (GER)—Takaniya (IRE) **S. A. Aga Khan**
135 **TCHAKOVKA (GER)**, ch f Lord of England (GER)—Ticinella (GER) **A. Jathiere**
136 **TELL ME NOW (IRE)**, b f Galileo (IRE)—Sing Softly (USA) **J. Allen**
137 **THE TURNING POINT (FR)**, b c Hurricane Cat (USA)—
L'ete (CHI) **J. Seche, J.-P. Barjon, Ec. La Vallee Martigny, J.-C. Rouget**

MR J. - C. ROUGET - Continued

138 **THEWAYYOUWISH (IRE)**, b c Thewayyouare (USA)—Faby Douglas (IRE) **C. Marzocco**
139 **VALDAYA (FR)**, b f Acclamation—Valima (FR) **H. H. Aga Khan**
140 **VOLKHOV (IRE)**, gr g Kendargent (FR)—Blue Blue Sea **A. Jathiere, G. Laboureau**
141 **VOLOSHKINE (FR)**, b c Sir Percy—Silver Miss **A. Jathiere**
142 **VOTKA (IRE)**, b f Rock of Gibraltar (IRE)—Conference (IRE) **A. Jathiere**
143 **WAR FLAG (USA)**, b f War Front (USA)—Black Speck (USA) **J. Allen**
144 **WESTADORA (IRE)**, b f Le Havre (IRE)—Stranded **Ecurie du Grand Chene**
145 **ZALAMEA (IRE)**, b c Lope de Vega (IRE)—Tanzania (IRE) **M. Zerolo, E. Puerari**
146 **ZELZAL**, b c Sea The Stars (IRE)—Olga Prekrasa (USA) **Al Shaqab Racing**
147 **ZGHORTA DANCE (FR)**, ch f Le Havre (IRE)—Ana Zghorta **Ecurie I. M. Fares**
148 **ZVALINSKA (FR)**, b f Sea The Stars (IRE)—Peinture Rose (USA) **A. Jathiere**

TWO-YEAR-OLDS

149 B c 5/3 Nathaniel (IRE)—Alabastrine (Green Desert (USA)) (147655) **Al Shaqab Racing**
150 **ANGEL BABY (FR)**, b f 21/4 Canford Cliffs (IRE)—Shabanou (FR) (Shamardal (USA)) (33222) **D.-Y. Treves**
151 **ASCOT ANGEL (FR)**, b c 9/2 Dark Angel (IRE)—Lady Ascot (FR) (Excellent Art) (33222) **Ecurie A. Caro**
152 **ASK ME ANOTHER (USA)**, ch f 1/4 Giant's Causeway (USA)—Storybook (UAE) (Halling (USA)) **J. Allen**
153 **BATTLE FLAG (USA)**, gr ro f 13/3 War Front (USA)—Photograph (USA) (Unbridled's Song (USA)) **J. Allen**
154 **BEAUDOUVILLE (FR)**, b f 6/4 Air Chief Marshal (IRE)—Langrune (FR) (Fasliyev (USA)) **G. Augustin-Normand**
155 **BLUESOLOGY (IRE)**, b f 30/3 Zoffany (IRE)—Khaleejiya (IRE) (Jeremy (USA)) (26578) **D.-Y. Treves**
156 **BOCCA DE LA VERITA (FR)**, gr f 9/3 Literato (FR)—Burghelarab (IRE) (Dubai Destination (USA))
       N. Saltiel, Ecurie La Vallee Martigny, T. Pien, Mme M. Leblan
157 **BRAMETOT (IRE)**, b c 24/2 Rajsaman (FR)—
       Morning Light (GER) (Law Society (USA)) **G. Augustin-Normand / Mme E. Vidal**
158 B f 19/5 Kyllachy—Brofalya (FR) (Fasliyev (USA)) **H. H. Aga Khan**
159 B c 10/3 Dalakhani (IRE)—Bryanka (FR) (Anabaa Blue) **H. H. Aga Khan**
160 B f 29/1 Frankel—Cassydora (Darshaan) **Andrew-James Smith**
161 **CHAPKA (FR)**, b f 7/2 Exchange Rate (USA)—Cheriearch (USA) (Arch (USA)) **A. Jathiere**
162 **CHILPERIC**, b c 14/3 Medicean—Mrs Mogg (Green Desert (USA)) (20000) **Ecurie M. Sardou**
163 **CHRISTMAS JOY (IRE)**, b br f 8/4 Galileo (IRE)—Wana Doo (USA) (Grand Slam (USA)) **J. Allen**
164 B f 23/3 Exceed And Excel (AUS)—Clarinda (FR) (Montjeu (IRE)) **H. H. Aga Khan**
165 **CORBON (FR)**, b c 31/1 Le Havre (IRE)—Sainte Adresse (Elusive City (USA)) **G. Augustin-Normand**
166 **CROPUS (FR)**, ch c 23/2 Le Havre (IRE)—Sabi Sabi (FR) (Orpen (USA)) **G. Augustin-Normand**
167 B c 1/1 Exceed And Excel (AUS)—Crystal Reef (Miss's Best (USA)) **Al Shaqab Racing**
168 **DAISY MILLER**, gr f 1/4 Smart Strike (CAN)—Gracie Square (USA) (Awesome Again (CAN)) **J. Allen**
169 **DARK AMERICAN (FR)**, gr c 1/1 Dark Angel (IRE)—
       Tres Americanqueen (FR) (American Post) (59062) **Ecurie A. Caro**
170 Ch c 13/3 Zamindar (USA)—Dayita (FR) (Dansili) **S. A. Aga Khan**
171 B f 6/3 Galileo (IRE)—
       Devoted To You (IRE) (Danehill Dancer (IRE)) (147655) **M. Tabor, Mrs S. Magnier, D. Smith**
172 **DORA BRUDER (FR)**, b f 14/4 Le Havre (IRE)—Fashion School (Shamardal (USA)) (59062) **D.-Y. Treves**
173 **DREAM AWHILE (USA)**, b f 29/4 War Front (USA)—Baroness Richter (USA) (Montjeu (IRE)) **J. Allen**
174 **EARL (FR)**, gr c 19/1 Peer Gynt (JPN)—
       Kanonette (FR) (Kaldoun (FR)) (31007) **J. Seche, J.P. Barjon, J.C. Rouget, J.P. Vallee Lambert**
175 **EIFFEL IN PARIS (FR)**, b c 28/2 Hurricane Cat (USA)—
       Miss Fine (FR) (Kaldoun (FR)) (23624) **Ecurie J.-L. Tepper / F. McNulty**
176 **EIGHTH AND I (USA)**, b f 19/4 Exchange Rate (USA)—
       Whipsaw City (FR) (Elusive City (USA)) **M. S. Schwartz Racing**
177 **ELDO BERE (FR)**, b c 1/3 Hurricane Cat (USA)—
       Former Probe (USA) (Dynaformer (USA)) (25839) **G. Augustin-Normand, SNC Regnier, Mme E de Seroux**
178 **ELVIS (FR)**, b c 8/4 Della Francesca (USA)—
       Fitness Queen (Gilded Time (USA)) (11812) **J.P. Barjon, J. Seche, J.C. Rouget, J.P. Vallee Lambert**
179 **EMPTY PAGES (IRE)**, b f 28/2 Holy Roman Emperor (IRE)—
       Just Little (FR) (Grand Slam (USA)) (22148) **M. Zerolo, Mme A. Gravereaux**
180 **ETTA (FR)**, b f 30/1 Hurricane Cat (USA)—Centralienne (USA) (Dixie Union (USA)) **F. McNulty**
181 **EVERLY (FR)**, b c 10/5 Hurricane Cat (USA)—
       Magic Cara (FR) (Akarad (FR)) **J.P. Vallee Lambert, F. McNulty, F. Nicolle**
182 **FAHADAN**, b c 22/2 Siyouni (FR)—Fraloga (IRE) (Grand Lodge (USA)) **H. H. Aga Khan**
183 **FEELIN ALRIGHT (IRE)**, b c 7/3 Clodovil (IRE)—Littlepromisedland (IRE) (Titus Livius (FR)) (45000) **D.-Y. Treves**
184 **FIRST OF SPRING (IRE)**, ch f 21/3 Galileo (IRE)—Homecoming Queen (IRE) (Holy Roman Emperor (IRE)) **J. Allen**
185 **FOLLOWME IN PARIS**, b f 4/3 So You Think (NZ)—Valera (IRE) (Ad Valorem (USA)) (81210) **Ecurie J.-L. Tepper**
186 **GALINKA**, b f 23/2 Soldier Hollow—Syllable (Halling (USA)) (44296) **A. Jathiere**
187 **GARANCE**, b f 1/1 Teofilo (IRE)—Germance (USA) (Silver Hawk (USA)) **Riviera Equine, Haras d'Etreham**
188 **GHURFAH**, ch f 13/4 Tamayuz—Indian Ink (IRE) (Indian Ridge) **Hamdan Al Maktoum**
189 Ch f 1/1 Dalakhani (IRE)—Grand Vadla (FR) (Grand Lodge (USA)) **H. H. Aga Khan**

MR J. - C. ROUGET - Continued

190 B c 9/2 Dubawi (IRE)—Harmonious (USA) (Dynaformer (USA)) **Al Shaqab Racing**

191 HEBAH (IRE), b f 31/3 Sea The Stars (IRE)—Lia (IRE) (Desert King (IRE)) **Hamdan Al Maktoum**

192 JEU CELEBRE (IRE), b c 8/4 Excelebration (IRE)—
Jeu de Vivre (IRE) (Montjeu (IRE)) (77519) **Ecurie A. Caro, G. Augustin-Normand**

193 B f 7/5 Acclamation—Kalidaha (IRE) (Cadeaux Genereux) **S. A. Aga Khan**

194 B f 18/3 Exceed And Excel (AUS)—Karasiyra (IRE) (Alhaarth (IRE)) **S. A. Aga Khan**

195 B f 19/1 Azamour (IRE)—Kastania (USA) (Gone West) **S. A. Aga Khan**

196 KESTILA, b f 5/5 Siyouni (FR)—Kerasha (FR) (Daylami (IRE)) **S. A. Aga Khan**

197 KHORODOV, b c 1/1 Dark Angel (IRE)—Blue Blue Sea (Galileo (IRE)) (66445) **A. Jathiere, Ecurie Skymarc Farm**

198 KHYROVA (IRE), b f 2/5 Canford Cliffs (IRE)—Excellent Girl (Exceed And Excel (AUS)) (88593) **A. Jathiere**

199 LA COCHERE (FR), b f 28/2 Le Havre (IRE)—Lady Meydan (FR) (American Post) **G. Augustin-Normand**

200 B c 1/4 Zoffany (IRE)—La Jalousie (FR) (Muhtathir) (110741) **Al Shaqab Racing**

201 LA MICHODIERE (IRE), gr f 19/1 Power—Lady Gray (IRE) (High Chaparral (IRE)) (18456) **Ecurie M. Sardou**

202 LAAMATHEEL, b c 30/3 New Approach (IRE)—Safwa (IRE) (Green Desert (USA)) **Hamdan Al Maktoum**

203 LADY'S BEAUTY (IRE), b f 13/2 Lope de Vega (IRE)—
Truth Beauty (IRE) (Dubai Destination (USA)) (60000) **Ecurie I. M. Fares**

204 LE CANDIDAT (FR), ro c 13/2 Literato (FR)—Creamcake (USA) (Mr Greeley (USA))
C. H. de Villeneuve, Ec. La Vallee Martigny, Ecurie du Loup, Mme M. Leblan

205 LION'S POWER, b f 2/4 Power—Calahorra (FR) (Soave (GER)) **O. Carli**

206 LONGROY (IRE), b c 22/3 Oasis Dream—Leaupartie (IRE) (Stormy River (FR)) **G. Augustin-Normand**

207 Ch f 16/3 Galileo (IRE)—Look At Me (IRE) (Danehill Dancer (USA)) **J. Allen**

208 LOUVE SAGE, b f 16/2 Sageburg (IRE)—
Louve Rouge (FR) (Gold Away (IRE)) (50203) **Ecurie A. Caro, G. Augustin-Normand**

209 B f 7/4 Redoute's Choice (AUS)—Mantilla (USA) (Gone West (USA)) (61050) **Ecurie des Charmes**

210 MARKAZI, gr c 9/4 Dark Angel (IRE)—Marasima (IRE) (Barathea (IRE)) **S. A. Aga Khan**

211 MASHAWAAR, b c 12/3 Dansili—
Alsace Lorraine (IRE) (Giant's Causeway (USA)) (260000) **Hamdan Al Maktoum**

212 MATHONVILLE (FR), b f 12/2 Rajsaman (FR)—
Tunis (FR) (Dubai Destination (USA)) (10335) **G. Augustin-Normand, Mme E. Vidal**

213 B c 1/3 Galileo (IRE)—
Melito (AUS) (Redoute's Choice (AUS)) **M. Tabor, Mrs S. Magnier, D. Smith, China Horse**

214 MICHIGAN (USA), ch c 22/2 Galileo (IRE)—I'm So Excited (USA) (Street Cry (IRE)) (65000) **J. Allen**

215 MIDNIGHT WATCH, b f 1/2 Harbour Watch (IRE)—Midnight M (Green Desert (USA)) (55000) **Ecurie I. M. Fares**

216 MILLE PIEDS, b c 26/2 Zoffany (IRE)—Providanza (FR) (Okawango (USA)) (55370) **Ecurie J.-L. Tepper**

217 B c 1/1 Zoffany (IRE)—Miryale (FR) (Anabaa (USA)) (95976) **Al Shaqab Racing**

218 Ch c 7/4 More Than Ready (USA)—Miss Cato (Notnowcato) (110741) **Al Shaqab Racing**

219 MUTANAASEB (USA), ch c 2/4 Kitten's Joy (USA)—
Queen's Causeway (USA) (Giant's Causeway (USA)) (100000) **Hamdan Al Maktoum**

220 NEGUEV (IRE), b c 12/3 So You Think (NZ)—Lady Bering (Bering) (88593) **D.-Y. Treves**

221 NEVER FALL AGAIN, gr c 15/2 Never On Sunday (FR)—
Masseria (FR) (Della Francesca (USA)) (29531) **D.-Y. Treves**

222 ONCLE FERNAND, b c 14/2 Aqlaam—Mixfeeling (IRE) (Red Ransom (USA)) (22148) **D.-Y. Treves**

223 ONTHEMOONAGAIN, b f 1/1 Cape Cross (IRE)—
Ma Preference (FR) (American Post) (40605) **Ecurie J.-L. Tepper, G. Augustin-Normand**

224 PARTNER IN CRIME, ch c 1/1 Dutch Art—Peach Pearl (Invincible Spirit (IRE)) (77519) **P. Segalot**

225 PAZEER, b c 2/3 Siyouni (FR)—Parandeh (FR) (Kahyasi) **H. H. Aga Khan**

226 B c 21/3 Fastnet Rock (AUS)—Penny's Gold (Kingmambo (USA)) **OTI Management, Mrs S. Magnier**

227 PLEIN SOLEIL (IRE), ch c 11/3 Shamardal (USA)—
Espirita (FR) (Iffraaj) (92284) **Ecurie J.-L. Tepper, F. McNulty**

228 PREMIERE GACHETTE (IRE), b f 22/3 Excelebration (IRE)—Time Pressure (Montjeu (IRE)) (51679) **D.-Y. Treves**

229 PRETTY STRANGE (IRE), b f 10/3 Siyouni (FR)—Shanghai Noon (FR) (Turtle Bowl (IRE)) (59062) **D.-Y. Treves**

230 PRINCESS KAINE (IRE), b f 14/3 Iffraaj—Kandykaine (IRE) (Montjeu (IRE)) (31007) **D.-Y. Treves**

231 QUBTAAN, b c 7/3 Oasis Dream—Shaleela (IRE) (Galileo (IRE)) **Hamdan Al Maktoum**

232 RELIEF QUEST (IRE), b f 22/3 Iffraaj—Supreme Quest (Exceed And Excel (AUS)) (80000) **Ecurie I. M. Fares**

233 REPRESAILLES (IRE), b f 24/5 Canford Cliffs (IRE)—
Pretty Pebble (IRE) (Cape Cross (IRE)) (19195) **Ecurie M. Sardou**

234 RHAAGHIB, ch c 25/2 Dutch Art—Safe House (IRE) (Exceed And Excel (AUS)) (118000) **Hamdan Al Maktoum**

235 RONCEY (FR), b c 1/1 Pivotal—Mixed Intention (IRE) (Elusive City (USA)) **G. Augustin-Normand**

236 ROUBAIX (IRE), b f 10/3 Acclamation—Rising Wind (IRE) (Shirocco (GER)) (118124) **Ecurie des Monceaux**

237 RYTHMIQUE (IRE), b f 6/3 Casamento (IRE)—
Reclamation (FR) (Red Ransom (USA)) (38390) **Ecurie de Monceaux**

238 B f 1/1 Zamindar (USA)—Sagalina (IRE) (Linamix (FR)) **H. H. Aga Khan**

239 SAMBA PA TI (IRE), b f 9/3 Hat Trick (JPN)—
Amourette (FR) (Halling (USA)) (22148) **J.P. Barjon, J. Seche, J.C. Rouget, J.P. Vallee Lambert**

240 B c 1/1 Galileo (IRE)—Seeharn (IRE) (Pivotal) **Al Shaqab Racing**

MR J. - C. ROUGET - Continued

241 B c 24/3 Medicean—Shamsa (FR) (Selkirk (USA)) **S. A. Aga Khan**
242 B f 3/2 Sea The Stars (IRE)—Sindirana (IRE) (Kalanisi (IRE)) **S. A. Aga Khan**
243 **SORQUAINVILLE,** b f 29/4 Martaline—Saffarona (Red Ransom (USA)) (23624) **G. Augustin-Normand**
244 **SUNITA (FR),** b f 12/4 Motivator—Serasana (Red Ransom (USA)) **S. A. Aga Khan**
245 **SUPERMENSCH,** b c 1/1 Canford Cliffs (IRE)—
    Spring Morning (FR) (Ashkalani (IRE)) (118124) **D.-Y. Treves, Ecurie J.-L. Tepper, F. McNulty**
246 **TEAM OF TEAMS,** gr f 4/4 Elusive Quality (USA)—Teammate (USA) (A P Indy (USA)) **J. Allen**
247 **TEGEREK (FR),** b c 28/3 Mount Nelson—Takaniya (IRE) (Rainbow Quest (USA)) **S. A. Aga Khan**
248 **TERENURE (IRE),** b f 30/3 Casamento (IRE)—
    Ten Commandments (IRE) (Key of Luck (USA)) (10335) **Ecurie A. Caro**
249 **THE BOXER,** gr c 28/3 Martaline—Ealore (FR) (Kendor (FR)) (59062) **D.-Y. Treves**
250 **TROARN,** b f 24/3 Wootton Bassett—
    Darkova (FR) (Maria's Mon (USA)) (81210) **G. Augustin-Normand, Ecurie A. Caro**
251 **TWIZZLE,** b c 8/4 Palace Episode (USA)—Green Delight (IRE) (Green Desert (USA)) (38390) **O. Carli**
252 B c 28/1 Azamour (IRE)—Vaderana (FR) (Monsun (GER)) **H. H. Aga Khan**
253 **VADYSKA (IRE),** b f 27/4 So You Think (NZ)—Rockatella (IRE) (Rock of Gibraltar (IRE)) (73827) **A. Jathiere**
254 **VENON (IRE),** b c 18/3 Le Havre (FR)—Vauville (IRE) (Invincible Spirit (IRE)) **G. Augustin-Normand**
255 **VOILOUP (IRE),** b f 8/3 So You Think (NZ)—
    Foolish Ambition (GER) (Danehill Dancer (IRE)) (31007) **Ecurie du Loup**
256 **VUE DU CIEL,** b f 3/4 Canford Cliffs (IRE)—Al Ribh (USA) (A P Indy (USA)) (62753) **P. Segalot**
257 **WALTZ KEY,** ro f 1/1 Henrythenavigator (USA)—
    Lia Waltz (FR) (Linamix (FR)) **Ec. La Vallee Matigny, Ecurie du Loup, F&F Horses**
258 **WAR MINISTER (IRE),** b c 20/3 Iffraaj—Core Element (Consolidator (USA)) (66445) **D.-Y. Treves**
259 **WESSEX (FR),** ch c 1/1 Mount Nelson—Atlanda (FR) (Hernando (FR)) (34699) **Ecurie du Loup, J.-P. Elissalt**
260 **WHAT'S IN A KISS (IRE),** ch f 15/1 Fast Company (IRE)—
    Ser Cecil's Girl (IRE) (Thunder Gulch (USA)) (11074) **C. Lauffer, J.C. Rouget**
261 **WHOLE WORLD (FR),** b c 27/3 Rajsaman (FR)—
    Salon Musique (GER) (Black Sam Bellamy (IRE)) (20671) **P. Beziat, Mme C. Taffet**
262 **YAABALADY (USA),** b f 27/3 Smart Strike (CAN)—Hatheer (USA) (Storm Cat (USA)) **Hamdan Al Maktoum**
263 B c 1/3 Azamour (IRE)—Zarebiya (IRE) (Galileo (IRE)) **S. A. Aga Khan**
264 B f 25/4 Holy Roman Emperor (IRE)—Zewara (BEL) (Alhaarth (IRE)) **S. A. Aga Khan**
265 **ZGHORTA RIDE,** gr f 10/4 Rajsaman (FR)—Ana Zghorta (Anabaa (USA)) (27316) **Ecurie I. M. Fares**

Assistant Trainers Jean Bernard Roth, Jean Rene Dubosq

Jockey (flat): Jean-Bernard Eyquem, Ioritz Mendizabal, Christophe Soumillon.

---

522 **MR RICHARD ROWE, Pulborough**
Postal: **Ashleigh House Stables, Sullington Lane, Storrington, Pulborough, West Sussex, RH20 4AE**
Contacts: **PHONE (01903) 742871 MOBILE (07831) 345636**
E-MAIL r.rowe.racing@virgin.net WEBSITE www.richardrowe-racing.co.uk

1 **CANADIAN DIAMOND (IRE),** 9, ch g Halling (USA)—Six Nations (USA) **Nicholls Family**
2 **DARK FLAME (IRE),** 7, b g Gold Well—Glorys Flame (IRE) **The Encore Partnership III**
3 **FULL OF MISCHIEF (IRE),** 8, ch m Classic Cliche—Drama Chick **The Chicanery Partnership**
4 **GRACE AND FORTUNE,** 9, b m Grape Tree Road—Nouveau Cheval
5 **LIKE SULLY (IRE),** 8, b br g Presenting—Swing Into Action (IRE) **Winterfields Farm Ltd**
6 **MEDIATE,** 5, ch g New Approach (IRE)—Miss Prim **Mr E. Wilson**
7 **PASTORAL DANCER,** 8, b g Pastoral Pursuits—Dancing Flame **R. Rowe**
8 **PASTORAL JET,** 8, b br h Pastoral Pursuits—Genteel (IRE) **R. Rowe**
9 **QUINLANDIO (IRE),** 6, b g Thousand Words—La Shalak (IRE) **Mr T. M. Clarke**
10 **RAIL DANCER,** 4, b g Rail Link—Mara Dancer **Mr M. R. Cashmore**
11 **REMEMBER FOREVER (IRE),** 6, b g Indian River (FR)—Running Wild (IRE)
12 **SECRET GLANCE,** 4, b g Sakhee's Secret—Look Here's Dee **Mrs S. T. M. McCarthy**
13 **SIR HUBERT,** 6, b g Multiplex—Lacounsel (FR) **Capt Adrian Pratt & Friends**
14 **STRANGE BIRD (IRE),** 11, b m Revoque (IRE)—Ethel's Bay (IRE) **Richard Rowe Racing Partnership**
15 **SWEET'N'CHIC (IRE),** 6, bm Midnight Legend—Sweetbitter (FR) **The Chicanery Partnership**
16 **WHIP UP A FRENZY (IRE),** 4, b g Vale of York (IRE)—Answer Do **Mr E. Wilson**

THREE-YEAR-OLDS

17 **FISHERGATE,** b g Pastoral Pursuits—Miss Meggy **Mr E. Wilson**

MR RICHARD ROWE - Continued

Other Owners: Mr C. J. Baldwin, Mr D. M. Bradshaw, Mrs H. C. G. Butcher, Mr N. S. Campbell, Mrs J. Case, Mrs J. E. Debenham, Mr C. B. Hatch, Mrs E. Nicholls, Mr R. Nicholls, Capt A. Pratt, T. W. Wellard.

---

523 MISS MANDY ROWLAND, Lower Blidworth
Postal: **Kirkfields, Calverton Road, Lower Blidworth, Nottingham, Nottinghamshire, NG21 0NW**
Contacts: **PHONE** (01623) 794831 **MOBILE** (07768) 224666
E-MAIL kirkfieldsriding@hotmail.co.uk

1 **CHINA EXCELS**, 9, b g Exceed And Excel (AUS)—China Beauty **Miss M. E. Rowland**
2 **MIXED MESSAGE (IRE)**, 6, b m Kodiac—Berenica (IRE) **W. I. Bloomfield**
3 **PIPERS PIPING (IRE)**, 10, b g Noverre (USA)—Monarchy (USA) **Miss M. E. Rowland**
4 **ROXY MADAM**, 7, br m Generous (IRE)—Masouri Sana (IRE) **Miss M. E. Rowland**

Assistant Trainer: Sarah Mitchel

Jockey (flat): Adam Kirby, Jimmy Quinn. **Jockey (NH):** Adam Pogson. **Apprentice:** Rob Hornby.

---

524 MR A. DE ROYER-DUPRE, Chantilly
Postal: **3 Chemin des Aigles, 60500 Chantilly, France**
Contacts: **PHONE** (0033) 34458 0303 **MOBILE** (0033) 6702 32901
E-MAIL de-royer-dupre@wanadoo.fr

1 **ALMIYR (FR)**, 4, gr c Dubawi (IRE)—Alnamara (FR) **H. H. Aga Khan**
2 **ASHIRA (FR)**, 4, b f Rock of Gibraltar (IRE)—Ashalina (FR) **Antoine Fontaine**
3 **DARIYAN (FR)**, 4, b c Shamardal (USA)—Daryakana (FR) **S. A. Aga Khan**
4 **DOUNYAPOUR (IRE)**, 20, b h Lahib (USA)—Dounya (USA) **H. H. Aga Khan**
5 **GRACIOUSLY**, 5, b m Shamardal (USA)—Gracefully (IRE) **Marquise de Moratalla**
6 **KARAKTAR (IRE)**, 4, b c High Chaparral (IRE)—Karawana (IRE) **S. A. Aga Khan**
7 **MARUNOUCHI (IRE)**, 4, ch f Peintre Celebre (USA)—Morning Line (FR) **Wildenstein Stables Limited**
8 **ONE FOOT IN HEAVEN (IRE)**, 4, b c Fastnet Rock (AUS)—Pride (FR) **Fair Salinia Ltd**
9 **PERLE RARE (USA)**, 4, ch f Distorted Humor (USA)—Peinture Rare (IRE) **Wildenstein Stables Limited**
10 **PRUDENTE (FR)**, 4, b f Dansili—Platonic **Ecurie des Monceaux, Ecurie Skymarc Farm**
11 **REMAKE**, 4, b f Dansili—Reggane **SCAG Haras de la Perelle**
12 **SANDY'S CHOICE**, 5, b m Footstepsinthesand—Zafonia (FR) **M. O. Bryant**
13 **SAYANA (FR)**, 4, b f Galileo (IRE)—Sichilla (IRE) **H. H. Aga Khan**
14 **SECRETARIAT HUMOR (USA)**, 4, ch f Distorted Humor (USA)—Secretariat's Soul (IRE) **Charles E. Fipke**
15 **SULTANA GOLD**, 4, b f Sea The Stars (IRE)—Sudarynya (IRE) **Viktor Timoshenko**
16 **SYLVANES (IRE)**, 4, b f Teofilo (IRE)—Sierra Slew **AB Ascot**
17 **VAZIRABAD (FR)**, 4, b g Manduro (GER)—Visorama (IRE) **H. H. Aga Khan**
18 **VERMONT (IRE)**, 6, b g Muhtathir—Venetian Beauty **Anton Krauliger**
19 **ZARKAR (FR)**, 4, b c Galileo (IRE)—Zarkava (IRE) **S. A. Aga Khan**

THREE-YEAR-OLDS

20 **ANDREA MANTEGNA (USA)**, ch c Giant's Causeway (USA)—
Adventure Seeker (FR) **Wildenstein Stables Limited**
21 **ASHIQANA (FR)**, b br f Giant's Causeway (USA)—Ashiyla (FR) **S. A. Aga Khan**
22 **ASHKOUL (FR)**, b c Tamayuz—Asharna (IRE) **S. A. Aga Khan**
23 **ASTERINA**, ch f Dalakhani (IRE)—Altamira **Wildenstein Stables Limited**
24 **BARHANPOUR (FR)**, b c Raven's Pass (USA)—Balankiya (IRE) **S. A. Aga Khan**
25 **BESHARA (FR)**, b f Cape Cross (IRE)—Bekhara (IRE) **S. A. Aga Khan**
26 **BOLD EMPEROR (IRE)**, b c Galileo (IRE)—Bastet (IRE) **Wildenstein Stables Limited**
27 **BRYZYNA (FR)**, b f Sinndar (IRE)—Brofalya (FR) **H. H. Aga Khan**
28 **CHARISMATIC MAN (IRE)**, b c Dalakhani (IRE)—
On Fair Stage (IRE) **Whitehaven Investments Pty Ltd, AB Ascot, Salinity Service AB**
29 **CIACONA (IRE)**, b f Oasis Dream—Caesarine (FR) **SCAG Haras de la Perelle**
30 **COSSONAY**, b f Pivotal—Celenza (FR) **SCAG Haras de la Perelle**
31 **DALDIYNA (FR)**, b f Dansili—Daltama (FR) **S. A. Aga Khan**
32 **DALMENYA (IRE)**, b f Authorized (IRE)—Daltaya (FR) **S. A. Aga Khan**
33 **DALSHAND (FR)**, ch c New Approach (IRE)—Daltaiyma (IRE) **S. A. Aga Khan**
34 **DARABAD (FR)**, b c Dansili—Darykana (FR) **S. A. Aga Khan**
35 **DARINJA (FR)**, b f Shamardal (USA)—Darjana (IRE) **Princess Z. P. Aga Khan**

MR A. DE ROYER-DUPRE - Continued

36 **DARIYBA (FR)**, b f Monsun (GER)—Daryaba (IRE) **S. A. Aga Khan**
37 **DEREMAH (USA)**, b br f More Than Ready (USA)—Darma (FR) **S. A. Aga Khan**
38 **DIMANIYA (FR)**, ch f Dalakhani (IRE)—Diampilina (FR) **H. H. Aga Khan**
39 **DOURDANA (FR)**, gr f Exceed And Excel (AUS)—Dardania **S. A. Aga Khan**
40 **ERETAN (FR)**, b c Rock of Gibraltar (IRE)—Erdiyna (IRE) **S. A. Aga Khan**
41 **GALILEO'S SPEAR (FR)**, b c Galileo (IRE)—Lady Shakespeare (USA) **Charles E. Fipke**
42 **GARALIYA (IRE)**, br f New Approach (IRE)—Grand Vadla (FR) **H. H. Aga Khan**
43 **LACHARES (IRE)**, ch c Manduro (GER)—Louve Imperiale (USA) **Wildenstein Stables Limited**
44 **LAILOMA (FR)**, ch f Teofilo (IRE)—Ludiana (FR) **H. H. Aga Khan**
45 **LOOK AT THAT (FR)**, b f Monsun (GER)—Peaceful Love (GER) **Al Shahania Stud**
46 **LYRICAL DUNES**, b f Sea The Stars (IRE)—Our Queen of Kings **Al Shahania Stud**
47 **MAJESTIC (FR)**, b c King's Best (USA)—Gamma (FR) **Bloomsbury Stud**
48 **MILKIPOUR (FR)**, b c Azamour (IRE)—Mintly Fresh (USA) **S. A. Aga Khan**
49 **MINAMYA (FR)**, gr f Makfi—Minatlya (FR) **H. H. Aga Khan**
50 **OTWO (USA)**, b c Medaglia d'oro (USA)—Vacare (USA) **Al Shahania Stud**
51 **PAINTER'S MUSE**, b f Smart Strike (CAN)—Peinture Rare (IRE) **Ecurie Wildenstein**
52 **PANDORA'S STAR (IRE)**, ch f Smart Strike (CAN)—Parade Militaire (IRE) **Wildenstein Stables Limited**
53 **QUERETARA (IRE)**, b f Exceed And Excel (AUS)—Quezon Sun (GER) **SCAG Haras de la Perelle**
54 **RAGAZZA D'ORO (IRE)**, gr f Dalakhani (IRE)—Aquarelle d'or **Ron Finemore**
55 **RASHKANI (FR)**, b c Pivotal—Radiyya (IRE) **H. H. Aga Khan**
56 **REMEMBER THE MAN (IRE)**, b c Dalakhani (IRE)—
    Perfect Hedge **Whitehaven Investments Pty Ltd, Fair Salinia Ltd**
57 **ROBIANO (IRE)**, b c Dubawi (IRE)—Reggane **San Paolo Agri Stud Srl, SCAG Haras de la Perelle**
58 **ROSHANARA (FR)**, b f Sea The Stars (IRE)—Rosawa (FR) **H. H. Aga Khan**
59 **ROSVANA (FR)**, b f Dansili—Rosanara (FR) **H. H. Aga Khan**
60 **SARZAMEEN (FR)**, b f Siyouni (FR)—Sarlisa (FR) **S. A. Aga Khan**
61 **SAYED (FR)**, b br c Stormy Atlantic (USA)—Saliyna (FR) **H. H. Aga Khan**
62 **SHAHMEEN (FR)**, b f Shamardal (USA)—Shamanova (IRE) **S. A. Aga Khan**
63 **SHAMSHAD (FR)**, b c Sea The Stars (IRE)—Shamakiya (IRE) **S. A. Aga Khan**
64 **SHEHIYR (FR)**, b c Acclamation—Shemiyla (FR) **S. A. Aga Khan**
65 **SHUMAILA (FR)**, b f Azamour (IRE)—Shemima **S. A. Aga Khan**
66 **SIMAVIYA (IRE)**, b f Zamindar (USA)—Simawa (IRE) **S. A. Aga Khan**
67 **SWERTIA**, ch f Pivotal—Sanjida (IRE) **SCAG Haras de la Perelle**
68 **TASHARMAN (FR)**, ch c Siyouni (FR)—Tashiriya (IRE) **S. A. Aga Khan**
69 **VALARIK (FR)**, ch c Rock of Gibraltar (IRE)—Valasyra (FR) **H. H. Aga Khan**
70 **VARDAK (FR)**, b c Dalakhani (IRE)—Vadiya (FR) **S. A. Aga Khan**
71 **VEDEVANI (FR)**, b c Dubawi (IRE)—Vadawina (FR) **H. H. Aga Khan**
72 **VIA VENETO (FR)**, b f Lawman (FR)—Via Saleria (IRE) **Salinity Service AB**
73 **ZAIBA (FR)**, b f King's Best (USA)—Zaidiyna (FR) **S. A. Aga Khan**
74 **ZARAK (FR)**, b c Dubawi (IRE)—Zarkava (IRE) **S. A. Aga Khan**
75 **ZARIYMA (IRE)**, b f Authorized (IRE)—Zariziyna (IRE) **S. A. Aga Khan**
76 **ZARKATALA (IRE)**, b f Desert Style (IRE)—Zarkalia (IRE) **S. A. Aga Khan**
77 **ZAYVA (FR)**, ch f Raven's Pass (USA)—Zayanida (FR) **S. A. Aga Khan**

TWO-YEAR-OLDS

78 **ACHIBUENO (FR)**, b c 27/4 Dansili—Altamira (Peintre Celebre (USA)) **Wildenstein Stables Limited**
79 **AMBEREEN (FR)**, b f 1/4 Exceed And Excel (AUS)—Alnamara (FR) (Linamix (FR)) **H. H. Aga Khan**
80 **ANDIRA (USA)**, ch f 24/1 Elusive Quality (USA)—
    Andromeda Galaxy (FR) (Peintre Celebre (USA)) **Ecurie Wildenstein**
81 **ARACA (FR)**, b f 26/3 Elusive Quality (USA)—Adventure Seeker (FR) (Bering) **Ecurie Wildenstein**
82 **ARJAL (FR)**, b c 21/1 Sinndar (IRE)—Artanava (Bahri) (Darshaan) **H. H. Aga Khan**
83 **ASHUTOR (FR)**, gr c 29/1 Redoute's Choice (AUS)—Ashalanda (FR) (Linamix (FR)) **H. H. Aga Khan**
84 **BAIYOUNA (FR)**, b f 20/3 Sea The Stars (IRE)—Balankiya (IRE) (Darshaan) **S. A. Aga Khan**
85 B f 15/3 Dalakhani (IRE)—Candara (FR) (Barathea (IRE)) **H. H. Aga Khan**
86 B f 17/2 Sinndar (IRE)—Clariyn (FR) (Acclamation) **H. H. Aga Khan**
87 B c 18/5 Holy Roman Emperor (IRE)—Daltaiyma (IRE) (Doyoun) **S. A. Aga Khan**
88 Gr f 2/5 Acclamation—Dardania (Dalakhani (IRE)) **S. A. Aga Khan**
89 **DJAMBA (FR)**, gr f 15/3 Dalakhani (IRE)—Darjana (IRE) (Invincible Spirit (IRE)) **Princess Z. P. Aga Khan**
90 **DOLIANOVA (FR)**, b f 1/3 Rock of Gibraltar (IRE)—Daltama (IRE) (Indian Ridge) **S. A. Aga Khan**
91 **LAMBARI (FR)**, b f 1/1 Medicean—Louve Imperiale (USA) (Giant's Causeway (USA)) **Ecurie Wildenstein**
92 **LAYLIYA (FR)**, ch f 14/4 Raven's Pass (USA)—Ludiana (FR) (Dalakhani (IRE)) **H. H. Aga Khan**
93 **MINDENA (IRE)**, ch f 24/2 Giant's Causeway (USA)—
    Mandesha (FR) (Desert Style (IRE)) **Princess Z. P. Aga Khan**
94 **MOCAMBO (FR)**, b c 22/2 High Chaparral (IRE)—Morning Line (FR) (Anabaa (USA)) **Ecurie Wildenstein**
95 **PAVINI (FR)**, b f 27/2 Dubawi (IRE)—Peinture Rare (IRE) (Sadler's Wells (USA)) **Ecurie Wildenstein**

MR A. DE ROYER-DUPRE - Continued

96 **PRAIRIE BLOSSOM (FR)**, ch f 2/4 Dalakhani (IRE)—Prairie Runner (IRE) (Arazi (USA)) **Ecurie Wildenstein**
97 **PUELO (FR)**, b c 9/4 Sinndar (IRE)—Premiere Danseuse (Gold Away (IRE)) **Ecurie Wildenstein**
98 B c 22/2 Sinndar (IRE)—Raiysina (Zamindar (USA)) **S. A. Aga Khan**
99 **RESHOUN (FR)**, b c 24/4 Shamardal (USA)—Radiyya (IRE) (Sinndar (IRE)) **S. A. Aga Khan**
100 **RONDONIA (IRE)**, b f 3/4 Raven's Pass (USA)—Raydiya (IRE) (Marju (IRE)) **S. A. Aga Khan**
101 B c 5/5 Redoute's Choice (AUS)—Sagawara (Shamardal (USA)) **H. H. Aga Khan**
102 **SAJJAD (FR)**, b c 15/2 Siyouni (FR)—Sage Et Jolie (Linamix (FR)) **H. H. Aga Khan**
103 B f 15/3 Harlan's Holiday (USA)—Saliyna (FR) (Linamix (FR)) **H. H. Aga Khan**
104 B c 22/2 Cape Cross (IRE)—Sanaya (IRE) (Barathea (IRE)) **S. A. Aga Khan**
105 **SAROSH (FR)**, b c 5/3 Sea The Stars (IRE)—Sarlisa (FR) (Rainbow Quest (USA)) **S. A. Aga Khan**
106 **SHAHINDA (FR)**, b f 31/3 Sea The Stars (IRE)—Shamanova (IRE) (Danehill Dancer (IRE)) **S. A. Aga Khan**
107 B c 19/2 Dalakhani (IRE)—Shamiyra (FR) (Medicean) **S. A. Aga Khan**
108 **SHEERLAR (FR)**, ch c 20/4 Shamardal (USA)—Shemiyla (FR) (Dalakhani (IRE)) **S. A. Aga Khan**
109 **SIKANDARI (FR)**, b c 17/2 Sea The Stars (IRE)—Sichilla (IRE) (Danehill (USA)) **H. H. Aga Khan**
110 **TRIPLICATE (FR)**, b f 23/2 Lawman (FR)—Gamma (FR) (Sadler's Wells (USA)) **Bloomsbury Stud**
111 B c 9/3 Azamour (FR)—Vadapolina (FR) (Trempolino (USA)) **H. H. Aga Khan**
112 B f 26/3 Exceed And Excel (AUS)—Valasyra (FR) (Sinndar (IRE)) **S. A. Aga Khan**
113 B c 30/1 Sinndar (IRE)—Visinova (FR) (Anabaa (USA)) **H. H. Aga Khan**
114 **ZAHID (FR)**, b c 5/5 Cape Cross (IRE)—Zaidiyna (FR) (Azamour (IRE)) **S. A. Aga Khan**
115 B f 29/5 New Approach (IRE)—Zarkasha (IRE) (Kahyasi) **S. A. Aga Khan**
116 **ZARMITAN (FR)**, b c 10/3 Redoute's Choice (AUS)—Zarkava (IRE) (Zamindar (USA)) **S. A. Aga Khan**
117 **ZEYZOUN (FR)**, b c 10/3 Excelebration (IRE)—Zayanida (IRE) (King's Best (USA)) **S. A. Aga Khan**

Assistant Trainers: Laurent Metais, Pierre Groualle

Jockey (flat): Alexis Badel, Mickael Berto, Christophe Soumillon.

---

525 MS LUCINDA RUSSELL, Kinross
Postal: **Arlary House Stables, Milnathort, Kinross, Tayside, KY13 9SJ**
Contacts: **PHONE** (01577) 865512 **FAX** (01577) 861171 **MOBILE** (07970) 645261
E-MAIL lucinda@arlary.fsnet.co.uk WEBSITE www.lucindarussell.com

1 4, B g Kalanisi (IRE)—Aboo Who (IRE) **Mrs E. Conetta**
2 **ALIZEE DE JANEIRO (FR)**, 6, b m Network (GER)—Katana (GER) **Ms D. Thomson**
3 **BACK TO BRACKA (IRE)**, 9, b g Rudimentary (USA)—
 Martha's Glimpse (IRE) **Mr Peter J S Russell & Mr John J Murray**
4 **BADGER FOOT (IRE)**, 11, br g Beneficial—Droim Alton Gale (IRE) **P. J. S. Russell**
5 **BALLYBEN (IRE)**, 8, ch g Beneficial—I'm Maggy (NZ) **Drew & Ailsa Russell**
6 **BALLYBILL (IRE)**, 6, ch g Presenting—Corrieann (IRE) **Drew & Ailsa Russell**
7 **BALLYCOOL (IRE)**, 9, b g Helissio (FR)—Carnoustie (USA) **Mr & Mrs T. P. Winnell**
8 **BESCOT SPRINGS (IRE)**, 11, b g Saddlers' Hall (IRE)—Silver Glen (IRE) **Kelso Lowflyers & Mr PJS Russell**
9 **BIG RIVER (IRE)**, 6, b g Milan—Call Kate (IRE) **Two Black Labs**
10 **BLENHEIM BROOK (IRE)**, 11, br g Alderbrook—Blenheim Blinder (IRE) **The County Set Three**
11 **BOLD SIR BRIAN (IRE)**, 10, b g Brian Boru—Black Queen (IRE) **Mr A R Trotter & Peter J S Russell**
12 **CASTLELAWN (IRE)**, 9, b g Runyon (IRE)—Pure Magic (IRE) **J. R. Adam**
13 **CATCHTHEMOONLIGHT**, 8, b m Generous (IRE)—Moon Catcher (IRE) **Dig In Racing**
14 **CHASSEUR DE TETE (FR)**, 4, b br g Coastal Path—Escomptee (FR) **Skye Larks**
15 **CLONDAW KNIGHT (IRE)**, 8, b g Heron Island (IRE)—
 Sarah Supreme (IRE) **Mr & Mrs Raymond Anderson Green**
16 **COBAJAYISLAND (IRE)**, 8, b g Heron Island (IRE)—Shinora (IRE) **Mrs L. Maclennan**
17 **DAYTRIPPER**, 5, gr m Daylami (IRE)—Stravaigin **Drew & Ailsa Russell**
18 **DROP A GEAR (IRE)**, 6, b g Presenting—Indian Love (FR) **P. J. S. Russell**
19 **EGRET (IRE)**, 6, b g Definite Article—Bright Sprite (IRE) **Mrs S Russell & A M Russell**
20 **FARRAGON (IRE)**, 6, b g Marienbard (IRE)—Oath of Allegiance (IRE) **Mrs S Russell & A M Russell**
21 **FIFTEEN KINGS (IRE)**, 6, b g King's Theatre—Mistletoeandwine (IRE) **E. Bruce**
22 **FINAL ASSAULT (IRE)**, 7, b br g Beneficial—Last Campaign (IRE) **Mrs S Russell & A M Russell**
23 **GAYE FLIER (IRE)**, 5, b m Milan—Gaye Preskina (IRE) **J. R. Adam**
24 **GREEN FLAG (IRE)**, 9, b g Milan—Erin Go Brea (IRE) **J. R. Adam**
25 **GREXIT (IRE)**, 5, b g Oratorio (IRE)—Baboosh (IRE) **P. J. S. Russell**
26 **HAPPY RIVER (IRE)**, 9, b g Pierre—Breezy River (IRE) **BSN Racing**
27 **HAUL US IN (IRE)**, 4, b f Kalanisi (IRE)—Shuilan (IRE) **Mr & Mrs J. Morrison-Bell**
28 **IMJOEKING (IRE)**, 9, b g Amilynx (FR)—Go Franky (IRE) **Mr K. Alexander**
29 **ISLAND CONFUSION (IRE)**, 8, b g Heron Island (IRE)—Anshan Gail (IRE) **Mrs A. E. Giles**
30 **ISLAND HEIGHTS (IRE)**, 7, b g Heron Island (IRE)—La Reina (IRE) **Mr G. R. McGladery**

MS LUCINDA RUSSELL - Continued

31 **ITSTIMEFORAPINT (IRE)**, 8, b g Portrait Gallery (IRE)—Executive Pearl (IRE) **IMEJ Racing**
32 **JACK STEEL (IRE)**, 6, b g Craigsteel—Wake Me Gently (IRE) **J. P. McManus**
33 **KAI BROON (IRE)**, 9, b g Marju (IRE)—Restiv Star (FR) **John R. Adam & Sons Ltd**
34 **KILBREE CHIEF (IRE)**, 8, b g Dr Massini (IRE)—Lame Excuse (IRE) **J. R. Adam**
35 **KINGS FOLLY (IRE)**, 8, b g Dushyantor (USA)—Beltane Queen (IRE) **Mrs M. C. Coltman**
36 **KRIS CROSS (IRE)**, 9, ch g Kris Kin (USA)—Perfidia **Ms D. Thomson**
37 **KUMBESHWAR**, 9, b g Doyen (IRE)—Camp Fire (IRE) **P. J. S. Russell**
38 **LE FRANK (IRE)**, 4, b g King's Theatre (IRE)—Dream Lass (IRE) **S. M. Smith**
39 **LONE FOOT LADDIE (IRE)**, 7, b g Red Clubs (IRE)—Alexander Phantom (IRE) **G. F. Bear**
40 **LORD OF DRUMS (IRE)**, 10, b g Beat of Drums—Treat A Lady (IRE) **The Ormello Way**
41 **MAKE IT HAPPEN (IRE)**, 7, b g Saffron Walden (FR)—Kelpie (IRE) **Wright Mitchell Stobart**
42 **MARAWEH (IRE)**, 6, b g Muhtathir—Itqaan (USA) **Tay Valley Chasers Racing Club**
43 **MARCUS ANTONIUS**, 9, b g Mark of Esteem (IRE)—Star of The Course (USA) **K C Partnership**
44 **MISFITS (IRE)**, 5, b g Beneficial—Park Rose (IRE) **County Set Four & Keith Hunter**
45 **MISS BLANCHE**, 5, b g King's Theatre (IRE)—Keys Pride (IRE) **Mr K. Alexander**
46 **MISS HIGH TIME**, 5, b m Kalanisi (IRE)—Windsor Dancer (IRE) **P. J. S. Russell**
47 **MISS JOEKING (IRE)**, 5, b m Alkaadhem—Go Franky (IRE) **P. J. S. Russell**
48 **MISS TIGGY (IRE)**, 6, b m Milan—Rockwell College (IRE) **John R. Adam & Sons Ltd**
49 **MOMKINZAIN (USA)**, 9, b g Rahy (USA)—Fait Accompli (USA) **P. J. S. Russell**
50 **MOORSTOWN (IRE)**, 6, b g Oscar (IRE)—Glacial Princess (IRE) **The County Set and Team Kirkton**
51 **MORNING TIME (IRE)**, 10, b g Hawk Wing (USA)—Desert Trail (IRE) **Mr W. G. H. Forrester**
52 **MUMGOS DEBUT (IRE)**, 8, b g Royal Anthem (USA)—Black Queen (IRE) **Mrs Suzy Brown & Mr Peter R Brown**
53 **MYSTEREE (IRE)**, 8, b g Gold Well—Hillside Native (IRE) **Mrs L. Maclennan**
54 **NEAR TO TEARS (IRE)**, 6, br m Robin des Pres (FR)—Tears of Jade (IRE) **Mr & Mrs J. Morrison-Bell**
55 **NEWTOWN LAD (IRE)**, 6, b g Craigsteel—Rocher Lady (IRE) **Mr John J Murray & Mrs Lynne MacLennan**
56 **ONE FOR ARTHUR (IRE)**, 7, b g Milan—Nonnetia (FR) **Two Golf Widows**
57 **ORIONINVERNESS (IRE)**, 5, b g Brian Boru—Woodville Leader (IRE) **Tay Valley Chasers Racing Club**
58 **PRESENT FLIGHT (IRE)**, 7, ch g Presenting—Grangeclare Flight (IRE) **Kilco (International) Ltd**
59 **PRESENT LODGER (IRE)**, 8, b g Presenting—Hannigan's Lodger (IRE) **Mr A. N. Seymour**
60 **QUITO DU TRESOR (FR)**, 12, b g Jeune Homme (FR)—Itiga (FR) **Kelso Lowflyers & Mr PJS Russell**
61 **REAPING THE REWARD (IRE)**, 12, b g Sylvan Express—Zamaine (IRE) **Mr & Mrs Raymond Anderson Green**
62 **REVOCATION (IRE)**, 8, b g Revoque (IRE)—Fenella **Mr Michael & Lady Jane Kaplan**
63 **RISING TIDE (IRE)**, 5, b g Dubai Destination (USA)—Erins Love (IRE) **R. A. Bartlett**
64 **RIVABODIVA (IRE)**, 6, ch m Flemensfirth (USA)—Sheebadiva (IRE) **Mrs S Russell & A M Russell**
65 **ROWDY ROCHER (IRE)**, 10, br g Winged Love (IRE)—Madam Rocher (IRE) **Michelle And Dan Macdonald**
66 **RYALEX (IRE)**, 5, b g Arcadio (GER)—Lady Ramona (IRE) **P. J. S. Russell**
67 **SAMMY B**, 6, br g Overbury (IRE)—This Thyne **G. S. Brown**
68 **SELKIRK'S ISLAND**, 5, b m Yeats (IRE)—Classic Gale (USA) **Allson Sparkle Ltd**
69 **SETTLEDOUTOFCOURT (IRE)**, 10, b g Court Cave (IRE)—Ardash Princess **Mr A. McAllister**
70 **SEVEN DEVILS (IRE)**, 6, b g Definite Article—Top Lot (IRE) **Mrs S Russell & A M Russell**
71 **SHANROE STREET (IRE)**, 6, b g Mustameet (USA)—Zaffran Lady (IRE) **Netherfield House Stud**
72 **SHINE A DIAMOND (IRE)**, 8, gr g St Jovite (USA)—Mossy Grey (IRE) **Kilco (International) Ltd**
73 **SIMARTHUR**, 9, gr g Erhaab (USA)—Dusty Too **Dig In Racing**
74 **SKY KHAN**, 7, b g Cape Cross (IRE)—Starlit Sky **The Ormello Way**
75 **SPIRIT OSCAR (IRE)**, 8, b m Oscar (IRE)—Grange Classic (IRE) **Ms D. Thomson**
76 **SUPERIOR COMMAND (IRE)**, 7, b g Lahib (USA)—Decent Dime (IRE) **Mr Willie Scott & Mr Peter J S Russell**
77 **SWEET HOLLY**, 5, b m Kayf Tara—Presuming **Drew & Ailsa Russell**
78 **TANTAMOUNT**, 7, b g Observatory (USA)—Cantanta **Mutual Friends**
79 **TAP NIGHT (USA)**, 9, ch g Pleasant Tap (USA)—Day Mate (USA) **J. P. McManus**
80 **THE COBBLER SWAYNE (IRE)**, 7, b g Milan—Turtle Lamp (IRE) **Mrs R. A. Stobart**
81 **THE COMPELLER (IRE)**, 4, b g Lawman (FR)—Mark Too (IRE) **W M D Racing**
82 **THE SQUINTY BRIDGE**, 8, b g Heron Island (IRE)—The Storm Bell (IRE) **Mrs J. Perratt**
83 **THE TOFT**, 7, b m Kayf Tara—Gretton **P. J. S. Russell**
84 **THROTHETHATCH (IRE)**, 7, b g Beneficial—Castletownroche (IRE) **Mrs A. E. Giles**
85 **TRADEWINDS (FR)**, 8, b g Kapgarde (FR)—Royale Floriane (FR) **Mr G. R. McGladery**
86 **URBAN KODE (IRE)**, 8, b g Kodiac—Urbanize (USA) **Suzy Brown, John Baird, Tony Evans**
87 **VENGEUR DE GUYE (FR)**, 7, b g Dom Alco (FR)—Mascotte de Guye (FR) **Brahms & Liszt**
88 **VOYAGE A NEW YORK (FR)**, 7, b g Kapgarde (FR)—Pennsylvanie (FR) **Fyffees**
89 **WHERE'S TIGER**, 5, b g Tiger Hill (IRE)—Where's Broughton **Mr Michael & Lady Jane Kaplan**
90 4, B g Big Bad Bob (IRE)—Whizz **Mr Gerry McGladery & Mr PJS Russell**

Other Owners: Mr W. Agnew, Mr J. A. Aitkenhead, Mr J. B. Baird, Mrs S. Brown, Mr P. R. Brown, A. Cadger, Mr C. Dempster, Mr E. W. Dempster, Mr R. Doak, Mrs B. V. Evans, Mr A. Evans, Mr J. Fyffe, Gilbert McClung (Kelso) Ltd, G. Godsman, Mrs I. M. Grant, Mrs A. Green, A. A. Green, E. D. Haggart, K. L. Hunter, Kelso Members Lowflyers Club, Mrs M Kennedy, Mrs C. J. Lamb, Mrs Y. M. V. Learmonth, Mr J. S. Lessells, Mr C. W. Levein, Mrs J. Lightbody, M. W. Lightbody, Ms F. E. MacInnes, Mrs M. Macdonald, Mr W. D. Macdonald, M. F. Mackay, Mr K. J. Mackie, Mr M. G. Mellor,

MS LUCINDA RUSSELL - Continued

Mr J. Mitchell, Mrs K. A. Morrison-Bell, Mr J. Morrison-Bell, Mr J. J. Murray, Mr W. E. Nicholson, Mr G. G. Ritchie, A. J. R. Russell, Mrs A. Russell, Mr A. M. Russell, Ms L. V. Russell, Mrs S. C. Russell, Mr W. T. Scott, A. W. Sinclair, Mr D. R. Skinner, Major A. R. Trotter, Mr N. J. Turnbull, Mrs M. Winnell, Mr T. P. Winnell, Mr D. J. Gordon Wright.

Assistant Trainers: Peter Scudamore, Jaimie Duff, Nick Orpwood, Jamie Turnbull

Jockey (NH): Peter Buchanan. **Conditional:** Ross Chapman, Grant Cockburn, Derek Fox.
Amateur: Mr Nick Orpwood, Mr Harry Reed.

---

526 **MR JOHN RYALL, Yeovil**
Postal: **Higher Farm, Rimpton, Yeovil, Somerset, BA22 8AD**
Contacts: **PHONE/FAX (01935) 850222 MOBILE (07592) 738848**
E-MAIL bjmryall@btconnect.com

1 BIT OF A CHARLIE, 7, b g Emperor Fountain—Win A Hand **B. J. M. Ryall**
2 HELLO JAZZ, 6, b m Helissio (FR)—Just Jasmine **Mrs A. Davis**
3 HI BRONCO, 9, b g Emperor Fountain—Win A Hand **B. J. M. Ryall**
4 SPRING BLOSSOM, 6, b m Apple Tree (FR)—Spring Grass **B. J. M. Ryall**
5 SPRING WOLF, 8, br g Loup Sauvage (USA)—Spring Grass **B. J. M. Ryall**
6 6, B g Franklins Gardens—Tin Symphony **B. J. M. Ryall**

Assistant Trainer: Mrs R C Ryall

---

527 **MR JOHN RYAN, Newmarket**
Postal: **Cadland Stables, Moulton Road, Newmarket, Suffolk, CB8 8DU**
Contacts: **PHONE (01638) 664172 MOBILE (07739) 801235**
E-MAIL john.ryan@jryanracing.com WEBSITE www.jryanracing.com Twitter: @JohnRyanRacing

1 BATTLE OF MARATHON (USA), 4, b g War Front (USA)—Sayedah (IRE) **Mr Graham Smith Bernal**
2 BIG MCINTOSH (IRE), 4, b g Bushranger (IRE)—Three Decades (IRE) **Kilco (International) Ltd**
3 EVACUSAFE LADY, 5, ch m Avonbridge—Snow Shoes **Coutts & Ryan Partnership**
4 HONCHO (IRE), 4, gr g Dark Angel (IRE)—Disco Lights **Mr G. R. McGladery**
5 MERCY ME, 4, b f Mawatheeq (USA)—Fantastic Santanyi **Mr G Smith-Bernal & Mr A Dee**
6 MERHOOB (IRE), 4, b g Cape Cross (IRE)—Lady Slippers (IRE) **Mr G. R. McGladery**
7 OCEAN TEMPEST, 7, gr g Act One—Ipsa Loquitur **Mr W McLuskey & Mr C Little & Mr John Ryan**
8 OPUS TOO (IRE), 5, b g Lawman (FR)—Jerez (IRE) **Mr Peter Close**
9 PLUCKY DIP, 5, b g Nayef (USA)—Plucky **Mr Byron, Mr Lavallin, Mr Donnison, Mr John Ryan**
10 SANDRO BOTTICELLI (IRE), 4, b g Galileo (IRE)—
                    Ask For The Moon (FR) **Mr Alan Dee & Mr Graham Smith Bernal**
11 TENGRI, 4, b g Aqlaam—Jackie's Opera (FR) **The High Tailors**
12 TENOR (IRE), 6, b g Oratorio (IRE)—Cedar Sea (IRE) **Kilco International Ltd**
13 THE GAY CAVALIER, 5, b g Henrythenavigator (USA)—Dear Daughter **The Gay Cavaliers Partnership**
14 THECORNISHBARRON (IRE), 4, b g Bushranger (IRE)—Tripudium (IRE) **Mr C Letcher & Mr John Ryan**

THREE-YEAR-OLDS

15 BELLA'S BOY (IRE), b g Lovelace—Cosa Deasa (IRE) **Mr John Ryan**
16 CADLAND LAD (IRE), b g Lilbourne Lad (IRE)—Hari's Gift (IRE) **Bourne To Be Wild**
17 CAPTAIN GERALD, b g Captain Gerrard (IRE)—My Heart's On Fire (IRE) **John Ryan Racing Partnership**
18 MISTYMOISTYMORNING (IRE), gr f Alhaarth (IRE)—Bermuxa (FR) **Mr G. F. Smith-Bernal**
19 OCEAN ELEVEN, b g Equiano (FR)—Fittonia (FR) **Mr W. McLuskey**
20 THECORNISHCAVALIER (IRE), b g Frozen Power (IRE)—Structura (USA) **Mr John Ryan**

TWO-YEAR-OLDS

21 GREY BRITAIN, gr c 15/3 Arcano (IRE)—
                    Reaching Ahead (USA) (Mizzen Mast (USA)) (20000) **Mr Alan Dee & Mr Graham Smith Bernal**
22 B f 19/2 Equiano (FR)—Ipsa Loquitur (Unfuwain (USA)) (13000) **Mr John Ryan**
23 SPELLO (IRE), br c 21/4 Born To Sea (IRE)—
                    Carina Ari (IRE) (Imperial Ballet (IRE)) (21000) **Mr Alan Dee & Mr Graham Smith Bernal**

MR JOHN RYAN - Continued

24 **WALTER RALEIGH (IRE)**, b c 25/4 Nathaniel (IRE)—
        Regrette Rien (USA) (Unbridled's Song (USA)) (45000) **Mr Alan Dee & Mr Graham Smith Bernal**
25 Gr ro f 6/2 Zebedee—White Shift (IRE) (Night Shift (USA)) (11000) **Mr John Ryan**

Other Owners: Mrs Helene Bonney, Mr Bob Bonney, Mrs Karen Coutts, Mr A. Dee, Mr Neil Hooper, Mr Simon Kerr, Mr Christopher Letcher, Mr C. W. Little, Mr W. McLuskey, Mr Gurmit Samra, Mr G. Smith-Bernal, Mrs J. Williams.

---

528   MR KEVIN RYAN, Hambleton
Postal: **Hambleton Lodge, Hambleton, Thirsk, North Yorkshire, YO7 2HA**
Contacts: PHONE Office **(01845) 597010 / (01845) 597622 FAX (01845) 597622**
MOBILE **(07768) 016930**
E-MAIL **kevin.hambleton@virgin.net** WEBSITE **www.kevinryanracing.com**

1 **AL KHAN (IRE)**, 7, b g Elnadim (USA)—Popolo (IRE) **C. G. J. Chua**
2 **ARDMAY (IRE)**, 7, b g Strategic Prince—Right After Moyne (IRE) **A. C. Henson**
3 **BAPAK ASMARA (IRE)**, 4, ro g Zebedee—Sheba Five (USA) **Mr T. A. Rahman**
4 **BOGART**, 7, ch g Bahamian Bounty—Lauren Louise **Mrs A. Bailey**
5 **BRANDO**, 4, ch g Pivotal—Argent du Bois (USA) **Mrs Angie Bailey**
6 **COMINO (IRE)**, 5, b g Tagula—Malta (USA) **Exors of the Late Mr D. W. Barker**
7 **COOPER**, 4, b g Sir Percy—Blossom **Hale Racing Ltd**
8 **COUNT MONTECRISTO (FR)**, 4, b g Siyouni (FR)—Blackberry Pie (USA) **Middleham Park Racing XLVI**
9 **CYRIL**, 4, b g Rail Link—Nurse Gladys **Guy Reed Racing**
10 **DISTANT PAST**, 5, b g Pastoral Pursuits—Faraway Lass **Mr M. Wynne**
11 **ELEUTHERA**, 4, ch g Bahamian Bounty—Cha Cha Cha **Guy Reed Racing**
12 **ERIK THE RED (FR)**, 4, b g Kendargent (FR)—Norwegian Princess (IRE) **Mr F. Gillespie**
13 **FAST ACT (IRE)**, 4, ch g Fast Company (IRE)—Nullarbor **Hambleton Racing Ltd XXXII**
14 **FLAMING SPEAR (IRE)**, 4, ch g Lope de Vega (IRE)—Elshamms **Mr Tony Bloom**
15 **GOKEN (FR)**, 4, b c Kendargent (FR)—Gooseley Chope (FR) **Mr G. Pariente**
16 **KELINNI (IRE)**, 8, b g Refuse To Bend (IRE)—Orinoco (IRE) **Amplitudo Partnership**
17 **KIBAAR**, 4, b g Pastoral Pursuits—Ashes (IRE) **Course & Distance Racing**
18 **LEXINGTON ABBEY**, 5, b g Sleeping Indian—Silvereine (FR) **Middleham Park Racing XIX**
19 **LIGHTNING SPREE (IRE)**, 4, gr g Jeremy (USA)—Spree (IRE) **Hambleton Racing Ltd XXXIV**
20 **MAYO STAR (IRE)**, 4, b g Stowaway—Western Whisper (IRE) **Charlie Doocey / Cathal Doocey**
21 **MERCURY**, 4, ch g Showcasing—Miss Rimex (IRE) **Mrs A. Bailey**
22 **MIGHTY ZIP (USA)**, 4, ch g City Zip (USA)—Incredulous (FR) **Mrs J. H. Ryan**
23 **MOONLIGHT VENTURE**, 5, ch g Tobougg (IRE)—Evening **Mrs J. Ryan**
24 **MOUNT TAHAN (IRE)**, 4, b g Lope de Vega (IRE)—Sorpresa (USA) **Mr T. A. Rahman**
25 **MUKAYNIS (IRE)**, 5, b g Tamayuz—Wild Ways **Mrs J. H. Ryan**
26 **PIAZON**, 5, br g Striking Ambition—Colonel's Daughter **Mr F. Gillespie**
27 **SIGURD (GER)**, 4, ch g Sholokhov (IRE)—Sky News (GER) **F. Gillespie**
28 **SIR DOMINO (FR)**, 4, b g Evasive—Domino Queen (USA) **Hambleton Racing Ltd XXXV**
29 **STRAITS OF MALACCA**, 5, ch g Compton Place—Cultural Role **JCG Chua & CK Ong**
30 **SWIFT APPROVAL (IRE)**, 4, ch g Approve (IRE)—Tiltili (IRE) **Middleham Park Racing XLIX**
31 **TERUNTUM STAR (FR)**, 4, ch g Dutch Art—Seralia (USA) **Mr T. A. Rahman**
32 **THE GREY GATSBY (IRE)**, 5, gr h Mastercraftsman (IRE)—Marie Vison (IRE) **Mr F. Gillespie**
33 **THE WEE BARRA (IRE)**, 4, b f Rock of Gibraltar (IRE)—Gamra (USA) **Slaters Arms Racing Club**
34 **TRAIL BLAZE (IRE)**, 7, b g Tagula (IRE)—Kingpin Delight **Mr & Mrs Julian & Rosie Richer**
35 **UPTIGHT (IRE)**, 4, b g Zamindar (USA)—Terre d'espoir (FR) **Matt & Lauren Morgan**

THREE-YEAR-OLDS

36 **ALOYSIUS HANSOM**, b c High Chaparral (IRE)—Crystany (IRE) **Mr F. Gillespie**
37 **ASHADIHAN**, b f Kyllachy—Miss Delila (USA) **Mr T. A. Rahman**
38 **BAY MIRAGE (IRE)**, b g Kheleyf (USA)—Choosey Girl (IRE) **NAD Partnership**
39 **BINT ALDAR**, b f Zoffany (IRE)—Maggie Lou (IRE) **Mr Abdulla Ahmad Al Shaikh**
40 **BLUE SASH**, gr f Sir Percy—Blue Moon **Guy Reed Racing**
41 **BRILLIANT VANGUARD (IRE)**, b g Fast Company (IRE)—Alyska (IRE) **JCG Chua & CK Ong**
42 **BRIYOUNI (FR)**, b g Siyouni (FR)—Brianza (USA) **Matt & Lauren Morgan**
43 **CANDY BANTER (USA)**, b f Distorted Humor (USA)—Sweet Hope (USA) **J. J. Cullinan**
44 **CANNY STYLE**, b f Canford Cliffs (IRE)—Stylish One (IRE) **Hambleton Racing Ltd XXXVII**
45 **CAPTAIN DION**, gr c Equiano (FR)—Bandanna **Mr T. A. Rahman**
46 **COMPANY ASSET (IRE)**, ch f Fast Company (IRE)—Changari (USA) **Hambleton Racing Ltd XLII**

MR KEVIN RYAN - Continued

47 **DANCE ALONE**, gr g Bahamian Bounty—Palais Glide **Guy Reed Racing**
48 **DEBEN**, b g Lilbourne Lad (IRE)—Mocca (IRE) **Mrs J. H. Ryan**
49 **DODGY BOB**, b g Royal Applause—Rustam **Jack Berry & John Nixon**
50 **FINE EXAMPLE**, b g Showcasing—Belle Reine **Hambleton Racing Ltd XLIV**
51 **FUTOON (IRE)**, b f Kodiac—Vermilliann (IRE) **Course & Distance Racing**
52 **GENO (IRE)**, b g Holy Roman Emperor—Abama Lady (CAN) **Matt & Lauren Morgan**
53 **GLORIOUS TIMES (IRE)**, b f Galileo (IRE)—Quiet Mouse (USA) **Mr Ahmad Abdulla Al Shaikh**
54 **GOODKNIGHT PERCY (IRE)**, ch g Sir Percy—Ekhraaj (USA) **The Better Together Partnership**
55 **HEAD HIGH (IRE)**, gr c Mastercraftsman (IRE)—Elisium **Rathordan Partnership**
56 **HEIR TO A THRONE (IRE)**, ch g Siyouni (FR)—Boaka (FR) **STS Racing Ltd**
57 **ICE GALLEY (IRE)**, b c Galileo (IRE)—Ice Queen (IRE) **Mrs Jayne Sivills**
58 **JESS**, b f Equiano (FR)—Poyle Meg **Mrs J. H. Ryan**
59 **KAJAKI (IRE)**, gr g Mastercraftsman (IRE)—No Quest (IRE) **F. Gillespie**
60 **LAGENDA**, b g Dick Turpin (IRE)—Whirly Dancer **Mr T. A. Rahman**
61 **LAUGHTON**, b c Acclamation—Peach Pearl **Mrs Angie Bailey**
62 **MAGICAL LASSO (IRE)**, ch g Monsieur Bond (IRE)—How Sweet It Is (IRE) **Middleham Park Racing CXX**
63 **MASTER MIRASOL (IRE)**, b g Arcano (IRE)—Hidden Meaning **Mrs M. Forsyth**
64 **MOHAB**, b c Sir Percy—Princess Aurora (USA) **Mr Khalid Mishref**
65 **MONT KIARA (FR)**, b g Kendargent (FR)—Xaarienne **JCG Chua & CK Ong 1**
66 B f Piccolo—Peggy Spencer **Guy Reed Racing**
67 **PERMAISURI (IRE)**, b f Sea The Stars (IRE)—Puteri Wentworth **Mr T. A. Rahman**
68 **ROYAL DISPLAY**, ch g Showcasing—Amouage Royale (IRE) **Mrs J. H. Ryan**
69 **SAYEDAATI SAADATI (IRE)**, b c Montjeu (IRE)—Guessing (USA) **Ahmad Abdulla Al Shaikh & Co**
70 **SILVA ECLIPSE**, gr c Multiplex—Linen Line **Geoff & Sandra Turnbull**
71 Ch f Peintre Celebre (USA)—Sincerely **Guy Reed Racing**
72 **STRUMMER (IRE)**, b g Frozen Power (IRE)—Question (USA) **J E Pallister & J G Pallister**
73 **TAKING LIBERTYS**, b g Makfi—Liberty Chery **Hambleton Racing Ltd XXXVIII**
74 **THE MAGIC PENCIL (IRE)**, b g Dream Ahead (USA)—Kylemore (IRE) **Mrs J. M. Dwyer**
75 **TIGA TUAN (FR)**, b f Le Havre (IRE)—Ramita (IRE) **Mr T. A. Rahman**
76 **TOP OF THE BANK**, b g Piccolo—America Lontana (FR) **Mr J. Hanson**
77 **TORREMAR (FR)**, br g Excellent Art—Sabela (IRE) **Mrs M. Forsyth**
78 **WALKING PRIMROSE (FR)**, ch f Raven's Pass (USA)—Celebre Fragance (FR) **Matt & Lauren Morgan**
79 **WEEKEND OFFENDER (FR)**, ch g Lope de Vega (IRE)—Huroof (IRE) **Matt & Lauren Morgan**
80 **WELD AL KHAWANEEJ (IRE)**, ch g Fast Company (IRE)—Law Review (IRE) **Course & Distance Racing**
81 **WERNOTFAMUSANYMORE (IRE)**, b g Oasis Dream—Dhanyata (IRE) **Highbank Stud**

TWO-YEAR-OLDS

82 Ch c 9/5 Piccolo—Card Games (First Trump) **Guy Reed Racing**
83 Ch f 24/4 Dutch Art—Carraigoona (IRE) (Rock of Gibraltar (IRE)) (42857)
84 B f 20/2 Quality Road—Celestic (USA) (Sky Classic (CAN)) (25000) **Mrs Clodagh McStay**
85 B g 5/3 Bahamian Bounty—Cha Cha Cha (Efisio) **Guy Reed Racing**
86 B f 4/3 Exceed And Excel (AUS)—Chili Dip (Alhaarth (IRE)) (31000)
87 B c 12/2 Firebreak—Dayville (IRE) (Dayjur (USA)) (33333)
88 Ch c 12/3 Dragon Pulse (IRE)—Degree of Honor (FR) (Highest Honor (FR)) (38095)
89 Ch f 25/3 Distorted Humor (USA)—Easterette (USA) (Hard Spun (USA)) **Mr Sutong Pan**
90 B c 5/3 Dandy Man (IRE)—Fields of Joy (GER) (Waky Nao) (16190) **Hambleton Racing Ltd XLVI**
91 B c 22/2 Equiano (FR)—George's Gift (Haafhd) (31428) **Mrs A. Bailey**
92 B f 21/2 Sixties Icon—Gillstown Great (Royal Applause) (14285) **Hambleton Racing Ltd XLIX**
93 B g 14/4 Royal Applause—Giusina Mia (USA) (Diesis) (28571) **Ontoawinner 8**
94 Ch g 16/3 Piccolo—Give Her A Whirl (Pursuit of Love) **Guy Reed Racing**
95 **GOKENA (FR)**, bl f 1/1 Kendargent (FR)—Gooseley Chope (FR) (Indian Rocket) **Mr Guy Pariente**
96 B g 22/4 Kheleyf (USA)—Golden Nun (Bishop of Cashel) (15000)
97 Gr c 8/3 Zebedee—Gone Sailing (Mizzen Mast (USA)) (35238) **Mr T. A. Rahman**
98 **HEIR OF EXCITEMENT (IRE)**, b c 15/3 Tagula (IRE)—
                            Gimli's Treasure (IRE) (King's Best (USA)) (30476) **STS Racing Limited**
99 Ch f 27/4 Monsieur Bond (IRE)—Jord (IRE) (Trans Island) **Mr A. Grice**
100 **LANJANO**, ch c 28/3 Foxwedge (AUS)—
                            Hot Property (USA) (Thunder Gulch (USA)) (17000) **Collier Holmes Racing**
101 **LUALIWA**, b c 9/3 Foxwedge (AUS)—Sunpearl (Compton Place) (38095) **Mr & Mrs Julian & Rosie Richer**
102 B c 2/2 Harbour Watch (IRE)—Mania (IRE) (Danehill (USA)) (45000) **Mr J. Hanson & Sir Alex Ferguson**
103 B c 12/4 Pivotal—Miss Delila (USA) (Malibu Moon (USA)) (75000) **Mr T. A. Rahman**
104 B f 27/2 Dark Angel (IRE)—Miss Otis (Danetime (IRE)) (27619) **Hambleton Racing Ltd XLV**
105 **NORWEGIAN DUCHESS (FR)**, ch f 12/2 Kendargent (FR)—
                            Norwegian Lady (FR) (Hold That Tiger (USA)) **Mr Guy Pariente**

MR KEVIN RYAN - Continued

106 **NORWEGIAN HIGHNESS (FR),** ch f 3/5 Kendargent (FR)—
Norwegian Princess (IRE) (Fairy King (USA)) **Mr Guy Pariente**
107 B g 3/4 Bahamian Bounty—Nurse Gladys (Dr Fong (USA)) **Guy Reed Racing**
108 **PERCY TOPLIS,** b g 3/4 Kheleyf (USA)—West Lorne (USA) (Gone West (USA)) (7000)
109 Ch c 23/4 Sepoy (AUS)—Samira Gold (FR) (Gold Away (IRE)) (20000) **Mr Jaber Abdullah**
110 **SHANNAH BINT ERIC,** ch f 17/4 Poet's Voice—
Crystal Mountain (USA) (Monashee Mountain (USA)) **Mr Saeed Jaber**
111 B f 19/4 Medicean—Show Flower (Shamardal (USA)) **Mr Jaber Abdullah**
112 B f 12/3 Acclamation—Soul Mountain (IRE) (Rock of Gibraltar (IRE)) (42857) **Mr T. A. Rahman**
113 B f 4/3 Speightstown (USA)—Sweet Hope (USA) (Lemon Drop Kid (USA)) (26000) **Highbank Stud**
114 **TEOMARIA,** b f 7/2 Teofilo (IRE)—Sylvestris (IRE) (Arch (USA)) **Mr David Blunt**
115 Ch c 7/2 Dream Ahead (USA)—Vasilia (Dansili) (41904) **Prostock Ltd**
116 Ch c 14/4 Tagula (IRE)—Westcote (USA) (Gone West (USA)) (26666) **Andy Turton & John Blackburn**

Other Owners: Mr Ahmad Abdulla Al Shaikh, Mr Abdulla Ahmad Al Shaikh, J. Airey, Mr J. E. Barnes, J. Cannon, Mr J. C. G. Chua, R. Crosbie, Mr Ian Cruddas, Mrs A. Dawson, Mr N. Dawson, Mr A. Denham, Mr Cathal Doocey, Mr Charles Doocey, Hambleton Racing Ltd, Mr Matthew Morgan, Mrs Lauren Morgan, Mr C. K. Ong, Mr J. Richer, Mrs Rosie Richer, Mr S. R. H. Turner, Mrs I. M. Wainwright, Mr M. Wainwright.

Assistant Trainer: Joe O'Gorman

Jockey (flat): Shane Gray, Amy Ryan.

---

529 **MR AYTACH SADIK, Kidderminster**
Postal: Wolverley Court Coach House, Wolverley, Kidderminster, Worcestershire, DY10 3RP
Contacts: **PHONE (01562) 852362 MOBILE (07803) 040344**

1 **CAPTAIN STARLIGHT (IRE),** 6, b g Captain Marvelous (IRE)—Jewell In The Sky (IRE) **A. M. Sadik**
2 **FINCH FLYER (IRE),** 9, ch g Indian Ridge—Imelda (USA) **A. M. Sadik**
3 **SADIKS BOY (IRE),** 7, b g Robert Emmet (IRE)—Lough N Uisce (IRE) **A. M. Sadik**
4 **SUSSEX ROAD (IRE),** 6, b g Mahler—Rose Island **A. M. Sadik**

---

530 **MRS DEBORAH SANDERSON, Retford**
Postal: Poplar Cottage, Wheatley Road, Sturton-le-Steeple, Retford, Nottinghamshire, DN22 9HU
Contacts: **PHONE (01427) 884692 FAX (01427) 884692 MOBILE (07968) 821074**
E-MAIL debsando999@gmail.com

1 **DIAMOND RUNNER (IRE),** 4, b g Amadeus Wolf—Hawk Eyed Lady (IRE) **Bawtry Racing Club**
2 **MUNAAWIB,** 8, b g Haafhd—Mouwadh (USA) **Bawtry Racing Club**
3 **PRIGSNOV DANCER (IRE),** 11, ch g Namid—Brave Dance (IRE) **Mr J. M. Lacey**
4 **ROGER THORPE,** 7, b g Firebreak—Nunthorpe **Mr J. M. Lacey**

THREE-YEAR-OLDS
5 **SIEGE OF BOSTON (IRE),** ch c Starspangledbanner (AUS)—Milton of Campsie **Mr M. Mckay**

Other Owners: Mrs Amanda Barrett, Mr M. McKay, Mrs Debbie Sanderson.

Assistant Trainer: Mark Sanderson

531 **MRS KATHLEEN SANDERSON, Calverleigh**
Postal: **New Cottage, Rackenford Road, Calverleigh, Tiverton, Devon, EX16 8BE**
Contacts: **PHONE (01884) 254217**
E-MAIL **h9bas@live.co.uk**

1 BLINDING LIGHTS (IRE), 11, b g Snurge—Tender Return (IRE) **Mrs K. M. Sanderson**

Jockey (NH): Micheal Nolan. **Amateur:** Mr Matthew Hampton.

532 **MR JOSE SANTOS, Upper Lambourn**
Postal: **The Croft, Upper Lambourn, Hungerford, Berkshire, RG17 8QH**

1 BALDADASH (IRE), 11, b g Beneficial—Balda Girl (IRE) **R. Cooper Racing Ltd**
2 BOLD RUNNER, 5, ch g Mount Nelson—Music In Exile (USA) **R. Cooper Racing Ltd**
3 HAGREE (IRE), 5, b g Haatef (USA)—Zuniga's Date (USA) **Mr W. Burn**
4 OPERA BUFF, 7, b g Oratorio (IRE)—Opera Glass **R. Cooper Racing Ltd**
5 PAO DE ACUCA (IRE), 4, b g Rip Van Winkle (IRE)—Splendeur (FR) **Mr J. M. Dos Santos**

THREE-YEAR-OLDS

6 BOB'S BOY, b g Showcasing—Tech Zinne **R. Cooper Racing Ltd**
7 Ch g Champs Elysees—Pilcomayo (IRE) **Mr W. Burn**

TWO-YEAR-OLDS

8 Ch c 30/4 Byron—Can She Dance (IRE) (Danehill Dancer (IRE)) (1623) **Mr J. M. Dos Santos**
9 Ch c 19/5 Dandy Man (IRE)—Nouveau Riche (IRE) (Entrepreneur) (885) **Mr J. M. Dos Santos**
10 Ch f 28/4 Helmet (AUS)—Symphonic Dancer (USA) (Smart Strike (CAN)) (571) **R. Cooper Racing Ltd**
11 Br c 23/4 Foxwedge (AUS)—Tech Zinne (Zinaad) **R. Cooper Racing Ltd**

533 **MR MALCOLM SAUNDERS, Wells**
Postal: **Blue Mountain Farm, Wells Hill Bottom, Haydon, Wells, Somerset, BA5 3EZ**
Contacts: **OFFICE/FAX (01749) 841011 MOBILE (07771) 601035**
E-MAIL **malcolm@malcolmsaunders.co.uk** WEBSITE **www.malcolmsaunders.co.uk**

1 BABYFACT, 5, b m Piccolo—Pennyspider (IRE) **Mrs V. L. Nicholas**
2 CAMELEY DAWN, 5, b m Alhaarth (IRE)—Apply Dapply **Mr & Mrs J Harris**
3 GINZAN, 8, b m Desert Style (IRE)—Zyzania **Mr P. S. G. Nicholas**
4 HENRIETTA DANCER, 4, ch f Sakhee's Secret—Craic Sa Ceili (IRE) **M. S. Saunders**
5 LADY BAYSIDE, 8, ch m Ishiguru (USA)—Seldemosa **M. S. Saunders**
6 LIBERTY RULES (IRE), 4, b g Aussie Rules (USA)—Polynesian Queen (IRE) **M. S. Saunders**
7 LUCKY CLOVER, 5, ch m Lucky Story (USA)—Willisa **Lockstone Business Services Ltd**
8 PIXELEEN, 4, b f Pastoral Pursuits—Ballyalla
9 SARANGOO, 8, b m Piccolo—Craic Sa Ceili (IRE) **Lockstone Business Services Ltd**
10 SILVERRICA (IRE), 6, gr m Ad Valorem (USA)—Allegorica (IRE) **Mrs V. L. Nicholas**
11 SPIRIT IN TIME (IRE), 4, b f Vale of York (IRE)—Star Port **M. S. Saunders**
12 SUNNY FUTURE (IRE), 10, b g Masterful (USA)—Be Magic **M. S. Saunders**
13 SUPER ICON, 4, b g Sixties Icon—Brigadiers Bird (IRE) **Mr P. S. G. Nicholas**
14 TITUS SECRET, 4, ch g Sakhee's Secret—Crimson Fern (IRE) **Lockstone Business Services Ltd**

THREE-YEAR-OLDS

15 ARCANISTA (IRE), ch f Arcano (IRE)—Cattiva Generosa **Mr & Mrs J Harris**
16 SECRETFACT, br c Sakhee's Secret—Matterofact (IRE) **Premier Conservatory Roofs**
17 SHOWMETHEWAYAVRILO, ch c Showcasing—Avrilo **Pat Hancock & Eric Jones**

Other Owners: D. J. Collier, Mr P. K. Hancock, Mr J. E. Harris, Mrs P. A. Harris, E. W. Jones.

534 MRS DIANNE SAYER, Penrith
Postal: **Town End Farm, Hackthorpe, Penrith, Cumbria, CA10 2HX**
Contacts: **PHONE (01931) 712245 MOBILE (07980) 295316**

1 BAILEYS CONCERTO (IRE), 10, b g Bach (IRE)—None The Wiser (IRE) **United Five Racing & Mr Andrew Sayer**
2 BELL WEIR, 8, gr g Tobougg (IRE)—Belly Dancer (IRE) **SJD Racing & Dianne Sayer**
3 BLUE JACKET (USA), 5, ro m Mizzen Mast (USA)—Complex (USA) **J. A. Sayer**
4 BONNIE LIZZIE, 5, ch m Alflora (IRE)—Caitlin Ash
5 BORUMA (IRE), 6, b g Brian Boru—Itfallendintears (IRE) **Tony Price & Mrs Linda White**
6 COOL BARANCA (GER), 10, b m Beat Hollow—Cool Storm (IRE) **Mr D. J. Coppola**
7 DALBY SPOOK (IRE), 6, b m Jeremy (USA)—Lamassu (IRE) **A. R. White**
8 ENDEAVOUR, 11, ch g Selkirk (USA)—Midnight Mambo **Mrs M. Coppola**
9 GOLD CHAIN (IRE), 6, b m Authorized (IRE)—Mountain Chain (USA) **Mrs M. Coppola**
10 GREAT DEMEANOR (USA), 6, b g Bernstein (USA)—Hangin Withmy Buds (USA) **Mr D. J. Coppola**
11 HONEYCHILE RYDER, 5, ch m Black Sam Bellamy (IRE)—Dusky Dante (IRE) **The Transatlantics & Diane Sayer**
12 LIPSTICKANDPOWDER (IRE), 4, gr f Mastercraftsman (IRE)—Raphimix (FR) **Mrs M. Coppola**
13 OCTAGON, 6, b g Overbury (IRE)—Dusky Dante (IRE) **Mr A. S. Ambler**
14 RONALDINHO (IRE), 6, b g Jeremy (USA)—Spring Glory **Mr D. J. Coppola**
15 SACKETT, 5, b g Midnight Legend—Gloriana **Mr A. S. Ambler**
16 SENDIYM (FR), 9, b g Rainbow Quest (USA)—Seraya (FR) **United Five Racing & Mr Andrew Sayer**
17 SERGEANT PINK (IRE), 10, b g Fasliyev (USA)—Ring Pink (USA) **J. A. Sayer**
18 SILVER SHUFFLE (IRE), 9, ch g Big Shuffle (USA)—Silvetta **E G Tunstall,G A Barker & Dianne Sayer**
19 THE PHANTOM (FR), 4, b g Apsis—Idee Recue (FR) **Mr A. S. Ambler**
20 TURTLE CASK (IRE), 7, b g Turtle Island (IRE)—Sayce (IRE) **Mellissa Lamb & Andrew Sayer**
21 WEAPON OF CHOICE (IRE), 8, b g Iffraaj—Tullawadgeen (IRE) **Appleby Racing & Dianne Sayer**

THREE-YEAR-OLDS
22 BIG TIME DANCER (IRE), b g Zoffany (IRE)—Final Opinion (IRE) **Andy Bell Anna Noble Arnie Flower**
23 MY VALENTINO (IRE), ch g Duke of Marmalade (IRE)—Nadwah (USA) **Dianne Sayer Anna Noble Arnie Flower**

Other Owners: Mr G. A. Barker, Mr A. Bell, Mr K. J. Burrow, Mr A. J. Burrow, Mr I. T. Conroy, Mr T. W. Ewbank, Mrs C Fitzgerald, Mr S. A. Flower, Mrs J. D. Howard, Mr D. Hunter, Miss M. Lamb, Mrs J. Macrae, Mr P. Moorby, Mr K. E. Moorby, Mr S. Nicholson, Mrs A. M. Noble, Mr D. A. Price, Mrs H. D. Sayer, E. G. Tunstall, Mrs L. White.

Assistant Trainer: Miss Joanna Sayer

Conditional: Emma Sayer. **Apprentice:** Emma Sayer. **Amateur:** Miss Liz Butterworth.

535 DR JON SCARGILL, Newmarket
Postal: **Red House Stables, Hamilton Road, Newmarket, Suffolk, CB8 0TE**
Contacts: **PHONE (01638) 667767 MOBILE (07785) 350705**
E-MAIL scargill@redhousestables.freeserve.co.uk WEBSITE www.jonscargill.co.uk

1 FRIDGE KID, 4, b f Kheleyf (USA)—Snow Shoes **Strawberry Fields Stud**
2 HAPPISBURGH MAN, 4, br g Footstepsinthesand—Contemplate **Strawberry Fields Stud**
3 THE GINGER BERRY, 6, ch g First Trump—Dolly Coughdrop (IRE) **Silent Partners**
4 VIVO PER LEI (IRE), 4, gr f Mastercraftsman (IRE)—Sabancaya **Newpinewood Stables Ltd**

THREE-YEAR-OLDS
5 DANGEROUS SECRET, gr f Medicean—Holamo (IRE) **Newpinewood Stables Ltd**
6 FEN TIGRESS, b f Iffraaj—Alybgood (CAN) **Mr D. Tunmore**
7 HAPPY GIRL, b f Aqlaam—Gwyneth **Newpinewood Stables Ltd**
8 TRODERO, b f Mastercraftsman (IRE)—Jules (IRE) **Newpinewood Stables Ltd**

TWO-YEAR-OLDS
9 Br f 11/5 Harbour Watch (IRE)—Alybgood (CAN) (Alydeed (CAN)) (14500) **Mr D. Tunmore**

Other Owners: G. F. L. Robinson, Mrs S. M. Scargill, F. B. B. White.

536 **MR DERRICK SCOTT, Minehead**
Postal: **East Lynch, Minehead, Somerset, TA24 8SS**
Contacts: **PHONE (01643) 702430 FAX (01643) 702430**

1 LUPITA (IRE), 12, ch m Intikhab (USA)—Sarah (IRE) **Mrs R. Scott**
2 ROYBUOY, 9, b g Royal Applause—Wavy Up (IRE) **Mrs R. Scott**

537 **MR GEORGE SCOTT, Newmarket**
Postal: **44 Rous Road, Newmarket, Suffolk, CB8 8DL**
Contacts: **MOBILE (07833) 461294**
E-MAIL **george@georgescottracing.com** WEBSITE **www.georgescottracing.com**

1 DOMINATE, 6, b g Assertive—Blue Goddess (IRE) **G. A. Wilson**
2 FIELDSMAN (USA), 4, b g Hard Spun (USA)—R Charlie's Angel (USA) **Chelsea Thoroughbreds - Lazenby**
3 GEORGE CINQ, 6, b g Pastoral Pursuits—Fairnilee **Breen, Bryan, Humphreys & Randle**
4 HAMELIN (IRE), 6, b g Cape Cross (IRE)—Love Divine **Lordship Stud**
5 ILLUSIVE (IRE), 5, b g Galileo (IRE)—Looking Back (IRE) **The Done At One-O-Ones**
6 MIGHTY YAR (IRE), 6, gr g Teofilo (IRE)—Karaliyfa (IRE) **R. A. H. Evans**
7 PHOSPHORESCENCE (IRE), 6, b g Sakhee (USA)—Eccentricity (USA) **Niarchos Family**
8 SIX CENTS (IRE), 4, b f Shirocco (GER)—Slawomira (GER) **Hunscote Stud**

THREE-YEAR-OLDS

9 CAJOLED (FR), b f High Chaparral (IRE)—Dolphina (USA) **Niarchos Family**
10 GRANITA (USA), b f Blame (USA)—Youre So Sweet (USA) **Flaxman Stables Ireland Ltd**
11 IMPERIAL STATE, b g Holy Roman Emperor (IRE)—Seldemosa **The Harnage Partnership**
12 ROYAL BEEKEEPER, ch g Champs Elysees—Lasso **Wellington Group Syndicate**
13 SHADEN (IRE), b f Kodiac—Lady Avenger (IRE) **Saleh Al Homaizi & Imad Al Sagar**

TWO-YEAR-OLDS

14 B f 4/3 Sayif (IRE)—Aramam (Kyllachy)
15 B f 30/4 Kodiac—Baltic Belle (IRE) (Redback) (140000) **Saleh Al Homaizi & Imad Al Sagar**
16 CHOTTO (IRE), b f 2/2 Royal Applause—Alta Definizione (IRE) (Hawk Wing (USA)) (9523) **The Old Guard**
17 B c 31/3 Intense Focus (USA)—Cuiseach (IRE) (Bachelor Duke (USA)) (19047) **Saffron Racing**
18 B c 18/4 Foxwedge (AUS)—Flaming Cliffs (USA) (Kingmambo (USA)) **Niarchos Family**
19 Ch c 2/4 Dandy Man (IRE)—Friendly Heart (CAN) (Lion Heart (USA)) (38095)
20 HI LA MAL, ch c 27/2 Nathaniel (IRE)—Princess Luna (GER) (Grand Lodge (USA)) (7000)
21 Ch f 20/3 Dutch Art—Injaaz (Sheikh Albadou) (50000)
22 B c 29/3 Canford Cliffs (IRE)—Mystiara (IRE) (Orpen (USA)) (24761) **The Foundation Partnership**
23 Br c 24/3 Sayif (IRE)—Pearl Magic (USA) (Speightstown (USA)) (15238) **Saleh Al Homaizi & Imad Al Sagar**
24 B c 10/4 Pivotal—Something Blue (Petong) (50000) **The Pivotal Club**
25 STANHOPE, b c 12/4 Equiano (FR)—Nicoise (IRE) (Lear Spear (USA)) **R. C. Tooth**
26 TREASURE REALM (FR), gr c 27/3 Kendargent (FR)—
Rose du Roi (IRE) (Royal Academy (USA)) (30000) **Redman, Philipps & Hodge**

Other Owners: I. J. Al-Sagar, Mr H. Black, T. P. Bostwick, Mr A. R. Boyd-Rochfort, Mr K. J. Breen, Mr J. A. Bryan, Mr E. Carroll, Chelsea Thoroughbreds Ltd, Mr H. Cram, Mr P. M. Fagan, Mr D. T. Fish, T. C. O. Gredley, T. F. Harris, Mrs E. A. Harris, Mrs P. N. D. Hodge, Saleh Al Homaizi, Mr V. Humphreys, Mr I. Marmion, Mr M. Morris, Mr C. E. L. Philipps, P. A. Philipps, Mr T. J. Ramsden, Mr A. Randle, T. S. Redman, Mrs A. Scotney, S. M. Smith, Mrs L. A. Smith, Mr M. Walsh, Mr C. Woodhouse.

538 **MR JEREMY SCOTT, Dulverton**
Postal: **Higher Holworthy Farm, Brompton Regis, Dulverton, Somerset, TA22 9NY**
Contacts: **PHONE (01398) 371414 MOBILE (07709) 279483**
E-MAIL **holworthyfarm@yahoo.com**

1 ALBEROBELLO (IRE), 8, b g Old Vic—Tourist Attraction (IRE) **Bradley Partnership**
2 ANYTHINGMAYHAPPEN (IRE), 5, b g Publisher (USA)—Wild Coast (IRE) **Bradley Partnership**
3 BEST BOY BARNEY (IRE), 10, b g Rashar (USA)—Graigue Lass (IRE) **Mr G. T. Lever**
4 BLUE APRIL (FR), 5, b g Blue Bresil (FR)—Royale Little (FR) **Mr J P Carrington & Partner**
5 BRAVE DEED (IRE), 10, b g Kadeed (IRE)—Merlins Return (IRE) **Gale Force Seven**
6 COLMERS HILL, 6, b g Crosspeace (IRE)—My Dancing Kin **Gale Force Four**

MR JEREMY SCOTT - Continued

7 **COMRAGH (IRE)**, 6, br m Desert King (IRE)—Akica (IRE) **London Erratics Racing Club**
8 **DAINTY DIVA (IRE)**, 8, b m Indian Danehill (IRE)—She's So Dainty (IRE) **Langleys**
9 **DASHAWAY (IRE)**, 7, ch g Shantou (USA)—Backaway (IRE) **The Town & Country Partnership 2**
10 **DAVERON (IRE)**, 8, b g Winged Love (IRE)—Double Doc (IRE) **Mr N. A. Holder**
11 **DAY OF ROSES (IRE)**, 7, b g Acambaro (GER)—Dan's Choice (IRE) **Derek Coles & John H W Finch**
12 **DECIMUS (IRE)**, 9, b g Bienamado (USA)—Catch Me Dreaming (IRE) **The Ten 2 One Gang**
13 **DUKE'S AFFAIR (IRE)**, 8, b g Fair Mix (IRE)—Dunsfold Duchess (IRE) **Mrs H. L. Stoneman**
14 **EXECUTIVE PRINCE (IRE)**, 6, bl g Presenting—Callanagh Pride (IRE)
15 **I'M OSCAR (IRE)**, 6, b g Oscar (IRE)—I'm Maggy (NZ) **The Free Spirits Partnership**
16 **ISLAND RENDEZVOUS (IRE)**, 6, b g Trans Island—Verlaya (FR) **Cash For Honours**
17 **JACK SNIPE**, 7, b g Kirkwall—Sea Snipe **Mrs L. J. C. Tylor**
18 **KILMURVY (IRE)**, 8, b g Shantou (USA)—Spagna (IRE) **I. R. Murray**
19 **LADY LONGSHOT**, 5, b m Needle Gun (IRE)—So Long **Mr R. J. Lock**
20 **MASTER BENJAMIN**, 9, b g Fair Mix (IRE)—Morning Flight (IRE) **The Master Partners 2**
21 **MELODIC RENDEZVOUS**, 10, ch g Where Or When (IRE)—Vic Melody (FR) **Cash For Honours**
22 **MISS SERIOUS (IRE)**, 6, br m Kalanisi (IRE)—Burnt Out (IRE) **Pillhead House Partners**
23 **MOORLANDS GEORGE**, 8, b g Grape Tree Road—Sandford Springs (USA) **Mrs L. M. Williams**
24 **MOORLANDS JACK**, 11, b g Cloudings (IRE)—Sandford Springs (USA) **Mrs L. M. Williams**
25 **NATIVE ROBIN (IRE)**, 6, br g Robin des Pres (FR)—Homebird (IRE) **The Punchestown Syndicate**
26 **NOTARFBAD (IRE)**, 10, b g Alderbrook—Angels Flame (IRE) **Govier & Brown**
27 **ON THE BRIDGE (IRE)**, 11, b g Milan—Bay Dove **Mr C. J. James**
28 **POPPING ALONG**, 7, ch m Volochine (IRE)—So Long **Mrs C. C. Scott**
29 **PORTERS WAR (IRE)**, 14, ch g Flemensfirth (USA)—Grainne Geal **Sarah Waugh & Paul Porter**
30 **SEEANYTHINGYOULIKE (IRE)**, 5, b g Fruits of Love (USA)—California Dreamin **Jeremy Scott Racing Club**
31 **SHOOFLY MILLY (IRE)**, 7, b m Milan—Jacksister (IRE) **Gale Force One**
32 **SPEEDALONG (IRE)**, 5, b g Vertical Speed (FR)—Emily's Bracelet (IRE) **Mrs S. J. Lanz**
33 **THAT'S GONNA STING (IRE)**, 5, b g Scorpion (IRE)—Creme d'arblay (IRE) **Mr C. J. James**
34 **THE SNAPPY POET**, 7, ch g Byron—Runaway Star **Jeremy Scott Racing Club**
35 **THREEBARMYMEN (IRE)**, 5, b g Winged Love (IRE)—Midnight Susie (IRE) **The Barmy Men**
36 **UNISON (IRE)**, 6, b g Jeremy (USA)—Easter Song (USA) **Mr J. P. Carrington**

Other Owners: Mr M. P. Ansell, Mr J. Bagwell-Purefoy, Mr P. W. Brockman, G. S. Brown, R. Coates, Mrs S. S. Cole, Mrs M. A. Cole, Mr C. Cole, D. J. Coles, J. H. W. Finch, Mr R. J. L. Flood, Mr A. P. Gale, Mrs G. D. Giles, Mr P. F. Govier, Mr P. Govier, M. D. Greatorex, Mr C. F. Hayes, Mr J. L. T. Illingworth, Mr W. M. Izaby-White, R. W. S. Jevon, Mr D. E. Langley, Mr S. J. Loosemore, Mr C. J. Lyles, Miss N. Martin, Mr P. D. Moore, P Porter, Mrs S. M. Ragg, Mr A. M. Rennison, Mr J. R. M. Scott, Mr J. Simpson, Mr M. J. Swallow, Mrs B. J. Tully, Miss S. M. Waugh.

Assistant Trainer: Camilla Scott

Jockey (NH): Nick Scholfield. **Conditional:** Matt Griffiths, David Pritchard. **Amateur:** Mr Rob Hawker, Miss Laura Scott, Miss V. Wade.

---

539 MISS KATIE SCOTT, Galashiels
Postal: **Stables Cottage, Millhaugh, Lindean, Galashiels, Scottish Borders**
Contacts: **MOBILE (07826) 344577**

1 **BENEFIT IN KIND (IRE)**, 8, b g Beneficial—She's So Beautiful (IRE) **Mr E. Cassie**
2 **BOLTON BLUE (IRE)**, 7, b g Blueprint (IRE)—Ebony Countess (IRE) **Mr E. Cassie**
3 **CALTON ENTRY (IRE)**, 7, b g Bahri (USA)—Gaybrook (IRE) **Mr G. H. Smith**
4 **COACHIE BEAR**, 5, ch g Grape Tree Road—Gentle Approach **Mr Edward Cassie and Mr William Muir**
5 **GALLEONS WAY**, 7, gr g Generous (IRE)—Yemaail (IRE) **Mr A. Dawson & Mrs K. Campbell**
6 **HERECOMESNELSON (IRE)**, 7, b g Morozov (USA)—Undesperado View (IRE) **Millhaugh Racing**
7 **JEWELLERY (IRE)**, 9, b br m King's Best (USA)—Eilean Shona **Mrs S. Scott**
8 **KALAHARRY (IRE)**, 4, b g Kalanisi (IRE)—Full Imperatrice (FR) **Matros Racing & Mr William Muir**
9 **KALASTAR (IRE)**, 7, b g Kalanisi (IRE)—Katsura **Mr K. Telfer**
10 **KNOCKLAYDE (IRE)**, 4, b g Mountain High (IRE)—Foret Noire (IRE) **The Jackson Partnership**
11 **LOCHALSH (IRE)**, 5, ch g Duke of Marmalade (IRE)—Kylemore (IRE) **Millhaugh Racing**
12 **MOSCOW MENACE (IRE)**, 9, b g Moscow Society (USA)—Sky Flagship (FR) **Miss E. Dunkley**
13 **STORMION (IRE)**, 11, b g Flemensfirth (USA)—El Moss (IRE) **Mrs S. Scott**
14 **WHATSTHESTORYMAN (IRE)**, 8, b g Alderbrook—Express Way Lady (IRE) **Miss E. Dunkley**

Other Owners: Mrs K. Campbell, A. Dawson, Mr S. P. Gillie, Dr D. E. McGuiness, Mr W. J. Muir, Miss K. Scott, Mr R. Thayne, Mr M. Wright.

540 **MR MICHAEL SCUDAMORE, Bromsash**
Postal: **Eccleswall Court, Bromsash, Nr. Ross-on-Wye, Herefordshire, HR9 7PP**
Contacts: **PHONE (01989) 750844 FAX (01989) 750281 MOBILE (07901) 853520**
E-MAIL michael.scu@btconnect.com WEBSITE www.michaelscudamoreracing.co.uk

1 **ARABIAN LEADER**, 4, b c Cape Cross (IRE)—Queen Consort (USA) **M. Scudamore**
2 **BENENDEN (IRE)**, 8, b g Moscow Society (USA)—Ashanti Dancer (IRE) **Mr M. R. Blandford**
3 **COTTONWOOL BABY (IRE)**, 5, b m Gold Well—Golden Steppes (IRE) **M. Scudamore**
4 **DAN EMMETT (USA)**, 6, ch g Flower Alley (USA)—Singing Dixie (USA) **Mrs L. Maclennan**
5 **DAWNIERIVER (IRE)**, 6, br m Indian River (FR)—In Sin (USA) **Don't Tell Ken**
6 **FAR FROM DEFEAT (IRE)**, 6, b g Robin des Pres (FR)—Clonsingle Native (IRE) **The Raise A Glass Partnership**
7 **GAELIC MAGNUM (IRE)**, 4, b g Lawman (FR)—Lapland (FR) **Lynne & Angus Maclennan**
8 **GRACE TARA**, 7, b m Kayf Tara—Fenney Spring **Having A Mare I**
9 **JUPITER CUSTOS (FR)**, 4, b br g Le Havre (IRE)—Angel Rose (IRE) **C. G. J. Chua**
10 **JUSTICE KNIGHT (IRE)**, 4, b g Raven's Pass (USA)—New Story (USA) **M. Scudamore**
11 **KINGSWELL THEATRE**, 4, b g King's Theatre (IRE)—Cresswell Native (IRE) **Mr J. J. Murray**
12 **KRAFTY ONE**, 4, ch f Mastercraftsman (IRE)—Wonderful Desert **Mr M. Jones**
13 **MESTI BOLEH**, 5, b g Cape Cross (IRE)—Miss Meltemi (IRE) **JCG Chua & CK Ong**
14 **MONBEG AQUADUDE (IRE)**, 5, b g Flemensfirth (USA)—Mite Dash (IRE) **Mr M. R. Blandford**
15 **MONBEG DUDE (IRE)**, 11, b g Witness Box (USA)—Ten Dollar Bill (IRE) **Oydunow**
16 **NEXT SENSATION (IRE)**, 9, b g Brian Boru—Road Trip (IRE) **Mr M. R. Blandford**
17 **NO THROUGH ROAD**, 9, b g Grape Tree Road—Pendil's Delight **A. P. Barwell**
18 **PRINCESSE FLEUR**, 6, b m Grape Tree Road—Princesse Grec (FR) **The Honfleur Syndicate**
19 **QUENCH TARA**, 9, b m Kayf Tara—Madam Min **Quench Racing Partnership**
20 **RIPTIDE**, 10, b g Val Royal (FR)—Glittering Image (IRE) **Having A Mare II**
21 **STATE SOVEREIGNTY**, 4, b f Authorized (IRE)—Sovereign's Honour (USA) **M. Scudamore**
22 **STREETS OF PROMISE (IRE)**, 7, b m Westerner—Miracle Lady **Gempro**
23 **SUNGAI LONG**, 4, b g Lawman (FR)—Ammo (IRE) **C. G. J. Chua**
24 **TWENTY EIGHT GUNS**, 6, b m Black Sam Bellamy (IRE)—Glory Be **Mason Scudamore Racing**
25 **ZAYFIRE ARAMIS**, 7, ch g Zafeen (FR)—Kaylifa Aramis **Aramis Racing**

THREE-YEAR-OLDS

26 **GAELIC ANGEL (IRE)**, b f Pour Moi (IRE)—Missionary Hymn (USA) **Mrs L. Maclennan**
27 **GAELIC MASTER (IRE)**, b g Mastercraftsman (IRE)—Colomone Cross (IRE) **Mrs L. Maclennan**

Other Owners: Mrs P. A. Baker, Mr C. Breeze, Mrs S. A. Brown, Mr D. E. Coltman, Mr B. Downard, W. J. Fenn, Mr T. S. Hopkins, K. L. Hunter, Mr A. Maclennan, Mr A. Mason, Mr N. McGawley, A. D. Middleton, Mr F. Ong, Mrs I. Phipps Coltman, Mr M. Preedy, Dr S. M. Readings, Mr N. J. Robinson, Mr S. Robson, Mr J. D. Simpson-Daniel, Mrs L. J. Sluman.

Assistant Trainer: Miss Kate Hanson

---

541 **MR DEREK SHAW, Sproxton**
Postal: **The Sidings, Saltby Road, Sproxton, Melton Mowbray, Leicestershire, LE14 4RA**
Contacts: **PHONE (01476) 860578 FAX (01476) 860578 MOBILE (07721) 039645**
E-MAIL mail@derekshawracing.com WEBSITE www.derekshawracing.com

1 **AGE OF INNOCENCE**, 5, b g Invincible Spirit (IRE)—Elusive Legend (USA) **Mr B. Johnson**
2 **BOROUGH BOY (IRE)**, 6, b g Jeremy (USA)—Ostrusa (AUT) **Mr B. Johnson**
3 **CAPTAIN LARS (SAF)**, 7, b g Captain Al (SAF)—Polar Charge **Mr C. B. Hamilton**
4 **DANCINGTOTHESTARS**, 5, b m Tiger Hill (IRE)—Dancing Duo **Mrs L. J. Shaw**
5 **DARING DRAGON**, 6, gr g Intikhab (USA)—The Manx Touch **Mr D. Shaw**
6 **DEVILUTION (IRE)**, 4, b g Bluegrass Cat (USA)—Meniatarra (USA) **Mr B. Johnson**
7 **DYNAMO WALT**, 5, b g Acclamation—Cambara **Mr B. Johnson**
8 **EXTREME SUPREME**, 5, b g Piccolo—Kitty Kitty Cancan **Mrs L. J. Shaw**
9 6, B g Deportivo—Haunt The Zoo
10 **ILLUSIVE FORCE (IRE)**, 4, ch g Iffraaj—Geesala (IRE) **Mr B. Johnson**
11 **INVECTUS HERO**, 4, b g Paco Boy (IRE)—Blur (IRE) **Mr B. Johnson**
12 4, B c Piccolo—Kitty Kitty Cancan **Mrs L. J. Shaw**
13 **LA BRANA**, 4, b g Exceed And Excel (AUS)—Oatcake **Mr B. Johnson**
14 **LOYALTY**, 9, b g Medicean—Ecoutila (USA) **Mr B. Johnson**
15 **MAGIC DELIGHT (IRE)**, 4, ch f Exceed And Excel (AUS)—Stravella (IRE) **Mr B. Johnson**
16 **MIDNIGHT DESTINY (IRE)**, 4, ro f Dark Angel (IRE)—Cappella (IRE) **Mr B. Johnson**
17 **POLARBROOK (IRE)**, 9, br g Alderbrook—Frozen Cello (IRE) **Mr J. R. Saville**

MR DEREK SHAW - Continued

18 **RUN WITH PRIDE (IRE)**, 6, b g Invincible Spirit (IRE)—Zibilene **The Whiteman Partnership**
19 **SHAWKANTANGO**, 9, b g Piccolo—Kitty Kitty Cancan **Shawthing Racing Partnership**
20 **STUN GUN**, 6, b g Medicean—Tapas En Bal (FR) **Mr J. R. Saville**
21 **SYNOPTIC DREAM (USA)**, 4, b f Medicean—Specific Dream **Mr B. Johnson**
22 **TOP BOY**, 6, b g Exceed And Excel (AUS)—Injaaz **Mr B. Johnson**
23 **UNEX MODIGLIANI (IRE)**, 7, ch g Hurricane Run (IRE)—Chronicle **Mr B. Johnson**
24 **WELLIESINTHEWATER (IRE)**, 6, b g Footstepsinthesand—Shadow Ash (IRE) **The Whiteman Partnership**

THREE-YEAR-OLDS

25 **CORRIDOR KID (IRE)**, b g Kodiac—All In Clover (IRE) **Mr D. Shaw**
26 **CRINKLEY BOTTOM**, b f Dick Turpin (IRE)—Crinkle (IRE) **P. E. Barrett**
27 **DEFIANT CHOICE**, b c Teofilo (IRE)—Endorsement **Mr B. Johnson**
28 **DIVASESQUE (IRE)**, ch f Poet's Voice—Lily Again **Mr B. Johnson**
29 **LE MANEGE ENCHANTE (IRE)**, gr g Zebedee—Beth **Mr B. Johnson**
30 **MANIPURA**, gr f Sleeping Indian—Ming Meng (IRE) **P. E. Barrett**
31 **MEMYSELFIE (IRE)**, b f Kodiac—Cool Tarifa (IRE) **Mr B. Johnson**
32 **NAME THAT TOON**, b f Paco Boy (IRE)—Saktoon (USA) **Mrs L. J. Shaw**
33 **NOFIZZOPHOBIA**, ch f Bahamian Bounty—Croeso Cusan **Mrs L. J. Shaw**
34 **TARONEESH**, b g Canford Cliffs (IRE)—Blur **Mr B. Johnson**
35 **TEMUJINS QUEST (IRE)**, b g Dream Ahead (USA)—Chinese Wall (IRE) **Mr B. Johnson**
36 **YISTY**, ch f Compton Place—Meditation **P. E. Barrett**

Other Owners: S. A. Whiteman.

Yard Sponsor: Grosvenor Contracts Leasing Ltd

Apprentice: Jack Osborn.

---

542   **MRS FIONA SHAW, Dorchester**
Postal: **Skippet Cottage, Bradford Peverell, Dorchester, Dorset, DT2 9SE**
Contacts: PHONE **(01305) 889350** MOBILE **(07970) 370444**
E-MAIL **fiona.shaw05@gmail.com**

1 **BOUND HILL**, 7, b g Kayf Tara—Ardent Bride **John & Heather Snook**
2 **DARWINS THEORY (IRE)**, 8, b g Montjeu—Thrift (IRE) **Mrs F. M. Shaw**
3 **TIMES OF TROUBLE**, 6, b g Tobougg (IRE)—Let It Be **Mrs F. M. Shaw**

Other Owners: Mrs H. A. Snook, J. W. Snook.

---

543   **MRS PATRICIA SHAW, Looe**
Postal: **Kilminorth Park, Looe, Cornwall, PL13 2NE**

1 **ACADEMY GENERAL (IRE)**, 10, b g Beneficial—Discerning Air **Mr D. C. Odgers**

---

544   **MR MARK SHEARS, Chagford**
Postal: **Lower Nattadon, Chagford, Newton Abbot, Devon, TQ13 8ER**
Contacts: PHONE **(01647) 432356** FAX **(01647) 432356** MOBILE **(07881) 745314**
E-MAIL **markshearsracing@gmail.com**

1 **BLACK MARBLE**, 5, br m Passing Glance—Pinegar Lady **Mr M. B. Shears**
2 **GHOST RUNNER (IRE)**, 6, b g Tagula (IRE)—Ball Cat (FR) **Mr M. B. Shears**

Assistant Trainer: Mrs H. Shears

Jockey (NH): Mark Quinlan. **Conditional:** David Noonan,.

545 **MR MATT SHEPPARD, Ledbury**
Postal: **Home Farm Cottage, Eastnor, Ledbury, Herefordshire, HR8 1RD**
Contacts: **FAX** (01531) 634846 **MOBILE** (07770) 625061
E-MAIL matthew.sheppard@cmail.co.uk

1 BEALLANDENDALL (IRE), 8, b g Beneficial—Railstown Lady (IRE) **Mr D. R. Bevan**
2 BUS NAMED DESIRE, 8, b m Alflora (IRE)—Arctic Ring **Mr E. J. Ford**
3 HILL FORT, 6, ch g Pivotal—Cairns (UAE) **Mr A. J. Scrivin**
4 IKTIVIEW, 8, ch g Iktibas—Eastview Princess **Mr E. J. Ford**
5 KERRYHEAD STORM (IRE), 11, b g Glacial Storm (USA)—Kerryhead Girl (IRE) **S. J. D. Gegg**
6 KEY TO THE WEST (IRE), 9, b g Westerner—Monte Solaro (IRE) **Miss R S Newell & Mr T P Morrissey**
7 LOUGHALDER (IRE), 10, ch g Alderbrook—Lough Lein Leader (IRE) **Mr Simon Gegg & Mr Tony Scrivin**
8 MODELIGO (IRE), 7, b g Indian Danehill (IRE)—Glens Lady **S. J. D. Gegg**
9 ROCK ON ROCKY, 8, b g Overbury (IRE)—Tachometer (IRE) **Jan Johnson & Terry Harman**
10 SYLVAN LEGEND, 8, b g Midnight Legend—Sylvan Warbler (USA) **Mr E. J. Ford**

Other Owners: Mr T. A. Harman, Mrs J. M. Johnson, Mr T. P. Morrissey, Miss R. S. Newell.

Amateur: Mr S. Sheppard.

---

546 **MR OLIVER SHERWOOD, Upper Lambourn**
Postal: **Rhonehurst House, Upper Lambourn, Hungerford, Berkshire, RG17 8RG**
Contacts: **PHONE** (01488) 71411 **FAX** (01488) 72786 **MOBILE** (07979) 591867
E-MAIL oliver.sherwood@virgin.net **WEBSITE** www.oliversherwood.com

1 4, B g Flemensfirth (USA)—Ballerina Queen (IRE) **O. M. C. Sherwood**
2 BEFOREALL (IRE), 8, b g Spadoun (FR)—Maggie Howard (IRE) **Beforeall Partnership**
3 BERTIE'S DESIRE, 8, b g King's Theatre (IRE)—Temptation (FR) **T. D. J. Syder**
4 BLAMEITALONMYROOTS (IRE), 6, b m Turtle Island (IRE)—Makingyourmindup (IRE) **T. D. J. Syder**
5 BOUNTIFUL SIN, 5, ch g Sinndar (IRE)—Tropical Barth (IRE) **Amity Finance Ltd**
6 CARRY ON SYDNEY, 6, b g Notnowcato—River Fantasy (USA) **Carry On Sydney Partnership**
7 COCO DES CHAMPS (IRE), 6, br m Robin des Champs (FR)—American Chick (IRE) **Michael & Gerry Worcester**
8 COCO SHAMBHALA, 7, b m Indian Danehill (IRE)—Kohinor **Mr R. J. Chugg**
9 COME ON LAURIE (IRE), 8, b g Oscar (IRE)—Megan's Magic **Mr P. Mellett**
10 CRUNCH TIME (IRE), 5, b g Scorpion (IRE)—Ash **Michael & Gerry Worcester**
11 DANVINNIE, 7, b g Midnight Legend—Top Gale (IRE) **John Rathbone**
12 DAYTIME AHEAD (IRE), 5, gr m Daylami (IRE)—Bright Times Ahead (IRE) **Mackenzie's Friends**
13 DEPUTY DAN (IRE), 8, b g Westerner—Louisas Dream (IRE) **T. D. J. Syder**
14 DRUM VALLEY, 8, b g Beat Hollow—Euippe **A Taylor & A Signy**
15 DUKE ARCADIO (IRE), 7, b g Arcadio (GER)—Kildowney Duchess (IRE) **Mr & Mrs Paul & Clare Rooney**
16 FIGHT COMMANDER, 7, b g Oscar (IRE)—Creidim (IRE) **Mr J. C. D. Rathbone**
17 FINANCIAL CLIMATE (IRE), 9, b g Exit To Nowhere (USA)—Claudia's Pearl **Sara Fillery & Friends**
18 FURROWS, 11, b g Alflora (IRE)—See More Furrows **Furrows Ltd**
19 GLOBAL POWER (IRE), 10, b g Subtle Power (IRE)—Bartelko (IRE) **It Wasn't Us**
20 HAUT BAGES (FR), 4, b g Archange d'or (IRE)—Rotina (FR) **Mr Simon Munir & Mr Isaac Souede**
21 HITHERJACQUES LADY (IRE), 4, br f Robin des Champs (FR)—Crackin' Liss (IRE) **Mr A. F. Lousada**
22 HORSEHILL (IRE), 7, b g Flemensfirth (USA)—
   Maid For Adventure (IRE) **Ian Barratt, Stephen Short & Adam Signy**
23 ICING ON THE CAKE (IRE), 6, b g Spadoun (FR)—
   Honeyed (IRE) **Palmer-Brown Worcester Lousada Shrubsall**
24 ITS A STING (IRE), 7, b g Scorpion (IRE)—Wyndham Sweetmarie (IRE) **Mr M. A. Burton**
25 KINGS BANDIT (IRE), 8, b g King's Theatre (IRE)—Gentle Lady (IRE) **Mrs D. L. Whateley**
26 LEGEND LADY, 5, b m Midnight Legend—Aoninch **Legend Lady Partnership**
27 LEMTARA BAY, 5, b m Kayf Tara—Lemon's Mill (USA) **G. R. Waters**
28 MANY CLOUDS (IRE), 9, br g Cloudings (IRE)—Bobbing Back (IRE) **T. J. Hemmings**
29 MCKENZIE'S FRIEND (IRE), 5, b g Flemensfirth (USA)—Escrea (IRE) **Jeremy Dougall & Will Watt**
30 MILGEN BAY, 10, br g Generous (IRE)—Lemon's Mill (USA) **James & Clare Luck**
31 MISCHIEVOUS MILLY, 8, b m Old Vic—Jennifers Diary (IRE) **A. Stewart & A. Taylor**
32 MORNING REGGIE, 7, gr g Turgeon (USA)—Nile Cristale (FR) **T. D. J. Syder**
33 MY CHARITY (IRE), 5, b g King's Theatre (IRE)—Benefit Ball (IRE) **T. J. Hemmings**
34 PITON PETE (IRE), 5, b g Westerner—Glenair Lucy (IRE) **Mr P. Mellett**
35 PUFFIN BILLY (IRE), 8, b g Heron Island (IRE)—Downtown Train (USA) **T. D. J. Syder**
36 QUEEN OLIVIA, 8, b m King's Theatre (IRE)—Queen's Leader (IRE) **Mr R. Hunnisett**
37 RAYVIN BLACK, 7, b g Halling (USA)—Optimistic **Mr R. White & Mr V. J. Walsh**

MR OLIVER SHERWOOD - Continued

38 **ROBINESSE (IRE)**, 5, ch m Robin des Champs (FR)—
Jennifers Diary (IRE) **Mr A Taylor & The Three Underwriters**
39 **ROBINSSON (IRE)**, 6, b g Robin des Champs (FR)—Silver Proverb **A. Taylor**
40 **ROMULUS DU DONJON (IRE)**, 5, gr g Stormy River (FR)—
Spring Stroll (USA) **Mr Simon Munir & Mr Isaac Souede**
41 **ROUGE ET BLANC (FR)**, 11, ch g Mansonnien (FR)—Fidelety (FR) **O Sherwood & Tim Syder**
42 **ROYALRAISE (IRE)**, 7, b g Royal Anthem (USA)—
Raise The Issue (IRE) **Ian Barratt, Stephen Short & Adam Signy**
43 **SAFE HARBOUR (IRE)**, 4, b g Stowaway—Beharista (FR) **Jeremy Dougall & Will Watt**
44 **SALTO CHISCO (IRE)**, 8, b g Presenting—Dato Fairy (IRE) **Mrs D. L. Whateley**
45 **SANTA'S SECRET (IRE)**, 8, b g Basanta (IRE)—Rivers Town Rosie (IRE) **Barratt, Gumienny, Johnsons & Signys**
46 **SERPICO (IRE)**, 5, br g Scorpion (IRE)—Call Her Again (IRE) **Diana Whateley & Tim Syder**
47 **SPORTING MILAN (IRE)**, 5, b g Milan—Sports Leader (IRE) **Mr M. A. Burton**
48 **STIFF UPPER LIP (IRE)**, 6, b g Sakhee's Secret—Just In Love (FR) **Richard Hitchcock Alan King**
49 **SURTEE DU BERLAIS (IRE)**, 6, b m High Chaparral (IRE)—Marina du Berlais (FR) **Mrs S. Griffiths**
50 **TANIOKEY (IRE)**, 6, b m Scorpion (IRE)—Creation (IRE) **Mr M. A. Burton**
51 **THE FRESH PRINCE (IRE)**, 6, b g Robin des Pres (FR)—Hayley Cometh (IRE) **T. J. Hemmings**
52 **THE ORGANIST (IRE)**, 5, b m Alkaadhem—Go On Eileen (IRE) **Million in Mind Partnership**
53 **TOVIERE (IRE)**, 5, ch g Presenting—Aventia (IRE) **Diana Whateley & Tim Syder**
54 4, B f King's Theatre (IRE)—Valdas Queen (GER) **Mr P. J. O'Neill**
55 **WESTSTREET (IRE)**, 6, b g Westerner—Klipperstreet (IRE) **Weststreet Partnership**
56 **WHAT A SCORCHER**, 5, b m Authorized (IRE)—Street Fire (IRE) **Mr & Mrs I Barratt**

Other Owners: Mr Ian Barratt, Mrs C. Barratt, Mr A. R. Bromley, Mr Brian Carpenter, Mr Herbert Cox, Mr J. Dougall, Mrs Rollo Duckworth, Mrs Sara Fillery, Mrs Caroline Frewer, Mr A. E. Frost, Mr Graham Goode, Mr Marek Gumienny, Mr R. G. Hitchcock, Mr A. Holt, Mr A. E. King, Mrs Michael Lambert, Mr A. F. Lousada, Mr James Luck, Mrs Clare Luck, Mr C. Mackenzie, Mr Peter Mellett, Mr D. Minton, Mr S. Munir, Mrs D. Nicholson, Mr J. Palmer-Brown, Mr H. M. J. Pope, Mrs Maryclare Prowse, Mr J. Robinson, Mrs C. Rooney, Mr P. A. Rooney, Mr O. M. C. Sherwood, Mr B. T. E. Shrubsall, Mr Adam Signy, Mr Isaac Souede, Mr Adrian Stewart, Tim Syder, Mr A. Taylor, Mr V. J. Walsh, Mr W. S. Watt, Mrs Diana L. Whateley, Mr Raymond White, Winterfields Farm Ltd, Mrs G. S. Worcester, Mr Michael Worcester.

Assistant Trainer: Andy Llewellyn **Head Lad:** Stefan Namesansky **Secretary:** Emma Chugg

Jockey (NH): Leighton Aspell. **Conditional:** Harrison Beswick, Ben Ffrench-Davis, Thomas Garner. **Amateur:** Mr Conor Bruen.

---

547 | MR RAYMOND SHIELS, Jedburgh
Postal: **Thickside Farm, Jedburgh, Roxburghshire, TD8 6QY**
Contacts: **PHONE (01835) 864060 MOBILE (07790) 295645**

1 **DAMSON GIN**, 9, b m Fair Mix (IRE)—Sing And Dance **R. Shiels**
2 **LUCARNO DANCER**, 6, b m Lucarno (USA)—Sing And Dance **R. Shiels**
3 **TIKKANDEMICKEY (IRE)**, 10, gr g Tikkanen (USA)—Miss Vikki (IRE) **R. Shiels**

---

548 | MISS LYNN SIDDALL, Tadcaster
Postal: **Stonebridge Farm, Colton, Tadcaster, North Yorkshire, LS24 8EP**
Contacts: **PHONE (01904) 744291 FAX (01904) 744291 MOBILE (07778) 216692/4**

1 **BETHELLIE PRIDE**, 6, b m Misu Bond (IRE)—Sunset Lady (IRE) **Ms J. A. French**
2 **BLUE COVE**, 11, ch g Karinga Bay—Meadow Blue **G. Kennington**
3 **CADGERS HOLE**, 9, b g Helissio (FR)—Not So Prim **Mrs D. Ibbotson & Miss J. M. Slater**
4 **FIRST OF NEVER (IRE)**, 10, b g Systematic—Never Promise (FR) **Lynn Siddall Racing II**
5 **HARPERS RUBY**, 6, b m Byron—La Belle Katherine (USA) **Mr J. A. Kay**
6 **I KNOW THE CODE (IRE)**, 11, b g Viking Ruler (AUS)—Gentle Papoose **Lynn Siddall Racing II**
7 **IN VINO VERITAS (IRE)**, 5, b g Art Connoisseur (USA)—Robin **Mr J. A. Kay**
8 **LA HAVRESE (FR)**, 5, ch m Le Havre (IRE)—La Buena (IRE) **Mr J. A. Kay**
9 **LISDONAGH HOUSE (IRE)**, 14, b g Little Bighorn—Lifinsa Barina (IRE) **Mr J. P. Cooke**
10 **PADDY'S ROCK (IRE)**, 5, b g Whipper (USA)—Hedera (USA) **Mr J. A. Kay**
11 **YORKSHIREMAN (IRE)**, 6, b g Red Clubs (IRE)—Ossiana (IRE) **Jan Slater & Partners**

THREE-YEAR-OLDS

12 **MR CONUNDRUM**, b c Paco Boy (IRE)—Folly Drove **Mr J. A. Kay**

MISS LYNN SIDDALL - Continued

Other Owners: Mr C. Abbott, Mrs P. Clark, Mrs W. Cooper, Mr B. Donkin, Mr I. Grice, Mrs P. M. Hornby, Mrs K. Kennington, Ms S. Lythe, Mr D. McGhee, Miss L. C. Siddall, Miss J. M. Slater, Miss Sue Vinden, Mrs A. Walker, Mr C. Wilkinson.

Assistant Trainer: Stephen Hackney

549	**MR DAVID SIMCOCK, Newmarket**

Postal: **The Office, Trillium Place, Birdcage Walk, Newmarket, Suffolk, CB8 0NE**
Contacts: **PHONE (01638) 662968 FAX (01638) 663888 MOBILE (07808) 954109**
E-MAIL david@davidsimcock.co.uk WEBSITE www.davidsimcock.co.uk

1 BALIOS (IRE), 4, ch c Shamardal (USA)—Elle Galante (GER)
2 BATEEL (IRE), 4, b f Dubawi (IRE)—Attractive Crown (USA)
3 BEYOND ARGUMENT (IRE), 4, b g Galileo (IRE)—Thought Is Free
4 BRETON ROCK (IRE), 6, b g Bahamian Bounty—Anna's Rock (IRE)
5 CALLING OUT (IRE), 5, b br g Martaline—Exit The Straight (IRE)
6 CAN'T CHANGE IT (IRE), 5, gr g Verglas (IRE)—All Tied Up (IRE)
7 CAPTAIN MORLEY, 5, b g Hernando (FR)—Oval Office
8 CARNACHY (IRE), 4, gr f Mastercraftsman (IRE)—Market Day
9 CARTIER (IRE), 4, b f Montjeu (IRE)—Rosamixa (FR)
10 CASPAR NETSCHER, 7, b h Dutch Art—Bella Cantata
11 CURBYOURENTHUSIASM (IRE), 5, gr g Mastercraftsman (IRE)—Mohican Princess
12 DESERT ENCOUNTER (IRE), 4, b g Halling (USA)—La Chicana (IRE)
13 DOCTOR SARDONICUS, 5, ch g Medicean—Never A Doubt
14 GLAN Y GORS (IRE), 4, b g High Chaparral (IRE)—Trading Places
15 GLORY AWAITS (IRE), 6, ch g Choisir (AUS)—Sandbox Two (IRE)
16 HIGHLAND GAMES, 4, b g Cape Cross (IRE)—High Barn
17 HOPE YOU DANCE (FR), 4, ch f Mastercraftsman (IRE)—Anna of Dubai (GER)
18 HORSTED KEYNES (IRE), 6, ch g Giant's Causeway (USA)—Viking's Cove (USA)
19 INTRUDE, 4, b g Intikhab (USA)—Don't Tell Mum (IRE)
20 LIGHTNING SPEAR, 5, ch h Pivotal—Atlantic Destiny (IRE)
21 MAJEED, 6, b g Mount Nelson—Clever Millie (USA)
22 ORACOLO (IRE), 4, b g Cape Cross (IRE)—Illuminise (IRE)
23 PRINCESS TANSY, 4, b f Equiano (FR)—Tanasie
24 RED CARDINAL (IRE), 4, b c Montjeu (IRE)—Notable
25 SHEIKHZAYEDROAD, 7, b g Dubawi (IRE)—Royal Secrets (IRE)
26 THE CASHEL MAN (IRE), 4, b g High Chaparral (IRE)—Hadarama (IRE)
27 THE CORSICAN (IRE), 5, b h Galileo (IRE)—Walklikeanegyptian (IRE)
28 UNDER SIEGE (IRE), 4, b g Invincible Spirit (IRE)—Interpose
29 WHISPERING WARRIOR (IRE), 7, b g Oasis Dream—Varenka (IRE)

THREE-YEAR-OLDS

30 ADALENE, b f Makfi—Marine Bleue (IRE)
31 ALGOMETER, gr c Archipenko (USA)—Albanova
32 BLYNX, b f Equiano (FR)—Desert Lynx (IRE)
33 BYBROOK, b f Dubawi (IRE)—Diary (IRE)
34 CAFE AMERICAIN (IRE), b c Holy Roman Emperor (IRE)—Sister Golightly
35 CERSEI, b f Invincible Spirit (IRE)—Elle Galante (GER)
36 CHINOISERIES, b f Archipenko (USA)—Robe Chinoise
37 DISQUOTATIONAL, ch f Nayef (USA)—Doggerbank (IRE)
38 DRAGON MALL (USA), b c Blame (USA)—Petition the Lady (USA)
39 FORESIGHT (FR), b c Dream Ahead (USA)—Madhya (USA)
40 FOUR POETS, ch g Poet's Voice—O Fourlunda
41 GOLDMEMBER, ch c New Approach (IRE)—Sister Act
42 GREAT THOUGHTS (IRE), ch f Iffraaj—Fascination (IRE)
43 HIGH HOPES, b f Zamindar (USA)—Dixielake (IRE)
44 KING OF DREAMS, ch c Dream Ahead (USA)—Complexion
45 MS GILLARD, b f Aussie Rules (USA)—Oval Office
46 NOTICE (IRE), ch f New Approach (IRE)—Classic Remark (IRE)
47 B f Shirocco (GER)—Pelagia (IRE)
48 PLAYFUL DUDE (USA), b c Drosselmeyer (USA)—Choice Play (USA)
49 PROSECUTE (FR), b g Lawman (FR)—Dissitation (IRE)

MR DAVID SIMCOCK - Continued

50 **RAGNER,** ch g New Approach (IRE)—Frivolity
51 **RUBENSIAN,** ch c Medicean—Hymnsheet
52 **SINGYOURSONG (IRE),** b f Aqlaam—Dhan Dhana (IRE)
53 **TELL A STORY,** b f Dutch Art—Ghenwah (FR)
54 **TURNING THE TABLE (IRE),** gr f Mastercraftsman (IRE)—Duchess Dee (IRE)
55 **ULTIMATE STAR,** gr c Starspangledbanner (AUS)—Ultimate Best
56 **UNSUSPECTED GIRL (IRE),** b f Rip Van Winkle (IRE)—Sweet Sioux
57 **VEENA (FR),** b f Elusive City (USA)—Kensita (FR)
58 **WEST COAST FLYER,** b c Cape Cross (IRE)—La Felicita

TWO-YEAR-OLDS

59 B f 28/1 High Chaparral (IRE)—Albanka (USA) (Giant's Causeway (USA))
60 B c 20/2 Manduro (GER)—Adjudicate (Dansili) (103359)
61 **AKRANTI,** ch f 26/4 Pivotal—Akdarena (Hernando (FR))
62 **BAB EL MANDEB (USA),** b c 25/2 Blame (USA)—April Pride (Falbrav (IRE)) (42735)
63 B c 6/4 Sir Percy—Balatoma (IRE) (Mr Greeley (USA))
64 B c 19/2 Lope de Vega (IRE)—Black Dahlia (Dansili) (44296)
65 Ch f 14/4 Arcano (IRE)—Boo Boo Bear (IRE) (Almutawakel (40000)
66 B c 14/2 Canford Cliffs (IRE)—Can Dance (Manduro (GER)) (95976)
67 B f 16/2 Acclamation—Choral (Oratorio (IRE)) (60000)
68 **COOL BREEZE (IRE),** b f 10/3 Dream Ahead (USA)—Dead Cool (Kyllachy) (68000)
69 **DALAVIDA (FR),** gr f 4/2 Kendargent (FR)—Dalawysa (FR) (Dalakhani (IRE)) (68000)
70 B c 11/2 Medicean—Despatch (Nayef (USA)) (105000)
71 B c 16/2 Frankel—Drifting (IRE) (Sadler's Wells (USA)) (140273)
72 B f 9/2 Frankel—First (Highest Honor (FR))
73 Ch f 19/2 Dragon Pulse (IRE)—Free Lance (IRE) (Grand Lodge (USA)) (55370)
74 B f 30/3 Oasis Dream—Frivolity (Pivotal)
75 B f 18/4 Canford Cliffs (IRE)—Gilded Vanity (IRE) (Indian Ridge) (200000)
76 B c 21/1 Rip Van Winkle (IRE)—Happy Holly (IRE) (Holy Roman Emperor (IRE)) (40000)
77 B c 22/2 Frankel—Hasten (IRE) (Montjeu (IRE))
78 B c 6/3 Deep Impact (JPN)—Keiai Gerbera (JPN) (Smarty Jones (USA))
79 B c 16/2 Holy Roman Emperor (IRE)—Kentucky Warbler (IRE) (Spinning World (USA)) (180000)
80 B f 26/4 Makfi—Liberty Chery (Statue of Liberty (USA))
81 B c 18/2 Dream Ahead (USA)—Malladore (IRE) (Lawman (FR)) (115000)
82 B c 13/3 Frankel—Marine Bleue (IRE) (Desert Prince (IRE))
83 **MISS SUGARS,** ch f 26/1 Harbour Watch (IRE)—Three Sugars (AUS) (Starcraft (NZ)) (10000)
84 B c 30/1 Deep Impact (JPN)—Musical Way (FR) (Gold Away (IRE))
85 B c 12/2 Kheleyf (USA)—My Lucky Liz (IRE) (Exceed And Excel (AUS))
86 B c 21/2 Teofilo (IRE)—Night And Dance (IRE) (Danehill Dancer (IRE))
87 B c 26/2 Archipenko (USA)—Oval Office (Pursuit of Love) (25000)
88 B f 1/5 Dutch Art—Plethora (Sadler's Wells (USA))
89 B f 5/2 Dutch Art—Rare Ransom (Oasis Dream)
90 B c 27/4 Harbour Watch (IRE)—Rock Lily (Rock of Gibraltar (IRE)) (110000)
91 **ROMAN SAINTS,** b c 16/2 Holy Roman Emperor (IRE)—Anything Goes (IRE) (Nayef (USA)) (20000)
92 **SABADILLA,** b f 9/4 Archipenko (USA)—Songerie (Hernando (FR))
93 B c 17/3 Pivotal—Shatter (IRE) (Mr Greeley (USA)) (40000)
94 B c 23/2 Blame (USA)—She Has Aptitude (USA) (Aptitude (USA)) (61050)
95 B c 5/2 Galileo (IRE)—Simply Perfect (Danehill (USA))
96 Ch c 17/4 Mastercraftsman (IRE)—Swirling (IRE) (Galileo (IRE)) (105000)
97 Ch c 16/2 Galileo (IRE)—Tereschenko (IRE) (Giant's Causeway (USA))
98 B c 18/2 Oasis Dream—Tingling (USA) (Storm Cat (USA))
99 B c 27/4 Galileo (IRE)—Walklikeanegyptian (IRE) (Danehill (USA))
100 B f 14/3 Kodiac—When Not Iff (IRE) (Iffraaj) (52380)
101 B f 21/2 Invincible Spirit (IRE)—Zallerina (Zamindar (USA))
102 B c 7/2 Henrythenavigator (USA)—Zimira (IRE) (Invincible Spirit (IRE))

Owners: Abdullah Al Mansouri, Al Asayl Bloodstock Ltd, Sultan Ali, Mrs Yvonne Allsop, Mr Roger Allsop, Julia Annable, Mr William Baker, Mr James Barnett, Jonathen Barnett, Black Gold Partnership, R. G. W. Brown, Mr Leon Caine, Malcolm Caine, Chippenham Lodge Stud, John Cook, Sheikh Juma Dalmook, Khalifa Dasmal, Mr M. P. Gibbens, Happy Valley Racing & Breeding Ltd, Mrs Fitri Hay, The Hon H. M. Herbert, Hesmonds Stud, Highclere Thoroughbred Racing Ltd, Mr Andrew Howells, Mohammed Jaber, Ahmed Jaber, Alison Jackson, Karmaa Racing Ltd, Roger MacNair, Mrs John Magnier, Saeed Manana, Manor Farm Stud, Millingbrook Racing, Pearl Bloodstock Ltd, Daniel Pittack, Qatar Racing Ltd, Miss Kirsten Rausing, Mrs Sonia Rogers, Ali Saeed, Gerhard Schoeningh, Dr Arujuna Sivananthan, Mrs Karthika Sivananthan, Mr Derrick Smith, St Albans Bloodstock Ltd, Mrs M. F. Stone, Mr Andrew Stone, Mr M. Tabor, Mrs Doreen Tabor, Dai Walters, Charles Wentworth, Andrew Whitlock, Mr C. G. P. Wyatt, Major M. G. Wyatt.

MR DAVID SIMCOCK - Continued

Assistant Trainer: Tom Clover

Jockey (flat): Jamie Spencer. **Apprentice:** George Buckell, Sophie Killoran, Daryl McLaughlin.
Amateur: Mr Matthew Johnson.

550

MR DAN SKELTON, Alcester
Postal: **Lodge Hill, Shelfield Green, Shelfield, Alcester, Warwickshire, B49 6JR**
Contacts: **PHONE** (01789) 336339
E-MAIL office@danskeltonracing.com **WEBSITE** www.danskeltonracing.com

1 ABRICOT DE L'OASIS (FR), 6, b g Al Namix (FR)—La Normandie (FR) **Mr F. McAleavy**
2 AGE OF DISCOVERY, 5, b g Nayef (USA)—Magic Tree (UAE) **The LAM Partnership**
3 AIR GLIDER (IRE), 6, b g Mountain High (IRE)—California Blue (FR) **Mr C. Buckingham**
4 AL FEROF (FR), 11, gr g Dom Alco (FR)—Maralta (FR) **Mr J. R. Hales**
5 AL REESHA (IRE), 5, b m Kayf Tara—Simply Kitty (IRE) **Mr N. J. G. Allsop**
6 ARTHAMINT, 8, b g Passing Glance—Araminta **Mrs A. J. Higgins**
7 ASHOKA (IRE), 4, gr g Azamour (IRE)—Jinskys Gift (IRE) **Mr F. McAleavy**
8 ASUM, 5, b g Kayf Tara—Candy Creek (IRE) **Mrs G. Widdowson & Mrs R. Kelvin-Hughes**
9 AT THE TOP (FR), 6, b m Network (GER)—Quaiou (FR) **Nick Skelton & Judy Craymer**
10 AZZURI, 4, b g Azamour (IRE)—Folly Lodge **The Blind Squirrels**
11 BANDSMAN, 5, b g Bandmaster (USA)—Soleil Sauvage **Mrs S. J. Faulks**
12 BARATINEUR (FR), 5, ch g Vendangeur (IRE)—Olmantina (FR) **Grech & Parkin**
13 BEAUTIFUL GEM (FR), 6, ch m Muhtathir—Hunorisk (FR) **Mr & Mrs J. D. Cotton**
14 BEKKENSFIRTH, 7, b g Flemensfirth (USA)—Bekkaria (FR) **Mrs P. M. Scott**
15 BELLENOS (FR), 8, b g Apsis—Palmeria (FR) **Mr & Mrs J. D. Cotton**
16 BENISSIMO (IRE), 6, b g Beneficial—Fennor Rose (IRE) **A Chandler,L Westwood,D Balchin,K Jones**
17 BETAMECHE (FR), 5, gr g Kapgarde (FR)—Kaldona (FR) **Miss J. Craymer**
18 BILZIC (FR), 5, b br g Axxos (GER)—Izellane (FR) **Donlon, Doyle & MacDonald**
19 BLUE HERON (IRE), 8, b g Heron Island (IRE)—American Chick (IRE) **Horwood Harriers Partnership**
20 BLUE PRAIRIE, 5, b g Tobougg (IRE)—Prairie Sun (GER) **Horwood Hunters**
21 BON CHIC (FR), 7, b m Presenting—Homebird (IRE) **Coral Champions Club**
22 BORN SURVIVOR (IRE), 5, b g King's Theatre—
　　　　　　　　　　　　　　　　　　　Bob's Flame (IRE) **Mrs G. Widdowson & Mrs R. Kelvin-Hughes**
23 BOSS DES MOTTES (FR), 5, b g Califet (FR)—Puszta des Mottes (FR) **Mr C. A. Donlon**
24 BUBBA N SQUEAK (FR), 5, ch g Dom Alco (FR)—Naiade du Moulin (FR) **Mr C. A. Donlon**
25 CAPTAIN CHAOS (IRE), 5, ch g Golan (IRE)—Times Have Changed (IRE) **Mike and Eileen Newbould**
26 CAPTAIN KELLY (IRE), 9, b g Oscar (IRE)—Tri Folene (FR) **Donlon, Doyle, MacDonald & Webb**
27 CH'TIBELLO (FR), 5, b g Sageburg (IRE)—Neicha (FR) **The Can't Say No Partnership**
28 CHAP, 6, ch g Midnight Legend—Silver Solace **Fruits Incorporated, P Castle, Mahon**
29 CHARLIE'S OSCAR (IRE), 6, b g Oscar (IRE)—Blue Gallery (IRE) **Universal Recycling & Dan Skelton**
30 CHATEAU CHINON (FR), 4, b g Dream Well (FR)—Liesse de Marbeuf (FR) **Mike and Eileen Newbould**
31 CHRISTMAS HAMPER (IRE), 4, b g Dubawi (IRE)—Gift Range (IRE) **Mr C. Buckingham**
32 CHURCHTOWN CHAMP (IRE), 5, b g Robin des Champs (FR)—Annagh Lady (IRE) **Priority Racing Partnership**
33 CLOSEST FRIEND, 7, b g Kayf Tara—Princess of War **Lottie Parsons & Sue Raymond**
34 COBRA DE MAI (FR), 4, b g Great Pretender (IRE)—Miria Galanda (FR) **Norman Lake & Susan Carsberg**
35 CROCKERY, 6, b m Croco Rouge (IRE)—Always Forgiving **Mrs S. C. Welch**
36 DEBDEBDEB, 6, b m Teofilo (IRE)—Windmill **The Sea Breeze Partnership**
37 DRAGON DE LA TOUR (FR), 5, b g Royal Dragon (USA)—Turga de La Tour (FR) **Three Celts**
38 FAIRYTALE THEATRE (IRE), 9, b m King's Theatre (IRE)—Bay Dove **Mr M. Fennessy**
39 FOCACCIA (IRE), 5, b g Milan—Dantes Term (IRE) **Mr T. Spraggett**
40 FOU ET SAGE (FR), 5, b g Sageburg (IRE)—Folie Lointaine (FR) **Mr A. L. Brooks**
41 FOUBURG (FR), 4, b g Sageburg (IRE)—Folie Lointaine (FR) **Brooks & Bromet Families**
42 FREE STONE HILL (IRE), 6, b g Beneficial—Claramanda (IRE) **Martin & Anna Rashdi & Richard Ward**
43 GIRLY GIRL (IRE), 7, b m Golan (IRE)—Clan Music (IRE) **Mr T. Crowe**
44 GO ODEE GO (IRE), 8, b g Alkaadhem—Go Franky **N. W. Lake**
45 GREAT LINK, 7, b g Rail Link—The Strand **Mr C. Hodgson**
46 HERONS HEIR (IRE), 8, b g Heron Island (IRE)—Kyle Lamp (IRE) **HighclereThoroughbredRacing-Herons Heir**
47 HURRICANE HOLLOW, 6, b g Beat Hollow—Veenwouden **Mr M. J. Rozenbroek**
48 INDIETIR (IRE), 4, b br g Muhtathir—Indietra (USA) **Mr A. L. Brooks**
49 ISTIMRAAR (IRE), 5, b g Dansili—Manayer (IRE) **Grech & Parkin**
50 ITS'AFREEBEE (IRE), 6, b g Danroad (AUS)—Aphra Benn (IRE) **Rebel Jumping**
51 JUST A NORMAL DAY (IRE), 6, b g High Chaparral (IRE)—Thats Luck (IRE) **CNC Routing Limited**
52 KAFELLA, 4, gr g Kayf Tara—Sisella (IRE) **P. E. Atkinson**
53 KASAKH NOIR (FR), 4, ch g Redback—Vale of Honor (FR) **Mr T. P. Radford**

MR DAN SKELTON - Continued

54 **KING BORU (IRE)**, 8, b g Brian Boru—Final Instalment (IRE) **The Can't Say No Partnership**
55 **KNOCKGRAFFON (IRE)**, 6, b g Flemensfirth (USA)—Gleaming Spire **Ms B. J. Abt**
56 **LATE NIGHT LILY**, 5, b m Midnight Legend—Ready To Crown (USA) **Braybrooke Lodge Partnership**
57 **LE BACARDY (FR)**, 10, b g Bahhare (USA)—La Balagna **Mr C. Hodgson**
58 **LE BRAYE (IRE)**, 4, b g Court Cave (IRE)—Salsaparilla (FR)
59 **LEVELLING**, 4, ch f Pivotal—Lane County (USA) **Mr C. Buckingham**
60 **LISTEN TO THE MAN (IRE)**, 6, b m Court Cave (IRE)—Badia Dream (IRE) **M. Boothright**
61 **LONG HOUSE HALL (IRE)**, 8, b g Saddlers' Hall (IRE)—Brackenvale (IRE) **J. D. Duggan**
62 **LOVEFROMABOVE (IRE)**, 5, b m Flemensfirth (USA)—Good Looking Woman (IRE) **Mr D. N. Skelton**
63 **LYNDA'S BOY**, 5, b g Rainbow High—Braybrooke Lady (IRE) **The On The Bridle Partnership**
64 **MASTER JAKE (IRE)**, 8, b g Pyrus (USA)—Whitegate Way **Mr C. Buckingham**
65 **MEET THE LEGEND**, 5, b g Midnight Legend—Combe Florey **Highclere Thoroughbred Racing - Legend**
66 **MICKS LAD (IRE)**, 6, b g Beneficial—Floreen (IRE) **Mr T. P. Radford**
67 **MINELLA EXPERIENCE (IRE)**, 5, br g Westerner—Southern Skies (IRE) **Mr & Mrs Gordon Pink**
68 **MISTER KALANISI (IRE)**, 7, b g Kalanisi (IRE)—Maxis Girl (IRE) **Paul & Linda Dixon & Mike Rozenbroek**
69 **MISTER MIYAGI (IRE)**, 7, b g Zagreb (USA)—Muckle Flugga (IRE) **Ben Turner & Jay Tabb**
70 **NORTH HILL HARVEY**, 5, b g Kayf Tara—Ellina **Mrs G. Widdowson & Mrs R. Kelvin-Hughes**
71 **OLDGRANGEWOOD**, 5, b g Central Park (IRE)—Top of The Class (IRE) **Chris Giles & Sandra Giles**
72 **OPEN HEARTED**, 9, b g Generous (IRE)—Romantic Dream **Mr C. Buckingham**
73 **PAIN AU CHOCOLAT (FR)**, 5, b g Enrique—Clair Chene (FR) **Mike and Eileen Newbould**
74 **PUMPED UP KICKS (IRE)**, 9, b m Flemensfirth (USA)—Beauty Star (IRE) **Grech & Parkin**
75 **RED TORNADO (IRE)**, 4, ch g Dr Fong (USA)—Encircle (USA) **Notalotterry**
76 **RENE'S GIRL (IRE)**, 6, b m Presenting—Brogella (IRE) **Andy & Sharon Measham**
77 **ROBIN OF LOCKSLEY (IRE)**, 6, b g Robin des Pres (FR)—Duggary Dancer (IRE) **Simon Caunce & J Tierney**
78 **ROBIN ROE (IRE)**, 5, b g Robin des Champs (FR)—Talktothetail (IRE) **Ms B. J. Abt**
79 **ROCK CHICK SUPREMO (IRE)**, 5, b m Scorpion (IRE)—Ballerina Queen (IRE) **Judy Craymer & Nick Skelton**
80 **ROYAL MANDATE (IRE)**, 4, ch g Manduro (GER)—Hesperia **Mike and Eileen Newbould**
81 **SAMTU (IRE)**, 5, b g Teofilo (IRE)—Samdaniya **Mr C. Buckingham**
82 **SAVELLO (IRE)**, 10, ch g Anshan—Fontaine Frances (IRE) **S Smith & S Campion**
83 **SEA THE SPRINGS (FR)**, 5, gr g Slickly (FR)—Cristal Springs (FR) **Mr K. Sumner**
84 **SHELFORD (IRE)**, 7, b g Galileo (IRE)—Lyrical **Mr C. Hodgson**
85 **SIR MANGAN (IRE)**, 8, b g Darsi (FR)—Lady Pep (IRE) **Mr F. McAleavy**
86 **SOLOMON GREY (FR)**, 4, gr g Sulamani (IRE)—Sardagna (FR) **Mrs S. J. Faulks**
87 **SQUIRE TRELAWNEY**, 10, b g Domedriver (IRE)—Crockadore (USA) **P. J. Haycock**
88 **STAGE ONE (IRE)**, 5, b g King's Theatre (IRE)—Tara Tara (IRE) **Walters Plant Hire & James & Jean Potter**
89 **STARLIGHT COURT (IRE)**, 5, b g Court Cave (IRE)—Marie The (FR)
90 **STEPHANIE FRANCES (IRE)**, 8, b m King's Theatre (IRE)—Brownlow Castle (IRE) **Miss M. J. Hall**
91 **STORM OF SWORDS (IRE)**, 8, ch g Beneficial—Crossbar Lady (IRE) **The McKilocon Syndicate**
92 **SULAMANI THE LATE (IRE)**, 4, b g Sulamani (IRE)—Delayed (FR) **Holt, Clark, Macnabb, Nugent & Robinson**
93 **SUPERB STORY (IRE)**, 5, b g Duke of Marmalade (IRE)—
                                             Yes My Love (FR) **A Holt, J Robinson, A Taylor & S Miller**
94 **SWANSEA MILE (IRE)**, 6, b g Dylan Thomas (IRE)—Hurry Up Helen (IRE) **Mr C. Buckingham**
95 **TARA POTTER**, 6, b m Kayf Tara—Lily Potter **James & Jean Potter**
96 **THE LAST BAR**, 6, b m Kayf Tara—Ardenbar **Mrs C. A. Wyatt**
97 **THINGER LICHT (FR)**, 7, b g Clety (FR)—Family Saga (FR) **Mr C. Hodgson**
98 **THREE MUSKETEERS (IRE)**, 6, b g Flemensfirth (USA)—
                                             Friendly Craic (IRE) **Mrs G. Widdowson & Mrs R. Kelvin-Hughes**
99 **TIPPERAIRY (IRE)**, 5, b g Flemensfirth (USA)—Bambootcha (IRE) **Oliver & K P Ryan & Tony Ahern Ptn.**
100 **TOBY LERONE (IRE)**, 9, b g Old Vic—Dawn's Double (IRE) **Mrs Gill Duckworth & Mrs Pat Dry**
101 **TOMMY RAPPER (IRE)**, 5, b g Milan—Supreme Evening (IRE) **Judy Craymer & Nick Skelton**
102 **TWO TAFFS (IRE)**, 6, b g Flemensfirth (USA)—Richs Mermaid (IRE) **Walters Plant Hire & James & Jean Potter**
103 **ULIS DE VASSY (FR)**, 8, b g Voix du Nord (FR)—Helathou (FR) **Len&White,Hewlett,Robinson,Banyard&Booth**
104 **UPEPITO (FR)**, 8, b g Khalkevi (IRE)—Friandise II (FR) **Mr A. L. Brooks**
105 **VALUE AT RISK**, 7, b g Kayf Tara—Miss Orchestra (IRE) **D. M. Huglin**
106 **VERONAISE (FR)**, 5, ch m Epalo (GER)—Duchesse Pierji (FR) **Mr C. A. Donlon**
107 **VIRGILIO (FR)**, 7, b g Denham Red (FR)—Liesse de Marbeuf (FR) **C J Edwards, D Futter, A H Rushworth**
108 **WALK ON AL (IRE)**, 8, b g Alflora (IRE)—Wave Back (IRE) **Donlon, MacDonald & McGowan**
109 **WALKING IN THE AIR (IRE)**, 6, b g Flemensfirth (USA)—Rossavon (IRE) **Ms B. J. Abt**
110 **WELSH SHADOW (IRE)**, 6, b g Robin des Champs (FR)—What A Mewsment (IRE) **Walters Plant Hire Ltd**
111 **WHAT A GOOD NIGHT (IRE)**, 8, br g Westerner—Southern Skies (IRE) **Mr & Mrs Gordon Pink**
112 **WHAT A WARRIOR (IRE)**, 9, b g Westerner—Be Right (IRE) **Mr & Mrs Gordon Pink**
113 **WILLOW'S SAVIOUR**, 9, ch g Septieme Ciel—Willow Gale **Triple F Partnership**
114 **WILTON MILAN (IRE)**, 8, b g Milan—Biondo (IRE) **J. T. Warner**
115 **WINTERFELL (IRE)**, 8, b g Voix du Nord (FR)—Goldville (IRE) **Mr A. L. Brooks**
116 **WORK IN PROGRESS (IRE)**, 6, b g Westerner—Parsons Term (IRE) **Donlon & Doyle**

MR DAN SKELTON - Continued

117 **WORKBENCH (FR)**, 8, b g Network (GER)—Danhelis (FR) **N. W. Lake**
118 **YES I DID (IRE)**, 6, b m Craigsteel—Younevertoldme (IRE) **The Can't Say No Partnership**
119 **ZARIB (IRE)**, 5, b g Azamour (IRE)—Zariziyna (IRE) **Notalotterry**

THREE-YEAR-OLDS

120 **MONT LACHAUX (FR)**, b c Astarabad (USA)—Belle Yepa (FR) **P. E. Atkinson**

Other Owners: Mr D. Balchin, M. A. Bates, Dr M. Booth, Mr H. F. Bowley, Mrs J. E. Bromet, Mr T. Buttle, Ms J. S. Campion, Mrs S. Carsberg, Mr P. J. Castle, Mr S. A. Caunce, Mr A. Chandler, P. F. Charter, S. J. Clare, Mr C. N. Clark, J. D. Cotton, Mrs B. Cotton, Mrs M. A. Cuff, P. M. Cunningham, P Dixon, Mrs L. J. Dixon, Mr A. Doyle, Mr P. Dry, Mrs G. Duckworth, Mr C. J. Edwards, Dr M. F. Ford, Mr D. Futter, Mr P. E. Gardener, Mrs A. E. Giles, Mr C. M. Giles, Mr J. B. Gilruth, Mr T. J. Good, Mr M. Gowing, Mr C. M. Grech, Miss L. J. Hales, Mr P. R. Halkett, Mr D. Hanafin, Mr T. Hanrahan, The Hon H. M. Herbert, Highclere Nominated Partner Limited, Highclere Thoroughbred Racing Ltd, Mr A. Holt, L. J. Jakeman, N. R. Jennings, Mr K. D. Jones, Mrs E. A. Kelvin-Hughes, R. G. Kelvin-Hughes, Mr T. Kilroe, Mr A. F. Lousada, Mr I. Macnabb, Mr J. G. Mahon, Mr I. Marmion, Mr I. McAleavy, Mr A. N. McGowan, Mr A. R. Measham, Mrs S. M. Measham, Mr P. J. Mercer, Mr S. R. Miller, Mrs K. J. Morgan, Mr L. M. Mulcahy, J. M. Newbould, Mrs E. E. Newbould, T. H. Northwood, Mr J. O. Nugent, Mr T. O'Connor, Mr S. J. Parkin, Mrs C. L. Parsons, Mrs K. M. Pink, Mr G. K. G. Pink, Mrs M. J. Potter, J. E. Potter, Mr A. Randle, Mr M. Rashdi, Mrs A. E. H. Rashdi, Mrs A. S. C. Raymond, Mr J. D. Robinson, Mr A. H. Rushworth, Mr O. F. Ryan, K. P. Ryan, Mrs L. Scott-MacDonald, Mr N. Skelton, Mrs S. Smith, Mr J. A. Tabb, A. Taylor, Mr P. J. Tierney, Mr J. Torrington, Mr B. H. Turner, Universal Recycling Company, Mr R. Ward, Mr R. A. Webb, Mr L. J. Westwood, Mr I. Whitfield, Mrs B. A. Widdowson.

Assistant Trainer: Josh Guerriero

Jockey (NH): Harry Skelton. **Amateur:** Miss Bridget Andrews.

---

551 | **MR KENNETH SLACK, Hilton**
Postal: **Heather Bank, Brackenber, Appleby-In-Westmorland, Cumbria, CA16 6LP**
Contacts: **PHONE (01768) 351354 MOBILE (07931) 137413**

1 **ALMOST GEMINI (IRE)**, 7, gr g Dylan Thomas (IRE)—Streetcar (IRE) **A. Slack**
2 **APACHE BLUE (IRE)**, 12, b g Presenting—La Eile (IRE) **A. Slack**
3 **CUMBRIAN FARMER**, 9, ch g Alflora (IRE)—Quark Top (FR) **A. Slack**
4 **DISCOVERIE**, 8, b g Runyon (IRE)—Sri (IRE) **A. Slack**
5 **FLYBALL**, 4, gr g Proclamation (IRE)—Bella Bertolini **Mrs D. E. Slack**
6 **KILLIECRANKIE**, 8, b g Kayf Tara—Bella Macrae **A. Slack**
7 **MY FRIEND GEORGE**, 10, ch g Alflora (IRE)—Snowgirl (IRE) **A. Slack**
8 **OMID**, 8, b g Dubawi (IRE)—Mille Couleurs (FR) **Mrs D. E. Slack**
9 **RUNSWICK RELAX**, 10, ch g Generous (IRE)—Zany Lady **A. Slack**
10 **TONTO'S SPIRIT**, 4, b g Authorized (IRE)—Desert Royalty (IRE) **A. Slack**

Other Owners: Mrs Dianne Sayer.

---

552 | **MRS PAM SLY, Peterborough**
Postal: **Singlecote, Thorney, Peterborough, Cambridgeshire, PE6 0PB**
Contacts: **PHONE (01733) 270212 MOBILE (07850) 511267**
E-MAIL pamslyracing@btconnect.com

1 **ACTINPIECES**, 5, ro gr m Act One—Bonnet's Pieces **Mrs P. M. Sly**
2 **ALL MY LOVE (IRE)**, 4, b f Lord Shanakill (USA)—Afilla **D. L. Bayliss**
3 **ARKAIM**, 8, b g Oasis Dream—Habariya (IRE) **G.A.Libson D.L.Bayliss G.Taylor P.M.Sly**
4 **BONNET'S VINO**, 8, b m Grape Tree Road—Bonnet's Pieces **G.A.Libson D.L.Bayliss G.Taylor P.M.Sly**
5 4, B f Midnight Legend—Forget The Ref (IRE) **Mr I. Thurtle & Mr R. Abrey**
6 **GHINIA (IRE)**, 5, b m Mastercraftsman (IRE)—Jorghinia (FR) **D. L. Bayliss**
7 **INDULGENCE**, 4, b f Sir Percy—Kaloni (IRE) **Mrs P. M. Sly**
8 **LOTARA**, 4, b f Monsieur Bond (IRE)—Cheviot Heights **Mr & Mrs S. Bone**
9 **MORTENS LEAM**, 4, b g Sulamani (IRE)—Bonnet's Pieces **G. Libson & Mrs P. M. Sly**
10 **POPELYS GULL (IRE)**, 4, ch g Recharge (IRE)—Circus Rose **G. & W. Edmondson & Mrs P. M. Sly**
11 **ROXIE LOT**, 4, b f Exceed And Excel (AUS)—Orlena (USA) **Mr G. A. Libson**
12 **STAND 'N' BOOGIE**, 6, ch m Tobougg (IRE)—Standing Bloom **The Stablemates**

MRS PAM SLY - Continued

13 **SYNCOPATE**, 7, b g Oratorio (IRE)—Millistar **Mrs P. M. Sly**
14 **TAWEYLA (IRE)**, 5, b m Teofilo (IRE)—Qasirah (IRE) **Pam's People**

THREE-YEAR-OLDS

15 **SHIFT ON SHEILA**, b f Aussie Rules (USA)—Black Salix (USA) **Mrs P. M. Sly**
16 B f Teofilo (IRE)—Speciosa (IRE) **M. H. Sly, Dr T. Davis, Mrs P. M. Sly**
17 **SPINART**, ch g Dutch Art—Spinneret **David Bourne**
18 **WALSINGHAM GRANGE (USA)**, b c Paddy O'prado (USA)—Mambo Queen (USA) **Pam's People**

TWO-YEAR-OLDS

19 **KEEPUP KEVIN**, b g 30/4 Haafhd—Black Salix (USA) (More Than Ready (USA)) **Mrs P. M. Sly**
20 B c 28/4 Dutch Art—Speciosa (IRE) (Danehill Dancer (IRE)) **M. H. Sly, Dr T. Davis, Mrs P. M. Sly**

Other Owners: Mr David L. Bayliss, Dr T. J. W. Davies, Mrs S. E. Godfrey, Mr G. A. Libson, Mr Michael H. Sly, Mrs P. M. Sly, Mr G. Taylor.

Assistant Trainer: Chris Scudder

Jockey (NH): Kielan Woods. **Amateur:** Miss Gina Andrews.

---

553 **MR DAVID SMAGA, Lamorlaye**
Postal: **17 Voie de la Grange des Pres, 60260 Lamorlaye, France**
Contacts: **PHONE (0033) 3442 15005 FAX (0033) 3442 15356**
E-MAIL david_smaga@wanadoo.fr

1 **ALMERIA (FR)**, 5, b m Shamardal (USA)—Suedoise **Alain Michel Haddad**
2 **BOMBA NOVA (FR)**, 4, b f Whipper (USA)—Larme (FR) **Robert Nahas**
3 **BRAZILIAN CHAP (FR)**, 4, b c High Chaparral (IRE)—Vezara (IRE) **Robert Nahas**
4 **DJIGUITE (FR)**, 4, b c Makfi—Envoutement (FR) **Alain Louis-Dreyfus**
5 **DON BOSCO (FR)**, 9, ch h Barathea (IRE)—Perfidie (IRE) **Tarek El Sharif**
6 **FRED LALLOUPET**, 9, b h Elusive City (USA)—Firm Friend (IRE) **Maurice Lagasse**
7 **I LOVE YOU (FR)**, 4, b f Aqlaam—Pyrana (USA) **Benjamin Steinbruch**
8 **MAGICIENMAKE MYDAY**, 5, b h Whipper (USA)—Whisper To Dream (USA) **Robert Nahas**
9 **MASTERMAMBO (IRE)**, 5, b m Mastercraftsman (IRE)—Poltava (FR) **David Smaga**
10 **MEZZO MEZZO (FR)**, 4, ch f Mount Nelson—Ibizane (USA) **Marie Benedict Fougy**
11 **PRIMUS INCITATUS (IRE)**, 5, ch h Mastercraftsman (IRE)—Chaibia (IRE) **Alain Michel Haddad**
12 **RAFFINEE (FR)**, 5, b m Air Eminem (IRE)—Gioconda Umbra (ITY) **Marie Benedick Fougy**
13 **RODEIO (FR)**, 4, b f King's Best (USA)—Arrow of Desire **Robert Nahas**
14 **ROYAL MANIFICO (IRE)**, 6, b h Hannouma (IRE)—Poltava (FR) **David Smaga**
15 **SAPHIRSIDE (IRE)**, 7, b g Elusive City (USA)—Silirisa (FR) **Gerard Augustin-Normand**
16 **SONHO NOVO (FR)**, 4, b f Makfi—Whisper To Dream (USA) **Robert Navas**
17 **STRELKITA (FR)**, 4, b f Dr Fong (USA)—Olonella **Alain Louis-Dreyfus**
18 **VICTORIOUS CHAMP (FR)**, 5, b g New Approach (IRE)—Sasanuma (USA) **Robert Nahas**
19 **ZIGOTO (FR)**, 4, b c Whipper (USA)—Sometime (FR) **Robert Nahas**

THREE-YEAR-OLDS

20 **BARTIZAN**, b c Cacique (IRE)—Well Warned **Khalid Abdullah**
21 **COHESION**, b c Champs Elysees—Winter Bloom (USA) **Khalid Abdullah**
22 **COSMICA SIDERA (IRE)**, b f Galileo (IRE)—Bywayofthestars **John Kalmanson**
23 **DOCUMENTING**, b c Zamindar (USA)—Namaskar **Khalid Abdullah**
24 **DON TOMMASINO (IRE)**, b c Fastnet Rock (AUS)—M'oubliez Pas (USA) **Alain Michel Haddad**
25 **EXONERATE**, b f Cacique (IRE)—Posteritas (USA) **Khalid Abdullah**
26 **FIXED RATE**, b c Oasis Dream—Pretty Face **Khalid Abdullah**
27 **FLYING DESIRE**, b c Rail Link—Arrow of Desire **Robert Nahas**
28 **GAETANO DONIZETTI (IRE)**, b c Makfi—Galipette **Maurice Lagasse**
29 **GRAND JETE**, b f Dansili—Modern Look **Khalid Abdullah**
30 **GYMKHANA**, ch c Equiano (FR)—Village Fete **Khalid Abdullah**
31 **JORVICK (USA)**, gr c Mizzen Mast (USA)—Deep Feeling (USA) **Khalid Abdullah**
32 **LEEWARD (USA)**, b f First Defence (USA)—Introducing (USA) **Khalid Abdullah**
33 **LITTLE STEFY (IRE)**, ch c Makfi—Stefer (USA) **Robert Nahas**
34 **MAD SPEED**, b c Makfi—La Fee de Breizh (FR) **Alain Louis Dreyfus**

MR DAVID SMAGA - Continued

35 **MAIN FACT (USA),** b c Blame (USA)—Reflections **Khalid Abdullah**
36 **MILLFIELD (FR),** b c Whipper (USA)—Victoria College (FR) **Alain Michel Haddad**
37 **PHANTARA (USA),** b f Lonhro (AUS)—Gateway (USA) **Khalid Abdullah**
38 **PRIVATE SCHOOL (IRE),** ch f Mastercraftsman (IRE)—Poltava (FR) **Ecurie Haras du Cadran**
39 **PROVINCETOWN,** b c High Chaparral (IRE)—Flood Plain **Khalid Abdullah**
40 **RAISE ME UP (FR),** b c Makfi—Punta Rosa (USA) **Aleyrion Bloodstock**
41 **SAO PAOLO MENINA (FR),** b f Elusive City (USA)—Vezara (IRE) **Robert Nahas**
42 **SUMMER IN BRAZIL (FR),** b c Whipper (USA)—Sometime (FR) **Robert Nahas**
43 **THURGOVIA (IRE),** b f Fastnet Rock (AUS)—T'as d'Beaux Yeux **Maurice Lagasse**
44 **VILARO (FR),** b c Whipper (USA)—Envoutement (FR) **Alain Louis-Dreyfus**
45 **WHISPER NOT (FR),** b f Whipper (USA)—Flavignana (FR) **Kathleen Bokobsa**
46 **ZACHARO,** b c Zamindar (USA)—Winter Silence **Khalid Abdullah**

TWO-YEAR-OLDS

47 B f 25/1 Makfi—Arrow of Desire (Danehill Dancer (IRE)) **Robert Nahas**
48 **BERRY (FR),** b f 8/5 Pour Moi (IRE)—Punta Rosa (USA) (War Chant (USA)) **Franck Amar**
49 **COMMENCE,** b f 20/1 Oasis Dream—Symposia (Galileo (IRE)) **Khalid Abdullah**
50 **COUNTY FAIR,** b c 26/4 Nayef (USA)—Village Fete (Singspiel (IRE)) **Khalid Abdullah**
51 **FACILITATE,** br f 18/2 Bated Breath—Emergency (Dr Fong (USA)) **Khalid Abdullah**
52 **GRAND MOGOL (FR),** ch c 21/2 Makfi—La Fee de Breizh (FR) (Verglas (IRE)) **Alain-Louis Dreyfus**
53 B c 1/4 Nayef (USA)—Ibizane (USA) (Elusive Quality (USA)) (29531) **Alain Michel Haddad**
54 B gr c 17/2 High Chaparral (IRE)—Ilhabela (IRE) (Azamour (IRE)) **Robert Nahas**
55 B c 1/2 Cape Cross (IRE)—Larme (IRE) (Soviet Star (USA)) **Robert Nahas**
56 B c 17/3 Shamardal—Lumiere du Soir (FR) (Anabaa (USA)) (103359) **Robert Nahas**
57 **MATE STORY (IRE),** b c 5/3 Makfi—Tierra Luna (IRE) (Giant's Causeway (USA)) (66445) **Aleyrion Bloodstock**
58 **RUFY,** b c 16/3 Makfi—Katchagua (FR) (Anabaa (USA)) **Alain-Louis Dreyfus**
59 **SECOND ATTEMPT (FR),** b c 3/5 New Approach (IRE)—Sefroua (USA) (Kingmambo (USA)) **Haras d'Etreham**
60 B c 15/5 Elusive City (USA)—Sometime (FR) (Anabaa (USA)) **Robert Nahas**
61 B c 19/4 Rip Van Winkle (IRE)—Stefer (USA) (Johannesburg (USA)) **Robert Nahas**
62 **TAMARAMA (FR),** b f 26/2 Vale of York (IRE)—
Happy Way (FR) (Kingsalsa (USA)) (20671) **Mme Jean-Etienne Dubois**
63 **TOUTAINVILLE (GER),** b f 19/2 Lope de Vega (IRE)—
Tomato Finish (GER) (Starborough) (40605) **Gerard Augustin-Normand**
64 Ch f 28/3 Falco (USA)—Victoria College (FR) (Rock of Gibraltar (IRE)) **Alain Michel Haddad**
65 B f 3/2 Cape Cross (IRE)—Whisper To Dream (USA) (Gone West (USA)) **Robert Nahas**

---

554 MR BRYAN SMART, Hambleton
Postal: **Hambleton House, Sutton Bank, Thirsk, North Yorkshire, YO7 2HA**
Contacts: **PHONE** (01845) 597481 **FAX** (01845) 597480 **MOBILE** (07748) 634797
E-MAIL office@bryansmart.plus.com **WEBSITE** www.bryansmart-racing.com

1 **ALPHA DELPHINI,** 5, b g Captain Gerrard (IRE)—Easy To Imagine (USA) **The Alpha Delphini Partnership**
2 **COMPTON RIVER,** 4, b g Compton Place—Inagh River **The Smart Inagh River Partnership**
3 **EMBLAZE,** 4, b f Showcasing—Chuskha **Crossfields Racing**
4 **GERRARD'S SLIP,** 4, b g Captain Gerrard (IRE)—Park's Girl **Mr B. Smart**
5 **HELVIS,** 4, gr g Hellvelyn—Easy Mover (IRE) **Woodcock Electrical Limited**
6 **KI KI,** 4, ch f Kheleyf (USA)—Peryllys **Mr B. Smart**
7 **KYLLACH ME (IRE),** 4, b g Kyllachy—Good For Her **The Smart Stoneacre Sarah Partnership**
8 **MEADWAY,** 5, b g Captain Gerrard (IRE)—Tibesti **Mr Michael Moses & Mr Terry Moses**
9 **MYTHMAKER,** 4, b c Major Cadeaux—Mythicism **Crossfields Racing**
10 **NAMEITWHATYOULIKE,** 7, b g Trade Fair—Emma Peel **Simon Chappell**
11 **ORWELLIAN,** 7, b g Bahamian Bounty—Trinny **Mr B. Smart**
12 **PLAYTOTHEWHISTLE,** 5, b g Sakhee's Secret—Prima Ballerina **Mr B. Smart**
13 **RED PIKE (IRE),** 5, ch g Kheleyf (USA)—Fancy Feathers (IRE) **Sir A Ferguson, P Deal & G Lowe**
14 **SHOOTINGSTA (IRE),** 4, b g Fast Company (IRE)—Kiva **Redknapp, Glendinning, Shaw**
15 **SMALLJOHN,** 10, ch g Needwood Blade—My Bonus **Mr B. Smart**
16 **STRAIGHTTOTHEPOINT,** 4, b g Kyllachy—Choisette **Crossfields Racing**
17 **YTHAN WATERS,** 4, b g Hellvelyn—Primrose Queen **BEFG Partnership**

THREE-YEAR-OLDS

18 **AYRESOME ANGEL,** ch f Captain Gerrard (IRE)—Almunia (IRE) **Mr D. S. Blake**
19 **BLACK HAMBLETON,** b g Dick Turpin (IRE)—Duena **The Smart Duena Partnership**

MR BRYAN SMART - Continued

20 **CHASE THE STARS (USA)**, b br f Henrythenavigator (USA)—
Always A Star (IRE) **Mr Albert Welch, Mr David Williams**
21 **EXTORTION**, b g Kheleyf (USA)—Virtuality (USA) **Crossfields Racing**
22 **FOOL'S DREAM**, ch f Showcasing—Folly Lodge **Mr B. Smart**
23 **HELLRACER**, b g Hellvelyn—Racina **The Smart Racina Partnership**
24 **JAY EM GEE (IRE)**, gr c Mastercraftsman (IRE)—Pallas Athena (IRE) **Mr J. M. Glendinning**
25 **KENTUCKYCONNECTON (USA)**, b c Include (USA)—Youcanringmybell (USA) **Woodcock Electrical Limited**
26 **KING ROBERT**, b c Royal Applause—Generously Gifted **Ceffyl Racing**
27 **LIFE OF FAME**, b f Equiano (FR)—Fame Is The Spur **Biddestone Racing Partnership XIII**
28 **LOVIN' SPOONFUL**, b f Kodiac—Dispol Veleta **Albert Welch & Partners**
29 **MADAME BARKER (IRE)**, ch f Frozen Power (IRE)—
Shadow Mountain **Middleham Park Racing XLII & The Barkers**
30 **MIDNIGHT ROBBERY**, br g Dick Turpin (IRE)—Zietunzeen (IRE) **The Smart Zietunzeen Partnership**
31 **PORTLAND STREET (IRE)**, b c Dream Ahead (USA)—Danaskaya (IRE) **Mr Michael Moses & Mr Terry Moses**
32 **SATIN CHIC**, ch f Monsieur Bond (IRE)—Satin Doll **Middleham Park Racing XXIV & Mrs A.D. Bourne**

TWO-YEAR-OLDS

33 **ALFIE'S ANGEL (IRE)**, b c 22/1 Dark Angel (IRE)—Penolva (IRE) (Galileo (IRE)) (15000) **Mr B. Smart**
34 B c 7/4 Excelebration (IRE)—Auntie Kathryn (IRE) (Acclamation) (18095) **The Smart Set**
35 **CHILLILILLI**, ch f 2/2 Monsieur Bond (IRE)—Stunning Icon (Dr Fong (USA)) **Mr B. Smart**
36 **CHOCHENYO**, b c 26/2 Kheleyf (USA)—Unwrapit (USA) (Tapit (USA)) **Crossfields Racing**
37 Ch f 17/1 Bated Breath—Deora De (Night Shift (USA)) (28571) **Gee Gee Racing**
38 Gr f 18/4 Hellvelyn—First Term (Acclamation) (11428) **The Smart Set**
39 B c 21/3 Aqlaam—Generously Gifted (Sakhee (USA)) (12500) **Mr B. Smart**
40 Ch c 20/3 Helmet (AUS)—Kalabunga (IRE) (Val Royal (FR)) (3333) **Mr B. Smart**
41 B f 19/4 Monsieur Bond (IRE)—Keyaki (IRE) (Shinko Forest (IRE)) **M. Barber**
42 Ch c 3/5 Kheleyf (USA)—La Peinture (GER) (Peintre Celebre (USA)) **Mr B. Smart**
43 **OUTFOX**, b f 20/3 Foxwedge (AUS)—Spontaneity (IRE) (Holy Roman Emperor (IRE)) **Crossfields Racing**
44 Gr g 31/3 Hellvelyn—Satin Doll (Diktat) **Mrs A. D. Bourne**
45 Ch c 27/4 Equiano (FR)—Sofonisba (Rock of Gibraltar (IRE)) (5000) **Mr B. Smart**
46 B f 23/3 Lilbourne Lad (IRE)—Subtle Affair (IRE) (Barathea (IRE)) (9523) **Mr B. Smart**
47 **TIVRA (IRE)**, b f 20/4 Kodiac—Bokhara Silk (IRE) (Barathea (IRE)) (33333) **Mr S. E. Chappell**
48 B f 31/3 Exceed And Excel (AUS)—Transfix (Pivotal) (25000) **Ceffyl Racing**
49 B c 26/2 Helmet (AUS)—Watsdaplan (IRE) (Verglas (IRE)) (18095) **The Smart Set**
50 **WHITEANDGOLD**, b f 16/2 Major Cadeaux—Irrational (Kyllachy) (5000) **Crossfields Racing**

Other Owners: Mr Tareq Al-Mazeedi, Mrs Zahidah Barker, Mr Peter Barker, Mr S. A. Barningham, Mr Tim Bostwick, Mrs A. D. Bourne, Mrs Tina Bullock, Mr M. G. Bullock, Mr P. A. Deal, Mr Dave Elders, Sir Alex Ferguson, Mr Bill Fraser, Mr Anthony D. Gee, Mr Richard G. Gee, Mr John M. Glendinning, Mrs A. C. Hudson, Mr G. Lowe, Mr T. J. Moses, Mr M. Moses, Mr Richard Page, Mr T. S. Palin, Mr M. Prince, Mr Harry Redknapp, Mr Phil Shaw, Mr B. Smart, Mrs V. R. Smart, Mr Shaun Tolley, Mr A. Welch.

Assistant TrainerS: Mrs V. R. Smart, Mr K. Edmunds **Pupil Assistant:** Miss Beth Smart

Jockey (flat): Fergal Lynch, Phil Makin, Paul Mulrennan. **Apprentice:** Adam Carter.

---

555 MR CHARLES SMITH, Temple Bruer
Postal: **6-7 Thompsons Bottom, Temple Bruer, Lincoln, Lincolnshire, LN5 0DE**
Contacts: **PHONE/FAX (01526) 833245 MOBILE (07778) 149188**

1 **ALPHA TAURI (USA)**, 10, b g Aldebaran (USA)—Seven Moons (JPN) **Mr J. R. Theaker**
2 **GENERAL TUFTO**, 11, b g Fantastic Light (USA)—Miss Marianne (FR) **Mr J. R. Theaker**
3 **MUHTADIM (IRE)**, 4, b g Dubawi (IRE)—Dhelaal **Mr M. J. Smeed**
4 **ROBBIAN**, 5, b g Bertolini (USA)—Crathes **R. J. Lewin**
5 **SAIRAAM (IRE)**, 10, b m Marju (IRE)—Sayedati Eljamila (USA) **J. Martin-Hoyes**

THREE-YEAR-OLDS

6 **VOCALISE**, gr f Hellvelyn—Church Hill Queen **Mr N. J. Baines**

556 MR JULIAN SMITH, Tirley
Postal: **Tirley Court, Tirley, Gloucester**
Contacts: PHONE **(01452) 780461** FAX **(01452) 780461** MOBILE **(07748) 901175**
E-MAIL nicola.smith9156@o2.co.uk

1 **EMERALD ROSE,** 9, b m Sir Harry Lewis (USA)—Swiss Rose **Grand Jury Partnership**
2 **FORTUNA ROSE,** 10, b m Sir Harry Lewis (USA)—Swiss Rose **Grand Jury Partnership**
3 **HARRIET'S ARK,** 9, ch m Sir Harry Lewis (USA)—Brush The Ark **Exors of the Late Mr D. E. S. Smith**
4 **IONA DAYS (IRE),** 11, br g Epistolaire (IRE)—Miss Best (FR) **Mrs J.A. Benson & Miss S.N. Benson**
5 **NO PRINCIPLES,** 13, b g Overbury (IRE)—Selective Rose **Exors of the Late Mr D. E. S. Smith**
6 **PASS ON THE MANTLE,** 8, b g Bollin Eric—Swiss Rose **Grand Jury Partnership**
7 **PENNIES AND POUNDS,** 9, b m Sir Harry Lewis (USA)—Sense of Value **Exors of the Late Mr D. E. S. Smith**

Other Owners: Mrs J. A. Benson, Miss S. N. Benson, A. W. Brookes, R. Brookes.

Assistant Trainer: Mrs Nicky Smith

Jockey (NH): Mark Grant, Sam Twiston-Davies. **Amateur:** Mr J. M. Ridley.

557 MR MARTIN SMITH, Newmarket
Postal: **Stable Cottage, Calder Park, Hamilton Road, Newmarket, Suffolk, CB8 0NY**
Contacts: MOBILE **(07712) 493589**
WEBSITE www.martinsmithracing.com

1 **ALWAYS WITH YOU (IRE),** 7, b g Heron Island (IRE)—Greenacre Mandalay (IRE) **Mr M. P. B. Smith**
2 **BRIDGE OF SIGHS,** 4, ch g Avonbridge—Ashantiana **SN Racing VI**
3 **EXECUTIVE ORDER,** 7, b g Overbury (IRE)—Maiden Aunt (IRE) **Smith & Rennie**
4 **IFWECAN,** 5, b g Exceed And Excel (AUS)—Kirk **D. C. Livingston**
5 **INDOMITABLE SPIRIT,** 4, b g Zebedee—Gayala (IRE) **Michelle Smith and Friends**
6 **NOTEBOOK,** 5, b g Invincible Spirit (IRE)—Love Everlasting **Little Princess Racing**
7 **WATER FOR LIFE,** 5, ch m Mount Nelson—Echo River (USA) **D. P. Fremel**
8 **YARD OF ALE,** 5, ch g Compton Place—Highly Liquid **Mr M. P. B. Smith**

THREE-YEAR-OLDS
9 Ch c Major Cadeaux—Ashantiana
10 **DARING KNIGHT,** b g Dick Turpin (IRE)—Fairy Slipper **Four Winds Racing & Martin Smith**
11 **GORGEOUS GEEZER,** b c Kheleyf (USA)—Arctic High **Stewart Turner & Amanda Wilson-Martin**
12 **PRIORY,** b f Mullionmileanhour (IRE)—Alectrona (FR) **Mrs M. E. Smith**

TWO-YEAR-OLDS
13 B f 21/1 Sleeping Indian—Castalian Spring (IRE) (Oasis Dream) **M & M Bloodstock**
14 **LAURAMAN,** ch f 20/2 Bated Breath—Dance Away (Pivotal) (7000) **Mr M. Nundram**
15 Ch f 30/3 Major Cadeaux—So Discreet (Tragic Role (USA)) (2200) **M & M Bloodstock**

Other Owners: Miss N. F. Davey, Mrs E. A. Mear, Mr R. J. Mear, S. Nunn, Mrs R. T. Rennie, Mr S. J. A. Turner, Ms A. V. Wilson-Martin.

Apprentice: Tim Clark. **Amateur:** Mr James Smith.

558 MR MICHAEL SMITH, Newcastle Upon Tyne
Postal: **Toft Hall Farm, Kirkheaton, Newcastle Upon Tyne, Tyne and Wear, NE19 2DH**
Contacts: PHONE **(01830) 530044** MOBILE **(07976) 903233**
E-MAIL michaelsmithracing@hotmail.com

1 **APPLEJACK LAD,** 5, ch g Three Valleys (USA)—Fittonia (FR) **Ownaracehorse Ltd**
2 **BLACK INK,** 5, b g Black Sam Bellamy (IRE)—Incony **M. Smith**
3 **BRUNELLO,** 8, b g Leporello (IRE)—Lydia Maria **Ownaracehorse Ltd**
4 **DREAM FLYER (IRE),** 9, ch g Moscow Society (USA)—Bright Choice (IRE) **T. Alderson & S. Smith**
5 **HAIL THE BRAVE (IRE),** 7, ch g Lahib (USA)—Parverb (IRE) **Alderclad Ltd**
6 **KID VALENTINE (IRE),** 6, b g Scorpion (IRE)—Supreme Nova **D. Gilbert, M. Lawrence, A. Bruce**
7 **KILGEFIN STAR (IRE),** 8, b g Saddlers' Hall (IRE)—
                              High Church Annie (IRE) **Mrs Sandra Smith, Ownaracehorse**
8 **MAHLER BAY (IRE),** 6, b g Mahler—Belalzao (IRE) **Simpson Blacklock & Smith**

MR MICHAEL SMITH - Continued

9 **MAKBULLET**, 9, gr g Makbul—Gold Belt (IRE) **Mrs S. Smith & D & D Armstrong Ltd**
10 **MISTER SPINGSPRONG (IRE)**, 9, b g Flemensfirth (USA)—Watts Hill (IRE) **D. Gilbert, M. Lawrence, A. Bruce**
11 **MR WITMORE (IRE)**, 6, b g Whitmore's Conn (USA)—Bright Future (IRE) **Smith & Blacklock**

Other Owners: Mr I. M. Blacklock, D&D Armstrong Ltd, Mr Dan Gilbert, Mr Mark Lawrence, Ownaracehorse Ltd (ownaracehorse.co.uk), Mr Ian Simpson, Mrs Sandra Smith.

Assistant Trainer: Sandra Smith

Jockey (NH): Henry Brooke, Danny Cook, Brian Hughes. **Conditional:** Adam Nicol.

---

559 **MR R. MIKE SMITH, Galston**
Postal: **West Loudoun Farm, Galston, Ayrshire, KA4 8PB**
Contacts: **PHONE (01563) 822062 MOBILE (07711) 692122**
E-MAIL mike@mikesmithracing.co.uk WEBSITE www.mikesmithracing.co.uk

1 **A LOVABLE ROGUE**, 4, b g Dutch Art—Dance Card **Belstane Racing Partnership & M Friel**
2 **ARANTES**, 5, b g Sixties Icon—Black Opal **Smith Millar Russell**
3 **FIRSTYMINI (FR)**, 5, gr g Slickly (FR)—Jolie Lola (FR) **R. M. Smith**
4 **GWORN**, 6, b g Aussie Rules (USA)—Crochet (IRE) **Smith & Gibson**
5 **HAYMARKET**, 7, b g Singspiel (IRE)—Quickstyx **Mr A. M. Ross**
6 **HOPEFULL**, 6, br bl m Overbury (IRE)—Maryscross (IRE) **R. M. Smith**
7 **KATIES CHOICE (IRE)**, 8, gr g Croco Rouge (IRE)—Rosetown Girl (IRE) **R. M. Smith**
8 **MISS MACKIE (IRE)**, 5, b m Mr Combustible (IRE)—Grannys Kitchen (IRE) **Smith Millar Hynd Russell**
9 **NAKADAM (FR)**, 6, b g Nickname (FR)—Cadoudame (FR) **Smith & Spittal**
10 **OUTLAW JOSEY WALES (IRE)**, 5, b g Jeremy (USA)—Trinity Scholar (IRE) **Bryson & Wales**
11 **RUNNING BROOK (IRE)**, 9, b g Alderbrook—May As Well **Mr J. G. Matheson**
12 **U NAME IT (IRE)**, 8, b g Gold Well—Bypharthebest (IRE) **Smith & Spittal**
13 **URIAH HEEP (FR)**, 7, b g Danehill Dancer (IRE)—Canasita **Mrs P. McLeish**

Other Owners: W. Brand, Mrs L. J. Bryson, Mr M. Friel, Mr R. Gibson, Mr J. Hampson, Ms M. Hynd, Mrs L. M. Millar, Mr M. J. Russell, Mr D. J. Smith, Miss B. Spittal, W. W. Wales.

---

560 **MR RALPH SMITH, Chipstead**
Postal: **Stud Managers Cottage, Cheval Court Stud, High Road, Chipstead, Surrey, CR5 3SD**
Contacts: **PHONE (01737) 201693 FAX (01737) 201693 MOBILE (07795) 327003**
E-MAIL rjsmith.racing@hotmail.com WEBSITE www.rjsmithracing.com

1 **CHELLA THRILLER (SPA)**, 7, b m Chevalier (IRE)—Arundhati (IRE) **Kevin Old & Clear Racing**
2 **HURRICANE VOLTA (IRE)**, 5, ch h Hurricane Run (IRE)—Haute Volta (FR) **Cheval, S Piper, Clear Racing**
3 **NEW LOOK (IRE)**, 6, b g New Approach (IRE)—Lady Miletrian (IRE) **The New Look Partnership**
4 **THE CASH GENERATOR (IRE)**, 8, b g Peintre Celebre (USA)—
Majestic Launch **Kevin Old & The Cash Generator Corp**
5 **TOPTEMPO**, 7, ch m Halling (USA)—Topatoo **Mrs J. C. Smith**
6 **TWO IN THE PINK (IRE)**, 6, gr ro m Clodovil (IRE)—Secret Circle **Homecroft Wealth Racing & Mr Kevin Old**
7 **VICTOR'S BET (SPA)**, 7, b g Leadership—Marmaria (SPA) **Homecroft Wealth & Clear Racing**
8 **WATTABOUTSTEVE**, 5, b g Araafa (IRE)—Angel Kate (IRE) **The Wattever Partnership**

THREE-YEAR-OLDS

9 B f Excellent Art—Coup de Torchon (FR)

Other Owners: Mr H. B. Bulteel, B. J. Greening, Mrs M. M. Greening, T. Hirschfeld, K. Old, S. J. Piper, Mr N. Pogmore, Mr S. Wilkinson, F. J. E. Willson, Mr A. C. de Lemos.

Assistant Trainer: Jayne Smith

Amateur: Miss Ella Smith.

561 MRS SUE SMITH, Bingley

Postal: **Craiglands Farm, High Eldwick, Bingley, West Yorkshire, BD16 3BE**
Contacts: **PHONE (01274) 564930 FAX (01274) 560626**
E-MAIL craiglandsracing@yahoo.co.uk

1 ABSOLUTE (IRE), 5, b g Danehill Dancer (IRE)—Beyond Belief (IRE) **Mrs S. J. Smith**
2 ALTA ROCK (IRE), 11, b g Luso—Princess Lulu (IRE) **Mrs S. J. Smith**
3 BE A DREAMER, 8, ch g Dreams End—Miss Fahrenheit (IRE) **Mrs S. J. Smith**
4 BENNYS WELL, 10, b g Beneficial—Alure (IRE) **Mrs A. Ellis**
5 BLAKE DEAN, 8, b g Halling (USA)—Antediluvian **Widdop Wanderers**
6 BLAKEMOUNT (IRE), 8, br g Presenting—Smashing Leader (IRE) **Mrs J. Conroy**
7 BRONTE JANE, 4, b f Recharge (IRE)—Last Dream (IRE) **Mrs S. J. Smith**
8 BROTHER SCOTT, 9, b g Kirkwall—Crimson Shower **Mrs S. J. Smith**
9 CAPTAIN MOIRETTE (FR), 4, gr g Kap Rock (FR)—Rahana Moirette (FR) **Mrs A. Clarke**
10 CHARLIE WINGNUT (IRE), 9, br g Westerner—Back To Stay (IRE) **McGoldrick Racing 4**
11 CLOUDY TOO (IRE), 10, b g Cloudings (IRE)—Curra Citizen (IRE) **Formulated Polymer Products Ltd**
12 CROSS TO BOSTON (IRE), 10, b g Oscar (IRE)—Collopy's Cross **Mrs S. J. Smith**
13 DARTFORD WARBLER (IRE), 9, b br g Overbury (IRE)—Stony View (IRE) **Mrs S. J. Smith**
14 DE BOITRON (FR), 12, b g Sassanian (USA)—Pondiki (FR) **Mrs J. Morgan & Mrs Lindsey J. Shaw**
15 DE VOUS A MOI (FR), 8, b g Sinndar (IRE)—Dzinigane (FR) **Mrs J. Morgan**
16 DELUSIONOFGRANDEUR (IRE), 6, b g Mahler—Olivia Rose (IRE) **McGoldrick Racing Syndicates (3)**
17 FILL THE POWER (IRE), 10, b g Subtle Power (IRE)—Our Alma (IRE) **McGoldrick Racing**
18 FLEMERINA (IRE), 7, b m Flemensfirth (USA)—Ballerina Laura (IRE) **Mrs S. J. Smith**
19 FOCAL POINT, 6, ch g Pivotal—Centreofattention (AUS) **D G Pryde, J Beaumont & D Van Der Hoeven**
20 FRIENDLY ROYAL (IRE), 7, b g Royal Anthem (USA)—Friendly Girl (IRE) **Formulated Polymer Products Ltd**
21 GLEN COUNTESS (IRE), 9, b m Pilsudski (IRE)—Countessdee (IRE) **The Naughty Partnership**
22 GOOD VIBRATION (FR), 5, gr g Saddler Maker (IRE)—Queenhood (FR) **Mrs A. Clarke**
23 GRATE FELLA (IRE), 8, b g King's Best (USA)—Moonlight Paradise (USA) **Mrs M. Ashby**
24 GREEN WIZARD (IRE), 10, b g Wizard King—Ajo Green (IRE) **Mrs S. J. Smith**
25 GROOMED (IRE), 8, b g Acclamation—Enamoured **Mrs S. J. Smith**
26 HAINAN (FR), 5, gr g Laveron—Honor Smytzer **Mrs J. Morgan & Mrs Lindsey J. Shaw**
27 HERISING (IRE), 8, b g Heron Island (IRE)—Lady Rising (IRE) **Mrs S. J. Smith**
28 HIT THE TOP (IRE), 9, b g Gold Well—Smooth Leader (IRE) **Mrs S. J. Smith**
29 I JUST KNOW (IRE), 6, b g Robin des Pres (FR)—Desperado Queen (IRE) **M. B. Scholey & R. H. Scholey**
30 JUST GEORGIE, 6, b g Kayf Tara—Just Kate **M. B. Scholey & R. H. Scholey**
31 KARISMA KING, 7, br g Supreme Sound—Hollybush (IRE) **Broadway Racing Club 15**
32 LACKAMON, 11, b g Fleetwood (IRE)—Pearlossa **Mrs S. J. Smith**
33 LAVELLA WELLS, 8, b m Alflora (IRE)—Jazzy Refrain (IRE) **Mrs S. J. Smith**
34 LUCKY LUCARNO, 4, b g Lucarno (USA)—Sari Rose (FR) **Mrs S. J. Smith**
35 MAXED OUT KING (IRE), 8, ch g Desert King (IRE)—Lady Max (IRE) **Mrs S. J. Smith**
36 MINELLA FIVEO (IRE), 8, b g Westerner—Autumn Sky (IRE) **Mrs S. J. Smith**
37 MISTER JONES, 8, b g Val Royal (FR)—Madame Jones (IRE) **Mrs S. J. Smith**
38 MR MOONSHINE (IRE), 12, b g Double Eclipse (IRE)—Kinross **DG Pryde,J Beaumont,DP van der Hoeven 1**
39 MR PEPPERPOT, 7, b g Sir Harry Lewis (USA)—Parslin **The Trevor-McDonald Partnership**
40 MUTAWAASEL, 4, b g Teofilo (IRE)—Muwakleh **Mrs S. J. Smith**
41 MWALESHI, 11, b g Oscar (IRE)—Roxy River **Mrs S. J. Smith**
42 MY FIRST ACE (IRE), 6, b g Scorpion (IRE)—Welsh Rhapsody (IRE) **John Regan & John Conroy**
43 NO PLANNING, 9, b g Kayf Tara—Poor Celt **Mrs J. Conroy**
44 NOT A BOTHER BOY (IRE), 8, b g Flemensfirth (USA)—Cab In The Storm (IRE) **Mrs S. J. Smith**
45 OORAYVIC (IRE), 9, ch g Snurge—Miss Murtle (IRE) **Mrs S. J. Smith**
46 OPTICAL HIGH, 7, b g Rainbow High—Forsweets **Mrs S. J. Smith**
47 PALM GREY (IRE), 8, gr g Great Palm (USA)—Lucy Cooper (IRE) **Mrs S. J. Smith**
48 PERSEID (IRE), 6, br g Robin des Pres (FR)—Cowanstown Miss (IRE) **Mrs S. J. Smith**
49 PURE SCIENCE (IRE), 8, ch g Galileo (IRE)—Rebelline (IRE) **Mrs S. J. Smith**
50 QUIETLY (IRE), 5, b g Oscar (IRE)—Gimme Peace (IRE) **T. J. Hemmings**
51 RED DANAHER (IRE), 9, ch g Shantou (USA)—Red Rover **Mrs S. J. Smith**
52 SHINE AWAY (IRE), 6, b m Robin des Pres (FR)—Bramble Bree (IRE) **Mrs S. J. Smith**
53 SILVER VOGUE, 8, gr g Revoque (IRE)—Pusslin **Mrs S. J. Smith**
54 SMOOTH STEPPER, 7, b g Alflora (IRE)—Jazzy Refrain (IRE) **Mrs A. Clarke**
55 SPECIAL WELLS, 7, ch g Alflora (IRE)—Oso Special **Mr D. Sutherland**
56 STRAIDNAHANNA (IRE), 7, gr g Medaaly—Sue's Song **M. B. Scholey & R. H. Scholey**
57 SUNNY WEST (IRE), 7, b g Westerner—Lunar Beauty **John Conroy Jaqueline Conroy**
58 SWING HARD (IRE), 8, br g Zagreb (USA)—Hurricane Jane (IRE) **DP van der Hoeven, DG Pryde & J Beaumont**
59 TELL US A TALE, 6, b g Lucky Story (USA)—Alumisiyah (USA) **Mrs S. J. Smith**
60 TROOPER ROYAL, 6, b g Zafeen (FR)—Faithful Beauty (IRE) **Mrs C. Steel**
61 VENDOR (FR), 8, gr g Kendor (FR)—Village Rainbow (FR) **Mrs A. Ellis**

MRS SUE SMITH - Continued

62 **VINTAGE CLOUDS (IRE)**, 6, gr g Cloudings (IRE)—Rare Vintage (IRE) **T. J. Hemmings**
63 **WAKANDA (IRE)**, 7, b g Westerner—Chanson Indienne (FR) **M. B. Scholey & R. H. Scholey**
64 **WHISKEY RIDGE (IRE)**, 10, b g High-Rise (IRE)—Little Chartridge **Widdop Wanderers**

Other Owners: J. J. Beaumont, Mr P. Butters, J. Conroy, A. D. Hollinrake, W. S. D. Lamb, R. J. Longley, C. C. S. MacMillan, P. J. Martin, S. McDonald, Mr A. M. Phillips, D. G. Pryde, J. Regan, Mrs M. B. Scholey, R. H. Scholey, Mrs L. J. Shaw, Mrs E. Smith, S. P. Trevor, Mr D. P. van der Hoeven.

Assistant Trainer: Ryan Clavin

Jockey (NH): Danny Cook, Sean Quinlan. **Conditional:** Stephen McCarthy, Trevor Ryan. **Amateur:** Mr Robert Hogg.

562

MISS SUZY SMITH, Lewes
Postal: **County Stables, The Old Racecourse, Lewes, East Sussex, BN7 1UR**
Contacts: **PHONE (01273) 477173 FAX (01273) 477173 MOBILE (07970) 550828**
E-MAIL suzy@suzysmithracing.co.uk WEBSITE www.suzysmithracing.co.uk

1 **BEAU LAKE (IRE)**, 12, b g Heron Island (IRE)—
Brennan For Audits (IRE) **Sergio Gordon-Watson & Graham Willetts**
2 **BOLD IMAGE (IRE)**, 5, b m Milan—Golden Bay **Mrs S. A. Addington-Smith**
3 **CLONDAW BISTO (IRE)**, 5, b g September Storm (GER)—Solo Venture (IRE) **Mr J. M. F. Gordon-Watson**
4 **CLONDAW CIAN (IRE)**, 6, br g Gold Well—Cocktail Bar (IRE) **Wolf Allisat & Chris Ames**
5 **FIN D'ESPERE (IRE)**, 5, b g Zagreb (USA)—Rapsan (IRE) **Roger & Yvonne Allsop**
6 **GENERAL BUX**, 5, b g Lucarno (USA)—Cadoutene (FR) **The Scoobyless Partnership**
7 **GINNY'S TONIC (IRE)**, 7, b m Oscar (IRE)—Golden Bay **Mrs H. Norman**
8 **HUNTRESS (IRE)**, 4, b f Flemensfirth (USA)—Madgehil (IRE)
9 **INVICTA LAKE (IRE)**, 9, b g Dr Massini (IRE)—Classic Material **Bernard & Jan Wolford**
10 **JENNIFER ECCLES (IRE)**, 6, b m Midnight Legend—Cherrygayle (IRE) **P Mercer & K W Allisat**
11 **KING CHARLIE (IRE)**, 6, b g Chevalier (IRE)—Desert Treat (IRE)
12 **LAUGHTON PARK**, 11, ch g Karinga Bay—Brass Castle (IRE) **S Smith, M. Forbes-Wood & R. Knight**
13 **LITTLE BOY BORU (IRE)**, 8, b g Brian Boru—How Is Things (IRE) **J Logan, D Harrison, T Loftus & S Smith**
14 **MARIET**, 7, ch m Dr Fong (USA)—Medway (IRE) **Miss S. Smith**
15 **MIGHTY VIC (IRE)**, 8, b g Old Vic—Mighty Marble (IRE) **Mr S. N. Riley**
16 **OURMANMASSINI (IRE)**, 8, b g Dr Massini (IRE)—Aunty Dawn (IRE) **The Seagull Partnership**
17 **RED DEVIL STAR (IRE)**, 6, b g Beneficial—Gortbofearna (IRE) **Mrs V. Palmer**
18 **STORM PATROL**, 5, b m Shirocco (GER)—Material World **Storm Force Ten**
19 **TED SPREAD**, 9, b g Beat Hollow—Highbrook (USA) **False Nose 'n Glasses Partnership**

THREE-YEAR-OLDS
20 **THE GINGER NINJER**, ch f Malinas (GER)—Atabaas Allure (FR)

Other Owners: Mrs K. H. Allisat, Mr W. Allisat, R. Allsop, Mrs Y. E. Allsop, Mr C. B. Ames, Mr S. A. Ashley, Mr G. Barrett, Mr M. T. Forbes-Wood, S. Gordon-Watson, Mr D. J. Harrison, Mr M. Hess, Mr R. I. Knight, Mr T. H. Loftus, J. A. A. S. Logan, P. J. Mercer, Mr G. Pettit, Mr A. R. Purvis, R. F. Smith, Mr G. J. Willetts, Mrs J. Wolford, B. Wolford, Mrs H. M. T. Woods.

Assistant Trainer: Mr S E Gordon-Watson

Jockey (flat): Luke Morris. **Jockey (NH):** Paddy Brennan, Tom O'Brien. **Conditional:** Harry Bannister, Freddie Mitchell.

563

MR GILES SMYLY, Broadway
Postal: **Garden Cottage, Wormington Grange, Broadway, Worcestershire, WR12 7NJ**
Contacts: **PHONE (01386) 584085 FAX (01386) 584085 MOBILE (07747) 035169**
E-MAIL gilessmiler@aol.com WEBSITE www.smylyracing.co.uk

1 **BADGER WOOD**, 7, b g Overbury (IRE)—Parlour Game **A. C. Ward-Thomas**
2 **CHELTENAM DE VAIGE (FR)**, 4, b g Forestier (FR)—Ratina de Vaige (FR) **M. Burford**
3 **GALICE DU CIEL**, 5, br g Septieme Ciel (USA)—Galice Du Soleil (FR) **Ms Gillian Metherell**
4 **HIT THE HIGHWAY (IRE)**, 7, b g Pierre—Highway Belle (FR) **A. C. Ward-Thomas**
5 **LETEMGO (IRE)**, 8, b g Brian Boru—Leteminletemout (IRE) **A. C. Ward-Thomas**
6 **MAYBE PLENTY**, 7, b m Overbury (IRE)—Mays Delight (IRE) **Nick Sutton & Adam Waugh**
7 **STELLA'S FELLA**, 8, b g Septieme Ciel (USA)—Gaspaisie (FR) **A E Agnew & A Ward Thomas**

MR GILES SMYLY - Continued

  8 **TAIGAN (FR)**, 9, b g Panoramic—Lazary (FR) **M. Burford**
  9 **VENEZ HORACE (FR)**, 7, b g Polish Summer—Fripperie (FR) **M. Burford**

Other Owners: Mr A. Agnew, N. R. A. Sutton, A. R. G. Waugh.

Assistant Trainer: Kim Smyly

Jockey (NH): David England, Liam Treadwell. **Conditional:** Ed Cookson.

564

MR JAMIE SNOWDEN, Lambourn
Postal: **Folly House, Upper Lambourn Road, Lambourn, Hungerford, Berkshire, RG17 8QG**
Contacts: **PHONE (01488) 72800 (office) Twitter: @jamiesnowden MOBILE (07779) 497563**
E-MAIL info@jamiesnowdenracing.co.uk WEBSITE www.jamiesnowdenracing.co.uk

  1 **AGENOR (GER)**, 5, b g Medicean—Acerba (GER) **Sir Chips Keswick**
  2 **ARCAMANTE (ITY)**, 5, b g High Chaparral—Caractere (GER) **Tim Dykes**
  3 **ARDKILLY WITNESS (IRE)**, 10, b g Witness Box (USA)—Ardkilly Angel (IRE) **The Cherry Pickers**
  4 **BARAYMI (FR)**, 4, b g Makfi—Brusca (USA) **The GD Partnership**
  5 **BE ON TIME (FR)**, 5, b g Linda's Lad—One More Time (FR) **The Folly Partnership**
  6 **BEAUCHAMP EAGLE**, 4, ch g Compton Admiral—Ashford Castle (USA) **E. Penser**
  7 **BELCANTO (IRE)**, 6, b m Bach (IRE)—Love Divided (IRE) **Jamie Snowden Racing Club**
  8 **BLUE BULLET (FR)**, 5, b g Le Fou (IRE)—Jiletta (FR) **Mrs L. E. Snowden**
  9 **BREAKING BITS (IRE)**, 9, br g Oscar (IRE)—Lantern Lark (IRE) **Mr C. Peake**
 10 **BUCHE DE NOEL (FR)**, 5, ch m Coastal Path—Kyrie (FR) **Mr David Brownlow**
 11 **DARK LOVER (GER)**, 11, b g Zinaad—Dark Lady (GER) **The Dark Lovers**
 12 **DENBOY (IRE)**, 6, b g King's Theatre (IRE)—Miss Denman (IRE) **Sir Martin Broughton**
 13 **DETROIT BLUES**, 6, ch g Tobougg (IRE)—Blue Missy (USA) **Ade & The Winettes**
 14 **DOUBLE TREASURE**, 5, b g King's Theatre (IRE)—Double Red (IRE) **Sir Chips Keswick**
 15 **EBADANI (IRE)**, 6, ch g Halling (USA)—Ebatana (IRE) **The Brook House Syndicate**
 16 **FACT OF THE MATTER (IRE)**, 6, b g Brian Boru—Womanofthemountain (IRE) **The Sandylini Racing Partnership**
 17 **FUTURE GILDED (FR)**, 7, b g Lost World (USA)—Doree du Pin (FR) **Owners For Owners: Future Gilded**
 18 **HERONRY (IRE)**, 8, b g Heron Island (IRE)—In A Tizzy **Chalke Valley Racing Partnership**
 19 **INCLUDED**, 4, b f Champs Elysees—Cordoba **ValueRacingClub.co.uk**
 20 **JEAN FLEMING (IRE)**, 9, b m Flemensfirth (USA)—Dromhale Lady (IRE) **Mrs K. Gunn**
 21 **KAPGARDE KING (FR)**, 5, ch g Kapgarde (FR)—Cybertina (FR) **The Konkerers**
 22 **KASPIAN TERN**, 5, b m Kadastrof (FR)—Little Tern (FR) **The Galloping Grannies**
 23 **KASSIS**, 7, b m Kalanisi (IRE)—Gastina (FR) **Mrs J. A. Thomas**
 24 **KENOBE STAR (IRE)**, 4, b g Clodovil (IRE)—Maimana (IRE) **ValueRacingClub.co.uk**
 25 **LEY LADY GREY**, 6, gr m With Approval (CAN)—Prospectress (USA) **Fawley House Stud**
 26 **LORD WESTY (IRE)**, 5, b g Westerner—Smile Later (IRE) **Fawley House Stud**
 27 **LUNAR FLOW**, 5, b g With The Flow (USA)—Misty Move (IRE) **L G Partnership**
 28 **MAJOR MILBORNE**, 8, ch g Exit To Nowhere (USA)—Motown Melody (IRE) **Mr & Mrs R. H. F. Fuller**
 29 **MIDNIGHT CHILL**, 4, b g Midnight Legend—Chilla Cilla **League Of Nations**
 30 **MIDNIGHT SILVER**, 6, gr m Midnight Legend—Ruggtah **Foxtrot NH Racing Partnership IX**
 31 **MISS TIGER LILY**, 6, b m Tiger Hill (GER)—Waitingonacloud **Mr & Mrs D. Hearson**
 32 **MOLLYANNA (IRE)**, 7, b m Oscar (IRE)—Baywatch Star (IRE) **The Duchess Of Cornwall & Mr D Brownlow**
 33 **MONBEG THEATRE (IRE)**, 7, b g King's Theatre (IRE)—Amberina (IRE) **Tim Dykes & Lynda Lovell**
 34 **NARANJA**, 4, ch f Black Sam Bellamy (IRE)—Full of Fruit (FR) **White Diamond Racing & Kate Austin**
 35 **ORCHARD PARK (IRE)**, 5, b g Milan—Tough As Leather (IRE) **Mr D. I. Ryder**
 36 **OUR REWARD (IRE)**, 6, b g Morozov—Paddyeoin (IRE) **EPDS Racing Partnership 17**
 37 **OUR THREE SONS (IRE)**, 5, b g Shantou (USA)—Ballyquinn (IRE) **A. J. & Mrs J. Ward**
 38 **PRESENT VIEW**, 8, b g Presenting—Carry Me (IRE) **Sir Chippendale Keswick**
 39 **RHYTHM STAR**, 6, b m Beat All (USA)—Star Award (IRE) **ValueRacingClub.co.uk**
 40 **SHOCKINGTIMES (IRE)**, 9, b g Wareed (USA)—Jolly Lady (USA) **S Beccle, Lady Hart, Boscobel Estates Ltd**
 41 **SOURIYAN (FR)**, 5, b g Alhaarth (IRE)—Serasana **The GD Partnership**
 42 **TEA CADDY**, 10, b m Kadastrof (FR)—Little Tern (FR) **R. T. S. Matthews**
 43 **THREE WAYS**, 5, b g Flemensfirth (USA)—Serenique **Mr David Brownlow**
 44 , B g Notnowcato—Tremiere (FR) **Apache Racing**
 45 **VAL DE LAW (FR)**, 7, b g Epalo (GER)—Law (FR) **Sir Chippendale Keswick**
 46 **VENTURA CASTLE**, 4, b g Paco Boy (IRE)—Bisaat (USA) **Mr A. C. T. Bath**
 47 **WILDEHEARTED WOMAN (IRE)**, 5, b m Oscar (IRE)—Burrator **EPDS Racing Partnership 13**
 48 **ZADOK**, 6, b g Nayef (USA)—Panna **Lady Halifax & Sir Chips Keswick**
 49 **ZAKTI (IRE)**, 6, gr m Shirocco (GER)—Inner Strength (FR) **Mr T. J. Dykes**

MR JAMIE SNOWDEN - Continued

THREE-YEAR-OLDS

50 FATIMA BLUSH, b f Black Sam Bellamy (IRE)—Samar Qand **Kristina Dalborg**

Other Owners: Mrs J. Abraham, Mr D. Abraham, Mr J. Anthony, Ms K. J. Austin, Mr S. Beccle, Mr Phil Bell, Mr Glynn Berrington-Evans, Boscobel Estates Limited, Mr M. Bower-Dyke, Mr Paul Boyle, Mr Stephen Broughton, Mr A. P. Brown, Mr Tom Castle, Duchess of Cornwall, Mr Paul Couldwell, Mr James Couldwell, Mrs Jane Glyn-Davies, Mr H. M. Glyn-Davies, Lady Halifax, Mr Mike Hammond, Lady Hart, Mr D. Hearson, Mrs David Hearson, Mr M. Holman, Mr E. J. Hughes, Mr Andrew J. Huntly, Mr P. Hurst, Mr R. J. Kilford, Mr O. C. S. Lazenby, Mrs L. R. Lovell, Mr Julian Makin, Mrs S. McGrath, Mr Brendan McManus, Mr R. McGrath, Mr A. Morley, Dr M. M. Ogilvy, Mr John Powell, Mr Darren Price, Mr J. Prosser, Mr H. J. Shapter, W. G. C. Shaw, Miss T. Sloan, Mr B. D. Smith, Mr Ben Spiers, Mr R. W. Stirling, Mr J. R. Sykes, Mr William Wallace, Mrs Janet Ward, Mr A. J. Ward, Miss Claire Wills, Mr Jordan Wylie, Miss A. L. Yorke.

Assistant Trainer: James Ward **Head Girl:** Kate Robinson

Jockey (NH): Micheal Nolan, Brendan Powell, Gavin Sheehan. **Conditional:** Graham Carson, Conor Shoemark. **Amateur:** Miss Page Fuller.

---

565 | MR MIKE SOWERSBY, York
Postal: **Southwold Farm, Goodmanham Wold, Market Weighton, York, East Yorkshire, YO43 3NA**
Contacts: **PHONE (01430) 810534 MOBILE (07855) 551056**

1 AGENT LOUISE, 8, b m Alflora (IRE)—Oso Special **M. E. Sowersby**
2 ENCOURAGING (IRE), 7, ch g Rock of Gibraltar (IRE)—Unreachable Star **M. E. Sowersby**
3 FEAST OF FIRE (IRE), 9, ch g St Jovite (USA)—Bellagrana **Mrs E. A. Verity**
4 LARKHALL, 9, b g Saddlers' Hall (IRE)—Larkbarrow **T. J. Stubbins**
5 LAWSONS THORNS (IRE), 7, b g Presenting—Ardnurcher (IRE) **Mrs E. A. Verity**
6 LILY LITTLE LEGS (IRE), 7, gr m Westerner—Silvers Promise (IRE) **Mrs J. H. Cooper**
7 STRICTLY GLITZ (IRE), 5, b m Kodiac—Dancing Steps **R. D. Seldon**
8 STRICTLY THE ONE (IRE), 6, b g Robin des Pres (FR)—Rita's Charm (FR) **B. Valentine**
9 TENNESSEE BIRD, 8, b g Danbird (AUS)—Tennessee Star **Queens Head Racing Club**
10 TREGARO (FR), 10, b g Phantom Breeze—Touques (FR) **A. Lyons**

Other Owners: Mr J. Heslop, Mrs J. Wiltschinsky, Mrs C. J. Zetter-Wells.

Assistant Trainer: Mary Sowersby

Jockey (flat): Tom Eaves, James Sullivan. **Jockey (NH):** Brian Hughes. **Conditional:** Adam Nichol, Gavin Sheehan. **Amateur:** Mr Russell Lindsay.

---

566 | MR JOHN SPEARING, Kinnersley
Postal: **Kinnersley Racing Limited, Kinnersley Racing Stables, Kinnersley, Severn Stoke, Worcestershire, WR8 9JR**
Contacts: **PHONE (01905) 371054 FAX (01905) 371054 MOBILE (07801) 552922**
E-MAIL jlspearing@aol.com

1 A TOUCH OF SASS (IRE), 6, b m Mahler—Lwitikila **Miss C. J. Ive**
2 AWAY IN MAY, 5, gr m Proclamation (IRE)—Loch Shiel (IRE) **Mrs C. J. Welch**
3 BARTON GIFT, 9, b g Alflora (IRE)—Marina Bird **Mercy Rimell & Kate Ive**
4 CLEAR SPRING (IRE), 8, b h Chineur (FR)—Holly Springs **Mr H. James**
5 HAWK MOTH (IRE), 8, b g Hawk Wing (USA)—Sasimoto (USA) **Kinnersley Partnership**
6 OVER THE AIR, 8, br m Overbury (IRE)—Moonlight Air **Mrs W. M. Badger**
7 OVERSTONE LASS (IRE), 4, b f Excellent Art—Clinging Vine (USA) **G. M. Eales**
8 PEARLS LEGEND, 9, b g Midnight Legend—Pearl's Choice (USA) **The Corsairs**
9 PINTLE'S IMAGE, 4, b f Paco Boy (IRE)—Pintle **The Two Old Timers**
10 SWEEPING ROCK (IRE), 6, b g Rock of Gibraltar (IRE)—Sweeping Story (USA) **Kinnersley Partnership II**
11 WHITECREST, 8, ch m Ishiguru (USA)—Risky Valentine **G. M. Eales**

THREE-YEAR-OLDS

12 B f Dick Turpin (IRE)—Loch Shiel (IRE)
13 B f Paco Boy (IRE)—Pintle **R. Heathcote**

MR JOHN SPEARING - Continued

TWO-YEAR-OLDS

- **14** B f 26/4 Approve (IRE)—Alinda (IRE) (Revoque (IRE)) (5167)
- **15** B c 8/4 Pastoral Pursuits—Croeso Bach (Bertolini (USA)) (761)
- **16** B f 8/5 Approve (IRE)—Emerald Fire (Pivotal) (3691)
- **17** B f 14/2 Sir Prancealot (IRE)—Johar Jamal (Chevalier (IRE)) (5315)

Other Owners: Mr Robert Heathcote, Miss C. Ive, Mr Henry Porter, Mrs Mercy Rimell, Mr J. Spearing.

Assistant Trainer: Miss C Ive

---

567 **MR HENRY SPILLER, Newmarket**
Postal: Henry Spiller Racing Ltd, Saffron House Stables, Hamilton Road, Newmarket, Suffolk, CB8 0NY
Contacts: **PHONE (01638) 662899 MOBILE (07786) 263997**
E-MAIL office@henryspillerracing.com WEBSITE www.henryspillerracing.com

- **1** ANNE OF BRITTANY (FR), 4, b f King's Best (USA)—Abyaan (IRE) **Mr R. P. A. Spiller**
- **2** ROYAL MEZYAN (IRE), 5, b g Royal Applause—Rice Mother (IRE) **Mr R. P. A. Spiller**
- **3** THE THIRD MAN, 5, gr g Dalakhani (IRE)—Spinning Queen **Mrs D. Spiller**
- **4** VAN DIEST, 4, b g Hurricane Run (IRE)—Miracle **Mr R. P. A. Spiller**

THREE-YEAR-OLDS

- **5** CAPITAL GEARING, b g Makfi—Dicara (GER) **Mrs Nicky Cannon Brookes & Peter Spiller**
- **6** COMBE HAY (FR), b f Elusive City (USA)—Coiffure **Mr R. P. A. Spiller**
- **7** DEMAND RESPECT, ch g Paco Boy (IRE)—Brilliance **Dethrone Racing**
- **8** FEARLESS POPPY, ch f Kyllachy—Cesseras (IRE) **Chippenham Lodge Stud Limited**
- **9** LAST STAR FALLING (IRE), b f Acclamation—Star Port **Dethrone Racing**
- **10** STAR GLIMMER (IRE), b f Kodiac—Skyscape **Dethrone Racing**

TWO-YEAR-OLDS

- **11** CANTERBURY QUAD (FR), b f 16/2 Motivator—Coiffure (King's Best (USA)) **Mr R. P. A. Spiller**
- **12** B c 12/2 Street Boss (USA)—Distorted Promise (USA) (Distorted Humor (USA)) (40000) **Mr R. P. A. Spiller**
- **13** B f 1/1 Zoffany (IRE)—Irisijana (GER) (Diktat) (14765)
- **14** B f 17/5 Foxwedge (AUS)—Queensgate (Compton Place) (1500)
- **15** B f 18/3 Royal Applause—Shadow of The Sun (Red Ransom (USA)) (800)
- **16** STAFF COLLEGE (FR), b c 7/4 Slickly (FR)—School of Music (FR) (Green Tune (USA)) **Mr R. P. A. Spiller**

Other Owners: Mrs M. Cannon Brookes, Miss J. S. Gill, Mr H. C. Spiller.

---

568 **MR TOMMY STACK, Cashel**
Postal: Thomastown Castle Stud, Golden, Cashel, Co. Tipperary, Ireland
Contacts: PHONE (00353) 62 54129
E-MAIL tommystack@eircom.net

- **1** BARBEQUE (IRE), 6, b m Elusive City (USA)—Babberina (IRE)
- **2** CURRENT STATE (IRE), 4, b f High Chaparral (USA)—Thoughtful (IRE)
- **3** GREAT MINDS (IRE), 6, ch g Bahamian Bounty—Raja (IRE)
- **4** HURRICANE CASS (IRE), 4, b g Hurricane Run (IRE)—Rahya Cass (IRE)
- **5** ONENIGHTIDREAMED (IRE), 5, ch h Footstepsinthesand—Pivotalia (IRE)
- **6** SALARIAQ (USA), 5, b m Daaher (CAN)—Alabaq (USA)
- **7** TANSANITE (IRE), 4, gr g Zebedee—Unfortunate
- **8** TOOREEN LEGEND (IRE), 6, ch g Rakti—Annmary Girl

THREE-YEAR-OLDS

- **9** A SHIN IMPALA (IRE), b g Evasive—Muzayadah
- **10** B f Cape Blanco (IRE)—Alabaq (USA)
- **11** ASPAR (IRE), b g Holy Roman Emperor (IRE)—Lisa Gherardini (IRE)
- **12** BALCONY (IRE), b f Fastnet Rock (AUS)—Front House (IRE)
- **13** BAMBARI (IRE), b g Arcano—Blue Dahlia (IRE)
- **14** CIAVENNA (IRE), b f Canford Cliffs (IRE)—Chantarella (IRE)
- **15** CRY ME A RIVER (IRE), b f Danehill Dancer (IRE)—River Flow (USA)

MR TOMMY STACK - Continued

16 **DIAMOND FIELDS (IRE)**, b f Fastnet Rock (AUS)—Question Times
17 **DUKE OF WASPINGTON (IRE)**, b c Duke of Marmalade (IRE)—Queen Wasp (IRE)
18 **FREEMAN (IRE)**, b g Arcano (IRE)—Sassy Gal (IRE)
19 **HE'S COMPLETE**, b c Royal Applause—Rhapsilian
20 **JUST JOAN (IRE)**, b f Pour Moi (IRE)—Wanna (IRE)
21 **KEYTOTHEOPERATION (USA)**, b c Henrythenavigator (USA)—Tashawak (IRE)
22 **LADY OAK (IRE)**, b f Arcano (IRE)—Lady of Kildare (IRE)
23 **LADY SEVILLE (IRE)**, b f Duke of Marmalade (IRE)—Heaven's Vault (IRE)
24 **NAME FOR THE BLAME (USA)**, b c Blame (USA)—Whenthetimeisright (USA)
25 **NO WOMAN NO KRY**, b f Champs Elysees—Looby Loo
26 **OFF AND ON (IRE)**, br g Cacique (IRE)—Elegant Beauty
27 **OROMO (IRE)**, b g High Chaparral (IRE)—Miss Beatrix (IRE)
28 B g Dylan Thomas (IRE)—Pure Greed (IRE)
29 B g Approve (IRE)—Reign of Fire (IRE)
30 **ROSSIE (IRE)**, b f Thewayyouare (USA)—Waroonga (IRE)
31 **SEE YOU IN MALTA (IRE)**, b c Holy Roman Emperor (IRE)—Ice Box (IRE)
32 Br f Rip Van Winkle (IRE)—Sheezalady
33 **SHORT STACKED**, b g Dutch Art—Rotunda
34 **VERUS CASS (IRE)**, b f High Chaparral (IRE)—Fand (USA)
35 **VICTORIOUS SECRET (IRE)**, b f Holy Roman Emperor (IRE)—Highindi
36 **ZAPPY CASS (IRE)**, b f Pour Moi (IRE)—Golden Mask (USA)

TWO-YEAR-OLDS

37 B c 25/4 Choisir (AUS)—Alexiade (IRE) (Montjeu (IRE)) (20671)
38 B f 3/2 Choisir (AUS)—Blue Dahlia (IRE) (Shamardal (USA))
39 B f 17/4 Henrythenavigator (USA)—Catch The Moon (IRE) (Peintre Celebre (USA))
40 B c 22/4 Holy Roman Emperor (IRE)—Clara Bow (IRE) (Sadler's Wells (USA)) (22000)
41 B f 27/3 Iffraaj—Desert Alchemy (IRE) (Green Desert (USA)) (32000)
42 B f 20/2 Fastnet Rock (AUS)—Front House (IRE) (Sadler's Wells (USA))
43 B c 26/4 Fastnet Rock (AUS)—Green Castle (IRE) (Indian Ridge) (58000)
44 B c 19/3 Pivotal—Hightime Heroine (IRE) (Danetime (IRE)) (51679)
45 B f 26/1 Fastnet Rock (AUS)—Ittasal (Any Given Saturday (USA)) (50000)
46 B f 20/3 Pour Moi (IRE)—Many Hearts (USA) (Distorted Humor (USA))
47 Ch c 10/3 Choisir (AUS)—Margaret's Dream (IRE) (Muhtarram (USA)) (42857)
48 B f 18/2 Royal Applause—Nasij (USA) (Elusive Quality (USA)) (49464)
49 B g 26/2 High Chaparral (IRE)—Rock Queen (IRE) (Rock of Gibraltar (IRE)) (18456)
50 Gr f 10/2 The Factor (USA)—Sayedah (IRE) (Darshaan) (97680)
51 B f 25/1 Cape Blanco (IRE)—Shermeen (IRE) (Desert Style (IRE)) (140000)
52 B br f 23/3 Bated Breath—Time Ahead (Spectrum (IRE)) (47988)
53 B c 7/5 Power—Varmint Lady (IRE) (Orpen (USA)) (32380)
54 B f 9/2 Lawman (FR)—Vespetta (FR) (Vespone (IRE))

Owners: Mr Michael Begley, Mr Sam Britt, Mr John Byrne, Mr Justin Caffrey, Mr Arunas Cicenas, Mr Terry Corden, Mr M. L. House, Mr T. Hyde Jnr, JSC Kasandros Grupe, Mr D. Keoghan, Mrs J. Magnier, Mr Casey McLiney, Mr J. P. McManus, The New Pension Fund Syndicate, Mr B. Parker, Mr P. Piller, G. A. Rupert, Mary Slack, Mr David Slater, Mr Michael Tabor.

Jockey (flat): Wayne Lordan. **Jockey (NH):** W. J. Lee.

---

569   MR EUGENE STANFORD, Newmarket
Postal: **Flat 4, MacDonald Buchanan House, Howard De Walden Way, Newmarket, Suffolk, CB8 0LT**
Contacts: **PHONE (01638) 665507 MOBILE (07761) 223096**
E-MAIL e.stanford077@btinternet.com WEBSITE www.eugenestanfordracing.com

1 **DAPHIGLOTE (FR)**, 7, b g Poliglote—Daphnee (FR) **Mr E. V. Stanford**
2 **HONEY BADGER**, 5, b br g Pastoral Pursuits—Taminoula (IRE) **Mrs D. J. Black**
3 **ISLAND AUTHORITY**, 4, b f Authorized (IRE)—Island Odyssey **Mr E. V. Stanford**
4 **LADY OF YUE**, 6, b m Manduro (GER)—Desert Royalty (IRE) **Mrs J. M. Quy**
5 **LITTLE VIC**, 5, b g Overbury (IRE)—Vicky Bee **Fare Dealing Partnership**
6 **THE HAPPY HAMMER (IRE)**, 10, b g Acclamation—Emma's Star (ITY) **Newmarketracingclub.co.uk**
7 **TWO MINDS (FR)**, 9, ch g Choisir (AUS)—Dynamic Dream (USA) **Mr E. V. Stanford**
8 **UNTIL MIDNIGHT (IRE)**, 6, b g Moss Vale (IRE)—Emma's Star (ITY) **Newmarketracingclub.co.uk**
9 **WHITE DOG (IRE)**, 4, b g Le Cadre Noir (IRE)—Little Annie **Green Stone Stud Ltd**

MR EUGENE STANFORD - Continued

THREE-YEAR-OLDS

10 Ch f Notnowcato—Baidawi **Baron F. Von Oppenheim**
11 Q CEE, b g Denounce—Gibraltar Lass (USA) **Mr M. Goodridge QC**

Other Owners: Mr Paul Burling, Mrs Mary Burling, Laurance Dixon, John Ferguson, New Sports Media Ltd, Ian Purkiss, Dan Roach, Mr Eugene Stanford, Mrs J. Thomason-Murphy, Mr Cliff Woof.

Jockey (flat): Jimmy Quinn, Robert Tart. **Jockey (NH):** Jack Quinlan.

570

MR DANIEL STEELE, Henfield
Postal: **Blacklands House, Wheatsheaf Road, Wineham, nr Henfield, West Sussex, BN5 9BE**
Contacts: **MOBILE (07500) 556398**
E-MAIL danielsteele14@hotmail.co.uk

1 ACCORDING TO THEM (IRE), 12, ch g Quws—Any Old Music (IRE) **Mr D. R. Steele**
2 KNOCKGRAFFON KING (IRE), 11, ch g Beneficial—Kilternan Gale (IRE) **Mr D. R. Steele**
3 MAD MOLL (IRE), 8, b m Heron Island (IRE)—Rose Gold (IRE) **Miss M. E. Spencer**
4 UTALY (FR), 8, b g Shaanmer (IRE)—Nataly (FR) **Mr D. R. Steele**

571

MRS JACKIE STEPHEN, Inverurie
Postal: **Conglass Farmhouse, Inverurie, Aberdeenshire, AB51 5DN**
Contacts: **PHONE (01467) 621267 FAX (01467) 620511 MOBILE (07980) 785924**
E-MAIL jackieprovan123@hotmail.co.uk

1 AMILLIONTIMES (IRE), 8, b g Olden Times—Miss Million (IRE) **Mr P. G. Stephen**
2 BALLINVEGGA (IRE), 6, gr g Royal Anthem (USA)—Gill's Honey (IRE) **Mrs J. S. Stephen**
3 BRIGHT PROSPECT (IRE), 7, b g Kutub (IRE)—Bright Future (IRE) **Lessells, Pirie, Ritchie & Stephen**
4 MO ROUGE (IRE), 8, b g Croco Rouge (IRE)—Just A Mo (IRE) **Mrs J. S. Stephen**
5 WELCOME BEN (IRE), 7, b g High Roller (IRE)—Bramble Cottage **Ben's Men**

Other Owners: Mr P. Gorman, Mr J. S. Lessells, Mr A. C. Pirie, Mr G. G. Ritchie, Mr T. S. Wordsworth.

572

MRS KATIE STEPHENS, Shaldon
Postal: **Sikymsa Meadow, Short Lane, Shaldon, Devon, TQ14 0HE**

1 CAPTAIN CANADA, 9, br g Tamayaz (CAN)—Hattie **Mrs K. Stephens**
2 CHAKISTO (FR), 8, b g Discover d'auteuil (FR)—Chattawakie (FR) **Mrs K. Stephens**
3 DRUMMOND, 7, b g Zamindar (USA)—Alrisha (IRE) **Mrs K. Stephens**
4 5, B m Primo Valentino (IRE)—Emmasflora **Mrs K. Stephens**
5 I'LLHAVEALOOK (IRE), 11, b g Milan—Kelly's Native (IRE) **Mrs K. Stephens**
6 POETS DAY, 6, ch m Apple Tree (FR)—Lady Blade (IRE) **Mrs K. Stephens**
7 STAG HILL (IRE), 7, ch g Redback—Counting Blessings **Mrs K. Stephens**

573

MR ROBERT STEPHENS, Caldicot
Postal: **The Knoll, St. Brides Netherwent, Caldicot, Gwent, NP26 3AT**
Contacts: **MOBILE (07717) 477177**
E-MAIL robertdavidstephens@btinternet.com

1 ALL FOR THE BEST (IRE), 4, b g Rip Van Winkle (IRE)—Alleluia **Mr E. A. Elliott**
2 BELTOR, 5, b g Authorized (IRE)—Carahill (AUS) **A. J. Mossop**
3 BON GENRE (IRE), 5, b g Fruits of Love (USA)—Cobblers Hall (IRE) **WHW Thoroughbreds**
4 BUMBLE BAY, 6, b g Trade Fair—Amica **A Mossop, H Scale, M Duthie**
5 CASTLE CAVALIER, 4, b g Nayef (USA)—Jardin **Castle Farm Racing**
6 CHARMED ONE, 5, b m Darnay—Bonnie Flora **Two Magpies Racing Club**
7 DIAMOND BENNY (IRE), 4, b g Milan—Ben's Pride **Paul Duffy Diamond Partnership**

MR ROBERT STEPHENS - Continued

8 **DISTRACTED (IRE)**, 8, b m Publisher (USA)—Richmond Usa (IRE) **Mr A. Roberts**
9 **DOUBLE MISS**, 5, b m Double Trigger (IRE)—Ladyalder **Paul Williams**
10 **INNER LOOP**, 4, b f Rail Link—Sailing Days **Mrs E. Morris**
11 **KAWARTHA**, 4, b f Royal Applause—Zarkavean **D. J. Deer**
12 **MAKDAY**, 4, b g Makfi—Flag Day **D. J. Deer**
13 **MERE ANARCHY (IRE)**, 5, b g Yeats (IRE)—Maracana (IRE) **The Warriors**
14 **MILAN OF CRYSTAL (IRE)**, 7, b m Milan—Native Crystal (IRE) **Castle Farm Racing**
15 **MILE HOUSE (IRE)**, 8, b g Close Conflict (USA)—Clogheen Lass (IRE) **Castle Farm Racing**
16 **NORTHERN MEETING (IRE)**, 6, b m Dylan Thomas (IRE)—Scottish Stage (IRE) **The Go Slow Club**
17 **RENDL BEACH (IRE)**, 9, b g Milan—Erins Emblem (IRE) **M Duthie & A Mossop**
18 **RULER OF THE NILE**, 4, b g Exceed And Excel (AUS)—Dinka Raja (USA) **Threes Company**

THREE-YEAR-OLDS

19 **EQUIJADE**, b f Equiano (FR)—Royal Jade **D. J. Deer**

Other Owners: Mr Paul Duffy, Mr M. Duthie, Mr A. C. Elliott, Mr Tony Gale, Mr S. Harrison, Mr B. J. Matthews, Alison Mossop, Mr Hugh Scale, Mr R. Stephens, Ms A. C. Tite.

Assistant Trainer: Rosie Stephens

Jockey (NH): Robert Dunne, Tom O'Brien. **Conditional** Ciaran Gethings.

574	**MISS ANN STOKELL, Southwell** Postal: **2 Chippendale Road, Lincoln, Lincolnshire, LN6 3PP** Contacts: **MOBILE (07814) 579982** E-MAIL ann.stokell@gmail.com

1 **ANJUNA BEACH (USA)**, 6, b g Artie Schiller (USA)—Hidden Temper (USA) **Mr G. B. Pacey**
2 **BAPAK BANGSAWAN**, 6, b g Pastoral Pursuits—Nsx **Mr G. B. Pacey**
3 8, Ch m Blue Dakota (IRE)—Fizzy Whizzy
4 **GEORGE FENTON**, 7, ch g Piccolo—Mashmoum **Mr G. B. Pacey**
5 **HOLD THE STAR**, 10, b m Red Ransom (USA)—Sydney Star **Mr G. B. Pacey**
6 **INCENDO**, 10, ch g King's Best (USA)—Kindle **Mr G. B. Pacey**
7 **ISLAND EXPRESS (IRE)**, 9, b g Chineur (FR)—Cayman Expresso (IRE) **Mr G. B. Pacey**
8 **KUANYAO (IRE)**, 10, b g American Post—Nullarbor **Mr G. B. Pacey**
9 **MRS MEDLEY**, 10, b m Rambling Bear—Animal Cracker **Ms C. Stokell**
10 **SIMPLY BLACK (IRE)**, 5, br m Kheleyf (USA)—Tashyra (IRE) **Mr G. B. Pacey**
11 **SIRDAAB (USA)**, 4, b g City Zip (USA)—Stormy Union (USA) **Mr G. B. Pacey**
12 **SPEIGHTOWNS KID (USA)**, 8, gr ro g Speightstown (USA)—Seize the Wind (USA) **Mr G. B. Pacey**
13 **STEEL CITY BOY (IRE)**, 13, b g Bold Fact (USA)—Balgren (IRE) **Mr G. B. Pacey**

THREE-YEAR-OLDS

14 **VALTASHYRA (IRE)**, br f Vale of York (IRE)—Tashyra (IRE) **Mr G. B. Pacey**

Assistant Trainer: Caron Stokell

575	**MR WILLIAM STONE, West Wickham** Postal: **The Meadow, Streetly End, West Wickham, Cambridge, Cambridgeshire, CB21 4RP** Contacts: **PHONE (01223) 894617 MOBILE (07788) 971094** E-MAIL williamstone1@hotmail.co.uk

1 **DIAMOND LADY**, 5, b m Multiplex—Ellen Mooney **The Going Great Guns Partnership**
2 **EAST COAST LADY (IRE)**, 4, b f Kodiac—Alexander Anapolis (IRE) **Miss C. M. Scott**
3 **EVENING ATTIRE**, 5, b g Pastoral Pursuits—Markova's Dance **Miss C. M. Scott**
4 **IMJIN RIVER (IRE)**, 9, b g Namid—Lady Nasrana (FR) **Miss C. M. Scott**
5 **LITTLE FLO**, 5, ch m Midnight Legend—Sweet Robinia (IRE) **Miss C. M. Scott**

MR WILLIAM STONE - Continued

   6 TOUCH THE CLOUDS, 5, b g Sleeping Indian—Aptina (USA) **Miss C. M. Scott**
   7 WARDEN BOND, 8, ch g Monsieur Bond (IRE)—Warden Rose **Mr J A Ross & Miss C Scott**

THREE-YEAR-OLDS

   8 HEATHFIELD PARK (IRE), b f Bushranger (IRE)—Alexander Anapolis (IRE) **The Plenipo Partnership**

TWO-YEAR-OLDS

   9 B f 5/3 Aqlaam—Aditi (Dansili) (3000)

Other Owners: Mr J. A. Ross.

576	**MR BRIAN STOREY, Kirklinton** Postal: **Low Dubwath, Kirklinton, Carlisle, Cumbria, CA6 6EF** Contacts: **PHONE (01228) 675168 FAX (01228) 675977 MOBILE (07950) 925576/ (07912) 898740** E-MAIL bstoreyracing@aol.com WEBSITE www.brianstoreyracing.co.uk

   1 4, Ch f And Beyond (IRE)—Enlisted (IRE)

Assistant Trainer: Mrs Jackie Storey

Jockey (flat): P. J. McDonald. **Jockey (NH):** Brian Hughes. **Conditional:** Jamie Hamilton.
Amateur: Miss Jackie Coward, Mr Tom Hamilton.

577	**MR WILF STOREY, Consett** Postal: **Grange Farm & Stud, Muggleswick, Consett, Co. Durham, DH8 9DW** Contacts: **PHONE (01207) 255259 FAX (01207) 255259 MOBILE (07860) 510441** E-MAIL wlstorey@metronet.co.uk WEBSITE www.wilfstorey.com

   1 CARD HIGH (IRE), 6, b g Red Clubs (IRE)—Think (FR) **Gremlin Racing**
   2 FAIR TRADE, 9, ch g Trade Fair—Ballet **W. L. Storey**
   3 JAN SMUTS (IRE), 8, b g Johannesburg (USA)—Choice House (USA) **H. S. Hutchinson & W. Storey**
   4 MR SUNDOWNER (USA), 4, b br g Scat Daddy (USA)—Bold Answer (USA) **W. L. Storey**
   5 NELSON'S BAY, 7, b g Needwood Blade—In Good Faith (USA) **The Durham Company & W. Storey**
   6 NONAGON, 5, b g Pastoral Pursuits—Nine Red **Geegeez.co.uk 1**
   7 ZINGIBER, 4, ch g Manduro (GER)—Titoli di Coda (IRE) **W. L. Storey**

Other Owners: Mr M. Bisogno, Mr M. Burton, The Durham Company, Mr D. D. Gillies, Mr H. S. Hutchinson, Mr D. McPharlane, Mr P. McVey, Mr S. Meikle, Mr A. Russ, Mr W. Storey.

Assistant Trainer: Miss S. Storey

Amateur: Miss S. M. Doolan.

578	**SIR MICHAEL STOUTE, Newmarket** Postal: **Freemason Lodge, Bury Road, Newmarket, Suffolk, CB8 7BY** Contacts: **PHONE (01638) 663801 FAX (01638) 667276**

   1 ARAB SPRING (IRE), 6, b h Monsun (GER)—Spring Symphony (IRE)
   2 CANNOCK CHASE (USA), 5, b h Lemon Drop Kid (USA)—Lynnwood Chase (USA)
   3 CONVEY, 4, b r Dansili—Insinuate (USA)
   4 CRYSTAL ZVEZDA, 4, ch f Dubawi (IRE)—Crystal Star
   5 DANNYDAY, 4, b c Dansili—Dayrose
   6 DARSHINI, 4, b g Sir Percy—Fairy Flight (USA)
   7 DARTMOUTH, 4, b c Dubawi (IRE)—Galatee (FR)
   8 EXOSPHERE, 4, b c Beat Hollow—Bright And Clear
   9 GOSPEL CHOIR, 7, ch g Galileo (IRE)—Chorist
   10 GRAND INQUISITOR, 4, b c Dansili—Dusty Answer
   11 HORSESHOE BAY (IRE), 4, b g Arch (USA)—Sweepstake (IRE)
   12 INTIMATION, 4, b f Dubawi (IRE)—Infallible
   13 MUSTAAQEEM (USA), 4, b g Dynaformer (USA)—Wasseema (USA)
   14 MUTAMAKKIN (IRE), 5, br g Shamardal (USA)—Princess Speedfit (FR)

SIR MICHAEL STOUTE - Continued

15 **PETRUCCI (IRE)**, 4, b g Azamour (IRE)—Spring Symphony (IRE)
16 **SONG OF NAMIBIA (IRE)**, 5, br g Cape Cross (IRE)—Spring Symphony (IRE)
17 **YARROW (IRE)**, 4, b f Sea The Stars (IRE)—Highland Gift (IRE)

THREE-YEAR-OLDS

18 **ABDON**, b c Cacique (IRE)—Kinnaird (IRE)
19 **ABERLADY (USA)**, br f Arch (USA)—Visit
20 **ABINGDON (USA)**, b f Street Cry (IRE)—Justlookdontouch (IRE)
21 **ACROSS THE STARS (IRE)**, b c Sea The Stars (IRE)—Victoria Cross (IRE)
22 **AFLAME**, b f Shamardal (USA)—Magical Romance (IRE)
23 **AL FALAK (USA)**, b c Cape Blanco (IRE)—Chic Shanique (USA)
24 **ALYDAY**, ch f Kyllachy—Dayrose
25 **ARAB POET**, ch c Poet's Voice—Floral Beauty
26 **ARISTOCLES (IRE)**, b g High Chaparral (IRE)—Amathusia
27 **ARISTOCRATIC**, b f Exceed And Excel (AUS)—Peeress
28 **ATONE**, b f Oasis Dream—Midsummer
29 **AUTOCRATIC**, b c Dubawi (IRE)—Canda (USA)
30 **BALLET CONCERTO**, b c Dansili—Ballet Ballon (USA)
31 **BARLEYSUGAR (IRE)**, b f Kyllachy—Caster Sugar (USA)
32 **CANONBURY (IRE)**, b br f Oasis Dream—Islington (IRE)
33 **CAT SILVER**, b c Dansili—Catopuma (USA)
34 **CLEAR EVIDENCE**, b c Cape Cross (IRE)—Rainbow's Edge
35 **COMMODITY (IRE)**, ch c Dutch Art—Royale Danehill (IRE)
36 **DELVE (IRE)**, b f Dansili—Cool And Composed (USA)
37 **DESERT ISLE (IRE)**, b c Fastnet Rock (AUS)—Desert Bloom (IRE)
38 **DIPLOMA**, b f Dubawi (IRE)—Enticement
39 **DIVINE QUICKSTEP (IRE)**, b f Dansili—La Divina (IRE)
40 **DIVISIONIST**, b c Oasis Dream—Exemplify
41 **DOLLAR REWARD**, b c Shamardal (USA)—Cape Dollar (IRE)
42 **DU MOTO (IRE)**, b c Galileo (IRE)—Mauralakana (FR)
43 **DUBKA**, b f Dubawi (IRE)—Rosika
44 **EL HAYEM (IRE)**, b c Invincible Spirit (IRE)—Winning Sequence (FR)
45 **ENGAGE (IRE)**, b f Pour Moi (IRE)—Brooklyn's Storm (USA)
46 **ESTIDRAAK (IRE)**, ch c Iffraaj—Gold Hush (USA)
47 **FIDAAWY**, ch g New Approach (IRE)—Haymana (IRE)
48 **FORGE**, b c Dubawi (IRE)—Heat Haze
49 **FORTH BRIDGE**, b c Bernardini (USA)—Sally Forth
50 **GALVANIZE (USA)**, b c Medaglia d'oro (USA)—Enthused (USA)
51 **HADDAJAH (IRE)**, b f Sea The Stars (IRE)—Ardbrae Lady
52 **HAMMER GUN (USA)**, b c Smart Strike (CAN)—Caraboss
53 **HAWKER HUNTER (IRE)**, gr c Dalakhani (IRE)—Kitty Hawk
54 **HEAVENLY NOTE**, ch f Dutch Art—Heavenly Dawn
55 **HEDGEROSE**, b f Zamindar (USA)—Rosacara
56 **HONORINA**, ch f Sea The Stars (IRE)—Honorine (IRE)
57 **IDYLLIC (IRE)**, b f Rip Van Winkle (IRE)—Cilium (IRE)
58 **IMPEDIMENT (IRE)**, ch g Pivotal—Pediment
59 **INFATUATION**, b f Invincible Spirit (IRE)—Fantasize
60 **JANTINA**, ch f Dutch Art—Zykina
61 **JUSTICE SMART (IRE)**, ch c Kyllachy—Laurentina
62 **KHAIRAAT (IRE)**, b c Shamardal (USA)—Mumayeza
63 **KOKONI (IRE)**, b g Acclamation—Belgique (IRE)
64 **LABYRINTH (IRE)**, b f Lawman (FR)—Kerry Gal (IRE)
65 **LIFE OF PI**, b f Sea The Stars (IRE)—Noahs Ark (IRE)
66 **LOLWAH**, ch f Pivotal—Palace Affair
67 **MAINSTREAM**, b c Dansili—Golden Stream (IRE)
68 **MASTER GUNNER (USA)**, b c War Front (USA)—Queen of The Night
69 **MAWAANY (IRE)**, gr g Teofilo (IRE)—Middle Persia
70 **MIDTERM**, b c Galileo (IRE)—Midday
71 **MISCHIEVOUS**, b f Holy Roman Emperor (IRE)—Mango Mischief (IRE)
72 **MOKHALAD**, ch c Dubawi (IRE)—Model Queen (USA)
73 **MULK**, ch c New Approach (IRE)—Nannina
74 **MUSDAM (USA)**, b c Exchange Rate (USA)—Valid Lilly (USA)
75 **MUSTASHRY**, b br c Tamayuz—Safwa (IRE)
76 **MYSTIC STORM**, ch f Pivotal—Moon Goddess
77 **PAVONINE**, b f High Chaparral (IRE)—Pearl City (IRE)

SIR MICHAEL STOUTE - Continued

78 **PELOPONNESE (FR)**, b f Montjeu (IRE)—Mimalia (USA)
79 **PERCY'S ROMANCE**, ch f Sir Percy—Top Romance (IRE)
80 **PLATITUDE**, b g Dansili—Modesta (IRE)
81 **PLAYFUL SOUND**, b f Street Cry (IRE)—Giants Play (USA)
82 **POET'S WORD (IRE)**, b c Poet's Voice—Whirly Bird
83 **QUEEN'S TRUST**, b f Dansili—Queen's Best
84 **ROSTOVA (USA)**, b f Arch (USA)—Tsar's Pride
85 **RUSCOMBE**, b f Dansili—Eva Luna (USA)
86 **SCOTTISH SUMMIT (IRE)**, b c Shamardal (USA)—Scottish Stage (IRE)
87 **SHABBAH (IRE)**, br c Sea The Stars (IRE)—Alizaya (IRE)
88 **SHALL WE (IRE)**, b f Dansili—Insight (FR)
89 **SHRAAOH (IRE)**, b c Sea The Stars (IRE)—Jumooh
90 **SIDLE (IRE)**, b f Lawman (FR)—Slink
91 **SIR GEORGE SOMERS (USA)**, ch c Cape Blanco (IRE)—Sense of Class (USA)
92 **SKY SHIP**, ch c Raven's Pass (USA)—Angara
93 **STARGAZER (IRE)**, b c Canford Cliffs (IRE)—Star Ruby (IRE)
94 **STATUESQUE**, b f Sea The Stars (IRE)—Kahara
95 **STREET POET (IRE)**, b c Poet's Voice—Street Star (USA)
96 **SUPERYACHT (IRE)**, b c Fastnet Rock (AUS)—Olympienne (IRE)
97 **SWEET FREEDOM (IRE)**, b g Iffraaj—Sweet Nicole
98 **SWIFT RESPONSE (USA)**, br c Hat Trick (JPN)—Promptly (IRE)
99 **THETIS (IRE)**, b f Invincible Spirit (IRE)—Serres (IRE)
100 **THIKRIYAAT (IRE)**, b g Azamour (IRE)—Malaspina (IRE)
101 **THIRD ROCK (IRE)**, b g Hat Trick (JPN)—Rochitta (USA)
102 **TRANSMITTING**, b c Cacique (IRE)—Shuttle Mission
103 **TRIATHLON (USA)**, br f Hat Trick (JPN)—Relaxed (USA)
104 **ULYSSES (IRE)**, ch c Galileo (IRE)—Light Shift (USA)
105 **UNDER ATTACK (IRE)**, b g Dubawi (IRE)—Ship's Biscuit
106 **VAUNTING (USA)**, gr f Exchange Rate (USA)—Boasting (USA)
107 **VOLITION (IRE)**, gr f Dark Angel (IRE)—Warshah (IRE)
108 **YANGTZE**, b g Dansili—Hi Calypso (IRE)

TWO-YEAR-OLDS

109 B c 6/5 Elusive City (USA)—Ammo (IRE) (Sadler's Wells (USA)) (250000)
110 **ARRIGO BOITO (IRE)**, b c 28/3 Dansili—Eleanora Duse (IRE) (Azamour (IRE))
111 **AWFAA (IRE)**, b f 14/3 Shamardal (USA)—Elraabeya (CAN) (Seeking The Gold (USA))
112 **BELIEVABLE**, b f 6/4 Acclamation—Irresistible (Cadeaux Genereux)
113 **BLUSHING ROSE**, ch f 23/1 Dalakhani (IRE)—Russelliana (Medicean)
114 **BORDER TERRITORY (IRE)**, b c 3/3 Shamardal (USA)—Scottish Stage (IRE) (Selkirk (USA))
115 B c 16/2 Zamindar (USA)—Coraline (Sadler's Wells (USA))
116 **COUNTERWEIGHT (IRE)**, b f 7/3 Azamour (IRE)—Drama Class (IRE) (Caerleon (USA))
117 **CRYSTAL OCEAN (IRE)**, b c 8/2 Sea The Stars (IRE)—Crystal Star (Mark of Esteem (IRE))
118 **DESERT CAPELLA**, b c 4/2 Dubawi (IRE)—Crystal Capella (Cape Cross (IRE))
119 **DESERT DREAM**, b c 14/3 Oasis Dream—Rosika (Sakhee (USA))
120 **EDITH WHARTON (IRE)**, b f 18/1 Dubawi (IRE)—Islington (IRE) (Sadler's Wells (USA))
121 **EL CAP (USA)**, b c 18/1 Speightstown (USA)—Divine Presence (A P Indy (USA))
122 Ch c 31/1 Dutch Art—Elysian (Galileo (IRE)) (170000)
123 **FRONTISPIECE**, b c 6/2 Shamardal (USA)—Free Verse (Danehill Dancer (USA))
124 **HAWKER HURRICANE (IRE)**, gr c 10/4 Dalakhani (IRE)—Kitty Hawk (Danehill Dancer (IRE))
125 **INTERWEAVE**, ch f 13/3 Dutch Art—Interlace (Pivotal)
126 **KARAWAAN (IRE)**, b c 12/2 Sea The Stars (IRE)—Magic Sister (Cadeaux Genereux)
127 B c 2/5 Cacique (IRE)—Katy Nowaitee (Komaite (IRE)) (180000)
128 B c 24/2 Nathaniel (IRE)—Kinnaird (IRE) (Dr Devious (IRE)) (525000)
129 **LA DONNA E MOBILE (IRE)**, b f 5/2 Pivotal—La Divina (IRE) (Sadler's Wells (USA))
130 B f 22/5 Galileo (IRE)—Landmark (USA) (Arch (USA)) (500000)
131 **LUCREZIA**, b f 4/4 Nathaniel (IRE)—Nannina (Medicean)
132 **LUPIN (USA)**, b f 13/4 Medaglia d'oro (USA)—Promising Lead (Danehill (USA))
133 **MAWQED (IRE)**, b f 25/3 Invincible Spirit (IRE)—Mumayeza (Indian Ridge)
134 **MELTING DEW**, b c 2/5 Cacique (IRE)—Winter Sunrise (Pivotal)
135 **MIDNIGHT VIXEN**, b f 9/4 Foxwedge (AUS)—Midnight Ransom (Red Ransom (USA))
136 B c 26/2 Oasis Dream—Mimalia (USA) (Silver Hawk (USA))
137 **MIRAGE DANCER**, b c 18/4 Frankel—Heat Haze (Green Desert (USA))
138 **MISSED**, b c 7/3 So You Think (NZ)—Daring Aim (Daylami (IRE))
139 **MORI**, b f 1/2 Frankel—Midday (Oasis Dream)
140 **NATHAN MAYER**, b c 15/3 Nathaniel (IRE)—Rosacara (Green Desert (USA))

SIR MICHAEL STOUTE - Continued

141 **OLIVE BRANCH (IRE)**, b f 16/5 Arcano (IRE)—Athene (IRE) (Rousillon (USA))
142 **PANOVA**, b f 14/3 Invincible Spirit (IRE)—Safina (Pivotal)
143 **PARADISE LAKE (IRE)**, b c 21/2 Siyouni (FR)—Kalandara (IRE) (Rainbow Quest (USA)) (320000)
144 **PARLANCE (IRE)**, b f 11/2 Invincible Spirit (IRE)—Pleasantry (Johannesburg (USA)) (450000)
145 **PARTITIA**, b f 7/2 Bated Breath—Palmette (Oasis Dream)
146 B c 2/3 Galileo (IRE)—Pearl Earrine (FR) (Kaldounevees (FR)) (184569)
147 **PIVOINE (IRE)**, b c 2/1 Redoute's Choice (AUS)—Fleur de Cactus (IRE) (Montjeu (IRE))
148 **QUEEN'S CASTLE**, b f 11/4 Dansili—Queen's Best (King's Best (USA))
149 **RAINBOW LEGACY (IRE)**, b c 4/3 Frankel—Gift Range (IRE) (Spectrum (IRE))
150 **RAMYA (IRE)**, ch f 11/2 Pivotal—Ebtisama (USA) (Kingmambo (USA))
151 B c 13/4 Harlan's Holiday (USA)—Reflections (Sadler's Wells (USA))
152 **ROMANTICUM (USA)**, b f 9/2 War Front (USA)—Sightseek (USA) (Distant View (USA))
153 **SABLE ISLAND (IRE)**, b c 18/3 New Approach (IRE)—Ratukidul (FR) (Danehill (USA))
154 Ch f 20/1 Galileo (IRE)—Saturn Girl (IRE) (Danehill Dancer (IRE))
155 B c 22/3 Nathaniel (IRE)—Shesasmartlady (IRE) (Dolphin Street (FR)) (145000)
156 **SPATIAL**, b f 7/3 New Approach (IRE)—Spacious (Nayef (USA))
157 Ch c 10/4 Nathaniel (IRE)—Splashdown (Falbrav (IRE)) (160000)
158 B f 19/2 So You Think (NZ)—Star Ruby (IRE) (Rock of Gibraltar (IRE))
159 **SUPERIORITYCOMPLEX (IRE)**, ch f 10/2 Hard Spun (USA)—Justlookdontouch (IRE) (Galileo (IRE))
160 **TAAMOL (IRE)**, b c 11/1 Helmet (AUS)—Supreme Seductress (IRE) (Montjeu (IRE)) (140000)
161 **TEXTURED (IRE)**, b f 23/1 Dark Angel (IRE)—Timbre (Dubai Destination (USA)) (73827)
162 **TIME'S ARROW (IRE)**, b c 21/1 Redoute's Choice (AUS)—Gilt Edge Girl (Monsieur Bond (IRE))
163 **VERITY**, b f 29/4 Redoute's Choice (AUS)—Virtuous (Exit To Nowhere (USA))
164 **VICE VERSA**, b f 27/2 Oasis Dream—Mascarene (USA) (Empire Maker (USA))
165 B c 15/4 New Approach (IRE)—Wild Mimosa (IRE) (Dynaformer (USA)) (300000)

Owners: HM The Queen, Mr Khalid Abdullah, Mr Athos Christodoulou, Mr Peter Done, Sir Alex Ferguson, Flaxman Stables Ireland Ltd, Mrs Elizabeth Haynes, Highclere Thoroughbred Racing, Mrs John Magnier, Newsells Park Stud, Mr Saeed Suhail, Mr George Strawbridge, Mrs Doreen Tabor, Mr Michael Tabor, Mrs Anita Wigan, Mr James Wigan.

---

579 MRS ALI STRONGE, Eastbury
Postal: **Castle Piece Racing Stables, Eastbury, Hungerford, Berkshire, RG17 7JR**
Contacts: **PHONE** (01488) 72818 **FAX** (01488) 670378 **MOBILE** (07779) 285205
E-MAIL office@castlepiecestables.com **WEBSITE** www.castlepiecestables.com

1 **AGENT GIBBS**, 4, ch g Bertolini (USA)—Armada Grove **EPDS Racing 14**
2 **BAKU BAY (IRE)**, 8, b g Flemensfirth (USA)—The Girlfriend (IRE) **Mr I Kidger, Mr I Mason & The Lanza Boys**
3 **BOWBERRY**, 5, b m Cockney Rebel (IRE)—Blaeberry **Lady Bland**
4 **CALL THE DETECTIVE (IRE)**, 7, b g Winged Love (IRE)—Aneeza (IRE) **Mr J. J. King**
5 **CAMAKASI (IRE)**, 5, b g Camacho—Innocence **Friends Of Castle Piece**
6 **CAPPIELOW PARK**, 7, b g Exceed And Excel (AUS)—Barakat **Mr T. J. Dykes & Miss A. Yorke**
7 **CLANVILLE LASS**, 4, b f Tobougg (IRE)—Mulberry Wine **Lady Bland**
8 **DEEPSAND (IRE)**, 7, br g Footstepsinthesand—Sinamay (USA) **Mrs B. V. Evans**
9 **HATTERS RIVER (IRE)**, 9, b g Milan—Curzon Ridge (IRE) **Mr & Mrs G. Nock**
10 **HERESMYNUMBER (IRE)**, 6, b g Kalanisi (IRE)—Broken Rein (IRE) **Pieces Of Eight Racing**
11 **MAVERIK**, 8, ch g Iceman—Nouvelle Lune **Mr S Leigh & Mrs I Kidger**
12 **MEETINGS MAN**, 9, gr g Footstepsinthesand—Missella (IRE) **Mrs B. Evans**
13 4, Ch g Flemensfirth (USA)—On Galley Head (IRE) **EPDS Racing 19**
14 **PETITE POWER**, 7, b g Subtle Power (IRE)—Little Serena **Mr J. J. King**
15 **PROUD TIMES**, 10, b br g Proud Citizen (USA)—Laura's Pistolette (USA) **Mrs A. J. Stronge**
16 **ROYAL GUARDSMAN (IRE)**, 9, b br g King's Theatre (IRE)—Lisa du Chenet (FR) **Camilla & Rosie Nock**
17 **SKINT**, 10, b g King's Theatre (IRE)—No More Money **Mrs B. V. Evans**
19 **STYNES (IRE)**, 6, b g Aussie Rules (USA)—Magic Princess **EPDS Racing 18**
20 **SURGING SEAS (IRE)**, 7, b g Tiger Hill (IRE)—Musardiere **The Hot Hooves Syndicate**
21 **THOMAS BLOSSOM (IRE)**, 6, b g Dylan Thomas (IRE)—Woman Secret (IRE) **Mr I. Beach**
21 **TONYTHETARMACKER (IRE)**, 5, b g Westerner—Dianeme **Mr F. J. Walters**
22 **VALANTINO OYSTER (IRE)**, 9, b g Pearl of Love (IRE)—Mishor **Mrs A. J. Stronge**

THREE-YEAR-OLDS

23 **COOPERESS**, b f Sixties Icon—Vilnius **Mr T. J. Dykes**
24 B f Sixties Icon—Mighty Splash **ROA V**

MRS ALI STRONGE - Continued

Other Owners: Mr Ian Kidger, Mr S. C. Leigh, Mr I. P. Mason, Miss R. Nock, Miss C. D. Nock, Mr C. J. Orme, Mr N. D. Peppiatt, Mrs V. Peppiatt, Miss Anna Yorke.

Assistant Trainer: Sam Stronge

---

580 **MISS KRISTIN STUBBS, Malton**
Postal: **Beverley House, Beverley Road, Norton, Malton, North Yorkshire, YO17 9PJ**
Contacts: **PHONE (01653) 698731 FAX (01653) 698724 MOBILE (07932) 977279 / (07801) 167707**
E-MAIL l.stubbs@btconnect.com

1 BOGSNOG (IRE), 6, b g Moss Vale (IRE)—Lovers Kiss **Facts & Figures**
2 BRONZE BEAU, 9, ch g Compton Place—Bella Cantata **D. G. Arundale**
3 COMPETENT, 4, b g Compton Place—Pantita **Mr R. W. Stubbs**
4 DEPTH CHARGE (IRE), 4, b g Fastnet Rock (AUS)—Myrtle **Paramount Racing III**
5 GOLD BEAU (FR), 6, b g Gold Away (IRE)—Theorie (FR) **Mr D Arundale & Mr N Lyons**
6 HANK WILLIAMS, 4, b g Schiaparelli (GER)—Jezadil (IRE) **O. J. Williams**
7 KEENE'S POINTE, 6, br g Avonbridge—Belle's Edge **P. A. Saxton**
8 LET'S TWIST, 4, ch g Piccolo—Takes Two To Tango **Paramount Racing II**
9 LYNNGALE, 5, b m Myboycharlie (IRE)—Belle Annie (USA) **Mrs L. Gale**
10 RED PALADIN (IRE), 6, b g Red Clubs (IRE)—Alexander Goldmine **PG Shorrock, DR Grieve, T Baker & Clark**
11 SOIE D'LEAU, 4, b g Monsieur Bond (IRE)—Silky Silence **F.A.T.J Partnership**
12 SOMETHING LUCKY (IRE), 4, gr g Clodovil (IRE)—Lucky Leigh **Paul & Linda Dixon**

THREE-YEAR-OLDS

13 FASHIONATA (IRE), ch f Fast Company (IRE)—Red Red Rose **Mr Paul Saxton & Mr P G Shorrock**
14 RONNIE BAIRD, ch g Poet's Voice—Fleur de Lis **Paramount Racing I**

TWO-YEAR-OLDS

15 B g 11/5 Mullionmileanhour (IRE)—Cheap N Chic (Primo Valentino (IRE)) **O. J. Williams**
16 ROYS DREAM, b f 20/1 Monsieur Bond (IRE)—Velvet Jaguar (Hurricane Run (IRE)) **Mrs A. Pickering**

Other Owners: Mr D. Arundale, Mr Terence Baker, Miss Donna Clark, Mr Iain Clark, Mr Paul W. H. Dixon, Mrs L. J. Dixon, Mr David Grieve, Mr J. P. Hames, Mr F. Harrison, Mr Nigel Lyons, Mrs Valerie Pittman, Mr T S Pople, Mr P. A. Saxton, Mr P. G. Shorrock, Miss Kristin Stubbs.

Jockey (flat): Tony Hamilton. **Apprentice:** Jacob Butterfield. **Amateur:** Mr Ben Stephens.

---

581 **MR ROB SUMMERS, Solihull**
Postal: **Summerhill Cottage, Danzey Green, Tanworth-in-Arden, Solihull, B94 5BJ**
Contacts: **PHONE (01564) 742667 MOBILE (07775) 898327**

1 ARCTIC DIXIE, 8, ch m Desideratum—Arctic Oats **R. P. D. T. Dineen**
2 DIRECT FLO (IRE), 9, b m Mr Combustible (IRE)—Direct Pursuit (IRE) **Mrs G. M. Summers**
3 MASSACHUSETTS, 9, ch g Singspiel (IRE)—Royal Passion **Miss G. L. Henderson**
4 MR ROBINSON (FR), 9, b g Robin des Pres (FR)—Alberade (FR) **Mrs G. M. Summers**
5 RED ROSSO, 11, ch g Executive Perk—Secret Whisper **Mrs G. M. Summers**
6 RED WHISPER, 12, ch g Midnight Legend—Secret Whisper **Mrs G. M. Summers**
7 ROSE RED, 9, ch m Weld—Secret Whisper **Mrs G. M. Summers**
8 ROSEINI (IRE), 10, b m Dr Massini (IRE)—Deise Rose (IRE) **Mrs G. M. Summers**

Assistant Trainer: Mrs G. M. Summers

---

582 **MR ALAN SWINBANK, Richmond**
Postal: **Western House Stables, East Road, Melsonby, Richmond, North Yorkshire, DL10 5NF**
Contacts: **PHONE (01325) 339964 FAX (01325) 377113 MOBILE (07860) 368365 / (07711) 488341**
E-MAIL info@alanswinbank.com WEBSITE www.alanswinbank.com

1 ARAMIST (IRE), 6, gr g Aussie Rules (USA)—Mistic Sun **Pam & Richard Ellis**
2 BIG WATER (IRE), 8, ch g Saffron Walden (FR)—Magic Feeling (IRE) **B. Valentine**

MR ALAN SWINBANK - Continued

3 **BUSY STREET**, 4, b g Champs Elysees—Allegro Viva (USA)
4 **CODESHARE**, 4, b g Dansili—Clepsydra **Elsa Crankshaw & G. Allan**
5 **DANCIN ALPHA**, 5, ch g Bahamian Bounty—Phoebe Woodstock (IRE) **Elm Row Racing Syndicate**
6 **DARK RULER (IRE)**, 7, b g Dark Angel (IRE)—Gino Lady (IRE) **Mr K. Walters**
7 **DEEP RESOLVE (IRE)**, 5, b g Intense Focus (USA)—I'll Be Waiting **Panther Racing Limited**
8 **DIVINE PORT (USA)**, 4, b g Arch (USA)—Out of Reach **Mr C. G. Harrison**
9 **DOWN THE LINE (IRE)**, 6, b g Celtic Swing—Aweigh **Ontoawinner 2**
10 **DUSKY DAWN**, 4, b f Kheleyf (USA)—Piddies Pride (IRE) **Countrywide Classics Ltd**
11 **EUTROPIUS (IRE)**, 7, b g Ad Valorem (USA)—Peps **D. C. Young**
12 **FINAL VENTURE**, 4, b g Equiano (FR)—Sharplaw Venture **B. Valentine**
13 **FLY HOME HARRY**, 7, b g Sir Harry Lewis (USA)—Fly Home **Mrs J. M. Penney**
14 **GENRES**, 4, b g Champs Elysees—Musical Horizon (USA) **Miss M. Swinbank**
15 **HAPPY HOLLOW**, 4, b g Beat Hollow—Dombeya (IRE) **Elsa Crankshaw & G. Allan**
16 **IN FOCUS (IRE)**, 5, ch g Intense Focus (USA)—Reine de Neige **Mr G. H. Bell**
17 **KINEMA (IRE)**, 5, b g Galileo (IRE)—Bon Nuit (IRE) **Mrs T. Blackett**
18 **LAVETTA**, 4, b f Peintre Celebre (USA)—Card Games **Guy Reed Racing**
19 **LOTHAIR (IRE)**, 7, b g Holy Roman Emperor (IRE)—Crafty Example (USA) **Mrs J. Porter**
20 **MICKLEGATE RUN**, 5, b g Tiger Hill (IRE)—Mamoura (IRE) **Mr A. J. Sparks**
21 **MOONSHINE RIDGE (IRE)**, 5, b m Duke of Marmalade (IRE)—
Dreams Come True (FR) **Elm Row Racing Syndicate**
22 **MUTDULA (IRE)**, 6, b g Gamut (IRE)—Calendula **Mr & Mrs Paul & Clare Rooney**
23 **NORTHSIDE PRINCE (IRE)**, 10, b g Desert Prince (IRE)—Spartan Girl (IRE) **Mrs J. M. Penney**
24 **PATIENCE TONY (IRE)**, 5, b g Windsor Knot (IRE)—Johar Jamal (IRE) **Mr D. C. Young**
25 **PHANTOM DANCER (IRE)**, 4, gr f Arakan (USA)—Zibaline (IRE) **Panther Racing Limited**
26 **PLANE SONG (IRE)**, 4, ch g Nayef (USA)—Kitty Hawk **Elm Row Racing Syndicate**
27 **RALPHY LAD (IRE)**, 5, b g Iffraaj—Hawattef (IRE) **The Trio Syndicate**
28 **ROSETTE**, 4, b f Archipenko (USA)—Roses **Exors of the Late Mr G. Reed**
29 **SKIDDAW VALLEYS**, 4, ch g Three Valleys (USA)—Skiddaw Wolf **Mr John Wills**
30 **STANARLEY PIC**, 5, b g Piccolo—Harlestone Lady **The Twopin Partnership**
31 **TEN TREES**, 6, b m Millkom—Island Path (IRE) **Spencer, Bradbury & Parsons**
32 **VIRNON**, 5, b g Virtual—Freedom Song **Mr M. J. Pearce**

THREE-YEAR-OLDS

33 **AUSTERITY (IRE)**, br g Elnadim (USA)—Royal Reprieve (FR) **Elm Row Racing Syndicate**
34 **BLUE VISION (IRE)**, ch g Loup Breton (IRE)—Blueprint (USA) **Mr D. G. Clayton**
35 **DOMINANNIE (IRE)**, b f Paco Boy (IRE)—English Rose (USA) **Mrs J. Forrest**
36 **FIDRA BAY (IRE)**, b f Roderic O'Connor (IRE)—Halicardia **Elm Row Racing Syndicate III**
37 Gr g Strategic Prince—Golden Rose (GER) **B. Valentine**
38 Gr g Zebedee—La Bella Grande (IRE)
39 **SHULAMMITE MAN (IRE)**, ch g Arcano (IRE)—Shulammite Woman (IRE) **Mr D. C. Young**
40 **STECCANDO (IRE)**, b g Lawman (FR)—Second Act **Mrs J. Porter**
41 **TRIKINGDOM**, b g Showcasing—Spritzeria **Elm Row Racing Syndicate**
42 **YOUNG SUNSHINE (IRE)**, b f Pour Moi (IRE)—Garra Molly (IRE) **Mr D. C. Young**
43 **ZEALOUS (IRE)**, br g Intense Focus (USA)—Velvet Kiss (IRE) **Mrs J. Porter**

TWO-YEAR-OLDS

44 B f 24/3 Red Rocks (IRE)—Coimbra (USA) (Trempolino (USA)) (36913) **Mrs J. Porter**
45 B g 14/5 Lawman (FR)—Green Lassy (FR) (Green Tune (USA)) (9000) **Mrs J. Porter**
46 B f 1/3 Canford Cliffs (IRE)—Love Thirty (Mister Baileys) (20671) **B. Valentine**
47 B c 24/1 Power—Parade Scene (USA) (Parade Ground (USA)) (16242) **John Latis**
48 B c 27/2 Rip Van Winkle (IRE)—Parvenue (FR) (Ezzoud (IRE)) (22148) **John Latis**
49 B g 12/3 Intikhab (USA)—Pink Moon (IRE) (Namid) (18456) **Mrs J. Porter**
50 B c 10/4 Nathaniel (IRE)—Ragiam (ITY) (Martino Alonso (IRE)) (31007) **John Latis**

Other Owners: Mr G. Allan, Mr J. Bradbury, Miss Elsa Crankshaw, Miss Sally R. Haynes, Mr K. Hogg, Mrs D. Jeromson, Mr N. J. O'Brien, Mr Ray Parsons, Mr P. A. Rooney, Mrs C. Rooney, Mrs Ben Sangster, Mr Ray Spencer, Miss M. Swinbank.

Assistant TrainerS: Mr W.W. Haigh, Miss Sally Haynes

Jockey (flat): Ben Curtis, Neil Farley. **Jockey (NH):** Leighton Aspell, Jake Greenall, Paul Moloney.
Apprentice: Megan Nicholls. **Amateur:** Mr A. Bartlett.

583 MR TOM SYMONDS, Hentland
Postal: **Dason Court Cottage, Hentland, Ross-On-Wye, Herefordshire, HR9 6LW**
Contacts: PHONE **(01989) 730869 MOBILE (07823) 324649**
E-MAIL **dasoncourt@gmail.com** WEBSITE **www.thomassymonds.co.uk**

1 ALBERTO'S DREAM, 7, b g Fantastic Spain (USA)—Molly's Folly **Wallys Dream Syndicate**
2 BABYLONE COLOMBE (FR), 5, b m Coastal Path—
Ruse de Guerre (FR) **G&M Roberts Churchwood Green Hay W-Williams**
3 CARHUE PRINCESS (IRE), 10, b m Desert Prince (IRE)—Carhue Journey (IRE) **The Mumbo Jumbos**
4 CHOOCHOOBUGALOO, 4, b f Rail Link—Charmante Femme **G. E. Amey**
5 DIXIE BULL (IRE), 11, br g Milan—Calora (USA) **Bailey-Carvill Equine**
6 DUBLIN INDEMNITY, 4, b g Presenting—Tazzarine (IRE) **Bailey-Carvill Equine**
7 EATON ROCK (IRE), 7, b g Rocamadour—Duchess of Kinsale (IRE) **Mr K. J. Price**
8 FALCONS FALL (IRE), 5, ch g Vertical Speed—Ellie Park (IRE) **The Eventful Partnership**
9 FOXCUB (IRE), 8, b g Bahri (USA)—Foxglove **Celia & Michael Baker**
10 FRANKLY SPEAKING, 6, ch g Flemensfirth (USA)—No More Money **David Jenks & Celia & Michael Baker**
11 GAYEBURY, 6, b g Overbury (IRE)—Gaye Sophie **Mrs S. D. Knipe**
12 HOLLYWOODIEN (FR), 5, gr g Martaline—Incorrigible (FR) **Sir Peter & Lady Gibbings**
13 KAKI DE LA PREE (FR), 9, b g Kapgarde (FR)—Kica (FR) **Sir Peter & Lady Gibbings**
14 4, B f Yeats (IRE)—Kerada (FR) **The Nigel Jones & Roy Ovel Syndicate**
15 KINGS APOLLO, 7, b g King's Theatre (IRE)—
Temple Dancer **G&M Roberts Churchward Frost Green W-Williams**
16 LAST ECHO (IRE), 5, b m Whipper—Priory Rock (IRE) **Wainwright, Hill, Cheshire & Rowlinson**
17 LEWIS, 7, b g Kayf Tara—Island of Memories (IRE) **Celia & Michael Baker**
18 LIME STREET (IRE), 5, b g Presenting—Specifiedrisk (IRE) **Valda Burke & Bryan Burrough**
19 LLANTARA, 5, b m Kayf Tara—Lady Llancillo (IRE) **Bailey-Carvill Equine**
20 MIDNIGHT BELLE, 9, b m Midnight Legend—Cherry Alley (IRE) **Mrs P. E. Holtorp**
21 MURPHY'S NAILS, 4, b g Milan—Definite Artist (IRE) **Bailey-Carvill Equine**
22 NEVER BEEN WRONG (IRE), 5, b m Robin des Champs (FR)—
Main Dans La Main (FR) **Valda Burke, J. Palmer-Brown, D.Redvers**
23 OSCARS WAY (IRE), 8, b g Oscar (IRE)—Derrigra Sublime (IRE) **Chris & Nick Nenadich**
24 POLITICAL QUIZ, 6, b g Lucarno (USA)—Quiz Night **I. A. Low**
25 REINE DES CHAMPS (IRE), 5, ch m Robin des Champs (FR)—Town Gossip (IRE) **Pearl Bloodstock Limited**
26 SNATCHITBACK, 5, b g Overbury (IRE)—Talk The Talk **Mark & Jane Frieze**
27 STRAITS OF MESSINA (IRE), 7, b g Mountain High (IRE)—Scylla **Lost In Space**
28 SUMMER SOUNDS (IRE), 7, b br g Definite Article—Marble Sound (IRE) **Sir Peter & Lady Gibbings**
29 TOOSEY, 5, b g Lucarno (USA)—Quiz Night **I. A. Low**

Other Owners: Mr P. J. Andrews, R. F. Bailey, Mrs C. A. M. Baker, Mr M. J. Baker, Mrs P. J. Buckler, Mrs V. F. Burke, B. R. H. Burrough, R. K. Carvill, Mrs J. Frieze, Mr M. A. Frieze, Sir Peter Gibbings, The Hon Lady Gibbings, F. M. Green, Mr M. Hill, M. D. C. Jenks, Mr N. A. Jones, J. G. G. Mason, Mr N. Nenadich, C. Nenadich, Mr R. M. Ovel, J. Palmer-Brown, Mr D. Redvers, G. A. Roberts, Mrs J. Rowlinson, Mrs J. E. Symonds, Mr T. R. Symonds, Mr M. J. Wainwright, Mr E. B. Whittall-Williams.

Conditional: Ben Poste. Amateur: Mr James Nixon.

584 MR JAMES TATE, Newmarket
Postal: **Jamesfield Place, Hamilton Road, Newmarket, Suffolk, CB8 7JQ**
Contacts: PHONE **(01638) 669861 FAX (01638) 676634 MOBILE (07703) 601283**
E-MAIL **james@jamestateracing.com** WEBSITE **www.jamestateracing.com**

1 ACCLIO (IRE), 5, b m Acclamation—Hovering (IRE) **S. Manana**
2 AMAZING CHARM, 4, ch f King's Best (USA)—Bint Doyen **M. Al Nabouda**
3 BRAZOS (IRE), 5, gr h Clodovil (IRE)—Shambodia (IRE) **S. Manana**
4 CEASELESS (IRE), 4, b f Iffraaj—Sheer Bliss (IRE) **Sheikh R. D. Al Maktoum**
5 CRACK SHOT (IRE), 4, ch c Lope de Vega (IRE)—Slap Shot (IRE) **S. Manana**
6 FIT THE BILL (IRE), 4, b c Iffraaj—Najam **S. Manana**
7 GOLD SANDS (IRE), 4, b f Cape Cross (IRE)—Lil's Jessy (IRE) **S. Manana**
8 HAALAN, 4, b f Sir Percy—Fin **S. Manana**
9 LADY MOSCOU (IRE), 4, b f Sir Percy—Place de Moscou (IRE) **S. Manana**
10 LAMAR (IRE), 5, b m Cape Cross (IRE)—Deveron (USA) **S. Ali**
11 LIGHT AND SHADE, 4, b f Aqlaam—Tara Moon **S. Manana**
12 MEDICEAN QUEEN, 5, b m Medicean—Qui Moi (CAN) **S. Manana**
13 NAMHROODAH (IRE), 4, br gr f Sea The Stars (IRE)—Independant **S. Manana**
14 QUEEN'S NOVEL, 4, b f King's Best (USA)—Jane Austen (IRE) **S. Manana**

MR JAMES TATE - Continued

15 **RUWAIYAN (USA)**, 7, b br h Cape Cross (IRE)—Maskunah (IRE) **S. Manana**
16 **RUWASI**, 5, b h Authorized (IRE)—Circle of Love **S. Manana**
17 **SBRAASE**, 5, ch h Sir Percy—Hermanita **S. Manana**
18 **SLOVAK (IRE)**, 4, ch f Iffraaj—Bratislava **S. Manana**
19 **SURETY (IRE)**, 5, b h Cape Cross (IRE)—Guarantia **S. Manana**
20 **TEOFILO'S PRINCESS (IRE)**, 4, b f Teofilo (IRE)—Very Nice **S. Manana**
21 **VIA VIA (IRE)**, 4, b c Lope de Vega (IRE)—Atalina (FR) **S. Manana**
22 **ZAMANI (IRE)**, 4, ch f Teofilo (IRE)—Zam Zoom (IRE) **S. Manana**

THREE-YEAR-OLDS

23 **ADHAM (IRE)**, b c Dream Ahead (USA)—Leopard Creek **Sheikh R. D. Al Maktoum**
24 **AMAZEMENT (GER)**, ch c Lope de Vega (IRE)—Aglow **Sheikh J. D. Al Maktoum**
25 **ASAAYL (IRE)**, b f Iffraaj—Mitawa (IRE) **Sheikh R. D. Al Maktoum**
26 **AWESOME QUALITY (USA)**, b c Elusive Quality (USA)—Awesome Maneuver (USA) **Sheikh R. D. Al Maktoum**
27 **BAHAMIAN DOLLAR**, b c Bahamian Bounty—Penny Ha'penny **S. Manana**
28 **BAHIYAH (IRE)**, b f Kyllachy—Eucharist (IRE) **Sheikh R. D. Al Maktoum**
29 B f Arch (USA)—Banyan Street (USA) **Sheikh J. D. Al Maktoum**
30 **CALM SPIRIT**, b c Dream Ahead (USA)—Anadolu (IRE) **S. Manana**
31 **CAPE OF GLORY (IRE)**, br c Cape Cross (IRE)—Stairway To Glory (IRE) **S. Ali**
32 **CAPE PENINSULAR**, b f Cape Cross (IRE)—Najam **S. Manana**
33 **CERTIFIED (IRE)**, ch f Raven's Pass (USA)—Guarantia **S. Manana**
34 **CORONATION DAY**, b f Bahamian Bounty—Queensgate **James Tate Racing Limited**
35 **DREAM VOICE (IRE)**, b f Approve—Louve Sereine (FR) **S. Manana**
36 **DREAMING LADY (IRE)**, b f Dream Ahead (USA)—Ballymore Lady (USA) **S. Manana**
37 **DUBAWI FIFTY**, b c Dubawi (IRE)—Plethora **S. Ali**
38 **DUBAWI HUNDRED (IRE)**, b c Dubawi (IRE)—Casanga (IRE) **S. Ali**
39 **FUN FOR ALL**, ch f Iffraaj—Funday **S. Ali**
40 **GAMRAH (IRE)**, ch f Exceed And Excel (AUS)—Fashionable **Sheikh J. D. Al Maktoum**
41 **GRECIAN KING**, b c Kheleyf (USA)—Grecian Air (FR) **S. Manana**
42 **HILLSIDE DREAM (IRE)**, b f Dream Ahead (USA)—Knapton Hill **S. Ali**
43 **IF WINTER COMES**, br f Dick Turpin (IRE)—Misty Eyed (IRE) **S. Manana**
44 **IL PICCOLO GRANDE (IRE)**, ch c Iffraaj—Soxy Doxy (IRE) **S. Manana**
45 **JAMEERAH**, b f Dansili—Jira **S. Manana**
46 **JIVE TIME**, b c Motivator—Lindy Hop (IRE) **S. Manana**
47 **KEEP THE SILENCE (IRE)**, b f Iffraaj—Lysandra (IRE) **James Tate Racing Limited**
48 **MAYASA (IRE)**, ch f Iffraaj—Lanzana (IRE) **Sheikh R. D. Al Maktoum**
49 **MIRSAALAH**, b f Sir Percy—Lyric Art (USA) **S. Ali**
50 **MUKAABRA**, b f Iffraaj—Peace Signal (USA) **Sheikh J. D. Al Maktoum**
51 **MUNEEB (IRE)**, b c Lilbourne Lad (IRE)—Gold Again (USA) **Sheikh R. D. Al Maktoum**
52 **MY ISLA**, br f Makfi—Islandia (USA) **S. Manana**
53 B f Diktat—Najraan **S. Manana**
54 **ON THE CLOCK**, b f Aqlaam—Azzoom (IRE) **S. Manana**
55 **PARTY ANIMAL**, b f Makfi—Party (IRE) **S. Ali**
56 **PIRATE'S TREASURE**, b c Iffraaj—Musical Sands **S. Ali**
57 **PRETTY JEWEL**, b f Aqlaam—Highland Jewel (IRE) **S. Manana**
58 B c Medicean—Red Camellia **S. Manana**
59 **ROCKET POWER**, ch c Kyllachy—Rhal (IRE) **S. Manana**
60 B f Pivotal—Saadiah (IRE) **S. Manana**
61 **SABAANI**, b c Aqlaam—Sabaweeya **S. Ali**
62 Ch c Medicean—Stagecoach Jade (IRE) **S. Manana**
63 **STANZA DANCER (IRE)**, ch c Poet's Voice—Calakanga **S. Manana**
64 **SUNSET DAZZLE (IRE)**, b f Teofilo (IRE)—Sunset Avenue (USA) **S. Ali**
65 **TEAJAN (IRE)**, gr c Dandy Man (IRE)—Red Riddle (IRE) **Sheikh R. D. Al Maktoum**
66 **TRANQUIL TIME**, b f Poet's Voice—Peaceful Soul (USA) **S. Manana**
67 **WEATHER FRONT (USA)**, ch g Stormy Atlantic (USA)—Kiswahili (USA) **S. Ali**
68 B c Sir Percy—Whole Grain **S. Manana**
69 **WILD SIDE (IRE)**, b c Dark Angel (IRE)—Miss Windley (IRE) **S. Manana**

TWO-YEAR-OLDS

70 B f 24/1 Cape Cross (IRE)—Al Joza (Dubawi (IRE)) (28000) **S. Manana**
71 B f 19/5 Camacho—Asinara (GER) (Big Shuffle (USA)) (22000) **S. Manana**
72 B f 2/4 Dragon Pulse—Call This Cat (IRE) (One Cool Cat (USA)) (28000) **S. Manana**
73 B c 15/2 Lawman (FR)—Catbells (IRE) (Rakti) (40000) **S. Manana**
74 B f 11/2 Teofilo (IRE)—Dixie Belle (Diktat) (36000) **S. Manana**

MR JAMES TATE - Continued

75 B f 2/2 Sea The Stars (IRE)—Dream Vision (USA) (Distant View (USA)) (35000) **S. Ali**
76 B f 16/4 Royal Applause—Garbah (IRE) (Kodiac) **S. Manana**
77 Ch c 7/3 Kheleyf (USA)—Golden Waters (Dubai Destination (USA)) (8000) **S. Manana**
78 B f 21/4 Royal Applause—Hadba (IRE) (Cape Cross (IRE)) **S. Manana**
79 B f 17/2 Cape Cross (IRE)—Happy Wedding (IRE) (Green Tune (USA)) (40000) **S. Ali**
80 B c 26/2 Helmet (AUS)—Kerrys Requiem (IRE) (King's Best (USA)) (32000) **S. Manana**
81 B f 7/4 Foxwedge (AUS)—Locharia (Wolfhound (USA)) (18000) **S. Manana**
82 B f 31/1 Foxwedge (AUS)—Lomapamar (Nashwan (USA)) (10000) **S. Manana**
83 B c 15/2 Sir Percy—Mexican Hawk (USA) (Silver Hawk (USA)) (9000) **S. Manana**
84 B c 3/3 Helmet (AUS)—Picture of Lily (Medicean) (28000) **S. Manana**
85 B f 23/4 Medicean—Plucky (Kyllachy) (115000) **S. Manana**
86 B f 18/2 Mayson—Purple Tiger (IRE) (Rainbow Quest (USA)) (10000) **S. Ali**
87 B f 16/3 Clodovil (IRE)—Shambodia (IRE) (Petardia) (30000) **S. Manana**
88 Ch c 21/3 Helmet (AUS)—Shimna (Mr Prospector (USA)) (24000) **S. Manana**
89 B c 28/4 Clodovil (IRE)—Shining Vale (USA) (Twilight Agenda (USA)) (11000) **S. Manana**
90 B c 26/3 Sea The Stars (IRE)—Silent Serenade (Bertolini (USA)) (70000) **S. Manana**
91 B c 29/4 Rio de La Plata (USA)—Silver Miss (FR) (Numerous (USA)) (26000) **S. Manana**

Assistant Trainer: Mrs Lucinda Tate

---

585 **MR TOM TATE, Tadcaster**
Postal: **Castle Farm, Hazelwood, Tadcaster, North Yorkshire, LS24 9NJ**
Contacts: **PHONE (01937) 836036 FAX (01937) 530011 MOBILE (07970) 122818**
E-MAIL tomtate@castlefarmstables.fsnet.co.uk WEBSITE www.tomtate.co.uk

1 AUSPICION, 4, b g Dansili—Superstar Leo (IRE) **Mr David Storey & Mr T. P. Tate**
2 ELLERSLIE JOE, 4, b g Captain Gerrard (IRE)—Madam Bijou **Mr Peter Mina**
3 EMPRESS ALI (IRE), 5, b m Holy Roman Emperor (IRE)—Almanza (IRE) **T T Racing**
4 4, ch g Shirocco (GER)—Leonica **T T Racing**
5 PRINCE OF JOHANNE (IRE), 10, gr g Johannesburg (USA)—Paiute Princess (FR) **Mr David Storey**
6 RED HARRY (IRE), 4, ch g Manduro (GER)—Iktidar **Mr D. P. Harrison**

THREE-YEAR-OLDS

7 B g Captain Gerrard (IRE)—Blades Princess **T T Racing**
8 FRIEND OR FOE, b g Dick Turpin (IRE)—Presto Levanter **Miss Fionnuala Cassidy & Mr T. P. Tate**
9 LE ROI DU TEMPS (USA), ch g Leroidesanimaux (BRZ)—Minute Limit (IRE) **Mr D. P. Harrison**
10 WAITING FOR RICHIE, b g Rail Link—Heart of Hearts **The Ivy Syndicate**
11 YOUNG CHRISTIAN, b g Captain Gerrard (IRE)—Shallow Ground (IRE) **T T Racing**

TWO-YEAR-OLDS

12 Ch f 20/3 Sepoy (AUS)—Camp Riverside (USA) (Forest Camp (USA)) (23809) **T T Racing**
13 B f 6/2 Lawman (FR)—Lucy Limelites (Medicean) (8571) **T T Racing**
14 B c 13/3 Equiano (FR)—Spring Clean (FR) (Danehill (USA)) (15238) **T T Racing**
15 Ch g 11/3 Roderic O'Connor (IRE)—Sweet Chilli (IRE) (Intikhab (USA)) (19047) **T T Racing**

Other Owners: Mrs Hazel Tate, Mr T. P. Tate.

Assistant Trainer: Hazel Tate

Jockey (flat): Andrew Elliott, James Sullivan.

---

586 **MRS SUE TAYLOR, Morpeth**
Postal: **The Gate, Longframlington, Morpeth, Northumberland, NE65 8EL**

1 RAKERIN LAD (IRE), 13, b g New Frontier (IRE)—Lotta (IRE)

587 MR COLIN TEAGUE, Wingate
Postal: **Bridgefield Farm, Trimdon Lane, Station Town, Wingate, Co. Durham, TS28 5NE**
Contacts: **PHONE (01429) 837087 MOBILE (07967) 330929**
E-MAIL colin.teague@btopenworld.com

1 **INGLEBY ANGEL (IRE)**, 7, br g Dark Angel (IRE)—Mistress Twister **Mr D. Scott**
2 **LEES ANTHEM**, 9, b g Mujahid (USA)—Lady Rock **Collins Chauffeur Driven Executive Cars**
3 **MONTE PATTINO (USA)**, 12, ch g Rahy (USA)—Jood (USA) **A. Rice**
4 **ON THE HIGH TOPS (IRE)**, 8, b g Kheleyf (USA)—Diplomats Daughter **A. Rice**
5 **RUBICON BAY (IRE)**, 9, b m One Cool Cat (USA)—Mrs Moonlight **Collins Chauffeur Driven Executive Cars**
6 **SATNAV STAN**, 4, ch c Phoenix Reach (IRE)—Pink Supreme **A. Rice**
7 **THORNABY NASH**, 5, br g Kheleyf (USA)—Mistress Twister **Mr D. Scott**
8 **THORNABY PRINCESS**, 5, b m Camacho—Ingleby Princess **Mr D. Scott**
9 **TSARGLAS**, 5, gr g Verglas (IRE)—Russian Empress (IRE) **T. B. Tarn**

THREE-YEAR-OLDS
10 B g Misu Bond (IRE)—Davana **T. B. Tarn**
11 **IVY MATILDA**, b f Monsieur Bond (IRE)—Ingleby Princess **Ingleby Bloodstock Ltd & The Ivy League**
12 Ch f Monsieur Bond (IRE)—Jaldarshaan (IRE) **T. B. Tarn**
13 B f Prime Defender—Lady Rock

Other Owners: Mr P. I. Baker, Mr C. M. Hills, Ingleby Bloodstock Limited.

588 MR ROGER TEAL, Great Shefford
Postal: **Shefford Valley Stables, Great Shefford, Hungerford, Berkshire, RG17 7EF**
Contacts: **PHONE (01488) 649869 MOBILE (07710) 325521**
E-MAIL info@rogertealracing.com WEBSITE www.rogertealracing.co.uk

1 **BERKELEY VALE**, 5, b g Three Valleys (USA)—Intriguing Glimpse **Mrs Muriel Forward & Dr G C Forward**
2 **DARING INDIAN**, 8, ch g Zamindar (USA)—Anasazi (IRE) **Mr B. M. Parish**
3 **JACK OF DIAMONDS (IRE)**, 7, b g Red Clubs (IRE)—Sakkara Star (IRE) **Inside Track Racing Club**
4 **JOHNNY SPLASH (IRE)**, 7, b g Dark Angel (IRE)—Ja Ganhou **Mr B. Kitcherside**
5 **LANGLEY VALE**, 7, b g Piccolo—Running Glimpse (IRE) **Mrs Muriel Forward & Dr G C Forward**
6 **MISS LILLIE**, 5, b m Exceed And Excel (AUS)—Never Lose **The Rat Racers**
7 **PUCON**, 7, b m Kyllachy—The Fugative **Mr J. A. Redmond**
8 **RACHAEL'S RUBY**, 9, b m Joe Bear (IRE)—Fajjoura (IRE) **Ms R. Bezuidenhout**
9 **ROSIE ROYALE (IRE)**, 4, gr f Verglas (IRE)—Fearn Royal (IRE) **The Idle B'S**
10 **STONEMADFORSPEED (IRE)**, 8, b g Fruits of Love (USA)—Diamond Forever **Mr Roger Teal**
11 **STORM RUN (IRE)**, 5, ch m Hurricane Run (IRE)—Jabroot (IRE) **Mr R. Teal**
12 **THE TICHBORNE (IRE)**, 8, b g Shinko Forest (IRE)—Brunswick **Mr Chris Simpson & Mick Waghorn**
13 **TILSTARR (IRE)**, 6, b m Shamardal (USA)—Vampire Queen (IRE) **Homecroft Wealth Racing**

THREE-YEAR-OLDS
14 Ch c Dutch Art—Ardessie **Mr Mark Vickers**
15 **MILYAAR (IRE)**, b c Vale of York (IRE)—Central Force **Mr B. M. Parish**
16 **ORMERING**, b f Kyllachy—Lihou Island **The Idle B's 2**

TWO-YEAR-OLDS
17 B f 22/1 Mayson—High Class Girl (Royal Applause) (28571) **Mr Mark Vickers**
18 B c 21/5 Equiano (FR)—The Fugative (Nicholas (USA)) (15000) **Mr John Redmond**

Other Owners: Mr Barry Kitcherside, Mr R. Kolien, Mr S. J. Piper, Mr E. Sames, Mr Chris Simpson, Mr Mick Waghorn, Mr Darren Waterer.

Amateur: Mr Harry Teal.

589 MR HENRY TETT, Lambourn
Postal: **Delamere Cottage Stables, Folly Road, Lambourn, Hungerford, Berkshire, RG17 8QE**
Contacts: **MOBILE (07796) 098220**
WEBSITE www.henrytettracing.co.uk

1 **ALANJOU (FR)**, 6, b g Maresca Sorrento (FR)—Partie Time (FR) **The Cap All Partnership**
2 **GYPSY RIDER**, 7, b g Ishiguru (USA)—Spaniola (IRE) **The Racing 4 Fun Partnership**
3 **MOVEABLE ASSET (IRE)**, 8, b g Trans Island—Mica Male (ITY) **The Collective Dreamers**
4 **PLAY THE BLUES (IRE)**, 9, gr m Refuse To Bend (IRE)—Paldouna (IRE) **The Cool Blue Partnership**
5 **RECTITUDE**, 5, b m Virtual—Evasive Quality (IRE) **The Rectitude Partnership**
6 **VICTORY RICH (IRE)**, 5, b g Kheleyf (USA)—Imperial Graf (USA) **Mrs Victoria Tett**

Other Owners: Mr M. A. Allen, Mr A. Crichton, Mrs D. S. Gibbs, Mr P. D. Hensher, Mrs C. Lowman, B. Newman, Mr C. C. Tett, Mr H. G. M. Tett.

590 MR SAM THOMAS, Northleach
Postal: **Winterwell Farm, Northleach, Cheltenham, Gloucestershire, GL54 3QD**
Contacts: **MOBILE (07929) 101751**
E-MAIL samthomasracing@outlook.com WEBSITE www.samthomasracing.com

1 **BALLYBROWNEYBRIDGE (IRE)**, 6, b m Kalanisi (IRE)—Ballybrowney Hall (IRE) **D. A. Hunt**
2 5, B m Westerner—Claudia's Pearl **Third Match Officials**
3 **EL TIBURON (IRE)**, 4, b g Court Cave (IRE)—Rongo's Last (IRE) **St Mamadasado**
4 **ENJOY RESPONSIBLY (IRE)**, 7, b g Flemensfirth (USA)—Spice Patrol (IRE) **Mr J. Beswick**
5 **FORT SMITH (IRE)**, 7, b g Presenting—Land of Honour **Mr J. Beswick**
6 **JAMRHAM (IRE)**, 9, b g Great Palm (USA)—Appleway (IRE) **Sarah McQueen**
7 **MISS GISELLE**, 7, b m Desideratum—Pride of The Oaks **Lilling Hall Racing**
8 **ON THE COUCH (IRE)**, 7, b br m Heron Island (IRE)—Miss Serenade (FR) **Third Match Officials**
9 **PENNINE PANTHER**, 5, b g Notnowcato—Kozmina (IRE) **Raso Hedd Win Racing**
10 **SAMDIBIEN (FR)**, 4, b g Day Flight—Sambirane (FR) **Sam's Six**
11 **TORHOUSEMUIR**, 5, b g Sagamix (FR)—Royal Musical

Other Owners: John Beswick, Mr Tom Fillery, Mrs Sara Fillery, Chris Haslam, Mr Carwyn James, Mr Rhys Jones, Sarah McQueen, Sam's Six Syndicate, Mr G. Sanderson, Mr Neil Woods.

Jockey (NH): James Banks, Sam Thomas. **Conditional:** Harry Beswick.

591 MRS JOANNE THOMASON-MURPHY, Chelmsford
Postal: **Oakview, Leighams Road, Bicknacre, Chelmsford, Essex, CM3 4HF**

1 **KERRY'S LORD (IRE)**, 7, b g Lend A Hand—Tesses Express (IRE) **Mrs J. Thomason-Murphy**

592 MR DAVID THOMPSON, Darlington
Postal: **South View Racing, Ashley Cottage, South View, Bolam, Darlington, Co. Durham, DL2 2UP**
Contacts: **PHONE (01388) 835806 (01388) 832658 FAX (01325) 835806 MOBILE (07795) 161657**
E-MAIL dwthompson61@hotmail.co.uk WEBSITE www.dwthompson.co.uk

1 **BALLYTHOMAS**, 9, b g Kayf Tara—Gregale **Mr Alan Moore & Mr Tony Livingston**
2 **BOWDLER'S MAGIC**, 9, b g Hernando (FR)—Slew The Moon (ARG) **Mr N. Park**
3 **GRAMMAR**, 7, b g Rail Link—Comma (USA) **Mr T. J. A. Thompson**
4 **HIGHER COURT (USA)**, 8, b g Shamardal (USA)—Nawaiet (USA) **Seneca Investments & Developments Ltd**
5 **IZBUSHKA (IRE)**, 5, b g Bushranger (IRE)—Zaynaba (IRE) **J. A. Moore**
6 **LETHIRATIT (IRE)**, 6, b m Zagreb (USA)—Clogga Native (IRE) **Mr T. J. A. Thompson**
7 **LORD ROB**, 5, b g Rob Roy (USA)—First Grey **A. Suddes**
8 **MOLIVIAS LAD**, 5, b g Monsieur Bond (IRE)—Mississippi Millie (IRE) **Mr K. M. Everitt**
9 **ROJA DOVE (IRE)**, 7, b m Jeremy (USA)—Knight's Place (IRE) **Mr N. Saint**
10 **ROMAN NUMERAL (IRE)**, 8, b g King's Best (USA)—Trespass **Mr S. Murray**
11 **SARAFINA**, 4, b f Mullionmileanhour (IRE)—Nala (USA) **The Cartmel Syndicate**
12 **SHAIYZAR (IRE)**, 7, b g Azamour (IRE)—Shaiyzima (IRE) **J. A. Moore**
13 **SLIDE SHOW**, 8, b m Galileo (IRE)—First Exhibit **Seneca Investments & Developments Ltd**

MR DAVID THOMPSON - Continued

14 **TARTAN JURA**, 8, b g Green Desert (USA)—On A Soapbox (USA) **J. A. Moore**
15 **TESTING (FR)**, 5, gr m New Approach (IRE)—Testama (FR) **The Renaissance Partnership**
16 **THATS DIGBY**, 6, ch g Cayman Kai (IRE)—Jupiter's Fancy **Mr M. V. Coglan**
17 **WEYBRIDGE LIGHT**, 11, b g Fantastic Light (USA)—Nuryana **J. A. Moore**
18 **ZAMASTAR**, 5, b g Zamindar (USA)—Kissogram **Wildcard Racing Syndicate**
19 **ZRUDA**, 5, b m Observatory (USA)—Pagan Princess **Mr K. M. Everitt**

THREE-YEAR-OLDS

20 **MOLIVIAS GEM**, b f Baltic King—Mississippi Millie (IRE) **Mr K. M. Everitt**

Other Owners: Mr D. F. L. Bishop, Mr A. J. Bonarius, Mr N. J. Bonarius, Mr M. Kay, Mr A. J. Livingston, D. Musgrave, Mrs J. B. Pye.

Assistant Trainer: A Dickman

Jockey (flat): Andrew Elliott, Tony Hamilton.

---

593 · MR RONALD THOMPSON, Stainforth

Postal: **No 2 Bungalow, Haggswood Racing Stable, Stainforth, Doncaster, South Yorkshire, DN7 5PS**
Contacts: **PHONE (01302) 845904 FAX (01302) 845904 MOBILE (07713) 251141**
E-MAIL ronracing@gmail.com

1 **ANNOUNCEMENT**, 5, ch m Proclamation (IRE)—Anapola (GER) **O C Racing**
2 **BELYNDA'S PRIDE (IRE)**, 5, b m Oscar (IRE)—Back To Bavaria (IRE) **Mr D. H. Slater**
3 **DAVE THE RAVE (IRE)**, 6, b g Craigsteel—Coolharbour Lady (IRE) **Mr P. Slater**
4 **GEORDAN MURPHY**, 5, b g Firebreak—Sukuma (IRE) **Mr P. Slater**
5 **JOHNNY CAVAGIN**, 7, b g Superior Premium—Beyond The Rainbow **A. Bell**
6 **MAGNA CARTOR**, 6, b g Motivator—Hora **Mr P. Slater**
7 **NOBLE REACH**, 5, b m Phoenix Reach (IRE)—Comtesse Noire (CAN) **G.B Racing Club**
8 **NUBAR BOY**, 9, ch g Compton Place—Out Like Magic **Mr P. Slater**
9 **ROCK CHARM**, 5, b g Araafa (IRE)—Evening Charm (IRE) **Mr P. Slater**
10 **ROMAN DE BRUT (IRE)**, 4, ch g Rock of Gibraltar (IRE)—Nesmeh (USA) **Mr P. Slater**
11 **SAILORS WARN (IRE)**, 9, b g Redback—Coral Dawn (IRE) **Mr P. Slater**

THREE-YEAR-OLDS

12 **BALLYER RALLYER (IRE)**, ch c Dylan Thomas (IRE)—Ridiforza (FR) **Mr P. Slater**
13 **BLUE JAY (FR)**, b c Anabaa Blue—Romantic Notion (IRE) **Ronald Thompson**
14 **BOND'S TRICKS**, ch g Monsieur Bond (IRE)—Triple Tricks (IRE) **Mr P. Slater**
15 **CHECK 'EM TUESDAY (IRE)**, b f Kodiac—Wait Watcher (IRE) **Mr D. H. Slater**
16 **HANNAHS LAD**, b g Assertive—Beyond The Rainbow **A. Bell**
17 **HEY BEN**, ch g Sakhee's Secret—Gib (IRE) **Mr P. Slater**
18 **JON H THE LAWMAN (IRE)**, b c Lawman (FR)—Lan Pham Ti (IRE) **Mrs A. Harrison**
19 **RAVEN BANNER (IRE)**, b f Raven's Pass (USA)—Ask Annie (IRE) **Mr D. H. Slater**
20 B c Majestic Missile (IRE)—Windomen (IRE) **Ronald Thompson**

Other Owners: Mr A. Bell, Mrs T. Nason, Mr W. Nason, Mr R. P. O'Donnell, Mr J. Parker.

Jockey (flat): T. Eaves, F. Lynch, J. Quinn. **Apprentice:** Jordan Nason.

---

594 · MR VICTOR THOMPSON, Alnwick

Postal: **Link House Farm, Newton By The Sea, Embleton, Alnwick, Northumberland, NE66 3ED**
Contacts: **PHONE (01665) 576272 MOBILE (07739) 626248**

1 **ANZINGER (IRE)**, 10, b g Milan—Tarmons Duchess (IRE) **V. Thompson**
2 **CHANCEOFA LIFETIME (IRE)**, 9, ch g Beneficial—Bounty Queen (IRE) **V. Thompson**
3 **COBH NATIONAL (IRE)**, 8, b g Millenary—Not A Bother Tohim (IRE) **V. Thompson**
4 **COURT PAINTER (IRE)**, 6, b g Court Cave—Comings (IRE) **V. Thompson**
5 **DUHALLOWCOUNTRY (IRE)**, 10, b g Beneficial—Milltown Lass (IRE) **V. Thompson**
6 **GIN COBBLER**, 10, b g Beneficial—Cassia **V. Thompson**
7 **HAVE ONE FOR ME (IRE)**, 9, b g Sonus (IRE)—Dunmanogue (IRE) **V. Thompson**
8 **KING OF THE DARK (IRE)**, 9, b g Zagreb (USA)—Dark Bird (IRE) **V. Thompson**
9 **MILLFIRTH (IRE)**, 9, b g Flemensfirth (USA)—Northern Mill (IRE) **V. Thompson**

MR VICTOR THOMPSON - Continued

10 **MOYACOMB (IRE)**, 8, b m Darsi (FR)—Matt Wood (IRE) **V. Thompson**
11 **MR SHAHADY (IRE)**, 11, b g Xaar—Shunaire (USA) **V. Thompson**
12 **MY LADY WEST (IRE)**, 7, b m Westerner—River Action (IRE) **V. Thompson**
13 **NELLY LA RUE (IRE)**, 9, b m Flemensfirth (USA)—Desperately Hoping (IRE) **V. Thompson**
14 **S FOR ESTUARY (IRE)**, 7, b g Milan—Princess Supreme (IRE) **V. Thompson**
15 **SENOR ALCO (FR)**, 10, gr g Dom Alco (FR)—Alconea (FR) **V. Thompson**
16 **SHARIVARRY (FR)**, 10, ch g Ballingarry (IRE)—Sharsala (IRE) **V. Thompson**
17 **STONEY (IRE)**, 9, b g Stowaway—Classical Rachel (IRE) **V. Thompson**
18 **TOMMYSTEEL (IRE)**, 11, br g Craigsteel—Sarahs Music (IRE) **V. Thompson**
19 **TRUST ME I'M A DR (IRE)**, 7, b g Dr Massini (IRE)—Friendly Flick (IRE) **V. Thompson**
20 **TWO STROKE (IRE)**, 10, b br g Turtle Island (IRE)—Bannockburn (IRE) **V. Thompson**

Assistant Trainer: M Thompson

595

MR SANDY THOMSON, Greenlaw
Postal: **Lambden, Greenlaw, Duns, Berwickshire, TD10 6UN**
Contacts: PHONE **(01361) 810211** MOBILE **(07876) 142787**
E-MAIL **sandy@lambdenfarm.co.uk** WEBSITE **www.sandythomsonracing.co.uk**

1 **BLUE KASCADE (IRE)**, 9, ch g Kaieteur (USA)—Lydia Blue (IRE) **Mrs Q. R. Thomson**
2 **BUCKLED**, 6, b g Midnight Legend—Mulberry Wine **Mr M. Wright**
3 **CHAIN OF BEACONS**, 7, b g Midnight Legend—Millennium Girl **Mr M. Wright & Mr G. Topham**
4 **FLY VINNIE (IRE)**, 7, b g Vinnie Roe (IRE)—Great Days (IRE) **Mr M. Wright**
5 **HARRY THE VIKING**, 11, ch g Sir Harry Lewis (USA)—
Viking Flame **JimBeaumont,DouglasPryde&QuonaThomson**
6 **IMPERIAL PRINCE (IRE)**, 7, b g Subtle Power (IRE)—Satco Rose (IRE) **Mr William Muir & Matros Racing 2**
7 **JOHN WILLIAMS (IRE)**, 7, b g Presenting—Duhallow Park (IRE) **Mrs C. S. Stephenson**
8 **KILQUIGGAN (IRE)**, 8, gr g Vinnie Roe (IRE)—Irene's Call (IRE) **Mrs Q. R. Thomson**
9 **MOSSIES WELL (IRE)**, 7, b g Morozov (USA)—Kidora (IRE) **Mr M. Wright**
10 **NEPTUNE EQUESTER**, 13, b g Sovereign Water (FR)—All Things Nice **J. J. Beaumont**
11 **OSCAR LATEEN (IRE)**, 8, b g Oscar (IRE)—Storm Call **Sprayclad UK & CSS Group**
12 **PRAIRIE LAD**, 8, b g Alflora (IRE)—An Bothar Dubh **Mr J. R. Adam**
13 **RAISE HELL (IRE)**, 9, b g Presenting—Markiza (IRE) **Mrs P. F. Payne**
14 **SEEYOUATMIDNIGHT**, 8, b g Midnight Legend—Morsky Baloo **Mrs Q. R. Thomson**
15 **SELDOM INN**, 8, ch g Double Trigger (IRE)—Portland Row (IRE) **W. A. Walker**
16 **SO SATISFIED**, 8, b g Aqlaam—Pirouetting **Mr M. Wright**
17 **SPIRIT OF KAYF**, 5, b g Kayf Tara—Over Sixty **Sprayclad UK & CSS Group**
18 **SPUR O THE MOMENT**, 7, b m Kayf Tara—Portland Row (IRE) **W. A. Walker**
19 **STRADATER (IRE)**, 7, b g Catcher In The Rye (IRE)—Starring Role (IRE) **Lambden Racing Club**
20 **THE DUTCHMAN (IRE)**, 6, b g King's Theatre (IRE)—Shivermetimber (IRE) **Sprayclad UK & CSS Group**
21 **WAKHAN (IRE)**, 8, b g Dalakhani (IRE)—Wrapitraise (USA) **J. Beaumont, D. Pryde & G. Thomson**

Other Owners: Mr Lee Aldsworth, Mr Jim Beaumont, Mr L. Ellison, Mr Kevin McMunigal, Mr William Muir, Mr D. G. Pryde, Mr D. Spratt, Mr R. Thayne, Mrs A. M. Thomson, Mr A. M. Thomson, Mr M. Wright.

Assistant Trainer: Mrs A. M. Thomson

596

MR NIGEL TINKLER, Malton
Trainer did not wish for details of his string to appear

597

MR COLIN TIZZARD, Sherborne
Postal: **Venn Farm, Milborne Port, Sherborne, Dorset, DT9 5RA**
Contacts: PHONE **(01963) 250598** FAX **(01963) 250598** MOBILE **(07976) 778656**
E-MAIL **info@colintizzard.co.uk** WEBSITE **www.colintizzard.co.uk**

1 **ALLCHILLEDOUT**, 7, b g Alflora (IRE)—Miss Chinchilla **Gale Force Six**
2 **BEARS RAILS**, 6, b g Flemensfirth (USA)—Clandestine **P. M. Warren**
3 **BILLY NO NAME (IRE)**, 8, b g Westerner—Just Little **Mrs J. R. Bishop**
4 **BRAMBLE BROOK**, 6, b g Kayf Tara—Briery Ann **Brocade Racing**

MR COLIN TIZZARD - Continued

5 **BUCKHORN TIMOTHY**, 7, b g Tamure (IRE)—Waimea Bay **The Buckhorn Racing Team**
6 **BUCKHORN TOM**, 8, b g Tamure (IRE)—Waimea Bay **The Buckhorn Racing Team**
7 **BURTON BORU (IRE)**, 4, b g Brian Boru—Tiffiny Gale (IRE) **The Gardens Entertainments Ltd**
8 **COR WOT AN APPLE**, 5, b g Apple Tree (FR)—Chipewyas (FR) **D. V. Stevens**
9 **COTSWOLD ROAD**, 6, b g Flemensfirth (USA)—Crystal Ballerina (IRE) **Chasing Gold Limited**
10 **CUCKLINGTON**, 5, b g Kayf Tara—Ardrom **C. L. Tizzard**
11 **CUE CARD**, 10, b g King's Theatre (IRE)—Wicked Crack (IRE) **Mrs J. R. Bishop**
12 **DUSKY LARK**, 6, b g Nayef (USA)—Snow Goose **Mrs Sara Biggins & Mrs Celia Djivanovic**
13 **FOURTH ACT (IRE)**, 7, b g King's Theatre (IRE)—Erintante (IRE) **Wendy & Malcolm Hezel**
14 **GENTLEMAN JON**, 8, b g Beat All (USA)—Sudden Spirit (FR) **Mr J. P. Romans**
15 **GOLDEN CHIEFTAIN (IRE)**, 11, b g Tikkanen (USA)—Golden Flower (GER) **Brocade Racing**
16 **HANDY ANDY (IRE)**, 10, b g Beneficial—Maslam (IRE) **Brocade Racing**
17 **HAWAIAN ROSE**, 6, b m Helissio (FR)—Waimea Bay **Wendy & Malcolm Hezel**
18 **JUMPS ROAD**, 9, b g Clerkenwell (USA)—Diletia **Chasing Gold Limited**
19 **JUSTATENNER**, 5, b g Northern Legend—Shelayly (IRE) **Mrs S. I. Tainton**
20 **KINGFISHER CREEK**, 6, b g Kayf Tara—Symbiosis **Brocade Racing**
21 **KINGS LAD (IRE)**, 9, b g King's Theatre (IRE)—Festival Leader (IRE) **G. F. Gingell**
22 **KINGS WALK (IRE)**, 5, b g King's Theatre (IRE)—Shuil Sionnach (IRE) **Mrs J. R. Bishop**
23 **KINGSCOURT NATIVE (IRE)**, 8, b g King's Theatre (IRE)—
　　　　　　　　　　　　　　　　　　Freydis (IRE) **K S B, Mr M Doughty & Mrs Sarah Tizzard**
24 5, B g Kayf Tara—Late For Class (IRE)
25 **LEG LOCK LUKE (IRE)**, 6, b g Indian River (FR)—Delirious Tantrum (IRE) **J. T. Warner**
26 **LILLINGTON (IRE)**, 4, br g Westerner—Kind Word (IRE)
27 5, B g Flemensfirth (USA)—Majic Times Ahead **J P Romans,A Selway,R G Tizzard,P Wavish**
28 **MARDEN COURT (IRE)**, 6, b g Tikkanen (USA)—Shilling Hill (IRE) **J K Farms**
29 **MASTERS HILL (IRE)**, 10, gr g Tikkanen (USA)—
　　　　　　　　　　　　　　　　　　Leitrim Bridge (IRE) **K S B, Mr M Doughty & Mrs Sarah Tizzard**
30 **MORELLO ROYALE (IRE)**, 6, b m King's Theatre (IRE)—Mystic Cherry (IRE) **Ann & Tony Gale**
31 **MUFFINS FOR TEA**, 6, ch g With The Flow (USA)—Countess Point **Mrs J. E. Purdie**
32 **MURRAYANA (IRE)**, 6, b g King's Theatre (IRE)—Royalrova (IRE) **Mrs S. I. Tainton**
33 **NATIVE RIVER (IRE)**, 6, ch g Indian River (FR)—Native Mo (IRE) **Brocade Racing**
34 **NEVER LEARN (IRE)**, 5, b g King's Theatre (IRE)—
　　　　　　　　　　　　　　　　　　Hamari Gold (IRE) **Brocade Racing J P Romans Terry Warner**
35 **PARSTARA**, 9, b m Kayf Tara—Castle Lynch (IRE) **Parstara Racing**
36 **QUITE BY CHANCE**, 7, b g Midnight Legend—Hop Fair **T Hamlin,J M Dare,J W Snook,J T Warner**
37 **QUIZ MASTER (IRE)**, 4, b g Ask—Good Bye Dolly (IRE) **Brocade Racing**
38 **ROBINSFIRTH (IRE)**, 7, b g Flemensfirth (USA)—Phardester (IRE) **Christine Knowles & Wendy Carter**
39 **ROYAL VACATION (IRE)**, 6, b g King's Theatre (IRE)—Summer Break (IRE) **Mrs J. R. Bishop**
40 **SANDY BEACH**, 6, b g Notnowcato—Picacho (IRE) **Brocade Racing**
41 **SARTORIAL ELEGANCE**, 5, b g Kayf Tara—Blue Ride (IRE) **R. G. Tizzard**
42 **SEW ON TARGET (IRE)**, 11, b g Needle Gun (IRE)—Ballykea (IRE) **A. G. Selway**
43 **SONNY THE ONE**, 6, ch g Tobougg (IRE)—Annie Fleetwood **Mr R. E. G. Nuttall**
44 5, B g King's Theatre (IRE)—Steel Grey Lady (IRE) **J. W. Snook**
45 **THE CIDER MAKER**, 6, b g Kayf Tara—Dame Fonteyn **Mrs C Djivanovic, Joanna Tizzard, KSB**
46 **THEATRE GUIDE (IRE)**, 9, b g King's Theatre (IRE)—Erintante (IRE) **Mrs J. R. Bishop**
47 **THEATRICAL STAR**, 10, b g King's Theatre (IRE)—Lucy Glitters **Brocade Racing**
48 **THIRD ACT (IRE)**, 7, b g King's Theatre (IRE)—Starry Lady (IRE) **Blackmore Vale Syndicate**
49 **THIRD INTENTION (IRE)**, 9, b g Azamour (IRE)—Third Dimension (IRE) **Mr & Mrs R. Tizzard**
50 **THISTLECRACK**, 8, b g Kayf Tara—Ardstown **John & Heather Snook**
51 **TIKKAPICK (IRE)**, 6, b g Tikkanen (USA)—Takeanotherpick (IRE) **The Con Club**
52 **ULTRAGOLD (FR)**, 8, b br g Kapgarde (FR)—Hot d'or (FR) **Brocade Racing J P Romans Terry Warner**
53 **VALHALLA (IRE)**, 6, b g Scorpion (IRE)—Fox Theatre (IRE) **J P Romans & Terry Warner**
54 **WATERLOO WARRIOR (IRE)**, 4, b g Kalanisi (IRE)—Vindonissa (IRE) **Brocade Racing**
55 **WEST APPROACH**, 6, b g Westerner—Ardstown **John & Heather Snook**
56 **WESTEND PRINCE**, 5, gr g King's Theatre (IRE)—Caltra Princess (IRE) **The Steal Syndicate**
57 **WIZARDS BRIDGE**, 7, b g Alflora (IRE)—Island Hopper **The Butterwick Syndicate**
58 **YENSTON (IRE)**, 5, b g Ashkalani (USA)—Stylish Type (IRE) **C. L. Tizzard**
59 **ZANSTRA (IRE)**, 6, b g Morozov (USA)—Enistar (IRE) **Moonrakers**

Other Owners: Mrs S. J. Biggins, Mr K. W. Biggins, Mr G. R. Broom, Mrs A. E. M. Broom, G. S. Brown, Mrs W. Carter, T. H. Chadney, Mr C. Cole, Mr C. E. G. Collier, Mr J. M. Dare, Mrs C. J. Djivanovic, Mr M. Doughty, Mrs A. G. Gale, Mr A. P. Gale, Mr R. Goodfellow, Mr P. Govier, Mr P. F. Govier, T. Hamlin, Mrs W. M. Hezel, Mr M. W. Hezel, Mr K. F. Honeybun, Mrs J. Honeybun, M. M. Hooker, Mr M. R. Kley, Mrs A. M. Kley, Mrs C. Knowles, Mr E. N. Liddiard, Mr D. A. Mayes, Mr C. D. Pritchard, Mrs H. A. Snook, Mr D. J. Stevens, P. A. Stranger, Miss J. Tizzard, Mrs S. L. Tizzard, Mr E. R. Vickery, Mr P. T. J. Wavish.

MR COLIN TIZZARD - Continued

Assistant Trainers: Mrs K. Gingell, Joe Tizzard

Jockey (NH): Daryl Jacobs, Brendan Powell. **Conditional:** Paul O'Brien.

MR MARTIN TODHUNTER, Penrith
Postal: **The Park, Orton, Penrith, Cumbria, CA10 3SD**
Contacts: **PHONE (01539) 624314 FAX (01539) 624314 MOBILE (07976) 440082**
WEBSITE www.martintodhunter.co.uk

1 BONZO BING (IRE), 8, b g Gold Well—She's A Dreamer (IRE) **Leeds Plywood & Doors Ltd**
2 CLARAGH NATIVE (IRE), 11, ch g Beneficial—Susy In The Summer (IRE) **Mrs S. J. Matthews**
3 CLOUD MONKEY (IRE), 6, b br g Marju (IRE)—Sweet Clover **Mr & Mrs Ian Hall**
4 CORONA BOREALIS, 5, b g Galileo (IRE)—Incheni **Leeds Plywood & Doors Ltd**
5 ELLA'S DELIGHT (IRE), 6, b m Camacho—Swift Alchemist **Mr & Mrs Ian Hall**
6 KILMAINHAM (IRE), 8, b g Celtic Swing—Newhall (IRE) **Park Farms Racing Syndicate 1**
7 LANDMEAFORTUNE (IRE), 7, gr g Touch of Land (FR)—Mayrich (IRE) **The Surf & Turf Partnership**
8 MARTIN CHUZZLEWIT (IRE), 7, ch g Galileo (IRE)—Alta Anna (FR) **Mr L. Richards**
9 MISS BARBOSSA (IRE), 5, b m Gold Well—Queens Quay **Mr & Mrs Ian Hall**
10 MONBEG RIVER (IRE), 7, b br g Indian River (FR)—So Pretty (IRE) **V Vyner-Brookes & Bill Hazeldean**
11 MORNING WITH IVAN (IRE), 6, b m Ivan Denisovich (IRE)—Grinneas (IRE) **Mr L. Richards**
12 PEKANHEIM (IRE), 8, b g Putra Pekan—Delheim (IRE) **Mr A. Bell**
13 PRESENTING JUNIOR (IRE), 9, b g Presenting—Dr Alice (IRE) **Mr W. & Mrs J. Garnett**
14 PRETTY MISS MAHLER (IRE), 5, b m Mahler—So Pretty (IRE) **Murphy's Law Partnership**
15 QUESTION OF FAITH, 8, b m Yeats (IRE)—Anastasia Storm **Mr K. Fitzsimons & Mr G. Fell**
16 ROCKABILLY RIOT (IRE), 6, br g Footstepsinthesand—Zawariq (IRE) **J. D. Gordon**
17 TOMMY DYLON (IRE), 6, b g Dylan Thomas (IRE)—Love of The Game (IRE) **P. G. Airey**

Other Owners: P. W. Clement, Mr P. M. Croan, W. Downs, Mr G. Fell, K. Fitzsimons, Mr W. W. Garnett, Mrs J. M. Garnett, J. W. Hazeldean, Mr C. G. Snoddy, D. M. Todhunter, Mr V. R. Vyner-Brookes.

Jockey (flat): Graham Lee, P. J. McDonald. **Jockey (NH):** Henry Brooke, Graham Watters.

MR MARK TOMPKINS, Newmarket
Postal: **Exeter Ride, The Watercourse, Newmarket, Suffolk, CB8 8LW**
Contacts: **PHONE (01638) 661434 FAX (01638) 668107 MOBILE (07799) 663339**
E-MAIL mht@marktompkins.co.uk WEBSITE www.marktompkins.co.uk

1 BLUE BOUNTY, 5, ch g Bahamian Bounty—Laheen (IRE) **Raceworld**
2 BRACKEN BRAE, 4, b f Champs Elysees—Azure Mist **Mr D. P. Noblett**
3 COMRADE BOND, 8, ch g Monsieur Bond (IRE)—Eurolink Cafe **Raceworld**
4 HOLD FIRM, 4, b c Refuse To Bend (IRE)—Four Miracles **Raceworld**
5 HUMPHRY REPTON, 4, b g Virtual—Qilin (IRE) **Dullingham Park**
6 PEEPS, 4, ch f Halling (USA)—Twelfth Night (IRE) **Judi Dench & Bryan Agar**
7 PRAYER TIME, 4, ch g Pastoral Pursuits—Nice Time (IRE) **Sarabex**
8 SANT'ELIA, 4, b f Authorized (IRE)—Trew Class **Russell Trew Ltd**
9 SMILE THAT SMILE, 4, b f Champs Elysees—Tenpence **Dahab Racing & Mark Tompkins**
10 TOPALING, 5, ch m Halling (USA)—Topatori (IRE) **M. P. Bowring**
11 TOPAMICHI, 6, b g Beat Hollow—Topatori (IRE) **Roalco Ltd**

THREE-YEAR-OLDS

12 ASTROSECRET, b f Halling (USA)—Optimistic **Mystic Meg Limited**
13 ASTROWIZARD, ch c Zamindar (USA)—Mega (IRE) **Mystic Meg Limited**
14 CARELESS RAPTURE, ch f Champs Elysees—Cushat Law (IRE) **J. A. Reed**
15 DESERT RIVER (IRE), b c Showcasing—Kathy's Rocket (USA) **Dullingham Park**
16 DOT GREEN (IRE), b f Lawman (FR)—Katajan **Dahab Racing**
17 HEAVENSFIELD, b f Motivator—Astrodiva **Mr M. Franklin**
18 IXCHELL, b f Equiano (FR)—Amanda Carter **Mrs J. M. MacPherson**
19 LOST THE MOON, b f Authorized (IRE)—Missouri **Dullingham Park**
20 MR TURNER, b c Nayef (USA)—Seasonal Blossom (IRE) **Sarabex 23**
21 PERMERA, b f Sir Percy—Four Miracles **Raceworld**

MR MARK TOMPKINS - Continued

22 **REGAL GALAXY,** b f Royal Applause—Astromancer (USA) **Dahab Racing**
23 **SING ME SING ME,** b f Motivator—Tenpence **Dullingham Park**
24 **SWEEPING BEAUTY,** b f Authorized (IRE)—Brushing **J. Brenchley**
25 **TOPALOVA,** ch f Champs Elysees—Topatori (IRE) **Roalco Ltd**

TWO-YEAR-OLDS

26 B c 7/2 Medicean—Astrolibra (Sakhee (USA)) **Mystic Meg Limited**
27 **ASTROSHADOW,** gr f 19/2 Aussie Rules (USA)—Astrodiva (Where Or When (IRE)) **Mystic Meg Limited**
28 B c 13/2 Mount Nelson—Azure Mist (Bahamian Bounty) **Mr David Noblett**
29 Gr f 24/4 Mastercraftsman (IRE)—Delitme (IRE) (Val Royal (FR)) (32000) **Dahab Racing**
30 B f 4/2 Footstepsinthesand—Diverting (Nayef (USA)) **J. A. Reed**
31 **DIXON,** b c 11/4 Lawman (FR)—Pure Song (Singspiel (IRE)) (45000) **Dahab Racing**
32 B c 25/4 Authorized (IRE)—Four Miracles (Vettori (IRE)) **Mr Richard Farleigh**
33 Ch c 19/3 Sir Percy—Missouri (Charnwood Forest (IRE)) **Dullingham Park**
34 B c 5/5 Aussie Rules (USA)—Nice Time (IRE) (Tagula (IRE)) **Sarabex**
35 **VELVET VOICE,** b f 11/3 Azamour (IRE)—Battery Power (Royal Applause) **Sarabex**

Other Owners: Mr Bryan Agar, Mr C. Bird, Mr M. P Bowring, Judi Dench, Mr R. D. E. Marriott, Mrs W. L. Marriott, Mystic Meg Limited, Mr David Tompkins, Mrs M. H. Tompkins, Mr M. H. Tompkins, Ms Sylvia Vrska.

Assistant Trainer: Barry Denvir

600

MR MARCUS TREGONING, Whitsbury
Postal: **Whitsbury Manor Racing Stables, Whitsbury, Fordingbridge, Hampshire, SP6 3QQ**
Contacts: **PHONE (01725) 518889 FAX (01725) 518042 MOBILE (07767) 888100**
E-MAIL info@marcustregoningracing.co.uk WEBSITE www.marcustregoningracing.co.uk

1 **ATALANTA BAY (IRE),** 6, b m Strategic Prince—Wood Sprite **Miss S. M. Sharp**
2 **BOWSERS BOLD,** 5, gr g Firebreak—Cristal Clear (IRE) **Mrs J. R. A. Aldridge**
3 **BRONZE ANGEL (IRE),** 7, b g Dark Angel (IRE)—Rihana (IRE) **Lady Tennant**
4 **BURMESE,** 4, b g Sir Percy—Swan Queen **Sir Thomas Pilkington**
5 **CLOVELLY BAY (IRE),** 5, b g Bushranger (IRE)—Crystalline Stream (FR) **M. P. Tregoning**
6 **COBHAM'S CIRCUS (IRE),** 5, ch g Hernando (FR)—Protectorate **Lady N. F. Cobham**
7 **COLDWATER CANYON,** 4, b g Zamindar (USA)—Femme de Fer **Wedgewood Estates**
8 **CONCORD (IRE),** 4, b g Mawatheeq (USA)—Amhooj **Park Walk Racing**
9 **CRANWELL,** 4, b f Nayef (USA)—First Bloom (USA) **Lady N. F. Cobham**
10 **PARADISE BIRD,** 4, ch f Kyllachy—Amanjena **Mrs M. E. Wates**
11 **RIVER DART (IRE),** 4, ch g Dutch Art—Sky Galaxy (USA) **Mr G. C. B. Brook**
12 **SERENA GRAE,** 5, gr m Arakan (USA)—Success Story **Mrs H. B. Raw**
13 **SILVER LINING (IRE),** 4, gr g Dark Angel (IRE)—Out of Woods (USA) **M. P. Tregoning**
14 **SWEET P,** 5, b m Sir Percy—Desert Run (IRE) **M. P. Tregoning**
15 **THAMES KNIGHT,** 4, b g Sir Percy—Bermondsey Girl **R. C. C. Villers**

THREE-YEAR-OLDS

16 **ALAMODE,** ch f Sir Percy—Almamia **Miss K. Rausing**
17 **DANCE THE DREAM,** b f Sir Percy—Shadow Dancing **Mrs M. A. Dalgety**
18 **DAWREYA (IRE),** b f Acclamation—Darajaat (USA) **Hamdan Al Maktoum**
19 **FRANK COOL,** b c Royal Applause—Queen of Heaven (USA) **Wedgewood Estates**
20 **HAWKERLAND (IRE),** b c Sea The Stars (IRE)—Zarara (USA) **Mr G. C. B. Brook**
21 **LADY VESTA,** b f Sir Percy—Lady Hestia (USA) **Mr & Mrs A. E. Pakenham**
22 **LAZIZAH,** b f Medicean—Atyaab **Wedgewood Estates**
23 **MAER ROCKS (IRE),** br f Dream Ahead (USA)—Dream of The Hill (IRE) **Mr G. C. B. Brook**
24 **MISS BLONDELL,** ch f Compton Place—Where's Broughton **Miss S. M. Sharp**
25 **MORNINGTON,** b c Aussie Rules (USA)—Giusina Mia (USA) **Allendale, Allison, Gaskell & Partner**
26 **MYSTIKANA,** ch f Sir Percy—Peintre d'argent (IRE) **Mrs V. M. Brown**
27 **POET'S SONG (IRE),** b g Poet's Voice—Bee Eater (IRE) **Lady Tennant**
28 **PORT GAVERNE (IRE),** b g Lord Shanakill (USA)—Jillian (USA) **M. P. Tregoning**
29 **PORT ISAAC (IRE),** b g Sakhee's Secret—Dombeya (IRE) **M. Tregoning & It's Better Than Fishing**
30 **STORM AHEAD (IRE),** b g Iffraaj—Loose Julie (IRE) **Mr G. C. B. Brook**
31 **SUMOU (IRE),** b g Arcano (IRE)—Three Times **Hamdan Al Maktoum**
32 **TAZAAYUD,** b g Kodiac—Esteemed Lady (IRE) **Hamdan Al Maktoum**

MR MARCUS TREGONING - Continued

33 **THAQAFFA (IRE)**, b c Kodiac—Incense **Hamdan Al Maktoum**
34 **TUKHOOM (IRE)**, b g Acclamation—Carioca (IRE) **Hamdan Al Maktoum**

TWO-YEAR-OLDS

35 **ARGENTERIE**, ch f 14/2 Archipenko (USA)—Sterling Sound (USA) (Street Cry (IRE)) **Miss K. Rausing**
36 **CELSIANA**, ch f 12/4 Sepoy (AUS)—Generous Lady (Generous (IRE)) (15000)
37 **CHEEKY FOX**, b f 14/3 Foxwedge (AUS)—Cheeky Girl (College Chapel) (19047) **FTP Equine Holdings Ltd**
38 **DEAUVILLE DIVA (IRE)**, b f 18/3 Lawman (FR)—
Sheila Toss (IRE) (Galileo (IRE)) (70136) **FTP Equine Holdings Ltd**
39 **DIVA POWER (IRE)**, b f 22/4 Power—Kotdiji (Mtoto) (40605) **FTP Equine Holdings Ltd**
40 B c 17/5 Acclamation—Ellen (IRE) (Machiavellian (USA)) (62000) **R. C. C. Villers**
41 B f 1/4 Cape Cross (IRE)—Estedaama (IRE) (Marju (IRE)) **Hamdan Al Maktoum**
42 B c 2/2 Aqlaam—Femme de Fer (Hamas (IRE)) (6000) **Wedgewood Estates**
43 **KNIGHTHOOD**, b c 14/4 Delegator—Love Roi (ITY) (Roi Danzig (USA)) (55000) **Lady Tennant**
44 B c 6/4 Sir Percy—Lady Hestia (USA) (Belong To Me (USA)) (32000) **The FOPS**
45 B c 19/5 Dalakhani (IRE)—Marque Royale (Royal Academy (USA)) (28054)
46 **MOHSEN**, b r 9/3 Bated Breath—Harryana (Efisio) (80000) **Hamdan Al Maktoum**
47 **MONAADHIL (IRE)**, b c 16/2 Dark Angel (IRE)—
Urban Daydream (IRE) (Oasis Dream) (160000) **Hamdan Al Maktoum**
48 B c 27/3 Nathaniel (IRE)—Navajo Rainbow (Rainbow Quest (USA)) (75000) **Mrs H. I. Slade**
49 **NEVALYASHKA**, b f 15/3 Sir Percy—Ninotchka (USA) (Nijinsky (CAN)) **Miss K. Rausing**
50 Br c 9/5 Henrythenavigator (USA)—Rose of Petra (IRE) (Golan (IRE)) (11074) **Marcus Tregoning Racing**
51 B c 14/4 Royal Applause—Scarlet Royal (Red Ransom (USA)) (17000) **R. C. C. Villers**
52 **SILVER LINK (IRE)**, b f 14/3 Arcano (IRE)—Miss Bellbird (IRE) (Danehill (USA)) **Airlie Stud**
53 **TAWFEER**, b c 8/3 Lawman (FR)—Wild Gardenia (Alhaarth (IRE)) (22857) **Hamdan Al Maktoum**
54 **WAQT (IRE)**, b c 17/1 Acclamation—Needles And Pins (IRE) (Fasliyev (USA)) (47619) **Hamdan Al Maktoum**

Other Owners: Viscountess Allendale, Mr Austin Allison, Mrs C. Baker, Mr Giles Blomfield, Mr Guy Brook, Mr Nicholas Brown, Mr Colin Chisholm, Mr R. F. U. Gaskell, Mr James Green, Mr Victor Hoare, Mr John Raw, Mr J. R. Wallis.

Assistant Trainer: Angie Kennedy

Jockey (flat): Martin Dwyer. **Apprentice:** Tyler Saunders. **Amateur:** Mr George Tregoning.

601
MR EDWIN TUER, Northallerton
Postal: **Granary Barn, Birkby, Northallerton, North Yorkshire, DL7 0EF**
Contacts: **PHONE** (01609) 881798 **FAX** (01609) 881798 **MOBILE** (07808) 330306

1 **BLUE MAISEY**, 8, b m Monsieur Bond (IRE)—Blue Nile (IRE) **E. Tuer**
2 **BULAS BELLE**, 6, b m Rob Roy (USA)—Bula Rose (IRE) **E. Tuer**
3 **FAZZA**, 9, ch g Sulamani (IRE)—Markievicz (IRE) **E. Tuer**
4 **GOLD SHOW**, 7, gr m Sir Percy—Pearl Bright (FR) **E. Tuer**
5 **MYSTICAL MOMENT**, 6, ch m Dutch Art—Tinnarinka **E. Tuer**
6 **THE BLUE BANANA (IRE)**, 7, b g Red Clubs (IRE)—Rinneen (IRE) **E. Tuer**

THREE-YEAR-OLDS

7 **MOJOLATION**, b f Stimulation (IRE)—Demolition Jo **E. Tuer**
8 **WAANEBE RANGER (IRE)**, b f Bushranger (IRE)—Jawaaneb (USA) **E. Tuer**

Assistant Trainer: Fergus King (07813) 153982

602
MR JOSEPH TUITE, Lambourn
Postal: **Felstead Stables, Folly Road, Lambourn, Hungerford, Berkshire, RG17 8QE**
Contacts: **MOBILE** (07769) 977351
E-MAIL joe.tuite@tuiteracing.com **WEBSITE** www.tuiteracing.co.uk

1 **BOHEMIAN RHAPSODY (IRE)**, 7, b g Galileo (IRE)—Quiet Mouse (USA) **Mr A. A. Byrne**
2 **CEYHAN**, 4, ch c Rock of Gibraltar (IRE)—Alla Prima (IRE) **Mr M. Kurt**
3 **CINCUENTA PASOS (IRE)**, 5, ch g Footstepsinthesand—
Sweet Nicole **Mr Mark Wellbelove & Mr Peter Gleeson**
4 **FAST DANCER (IRE)**, 4, b g Fast Company (IRE)—Tereed Elhawa **Alan & Christine Bright**
5 **FLASHY QUEEN (IRE)**, 5, ch m Bahamian Bounty—Somersault **Penny/Adrian Burton, Bob/Angela Lampard**
6 **FOR AYMAN**, 5, b g Bertolini (USA)—Saharan Song (IRE) **I & K Prince**

MR JOSEPH TUITE - Continued

7 **GEORGIAN HERO**, 6, b g Arkadian Hero (USA)—Zulu Rose **Mrs B. C. Tucker**
8 **LITIGANT**, 8, b g Sinndar (IRE)—Jomana (IRE) **Mr A. A. Byrne**
9 **POSH BOUNTY**, 5, ch m Bahamian Bounty—Fission **The Lamb Inn - Pethy**
10 **PRESBURG (IRE)**, 7, b g Balmont (USA)—Eschasse (USA) **Mr L. Eke**
11 **START SEVEN**, 4, br g Dilum (USA)—Dancingintheclouds (IRE) **Mr M. Kurt**
12 **THANE OF CAWDOR (IRE)**, 7, b g Danehill Dancer (IRE)—Holy Nola (USA) **Alan & Christine Bright**
13 **TIME TO TANGO (IRE)**, 5, b g Tiger Hill (IRE)—Bravo Dancer **Mr J. M. Tuite**
14 **WASEEM FARIS (IRE)**, 7, b g Exceed And Excel (AUS)—Kissing Time **Hillen, Cooper, Peppiatt & EGM**
15 **ZIPEDEEDODAH (IRE)**, 4, gr g Zebedee—Beverley Macca **D.M Synergy & Mark Wellbelove**

THREE-YEAR-OLDS

16 **CLEVER BOB (IRE)**, br c Big Bad Bob (IRE)—Clever Millie (USA) **Spear Family**
17 **FIELD OF VISION (IRE)**, b c Pastoral Pursuits—Grand Design **Shefford Valley Racing**
18 **FLASHY KING (IRE)**, b c Tagula (IRE)—Trixiebelle (IRE) **Penny/Adrian Burton, Bob/Angela Lampard**
19 **OCCASIONAL DREAM (IRE)**, b f Dream Ahead (USA)—Almaviva (IRE) **Mr R Paterson & Mr P Gleeson**
20 **PINK MARTINI (IRE)**, b f Tagula (IRE)—Ohwhatalady (IRE) **Mr L. Eke**
21 **RED HOT CHILLY (IRE)**, ch g Frozen Power (IRE)—She's Got The Look **Mr & Mrs A J Mutch 1**
22 **ROJINA (IRE)**, ch f Intense Focus (USA)—Hurricane Havoc (IRE) **Mr A. L. Al Zeer**
23 **TOPOLOGY**, br g Passing Glance—Bold Byzantium **The Singleton Park Partnership 2**

TWO-YEAR-OLDS

24 Ch c 20/4 Arakan (USA)—Brioney (IRE) (Barathea (IRE)) (3000) **C.R. Lambourne, M. Forbes, D. Losse**
25 B f 18/2 Canford Cliffs (IRE)—Circle (IRE) (Galileo (IRE)) (18456) **Mr A A Byrne & Mr Mark Wellbelove**
26 B c 14/3 Bahamian Bounty—Crinkle (IRE) (Distant Relative) (26666) **Spear Family**
27 **HARBOUR FORCE (FR)**, b c 12/3 Harbour Watch (IRE)—Dam Beautiful (Sleeping Indian) (88593) **Mr A. A. Byrne**
28 B c 26/3 Acclamation—Miss Work of Art (Dutch Art) (31007)
29 B c 1/3 Helmet (AUS)—Oeuvre d'art (IRE) (Marju (IRE)) (30476) **Mr J. M. Tuite**
30 Ch c 11/4 Foxwedge (AUS)—Shaken And Stirred (Cadeaux Genereux) (8121)
31 Ch f 12/2 Bated Breath—Today's The Day (Alhaarth (IRE)) (17142) **Felstead Court Flyers**

Other Owners: Mrs D. M. Barrett, Mr D. Barrett, Mr A. D. Bright, Mrs C. Bright, Mrs P. C. Burton, Mr M. Chesney, M. I. Forbes, P. J. Gleeson, Mrs R. G. Hillen, Mrs A. Johnson, Mr C. R. Lambourne, Mr R. J. Lampard, Mr D. R. Losse, Mrs L. J. Losse, Mr D. Marsh, Mr A. J. Mutch, Mrs S. Mutch, Mr R. Paterson, Mr G. R. Pooley, Mr I. D. Prince, Mrs K. Prince, Mr P. Spear, Mr A. Spear, R. L. Squire, Mr M. J. Wellbelove.

---

603 MR BILL TURNER, Sherborne
Postal: **Sigwells Farm, Sigwells, Corton Denham, Sherborne, Dorset, DT9 4LN**
Contacts: **PHONE (01963) 220523 FAX (01963) 220046 MOBILE (07932) 100173**
E-MAIL billturnerracing@gmail.com

1 **BREAN GOLF BIRDIE**, 4, br f Striking Ambition—Straight As A Die **Unity Farm Holiday Centre Ltd**
2 **BREAN SPLASH SUSIE**, 5, b m Tobougg (IRE)—Straight As A Die **Unity Farm Holiday Centre Ltd**
3 **DADDY'S FAVOURITE**, 4, b g Hellvelyn—Wavet **B. J. Goldsmith**
4 **EDLOMOND (IRE)**, 10, gr g Great Palm (USA)—Samardana (IRE) **Mrs P. A. Turner**
5 **EL DUQUE**, 5, b g Byron—Royal Tavira Girl (IRE) **Mrs P. A. Turner**
6 **FLORAL SPINNER**, 9, b m Alflora (IRE)—Dawn Spinner **The Floral Farmers**
7 **GUARACHA**, 5, ch g Halling (USA)—Pachanga **R. A. Bracken**
8 **TURBO CHARGED (IRE)**, 4, b g Jeremy (USA)—House Rebel (IRE) **E. A. Brook**
9 **TWO MANY WORDS (IRE)**, 4, b g Thousand Words—Three Days In May **Mrs Tracy Turner**

THREE-YEAR-OLDS

10 **ARTHUR'S CHOICE**, b g Dandy Man (IRE)—Miss Sharapova (IRE) **E. A. Brook**
11 **DON'T TELL JO JO**, b g Hellvelyn—Shake Baby Shake **The Harefield Racing Club**
12 **DRAWN TO BE A LADY**, b f Avonbridge—Lady Killer (IRE) **Mrs M. S. Teversham**
13 **LAGAN ZORO**, b f Tobougg (IRE)—Lagan Katie **Mr Ron Clark**
14 **MUSTN'T GRUMBLE (IRE)**, ch g Intense Focus (USA)—Lough Mist (IRE) **E. A. Brook**
15 **RAISE THE GAME (IRE)**, b g Bushranger (IRE)—Fancy Feathers (IRE) **E. A. Brook**
16 **THE TIME HAS COME (IRE)**, gr g Elusive Pimpernel (USA)—Sidecar (IRE) **E. A. Brook & Tracy Turner**
17 **THIEF OF HEARTS**, br f Dick Turpin (IRE)—Constant Craving **Mascalls Stud**

MR BILL TURNER - Continued

TWO-YEAR-OLDS

18 Ch c 18/2 Phoenix Reach (IRE)—Calgary (Pivotal) (9523) **Eric Brook**
19 B f 15/4 Royal Applause—Constant Craving (Pastoral Pursuits) **Mascalls Stud**
20 Ch f 2/2 Firebreak—Day By Day (Kyllachy) (3200) **Tracy Turner**
21 B c 17/3 Lilbourne Lad (IRE)—Gemma's Delight (IRE) (Clodovil (IRE)) **Tracy Turner**
22 B f 5/3 Kyllachy—Just Like A Woman (Observatory (USA)) **Mascalls Stud**
23 B f 12/4 Dandy Man (IRE)—Monet's Lady (IRE) (Daylami (IRE)) (3691) **Tracy Turner**
24 B c 6/2 Pivotal—Moonglow (Nayef (USA)) (38095) **Eric Brook, Tracy Turner**
25 Ch c 3/3 Haafet (USA)—Rainbow Melody (IRE) (Rainbows For Life (CAN)) (9228) **Tracy Turner**
26 B c 2/2 Bushranger (IRE)—Shenkara (IRE) (Night Shift (USA)) (4500) **Harefield Racing Club**
27 Ch c 24/4 Sleeping Indian—Trust Fund Babe (IRE) (Captain Rio) **Tracy Turner**

Other Owners: Mr G. Bennett, Mr R. A. Bracken, Mrs Susan Hearn, Mr Barry Hearn, Mr T. Robinson-Gamby, Mr E. Vickery.

Conditional: Ryan While. **Apprentice:** Ryan While. **Amateur:** Miss Poppy Skipper.

604

MR JAMES TURNER, Helperby
Postal: **Mayfield Farm, Norton-le-Clay, Helperby, York**
Contacts: **PHONE (01423) 322239 FAX (01423) 322239**

1 BONDI BEACH BABE, 6, b m Misu Bond (IRE)—Nice One **Mr G. R. Turner & Mr H. Turner**
2 BONDI BEACH BOY, 7, b g Misu Bond (IRE)—Nice One **Mr G. R. Turner & Mr H. Turner**
3 SINGING STAR (IRE), 5, b m Iffraaj—Seven Sing (USA) **J. R. Turner**
4 TEMPLE TIGER, 6, b g Tamure (IRE)—Filey Flyer **J. R. Turner**
5 ZAKETY ZAK, 5, b g Overbury (IRE)—Jeanne d'arc **Mr D. M. Wordsworth**

Other Owners: Mr H. Turner, Mr G. R. Turner.

Assistant Trainer: Oliver J. Turner

605

MRS KAREN TUTTY, Northallerton
Postal: **Trenholme House Farm, Osmotherley, Northallerton, North Yorkshire, DL6 3QA**
Contacts: PHONE **(01609) 883624** FAX **01609 883624** MOBILE **(07967) 837406**
E-MAIL **karentutty@btinternet.com** WEBSITE **www.karentuttyracing.co.uk**

1 I'M SUPER TOO (IRE), 9, b g Fasliyev (USA)—Congress (IRE) **Grange Park Racing**
2 LOOK HERE'S AL, 5, gr g Alhaarth (IRE)—Look Here's Dee **Thoroughbred Homes Ltd**
3 MOROCCO, 7, b g Rock of Gibraltar (IRE)—Shanghai Lily (IRE) **Max Europe Limited**
4 ORICANO, 4, ch f Arcano (IRE)—Dhuyoof (IRE) **Thoroughbred Homes Ltd**
5 PERCY'S GAL, 5, ch m Sir Percy—Galette **Max Europe Ltd & Thoroughbred Homes Ltd**
6 TALENT SCOUT (IRE), 10, b g Exceed And Excel (AUS)—Taalluf (USA) **Thoroughbred Homes Ltd**
7 UNDER APPROVAL, 5, b g Captain Gerrard (IRE)—Dockside Strike **Grange Park Racing**

THREE-YEAR-OLDS

8 DIAL A LOG, b g Mullionmileanhour (IRE)—Angelic Kitten (IRE) **Mr J. Hamilton**
9 RISE UP SINGING, b f Showcasing—Sambarina (IRE) **Mr J. Hamilton**

Other Owners: A. D. Crombie, Mr E. Surr.

Apprentice: Gemma Tutty.

606

MR NIGEL TWISTON-DAVIES, Cheltenham
Postal: **T/a Grange Hill Farm Limited, Grange Hill Farm, Naunton, Cheltenham, Gloucestershire, GL54 3AY**
Contacts: **PHONE (01451) 850278 FAX (01451) 850101 MOBILE (07836) 664440**
E-MAIL **nigel@nigeltwistondavies.co.uk** WEBSITE **www.nigeltwistondavies.co.uk**

1 ABIGAIL LYNCH (IRE), 8, b m Oscar (IRE)—Tanit Lady (IRE) **Rose Tinted Racing**
2 AFRICAN GOLD (IRE), 8, b g King's Theatre (IRE)—Mrs Dempsey (IRE) **Walters Plant, J & J Potter & Egan**
3 ALDEBURGH, 7, b g Oasis Dream—Orford Ness **W. E. Sturt**

MR NIGEL TWISTON-DAVIES - Continued

4 ALGERNON PAZHAM (IRE), 7, b g Milan—Kitty Star (IRE) **Graham & Alison Jelley**
5 ANOTHER FRONTIER (IRE), 5, b g Darsi (FR)—Scent With Love (IRE) **Jump For Fun Racing**
6 ARCTIC GOLD (IRE), 5, b g Gold Well—Arctic Warrior (IRE) **Geoffrey & Donna Keeys**
7 ARTHUR MC BRIDE (IRE), 7, b br g Royal Anthem (USA)—Lucky Diverse (IRE) **John Gaughan & Rob Rexton**
8 ARTHUR'S GIFT (IRE), 5, b g Presenting—Uncertain Affair (IRE) **Mrs C. M. Mould**
9 ASTRACAD (FR), 10, br g Cadoudal (FR)—Astre Eria (FR) **Mrs C. M. Mould**
10 BABY BEE JAY, 5, b m King's Theatre (IRE)—Belle Magello (FR) **Banjax's Girls Plus One**
11 BALLY BEAUFORT (IRE), 8, b g Old Vic—Miss Compliance (IRE) **Mr R. J. Rexton**
12 BALLYANDREW (IRE), 5, b g Westerner—Royale Acadou (FR) **N. A. Twiston-Davies**
13 BALLYANDY, 5, b g Kayf Tara—Megalex **Options O Syndicate**
14 BALLYARTHUR (IRE), 6, b g Kayf Tara—Ariels Serenade (IRE) **Graham & Alison Jelley**
15 BALLYBOLLEY (IRE), 7, b g Kayf Tara—Gales Hill (IRE) **Mr Simon Munir & Mr Isaac Souede**
16 BALLYCASH (IRE), 5, b g Kalanisi (IRE)—Waterlily (IRE) **Million in Mind Partnership**
17 BALLYCROSS, 5, b g King's Theatre (IRE)—Ninna Nanna (FR) **The Autism Rockers**
18 BALLYHILL (FR), 5, b br g Al Namix (FR)—Laly Light (FR) **S Such & CG Paletta**
19 BALLYKAN, 6, b g Presenting—La Marianne **Mr Simon Munir & Mr Isaac Souede**
20 BALLYMALIN (IRE), 6, b g Presenting—Murrurundi (IRE) **N. A. Twiston-Davies**
21 BALLYPOINT (IRE), 5, b g Mahler—Angel Trix (IRE) **N. A. Twiston-Davies**
22 BALLYRATH (IRE), 5, gr g Flemensfirth (USA)—Rose Wee (IRE) **The Stirling Partnership**
23 BAR A MINE (FR), 7, b g Martaline—Treekle Toffee (FR) **Walters Plant Hire Ltd**
24 BELMOUNT (IRE), 7, b g Westerner—Artist's Jewel **Mrs S. Jones**
25 BENBENS (IRE), 11, ch g Beneficial—Millicent Bridge (IRE) **S Such & CG Paletta**
26 BENDOMINGO (IRE), 5, b g Beneficial—Bobbies Storm (IRE) **DG Partners**
27 BETTER DAYS (IRE), 5, gr g Daylami (IRE)—Miss Edgehill (IRE) **Mrs L. M. Berryman**
28 BIG CASINO, 10, b g Court Cave (IRE)—Migsy Malone **The Jukes Family**
29 BIG TOUCH (FR), 5, b g Network (GER)—Etoile d'or II (FR) **Walters Plant Hire Ltd**
30 BLAKLION, 7, b g Kayf Tara—Franciscaine (FR) **S Such & CG Paletta**
31 BOMBER'S MOON, 5, b g Erhaab (USA)—Flaviola (IRE) **W. E. Sturt**
32 BRISTOL DE MAI (FR), 5, gr g Saddler Maker (IRE)—La Bole Night (FR) **Mr Simon Munir & Mr Isaac Souede**
33 BROWNVILLE, 7, b g Kayf Tara—Cool Spice **Mrs F. E. Griffin**
34 BUDDY LOVE, 9, gr m Silver Patriarch (IRE)—O My Love **Mr S. Cottrill**
35 COGRY, 7, b g King's Theatre (IRE)—Wyldello **Graham & Alison Jelley**
36 COLIN'S BROTHER, 6, b g Overbury (IRE)—Dd's Glenalla (IRE) **Mrs C. S. C. Beresford-Wylie**
37 COUNT GUIDO DEIRO (IRE), 9, b g Accordion—Ivy Lane (IRE) **R. Bevis**
38 COUNT MERIBEL, 4, ch c Three Valleys (USA)—Bakhtawar (IRE) **Jim Old**
39 DEPUTY COMMANDER (IRE), 7, b g Shantou (USA)—Artic Native (IRE) **Imperial Racing**
40 DOUBLE COURT (IRE), 5, b g Court Cave (IRE)—Miss Top (IRE) **Synergy Racing**
41 DOUBLE ROSS (IRE), 10, ch g Double Eclipse (IRE)—Kinross **Options O Syndicate**
42 FIVE STAR WILSHAM (IRE), 12, b g Bob's Return (IRE)—Riverpauper (IRE) **N. A. Twiston-Davies**
43 FLORRIE BOY (IRE), 5, b g Milan—Second Best (IRE) **Options O Syndicate**
44 FLYING ANGEL (IRE), 5, gr g Arcadio (GER)—Gypsy Kelly (IRE) **Mr R. J. Rexton**
45 FOND MEMORY (IRE), 8, b g Dr Massini (IRE)—Glacier Lilly (IRE) **The Stirling Partnership**
46 FOXBRIDGE (IRE), 10, b g King's Theatre (IRE)—Fairy Native (IRE) **Walters Plant Hire Spiers & Hartwell**
47 FOXTAIL HILL (IRE), 7, b g Dr Massini (IRE)—Flynn's Girl (IRE) **Options O Syndicate**
48 FRONTIER VIC, 9, b g Old Vic—Right On Target (IRE) **Jump For Fun Racing**
49 GOLDEN JUBILEE (USA), 7, b br g Zavata (USA)—Love Play (USA) **Mrs J. K. Powell**
50 GOODBYE DANCER (IRE), 5, b g Dragon Dancer—Maribia Bella (FR) **The Yes No Wait Sorries**
51 GUITING POWER, 5, b g Lucarno (USA)—Sparkling Jewel **Mr DJ Langdon & Mr AW Morgan**
52 HOLLOW BLUE SKY (FR), 9, gr g Turgeon (USA)—Run For Laborie (FR) **Hollow Bottom**
53 HORSEGUARDSPARADE, 7, b g Montjeu (USA)—Honorlina (FR) **Walters Plant Hire Ltd**
54 I AM COLIN, 7, b g Zafeen (FR)—Dd's Glenalla (IRE) **Mrs C. S. C. Beresford-Wylie**
55 IMPERIAL LEADER (IRE), 8, b g Flemensfirth (USA)—
                                        Glamorous Leader (IRE) **Imperial Racing Partnership No.2**
56 KERISPER (FR), 7, b g Robin des Champs (FR)—Tina Rederie (FR) **The Autism Rockers**
57 KILRONAN HIGH (IRE), 7, b m Mountain High (IRE)—Broadcast **Mrs J. K. Powell**
58 LIGHT BREAKS (IRE), 4, b g Dylan Thomas (IRE)—Anywaysmile (IRE) **N. A. Twiston-Davies**
59 LISTEN BOY (IRE), 10, ch g Presenting—Buckalong (USA) **Bryan & Philippa Burrough**
60 LITTLE JAMES (IRE), 7, b g Craigsteel—Brymar Lass (IRE) **The Yes No Wait Sorries**
61 LITTLE JON, 8, b g Pasternak—Jowoody **Mr R Frosell & Mrs L Taylor**
62 LITTLE POP, 8, b g Pasternak—Flagship Daisy May (IRE) **S Such & G Paletta**
63 MAJOR MALARKEY (IRE), 13, b g Supreme Leader—Valley (IRE) **Baker Dodd & Cooke**
64 MARGARET'S ROSE (IRE), 6, b m Milenary—Alannah Rose (IRE) **Miss A. J. Holland**
65 MILLICENT SILVER, 7, gr m Overbury (IRE)—Common Girl (IRE) **Mr J. Goodman**
66 MINELLA RECEPTION (IRE), 10, b g King's Theatre (IRE)—Cadourova (FR) **Options O Syndicate**
67 MINI MUCK, 10, b m Kayf Tara—Madam Muck **Jilly Scott & Sarah MacEchern**

MR NIGEL TWISTON-DAVIES - Continued

68 **MONT CHOISY (FR)**, 6, b g Vic Toto (FR)—Rhapsodie St Eloi (FR) **Mrs N. Unsworth**
69 **MUCKLE ROE (IRE)**, 7, b g Westerner—Island Crest **Mrs V. J. Lane**
70 **NORTHANDSOUTH (IRE)**, 6, ch g Spadoun (FR)—Ennel Lady (IRE) **Mills & Mason Partnership**
71 **OSCAR MAGIC (IRE)**, 9, b br g Oscar (IRE)—Just An Illusion (IRE) **Mrs L. M. Berryman**
72 **PARADIS BLANC (FR)**, 5, b g Early March—Mont Paradis (FR) **Fourway Flyers**
73 **PINK GIN**, 8, ch g Alflora (IRE)—Miss Mailmit
74 **RANSOM NOTE**, 9, b g Red Ransom (USA)—Zacheta **Mrs C. M. Mould**
75 **RED RIVERMAN**, 8, b g Haafhd—Mocca (IRE) **N. A. Twiston-Davies**
76 **ROBINSHILL (IRE)**, 5, ch g Robin des Champs (FR)—I Remember It Well (IRE) **Mrs C. M. Mould**
77 **SERANWEN (IRE)**, 9, b g Old Vic—Glenarb Molly (IRE) **Walters Plant Hire Ltd Egan Waste Ltd**
78 **SOUTHERLY BUSTER**, 4, b g Shirocco (GER)—Appleby **Julie Fowler & Alan Britten**
79 **SPEED MASTER (IRE)**, 10, b g King's Theatre (IRE)—Handy Lass **Spiers & Hartwell and N A Twiston-Davies**
80 **SPLASH OF GINGE**, 8, b g Oscar (IRE)—Land of Honour **Mr J. Neild**
81 **SUSTAINABLE**, 4, b f Sulamani (IRE)—Attainable **C. J. Jenkins**
82 **SWORD OF THE BLUE**, 6, b g Kheleyf (USA)—Shona Yes No Wait Sorries
83 **SYBARITE (FR)**, 10, b br g Dark Moondancer—Haida III (FR) **N. A. Twiston-Davies**
84 **TEMPLEROSS (IRE)**, 5, b br g Presenting—Dame O'neill (IRE) **N. A. Twiston-Davies**
85 **THE NEW ONE (IRE)**, 8, b g King's Theatre (IRE)—Thuringe (IRE) **S Such & CG Paletta**
86 **THUNDER SHEIK (IRE)**, 8, b g Green Tune (USA)—Realy Queen (USA) **Mr R. J. Rexton**
87 **TOUR DES CHAMPS (FR)**, 9, b br g Robin des Champs (FR)—Massada (FR) **Mrs C. M. Mould**
88 **TWIST ON GINGE (IRE)**, 4, b g Craigsteel—Miss Top (IRE) **J Neild, A Bridges & N A Twiston-Davies**
89 **VALID POINT (IRE)**, 10, b g Val Royal (FR)—Ricadonna **W. E. Sturt**
90 **WEST WIZARD (FR)**, 7, b br g King's Theatre (IRE)—Queen's Diamond (GER) **Walters Plant Hire Ltd**
91 **WHOLESTONE (IRE)**, 5, br g Craigsteel—Last Theatre (IRE) **Mr Simon Munir & Mr Isaac Souede**
92 **WICKED WILLY**, 5, br g Arcadio (GER)—How Provincial **N. A. Twiston-Davies**
93 **WINGED CRUSADER (IRE)**, 8, b g Winged Love (IRE)—Reine Berengere (FR) **Imperial Racing Partnership No.6**
94 **WOOD YER (IRE)**, 10, ch g Anshan—Glenasheen (IRE) **Miss K. J. Holland**
95 **YANMARE (IRE)**, 6, b g Soapy Danger—Bell Walks Caroll (IRE) **Bryan & Philippa Burrough**

Other Owners: Mrs C. Beresford Wylie, Mr A. P. Bridges, Mr A. J. Britten, Mrs Philippa Burrough, Mr B. R. H. Burrough, Mr Chris Coley, Egan Waste Services Ltd, Mr J. Flannery, Mrs J. Fowler, Mr Robert Frosell, Mr A. B. Greenfield, Mrs Alison Jelley, Mr Graham Jelley, Mr R. Jukes, Mrs Margaret Jukes, Mr Geoffrey Keeys, Mrs Donna Keeys, Mr David Langdon, Mrs James Layton, Mrs S. A. MacEchern, Mr David Mason, Mr F. J. Mills, Mr W. R. Mills, Mr A. W. Morgan, Mr S. Munir, Mr J. D. Neild, Mr C. G. Paletta, Mrs J. E. Potter, Mr J. E. Potter, Mr G. M. Powell, Mr Paul Preston, Mr R. J. Rexton, Mr Ian A. Robinson, Mrs C. M. Scott, Mr Sanjay Shah, Mr Isaac Souede, Spiers & Hartwell Ltd, Mrs Deborah Stoneham, Mrs S. Such, Mrs L. C. Taylor, Mr Charles C. Walker, Walters Plant Hire Ltd, Mr S. Wignall.

Jockey (flat): William Twiston-Davies. **Jockey (NH):** Sam Twiston-Davies. **Conditional:** Jamie Bargary, Ryan Hatch.

---

 607 **MR JAMES UNETT, Wolverhampton**
Postal: 1 Dunstall Mews, Gorsebrook Road, Wolverhampton, West Midlands, WV6 0PE
Contacts: PHONE (01691) 610001 FAX (01691) 610001 MOBILE (07887) 534753
E-MAIL jamesunett1327@yahoo.co.uk WEBSITE www.jamesunettracing.com

1 **CLARATY**, 6, b m Firebreak—Claradotnet **G. D. Kendrick**
2 **CLARY (IRE)**, 6, b m Clodovil (IRE)—Kibarague **J. W. Unett**
3 **HEAT STORM (IRE)**, 5, b g Lawman (FR)—Coconut Show **Northern Line Racing Ltd**
4 **MARCRET (ITY)**, 9, b g Martino Alonso (IRE)—Love Secret (USA) **Northern Line Racing Ltd**
5 **MCCOOL RUNNINGS**, 5, b g Cockney Rebel (IRE)—Dances With Angels (IRE) **Mr M. A. Sheehy**
6 **MONUMENTAL MAN**, 7, b g Vital Equine (IRE)—Spark Up **R Milner & Partners**
7 **THE FENLAND MAN**, 5, b g Rob Roy (USA)—Spark Up **Mr M. B. Hall**
8 **VIVRE LA REVE**, 4, b f Assertive—Noor El Houdah (IRE) **J. W. Unett**
9 **WATERLOO DOCK**, 11, b g Hunting Lion (IRE)—Scenic Air **Mr M. Watkinson**

THREE-YEAR-OLDS

10 **ARTFUL MIND**, b c Cape Cross (IRE)—Tiriana **Northern Line Racing Ltd**
11 **CAFE NERVOSA (IRE)**, b f Excellent Art—Namoos (USA) **Miss C. Doyle**
12 **DREAM REVIVAL**, br f Captain Gerrard (IRE)—Passkey **Ms R. E. Taylor**
13 **NONEEDTOTELLME (IRE)**, gr f Fast Company (IRE)—Gemma's Delight (IRE) **Mr R. J. Roberts**
14 **Q TEN GIRL (IRE)**, ch f Zebedee—Regresa A Mi (IRE) **Northern Line Racing Ltd**

MR JAMES UNETT - Continued

Other Owners: Mrs B. Clarke, Mr M. J. Legge, W. R. Milner.

Assistant Trainer: Miss C. H. Jones

---

608 **MR JOHN UPSON, Towcester**
Postal: Glebe Stables, Blakesley Heath, Maidford, Towcester, Northamptonshire, NN12 8HN
Contacts: **PHONE** (01327) 860043 **FAX** (01327) 860238

1 BLACKWELL SYNERGY (FR), 10, b g Antarctique (IRE)—Pyu (GER) **The Peter Partnership**
2 ISAAC'S WARRIOR (IRE), 10, b g Pushkin (IRE)—Point The Finger (IRE) **Lord Nicholas Wilson**
3 STEEL GOLD (IRE), 10, b g Craigsteel—It Time To Run (IRE) **The Marron Partnership**
4 THEFRIENDLYGREMLIN, 8, b g Vinnie Roe (IRE)—Queens Fantasy **The Nap Hand Partnership**

Other Owners: M. H. Beesley, D. Deveney, Mr J. D. Horgan, Mrs J. M. Letts, Miss K. J. Letts, M. E. White.

---

609 **MR MARK USHER, Lambourn**
Postal: Rowdown Stables, Upper Lambourn, Hungerford, Berkshire, RG17 8QP
Contacts: **PHONE** (01488) 72598 (01488) 73630 **MOBILE** (07831) 873531
E-MAIL markusherracing@btconnect.com **WEBSITE** www.markusherracing.co.uk

1 ARLECCHINO'S LEAP, 4, br g Kheleyf (USA)—Donna Giovanna **Mr K. Senior**
2 BLACK TRUFFLE (FR), 6, b g Kyllachy—Some Diva **Ushers Court**
3 LEITH BRIDGE, 4, b g Avonbridge—Ishibee (IRE) **Saxon House Racing**
4 MISU PETE, 4, b g Misu Bond (IRE)—Smart Ass (IRE) **Saxon House Racing**
5 REGINALD CLAUDE, 8, b g Monsieur Bond (IRE)—Miller's Melody **High Five Racing**
6 SET TO GO, 9, b g Reset (AUS)—Golubitsa (IRE) **Miss W. Gill**
7 SPICE FAIR, 9, ch g Trade Fair—Focosa (ITY) **Saxon House Racing**

THREE-YEAR-OLDS

8 KIMBELLE, b f Compton Place—Engaging **Ushers Court**
9 MANY DREAMS (IRE), b f Kodiac—Deeday Bay (IRE) **Mr B. Fry**
10 MISS VICTORY (IRE), b f Mount Nelson—Wars (IRE) **Ushers Court**
11 MISTRY, b f Mullionmileanhour (IRE)—Smart Ass (IRE) **Ushers Court**
12 ROSIE'S VISION, b f Passing Glance—Bold Rose **Ushers Court**
13 STIMULATOR, b g Motivator—Fleeting Echo **P. J. Haycock**
14 WINDOW SHOPPING (IRE), b f Lilbourne Lad (IRE)—Stained Glass **M. D. I. Usher**

TWO-YEAR-OLDS

15 B c 29/3 Dick Turpin (IRE)—Bob's Princess (Bob's Return (IRE)) **Mark Usher**
16 B f 12/4 Stimulation (IRE)—Heart Felt (Beat Hollow) **Mark Usher**
17 Br c 15/2 Big Bad Bob (IRE)—Jessica Ennis (USA) (English Channel (USA)) (13500) **High Five Racing**
18 Ch f 7/3 Bated Breath—Kootenay (IRE) (Selkirk (USA)) (19047) **Rowdown Racing**
19 Ch f 20/4 Sixties Icon—Phoebe Woodstock (IRE) (Grand Lodge (USA)) (3333) **Mark Usher**
20 B c 25/3 Zoffany (IRE)—Queens Flight (King's Best (USA)) (24761) **Rowdown Racing**
21 B f 25/3 Elusive Pimpernel (USA)—Shamora (FR) (Oratorio (IRE)) **Mrs Jill Pellett**
22 Ch f 3/5 Kheleyf (USA)—Sweetest Revenge (IRE) (Daggers Drawn (USA)) **Ridgeway Alchemists**

Other Owners: Mr R. H. Brookes.

Assistant Trainer: Michael Usher

Jockey (flat): Liam Keniry. Jockey (NH): David Crosse.

---

610 **MR ROGER VARIAN, Newmarket**
Postal: Kremlin House Stables, Fordham Road, Newmarket, Suffolk, CB8 7AQ
Contacts: **PHONE** (01638) 661702 **FAX** (01638) 667018
E-MAIL office@varianstable.com **WEBSITE** www.varianstable.com

1 AJMAN BRIDGE, 6, ch g Dubawi (IRE)—Rice Mother (IRE) **Sheikh Mohammed Obaid Al Maktoum**
2 AMERICAN ARTIST (IRE), 4, ch c Danehill Dancer (IRE)—
American Adventure (USA) **Thurloe Thoroughbreds XXXV**

MR ROGER VARIAN - Continued

3 APPEARED, 4, b c Dubawi (IRE)—Appearance **Sheikh Mohammed Obaid Al Maktoum**
4 BARCHAN (USA), 4, b g War Front (USA)—Malamado (USA) **Godolphin Management Company Ltd**
5 BARSANTI (IRE), 4, b g Champs Elysees—Silver Star **Sheikh Mohammed Obaid Al Maktoum**
6 BATTERSEA, 5, b h Galileo (IRE)—Gino's Spirits **H.R.H. Sultan Ahmad Shah**
7 BELARDO (IRE), 4, b c Lope de Vega (IRE)—Danaskaya (IRE) **Godolphin & Prince A A Faisal**
8 CENTRAL SQUARE (IRE), 4, b g Azamour (IRE)—Lucky Clio (IRE) **Clipper Group Holdings Ltd**
9 CERTIFICATE, 5, ch g Pivotal—Graduation **Cheveley Park Stud Limited**
10 DOUBLE UP, 5, b g Exceed And Excel (AUS)—My Love Thomas (IRE) **Mr A D Spence & Mr M B Spence**
11 EKTIHAAM (IRE), 7, b g Invincible Spirit (IRE)—Liscune (IRE) **Hamdan bin Rashid Al Maktoum**
12 EL TEL, 4, ch g Sixties Icon—Chelsea (USA) **Ballymore Sterling Syndicate**
13 IMTIYAAZ (IRE), 4, b f Starspangledbanner (AUS)—Endure (IRE) **Mr M. Al-Qatami & Mr K. M. Al-Mudhaf**
14 INTILAAQ (USA), 4, b c Dynaformer (USA)—Torrestrella (IRE) **Hamdan bin Rashid Al Maktoum**
15 KING BOLETE (IRE), 4, b c Cape Cross (IRE)—Chanterelle (FR) **Sheikh Mohammed Obaid Al Maktoum**
16 LADY OF DUBAI, 4, b f Dubawi (IRE)—Lady of Everest (USA) **Sheikh Mohammed Obaid Al Maktoum**
17 MAKAFEH, 6, br g Elusive Quality (USA)—Demisemiquaver **Sheikh Mohammed Obaid Al Maktoum**
18 MALJAA, 4, ch g Paco Boy (IRE)—Kerry's Dream **Hamdan bin Rashid Al Maktoum**
19 MEDIATION, 4, b f Azamour (IRE)—Macleya (GER) **Cheveley Park Stud Limited**
20 MINDUROWNBUSINESS (IRE), 5, b h Cape Cross (IRE)—Whos Mindin Who (IRE) **Mr Alan Spence**
21 MONOTYPE (IRE), 4, b g Makfi—Mill Guineas (USA) **Sheikh Mohammed Obaid Al Maktoum**
22 MOUNT LOGAN (IRE), 5, ch h New Approach (IRE)—Vistaria (USA) **Sheikh Mohammed Obaid Al Maktoum**
23 MUJASSAM, 4, ch g Kyllachy—Naizak **Hamdan bin Rashid Al Maktoum**
24 ONE PEKAN (IRE), 5, b g Hard Spun (USA)—Stormy Blessing (USA) **Mrs H. Varian**
25 POSTPONED (IRE), 5, b h Dubawi (IRE)—Ever Rigg **Sheikh Mohammed Obaid Al Maktoum**
26 QUEEN'S PEARL (IRE), 4, b f Exceed And Excel (AUS)—Gimasha **Z. A. Galadari**
27 RAISING SAND, 4, b g Oasis Dream—Balalaika **Castle Down Racing & Mrs H. Varian**
28 REALTRA (IRE), 4, gr f Dark Angel (IRE)—Devious Diva (IRE) **Mr Y. Kubota**
29 ROSEBURG (IRE), 4, b g Tamayuz—Raydaniya (IRE) **Sheikh Mohammed Obaid Al Maktoum**
30 SPANGLED, 4, ch f Starspangledbanner (AUS)—Zykina **Cheveley Park Stud Limited**
31 SPIRITING (IRE), 4, b g Invincible Spirit (IRE)—Gold Bubbles (USA) **Sheikh Mohammed Obaid Al Maktoum**
32 STEPS (IRE), 8, gr g Verglas—Killinallan **Michael Hill**
33 STEVE ROGERS (IRE), 5, b g Montjeu (IRE)—Three Owls (IRE) **N. Bizakov**
34 STOCKING, 4, gr f Acclamation—Red Boots (USA) **Highclere T'Bred Racing(Prince Of Wales)**
35 SYLVETTE, 4, ch f Selkirk (USA)—Souvenance **Miss K. Rausing**
36 TARAZ, 4, b g Oasis Dream—Tamarind (IRE) **N. Bizakov**
37 WHITE LAKE, 4, b g Pivotal—White Palace **Sheikh Mohammed Obaid Al Maktoum**

THREE-YEAR-OLDS

38 ABSOLUTE ZERO (IRE), b g Cape Cross (IRE)—Emsiyah (USA) **J. Collins, C. Fahy & S. Piper**
39 AGHAANY, gr f Dubawi (IRE)—Hathrah (USA) **Hamdan bin Rashid Al Maktoum**
40 AJMAN PRINCE (IRE), b g Manduro (GER)—Jumaireyah **Sheikh Mohammed Obaid Al Maktoum**
41 AJMAN PRINCESS (IRE), b f Teofilo (IRE)—Reem Three **Sheikh Mohammed Obaid Al Maktoum**
42 ALIZOOM (IRE), gr g Invincible Spirit (IRE)—Lady Springbank (IRE) **Khalifa Dasmal & A Merza**
43 ALJULJALAH (USA), b f Exchange Rate (USA)—Ruler's Charm (USA) **Mr S. Rashid**
44 ALLE STELLE, b f Sea The Stars (IRE)—Alta Moda **Miss K. Rausing**
45 ALQUFFAAL, br c Dansili—Cuis Ghaire (IRE) **Hamdan bin Rashid Al Maktoum**
46 Ch c Danehill Dancer (IRE)—Alsace Lorraine (IRE) **Mr P. D. Smith**
47 ANDAZ, b f Makfi—Waafiah **Z. A. Galadari**
48 AROSE, b f Fastnet Rock (AUS)—Up At Dawn **China Horse Club (HK) Investment Holdings Limited**
49 ASKARI, b c Sea The Stars (IRE)—Loulwa (IRE) **Saleh Al Homaizi & Imad Al Sagar**
50 AZIZAAN, b c Dubawi (IRE)—Pearling (USA) **Saleh Al Homaizi & Imad Al Sagar**
51 CATSKILL MOUNTAINS (IRE), b c Rip Van Winkle (IRE)—Cawett (IRE) **China Horse Club (HK) Investment Holdings Limited**
52 CHASE THE LIGHT (IRE), b f Lawman (FR)—Solar Event **Qatar Racing Limited**
53 CHOREOGRAPHER (IRE), ch c Sea The Stars (IRE)—Evensong (GER) **China Horse Club (HK) Investment Holdings Limited**
54 CLIFF EDGE (IRE), b g Canford Cliffs (IRE)—That's My Style **Thurloe Thoroughbreds XXXVI**
55 COMPAS SCOOBIE, br g Kheleyf (USA)—Fantastic Santanyi **Michael Hill**
56 CORINTHIAN, b c Sea The Stars (IRE)—Contradictive (USA) **Highclere Thoroughbred Racing(Gladstone)**
57 DAILY NEWS, b c Street Cry (IRE)—Zeeba (IRE) **Sheikh Mohammed Obaid Al Maktoum**
58 DANCE BAND (IRE), b f Danehill Dancer (IRE)—Maidin Maith (IRE) **Cheveley Park Stud Limited**
59 DAWN OF HOPE (IRE), ch f Mastercraftsman (IRE)—Sweet Firebird (IRE) **Saleh Al Homaizi & Imad Al Sagar**
60 DREAM TRADER (IRE), b c Oasis Dream—Vakiyla (FR) **Mr H. R. Bin Ghedayer**
61 EBONY N IVORY, b c Equiano (FR)—Ile Deserte **Newsells Park Stud Limited**
62 ENNAADD, b c King's Best (USA)—Zayn Zen **Sheikh Ahmed Al Maktoum**
63 EX LOVER, ch c Monsun (GER)—Tu Eres Mi Amore (IRE) **Sheikh Mohammed Obaid Al Maktoum**

MR ROGER VARIAN - Continued

64 **FACTS AND FIGURES (IRE)**, gr c Galileo (IRE)—
Laddies Poker Two (IRE) **Mr D Smith, Mrs J Magnier & Mr M Tabor**
65 **FALAK (IRE)**, b c Teofilo (IRE)—Family (USA) **Al Shaqab Racing UK Limited**
66 **FASHAAR**, b c Showcasing—Avessia **Sheikh Ahmed Al Maktoum**
67 **FIRST RATE**, b c Kyllachy—Hooray **Cheveley Park Stud Limited**
68 **FOOL TO CRY (IRE)**, ch f Fast Company (IRE)—Islandagore (IRE) **J. Shack**
69 **FORBIDDING (USA)**, ch c Kitten's Joy (USA)—La Coruna (USA) **Prince A. A. Faisal**
70 **FOURTH WAY (IRE)**, b f Iffraaj—Spiritual Air **Qatar Racing Limited**
71 Gr c Mastercraftsman (IRE)—Gold Charm (GER) **Mr P. D. Smith**
72 **HAALICK (IRE)**, ch c Roderic O'Connor (IRE)—Lucky Pipit **Sheikh Ahmed Al Maktoum**
73 **HEART SPRINKLED (IRE)**, b f Galileo (IRE)—Heart Shaped (USA) **T. Yoshida**
74 **HIGH COMMAND (IRE)**, b c High Chaparral (IRE)—Plaza (USA) **H.R.H. Sultan Ahmad Shah**
75 **IDEALIST**, b f Rip Van Winkle (IRE)—Illusion **Cheveley Park Stud Limited**
76 **IKRAAMM**, b c Street Cry (IRE)—Red Dune (IRE) **Sheikh Ahmed Al Maktoum**
77 **KALAMATA**, b f Sir Percy—Kalamkas (USA) **N. Bizakov**
78 **KARAKOZ**, b f Danehill Dancer (IRE)—Card Shop (USA) **N. Bizakov**
79 **KARISMA (IRE)**, gr f Lawman (FR)—Lucky Clio (IRE) **Miss Y. M. G. Jacques**
80 B c Cape Blanco (IRE)—Keepers Hill (IRE) **Mr P. D. Smith**
81 **KHARBETATION (IRE)**, b g Dream Ahead (USA)—Anna's Rock (IRE) **Mr S. Rashid**
82 **LAQAB (IRE)**, b c Teofilo (IRE)—Ghaidaa (IRE) **Hamdan bin Rashid Al Maktoum**
83 **MAJDOOL (IRE)**, b g Acclamation—Maany (USA) **Hamdan bin Rashid Al Maktoum**
84 **MALHAMA**, br f New Approach (IRE)—Mahaatheer (IRE) **Hamdan bin Rashid Al Maktoum**
85 **MORANDO (FR)**, b c Kendargent (FR)—Moranda (FR) **H.H. Sheikh Mohammed bin Khalifa Al-Thani**
86 **MORMILL**, b c Authorized (IRE)—Sakhya (IRE) **Z. A. Galadari**
87 **MOUEENN**, ch g Lope de Vega (IRE)—Quesada (IRE) **Sheikh Ahmed Al Maktoum**
88 **MUTARAJJIL (IRE)**, b g Acclamation—Rouge Noir (USA) **Hamdan bin Rashid Al Maktoum**
89 **MUTAWAALY (IRE)**, b c Cape Cross (IRE)—Sana Abel (USA) **Hamdan bin Rashid Al Maktoum**
90 **MY FAVOURITE THING**, b f Oasis Dream—The Sound of Music (IRE) **Sheikh Mohammed Obaid Al Maktoum**
91 **MYSTIC IMAGE (USA)**, b f Distorted Humor (USA)—Time Control **Merry Fox Stud Limited**
92 **MYTIMEHASCOME**, b f Montjeu (IRE)—Vital Statistics **M. Abdullah**
93 **NADA (IRE)**, b f Teofilo (IRE)—Zomaradah **Sheikh Mohammed Obaid Al Maktoum**
94 **NEW WORLD POWER (JPN)**, b c Deep Impact (JPN)—Listen (IRE) **Qatar Racing Limited**
95 **NEZWAAH**, b f Dubawi (IRE)—Ferdoos **Sheikh Ahmed Al Maktoum**
96 **NOTARY**, b f Lawman (FR)—Purity **Cheveley Park Stud Limited**
97 **OWASEYF (USA)**, b f Medaglia d'oro (USA)—Nasmatt **Sheikh Ahmed Al Maktoum**
98 **PAPER FACES (USA)**, ch f Lemon Drop Kid (USA)—Liffey Dancer (IRE) **Merry Fox Stud Limited**
99 **PENNY LANE FOREVER**, b f Pivotal—Ventura Highway **Helena Springfield Ltd**
100 **PHILADELPHIA (IRE)**, b g Roderic O'Connor (IRE)—Harvest Joy (IRE) **The Philadelphia Partnership**
101 **POINT OF VIEW (IRE)**, b c New Approach (IRE)—Artisti **Sheikh Mohammed Obaid Al Maktoum**
102 **PRINCESS MOMOKA**, b f Exceed And Excel (AUS)—Impressionism (IRE) **Saleh Al Homaizi & Imad Al Sagar**
103 **PRINCESS PEARL (IRE)**, b f Teofilo (IRE)—Gimasha **Z. A. Galadari**
104 **RATTLE ON**, ch c Pivotal—Sabreon **Sheikh Mohammed Obaid Al Maktoum**
105 **RECOGNITION (IRE)**, gr c Rip Van Winkle (IRE)—Bali Breeze (IRE) **Mr Alan Spence**
106 **REDEMPTION**, b f Olden Times—Gentle On My Mind **Prince A. A. Faisal**
107 **SAIDDAA (USA)**, b f Hard Spun (USA)—My Dubai (IRE) **Sheikh Ahmed Al Maktoum**
108 **SHABEEB (USA)**, b c Smart Strike (CAN)—Sortita (GER) **Hamdan bin Rashid Al Maktoum**
109 **SHAHABAD**, b f Shamardal (USA)—Gulbarg **Sheikh Mohammed Obaid Al Maktoum**
110 **SHARJA QUEEN**, b f Pivotal—Dubai Queen **Sheikh Mohammed Obaid Al Maktoum**
111 **SHERDAT (IRE)**, b f Shirocco (GER)—Jathaabeh **Sheikh Ahmed Al Maktoum**
112 **SPANISH CITY**, ch c Exceed And Excel (AUS)—Annabelle's Charm (IRE) **Merry Fox Stud Limited**
113 **ST MALO (USA)**, b c Street Cry (IRE)—Arkadina (IRE) **China Horse Club (HK) Investment Holdings Limited**
114 **SUBOTAL (IRE)**, ch g Pivotal—Suba (USA) **Sheikh Mohammed Obaid Al Maktoum**
115 **SUN LOVER**, b c Oasis Dream—Come Touch The Sun (IRE) **Sheikh Mohammed Obaid Al Maktoum**
116 B g Rip Van Winkle (IRE)—Superfonic (FR) **Mr M. Almutairi**
117 **TAILWIND**, b c Dubawi (IRE)—Time Saved **R. Barnett**
118 **TALENT TO AMUSE (IRE)**, b f Manduro (GER)—Burn Baby Burn (IRE) **J. Shack**
119 **TANEEN (USA)**, b br c Speightstown (USA)—Moon And Sun (USA) **Hamdan bin Rashid Al Maktoum**
120 **TANGBA**, b f Dansili—Tamarind (IRE) **N. Bizakov**
121 **TARSEEKH**, b c Kyllachy—Constitute (USA) **Hamdan bin Rashid Al Maktoum**
122 **TESTIMONY**, b f Lawman (FR)—Macleya (GER) **Cheveley Park Stud Limited**
123 **TIERCEL**, b c Olden Times—Sharp Mode (USA) **Prince A. A. Faisal**
124 **TIFL**, ch g Approve (IRE)—Isobel Rose (IRE) **Hamdan bin Rashid Al Maktoum**
125 **TOUMAR**, ch f Sea The Stars (IRE)—Tingling (USA) **N. Bizakov**
126 **UAE PRINCE (IRE)**, b c Sea The Stars (IRE)—By Request **Sheikh Mohammed Obaid Al Maktoum**
127 **VIZIER**, b g Pivotal—Rare Ransom **N. Bizakov**

MR ROGER VARIAN - Continued

128 ZABEEL PRINCE (IRE), ch c Lope de Vega (IRE)—
Princess Serena (USA) **Sheikh Mohammed Obaid Al Maktoum**
129 ZABEEL PRINCESS, b f Dubawi (IRE)—Mundana (IRE) **Sheikh Mohammed Obaid Al Maktoum**

TWO-YEAR-OLDS

130 AJAMAN KING (IRE), ch c 30/3 Lope de Vega (IRE)—
Third Dimension (FR) (Suave Dancer (USA)) (95976) **Sheikh Mohammed Obaid Al Maktoum**
131 AKDAAR, b c 15/3 Dubawi (IRE)—Min Banat Alreeh (IRE) (Oasis Dream) **Hamdan bin Rashid Al Maktoum**
132 ALAMTHAL (IRE), b f 16/5 Oasis Dream—Cuis Ghaire (IRE) (Galileo (IRE)) **Hamdan bin Rashid Al Maktoum**
133 B f 28/1 High Chaparral (IRE)—Albanka (IRE) (Giant's Causeway (USA)) **N. Bizakov**
134 B br c 17/3 Lonhro (AUS)—Alzerra (UAE) (Pivotal) **Sheikh Ahmed Al Maktoum**
135 B f 24/2 Dubawi (IRE)—
Badee'a (IRE) (Marju (IRE)) (900000) **China Horse Club (HK) Investment Holdings Limited**
136 CAPE BYRON, ch c 3/3 Shamardal (USA)—
Reem Three (Mark of Esteem (IRE)) **Sheikh Mohammed Obaid Al Maktoum**
137 DAIRA BRIDGE (IRE), b c 5/3 Dream Ahead (USA)—
Lady Livius (IRE) (Titus Livius (FR)) (110000) **Sheikh Mohammed Obaid Al Maktoum**
138 DAIRA PRINCE (IRE), b c 12/5 Dubawi (IRE)—
Chiang Mai (IRE) (Sadler's Wells (USA)) (110000) **Sheikh Mohammed Obaid Al Maktoum**
139 B c 7/2 Bahamian Bounty—Dare To Dream (Exceed And Excel (AUS)) (130000) **Sheikh Ahmed Al Maktoum**
140 Ch c 26/3 Lope de Vega (IRE)—Dashing (Sadler's Wells (USA)) **Saleh Al Homaizi & Imad Al Sagar**
141 B c 24/4 Zoffany (IRE)—Dashing Beauty (IRE) (Daggers Drawn) (200000) **Mr M. Almutairi**
142 DAWN CHOIR, b f 15/4 Fastnet Rock (AUS)—Heavenly Dawn (Pivotal) **Cheveley Park Stud Limited**
143 DEALER'S CHOICE (IRE), gr f 14/3 Exchange Rate (USA)—
Micaela's Moon (USA) (Malibu Moon (USA)) (33000) **J. Shack**
144 DEFOE (IRE), br gr c 8/5 Dalakhani (IRE)—Dulkashe (Pivotal) **Sheikh Mohammed Obaid Al Maktoum**
145 DHAJEEJ (IRE), b c 18/2 Cape Cross (IRE)—
Nimboo (USA) (Lemon Drop Kid (USA)) (130000) **Hamdan bin Rashid Al Maktoum**
146 DUBAWI PRINCE, b c 22/2 Dubawi (IRE)—Flawly (Old Vic) (725000) **Sheikh Mohammed Obaid Al Maktoum**
147 Gr f 26/3 Exceed And Excel (AUS)—
Ela Athena (Ezzoud (IRE)) (177187) **China Horse Club (HK) Investment Holdings Limited**
148 ELERFAAN (IRE), b c 27/4 Shamardal (USA)—
Gorband (USA) (Woodman (USA)) (100000) **Hamdan bin Rashid Al Maktoum**
149 B c 16/3 Mastercraftsman (IRE)—Endure (IRE) (Green Desert (USA)) (205000) **Mr M. Almutairi**
150 EQUITATION, b c 13/2 Equiano (FR)—Sakhee's Song (Sakhee (USA)) (47000) **The Equitation Partnership**
151 FAIRY LIGHTS, b f 29/3 Shamardal (USA)—
Suba (USA) (Seeking The Gold (USA)) **Sheikh Mohammed Obaid Al Maktoum**
152 B f 17/3 Oasis Dream—Firdaws (USA) (Mr Greeley (USA)) **Hamdan bin Rashid Al Maktoum**
153 FUJAIRA BRIDGE (IRE), b c 14/3 Sea The Stars (IRE)—
Garanciere (FR) (Anabaa (USA)) (310000) **Sheikh Mohammed Obaid Al Maktoum**
154 FUJAIRA PRINCE (IRE), gr ro c 19/4 Pivotal—
Zam Zoom (IRE) (Dalakhani (IRE)) (90000) **Sheikh Mohammed Obaid Al Maktoum**
155 B c 1/2 Showcasing—Funny Enough (Dansili) (85000) **Sheikh Ahmed Al Maktoum**
156 Ch f 19/2 Pivotal—Gakalina (IRE) (Galileo (IRE)) **N. Bizakov**
157 Ch c 5/3 Dragon Pulse (IRE)—Galistic (IRE) (Galileo (IRE)) (48000) **Jon Collins, Chris Fahy & Mrs H. Varian**
158 HAMMERSTEIN, b c 30/4 Dansili—
The Sound of Music (IRE) (Galileo (IRE)) **Sheikh Mohammed Obaid Al Maktoum**
159 B c 20/2 Dutch Art—Jamboretta (IRE) (Danehill (USA)) (150000) **Mr P. D. Smith**
160 JUMIRA BRIDGE, b c 24/3 Invincible Spirit (IRE)—
Zykina (Pivotal) (85000) **Sheikh Mohammed Obaid Al Maktoum**
161 JUMIRA PRINCE (IRE), ch c 6/3 Exceed And Excel (AUS)—
Aoife Alainn (IRE) (Dr Fong (USA)) (295311) **Sheikh Mohammed Obaid Al Maktoum**
162 JUMIRA PRINCESS (IRE), b f 17/2 Redoute's Choice (AUS)—
Blaze of Colour (Rainbow Quest (USA)) (125507) **Sheikh Mohammed Obaid Al Maktoum**
163 B c 26/3 Zoffany (IRE)—Knysna (IRE) (Rock of Gibraltar (IRE)) (118124) **Saleh Al Homaizi & Imad Al Sagar**
164 B c 8/5 Shamardal (USA)—Littlefeather (IRE) (Indian Ridge) (95000) **Mr W. Y. C. Leung**
165 B f 6/3 Oasis Dream—Loulou (USA) (El Prado (IRE)) **Saleh Al Homaizi & Imad Al Sagar**
166 B f 24/4 Dream Ahead (USA)—
Love And Laughter (IRE) (Theatrical) (214101) **China Horse Club (HK) Investment Holdings Limited**
167 MAAZEL (IRE), b c 16/4 Elzaam (AUS)—Laylati (IRE) (Green Desert (USA)) (45000) **The Maazel Partnership**
168 Gr f 28/3 Dark Angel (IRE)—Mahaazen (IRE) (Cape Cross (IRE)) (49523)
169 MARGHERITA, b f 11/2 Mayson—Phillipina (Medicean) **Cheveley Park Stud Limited**
170 MATERIALIST, b c 13/3 Dansili—Mundana (IRE) (King's Best (USA)) **Sheikh Mohammed Obaid Al Maktoum**
171 B c 28/4 Holy Roman Emperor (IRE)—Miss Rochester (IRE) (Montjeu (IRE)) (120000) **Mr W. Y. C. Leung**

MR ROGER VARIAN - Continued

172 B c 15/3 Frankel—
      Model Queen (USA) (Kingmambo (USA)) (670000) **China Horse Club (HK) Investment Holdings Limited**
173 B c 21/5 Rock of Gibraltar (IRE)—Moiava (FR) (Bering) (42000) **Unregistered Partnership**
174 B f 5/3 Holy Roman Emperor (IRE)—Monshak (IRE) (Monsun (GER)) **N. Bizakov**
175 **MOUNTAIN ANGEL (IRE)**, b c 22/4 Dark Angel (IRE)—
      Fanciful Dancer (Groom Dancer (USA)) (100000) **Z. A. Galadari**
176 **NEWCOMER**, ch f 10/1 New Approach (IRE)—
      Khor Sheed (Dubawi (IRE)) **Sheikh Mohammed Obaid Al Maktoum**
177 **NOTHING BUT DREAMS**, b f 27/1 Frankel—Danedream (GER) (Lomitas) **T. Yoshida**
178 **PALACE GATE**, ch c 7/2 Street Cry (IRE)—
      Princess Nada (Barathea (IRE)) **Sheikh Mohammed Obaid Al Maktoum**
179 **PICHOLA DANCE (IRE)**, ch f 16/2 Distorted Humor (USA)—
      Liffey Dancer (IRE) (Sadler's Wells (USA)) **Merry Fox Stud Limited**
180 **PLAYING TRIX**, b f 27/2 War Front (USA)—Time Control (Sadler's Wells (USA)) **Merry Fox Stud Limited**
181 **PLEAD**, ch f 13/4 Dutch Art—Entreat (Pivotal) **Cheveley Park Stud Limited**
182 B c 13/2 Invincible Spirit (IRE)—
      Prima Luce (IRE) (Galileo (IRE)) (428202) **China Horse Club (HK) Investment Holdings Limited**
183 **PROMINENCE**, br f 26/4 Pivotal—Dublino (USA) (Lear Fan (USA)) **Cheveley Park Stud Limited**
184 B c 24/3 Invincible Spirit (IRE)—Rock Salt (Selkirk (USA)) **N. Bizakov**
185 **ROSENCRANZ**, gr c 7/4 Dubawi (IRE)—
      Rose Diamond (IRE) (Daylami (IRE)) **Sheikh Mohammed Obaid Al Maktoum**
186 B f 1/2 Azamour (IRE)—Serres (IRE) (Daylami (IRE)) **N. Bizakov**
187 B c 29/1 Pivotal—Shabyt (Sadler's Wells (USA)) **N. Bizakov**
188 **SHARJA BRIDGE**, b c 26/3 Oasis Dream—
      Quetena (GER) (Acatenango (GER)) (500000) **Sheikh Mohammed Obaid Al Maktoum**
189 Ch c 2/3 Pastoral Pursuits—Strawberry Leaf (Unfuwain (USA)) (14285)
190 **SUBHAAN**, ch c 22/3 Dutch Art—
      Mamma Morton (IRE) (Elnadim (USA)) (195238) **Hamdan bin Rashid Al Maktoum**
191 B f 8/3 Dansili—Tamarind (IRE) (Sadler's Wells (USA)) **N. Bizakov**
192 **TANBEEH (IRE)**, b c 26/3 Approve (IRE)—
      White Daffodil (IRE) (Footstepsinthesand) (68571) **Hamdan bin Rashid Al Maktoum**
193 B f 10/2 Invincible Spirit (IRE)—Totally Devoted (IRE) (Seeking The Gold (USA)) **N. Bizakov**
194 **UAE KING (IRE)**, b c 8/2 Oasis Dream—
      Caphene (Sakhee (USA)) (750000) **Sheikh Mohammed Obaid Al Maktoum**
195 **UAE QUEEN**, b f 16/4 Oasis Dream—Pongee (Barathea (IRE)) (450000) **Sheikh Mohammed Obaid Al Maktoum**
196 **VICTORY ANGEL (IRE)**, b c 9/3 Acclamation—Golden Shadow (IRE) (Selkirk (USA)) (140000) **Z. A. Galadari**
197 B c 11/2 Dalakhani (IRE)—Wahylah (IRE) (Shamardal (USA)) (105000) **Sheikh Ahmed Al Maktoum**
198 **WATCHMAN**, b c 10/3 Frankel—Zomaradah (Deploy) **Sheikh Mohammed Obaid Al Maktoum**
199 **ZEELANDER**, b c 18/3 Dubawi (IRE)—Zeeba (IRE) (Barathea (IRE)) **Sheikh Mohammed Obaid Al Maktoum**

Other Owners: K. M. Al-Mudhaf, Mohammed Jasem Al-Qatami, I. J. Al-Sagar, Mrs J. A. Allen, Mr K. Allen, G. M. Barnard, Mr J. A. Collins, K. A. Dasmal, Mrs H. S. Ellingsen, Mr C. J. Fahy, Dowager Countess of Harrington, The Hon H. M. Herbert, Highclere Thoroughbred Racing Ltd, Saleh Al Homaizi, Mrs G. A. S. Jarvis, Mr R. P. Legh, Mrs S. Magnier, Mr R. P. Marchant, Mr S. Marchant, Mr A. A. Merza, Mr M. D. Moroney, Mr G. Moss, Mr O. J. W. Pawle, S. J. Piper, D. Smith, Mr M. B. Spence, Mr J. A. B. Stafford, M. Tabor, M. Weinfeld.

Assistant Trainer: Will Johnson

Jockey (flat): Andrea Atzeni. **Apprentice:** Cameron Noble.

---

611 **MR ED VAUGHAN, Newmarket**
Postal: **Machell Place Cottage, Old Station Road, Newmarket, Suffolk, CB8 8DW**
Contacts: **PHONE (01638) 667411 FAX (01638) 667452 MOBILE (07799) 144901**
E-MAIL ed@efvaughan.com WEBSITE www.efvaughan.com

1 **ADVENTURE SEEKER (IRE)**, 5, gr h Dalakhani (IRE)—Adventure (USA)
2 **CLAIM THE ROSES (USA)**, 5, b br h Speightstown (USA)—Reboot (USA)
3 **COSTA FILEY**, 5, b g Pastoral Pursuits—Cosmic Destiny (IRE)
4 **INTERCONNECTION**, 5, ch g Mount Nelson—Lacework
5 **MEHRONISSA**, 4, ch f Iffraaj—Miss University (USA)
6 **PRIMROSE VALLEY**, 4, b f Pastoral Pursuits—Cosmic Destiny (IRE)
7 **SI SENOR (IRE)**, 5, b g Dansili—Kotsi (IRE)

MR ED VAUGHAN - Continued

THREE-YEAR-OLDS

8 **BONNEFIO**, b f Teofilo (IRE)—Crimson Ribbon (USA)
9 **COLD FUSION (IRE)**, b f Frozen Power (IRE)—Tuscania (USA)
10 **KHALEESI WIND (IRE)**, b f Exceed And Excel (AUS)—Madam Ninette
11 **LAJATICO**, b f Equiano (FR)—Italian Connection
12 **RECONCILLIATION**, b g Aqlaam—Gretna
13 **ROMAN HOLIDAY (IRE)**, b f Holy Roman Emperor (IRE)—Burn The Breeze (IRE)
14 **ROYAL DEBT**, b f Royal Applause—Caldy Dancer (IRE)
15 **STAINTONDALE LASS (IRE)**, b f Bushranger (IRE)—Siphon Melody (USA)
16 **WILD BLOOM**, b f Exceed And Excel (AUS)—Wild Gardenia
17 **XCELERATION**, b c Acclamation—Hijab

TWO-YEAR-OLDS

18 B c 25/4 Jeremy (USA)—Ballyologue (IRE) (Montjeu (IRE)) (29531)
19 **GEORGE RAVENSCAR**, b c 21/4 Pastoral Pursuits—Cosmic Destiny (IRE) (Soviet Star (USA))
20 Ch c 1/2 Windsor Knot (IRE)—Halliard (Halling (USA)) (11074)
21 **LITTLEBECK LADY**, b f 1/2 Sir Percy—Mrs Snaffles (IRE) (Indian Danehill (IRE)) (16000)
22 B c 8/2 Clodovil (IRE)—Nordkappe (GER) (High Chaparral (IRE)) (26000)
23 B c 11/5 Kalanisi (IRE)—Peratus (IRE) (Mujadil (USA)) (13289)
24 B c 6/3 Tin Horse (IRE)—Plebeya (IRE) (Dubawi (IRE)) (48000)
25 B f 19/1 Sir Prancealot (IRE)—Really Polish (USA) (Polish Numbers (USA)) (14285)
26 B c 5/5 Arcano (IRE)—Spa (Sadler's Wells (USA)) (19195)
27 Ch c 1/4 Bahamian Bounty—Starlit Sky (Galileo (IRE)) (32000)
28 B c 11/2 Kyllachy—Violet Ballerina (IRE) (Namid) (65000)

Owners: Mr H. R. Bin Ghadayer, Bloomsbury Stud, Mr Jonathan A. Bryan, Mr M. J. C. Hawkes, Mr Hugo Lascelles, Mrs Hugo Lascelles, Mr Rupert P. Legh, Mr P. A. Moroney, Mr Michael D. Moroney, Mr A. E. Oppenheimer, Mr A. M. Pickering, Mr S. Rashid, Mr G. Sharp, Mr D. Thorpe, Mr G. Van Ameyden, Mr E. F. Vaughan.

---

612 **MR TIM VAUGHAN, Cowbridge**
Postal: **Pant Wilkin Stables, Llanquian Road, Aberthin, Cowbridge, South Glamorgan, CF71 7HE**
Contacts: **PHONE** (01446) 771626 **FAX** (01446) 774371 **MOBILE** (07841) 800081
E-MAIL tim@timvaughanracing.com **WEBSITE** www.timvaughanracing.com

1 **AIR APPROACH**, 4, b br g New Approach (IRE)—Grecian Air (FR) **Mr J. H. Frost**
2 4, B g Westerner—Allfreeze **T. E. Vaughan**
3 **ALPHABETICAL ORDER**, 8, b g Alflora (IRE)—Lady Turk (FR) **Great Northern Partnership**
4 **ASHFORD WOOD (IRE)**, 8, b g Stowaway—Shambala (IRE) **David & Susan Luke**
5 **ASHKOUN (FR)**, 5, b g Sinndar (IRE)—Ashalina (FR) **Galopp Syndicate Ltd**
6 **ASOCKASTAR (IRE)**, 8, b g Milan—Baie Barbara (IRE) **Oceans Racing**
7 4, B g Flemensfirth (USA)—Aventia (IRE) **T. E. Vaughan**
8 **BALLYROCK (IRE)**, 10, b g Milan—Ardent Love (IRE) **Pearn's Pharmacies Ltd**
9 5, B g Alflora (IRE)—Barton Flower **T. E. Vaughan**
10 **BASSARABAD (FR)**, 5, b g Astarabad (USA)—Grivette (FR) **Pearn's Pharmacies Ltd**
11 **BEAT THE TIDE**, 6, b g Black Sam Bellamy (IRE)—Sablonne (USA) **The Mount Fawcus Partnership**
12 **BELIZE**, 5, b g Rail Link—Costa Rica (IRE) **Mr D. R. Passant**
13 **BELLS OF AILSWORTH (IRE)**, 6, b g Kayf Tara—Volverta (FR) **Mr S. Grys & Mr M. O'Boyle**
14 **BELLS OF SUTTON (IRE)**, 4, b g Kalanisi (IRE)—Out Performer (IRE) **Mr S. Grys & Mr M. O'Boyle**
15 **BENABILITY (IRE)**, 6, b g Beneficial—Whataliability (IRE) **Mrs L. Bowtell**
16 **BENEFIT OF YOUTH (IRE)**, 9, b g Beneficial—Persian Avenue (IRE) **The Eternal Optimists**
17 **BENNACHIE (IRE)**, 7, b g Milan—Stormy Lady (IRE) **Oceans Racing**
18 **BLANVILLE (FR)**, 5, gr g High Rock (IRE)—Paricolombieres (FR) **T. E. Vaughan**
19 **BLEU ET NOIR**, 5, b g Enrique—Gastina (FR) **A. E. Peterson**
20 **BONVILSTON BOY**, 5, b g Martaline—Lisa du Chenet (FR) **Mr N. Harris**
21 **BROOME LANE**, 7, b m Kayf Tara—Aranga (IRE) **T. E. Vaughan**
22 **BUCKING THE TREND**, 8, b g Kayf Tara—Macklette (IRE) **The Marinades**
23 **BUY BACK BOB (IRE)**, 9, b g Big Bad Bob—Abeyr **R P B Michaelson & Robin Clay**
24 **C'EST DU GATEAU (FR)**, 4, b g Laveron—Programmee (FR) **Pearn's Pharmacies Ltd**
25 **CANTON PRINCE (IRE)**, 5, b g Shantou (USA)—Hasainm (USA) **Tertia Racing**
26 **CASPIAN PIPER (IRE)**, 9, b g Millenary—Pepsi Starlet (IRE) **Oceans Racing**
27 **CHAMPAGNE CHASER**, 6, b g Tobougg (IRE)—Champagne Lil **Mrs M. A. O'Sullivan**
28 4, Br g Stowaway—Clairefontaine **T. E. Vaughan**
29 **CREATEUR (IRE)**, 5, b g Muhtathir—Cracovie **Oceans Racing**

MR TIM VAUGHAN - Continued

30 **DADSINTROUBLE (IRE)**, 6, b g Presenting—Gemini Lucy (IRE) **Mr J. P. M. Bowtell**
31 **DALAMAN (IRE)**, 5, b g Duke of Marmalade (IRE)—Crimphill (IRE) **Diamond Racing Ltd**
32 **DEBECE**, 5, b g Kayf Tara—Dalamine (FR) **R. M. Kirkland**
33 **DESHAN (GER)**, 5, b g Soldier Hollow—Desimona (GER) **S. Clarke & and the Late Mr M. S. Clarke**
34 **DIRECTIONAL**, 4, b g Raven's Pass (USA)—Rose Street (USA) **Mr P. C. Etty**
35 **DOVILS DATE**, 7, gr g Clodovil (IRE)—Lucky Date (IRE) **T. E. Vaughan**
36 **DUBH EILE (IRE)**, 8, br m Definite Article—Aine Dubh (IRE) **Mr Paul Bowtell & Mr Jonathan Shinton**
37 **ESSTEEPEE**, 7, b g Double Trigger (IRE)—Lamper's Light **T. E. Vaughan**
38 **EXPLAINED (IRE)**, 9, b g Exit To Nowhere (USA)—All Told (IRE) **D N V Churton & Mrs C Wilson**
39 **FALCARRAGH (IRE)**, 9, ch g Alderbrook—Maghereareagh Lady (IRE) **Mr M. A. Stratford**
40 **FAYETTE COUNTY (IRE)**, 9, b g Golden Lariat (USA)—Midsyn Lady (IRE) **J. P. McManus**
41 **FIELDS OF GLORY (FR)**, 6, b g King's Best (USA)—Lavandou **Pearn's Pharmacies Ltd**
42 **FIRST FANDANGO**, 9, b g Hernando (FR)—First Fantasy **WRB Racing 40 & Premier Chance Racing**
43 **FRASER CANYON**, 4, b g Halling (USA)—Valley of Gold (FR) **Bovian Racing**
44 **GIFTED ISLAND (IRE)**, 6, b g Turtle Island (IRE)—Life Support (USA) **Oceans Racing**
45 **GLIMPSE OF GOLD**, 5, b g Passing Glance—Tizzy Blue (IRE) **The Craftsmen**
46 **HAWKHILL (IRE)**, 10, b g Hawk Wing (USA)—Crimphill (IRE) **Mr L. Helps**
47 **HONEY POUND (IRE)**, 8, b g Big Bad Bob (IRE)—
        Moon Review (USA) **D&S Luke & Great Northern Partnership II**
48 **IFAN (IRE)**, 8, b g Ivan Denisovich (IRE)—Montana Miss (IRE) **WRB Racing 61 & Derek & Jean Clee**
49 4, B g Flemensfirth (USA)—In Our Intrest (IRE) **Pearn's Pharmacies Ltd**
50 **JIMMY SHAN (IRE)**, 8, b g Milan—Divine Prospect (IRE) **T. E. Vaughan**
51 **KALIMANTAN (IRE)**, 6, b g Azamour (IRE)—Kalamba (IRE) **T. E. Vaughan**
52 **KENDARI RACING (IRE)**, 5, b g Misternando—Native Mistress (IRE) **Kendari Racing**
53 **KNIGHT'S REWARD**, 6, b g Sir Percy—Wardeh **optimumracing.co.uk**
54 4, B g Getaway (GER)—Knock Down (IRE) **Pearn's Pharmacies Ltd**
55 **LAKE CHAPALA (IRE)**, 7, b g Shantou (USA)—Rathcolman Queen (IRE) **Mr B. M. Jones**
56 **LAWLESS ISLAND (IRE)**, 7, b g Heron Island (IRE)—Nylon (GER) **Pearn's Pharmacies Ltd**
57 **LIBERTY COURT (IRE)**, 9, b g Court Cave (IRE)—Miss Vikki (IRE) **Passant & Butt**
58 **LOOKSNOWTLIKEBRIAN (IRE)**, 5, b g Brian Boru—Sheebadiva (IRE) **SC Botham & RG Botham**
59 **LORD LIR (IRE)**, 10, b g Oscar Schindler (IRE)—Milford Woman (IRE) **Two Gents & An Orange Bloke Racing**
60 **LOUIS LUDWIG (IRE)**, 11, b g Mull of Kintyre (USA)—Fantastic Bid (USA) **Oceans Racing**
61 **LOVELY BUBBLY**, 5, gr g Kayf Tara—Champagne Lil **R. M. Kirkland**
62 **MAKETHEDIFFERENCE (IRE)**, 8, b g Shantou (USA)—La Panthere (USA) **Mr B. M. Jones**
63 **MAN OF GOD (IRE)**, 8, b g Sadler's Wells (USA)—Jude **optimumracing.co.uk**
64 **MASSINI'S MAGUIRE (IRE)**, 15, b g Dr Massini (IRE)—Molly Maguire (IRE) **A. E. Peterson**
65 **MASTER DANCER**, 5, gr g Mastercraftsman (IRE)—Isabella Glyn (IRE) **select-racing-club.co.uk & Mr C Davies**
66 **MATTS LEGACY (IRE)**, 4, b g Arcadio (GER)—How Provincial (IRE) **T. E. Vaughan**
67 **MESSERY (FR)**, 5, b g Poliglote—Iris du Berlais (FR) **Mrs B. N. Ead**
68 **MIST THE BOAT**, 8, b g Generous (IRE)—Baily Mist (IRE) **Twenty Four 7 Racing**
69 **MOREECE (IRE)**, 7, b g Chevalier (IRE)—Jumbo Romance (IRE) **Newport Rangers**
70 **MURCHU (IRE)**, 10, b g Oscar (IRE)—Bottle A Knock (IRE) **Oceans Racing**
71 **NATHANS PRIDE (IRE)**, 8, ch g Definite Article—Tricias Pride (IRE) **Mr J. P. M. Bowtell**
72 **NELLIE THE ELEGANT**, 5, b m Mount Nelson—Mexican Hawk (USA) **W R B Racing 53**
73 **NOBLE GALILEO (GER)**, 6, b g Galileo (IRE)—Nordtanzerin (GER) **Newport Rangers**
74 **NORMANDY KING (IRE)**, 5, b g King's Theatre (IRE)—Clairefontaine **The 600 Club**
75 **NUMBER ONE LONDON (IRE)**, 6, b g Invincible Spirit (IRE)—Vadorga **D. J. Wallis**
76 **OFFICER HOOLIHAN**, 6, b g Kayf Tara—Major Hoolihan **R. M. Kirkland**
77 **ONE LEADER (IRE)**, 5, b g Oscar (IRE)—Be My Leader (IRE) **Tertia Racing**
78 **OSCAR FIAIN (IRE)**, 8, b g Oscar (IRE)—Produzione (FR) **David & Susan Luke**
79 **OSKAR'S EVA (IRE)**, 6, gr m Black Sam Bellamy (IRE)—Sardagna (FR) **Sally Morgan & Richard Prince**
80 **PANIS ANGELICUS (FR)**, 7, b g Panis (USA)—Pyu (GER) **Oceans Racing**
81 **PARTING WAY (IRE)**, 8, b g Golan (IRE)—Best Mother (IRE) **Brian Ead & Martin Moore**
82 **PRESENTING RED (IRE)**, 6, b g Presenting—Bolly (IRE) **R. M. Kirkland**
83 **QUASI (IRE)**, 4, ch g Presenting—Pink Mist (IRE) **Mr D. R. Passant**
84 **REDDINGTON (IRE)**, 4, b g Getaway (GER)—Nikkis Alstar (IRE) **Mrs B. N. Ead**
85 **RENFREW (IRE)**, 6, b g Robin des Pres (FR)—Allstar Rose (IRE) **T. E. Vaughan**
86 **ROYALE DJANGO (IRE)**, 7, b g Kayf Tara—Royale Boja (FR) **Mr J Durston & Mr N Harris**
87 **RUSTAMABAD (FR)**, 6, ch g Dylan Thomas (IRE)—Rosawa (FR) **Mr D. R. Passant**
88 **RYE HOUSE (IRE)**, 7, b g Dansili—Threefold (USA) **Oceans Racing**
89 **SACRED SUMMIT (IRE)**, 5, ch g Mountain High (IRE)—D'ygrande (IRE) **Oceans Racing**
90 4, B g Kayf Tara—Salamaite (FR) **T. E. Vaughan**
91 **SATELLITE (IRE)**, 5, b g Danehill Dancer (IRE)—Perihelion (IRE) **Paul & Louise Bowtell**
92 4, B g Brian Boru—Sheebadiva (IRE) **T. E. Vaughan**
93 **SHOUT IT ALOUD**, 7, b g Proclamation—Party Charmer **The Mount Fawcus Partnership**

MR TIM VAUGHAN - Continued

94 **SHOW'S OVER (IRE)**, 5, b g Curtain Time (IRE)—Sailors Run (IRE) **Mr B. M. Jones**
95 5, B g Double Trigger (IRE)—Soloism **T. E. Vaughan**
96 **SPECTATOR**, 5, br g Passing Glance—Averami **Pearn's Pharmacies Ltd**
97 **TANACANDO (FR)**, 4, b g Ballingarry (IRE)—Tamaziya (IRE) **Mr M. Trezise**
98 **TANIT RIVER (IRE)**, 6, br g Indian River (FR)—Tanit Lady (IRE) **Brian Ead & Martin Moore**
99 **TARA MAC**, 7, b m Kayf Tara—Macklette (IRE) **Mr W. Jones**
100 **THE MYTHOLOGIST (IRE)**, 8, ch g Motivator—Dilemma **Oceans Racing**
101 **THE OMEN**, 10, b g Sir Harry Lewis (USA)—High Sturt **Oceans Racing & Out Of Bounds Racing**
102 **THE WALLACE LINE (IRE)**, 5, b g Mastercraftsman (IRE)—Surval (IRE) **Diamond Racing Ltd**
103 **THELIGNY (FR)**, 5, gr g Martaline—Romilly (FR) **Pearn's Pharmacies Ltd**
104 **TIDESTREAM**, 6, b g Galileo (IRE)—Sweet Stream (ITY) **Delamere Cottage Racing Partners (1996)**
105 **TIME AND AGAIN (FR)**, 6, b g Sassanian (USA)—Petillante Royale (FR) **Oceans Racing**
106 **TOBACCO ROAD (IRE)**, 6, b g Westerner—Virginias Best **Mr S. Quinlan**
107 **TOMSK (FR)**, 6, ch g Priolo (USA)—Kauto Relstar (FR) **Oceans Racing**
108 **ULTIMATE HORSEMAN (IRE)**, 6, b g Kalanisi (IRE)—Dawn's Double (IRE) **Mr M. A. Stratford**
109 **UNCLE TONE (IRE)**, 7, b g Pelder (IRE)—Daisy A Day (IRE) **Kings Head Duffield Racing Partnership**
110 **UP THE JUNCTION**, 5, b g New Approach (IRE)—Hyabella **The Junction Partnership**
111 **VODKA ISLAND (IRE)**, 7, b m Turtle Island (IRE)—Fromrussiawithlove **Folly Road Racing Partners (1996)**
112 **WINGS OF SMOKE (IRE)**, 11, gr g King's Theatre (IRE)—Grey Mo (IRE) **Pearn's Pharmacies Ltd**
113 **WINIDO**, 4, b g Sulamani (IRE)—Princess Claudia (IRE) **JRFB Ltd**
114 **WITHOUT FRONTIER (IRE)**, 4, b g Stowaway—Hollygrove Samba (IRE) **Mr J Durston & Mr N Harris**
115 4, B f King's Theatre (IRE)—Wyldello **The Oxymorons**

Other Owners: A. W. A. Bates, Mr M. Batters, Mr N. Berrisford, S. C. Botham, Mr R. G. Botham, Mr A. Bott, Mr G. W. T. Butt, Mr D. N. V. Churton, S. J. Clare, Mr A. Clarke, Mr S. A. Clarke, Exors of the Late Mr M. S. Clarke, Mr R. I. Clay, D. D. Clee, Mrs J. P. Clee, Mr M. J. Curtis, Mr C. Davies, Mr R. Denness, Mr J. Durston, Mr D. Ead, Mr D. S. Fawcus, Mrs M. W. Fawcus, K. H. Foster, Mr A. L. Gregg, Mr S. Grys, Mr M. Hall, Mr G. Handley, Mr M. E. Harris, Mr S. R. Hartley, Mrs K. E. Hollingworth, Mr C. M. Ingram, Mr R. Jackson, Mr B. Jagger, D. M. Jenkins, T. E. Kerfoot, Mr M. D. Kilsby, J. K. S. Law, Mr G. T. Lever, Mrs D. J. Lowrie, A. D. Lowrie, Mr D. A. Luke, Mrs S. Luke, Dr C. H. Mason, R. P. B. Michaelson, Mr M. E. Moore, Mr J. M. Mordecai, Mrs S. Morgan, Mr M. O'Boyle, Mr G. P. O'Shea, Mr J. C. Peak, Miss D. E. Pettle, Mr J. T. Phillips, Mr A. J. Pigott, Mr R. G. Price, R. J. Prince, Mr N. S. C. Proctor, A. Robinson, Mr R. M. Rose, Mr J. Sanders, The Select Racing Club Limited, D. A. Shinton, Mr J. Shinton, Mr A. Spencer, Wetherby Racing Bureau Ltd, Mr N. D. Whitham, Mrs C. S. Wilson.

Jockey (flat): David Probert, Fergus Sweeney. **Jockey (NH):** Richard Johnson, Michael Byrne, Alan Johns.
Conditional: George Blackwell. **Amateur:** Mr Evan David, Ms Rachel Leyshon.

---

613 **MR CHRISTIAN VON DER RECKE, Weilerswist**
Postal: **Rennstall Recke GmbH, Hovener Hof, D-53919, Weilerswist, Germany**
Contacts: **PHONE (0049) 2254 84 53 14 FAX (0049) 2254 845315 MOBILE (0049) 171 542 50 50**
E-MAIL recke@t-online.de WEBSITE www.rennstall-recke.de

1 **AZYAAN (IRE)**, 4, gr f Mastercraftsman (IRE)—Hidden Heart (USA) **Frau Caroline Fuchs**
2 **BAVARIAN BEAUTY (GER)**, 5, b m Desert Prince (IRE)—Best Moving (GER) **Martin Ernst Veeck**
3 **CALL ME NUMBER ONE (GER)**, 4, b g Touch Down (GER)—Carrie Anne **H. H. Brand u.a.**
4 **CATTERMOLE (GER)**, 4, b g Mamool (IRE)—Chandos Rose (IRE) **H. H. Brand u.a.**
5 **CIOCCO SAM (GER)**, 8, bl g Samum (GER)—Cioccolata (GER) **Stall Blankenese**
6 **DREAMSPEED (IRE)**, 9, b g Barathea (IRE)—Kapria (IRE) **BMK Racing**
7 **EASTSITE ONE (GER)**, 4, b g Mamool (IRE)—Ericarrow (IRE) **Frau Gabriele Gaul**
8 **ERIC (GER)**, 5, ch h Tertullian (USA)—Ericarrow (IRE) **Frau Gabriele Gaul**
9 **FROM FROST**, 5, b g Nayef (USA)—Salutare (IRE) **Stall Saarbrucken**
10 **HOT BED (IRE)**, 7, b g Dashing Blade—Mer de Corail (IRE) **Stall Chevalex**
11 **INTERIOR MINISTER**, 6, b g Nayef (USA)—Sister Maria (USA) **Eugen-Andreas Wahler**
12 **JUNGLEBOOGIE (GER)**, 4, b c Nicaron (GER)—Jive (GER) **Stall Nizza**
13 **KINGDOM (IRE)**, 6, b g Montjeu (IRE)—Shadow Song (IRE) **Rennstall Recke GmbH**
14 **KOLONEL KIRKUP**, 6, b g Dr Fong (USA)—Strawberry Lolly (GER) **Stall Rettstadt**
15 **LINCOLN COUNTY**, 5, b g Authorized (IRE)—Lane County (USA) **Stall Alemannia**
16 **LIRO**, 6, b g Samum (GER)—La Donna **Stall Winterhude**
17 **LOS CERRITOS (SWI)**, 4, ch c Dr Fong (USA)—La Coruna (SWI) **Stall Leon**
18 **MAXIM GORKY (IRE)**, 9, b g Montjeu (IRE)—Altruiste (USA) **M-B-A Racing**
19 **MY MAJOR (IRE)**, 5, b g Holy Roman Emperor (IRE)—Greek Easter (IRE) **James Hanly**
20 **NESSAYA (GER)**, 4, b f Soldier of Fortune (IRE)—Nouvelle Princesse (GER) **Gestut Romerhof**
21 **PARIGINO (FR)**, 8, b g Panis (USA)—Loretta Gianni (FR) **M-B-A Racing**
22 **POLSKI POSEIDON (GER)**, 5, b g Areion (GER)—Polska Infa (GER) **Gestut IDEE GmbH & Co. KG**

MR CHRISTIAN VON DER RECKE - Continued

23 **RENNY STORM (CZE)**, 6, b g Stormy Jail (IRE)—Renaissance (CZE) **Rennstall Recke GmbH**
24 **RONNIE ROCKCAKE**, 6, b g Tiger Hill (IRE)—Vitesse (IRE) **Stall Ullenboomshof**
25 **SACRED DRAGON (USA)**, 6, b br g Bernstein (USA)—Night Breeze (USA) **Rennstall Recke GmbH**
26 **SEE YOU SOON**, 5, ch m Sholokhov (IRE)—See Me Well (IRE) **Schwindibode AG**
27 **SHADOW SADNESS (GER)**, 4, b c Soldier Hollow—Shadow Queen (GER) **Stall Weiss-Blau**
28 **SIMBA**, 5, ch h Teofilo (IRE)—Sarabia (GER) **M-B-A Racing**
29 **TABLEFORTEN**, 5, ch g Pastoral Pursuits—Twitch Hill **Frau Caroline Fuchs**
30 **TIREX (GER)**, 5, b g Sabiango (GER)—Think Twice (GER) **Frau Anne-Claire Bresges**
31 **VABINSARU (FR)**, 5, b g Enrique—Yolaine (FR) **Stall Walcheren**
32 **VAIHAU (FR)**, 7, br g Lavirco (GER)—Niponne (FR) **Rennstall Recke GmbH**
33 **ZARAGOZA (GER)**, 5, b m Zamindar (USA)—Zayraba (IRE) **Gestut Romerhof**

THREE-YEAR-OLDS

34 **AUSTIN (GER)**, b g Nicaron (GER)—Alte Rose (GER) **Stall Burg Muggenhausen**
35 **CHANDOS BELLE (GER)**, b f Mamool (IRE)—Chandos Rose (IRE) **H. H. Brand u.a.**
36 **CLASSIC BRIGHT (FR)**, b f Volfonic (IRE)—Classic Night (GER) **van der Hulst Special**
37 Gr f Getaway (GER)—Courting Shinney **Andrew Smith**
38 **CUMBRIANO (GER)**, b g Wiener Walzer (GER)—Carrie Anne **H. H. Brand u.a.**
39 **ERICA (GER)**, b f Mamool (IRE)—Ericarrow (IRE) **Frau Gabriele Gaul**
40 **EXCEED MY BUDGET**, ch f Exceed And Excel (AUS)—Best Side (IRE) **M-B-A Racing**
41 **IBIZA EMPRESS (IRE)**, b f Tertullian (USA)—Ibiza Dream **M-B-A Racing**
42 **JOKER (GER)**, b c Nicaron (GER)—Jive (GER) **Stall Nizza**
43 **LAROX (GER)**, b f Tertullian (USA)—Lajana (GER) **Stall Lydien**
44 **NARGIS QUEEN (FR)**, b f Slickly (FR)—Quiet Queen **M-B-A Racing**
45 **NINARO (GER)**, b c Areion (GER)—Ninigretta (GER) **Frau M. Haller**
46 **PURO AMIGO (GER)**, ch c Manduro (GER)—Power Penny (USA) **Gestut IDEE GmbH & Co. KG**
47 **QUICK STEP (GER)**, ch c Distant Music (USA)—Quadraga (GER) **Marquardt von Hodenberg**
48 **ZASADA (IRE)**, gr f Mastercraftsman (IRE)—Zagreb Flyer **M-B-A Racing**

TWO-YEAR-OLDS

49 **AMUN (GER)**, b c 3/3 Soldier Hollow—Albula (GER) (Dashing Blade) (23624) **Stall Nizza**
50 **LADY DONCASTER (IRE)**, b f 20/4 Harbour Watch (IRE)—
Ronja (USA) (El Corredor (USA)) (17142) **Stall Alemannia**
51 **MANDALA (GER)**, b f 21/3 Cacique (IRE)—Moonlight Danceuse (IRE) (Bering) **Gestut Am Schlossgarten**
52 **ROYAL FLAG (GER)**, ch c 8/4 Jukebox Jury (IRE)—Royal Lomita (GER) (Lomitas) (11074) **Frau R.u.A. Hacker**
53 **VOTEC (IRE)**, br c 15/4 Rock of Gibraltar (IRE)—Vestavia (IRE) (Alhaarth (IRE)) (40000) **Stall Nizza**

---

614 | **MR JOHN WADE, Sedgefield**
Postal: Howe Hills, Mordon, Sedgefield, Cleveland, TS21 2HG
Contacts: **PHONE (01740) 630310 FAX (01740) 630310 MOBILE (07831) 686968**

1 **ALLEZ COOL (IRE)**, 7, ch g Flemensfirth (USA)—La Fisarmonica (IRE) **J. Wade**
2 **ALWAREED**, 4, ch g Makfi—Sinduda **J. Wade**
3 **CASUAL CAVALIER (IRE)**, 8, br g Presenting—Asklynn (IRE) **J. Wade**
4 **CLUES AND ARROWS (IRE)**, 8, b g Clerkenwell (USA)—Ballela Girl (IRE) **J. Wade**
5 **CORRELATE**, 6, ch g Zamindar (USA)—Snow Blossom **J. Wade**
6 **DEAN'S WALK (IRE)**, 7, b g Craigsteel—Killashee (IRE) **J. Wade**
7 **DUBAI CELEBRITY**, 4, b g Sakhee (USA)—Aljana (IRE) **J. Wade**
8 **FORTY CROWN (IRE)**, 10, b g Court Cave—Forty Quid (IRE) **Miss M. D. Myco**
9 **FOURTH ESTATE (IRE)**, 10, b g Fantastic Light (USA)—Papering (IRE) **J. Wade**
10 **HARRIS HAWK**, 11, b g Karinga Bay—Harristown Lady **J. Wade**
11 **NAY MORE**, 5, b g Distant Peak (IRE)—Naywye **J. Wade**
12 **NEW ACADEMY**, 8, ch g Zamindar (USA)—New Abbey **J. Wade**
13 **NEWSPAGE (IRE)**, 10, b g Blueprint—Newlineview (IRE) **J. Wade**
14 **NORTONTHORPELEGEND (IRE)**, 6, b g Midnight Legend—Tanit **Miss M. D. Myco**
15 **PIKARNIA**, 6, b g Authorized (IRE)—Kartuzy (JPN) **J. Wade**
16 **PUDSEY HOUSE**, 9, b g Double Trigger (IRE)—Dara's Pride (IRE) **J. Wade**
17 **RISKIER**, 11, gr g Kier Park (IRE)—Risky Girl **J. Wade**
18 **RONN THE CONN (IRE)**, 4, ch g Whitmore's Conn (USA)—Speedy Fairy (IRE) **J. Wade**
19 **ROSEVILLE COTTAGE (IRE)**, 9, b g Kris Kin (USA)—Johnny's Idea (IRE) **J. Wade**
20 **RUNSWICK DAYS (IRE)**, 9, b g Presenting—Miss Lauren Dee (IRE) **J. Wade**
21 **SHEPHERD STORM (IRE)**, 6, b g September Storm (GER)—Clerhane Belle (IRE) **J. Wade**
22 **SILVER BULLION**, 5, br g Three Valleys (USA)—Silver Yen (USA) **J. Wade**

MR JOHN WADE - Continued

23 **SKA RIDGE**, 4, b g Distant Peak (IRE)—Tandawizi **J. Wade**
24 **SPANISH FLEET**, 8, b g Cadeaux Genereux—Santisima Trinidad (IRE) **J. Wade**
25 **STILO BLUE NATIVE (IRE)**, 8, gr g Blueprint (IRE)—Reconciliation (IRE) **J. Wade**
26 **VANILLA RUN (IRE)**, 5, b m Hurricane Run (IRE)—Vanilla Delight (IRE) **J. Wade**
27 **WALSER (IRE)**, 9, b g Milan—Brass Neck (IRE) **J. Wade**

Assistant Trainer: Miss Maria Myco (07798) 775932

Jockey (NH): Brian Hughes, Wilson Renwick, James Reveley. **Amateur:** Mr John Dawson, Mr C. M. O'Mahony.

---

615 **MRS LUCY WADHAM, Newmarket**
Postal: **The Trainer's House, Moulton Paddocks, Newmarket, Suffolk, CB8 7PJ**
Contacts: **PHONE (01638) 662411 FAX (01638) 668821 MOBILE (07980) 545776**
E-MAIL lucy.wadham@virgin.net **WEBSITE** www.lucywadhamracing.co.uk

1 **A BOY NAMED SUZI**, 8, b g Medecis—Classic Coral (USA) **ABS Partnership**
2 **ALIZEE JAVILEX (FR)**, 6, b m Le Fou (IRE)—
Etoile du Lion (FR) **J. J. W. Wadham, B. M. A. Hopkins, A. F. Lousada**
3 **AMIDON (FR)**, 6, b g Dom Alco (FR)—Immage (FR) **P. H. Betts**
4 **AMTHAL (IRE)**, 7, b m Dalakhani (IRE)—Al Ihtithar (IRE) **Mr Clive Brittain**
5 **ARTIFICE SIVOLA (FR)**, 6, gr g Dom Alco (FR)—Kerrana (FR) **R. B. Holt**
6 **ATWIX**, 4, br f Sakhee (USA)—Atwirl **The Calculated Speculators**
7 **AVIADOR (GER)**, 10, b g Paolini (GER)—Albarana (GER) **J. J. W. Wadham**
8 **BANJO GIRL (IRE)**, 4, ch f Presenting—Oh Susannah (FR) **Living In Hope Partnership**
9 **COURTSIDER**, 4, b f Kyllachy—Elhareer (IRE) **The Calculated Speculators**
10 4, B g Gamut (IRE)—Dar Dar Supreme **J. J. W. Wadham**
11 **IRON IN THE SOUL**, 4, ch g Sulamani—Go Classic **Mr R. S. Keeley**
12 **KALAHARI (IRE)**, 7, b g Halling (USA)—Semaphore **Lough Derg Syndicate**
13 **LANCEUR (FR)**, 7, b g Rail Link—Lanciana (USA) **P. H. Betts**
14 **LE REVE (IRE)**, 8, br g Milan—Open Cry (IRE) **P. H. Betts**
15 **LETTER EXIT (IRE)**, 6, b g Exit To Nowhere (USA)—Letterwoman (IRE) **Mr B. M. A. Hopkins**
16 **MINSTRELS GALLERY (IRE)**, 7, ch g Refuse To Bend (IRE)—Lilakiya (IRE) **G. Pascoe & S. Brewer**
17 **MISS SPENT (IRE)**, 6, b m Presenting—Cash And New (IRE) **The Wynn Partnership**
18 **MYSTIC SKY**, 5, b m Midnight Legend—Kentucky Sky **Mr T. R. Wood**
19 **NOBLE SILK**, 7, gr g Sir Percy—Tussah **The FOPS**
20 **PERSIAN BREEZE**, 4, b f Pivotal—Persian Jasmine **Dr Jamal Ahmadzadeh**
21 **PHOENICIANA**, 5, b m Phoenix Reach (IRE)—Viciana **G. W. Paul**
22 **POTTERS LADY JANE**, 4, b f Sir Percy—Arabescato (UAE) **Mrs J. May**
23 **POTTERS LEGEND**, 6, b g Midnight Legend—Loose Morals (IRE) **Mrs J. May**
24 **POTTERS MIDNIGHT**, 6, b m Midnight Legend—Craughwell Suas (IRE) **Mrs J. May**
25 **ROAD TO FREEDOM**, 7, b g Revoque (IRE)—Go Classic **Mr R. S. Keeley**
26 **RUBY RAMBLER**, 6, b m Notnowcato—Arruhan (IRE) **Sara Dennis,J J W Wadham & J C S Wilson**
27 **SHANROE SANTOS (IRE)**, 7, b g Definite Article—Jane Hall (IRE) **Mr James Summers**
28 **SONGSMITH**, 8, b g Librettist (USA)—Venus Rising **Team Supreme**
29 **SUNSHINE CORNER**, 5, b m King's Theatre (IRE)—Coolgreaney (IRE) **P A Philipps & Mrs G J Redman**
30 **WATERBERRY**, 5, gr m Sagamix (FR)—Eneeymeenymineeymo (USA) **Adam & Clare Signy**
31 **WHISPERING SPEED (IRE)**, 6, ch g Vertical Speed (FR)—Midnight Lover **The A. T. Partnership**
32 **WIESENTRAUM (GER)**, 10, ch g Next Desert (IRE)—Wiesenblute (GER) **G. Pascoe & S. Brewer**

THREE-YEAR-OLDS

33 **GREGARIOUS (IRE)**, gr g Big Bad Bob (IRE)—Sense of Greeting (IRE) **Mr J. Summers**
34 **ICONIC SKY**, gr f Sixties Icon—Kentucky Sky **Mr T. R. Wood**
35 **MONET'S SKY (IRE)**, ch g Roderic O'Connor (IRE)—La Sibilla **Mr T. R. Wood**
36 **PERNICKETY**, b f Sir Percy—Nicola Bella (IRE) **Mr & Mrs A. E. Pakenham**
37 **POTTERS SAPPHIRE**, gr f Aussie Rules (USA)—Arabescato (UAE) **Mrs J. May**
38 **PUMBLECHOOK**, b c Dalakhani (IRE)—Chiang Mai (IRE) **Mr Christopher W. T. Johnston**
39 **TAFFETA LADY**, ch f Sir Percy—Bombazine (IRE) **Mr & Mrs A. E. Pakenham**
40 **VICTRICE**, b f Invincible Spirit (IRE)—Cassique Lady (IRE) **Mr & Mrs A. E. Pakenham**

TWO-YEAR-OLDS

41 B f 17/3 Sir Percy—Bermondsey Girl (Bertolini (USA)) (19047) **The FOPS**
42 B f 16/3 Sir Percy—Crystal Gal (IRE) (Galileo (IRE)) (170000) **Chasemore Farm**

MRS LUCY WADHAM - Continued

Other Owners: Mr S. J. Brewer, Mrs Sara Dennis, Mr Charles Hamilton, Mr S. J. High, Mr R. Maddison, Mr Jeff O'Leary, Mrs S. F. O'Leary, Mrs Victoria Pakenham, Mr A. E. Pakenham, Mr G. J. Pascoe, Mr P. A. Phillipps, Mrs G. J. Redman, Mrs L. E. Redman, Mr T. S. Redman, Mr Adam Signy, Mrs Clare Signy, Mrs Lucy Wadham, Mr J. J. W. Wadham, Mr Edward Wakelin, Mr J. C. S. Wilson.

Jockey (NH): Leighton Aspell. Conditional: Luke Ingram.

---

616 **MISS TRACY WAGGOTT, Spennymoor**
Postal: Awakening Stables, Vyners Close, Merrington Lane, Spennymoor, Co. Durham, DL16 7HB
Contacts: PHONE (01388) 819012 MOBILE (07979) 434498

1 BORDER BANDIT (USA), 8, b g Selkirk (USA)—Coretta (IRE) **Mr D. Tate**
2 CAPTAIN ROYALE (IRE), 11, ch g Captain Rio—Paix Royale **H. Conlon**
3 CHORUS OF LIES, 4, b g Teofilo (IRE)—Cherry Orchard (IRE) **Mr S. Roberts**
4 COPT HILL, 8, b g Avonbridge—Lalique (IRE) **H. Conlon**
5 DESERT SENSATION (IRE), 4, b g Authorized (IRE)—Awwal Malika (USA) **Gordon Allan Elsa Crankshaw**
6 GABRIAL'S HOPE (FR), 7, b g Teofilo (IRE)—Wedding Night (FR) **Mr D. Tate**
7 GRANDAD CHUNK (IRE), 5, gr ro h Acclamation—Silverdreammachine (IRE) **Mr S. Roberts**
8 HENLEY, 4, b g Royal Applause—Making Waves (IRE) **Mr D. Tate**
9 IMPERIALISTA, 4, ch f Halling (USA)—Empress Maud (USA) **Mr D. Tate**
10 MIGHTY BOND, 4, b g Misu Bond (IRE)—Mighty Flyer (IRE) **Mr D. Tate**
11 MISSION IMPOSSIBLE, 11, gr g Kyllachy—Eastern Lyric **H. Conlon**
12 QUESTO, 4, ch g Monsieur Bond (IRE)—Ex Gracia **J. J. Maguire**
13 RONYA (IRE), 5, b m Bushranger (IRE)—Beenablaw (IRE) **Mr D. Tate**
14 SHADOWTIME, 11, b g Singspiel (IRE)—Massomah (USA) **H. Conlon**
15 SHEARIAN, 6, b g Royal Applause—Regal Asset (USA) **Mr D. Tate**
16 SOLAR SPIRIT (IRE), 11, b g Invincible Spirit (IRE)—Misaayef (USA) **Elsa Crankshaw Gordon Allan**
17 WINDFORPOWER (IRE), 6, b g Red Clubs (IRE)—Dubai Princess (IRE) **Mr D. Tate**

THREE-YEAR-OLDS

18 CAYMUS, b f Compton Place—Midnight Sky **Mr D. Tate**
19 CONNEMERA QUEEN, ch f Major Cadeaux—Cashleen (USA) **Northumbria Leisure Ltd**
20 HADLEY, b g Royal Applause—Brush Strokes **Mr D. Tate**

Other Owners: G. Allan, Miss E. Crankshaw.

---

617 **MR JOHN WAINWRIGHT, Malton**
Postal: Granary House, Beverley Road, Norton, Malton, North Yorkshire, YO17 9PJ
Contacts: PHONE (01653) 692993 MOBILE (07798) 778070
E-MAIL jswainwright@googlemail.com

1 EENY MAC (IRE), 9, ch g Redback—Sally Green (IRE) **Chatterbox Racing Partnership**
2 EXIT TO FREEDOM, 10, ch g Exit To Nowhere (USA)—Bobanvi **I. J. Barran**
3 FLEET DAWN, 10, b g Polish Precedent (USA)—Wychnor Dawn (IRE) **Chatterbox Racing Partnership 2**
4 FOREST MISSILE (IRE), 4, b g Majestic Missile (IRE)—Garnock Academy (USA) **P. W. Cooper**
5 KNOCKAMANY BENDS (IRE), 6, b g Majestic Missile (IRE)—Sweet Compliance **D. R. & E. E. Brown**
6 NORTH BAY LADY (IRE), 4, b f Fast Company (IRE)—Straight Sets (IRE) **Mr A. P. Bluck**
7 PINE RUN, 6, b m Bertolini (USA)—Kudbeme **N. Bycroft**
8 ROSIE HALL (IRE), 6, ch m Lion Heart (USA)—Baltic Dip (IRE) **R & E Hall & Son**
9 ROSSINGTON, 7, b g Gentleman's Deal (IRE)—Ettrbee (IRE) **Brian Robb. David Hoyes. Mark Phillips.**

THREE-YEAR-OLDS

10 CITADEL, ch g Haafhd—Preference **Chatterbox Racing Partnership 2**

MR JOHN WAINWRIGHT - Continued

TWO-YEAR-OLDS

  11 B f 19/2 Rock of Gibraltar (IRE)—Bright Enough (Fantastic Light (USA)) (4800)
  12 **HENRIETTA'S DREAM,** b f 17/3 Henrythenavigator (USA)—
                        Timeless Dream (Oasis Dream) (7000) **Chatterbox Racing Partnership**
  13 B f 8/4 Avonbridge—Zarkavean (Medicean) (3690)

Other Owners: Mrs E. E. Brown, D. R. Brown, Mr R. Hall, Mr R. C. Hall, Mr D. N. Hoyes, Mr M. D. Phillips, Mr B. W. Robb, J. S. Wainwright, Mr P. Walker.

Assistant Trainer: Mrs Fiona Wainwright

Jockey (flat): Tom Eaves, Paddy Aspell, Tony Hamilton. **Amateur:** Mr Alexander French, Mr Kaine Wood.

618

MR ROBERT WALEY-COHEN, Banbury
Postal: **Upton Viva, Banbury, Oxfordshire, OX15 6HT**
Contacts: **PHONE (02072) 446022 MOBILE (07831) 888778**
E-MAIL rwc@uptonviva.co.uk WEBSITE www.uptonestate.co.uk

  1 **ANQUETTA (IRE),** 12, b g Anshan—Quetta (IRE) **R. B. Waley-Cohen**
  2 **LONG RUN (FR),** 11, b br g Cadoudal (FR)—Libertina (FR) **R. B. Waley-Cohen**
  3 **MAKADAMIA,** 7, b m Kahyasi—Makounji (FR) **R. B. Waley-Cohen**
  4 **MR SIMPKINS,** 8, b g Presenting—Violet Express (FR) **R. B. Waley-Cohen**
  5 **SING TO ME,** 6, ch m Presenting—Symphonique (FR) **Team Max Scarlett**
  6 **STORM FORCE TEN,** 5, b g Shirocco (GER)—Stravinsky Dance **R. B. Waley-Cohen**
  7 **WARNE (IRE),** 12, b g Bob Back (USA)—Dusky Diva **R. B. Waley-Cohen**

Other Owners: Mr S. B. Waley-Cohen.

Assistant Trainer: Kate Mawle

Amateur: Mr S. Waley-Cohen.

619

MR MARK WALFORD, Sheriff Hutton
Postal: **Cornborough Manor, Cornborough Road, Sheriff Hutton, York, North Yorkshire, YO60 6QN**
Contacts: **MOBILE (07734) 265689**
E-MAIL info@markwalfordracing.com WEBSITE www.markwalfordracing.com

  1 **ADAM'S ALE,** 7, b g Ishiguru (USA)—Aqua **Mrs M. J. Hills**
  2 **BIG SOUND,** 9, b g Supreme Sound—Tarbolton Moss **Hanson & Hamilton**
  3 **CAPE HIDEAWAY,** 4, b g Mount Nelson—Amiata **Cornborough Racing Club**
  4 **CORNBOROUGH,** 5, ch g Sir Percy—Emirates First (IRE) **Cornborough Racing Club**
  5 **CRAGGAKNOCK,** 5, b g Authorized (IRE)—Goodie Twosues **Mrs M. Longstaff**
  6 **HERE COMES ARTHUR (FR),** 6, b g Smadoun (FR)—Toulouzette (IRE) **Mr J Toes & Mr J O'Loan**
  7 **HOME FLYER (IRE),** 5, b g Tagula (IRE)—Lady Flyer (IRE) **Mrs J Collins,Mrs H Forman,Miss J Sawney**
  8 **LACKADAY,** 4, gr g Kyllachy—Day Creek **Mrs G. B. Walford**
  9 **LILLY'S LEGEND,** 6, ch m Midnight Legend—Dalticia (FR) **Mr C J Grindal & Partner**
 10 **LOCH LINNHE,** 4, b g Tobougg (IRE)—Quistaquay **Mrs M. Cooper**
 11 **LORIMER'S LOT (IRE),** 5, ch m Camacho—Alwiyda (USA) **Lorimer Walford**
 12 **LOUGH SALT (IRE),** 5, b g Brian Boru—Castlehill Lady (IRE) **Mr J Toes & Mr J O'Loan**
 13 **MAGNOLIA RIDGE (IRE),** 5, b g Galileo (IRE)—Treasure The Lady (IRE) **Mr H. J. Kinder**
 14 **MISS CONWAY,** 5, br m Midnight Legend—Miss Pross **Mrs G Bartle & Mrs S Morrell**
 15 **MR SNOOZY,** 7, b g Pursuit of Love—Hard To Follow **T. W. Heseltine**
 16 **OLIVER'S GOLD,** 8, b g Danehill Dancer (IRE)—Gemini Gold (IRE) **CW Racing Club & Partner**
 17 **REGAL MISSILE (IRE),** 4, b g Royal Applause—Leenane **Dickson, Hamilton & Smeaton**
 18 4, Br f Kalanisi (IRE)—Senorita Rumbalita **Margaret Walton & Le Dream Team**
 19 **SHIMLA DAWN (IRE),** 8, b g Indian Danehill (IRE)—Tina Thyne (IRE) **Mrs M. Cooper**
 20 **SOUTHVIEW LADY,** 4, b f Misu Bond (IRE)—Salalah **Cornborough Racing Club**
 21 **TARA'S ROCKET,** 5, b g Kayf Tara—Whizz Back (IRE) **Mrs R. Haggie**
 22 **UNO VALOROSO (FR),** 8, b g Voix du Nord (FR)—Danse d'avril (FR) **Mr C. N. Herman**
 23 **VEROCE (FR),** 7, b br g Assessor (IRE)—Pyvoine (FR) **D. J. Dickson**

MR MARK WALFORD - Continued

24 **WESTERN BREEZE (IRE)**, 7, b m Westerner—Winsome Breeze (IRE) **The Western Breeze Partnership**
25 **WOODY BAY**, 6, b g New Approach (IRE)—Dublino (USA) **Mr P. C. Thompson**

THREE-YEAR-OLDS

26 **BIT OF A QUIRKE**, ch g Monsieur Bond (IRE)—Silk (IRE) **Mr A. K. Quirke**
27 B f Sir Percy—Bruma (IRE)
28 **DRUID'S DIAMOND**, b g Piccolo—Faithful Beauty (IRE) **Mr A Brown & Mrs Cherry Steel**

TWO-YEAR-OLDS

29 B c 15/4 Haafhd—Diablo Dancer (Zafeen (FR)) (761) **Miss J. L. Gittus**
30 B f 5/2 Mullionmileanhour (IRE)—La Corujera (Case Law) (952)
31 B f 17/3 Piccolo—Princess Almora (Pivotal) (5714) **Cornborough Racing Club**

Other Owners: Mrs G. M. Bartle, Mr A. J. Brown, Mr P. A. P. Clays, Mrs J. Collins, Mr J. Craggs, Mrs W. A. D. Craven, P. F. Crowley, Mrs H. Forman, C. J. Grindal, Mr K. Hamilton, Mr K. Hanson, S. N. Lorimer, Mr P. P. Lorimer, Mrs S. E. Morrell, A. Nicholls, Mr John O'Loan, Mr D. Percival, Miss J. Sawney, Mr R. J. Smeaton, Mrs C. Steel, Mr J. Toes, Mrs J. M. Walton, Miss L. Jayne Watson.

Assistant Trainer: Tim Walford

Conditional: Jamie Hamilton.

---

620 | **MR ROBERT WALFORD, Blandford**
Postal: Heart of Oak Stables, Okeford Fitzpaine, Blandford, Dorset, DT11 0LW
Contacts: **MOBILE (07815) 116209**
E-MAIL robertwalford1@gmail.com

1 **ALBERT D'OLIVATE (FR)**, 6, b br g Alberto Giacometti (IRE)—Komunion (FR) **Chris Pugsley & Nigel Skinner**
2 **ASTRE DE LA COUR (FR)**, 6, b br g Khalkevi (IRE)—Gracieuse Delacour (FR) **The Front Runners Partnership**
3 **BRODY BLEU (FR)**, 9, b g Kotky Bleu (FR)—Brodie Blue (FR) **Mr R. J. Brown**
4 **CAMPING GROUND (FR)**, 6, b g Goldneyev (USA)—Camomille (GER) **G. L. Porter**
5 **CASTARNIE**, 8, b g Alflora (IRE)—Just Jenny (IRE) **Sue & Clive Cole & Ann & Tony Gale**
6 **CRAZY TRAIN**, 7, ch m Sir Harry Lewis (USA)—Vent d'aout (IRE) **Withyslade**
7 **FLIGHTS**, 5, b m King's Theatre (IRE)—Motcombe (IRE) **Lady N. F. Cobham**
8 **HOIST THE COLOURS (IRE)**, 5, b g Sea The Stars (IRE)—Multicolour Wave (IRE) **R. H. Alner**
9 **JULLY LES BUXY**, 6, b m Black Sam Bellamy (IRE)—Jadidh **Mr A. F. G. Brimble**
10 **LADY ASH (IRE)**, 6, gr m Scorpion (IRE)—La Fiamma (FR) **JP Romans & R Selway**
11 **LE BOIZELO (FR)**, 5, b g Irish Wells (FR)—Bois Tendre (FR) **Dr & Mrs John Millar**
12 **LIZZIE LANGTON**, 5, b m Kayf Tara—Madam Flora **Wendy Pope & Tim Swaffield**
13 **MAD ABOUT THE BOY**, 6, b g Robin des Pres (FR)—Dalamine (FR) **A. J. M. Trowbridge**
14 **MR MEDIC**, 5, b g Dr Massini (IRE)—Danse Slave (FR) **The White Hart Company**
15 **PILGREEN (FR)**, 11, ch g Green Tune (USA)—Galinetta (FR) **Mrs S. De Wilde**
16 **SAINT RAPH (FR)**, 8, gr g Saint des Saints (FR)—Speed Padoline (FR) **Mrs C. M. Hinks**
17 **SHADDAII (FR)**, 10, gr g April Night (FR)—Gypsie d'artois (FR) **Mrs C. E. Davies**
18 **SUN WILD LIFE (FR)**, 6, b g Antarctique (IRE)—Nidelia (FR) **The Keightley Lambert Partnership**
19 **SYDNEY DE BAUNE (FR)**, 5, b g Califet (FR)—Perle De Baune (FR) **Mrs S. De Wilde**
20 **TOM NEARY (IRE)**, 9, b g Atraf—La Fandango (IRE) **Mrs C. A. Lewis-Jones**
21 **UMBERTO D'OLIVATE (FR)**, 8, b g Alberto Giacometti (IRE)—Komunion (FR) **Mrs S. De Wilde**
22 **WALK IN THE MILL (FR)**, 6, b g Walk In The Park (IRE)—Libre Amour (FR) **Baroness D. M. Harding**

Other Owners: Mr David Bond, Mr C. Cole, Mrs S. S. Cole, Mrs A. G. Gale, Mr A. P. Gale, Mr P. Goodwin, Mr A. G. Ham, Mrs C. Keightley, Mr T. P. Lambert, Dr J. W. Millar, Mrs J. D. Millar, Miss H. Pease, Mrs W. M. Pope, C. C. Pugsley, Mr S. Reed, Mr J. P. Romans, Mr R. Selway, N. Skinner, Mr T. J. Swaffield, Mr E. W. White.

Jockey (NH): Daryl Jacob.

621 MR ED WALKER, Newmarket
Postal: **Eve Lodge Stables, Hamilton Road, Newmarket, Suffolk, CB8 0NY**
Contacts: **PHONE (01638) 660464 MOBILE (07787) 534145**
E-MAIL ed@edwalkerracing.com WEBSITE www.edwalkerracing.com

1 AEOLUS, 5, b g Araafa (IRE)—Bright Moll **A. R. F. Buxton**
2 BETTY THE THIEF, 5, b m Teofilo (IRE)—Siphon Melody (USA) **Mr D. Ward**
3 BOLD PREDICTION (IRE), 6, b g Kodiac—Alexander Eliott (IRE) **John Nicholls (Trading) & Matthew Cottis**
4 DOUBLE HEAVEN, 4, b g Dutch Art—Popocatepetl (FR) **Mr C. F. Ma**
5 GHALIB (IRE), 4, ch c Lope de Vega (IRE)—Gorband (USA) **Saleh Al Homaizi & Imad Al Sagar**
6 GLORIOUS EMPIRE (IRE), 5, br g Holy Roman Emperor (IRE)—Humble And Proud (IRE) **Mr P. K. Siu**
7 GLORIOUS PROTECTOR (IRE), 6, b g Azamour (IRE)—Hasaiyda (IRE) **Ms A. A. Lau Yap**
8 INVINCIBLE GOLD (IRE), 4, b c Invincible Spirit (IRE)—Urgele (FR) **Mr John Coleman & Mr Clarence Cheng**
9 JUSTICE BELLE (IRE), 4, b f Montjeu (IRE)—Metaphor (USA) **Mr R. Ng**
10 MEZAJY (IRE), 4, b g Makfi—Maidin Maith (IRE) **Saleh Al Homaizi & Imad Al Sagar**
11 PERSONA GRATA, 5, b m Sir Percy—Kaldounya **Middleham Park Racing XLI**
12 RIGGINS (IRE), 12, b g Cape Cross—Rentless **Dubai Thoroughbred Racing**
13 RUSTIQUE, 4, ch f Pastoral Pursuits—Nihal (IRE) **Dubai Thoroughbred Racing**

THREE-YEAR-OLDS
14 ATLANTEIA (IRE), ch f Duke of Marmalade (IRE)—Teide Lady **Mr M. J. Cottis**
15 BEST OF OREGON (USA), ch c Cape Blanco (IRE)—Wicked Sting (USA) **Mr P. K. Siu**
16 BOYCHICK (IRE), b g Holy Roman Emperor (IRE)—Al Saqiya (USA) **L. A. Bellman**
17 BRYGHT BOY, b g Paco Boy—Bright Moll **A. R. F. Buxton**
18 CAPTAIN COURAGEOUS (IRE), b g Canford Cliffs (IRE)—Annacloy Pearl (IRE) **L. A. Bellman**
19 CEECUBED (IRE), b f Canford Cliffs (IRE)—Chincoteague (IRE) **Mr M. Keller**
20 COZ I DO, b f Pivotal—Bea Menace (USA) **Chasemore Farm LLP**
21 DARK SIEGE, b g Iffraaj—Green Poppy **Mr C. U. F. Ma**
22 DREAM FARR (IRE), b g Dream Ahead (USA)—French Lady (NZ) **Mr P. K. Siu**
23 DREAM GLORY (IRE), b c Dream Ahead (USA)—Do The Honours (IRE) **Kangyu Int. Racing (HK) Ltd & Mr F Ma**
24 EASY GOLD (IRE), ch c Mastercraftsman (IRE)—Aiming Upwards (IRE) **Mr J. A. Coleman**
25 EDGE OF REASON, b f Authorized (IRE)—Forest Express (AUS) **The Forest Partners**
26 EXCEL QUEST, b c Exceed And Excel (AUS)—Rayyana (IRE) **Mr M. H. Lui**
27 EXPERTO CREDE (IRE), b g Exceed And Excel (AUS)—Shepherdia (IRE) **Mr P. K. Siu**
28 GALE SONG, b f Invincible Spirit (IRE)—Please Sing **Lordship Stud**
29 GLADYS COOPER (IRE), b f Arcano (IRE)—Anthyllis (GER) **Buckmaster Racing**
30 GLORIOUS LEGEND (IRE), b c Pour Moi (IRE)—Endearing **Kangyu International Racing (HK) Limited**
31 GLORIOUS POET, ch c Poet's Voice—Sky Wonder **Kangyu International Racing (HK) Limited**
32 HIDDEN GEM, b f Shamardal (USA)—Hidden Brief **Lordship Stud**
33 HOPE COVE, b c Shamardal (USA)—Deveron (USA) **Mr M. H. Lui**
34 JUDICIAL ENQUIRY, b g Lawman (FR)—Koniya (IRE) **Greenwood, James & McVeigh**
35 KENSINGTON PALACE (IRE), b c Kodiac—Anthyllis (GER) **Laurence Bellman, Kerr-Dineen, De La Warr**
36 LOBSTER COCKTAIL (IRE), b c Footstepsinthesand—Sanpala **De La Warr Racing**
37 MARYLEBONE, b c Shamardal (USA)—Mary Boleyn (IRE) **Chasemore Farm LLP**
38 MERCIFILLY (FR), b f Whipper (USA)—Coco (USA) **L. A. Bellman**
39 RECKLESS WAVE (IRE), b f Cape Cross (IRE)—Fairybook (USA) **rs G. Walker**
40 ROCOCOA (IRE), b f Zebedee—Nightbird (IRE) **Elaine Chivers & Merlin Racing**
41 SHADELE (IRE), b f Rip Van Winkle (IRE)—Zadalla **Mr M. Keller**
42 SHOW AYA (IRE), ch f Showcasing—Mimiteh (USA) **S. Al Ansari**
43 SHRUBLAND, b g High Chaparral (IRE)—Ratukidul (IRE) **Mr M. H. Lui**
44 SILQUE, b f Aqlaam—Tamzin **Mr M. Keller**
45 SMILEY BAGEL (IRE), b g Kyllachy—Epistoliere (IRE) **L. A. Bellman**
46 STORMY ANTARCTIC, ch c Stormy Atlantic (USA)—Bea Remembered **Mr P. K. Siu**
47 THE PERFECT SHOW, ch g Showcasing—Nizhoni (USA) **Mr P. K. Siu**
48 TOGETHERNESS (IRE), b c Pour Moi (IRE)—Madeira Mist (IRE) **Weston Brook Farm Bromfield & Whitaker**

TWO-YEAR-OLDS
49 BAKERLOO, b c 16/3 Teofilo (IRE)—Looby Loo (Kyllachy) (20000) **Chasemore Farm LLP**
50 B c 19/2 Medicean—Bluebelle (Generous (IRE)) (42000) **Laurence Bellman & Billy Mills**
51 B c 8/5 Fastnet Rock (AUS)—Bright Bank (Sadler's Wells (USA)) **O.T.I. Racing & Partner**
52 B c 15/3 Excelebration (IRE)—Dance Avenue (IRE) (Sadler's Wells (USA)) (251015) **Mr P. K. Siu**
53 B c 24/3 Lawman (FR)—Evensong (GER) (Waky Nao) (38390)
54 Ch c 11/5 Tagula (IRE)—Fashion Guide (IRE) (Bluebird) (20671) **S Al Ansari & E C D Walker**
55 B c 15/4 Mount Nelson—Helena Molony (IRE) (Sadler's Wells (USA)) (80000) **Laurence Bellman & David Ward**

MR ED WALKER - Continued

56 Ch c 24/2 Archipenko (USA)—
Here To Eternity (USA) (Stormy Atlantic (USA)) (110000) **Kangyu International Racing (HK) Limited**
57 HERNANDES (FR), gr c 22/3 Clodovil (IRE)—
Gontcharova (IRE) (Zafonic (USA)) (33222) **John Moorhouse & John Nicholls (Trading)**
58 Ch f 1/4 Mayson—High Reserve (Dr Fong (USA)) (9523) **Mr Bobby Donworth**
59 B c 10/4 Big Bad Bob (IRE)—Indienne (IRE) (Indian Ridge) (28792) **L. A. Bellman**
60 B c 26/4 Sepoy (AUS)—Kournikova (SAF) (Sportsworld (USA)) (88593) **Mr C. U. F. Ma**
61 B c 13/2 Dutch Art—Loquacity (Diktat) (77000)
62 B c 19/3 Born To Sea (IRE)—Luanas Pearl (IRE) (Bahri (USA)) (70000) **Mr C. U. F. Ma**
63 MADAME BOUNTY (IRE), b f 29/4 Bahamian Bounty—
Madame Boulangere (Royal Applause) (54000) **Paola Hewins Olivia Hoare**
64 Ch f 3/5 Dutch Art—Makara (Lion Cavern (USA)) (58000) **Laurence Bellman & David Ward**
65 Ch c 23/2 Born To Sea (IRE)—Maskaya (IRE) (Machiavellian (USA)) (236249) **Mr P. K. Siu**
66 B f 8/5 Galileo (IRE)—Miss Cap Ferrat (Darshaan) **J. L. C. Pearce**
67 NASTENKA, b f 1/2 Aussie Rules (USA)—Nezhenka (With Approval (CAN)) **Miss K. Rausing**
68 B c 14/3 Sayif (IRE)—Native Picture (IRE) (Kodiac) **Saleh Al Homaizi & Imad Al Sagar**
69 Ch c 27/3 Lope de Vega (IRE)—Penelope Star (GER) (Acatenango (GER)) (160000) **Mr M. Betamar**
70 Ch c 27/3 Tamayuz—Rapid Ransom (USA) (Red Ransom (USA)) (73827) **Mr B. T. C. Liu**
71 B c 16/2 Frankel—Reaching (IRE) (Dansili) (500000) **Reiko Baum & Michael Baum**
72 B c 17/3 Bahamian Bounty—Regent's Park (Green Desert (USA)) (40605) **L. A. Bellman**
73 B c 16/3 Holy Roman Emperor (IRE)—Salinia (IRE) (Rainbow Quest (USA)) (73827) **Mr P. K. Siu**
74 TINOS (GER), b c 1/1 Soldier Hollow—
Ticinella (GER) (Hernando (FR)) (49464) **HH Sheikh Mohammed Bin Khalifa Al Thani**
75 B f 24/3 Sayif (IRE)—Usem (Bahamian Bounty) **Saleh Al Homaizi & Imad Al Sagar**
76 Gr f 24/2 Mastercraftsman (IRE)—Waldena (USA) (Storm Cat (USA)) (70000) **Laurence Bellman & David Ward**
77 B c 12/4 Zoffany (IRE)—Wing Diva (IRE) (Hawk Wing (USA)) (50000) **Kangyu International Racing (HK) Limited**
78 c 27/1 Fastnet Rock (AUS)—
Wonder of Wonders (USA) (Kingmambo (USA)) (213675) **H.H. Sheikh Mohammed Bin Khalifa Al Thani**
79 Ch f 15/3 Dutch Art—Zenella (Kyllachy) (40000) **Laurence Bellman & Billy Mills**

Assistant Trainer: Jack Steels

---

622 **MR CHRIS WALL, Newmarket**
Postal: **Induna Stables, Fordham Road, Newmarket, Suffolk, CB8 7AQ**
Contacts: **OFFICE (01638) 661999 HOME (01638) 668896 FAX (01638) 667279**
MOBILE (07764) 940255
E-MAIL christianwall@btconnect.com WEBSITE www.chriswallracing.co.uk

1 ATAMAN (IRE), 4, b c Sholokhov (IRE)—Diora (IRE) **Alan & Jill Smith**
2 CLOUD SEVEN, 4, br g New Approach (IRE)—Regrette Rien (USA) **Ms A. Fustoq**
3 ENCHANTED MOMENT, 4, b f Lawman (FR)—Gentle Thoughts **Mr D. S. Lee**
4 FEVER FEW, 7, b m Pastoral Pursuits—Prairie Oyster **Mrs C A Wall & Mr R Wayman**
5 FIRST SITTING, 5, b g Dansili—Aspiring Diva (USA) **Bringloe & Clarke**
6 KRISTJANO (GER), 4, b g Nayef (USA)—Kalahari Dancer **B. R. Westley**
7 LONDON CITIZEN (USA), 6, ch h Proud Citizen (USA)—Sally Bowles (SAF) **Ms A. Fustoq**
8 NOT ANOTHER BILL, 5, ch g Notnowcato—Composing (IRE) **Mr P. Botham**
9 OASIS SPEAR, 4, b g Oasis Dream—Sunspear (IRE) **Ms A. Fustoq**
10 OH SO SASSY, 6, b m Pastoral Pursuits—Almasi (IRE) **The Eight of Diamonds**
11 SAHARA (IRE), 4, b f Clodovil (IRE)—Celtic Lynn (IRE) **Mr M. Bringloe**
12 SONG OF NORWAY, 5, b m Halling (USA)—Amarullah (FR) **Mr B Chandler & Mr R Henley**
13 SOUVILLE, 5, b m Dalakhani (IRE)—Royale Danehill (USA) **Hughes & Scott**
14 STAMP OF APPROVAL (IRE), 4, b f Approve (IRE)—Wassendale **Induna Racing Partners (Two)**
15 SYRIAN PEARL, 5, gr m Clodovil (IRE)—Syrian Queen **The Clodhoppers**
16 THE NEW PHARAOH (IRE), 5, b g Montjeu (IRE)—Out West (USA) **Ms A. Fustoq**
17 TTAINTED LOVE, 4, b f Mastercraftsman (IRE)—Eve **Mr D. S. Lee**

THREE-YEAR-OLDS

18 ALWAYS A DREAM, b f Oasis Dream—Always Remembered (IRE) **Ms A. Fustoq**
19 CAMBODIA (IRE), ch g Fast Company (IRE)—Remarkable Story **Mr D. M. Thurlby**
20 I CAN'T STOP, gr f Kyllachy—Vellena **Sheikh Rashid Dalmook Al Maktoum**
21 LONDON GLORY, b c Archipenko (USA)—Reflected Image (IRE) **Mr Fung Lok Li**
22 LUANG PRABANG (IRE), b f Invincible Spirit (IRE)—Sauvage (FR) **Mr D. M. Thurlby**

MR CHRIS WALL - Continued

23 **LUDI LU (FR)**, b f New Approach (IRE)—Sunspear (IRE) **Ms A. Fustoq**
24 **MATILDA'S LAW**, b f Aussie Rules (USA)—Oatey **Archangels 2**
25 **MIX AND MINGLE (IRE)**, ch f Exceed And Excel (AUS)—Mango Lady **Ms A. Fustoq**
26 **NORTH CREEK**, b c Iffraaj—Maine Rose **Sheikh Rashid Dalmook Al Maktoum**
27 **PARTY THYME**, ch f Medicean—Thymesthree (IRE) **Mr P. Botham**
28 **SEA THE BLUE (IRE)**, b g Dark Angel (IRE)—Bowness **Sheikh Rashid Dalmook Al Maktoum**
29 **SONG OF PARADISE**, ch f Kyllachy—Merry Diva **The Equema Partnership**

TWO-YEAR-OLDS

30 Ch f 20/3 Elusive Quality (USA)—Any For Love (ARG) (Southern Halo (USA)) (61050) **Ms A. Fustoq**
31 **ATLANTA BELLE (IRE)**, ch f 14/2 Zebedee—Tara Too (IRE) (Danetime (IRE)) (11000) **The Leap Year Partnership**
32 **BABY CATO**, b f 15/4 Notnowcato—Ambala (Intikhab (USA)) **Webster, Wall & Traylor**
33 **CALM CHARM (IRE)**, ch f 21/3 Teofilo (IRE)—Mango Lady (Dalakhani (IRE)) (50000) **Ms A. Fustoq**
34 **DUTCH MELODY**, b f 27/2 Dutch Art—Mystic Melody (IRE) (Montjeu (IRE)) **Mr D. S. Lee**
35 B c 27/3 Cape Cross (IRE)—Eclaircie (IRE) (Thunder Gulch (USA)) (70000) **Sheikh J. D. Al Maktoum**
36 **ENFORCING (IRE)**, b c 19/1 Canford Cliffs (IRE)—
        Black Mascara (IRE) (Authorized (IRE)) (100000) **Mr Ben C. M. Wong**
37 **ENTANGLING (IRE)**, b c 17/1 Fastnet Rock (AUS)—
        Question Times (Shamardal (USA)) (280546) **Mr Ben C. M. Wong**
38 **MARILYN**, ch f 14/2 Sixties Icon—Donatia (Shamardal (USA)) (4000) **Tadgell, Swinburn & Wall**
39 **MINUTE TO WIN IT**, b f 14/4 Nathaniel (IRE)—Vanishing Point (USA) (Caller I D (USA)) **Ms A. Fustoq**
40 B f 24/3 Bated Breath—Miss Meltemi (IRE) (Miswaki Tern (USA)) (48000) **Sheikh J. D. Al Maktoum**
41 **OH IT'S SAUCEPOT**, b f 2/3 Sir Percy—Oh So Saucy (Imperial Ballet (IRE)) **The Eight Of Diamonds**
42 B f 3/3 Iffraaj—Relinquished (Royal Applause) (20000) **Sheikh Rashid Dalmook Al Maktoum**
43 **SO CUTE (IRE)**, ch f 9/2 Lope de Vega (IRE)—
        Lizzy's Township (USA) (Delaware Township (USA)) (78000) **Ms A. Fustoq**
44 Ch c 3/2 Raven's Pass (USA)—Sospira (Cape Cross (IRE)) (20000) **Sheikh Rashid Dalmook Al Maktoum**
45 **TIP OF THE CITY**, b f 15/4 Oasis Dream—Always Remembered (IRE) (Galileo (IRE)) **Ms A. Fustoq**
46 **UPENDED**, b g 24/3 Paco Boy—Upskittled (Diktat) (17000) **Mr Des Thurlby**
47 B f 19/2 Henrythenavigator (USA)—Whatizzit (Galileo)) **Moyns Park Stud**

Other Owners: Mr T. J. Bater, Mr Michael Bringloe, Mrs Valerie Carpenter, Mr David Cherry, Mr Jeremy Davies, Mrs J. E. Dobie, Mr Stuart Feast, Mr R. Fraiser, Mr C. J. A. Hughes, Mrs Jill Kerr-Smiley, Mr Roger Nash, Mr Ray Rice, Mr Pierpont Scott, Mr Kieran D. Scott, Mr R. A. Smith, Mrs Jill Smith, Mrs Doreen M. Swinburn, Mrs C. A. Wall, Mr R. J. Wayman.

Assistant Trainer: Richard Freeman

Jockey (flat): George Baker, Ted Durcan. **Apprentice:** Sam Clarke, Cheryl Wilson.

---

623 **MR MARK WALL, Chedworth**
Postal: 5 Hemplands, Chedworth, Cheltenham, Gloucestershire, GL54 4NH

1 **CARDINAL ROSE**, 9, ch g Karinga Bay—Miniature Rose **Mr M. J. Wall**
2 **CRACK DU TAY (FR)**, 4, b g Ballingarry (IRE)—Bonjour Jandrer (FR)
3 **STOICAL PATIENT (IRE)**, 7, b m Shantou (USA)—Dust Gale (IRE) **A. Carr**
4 **SWIVEL**, 5, ch g Shirocco (GER)—Pivotal Drive (IRE) **Mrs R. J. Tufnell**

---

624 **MR CHARLIE WALLIS, Ardleigh**
Postal: Benson Stud, Harts Lane, Ardleigh, Colchester, Essex, CO7 7QE
Contacts: PHONE (01206) 230779 MOBILE (07725) 059355
E-MAIL cwallis86@hotmail.com

1 **CHETAN**, 4, b g Alfred Nobel (IRE)—Island Music (IRE) **Roger & Val Miles, Tony Stamp**
2 **COLOURBEARER (IRE)**, 9, ch g Pivotal—Centifolia (IRE) **Roalco Ltd**
3 **GLADSOME**, 8, b m Resplendent Glory—Christening (IRE) **Miss V. Pratt**
4 **KUWAIT STAR**, 7, ch g Resplendent Glory (IRE)—Mofeyda (IRE) **Miss V. Pratt**
5 **MANGE ALL**, 5, b g Zamindar (USA)—Blancmange **P. E. Axon**
6 **POWERFUL WIND (IRE)**, 7, ch g Titus Livius (FR)—Queen of Fools (IRE) **Mr A. D. Cooke**
7 **REGAL PARADE**, 12, ch g Pivotal—Model Queen (USA) **Roalco & J Goddard**

MR CHARLIE WALLIS - Continued

8 **STENCIVE**, 7, b g Dansili—Madeira Mist (IRE) **Mr S. C. Wood**
9 **THE QUARTERJACK**, 7, b g Haafhd—Caressed **P. E. Axon**
10 **WINOLA**, 6, ch m Lucarno (USA)—Wolnai **I. A. Low**

TWO-YEAR-OLDS

11 B f 31/3 Champs Elysees—Artistic Blue (USA) (Diesis) (2500) **P. E. Axon**

Other Owners: Mr J. W. Goddard, K. R. Miles, Mrs V. Miles, Mr A. P. Stamp.

Assistant Trainer: Hayley Wallis

625
MRS JANE WALTON, Otterburn
Postal: **Dunns Houses, Otterburn, Newcastle Upon Tyne, Tyne and Wear, NE19 1LB**
Contacts: **PHONE (01830) 520677 FAX (01830) 520677 MOBILE (07808) 592701**
E-MAIL dunnshouses@hotmail.com WEBSITE www.janewaltonhorseracing.co.uk

1 **ALWAYSRECOMMENDED (IRE)**, 7, ch g Gamut (IRE)—
Awbeg Beauty (IRE) **Highly Recommended Partnership 2**
2 **HAVE YOU HAD YOURS (IRE)**, 10, br g Whitmore's Conn (USA)—
Mandys Moynavely (IRE) **Highly Recommended Partnership**
3 4, B g Court Cave (IRE)—Kindle Ball (FR) **Mrs J. M. Walton**
4 **MASTER MURPHY (IRE)**, 11, b g Flemensfirth (USA)—Awbeg Beauty (IRE) **Mrs J. M. Walton**
5 **REVERSE THE CHARGE (IRE)**, 9, b g Bishop of Cashel—Academy Jane (IRE) **Fresh Start Partnership**
6 **WESTEND THEATRE (IRE)**, 7, b g Darsi (FR)—Ballyvelig Lady (IRE) **Mrs J. M. Walton**
7 **WILDEST DREAMS (IRE)**, 7, b g Flemensfirth (USA)—Suspicious Minds **Joyce Rutherford Jane Walton**

Other Owners: Mrs L. Duncan, Mr John McCreanor, Mr David J. Parkins, Recommended Freight Ltd, Mrs M. Ridley, Miss J. Rutherford, Mrs J. M. Walton.

Assistant Trainer: Mrs Patricia Robson

Conditional: Dale Irving.

626
MR JASON WALTON, Morpeth
Postal: **Flotterton Hall, Thropton, Morpeth, Northumberland, NE65 7LF**
Contacts: **PHONE (01669) 640253 FAX (01669) 640288 MOBILE (07808) 592701**

1 **CATCHAMAT**, 7, b m Overbury (IRE)—More Flair **Messrs F. T. Walton**
2 **CENTRAL FLAME**, 8, ch g Central Park (IRE)—More Flair **Messrs F. T. Walton**
3 **COQUET HEAD**, 10, br g Alflora (IRE)—Coquet Gold **Messrs F. T. Walton**
4 **DON'T POINT**, 7, ch m Double Trigger (IRE)—Posh Stick **Messrs F. T. Walton**
5 **MATTHEW MAN**, 5, b g Bollin Eric—Garden Feature **Messrs F. T. Walton**
6 **PLAY PRACTICE**, 6, b m Josr Algarhoud (IRE)—More Flair **Messrs F. T. Walton**
7 **ROLL OF THUNDER**, 7, b g Antonius Pius (USA)—Ischia **Messrs F. T. Walton**
8 **RUPERT BEAR**, 10, b g Rambling Bear—Glittering Stone **Messrs F. T. Walton**
9 **STRATEGIC ISLAND (IRE)**, 5, b m Strategic Prince—Island Music (IRE) **Messrs F. T. Walton**

Other Owners: F. A. Walton, J. B. Walton.

627
MRS SHEENA WALTON, Hexham
Postal: **Linacres, Wark, Hexham, Northumberland, NE48 3DP**
Contacts: **PHONE (01434) 230656 MOBILE (07752) 755184**
E-MAIL linacres@btconnect.com

1 **DYSTONIA'S REVENGE (IRE)**, 11, b g Woods of Windsor (USA)—
Lady Isaac (IRE) **John Blacklock & Margaret Rogerson**
2 **ETHAN (IRE)**, 7, b g Beneficial—Timissa (IRE) **R. H. & S. C. Walton**
3 **FOZY MOSS**, 10, b g And Beyond (IRE)—Peggy Sioux (IRE) **Mrs C. Hogg**

MRS SHEENA WALTON - Continued

   4 NATIVE OPTIMIST (IRE), 9, b g Broadway Flyer (USA)—Native Orchid (IRE) **R. H. & S. C. Walton**
   5 WARKSBURN BOY, 6, b g Kayf Tara—Bonchester Bridge **Rede Tyne Racing**

Other Owners: Mr J. L. Blacklock, Mrs M. Rogerson, Mrs S. Walton, R. H. Walton.

Assistant Trainer: Mr R. H. Walton

Amateur: Miss C. Walton.

---

628   MR JASON WARD, Middleham
Postal: **The Dante Yard, Manor House Stables, Middleham, Leyburn, North Yorkshire, DL8 4QL**
Contacts: **PHONE (01969) 622730 MOBILE (07967) 357595**
E-MAIL **info@jasonwardracing.co.uk** WEBSITE **www.jasonwardracing.co.uk**

   1 LONGSHADOW, 6, ch g Monsun (GER)—La Felicita **David Robertson & J Ward**
   2 PANCAKE DAY, 4, b g Mullionmileanhour (IRE)—Fangfoss Girls **Trojan Racing**
   3 PETERHOUSE (USA), 4, ch g Elusive Quality (USA)—Dynaire (USA) **Mr Peter Ward**
   4 THIEPVAL, 4, ch g Kyllachy—Lady Broughton (IRE) **T Walton & J Ward**
   5 YPRES, 7, b g Byron—Esligier (IRE) **B Harker, M Walmsley, S Roebuck, J Teal**

THREE-YEAR-OLDS

   6 NEVER SAY (IRE), b f Monsieur Bond (IRE)—Wong Again **Dante Yard Racing Club**
   7 ROLL ON RORY, b g Mullionmileanhour (IRE)—Fangfoss Girls **P Adams, P Clarke, T Wickins, J Sutton**

TWO-YEAR-OLDS

   8 B c 24/3 Bushranger (IRE)—Invincible Me (IRE) (Invincible Spirit (IRE)) (8121)
   9 Ch f 15/2 Power—Jessie Jane (IRE) (Dylan Thomas (IRE)) (7382)
  10 Ch f 17/2 Intense Focus (USA)—Zawariq (IRE) (Marju (IRE)) (7382)

Other Owners: Mr P. Adams, Mr A. Bennett, Mr Paul Clarke, Mr Jon Ellis, Mr J. Hetherington, Mr K. Holland, Mr T. Walton, Mrs Jill Ward.

Assistant Trainer: Tim Ward

Jockey (flat): B. Curtis, P J McDonald. **Jockey (NH):** Brian Hughes. **Amateur:** Mr D. Houlbrook.

---

629   MISS TRACEY WATKINS, Kington
Postal: **Rose Villa, Holmes Marsh, Lyonshall, Kington, Herefordshire, HR5 3JS**
Contacts: **PHONE (01544) 340471 MOBILE (07812) 804758**
E-MAIL **traceyswatkins@googlemail.com**

   1 ONE COOL BOY (IRE), 7, b br g One Cool Cat (USA)—Pipewell (IRE) **K. M. Parry**
   2 SANNDIYR (IRE), 8, b g Red Ransom (USA)—Sinndiya (IRE) **K. M. Parry**

Assistant Trainer: Kevin Parry

Jockey (NH): Ben Poste. **Amateur:** Miss Brodie Hampson.

---

630   MR FREDERICK WATSON, Sedgefield
Postal: **Beacon Hill, Sedgefield, Stockton-On-Tees, Cleveland, TS21 3HN**
Contacts: **PHONE (01740) 620582 MOBILE (07773) 321472**
E-MAIL **fredwatson@talktalk.net**

   1 BRETON BLUES, 6, b g Street Cry (IRE)—Many Colours **F. Watson**
   2 DESTINATION AIM, 9, b g Dubai Destination (USA)—Tessa Reef (IRE) **F. Watson**
   3 FREDDIE BOLT, 10, b g Diktat—Birjand **F. Watson**
   4 JOYFUL STAR, 6, b g Teofilo (IRE)—Extreme Beauty (USA) **F. Watson**
   5 NEWSPEAK (IRE), 4, b g New Approach (IRE)—Horatia (IRE) **F. Watson**
   6 SPOKESPERSON (USA), 8, b g Henny Hughes (USA)—Verbal (USA) **F. Watson**

631 **MRS SHARON WATT, Richmond**
Postal: **Rosey Hill Farm, Scorton Road, Brompton on Swale, Richmond, North Yorkshire, DL10 7EQ**
Contacts: **PHONE (01748) 812064 FAX (01748) 812064 MOBILE (07970) 826046**
E-MAIL wattfences@aol.com

1 CHAMPAGNE RULES, 5, gr g Aussie Rules (USA)—Garabelle (IRE) **Rosey Hill Partnership**
2 MADAM LILIBET (IRE), 7, b m Authorized (IRE)—Foxilla (IRE) **D. H. Montgomerie**
3 RUBY VODKA, 5, b m Oscar (IRE)—Auntie Kathleen **Major E. J. Watt**
4 SERAFFIMO, 4, ch g Monsieur Bond (IRE)—Hula Ballew **Major E. J. Watt**

TWO-YEAR-OLDS

5 B g 5/4 Fast Company (IRE)—Akariyda (IRE) (Salse (USA)) (14765) **D. H. Montgomerie**
6 B f 28/3 Tagula (IRE)—Silk Affair (IRE) (Barathea (IRE)) (5906) **D. H. Montgomerie**
7 B f 5/2 Sir Prancealot (IRE)—Straight Sets (IRE) (Pivotal) **D. H. Montgomerie**

Other Owners: F. C. Previtali.

632 **MR SIMON WAUGH, Morpeth**
Postal: **A G Waugh & Sons Limited, Molesden House, Molesden, Morpeth, Northumberland, NE61 3QF**
Contacts: **MOBILE (07860) 561445**
E-MAIL swaugh@dircon.co.uk

1 ANNA GREY, 7, gr m Fair Mix (IRE)—Little Flora **Mrs E. Annett**
2 BAMBI DU NOYER (FR), 5, b g Sageburg (IRE)—Zouk Wood (USA)
3 BOLERO COLLONGES (FR), 5, gr g Fragrant Mix (IRE)—Katy Collonges (FR) **Mr R. G. Green**
4 BORIC, 8, b g Grape Tree Road—Petrea **Mrs S. A. York**
5 DARK AND DANGEROUS (IRE), 8, b g Cacique (IRE)—Gilah (IRE) **Yacht London Racing Ltd**
6 DEVON RIVER (FR), 6, gr g Stormy River (FR)—Devon House (USA) **Mr R. G. Green**
7 JACK RIDDELL, 8, br g Grape Tree Road—Little Blackie **Northumberland Racing Club**
8 MY ESCAPADE (IRE), 5, ch m Tamayuz—Highly Respected (IRE) **Yacht London Racing Ltd**
9 NEWYEARSRESOLUTION (IRE), 12, b g Mr Combustible (IRE)—That's Magic (IRE) **S. G. Waugh**
10 ROXY THE REBEL, 6, b m Bollin Eric—Petrea **Mrs S. A. York**
11 SPEEDY TUNES (IRE), 9, b g Heron Island (IRE)—Art Lover (IRE) **Jimmy Hack Racing Partners**
12 TELEX DU BERLAIS (FR), 7, b br g Irish Wells (FR)—Textos (FR) **Northumberland Racing Club**
13 TOTAL ASSETS, 8, b m Alflora (IRE)—Maid Equal **Northumberland Racing Club**

THREE-YEAR-OLDS

14 IMPERIAL FOCUS (IRE), b c Intense Focus (USA)—Mrs Cee (IRE) **Yacht London Racing Ltd**
15 INVINCIBLE BOND, b c Monsieur Bond (IRE)—Royal Pardon **Yacht London Racing Ltd**

Other Owners: Mr S. W. Buckley, Mr S. F. Coton, Mrs V. A. Y. Knox.

633 **MR PAUL WEBBER, Banbury**
Postal: **Cropredy Lawn, Mollington, Banbury, Oxfordshire, OX17 1DR**
Contacts: **PHONE (01295) 750226 FAX (01295) 758482 MOBILE (07836) 232465**
E-MAIL paul@paulwebberracing.com WEBSITE www.paulwebberracing.com

1 ALFIBOY, 6, b g Alflora (IRE)—Cloudy Pearl **Exors of the Late Mr D. C. R. Allen**
2 ALHAMAREER (IRE), 4, ch g Teofilo (IRE)—Ribot's Guest (IRE) **Mr S. A. Al Helaissi**
3 BAYLEY'S DREAM, 7, b g Presenting—Swaythe (USA) **The Sweep Stakes Partnership**
4 BREATH OF BLIGHTY (FR), 5, b br g Policy Maker (IRE)—Nosika d'airy (FR) **John Nicholls (Trading) Ltd**
5 BURMA (FR), 5, b br m Charming Groom (FR)—Tadorna (FR) **The Smillie Watters Partnership**
6 COPPERFACEJACK (IRE), 6, b g Robin des Pres (FR)—Leone Des Pres (FR) **R. W. Barnett**
7 COSMIC DIAMOND, 6, b m Multiplex—Lucy Glitters **Economic Security 1**
8 DUNNSCOTIA, 4, b g Showcasing—Black And Amber **Mrs P. A. Scott-Dunn**
9 FINGERS CROSSED (IRE), 6, b g Bach (IRE)—Awesome Miracle (USA) **Exors of the Late Mr D. C. R. Allen**
10 FIRM ORDER (IRE), 11, b g Winged Love (IRE)—Fairylodge Scarlet (IRE) **The Syndicators**
11 GLENLYON, 4, b g Thewayyouare (USA)—Helena **R. C. Moody**
12 GWAFA (IRE), 5, gr g Tamayuz—Atalina (FR) **Saleh Al Homaizi & Imad Al Sagar**
13 HOLLOW BAY, 6, ch m Beat Hollow—Cavernista **Exors of the Late Mr D. C. R. Allen**

MR PAUL WEBBER - Continued

14 HONOUR A PROMISE, 8, b m Norse Dancer (IRE)—Motcombe (IRE) **R. C. Moody**
15 IDDER (IRE), 5, bl g Authorized (IRE)—Epiphany **Saleh Al Homaizi & Imad Al Sagar**
16 INNOVATE (FR), 4, ch f Full of Gold (FR)—Ryde (FR) **Cropredy Lawn Racing**
17 JUST A FEELING, 6, ch m Flemensfirth (USA)—Precious Lady **Swanbridge Bloodstock Limited**
18 KOOLALA (IRE), 8, b m Kayf Tara—Squaw Talk (USA) **Lady Wellesley**
19 LEMON'S GENT, 9, br g Generous (IRE)—Lemon's Mill (USA) **G. R. Waters**
20 MAETRUFEL ANNIE, 7, b m Flemensfirth (USA)—Materiality **Jolly Wolf Racing**
21 MERRY DANCER (IRE), 4, ch f Duke of Marmalade (IRE)—Starlit Sky **Caroline Ellis and Matthew Hunt**
22 MICHAELA, 4, ch f Sholokhov (IRE)—La Capilla **John Nicholls (Trading) Ltd**
23 MISS TONGABEZI, 7, b m Overbury (IRE)—Shiwa **Turf 2014 & Mrs J Webber**
24 MONAR LAD (IRE), 4, b g Mountain High (IRE)—Cottage Lady (IRE) **Exors of the Late Mr D. C. R. Allen**
25 MR BANKS (IRE), 5, br g Kalanisi (IRE)—She's Supersonic (IRE) **Cropredy Lawn Racing**
26 MR K (IRE), 5, b g Kheleyf (USA)—Undertone (IRE) **Exors of the Late Mr D. C. R. Allen**
27 MY JUDGE, 4, b g Nayef (USA)—Full Steam **Saleh Al Homaizi & Imad Al Sagar**
28 NEW AGENDA, 4, b g New Approach (IRE)—Prove **Bowden C Magee**
29 PERFECT TIMING (FR), 6, b g Sassanian (USA)—Royale Sulawesie (FR) **Exors of the Late Mr D. C. R. Allen**
30 PINAMAR, 6, ch m Shirocco (GER)—Highland Ceilidh (IRE) **C. Humphris**
31 PRETTY MOBILE (FR), 5, gr m Al Namix (FR)—Gobeline (FR) **Mrs A. W. Timpson**
32 RED COSSACK (CAN), 5, ch g Rebellion—Locata (USA) **Mrs G. Thomas**
33 ROYAL DEBUTANTE (IRE), 5, b m Presenting—Chinatownqueen (IRE) **The Ping Partnership**
34 SEPTEMBER BLAZE, 9, b m Exit To Nowhere (USA)—Mid Day Chaser (IRE) **The Blaze Partnership**
35 SIXTY SOMETHING (FR), 10, gr g Dom Alco (FR)—Jaunas (FR) **Mrs A. W. Timpson**
36 SPEEDY RUNAWAY (IRE), 5, br g Presenting—Toasted Oats (IRE) **Mrs M. A. Houghland**
37 SUGAR TRAIN, 6, b g Rail Link—Plum Fairy **Cropredy Lawn Racing**
38 THE BOTTOM BAR (IRE), 4, br g Stowaway—Serenade Leader (IRE) **Richard Morecombe**
39 THE VENERABLE BEDE (IRE), 5, b g Kalanisi (IRE)—Feedthegoodmare (IRE) **Mrs A. W. Timpson**
40 THECORRUPTOR (IRE), 6, b br g Robin des Pres (FR)—Cappard View (IRE) **P. R. Webber**
41 TINDARO (FR), 9, gr g Kingsalsa (USA)—Star's Mixa (FR) **The Tindaro Partnership**
42 TOO MUCH TOO SOON (IRE), 7, b g Craigsteel—Zara Rose (IRE) **Mr I. R. Watters**
43 UNSEEN (FR), 8, gr g Dom Alco (FR)—Cathou (FR) **The Virbac Partnership**
44 VERY LIVE (FR), 7, b g Secret Singer (FR)—Iona Will (FR) **R. V. Shaw**
45 VIKING QUEEN, 5, b m Presenting—Swaythe (USA) **Higgy, Mette & Friends 1**

THREE-YEAR-OLDS

46 DETONATE (FR), gr g Al Namix (FR)—Tadorna (FR) **Michael Kerr-Dineen & Martin Hughes**
47 KERRERA, ch f Champs Elysees—Questa Nova **Paul Webber**
48 B g Beat Hollow—Swaythe (USA) **Higgy, Mette & Friends**

TWO-YEAR-OLDS

49 STARJAC (FR), b g 22/3 Linda's Lad—Star's Mixa (FR) (Linamix (FR)) **The Starjac Partnership**

Other Owners: Imad Al-Sagar, R. K. Aston, Mr N. M. Birch, Mr P. Bowden, Mr S. K. I. Double, Mrs S. M. Drysdale, Miss Caroline Ellis, Mrs M. F. Gardiner, D. W. Higgins, Saleh Al Homaizi, Mr M. Hunt, Mr P. S. Lewis, Sir I. Magee, Professor David Metcalf, R. P. Rocher, Mr Iain Russell Watters, Mr J. Smillie, Turf Club 2014, Mr Paul Webber, Mrs D. J. Webber, E. E. Williams.

Jockey (NH): Liam Treadwell.

---

634 **MR D. K. WELD, The Curragh**
Postal: **Rosewell House, Curragh, Co. Kildare, Ireland**
Contacts: **PHONE (00353) 4544 1273 / 441 476 FAX (00353) 4544 1119**
E-MAIL dkweld@eircom.net

1 ALMELA (IRE), 4, b f Sea The Stars (IRE)—Aliya (IRE) **H. H. Aga Khan**
2 ASHRAF (IRE), 4, b c Cape Cross (IRE)—Askeria (IRE) **H. H. Aga Khan**
3 DONT TELL NO ONE (IRE), 8, b g Westerner—Kings Rose (IRE) **Mr Brian Gleeson**
4 FASCINATING ROCK (IRE), 5, b h Fastnet Rock (AUS)—Miss Polaris **Newtown Anner Stud**
5 FIRST FIGARO (GER), 6, ch g Silvano (GER)—Felina (GER) **The Bellamy Syndicate**
6 FORGOTTEN RULES (IRE), 6, b g Nayef (USA)—Utterly Heaven (IRE) **Moyglare Stud Farm**
7 JOAILLIERE (IRE), 4, b f Dubawi (IRE)—Majestic Silver (IRE) **Moyglare Stud Farm**
8 RADANPOUR (IRE), 4, b c Sea The Stars (IRE)—Rose Quartz **H. H. Aga Khan**
9 SHINGHARI (IRE), 4, b c Cape Cross (IRE)—Sindiyma (IRE) **H. H. Aga Khan**
10 SHOW COURT (IRE), 7, b g Vinnie Roe (IRE)—Sparkling Gem (IRE) **Mr Kris Weld**
11 SILVER CONCORDE, 8, b g Dansili—Sacred Pearl (IRE) **Dr Ronan Lambe**

MR D. K. WELD - Continued

12 **TANDEM,** 7, b g Dansili—Light Ballet **The Bellamy Syndicate**
13 **VIGIL (IRE)**, 7, b g Dansili—Magnolia Lane (IRE) **Mr N. Furlong**
14 **ZANNDA (IRE)**, 4, b f Azamour (IRE)—Zanoubiya (IRE) **H. H. Aga Khan**
15 **ZHUKOVA (IRE)**, 4, b f Fastnet Rock (AUS)—Nightime (IRE) **Mrs C. C. Regalado Gonzalez**

THREE-YEAR-OLDS

16 **A LIKELY STORY (IRE)**, b g Exceed And Excel (AUS)—Where We Left Off **Moyglare Stud Farm**
17 **A SHIN KILDARE (USA)**, b br f Kitten's Joy (USA)—Bala (CAN) **Mr K. Hirai**
18 **AASHEQ (IRE)**, b c Dubawi (IRE)—Beach Bunny (IRE) **Sheikh Hamdan Al Maktoum**
19 **ACE OF DIAMONDS (IRE)**, b c Oasis Dream—Perfect Touch (USA) **Mr Noel Furlong**
20 **ADOOL (IRE)**, ch f Teofilo (IRE)—Khulood (USA) **Sheikh Hamdan Al Maktoum**
21 **ALMANAARA (IRE)**, gr c Shamardal (USA)—Midnight Angel **Sheikh Hamdan Al Maktoum**
22 **AMPLE SUFFICIENCY (USA)**, b c English Channel (USA)—Between Raindrops (USA)
23 **ARAQEEL (IRE)**, b c Dutch Art—Alice Alleyne (IRE) **Sheikh Hamdan Al Maktoum**
24 **ASMEEN (IRE)**, b f Shamardal (USA)—Askeria (IRE) **H. H. Aga Khan**
25 **BALIYKA (IRE)**, b f Cape Cross (IRE)—Baliyana (IRE) **H. H. Aga Khan**
26 **BURMA STAR**, ch f Shamardal (USA)—Shamayel **Mr D. K. Weld**
27 **COLOUR BRIGHT (IRE)**, b f Dream Ahead (USA)—Flashing Green **Moyglare Stud Farm**
28 **CREME DE LA (USA)**, ch f English Channel (USA)—Treysta (USA) **Calumet Farm**
29 **DALTON HIGHWAY (IRE)**, b g Zoffany (IRE)—Poinsettia (IRE) **Dr Ronan Lambe**
30 **DISCIPLINE,** b f Dansili—Fame At Last (USA) **Mr K. Abdullah**
31 **EBEDIYIN (IRE)**, b c Raven's Pass (USA)—Ebadiyla (IRE) **H. H. Aga Khan**
32 **EMBIRAN (IRE)**, b c Shamardal (USA)—Emiyna (IRE) **H. H. Aga Khan**
33 **EMERGENT,** b f Oasis Dream—Trojan Queen (USA) **Mr K. Abdullah**
34 **EZANAK (IRE)**, b c Sea The Stars (IRE)—Ebaza (IRE) **H. H. Aga Khan**
35 **FAST CANDY (IRE)**, b f Fastnet Rock (AUS)—Maryellen's Spirit (IRE) **Newtown Anner Stud**
36 **FAWZ (IRE)**, b f Medaglia d'oro (USA)—Lahudood **Sheikh Hamdan Al Maktoum**
37 **FLAGSTAFF,** b f Dansili—Etoile Montante (USA) **Mr K. Abdullah**
38 **FLYING BULLET (USA)**, b c Smart Strike (CAN)—Perfect Sting (USA) **Stronach Stables**
39 **FOXTROT CHARLIE (USA)**, ch c English Channel (USA)—Flashy Four (USA) **Calumet Farm**
40 **HARZAND (IRE)**, br c Sea The Stars (IRE)—Hazariya (IRE) **H. H. Aga Khan**
41 **HAZMIYRA (IRE)**, ch f Pivotal—Haziyna (IRE) **H. H. Aga Khan**
42 **HEARTFUL (IRE)**, br b f Shamardal (USA)—Mad About You (IRE) **Moyglare Stud Farm**
43 **JULIETTE FAIR (IRE)**, gr f Dark Angel (IRE)—Capulet Monteque (IRE) **Moyglare Stud Farm**
44 **KARALARA (IRE)**, b f Shamardal (USA)—Karasiyra (IRE) **H. H. Aga Khan**
45 **KIDD MALIBU (USA)**, ch c Malibu Moon (USA)—Kiddari (USA) **Sheikh Hamdan Al Maktoum**
46 **KIROUNA (FR)**, ch f Sea The Stars (IRE)—Katiyra (IRE) **H. H. Aga Khan**
47 **LOOK CLOSER (IRE)**, ch c Danehill Dancer (IRE)—Key Secure (IRE) **Moyglare Stud Farm**
48 **LOST STARS (IRE)**, b f Sea The Stars (IRE)—Moving Heart (IRE) **Moyglare Stud Farm**
49 **LOVE IN THE SUN (IRE)**, b f Kodiac—Summer Trysting (USA) **Moyglare Stud Farm**
50 **LUNE DE SABLE (IRE)**, b f Medicean—Token Gesture (IRE) **Moyglare Stud Farm**
51 **MAGNOLIA ROSE (IRE)**, b f Fastnet Rock (AUS)—Magnolia Lane (IRE) **Calumet Farm**
52 **MANEEN (IRE)**, b c Paco Boy (IRE)—Tereshkina (IRE) **Chanelle Pharmaceuticals Ltd.**
53 **MONOCLE,** b gr c King's Best (USA)—Spectacle **Mr K. Abdullah**
54 **MOUNIRA (IRE)**, ch f Raven's Pass (USA)—Mouramara (IRE) **H. H. Aga Khan**
55 **MUNAASHID (USA)**, b br c Lonhro (AUS)—Freefourracing (USA) **Sheikh Hamdan Al Maktoum**
56 **MURRAQIB (USA)**, ch c Summer Bird (USA)—Golden Party (USA) **Sheikh Hamdan Al Maktoum**
57 **NOBLE BEQUEST (USA)**, b br c Lonhro (AUS)—Supposition **Mr K. Abdullah**
58 **NUDGE,** b f Dansili—Take The Hint **Mr K. Abdullah**
59 **ONSHORE,** ch f Sea The Stars (IRE)—Kalima **Mr K. Abdullah**
60 **ORANGEY RED (IRE)**, b f Lawman (FR)—Triple Try (IRE) **Moyglare Stud Farm**
61 **ORILLION,** b g Cacique (IRE)—Pure Joy **Mr K. Abdullah**
62 **PALMETTO DUNES (USA)**, b c First Defence (USA)—Gainful (USA) **Mr K. Abdullah**
63 **PARTY ANGEL (IRE)**, b f Dark Angel (IRE)—Lady Docker (IRE) **Mr J. Higgins**
64 **PROPRIANO (USA)**, b c More Than Ready (USA)—Primadona (IRE) **Moyglare Stud Farm**
65 **RAYMONDA (USA)**, b f Lonhro (AUS)—Daring Diva **Mr K. Abdullah**
66 **READY INDY (USA)**, ch f More Than Ready (USA)—Gatherindy (USA) **Calumet Farm**
67 **ROSE DE PIERRE (IRE)**, b f Dubawi (IRE)—Profound Beauty (IRE) **Moyglare Stud Farm**
68 **SCARLET BLUE (IRE)**, gr c Dark Angel (IRE)—Scarlet O'hara (IRE) **Calumet Farm**
69 **SEA SWIFT (IRE)**, b f High Chaparral (IRE)—Agnetha (GER) **Calumet Farm**
70 **SHAMREEN (IRE)**, b f Dubawi (IRE)—Shareen (IRE) **H. H. Aga Khan**
71 **SHARLIYNA (IRE)**, b f Pivotal—Sharleez (IRE) **H. H. Aga Khan**
72 **SIKANDARABAD (IRE)**, b g Dr Fong (USA)—Sindiyma (IRE) **H. H. Aga Khan**
73 **SIMANNKA (IRE)**, gr f Mastercraftsman (IRE)—Simkana (IRE) **H. H. Aga Khan**
74 **SMOKEY QUARTZ (IRE)**, gr f Dark Angel (IRE)—Instant Sparkle (IRE) **Moyglare Stud Farm**

MR D. K. WELD - Continued

75 **SOCIAL TREASURE (IRE)**, ch c Galileo (IRE)—Society Hostess (USA) **Moyglare Stud Farm**
76 **SURPRISINGLY (IRE)**, b f Galileo (IRE)—Lesson In Humility (IRE) **Mrs J. Magnier**
77 **TANAZA (IRE)**, b f Dubawi (IRE)—Tanoura (IRE) **H. H. Aga Khan**
78 **TARAYEF (IRE)**, br f Teofilo (IRE)—Grecian Bride (IRE) **Sheikh Hamdan Al Maktoum**
79 **TARAZANI (IRE)**, ch g Dutch Art—Tarakala (IRE) **H. H. Aga Khan**
80 **TIRMIZI (FR)**, b c Sea The Stars (IRE)—Timabiyra (IRE) **H. H. Aga Khan**
81 **TOPAZ CLEAR (IRE)**, b f Pivotal—Utterly Heaven (IRE) **Moyglare Stud Farm**
82 **TRUE SOLITAIRE (IRE)**, b c Oasis Dream—Majestic Silver (IRE) **Moyglare Stud Farm**
83 **VA PENSIERO (IRE)**, b f High Chaparral (IRE)—Thoughtless Moment (IRE) **Moyglare Stud Farm**
84 **WADALANI (IRE)**, b g Dalakhani (IRE)—Wilde Perle **Calumet Farm**
85 **WHISKEY ZULU (IRE)**, b c Canford Cliffs (IRE)—Zanzibar Girl (USA) **Calumet Farm**
86 **YASOOD (IRE)**, b c Acclamation—Lucina **Sheikh Hamdan Al Maktoum**
87 **ZABALAN (IRE)**, b c Dutch Art—Zanoubiya (IRE) **H. H. Aga Khan**
88 **ZALFANA (IRE)**, ch f Dutch Art—Zafayra (IRE) **H. H. Aga Khan**
89 **ZAMIRA (IRE)**, b f New Approach (IRE)—Zanara (IRE) **H. H. Aga Khan**
90 **ZULU ALPHA (USA)**, b c Street Cry (IRE)—Zori (USA) **Calumet Farm**

TWO-YEAR-OLDS

91 B c 2/3 Famous Name—Agnetha (GER) (Big Shuffle (USA)) (65000) **Dr Ronan Lambe**
92 **ALAHIDA (IRE)**, b br f 23/1 Redoute's Choice (AUS)—Alanza (IRE) (Dubai Destination (USA)) **H. H. Aga Khan**
93 **ALDHARA**, b f 5/1 Dubawi (IRE)—Bethrah (IRE) (Marju (IRE)) **Sheikh Hamdan Al Maktoum**
94 **ALJUNOOD (IRE)**, br c 18/3 Bated Breath—Ataraxy (Zamindar (USA)) **Sheikh Hamdan Al Maktoum**
95 **ALL CRAZY NOW (IRE)**, ch c 25/3 Dutch Art—Supernovae (IRE) (Dalakhani (IRE)) **Moyglare Stud Farm**
96 B f 12/2 Dansili—Askeria (IRE) (Sadler's Wells (USA)) **H. H. Aga Khan**
97 **ASSAM**, b f 20/2 Dansili—Sense of Pride (Sadler's Wells (USA)) **Mr K. Abdullah**
98 **BEE QUEEN**, b f 29/3 Makfi—Trojan Queen (Empire Maker (USA)) **Mr K. Abdullah**
99 **BID ADIEU (IRE)**, b c 14/5 Pour Moi (IRE)—Thoughtless Moment (IRE) (Pivotal) **Moyglare Stud Farm**
100 B f 24/4 Big Bad Bob (IRE)—Brazilian Bride (IRE) (Pivotal) **Lady Chryss O'Reilly**
101 **BREVARD**, br c 30/3 Bated Breath—Rare Virtue (USA) (Empire Maker (USA)) **Mr K. Abdullah**
102 **CASCAVELLE (IRE)**, gr c 4/5 Shamardal—Majestic Silver (IRE) (Linamix (FR)) **Moyglare Stud Farm**
103 Ch c 28/2 Galileo (IRE)—Caumshinaun (IRE) (Indian Ridge) **Mr Noel Furlong**
104 **CROIS LION (USA)**, b br c 5/2 More Than Ready (USA)—
          Endless Expanse (IRE) (Red Ransom (USA)) **Moyglare Stud Farm**
105 B gr f 23/1 Siyouni (FR)—Dabista (IRE) (Highest Honor (FR)) **H. H. Aga Khan**
106 **DANCINGWITH STORMS (IRE)**, ch c 19/5 New Approach (IRE)—
          Mad About You (IRE) (Indian Ridge) **Moyglare Stud Farm**
107 **DELTA DREAMER**, b f 12/3 Oasis Dream—Kilo Alpha (King's Best) **Mr K. Abdullah**
108 **DHAJEEJ (USA)**, b f 20/1 Lemon Drop Kid (USA)—Saraama (USA) (Bahri (USA)) **Sheikh Hamdan Al Maktoum**
109 B c 4/3 Sir Prancealot (IRE)—Dream Date (IRE) (Oasis Dream) (59061) **Mr Kenneth Ramsey**
110 B f 31/3 Sepoy (AUS)—Elbasana (IRE) (Indian Ridge) **H. H. Aga Khan**
111 **ESPOIR D'SOLEIL (IRE)**, ch f 17/4 Galileo (IRE)—Lady Luck (IRE) (Kris) **Moyglare Stud Farm**
112 **EUROPIUM**, b f 4/4 Frankel—Revered (Oasis Dream) **Mr K. Abdullah**
113 **EZYIRA (IRE)**, ch f 3/2 Teofilo (IRE)—Eytarna (IRE) (Dubai Destination (USA)) **H. H. Aga Khan**
114 **FIDAAHA (IRE)**, ch f 27/2 New Approach (IRE)—
          Ceist Eile (IRE) (Noverre (USA)) (147655) **Sheikh Hamdan Al Maktoum**
115 **FIREY SPEECH (USA)**, b c 11/4 Street Cry (IRE)—Firey Red (IRE) (Pivotal) **Moyglare Stud Farm**
116 **FURUD (IRE)**, gr c 24/3 Zebedee—Kahira (IRE) (King's Best) (147655) **Sheikh Hamdan Al Maktoum**
117 **HARIPOUR (IRE)**, br c 2/4 Shamardal—Hazariya (IRE) (Xaar) **H. H. Aga Khan**
118 Gr f 15/3 New Approach (IRE)—Hazarafa (IRE) (Daylami (IRE)) **H. H. Aga Khan**
119 **IMPART**, b f 8/2 Oasis Dream—Disclose (Dansili) **Mr K. Abdullah**
120 **JANUARY MORN (USA)**, b f 17/1 Elusive Quality (USA)—Primadona (IRE) (Galileo (IRE)) **Moyglare Stud Farm**
121 Gr f 22/3 Dark Angel (IRE)—Kaladena (IRE) (Daylami (IRE)) **H. H. Aga Khan**
122 **KARAGANDA (IRE)**, b f 13/2 Cape Cross (IRE)—Karawana (IRE) (King's Best) **H. H. Aga Khan**
123 Ch f 19/2 Raven's Pass (USA)—Kasanka (IRE) (Galileo (IRE)) **H. H. Aga Khan**
124 B f 17/2 Dutch Art—Katiola (IRE) (Oratorio (IRE)) **H. H. Aga Khan**
125 **KEREMAN (IRE)**, bc 20/4 Azamour (IRE)—Kerania (IRE) (Daylami (IRE)) **H. H. Aga Khan**
126 **KING'S SHILLING (USA)**, b br c 16/2 Bellamy Road (USA)—Gainful (USA) (Gone West (USA)) **Mr K. Abdullah**
127 **KNOWING YOU (IRE)**, ch f 19/3 Pivotal—She's Our Mark (Ishiguru (USA)) **Moyglare Stud Farm**
128 **KRYPTOS**, b c 5/4 Cacique (IRE)—Posteritas (USA) (Lear Fan (USA)) **Mr K. Abdullah**
129 **LE MORNE (IRE)**, b c 10/4 Henrythenavigator (USA)—
          Profound Beauty (IRE) (Danehill (USA)) **Moyglare Stud Farm**
130 Ch c 6/3 Famous Name—Let Your Love Flow (IRE) (Iffraaj) (47988) **Dr Ronan Lambe**
131 **LIGHT LAUGHTER (IRE)**, ch f 19/3 Distorted Humor (USA)—
          Sense of Purpose (IRE) (Galileo (IRE)) **Moyglare Stud Farm**

MR D. K. WELD - Continued

132 **LOST IN SILENCE (IRE)**, b f 25/5 Holy Roman Emperor (IRE)—
Suitably Discreet (USA) (Mr Prospector (USA)) **Moyglare Stud Farm**
133 **MAKING LIGHT (IRE)**, b f 4/4 Tamayuz—Instant Sparkle (Danehill (USA)) **Moyglare Stud Farm**
134 Ch f 28/2 Rip Van Winkle (IRE)—Masiyma (IRE) (Dalakhani (IRE)) **H. H. Aga Khan**
135 **MEMORIAL ROSE (IRE)**, ch f 17/2 Dalakhani (IRE)—Moving Heart (IRE) (Anabaa (USA)) **Moyglare Stud Farm**
136 **MILITARY POET (IRE)**, b c 14/5 High Chaparral (IRE)—
Utterly Heaven (IRE) (Danehill (USA)) **Moyglare Stud Farm**
137 **MOGHRAMA (IRE)**, ch f 27/1 Harbour Watch (IRE)—Mythie (FR) (Octagonal (NZ)) **Sheikh Hamdan Al Maktoum**
138 **MOMOUR (USA)**, b c 14/3 Mizzen Mast (USA)—Mouraniya (IRE) (Azamour (IRE)) **H. H. Aga Khan**
139 **MOTAHASSEN (IRE)**, br c 13/5 Lonhro (AUS)—
Journalist (IRE) (Night Shift (USA)) (100000) **Sheikh Hamdan Al Maktoum**
140 **MUJAAZY (IRE)**, b f 8/3 New Approach (IRE)—Qaadira (USA) (Mr Greeley (USA)) **Sheikh Hamdan Al Maktoum**
141 **MUQTANNY (IRE)**, b c 9/4 Oasis Dream—Rifqah (USA) (Elusive Quality (USA)) **Sheikh Hamdan Al Maktoum**
142 **MUZBID (IRE)**, b c 22/4 Lope de Vega (IRE)—
Kartiste (IRE) (Kalanisi (IRE)) (70000) **Sheikh Hamdan Al Maktoum**
143 **NEOCLASSICAL (USA)**, b c 15/4 First Defence (USA)—Rio Carnival (USA) (Storm Cat (USA)) **Mr K. Abdullah**
144 B c 24/4 Shamardal (USA)—Perfect Touch (USA) (Miswaki (USA)) (200000) **Mrs C. C. Regalado-Gonzalez**
145 **QUICK CHAT (USA)**, b br f 2/5 First Defence (USA)—Discuss (USA) (Danzig (USA)) **Mr K. Abdullah**
146 **RICH HISTORY (IRE)**, ch c 6/2 Dubawi (IRE)—Polished Gem (IRE) (Danehill (USA)) **Moyglare Stud Farm**
147 Gr c 17/2 Dalakhani (IRE)—Rose Quartz (Lammtarra (USA)) **H. H. Aga Khan**
148 **ROYAL VIGIL (IRE)**, b c 31/3 Shamardal (USA)—
Spoil Yourself (USA) (Distorted Humor (USA)) **Moyglare Stud Farm**
149 **SANSIBAR JEWEL (USA)**, b f 2/5 Street Cry (IRE)—
Irresistible Jewel (IRE) (Danehill (USA)) **Moyglare Stud Farm**
150 **SAQR**, b c 2/5 Tamayuz—Tumooh (USA) (Authorized (IRE)) **Sheikh Hamdan Al Maktoum**
151 **SECRETS SHARED (USA)**, b f 9/4 Street Cry (IRE)—Miss Kilroy (USA) (A P Indy (USA)) **Moyglare Stud Farm**
152 B c 7/3 Makfi—Simawa (IRE) (Anabaa (USA)) **H. H. Aga Khan**
153 **SINGLE NOTE (IRE)**, b c 7/2 Big Bad Bob (IRE)—
Sparkling View (IRE) (Danehill Dancer (IRE)) **Moyglare Stud Farm**
154 **SOLO SAXOPHONE (IRE)**, b c 18/4 Frankel—
Society Hostess (USA) (Seeking The Gold (USA)) **Moyglare Stud Farm**
155 **SORELLE DELLE ROSE (IRE)**, gr f 16/3 Dark Angel (IRE)—
Kelsey Rose (Most Welcome) (258397) **Moyglare Stud Farm**
156 **SWITCH IN TIME (IRE)**, b f 2/3 Galileo (IRE)—Switch (USA) (Quiet American (USA)) **Moyglare Stud Farm**
157 **TEMPERA**, b f 9/2 Dansili—Portodora (USA) (Kingmambo (USA)) **Mr K. Abdullah**
158 **TILLY TROTTER (IRE)**, b f 10/3 Kodiac—Inourthoughts (IRE) (Desert Style (IRE)) (90000) **Mr Frank Gillespie**
159 **TITUS**, b c 26/2 Dansili—Mirror Lake (Dubai Destination (IRE)) **Mr K. Abdullah**
160 **TOCCO D'AMORE (IRE)**, b f 19/4 Raven's Pass (USA)—
Spirit of Tara (IRE) (Sadler's Wells (USA)) (1476559) **Moyglare Stud Farm**
161 **TOURSOUN (IRE)**, b c 22/4 Sea The Stars (IRE)—Tarakala (IRE) (Dr Fong (USA)) **Moyglare Stud Farm**
162 B f 7/2 Pour Moi (IRE)—Truly Mine (IRE) (Rock of Gibraltar (IRE)) **Mr D. K. Weld**
163 **UGNEYA (IRE)**, br f 7/3 Teofilo (IRE)—Zahoo (IRE) (Nayef (USA)) **Sheikh Hamdan Al Maktoum**
164 B f 30/1 Lawman (FR)—Zalanga (IRE) (Azamour (IRE)) **H. H. Aga Khan**
165 **ZIRCONIA**, b c 26/1 Dansili—Zaminast (Zamindar (USA)) **Mr K. Abdullah**

Jockey (flat): P. J. Smullen, L. F. Roche. **Apprentice:** Jamie Cattigan.

---

635 MISS SHEENA WEST, Lewes

Postal: **5 Balmer Farm Cottages, Brighton Road, Lewes, East Sussex, BN7 3JN**
Contacts: PHONE **(01273) 621303** FAX **(01273) 622189** MOBILE **(07748) 181804**
E-MAIL **sheenawest11@aol.com** WEBSITE **www.sheenawest.com**

1 **BRILLIANT BARCA**, 8, b g Imperial Dancer—Fading Away **G. West**
2 **CANNON FODDER**, 9, b m Nomadic Way (USA)—Grace Dieu **The Cheapskates**
3 **CRASHING THEW LIFE**, 6, b g Tobougg (IRE)—Kalmina (USA) **G. West**
4 **DING DING**, 5, ch m Winker Watson—Five Bells (IRE) **G. West**
5 **FEB THIRTYFIRST**, 7, ch g Shirocco (GER)—My Mariam **M. Moriarty**
6 **HI NOTE**, 8, b m Acclamation—Top Tune **G. West**
7 **JENNY SPARKS**, 5, b m Winker Watson—Stephanie's Mind **M. R. Channon**
8 **JUSTANOTHER MUDDLE**, 9, gr g Kayf Tara—Spatham Rose **Saloop**
9 **LEG IRON (IRE)**, 11, b g Snurge—Southern Skies (IRE) **M. Moriarty**
10 **MR MUDDLE**, 9, gr g Imperial Dancer—Spatham Rose **Saloop**
11 **NOT ANOTHER MUDDLE**, 5, b g Kayf Tara—Spatham Rose **Saloop**

MISS SHEENA WEST - Continued

12 **SCREAMING BRAVE**, 10, br g Hunting Lion (IRE)—Hana Dee
13 **SPANISH FORK (IRE)**, 7, br g Trans Island—Wings Awarded **G. West**
14 **WARRANT OFFICER**, 6, gr g Misu Bond (IRE)—Kilmovee **M. Moriarty**
15 **YA HAFED**, 8, ch g Haafhd—Rule Britannia **G. West**

Other Owners: Mr L. T. Morris, Mrs C. S. Muddle, Miss C. Stewart, Mrs E. Turner.

Jockey (NH): M. Goldstein.

---

636 **MR SIMON WEST, Middleham**
Postal: **14A St Alkeldas Road, Middleham, Leyburn, North Yorkshire, DL8 4PW**
Contacts: **MOBILE (07855) 924529**
E-MAIL simonwest21@hotmail.co.uk WEBSITE www.mkmracing.co.uk

1 **ABONOS (IRE)**, 4, b f Approve (IRE)—Topiary (IRE) **Mr S. G. West**
2 **AFIENYA (IRE)**, 6, gr m Tikkanen (USA)—Tullytoyle (IRE) **Mr P. Hothersall**
3 **AMOOD (IRE)**, 5, ch g Elnadim (USA)—Amanah (USA) **Mr C. R. Hirst**
4 **KODIAC LADY (IRE)**, 4, b f Kodiac—Weeping Willow (IRE) **Mr P. Hothersall**
5 **LADY BRIENNE (IRE)**, 7, b m Flemensfirth (USA)—Spirit Rock (IRE) **Red Squares**
6 **LOVEY DOVEY (IRE)**, 12, b m Winged Love (IRE)—Dansana (IRE) **J. D. Gordon**
7 **MADAKHEEL (USA)**, 5, b m Mr Greeley (USA)—Manaal (USA) **Miss K Milligan & Mr P Fowlie**
8 **MAXIMISER (IRE)**, 8, gr g Helissio (FR)—Clydeside (IRE) **J. D. Gordon**
9 **OVERTHEEDGE (IRE)**, 7, b g Morozov (USA)—Ballyroe Hill (IRE) **Mr P. Hothersall**
10 **SAINT BRIEUC (FR)**, 7, b br g Saint des Saints (FR)—Merci Alkmene (FR) **Mr C. R. Hirst**
11 **SLIM CHANCE (IRE)**, 7, b m Clodovil (IRE)—Valluga (IRE) **Mrs B. Hothersall**
12 **SLIPPER SATIN (IRE)**, 6, b m Excellent Art—In The Ribbons **Mrs J. M. L. Milligan**
13 **VILMAN (IRE)**, 4, b g Mastercraftsman (IRE)—Velandia (IRE) **J. D. Gordon**

THREE-YEAR-OLDS

14 **DARK FOREST**, b g Iffraaj—Through The Forest (USA) **Mr C. R. Hirst**
15 **HOLY GRAIL (IRE)**, b f Canford Cliffs (IRE)—Dashing Beauty (IRE) **Mr C. R. Hirst**
16 **MIDDLEMAN**, b g Oasis Dream—Sense of Pride **Mr C. R. Hirst**

Other Owners: Mr K. Flint, Mr S. Flint, Mr P. Fowlie, Miss M. K. Milligan.

---

637 **MR DAVID WESTON, West Overton**
Postal: **c/o Flintstone Stud, West Overton, Marlborough, Wiltshire, SN8 4ER**
Contacts: **MOBILE (07966) 641001**

1 **AT FIRST LIGHT**, 7, b m Echo of Light—Bisaat (USA) **Miss E. Tanner**
2 **BEDROCK FRED**, 10, ch g Monsieur Bond (IRE)—Sea Mist (IRE) **Miss E. Tanner**
3 **EASY TIGER**, 4, b g Refuse To Bend (IRE)—Extremely Rare (IRE) **Miss E. Tanner**
4 **SOLSTALLA**, 4, b f Halling (USA)—Solstice **Miss E. Tanner**

---

638 **MR TOM WESTON, Hindlip**
Postal: **Offerton Farm, Offerton Lane, Hindlip, Worcester, Worcestershire, WR3 8SX**
Contacts: **MOBILE (07752) 313698**

1 **DIAMOND REFLECTION (IRE)**, 4, b g Oasis Dream—Briolette (IRE) **Int-Ex Contracting Limited**
2 **DOS'NTSUITME (IRE)**, 7, b g Acambaro (GER)—Divine Rapture (IRE) **Int-Ex Contracting Limited**
3 **HARD TO SWALLOW (IRE)**, 10, b g Snurge—Nicat's Daughter (IRE) **Int-Ex Contracting Limited**
4 **MR JALFRAZY (IRE)**, 7, b g Pierre—Brushaside Spa (IRE) **Int-Ex Contracting Limited**
5 **THOONAVOLLA (IRE)**, 8, ch g Beneficial—Another Partner **The Troubled Pink Partnership**

Other Owners: Mrs D. Grove, M. H. Weston.

639   MISS JESSICA WESTWOOD, Chulmleigh
Postal: Molland Ridge Farm, Chulmleigh, Devon, EX18 7EF
Contacts: MOBILE (07536) 021449
E-MAIL Jesswestwoodracing@gmail.com WEBSITE www.jesswestwoodracing.com

1 DONT CALL ME DORIS, 6, b m Franklins Gardens—Grove Dancer **Holnicote Partnership**
2 GREYWELL BOY, 9, gr g Fair Mix (IRE)—Rakajack **Chasing Gold Limited**
3 INTHENICOFTIME, 6, b g With The Flow (USA)—Rose Lir **Mrs F. L. Heal**
4 MONKERTY TUNKERTY, 13, b g Silver Patriarch (IRE)—Orphan Annie **Miss J. J. Westwood**
5 4, B g Hamairi (IRE)—Rose Lir **Mrs F. L. Heal**

THREE-YEAR-OLDS
6 Gr f Dream Eater (IRE)—State of Grace **Miss J. J. Westwood**

Other Owners: Mr M. L. J. Fooks, Mr A. Westwood.

640   MR JOHN WEYMES, Middleham
Trainer did not wish details of his string to appear

641   MR ERIC WHEELER, Marlborough
Postal: Westcourt Stables, Westcourt, Burbage, Marlborough, Wiltshire, SN8 3BW
Contacts: PHONE (07795) 844185 (01672) 811423 MOBILE (07795) 844185

1 BEGGERS LUCK, 6, b m Lucky Story (USA)—Dropitlikeit's Hot (IRE) **Mr G. W. Witheford**
2 MALIH, 7, b g Echo of Light—Sultry Lass (USA) **Wedgewood Estates**

THREE-YEAR-OLDS
3 LINKS BAR MARBELLA (IRE), ch g Intense Focus (USA)—Silesian (IRE) **Links Bar Amigos**

TWO-YEAR-OLDS
4 MISTRAL SONG (FR), b f 9/3 Hurricane Cat (USA)—Song of India (Dalakhani (IRE))

Other Owners: Mr Tony Arnold, Mr Tony Preece.

Assistant Trainer: Mr C. Witheford

642   MR ALISTAIR WHILLANS, Hawick
Postal: Esker House, Newmill-On-Slitrig, Hawick, Roxburghshire, TD9 9UQ
Contacts: PHONE (01450) 376642 FAX (01450) 376082 MOBILE (07771) 550555
E-MAIL acwracing@hotmail.com

1 AHHDEHKEN, 11, b g Cloudings (IRE)—Swazi Princess (IRE) **A. C. Whillans**
2 ALEXANDRAKOLLONTAI (IRE), 6, b m Amadeus Wolf—Story **Chris Spark & William Orr**
3 APACHEE PRINCE (IRE), 7, b g Indian Danehill (IRE)—Wheredidthemoneygo (IRE) **J. D. Wright**
4 BOP ALONG (IRE), 9, b g Double Eclipse (IRE)—Bob Girl (IRE) **East-West Partnership**
5 BRACKENMOSS RORY, 4, b g Overbury (IRE)—Thorterdykes Lass **John & Liz Elliot**
6 CLAUDE CARTER, 12, b g Elmaamul (USA)—Cruz Santa **Mrs L. M. Whillans**
7 CLEAR SPELL (IRE), 5, b g Tamayuz—Beat The Rain **Still Game Racing Syndicate**
8 COURT BALOO (IRE), 5, b g Court Cave (IRE)—Tremplin (IRE) **Akela Construction Ltd**
9 DUBAI SHEN (IRE), 5, b g Dubai Destination (USA)—Graineuaile (IRE) **Akela Construction Ltd**
10 FUNKY MUNKY, 11, b g Talaash (IRE)—Chilibang Bang
11 GALILEE CHAPEL (IRE), 7, b g Baltic King—Triple Zero (IRE) **A. C. Whillans**
12 GLACIAL ROCK (IRE), 10, b g Sonus (IRE)—Glacial Princess (IRE) **Mr M. Bell**
13 GLEANN NA NDOCHAIS (IRE), 10, b g Zagreb (USA)—Nissereen (USA) **Mr W J E Scott & Mrs M A Scott**
14 HIDDEN REBEL, 4, b f Cockney Rebel (IRE)—Medicea Sidera **J. D. Wright**
15 JONNY EAGER (IRE), 7, b g Craigsteel—Dishy (IRE) **Mr & Mrs Paul & Clare Rooney**
16 KIND OF EASY (IRE), 10, b g Kalanisi (IRE)—Specifiedrisk (IRE) **Mrs L. J. McLeod**

MR ALISTAIR WHILLANS - Continued

17 **LOVE MARMALADE (IRE)**, 6, ch g Duke of Marmalade (IRE)—Green Castle (IRE) **Akela Construction Ltd**
18 **MAHLER AND ME (IRE)**, 6, ch g Mahler—Tisindabreedin (IRE) **Mr & Mrs Paul & Clare Rooney**
19 **MAYZE BELL**, 7, br m And Beyond (IRE)—Eleanor May **A. C. Whillans**
20 **MEADOWCROFT BOY**, 7, b g Kayf Tara—Blackbriery Thyne (IRE) **Mr W J E Scott & Mrs M A Scott**
21 **MONBEG DOLLY (IRE)**, 6, ch m Flemensfirth (USA)—Laughing Lesa (IRE) **Mr & Mrs Paul & Clare Rooney**
22 **OLIVIA JOAN**, 5, ch m Grape Tree Road—Thorterdykes Lass (IRE) **John & Liz Elliot**
23 **OPT OUT**, 6, ch g Pivotal—Easy Option (IRE) **Akela Construction Ltd**
24 **PIXIE CUT (IRE)**, 6, b m Chineur (FR)—Fantastic Cee (IRE) **Chris Spark & William Orr**
25 **RALPHY BOY (IRE)**, 7, b g Acclamation—Silcasue **Mr F. Lowe**
26 **RED STORY**, 5, b g Kayf Tara—Marabunta (SPA) **Mr W J E Scott & Mrs M A Scott**
27 **TAGTALE (IRE)**, 4, b f Tagula (IRE)—Story **A. C. Whillans**
28 **VICKY VALENTINE**, 6, b m Rock of Gibraltar (IRE)—Silcasue **Mr F. Lowe**
29 **W SIX TIMES**, 10, b m Double Trigger (IRE)—Be My Mot (IRE) **Mrs L. M. Whillans**
30 **WEE JOCK ELLIOT**, 6, b g Overbury (IRE)—Caitlin Ash **John & Liz Elliot**
31 **WYFIELD ROSE**, 7, b m Kayf Tara—Miniature Rose **John & Liz Elliot**

Other Owners: Mr E. Cassie, K. Creighton, Mrs E. J. Elliot, J. J. Elliot, Mr K. Little, Mr W. J. Muir, Mr W. Orr, Mr P. A. Rooney, Mrs C. Rooney, W. J. E. Scott, Mrs M. A. Scott, Mr C. Spark, Mrs S. L. Wright.

---

643 **MR DONALD WHILLANS, Hawick**
Postal: **Dodlands Steading, Hawick, Roxburghshire, TD9 8LG**
Contacts: **BUSINESS (01450) 373128 HOME (01450) 379810 FAX (01450) 376082**
MOBILE (07840) 997570
E-MAIL helenwhillans24@gmail.com WEBSITE www.donaldwhillansracing.com

1 **BEARSKIN (IRE)**, 5, br g Kodiac—Dark Arts (USA) **D. W. Whillans**
2 **BOLLIN FIONA**, 12, ch m Silver Patriarch (IRE)—Bollin Nellie **C. N. Whillans**
3 **BOLLIN JULIE**, 9, b m Bollin Eric—Bollin Nellie **C. N. Whillans**
4 **CHAMPAGNE AGENT (IRE)**, 10, b g Smadoun (FR)—Madame Jean (FR) **Star Racing**
5 4, B g Definite Article—Couture Daisy (IRE) **Mr A. J. M. Duncan**
6 **EGON SPENGLAR**, 8, b g River Falls—Wee Willow **D. W. Whillans**
7 **ELLISTRIN BELLE**, 8, b m Helissio (FR)—Hannah Park (IRE) **Mrs E. Smith**
8 **HARTFORTH**, 8, ch g Haafhd—St Edith (IRE) **The Brave Lads Partnership**
9 **MACMIDNIGHT**, 4, b f Mawatheeq (USA)—Rehlaat (USA) **Star Racing**
10 **PAPER ROSES (IRE)**, 5, b m Gamut (IRE)—Rose Vic (IRE) **Mrs E. Smith**
11 4, B f Beneficial—Roses And Wine (IRE) **Mr A. J. M. Duncan**
12 **SHADES OF MIDNIGHT**, 6, b g Midnight Legend—Hannah Park (IRE) **The Potassium Partnership**
13 **SNAPPING TURTLE (IRE)**, 11, b g Turtle Island (IRE)—Rachael's Dawn **D. W. Whillans**
14 **TOMAHAWK WOOD**, 7, ch g Courteous—Meda's Song **Mr G. Aitken**

Other Owners: Mr N. Bannerman, Mr H. G. Beeby, Mrs Alison Rhind, Mr S. A. Taylor, Mr D. W. Whillans, Mrs H. M. Whillans.

Assistant Trainer: Garry Whillans

Jockey (flat): Garry Whillans. **Jockey (NH):** Callum Whillans. **Amateur:** Mr Ryan Nichol.

---

644 **MR RICHARD WHITAKER, Scarcroft**
Postal: **Hellwood Racing Stables, Hellwood Lane, Scarcroft, Leeds, West Yorkshire, LS14 3BP**
Contacts: **PHONE (01132) 892265 MOBILE (07831) 870454**
E-MAIL rmwhitaker@btconnect.com WEBSITE www.richardwhitaker.org

1 **AVON BREEZE**, 7, b m Avonbridge—African Breeze **Grange Park Racing II & Partner**
2 **DESERT CHIEF**, 4, b g Kheleyf (USA)—African Breeze **Nice Day Out Partnership**
3 **ICY BLUE**, 8, b g Iceman—Bridal Path **Country Lane Partnership**
4 **JUBILEE SONG**, 4, b f Royal Applause—Cosmic Song **Mr D. A. Walker**
5 **LOVE ISLAND**, 7, b m Acclamation—Sally Traffic **R. M. Whitaker**
6 **MIDLIGHT**, 4, b g Elusive City (USA)—My Heart's Deelite (USA) **Cragg Wood Racing**
7 **PIPERS NOTE**, 6, ch g Piccolo—Madam Valentine **Cragg Wood Racing & Partner**
8 **PRECISION STRIKE**, 5, b g Multiplex—Dockside Strike **Resdev Ltd**
9 **PUMAFLOR (IRE)**, 4, b g Aussie Rules (USA)—Krasotka (IRE) **Resdev Ltd**
10 **ROCKY'S PRIDE (IRE)**, 10, b g Rock of Gibraltar (IRE)—L'animee **R. M. Whitaker**
11 **SPARKLING SAPPHIRE**, 4, ro f Monsieur Bond (IRE)—Velvet Band **Nice Day Out Partnership**

MR RICHARD WHITAKER - Continued

12 **TOTALLY MAGIC (IRE)**, 4, b f Captain Rio—Hypocrisy **Mr James Marshall & Mr Chris Marshall**
13 **TUMBLEWIND**, 6, ch m Captain Rio—African Breeze **Nice Day Out Partnership**
14 **WOODACRE**, 9, b g Pyrus (USA)—Fairy Ring (IRE) **Mrs R. M. Whitaker**

THREE-YEAR-OLDS

15 **COSMIC DUST**, b f Equiano (FR)—Cosmic Song **Mrs J. Robinson**
16 **MISS MOZAICO**, b f Pastoral Pursuits—Grin **Resdev Ltd**
17 **NEVER IN DOUBT**, b g Royal Applause—African Breeze **Mrs J. D. M. Thompson**
18 **PENNY POT LANE**, b f Misu Bond (IRE)—Velvet Band **Mr A. Melville**
19 **ROUND THE ISLAND**, b g Royal Applause—Luanshya **Robin Dollar & David Horner**
20 **SEBASTIAN'S WISH (IRE)**, b g Aqlaam—Swish (GER) **Two Goldfish & A Balloon**
21 **THE RESDEV WAY**, b g Multiplex—Lady Duxyana **Resdev Ltd**
22 **WOTABOND**, ch g Monsieur Bond (IRE)—Wotatomboy **Mrs J. M. Willows**

TWO-YEAR-OLDS

23 B f 9/2 Equiano (FR)—Charlevoix (IRE) (King Charlemagne (USA)) (9000)
24 Ch c 1/4 Piccolo—Dahshah (Mujtahid (USA)) (11500)
25 B g 31/3 Piccolo—Marysienka (Primo Dominie) (12000)
26 Ch f 5/3 Compton Place—Oriental Girl (Dr Fong (USA)) (2666)
27 **TEDDY EDWARD**, ch g 6/5 Medicean—Pinkai (IRE) (Caerleon (USA)) (4000) **A. D. Copley**

Other Owners: A. D. Crombie, R. C. Dollar, Mr D. A. Horner, Dr K. Howard, Mrs P. Howard, Robert Macgregor, Mr C. R. Marshall, J. R. Marshall, Mr A. Norrington.

Assistant Trainer: Simon R Whitaker

Jockey (flat): George Chaloner, Keagan Latham.

---

645 **MR ARTHUR WHITEHEAD, Craven Arms**
Postal: Lawn Farm, Beambridge, Aston on Clun, Craven Arms, Shropshire, SY7 0HA
Contacts: **PHONE (01588) 660424**

1 **DELLA SUN (FR)**, 10, b g Della Francesca (USA)—Algarve Sunrise (IRE) **A. J. Whitehead**
2 **JAWAHAL DU MATHAN (FR)**, 8, b g Smadoun (FR)—Stone's Glow (USA) **A. J. Whitehead**
3 **ZALGARRY (FR)**, 9, b g Ballingarry (IRE)—Spleen (FR) **A. J. Whitehead**

Conditional: Josh Wall.

---

646 **MR ARTHUR WHITING, Dursley**
Postal: 38 Barrs Lane, North Nibley, Dursley, Gloucestershire, GL11 6DT
Contacts: **PHONE (01453) 546375 MOBILE (07786) 152539**

1 **BARRS LANE**, 8, b m Sir Harry Lewis (USA)—Cashel Dancer **A. J. Whiting**
2 **BONNIE BLACK ROSE**, 6, b m Black Sam Bellamy (IRE)—Fragrant Rose **A. J. Whiting**
3 **ITSUPTOYOU (IRE)**, 12, b g Dr Massini—I Blame Theparents **A. J. Whiting**
4 **THE WEE MIDGET**, 11, b g Mtoto—Fragrant Rose **A. J. Whiting**

---

647 **MR CHARLES WHITTAKER, Frome**
Postal: West Forest Farm, Gare Hill, Frome, Somerset, BA11 5EZ
Contacts: **PHONE (01373) 836500 MOBILE (07966) 762109**
WEBSITE www.westforestfarmracing.co.uk

1 **BANCO DE LOGOS (FR)**, 5, b g Laverock (IRE)—Funkia (FR) **Miss H. E. Hodge**
2 **CAP HORNER (FR)**, gr g Apsis—Rapsodie Sea (FR)
3 **CHINATOWN BOY (IRE)**, 8, ch g Presenting—Asian Maze (IRE)
4 **GARDE FORESTIER (FR)**, 4, b g Forestier (FR)—Nette Rousse (FR)
5 **RUAPEHU (IRE)**, 10, b g Presenting—Silver Prayer (IRE) **C. R. Whittaker**
6 **SOUTHFIELD FAIRY**, 5, b m Victory Note (USA)—Laureldean Belle (IRE) **Mrs A. B. Yeoman**

648 **MR HARRY WHITTINGTON, Sparsholt**
Postal: Hill Barn, Sparsholt, Wantage, Oxfordshire, OX12 9XB
Contacts: **PHONE (01235) 751869 MOBILE (07734) 388357**
E-MAIL harry@harrywhittington.co.uk WEBSITE www.harrywhittington.co.uk

1 **AFFAIRE D'HONNEUR (FR)**, 5, ch g Shirocco (GER)—Affaire de Moeurs (FR) **Mr A. Holt**
2 **ARZAL (FR)**, 6, b br g Vendangeur (IRE)—Ghostaline (FR) **The Hennessy Six**
3 **BIG SOCIETY (IRE)**, 10, b g Flemensfirth (USA)—Choice of Kings (IRE) **Hill Barn Racing Club**
4 **BIGMARTRE (FR)**, 5, b g Montmartre (FR)—Oh La Miss (FR) **P. J. Dixon**
5 **CRISTAL DE SIENNE (FR)**, 4, b g Montmartre (FR)—Heroine de Sienne (FR)
6 **DRIFTER (IRE)**, 5, b g Footstepsinthesand—Bright Bank (IRE) **The Boardwalk Partnership**
7 **DUKE OF MEDINA (IRE)**, 4, br g Rock of Gibraltar (IRE)—Daruliyya (IRE) **Exors of the late Mr H. J. M. Webb**
8 **EMERGING FORCE (IRE)**, 6, b g Milan—Danette (GER) **Webb Holt Carpenter Tucker**
9 **FATCATINTHEHAT**, 7, b g Authorized (IRE)—Fin **The Felix Partnership**
10 **FOUROVAKIND**, 11, b g Sir Harry Lewis (USA)—Four M's **Andrew F. Sawyer, G. W. Hazell & C. Bosley**
11 **FRIZZO (FR)**, 9, ch g Ballingarry (IRE)—Floridene (FR) **Hill Barn Racing Club**
12 **HOKE COLBURN (IRE)**, 4, br g Beneficial—Ravaleen (IRE) **Aylett, Batcheler, Cox, McCarthy**
13 **MOLLASSES**, 5, b m Authorized (IRE)—Muscovado (USA) **Atkin, Bullen-Smith, Gamon, Pelly**
14 **PASSING DU MOULIN (FR)**, 5, gr g Passing Sale (FR)—
　　　　　　　　　　　　　　　　　　　Ruaha River (FR) **Holt,Macnabb,Robinson,Taylor,Tucker**
15 **PATRONNE (FR)**, 4, b f Solon (GER)—Parla (GER) **Mrs C. Atkin and Mrs L. Bullen-Smith**
16 **PINK PLAY (IRE)**, 5, b m King's Theatre (IRE)—Strawberry Fool (FR) **P. G. Jacobs**
17 **POLSTAR (FR)**, 7, b g Poliglote—Star Dancing **Dixon,Ellis,Lynds,Travers,Watkins**
18 **QASSER (IRE)**, 7, b g Intikhab (USA)—Surrender To Me (USA) **Lead The Way Syndicate**
19 **SCARPER (IRE)**, 4, ch g Getaway (GER)—Whats Anothershuil (IRE) **P. G. Jacobs & Partners**
20 **TIERRA VERDE**, 5, b m Josr Algarhoud (IRE)—La Corujera **Greenlands Farm Stud**
21 **WOOLSTONE ONE**, 4, b f Authorized (IRE)—Saralea (FR) **P. G. Jacobs**
22 **ZEPHYROS BLEU (IRE)**, 6, b g Westerner—Quel Bleu (IRE) **Atkin, Bellman, Chamberlain, Murray**

Other Owners: Mrs Catherine Atkin, Mr T. Aylett, Mr S. Batcheler, Mr Laurence A. Bellman, Mr C. Bosley, Mr David J. Buckley, Mrs L. Bullen-Smith, Mr Brian Carpenter, Mr K. Cox, Mr P. J. Dixon, Mr D. Ellis, Mrs A. Fitzgerald-O'Connor, Mrs Michele Gamon, Mrs Helen Harvey, Mr G. Hazell, Mr M. G. Hazell, Mr A. Holt, Mr Ian Macnabb, Mr K. McCarthy, Mr Ian Murray, Mrs Susie Pelly, Mr J. Robinson, Mr Andrew F. Sawyer, Mr G. M. Spencer, Mr A. Taylor, Mr A. Tucker, Mrs Isobel Webb, Mr H. Whittington, Mr Steven Willis.

Assistant Trainer: Paul O'Brien

649 **MR MICHAEL WIGHAM, Newmarket**
Postal: Hamilton Stables, Hamilton Road, Newmarket, Suffolk, CB8 7JQ
Contacts: **PHONE (01638) 668806 FAX (01638) 668806 MOBILE (07831) 456426**
E-MAIL michaelwigham@hotmail.co.uk WEBSITE www.michaelwighamracing.co.uk

1 **ALI BIN NAYEF**, 4, b g Nayef (USA)—Maimoona (IRE) **P J Edwards & M Wigham**
2 **CREDIT SWAP**, 11, b g Diktat—Locharia **Palatinate Thoroughbred Racing Limited**
3 **DEMBABA (IRE)**, 4, b g Moss Vale (IRE)—Wildsplash (USA) **Palatinate Thoroughbred Racing, D Hassan**
4 **ELIS ELIZ (IRE)**, 4, b f Lord Shanakill (USA)—Suailce (IRE) **Mr T. Akman**
5 **FAIRWAY TO HEAVEN (IRE)**, 7, b g Jeremy (USA)—Luggala (IRE) **Palatinate Thoroughbred Racing Limited**
6 **FOXY FOREVER (IRE)**, 6, b g Kodiac—Northern Tara (IRE) **D. Hassan, J. Cullinan**
7 **GIN AND TONIC**, 6, ch g Phoenix Reach (IRE)—Arctic Queen **The Gin & Tonic Partnership**
8 **HAPPY JACK (IRE)**, 5, b g Elusive City (USA)—Miss Pelling (IRE) **G. D. J. Linder**
9 **MY TARGET (IRE)**, 5, b g Cape Cross (IRE)—Chercheuse (USA) **Mr Tugay Akman & Mr John B Williams**
10 **NINETEENTH HOLE (IRE)**, 4, b g Dark Angel (IRE)—
　　　　　　　　　　　　　　　　　Kingpin Delight **Palatinate Thoroughbred Racing, D Hassan**
11 **TEXAS SCRAMBLE**, 4, b g Nayef (USA)—Footlight Fantasy (USA) **Palatinate Thoroughbred Racing, D Hassan**
12 **TOMBISH (FR)**, 4, ch c Three Valleys (USA)—Dalawala (IRE) **T Akman & D Hassan**
13 **TROJAN ROCKET (USA)**, 8, b g Elusive City (USA)—Tagula Bay (IRE) **G Linder, D Hassan, R Warner**

THREE-YEAR-OLDS

14 B c Zebedee—Nairobi (FR) **Palatinate Thoroughbred Racing, D Hassan**
15 **ROYAL BLOSSOM (IRE)**, b f Royal Applause—Dynacam (USA) **Follow The Flag Partnership**
16 B g Acclamation—Week End **Palatinate Thoroughbred Racing, D Hassan**

MR MICHAEL WIGHAM - Continued

TWO-YEAR-OLDS

17 B c 1/3 Zebedee—Tipperary Boutique (IRE) (Danehill Dancer (IRE)) (13000) **T Akman & D Hassan**

Other Owners: Mr C. T. Appleton, J. Cullinan, Mr P. J. Edwards, R. A. Popely, D. J. Popely, R. Warner, M. Wigham, Mr J. B. Williams.

Assistant Trainer: Sharon Kenyon

---

650 **MR MARTIN WILESMITH, Dymock**
Postal: **Bellamys Farm, Dymock, Gloucestershire, GL18 2DX**
Contacts: **PHONE (01531) 890410 (01684) 561238 FAX (01684) 893428 MOBILE (07970) 411638**
E-MAIL martin@mswilesmith.co.uk

1 FAIR ALICE, 7, gr m Fair Mix (IRE)—Mrs White (IRE) **M. S. Wilesmith**
2 GREENWAY CROSS, 9, b g Alflora (IRE)—Might Be **M. S. Wilesmith**
3 LORD BELLAMY (IRE), 14, b g Lord Americo—Paean Express (IRE) **M. S. Wilesmith**
4 MIDNIGHT FRENSI, 7, b g Midnight Legend—Flame O'frensi **M. S. Wilesmith**
5 6, B m Black Sam Bellamy (IRE)—Mrs White (IRE) **M. S. Wilesmith**
6 RED OATS, 10, ch m Alflora (IRE)—Silk Oats **M. S. Wilesmith**
7 SHE'SOLOVELY, 12, b m Alflora (IRE)—Cashmere Lady **M. S. Wilesmith**
8 SILK ROSE, 12, gr m Terimon—Silk Oats **M. S. Wilesmith**

Assistant Trainer: Ms E. C. Wilesmith (07976 926906)

---

651 **MR DAI WILLIAMS, Lambourn**
Postal: **21 Beales Farm Road, Lambourn, Hungerford, Berkshire, RG17 8PZ**
Contacts: **HOME (01488) 638636 FAX (01488) 638121 MOBILE (07879) 403160 (07879) 403595**

1 BALLYADEEN (IRE), 8, b g King's Theatre (IRE)—Akilara (IRE) **Mr F. Michael**
2 NEAREST THE PIN (IRE), 11, b g Court Cave (IRE)—Carnbelle (IRE) **R. J. Hewitt**
3 PETIT ECUYER (FR), 10, b g Equerry (USA)—Petite Majeste (FR) **Mr F. Michael**
4 PONIEL, 4, b g Bahri (USA)—Rafta (IRE) **Mr S. R. Williams**
5 WEST OF THE EDGE (IRE), 8, b g Westerner—Bermuda Bay (IRE) **Mr F. Michael**

Assistant Trainer: Miss Lucy Horner

Amateur: Miss L. Horner.

---

652 **MR EVAN WILLIAMS, Llancarfan**
Postal: **Aberogwrn Farm, Llancarfan, Nr Barry, Vale of Glamorgan**
Contacts: **PHONE (01446) 754069 FAX (01446) 754069 MOBILE (07950) 381227**
E-MAIL cath@evanwilliams.co.uk WEBSITE www.evanwilliamsracing.co.uk

1 AERLITE SUPREME (IRE), 9, b g Gold Well—Supreme Evening (IRE) **Mr M. J. Haines**
2 ALLEZ VIC (IRE), 10, b g Old Vic—Newgate Fairy **Mr R. J. Gambarini**
3 AQUA DUDE (IRE), 6, br g Flemensfirth (USA)—Miss Cozzene (FR) **Mr & Mrs William Rucker**
4 ARMCHAIR THEATRE (IRE), 6, b g King's Theatre (IRE)—Oh Susannah (FR) **Ms S. A. Howell**
5 BACH DE CLERMONT (FR), 5, b g Della Francesca (USA)—Fleur de Princesse (FR) **Mr & Mrs William Rucker**
6 BALLYGLASHEEN (IRE), 6, ch g Galileo (IRE)—Luas Line (IRE) **Mr R. J. Gambarini**
7 BARRAKILLA (IRE), 9, b g Milan—Kigali (IRE) **Mr & Mrs William Rucker**
8 BATTLECAT, 9, b g Tiger Hill (IRE)—Applecross **Gwili Syndicate**
9 BLANDFORDS GUNNER, 7, b g Needle Gun (IRE)—Miss Millbrook **Kevin & Anne Glastonbury**
10 BONOBO (IRE), 9, b g Quws—Better Folly (IRE) **Mary & Billy Evans**
11 BUCK MULLIGAN, 11, b g Robellino (USA)—Music Park (IRE) **Mr T. L. Fell**
12 BUYWISE (IRE), 9, b g Tikkanen (USA)—Greenogue Princess (IRE) **T. H. Jones**
13 CANICALLYOUBACK, 8, b g Auction House (USA)—Island Colony (USA) **Mrs D. E. Cheshire**
14 CAPE CASTER (IRE), 5, br g Cape Cross (IRE)—Playboy Mansion (IRE) **D P Barrie & D Redhead**
15 CAPILLA (IRE), 8, gr g Beneficial—Cap The Rose (IRE) **Mrs J. Davies**
16 CATCHER ON THE GO (IRE), 6, b g Catcher In The Rye (IRE)—Suspicious Minds **R. E. R. Williams**

MR EVAN WILLIAMS - Continued

17 **CLYNE**, 6, b g Hernando (FR)—Lauderdale (GER) **Mr D. M. Williams**
18 **COPPER BIRCH (IRE)**, 8, ch g Beneficial—Giverhertime (IRE) **Mrs J. Davies**
19 **COURT MINSTREL (IRE)**, 9, b g Court Cave (IRE)—Theatral **Mrs J. Davies**
20 **DARK SPIRIT (IRE)**, 8, b m Whipper (USA)—Dark Raider (IRE) **Richard Abbott & Mario Stavrou**
21 **DE BENE ESSE (IRE)**, 6, br g Scorpion (IRE)—Benedicta Rose (IRE) **Mr & Mrs William Rucker**
22 **DE FAOITHESDREAM (IRE)**, 10, br g Balakheri (IRE)—Cutteen Lass (IRE) **Mr R Abbott & Mr M Stavrou**
23 **DYE OF A NEEDLE (IRE)**, 6, ch g Lakeshore Road (USA)—Laskine (IRE) **A Turton & J Blackburn**
24 **ESSPRESSO (FR)**, 4, gr g Croco Rouge (IRE)—Kaldoubelle (FR) **Mr M. J. Haines**
25 **FILLE DES CHAMPS (IRE)**, 5, b m Robin des Champs (FR)—South Queen Lady (IRE) **Mrs J. Davies**
26 **FIREBIRD FLYER (IRE)**, 6, b g Winged Love (IRE)—Kiora Lady (IRE) **R. E. R. Williams**
27 **FORGIVIENNE**, 9, b m Alflora (IRE)—Always Forgiving **Gwili Syndicate**
28 5, B g Darsi (FR)—Geray Lady (IRE) **W. Williams**
29 **GO LONG (IRE)**, 6, b g Hurricane Run (IRE)—Monumental Gesture **Mr & Mrs William Rucker**
30 **GOING CONCERN (IRE)**, 9, b g Overbury (IRE)—Scorpio Girl **Mr P. M. Langford**
31 **GOLD BONNE RAINE (IRE)**, 5, b m Gold Well—Be My Bonne **Mr J. V. Byrne**
32 **GORMAN (FR)**, 5, ch g King's Best (USA)—Gerone (FR) **Mr M. J. Haines**
33 **GRANDASOWT (IRE)**, 7, b g Darsi (FR)—Cookscrove Rosie (IRE) **Mrs C. A. Williams**
34 **HUGHESIE (IRE)**, 7, b g Indian Danehill (IRE)—Collatrim Choice (IRE) **Mr A. Turton & Mr P. Langford**
35 **IN ON THE ACT**, 6, b g Act One—Pequenita **Mr D. M. Williams**
36 **IN THE HOLD (IRE)**, 6, b g Stowaway—Carrigeen Kerria (IRE) **Mr & Mrs William Rucker**
37 **IT'S A STEAL (IRE)**, 9, b g Craigsteel—Mimosa Rose (IRE) **Mr & Mrs William Rucker**
38 **JINSHA LAKE (IRE)**, 4, b c Galileo (IRE)—Al Ihsas (IRE) **Losing Control Partnership**
39 **JOHN CONSTABLE (IRE)**, 5, b h Montjeu (IRE)—Dance Parade (USA) **Walters Plant Hire Ltd**
40 **JUST BILL (IRE)**, 8, b g Blueprint (IRE)—Husdale (IRE) **Mrs C. A. Williams**
41 **KING MASSINI (IRE)**, 10, b g Dr Massini (IRE)—King's Linnet (IRE) **Border Pointers**
42 **KING'S ODYSSEY (IRE)**, 7, b g King's Theatre (IRE)—Ma Furie (FR) **Mr & Mrs William Rucker**
43 **KUDU COUNTRY (IRE)**, 10, gr g Captain Rio—Nirvavita (FR) **W. J. Evans**
44 **LASER HAWK (IRE)**, 9, b g Rashar (USA)—Alphablend (IRE) **W. J. Evans**
45 **LAVA LAMP (GER)**, 9, b g Shamardal (USA)—La Felicita **Mrs J. Davies**
46 **LITTLE DREAM (IRE)**, 9, b m Beneficial—Miss Franco (IRE) **Mrs E. Magee**
47 **MAC BERTIE**, 7, b g Beat All (USA)—Macnance (IRE) **Keith & Sue Lowry**
48 **MAC GREGORY**, 5, b g Multiplex—Macnance (IRE) **Keith & Sue Lowry**
49 **MAXANISI (IRE)**, 6, br g Kalanisi (IRE)—Maxis Girl (IRE) **Mrs J. Davies**
50 **MILESTONE (IRE)**, 6, b g Galileo (IRE)—Cassydora **Mr R. J. Gambarini**
51 **MONYJEAN (FR)**, 5, b g Califet (FR)—Rose Beryl (FR) **Mr & Mrs William Rucker**
52 **MOORLANDS MIST**, 9, gr g Fair Mix (IRE)—Sandford Springs (USA) **J. T. Warner**
53 **MR KIT CAT**, 6, ch g Lucarno (USA)—Makeabreak (IRE) **Mr & Mrs William Rucker**
54 **MY LIEGE (IRE)**, 5, b g Marienbard (IRE)—Smashing Leader (IRE) **Mr & Mrs William Rucker**
55 **NANSAROY**, 6, br g Indian River (FR)—Jurado Park (IRE) **T. H. Jones**
56 **NORDICAL (IRE)**, 6, b g Beneficial—Nordic Abu (IRE) **R. E. R. Williams**
57 **OMGNOTANOTHER (IRE)**, 5, b m Scorpion (IRE)—Hot Bunny (IRE) **David M. Manning Ltd**
58 **ON THE ROAD (IRE)**, 6, b g Stowaway—B Greenhill **Mrs C. A. Williams**
59 **ON TOUR (IRE)**, 8, b g Croco Rouge (IRE)—Galant Tour (IRE) **T. H. Jones**
60 **OSCAR SUNSET (IRE)**, 9, b g Oscar (IRE)—Derravarra Sunset (IRE) **Geoff & Anne Price**
61 **OXWICH BAY (IRE)**, 4, b g Westerner—Rose de Beaufai (FR) **Mr D. M. Williams**
62 **PADGE (IRE)**, 7, b g Flemensfirth (USA)—Mona Vic (IRE) **Mr & Mrs William Rucker**
63 **POBBLES BAY (IRE)**, 6, b g Oscar (IRE)—Rose de Beaufai (FR) **Mr D. M. Williams**
64 **POSITIVELY DYLAN**, 5, b g Multiplex—Wou Oodd **Mrs J. Davies**
65 **PRESENT TIMES (IRE)**, 5, b g Kalanisi (IRE)—Beguiling (IRE) **Mrs C. A. Waters**
66 **PRIME VENTURE (IRE)**, 5, br g Primary (IRE)—Next Venture (IRE) **Mrs J. Davies**
67 **PRIMO MILANO**, 7, b g Milan—She's Our Native (IRE) **I. C. Brice**
68 **ROADIE JOE (IRE)**, 7, b g Golan (IRE)—Granny Clampett (IRE) **Mr W. P. Bates**
69 5, B g Morozov (USA)—Saltee Great (IRE) **R. E. R. Williams**
70 5, B g Gold Well—Shamriyna (IRE) **R. E. R. Williams**
71 **SHREWD TACTICS (IRE)**, 5, ch g Broadway Flyer (USA)—Taking My Time (IRE) **Mr & Mrs William Rucker**
72 **STILL BELIEVING (IRE)**, 8, ch m Blueprint (IRE)—Im A Believer (IRE) **R. E. R. Williams**
73 **SUBLIME TALENT (IRE)**, 10, b g Sadler's Wells (USA)—Summer Trysting (USA) **Mrs C. A. Williams**
74 **TEA IN TRANSVAAL (IRE)**, 5, b m Teofilo (IRE)—Mpumalanga **Mr M. J. Haines**
75 **TENANT FARMER (IRE)**, 6, gr g Touch of Land (FR)—Miss McCormick (IRE) **R. E. R. Williams**
76 **THE BUGLER (IRE)**, 9, ch g Rock of Gibraltar (IRE)—Purple Spirit (IRE) **W. J. Evans**
77 **THE GIPPER (IRE)**, 8, b g King's Theatre (IRE)—Merrill Gaye (IRE) **POS Partnership**
78 5, B g Brian Boru—The Rebel Lady (IRE) **R. E. R. Williams**
79 **TORNADO IN MILAN (IRE)**, 10, b g Milan—Julika (GER) **Mrs C. A. Williams**
80 **WABANAKI (IRE)**, 6, b g Indian River (FR)—Treasure Island **Walters Plant Hire & James & Jean Potter**
81 **WILD BILL (IRE)**, 7, b g Westerner—Sarahall (IRE) **Mr & Mrs William Rucker**

MR EVAN WILLIAMS - Continued

82 **WYCHWOODS BROOK,** 10, b g Midnight Legend—Miss Millbrook **Kevin & Anne Glastonbury**
83 **WYLDE MAGIC (IRE),** 5, b g Oscar (IRE)—Voodoo Magic (GER) **Mr & Mrs William Rucker**
84 **ZAMA ZAMA,** 9, b g Sakhee (USA)—Insinuation (IRE) **Tony Cromwell & Partner**
85 **ZARZAL (IRE),** 8, b g Dr Fong (USA)—Zarwala (IRE) **Mrs J. Davies**

Other Owners: R. J. Abbott, D. P. Barrie, J. N. Blackburn, Mr C. T. Cromwell, M. V. Dawson, Mr W. J. Eddy-Williams, J. R. Edwards, Mrs M. Evans, Mr D. C. Footman, K. J. Glastonbury, Mrs A. J. Glastonbury, Mr P Griffiths, Ms L. Judah, Mrs S. B. Lowry, K. R. Lowry, W. J. G. Morse, Mrs M. J. Potter, Mr G. Price, Mrs A. C. Price, Mr D. P. Redhead, M. J. Rees, Mrs A. Rucker, W. J. Rucker, M. Stavron, Mr D. Thomas, D. I. Thomas, Mr C. Trigg, Mr A. Turton, Mr J. Whiting, Mr S. Williams.

Assistant Trainer: Cath Williams

Jockey (NH): Paul Moloney, Adam Wedge. **Conditional:** Lewis Gordon, Cian Maher, Conor Ring. **Amateur:** Mr Conor Orr, Miss Charlotte Pritchard, Mr Jamie Thomas, Miss Isabel Williams.

---

653 MR IAN WILLIAMS, Alvechurch
Postal: **Dominion Racing Stables, Seafield Lane, Alvechurch, Birmingham, B48 7HL**
Contacts: **PHONE (01564) 822392 FAX (01564) 829475 MOBILE (07976) 645384**
E-MAIL **info@ianwilliamsracing.com** WEBSITE **www.ianwilliamsracing.com**

1 **ADMAN SAM (IRE),** 5, b g Black Sam Bellamy (IRE)—Koral Bay (FR) **Mr P. A. Downing**
2 **AGHA DES MOTTES (FR),** 6, b g Mister Sacha (FR)—Java des Mottes (FR) **Mr A. L. R. Morton**
3 4, B g Mahler—Aos Dana (IRE)
4 **BALLYALTON (IRE),** 9, b g Pierre—Almilto (IRE) **Mr J. Westwood**
5 **BALLYFARSOON (IRE),** 5, ch g Medicean—Amzara (IRE) **P. Kelly**
6 **BAMAKO DU CHATELET (FR),** 5, gr g Voix du Nord (FR)—Royale du Chatelet (FR) **Macable Partnership**
7 **BARON DU PLESSIS (FR),** 5, b g Network (GER)—Larme A L'oeil (FR) **Mrs J. Hitchings**
8 **BOBCATBILLY (IRE),** 10, b g Overbury (IRE)—Cush Jewel (IRE) **The Ferandlin Peaches**
9 **BODEGA,** 8, b g Grape Tree Road—Gurleigh (IRE) **Mr P. R. Williams**
10 **BOY IN THE BAR,** 5, ch g Dutch Art—Lipsia (IRE) **Sovereign Racing**
11 **BYRON FLYER,** 5, b g Byron—Nursling (IRE) **Anchor Men**
12 **CALDEY,** 7, b m Overbury (IRE)—Barfleur (IRE) **Miss C. A. Smith**
13 **CHORLTON HOUSE,** 4, ch g Compton Place—Really Ransom **Ian Williams Racing Club**
14 **CONRY (IRE),** 10, ch g Captain Rio—Altizaf **Mr & Mrs H. Parmar**
15 **COOL SKY,** 7, b g Millkom—Intersky High (USA) **Norte Sur Partnership**
16 **COTILLION,** 10, b g Sadler's Wells (USA)—Riberac **Mr J. Roberts**
17 **DIAKTOROS (IRE),** 6, b g Red Clubs (IRE)—Rinneen (IRE) **Mr S Hassiakos & Sir Alex Ferguson**
18 **ETANIA,** 8, b m King's Theatre (IRE)—Linnet (GER) **Mr & Mrs H. Parmar**
19 **FERRYVIEW PLACE,** 7, b g Compton Place—Songsheet **Mr J. Rocke**
20 **FREDO (IRE),** 12, ch g Lomitas—Felina (GER) **Mrs J. S. Allen**
21 **FREUD (FR),** 6, b g Dalakhani (IRE)—Ailette **J. Tredwell**
22 **GAMBOL (FR),** 6, ch g New Approach (IRE)—Guardia (GER) **Eventmasters Racing**
23 **GASOLINE (IRE),** 4, b g Mahler—Judelle de Thou (FR) **Mr P. A. Downing**
24 **GHOST OF A SMILE (IRE),** 8, b g Oscar (IRE)—Dix Huit Brumaire (FR) **Mr S. Cox**
25 **GLENGRA (IRE),** 7, gr g Beneficial—Zaraza (IRE) **The Ferandlin Peaches**
26 **GOODWOOD MOONLIGHT,** 4, gr g Azamour (IRE)—Corrine (IRE) **Miss J. A. Leighs**
27 **GRAND GIGOLO (FR),** 7, b g Enrique—Belle D'ecajeul (FR) **Mr P. A. Downing**
28 **HENRYBROWNEYES (IRE),** 7, ch g Goldmark (USA)—The Vine Browne (IRE) **Mr P. R. Williams**
29 **HOPEFORDEBEST (IRE),** 6, b g Zagreb (USA)—Rapsan (IRE) **Macable Partnership**
30 **HOWABOUTNEVER (IRE),** 8, b g Shantou (USA)—Sarah's Cottage (IRE) **Brannon, Dick, Hernon & Holden**
31 **HOWABOUTNOW (IRE),** 9, ch g Shantou (USA)—Sarah's Cottage (IRE) **Brannon, Dick, Hernon & Holden**
32 **INDIAN CASTLE (IRE),** 8, b g Dr Massini (IRE)—Indian Legend (IRE) **Askew Dick Hernon Reynard**
33 **JACK HENRI (FR),** 5, ch g Kapgarde (FR)—Luba (FR) **Mr P. A. Downing**
34 **JAM SESSION (IRE),** 4, ch g Duke of Marmalade (IRE)—Night Dhu **M. H. Watt**
35 **KAPSTADT (FR),** 6, b br g Country Reel (USA)—King's Parody (IRE) **Anchor Men**
36 **KING OF REALMS (IRE),** 4, b g King's Theatre (IRE)—
  Sunny South East (IRE) **Chandler Ferguson Hanafin Kelly Westwood**
37 **LE MAITRE CHAT (USA),** 5, b g Tale of The Cat (USA)—Bedside Story **M. H. Watt**
38 **LEATH ACRA MOR (IRE),** 10, b g King's Theatre (IRE)—Happy Native (IRE) **I. P. Williams**
39 **MALVIA,** 4, b g Exceed And Excel (AUS)—Always On My Mind **Karmaa Racing Limited**
40 **MCDELTA,** 6, b g Delta Dancer—McNairobi **Jim Mellon & Partners**
41 **MIDTECH STAR (IRE),** 4, b g Kodiac—Royal Rival (IRE) **Midtech**

MR IAN WILLIAMS - Continued

42 **MIDTECH VALENTINE,** 5, b m Act One—Eveon (IRE) **Midtech**
43 **MONALEEN (IRE),** 5, b br m High Chaparral (IRE)—Dawn Air (USA) **Farranamanagh**
44 **MR BISSTO,** 4, b g High Chaparral (IRE)—Senta's Dream **S. & A. Mares & J. & L. Rawlings**
45 **MR VENDMAN (IRE),** 6, b g Whipper—So Precious (IRE) **Mr R. Little**
46 **MY DAD SYD (USA),** 4, b br g Acclamation—Weekend Fling (USA) **S. Rudolf**
47 **NO CEILING (IRE),** 6, b g Turtle Island (IRE)—Pyrexie (FR) **The Ferandlin Peaches**
48 **NORTH HILL (IRE),** 5, b g Westerner—Hill Fairy **D. A. Thorpe**
49 **PARIS SNOW,** 6, b g Montjeu (IRE)—Snow Key (USA) **Ian Williams Racing Club**
50 **PENSAX BOY,** 4, b g Rail Link—Cyclone Connie **S. & A. Mares**
51 **PERCELLA,** 4, b f Sir Percy—Temple of Thebes (USA) **I. P. Williams**
52 **PERFECT SUMMER (IRE),** 6, b m High Chaparral (IRE)—Power of Future (GER) **Mr G. Schoening**
53 **POKER SCHOOL (IRE),** 6, b g Gold Well—Broken Pockets (IRE) **Aniol Chandler Medcroft Turner Westwood**
54 **PORTWAY FLYER (IRE),** 8, br g King's Theatre (IRE)—Next Best Thing (IRE) **P. Kelly**
55 **PSYCHOCANDY (IRE),** 4, b f Oscar (IRE)—Derrigra Sublime (IRE) **Mr S. Cox**
56 **RED INFANTRY (IRE),** 6, ch g Indian River (FR)—Red Rover **Mr R. Little**
57 4, B f Kalanisi (IRE)—Reseda (GER)
58 **ROCKNROLLRAMBO (IRE),** 9, b g Winged Love (IRE)—Lady Padivor (IRE) **Ian Williams Racing Club**
59 **SHADY MCCOY (USA),** 6, b g English Channel (USA)—Raw Gold (USA) **Allwins Stables**
60 **SIR MAXIMILIAN (IRE),** 7, b g Royal Applause—Nebraska Lady (IRE) **Mr P. E. Wildes**
61 **SOLIX (FR),** 10, b br g Al Namix (FR)—Solimade (FR)
62 **SONOFAGUN (FR),** 10, b g Turgeon (USA)—Detonante (FR) **The Piranha Partnership**
63 **SUPER DUTY (IRE),** 10, b g Shantou (USA)—Sarah's Cottage (IRE) **Brannon, Dick, Hernon & Holden**
64 **SWINGING HAWK (GER),** 10, ch g Hawk Wing (USA)—Saldenschwinge (GER) **R. J. Turton**
65 **SWINTON DIAMOND (IRE),** 5, b g Dubai Destination (USA)—Absent Beauty (IRE) **Mr & Mrs I P Earnshaw**
66 **SWIZZLER (IRE),** 7, b g Scorpion (IRE)—Arch Hall Lady (IRE) **Mr P. P. Elliott**
67 **THE PERFECT CRIME (IRE),** 7, b g Oscar (IRE)—Gimme Peace (IRE) **Mr S. Cox**
68 **THEHOSSBEHIND (IRE),** 5, ch g Mahler—Bayloughbess (IRE) **The Piranha Partnership**
69 **TRUCKERS FIRST,** 8, b m Kayf Tara—Cheeky Trucker **S. F. Benton**
70 **TWOJAYSLAD,** 7, b g Kayf Tara—Fulwell Hill **J. Tredwell**
71 **VIRGIL EARP,** 9, b g Fasliyev (USA)—Karakorum (IRE) **Ian Williams Racing Club**
72 **WATT BRODERICK,** 7, ch g Hawk Wing (USA)—Kingsridge (IRE) **P. Kelly**
73 4, B g Robin des Pres (FR)—Wavering Bee (IRE)

THREE-YEAR-OLDS

74 **JAMINDEH,** b c Zamindar (USA)—Missy Wassie Gal (USA) **Mr N. Martin**
75 B c Ask—Reseda (GER)
76 **SIR RENOS SANTI,** b g Observatory (USA)—Diamond Reef **Karmaa Racing Limited**
77 **SO CELEBRE (GER),** ch g Peintre Celebre (USA)—Saldennahe (GER) **Michael Watt & Roy David**
78 **ST ANDREWS (IRE),** ch g Rip Van Winkle (IRE)—Stellavera (FR) **S. Rudolf**
79 **WHARANE (FR),** br g Diktat—Nova Lady (USA) **TMBS Solutions Ltd & Mr R Ryan**

Other Owners: Mr G. Anderson, Mr A. Aniol, Mr S. A. Cawkwell, Mr A. Chandler, A. Cocum, P. D. Cundell, Mr R. David, Mr A. D. Dick, Dr P. A. I. Doro, Mrs J. Earnshaw, Mr I. P. Earnshaw, Sir A. Ferguson, Mrs M. Forsyth, Mr D. Hanafin, P. V. Harris, Ms R. J. Harris, T. Hart, S. Hassiakos, Mr P. Holden, Mrs D. Hopkins, Mr S. Mackintosh, Mr F. W. Mackintosh, Mr C. R. Mander, Mrs A. Mares, Mr S. Mares, Mr J. R. Medcroft, Mr J. Mellon, Mr A. Miles, Mr M. Morrissey, Mrs A. Morrissey, Mr H. Parmar, Mrs K. Parmar, Mr P. Ratcliffe, Mr J. Rawlings, Mrs L. Rawlings, Mr J. A. Reynard, Mr R. Ryan, Mrs D. Sheasby, Mr E. J. N. Sheasby, Mr S. P. Skinner, TMBS Solutions Ltd, Mr S. W. Turner, Mr L. J. Westwood.

Assistant Trainer: Richard Ryan

Jockey (NH): Will Kennedy, Rob McCarth.

---

654 | **MR NICK WILLIAMS, South Molton**
Postal: **Culverhill Farm, George Nympton, South Molton, Devon, EX36 4JE**
Contacts: **PHONE (01769) 574174 MOBILE (07855) 450379**
E-MAIL nandjwilliams@live.co.uk

1 **AFTER EIGHT SIVOLA (FR),** 6, b g Shaanmer (IRE)—Eva de Chalamont (FR) **Larkhills Racing Partnership III**
2 **AGRAPART (FR),** 5, b b g Martaline—Afragha (FR) **The Gascoigne Brookes Partnership III**
3 **ALFIE SPINNER (IRE),** 11, b g Alflora (IRE)—Little Red Spider **Alan Beard & Brian Beard**
4 **AMOUR D'OR,** 5, b m Winged Love (IRE)—Diletia **French Gold**
5 **AUBUSSON (FR),** 7, b g Ballingarry (IRE)—Katioucha (FR) **Mrs J. R. Williams**
6 **BARRANCO VALLEY,** 5, b g Midnight Legend—Shali San (FR) **John White & Anne Underhill**
7 **BRISE COEUR (FR),** 5, b g Daramsar (FR)—Rose Bombon (FR) **French Gold**

MR NICK WILLIAMS - Continued

8 **CABERNET D'ALENE (FR)**, 4, b g Day Flight—Haifa du Noyer (FR) **Larkhills Racing Partnership**
9 **COO STAR SIVOLA (FR)**, 4, b g Assessor (IRE)—Santorine (FR) **Babbit Racing**
10 **CULTURE DE SIVOLA (FR)**, 4, b f Assessor (IRE)—Neva de Sivola (FR) **Larkhills Racing Partnership II**
11 **DOLORES DELIGHTFUL (FR)**, 6, b m Saint des Saints (FR)—Us Et Coutumes (FR) **Miss E. Morgan**
12 **GRAND COUREUR (FR)**, 4, b br g Grand Couturier—Iris du Berlais (FR) **You Can Be Sure**
13 **HORATIO HORNBLOWER (IRE)**, 8, b br g Presenting—Countess Camilla **H. Davies & R. Davies**
14 **LE ROCHER (FR)**, 6, b g Saint des Saints (FR)—Belle du Roi (FR) **John White & Anne Underhill**
15 **LIMONCELLO (FR)**, 4, b g Maresca Sorrento (FR)—Isarella (GER) **Mrs Jane Williams & Mr R. Stark**
16 **LORD OF THE HOSTS**, 5, gr g Saint des Saints (FR)—Telmar Flyer **Mrs J. N. Humphreys**
17 **MAN FROM MARS**, 4, b g Schiaparelli (GER)—Diletia **Chasing Gold**
18 **ME VOILA (FR)**, 4, b g Turgeon (USA)—Saintenitouche (FR) **Jane Williams, Len Jakeman & Martin Booth**
19 **ONE OF US**, 4, b g Presenting—One Gulp **Forty Winks Syndicate**
20 **QUEEN OF THE STAGE (IRE)**, 6, b m King's Theatre (IRE)—Supreme du Casse (IRE) **Mrs J. R. Williams**
21 **REVE DE SIVOLA (FR)**, 11, b g Assessor (IRE)—Eva de Chalamont (FR) **Paul Duffy Diamond Partnership**
22 **SKY LINO (FR)**, 4, b g Martaline—Sky Dance (FR) **K. Alexander/R. Watts**
23 **SWINCOMBE TOBY**, 4, b g Tobougg (IRE)—Soloism **Yeo Racing Partnership**
24 **TEA FOR TWO**, 7, b g Kayf Tara—One For Me **Mrs Jane Williams & Mr Len Jakeman**
25 **THE COFFEE HUNTER (FR)**, 4, gr g Doctor Dino (FR)—
                                      Mamamia (FR) **Allen, Dunn, Elliott, Hurst, Jones & Williams**
26 **THE ITALIAN YOB (IRE)**, 8, b g Milan—The Rebel Lady (IRE) **The Macaroni Beach Society**
27 **WHAT A SAGA**, 5, b m Sagamix (FR)—Born To Dream (IRE) **Mrs Jane Williams**

THREE-YEAR-OLDS

28 **ADMIRAL BARRATRY (FR)**, b g Soldier of Fortune (IRE)—Haskilclara (FR) **Mr R. Forster**
29 **DAIM PIERJI (FR)**, b g Coastal Path—Keensland (FR) **Mrs Jane Williams**
30 **DAISY DE SIVOLA (FR)**, b f Assessor (IRE)—Kerrana (FR) **Mr K. Alexander**
31 **DENTLEY DE MEE (FR)**, b g Lauro (GER)—Natty Twigy (FR) **Babbit Racing**
32 **DIABLE DE SIVOLA (FR)**, b g Noroit (GER)—Grande Route (IRE) **Mr R. Forster**
33 **DIAMANT BLEU (FR)**, b g Montmartre (FR)—Cate Bleue (FR) **Mrs Jane Williams & Mr Len Jakeman**
34 **FLYING TIGER (IRE)**, bl g Soldier of Fortune (IRE)—Ma Preference (FR) **The Macaroni Beach Society**
35 B g Saint des Saints (FR)—Nanouska (GER) **Mrs Jane Williams**
36 **NIGHT OF SIN (FR)**, gr g Sinndar (IRE)—Natt Musik (FR) **Mr R. Watts & Mr S. Brown**
37 **SIRUH DU LAC (FR)**, b g Turgeon (USA)—Margerie (FR) **John White & Anne Underhill**
38 **SONAR DE SIVOLA (FR)**, b g Noroit (GER)—Protege Moi (FR) **Mr R. Forster**

TWO-YEAR-OLDS

39 **ESPRIT DE SOMOZA (FR)**, b g 29/4 Irish Wells (FR)—
                                      Topaze de Somoza (FR) (Discover d'auteuil (FR)) (19195) **Mr R. Forster**
40 **HTAG (FR)**, b g 30/5 Diamond Boy (FR)—Draga (FR) (Smadoun (FR)) (22886) **Mrs Jane Williams**
41 Ch g 3/4 Gentlewave (IRE)—Imperia II (FR) (Beyssac (FR)) **Mrs Jane Williams**
42 Gr g 18/4 Soldier of Fortune (IRE)—Southwold (FR) (Take Risks (FR)) (22148) **K. Alexander & R. Watts**

Other Owners: Mr K. Alexander, Mr Dave Allen, Mr Kerry Barker, Mr B. Beard, Mr Alan Beard, Dr Martin Booth, Mr N. Brookes, Mr T. H. Chadney, Mrs V. J. Chadney, Mr Kevin Conlan, Dr Chris Cowell, Mr Paul Duffy, Mr B. Dunn, Mr Marcus Freer, Mr Tony Gale, Mr C. Garner, Mr D. A. Gascoigne, Mr A. Holt, Mr Len Jakeman, Mr Joe Lawrence, Mrs Sarah Ling, Miss Eliisa Morgan, Mr David Morgan, Mr K. B. W. Parkhouse, Mr Ian Paye, Mr Martin Pepper, Mr G. C. Pratt, Mr J. Robinson, Mrs Karen Salters, Miss Alice Simmons, Mrs A. Underhill, Mr Ron Watts, Mr A. J. White, Mrs Jane Williams, Mrs K. Y. Yeo.

Assistant Trainer: Mrs Jane Williams

Conditional: Lizzie Kelly. **Amateur:** Mr C. Williams.

---

655 **MR NOEL WILLIAMS, Blewbury**
Postal: **White Shoot, Woodway Road, Blewbury, Didcot, Oxfordshire, OX11 9EY**
Contacts: PHONE (01235) 850806 MOBILE (07887) 718678
E-MAIL info@noelwilliamsracing.co.uk WEBSITE www.noelwilliamsracing.co.uk

1 **AUTHORIZED TOO**, 5, b g Authorized (IRE)—Audaz **Stonepoint Racing Club**
2 **BINGO D'OLIVATE (FR)**, 5, b g Laverock (IRE)—Ombrelle de L'orme (FR) **Didntt Partnership**

MR NOEL WILLIAMS - Continued

3 BRIERY QUEEN, 7, b m King's Theatre (IRE)—Briery Gale **Helen Plumbly & Kathryn Leadbeater**
4 CHANCE TAKEN, 8, b m Overbury (IRE)—New Dawn **Calleva Bloodstock**
5 CINDERFELLA, 5, gr g Sagamix (FR)—Firecracker Lady (IRE) **J.C.Harrison Lee & T.Howard Partnership**
6 DALIANCE (IRE), 7, ch g Dalakhani (IRE)—Everlasting Love **EPDS Racing Partnership 15**
7 FRIENDLY SOCIETY (IRE), 11, ch g Moscow Society (USA)—Friendly Breeze **Whiteshoot Racing**
8 HOT WHISKEY N ICE (IRE), 7, b g Milan—Fair Gina (IRE) **Whitehorsemen**
9 KINCORA FORT (IRE), 7, b g Brian Boru—Glenview Rose (IRE) **EPDS Racing Partnership 8**
10 KING KAYF, 7, b g Kayf Tara—Firecracker Lady (IRE) **J.C.Harrison Lee & T.Howard Partnership**
11 5, B m Shirocco (GER)—Kohiba (IRE) **Withyslade**
12 KRACKATOA KING, 8, b g Kayf Tara—Firecracker Lady (IRE) **J.C.Harrison Lee & T.Howard Partnership**
13 MENACE, 5, ch g Papal Bull—Wishfully Tropical (IRE) **EPDS Racing Twitterati Partnership**
14 MIDNIGHT JITTERBUG, 4, b g Midnight Legend—Heebie Jeebie **Mrs Peter Prowting**
15 MIDNIGHT MERLOT, 4, b g Midnight Legend—Peel Me A Grape **Mrs Peter Prowting**
16 OAST HOUSE, 5, b g Fair Mix (IRE)—Amaretto Rose **Stonepoint Racing Club**
17 PATTARA, 7, b m Kayf Tara—Fortunes Course (IRE) **J. E. Garrett**
18 PRIMO BLUE, 6, b g Primo Valentino (IRE)—Flintwood **Mr R. Skillen**
19 QUANTUM OF SOLACE, 6, b m Kayf Tara—Fashion House **007 Partnership**
20 THEATRE GOER, 7, b m King's Theatre (IRE)—Clover Green (IRE) **Mr N. Williams**
21 TIGERS ROCK, 5, b m Tiger Hill (IRE)—Alexandra S (IRE) **Let's Live Racing**

Other Owners: Mr David Bellamy, Mr David Bond, Mr Alex Clark, Mr N. Clyne, Ms J. C. Harrison-Lee, Mr S. Hind, Miss T. Howard, Mrs Kathryn Leadbeater, Miss Clare Ludlow, Miss Helen Pease, Mrs Helen Plumbly, Mr John Powell, Mr Robert Skillen, Mrs Louise Skillen, Miss T. Sloan.

Jockey (NH): James Banks, Wayne Hutchinson.

---

656 **MR OLLY WILLIAMS, Market Rasen**
Postal: **Stone Stables, Nettleton Top, Market Rasen, Lincolnshire, LN7 6SY**
Contacts: **MOBILE (07793) 111600**
E-MAIL williams.olly@yahoo.co.uk WEBSITE www.ollywilliams.co.uk

1 BURNER (IRE), 4, b g High Chaparral (IRE)—Breathe (FR) **Mr S. Graham**
2 DANBY'S LEGEND, 9, b g Midnight Legend—Miss Danbys **Exors of the Late Mr D. T. Todd**
3 HOOLEY TIME (IRE), 4, b f Rugby (USA)—Rahelly Lady (IRE) **O. Williams**
4 NO RUM (IRE), 4, b g Alfred Nobel (IRE)—Common Rumpus (IRE) **All Right Partnership**
5 TOMMY ATKINS (IRE), 11, br g Blueprint (IRE)—Bit of The Past (IRE) **Mr E. Williams**
6 XENOPHON, 8, b g Phoenix Reach (IRE)—Comtesse Noire (CAN) **Milson Robinson**

THREE-YEAR-OLDS

7 TRICKY DICKY, b g Holy Roman Emperor (IRE)—Tricky Situation **Eight Gents & A Lady**

Other Owners: Mr Ralph Roberts, Mr Mark Spincer, Mrs S. Williams, Mr Evan Williams.

Assistant Trainer: Lynsey Williams

---

657 **MR STUART WILLIAMS, Newmarket**
Postal: **Diomed Stables, Hamilton Road, Newmarket, Suffolk, CB8 0PD**
Contacts: **STABLES/OFFICE (01638) 663984 HOME (01638) 560143 MOBILE (07730) 314102**
E-MAIL stuart@stuartwilliamsracing.co.uk
WEBSITE www.stuartwilliamsracing.co.uk Twitter:@Williamsstuart

1 CREW CUT (IRE), 8, gr g Acclamation—Carabine (USA) **Mr P. W. Stevens**
2 DAISY BOY (IRE), 5, b g Cape Cross (IRE)—Muluk (IRE) **Mr G. M. C. Johnson**
3 DOCTOR PARKES, 10, b g Diktat—Lucky Parkes **The Doctor Parkes Partnership**
4 EXCELLENT GEORGE, 4, b g Exceed And Excel (AUS)—Princess Georgina **D. A. Shekells**
5 FLYING FANTASY, 4, b g Oasis Dream—Disco Volante **Happy Valley Racing & Breeding Limited**
6 HARWOODS STAR (IRE), 6, b g Danehill Dancer (IRE)—Showbiz (IRE) **Mrs C. M. A. Seagroatt**
7 HIGHEST QUALITY (IRE), 4, b f Invincible Spirit (IRE)—Princess Taise (USA) **D. A. Shekells**
8 INVADE (IRE), 4, ch f Intense Focus (USA)—Spinning Well (IRE) **Happy Valley Racing & Breeding Limited**
9 J'ASPIRE, 4, b f Zamindar (USA)—Ipsa Loquitur **Alasdair Simpson**
10 LITTLE LORD NELSON, 4, b g Mount Nelson—Cactus Curtsey **W. E. Enticknap**
11 LUNAR DEITY, 7, b g Medicean—Luminda (IRE) **The Morley Family**

MR STUART WILLIAMS - Continued

12 **MONNA VALLEY**, 4, ch g Exceed And Excel (AUS)—
                                 Monnavanna (IRE) **Happy Valley Racing & Breeding Limited**
13 **MY TRINGALING (IRE)**, 4, ch f Summer Bird (USA)—Lady Amira (USA) **J. W. Parry**
14 **OAKLEY GIRL**, 4, b f Sir Percy—Pivotting **The Parry's**
15 **OHSOSECRET**, 4, ch f Sakhee's Secret—Warden Rose **The Secretly Hopeful Partnership**
16 **PACTOLUS (IRE)**, 5, b g Footstepsinthesand—Gold Marie (GER) **T W Morley & Mrs J Morley**
17 **REALIZE**, 6, b g Zafeen (FR)—Relkida **JKB Racing**
18 **ROYAL BIRTH**, 5, b g Exceed And Excel (AUS)—Princess Georgina **The Morley Family**
19 **RUBAN (IRE)**, 7, ch g Dubawi (IRE)—Piece Unique **Essex Racing Club et al**
20 **SPINNING COBBLERS**, 5, b g Royal Applause—Tychy **Brian Piper & David Cobill**
21 **SUZI'S CONNOISSEUR**, 5, b g Art Connoisseur (IRE)—Suzi Spends (IRE) **Qatar Racing Limited**
22 **UPAVON**, 6, b g Avonbridge—Blaina **Morley, Reynolds & Watkins**
23 **WELEASE BWIAN (IRE)**, 7, b g Kheleyf (USA)—Urbanize (USA) **W. E. Enticknap**

THREE-YEAR-OLDS

24 B g Distorted Humor (USA)—Argyle Pink (USA) **Champion Bloodstock Limited**
25 **BELLE MARE PLAGE**, b f Canford Cliffs (IRE)—Flora Trevelyan **J. W. Parry**
26 **BRING ON A SPINNER**, b g Kheleyf (USA)—Posy Fossil (USA) **J. W. Parry**
27 **CECILE ROYALE**, b f Royal Applause—George's Gift **Mrs M. Shone**
28 **CHERRY KOOL**, b f Kheleyf (USA)—Pretty Kool **Mr B Piper & Mr D Shekells**
29 **FABLE OF ARACHNE**, b f Dick Turpin (IRE)—Las Hilanderas (USA) **D. A. Shekells**
30 **LITTLE KIPLING**, b f Royal Applause—Victoria Montague **D. A. Shekells**
31 **SWEET TEMPTATION (IRE)**, b f Amadeus Wolf—Summer Spice (IRE) **The Morley Family**
32 **TAMARA LOVE (IRE)**, b f Tamayuz—Lovers Peace (IRE) **J. W. Parry**
33 **WORLD'S GREATEST (USA)**, ch f Discreet Cat (USA)—Say You Will (IRE) **D. A. Shekells**

TWO-YEAR-OLDS

34 B f 31/3 Bated Breath—Annapurna (IRE) (Brief Truce (USA)) (24000) **J. W. Parry**
35 B f 2/2 Notnowcato—Crystal Etoile (Dansili) (42000) **J. W. Parry & R. Levitt**
36 Gr c 30/3 Silver Frost (IRE)—Darairya (FR) (Refuse To Bend (IRE)) (1904) **Mr G. M. C. Johnson**
37 B f 9/2 Royal Applause—Eraadaat (IRE) (Intikhab (USA)) (1333) **Mr J. W. Parry**
38 Gr c 27/2 Aussie Rules (USA)—
                               Las Hilanderas (USA) (El Prado (IRE)) (17000) **Miss Emily Stevens and Paul Stevens**
39 Ch c 24/2 Paco Boy (IRE)—
                               Miss Bond (IRE) (Danehill Dancer (IRE)) (3500) **Morris J Russell O Doyle J Murphy Et Al**
40 B f 4/3 Kheleyf (USA)—Pretty Kool (Inchinor) **Mr B Piper & Mr B Riddell**
41 B c 7/2 Iffraaj—Princess Georgina (Royal Applause) (30000) **D. A. Shekells**
42 Ch f 11/4 Foxwedge (AUS)—Unasuming (IRE) (Orpen (USA)) (16000) **Whitsbury Manor Stud**

Other Owners: Mr David Cobill, Mr G. Johnson, Mr Robert Levitt, Mrs H. J. Lewis, Mrs F. M. Midwood, Mr T. W. Morley, Mrs J. Morley, Mr J. W. Parry, Mr B. Piper, Mr Bernard Ralph, Mr David N. Reynolds, Mr Barry Root, Mrs Joan Root, Mr D. A. Shekells, Mr C. D. Watkins, Mr Stuart C. Williams.

Assistant Trainer: Mr J W Parry

Apprentice: Aaron Jones, Milly Naseb.

658	**MISS VENETIA WILLIAMS, Hereford** Postal: **Aramstone, Kings Caple, Hereford, Herefordshire, HR1 4TU** Contacts: **PHONE (01432) 840646 MOBILE (07770) 627108** E-MAIL venetia.williams@virgin.net WEBSITE www.venetiawilliams.com

1 **AACHEN**, 12, b g Rainbow Quest (USA)—Anna of Saxony **Mr A. G. Bloom**
2 **ACHILLE**, 6, gr g Dom Alco (FR)—Hase (FR) **Mrs V. A. Bingham**
3 **ARTHUR'S OAK**, 8, b g Kayf Tara—Myumi **Mrs J. K. Burt**
4 **ASO (FR)**, 6, b br g Goldneyev (USA)—Odyssee du Cellier (FR) **The Bellamy Partnership**
5 **ASTIGOS (FR)**, 9, b br g Trempolino—Astonishing (BRZ) **Mr A. L. Brooks**
6 **AZERT DE COEUR (FR)**, 6, b g Tiger Groom—Eden de Coeur (FR) **Gay & Peter Hartley**
7 **BALLYOLIVER**, 12, b g Kayf Tara—Macklette (IRE) **Mr R. M. Britten-Long**
8 **BECAUSESHESAIDSO (IRE)**, 8, b g Winged Love—Huit de Coeur (FR) **Lady M. A. Bolton**
9 **BELAMI DES PICTONS (FR)**, 5, b g Khalkevi (IRE)—Nina des Pictons (FR) **Hills of Ledbury (AGA)**
10 **BENNYS KING (IRE)**, 5, b g Beneficial—Hellofafaithful (IRE) **Mezzone Family**
11 **BENNYS MIST (IRE)**, 10, b g Beneficial—Dark Mist (IRE) **Mezzone Family**
12 **BOBBLE BORU (IRE)**, 8, b m Brian Boru—Balreask Lady (IRE) **Mr T. Fawcett**

MISS VENETIA WILLIAMS - Continued

13 **BONNE QUESTION (FR)**, 7, gr g Tagula (IRE)—Amonita (GER) **Falcon's Line Ltd**
14 **BUTTERCUP (FR)**, 5, b m Limnos (JPN)—Paranoia (FR) **Boultbee Brooks Ltd**
15 **CASH AND GO (IRE)**, 9, b g Sulamani (IRE)—Calcida (GER) **Mrs C. G. Watson**
16 **CENTURIUS**, 6, ch g New Approach (IRE)—Questina (FR) **Andrew Brooks & Julian Taylor**
17 **CLOUDY BEACH (IRE)**, 9, gr g Cloudings (IRE)—Niki Beach (IRE) **The Beachcombers**
18 **COLD MARCH (FR)**, 6, b br g Early March—Tumultueuse (FR) **Mr A. L. Brooks**
19 **COUDEFOUDRE (FR)**, 4, gr g Martaline—Chamoss World (FR) **Miss V. M. Williams**
20 **DARE ME (IRE)**, 12, b g Bob Back (USA)—Gaye Chatelaine (IRE) **Shire Birds**
21 **DRUMVIREDY (IRE)**, 7, b m Flemensfirth (USA)—Leitrim Bridge (IRE) **The M. Shones**
22 **DU SOLEIL (FR)**, 4, ch g Zambezi Sun—Cykapri (FR) **Mr A. L. Brooks**
23 **DUBAWI ISLAND (FR)**, 7, b g Dubawi (IRE)—Housa Dancer (FR) **Andrew Brooks & Julian Taylor**
24 **ECO WARRIOR**, 6, b g Echo of Light—Kryssa **Mrs J. Blackwell**
25 **ELENIKA (FR)**, 8, gr g Martaline—Nika Glitters (FR) **Janet Bromet & Andrew Brooks**
26 **EMINENT POET**, 5, b g Montjeu (IRE)—Contare **B. C. Dice**
27 **EMPEROR'S CHOICE (FR)**, 9, b g Flemensfirth (USA)—House-of-Hearts (IRE) **The Bellamy Partnership**
28 **FIONN MAC CUL (IRE)**, 5, b g Oscar (IRE)—No Moore Bills **T. J. Hemmings**
29 **GARDEFORT (FR)**, 7, b br g Agent Bleu (FR)—La Fresnaie (FR) **Mr A. L. Brooks**
30 **GORGEHOUS LLIEGE (FR)**, 10, b g Lavirco (GER)—Charme d'estruval (FR) **Mr A. L. Brooks**
31 **GRAND TURINA**, 5, b m Kayf Tara—Cesana (IRE) **A. J. Taylor**
32 **GUANTOSHOL (IRE)**, 5, ch g Sholokhov (IRE)—Glicine (GER) **John Nicholls (Trading) & John Moorhouse**
33 **HOUBLON DES OBEAUX (FR)**, 9, b g Panoramic—Harkosa (FR) **Mrs J. Blackwell**
34 **HOWARD'S LEGACY (IRE)**, 10, b g Generous (IRE)—Ismene (FR) **A. G. Parker**
35 **HUFF AND PUFF**, 9, b g Azamour (IRE)—Coyote **Gay & Peter Hartley**
36 **INHERITANCE THIEF**, 4, b g Black Sam Bellamy (IRE)—Red And White (IRE) **F. M. P. Mahon**
37 **KAP JAZZ (FR)**, 6, b g Kapgarde (FR)—Jazz And Liquer (FR) **Brooks,Vando,Pummell,Martin & Armstrong**
38 **KATARA BAY**, 5, b g Kayf Tara—De Blanc (IRE) **You Can Be Sure**
39 **KATENKO (FR)**, 10, b g Laveron—Katiana (FR) **Mr A. L. Brooks**
40 **KINGS RIVER (FR)**, 7, b br g Lost World (IRE)—Si Parfaite (FR) **Mrs J. Blackwell**
41 **LADY KARINA**, 5, b m Kayf Tara—Lady Rebecca **Kinnersley Optimists**
42 **LEVIATHAN**, 9, b g Dubawi (IRE)—Gipsy Moth **H. E. Ansell**
43 **LIVE MIRACLE (USA)**, 4, b f Falco (USA)—Zaragoza Girl (BRZ) **ROA Arkle Partnership**
44 **LOCHNAGAR (GER)**, 7, b g Sholokhov (IRE)—Lindenblute **Richard Britten-Long & Sarah Williams**
45 **LOWER HOPE DANDY**, 9, gr g Karinga Bay—Cheeky Mare **Mr W. S. C. Richards**
46 **LUTECE**, 4, b f Cape Cross (IRE)—Loutka (FR) **ROA Arkle Partnership**
47 **MARCILHAC (FR)**, 7, b g Smadoun (FR)—One Way (FR) **Mr A. L. Brooks**
48 **MARKET OPTION (IRE)**, 10, b g Lord Americo—Ticklepenny (IRE) **The Gambling Cousins**
49 **MIXCHIEVOUS**, 5, gr g Fair Mix (IRE)—Cheeky Mare **Tolostley Partnership**
50 **ONE STYLE (FR)**, 6, b g Desert Style (IRE)—Arieta (FR) **A. J. Pye-Jeary**
51 **ONEIDA TRIBE (FR)**, 7, b g Turtle Island (IRE)—Glory Queen (IRE) **John Nicholls (Trading) Ltd**
52 **OPERA ROCK (FR)**, 5, b g Kap Rock (FR)—Open Up (FR) **Boultbee Brooks Ltd**
53 **OTAGO TRAIL (IRE)**, 8, b g Heron Island (IRE)—Cool Chic (IRE) **Mrs M. L. Shone**
54 **PINK TARA**, 5, b m Kayf Tara—Red And White (IRE) **F. M. P. Mahon**
55 **POLO (GER)**, 6, ch g Sholokhov (IRE)—Poule d'essai (GER) **Mrs J. Blackwell**
56 **PREMIER BLANC**, 6, b m Kayf Tara—De Blanc (IRE) **Mr Jeremy Hancock**
57 **PRESSURIZE (IRE)**, 10, b g Witness Box (USA)—Cockpit Rose (IRE) **Mrs S. A. Williams**
58 **REDMOND (IRE)**, 6, b g Tikkanen (USA)—Medal Quest (IRE) **Peaky Blinders**
59 **RELAX (FR)**, 11, b g Fragrant Mix (IRE)—Magik (FR) **The Bellamy Partnership**
60 **RENARD (FR)**, 11, b br g Discover d'auteuil (FR)—Kirmelia (FR) **ROA Arkle Partnership 1**
61 **RIGADIN DE BEAUCHENE (FR)**, 11, b br g Visionary (FR)—Chipie d'angron (FR) **Mr A. O. Wiles**
62 **ROSA FLEET (IRE)**, 8, b m Alflora (IRE)—Crimond (IRE) **Mezzone Family**
63 **ROYAL PALLADIUM (FR)**, 8, gr g King's Theatre (IRE)—Dent Sucree (FR) **Mrs A. W. Timpson**
64 **RUSSBOROUGH (FR)**, 7, b g Turgeon (USA)—Heritage River (FR) **Lady M. A. Bolton**
65 **SAROQUE (IRE)**, 9, b g Revoque (IRE)—Sarakin (IRE) **Mr A. L. Brooks**
66 **SHANGANI (USA)**, 10, b g Giant's Causeway (USA)—Tanzania (IRE) **The Bellamy Partnership**
67 **SHIVERMETIMBERS (IRE)**, 4, br g Black Sam Bellamy (IRE)—Kimouna (FR) **Old Carthusian Racing Society**
68 **SUMMERY JUSTICE (IRE)**, 12, b g Witness Box (USA)—Kinsellas Rose (IRE) **Mrs P. Brown**
69 **TAKE THE MICK**, 9, b g Ishiguru (USA)—Michaelmas Daizy **Sir Geoffrey & Lady Vos**
70 **TANGO DE JUILLEY (FR)**, 8, b g Lesotho (USA)—Lasalsa de Juilley (FR) **Mr M. N. Khan**
71 **TARA FLOW**, 6, b m Kayf Tara—Poppet **Kate & Andrew Brooks**
72 **TARA MACTWO**, 6, b m Kayf Tara—Macklette (IRE) **Babylon Five**
73 **TARRACO (FR)**, 9, b g Sassanian (USA)—Marie Esther (FR) **Mrs V. A. Bingham**
74 **TENOR NIVERNAIS (FR)**, 9, b g Shaanmer (IRE)—Hosanna II (FR) **Boultbee Brooks Ltd**
75 **THE CLOCK LEARY (IRE)**, 8, b g Helissio (FR)—Kiwi Babe **Brooks,Vando,Pummell,Martin & Armstrong**
76 **TIDAL DANCE (IRE)**, 9, b g Craigsteel—Musical Waves (IRE) **Pinks Gym & Leisure Wear Ltd**
77 **TOP AND DROP**, 5, b m Kayf Tara—Ismene (FR) **Graeme Moore, Kate & Andrew Brooks**

MISS VENETIA WILLIAMS - Continued

78 **TRIUMVIRATE**, 6, b m Rail Link—Strike Lightly **Lady M. A. Bolton**
79 **UHLAN BUTE (FR)**, 8, ch g Brier Creek (USA)—Jonquiere (FR) **R Elliott & N Coe, S Graham & C Watson**
80 **UN PROPHETE (FR)**, 5, gr g Carlotamix (FR)—Pollita (FR) **Mrs A. W. Timpson**
81 **UNION JACK D'YCY (FR)**, 8, b g Bonnet Rouge (FR)—Jacady (FR) **Mr I. R. P. Josephs**
82 **VIC DE TOUZAINE (FR)**, 7, gr g Dom Alco (FR)—Diana de Vonnas (FR) **A Brooks & G Moore**
83 **VIRTUOSE DU CHENET (FR)**, 7, b g Irish Wells (FR)—Lili Bleue (FR) **Let's Live Racing**
84 **VIVACCIO (FR)**, 7, b g Antarctique (IRE)—Cybelle (FR) **Boultbee Brooks Ltd**
85 **WALDORF SALAD**, 8, b g Millenary—Ismene (FR) **A. G. Parker**
86 **YALA ENKI (FR)**, 6, b br g Nickname (FR)—Cadiane (FR) **Hills of Ledbury Ltd**
87 **ZAMDY MAN**, 7, b g Authorized (IRE)—Lauderdale (GER) **Mr M. N. Khan**

Jockey (NH): Aidan Coleman, Liam Treadwell, Callum Whillans. **Conditional:** Charlie Deutsch.
Amateur: Mr Joe Knox, Miss Lucy Turner.

---

659 MRS LISA WILLIAMSON, Chester
Postal: **Saighton Hall, Saighton, Chester, Cheshire, CH3 6EE**
Contacts: **PHONE** (01244) 314254 **FAX** (01244) 314254 (please ring before sending)
MOBILE (07970) 437679
E-MAIL info@lisawilliamson.co.uk **WEBSITE** www.lisawilliamson.co.uk

1 **BERTIE BLU BOY**, 8, b g Central Park (IRE)—Shaymee's Girl **B & B Hygiene Limited**
2 **CHESTER DEELYTE (IRE)**, 8, b m Desert Style (IRE)—Bakewell Tart (IRE) **Hindford Oak Racing**
3 8, B g Pursuit of Love—Classic Quartet
4 4, B f Black Sam Bellamy (IRE)—Crystal Princess (IRE)
5 **GARDE VILLE (FR)**, 6, ch g Kapgarde (FR)—Ville Eagle (FR) **Mrs Y. Fleet**
6 **GO CHARLIE**, 5, b g Myboycharlie (IRE)—Branston Gem **Miss H. J. Roberts**
7 **HARPS OF BRETAGNE**, 4, b f Monsieur Bond (IRE)—Lavernock Lady **Mr J. Levenson**
8 **HINDFORD OAK GOLD**, 8, ch g Grape Tree Road—Sharp Susy
9 **LILY JICARO (IRE)**, 10, ch m Choisir (AUS)—Mourir d'aimer (USA)
10 **MISTY SECRET (IRE)**, 6, b m Clodovil (IRE)—Villafranca (IRE) **Simon&Jeanette Pierpoint&Paul Salisbury**
11 **PINBALL (IRE)**, 10, b m Namid—Luceball (IRE)
12 **RAT CATCHER (IRE)**, 6, b g One Cool Cat (USA)—Molly Marie (IRE) **Mr R. Jones**
13 **RYAN STYLE (IRE)**, 10, b g Desert Style (IRE)—Westlife (IRE) **Heath House Racing**
14 **SECRET ASSET (IRE)**, 11, gr g Clodovil (IRE)—Skerray **Simon&JeanettePierpoint/Dave&WendyHughes**
15 **SENORA LOBO (IRE)**, 6, b m Amadeus Wolf—Valencia (IRE) **Mr G. H. Briers**
16 **SERAPHIMA (IRE)**, 6, b m Fusaichi Pegasus (USA)—Millestan (IRE) **Heath House Racing**
17 **SIXTIES QUEEN**, 6, b m Sixties Icon—Lily of Tagula (IRE) **Tregarth Racing & Partner**
18 **TAMARIN**, 4, ch f Paco Boy (IRE)—Les Hurlants (IRE) **Heath House Racing**
19 **TAMBRINI LAD**, 6, b g Fair Mix (IRE)—Lady Lambrini **Hindford Oak Racing**
20 **YOUR GIFTED (IRE)**, 9, b m Trans Island—Dame Laura (IRE) **Mr A. T Sykes**

THREE-YEAR-OLDS
21 **EUREKA SPRINGS**, b f Mullionmileanhour (IRE)—Shaymee's Girl
22 **MATILDA GLEAM**, b f Arabian Gleam—Matilda Peace **Mange Tout**
23 **YALLA HABIBTI**, b f Kayf Tara—Majeeda (IRE)

TWO-YEAR-OLDS
24 B c 13/3 Jeremy (USA)—Ancone (FR) (Nikos)
25 B c 28/5 Jeremy (USA)—Blond's Addition (IRE) (Lord Americo) (9597)
26 B f 22/4 Captain Gerrard (IRE)—Lambrini Lace (IRE) (Namid)
27 **SASHEEDA**, b f 23/4 Putra Sas (IRE)—Majeeda (IRE) (Jeremy (USA))
28 B c 20/6 Kayf Tara—Special Choice (IRE) (Bob Back (USA)) (40000)

Other Owners: A. Bailey, Mrs E. L. Berry, Mrs A. Buchanan, Mr H. Hall, Exors of the Late M. S. Heath, Miss C. L. Howard, Mr D. R. Hughes, Mrs W. E. Hughes, Mr S. Jennings, Mr J. H. Martin, Mr S. W. Pierpoint, Mrs J. T. Pierpoint, Mr M. L. Rush, Mr P. J. Salisbury, Mr R. L. Williams.

Assistant Trainer: Mark Williamson

Jockey (NH): Brian Hughes. **Conditional:** Harry Challoner. **Amateur:** Mr C. Ellingham, Mr Alexander French.

660 **MR ANDREW WILSON, Greystoke**
Postal: **Silver Howe, Orton, Penrith, Cumbria, CA10 3RQ**
Contacts: **PHONE (01539) 624071 MOBILE (07813) 846768**
E-MAIL andywilsonorton@gmail.com

1 5, B g Coroner (IRE)—Catch Those Kisses **Mr A. C. Wilson**
2 **NABURN,** 8, b g Cape Cross (IRE)—Allespagne (USA) **Mr A. C. Wilson**
3 **TARA DEE (IRE),** 7, b m Golan (IRE)—Liberwoman (IRE) **Mr A. C. Wison**

661 **MR CHRISTOPHER WILSON, Darlington**
Postal: **Manor Farm, Manfield, Darlington, Co. Durham, DL2 2RW**
Contacts: **PHONE (01325) 374595 FAX (01325) 374595 MOBILE (07815) 952306/(07721) 379277**
E-MAIL wilsonracing@aol.com

1 **ESME RIDES A GAINE,** 14, gr m Doubletour (USA)—Silver Penny **Mrs J. Wilson**
2 **LATEST FASHION (IRE),** 10, ch m Ashkalani (IRE)—Musical Bramble (IRE) **Mrs J. Wilson**
3 **NO TIME TO CRY,** 7, b m Josr Algarhoud (IRE)—Autumn Bloom (IRE) **Mrs J. Wilson**

Assistant Trainer: Julie Wilson

Jockey (flat): Paddy Aspell, Silvestre De Sousa. **Jockey (NH):** Keith Mercer, Ewan Whillans.

662 **MR JIM WILSON, Cheltenham**
Postal: **Glenfall Stables, Ham, Charlton Kings, Cheltenham, Gloucestershire, GL52 6NH**
Contacts: **PHONE (01242) 244713 MOBILE (07932) 157243**
E-MAIL ajwglenfall@aol.com

1 **MAX DYNAMO,** 6, b g Midnight Legend—Vivante (IRE) **Mrs M. J. Wilson**
2 **SEYMOUR LEGEND,** 10, b g Midnight Legend—Rosehall **Mrs M. J. Wilson**
3 **VITARRA,** 7, b m Kayf Tara—Vivante (IRE) **Mrs M. J. Wilson**

663 **MISS MAIRI WILSON, Bawtry**
Postal: **Martin Common Farm, Bawtry, Doncaster, South Yorkshire, DN10 6DB**

1 6, B m Mahler—Angel Trix (IRE) **Mrs M. F. and Miss M. C. Wilson**
2 **COFFEE KING (IRE),** 7, b g King's Best (USA)—Passarelle (USA) **Mrs M. F. and Miss M. C. Wilson**

Other Owners: Miss M. C. Wilson, Mrs M. F. Wilson.

Assistant Trainer: Mrs M. Wilson

664 **MR NOEL WILSON, Middleham**
Postal: **Wold House Stables, Langton Road, Norton, Malton, North Yorkshire, YO17 9QG**
Contacts: **MOBILE (07718) 613206**
E-MAIL nlwilson69@live.com

1 **CROCKETT,** 5, b g Rail Link—Tarocchi (USA) **Mr L. Martell**
2 **GALVANIZE,** 5, b g Bahamian Bounty—Xtrasensory **Mr J. J. Blair**
3 **GHOSTLY ARC (IRE),** 4, b g Arcano (IRE)—Cheyenne's Spirit (IRE) **G. J. Paver**
4 **KINLOCH PRIDE,** 4, ch f Kyllachy—Pride of Kinloch **Mrs C. K. Paver**
5 **LILY MORETON (IRE),** 4, b f Kodiac—Hollow Haze (USA) **D. J. Emsley**
6 **LONGROOM,** 4, b g Oasis Dream—Phantom Wind (USA) **Mr L. Martell**
7 **PAVERS STAR,** 7, ch g Pastoral Pursuits—Pride of Kinloch **Mrs C. K. Paver**
8 **PENCAITLAND,** 4, b f Champs Elysees—Anthea **Hurn Racing Club & Gary Kennedy**
9 **REDVERS (IRE),** 8, b g Ishiguru (USA)—Cradle Brief (IRE) **Miss A. Porritt**
10 **UBEDIZZY (IRE),** 4, b g Captain Rio—Karenka (IRE) **Mr John Blair**

MR NOEL WILSON - Continued

THREE-YEAR-OLDS

11 **BLACK DIAMOND GIRL**, b f Kheleyf (USA)—Tripti (IRE) **Garry Swainston & John James Blair**
12 **COERCE**, ch f Motivator—New Design (IRE) **Mr L. Martell**
13 **FORMATIVE**, ch g Champs Elysees—Chasing Stars **Miss A. Porritt**
14 **I T GURU**, b c Bahamian Bounty—Never Say Deya **Mr L. Martell**
15 **MISS POPOV**, b f Monsieur Bond (IRE)—Priti Fabulous (IRE) **Miss A. Porritt**
16 **OUR PLACE IN LOULE**, ch g Compton Place—Show Off **G. J. Paver**
17 **SUNNYHILLS BELFORD**, ch f Monsieur Bond (IRE)—Zamindari **Ian & Debbie Paver**
18 **THE NAME'S PAVER**, ch c Monsieur Bond (IRE)—Pride of Kinloch **Mrs C. K. Paver**
19 **ZEPHYR BREEZE**, b c Piccolo—Bold Love **Glyn Budden & Roy Phillips**

TWO-YEAR-OLDS

20 Ch c 12/5 Bahamian Bounty—Pride of Kinloch (Dr Devious (IRE)) **Mrs C. K. Paver**
21 B c 23/4 Assertive—Selkirk Rose (IRE) (Pips Pride) (952) **Ian & Debbie Paver**

Other Owners: Mr John Blair, Mr Glyn Budden, Mrs I. M. Jessop, Mr Gary Kennedy, Mr John R. Owen, Mr Ian Paver, Mr G. J. Paver, Mrs Debbie Paver, Mr Roy Phillips, Miss Alex Porritt, Mr Garry Swainston.

Assistant Trainer: Miss Alex Porritt

Jockey (flat): Joe Fanning, Duran Fentiman, Tony Hamilton, Barry McHugh.

---

665 MR KEN WINGROVE, Bridgnorth
Postal: **6 Netherton Farm Barns, Netherton Lane, Highley, Bridgnorth, Shropshire, WV16 6NJ**
Contacts: **HOME (01746) 861534 MOBILE (07974) 411267**
E-MAIL kenwingrove@btinternet.com

1 **ADMIRAL BARTON (IRE)**, 10, b g Flemensfirth (USA)—Ashanti Dancer (IRE) **Mr D. G. Wingrove**
2 **COPPICE LAD**, 7, b g Thethingaboutitis (USA)—Coppice Lane **Miss S. N. Allington**
3 **EDE'S THE BUSINESS**, 5, ch m Halling (USA)—My Amalie (IRE) **Mr D. G. Wingrove**
4 **FERNANDO (IRE)**, 12, b g Fruits of Love (USA)—Dancing Venus **Mr D. G. Wingrove**
5 **JOHNNYS LEGACY (IRE)**, 9, b g Ecton Park (USA)—Lexy May (USA) **Mr D. G. Wingrove**
6 **KWANTO**, 6, b m Piccolo—Craic Sa Ceili (IRE) **Mr D. G. Wingrove**
7 **MY NOBLE FRIEND**, 5, b g Overbury (IRE)—Karinga Princess
8 **OSCAR ROBIN (IRE)**, 7, b m Oscar (IRE)—Bryan's Pet (IRE)
9 **STREELE (USA)**, 6, gr m Thunder Gulch (USA)—Crown Capers (USA) **Mr D. G. Wingrove**
10 **TONY (IRE)**, 9, ch g High Roller (IRE)—Plucky Hart (IRE) **Mr D. G. Wingrove**
11 **WINROB**, 10, b g Exceed And Excel (AUS)—High Standard

Assistant Trainer: Isobel Willer

---

666 MR PETER WINKS, Barnsley
Postal: **Homefield Stables, Rotherham Road, Little Houghton, Barnsley, South Yorkshire, S72 0HA**
Contacts: **MOBILE (07846) 899993**
E-MAIL lynnpwracing@outlook.com

1 **CHESTNUT BEN (IRE)**, 11, ch g Ridgewood Ben—Betseale (IRE) **Mr P. Winks**
2 **DOMTALINE (FR)**, 9, gr g Martaline—Domna Noune (FR) **Mr P. Winks**
3 **GROW NASA GROW (IRE)**, 5, ch g Mahler—Dereenavurrig (IRE) **Mr P. Winks**
4 **HARTSIDE (GER)**, 7, b g Montjeu (IRE)—Helvellyn (USA) **Mr P. Winks**
5 **PRESENTING STREAK (IRE)**, 7, b g Presenting—Kuwalla (IRE) **Mr P. Winks**
6 **SOLSTICE DAWN**, 8, b m Lyphento (USA)—Ryders Hill **Mr P. Winks**

Assistant Trainer: Ryan Winks

Amateur: Mr Ryan Winks.

667 MR ADRIAN WINTLE, Westbury-On-Severn
Postal: **Yew Tree Stables, Rodley, Westbury-On-Severn, Gloucestershire, GL14 1QZ**
Contacts: **MOBILE (07767) 351144**

1 **ANNIE HUGHES (IRE)**, 7, b m Golan (IRE)—Broadfield Cruiser (IRE) **Mr R. G. Owens**
2 **DAYS LIKE THESE**, 7, b m Westerner—One of Those Days **I. M. McGready**
3 **EXOTIC FRIEND (IRE)**, 8, ch g Croco Rouge (IRE)—Prima Nox **Mr S. R. Whistance**
4 **GENERAL ROSS (IRE)**, 9, b g Generous (IRE)—Rossmore Girl (IRE) **Mrs S. I. Tainton**
5 **HALLINGS COMET**, 7, ch g Halling (USA)—Landinium (ITY) **Lord J. Blyth**
6 **PEMBRIDGE**, 7, b m Kayf Tara—Supreme Gem (IRE) **A. A. Wintle**
7 **POETIC PRESENCE (IRE)**, 6, b m Presenting—Johnston's Crest (IRE) **A. J. Williams**
8 **PRAIRIE HAWK (USA)**, 11, b g Hawk Wing (USA)—Lady Carla **Mr R. G. Owens**
9 **ROSYGO (IRE)**, 8, b m Oscar (IRE)—Sharp Single (IRE) **Smith, Ratcliffe & Bowring**
10 **SHALONE**, 12, ch g Tobougg (IRE)—Let Alone **A. A. Wintle**
11 **STAR BENEFIT (IRE)**, 6, b g Beneficial—Beautiful Night (FR) **Search For Stars**
12 **TINCTORIA**, 6, b m Oratorio (IRE)—Blue Indigo (FR) **A. A. Wintle**
13 **VINTAGE VIXON (IRE)**, 9, b m Moscow Society (USA)—Bar Un'que (IRE) **D. J. Oseman**

Other Owners: Mr D. S. Bowring, Mr J. Ratcliffe, Mr W. L. Smith, Mr R. J. Williams.

668 MR STEVE WOODMAN, Chichester
Postal: **Parkers Barn Stables, 8 Pook Lane, East Lavant, Chichester, West Sussex, PO18 0AU**
Contacts: **OFFICE (01243) 527136 FAX (01243) 527136 MOBILE (07889) 188519**
E-MAIL stevewoodman83@msn.com

1 **CHEVISE (IRE)**, 8, b m Holy Roman Emperor (IRE)—Lipica (IRE) **The Chevise Partnership**
2 **CROWNING STAR (IRE)**, 7, b g Royal Applause—Dossier **Countrywide Classics Ltd**
3 6, B m Robin des Pres (FR)—Evangelica (USA)
4 **GOING TWICE**, 11, b g Josr Algarhoud (IRE)—Its Your Bid **Mrs S. B. Woodman**
5 5, B m Tikkanen (USA)—Like A Bolt (IRE)
6 **SOLVEIG'S SONG**, 4, b f Norse Dancer (IRE)—Ivory Lace **Sally Woodman & D. Mortimer**

Other Owners: Mr David Mortimer, Mrs Trish Tyler, Mrs Sally Woodman.

669 MR RICHARD WOOLLACOTT, South Molton
Postal: **Nethercott Manor, Rose Ash, South Molton, Devon, EX36 4RE**
Contacts: **PHONE (01769) 550483 MOBILE (07780) 006995**
E-MAIL info@richardwoollacottracing.co.uk WEBSITE www.richardwoollacottracing.co.uk

1 **COVE LODGE**, 6, b g Sakhee's Secret—Limonia (GER) **Mrs E. M. Roberts**
2 **FLORESCO (GER)**, 6, ch g Santiago (GER)—Fiori (GER) **D. G. Staddon**
3 **GETON XMOOR (IRE)**, 9, b g Heron Island (IRE)—Get On With It (IRE) **Mr J. Winzer**
4 **KUDU SHINE**, 10, b g Karinga Bay—Flora Bright **Mr D Stevens & Mrs S Stevens**
5 **LIBERTY ONE (IRE)**, 10, b g Milan—Same Old Story (IRE) **D. G. Staddon**
6 **MILLANISI BOY**, 7, b g Kalanisi (IRE)—Millennium Rose (IRE) **Mr D Stevens & Mrs S Stevens**
7 **MONDELLO (GER)**, 5, b g Soldier Hollow—Mandrella (GER) **M. J. Gallagher**
8 **ONEFORTHENURE (IRE)**, 7, b m Court Cave (IRE)—Shining Willow **Sue & Clive Cole & Ann & Tony Gale**
9 **SABROCLAIR (FR)**, 7, b g Robin des Champs (FR)—Malicka Madrik (FR) **Taunton Racecourse Owners Club**
10 **SAINT ELM (FR)**, 6, b g Poliglote—Place d'armes (IRE)
11 **SHEER POETRY (IRE)**, 5, b m Yeats (IRE)—Sassari (IRE) **R. J. Weeks**
12 **SHINTORI (FR)**, 4, b g Enrique—La Masai (FR) **Mrs R Vicary & Mr J Pratt**
13 **SPA HILL (IRE)**, 7, b g Fruits of Love (USA)—Calistoga (IRE) **Nethercott Manor Racing**
14 **TOO SCOOPS (IRE)**, 9, ch g Alderbrook—Accordion To Bob (IRE) **Nethercott Manor Racing 2**
15 **WEST HILL LEGEND**, 5, b m Midnight Legend—Bajan Blue **D. G. Staddon**

Other Owners: M. J. Bevan, Mr C. Cole, Mrs S. S. Cole, Mr A. P. Gale, Mrs A. G. Gale, Mr M. Higgs, Mr L. J. Pratt, Mr S. C. C. Stacey, Mrs S. E. Stevens, Mr D. J. Stevens, Mrs R. E. Vicary, R. Woollacott.

Assistant Trainer: Mrs Kayley Woollacott

670 MR RAYMOND YORK, Cobham
Postal: **Newmarsh Farm, Horsley Road, Cobham, Surrey, KT11 3JX**
Contacts: **PHONE (01932) 863594 MOBILE (07808) 344131**
E-MAIL ray.york@virgin.net

1 **ASHBROOK**, 7, b g Bollin Eric—Woodford Consult **R. H. York**
2 **BACHMAN (IRE)**, 8, ch g Bach (IRE)—Oak Lodge (IRE) **Mrs K. H. York**
3 **BROUGHTONS BANDIT**, 9, b g Kyllachy—Broughton Bounty **R. H. York**
4 **GERSJOEYCASEY (IRE)**, 7, b m Milan—Derrigra Sublime (IRE) **R. H. York**
5 **HARRY'S CHOICE**, 8, b g Sir Harry Lewis (USA)—Chosen (IRE) **R. H. York**
6 **IM STEEL HERE (IRE)**, 8, b g Craigsteel—Greeced Lightning (IRE) **Star Contractors Ltd**
7 8, Gr g Terimon—Kilshey
8 **MISS NORTH LIGHT (IRE)**, 7, ch m North Light (IRE)—Damask Rose (IRE) **R. H. York**
9 **ON YOUR MAX**, 8, b g Tobougg (IRE)—Maxilla (IRE) **R. H. York**
10 **SAMMARA**, 5, b m Black Sam Bellamy (IRE)—Aspra (FR) **Mrs D. A. T. Salmon**
11 **SPIRITOFCHARTWELL**, 8, ch g Clerkenwell (USA)—Rollin Rock **R. Gurney**
12 **VERAX**, 5, ch m Central Park (IRE)—Veredus **R. H. York**
13 4, B f Multiplex—Vic Trish **F. D. Camis**

Assistant Trainer: P. York **Amateur:** Mr P. York.

671 MRS LAURA YOUNG, Bridgwater
Postal: **Rooks Castle Stables, Broomfield, Bridgwater, Somerset, TA5 2EW**
Contacts: **PHONE (01278) 664595 FAX (01278) 661555 MOBILE (07766) 514414**
E-MAIL ljyracing@hotmail.com WEBSITE www.laurayoungracing.com

1 **ADMIRAL BLAKE**, 9, b g Witness Box (USA)—Brenda Bella (FR) **Mrs L. J. Young**
2 **AUENWIRBEL (GER)**, 5, b h Sholokhov (GER)—Auentime (GER) **Total Plumbing Supporters Club**
3 **BORDER STATION (IRE)**, 10, b g Shantou (USA)—Telemania (IRE) **Total Plumbing Supporters Club**
4 **BUCKBORU (IRE)**, 8, b m Brian Boru—Buckland Filleigh (IRE) **Mrs L. J. Young**
5 **CREATIVE BORU (IRE)**, 8, b g Brian Boru—Ruths Rhapsody (IRE) **The Isle Of Frogs Partnership**
6 **GILMER (IRE)**, 5, b g Exceed And Excel (AUS)—Cherokee Rose (IRE) **Total Plumbing Supporters Club**
7 **GOLD THIEF (IRE)**, 6, b g Gold Well—Mullaghcloga (IRE) **The Isle Of Frogs Partnership**
8 **JIGSAW FINANCIAL (IRE)**, 10, b g Brian Boru—Ardcolm Cailin (IRE) **Mrs L. J. Young**
9 **MY DIAMOND (IRE)**, 5, b g Brian Boru—Our Idol (IRE) **The Isle Of Frogs Partnership**
10 **SHIVSINGH**, 7, b g Montjeu (IRE)—Vistaria (USA) **Mrs L. J. Young**
11 **SPARKLING ICE (IRE)**, 5, gr m Verglas (IRE)—Sand Crystal (IRE) **Mrs L. J. Young**
12 **SUFFICE (IRE)**, 7, b g Iffraaj—Shallat (IRE) **Mrs L. J. Young**
13 **SURFING THE STARS (IRE)**, 5, b g Brian Boru—Golden Jorden (IRE) **The Isle Of Frogs Partnership**
14 **THE BIG MARE**, 7, b m Doyen (IRE)—Fizzy Lady **Mrs L. J. Young**
15 **TWYFORD**, 9, b g Bach (IRE)—Commanche Token (IRE) **Total Plumbing Supporters Club**
16 **WHISKEY JOHN**, 6, b g Westerner—Cherry Lane **The Isle Of Frogs Partnership**
17 **WHITE NILE (IRE)**, 7, b h Galileo (IRE)—Super Gift (IRE) **Total Plumbing Supporters Club**

THREE-YEAR-OLDS

18 **WOMBLE**, b c Equiano (FR)—Little Caroline (IRE) **D. R. Tucker**

Other Owners: C. E. Handford, Mr I. D. Moses, Mr G. C. Vining, Mr C. V. Vining.

Assistant Trainer: James Young **Jockey (NH):** Robert Dunne.

672 MR WILLIAM YOUNG, Carluke
Postal: **Watchknowe Lodge, Crossford, Carluke, Lanarkshire, ML8 5QT**
Contacts: **PHONE (01555) 860856 (01555) 860226 FAX (01555) 860137 MOBILE (07900) 408210**
E-MAIL watchknowe@talktalk.net

1 **FORMIDABLEOPPONENT (IRE)**, 9, b g Arakan (USA)—Sliding **W. G. Young**
2 **PHOENIX RETURNS (IRE)**, 8, br g Phoenix Reach (IRE)—Oscar's Lady (IRE) **W. G. Young**
3 **RAIFTEIRI (IRE)**, 9, b g Galileo (IRE)—Naziriya (FR) **W. G. Young**

Assistant Trainer: William G Young Snr

INDEX TO HORSES

The Figure before the name of the horse refers to the number of the team in which it appears and **The Figure after** the horse supplies a ready reference to each animal. Horses are indexed strictly alphabetically, e.g. THE FRESH PRINCE appears in the T's, MR BOSSY BOOTS IN THE MR'S, ST PATRICKS DAY IN THE ST'S ETC.

134 **AMBION LANE** (IRE) 3
134 **AMBION WOOD** (IRE) 4
311 **AMBITIOUS BOY** (GB) 1
261 **AMBITIOUS ICARUS** (GB) 1
93 **AMBITIOUS ROSIE** (GB) 3
7 **AMBIVALENT ABOUT** (GB) 1
285 **AMBONNAY** (GB) C 19
25 **AMBRE DES MARAIS** (FR) 1
429 **AMBUSCADE** (GB) 29
185 **AMELIA GRACE** (IRE) 81
158 **AMENABLE** (IRE) 1
104 **AMENTA** (IRE) 55
123 **AMERICA NOVA** (FR) C 48
224 **AMERICAN** (FR) 5
610 **AMERICAN ARTIST** (IRE) 2
266 **AMERICAN GIGOLO** (GB) 2
185 **AMERICAN HUSTLE** (IRE) 2
463 **AMERICAN LEGEND** (IRE) 4
367 **AMERICAN LIFE** (FR) 1
29 **AMERICAN PATROL** (IRE) 45
437 **AMERICAN TOM** (FR) 9
521 **AMERICAN WHIPPER** (FR) 35
67 **AMERICAN WORLD** (FR) 1
109 **AMETHYST ROSE** (IRE) 1
406 **AMI DESBOIS** (FR) 3
615 **AMIDON** (FR) 3
485 **AMIGO** (FR) 3
148 **AMILIYA** (IRE) 28
571 **AMILLIONTIMES** (IRE) 1
192 **AMIRAL COLLONGES** (FR) 1
31 **AMIS REUNIS** (GB) 1
200 **AMITIE WALTZ** (FR) 3
578 **AMMO** (IRE) C 109
636 **AMOOD** (IRE) 3
359 **AMOR INVICTO** (IRE) 9
101 **AMORAMA** (FR) C 20
200 **AMORE ALATO** (GB) 4
153 **AMOUAGE ROYALE** (IRE) C 43
654 **AMOUR D'OR** (GB) 4
494 **AMOUR DE NUIT** (IRE) 1
276 **AMOUR FOU** (IRE) F 124
634 **AMPLE SUFFICIENCY** (USA) 22
42 **AMTHAAL** (GB) 105
615 **AMTHAL** (IRE) 4
613 **AMUN** (GER) 49
418 **AMUSE ME** (GB) 2
130 **AMY BLAIR** (GB) 39
155 **AMYS CHOICE** (IRE) 1
48 **AN CAILIN ORGA** (IRE) 17
183 **AN CAPALL MOR** (IRE) 2
389 **AN DROICHEAD** (IRE) 50
213 **AN FEAR CIUIN** (IRE) 1
367 **AN POC AR BUILE** (IRE) 2
346 **AN TARBH OG** (IRE) 1
90 **ANAARUS** (FR) 34
339 **ANADOLU** (IRE) C 32
16 **ANAGALLIS** (IRE) 10
437 **ANALIFET** (FR) 10
265 **ANAMARKA** (GB) C 70
265 **ANAMATO** (AUS) F 71
265 **ANAMBA** (GB) 31
185 **ANANDA KANDA** (GB) F 82
78 **ANAPHORA** (IRE) F 63
423 **ANAPOLA** (GER) F 25
3 **ANASTASIA VENTURE** (GB) G 27
128 **ANASTAZIA** (GB) 1
451 **ANATOL** (FR) 8
456 **ANATOLA** (GER) C 89

286 **ANAY TURGE** (FR) 3
48 **ANAYID** (GB) F 72
500 **ANCIENT ASTRONAUT** (GB) 29
14 **ANCIENT GREECE** (GB) 2
276 **ANCIENT TRADE** (USA) 30
299 **ANCIENT WORLD** (USA) 21
659 **ANCONE** (FR) C 25
202 **AND AGAIN** (USA) C 17
98 **AND I** (GB) C 88
451 **AND THE NEW** (IRE) 9
315 **ANDA DE GRISSAY** (FR) 4
404 **ANDALUSITE** (GB) 10
120 **ANDANOTHERONE** (IRE) 6
28 **ANDAR** (GB) 24
610 **ANDAZ** (GB) 47
524 **ANDIRA** (USA) 80
524 **ANDREA MANTEGNA** (USA) 20
276 **ANDREYEV** (GB) 31
5 **ANDROEAH** (USA) C 91
364 **ANDY KELLY** (IRE) 2
185 **ANDYS GIRL** (IRE) 83
123 **ANEEDAH** (IRE) F 49
432 **ANEEDH** (GB) 1
501 **ANFIELD** (GB) 1
195 **ANGE DES MALBERAUX** (FR) 1
521 **ANGEL BABY** (FR) 150
42 **ANGEL CRAFT** (USA) F 106
23 **ANGEL ERIA** (GB) 12
352 **ANGEL FACE** (GB) 3
95 **ANGEL FLORES** (IRE) 1
410 **ANGEL GRACE** (IRE) 7
185 **ANGEL IN THE SNOW** (GB) 84
78 **ANGEL PALANAS** (GB) 64
663 **ANGEL TRIX** (IRE) F 1
78 **ANGEL VOICES** (IRE) F 65
227 **ANGEL WAY** (IRE) 2
342 **ANGEL'S TEARS** (GB) F 130
123 **ANGELA NORTH** (GB) 17
98 **ANGELIC GUEST** (IRE) 45
135 **ANGELIC LORD** (IRE) 1
376 **ANGELICAL** (IRE) 28
51 **ANGELICAL DANCER** (FR) 22
371 **ANGELITO** (GB) 1
423 **ANGIE BABY** (GB) 26
159 **ANGIE ERIA** (FR) F 33
116 **ANGIE'S GIRL** (GB) 25
149 **ANGINOLA** (IRE) 1
433 **ANGLO PADDY** (IRE) 2
5 **ANGLOPHILE** (GB) 2
431 **ANGRYWHITEPYJAMAS** (IRE) 17
149 **ANGUS GLENS** (IRE) 2
389 **ANIABLE FLY** (FR) 1
176 **ANIERES BOY** (GB) 2
299 **ANIF** (GB) 87
355 **ANIKNAM** (FR) 2
286 **ANIS DES MALBERAUX** (FR) 4
574 **ANJUNA BEACH** (USA) 1
20 **ANN MARIES REJECT** (IRE) 1
150 **ANN'S LOTTERY** (GB) 1
469 **ANNA AMALIA** (IRE) C 56
632 **ANNA GREY** (GB) 1
456 **ANNA KARENINA** (IRE) C 90
494 **ANNA MEDICI** (GB) 42
42 **ANNA PLATINI** (GB) 5
352 **ANNACOTTY** (IRE) 4
142 **ANNAKRISTA** (GER) 1
168 **ANNALINA** (USA) C 62

451 **ANNALULU** (IRE) 10
481 **ANNAMULT** (IRE) 1
657 **ANNAPURNA** (IRE) F 34
23 **ANNASANDRA** (FR) 50
567 **ANNE OF BRITTANY** (FR) 1
90 **ANNE OF BRITTANY** (FR) 2
334 **ANNE'S VALENTINO** (GB) 1
253 **ANNEANI** (IRE) 1
319 **ANNELIINA** (GB) C 21
242 **ANNIE GREENLAW** (GB) F 2
667 **ANNIE HUGHES** (IRE) 1
437 **ANNIE O** (IRE) 11
437 **ANNIE POWER** (IRE) 12
407 **ANNIE SALTS** (GB) 9
413 **ANNIE T** (GB) 22
497 **ANNIE'SBOYDAVE** (GB) 1
91 **ANNIGONI** (FR) 5
172 **ANNILOGS PALM** (IRE) G 2
454 **ANNIVERSARIE** (FR) 1
593 **ANNOUNCEMENT** (GB) 1
228 **ANNOUSHKA** (GB) 3
467 **ANNOUSKA** (IRE) C 49
436 **ANNS PRESENT** (IRE) G 4
190 **ANONYMOUS JOHN** (IRE) 3
256 **ANOTHER** (IRE) 1
512 **ANOTHER BILL** (IRE) 1
28 **ANOTHER BOY** (GB) 27
159 **ANOTHER DAY** (GB) 1
24 **ANOTHER DESPERADO** (IRE) 20
155 **ANOTHER DIMENSION** (IRE) 2
606 **ANOTHER FRONTIER** (IRE) 5
463 **ANOTHER HERO** (IRE) 5
139 **ANOTHER JOURNEY** (GB) 2
294 **ANOTHER LINCOLNDAY** (GB) 1
1 **ANOTHER MATTIE** (IRE) 3
299 **ANOTHER STORM** (USA) F 88
252 **ANOTHER SUNSHINE** (GB) 5
197 **ANOTHER TOUCH** (GB) 76
413 **ANOTHER WISE KID** (IRE) 1
618 **ANQUETTA** (IRE) 1
6 **ANSAAB** (GB) 2
451 **ANTARTICA DE THAIX** (FR) 11
148 **ANTEMIO** (FR) 29
367 **ANTEROS** (IRE) 3
151 **ANTI COOL** (IRE) 1
5 **ANTIMO** (GB) 28
428 **ANTIOCO** (GB) 14
301 **ANTIPHONY** (IRE) 4
5 **ANTIQUARIUM** (IRE) 3
265 **ANTIQUE** (IRE) F 72
396 **ANTON CHIGURH** (GB) 1
435 **ANTON DOLIN** (GB) 1
318 **ANTONIO JOLI** (IRE) 1
23 **ANTONOE** (USA) 13
422 **ANTONY** (FR) 4
476 **ANUSHKA NOO NOO** (GB) 8
347 **ANY CURRENCY** (IRE) 2
622 **ANY FOR LOVE** (ARG) F 30
388 **ANY GUEST** (GB) 15
285 **ANY JOY** (IRE) 12
358 **ANY QUESTIONS** (GB) 42
87 **ANYA** (GB) 1
135 **ANYAAS** (IRE) F 52
538 **ANYTHINGMAYHAPPEN** (IRE) 2
512 **ANYWAYTHEWINDBLOWS** (GB) 2
276 **ANZASI** (FR) 125
363 **ANZHELIKA** (IRE) 2
594 **ANZINGER** (IRE) 1

624 **ARTISTIC BLUE** (USA) F 11
54 **ARTISTIC FLIGHT** (IRE) 1
87 **ARTISTS MODEL** (IRE) 20
221 **ARTY BELLA** (GB) 3
370 **ARTY CAMPBELL** (IRE) 2
327 **ARU CHA CHA** (GB) 1
361 **ARVIOS** (GB) 1
42 **ARYAAMM** (IRE) C 107
80 **ARZAAK** (IRE) 30
648 **ARZAL** (FR) 2
194 **AS A DREAM** (IRE) 3
451 **AS AND WHEN** (IRE) 14
315 **AS DE FER** (FR) 5
437 **AS DE FERBET** (FR) 21
451 **AS DE MEE** (FR) 15
347 **AS JUSSINIERE** (FR) 3
584 **ASAAYL** (IRE) 25
263 **ASAMA BLUE** (IRE) 22
107 **ASCENDANCY** (GB) F 14
200 **ASCENDANT** (GB) 5
521 **ASCOT ANGEL** (FR) 151
195 **ASCOT DE BRUYERE** (FR) 3
12 **ASCOTDEUX NELLERIE** (FR) 5
469 **ASCRIPTION** (IRE) 2
109 **ASH PARK** (IRE) 2
528 **ASHADIHAN** (GB) 37
557 **ASHANTIANA** (GB) C 9
490 **ASHAZURI** (GB) 41
353 **ASHBRITTLE** (GB) 1
670 **ASHBROOK** (GB) 1
433 **ASHCOTT BOY** (GB) 4
279 **ASHES OF LOVE** (IRE) 2
439 **ASHFORD ISLAND** (GB) 14
612 **ASHFORD WOOD** (IRE) 4
524 **ASHIQANA** (FR) 21
524 **ASHIRA** (FR) 2
42 **ASHIRAH** (USA) F 108
98 **ASHJAN** (GB) 46
524 **ASHKOUL** (FR) 22
612 **ASHKOUN** (FR) 5
456 **ASHLEY HALL** (USA) C 92
435 **ASHLEYS PETALE** (IRE) C 2
550 **ASHOKA** (IRE) 7
634 **ASHRAF** (IRE) 2
22 **ASHTAROUTE** (USA) C 46
521 **ASHTIYNA** (FR) 37
344 **ASHTOWN** (IRE) 1
524 **ASHUTOR** (FR) 83
335 **ASHWELL ROSE** (GB) F 41
460 **ASI** (USA) C 22
91 **ASIAN TRADER** (GB) 6
584 **ASINARA** (GER) F 71
453 **ASK ANNIE** (IRE) C 43
521 **ASK ME ANOTHER** (USA) 152
9 **ASK THE GURU** (GB) 1
397 **ASKAMORE DARSI** (IRE) 3
610 **ASKARI** (GB) 49
142 **ASKER** (IRE) 2
395 **ASKERIA** (IRE) F 96
244 **ASKING PRICE** (USA) 107
63 **ASKNOTWHAT** (IRE) 3
634 **ASMEEN** (IRE) 24
658 **ASO** (FR) 4
612 **ASOCKASTAR** (IRE) 6
568 **ASPAR** (IRE) 11
59 **ASPASIAS TIZZY** (USA) F 17
422 **ASPASIUS** (GER) 8
410 **ASPEN AGAIN** (GB) 8

280 **ASPENS SHADOW** (GB) 1
5 **ASSABIYYA** (IRE) C 93
634 **ASSAM** (GB) 97
169 **ASSANILKA** (FR) 30
93 **ASSERTIVE AGENT** (GB) 4
477 **ASSISTED** (GB) 4
521 **ASSOUFID** 38
86 **ASTAROLAND** (FR) 1
88 **ASTER'S APPROVAL** (GB) 1
524 **ASTERINA** (GB) 23
244 **ASTERION** (GB) 108
307 **ASTEROID BELT** (IRE) 1
437 **ASTHURIA** (FR) 22
658 **ASTIGOS** (FR) 5
301 **ASTON CANTLOW** (GB) 5
6 **ASTRA HALL** (GB) 7
606 **ASTRACAD** (FR) 9
90 **ASTRE DE BALLON** (FR) 2
620 **ASTRE DE LA COUR** (FR) 2
599 **ASTROLIBRA** (GB) C 26
479 **ASTRONEREUS** (FR) 4
599 **ASTROSECRET** (GB) 12
599 **ASTROSHADOW** (GB) 27
599 **ASTROWIZARD** (GB) 13
347 **ASTRUM** (GB) 4
550 **ASUM** (GB) 8
411 **ASUNCION** (FR) 1
190 **ASWAAQ** (FR) F 43
637 **AT FIRST LIGHT** (GB) 1
126 **AT FISHERS CROSS** (IRE) 2
550 **AT THE TOP** (FR) 9
429 **ATALAN** (GB) 1
600 **ATALANTA BAY** (GB) 1
15 **ATALANTE** (GB) 50
622 **ATAMAN** (IRE) 1
148 **ATAMAN ERMAK** (IRE) 1
166 **ATHASACH** (IRE) 3
81 **ATHENIAN GARDEN** (USA) 2
243 **ATHENRY BOY** (IRE) 1
508 **ATHLETIC** (GB) 1
363 **ATHLON** (IRE) 13
303 **ATHOU DU NORD** (FR) 2
301 **ATIRELARIGO** (FR) 6
130 **ATISHOO** (FR) F 62
622 **ATLANTA BELLE** (IRE) 31
621 **ATLANTEIA** (FR) 14
169 **ATLANTIC BEAUTY** (IRE) 31
123 **ATLANTIC DESTINY** (IRE) C 50
375 **ATLANTIC GOLD** (IRE) 4
194 **ATLANTIC LADY** (GER) G 4
242 **ATLANTIC ROLLER** (IRE) 3
276 **ATLANTIC SUN** (GB) 32
521 **ATLANTIDE** (FR) 39
303 **ATOMIK D'OLIVATE** (FR) 3
361 **ATOMIQUE** (FR) 44
452 **ATOMIX** (GER) 2
578 **ATONE** (GB) 28
176 **ATREUS** (GB) 3
201 **ATTAIN** (GB) 2
460 **ATTASLIYAH** (IRE) C 23
361 **ATTENDU** (FR) 13
155 **ATTENTION PLEASE** (IRE) 3
177 **ATTENTION SEEKER** (GB) 3
479 **ATTEST** (GB) 19
162 **ATTIMO** (GB) 1
116 **ATTITUDE ROCKS** (GB) 26
433 **ATTRACTIVE LIASON** (IRE) 5
615 **ATWIX** (GB) 6

437 **AU QUART DE TOUR** (FR) 23
654 **AUBUSSON** (FR) 5
433 **AUCKLAND DE RE** (FR) 6
126 **AUDACIOUS PLAN** (IRE) 3
335 **AUDEN** (USA) 3
116 **AUDREY BROWN** (GB) C 63
671 **AUENWIRBEL** (GER) 2
421 **AUGEST BENEFIT** (IRE) 1
105 **AUGHCARRA** (IRE) 2
437 **AUGUSTA KATE** (GB) 24
437 **AUGUSTIN** (FR) 25
477 **AUJIANG** (GER) C 14
273 **AULDTHUNDER** (IRE) 5
378 **AUMERLE** (GB) 2
500 **AUMIT HILL** (GB) 30
554 **AUNTIE KATHRYN** (IRE) C 34
107 **AUNTIE MAY** (IRE) 1
244 **AUNTINET** (GB) 23
28 **AUREANA** (GB) 73
215 **AUREATE** (GB) 1
276 **AURIC GOLDFINGER** (IRE) 130
126 **AURILLAC** (FR) 4
437 **AURKO** (FR) 26
244 **AURORA GOLD** (GB) 109
429 **AURORA GRAY** (GB) 30
126 **AURORE D'ESTRUVAL** (FR) 5
585 **AUSPICION** (GB) 1
411 **AUSSIE OPERA** (IRE) C 23
376 **AUSSIE RULER** (FR) 3
582 **AUSTERITY** (GB) 33
613 **AUSTIN** (GER) 34
34 **AUSTIN FRIARS** (GB) 4
403 **AUSTRALASIA** (IRE) 1
339 **AUSTRALIA FAIR** (GB) C 33
186 **AUSTRALIAN QUEEN** (GB) 14
372 **AUTHENTICATION** (GB) 1
213 **AUTHENTICITY** (GB) 2
358 **AUTHOR'S DREAM** (GB) 19
333 **AUTHORA** (IRE) C 18
35 **AUTHORIZED SPIRIT** (GB) 1
655 **AUTHORIZED TOO** (GB) 1
578 **AUTOCRATIC** (GB) 29
201 **AUTOMOTIVE** (GB) 3
4 **AUTRE PRINCESS** (IRE) 3
342 **AUTUMN BLOSSOM** (USA) 32
184 **AUTUMN GLOW** (GB) 10
160 **AUTUMN TONIC** (IRE) 1
463 **AUVERGNAT** (FR) 6
451 **AUX PTITS SOINS** (FR) 16
313 **AUXILIARY** (GB) 22
359 **AV A WORD** (GB) 17
379 **AVAILABLE** (IRE) 1
431 **AVALANCHE EXPRESS** (GB) 2
437 **AVANT TOUT** (FR) 27
49 **AVEC LAURA** (GB) 14
286 **AVEL VOR** (FR) 5
437 **AVENIR D'UNE VIE** (FR) 28
612 **AVENTIA** (IRE) G 7
100 **AVENUE DES CHAMPS** (GB) 1
403 **AVENUE OF STARS** (GB) 12
15 **AVERAMI** (GB) C 119
42 **AVIACION** (BRZ) F 109
615 **AVIADOR** (GER) 7
23 **AVIANE** (GER) F 53
189 **AVIATOR** (GER) 1
437 **AVICHI** (IRE) 29
195 **AVIDITY** (GB) 4
352 **AVISPA** (GB) 7

546 **BERTIE'S DESIRE** (GB) 3
288 **BERTIELICIOUS** (GB) 1
22 **BERTIEWHITTLE** (GB) 4
411 **BERTORIZZIA** (FR) 24
517 **BERWIN** (IRE) 1
525 **BESCOT SPRINGS** (IRE) 8
524 **BESHARA** (FR) 7
263 **BESHARAH** (IRE) 27
273 **BESPOKE LADY** (IRE) 7
123 **BESS OF HARDWICK** (GB) 4
538 **BEST BOY BARNEY** (IRE) 3
42 **BEST EXAMPLE** (USA) 4
456 **BEST IN THE WORLD** (IRE) 15
190 **BEST NEW SHOW** (IRE) 19
621 **BEST OF OREGON** (USA) 15
42 **BEST OF TIMES** (GB) 5
153 **BEST TAMAYUZ** (GB) 3
263 **BEST TERMS** (GB) F 109
206 **BEST TRIP** (IRE) 1
279 **BESTOW** (IRE) 5
835 **BESTWORK** (FR) 7
342 **BETA** (GB) F 133
550 **BETAMECHE** (FR) 17
548 **BETHELLIE PRIDE** (GB) 1
65 **BETHNAL GREEN** (GB) 4
90 **BETISE BEAUCHENE** (FR) 6
15 **BETROTHED** (IRE) C 122
516 **BETSY BOO BOO** (GB) 1
352 **BETTATOGETHER** (GB) 11
606 **BETTER DAYS** (IRE) 27
512 **BETTER GETALONG** (IRE) 7
294 **BETTERCALLPHOENIX** (GB) 12
282 **BETTY BOO** (IRE) 2
489 **BETTY BORGIA** (GB) 1
469 **BETTY GRABLE** (IRE) 60
621 **BETTY THE THIEF** (IRE) 2
265 **BETWIXT** (USA) C 73
196 **BEVERLEY BULLET** (GB) 9
292 **BEWARE THE BEAR** (IRE) 17
474 **BEWDLEY** (GB) 2
123 **BEWITCHED** (IRE) F 51
521 **BEYCHEVELLE** (USA) 42
6 **BEYEH** (IRE) 10
521 **BEYNOSTORM** (IRE) 43
23 **BEYOND APOLLO** (IRE) 15
549 **BEYOND ARGUMENT** (IRE) 3
202 **BEYOND BELIEF** (IRE) C 18
263 **BEYOND DESIRE** (GB) F 110
89 **BEYOND MEASURE** (IRE) 1
123 **BEYOND RECALL** (GB) 52
391 **BEYOND THE EDGE** (GB) 1
246 **BEYOND THE GLEN** (GB) 5
288 **BEYONDTEMPTATION** (GB) 2
288 **BEYONDTHEFLAME** (GB) 1
244 **BEZIQUE** (GB) C 113
514 **BHAKTI** (IRE) 1
456 **BHUTAN** (IRE) 16
410 **BIANCA MINOLA** (FR) 18
122 **BIANCA SFORZA** (GB) G 11
406 **BIBI D'EOLE** (FR) 7
307 **BIBI'S PEARL** (IRE) G 7
327 **BICKERSHAW** (GB) 3
634 **BID ADIEU** (IRE) 99
23 **BIDDER** (GB) 16
485 **BIDOUREY** (FR) 11
159 **BIEN NOMMEE** (FR) 19
361 **BIENTEVEO** (IRE) 15
130 **BIFF JOHNSON** (IRE) 6

135 **BIG AMIGO** (IRE) 25
234 **BIG BAD DUDE** (IRE) 10
201 **BIG BANG** (GB) 21
431 **BIG BAZ** (IRE) 3
456 **BIG BEN** (GB) 17
606 **BIG CASINO** (GB) 28
352 **BIG CHIEF BENNY** (IRE) 12
97 **BIG CHILL** (IRE) 2
234 **BIG FELLA THANKS** (IRE) 11
435 **BIG FLOE** (GB) 2
11 **BIG GENERATOR** (GB) 3
397 **BIG HANDS HARRY** (GB) 7
264 **BIG JIM** (GB) 3
65 **BIG MAJOR** (GB) 7
527 **BIG MCINTOSH** (IRE) 2
353 **BIG MEADOW** (IRE) 2
322 **BIG MIKE** (IRE) 1
324 **BIG NIGHT OUT** (GB) 3
485 **BIG OCCASION** (IRE) 12
29 **BIG ORANGE** (GB) 1
24 **BIG RED** (GB) 2
525 **BIG RIVER** (GB) 9
299 **BIG SHOES** (IRE) 25
259 **BIG SMILE** (IRE) 1
648 **BIG SOCIETY** (IRE) 3
619 **BIG SOUND** (GB) 2
256 **BIG STORM COMING** (GB) 2
361 **BIG SUR** (IRE) 16
63 **BIG TALK** (GB) 6
273 **BIG THUNDER** (GB) 8
450 **BIG TIME** (IRE) 3
534 **BIG TIME DANCER** (IRE) 22
264 **BIG TIME FRANK** (IRE) 4
160 **BIG TOMS GIRL** (GB) 1
606 **BIG TOUCH** (FR) 29
582 **BIG WATER** (IRE) 2
35 **BIG WHISKEY** (IRE) 3
234 **BIG WINDMILL** (IRE) 12
432 **BIGBADBOY** (IRE) 10
126 **BIGBADJOHN** (IRE) 8
252 **BIGBURY BAY** (IRE) 10
276 **BIGGER AND BETTER** (GB) 35
459 **BIGGS** (IRE) 3
155 **BIGIRONONHISHIP** (IRE) 8
648 **BIGMARTRE** (FR) 4
410 **BIGMOUTH STRIKES** (IRE) 9
130 **BIJAN** (GB) C 63
148 **BILAPERFECTA** (FR) 3
311 **BILASH** (GB) 2
301 **BILBROOK BLAZE** (GB) 13
252 **BILKO'S BACK** (IRE) 11
195 **BILL D'ARON** (FR) 8
23 **BILLABONG** (MOR) 1
186 **BILLET DOUX** (IRE) 15
397 **BILLFROMTHEBAR** (IRE) 8
431 **BILLIE JEAN** (GB) C 44
521 **BILLIONNAIRE** (IRE) 44
352 **BILLY BISCUIT** (IRE) 3
197 **BILLY BOND** (GB) 9
161 **BILLY DUTTON** (GB) 2
224 **BILLY MERRIOTT** (IRE) 10
161 **BILLY MY BOY** (GB) 3
597 **BILLY NO NAME** (IRE) 1
335 **BILLY RED** (GB) 6
261 **BILLY ROBERTS** (IRE) 16
428 **BILLY SLATER** (GB) 2
297 **BILLY TWYFORD** (IRE) 2
279 **BILLY'S HOPE** (IRE) 6

22 **BILLYOAKES** (IRE) 5
550 **BILZIC** (FR) 18
224 **BIM BAM BOUM** (FR) 11
299 **BIMINI** (GB) C 92
301 **BINCOMBE** (GB) 14
134 **BINDON MILL** (GB) 5
126 **BINGE DRINKER** (IRE) 9
655 **BINGO D'OLIVATE** (FR) 2
15 **BINGO GEORGE** (IRE) 52
376 **BINKY BLUE** (FR) 5
5 **BINT AL REEM** (IRE) 31
528 **BINT ALDAR** (GB) 39
84 **BINT ARCANO** (FR) 10
173 **BINT DANDY** (IRE) 3
319 **BINT DOYEN** (GB) F 17
78 **BIODYNAMIC** (IRE) 26
263 **BIOLOGIST** (IRE) 111
176 **BIONIC INDIAN** (GB) 7
414 **BIOTIC** (FR) 2
292 **BIRCH HILL** (IRE) 18
197 **BIRCHWOOD** (IRE) 81
485 **BIRD D'ESTRUVAL** (FR) 13
428 **BIRDCAGE** (GB) 15
422 **BIRDIE QUEEN** (GB) 11
461 **BIRDMAN** (IRE) 7
224 **BIRETTA** (GB) 12
42 **BIRJAND** (GB) C 114
197 **BIRKDALE BOY** (IRE) 18
15 **BIRMANIE** (USA) C 123
165 **BIRRAFUN** (IRE) 9
355 **BIRTHDAY GUEST** (GER) 4
411 **BISHOP LIGHTFOOT** (IRE) 3
52 **BISHOP WULSTAN** (IRE) 6
433 **BISHOPS COURT** (GB) 10
366 **BISHOPS ROAD** (IRE) 3
526 **BIT OF A CHARLIE** (GB) 1
72 **BIT OF A LAD** (IRE) 18
619 **BIT OF A QUIRKE** (GB) 26
224 **BITOFAPUZZLE** (GB) 13
355 **BITUMEN BELLE** (IRE) 5
292 **BIVOUAC** (FR) 19
244 **BIZZARRIA** (GB) 114
408 **BLACK ACE** (IRE) 10
306 **BLACK ART** (GB) 2
145 **BLACK BARONESS** (GB) C 32
87 **BLACK BELT SHOPPER** (IRE) F 47
54 **BLACK BESS** (GB) 15
276 **BLACK BOLT** (IRE) 133
296 **BLACK CAESAR** (IRE) 3
276 **BLACK CHERRY** (GB) 2
451 **BLACK CORTON** (FR) 22
151 **BLACK COUNTRY BOY** (GB) 5
242 **BLACK COW** (IRE) 6
549 **BLACK DAHLIA** (GB) C 64
190 **BLACK DAVE** (IRE) 5
664 **BLACK DIAMOND GIRL** (GB) 11
176 **BLACK GRASS** (GB) 54
554 **BLACK HAMBLETON** (GB) 19
466 **BLACK HAWK** (IRE) 4
456 **BLACK HAWK WAR** (USA) 18
437 **BLACK HERCULES** (IRE) 47
93 **BLACK HOLE SUN** (GB) 9
475 **BLACK ICEMAN** (GB) 1
558 **BLACK INK** (GB) 2
176 **BLACK IS BLACK** (IRE) 55
461 **BLACK ISLE BOY** (IRE) 71
210 **BLACK JACK JAXON** (GB) 2
397 **BLACK JACK ROVER** (IRE) 9

134 **BOLVING** (IRE) 6
553 **BOMBA NOVA** (FR) 2
389 **BOMBA STICK** (FR) 5
100 **BOMBAY ROLL** (GB) 17
234 **BOMBER COMMAND** (FR) 13
153 **BOMBER ETCHES** (GB) 28
606 **BOMBER'S MOON** (GB) 31
5 **BOMBILATE** (USA) 35
550 **BON CHIC** (IRE) 21
252 **BON ENFANT** (FR) 12
573 **BON GENRE** (IRE) 3
437 **BON PAPA** (FR) 55
437 **BONBON AU MIEL** (FR) 56
468 **BONCHARD** (GB) 12
65 **BOND DEAL** (IRE) C 19
371 **BOND MYSTERY** (GB) 3
116 **BOND TRADER** (GB) 29
465 **BOND'S GIFT** (GB) 1
593 **BOND'S TRICKS** (GB) 14
456 **BONDI BEACH** (IRE) 1
604 **BONDI BEACH BABE** (GB) 1
604 **BONDI BEACH BOY** (GB) 2
233 **BONDI MIST** (IRE) 2
436 **BONDS CONQUEST** (GB) 7
171 **BONGO BELLE** (GB) 1
456 **BONHEUR** (IRE) C 96
90 **BONHEUR DE STARA** (FR) 7
29 **BONHOMIE** (GB) 16
78 **BONJOUR BABY** (GB) 27
521 **BONJOUR MAMIE** (FR) 46
496 **BONJOUR STEVE** (GB) 1
78 **BONNE** (GB) F 67
658 **BONNE QUESTION** (FR) 13
611 **BONNEFIO** (GB) 8
552 **BONNET'S VINO** (GB) 4
646 **BONNIE BLACK ROSE** (GB) 2
534 **BONNIE LIZZIE** (GB) 4
408 **BONNY KATE** (IRE) 12
135 **BONNY ROSE** (GB) F 58
652 **BONOBO** (IRE) 10
612 **BONVILSTON BOY** (GB) 20
598 **BONZO BING** (IRE) 4
549 **BOO BOO BEAR** (IRE) F 65
504 **BOOK AT BEDTIME** (GB) 4
60 **BOOK OF EXCUSES** (IRE) 1
62 **BOOKMAKER** (GB) 1
148 **BOOKRUNNER** (USA) 4
345 **BOOKTHEBAND** (IRE) 1
185 **BOOLASS** (IRE) 10
12 **BOOLAVARD KING** (IRE) 10
279 **BOOM BOX** (IRE) 9
93 **BOOM JUNIOR** (GB) 72
93 **BOOM THE GROOM** (GB) 11
467 **BOOMERANG BOB** (IRE) 1
14 **BOOMSHACKERLACKER** (IRE) 7
172 **BOOMTOWN** (GB) 2
102 **BOONGA ROOGETA** (GB) 1
426 **BOOOM** 15
168 **BOOSHBASH** (IRE) 63
494 **BOOST** (GB) 44
438 **BOOTED EAGLE** (GB) 1
72 **BOOTERY** (USA) F 33
153 **BOOTS AND SPURS** (GB) 4
359 **BOOTY FULL** (GB) 10
642 **BOP ALONG** (IRE) 4
265 **BORA BLUES** (GB) C 75
370 **BORAK** (IRE) 4
437 **BORBOLETA** (IRE) 57

32 **BORDEAUX BILL** (IRE) 3
616 **BORDER BANDIT** (USA) 1
470 **BORDER BLOOM** (GB) F 6
485 **BORDER BREAKER** (IRE) 15
671 **BORDER STATION** (IRE) 3
578 **BORDER TERRITORY** (IRE) 114
437 **BORDINI** (FR) 58
149 **BORED OR BAD** (IRE) 4
632 **BORIC** (GB) 4
550 **BORN SURVIVOR** (IRE) 22
258 **BORN TO BE FREE** (GB) 3
347 **BORN TO DREAM** (IRE) G 6
230 **BORN TO FINISH** (IRE) 16
171 **BORN TO FLY** (IRE) 4
51 **BORNTOSIN** (IRE) 82
541 **BOROUGH BOY** (IRE) 2
299 **BORTHWEN** (IRE) 94
34 **BORU'S BROOK** (IRE) 6
534 **BORUMA** (IRE) 5
176 **BOSHAM** (GB) 8
437 **BOSMAN RULE** (GB) 59
23 **BOSNORMAND** (FR) 55
156 **BOSPHORUS QUEEN** (FR) F 50
550 **BOSS DES MOTTES** (FR) 23
436 **BOSS IN BOOTS** (IRE) 8
65 **BOSSA NOVA** (GB) 9
177 **BOSSIPOP** (GB) 72
98 **BOSSY GUEST** (IRE) 4
457 **BOSTIN** (IRE) 1
93 **BOSTON BLUE** (GB) 12
437 **BOSTON BOB** (IRE) 60
373 **BOSTON DE LA ROCHE** (FR) 1
144 **BOSTON RED** (GB) 1
15 **BOTH SIDES** (GB) 54
276 **BOUCHERON** (GB) C 135
93 **BOUCLIER** (GB) 13
252 **BOUDRY** (FR) 13
87 **BOUNCE** (GB) 22
542 **BOUND HILL** (GB) 1
546 **BOUNTIFUL SIN** (GB) 5
477 **BOUNTY BOX** (GB) C 16
78 **BOUNTY BRIDGE** (IRE) 68
6 **BOUNTY TIME** (GB) 12
14 **BOUNTYBEAMADAM** (GB) 8
162 **BOURBON PRINCE** (GB) 2
13 **BOURDELLO** (GB) 3
397 **BOURNE** (GB) 10
78 **BOURNVILLE** (IRE) 69
16 **BOUTAN** (GB) 44
402 **BOUTIQUE** (GB) G 1
451 **BOUVREUIL** (FR) 27
5 **BOW AND ARROW** (GB) 4
579 **BOWBERRY** (GB) 3
592 **BOWDLER'S MAGIC** (GB) 2
351 **BOWIE** (IRE) 1
600 **BOWSERS BOLD** (GB) 2
176 **BOWSON FRED** (GB) 9
263 **BOX OF FROGS** (IRE) F 113
463 **BOX OFFICE** (IRE) 10
482 **BOXATRIX** (GB) 7
196 **BOXING SHADOWS** (GB) 1
12 **BOY IN A BENTLEY** (IRE) 11
653 **BOY IN THE BAR** (GB) 10
334 **BOY NAMED SIOUX** (GB) 2
621 **BOYCHICK** (IRE) 16
276 **BOYCIE** (GB) 37
234 **BOYHOOD** (IRE) 14
106 **BOYISSIME** (FR) 19

301 **BRAAVOS** (GB) 16
42 **BRABBLE** (USA) 39
1 **BRACING** (GB) 8
599 **BRACKEN BRAE** (GB) 2
257 **BRACKEN HILL** (GB) 1
510 **BRACKENMOSS** (IRE) G 5
642 **BRACKENMOSS RORY** (GB) 5
301 **BRADFORD BRIDGE** (IRE) 17
156 **BRADLEYSINTOWN** (IRE) 28
39 **BRAE ON** (GB) 2
239 **BRAES OF LOCHALSH** (GB) 2
309 **BRAGABOUT** (GB) 4
279 **BRAGADOCIOUS** (USA) C 88
429 **BRAHMA** (GB) 32
437 **BRAHMA BULL** (IRE) 61
292 **BRAIN POWER** (IRE) 24
597 **BRAMBLE BROOK** (GB) 4
5 **BRAMBLES** (GB) 36
521 **BRAMETOT** (IRE) 157
479 **BRAMSHILL LASS** (GB) 6
342 **BRANDBERG** (IRE) 37
375 **BRANDENBURG GATE** (IRE) 9
528 **BRANDO** (GB) 5
15 **BRANDON CASTLE** (GB) 6
51 **BRANDYBEND** (IRE) 3
470 **BRANGANE** (GB) C 7
117 **BRANSTON GEM** (GB) C 28
126 **BRAQUEUR D'OR** (FR) 11
159 **BRASS BELL** (IRE) 2
6 **BRASSBOUND** (USA) 13
108 **BRAVE ARCHIBALD** (IRE) 22
516 **BRAVE CUPID** (GB) 3
338 **BRAVE DECISION** (GB) 1
538 **BRAVE DEED** (IRE) 5
483 **BRAVE HELIOS** (GB) 6
42 **BRAVE HERO** (GB) 40
451 **BRAVE JAQ** (FR) 28
335 **BRAVE RICHARD** (IRE) 8
510 **BRAVE SPARTACUS** (IRE) 10
42 **BRAVE TIMES** (GB) 41
422 **BRAVE VIC** (IRE) 15
279 **BRAVE THE BULL** (IRE) 64
456 **BRAVERY** (IRE) 20
437 **BRAVISSIMO** (FR) 62
9 **BRAVO ECHO** (GB) 3
131 **BRAVO KING** (IRE) 3
455 **BRAVO ZOLO** (IRE) 1
12 **BRAW ANGUS** (GB) 12
116 **BRAZEN SPIRIT** (GB) 2
78 **BRAZILIAN BREEZE** (IRE) F 70
634 **BRAZILIAN BRIDE** (IRE) F 100
553 **BRAZILIAN CHAP** (FR) 3
407 **BRAZILIAN SAMBA** (IRE) F 32
358 **BRAZILIAN STYLE** (GB) F 44
584 **BRAZOS** (IRE) 3
177 **BREAKABLE** (GB) 7
407 **BREAKFAST** (IRE) 33
15 **BREAKHEART** (IRE) 7
564 **BREAKING BITS** (IRE) 9
500 **BREAKING FREE** (GB) 53
96 **BREAKING THE BANK** (GB) 3
603 **BREAN GOLF BIRDIE** (GB) 1
603 **BREAN SPLASH SUSIE** (GB) 2
633 **BREATH OF BLIGHTY** (FR) 4
514 **BREATH OF LIFE** (GB) 2
263 **BREDA CASTLE** (GB) 28
244 **BREDEN** (IRE) 1
229 **BREDON HILL LAD** (GB) 1

185 **BURNING BLAZE** (GB) 11
48 **BURNING BULLET** (GB) 19
319 **BURNING DESIRE** (IRE) 5
426 **BURNING LOVE** (IRE) 4
48 **BURNING SWORD** (IRE) 20
186 **BURNING THREAD** (IRE) 3
2 **BURNT CREAM** (GB) 2
276 **BURNT SUGAR** (IRE) 3
597 **BURTON BORU** (IRE) 1
84 **BURTONWOOD** (GB) 1
545 **BUS NAMED DESIRE** (GB) 2
4 **BUSH BEAUTY** (IRE) 1
469 **BUSH HOUSE** (IRE) 64
438 **BUSH WARRIOR** (IRE) 2
237 **BUSHEL** (GB) 3
226 **BUSHEPHALUS** (IRE) 3
57 **BUSHWISE** (IRE) 14
276 **BUSKIN RIVER** (IRE) 139
160 **BUSTA NELLIE** (GB) 16
142 **BUSTER BROWN** (GB) 4
31 **BUSY BIMBO** (IRE) 2
243 **BUSY BUSH** (IRE) 2
582 **BUSY STREET** (GB) 3
408 **BUTCHIES GIRL** (IRE) G 15
185 **BUTHELEZI** (USA) 12
658 **BUTTERCUP** (FR) 14
342 **BUTTERMERE** (USA) 39
292 **BUVEUR D'AIR** (FR) 27
612 **BUY BACK BOB** (IRE) 23
320 **BUYER BEWARE** (IRE) 1
652 **BUYWISE** (IRE) 13
9 **BUZZ LIGHTYERE** (GB) 28
437 **BUZZ OFF BARROSO** (IRE) 67
93 **BY RIGHTS** (GB) 14
12 **BY THE BOARDWALK** (IRE) 13
5 **BY THE LAW** (GB) 38
549 **BYBROOK** (GB) 33
340 **BYGONES FOR COINS** (IRE) 1
62 **BYRD IN HAND** (IRE) 2
236 **BYRON BLUE** (IRE) 3
653 **BYRON FLYER** (GB) 11
109 **BYRONEGETONEFREE** (GB) 4
407 **C NOTE** (IRE) 10
612 **C'EST DU GATEAU** (FR) 24
195 **CA LE FERRA** (FR) 9
277 **CABAL** (GB) 3
265 **CABARET** (IRE) C 77
213 **CABBIES LOU** (GB) 3
654 **CABERNET D'ALENE** (FR) 8
422 **CABIMAS** (GB) 18
6 **CABLE STREET** (USA) 16
190 **CABUCHON** (GER) 6
26 **CACICA** (GB) 8
176 **CACTUS VALLEY** (IRE) 10
153 **CADEAUX PEARL** (GB) 5
177 **CADEAUX POWER** (GB) 8
548 **CADGERS HOLE** (GB) 3
527 **CADLAND LAD** (IRE) 16
437 **CADMIUM** (FR) 68
453 **CADMIUM** (GB) 11
453 **CADORE** (IRE) 4
375 **CADOUDOFF** (FR) 10
549 **CAFE AMERICAIN** (IRE) 34
607 **CAFE NERVOSA** (IRE) 11
168 **CAFOO** (IRE) 19
241 **CAGED LIGHTNING** (IRE) 1
312 **CAHAR FAD** (IRE) 1
339 **CAHERASSDOTCOM** (GB) C 37

352 **CAHILL** (IRE) 19
280 **CAI SHEN** (IRE) 2
451 **CAID DU BERLAIS** (FR) 32
88 **CAILIN** (IRE) 2
265 **CAILIN MOR** (IRE) 3
164 **CAILLEACH ANNIE** (IRE) 3
108 **CAITIE** (IRE) 23
252 **CAITYS JOY** (GER) 15
512 **CAIUS MARCIUS** (IRE) 9
470 **CAJAMARCA** (FR) 8
148 **CAJARIAN** (FR) 32
135 **CAJMERE** (GB) 40
537 **CAJOLED** (FR) 9
352 **CAJUN FIDDLE** (IRE) 20
276 **CAKE** (IRE) C 140
115 **CAKESTOWN LADY** (IRE) C 54
195 **CALACH** (FR) 10
310 **CALAJANI** (FR) 7
352 **CALAMINTHA** (GB) C 21
5 **CALANDO** (USA) F 97
332 **CALCULATED RISK** (GB) 3
135 **CALDER PRINCE** (GB) 27
653 **CALDEY** (GB) 12
239 **CALEDONIA** (GB) 3
318 **CALEDONIA LAIRD** (GB) 2
603 **CALGARY** (GB) C 18
244 **CALIFORNIA** (IRE) 2
169 **CALIFORNIA LAD** (GB) 13
456 **CALIFORNIADREAMING** (IRE) 21
286 **CALIN DU BRIZAIS** (FR) 9
290 **CALINA** (FR) 10
42 **CALIPATRIA** (GB) F 116
451 **CALIPTO** (FR) 33
1 **CALIVIGNY** (IRE) 9
195 **CALIX DELAFAYETTE** (FR) 11
322 **CALL AT MIDNIGHT** (GB) 2
1 **CALL HER AGAIN** (IRE) F 10
355 **CALL IT ON** (IRE) 8
15 **CALL LATER** (USA) C 124
192 **CALL ME BEN** (IRE) 3
332 **CALL ME CROCKETT** (IRE) 4
483 **CALL ME EMMA** (IRE) 7
322 **CALL ME KAL** (IRE) 2
613 **CALL ME NUMBER ONE** (GER) 3
234 **CALL ME VIC** (IRE) 16
6 **CALL OUT LOUD** (IRE) 17
292 **CALL THE COPS** (IRE) 28
579 **CALL THE DETECTIVE** (IRE) 4
584 **CALL THIS CAT** (IRE) F 72
263 **CALL TO MIND** (IRE) 115
243 **CALLANISH** (GB) F 12
116 **CALLENDULA** (GB) 3
224 **CALLING DES BLINS** (FR) 17
549 **CALLING OUT** (IRE) 5
15 **CALLIOPE** (GB) 57
622 **CALM CHARM** (IRE) 33
584 **CALM SPIRIT** (GB) 30
539 **CALTON ENTRY** (IRE) 3
349 **CALTRA COLLEEN** (GB) 1
473 **CALVA D'HONORE** (FR) 1
431 **CALVADOS SPIRIT** (GB) 19
356 **CALYPSO CHOIR** (GB) 15
273 **CALYPSO DELEGATOR** (IRE) 76
411 **CALYPSO STORM** (IRE) 4
217 **CAMACHOICE** (IRE) 2
579 **CAMAKASI** (IRE) 5
285 **CAMANCHE GREY** (IRE) 1
475 **CAMARADORIE** (IRE) 13

622 **CAMBODIA** (IRE) 19
228 **CAMBRIDGE FAVORITE** (GB) 7
377 **CAMCHICA** (IRE) 4
467 **CAMDORA** (IRE) 2
533 **CAMELEY DAWN** (GB) 2
279 **CAMILE** (IRE) 65
230 **CAMINEL** (IRE) 1
442 **CAMINO** (GB) 11
432 **CAMLET** (GB) C 136
521 **CAMP COURAGE** (USA) 48
585 **CAMP RIVERSIDE** (USA) F 12
179 **CAMPINA** (GB) C 15
620 **CAMPING GROUND** (FR) 4
244 **CAMPOSANTO** (GB) 25
286 **CAMRON DE CHAILLAC** (FR) 10
549 **CAN DANCE** (GB) 64
532 **CAN SHE DANCE** (IRE) C 8
549 **CAN'T CHANGE IT** (IRE) 6
459 **CAN'T STOP** (GER) C 4
522 **CANADIAN DIAMOND** (IRE) 1
320 **CANALY** (IRE) 12
135 **CANCAN KATY** (GB) 28
524 **CANCELLARA** (GB) 3
451 **CANDARA** (FR) F 85
460 **CANDELISA** (IRE) 15
183 **CANDELITA** (GB) 4
201 **CANDESTA** (USA) 4
290 **CANDICANS** (GB) F 38
145 **CANDLE** (GB) F 2
456 **CANDLE ROCKS** (IRE) 22
279 **CANDLESTICK** (IRE) 11
528 **CANDY BANTER** (USA) 43
432 **CANDY EXPRESS** (GB) 5
442 **CANDYMAN CAN** (IRE) 4
148 **CANESSAR** (FR) 33
479 **CANFORD BELLE** (GB) 21
467 **CANFORD CHIMES** (IRE) 18
276 **CANFORD CROSSING** (IRE) 39
339 **CANFORD LILLI** (IRE) 17
281 **CANFORD STAR** (IRE) 26
51 **CANFORD THOMPSON** (GB) 24
87 **CANFORD TOR** (IRE) 48
652 **CANICALLYOUBACK** (GB) 14
20 **CANIVER QUEEN** (IRE) 2
281 **CANIZAY** (IRE) 34
123 **CANNED HEAT** (GB) 55
578 **CANNOCK CHASE** (USA) 2
635 **CANNON FODDER** (GB) 2
185 **CANNY KOOL** (GB) 13
528 **CANNY STYLE** (GB) 44
578 **CANONBURY** (IRE) 32
429 **CANOODLE** (GB) 3
202 **CANT HURRY LOVE** (GB) F 19
469 **CANTAL** (GB) C 65
376 **CANTANKEROUS** (GB) 6
567 **CANTERBURY QUAD** (FR) 11
314 **CANTON MASSINI** (GB) 1
612 **CANTON PRINCE** (IRE) 25
457 **CANTOR** (GB) 2
22 **CANUKEEPASECRET** (GB) F 51
197 **CANYARI** (IRE) 4
455 **CAP CANAILLE** (USA) 14
263 **CAP COZ** (FR) F 116
437 **CAP D'AUBOIS** (FR) 69
647 **CAP HORNER** (FR) 2
463 **CAPARD KING** (IRE) 12
387 **CAPATOSTA** (USA) 5
459 **CAPBRETON** (FR) 5

610 **DAWN OF HOPE** (IRE) 59
363 **DAWN SKY** (GB) 3
460 **DAWN SPINNER** (GB) G 4
135 **DAWN'S EARLY LIGHT** (IRE) 10
540 **DAWNIERIVER** (IRE) 5
600 **DAWREYA** (IRE) 18
262 **DAWSON CITY** (GB) 3
603 **DAY BY DAY** (GB) F 20
32 **DAY DAY** (IRE) 6
538 **DAY OF ROSES** (IRE) 11
174 **DAY OF THE EAGLE** (IRE) 15
521 **DAYANA** (FR) 54
318 **DAYBREAK LADY** (GB) 7
467 **DAYDREAM** (IRE) 20
503 **DAYDREAM BELIEVER** (GB) 1
176 **DAYITA** (FR) C 170
176 **DAYLIGHT** (GB) 16
186 **DAYLIGHT ROBBERY** (GB) 17
299 **DAYROSE** (GB) C 100
214 **DAYS AHEAD** (IRE) 3
667 **DAYS LIKE THESE** (GB) 2
292 **DAYS OF HEAVEN** (FR) 49
28 **DAYS OF SUMMER** (IRE) F 82
546 **DAYTIME AHEAD** (GB) 12
525 **DAYTRIPPER** (GB) 17
528 **DAYVILLE** (USA) C 87
148 **DAZARI** (FR) 36
294 **DAZEEKHA** (GB) 13
466 **DAZINSKI** (GB) 5
5 **DBOBE** (GB) 3
104 **DE AGUILAR** (USA) 23
519 **DE BEE KEEPER** (IRE) 2
652 **DE BENE ESSE** (GB) 22
422 **DE BLACKSMITH** (IRE) 27
561 **DE BOITRON** (FR) 14
652 **DE FAOITHESDREAM** (IRE) 23
63 **DE KERRY MAN** (IRE) 10
513 **DE LESSEPS** (USA) 1
408 **DE NAME ESCAPES ME** (IRE) 20
407 **DE VEER CLIFFS** (IRE) 13
561 **DE VOUS A MOI** (FR) 15
435 **DEADLINE DAY** (IRE) 4
139 **DEADLY APPROACH** (GB) 9
52 **DEADLY MOVE** (IRE) 12
433 **DEADLY STING** (GB) 22
610 **DEALER'S CHOICE** (IRE) 143
11 **DEALING RIVER** (GB) 6
614 **DEAN'S WALK** (IRE) 6
84 **DEANSGATE** (IRE) 11
342 **DEAR BELA** (ARG) C 147
456 **DEAUVILLE** (IRE) 30
149 **DEAUVILLE DANCER** (IRE) 11
600 **DEAUVILLE DIVA** (IRE) 38
135 **DEAUVILLE PRINCE** (FR) 11
550 **DEBDEBDEB** (GB) 36
612 **DEBECE** (GB) 32
528 **DEBEN** (GB) 48
306 **DEBIT** (GB) 4
213 **DEBT TO SOCIETY** (IRE) 4
42 **DECEMBER SECOND** (IRE) 121
146 **DECIDING MOMENT** (IRE) 1
538 **DECIMUS** (IRE) 1
94 **DECISIVE** (IRE) 2
286 **DECKERS DELIGHT** (GB) 11
467 **DECLAN** (GB) 4
37 **DECLAN** (GB) 4
256 **DECLINED** (GB) 5
104 **DECORATED KNIGHT** (GB) 5

276 **DECORATIVE** (IRE) F 150
165 **DECREES OF MOTION** (IRE) 41
19 **DEE BEES GIFT** (GB) 5
72 **DEE DEE GIRL** (IRE) F 36
96 **DEE TWO O TWO** (IRE) F 41
496 **DEEBAJ** (IRE) 3
499 **DEEP BLUE DIAMOND** (GB) 5
94 **DEEP BLUE SEA** (GB) 3
15 **DEEP DREAM** (GB) 61
582 **DEEP RESOLVE** (IRE) 7
96 **DEEP TROUBLE** (GB) 8
123 **DEEP WINTER** (GB) F 64
579 **DEEPSAND** (IRE) 8
62 **DEER SONG** (GB) 11
307 **DEES ROCK** (IRE) F 8
244 **DEFENCE COUNSEL** (USA) 124
541 **DEFIANT CHOICE** (GB) 27
393 **DEFINATELY VINNIE** (GB) 1
223 **DEFINING YEAR** (IRE) 4
366 **DEFINITE FUTURE** (IRE) 4
126 **DEFINITE OUTCOME** (IRE) 16
234 **DEFINITELY BETTER** (IRE) 20
112 **DEFINITELY GLAD** (IRE) 2
375 **DEFINITLY GREY** (IRE) 16
185 **DEFINITLY RED** (IRE) 16
610 **DEFOE** (IRE) 144
467 **DEFROCKED** (IRE) 21
480 **DEFTERA LAD** (IRE) 4
422 **DEGAS BRONZE** (IRE) 129
200 **DEGOOCH** (IRE) 7
528 **DEGREE OF HONOR** (FR) C 88
433 **DEJA BOUGG** (GB) 23
356 **DELAGOA BAY** (IRE) 4
50 **DELAIRE** (GB) 5
353 **DELGANY DEMON** (GB) 5
190 **DELIA** (IRE) F 45
244 **DELIBERATE** (GB) C 125
120 **DELIGHTFUL BELLE** (USA) 11
48 **DELIGHTFUL FOCUS** (IRE) 82
394 **DELINEATE** (IRE) 1
276 **DELIRA** (IRE) C 151
406 **DELIRIOUS LOVE** (IRE) 9
599 **DELITME** (IRE) F 29
485 **DELL' ARCA** (IRE) 24
645 **DELLA SUN** (FR) 1
480 **DELLBUOY** (IRE) 5
388 **DELMA** (IRE) F 24
634 **DELTA DREAMER** (GB) 107
561 **DELUSIONOFGRANDEUR** (IRE) 16
480 **DELUXE** (GB) 6
578 **DELVE** (IRE) 36
389 **DELVIN ROAD** (IRE) 10
171 **DELYSDREAM** (GB) 7
567 **DEMAND RESPECT** (GB) 7
649 **DEMBABA** (IRE) 3
179 **DEMI'S QUEST** (IRE) 17
364 **DEMOGRAPHIC** (USA) 17
333 **DEMONSTRATION** (IRE) 2
6 **DEMORA** (GB) 25
165 **DEMPSEY ROLL** (GB) 12
6 **DENALA** (GB) 26
11 **DENALI HIGHWAY** (IRE) 7
564 **DENBOY** (IRE) 12
23 **DENEBOLA** (USA) C 58
87 **DENHAM SOUND** (GB) 23
434 **DENISON FLYER** (GB) 1
346 **DENNY KERRELL** (GB) 4
654 **DENTLEY DE MEE** (FR) 31

156 **DENTON CARNIVAL** (IRE) 5
308 **DENY** (GB) 2
342 **DEODORO** (USA) 46
554 **DEORA DE** (GB) F 37
454 **DEPORTATION** (GB) 3
508 **DEPRESSED** (GB) F 8
580 **DEPTH CHARGE** (IRE) 4
606 **DEPUTY COMMANDER** (IRE) 39
546 **DEPUTY DAN** (IRE) 13
524 **DEREMAH** (USA) 37
292 **DERKSEN** (IRE) 50
224 **DERRAVARAGH SAYRA** (IRE) G 21
12 **DERRINTOGHER BLISS** (IRE) 20
403 **DERRYDOON** (GB) 4
213 **DERRYFADDA** (IRE) 5
142 **DERRYOGUE** (IRE) 5
184 **DESAFINADO** (IRE) 5
28 **DESDICHADO** (GB) 5
156 **DESERT ACE** (IRE) 6
568 **DESERT ALCHEMY** (IRE) F 41
578 **DESERT CAPELLA** (GB) 118
644 **DESERT CHIEF** (GB) 2
115 **DESERT COMMAND** (GB) 4
463 **DESERT CROSS** (GB) 106
397 **DESERT CRY** (IRE) 23
578 **DESERT DREAM** (GB) 119
549 **DESERT ENCOUNTER** (IRE) 12
276 **DESERT FORCE** (GB) 5
439 **DESERT FOX** (GB) 26
148 **DESERT GALE** (IRE) 37
342 **DESERT GAZELLE** (USA) C 148
28 **DESERT HAZE** (GB) 36
19 **DESERT ISLAND DUSK** (GB) 6
578 **DESERT ISLE** (GB) 37
352 **DESERT JOE** (IRE) 33
62 **DESERT KISS** (GB) F 15
413 **DESERT LAW** (IRE) 2
431 **DESERT LIAISON** (GB) F 48
94 **DESERT MORNING** (IRE) 4
85 **DESERT NOVA** (IRE) 3
224 **DESERT QUEEN** (GB) 22
466 **DESERT RECLUSE** (IRE) 30
301 **DESERT RETREAT** (IRE) 30
599 **DESERT RIVER** (IRE) 15
460 **DESERT RULER** (GB) 16
616 **DESERT SENSATION** (IRE) 5
115 **DESERT SKY** (IRE) C 57
480 **DESERT SONG** (GB) 25
158 **DESERT STRIKE** (GB) 4
276 **DESERT SUNRISE** (GB) F 152
490 **DESERT TANGO** (GB) 22
28 **DESERT WAY** (GB) 37
52 **DESERTMORE HILL** (IRE) 13
612 **DESHAN** (GB) 33
145 **DESIGNED** (GB) C 35
192 **DESILVANO** (GB) 4
429 **DESIRABLE** (GB) 36
197 **DESIRE** (IRE) 18
66 **DESKTOP** (GB) 3
549 **DESPATCH** (GB) C 70
151 **DESROCHES** (GER) 7
414 **DESSERT FLOWER** (IRE) C 26
342 **DESSERTOFLIFE** (IRE) 47
630 **DESTINATION AIM** (GB) 2
488 **DESTINY AWAITS** (IRE) 1
14 **DESTINY'S GOLD** (IRE) 10
14 **DESTINY'S SHADOW** (IRE) 11
463 **DESTINY'S STAR** (GB) 25

512 ECHO EXPRESS (IRE) 17
159 ECHO MAKER (FR) 7
185 ECHO OF LIGHTNING (GB) 23
399 ECHO SPRINGS (GB) 2
469 ECLAIRCIE (IRE) C 20
622 ECLAIRCIE (IRE) C 35
658 ECO WARRIOR (GB) 24
31 ECONOMIC CRISIS (IRE) 3
469 ECUREUIL (IRE) 21
130 ECUSSON (GB) F 42
127 EDAS (GB) 1
208 EDDIEMAURICE (IRE) 5
471 EDDY (GB) 1
226 EDDY MERCS (GB) 5
665 EDE'S THE BUSINESS (GB) 3
480 EDE'S THE MOVER (GB) 20
262 EDEIFF'S LAD (GB) 4
63 EDGAR (GER) 13
130 EDGAR BALTHAZAR (GB) 11
370 EDGE (IRE) 6
490 EDGE OF HEAVEN (GB) 6
153 EDGE OF LIGHT (GB) F 48
621 EDGE OF REASON (GB) 25
391 EDGED OUT (GB) 2
243 EDGY (IRE) 10
407 EDIFICATION (GB) 14
115 EDITH WESTON (GB) 30
578 EDITH WHARTON (IRE) 120
603 EDLOMOND (IRE) 4
271 EDMUND (IRE) 1
512 EDUARD (IRE) 18
419 EDUCATE (GB) 1
11 EDWARD ELGAR (GB) 10
617 EENY MAC (IRE) 1
130 EEZ EH (IRE) 43
72 EFFIGE (IRE) C 40
643 EGON SPENGLAR (GB) 6
525 EGRET (IRE) 19
455 EGYPTIAN (USA) 16
80 EHTIRAAS (GB) 10
521 EIFFEL IN PARIS (FR) 175
521 EIGHTH AND I (USA) 176
228 EINSTEIN (GB) 4
328 EIRENE (GB) 56
48 EIRIAMACH NA CASCA (IRE) 85
83 EIUM MAC (GB) 3
276 EJAAZAH (IRE) 46
122 EJAYTEEKAY (GB) 12
115 EJBAAR (GB) 5
610 EKTIHAAM (IRE) 11
500 EL ASTRONAUTE (IRE) 33
451 EL BANDIT (GB) 55
500 EL BEAU (IRE) 4
160 EL CAMPEON (GB) 6
578 EL CAP (USA) 121
98 EL CHE (GB) 7
603 EL DUQUE (GB) 5
422 EL FENIX (IRE) 35
578 EL HAYEM (IRE) 44
174 EL INDIO (IRE) 6
106 EL ISSIDRO (GB) 24
36 EL MASSIVO (IRE) 1
176 EL MOLINO BLANCO (GB) F 64
196 EL PRINCIPE (GB) 11
610 EL TEL (GB) 12
590 EL TIBURON (IRE) 3
9 EL TREN (IRE) 5
197 EL VIENTO (FR) 20

123 EL VIP (IRE) 24
610 ELA ATHENA (GB) F 147
102 ELA GOOG LA MOU (GB) 2
438 ELAND ALLY (GB) 4
244 ELAS DIAMOND (GB) F 128
634 ELBASANA (IRE) F 110
15 ELBERETH (GB) 16
22 ELBOW BEACH (GB) C 55
148 ELDACAR (GB) 6
521 ELDO BERE (FR) 177
122 ELEANOR ELOISE (USA) C 13
263 ELECTRA STAR (GB) C 129
431 ELECTRIC FEEL (GB) C 50
455 ELECTRIFY (IRE) 17
490 ELEGANT ANNIE (GB) 23
407 ELEGANT PRIDE (GB) C 37
28 ELEKTRA MARINO (GB) F 86
42 ELEMENT OF TRUTH (USA) C 124
492 ELEMENT QUARTET (IRE) 5
29 ELEMENTARY (GB) 52
400 ELEMENTO (GB) 22
658 ELENIKA (FR) 25
521 ELENNGA (FR) 60
610 ELERFAAN (IRE) 148
528 ELEUTHERA (GB) 11
352 ELGIN (GB) 39
23 ELIDE (IRE) 17
98 ELIDOR (GB) 8
137 ELIDORE (GB) F 15
649 ELIS ELIZ (IRE) 4
42 ELITE ARMY (GB) 7
104 ELITE FORCE (GB) 4
165 ELIZABELLE (IRE) F 43
328 ELJADDAAF (IRE) 3
263 ELJEEMI (IRE) 40
352 ELKSTONE (GB) 40
598 ELLA'S DELIGHT (IRE) 5
298 ELLA'S PROMISE (GB) 3
91 ELLAAL (GB) 14
72 ELLABLUE (GB) C 41
202 ELLBEEDEE (IRE) F 24
335 ELLCON (IRE) F 47
377 ELLE DORADO (GB) 6
64 ELLE REBELLE (GB) 2
35 ELLE S'VOYAIT DEJA (USA) C 27
600 ELLEN (IRE) C 40
198 ELLERINA (GB) 4
585 ELLERSLIE JOE (GB) 2
351 ELLESMERE (IRE) G 4
171 ELLINGHAM (IRE) 8
115 ELLIPTICAL (GB) 58
643 ELLISTRIN BELLE (GB) 7
351 ELLUSIVANCE (IRE) 5
15 ELM PARK (GB) 17
387 ELMORE BACK (IRE) 9
107 ELOCUTION (GB) 7
473 ELOPED (GB) 15
169 ELOUGES (IRE) C 35
299 ELRONAQ (GB) 34
276 ELTEZAM (IRE) 47
65 ELTHAM (GB) 12
149 ELUNA (GB) G 12
48 ELUSIVE APPROACH (IRE) 3
106 ELUSIVE DANCER (FR) 3
492 ELUSIVE ELLEN (IRE) 5
276 ELUSIVE GALAXY (IRE) F 48
49 ELUSIVE GIRL (FR) 16
388 ELUSIVE GUEST (FR) 1

249 ELUSIVE IN PARIS (IRE) 1
521 ELUSIVE MILLION (IRE) 61
42 ELUSIVE SPARKLE (USA) F 125
158 ELUSIVITY (IRE) 5
470 ELUSOUDA (FR) 13
521 ELVIS (FR) 178
494 ELYSEES PALACE 49
578 ELYSIAN (GB) C 122
479 ELYSIAN FIELDS (GB) 9
319 ELYSIAN FLYER (IRE) 10
353 ELYSIAN PRINCE (GB) 6
470 ELZEBIETA (IRE) 1
361 EMBAJADORES (IRE) 48
9 EMBANKMENT (GB) 6
634 EMBIRAN (IRE) 32
265 EMBIYRA (IRE) 37
554 EMBLAZE (GB) 3
169 EMBROIDERY (IRE) 16
276 EMELL (GB) 6
51 EMERALD (ITY) 6
413 EMERALD ASSET (IRE) 23
226 EMERALD BAY (GB) 19
566 EMERALD FIRE (GB) F 16
106 EMERALD ISLE (IRE) 25
28 EMERALD LOCH (GB) 40
383 EMERALD PETRINA (IRE) 2
556 EMERALD ROSE (GB) 1
413 EMERALD SECRET (IRE) 29
246 EMERALD THIEF (IRE) 13
47 EMERALDS SPIRIT (IRE) C 21
634 EMERGENT (GB) 33
648 EMERGING FORCE (IRE) 8
451 EMERGING TALENT (IRE) 56
198 EMILIE BRONTE (GB) 10
486 EMILIO LARGO (GB) 4
131 EMILY DAVISON (IRE) 7
400 EMILY GOLDFINCH (GB) 19
12 EMILY GRAY (IRE) 23
658 EMINENT POET (GB) 26
470 EMIR (FR) 15
42 EMIRATES AIRLINE (GB) 8
5 EMIRATES GIRL (USA) C 103
404 EMJAYEM (GB) 2
239 EMLY EXPRESS (IRE) G 39
470 EMMA KNOWS (IRE) 5
138 EMMA SODA (GB) 1
572 EMMASFLORA (GB) F 4
361 EMOTICON (FR) 19
342 EMOTION PARADE (ARG) F 157
5 EMOTIONLESS (IRE) 50
477 EMPERICAL (GB) 1
63 EMPEROR COMMODOS (GB) 14
15 EMPEROR NAPOLEON (GB) 63
320 EMPEROR OF EXMOOR (IRE) 16
403 EMPEROR SAKHEE (GB) 5
658 EMPEROR'S CHOICE (IRE) 27
473 EMPEROR'S HILL (IRE) 16
48 EMPEROR'S PALACE (IRE) 4
422 EMPERORS WARRIOR (IRE) 36
51 EMPIRE ROSE (ARG) C 86
23 EMPIRIC (GB) 18
585 EMPRESS ALI (IRE) 3
213 EMPRESS OF LIGHT (GB) G 3
199 EMPRESS ROCK (IRE) 29
166 EMPRESS SCORPION (IRE) 1
422 EMPTY MARMALADES (IRE) F 37
521 EMPTY PAGES (IRE) 179
54 EMPTY THE TANK (IRE) 3

634 **FLAGSTAFF** (GB) 37
202 **FLAMBEAU** (GB) C 26
169 **FLAMBEUSE** (GB) 4
432 **FLAME AND FORTUNE** (IRE) 13
456 **FLAMES** (GB) C 109
333 **FLAMETREESOFTHIKA** (GB) 22
477 **FLAMING ACE** (IRE) 7
537 **FLAMING CLIFFS** (USA) C 18
236 **FLAMING FYNN** (GB) 18
199 **FLAMING MARVEL** (IRE) 57
528 **FLAMING SPEAR** (IRE) 14
304 **FLAMING THISTLE** (GB) 7
171 **FLAMINGO BEAT** (GB) 9
319 **FLANAGAN** (GB) 28
370 **FLANAGANS FIELD** (IRE) 8
244 **FLANDERS** (IRE) F 130
367 **FLANS O MAN** (IRE) 11
91 **FLASH CITY** (ITY) 18
60 **FLASH CRASH** (GB) 3
194 **FLASH N SMART** (IRE) 21
422 **FLASHMAN** (GB) 41
602 **FLASHY KING** (IRE) 18
602 **FLASHY QUEEN** (IRE) 5
290 **FLAUTIST** (USA) 41
279 **FLAVIANA** (IRE) 15
469 **FLEABISCUIT** (IRE) 77
244 **FLECHE D'OR** (GB) F 131
158 **FLECKERL** (IRE) 7
149 **FLED OR PLED** (IRE) 14
329 **FLEDERMAUS** (IRE) 2
423 **FLEECED AGAIN** (IRE) 12
617 **FLEET DAWN** (GB) 3
461 **FLEETFOOT JACK** (IRE) 74
263 **FLEETING DREAM** (IRE) 46
15 **FLEETING GLIMPSE** (GB) 66
276 **FLEETING IMAGE** (GB) F 160
339 **FLEETING VISIT** (GB) 21
9 **FLEETWOOD BELLA** (GB) 3
9 **FLEETWOOD POPPY** (GB) 9
483 **FLEMENSBAY** (GB) 12
130 **FLEMENSFIRTHLEADER** (GB) 13
12 **FLEMENSMIX** (GB) 27
347 **FLEMENTIME** (GB) 12
561 **FLEMERINA** (IRE) 18
322 **FLEMI TWO TOES** (GB) 6
224 **FLETCHERS FLYER** (IRE) 25
106 **FLEUR D'IPANEMA** (FR) 28
29 **FLEUR DE LIS** (GB) F 54
23 **FLEUR DE SEL** (GB) F 61
289 **FLEUR DU WELD** (GB) 2
118 **FLEURTILLE** (GB) 3
114 **FLICHITY** (IRE) 1
117 **FLICKA'S BOY** (GB) 2
49 **FLICKER FLAME** (IRE) 26
487 **FLIGHT OFFICER** (GB) 9
513 **FLIGHT PLAN** (IRE) 28
48 **FLIGHT RISK** (IRE) F 5
620 **FLIGHTS** (GB) 7
479 **FLIGHTY FILIA** (IRE) 11
58 **FLINTHAM** (GB) 7
286 **FLINTS LEGACY** (GB) 13
188 **FLINTY FELL** (IRE) 25
365 **FLOBURY** (GB) 2
106 **FLOJO** (USA) 29
116 **FLOOD WARNING** (GB) 68
359 **FLOODED** (GB) 19
286 **FLORA AURORA** (GB) 14
320 **FLORA MAY** (GB) G 18

98 **FLORAL BEAUTY** (GB) C 103
510 **FLORAL BOUQUET** (GB) 28
603 **FLORAL SPINNER** (GB) 6
510 **FLORAMOSS** (GB) 10
431 **FLORENCIO** (GB) 24
198 **FLORENZA** (GB) 11
669 **FLORESCO** (GER) 2
234 **FLORIDA CALLING** (IRE) 26
199 **FLORISS** (GB) 3
5 **FLORISTRY** (GB) F 105
606 **FLORRIE BOY** (IRE) 43
380 **FLOWALONG** (IRE) 3
120 **FLOWER CUP** (GB) 16
339 **FLOWER MARKET** (GB) C 44
469 **FLOWER OF KENT** (USA) F 78
120 **FLOWER OF LOVE** (GB) 17
117 **FLOWER POWER** (GB) 3
190 **FLOWERS ON VENUS** (IRE) 10
197 **FLOWING CLARETS** (GB) 92
436 **FLUGZEUG** (GB) 12
422 **FLUTE BOWL** (GB) 42
14 **FLUTTERBEE** (GB) 15
199 **FLY** (GB) 4
292 **FLY CAMP** (IRE) 58
252 **FLY DU CHARMIL** (FR) 24
356 **FLY FREE** (GB) C 35
582 **FLY HOME HARRY** (GB) 13
230 **FLY TRUE** (GB) 21
595 **FLY VINNIE** (IRE) 4
206 **FLY WITH EMIRATES** (IRE) 4
551 **FLYBALL** (GB) 5
461 **FLYBOY** (IRE) 61
606 **FLYING ANGEL** (IRE) 44
235 **FLYING ANSWER** (IRE) G 9
229 **FLYING AWARD** (IRE) 8
230 **FLYING BEAR** (IRE) 7
634 **FLYING BULLET** (USA) 38
310 **FLYING CAPE** (IRE) 3
553 **FLYING DESIRE** (GB) 27
52 **FLYING EAGLE** (IRE) 18
657 **FLYING FANTASY** (GB) 5
106 **FLYING FLEUR** (FR) 30
94 **FLYING FOXY** (GB) 17
19 **FLYING JACK** (GB) 8
342 **FLYING LESSON** (IRE) 51
406 **FLYING LIGHT** (IRE) 13
39 **FLYING NATIVE** (IRE) 6
276 **FLYING NORTH** (GB) 161
244 **FLYING OFFICER** (USA) 5
454 **FLYING POWER** (GB) 5
177 **FLYING PURSUIT** (GB) 76
252 **FLYING SHADOW** (GER) 25
654 **FLYING TIGER** (IRE) 34
461 **FLYMAN** (GB) 16
494 **FLYMETOTHESTARS** (GB) 19
550 **FOCACCIA** (IRE) 39
131 **FOCAL** (GB) F 25
502 **FOCAL POINT** (GB) 15
166 **FOCAS MOR** (IRE) 3
48 **FOCUS ON GRASS** (IRE) 90
48 **FOCUS ON TAPIT** (IRE) 91
180 **FOCUSING** (GB) 6
244 **FOIBLE** (GB) 42
173 **FOIE GRAS** (GB) 5
263 **FOI O'YASMINE** (GB) 47
165 **FOLCUNGI** (IRE) F 44
477 **FOLGA** (GB) F 18
279 **FOLIDALWAYS** (FR) C 16

5 **FOLKSWOOD** (GB) 54
23 **FOLLE ALLURE** (FR) C 62
29 **FOLLE BLANCHE** (GB) C 55
383 **FOLLOW MY DREAM** (GB) F 5
98 **FOLLOW THE FAITH** (GB) 13
215 **FOLLOW THE MASTER** (GB) 4
20 **FOLLOW THE TRACKS** (IRE) 4
521 **FOLLOWME IN PARIS** 185
7 **FOLLOWMYBUTTONS** (IRE) 5
189 **FOLLY BERGERE** (IRE) 15
358 **FOLLY BRIDGE** (GB) C 48
332 **FOLLY BRIDGE** (GB) C 28
427 **FOLSOM BLUE** (IRE) 14
342 **FOND MEMORY** (IRE) 45
165 **FONDIE** (IRE) 52
339 **FONTEGIUSTA** (IRE) F 45
339 **FONTLEY** (GB) F 45
610 **FOOL TO CRY** (IRE) 68
554 **FOOL'S DREAM** (GB) 22
53 **FOOLAAD** (GB) 8
177 **FOOLISH LADY** (IRE) F 107
246 **FOOLISH MISTRESS** (IRE) 14
313 **FOOT THE BILL** (GB) 5
197 **FOOTLIGHT** (GB) 93
437 **FOOTPAD** (FR) 92
95 **FOOTSTEPSINTHERAIN** (IRE) 5
602 **FOR AYMAN** (GB) 6
301 **FOR GOOD MEASURE** (IRE) 39
252 **FOR GOODNESS SAKE** (IRE) 26
469 **FOR HENRY** (IRE) 79
463 **FOR INSTANCE** (IRE) 30
376 **FOR SHIA AND LULA** (IRE) 11
242 **FOR TWO** (FR) 12
363 **FOR WHAT** (USA) 4
610 **FORBIDDING** (USA) 66
299 **FORCE** (IRE) 38
228 **FORCE OF DESTINY** (GER) 1
14 **FORCED FAMILY FUN** (GB) 16
160 **FORCEFUL APPEAL** (USA) 7
347 **FORECAST** (GB) 1
29 **FORECASTER** (GB) 22
461 **FOREIGN DIPLOMAT** (GB) 17
65 **FOREIGN LANGUAGE** (USA) C 20
21 **FOREIGN RHYTHM** (IRE) 2
549 **FORESIGHT** (FR) 39
185 **FOREST BIHAN** (FR) 29
617 **FOREST MISSILE** (IRE) 4
423 **FOREST PRIZE** (GB) C 31
423 **FOREST STEPS** (IRE) 32
148 **FOREST WONDER** (GB) 42
130 **FOREVER A LADY** (IRE) 46
292 **FOREVER FIELD** (GB) 59
407 **FOREVER NOW** (GB) 2
263 **FOREVER POPULAR** (USA) 5
328 **FOREVER YOURS** (IRE) 31
104 **FOREWARNING** (GB) 70
578 **FORGE** (GB) 48
279 **FORGE MEADOW** (IRE) 17
552 **FORGET THE REF** (IRE) F 5
652 **FORGIVIENNE** (GB) 28
78 **FORGIVING FLOWER** (GB) 32
352 **FORGIVING GLANCE** (GB) 42
234 **FORGOTTEN GOLD** (IRE) 27
12 **FORGOTTEN HERO** (IRE) 28
276 **FORGOTTEN ME** (IRE) F 162
634 **FORGOTTEN RULES** (IRE) 6
664 **FORMATIVE** (GB) 13
672 **FORMIDABLEOPPONENT** (IRE) 1

459 JUMPTOCONCLUSIONS (IRE) 12
364 JUNCTION FOURTEEN (IRE) 30
433 JUNE FRENCH (FR) 40
100 JUNGLE BAY (GB) 6
613 JUNGLEBOOGIE (GER) 12
431 JUNIA TEPZIA (GB) C 52
485 JUNIOR PACKAGE (GB) 42
29 JUNIPER GIRL (IRE) F 63
263 JUNO MARLOWE (IRE) C 137
194 JUNO MONETA (IRE) 22
227 JUNOESQUE (GB) 17
202 JUPITER ASCENDING (GB) 28
540 JUPITER CUSTOS (FR) 9
334 JURBY (GB) 20
633 JUST A FEELING (GB) 17
165 JUST A GROOVE (IRE) 5
550 JUST A NORMAL DAY (IRE) 51
451 JUST A PAR (IRE) 69
451 JUST ACTING (IRE) 70
453 JUST ANNIE (GB) 6
443 JUST ARCHIE (IRE) 3
226 JUST BE LUCKY (IRE) 9
234 JUST BEFORE DAWN (IRE) 34
652 JUST BILL (IRE) 41
273 JUST CAMERON (GB) 27
427 JUST CAUSE (IRE) 18
51 JUST FAB (IRE) 42
107 JUST FRED (IRE) 9
561 JUST GEORGIE (GB) 30
281 JUST GLAMOROUS (IRE) 27
177 JUST HISS (IRE) 79
47 JUST ISLA (GB) 9
568 JUST JOAN (IRE) 20
172 JUST JOELLIOTT (IRE) 8
194 JUST LEWIS (GB) 5
603 JUST LIKE A WOMAN (GB) F 22
205 JUST LIKE BETH (GB) 1
441 JUST LIKE DYLAN (IRE) 6
247 JUST MARION (IRE) 3
115 JUST OVER (GB) 36
362 JUST SATISFACTION (GB) 1
278 JUST SKITTLES (GB) 1
149 JUST SO COOL (IRE) 19
187 JUST TALKING (IRE) 6
115 JUST US TWO (IRE) 14
97 JUST WHEN (GB) 11
635 JUSTANOTHER MUDDLE (GB) 8
597 JUSTATENNER (GB) 19
342 JUSTE POUR NOUS (GB) 68
328 JUSTICE (IRE) 33
186 JUSTICE ANGEL (IRE) 18
621 JUSTICE BELLE (IRE) 9
186 JUSTICE BOLD (IRE) 19
186 JUSTICE EARS (IRE) 20
168 JUSTICE FIRST (GB) 5
186 JUSTICE FOCUSED (IRE) 21
186 JUSTICE GOOD (IRE) 5
28 JUSTICE GRACE (IRE) 48
540 JUSTICE KNIGHT (IRE) 10
186 JUSTICE LADY (IRE) 22
186 JUSTICE LASS (IRE) 23
186 JUSTICE LAW (IRE) 24
186 JUSTICE LUCKY (USA) 25
186 JUSTICE PLEASING (GB) 26
186 JUSTICE ROCK (GB) 27
578 JUSTICE SMART (IRE) 61
186 JUSTICE SUPER (IRE) 28
186 JUSTICE WELL (GB) 6

422 JUSTIFICATION (GB) 67
115 JUSTINEO (GB) 15
469 JUSTLY ROYAL (USA) C 93
521 JUSTWANTACONTACT (IRE) 79
230 K'GARI SPIRIT (GB) 25
469 KAABARI (USA) F 94
69 KAABER (USA) 3
410 KAATSKILL NAP (FR) 11
279 KABJOY (IRE) 24
135 KACHESS (GB) 80
226 KACHOU (GB) 10
135 KACHY (GB) 36
286 KADALKIN (FR) 18
151 KADDYS DREAM (GB) 13
151 KADDYS GIRL (GB) 14
78 KADOOMENT DAY (IRE) 34
265 KADRA (IRE) 46
328 KADRIZZI (FR) 34
337 KAFEEL (USA) 12
550 KAFELLA (GB) 52
168 KAFOO (GB) 31
408 KAGNEY (IRE) 34
301 KAHALEESI (GB) 49
506 KAHDIAN (IRE) 1
431 KAHLUA KISS (GB) F 53
244 KAHYASI MOLL (IRE) C 143
525 KAI BROON (IRE) 33
29 KAISAN (GB) 2
528 KAJAKI (IRE) 59
438 KAKAPUKA (GB) 7
439 KAKATOSI (GB) 5
583 KAKI DE LA PREE (FR) 13
422 KALABUNGA (IRE) C 147
554 KALABUNGA (IRE) C 40
634 KALADENA (IRE) F 121
615 KALAHARI (IRE) 12
539 KALAHARRY (IRE) 8
610 KALAMATA (GB) 77
375 KALANE (IRE) 24
70 KALANI'S DIAMOND (IRE) 2
12 KALANISI GLEN (IRE) 35
246 KALANITI (IRE) 18
265 KALASADI (IRE) 47
424 KALASKADESEMILLEY (GB) 6
539 KALASTAR (IRE) 9
284 KALAWAR (USA) 16
521 KALIDAHA (IRE) F 193
485 KALIFOURCHON (FR) 43
612 KALIMANTAN (IRE) 51
279 KALINITE (IRE) 25
101 KALINOVA (IRE) F 26
176 KALK BAY (IRE) 26
437 KALKIR (FR) 108
445 KALMBEFORETHESTORM (GB) 3
102 KALON BRAMA (IRE) 3
433 KALONDRA (IRE) 41
361 KALVOS (FR) 23
463 KAMOOL (GER) 44
356 KAMPAI (GB) C 38
470 KANALETO (FR) 33
379 KANTARA CASTLE (IRE) 10
126 KANTURK BANK (IRE) 31
658 KAP JAZZ (FR) 37
564 KAPGARDE KING (FR) 21
367 KAPRICORNE (FR) 13
653 KAPSTADT (FR) 35
434 KARA TARA (GB) 4
265 KARADENIZA (IRE) 48

634 KARAGANDA (IRE) 122
610 KARAKOZ (GB) 78
524 KARAKTAR (IRE) 6
634 KARALARA (IRE) 44
437 KARALEE (FR) 109
335 KARAM ALBAARI (IRE) 18
521 KARASIYRA (IRE) F 194
578 KARAWAAN (FR) 126
510 KARCH (GB) 30
235 KARENS LAD (IRE) 14
312 KARENS STAR (GB) 13
352 KAREZAK (IRE) 59
224 KARINGA DANCER (GB) 37
453 KARINGO (GB) 7
610 KARISMA (FR) 79
561 KARISMA KING (GB) 31
236 KARL MARX (IRE) 8
469 KARLIYSHA (IRE) C 95
359 KARNAGE (IRE) 3
106 KARSA JET (IRE) 35
461 KARTELLA (IRE) F 77
361 KARYNIA (FR) 24
550 KASAKH NOIR (IRE) 15
634 KASANKA (IRE) F 123
148 KASATANA (IRE) C 80
370 KASHGAR (IRE) 13
500 KASHMIR PEAK (IRE) 10
283 KASHSTAREE (GB) 4
169 KASHTAN (GB) 21
564 KASPIAN TERN (GB) 22
98 KASSIA (IRE) 58
564 KASSIS (GB) 23
436 KASTANI BEACH (IRE) 22
521 KASTANIA (USA) F 195
207 KASTELA STARI (GB) 1
397 KATACHENKO (IRE) 41
658 KATARA BAY (GB) 38
58 KATARRHINI (GB) 11
437 KATE APPLEBY SHOES (IRE) 110
461 KATE THE GREAT (GB) C 78
658 KATENKO (FR) 39
373 KATERNER (FR) 5
451 KATGARY (FR) 71
146 KATH'S LEGACY (GB) 3
455 KATHERINE LEE (IRE) C 29
8 KATIE GALE (GB) 42
352 KATIE TOO (IRE) 60
78 KATIE'S DIAMOND (FR) 35
559 KATIES CHOICE (IRE) 7
469 KATIMONT (FR) F 96
634 KATIOLA (IRE) F 124
265 KATIYMANN (FR) 16
485 KATKEAU (FR) 44
578 KATY NOWAITEE (GB) F 127
279 KATY P (GB) 26
254 KAUTO RIKO (FR) 10
175 KAVANAGHS CORNER (IRE) 4
151 KAWA (FR) 15
573 KAWARTHA (GB) 11
31 KAY GEE BE (IRE) 6
447 KAY SERA (GB) 5
433 KAY THEATRE (IRE) C 42
301 KAYF ADVENTURE (GB) 50
406 KAYF BLANCO (GB) 22
44 KAYF CHARMER (GB) 1
292 KAYF GRACE (GB) 75
208 KAYF MOSS (GB) 7
151 KAYF TIGER (GB) 16

642 **MEADOWCROFT BOY** (GB) 20
554 **MEADWAY** (GB) 8
70 **MEANDMYSHADOW** (GB) 4
467 **MEANWHILE** (IRE) C 57
437 **MEASUREOFMYDREAMS** (IRE) 125
156 **MECCA'S ANGEL** (IRE) 18
293 **MEDBURN DREAM** (GB) 20
494 **MEDDLESOME** (GB) 23
522 **MEDIA WORLD** (IRE) 14
522 **MEDIATE** (GB) 6
610 **MEDIATION** (GB) 19
123 **MEDICEAN DREAM** (IRE) 83
230 **MEDICEAN MAN** (GB) 9
584 **MEDICEAN QUEEN** (IRE) 12
78 **MEDICI BANCHIERE** (GB) 80
87 **MEDICIMAN** (GB) 20
460 **MEDICINE HAT** (GB) 8
211 **MEDIEVAL BISHOP** (IRE) 2
352 **MEDINAS** (FR) 75
72 **MEDRANO** (GB) 8
279 **MEDUSE BLEU** (GB) F 97
335 **MEEBO** (GB) 22
279 **MEELICK FLYER** (IRE) G 33
345 **MEESON** (GB) 3
550 **MEET THE LEGEND** (GB) 65
579 **MEETINGS MAN** (IRE) 12
158 **MEGAMUNCH** (IRE) 12
422 **MEGASUE** (GB) F 80
611 **MEHRONISSA** (GB) 5
299 **MEIOSIS** (USA) C 121
464 **MEISTER ECKHART** (IRE) 11
521 **MEKHTAAL** (GB) 102
456 **MEKKO HOKTE** (USA) C 124
263 **MELABI** (IRE) 63
66 **MELANDRE** (GB) C 26
292 **MELANGERIE** (GB) 92
276 **MELFIT** (FR) 73
176 **MELGATE MELODY** (GB) 61
342 **MELHOR AINDA** (USA) F 178
494 **MELINOE** (GB) 54
521 **MELITO** (AUS) C 213
429 **MELLOW** (GB) 65
538 **MELODIC RENDEZVOUS** (GB) 21
454 **MELODINE** (GB) 55
186 **MELODIOUS** (GB) 10
28 **MELODY MAKER** (GB) C 105
437 **MELON** (GB) 126
578 **MELTING DEW** (GB) 134
15 **MELVIN THE GRATE** (IRE) 30
224 **MEME'S HORSE** (IRE) 41
42 **MEMORIAL DAY** (IRE) 20
634 **MEMORIAL ROSE** (GB) 135
169 **MEMORIES GALORE** (GB) 6
174 **MEMORY OF LIGHT** (IRE) 10
185 **MEMPHIS BELLE** (GB) C 112
541 **MEMYSELFIE** (IRE) 31
237 **MEN UNITED** (FR) 23
655 **MENACE** (GB) 13
299 **MENAI** (IRE) 60
23 **MENARDAIS** (FR) 5
14 **MENDACIOUS HARPY** (IRE) 33
5 **MENDACITY** (IRE) 67
301 **MENDIP EXPRESS** (IRE) 57
342 **MENEKINEKO** (USA) C 80
217 **MENELIK** (IRE) 7
469 **MENGLI KHAN** (IRE) 35
276 **MEON MIX** (GB) C 195
456 **MEOW** (IRE) C 125

106 **MER ET JARDIN** (GB) 9
353 **MERCERS COURT** (IRE) 17
294 **MERCERS ROW** (GB) 7
239 **MERCHANT OF DUBAI** (GB) 20
273 **MERCHANT OF MEDICI** (GB) 35
208 **MERCHANT OF MILAN** (GB) 9
621 **MERCIFILLY** (FR) 38
528 **MERCURY** (GB) 21
527 **MERCY ME** (GB) 5
91 **MERDON CASTLE** (IRE) 25
573 **MERE ANARCHY** (IRE) 13
527 **MERHOOB** (GB) 6
106 **MERI DEVIE** (FR) 43
224 **MERIBEL MILLIE** (GB) 42
122 **MERLE** (GB) F 14
122 **MERLE** (GB) F 20
29 **MERLIN** (GB) 68
347 **MERLIN'S WISH** (IRE) 19
169 **MEROULA** (FR) 23
494 **MERRITT ISLAND** (GB) 3
408 **MERRY BATIM** (IRE) G 45
633 **MERRY DANCER** (IRE) 21
413 **MERRY DIVA** (GB) F 34
293 **MERRY MAST** (USA) 9
15 **MERRY ME** (IRE) 31
437 **MERRY NIGHT** (IRE) 127
91 **MESHARDAL** (GER) 26
521 **MESONERO** (FR) 103
612 **MESSERY** (FR) 67
352 **MESSINA STRAIGHTS** (GB) 10
352 **MESSIRE DES OBEAUX** (FR) 76
540 **MESTI BOLEH** (GB) 13
322 **MESUT** (FR) 12
435 **METHAALY** (IRE) 12
414 **METTE** (GB) 19
298 **MEXICAN BORDER** (GER) 5
584 **MEXICAN HAWK** (GB) C 83
295 **MEXICAN JIM** (GB) 5
295 **MEXICAN MICK** (GB) 6
65 **MEYDAN PRINCESS** (IRE) F 24
371 **MEYREM ANA** (GB) 8
263 **MEYRICK** (GB) 148
621 **MEZAJY** (IRE) 10
86 **MEZEL** (GB) 6
521 **MEZIDON** (FR) 104
424 **MEZMAAR** (GB) 8
553 **MEZZO MEZZO** (FR) 10
95 **MEZZOTINT** (IRE) 11
197 **MFIFTYTHREEDOTCOM** (IRE) 47
290 **MI DICA** (GB) C 46
299 **MIA DIVINA** (GB) C 122
109 **MIA MATRIARCH** (GB) 13
237 **MIA TIA** (GB) 38
352 **MIA'S STORM** (IRE) 77
5 **MIALUNA** (GB) F 114
36 **MIAMI PRESENT** (IRE) 4
456 **MIARIXA** (FR) C 126
197 **MICA MIKA** (IRE) 48
168 **MICHAEL'S MOUNT** (GB) 33
633 **MICHAELA** (GB) 22
521 **MICHIGAN** (USA) 214
268 **MICHIGAN ASSASSIN** (IRE) 6
42 **MICHITA** (USA) F 141
46 **MICK DUGGAN** (GB) 7
224 **MICK JAZZ** (FR) 43
135 **MICKEY** (IRE) 38
115 **MICKLEBERRY** (IRE) F 63
582 **MICKLEGATE RUN** (GB) 20

550 **MICKS LAD** (IRE) 66
78 **MICOLYS** (FR) 81
233 **MICQUUS** (IRE) 8
342 **MID MON LADY** (IRE) C 179
373 **MIDAS GOLD** (IRE) 6
636 **MIDDLEMAN** (GB) 16
80 **MIDHMAAR** (GB) 15
644 **MIDLIGHT** (GB) 6
367 **MIDNIGHT APPEAL** (GB) 19
583 **MIDNIGHT BELLE** (GB) 20
192 **MIDNIGHT BROWNIE** (GB) 8
13 **MIDNIGHT CHARMER** (GB) 8
564 **MIDNIGHT CHILL** (GB) 29
264 **MIDNIGHT CHORISTER** (GB) 12
352 **MIDNIGHT COWBOY** (GB) 78
541 **MIDNIGHT DESTINY** (IRE) 16
397 **MIDNIGHT FLIRT** (IRE) G 52
473 **MIDNIGHT FOLIE** (GB) 22
650 **MIDNIGHT FRENSI** (GB) 4
375 **MIDNIGHT GEM** (GB) 33
301 **MIDNIGHT GLORY** (GB) 58
259 **MIDNIGHT JADE** (IRE) 2
96 **MIDNIGHT JAZZ** (GB) 17
655 **MIDNIGHT JITTERBUG** (GB) 14
72 **MIDNIGHT MACCHIATO** (IRE) 23
177 **MIDNIGHT MALIBU** (IRE) 82
108 **MIDNIGHT MARTINI** (GB) C 47
312 **MIDNIGHT MEMORIES** (GB) 6
655 **MIDNIGHT MERLOT** (GB) 15
177 **MIDNIGHT MOJITO** (GB) 31
510 **MIDNIGHT MONTY** (GB) 13
204 **MIDNIGHT MOOD** (GB) 13
42 **MIDNIGHT MUSIC** (IRE) C 142
390 **MIDNIGHT MUSTANG** (GB) 3
29 **MIDNIGHT MYSTIC** (GB) 27
174 **MIDNIGHT OWLE** (GB) 11
352 **MIDNIGHT PRAYER** (GB) 79
286 **MIDNIGHT REQUEST** (GB) 24
414 **MIDNIGHT RIDER** (IRE) 11
554 **MIDNIGHT ROBBERY** (GB) 30
433 **MIDNIGHT SEQUEL** (GB) 55
375 **MIDNIGHT SHOT** (GB) 34
564 **MIDNIGHT SILVER** (GB) 30
259 **MIDNIGHT TARGET** (GB) 3
347 **MIDNIGHT THOMAS** (GB) 20
373 **MIDNIGHT TOUR** (GB) 7
315 **MIDNIGHT TUNE** (GB) 18
301 **MIDNIGHT VELVET** (GB) 59
578 **MIDNIGHT VIXEN** (GB) 135
21 **MIDNIGHT WARRIOR** (GB) 4
521 **MIDNIGHT WATCH** (GB) 215
407 **MIDNIGHT WHISTLER** (USA) 4
653 **MIDTECH STAR** (IRE) 41
653 **MIDTECH VALENTINE** (GB) 42
578 **MIDTERM** (GB) 70
290 **MIDWEEK** (GB) 21
292 **MIGHT BITE** (IRE) 93
290 **MIGHT IS RIGHT** (IRE) 22
616 **MIGHTY BOND** (GB) 10
65 **MIGHTY LADY** (GB) 15
466 **MIGHTY LEADER** (IRE) 11
265 **MIGHTY LEGEND** (IRE) 51
390 **MIGHTY MUSTANG** (GB) 4
579 **MIGHTY SPLASH** (GB) F 24
511 **MIGHTY THOR** (GB) 7
562 **MIGHTY VIC** (IRE) 15
537 **MIGHTY YAR** (IRE) 6
528 **MIGHTY ZIP** (USA) 22

633 **MR BANKS** (IRE) 25
387 **MR BIG** (IRE) 18
485 **MR BIG SHOT** (IRE) 61
653 **MR BISSTO** (GB) 44
455 **MR BOOMER** (USA) 8
28 **MR BOSSY BOOTS** (IRE) 14
476 **MR C** (IRE) 18
135 **MR CHRISTOPHER** (IRE) 16
355 **MR CHUCKLES** (IRE) 52
548 **MR CONUNDRUM** (GB) 12
261 **MR COOL CASH** (GB) 9
376 **MR DANDY MAN** (IRE) 18
487 **MR ELEVATOR** (IRE) 11
364 **MR FENTON** (IRE) 37
422 **MR FICKLE** (IRE) 83
140 **MR FITZROY** (IRE) 10
483 **MR FRANKIE** (GB) 19
96 **MR GREY** (IRE) 19
130 **MR GRUMPY** (GB) 53
638 **MR JALFRAZY** (IRE) 4
633 **MR K** (IRE) 26
51 **MR KHALID** (GB) 52
652 **MR KIT CAT** (GB) 54
224 **MR KITE** (IRE) 47
25 **MR LANDO** (GB) 3
452 **MR LUCAS** (IRE) 16
93 **MR MAFIA** (IRE) 37
356 **MR MARCHWOOD** (GB) 23
131 **MR MCGREGOR** (IRE) 12
231 **MR MCGUINESS** (IRE) 7
620 **MR MEDIC** (GB) 14
451 **MR MIX** (FR) 87
451 **MR MOLE** (IRE) 88
334 **MR MONOCHROME** (GB) 26
561 **MR MOONSHINE** (IRE) 38
59 **MR MOROCCO** (GB) 5
185 **MR MORSE** (GB) 99
364 **MR MOUNTAIN** (IRE) 38
635 **MR MUDDLE** (GB) 10
459 **MR NICOLLS** (IRE) 16
413 **MR ORANGE** (IRE) 26
561 **MR PEPPERPOT** (GB) 39
199 **MR PICKWICK** (GB) 14
261 **MR POTTER** (GB) 23
6 **MR RED CLUBS** (IRE) 57
581 **MR ROBINSON** (FR) 4
14 **MR ROCK** (IRE) 34
276 **MR SCARAMANGA** (GB) 200
594 **MR SHAHADY** (IRE) 11
463 **MR SHANTU** (IRE) 62
396 **MR SHEKELLS** (GB) 3
618 **MR SIMPKINS** (GB) 4
244 **MR SINGH** (GB) 14
619 **MR SNOOZY** (GB) 15
348 **MR SQUIRREL** (IRE) 5
481 **MR STANDFAST** (GB) 7
577 **MR SUNDOWNER** (USA) 4
246 **MR SYNTAX** (IRE) 24
445 **MR TOY BOY** (GB) 4
599 **MR TURNER** (GB) 20
276 **MR TYRRELL** (IRE) 201
653 **MR VENDMAN** (IRE) 45
558 **MR WITMORE** (IRE) 11
92 **MRS BIGGS** (GB) 10
423 **MRS BUBBLES** (GB) 7
433 **MRS BURBIDGE** (GB) 61
10 **MRS EVE** (IRE) 9
432 **MRS FROSTY** (IRE) 12

288 **MRS GRASS** (GB) 5
48 **MRS KING** (IRE) 44
285 **MRS MAGS** (GB) 17
574 **MRS MEDLEY** (GB) 9
14 **MRS WARREN** (GB) 35
650 **MRS WHITE** (IRE) F 5
364 **MRSROBIN** (IRE) 39
59 **MS ARSENAL** (GB) 6
279 **MS BRINKLEYS** (IRE) 80
429 **MS CORDELIA** (USA) C 66
6 **MS EBORACUM** (IRE) 58
549 **MS GILLARD** (GB) 45
106 **MT OF BEATITUDES** (IRE) 45
244 **MUAITHER** (IRE) 79
404 **MUARA** (GB) C 20
80 **MUBAJAL** (GB) 17
513 **MUBROOK** (USA) 5
15 **MUCHO APPLAUSE** (IRE) 153
606 **MUCKLE ROE** (IRE) 69
299 **MUDAJAJ** (USA) 125
190 **MUDALALAH** (IRE) F 56
263 **MUFFRI'HA** (IRE) 7
72 **MUHAAFIZ** (IRE) 9
342 **MUHADATHAT** (GB) 83
80 **MUHAJJAL** (GB) 39
477 **MUHAZWARA** (IRE) 3
555 **MUHTADIM** (IRE) 3
192 **MUHTARIS** (IRE) 11
48 **MUNINEACH** (IRE) 114
14 **MUIR LODGE** (GB) 36
263 **MUJAAMIL** (GB) 64
634 **MUJAAZY** (IRE) 140
168 **MUJAMALA** (IRE) 34
610 **MUJASSAM** (GB) 23
450 **MUJAZIF** (IRE) 17
356 **MUJDEYA** (GB) C 41
584 **MUKAABRA** (GB) 50
528 **MUKAYNIS** (IRE) 25
177 **MUKHAYYAM** (GB) 35
299 **MULHIMATTY** (GB) 126
578 **MULK** (GB) 73
35 **MULLED WINE** (GB) 18
183 **MULLIGAN'S MAN** (IRE) 8
279 **MULLIGATAWNY** (IRE) 81
35 **MULLIONHEIR** (GB) 12
35 **MULLOVER** (GB) 19
429 **MULSANNE CHASE** (GB) 67
177 **MULTELLIE** (GB) 36
273 **MULTI GRAIN** (GB) 37
374 **MULTI QUEST** (GB) 4
382 **MULTIGIFTED** (GB) 9
195 **MULTIPEDE** (GB) 18
382 **MULTITASK** (GB) 5
123 **MULUK** (GB) C 85
168 **MULZIM** (GB) 80
318 **MUMBLES MAGIC** (IRE) 11
277 **MUMFORD** (GB) 8
525 **MUMGOS DEBUT** (IRE) 52
276 **MUMS THE WORD** (GB) 202
634 **MUNAASHID** (USA) 55
530 **MUNAAWIB** (IRE) 2
94 **MUNCHKIN** (GB) F 19
276 **MUNDUS NOVUS** (GB) F 203
584 **MUNEEB** (IRE) 51
72 **MUNFALLET** (IRE) 10
201 **MUNGO MADNESS** (GB) 27
371 **MUNICH** (IRE) 10

313 **MUNJALLY** (GB) 13
28 **MUNRO** (GB) 110
95 **MUNSARIM** (IRE) 13
15 **MUNSTEAD STAR** (GB) 154
377 **MUNTADAB** (IRE) 10
244 **MUNTAHAA** (IRE) 60
80 **MUNTAZAH** (GB) 18
276 **MUQAATIL** (USA) 204
377 **MUQARRED** (USA) 11
634 **MUQTANNY** (GB) 141
419 **MURAABIT** (GB) 4
244 **MURAAQEB** (GB) 155
469 **MURAD KHAN** (FR) 37
342 **MURAVKA** (IRE) F 182
612 **MURCHU** (IRE) 70
222 **MURDANOVA** (IRE) 25
101 **MURGAN** (GB) 5
148 **MURHIB** (IRE) 14
166 **MURMURATION** (IRE) 15
461 **MUROOR** (GB) 66
583 **MURPHY'S NAILS** (GB) 22
634 **MURRAQIB** (USA) 56
387 **MURRAY MOUNT** (IRE) 19
597 **MURRAYANA** (IRE) 32
283 **MURTYS DELIGHT** (IRE) 6
176 **MUSAAID** (IRE) 30
263 **MUSAANADA** (GB) 65
299 **MUSAWAAT** (GB) 127
276 **MUSCIKA** (GB) 205
276 **MUSDAM** (USA) 74
578 **MUSDAM** (USA) 74
1 **MUSEO** (GB) 72
168 **MUSHAREEFA** (IRE) 81
92 **MUSHARRIF** (GB) 11
521 **MUSHAWWEQ** (GB) 109
282 **MUSIC HALL** (FR) 12
424 **MUSIC MAJOR** (GB) 11
122 **MUSIC MAN** (IRE) 3
59 **MUSICAL BAR** (IRE) F 21
439 **MUSICAL COMEDY** (GB) 6
480 **MUSICAL TASTE** (GB) 22
549 **MUSICAL WAY** (FR) C 84
151 **MUST MEET MRSGRATH** (IRE) 18
578 **MUSTAAQEEM** (USA) 13
80 **MUSTAJEER** (GB) 19
299 **MUSTALLIB** (IRE) 65
351 **MUSTANG ON** (GB) 7
156 **MUSTAQBAL** (IRE) 19
461 **MUSTAQQIL** (IRE) 33
276 **MUSTARRID** (IRE) 206
578 **MUSTASHRY** (GB) 75
197 **MUSTIQUE DANCER** (IRE) 51
463 **MUSTMEETALADY** (IRE) 63
603 **MUSTN'T GRUMBLE** (IRE) 14
226 **MUSTN'T GRUMBLE** (IRE) 21
91 **MUTAFAAKIR** (IRE) 28
276 **MUTAHAADY** (IRE) 207
263 **MUTAKAYYEF** (GB) 8
521 **MUTAMADED** (IRE) 110
578 **MUTAMAKKIN** (IRE) 14
168 **MUTAMAYEL** (IRE) 82
521 **MUTANAASEB** (USA) 219
610 **MUTARAJJIL** (IRE) 88
610 **MUTAWAALY** (IRE) 89
561 **MUTAWAASEL** (GB) 40
120 **MUTAWATHEA** (GB) 2
276 **MUTAWATHEB** (IRE) 208
263 **MUTAYYAM** (GB) 66

600 NAVAJO RAINBOW (GB) C 48	54 NEVER TO BE (USA) 6	42 NICE FUTURE (IRE) 74
6 NAVAJO STORM (IRE) 105	279 NEVERUSHACON (IRE) 36	470 NICE MATIN (USA) C 47
485 NAVANMAN (IRE) 63	238 NEVILLE WOODS (GB) 2	451 NICE N EASY (GB) 90
407 NAVIGATE (IRE) 6	349 NEW ABBEY ANGEL (IRE) 18	485 NICE THOUGHTS (IRE) 64
467 NAWAASHI (GB) F 59	614 NEW ACADEMY (GB) 12	599 NICE TIME (IRE) C 34
521 NAWARAT (USA) 111	633 NEW AGENDA (GB) 28	500 NICE WEE GIRL (IRE) G 61
614 NAY MORE (GB) 11	22 NEW BIDDER (GB) 18	172 NICELY INDEED (IRE) 11
276 NAYEL (IRE) 13	411 NEW BLOSSOM (IRE) C 25	28 NICEOFYOUTOTELLME (GB) 15
410 NAZIBA (IRE) 4	342 NEW CALEDONIA (IRE) 84	358 NICEONECENTURION (GB) 32
244 NAZZAA (IRE) 63	5 NEW DISCOVERY (GB) 73	366 NICHOLASCOPERNICUS (IRE) 23
525 NEAR TO TEARS (IRE) 54	23 NEW GRANADA (GB) 34	437 NICHOLS CANYON (GB) 141
33 NEAR WILD HEAVEN (GB) 8	120 NEW HAPPINESS (IRE) 29	78 NICK VEDDER (GB) 84
430 NEARDOWN BEAUTY (IRE) F 11	225 NEW HORIZONS (IRE) 3	128 NICK'S NIKITA (IRE) F 11
651 NEAREST THE PIN (IRE) 2	437 NEW KID IN TOWN (IRE) 140	162 NICKI'S NIPPER (GB) 7
429 NEARLY CAUGHT (IRE) 15	130 NEW LEASE OF LIFE (GB) 30	292 NICOLAS CHAUVIN (IRE) 104
279 NEARLY FAMOUS (GB) 82	115 NEW LEGEND (IRE) 40	62 NIDNOD (GB) 13
320 NEARLY NAMA'D (IRE) 32	230 NEW LEYF (IRE) 11	185 NIETZSCHE (GB) 100
469 NEARTICA (FR) C 109	42 NEW LIST (GB) 70	400 NIFTY KIER (GB) 12
176 NEATH (GB) C 70	560 NEW LOOK (IRE) 3	165 NIFTY NIECE (IRE) 52
46 NEBULA STORM (IRE) 8	292 NEW MEMBER (IRE) 102	130 NIGELLA (GB) C 72
35 NECESSARY (GB) 30	456 NEW MILLENNIUM (IRE) 52	135 NIGH (IRE) C 87
407 NECKLACE (GB) F 43	170 NEW REACTION (GB) 14	549 NIGHT AND DANCE (IRE) C 86
352 NED STARK (IRE) 90	339 NEW RICH (GB) 3	15 NIGHT CARNATION (GB) F 155
98 NEEDLESS SHOUTING (IRE) 30	117 NEW ROAD SIDE (GB) 24	408 NIGHT GENERATION (GER) 50
118 NEEDWOOD PARK (GB) 4	78 NEW ROMANTIC (GB) C 83	510 NIGHT IN LONDON (IRE) 14
70 NEFETARI (GB) 11	42 NEW STRATEGY (IRE) 23	510 NIGHT IN MILAN (IRE) 15
397 NEFYN BAY (GB) 58	34 NEW STREET (IRE) 20	128 NIGHT LILY (IRE) F 12
521 NEGUEV (IRE) 220	279 NEW TO THIS TOWN (IRE) 37	654 NIGHT OF SIN (IRE) 36
456 NELL GWYN (IRE) C 129	224 NEW VENNTURE (FR) 48	153 NIGHT SHADOW (GB) 50
342 NELLIE MELBA (GB) F 184	610 NEW WORLD POWER (JPN) 94	28 NIGHT TO REMEMBER (IRE) 55
166 NELLIE NOLAN (USA) F 26	453 NEW YOUMZAIN (IRE) 8	375 NIGHTFLY (IRE) 37
612 NELLIE THE ELEGANT (GB) 72	279 NEWBERRY NEW (IRE) 38	357 NIGHTINGALE VALLEY (IRE) 18
594 NELLY LA RUE (IRE) 13	610 NEWCOMER (IRE) 176	375 NIGHTLINE (GB) 38
318 NELLY'S GLEN (GB) F 12	135 NEWERA (GB) 17	192 NIGHTSWIFT (GB) 12
230 NELSON QUAY (IRE) 10	332 NEWMARKET WARRIOR (IRE) 14	51 NIGHTSWIMMER (IRE) C 98
577 NELSON'S BAY (GB) 5	517 NEWNHAM FLYER (IRE) 3	469 NILE EMPRESS (GB) 110
144 NELSON'S HILL (GB) 3	303 NEWORLD (FR) 8	90 NILE KHALKEVIE (IRE) 23
327 NELSON'S PRIDE (GB) 8	614 NEWSPAGE (IRE) 13	387 NIMBUS GALE (IRE) 21
258 NELSON'S VICTORY (GB) 7	630 NEWSPEAK (IRE) 5	479 NIMOY (USA) 46
174 NELTARA (GB) 12	342 NEWSREEL (IRE) C 185	361 NIMPHEAS (USA) 3
455 NEMORALIA (USA) 20	22 NEWSTEAD ABBEY (GB) 19	15 NIMUE (USA) C 156
634 NEOCLASSICAL (USA) 143	292 NEWSWORTHY (IRE) 103	613 NINARO (GER) 45
319 NEPALI PRINCESS (IRE) F 39	494 NEWT (GB) 57	271 NINE ALTARS (IRE) 2
595 NEPTUNE EQUESTER (GB) 10	473 NEWTON GERONIMO (GB) 23	464 NINEPOINTSIXTHREE (GB) 12
459 NERANO (IRE) 18	473 NEWTON THISTLE (GB) 24	649 NINETEENTH HOLE (IRE) 10
299 NESHMEYA (GB) 129	218 NEWTOWN CROSS (IRE) 44	165 NINETTA (IRE) 23
613 NESSINA (GER) 20	525 NEWTOWN LAD (IRE) 55	413 NINJAGO (GB) 11
263 NESSINA (USA) C 151	632 NEWYEARSRESOLUTION (IRE) 9	484 NINNY NOODLE (GB) 3
469 NESSITA (GB) 38	451 NEXIUS (IRE) 89	361 NISEA (FR) 29
106 NESSUN DORMA (GER) 46	355 NEXT EDITION (IRE) 34	224 NITROGEN (IRE) 49
292 NESTERENKO (GER) 100	114 NEXT EXIT (IRE) 2	244 NITYA (FR) C 159
437 NET D'ECOSSE (FR) 139	288 NEXT HIGHT (IRE) 6	252 NIVALF (GB) G 41
12 NET WORK ROUGE (FR) 48	42 NEXT HOLY (IRE) C 147	382 NO BODY'S FOOL (GB) 10
422 NETHERBY (GB) 84	42 NEXT LIFE (GB) 71	63 NO BUTS (GB) 27
151 NETHERTON BOY (GB) 33	483 NEXT LOT (GB) 22	653 NO CEILING (IRE) 47
169 NETLEY ABBEY (GB) 39	42 NEXT MEETING (USA) 72	301 NO COMMENT (GB) 64
292 NEUMOND (GER) 101	540 NEXT SENSATION (IRE) 16	389 NO DICE (IRE) 30
600 NEVALYASHKA (GB) 49	42 NEXT STAGE (GB) 73	234 NO DUFFER (GB) 40
299 NEVER A DOUBT (GB) F 130	450 NEXT STOP (GB) 18	318 NO EDUCATION (GB) 13
583 NEVER BEEN WRONG (IRE) 23	306 NEXT TO THE TOP (GB) C 18	140 NO FRILLS (IRE) F 17
370 NEVER EQUALLED (IRE) 20	189 NEXT TRAIN'S GONE (IRE) 8	292 NO HERETIC (GB) 105
521 NEVER FALL AGAIN 221	29 NEYMAR (GB) 8	361 NO MOOD (GB) 4
644 NEVER IN DOUBT (GB) 17	500 NEZAR (IRE) 17	375 NO NO JOLIE (FR) 39
597 NEVER LEARN (IRE) 34	610 NEZWAAH (GB) 95	375 NO NO MAC (IRE) 40
332 NEVER NEVER (IRE) 13	408 NIAMH'S DREAM (IRE) G 49	101 NO PAIN NO GAIN (FR) 30
141 NEVER PERFECT (IRE) 3	256 NIAMH'S PET (IRE) C 18	561 NO PLANNING (GB) 43
628 NEVER SAY (IRE) 6	419 NIBLAWI (IRE) 5	556 NO PRINCIPLES (GB) 5
315 NEVER SAYS NEVER (GB) 19	87 NICARRA (IRE) 31	656 NO RUM (IRE) 4

98 **OCTOBER STORM** (GB) 66
182 **ODDS ON DAN** (IRE) 6
342 **ODE TO EVENING** (GB) 85
260 **ODE TO GLORY** (GB) 26
237 **ODEON** (GB) 11
166 **ODISHA** (USA) 16
91 **OEIL DE TIGRE** (FR) 41
15 **OEKAKI** (FR) G 157
602 **OEUVRE D'ART** (IRE) C 29
568 **OFF AND ON** (IRE) 26
177 **OFF ART** (GB) 39
320 **OFF THE CHARTS** (IRE) 33
375 **OFF THE GROUND** (IRE) 41
379 **OFF THE PULSE** (GB) 15
333 **OFF TO BOND STREET** (GB) 26
277 **OFFBEAT SAFARIS** (IRE) 16
403 **OFFICER CADET** (GB) 8
34 **OFFICER DRIVEL** (IRE) 21
612 **OFFICER HOOLIHAN** (GB) 76
408 **OFFICIEUX** (FR) 52
264 **OGARITMO** (GB) 14
299 **OGBOURNE DOWNS** (GB) 13
435 **OGWEN VALLEY GIRL** (GB) 16
426 **OH GENO** 20
48 **OH GRACE** (IRE) 117
622 **OH IT'S SAUCEPOT** (GB) 41
177 **OH JAMES** (GB) 86
353 **OH LAND ABLOOM** (IRE) 20
276 **OH SEDULOUS** (IRE) C 211
422 **OH SO FRUITY** (GB) 85
292 **OH SO GIGOLO** (IRE) 107
622 **OH SO SASSY** (GB) 10
276 **OH THIS IS US** (IRE) 78
31 **OH WHAT A SPECIES** (IRE) 19
244 **OHIYESA** (IRE) C 161
143 **OHMS LAW** (GB) 3
657 **OHSOSECRET** (GB) 15
389 **OIGHEAR DUBH** (IRE) 33
109 **OIL BURNER** (GB) 15
176 **OIL STRIKE** (GB) 32
19 **OISHIN** (GB) 16
328 **OJAI** (IRE) 36
292 **OK CORRAL** (IRE) 108
326 **OKANA** (GB) 31
80 **OKOOL** (FR) 41
389 **OKOTOKS** (IRE) 34
361 **OLANTHIA** (IRE) 5
353 **OLD FASHION** (GB) 21
451 **OLD GUARD** (GB) 91
367 **OLD MAGIC** (IRE) 22
373 **OLD PRIDE** (FR) 10
396 **OLD TOWN BOY** (GB) 4
550 **OLDGRANGEWOOD** (GB) 71
413 **OLDJOESAID** (GB) 12
157 **OLINDERA** (GER) F 15
578 **OLIVE BRANCH** (IRE) 141
148 **OLIVE D'HAGUENET** (FR) 16
461 **OLIVE MARY** (GB) 35
619 **OLIVER'S GOLD** (GB) 16
297 **OLIVER'S HILL** (IRE) 7
413 **OLIVIA FALLOW** (IRE) 13
642 **OLIVIA JOAN** (GB) 22
246 **OLLIE G** (GB) 26
234 **OLOFI** (FR) 43
367 **OLYMPIAN BOY** (IRE) 23
295 **OLYMPIC DUEL** (IRE) 15
299 **OLYMPIC MEDAL** (GB) C 131
263 **OLYMPIC RUNNER** (GB) 71

469 **OMEROS** (GB) 111
292 **OMESSA HAS** (FR) 109
652 **OMGNOTANOTHER** (IRE) 58
551 **OMID** (GB) 8
64 **OMOTESANDO** (GB) 7
177 **ON A PAR** (GB) 40
376 **ON A WHIM** (GB) 29
306 **ON DEMAND** (GB) 11
37 **ON FIRE** (GB) 20
579 **ON GALLEY HEAD** (IRE) G 13
263 **ON HER TOES** (IRE) 152
437 **ON HIS OWN** (IRE) 143
190 **ON MY KNESS** (IRE) F 57
492 **ON STAGE** (GB) 19
168 **ON THE BILL** (IRE) 36
538 **ON THE BRIDGE** (IRE) 27
234 **ON THE CASE** (GB) 44
584 **ON THE CLOCK** (GB) 54
590 **ON THE COUCH** (IRE) 8
131 **ON THE CUSP** (IRE) 13
153 **ON THE DARK SIDE** (IRE) C 51
421 **ON THE DRY** (IRE) 11
587 **ON THE HIGH TOPS** (IRE) 4
106 **ON THE LINE** (FR) F 67
423 **ON THE NILE** (FR) F 42
96 **ON THE PROWL** (IRE) 22
509 **ON THE RAZ** (GB) 2
365 **ON THE RIGHT PATH** (GB) 7
652 **ON THE ROAD** (IRE) 59
423 **ON THIN ICE** (IRE) F 43
339 **ON TO VICTORY** (GB) 49
502 **ON TOUR** (IRE) 60
670 **ON YOUR MAX** (GB) 9
106 **ONCEUPONASTAR** (IRE) 48
521 **ONCLE FERNAND** 222
213 **ONDA DISTRICT** (IRE) 15
364 **ONDERUN** (IRE) 41
197 **ONE BOY** (IRE) 55
629 **ONE COOL BOY** (IRE) 1
421 **ONE COOL POET** (IRE) 12
301 **ONE COOL SCORPION** (IRE) 65
317 **ONE COOL WESTERNER** (IRE) 7
524 **ONE FOOT IN HEAVEN** (IRE) 8
525 **ONE FOR ARTHUR** (IRE) 56
512 **ONE FOR HARRY** (IRE) 31
512 **ONE FOR HOCKY** (IRE) 32
76 **ONE FOR THE BOSS** (IRE) 8
292 **ONE FOR THE GUV'NR** (IRE) 110
333 **ONE GIANT LEAP** (IRE) C 27
121 **ONE IN A ROW** (IRE) 19
305 **ONE LAST DREAM** (GB) 6
612 **ONE LEADER** (IRE) 77
279 **ONE LINER** (GB) 99
448 **ONE MORE GO** (IRE) 14
654 **ONE OF US** (GB) 19
610 **ONE PEKAN** (IRE) 24
492 **ONE PURSUIT** (IRE) 20
658 **ONE STYLE** (FR) 50
126 **ONE TERM** (IRE) 41
272 **ONE TICK** (IRE) 4
252 **ONE TRACK MIND** (IRE) 43
177 **ONE WORD MORE** (IRE) 41
301 **ONEFITZALL** (IRE) 66
669 **ONEFORTHENURE** (IRE) 8
296 **ONEHELLUVATOUCH** (GB) 13
658 **ONEIDA TRIBE** (IRE) 51
568 **ONENIGHTIDREAMED** (IRE) 5
301 **ONENIGHTINVIENNA** (IRE) 67

51 **ONESIE** (IRE) 53
292 **ONLY FOR LOVE** (GB) 111
229 **ONLY GORGEOUS** (IRE) 10
123 **ONLY ME** (IRE) 34
418 **ONLY MILLIE** (GB) F 14
273 **ONLY ORSENFOOLSIES** (GB) 38
334 **ONLY ORVIETO** (IRE) 28
335 **ONLY TEN PER CENT** (IRE) 25
273 **ONLYFOOLSOWNHORSES** (IRE) 39
23 **ONLYJIM** (FR) 36
54 **ONORINA** (IRE) 7
634 **ONSHORE** (GB) 59
521 **ONTHEMOONAGAIN** 223
463 **ONTHEWESTERNFRONT** (IRE) 64
421 **ONTOPOFTHEWORLD** (IRE) 13
462 **ONURBIKE** (GB) 2
333 **ONWARDSANDUPWARDS** (GB) 12
242 **ONWITHTHEPARTY** (GB) 25
227 **OOLOGIST** (GB) 10
561 **OORAYVIC** (IRE) 45
104 **OOTY HILL** (GB) 10
98 **OPAL TIARA** (IRE) 67
63 **OPECHEE** (IRE) 29
437 **OPEN EAGLE** (IRE) 144
550 **OPEN HEARTED** (GB) 72
479 **OPEN THE RED** (GB) 14
479 **OPEN WIDE** (USA) 48
224 **OPENING BATSMAN** (IRE) 9
786 **OPENING TIME** (GB) 212
532 **OPERA BUFF** (GB) 4
342 **OPERA BUFFA** (IRE) 86
356 **OPERA DANCER** (GB) C 42
15 **OPERA GAL** (IRE) C 158
15 **OPERA GLASS** (GB) F 159
15 **OPERA LAD** (IRE) 35
658 **OPERA ROCK** (FR) 52
285 **OPERATEUR** (IRE) 7
145 **OPERATIVE** (GB) 26
299 **OPERISSIMO** (GB) C 132
299 **OPITO BAY** (IRE) 14
168 **OPPOSITION** (GB) 37
642 **OPT OUT** (GB) 23
561 **OPTICAL HIGH** (GB) 46
313 **OPTIMA PETAMUS** (GB) 14
463 **OPTIMISTIC BIAS** (IRE) 65
527 **OPUS TOO** (IRE) 8
320 **OR DE VASSY** (FR) 34
99 **ORACLE BOY** (GB) 7
549 **ORACOLO** (IRE) 22
104 **ORANGE GIN** (GB) 86
375 **ORANGE NASSAU** (FR) 42
96 **ORANGEADAY** (GB) 23
439 **ORANGECHERIE** (IRE) 19
390 **ORANGER** (FR) 6
634 **ORANGEY RED** (IRE) 60
456 **ORATE** (USA) C 130
437 **ORATORIANO** (FR) 145
411 **ORATORIO'S JOY** (IRE) 11
419 **ORATRIX** (IRE) F 26
451 **ORBASA** (FR) 92
292 **ORBIT LIGHT** (IRE) 112
280 **ORBIT THE MOON** (IRE) 11
564 **ORCHARD PARK** (IRE) 35
136 **ORCHARD ROAD** (USA) 4
459 **ORCHESTRAL RUN** (IRE) 20
63 **ORCHESTRATED** (FR) 30
161 **ORDENSRITTER** (GER) 18
282 **ORDER OF SERVICE** (GB) 14

486 **RYDE ON** (GB) C 9
298 **RYDON PYNES** (GB) 8
612 **RYE HOUSE** (IRE) 88
334 **RYEDALE RACER** (GB) 34
177 **RYEDALE RIO** (IRE) 92
422 **RYEOLLIEAN** (GB) 98
521 **RYTHMIQUE** (IRE) 237
594 **S FOR ESTUARY** (IRE) 14
195 **SA SUFFIT** (FR) 23
199 **SAAB ALMANAL** (GB) 17
584 **SAADIAH** (IRE) F 60
48 **SAAFARR** (GB) 52
521 **SAANE** (FR) 19
584 **SABAANI** (GB) 61
549 **SABADILLA** (GB) 92
15 **SABAH** (GB) F 170
578 **SABLE ISLAND** (IRE) 153
23 **SABLEROSE** (IRE) 40
190 **SABLONNE** (USA) F 60
479 **SABORIDO** (USA) 16
284 **SABRAGE** (IRE) 24
470 **SABRATAH** (GB) C 59
201 **SABRE ROCK** (GB) 13
101 **SABRE SQUADRON** (IRE) 17
115 **SABREWING** (IRE) 43
156 **SABRINA BRAZZO** (GB) 45
669 **SABROCLAIR** (FR) 9
534 **SACKETT** (GB) 15
190 **SACRAMENT** (IRE) 35
233 **SACRAMENTO KING** (IRE) 10
613 **SACRED DRAGON** (USA) 25
33 **SACRED ROCK** (IRE) 16
158 **SACRED SQUARE** (IRE) 14
612 **SACRED SUMMIT** (IRE) 89
469 **SACRED TRUST** (GB) 41
301 **SADDLERS ENCORE** (IRE) 80
85 **SADDLERS' SECRET** (IRE) 5
521 **SADIA** (GB) 125
197 **SADIE BABES** (IRE) 135
529 **SADIKS BOY** (IRE) 3
485 **SADLER'S GOLD** (IRE) 76
362 **SADMA** (GB) 4
51 **SAEEDAN** (IRE) 63
182 **SAFARI JOURNEY** (USA) 8
546 **SAFE HARBOUR** (IRE) 43
500 **SAFE VOYAGE** (IRE) 40
63 **SAFFRON PRINCE** (GB) 34
353 **SAFFRON WELLS** (IRE) 27
325 **SAFIRA MENINA** (GB) 1
411 **SAFQA** (GB) F 26
168 **SAGACIOUSLY** (IRE) 7
521 **SAGALINA** (IRE) F 238
63 **SAGAWARA** (GB) C 101
63 **SAGE MONKEY** (IRE) 35
168 **SAGELY** (IRE) 45
101 **SAGINA** (GB) F 33
51 **SAHALIN** (GB) 64
622 **SAHARA** (IRE) 11
499 **SAHARA DESERT** (IRE) 11
133 **SAHARA HAZE** (GB) F 150
422 **SAHARAN SONG** (IRE) F 54
423 **SAHARIRI** (IRE) F 50
299 **SAHREEJ** (IRE) 70
610 **SAIDDAA** (USA) 107
521 **SAIGON CITY** (GB) 14
433 **SAIL BY THE SEA** (IRE) 75
514 **SAIL WITH SULTANA** (GB) 8
59 **SAIL WITH THE WIND** (GB) F 25

332 **SAILING DAYS** (GB) C 32
349 **SAILOR MALAN** (GB) 8
593 **SAILORS WARN** (IRE) 11
234 **SAINT ARE** (FR) 49
250 **SAINT BREIZ** (FR) 7
636 **SAINT BRIEUC** (FR) 10
375 **SAINT CAJETON** (FR) 51
292 **SAINT CHARLES** (FR) 134
669 **SAINT ELM** (FR) 10
236 **SAINT HELENA** (IRE) 13
480 **SAINT HONORE** (GB) 19
106 **SAINT ISIDORE** (FR) 51
485 **SAINT JOHN HENRY** (FR) 77
414 **SAINT LUCIA** (IRE) C 30
93 **SAINT POIS** (FR) 49
620 **SAINT RAPH** (FR) 16
451 **SAINT ROQUE** (FR) 110
521 **SAINT SIMEON** (IRE) 126
12 **SAINTE LADYLIME** (FR) 57
263 **SAINTED** (GB) 80
224 **SAINTINGRID** (FR) 61
176 **SAINTS AND SINNERS** (IRE) 41
555 **SAIRAAM** (IRE) 5
524 **SAJJAD** (IRE) 102
335 **SAKHACITY** (GB) F 50
335 **SAKHACITY** (GB) F 45
261 **SAKHALIN STAR** (IRE) 12
171 **SAKHASTIC** (GB) 17
6 **SAKHEE STAR** (GB) 110
355 **SAKHEE'S CITY** (FR) 41
349 **SAKHEE'S JEM** (GB) 21
177 **SAKHEE'S RETURN** (GB) 52
404 **SAKHEE'S ROSE** (GB) 7
64 **SAKHRA** (GB) 9
104 **SALAD DAYS** (GB) 47
612 **SALAMAITE** (FR) G 90
342 **SALAMANQUE** (FR) F 98
568 **SALARIAQ** (USA) 6
461 **SALATEEN** (GB) 42
469 **SALEH** (FR) 42
9 **SALIENT** (GB) 23
621 **SALINIA** (IRE) C 73
524 **SALIYNA** (FR) F 103
116 **SALLANCHES** (USA) C 50
352 **SALMANAZAR** (GB) 104
276 **SALMON ROSE** (IRE) F 226
177 **SALMON SUSHI** (GB) 53
263 **SALONBLUE** (FR) F 165
463 **SALOPIEN** (IRE) 77
499 **SALT LAKE SOOTY** (GB) 14
206 **SALTARELLO** (IRE) 10
652 **SALTEE GREAT** (IRE) G 71
546 **SALTO CHISCO** (IRE) 44
451 **SALUBRIOUS** (IRE) 111
264 **SALUT HONORE** (FR) 17
93 **SALVADO** (IRE) 50
202 **SALVO** (GB) 14
452 **SAM FAIRYANN** (GB) 11
224 **SAM I** (FR) 76
418 **SAM LORD** (GB) 17
199 **SAM MISSILE** (IRE) 44
451 **SAM WINNER** (FR) 112
185 **SAM'S ADVENTURE** (GB) 62
264 **SAMALARR** (IRE) 18
489 **SAMARINTA** (GB) 4
130 **SAMASANA** (FR) F 75
141 **SAMAWI** (IRE) 4
521 **SAMBA PA TI** (IRE) 239

436 **SAMBA SOUND** (IRE) 35
441 **SAMBARA** (IRE) G 10
437 **SAMBREMONT** (FR) 170
244 **SAMDANIYA** (GB) F 181
590 **SAMDIBIEN** (FR) 10
252 **SAME DIFFERENCE** (IRE) 54
12 **SAME OLE TRIX** (IRE) 58
510 **SAMEDI SOIR** (GB) 17
451 **SAMETEGAL** (FR) 113
72 **SAMHAIN** (GB) 12
286 **SAMINGARRY** (FR) 35
528 **SAMIRA GOLD** (FR) C 109
23 **SAMIRE** (FR) 6
462 **SAMIZDAT** (FR) 3
670 **SAMMARA** (GB) 10
525 **SAMMY B** (GB) 67
77 **SAMMY'S CHOICE** (GB) 3
406 **SAMOSET** (GB) 31
222 **SAMRANA** (FR) F 13
429 **SAMSON** (GB) 18
411 **SAMSON COLLONGES** (FR) 14
117 **SAMSONITE** (IRE) 13
212 **SAMTHEMAN** (GB) 5
550 **SAMTU** (IRE) 81
451 **SAN BENEDETO** (FR) 114
91 **SAN CASSIANO** (IRE) 30
456 **SAN FRANCISCO** (IRE) 61
111 **SAN MARINO** (FR) 2
213 **SAN PIETRO** (FR) 20
328 **SAN QUENTIN** (FR) 14
78 **SAN SEBASTIANA** (GB) 89
180 **SAN TELM** (IRE) 15
197 **SANAADH** (GB) 136
292 **SANAIJA** (GB) 135
524 **SANAYA** (IRE) C 104
185 **SAND BLAST** (GB) 63
119 **SAND BY ME** (GB) 6
104 **SAND SHOE** (GB) 92
122 **SANDACRES** (GB) 16
505 **SANDEEL BAY** (IRE) 10
200 **SANDFORD CASTLE** (IRE) 22
119 **SANDFRANKSKIPSGO** (GB) 2
433 **SANDGATE** (GB) 76
252 **SANDHURST LAD** (IRE) 55
196 **SANDRA'S SECRET** (IRE) 13
527 **SANDRO BOTTICELLI** (IRE) 10
237 **SANDS CHORUS** (GB) 13
192 **SANDS COVE** (IRE) 18
290 **SANDSTONE** (GB) 29
98 **SANDTAIL** (IRE) C 127
597 **SANDY BEACH** (GB) 40
189 **SANDY COVE** (GB) 9
524 **SANDY'S CHOICE** (FR) 12
301 **SANDYGATE** (GB) 81
279 **SANDYMOUNT DUKE** (IRE) 49
221 **SANGRAM** (IRE) 13
361 **SANJITA** (FR) 59
629 **SANNDIYR** (IRE) 2
156 **SANS REWARD** (IRE) F 64
634 **SANSIBAR JEWEL** (USA) 149
599 **SANT'ELIA** (GB) 8
456 **SANTA ANITA** (GB) 62
546 **SANTA'S SECRET** (IRE) 45
461 **SANTACUS** (IRE) F 68
300 **SANTADELACRUZE** (GB) 6
299 **SANTE** (FR) 71
130 **SANTEFISIO** (GB) 32
222 **SANTIA** (GB) F 14

6 **STARS N ANGELS** (IRE) 114	546 **STIFF UPPER LIP** (IRE) 48	182 **STOW** (GB) 10
485 **STARS OVER THE SEA** (USA) 85	652 **STILL BELIEVING** (IRE) 74	292 **STOWAWAY MAGIC** (IRE) 143
235 **STARS ROYALE** (IRE) 23	87 **STILL I'M A STAR** (IRE) F 65	595 **STRADATER** (IRE) 19
494 **STARSHELL** (IRE) 64	400 **STILL KICKING** (IRE) 21	423 **STRADUFF** (IRE) 22
276 **STARSTONE** (GB) C 238	177 **STILL ON TOP** (GB) 16	561 **STRAIDNAHANNA** (IRE) 56
602 **START SEVEN** (GB) 11	355 **STILL SMALL VOICE** (GB) F 52	631 **STRAIGHT SETS** (IRE) F 7
263 **START THE MUSIC** (IRE) C 173	485 **STILL TOGETHER** (IRE) 86	554 **STRAIGHTTOTHEPOINT** (GB) 16
414 **STARVING MARVIN** (GB) 13	451 **STILLETTO** (IRE) 131	512 **STRAIT OF MAGELLAN** (IRE) 41
639 **STATE OF GRACE** (GB) F 6	614 **STILO BLUE NATIVE** (IRE) 25	273 **STRAIT RUN** (IRE) 58
284 **STATE OF ORIGIN** (IRE) 28	609 **STIMULATOR** (GB) 13	528 **STRAITS OF MALACCA** (GB) 29
95 **STATE OF THE UNION** (IRE) 18	436 **STING JET** (IRE) 41	583 **STRAITS OF MESSINA** (IRE) 28
540 **STATE SOVEREIGNTY** (GB) 21	185 **STIPULATE** (GB) 70	237 **STRANDS OF SILK** (IRE) 29
157 **STATE TROOPER** (IRE) 9	187 **STITCHED IN TIME** (IRE) 7	522 **STRANGE BIRD** (IRE) 14
389 **STATEN ISLAND** (IRE) 43	492 **STOCKHILL DIVA** (GB) 24	626 **STRATEGIC ISLAND** (IRE) 9
29 **STATION HOUSE** (IRE) C 78	610 **STOCKING** (GB) 34	299 **STRATH BURN** (GB) 16
578 **STATUESQUE** (GB) 94	87 **STOIC BOY** (GB) 16	29 **STRATHEARN** (IRE) 37
494 **STATUS QUO** (IRE) 35	623 **STOICAL PATIENT** (IRE) 3	514 **STRATHTAY** (GB) G 9
116 **STAUNCH** (GB) 21	437 **STONE HARD** (IRE) 185	290 **STRATONIKA** (FR) 53
112 **STAY IN MY HEART** (IRE) 12	456 **STONE MOUNTAIN** (IRE) 69	244 **STRATUM** (GB) 85
210 **STEADY EDDIE** (GB) 10	195 **STONE OF FOLCA** (GB) 28	122 **STRAVIE** (IRE) F 18
28 **STEAM AHEAD** (GB) 68	237 **STONE QUERCUS** (IRE) 28	263 **STRAW HAT** (IRE) 89
28 **STEAMING** (IRE) 129	104 **STONE THE CROWS** (GB) 97	346 **STRAWBERRY HILL** (IRE) 12
582 **STECCANDO** (IRE) 40	251 **STONEACRE OSKAR** (GB) 4	610 **STRAWBERRY LEAF** (GB) 189
415 **STEEL A TUNE** (GB) 6	356 **STONEACRE SARAH** (GB) C 52	116 **STRAWBERRY SORBET** (GB) 54
574 **STEEL CITY BOY** (IRE) 13	92 **STONEBOAT BILL** (GB) 16	157 **STRAWBERRYFIELDS** (GB) 11
44 **STEEL EXPRESS** (IRE) 5	397 **STONEBROOK** (IRE) 76	512 **STREAMS OF WHISKEY** (IRE) 42
608 **STEEL GOLD** (IRE) 3	425 **STONECOLDSOBA** (GB) 8	665 **STREELE** (USA) 9
597 **STEEL GREY LADY** (IRE) G 44	492 **STONECUTTER** (IRE) 25	439 **STREET ART** (IRE) 10
276 **STEEL OF MADRID** (IRE) 96	408 **STONEFORD** (IRE) 67	450 **STREET ARTIST** (IRE) 25
194 **STEEL RAIN** (GB) 13	422 **STONEGATE** (GB) 105	342 **STREET DUEL** (USA) 113
66 **STEEL STOCKHOLDER** (GB) 17	332 **STONEHAM** (GB) 23	6 **STREET FORCE** (USA) 81
461 **STEEL TRAIN** (FR) 48	588 **STONEMADFORSPEED** (IRE) 10	237 **STREET JAZZ** (GB) 41
353 **STEELING DOLLARS** (IRE) 28	594 **STONEY** (IRE) 17	42 **STREET OF DREAMS** (GB) 86
22 **STEELRIVER** (IRE) 25	199 **STONEY BROKE** (GB) 47	376 **STREET OUTLAW** (IRE) 35
336 **STEEPLEOFCOPPER** (IRE) 4	276 **STONEY COVE** (IRE) F 240	578 **STREET POET** (IRE) 95
553 **STEFER** (USA) C 61	352 **STONEY'S TREASURE** (GB) 114	319 **STREET STYLE** (GB) C 50
48 **STEIP AMACH** (IRE) 1	486 **STOP THE PRESS** (GB) 11	540 **STREETS OF PROMISE** (IRE) 22
563 **STELLA'S FELLA** (GB) 7	600 **STORM AHEAD** (IRE) 30	470 **STREETS OF RIO** (FR) 65
48 **STELLAR GLOW** (IRE) 12	229 **STORM ALERT** (GB) 13	276 **STRELA** (GER) C 241
48 **STELLAR MASS** (IRE) 58	618 **STORM FORCE TEN** (GB) 6	553 **STRELKITA** (FR) 17
451 **STELLAR NOTION** (IRE) 130	334 **STORM FORECAST** (IRE) 37	408 **STRETCHINGTHETRUTH** (IRE) 68
47 **STELLARTA** (GB) 13	468 **STORM HAWK** (IRE) 8	10 **STRICTLY ART** (IRE) 16
263 **STELLENBOSCH** (IRE) 174	256 **STORM KING** (GB) 10	10 **STRICTLY CARTER** (GB) 17
624 **STENCIVE** (GB) 8	134 **STORM KITTEN** (IRE) G 24	565 **STRICTLY GLITZ** (IRE) 7
48 **STENOGRAPHER** (USA) 59	64 **STORM LIGHTNING** (GB) 10	357 **STRICTLY LAMBADA** (GB) C 28
290 **STEP IN LATE** (FR) 32	342 **STORM LILY** (USA) F 205	565 **STRICTLY THE ONE** (IRE) 8
550 **STEPHANIE FRANCES** (IRE) 90	463 **STORM MELODY** (GB) 109	325 **STRIKE FORCE** (GB) 2
20 **STEPHEN HERO** (IRE) 12	550 **STORM OF SWORDS** (IRE) 91	331 **STRIKEMASTER** (IRE) 5
264 **STEPOVER** (GB) 22	562 **STORM PATROL** (GB) 18	311 **STRIKING FOR GOLD** (GB) 22
107 **STEPPE DAUGHTER** (IRE) 6	450 **STORM RIDER** (GB) 23	279 **STRIKING GOLD** (GB) 85
431 **STEPPER POINT** (GB) 15	276 **STORM RISING** (IRE) 97	99 **STRIKING NIGELLA** (GB) 12
9 **STEPPIN OUT** (GB) C 30	169 **STORM ROCK** (GB) 10	263 **STRINGS** (GB) C 175
610 **STEPS** (IRE) 32	588 **STORM RUN** (IRE) 11	29 **STRIVING** (IRE) C 80
463 **STEPS AND STAIRS** (IRE) 85	388 **STORM RUNNER** (IRE) 13	9 **STRIX** (GB) 9
113 **STERLING GENT** (IRE) 5	450 **STORM TROOPER** (IRE) 24	453 **STROBE** (GB) 15
276 **STERLING SILVA** (IRE) 239	108 **STORMBOUND** (FR) 15	7 **STROLLAWAYNOW** (IRE) 10
301 **STERNRUBIN** (GER) 90	177 **STORMIN TOM** (IRE) 60	42 **STRONG CHALLENGE** (IRE) 87
342 **STETCHWORTH** (IRE) 17	151 **STORMING HARRY** (GB) 23	172 **STRONG CONTENDER** (GB) 13
29 **STETCHWORTH PARK** (IRE) 36	234 **STORMING STRUMPET** (GB) 55	42 **STRONG FORCE** (GB) 88
157 **STEUBEN** (GER) 10	539 **STORMION** (IRE) 13	176 **STRONG MAN** (GB) 46
428 **STEVE PRESCOTT** (GB) 11	19 **STORMONT BRIDGE** (IRE) 21	301 **STRONG PURSUIT** (IRE) 91
610 **STEVE ROGERS** (IRE) 33	230 **STORMY ANGEL** (FR) 33	469 **STRONG STEPS** (GB) 8
72 **STEVIE BROWN** (IRE) 47	621 **STORMY ANTARCTIC** (GB) 46	42 **STRONG TEAM** (IRE) 89
273 **STHENIC** (FR) 56	156 **STORMY ART** (IRE) 46	463 **STRONGLY SUGGESTED** (GB) 86
252 **STICKEE FINGERS** (GB) 60	261 **STORMY WEATHER** (GB) G 29	460 **STRUCTURED NOTE** (IRE) 13
336 **STICKERS** (GB) 5	515 **STORYTALE** (GB) 5	52 **STRUMBLE HEAD** (IRE) 35
273 **STICKLEBACK** (GB) 57	349 **STOSUR** (IRE) 11	528 **STRUMMER** (IRE) 72
29 **STICKS MCKENZIE** (GB) 79	334 **STOUT CORTEZ** (GB) 38	176 **STUBYTUESDAY** (GB) 74

533 **TITUS SECRET** (GB) 14
554 **TIVRA** (IRE) 47
429 **TIYSHA** (IRE) C 79
490 **TIZ HERSELF** (IRE) 38
342 **TIZDUBAI** (USA) F 211
49 **TIZIANA** (FR) 8
375 **TJONGEJONGE** (FR) 66
469 **TO BE WILD** (IRE) 46
387 **TO BEGIN** (GB) 28
244 **TO ETERNITY** (GB) 94
427 **TOAD CORNER** (GB) 4
112 **TOARMANDOWITHLOVE** (IRE) 14
174 **TOAST AND JAM** (IRE) 15
612 **TOBACCO ROAD** (IRE) 106
459 **TOBAR NA GAOISE** (IRE) 29
268 **TOBEFAIR** (GB) 12
332 **TOBERANTHAWN** (IRE) C 34
165 **TOBOGGAN'S FIRE** (GB) 31
165 **TOBOGGAN'S GIFT** (GB) 8
357 **TOBUGGALOO** (GB) 15
6 **TOBOUGGAN RUN** (GB) 89
550 **TOBY LERONE** (IRE) 100
634 **TOCCO D'AMORE** (IRE) 160
602 **TODAY'S THE DAY** (GB) F 31
438 **TODD** (GB) 11
208 **TOE TO TOE** (IRE) 13
168 **TOFFEE APPLE** (IRE) 52
347 **TOFFEE HOLLAND** (GB) 30
299 **TOFFEE VODKA** (IRE) F 157
222 **TOGA TIGER** (IRE) 22
456 **TOGETHER** (IRE) F 146
621 **TOGETHERNESS** (IRE) 48
342 **TOGETHERWECAN** (IRE) 21
456 **TOI ET MOI** (IRE) C 147
332 **TOKARAMORE** (GB) 26
286 **TOKYO JAVILEX** (FR) 40
19 **TOLEDO GOLD** (IRE) 22
134 **TOLKEINS TANGO** (IRE) 26
461 **TOLOMEO** (IRE) 40
461 **TOLSTOY** (IRE) 70
191 **TOM BACH** (IRE) 2
353 **TOM HALL** (GB) 30
243 **TOM KETTLE** (IRE) 7
620 **TOM NEARY** (IRE) 20
84 **TOM SAWYER** (GB) 7
148 **TOM TOM D'HAGUENET** (FR) 22
507 **TOM'S ANNA** (IRE) 3
643 **TOMAHAWK WOOD** (GB) 14
130 **TOMBE GIRL** (GB) 59
649 **TOMBISH** (FR) 12
411 **TOMKEVI** (FR) 110
656 **TOMMY ATKINS** (IRE) 5
130 **TOMMY DOCC** (GB) 36
598 **TOMMY DYLON** (IRE) 17
550 **TOMMY RAPPER** (IRE) 101
451 **TOMMY SILVER** (GB) 137
86 **TOMMY THE RASCAL** (GB) 23
100 **TOMMY'S SECRET** (GB) 8
382 **TOMMYS GEAL** (GB) 7
594 **TOMMYSTEEL** (IRE) 38
185 **TOMNGERRY** (IRE) 75
612 **TOMSK** (FR) 107
224 **TONGANUI** (IRE) 69
93 **TONI'S A STAR** (GB) 64
265 **TONKINESE** (GB) 65
551 **TONTO'S SPIRIT** (GB) 10
665 **TONY** (IRE) 10
276 **TONY CURTIS** (GB) 104

579 **TONYTHETARMACKER** (IRE) 21
22 **TOO CLOSE** (IRE) F 68
239 **TOO COOL TO FOOL** (IRE) 37
352 **TOO FAR GONE** (IRE) 124
220 **TOO HOT TO BOUGGIE** (GB) 2
633 **TOO MUCH TOO SOON** (IRE) 42
669 **TOO SCOOPS** (IRE) 14
443 **TOO TRIGGER HAPPY** (GB) 7
78 **TOOCOOLFORSCHOOL** (IRE) 17
115 **TOOFI** (FR) 27
235 **TOOHIGHFORME** (IRE) 25
460 **TOOLA BOOLA** (GB) 14
568 **TOOREEN LEGEND** (IRE) 8
276 **TOORMORE** (IRE) 19
583 **TOOSEY** (GB) 30
301 **TOOWOOMBA** (IRE) 99
658 **TOP AND DROP** (GB) 77
429 **TOP BEAK** (IRE) 56
278 **TOP BENEFIT** (IRE) 3
512 **TOP BILLING** (GB) 45
541 **TOP BOY** (GB) 22
246 **TOP CAT DJ** (IRE) 39
448 **TOP CAT HENRY** (IRE) 22
281 **TOP COP** (GB) 21
252 **TOP DANCER** (FR) 66
422 **TOP DIKTAT** (GB) 109
366 **TOP GAMBLE** (IRE) 28
322 **TOP MAN MARTY** (IRE) 16
292 **TOP NOTCH** (FR) 151
528 **TOP OF THE BANK** (GB) 76
185 **TOP OF THE GLAS** (IRE) 76
135 **TOP OF THE ROCKS** (IRE) 46
428 **TOP OFFER** (GB) 12
382 **TOP POCKET** (GB) 8
463 **TOP PRIORITY** (FR) 92
483 **TOP SET** (IRE) 33
485 **TOP WOOD** (FR) 93
599 **TOPALING** (GB) 10
599 **TOPALOVA** (GB) 25
599 **TOPAMICHI** (GB) 11
634 **TOPAZ CLEAR** (IRE) 81
514 **TOPMAN TED** (GB) 10
602 **TOPOLOGY** (GB) 23
7 **TOPOLSKI** (GB) 12
281 **TOPSOIL** (GB) 30
560 **TOPTEMPO** (GB) 5
50 **TOPTHORN** (GB) 11
245 **TOQUICKLY** (GB) 7
276 **TORCH** (GB) 105
483 **TORDUFF STORM** (IRE) G 34
422 **TORERO** (GB) 110
370 **TORETTO** (IRE) 27
590 **TORHOUSEMUIR** (IRE) 11
189 **TORIANO** (GB) 24
652 **TORNADO IN MILAN** (IRE) 81
520 **TORNESEL** (GB) 9
494 **TORONTO SOUND** (GB) 65
169 **TORQUAY** (GB) 29
528 **TORREMAR** (FR) 77
437 **TORRENT DES MOTTES** (FR) 197
400 **TORREON** (IRE) 16
176 **TORRID** (GB) 50
265 **TOSCANINI** (IRE) 28
632 **TOTAL ASSETS** (GB) 13
185 **TOTAL POWER** (GB) 105
320 **TOTAL RECALL** (IRE) 53
123 **TOTAL STAR** (GB) 102
185 **TOTALIZE** (GB) 77

116 **TOTALLY COMMITTED** (GB) 57
610 **TOTALLY DEVOTED** (USA) F 193
437 **TOTALLY DOMINANT** (USA) 198
644 **TOTALLY MAGIC** (IRE) 12
422 **TOTHEMOONANDBACK** (IRE) 111
128 **TOTZO** (IRE) 9
27 **TOUCH BACK** (IRE) 15
451 **TOUCH KICK** (IRE) 138
470 **TOUCH OF ART** (FR) 70
195 **TOUCH OF STEEL** (IRE) 29
90 **TOUCH OF VELVETT** (GB) 28
575 **TOUCH THE CLOUDS** (GB) 6
186 **TOUCH THE SKY** (GB) 13
15 **TOUCHDOWN BANWELL** (USA) 110
419 **TOUCHED BY LOVE** (USA) 22
419 **TOUGH CALL** (IRE) 6
131 **TOUGH CHIC** (IRE) G 19
339 **TOULSON** (GB) 31
610 **TOUMAR** (GB) 125
172 **TOUR DE VILLE** (IRE) 16
606 **TOUR DES CHAMPS** (FR) 87
172 **TOURNAMENT** (GB) 17
634 **TOURSOUN** (IRE) 161
553 **TOUTAINVILLE** (GER) 63
546 **TOVIERE** (IRE) 53
292 **TOWER OF ALLEN** (IRE) 152
400 **TOWER POWER** (GB) 17
269 **TOWERBURN** (IRE) 7
292 **TOWERING** (GB) 153
29 **TOWERLANDS PARK** (IRE) 40
429 **TOWIE** (IRE) 80
353 **TOWN MOUSE** (GB) 31
213 **TOWN ORATOR** (GB) 22
42 **TOWN'S HISTORY** (USA) 93
437 **TOWNSHEND** (GER) 199
130 **TOWNSVILLE** (GB) 37
422 **TOXARIS** (IRE) 112
135 **TOY SHOW** (IRE) C 99
156 **TOY TOP** (USA) F 65
400 **TOYMAKER** (GB) 18
390 **TRACKING TIME** (GB) 8
192 **TRACKMATE** (GB) 20
525 **TRADEWINDS** (FR) 85
139 **TRAFALGAR** (FR) 21
448 **TRAFALGAR ROCK** (GB) 23
422 **TRAFFIC FLUIDE** (FR) 113
106 **TRAFFIC JAM** (FR) 54
528 **TRAIL BLAZE** (IRE) 34
263 **TRAINNAH** (GB) 92
306 **TRAKEUR** (FR) 14
376 **TRALANZA** (IRE) C 37
23 **TRANCOSO** (FR) 46
584 **TRANQUIL FLIGHT** (GB) F 12
288 **TRANQUIL TIME** (GB) 66
229 **TRANS EXPRESS** (IRE) 15
554 **TRANSFIX** (GB) F 48
355 **TRANSIENT BAY** (IRE) 45
19 **TRANSLUSCENT** (IRE) 23
578 **TRANSMITTING** (GB) 102
156 **TRANSPENNINE STAR** (GB) 47
78 **TRAP QUEEN** (IRE) 55
170 **TRAPPER PEAK** (IRE) 21
352 **TRAVERTINE** (IRE) 125
208 **TRAVIS BICKLE** (IRE) 14
293 **TREACY HOTELS BOY** (IRE) 18
456 **TREASURE CHEST** (IRE) 75
537 **TREASURE REALM** (IRE) 26
508 **TREASURE THE RIDGE** (IRE) 6

469 **VITA NOVA** (IRE) F 132
23 **VITAL SUN** (FR) 48
437 **VITALIZED** (IRE) 222
662 **VITARRA** (GB) 3
265 **VITELLO** (GB) 66
483 **VIVA RAFA** (IRE) 35
37 **VIVA STEVE** (FR) 41
376 **VIVA VERGLAS** (IRE) 23
658 **VIVACCIO** (FR) 84
226 **VIVACISSIMO** (IRE) 17
451 **VIVALDI COLLONGES** (FR) 149
224 **VIVANT POEME** (FR) 71
375 **VIVAS** (FR) 68
106 **VIVE LE GRIS** (FR) 55
375 **VIVE LE ROI** (IRE) 69
342 **VIVE MA FILLE** (GER) 22
535 **VIVO PER LEI** (FR) 4
607 **VIVRE LA REVE** (GB) 2
168 **VIVRE POUR VIVRE** (IRE) 53
299 **VIZ** (IRE) C 159
610 **VIZIER** (GB) 127
48 **VOCAL ACTIVITY** (IRE) 138
166 **VOCAL DEFENSE** (IRE) 19
166 **VOCAL HEIR** (IRE) 10
166 **VOCAL PERFECTION** (IRE) 20
166 **VOCAL RESPONSE** (IRE) 139
166 **VOCAL VELOCITY** (IRE) 11
555 **VOCALISE** (GB) 6
151 **VOCALISER** (GB) 30
243 **VOCIFEROUSLY** (IRE) 8
292 **VODKA 'N TONIC** (IRE) 157
106 **VODKA DOUBLE** (FR) 56
612 **VODKA ISLAND** (FR) 111
340 **VODKA RED** (IRE) 10
149 **VODKA SHOT** (USA) G 33
261 **VODKA SHOT** (USA) C 30
282 **VODKA TIME** (IRE) 23
273 **VODKA WELLS** (FR) 69
29 **VOGARTH** (GB) 15
51 **VOGUEATTI** (USA) 75
420 **VOICE CONTROL** (IRE) 19
313 **VOICE FROM ABOVE** (IRE) 19
71 **VOICE OF A LEADER** (IRE) 4
189 **VOICE OVER** (GB) 31
221 **VOICES OF KINGS** (GB) 39
55 **VOILOUP** (FR) 255
224 **VOIX D'EAU** (FR) 72
397 **VOLCANIC** (FR) 93
99 **VOLCANIC JACK** (IRE) 16
578 **VOLITION** (IRE) 107
521 **VOLKHOV** (IRE) 140
292 **VOLNAY DE THAIX** (FR) 158
521 **VOLOSHKINE** (FR) 141
98 **VOLUNTEER POINT** (IRE) 42
244 **VON BLUCHER** (IRE) 99
448 **VOSNE ROMANEE** (GB) 24
189 **VOTE** (GB) 32
613 **VOTEC** (IRE) 53
521 **VOTKA** (IRE) 142
525 **VOYAGE A NEW YORK** (FR) 88
202 **VROOM** (IRE) 16
437 **VROOM VROUM MAG** (FR) 223
49 **VUE DE L'ESPRIT** (FR) 30
521 **VUE DU CIEL** 256
123 **VUELA** (GB) 44
292 **VYTA DU ROC** (FR) 159
642 **W SIX TIMES** (GB) 29
244 **WAADY** (IRE) 17

601 **WAANEBE RANGER** (IRE) 8
652 **WABANAKI** (IRE) 82
634 **WADALANI** (GB) 84
149 **WADE HARPER** (IRE) 34
433 **WADSWICK COURT** (IRE) 94
120 **WAFI STAR** (IRE) 42
179 **WAGONER** (GB) 21
319 **WAHAAB** (IRE) 16
352 **WAHEEBA** (GB) 130
148 **WAHIB** (FR) 27
342 **WAHQA** (GB) 122
63 **WAHWONAISA** (GB) 42
610 **WAHYLAH** (IRE) C 197
115 **WAISHBOOSHBASH** (GB) 69
301 **WAIT FOR ME** (FR) 105
585 **WAITING FOR RICHIE** (GB) 10
510 **WAITING PATIENTLY** (IRE) 26
169 **WAITINGONACLOUD** (GB) C 44
42 **WAITRESS** (USA) F 162
244 **WAJEEZ** (IRE) 100
145 **WAKAME** (IRE) 29
561 **WAKANDA** (IRE) 63
86 **WAKE YOUR DREAMS** (IRE) 24
455 **WAKEA** (USA) 11
595 **WAKHAN** (IRE) 87
63 **WALDEN PRINCE** (IRE) 43
621 **WALDENA** (USA) F 76
658 **WALDORF SALAD** (GB) 85
148 **WALK IN BEAUTY** (IRE) F 93
620 **WALK IN THE MILL** (FR) 22
6 **WALK LIKE A GIANT** (GB) 94
449 **WALK OF GLEAMS** (GB) 7
550 **WALK ON AL** (IRE) 108
279 **WALK TO FREEDOM** (IRE) 58
463 **WALK WATERFORD** (GB) 99
220 **WALKABOUT CREEK** (IRE) 3
463 **WALKAMI** (FR) 100
276 **WALKING IN RHYTHM** (IRE) 110
550 **WALKING IN THE AIR** (IRE) 109
528 **WALKING PRIMROSE** (FR) 78
549 **WALKLIKEANEGYPTIAN** (IRE) C 99
135 **WALL OF LIGHT** (IRE) 47
170 **WALLAWALLABINGBANG** (GB) 23
469 **WALPOLE** (FR) 11
98 **WALRUS GUMBOOT** (GB) 43
614 **WALSAN** (FR) 12
552 **WALSINGHAM GRANGE** (USA) 18
292 **WALT** (IRE) 160
463 **WALTER ONEEIGHTONE** (IRE) 101
527 **WALTER RALEIGH** (IRE) 24
301 **WALTER WHITE** (IRE) 106
139 **WALTON MONEY** (GB) F 24
510 **WALTZ DARLING** (FR) 27
521 **WALTZ KEY** 257
248 **WALTZING TORNADO** (IRE) 2
123 **WANNABE FRIENDS** (GB) 45
116 **WANT THE FAIRYTALE** (GB) 58
363 **WAPPING** (USA) 30
80 **WAQAAD** (IRE) 23
299 **WAQAAS** (GB) 160
600 **WAQT** (IRE) 54
29 **WAR DEPARTMENT** (FR) 41
521 **WAR FLAG** (USA) 143
22 **WAR GIRL** (USA) 28
276 **WAR GLORY** (IRE) 111
521 **WAR MINISTER** (IRE) 258
29 **WAR OFFICE** (IRE) 82
200 **WAR SINGER** (USA) 25

301 **WAR SOUND** (GB) 107
123 **WAR STORY** (FR) 46
276 **WAR WHISPER** (FR) 112
123 **WARA** (GB) C 105
575 **WARDEN BOND** (GB) 7
98 **WARDEN HILL** (IRE) 44
39 **WARDEN LAW** (IRE) 17
207 **WARFARE** (GB) 5
627 **WARKSBURN BOY** (GB) 5
237 **WARM OASIS** (GB) 44
93 **WARM ORDER** (GB) 67
22 **WARM WELCOME** (GB) C 69
618 **WARNE** (IRE) 7
10 **WAROFINDEPENDENCE** (USA) 12
635 **WARRANT OFFICER** (GB) 14
252 **WARRANTOR** (IRE) 71
363 **WARRIOR OF LIGHT** (IRE) 10
168 **WARRIOR PRINCE** (GB) 54
276 **WARRIOR'S SPIRIT** (IRE) 252
451 **WARRIORS TALE** (GB) 150
154 **WARSAW PACT** (IRE) 4
602 **WASEEM FARIS** (IRE) 14
116 **WASHINGTON BLUE** (GB) 92
456 **WASHINGTON DC** (IRE) 80
101 **WASHINGTON WINKLE** (GB) 6
145 **WASSAIL** (GB) 30
120 **WASSEEM** (IRE) 43
610 **WATCHMAN** (GB) 198
471 **WATCHMETAIL** (IRE) 4
557 **WATER FOR LIFE** (GB) 7
429 **WATER FOUNTAIN** (GB) C 82
411 **WATER GARDEN** (FR) 18
175 **WATER RAIL** (GB) 6
320 **WATER ROCK** (GB) G 54
380 **WATER STRATFORD** (IRE) F 5
398 **WATER THIEF** (USA) 5
364 **WATER WAGTAIL** (GB) 55
224 **WATER WILLOW** (GB) 73
615 **WATERBERRY** (GB) 30
273 **WATERCLOCK** (FR) 70
456 **WATERLOO BRIDGE** (IRE) 81
607 **WATERLOO DOCK** (GB) 9
597 **WATERLOO WARRIOR** (FR) 54
342 **WATERSMEET** (GB) 23
319 **WATERVILLE DANCER** (IRE) 54
554 **WATSDAPLAN** (IRE) C 49
653 **WATT BRODERICK** (IRE) 72
560 **WATTABOUTSTEVE** (GB) 8
456 **WAVE** (IRE) C 151
49 **WAVE GOODBYE** (FR) F 31
48 **WAVE OF APPLAUSE** (GB) C 140
49 **WAVE POWER** (FR) 10
263 **WAVE REVIEWS** (GB) 95
28 **WAVELESS** (GB) 70
653 **WAVERING BEE** (IRE) G 73
408 **WAXIES DARGLE** (GB) 81
418 **WAY TO FINISH** (GB) 19
456 **WAY TO MY HEART** (IRE) 82
467 **WAYFARING STRANGER** (IRE) 46
156 **WAYSIDE MAGIC** (GB) 48
34 **WAYWARD FROLIC** (GB) 29
78 **WAYWARD HOOF** (GB) 57
273 **WAYWARD SUN** (GB) 71
397 **WAZOWSKI** (GB) 94
469 **WE ARE NINETY** (IRE) 49
131 **WE HAVE A DREAM** (GB) 21
78 **WE'LL SHAKE HANDS** (FR) 18
6 **WEALD OF KENT** (USA) 95

Join Members' Club for your definitive source of tipping, news, analysis, statistics and ratings. Membership starts from just 40p a day*

RACING POST.com/membersclub

LATE ENTRIES

MR PAUL COWLEY, Banbury

Postal: **Lodge Farm, Culworth, Banbury, Oxfordshire, OX17 2HL**
Contacts: **PHONE (01295) 768998   MOBILE (07775) 943346**
E-MAIL paulcowleyequine@yahoo.co.uk

1 **BUSY BARO (IRE),** 6, ch g Acambaro (GER)—Miss Busy Lizzy (IRE) **The BMWs**
2 **FRONTLINE (IRE),** 8, b g King's Theatre (IRE)—Thunder Road (IRE)
3 **GLENDERMOT (IRE),** 7, b g Portrait Gallery (IRE)—Native Bandit (IRE) **George Beyts & Stan West**
4 **NICOLOSIO (IRE),** 6, b h Peintre Celebre (USA)—Nicolaia (GER)
5 **SANOK (POL),** 4, b g Jape (USA)—Sun Queen (POL)
6 **SEAS OF GREEN,** 9, ch m Karinga Bay—Emerald Project (IRE) **CW Booth & The Grafton Hounds Choice Club**
7 **TRIGGERS GINGER,** 11, ch m Double Trigger (IRE)—New Dawn **Mr W. J. Lee**
8 **XHALE (FR),** 4, b g Halling (USA)—Xanadu Bliss (FR) **The Blue Harlequin Racing Club**

Other Owners: Mr R. J. Batchelor, Mr N. Becks, Mr George Beyts, Mr C. W. Booth, Mr Paul E. Cowley, Mrs Alana Cowley, Mr J. Leadbeater, Mr J. McConkey, Mrs M. Miller, Mrs P. Parsons, Mrs C. W. Richmond-Watson, Mrs J. Sheppard-Cross, Mr T. Shreeve, Mrs A. Sinclair, Mrs C. Smythe-Osbourne, Mr W. M. Welton, Mr Stan West, Mrs A. White, Mr D. E. Wilson.

MR W. HARNEY, Co. Tipperary

Postal: **Manna Cottage, Templemore, Co. Tipperary, Ireland**
Contacts: **PHONE (00353) 504 31534 FAX (00353) 504 31534 MOBILE (00353) 86 2498836**
E-MAIL harneyvet@gmail.com

1 **CHU CHU PERCY,** 5, b g Tobougg (IRE)—First Katoune (FR) **Mrs W. Harney**
2 **DESTINATION DEBBIE (IRE),** 5, br m Dubai Destination (USA)—Sorrentina (IRE)
Irene Fielding & Mrs W. Harney
3 **GANDHI (IRE),** 6, b g Indian River (FR)—French Class **Mrs W. Harney**
4 **ROBBINA (IRE),** 6, br m Robin des Champs (FR)—Sorrentina (IRE) **Mrs W. Harney**
5 **TARTAN TREASURE (IRE),** 5, ch g Indian River (FR)—Ballyburn Lady (IRE) **Patrick Harney & Liam Breslin**
6 **THE CANNY MAN (IRE),** 5, b g Indian River (FR)—Wimbledonian **Patrick Harney & Liam Breslin**
7 **THE CONKER CLUB (IRE),** 10, ch m Beneficial—Puff of Magic (IRE) **The Old Port Syndicate**

Assistant Trainer: Rachel Harney

Jockey (NH): R. C. Colgan. **Amateur:** Mr D. Crean.

LATE ENTRIES

MR GUILLAUME MACAIRE, Les Mathes
Postal: **Hippodrome de la Palmyre, Allee du Carre d'As, 17570 Les Mathes, France**
Contacts: **PHONE** (0033) 5462 36254 **FAX** (0033) 5462 25438 **MOBILE** (0033) 6076 54992
E-MAIL entrainement-g.macaire@wanadoo.fr

1 AIMAISSA (FR), 4, gr f Enrique—Chin'ba (FR) **Haras du Hoguenet**
2 AINSIQUE DE L'ISLE (FR), 6, b g Lavirco (GER)—Naiade de l'isle (FR) **Mr Terry Amos**
3 ALMA MIX, 4, br f Al Namix (FR)—Fortana (FR) **Mr Patrick Atkinson**
4 ARZEMBOUY PREMIER (FR), 6, b g Lavirco (GER)—Laurence (FR) **Mr Simon Munir**
5 AS D'ESTRUVAL (FR), 6, b g Nickname (FR)—Ombre d'estruval (FR) **Mme Bernard Le Gentil**
6 ATHENNY (GER), 4, b f Nicaron (GER)—Aughamore Beauty (IRE) **Mr Jean-Claude Zentz**
7 BALLOTIN (FR), 5, b g Enrique—Orphee de Vonnas (FR) **Mme Patrick Papot**
8 BEGUIN D'ESTRUVAL (FR), 5, ch g Martaline—Rose d'estruval (FR) **Mme Bernard Le Gentil**
9 BENEVOLAT (FR), 5, gr g Dom Alco (FR)—Platine (FR) **Mme Patrick Papot**
10 BLEU AZUR (FR), 4, b g Soldier of Fortune (IRE)—Black Dalhia (FR) **Mr Eckhard Sauren**
11 BRIO DES VILLERETS (FR), 5, b g Malinas (GER)—Qui L'eut Cru (FR) **Mr Patrick Joubert**
12 BUDDY BANKS (FR), 4, b g Saint des Saints (FR)—Madison Road (IRE) **Mr Jacques Detre**
13 CALL OF OUTY KLASS (FR), 4, ch g Network (GER)—Leathou (FR) **Mr Patrick Joubert**
14 CALLIA D'OUDAIRIES (FR), 4, b f Saint des Saints (FR)—Quecy de Chadzeau (FR) **Mr Michel de Gigou**
15 CARMEN DEJY (FR), 4, b f Martaline—Merci Jandrer (FR) **Mr Terry Amos**
16 CASTELAINYA (FR), 4, b g Network (GER)—Parpaillya (FR) **Mr Patrick Joubert**
17 CASTLETOWN (FR), 4, gr g Poliglote—Message Personnel (FR) **Mr RA Green**
18 CAVALLO (FR), 4, b g Network (GER)—Kadalia (FR) **Mr Patrick Joubert**
19 CHAHUTEUR (FR), 4, b g Saint des Saints (FR)—Redowa (FR) **Mme Magalen Bryant**
20 CHEF ETOILE (FR), 4, b g Coastal Path—Quephaeton (FR) **Mr Patrick Joubert**
21 COELHO (FR), 8, ch g Kapgarde (FR)—Exela (FR) **Melle Patricia Le Tellier**
22 CONTRE TOUS (FR), 4, b g Forestier (FR)—Orphee de Vonnas (FR) **Haras du Hoguenet**
23 CORSCIA (FR), 5, b m Nickname (FR)—Cardamine (FR) **Mr Michel Tessier**
24 CURIEUX (FR), 4, b g Nickname (FR)—Rouge Folie (FR) **Mr Stephane Szwarc**
25 DAMASAKO (FR), 4, gr g Turgeon (USA)—Formigny (FR) **Mr Gerard Brault**
26 DESCARTES (GER), 7, ch g Sholokhov (IRE)—Dynamica (GER) **Mr Gerald Laroche**
27 DEVICE (FR), 4, b g Poliglote—Westonne (FR) **Mme Magalen Bryant**
28 DOUAR DE KERBARH (FR), 4, b g Turgeon (USA)—Nik Bey (FR) **Mr Gilles Baratoux**
29 FUNKO DU PECOS (FR), 5, ch g Network (GER)—Falladore (FR) **Mr Patrick Joubert**
30 GRANDOUET (FR), 9, b br g Al Namix (FR)—Virginia River (FR) **Mr Simon Munir**
31 LADY POLIGLOTE (FR), 5, b m Poliglote—Madison Road (IRE) **Mr Donald Galt**
32 LAST PARCELLE (FR), 4, b f Poliglote—Parcelle Coloree (FR) **Mr John Cotton**
33 LE COSTAUD (FR), 5, ch g Forestier (FR)—Loya Lescribaa (FR) **Mr Terry Amos**
34 LOUEGARDE (FR), 4, b f Kapgarde (FR)—Loucessita (FR) **Mr Damien Coveliers**
35 MISS BALKANIA (FR), 4, b f Balko (FR)—Miss de Boulem (FR) **Mr Rene Tabart**
36 NOCES DE DIAMANT (FR), 4, b f Saint des Saints (FR)—Noces d'or A Estivaux (FR)
                                                                    Mr Charles de Chaisemartin
37 NOVALIS (GER), 4, b g Soldier Hollow—Naomia (GER) **Mr Eckhard Sauren**
38 OFF BY HEART (FR), 9, b g Kapgarde (FR)—Fassonwest (FR) **Mme Magalen Bryant**
39 OLE COMPANERO (GER), 10, b g Sholokhov (IRE)—Orsina (IRE) **Mme Patrick Papot**
40 ONSAIJAMAIS (FR), 5, b g Kap Rock (FR)—Romantique Cotte (FR) **Mr Terry Amos**
41 PASS KAT (FR), 4, b g Coastal Path—Spirit Katoune (FR) **Ecurie Couderc**
42 PERSEPOLIA (FR), 5, b m Poliglote—Darae (FR) **Mr Francis Picoulet**
43 POLITIKAR (FR), 4, b g Poliglote—Kitara (GER) **Mme Patrick Papot**
44 PROVOKATOR (FR), 4, ch g Trempolino (USA)—Pepples Beach (GER) **Mme Marie-Claude Tyssandier**
45 QUICK DAVIER (FR), 4, b g Early March—Double Melody (FR) **Mr Olivier Perroton**
46 RALIANKA (FR), 4, b f Martaline—Ravna (FR) **Mr Jacky Robin**
47 SAINT GOUSTAN BLUE (FR), 4, b g Blue Bresil (FR)—Les Saintes Glaces (FR) **Mr Simon Munir**
48 SANG DASHER (GER), 4, b g Dashing Blade—Sang Sun (GER) **Mr Bernd Glutsch**
49 SANPACO (FR), 4, b g Saint des Saints (FR)—Aimela (FR) **Mme Francis Montauban**
50 SINGAPUR (POL), 5, b g Belenus (GER)—Soneria (POL) **Mr Pierre Goral**
51 SO FRENCH (FR), 5, b g Poliglote—Westonne (FR) **Mme Magalen Bryant**
52 STORM OF SAINTLY (FR), 7, b g Saint des Saints (FR)—The Storm (FR) **Mr Jeannot Andt**

MR GUILLAUME MACAIRE—continued

53 **STYLINE (FR)**, 4, b f Martaline—Cayras Style (FR) **Mme Murielle Legriffon**
54 **SYSTEMIQUE (FR)**, 6, b g Saint des Saints (FR)—Gavotte de Brejoux (FR) **Mr Jacques Detre**
55 **TERRIFIC (FR)**, 5, b m Protektor (GER)—Fassination (FR) **Mme Magalen Bryant**
56 **UMBERTO (GER)**, 4, b c Lawman (FR)—Uryale (FR) **Famille Rothschild**
57 **VIZIR D'ESTRUVAL (FR)**, 7, b g Cachet Noir (USA)—Heure d'estruval (FR) **Mme Bernard Le Gentil**
58 **VOEUX D'ESTRUVAL (FR)**, 7, b g Daliapour (IRE)—Perle d'estruval (FR) **Mr Simon Munir**
59 **WALK SIBO (FR)**, 8, b g Balko (FR)—Walk Sibir (FR) **Mr Daniel Bonnaudet**

THREE-YEAR-OLDS

60 **AIE AIE AIE (FR)**, b f Saint des Saints (FR)—Arolla (FR) **Mme Benoit Gourdon**
61 **AMAULINO (FR)**, b g Saint des Saints (FR)—Sea Well (FR) **Mr Jacques Detre**
62 **ANNAMIX (FR)**, gr g Martaline—Tashtiyana (IRE) **Mme Dubuc-Grassa**
63 **BALLINE DE TEILLEE (FR)**, ch f Ballingarry (IRE)—Princesse d'orton (FR) **Mr Aurelien Kahn**
64 **BARKO (FR)**, ch g Balko (FR)—Katria (GER) **Mr Jacky Robin**
65 **BURN OUT (FR)**, b g Saddler Maker (IRE)—Queenhood (FR) **Mr David Lumet**
66 **BURROWS SAINT (FR)**, bc Saint des Saints (FR)—La Bombonera (FR) **Mme Dubuc-Grassa**
67 **CHITTA (FR)**, b f Saint des Saints (FR)—Dalkaresca (FR) **Mme Benoit Gourdon**
68 **DAME D'ESTRUVAL (FR)**, ch f Cachet Noir (USA)—Avoine de Beaufai (FR) **Mme Bernard Le Gentil**
69 **DEFIT D'ESTRUVAL (FR)**, b g Balko (FR)—Udine d'estruval (FR) **Mme Bernard Le Gentil**
70 **DIAMONT DROP (FR)**, b g Diamond Green (FR)—Tourmaline (FR) **Mr Andre Duboe**
71 **DICKENEK (FR)**, b g Dick Turpin (IRE)—Baladewa (GER) **Mr Patrick Papot**
72 **DINAMIQUE (FR)**, b f Balko (FR)—Medine (FR) **Mme Francis Montauban**
73 **DIONYSOS DE MEL (FR)**, b g Balko (FR)—Olympe Malta (FR) **Mr JN Touzaint**
74 **DIVINE (FR)**, b f Vision d'etat (FR)—Mayence (FR) **Mme Francis Montauban**
75 **DOLOS (FR)**, b g Kapgarde (FR)—Redowa (FR) **Mr Pierre de Maleissye**
76 **DOUMA DESBOIS (FR)**, gr f Smadoun (FR)—Strip Tease (FR) **Mr R. A. Green**
77 **DROP D'ESTRUVAL (FR)**, b g Balko (FR)—Tonelle d'estruval (FR) **Mme Bernard Le Gentil**
78 **DROWING (FR)**, b f Blue Bresil (FR)—Kandora (FR) **Mr Daniel Allard**
79 **DURKASH (FR)**, b g Blue Bresil (FR)—Meralda (FR) **Mr Francis Picoulet**
80 **EDWARD D'ARGENT (FR)**, gr g Martaline—Roquine (FR) **Mr Stephane Ruel**
81 **EFFIKAS (FR)**, b f Sholokhov (IRE)—Negresse de Cuta (FR) **Mr Jacques Bisson**
82 **EJO PRITCHARD (POL)**, b f Belenus (GER)—Enchanted Ocean (USA) **Mr J. C. Zentz**
83 **ELNATH (FR)**, b f Silver Frost (IRE)—Eva Kant **Mme Dubuc-Grassa**
84 **FAIRY TALE (FR)**, b f Spanish Moon (USA)—Haute Tension (FR) **Mme Patrick Papot**
85 **FULL GLASS (FR)**, b g Diamond Green (FR)—Full Tune (FR) **Mr Andre Duboe**
86 **GORVINO (FR)**, b g Lucarno (USA)—Rolandale (FR) **Mme Patrick Papot**
87 **INDIGA (FR)**, b f Sholokhov (IRE)—Shadline (FR) **Mr Pierre Goral**
88 **INVICTER (FR)**, b g Sholokhov (IRE)—Presidence (FR) **Mr Pierre Goral**
89 **JEDNO (FR)**, gr g Balko (FR)—Ascella (FR) **Mr Gildas Blain**
90 **KAP ET PAS CAP (FR)**, b g Kapgarde (FR)—Kitara (GER) **Mme Patrick Papot**
91 **LA PACOTILLE (FR)**, b f Al Namix (FR)—La Trattoria (FR) **Mr Denys Audouard**
92 **LADY OF GOLD (FR)**, b f Full of Gold (FR)—Ladykish (FR) **Mme Francis Montauban**
93 **LAPLOU (FR)**, b f Plouescop (FR)—Pic Saint Loup (FR) **Mme ML Oget**
94 **LAUYANN DE BODEAN (FR)**, b g Cadoubel (FR)—Cateleya (FR) **Mme Marie-Laurence Oget**
95 **LUDO SOL (FR)**, b f Enrique—First Wonder (FR) **Allard (S)**
96 **MA TORPILLE (FR)**, ch f Turgeon (USA)—Manmary (FR) **Mr Jeannot Andt**
97 **MICK TAROS (FR)**, gr g Blue Bresil (FR)—Mick Madona (FR) **Mr Daniel Robin**
98 **MISS SENAM (FR)**, b f Saint des Saints (FR)—Madison Road (IRE) **Mr Jacques Detre**
99 **MOI PRESIDENT (FR)**, b g Irish Wells (FR)—Savita (FR) **Mme Patrick Papot**
100 **MONSIEUR CO (FR)**, b g Turgeon (USA)—Cayras Style (FR) **Mme Murielle Legriffon**
101 **MOUNT KAILAS (FR)**, b g Kapgarde (FR)—Villa Joyeuse (FR) **Ecurie RIB**
102 **NEXT TO ME (FR)**, b g Early March—Surning Love (FR) **Mr Ry Simon**
103 **NURMI (GER)**, br g Samum (GER)—Nadin (GER) **D Allard (S)**
104 **OBELAMI (FR)**, b g Laverock (IRE)—Osterliz (FR) **Mr David Powell**
105 **OKAY SENAM (FR)**, b g Saint des Saints (FR)—Salvatrixe (FR) **Mr Jacques Detre**
106 **OLE CABALLERO (GER)**, b g Sholokhov (IRE)—Orsina (IRE) **Mme Patrick Papot**
107 **ON THE GO (FR)**, b g Kamsin (GER)—Sacral Nirvana (FR) **Mme Patrick Papot**

MR GUILLAUME MACAIRE—continued

108 **PARIS COLLECTION (FR)**, b f Saint des Saints (FR)—Line Ireland (FR) **Mme Bernard Le Gentil**
109 **ROOTSTER (FR)**, b g Saddler Maker (IRE)—Quadina (FR) **Mr David Lumet**
110 **ROYALE IPANEMA (FR)**, gr f Ballingarry (IRE)—Royale Punta Cana (FR) **Mr Terry Amos**
111 **SAINE ET SPEED (FR)**, b f Saint des Saints (FR)—Speed des Monceaux (FR) **Mme Benoit Gourdon**
112 **SAINT RAJH (FR)**, b g Saint des Saints (FR)—Jahra (FR) **Mr Jacques Detre**
113 **SAN PEDRO DE SENAM (FR)**, b g Saint Des Saints (FR)—Tetiaroa (FR) **Mr Jacques Detre**
114 **SENTENTZA**, b g Manduro (GER)—Forago (USA) **Mme Francis Montauban**
115 **SING TO THE MOON (FR)**, ch g Spanish Moon (USA)—Double Melody (FR) **Palmyr Racing**
116 **SOUFFLENHEIM (FR)**, b g Martaline—La Saone (FR) **Mr Jeannot Andt**
117 **SOUL EMOTION (FR)**, b g Martaline—Second Emotion (FR) **Mr Terry Amos**
118 **STARKHOV (FR)**, b g Sholokhov (IRE)—Free Sky (FR) **Mr Jacques Bisson**
119 **SUN FIZZ (FR)**, b g Blue Bresil (FR)—Sophie's Sun (FR) **Palmyr Racing**
120 **SUPER ROCK (FR)**, b g Laverock (IRE)—Super Vision (FR) **Mr Daniel Bonnaudet**
121 **TERREFORT (FR)**, gr g Martaline—Vie de Reine (FR) **Mme Francis Montauban**
122 **TOP AND GO (FR)**, b f Smadoun (FR)—Topira (FR) **Mme Marie Tyssandier**
123 **TOPISSIME (FR)**, b g Khalkevi (IRE)—Lhotse (FR) **D Allard (S)**
124 **WEST KAP (FR)**, b g Kapgarde (FR)—Westonne (FR) **Mme Magalen Bryant**

Jockey (NH): Lewis Conan, Herve Jumelle, Bertrand Lestrade, Kevin Nabet, James Reveley. **Conditional:** Kilian Dubourg.

MR W. M. ROPER, Curragh

Postal: **French Furze, Maddenstown, The Curragh, Co. Kildare, Ireland**
Contacts: **PHONE** (00353) 45 44182   **MOBILE** (00353) 86 823 4279
E-MAIL markroper1@eircom.net

1 **CLARIOR EX OBSCURO (IRE)**, 10, br g Morozov (USA)—Achates (IRE) **Mr W. M. Roper**
2 **LIGHT IN THE EYE (IRE)**, 5, b m Echo of Light—Woodland Dancer (IRE) **M. H. Keogh**
3 **PLAY THE PART (IRE)**, 5, b g Kutub (IRE)—Pretty Contender (IRE) **P. E. I. Newell**
4 **THE MAGPIE MAN (IRE)**, 5, b g Echo of Light—Inspectors Choice (IRE) **Piers Dennis**
5 **TOMMY WELSH (IRE)**, 4, b c Dylan Thomas (IRE)—Roshanak (IRE) **M. H. Keogh**
6 **VAALWATER (IRE)**, 11, b g Danehill Dancer (IRE)—Amaranthus (USA) **Mr W. M. Roper**

TWO-YEAR-OLDS

7 Ch g 1/5 Medicean—Moonlight Mystery (Pivotal) (8859) **Mr W. M. Roper**
8 **ROONEY MARA**, ch f 25/2 Dragon Pulse (IRE)—Date Mate (USA) (Thorn Dance (USA)) (18456) **M. H. Keogh**

LATE ENTRIES

MR TREVOR WALL, Craven Arms
Postal: **Hope Farm Stables, Twitchen, Clunbury, Craven Arms, Shropshire, SY7 0HN**
Contacts: **PHONE (01588) 660219   MOBILE (07972) 732080**

1 **BLURRED LINES (IRE)**, 7, ch m Shantou (USA)—Balda Girl (IRE)
2 **FAIRY ALISHA**, 8, ch m Doyen (IRE)—Regal Fairy (IRE) **D. Pugh**
3 **GRISEDENUIT (FR)**, 4, b br f Gris de Gris (IRE)—Ambacity (FR) **Michael & Lesley Wilkes**
4 **HELMSLEY FLYER (IRE)**, 6, b g Baltic King—Dorn Hill **The Wenlock Edge Optimists**
5 **HOT MADRAS (IRE)**, 8, b m Milan—Hot Fudge (IRE)
6 **INVINCIBLE WISH (IRE)**, 4, b g Vale of York (IRE)—Moonlight Wish (IRE) **Michael & Lesley Wilkes**
7 **MAXI MAC (IRE)**, 6, ch g Thousand Words—Crimada (IRE) **D. Pugh**
8 **MAY MIST**, 4, b f Nayef (USA)—Midnight Mist (IRE) **A. H. Bennett**

Other Owners: Mr P. Cowell, J. D. Evans, Mrs L. Wilkes, Mr M. H. A. Wilkes.

Assistant Trainer: Mrs J. A. Wall

Conditional: Josh Wall.

KEY TO RACECOURSES
○ NATIONAL HUNT
★ FLAT
● NATIONAL HUNT AND FLAT

PERTH ○
MUSSELBURGH ●
HAMILTON PARK ★
AYR ●
KELSO ○
NEWCASTLE ●
HEXHAM ○
CARLISLE ●
SEDGEFIELD ○
CARTMEL ○
REDCAR ★
CATTERICK ●
THIRSK ●
RIPON ★
YORK ★
WETHERBY ●
BEVERLEY ★
PONTEFRACT ★
DONCASTER ●
MARKET RASEN ○
AINTREE ○
HAYDOCK ●

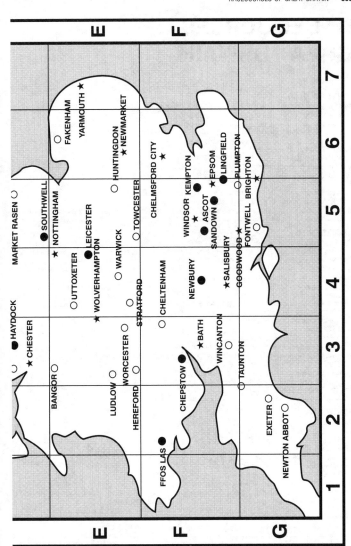

RACECOURSES OF GREAT BRITAIN

AINTREE (L.H)
Grand National Course: Triangular, 2m 2f (16) 494y run-in with elbow. Perfectly flat. A severe test for both horse and rider, putting a premium on jumping ability, fitness and courage.
Mildmay Course: Rectangular, 1m 4f (8) 260y run-in. A very fast, flat course with sharp bends.
Address: Aintree Racecourse, Ormskirk Road, Aintree, Liverpool, L9 5AS Tel: 0151 523 2600
Fax: 01515 222920 Website: www.aintree.co.uk
Regional Director: John Baker
Clerk of the Course: Andrew Tulloch 07831 315104
Going Reports: 01515 232600.
Stabling: Boxes allocated in strict rotation. Facilities are available on the course for up to 100 stable staff.
01515 222937.
By Road: North of the City, near the junction of the M57 and M58 with the A59 (Preston).
By Rail: Aintree Station is adjacent to the Stands, from Liverpool Central.
By Air: Liverpool (John Lennon) Airport is 10 miles. Helicopter landing facility by prior arrangement.

ASCOT (R.H)
Flat: Right-handed triangular track just under 1m 6f in length. The Round course descends from the 1m 4f start into Swinley Bottom, the lowest part of the track. It then turns right-handed and joins the Old Mile Course, which starts on a separate chute. The course then rises to the right-handed home turn over an underpass to join the straight mile course. The run-in is about 3f, rising slightly to the winning post. The whole course is of a galloping nature with easy turns.
N.H. Triangular, 1m 6f (10) 240y run-in mostly uphill. A galloping course with an uphill finish, Ascot provides a real test of stamina. The fences are stiff and sound jumping is essential, especially for novices.
Address: Ascot Racecourse, Ascot, Berkshire SL5 7JX Tel: 08707 271234 Fax: 08704 601250
Website: www.ascot.co.uk
Clerk of the Course: Chris Stickels 01344 878502 / 07970 621440
Chief Executive: Guy Henderson
Going Reports: Day: 01344 878502
Stabling: 175 boxes. Free, with shavings, straw or paper provided. Tel: 01344 878454 Fax: 08704 214755
By Road: West of the town on the A329. Easy access from the M3 (Junction 3) and the M4 (Junction 6).
Car parking adjoining the course and Ascot Heath.
By Rail: Regular service from Waterloo to Ascot (500y from the racecourse).
By Air: Helicopter landing facility at the course. London (Heathrow) Airport 15 miles, White Waltham Airfield 12 miles (01427) 718800.

AYR (L.H)
Flat: A left-handed, galloping, flat oval track of 1m 4f with a 4f run-in. The straight 6f is essentially flat.
N.H. Oval, 1m 4f (9) 210y run-in. Relatively flat and one of the fastest tracks in Great Britain. It is a well-drained course and the ground rarely becomes testing. The track suits the long-striding galloper.
Address: Ayr Racecourse, Whitletts Road, Ayr KA8 0JE Tel: 01292 264179 Fax: 01292 610140
Website: www.ayr-racecourse.co.uk
Clerk of the Course: Emma Marley 07881 908702
Managing Director: David Brown
Going Reports: Contact Clerk of the Course as above.
Stabling: 175 boxes. Free stabling and accommodation for lads and lasses. Tel: 01292 264179 ext 141.
By Road: East of the town on the A758. Free parking for buses and cars.
By Rail: Ayr Station (trains on the half hour from Glasgow Central). Journey time 55 minutes. Buses and taxis also to the course.
By Air: Prestwick International Airport (10 minutes), Glasgow Airport (1 hour).

BANGOR-ON-DEE (L.H)

N.H. Circular, 1m 4f (9) 325y run-in. Apart from some 'ridge and furrow', this is a flat course notable for three sharp bends, especially the paddock turn. Suits handy, speedy sorts.
Address: Bangor-On-Dee Racecourse, Overton Road, Bangor-On-Dee, Wrexham. LL13 0DA
Tel: 01978 782081, Fax: 01978 780985 Website: www.bangorondeeraces.co.uk
Racecourse Manager and Clerk of the Course: Andrew Morris
Chief Executive: Richard Thomas
General Manager: Jeannie Chantler
Going Reports: Contact Clerk of the Course as above.
Stabling: 85 stables, allotted on arrival. Shavings (straw on request). Applications to the Manager.
Tel: 01978 782081.
By Road: 5 miles southeast of Wrexham, off the B5069.
By Rail: Wrexham Station (bus or taxi to the course).
By Air: Helicopters may land by prior arrangement with Clerk of the Course at entirely their own risk.

BATH (L.H)

Flat: Galloping, left-handed, level oval of 1m 4f 25y, with long, stiff run-in of about 4f which bends to the left. An extended chute provides for sprint races.
Address: The Racecourse, Lansdown, Bath BA1 9BU. Tel: 01225 424609 Fax: 01225 444415.
Website: www.bath-racecourse.co.uk
Clerk of the Course: Jo Hall
Clerk of the Course: Katie Stephens
Going Reports: Contact Clerk of the Course as above.
Stabling: 120 boxes. Free stabling and accommodation for lads and lasses. Tel: 01225 424609
By Road: 2 miles northwest of the City (M4 Junction 18) at Lansdown. Unlimited free car and coach parking space immediately behind the stands. Special bus services operate from Bath to the racecourse.
By Rail: Bath Station (from Paddington).
By Air: Bristol or Colerne Airports. Helicopter landing facilities available by prior arrangement.

BEVERLEY (R.H)

Flat: A right-handed oval of 1m 3f, generally galloping, with an uphill run-in of two and a half furlongs. The 5f course is very stiff.
Address: Beverley Race Co. Ltd., York Road, Beverley, Yorkshire HU17 9QZ
Tel: 01482 867488 / 882645.Website: www.beverley-racecourse.co.uk
General Manager and Clerk of the Course: Sally Iggulden 07850 458605
Going Reports: Tel: 01482 867488 / 882645
Stabling: 111 boxes. Free stabling. Accommodation available for lads and lasses
Tel: 01482 867488 / 882645.
By Road: 7 miles from the M62 (Junction 38) off the A1035. Free car parking opposite the course. Owners and trainers use a separate enclosure.
By Rail: Beverley Station (Hull-Scarborough line). Occasional bus service to the course (1 mile).

BRIGHTON (L.H)

Flat: Left-handed, 1m 4f horseshoe with easy turns and a run-in of three and a half furlongs. Undulating and sharp, the track suits handy types.
Address: Brighton Racecourse, Brighton, East Sussex BN2 2XZ Tel: 01273 603580 Fax: 01273 673267
Website: www.brighton-racecourse.co.uk
Clerk of the Course: Ed Arkell 07977 587713
General Manager: Shaun Steel
Going Reports: Available on www.brighton-racecourse.co.uk or contact main office/Clerk of the Course as above
Stabling: 102 boxes. Stabling and accommodation: Tel: 01273 603580, available on request.
By Road: East of the city on the A27 (Lewes Road). Car park adjoins the course.
By Rail: Brighton Station (from Victoria on the hour, London Bridge or Portsmouth). Special bus service to the course from the station (approx 2 miles).
By Air: Helicopters may land by prior arrangement.

CARLISLE (R.H)

Flat: Right-handed, 1m 4f pear-shaped track. Galloping and undulating with easy turns and a stiff uphill run-in of three and a half furlongs. The 6f course begins on an extended chute.

N.H. Pear-shaped, 1m 5f (9) 300y run-in uphill. Undulating and a stiff test of stamina, ideally suited to the long-striding thorough stayer. Three-mile chases start on a chute, and the first fence is only jumped once.

Address: Carlisle Racecourse, Durdar Road, Carlisle CA2 4TS Tel: 01228 554700 Fax: 01228 554747
Website: www.carlisle-races.co.uk

Regional Director: John Baker

Clerk of the Course: Kirkland Tellwright

General Manager: Geraldine McKay

Going Reports: 01228 554700 recorded or contact Clerk of the Course above

Stabling: 98 boxes. Stabling and accommodation available on request. Please phone Head Groundsman on 07889 987542, or Fax Stable Office on 01228 554747 by 1pm day before racing.

By Road: 2 miles south of the city (Durdar Road). Easy access from the M6 (Junction 42). The car park is free (adjacent to the course).

By Rail: Carlisle Station (2 miles from the course).

By Air: Helicopter landing facility by prior arrangement.

CARTMEL (L.H)

N.H. Oval, 1m 1f (6) 800y run-in. Almost perfectly flat but very sharp, with the longest run-in in the country, approximately half a mile. The fences are stiff but fair.

Address: Cartmel Racecourse, Cartmel, nr Grange-Over-Sands, Cumbria LA11 6QF Tel: 01539 536340.
Out of season: 01539 533335 Fax: 01539 536004 Website: www.cartmel-racecourse.co.uk

Managing Director: Jonathan Garratt

Clerk of the Course: Anthea Morshead 07837 559861

Going Reports: 01539 536340 or contact Clerk of the Course as above.

Stabling: 75 boxes. Boxes and accommodation for lads and lasses is limited. Prior booking is required by 12 noon the day before racing 01539 534609.

By Road: 1 mile west of the town, 2 miles off the B5277 (Grange-Haverthwaite road). M6 (Junction 36).

By Rail: Cark-in-Cartmel Station (2 miles) (Carnforth-Barrow line). Raceday bus service.

By Air: Light aircraft facilities available at Cark Airport (4 miles from the course). Helicopter landing facility at the course, by prior arrangement only.

CATTERICK (L.H)

Flat: A sharp, left-handed, undulating oval of 1m 180y with a downhill run-in of 3f.

N.H. Oval, 1m 1f (9) 240y run-in. Undulating, sharp track that favours the handy, front-running sort, rather than the long-striding galloper.

Address: The Racecourse, Catterick Bridge, Richmond, North Yorkshire DL10 7PE Tel: 01748 811478
Fax: 01748 811082 Website: www.catterickbridge.co.uk

General Manager and Clerk of the Course: Fiona Needham 07831 688625

Going Reports: Contact Clerk of the Course as above

Stabling: 116 Boxes. Allotted on arrival.

By Road: The course is adjacent to the A1, 1 mile northwest of the town on the A6136. There is a free car park.

By Rail: Darlington Station (special buses to course - 14 mile journey).

By Air: Helicopters can land by prior arrangement. Fixed wing planes contact RAF Leeming Tel: 01677 423041

CHELMSFORD CITY (L.H)

Flat: A left-handed, Polytrack oval of 1m with sweeping bends and a 2f home straight. Races over 7f and 1m start from separate chutes.

Address: Chelmsford City Racecourse, Great Leighs, Essex, CM3 1QP Tel: 01245 362412
Fax: 01245 361850

Website: www.chelmsfordcityracecourse.com

Manager: Fraser Garritty

Clerk of the Course: Andy Waitt

By Road: At Great Leighs, five miles north of Chelmsford on the A31

By Rail: Chelmsford station (from Liverpool Street)

By Air: Stansted Airport (17 miles)

CHELTENHAM (L.H)

Old Course: Oval, 1m 4f (9) 350y run-in. A testing, undulating track with stiff fences. The ability to stay is essential.

New Course: Oval, 1m 5f (10) 220y run-in. Undulating, stiff fences, testing course, uphill for the final half-mile.

Address: Cheltenham Racecourse, Prestbury Park, Cheltenham, Gloucestershire GL50 4SH

Tel: 01242 513014 Fax: 01242 224227

Website: www.cheltenham.co.uk

Regional Director: Ian Renton

Director of Racing and Clerk of the Course: Simon Claisse 07785 293966

Going Reports: Available from six days before racing 01242 513014 (option 2, then 6)

Stabling: 299 boxes. Ample stabling and accommodation for lads.

Apply to the Stable Manager 01242 537602 or 521950.

By Road: 1.5 miles north of the town on the A435. M5 (Junction 10 or 11).

By Rail: Cheltenham Spa Station. Buses and taxis to course.

By Air: Helicopter landing site to the northeast of the stands.

CHEPSTOW (L.H)

Flat: A left-handed, undulating oval of about 2m, with easy turns, and a straight run-in of 5f. There is a straight track of 1m 14y.

N.H. Oval, 2m (11) 240y run-in. Many changing gradients, five fences in the home straight. Favours the long-striding front-runner, but stamina is important.

Address: Chepstow Racecourse, Chepstow, Monmouthshire NP16 6BE Tel: 01291 622260

Fax: 01291 627061 Website: www.chepstow-racecourse.co.uk

Clerk of the Course: Keith Ottesen 07813 043453

Executive Director: Phil Bell

Going Reports: Contact Clerk of the Course as above.

Stabling: 106 boxes, allotted on arrival. Limited accommodation for lads and lasses. Apply: 01291 622260.

By Road: 1 mile North-West of the town on the A466. (1 mile from Junction 22 of the M4 (Severn Bridge) or M48 Junction 2. There is a free public car park opposite the entrance.

By Rail: Chepstow Station (from Paddington, change at Gloucester or Newport). The course is a mile from the station.

By Air: Helicopter landing facility in the centre of the course.

CHESTER (L.H)

Flat: A level, sharp, left-handed, circular course of 1m 73y, with a short run-in of 230y.

Chester is a specialists' track which generally suits the sharp-actioned horse.

Address: The Racecourse, Chester CH1 2LY Tel: 01244 304600 Fax: 01244 304648

Website: www.chester-races.co.uk

Racecourse Manager and Clerk of the Course: Andrew Morris

Chief Executive: Richard Thomas

Going Reports: Contact Main Office 01244 304600

Stabling: 138 boxes and accommodation. Tel: 01244 324880 or 01244 304610

By Road: The course is near the centre of the city on the A548 (Queensferry Road). The Owners' and Trainers' car park is adjacent to the Leverhulme Stand. There is a public car park in the centre of the course.

By Rail: Chester Station (¾ mile from the course). Services from Euston, Paddington and Northgate.

By Air: Hawarden Airport (2 miles). Helicopters are allowed to land on the racecourse by prior arrangement only.

DONCASTER (L.H)

Flat: A left-handed, flat, galloping course of 1m 7f 110y, with a long run-in which extends to a straight mile.

N.H. Conical, 2m (11) 247y run-in. A very fair, flat track ideally suited to the long-striding galloper.

Address: Doncaster Racecourse, Leger Way, Doncaster DN2 6BB Tel: 01302 304200, Fax: 01302 323271

Email: info@doncaster-racecourse.co.uk Website: www.doncaster-racecourse.co.uk

Clerk of the Course: Roderick Duncan 07772 958685

Managing Director: Kieran Gallagher

Going Reports: Contact Clerk of the Course as above or Estate Manager 07831 260373.

Stabling: 147 boxes. Free stabling and accommodation. Tel: 01302 304200

By Road: East of the town, off the A638 (M18 Junctions 3 and 4). Club members' car park reserved. Large public car park free and adjacent to the course.

By Rail: Doncaster Central Station (from King's Cross). Special bus service from the station (1 mile).
By Air: Helicopter landing facility by prior arrangement only. Doncaster Robin Hood Airport is 15 minutes from the racecourse.

EPSOM (L.H)

Flat: Left-handed and undulating with easy turns, and a run-in of just under 4f. The straight 5f course is also undulating and downhill all the way, making it the fastest 5f in the world.
Address: The Racecourse, Epsom Downs, Surrey, KT18 5LQ. Tel: 01372 726311, Fax: 01372 748253
Website: www.epsomderby.co.uk
Regional Director: Rupert Trevelyan
Clerk of the Course: Andrew Cooper. Tel: 01372 726311, Mobile: 07774 230850
General Manager: Simon Durrant
Going Reports: Contact Clerk of the Course as above.
Stabling: 108 boxes. Free stabling and accommodation. Tel: 01372 460454
By Road: Two miles south of the town on the B290 (M25 Junctions 8 and 9). For full car park particulars apply to: The Club Secretary, Epsom Grandstand, Epsom Downs, Surrey KT18 5LQ. Tel: 01372 726311.
By Rail: Epsom, Epsom Downs or Tattenham Corner Stations (trains from London Bridge, Waterloo, Victoria). Regular bus services run to the course from Epsom and Morden Underground Station.
By Air: London (Heathrow) and London (Gatwick) are both within 30 miles of the course.
Heliport (Derby Meeting only) apply to Hascombe Aviation. Tel: 01279 680291.

EXETER (R.H)

N.H. Oval, 2m (11) 300y run-in uphill. Undulating with a home straight of half a mile. A good test of stamina, suiting the handy, well-balanced sort.
Address: Exeter Racecourse, Kennford, Exeter, Devon EX6 7XS Tel: 01392 832599 Fax: 01392 833454
Email: Exeter@thejockeyclub.co.uk Website: www.exeter-racecourse.co.uk
Regional Director: Ian Renton
Clerk of the Course: Barry Johnson 07976 791578
General Manager: Daniel Thompson
Going Reports: Contact Clerk of the Course as above.
Stabling: 90 loose boxes at the course. Sleeping accommodation and canteen for both lads and lasses by prior arrangement. Apply to Racecourse Office. Tel: 01392 832599 by 12 noon on day before racing.
By Road: The course is at Haldon, 5 miles southwest of Exeter on the A38 (Plymouth) road, 2 miles east of Chudleigh.
By Rail: Exeter (St Davids) Station. Free bus service to course.
By Air: Helicopters can land by prior arrangement.

FAKENHAM (L.H.)

N.H. Square, 1m (6) 200y run-in. On the turn almost throughout and undulating, suiting the handy front-runner. The going rarely becomes heavy.
Address: The Racecourse, Fakenham, Norfolk NR21 7NY Tel: 01328 862388 Fax: 01328 855908
email: info@fakenhamracecourse.co.uk Website: www.fakenhamracecourse.co.uk
Clerk of the Course and Chief Executive: David Hunter Tel: 01328 862388 Mobile: 07767 802206.
Going Reports: Contact Clerk of the Course as above.
Stabling: 70 boxes available. Tel: 01328 862388 Fax: 01328 855908.
By Road: A mile south of the town on the B1146 (East Dereham) road.
By Rail: Norwich Station (26 miles) (Liverpool Street line), King's Lynn (22 miles)
(Liverpool Street/Kings Cross).
By Air: Helicopter landing facility in the centre of the course by prior arrangement only.

FFOS LAS (L.H.)

Flat and N.H.: The track is a 60m wide, basically flat, 1m4f oval with sweeping bends. Races over 5f and 6f start on a chute.
Address: Ffos Las Racecourse, Trimsaran, Carmarthenshire, SA17 4DE Tel: 01554 811092
Fax: 01554 811037 Website: www.ffoslasracecourse.com
Commercial Director: Dave Clayton
Clerk of the Course: Keith Ottesen 07813 043453
Going Reports: Contact Clerk of the Course as above.
Stabling: 120 box stable yard.
By Road: From the east take J48 from the M4 and join the A4138 to Llanelli, then follow the brown tourist

signs to the racecourse. From the west take the A48 to Carmarthen then the A484 to Kidwelly before following the brown signs.

By Air: The course has the facilities to land helicopters on race days.

FOLKESTONE (R.H)
No 2016 fixtures scheduled by owners Arena Racing Company

FONTWELL PARK (Fig. 8)
N.H. 2m (7) 230y run-in with left-hand bend close home. The figure-of-eight chase course suits handy types and is something of a specialists' track. The left-handed hurdle course is oval, one mile round with nine hurdles per two and a quarter miles.

Address: Fontwell Park Racecourse, nr Arundel, West Sussex BN18 0SX Tel: 01243 543335
Fax: 01243 543904 Website: www.fontwellpark.co.uk
Clerk of the Course: Ed Arkell 07977 587713
General Manager: Simon Williams
Going Reports: 01243 543335 during office hours.
Stabling: 90 boxes. Limited accommodation. If arriving the day before the meeting, contact:
Tel: 01243 543335.
By Road: South of village at the junction of the A29 (Bognor) and A27 (Brighton-Chichester) roads.
By Rail: Barnham Station (2 miles). Brighton-Portsmouth line (access via London Victoria).
By Air: Helicopter landing facility by prior arrangement with the Clerk of the Course.

GOODWOOD (R.H)
Flat: A sharp, undulating, essentially right-handed track with a long run-in. There is also a straight 6f course.

Address: Goodwood Racecourse Ltd., Goodwood, Chichester, West Sussex PO18 0PX
Tel: 01243 755022, Fax: 01243 755025 Website: www.goodwood.co.uk
Managing Director: Adam Waterworth
Clerk of the Course: Seamus Buckley 07774 100223
Going Reports: 01243 755022 (recorded message) or Clerk of the Course.
Stabling: Free stabling and accommodation for runners (130 well equipped boxes at Goodwood House).
Please book in advance. Subsidised canteen and recreational facilities. Tel: 01243 755022 / 755036.
By Road: 6 miles north of Chichester between the A286 and A285. There is a car park adjacent to the course. Ample free car and coach parking.
By Rail: Chichester Station (from Victoria or London Bridge). Regular bus service to the course (6 miles).
By Air: Helicopter landing facility by prior arrangement 01243 755030. Goodwood Airport 2 miles (taxi to the course).

HAMILTON PARK (R.H)
Flat: Sharp, undulating, right-handed course of 1m 5f with a five and a half-furlong, uphill run-in. There is a straight track of 6f.

Address: Hamilton Park Racecourse, Bothwell Road, Hamilton, Lanarkshire ML3 0DW Tel: 01698 283806
Fax: 01698 286621 Website: www.hamilton-park.co.uk
Racing Manager and Clerk of the Course: Sulekha Varma
Chief Executive: Vivien Kyles 01698 283806
Going Reports: Track Manager: 07736 101130 or Clerk of the Course.
Stabling: Free stabling (102 boxes) and accommodation on request. Tel: 01698 284892 or Office.
By Road: Off the A72 on the B7071 (Hamilton-Bothwell road). (M74 Junction 5). Free parking for cars and buses.
By Rail: Hamilton West Station (1 mile).
By Air: Glasgow Airport (20 miles).

HAYDOCK PARK (L.H)
Flat: A galloping, almost flat, oval track, 1m 5f round, with a run-in of four and a half furlongs and a straight six-furlong course.
N.H. Oval, 1m 5f (10) 440y run-in. Flat, galloping chase course. The hurdle track, which is sharp, is inside the chase course and has some tight bends.

Address: Haydock Park Racecourse, Newton-le-Willows, Merseyside WA12 0HQ Tel: 01942 402609
Fax: 01942 270879 Website: www.haydock-park.co.uk

Regional Director: John Baker
General Manager: Jason Fildes
Clerk of the Course: Kirkland Tellwright 01942 725963 or 07748 181595
Going Reports: Contact Clerk of the Course as above or Head Groundsman 07831 849298
Stabling: 124 boxes. Applications to be made to the Racecourse for stabling and accommodation.
Tel: 01942 725963 or 01942 402615 (racedays).
By Road: The course is on the A49 near Junction 23 of the M6.
By Rail: Newton-le-Willows Station (Manchester-Liverpool line) is 2.5 miles from the course. Earlstown 3
miles from the course. Warrington Bank Quay and Wigan are on the London to Carlisle/Glasgow line.
By Air: Landing facilities in the centre of the course for helicopters and planes not exceeding 10,000lbs
laden weight. Apply to the Sales Office.

HEREFORD (R.H)

N.H. Square, 1m 4f (9) 300y run-in. The turns, apart from the final one that is on falling ground, are easily
negotiated, placing the emphasis on speed rather than stamina. A handy position round the home turn is
vital, as winners rarely come from behind. The hurdle track is on the outside of the chase course.
Address: Hereford Racecourse, Roman Road, Holmer, Hereford, HR4 9QU. Tel: (01432) 273560.
Fax: (01432) 352807 Website: www.hereford-racecourse.co.uk
General Manager: TBA
Clerk of the Course: Keith Ottesen
By Road: 1 mile North West of the City Centre off the A49 (Leominster) road.
By Rail: Hereford Station (1 mile from the course).

HEXHAM (L.H)

N.H. Oval, 1m 4f (10) 220y run-in. An undulating course that becomes very testing when the ground is soft,
it has easy fences and a stiff climb to the finishing straight, which is on a separate spur.
Address: Hexham Racecourse, The Riding, Hexham, Northumberland NE46 2JP Tel: 01434 606881
Fax: 01434 605814, Racedays: 01434 603738. Email: admin@hexham-racecourse.co.uk
Website: www.hexham-racecourse.co.uk
Chief Executive: Charles Enderby
Clerk of the Course: James Armstrong 01434 606881 or 07801 166820
Going Reports: Contact Clerk of the Course as above
Stabling: 93 Boxes allocated in rotation. Please book stabling and accommodation the day before by
Fax: 01434 605814.
By Road: 1.5 miles southwest of the town off the B6305.
By Rail: Hexham Station (Newcastle-Carlisle line). Free bus to the course.
By Air: Helicopter landing facility in centre of course (by special arrangement only).

HUNTINGDON (R.H)

N.H. Oval, 1m 4f (9) 200y run-in. Perfectly flat, galloping track with a tricky open ditch in front of the stands.
The two fences in the home straight can cause problems for novice chasers. Suits front runners.
Address: The Racecourse, Brampton, Huntingdon, Cambridgeshire PE28 4NL Tel: 01480 453373
Fax: 01480 455275 Website: www.huntingdon-racecourse.co.uk
Regional Director: Amy Starkey
Clerk of the Course: Jack Pryor
Managing Director: Sian Williams
Going Reports: Tel: 01480 453373 or 07990 774295
Stabling: 100 boxes available. Allotted on arrival. Telephone Racecourse Office.
By Road: The course is situated at Brampton, 2 miles west of Huntingdon on the A14. Easy access from
the A1 (½ mile from the course).
By Rail: Huntingdon Station. Buses and taxis to course.
By Air: Helicopter landing facility by prior arrangement.

KELSO (L.H)

N.H. Oval, 1m 3f (8), uphill run-in of just over a furlong. Rather undulating with two downhill fences opposite the stands, it suits the nippy, front-running sort, though the uphill finish helps the true stayer. The hurdle course is smaller and very sharp with a tight turn away from the stands.

Address: Kelso Racecourse, Kelso, Roxburghshire TD5 7SX Tel: 01668 280800

Website: www.kelso-races.co.uk

Clerk of the Course: Anthea Morshead

Managing Director: Richard Landale

Going Reports: Racecourse: 01573 224822 Groundsman Tel: 07774 172527

Stabling: 94 boxes allotted in rotation. Reservations for stabling and accommodation for lads and lasses at the racecourse, please phone Head Groundsman Tel: 01573 224767 or

Racecourse stables: 01573 224822 from 3pm the day before racing.

By Road: 1 mile north of the town, off the B6461.

By Rail: Berwick-upon-Tweed Station. 23-mile bus journey to Kelso.

By Air: Helicopters can land at course by arrangement, fixed wing aircraft Winfield, regular aircraft Edinburgh.

KEMPTON PARK (R.H)

Flat: A floodlit Polytrack circuit. A 1m 2f outer track accommodates races over 6f, 7f, 1m, 1m 3f, 1m 4f and 2m. The 1m inner track caters for races over 5f and 1m 2f.

N.H. Triangular, 1m 5f (10) 175y run-in. Practically flat; sharp course where the long run between the last obstacle on the far side and the first in the home straight switches the emphasis from jumping to speed. The hurdles track is on the outside of the chase track. The course crosses the Polytrack at two points on each circuit.

Address: Kempton Park Racecourse, Sunbury-on-Thames, Middlesex TW16 5AQ Tel: 01932 782292

Fax: 01932 782044 Raceday Fax: 01932 779525 Website: www.kempton.co.uk Email: kempton@rht.net

Regional Director: Rupert Trevelyan

Clerk of the Course and Director of Racing: Brian Clifford 07880 784484

General Manager: Steve Parlett

Going Reports: 01932 782292 if unavailable contact Clerk of the Course as above

Stabling: 117 boxes. Allocated on arrival. Prior booking required for overnight stay. Tel: 01932 782292

By Road: On the A308 near Junction 1 of the M3.

By Rail: Kempton Park Station (from Waterloo).

By Air: London (Heathrow) Airport 6 miles.

LEICESTER (R.H)

Flat: Stiff, galloping, right-handed oval of 1m 5f, with a 5f run-in. There is a straight course of seven furlongs.

N.H. Rectangular, 1m 6f (10) 250y run-in uphill. An undulating course with an elbow 150y from the finish, it can demand a high degree of stamina, as the going can become extremely testing and the last three furlongs are uphill.

Address: Leicester Racecourse, Oadby, Leicester LE2 4AL. Tel: 01162 716515 Fax: 01162 711746

Website: www.leicester-racecourse.co.uk

Clerk of the Course: Jimmy Stevenson 01162 712115 or 07774 497281

General Manager: Rob Bracken

Going Reports: Recorded message 01162 710875 or contact Clerk of the Course as above.

Stabling: 108 boxes. Allocated on arrival. Canteen opens at 7.30a.m. Tel: 01162 712115.

By Road: The course is 2.5 miles southeast of the City on the A6 (M1, Junction 21). The car park is free.

By Rail: Leicester Station (from St Pancras) is 2.5 miles.

By Air: Helicopter landing facility in the centre of the course.

LINGFIELD PARK (L.H)

Flat, Turf: A sharp, undulating left-handed circuit, with a 7f 140y straight course.

Flat, Polytrack: The left-handed Polytrack is 1m 2f round, with an extended chute to provide a 1m 5f start. It is a sharp, level track with a short run-in.

N.H. Conical, 1m 5f (10) 200y run-in. Severely undulating with a tight downhill turn into the straight, the chase course suits front runners and those of doubtful resolution.

Address: Lingfield Park Racecourse, Lingfield, Surrey RH7 6PQ Tel: 01342 834800 Fax: 01342 832833

Website: www.lingfieldpark.co.uk

Clerk of the Course: Ed Arkell

Executive Manager: Andrew Perkins

Going Reports: Contact Clerk of the Course as above.
Stabling: 106 boxes. For details of accommodation Tel: 01342 831718. Advance notice for overnight accommodation required before 12 noon on the day before racing.
By Road: Southeast of the town off the A22; M25 (Junction 6). Ample free parking.
By Rail: Lingfield Station (regular services from London Bridge and Victoria). ½ mile walk to the course.
By Air: London (Gatwick) Airport 10 miles. Helicopter landing facility south of wind-sock.

LUDLOW (R.H)

N.H. Oval, 1m 4f (9) 185y run-in. The chase course is flat and has quite sharp bends into and out of the home straight, although long-striding horses never seem to have any difficulties. The hurdle course is on the outside of the chase course and is not so sharp.
Address: Ludlow Race Club Ltd, The Racecourse, Bromfield, Ludlow, Shropshire SY8 2BT
Tel: 01584 856221 (Racedays) or see below. Website: www.ludlowracecourse.co.uk
Clerk of the Course: Simon Sherwood
General Manager: Bob Davies. Tel: 01584 856221, Mobile 07970 861533, Fax: 01584 856217
Email: bobdavies@ludlowracecourse.co.uk
Going Reports: Contact Clerk of the Course as above or Groundsman Tel: 01584 856289 or 07970 668353
Stabling: Free and allocated on arrival. 100 stables, mainly cardboard with a limited number of shavings and straw. Tel: 01584 856221.
By Road: The course is situated at Bromfield, 2 miles north of Ludlow on the A49.
By Rail: Ludlow Station (Hereford-Shrewsbury line) 2 miles.
By Air: Helicopter landing facility in the centre of the course by arrangement with the Clerk of the Course and entirely at own risk.

MARKET RASEN (R.H)

N.H. Oval, 1m 2f (8) 250y run-in. A sharp, undulating course with a long run to the straight, it favours the handy, front-running type.
Address: Market Rasen Racecourse, Legsby Road, Market Rasen, Lincolnshire LN8 3EA
Tel: 01673 843434 Fax: 01673 844532 Website: www.marketrasenraces.co.uk
Regional Director: Amy Starkey
Clerk of the Course: Jack Pryor
General Manager: Nadia Gollings
Going Reports: Contact Clerk of the Course.
Stabling: 86 boxes at the course, allocated on arrival. Accommodation for lads and lasses is by reservation only. Tel: 01673 842307 (racedays only)
By Road: The town is just off the A46, and the racecourse is one mile east of the town on the A631. Free car parks.
By Rail: Market Rasen Station 1 mile (King's Cross - Cleethorpes line).
By Air: Helicopter landing facility by prior arrangement only.

MUSSELBURGH (R.H)

Flat: A sharp, level, right-handed oval of 1m 2f, with a run-in of 4f. There is an additional 5f straight course.
N.H. Rectangular, 1m 3f (8) 150y run-in (variable). A virtually flat track with sharp turns, suiting the handy, front-running sort. Drains well.
Address: Musselburgh Racecourse, Linkfield Road, Musselburgh, East Lothian EH21 7RG
Tel: 01316 652859 (Racecourse) Fax: 01316 532083 Website:www.musselburgh-racecourse.co.uk
Clerk of the Course: Harriet Graham 07843 380401
General Manager: Bill Farnsworth 07710 536134
Going Reports: Contact main office as above or Clerk of the Course.
Stabling: 101 boxes. Free stabling. Accommodation provided. Tel: 07773 048638, Stables (racedays): 01316 652796.
By Road: The course is situated at Musselburgh, 5 miles east of Edinburgh on the A1. Car park, adjoining course, free for buses and cars.
By Rail: Waverley Station (Edinburgh). Local Rail service to Musselburgh.
By Air: Edinburgh (Turnhouse) Airport 30 minutes

NEWBURY (L.H)

Flat: Left-handed, oval track of about 1m 7f, with a slightly undulating straight mile. The round course is level and galloping with a four and a half furlong run-in. Races over the round mile start on the adjoining chute.

N.H. Oval, 1m 6f (11) 255y run-in. Slightly undulating, wide and galloping in nature. The fences are stiff and sound jumping is essential. One of the fairest tracks in the country.
Address: Newbury Racecourse, Newbury, Berkshire RG14 7NZ Tel: 01635 40015 Fax: 01635 528354
Website: www.newbury-racecourse.co.uk
Chief Executive: Julian Thick
Raceday Clerk: Richard Osgood 07977 426947
Going Reports: Clerk of the Course as above.
Stabling: 164 boxes. Free stabling and accommodation for lads and lasses. Tel: 01635 40015.
By Road: East of the town off the A34 (M4, Junction 12 or 13). Car park, adjoining enclosures, free.
By Rail: Newbury Racecourse Station adjoins the course.
By Air: Light Aircraft landing strip East/West. 830 metres by 30 metres wide. Helicopter landing facilities.

NEWCASTLE (L.H)
Flat: Flat racing on turf discontinued, to be replaced in 2016 with a Tapeta track outside the jumps course. The straight mile will be floodlit.
N.H. Oval, 1m 6f (11) 220y run-in. A gradually rising home straight of four furlongs makes this galloping track a true test of stamina, especially as the ground can become very heavy.
Address: High Gosforth Park, Newcastle-Upon-Tyne NE3 5HP Tel: 01912 362020 Fax: 01912 367761
Website: www.newcastle-racecourse.co.uk
Clerk of the Course: James Armstrong 07801 166820
Executive Director: David Williamson
Stabling: 135 boxes. Stabling Free. It is essential to book accommodation in advance. Apply via the Racecourse Office.
Going Reports: Contact Clerk of the Course as above or Head Groundsman 07860 274289.
By Road: 4 miles north of the city on the A6125 (near the A1).
By Rail: Newcastle Central Station (from King's Cross). A free bus service operates from South Gosforth and Regent Centre Metro Station.
By Air: Helicopter landing facility by prior arrangement. The Airport is 4 miles from the course.

NEWMARKET (R.H)
Rowley Mile Course: There is a straight ten-furlong course, which is wide and galloping. Races over 1m 4f or more are right-handed. The Rowley Mile course has a long run-in and a stiff finish.
July Course: Races up to a mile are run on the Bunbury course, which is straight. Races over 1m 2f or more are right-handed, with a 7f run-in. Like the Rowley Mile course, the July Course finish is stiff.
Address: Newmarket Racecourse, Newmarket, Suffolk CB8 0TG Tel: 01638 663482 (Main Office), 01638 663762 (Rowley), 01638 675416 (July) Fax: Rowley 01638 675340. Fax: July 01638 675410
Website: www.newmarketracecourses.co.uk
Clerk of the Course: Michael Prosser, Westfield House, The Links, Newmarket. Tel: 01638 675504 or 07802 844578
Regional Director: Amy Starkey
Going Reports: Contact main office or Clerk of the Course as above
Stabling: 100 boxes. Free accommodation available at the Links Stables. Tel: 01638 662200 or 07747 766614
By Road: Southwest of the town on the A1304 London Road (M11 Junction 9). Free car parking at the rear of the enclosure. Annual Badge Holders' car park free all days. Free courtesy bus service from Newmarket Station, Bus Station and High Street, commencing 90 minutes prior to the first race, and return trips up to 60 minutes after the last race.
By Rail: Infrequent rail service to Newmarket Station from Cambridge (Liverpool Street) or direct bus service from Cambridge (13-mile journey).
By Air: Landing facilities for light aircraft and helicopters on racedays at both racecourses. See Flight Guide. Cambridge Airport 11 miles.

NEWTON ABBOT (L.H)
N.H. Oval, 1m 2f (7) 300y run-in. Flat with two tight bends and a water jump situated three fences from home. The nippy, agile sort is favoured. The run-in can be very short on the hurdle course.
Address: Newton Abbot Races Ltd., Kingsteignton Road, Newton Abbot, Devon TQ12 3AF
Tel: 01626 353235 Fax: 01626 336972 Website: www.newtonabbotracing.com
Clerk of the Course: Jason Loosemore 07766 228109
Managing Director: Pat Masterson. Tel: 01626 353235 Fax: 01626 336972 Mobile: 07917 830144.
Going reports: Clerk of the Course as above.
Stabling: 80 boxes, allocated on arrival. Tel: 07766 202938

By Road: North of the town on the A380. Torquay 6 miles, Exeter 17 miles.
By Rail: Newton Abbot Station (from Paddington) ¾ mile. Buses and taxis operate to and from the course.
By Air: Helicopter landing pad in the centre of the course.

NOTTINGHAM (L.H)

Flat: Left-handed, galloping, oval of about 1m 4f, and a run-in of four and a half furlongs. Flat with easy turns.
Address: Nottingham Racecourse, Colwick Park, Nottingham NG2 4BE Tel: 0870 8507634
Fax: 01159 584515 Website: www.nottinghamracecourse.co.uk
Regional Director: Amy Starkey
Clerk of the Course: Jane Hedley
Managing Director: James Knox
Going Reports: Contact main office as above or Clerk of the Course.
Stabling: 122 boxes allotted on arrival. Hostel for lads and lasses. Tel: 08708 507634
By Road: 2 miles east of the city on the B686.
By Rail: Nottingham (Midland) Station. Regular bus service to course (2 miles).
By Air: Helicopter landing facility in the centre of the course.

PERTH (R.H)

N.H. Rectangular, 1m 2f (8) 283y run-in. A flat, easy track with sweeping turns. Not a course for the long-striding galloper. An efficient watering system ensures that the ground rarely gets hard.
Address: Perth Racecourse, Scone Palace Park, Perth PH2 6BB Tel: 01738 551597 Fax: 01738 553021
Website: www.perth-races.co.uk
Clerk of the Course: Harriet Graham 07843 380401
General Manager: Hazel Peplinski
Going Reports: Groundsman 07899 034012 or contact Clerk of the Course as above.
Stabling: 96 boxes and accommodation for lads and lasses Tel: 01738 551597. Stables Tel: 01738 621604
(racedays only).
By Road: 4 miles north of the town off the A93.
By Rail: Perth Station (from Dundee) 4 miles. There are buses to the course.
By Air: Scone Airport (3.75 miles). Edinburgh Airport 45 minutes.

PLUMPTON (L.H)

N.H. Oval, 1m 1f (7) 200y run-in uphill. A tight, undulating circuit with an uphill finish, Plumpton favours the handy, fast jumper. The ground often gets heavy, as the course is based on clay soil.
Address: Plumpton Racecourse, Plumpton, East Sussex, BN7 3AL Tel: 01273 890383 Fax: 01273 891557
Website: www.plumptonracecourse.co.uk
Clerk of the Course: Mark Cornford 07759 151617
Chief Executive: Kate Hills
Going Reports: Tel: 01273 890383 / 07759 151617.
Stabling: 76 boxes. Advance notice required for overnight arrival. Tel: 07759 151617
By Road: 2 miles north of the village off the B2116.
By Rail: Plumpton Station (from Victoria) adjoins course.
By Air: Helicopter landing facility by prior arrangement with the Clerk of the Course.

PONTEFRACT (L.H)

Flat: Left-handed oval, undulating course of 2m 133y, with a short run-in of 2f. It is a particularly stiff track with the last 3f uphill.
Address: Pontefract Park Race Co. Ltd., The Park, Pontefract, West Yorkshire Tel: 01977 781307
(Racedays) Fax: 01977 781850 Website: www.pontefract-races.co.uk
Managing Director and Clerk of the Course: Norman Gundill 01977 781307
Assistant Manager and Clerk of the Course: Richard Hamill
Going Reports: Contact Office as above, or Clerk of the Course
Stabling: 113 boxes. Stabling and accommodation must be reserved. They will be allocated on a first come-first served basis. Tel: 01977 702323
By Road: 1 mile north of the town on the A639. Junction 32 of M62. Free car park adjacent to the course.
By Rail: Pontefract Station (Tanshelf, every hour to Wakefield), 1½ miles from the course. Regular bus service from Leeds.
By Air: Helicopters by arrangement only. (Nearest Airfields: Robin Hood (Doncaster), Sherburn-in-Elmet, Yeadon (Leeds Bradford).

REDCAR (L.H)

Flat: Left-handed, level, galloping, oval course of 1m 6f with a straight run-in of 5f. There is also a straight mile.

Address: Redcar Racecourse, Redcar, Cleveland TS10 2BY Tel: 01642 484068 Fax: 01642 488272
Website: www.redcarracing.com

Clerk of the Course: Jonjo Sanderson Tel: 01642 484068 Mobile: 07766 022893

General Manager: Amy Fair

Going Reports: Contact main office as above or Clerk of the Course.

Stabling: 144 Boxes available. Tel: Stables 01642 484068 or racedays only 01642 484254.

By Road: In town off the A1085. Free parking adjoining the course for buses and cars.

By Rail: Redcar Station (¼ mile from the course).

By Air: Landing facilities at Turners Arms Farm (600yds runway) Yearby, Cleveland. Two miles south of the racecourse - transport available. Durham Tees Valley airport (18 miles west of Redcar).

RIPON (R.H)

Flat: A sharp, undulating, right-handed oval of 1m 5f, with a 5f run-in. There is also a 6f straight course.

Address: Ripon Racecourse, Boroughbridge Road, Ripon, North Yorkshire HG4 1UG Tel: 01765 530530
Fax: 01765 698900 E-mail: info@ripon-races.co.uk Website: www.ripon-races.co.uk

Clerk of the Course and Managing Director: James Hutchinson

Going Reports: Tel: 01765 603696 or Head Groundsman 07976 960177

Stabling: Trainers requiring stabling (103 boxes available) are requested to contact the Stable Manager prior to 12 noon the day before racing. Tel: 01765 604135

By Road: The course is situated 2 miles southeast of the city, on the B6265. There is ample free parking for cars and coaches. For reservations apply to the Secretary.

By Rail: Harrogate Station (11 miles), or Thirsk (15 miles). Bus services to Ripon.

By Air: Helicopters only on the course. Otherwise Leeds/Bradford airport.

SALISBURY (R.H)

Flat: Right-handed and level, with a run-in of 4f. There is a straight mile track. The last half-mile is uphill, providing a stiff test of stamina.

Address: Salisbury Racecourse, Netherhampton, Salisbury, Wiltshire SP2 8PN Tel: 01722 326461
Fax: 01722 412710 Website: www.salisburyracecourse.co.uk

Clerk of the Course and General Manager: Jeremy Martin 07880 744999

Going Reports: Contact Clerk of the Course as above

Stabling: Free stabling (114 boxes) and accommodation for lads and lasses, apply to the Stabling Manager 07722 327327.

By Road: 3 miles southwest of the city on the A3094 at Netherhampton. Free car park adjoins the course.

By Rail: Salisbury Station is 3.5 miles (from London Waterloo). Bus service to the course.

By Air: Helicopter landing facility near the 1m 2f start.

SANDOWN PARK (R.H)

Flat: An easy right-handed oval course of 1m 5f with a stiff straight uphill run-in of 4f. Separate straight 5f track is also uphill. Galloping.

N.H. Oval, 1m 5f (11) 220y run-in uphill. Features seven fences on the back straight; the last three (the Railway Fences) are very close together and can often decide the outcome of races. The stiff climb to the finish puts the emphasis very much on stamina, but accurate-jumping, free-running sorts are also favoured. Hurdle races are run on the Flat course.

Address: Sandown Park Racecourse, Esher, Surrey KT10 9AJ Tel: 01372 464348 Fax: 01372 470427
Website: www.sandown.co.uk

Regional Director: Rupert Trevelyan

General Manager: Phil White

Clerk of the Course: Andrew Cooper, Sandown Park, Esher, Surrey. Tel: 01372 461213
Mobile: 07774 230850.

Going Reports: 01372 461212.

Stabling: 110 boxes. Free stabling and accommodation for lads and lasses. Tel: 01372 463511.

By Road: Four miles southwest of Kingston-on-Thames, on the A307 (M25 Junction 10).

By Rail: Esher Station (from Waterloo) adjoins the course.

By Air: London (Heathrow) Airport 12 miles.

SEDGEFIELD (L.H)

N.H. Oval, 1m 2f (8) 200y run-in: Hurdles 200y run-in. Undulating with fairly tight turns, it doesn't suit big, long-striding horses.
Address: Sedgefield Racecourse, Sedgefield, Stockton-on-Tees, Cleveland TS21 2HW Tel: 01740 621925
Office Fax: 01740 620663 Website: www.sedgefield-racecourse.co.uk
Clerk of the Course: Sophie Barton
General Manager: Jill Williamson
Going Reports: Tel: 01740 621925 or contact Clerk of the Course as above
Stabling: 116 boxes filled in rotation. No forage. Accommodation for horse attendants: Tel: 01740 621925
By Road: ¾ mile southwest of the town, near the junction of the A689 (Bishop Auckland) and the A177 (Durham) roads. The car park is free.
By Rail: Darlington Station (9 miles). Durham Station (12 miles).
By Air: Helicopter landing facility in car park area by prior arrangement only.

SOUTHWELL (L.H)

Flat, Turf: Tight left-handed track.
Flat, Fibresand: Left-handed oval, Fibresand course of 1m 2f with a 3f run-in. There is a straight 5f. Sharp and level, Southwell suits front-runners.
N.H. Oval, 1m 1f (7) 220y run-in. A tight, flat track with a short run-in, suits front-runners.
Address: Southwell Racecourse, Rolleston, Newark, Nottinghamshire NG25 0TS Tel: 01636 814481
Fax: 01636 812271 Website: www.southwell-racecourse.co.uk
Managing Director: Dave Roberts
Clerk of the Course: Roderick Duncan 07772 958685
General Manager: Amanda Boby
Going Reports: Contact Clerk of the Course as above.
Stabling: 113 boxes at the course. Applications for staff and horse accommodation to be booked by noon the day before racing on 01636 814481.
By Road: The course is situated at Rolleston, 3 miles south of Southwell, 5 miles from Newark.
By Rail: Rolleston Station (Nottingham-Newark line) adjoins the course.
By Air: Helicopters can land by prior arrangement.

STRATFORD-ON-AVON (L.H)

N.H. Triangular, 1m 2f (8) 200y run-in. Virtually flat with two tight bends, and quite a short home straight. A sharp and turning course, Stratford-on-Avon suits the well-balanced, handy sort.
Address: Stratford Racecourse, Luddington Road, Stratford-upon-Avon, Warwickshire CV37 9SE
Tel: 01789 267949 Fax: 01789 415850 Website: www.stratfordracecourse.net
Managing Director: Ilona Barnett
Clerk of the Course: Nessie Lambert
Going reports: Contact main office as above or Head Groundsman Tel: 07770 623366.
Stabling: 89 boxes allotted on arrival. Advance notice must be given for overnight stays. Tel: 01789 267949.
By Road: A mile from the town centre, off the A429 (Evesham road).
By Rail: Stratford-on-Avon Station (from Birmingham New Street or Leamington Spa) 1 mile.
By Air: Helicopter landing facility by prior arrangement.

TAUNTON (R.H)

N.H. Elongated oval, 1m 2f (8) 150y run-in uphill. Sharp turns, especially after the winning post, with a steady climb from the home bend. Suits the handy sort.
Address: Taunton Racecourse, Orchard Portman, Taunton, Somerset TA3 7BL Tel: 01823 337172
Office Fax: 01823 325581 Website: www.tauntonracecourse.co.uk
Clerk of the Course: Jason Loosemore
General Manager: Bob Young
Going reports: Contact Clerk of the Course as above, or Head Groundsman (after 4.30pm) 07971 695132.
Stabling: 90 boxes allotted on arrival. Advance bookings for long journeys. Apply to the Stable Manager, 01823 337172
By Road: Two miles south of the town on the B3170 (Honiton) road (M5 Junction 25).
By Rail: Taunton Station 2 miles. There are buses and taxis to course.
By Air: Helicopter landing facility by prior arrangement.

THIRSK (L.H)

Flat: Left-handed, oval of 1m 2f with sharp turns and an undulating run-in of 4f. There is a straight 6f track.
Address: The Racecourse, Station Road, Thirsk, North Yorkshire YO7 1QL Tel: 01845 522276
Fax: 01845 525353. Website: www.thirskracecourse.net
Clerk of the Course and Managing Director: James Sanderson
Going reports: Contact main office or Clerk of the Course as above
Stabling: 110 boxes. For stabling and accommodation apply to the Racecourse Tel: 01845 522096
By Road: West of the town on the A61. Free car park adjacent to the course for buses and cars.
By Rail: Thirsk Station (from King's Cross). ½ mile from the course.
By Air: Helicopters can land by prior arrangement. Tel: Racecourse 01845 522276. Fixed wing aircraft can land at RAF Leeming. Tel: 01677 423041. Light aircraft at Bagby. Tel: 01845 597385 or 01845 537555.

TOWCESTER (R.H)

N.H. Square, 1m 6f (10) 200y run-in uphill. The final six furlongs are uphill. One of the most testing tracks in the country with the emphasis purely on stamina.
Address: The Racecourse, London Road, Towcester, Northants NN12 6LB Tel: 01327 353414
Fax: 01327 358534 Website: www.towcester-racecourse.co.uk
Clerk of the Course: Robert Bellamy 07836 241458
General Manager: Kevin Ackerman
Going Reports: Tel: 01327 353414 or contact Clerk of the Course as above.
Stabling: 101 stables in a new block. Allocated on arrival. Please contact racecourse in advance for overnight stabling / accommodation 01327 350200.
By Road: 1 mile southeast of the town on the A5 (Milton Keynes road). M1 (Junction 15a).
By Rail: Northampton Station (Euston) 9 miles, buses to Towcester; or Milton Keynes (Euston) 12 miles, taxis available.
By Air: Helicopters can land by prior arrangement with the Racecourse Manager.

UTTOXETER (L.H)

N.H. Oval, 1m 2f (8) 170y run-in. A few undulations, easy bends and fences and a flat home straight of over half a mile. Suits front-runners, especially on the 2m hurdle course.
Address: The Racecourse, Wood Lane, Uttoxeter, Staffordshire ST14 8BD Tel: 01889 562561
Fax: 01889 562786 Website: www.uttoxeter-racecourse.co.uk
Clerk of the Course: Charlie Moore 07764 255500
General Manager: David MacDonald
Going Reports: Contact main office or Clerk of the Course as above.
Stabling: 102 boxes, allotted on arrival. Tel: 01889 562561. Overnight and Accommodation requirements must be notified in advance as no hostel at course.
By Road: Southeast of the town off the B5017 (Marchington Road).
By Rail: Uttoxeter Station (Crewe-Derby line) adjoins the course.
By Air: Helicopters can land by prior arrangement with the raceday office.

WARWICK (L.H)

N.H. Circular, 1m 6f (10) 240y run-in. Undulating with tight bends, five quick fences in the back straight and a short home straight, Warwick favours handiness and speed rather than stamina.
Address: Warwick Racecourse, Hampton Street, Warwick CV34 6HN Tel: 01926 491553
Fax: 01926 403223 Website: www.warwickracecourse.co.uk
Regional Director: Ian Renton
Clerk of the Course: Jane Hedley
Managing Director: Andre Klein
Going Reports: Contact main office or Clerk of the Course as above.
Stabling: 117 boxes allocated on arrival or by reservation 01926 491553.
By Road: West of the town on the B4095 adjacent to Junction 15 of the M40.
By Rail: Warwick or Warwick Parkway Stations.
By Air: Helicopters can land by prior arrangement with the Clerk of the Course.

WETHERBY (L.H)

Flat: First used in 2015, the Flat course is left-handed with a 1m 4f circuit.
N.H. Oval, 1m 4f (9) 200y run-in slightly uphill. A flat, very fair course which suits the long-striding galloper.
Address: The Racecourse, York Road, Wetherby, LS22 5EJ Tel: 01937 582035 Fax: 01937 588021

Website: www.wetherbyracing.co.uk
Clerk of the Course and Chief Executive: Jonjo Sanderson 07831 437453
Going reports: Tel: 01937 582035, or Head Groundsman: 07880 722586
Stabling: 91 boxes allocated on arrival. Accommodation available. Tel: 01937 582035 or from 2pm the day before racing 01937 582074.
By Road: East of the town off the B1224 (York Road). Adjacent to the A1. Excellent bus and coach facilities. Car park free.
By Rail: Leeds Station 12 miles. Buses to Wetherby.
By Air: Helicopters can land by prior arrangement

WINCANTON (R.H)

N.H. Rectangular, 1m 3f (9) 200y run-in. Good galloping course where the going rarely becomes heavy. The home straight is mainly downhill.
Address: Wincanton Racecourse, Wincanton, Somerset BA9 8BJ Tel: 01963 32344 Fax: 01963 34668
Website: www.wincantonracecourse.co.uk
Regional Director: Ian Renton
Clerk of the Course: Barry Johnson 07976 791578
General Manager: Huw Williams
Going Reports: Contact Racecourse Office as above.
Stabling: 94 boxes allocated on arrival, overnight accommodation must be booked in advance. Apply to the Stable Manager, Wincanton Racecourse. Tel: 01963 32344.
By Road: 1 mile north of the town on the B3081.
By Rail: Gillingham Station (from Waterloo) or Castle Cary Station (from Paddington). Buses and taxis to the course.
By Air: Helicopter landing area is situated in the centre of the course.

WINDSOR (Fig. 8)

Flat: Figure of eight track of 1m 4f 110y. The course is level and sharp with a long run-in. The 6f course is essentially straight.
Address: Royal Windsor Racecourse, Maidenhead Road, Windsor, Berkshire SL4 5JJ Tel: 01753 498400
Fax: 01753 830156. Website: www.windsor-racecourse.co.uk
Clerk of the Course: Jeff Green
Executive Director: Stuart Dorn
Going Reports: Contact Clerk of the Course as above.
Stabling: 114 boxes available. Reservation required for overnight stay and accommodation only.
Tel: 07825 003236 or 01753 498405 (racedays).
By Road: North of the town on the A308 (M4 Junction 6).
By Rail: Windsor Central Station (from Paddington) or Windsor and Eton Riverside Station (from Waterloo).
By Air: London (Heathrow) Airport 15 minutes. Also White Waltham Airport (West London Aero Club) 15 minutes.
River Bus: Seven minutes from Barry Avenue promenade at Windsor.

WOLVERHAMPTON (L.H)

Flat: Left-handed oval Tapeta track of 1m, with a run-in of 380y. A level track with sharp bends.
Address: Wolverhampton Racecourse, Dunstall Park, Gorsebrook Road, Wolverhampton WV6 0PE
Tel: 01902 390000 Fax: 01902 421621 Website: www.wolverhampton-racecourse.co.uk
Clerk of the Course: Fergus Cameron 07971 531162
General Manager: Dave Roberts
Going Reports: Contact Main Office as above
Stabling: 103 boxes allotted on arrival. Applications for lads and lasses, and overnight stables must be made to Racecourse by noon on the day before racing. Tel: 07971 531162. Fax: 01902 421621.
By Road: 1 mile north of the city on the A449 (M54 Junction 2 or M6 Junction 12). Car parking free of charge.
By Rail: Wolverhampton Station (from Euston) 1 mile.
By Air: Halfpenny Green Airport 8 miles.

WORCESTER (L.H)

N.H. Elongated oval, 1m 5f (9) 220y run-in. Flat with easy turns, Worcester is a very fair, galloping track.
Address: Worcester Racecourse, Pitchcroft, Worcester WR1 3EJ Tel: 01905 25364 Fax: 01905 617563
Website: www.worcester-racecourse.co.uk
Clerk of the Course: Keith Ottesen

Managing Director: Dave Roberts 01905 25364.
Going Reports: Contact Clerk of the Course as above, or 01905 25364 (racedays).
Stabling: 97 boxes allotted on arrival. Overnight accommodation for lads and lasses in Worcester.
Tel: 01905 25364 Fax: 01905 617563.
By Road: West of the city off the A449 (Kidderminster road) (M5 Junction 8).
By Rail: Foregate Street Station, Worcester (from Paddington) ¾ mile.
By Air: Helicopter landing facility in the centre of the course, by prior arrangement only.

YARMOUTH (L.H)

Flat: Left-handed, level circuit of 1m 4f, with a run-in of 5f. The straight course is 1m long.
Address: The Racecourse, Jellicoe Road, Great Yarmouth, Norfolk NR30 4AU Tel: 01493 842527
Fax: 01493 843254 Website: www.greatyarmouth-racecourse.co.uk
Clerk of the Course: Richard Aldous 07738 507643
Executive Director: Glenn Tubby
Going Reports: Contact Main Office or Clerk of the Course as above
Stabling: 127 boxes available. Allocated on arrival. Tel: 01493 855651 (racedays only) or racecourse office.
By Road: 1 mile east of town centre (well signposted from A47 and A12).
By Rail: Great Yarmouth Station (1 mile). Bus service to the course.
By Air: Helicopter landing available by prior arrangement with Racecourse Office

YORK (L.H)

Flat: Left-handed, level, galloping track, with a straight 6f. There is also an adjoining course of 6f 214y.
Address: The Racecourse, York YO23 1EX Tel: 01904 683932 Fax: 01904 611071
Website: www.yorkracecourse.co.uk
Clerk of the Course and Chief Executive: William Derby 07812 961176
Assistant Clerk of the Course: Anthea Morshead
Going Reports: Contact 01904 683932 or Clerk of the Course as above.
Stabling: 177 boxes available Tel: 01904 706317 (Racedays) or 07712 676434.
By Road: 1 mile southeast of the city on the A1036.
By Rail: 1½ miles York Station (from King's Cross). Special bus service from station to the course.
By Air: Light aircraft and helicopter landing facilities available at Rufforth aerodrome (5,000ft tarmac runway). £20 landing fee - transport arranged to course. Leeds Bradford airport (25 miles).

THE INVESTEC DERBY STAKES (GROUP 1) EPSOM DOWNS ON SATURDAY 4TH JUNE 2016

SECOND ENTRIES BY NOON APRIL 5TH; SUPPLEMENTARY ENTRIES BY NOON MAY 30TH.

HORSE	TRAINER	HORSE	TRAINER
A YEAR TO REMEMBER (IRE)	Aidan O'Brien	CHATEAUDEMALMAISON (USA)	A. Fabre
AASHEQ (IRE)	D. K. Weld	CHELSEA'S BOY (IRE)	Clive Cox
ABDON (GB)	Sir Michael Stoute	CHESS GRAND MASTER (GB)	Aidan O'Brien
ABLE RIP (IRE)	John Gosden	CITY OF IDEAS (GB)	John Gosden
ABSOLUTE RULER (IRE)	Aidan O'Brien	CLAUDIO MONTEVERDI (IRE)	Aidan O'Brien
ACROSS THE STARS (IRE)	Sir Michael Stoute	CLE (IRE)	Rodolphe Collet
ACRUX (GB)	David Lanigan	CLOCK WATCHER (GB)	Charlie Appleby
AFNAAN (GB)	Saeed bin Suroor	COHESION (GB)	D. Smaga
AIR VICE MARSHAL (USA)	Aidan O'Brien	COLE PORTER (IRE)	Aidan O'Brien
AL FALAK (USA)	Sir Michael Stoute	COMBATIVE (GB)	Amanda Perrett
AL HARAM (FR)	Ellie Lellouche	CONFIDENT KID (GB)	Saeed bin Suroor
AL KHAFJI (GB)	Luca Cumani	COOK ISLANDS (IRE)	Aidan O'Brien
AL NEKSH (GB)		CORINTHIAN (GB)	Roger Varian
AL VALORE (IRE)	Charlie Appleby	COSMO VECCHIO (JPN)	M. Ogasa
ALAADEL (GB)	William Haggas	CRIMEAN TATAR (TUR)	Hugo Palmer
ALFAHAD (IRE)	Ed Dunlop	CROCODILE SHOES (IRE)	Aidan O'Brien
ALGOMETER (GB)	David Simcock	DAILY NEWS (GB)	Roger Varian
ALMANAARA (IRE)	D. K. Weld	DAQEEQ (IRE)	Simon Crisford
ALPHEUS (IRE)	David Simcock	DARABAD (FR)	A. de Royer Dupre
ALQUFFAAL (GB)	Roger Varian	DEAUVILLE (IRE)	Aidan O'Brien
AMAZING RED (IRE)	Ed Dunlop	DESERT ISLE (IRE)	Sir Michael Stoute
ANCIENT TRADE (USA)	Richard Hannon	DESERT RIVER (IRE)	Mark H. Tompkins
ANGRYWHITEPYJAMAS (IRE)	William Muir	DHAROOS (IRE)	John Gosden
ARCARIUS (GB)	Saeed bin Suroor	DINSDALE (IRE)	Charlie Appleby
ARCH STING (USA)	John M. Oxx	D'NIRO (IRE)	Harry Dunlop
ARCHIMENTO (GB)	Ed Dunlop	DOHA DREAM (FR)	A. Fabre
ARGYLE (IRE)	William Muir	DOWSING (JPN)	J. E. Hammond
ARTICLE BLEU (GB)	Luca Cumani	DU MOTO (IRE)	Sir Michael Stoute
ASKARI (GB)	Roger Varian	DUBAWI FLAME (GB)	Charlie Appleby
AWTAAD (IRE)	K. Prendergast	DWIGHT D (GB)	William Haggas
AZIZAAN (GB)	Roger Varian	EBEDIYIN (IRE)	D. K. Weld
BAILEYS ESQUIRE (GB)	Mark Johnston	EBTIHAAL (IRE)	Saeed bin Suroor
BALLET CONCERTO (GB)	Sir Michael Stoute	ECOUTE (IRE)	A. Fabre
BAN SHOOF (GB)	Ismail Mohammed	EHTIRAAS (IRE)	B. W. Hills
BANDIT BOB (IRE)	K. R. Burke	EL VIP (IRE)	Luca Cumani
BARWOD (GB)	A. Fabre	EMBIRAN (IRE)	D. K. Weld
BEACON ROCK (IRE)	Aidan O'Brien	EMOTIONLESS (IRE)	Charlie Appleby
BEAST MODE (IRE)	Peter Chapple-Hyam	EPOCH (IRE)	A. Fabre
BEIJING (GB)	A. Fabre	ET TOI (IRE)	Brian Meehan
BEYOND APOLLO (FR)	P. Bary	EX LOVER (GB)	Roger Varian
BHUTAN (IRE)	Aidan O'Brien	EXECUTOR (GB)	Roger Charlton
BIG BEN (GB)	Aidan O'Brien	EXOTERIC (GB)	Charles Hills
BIODYNAMIC (IRE)	K. R. Burke	EZANAK (IRE)	D. K. Weld
BIRTHPLACE (IRE)	Aidan O'Brien	FACE OF GLORY (IRE)	Ismail Mohammed
BLACK HAWK WAR (USA)	Aidan O'Brien	FACTS AND FIGURES (IRE)	Roger Varian
BLACK SEA (IRE)	Aidan O'Brien	FALAK (IRE)	Roger Varian
BLUE CREEK (GB)	Charlie Appleby	FANDANGO (GER)	Jeremy Gask
BOLD EMPEROR (IRE)	A. de Royer Dupre	FARADAY EFFECT (GB)	Charles Hills
BRAVERY (IRE)	Aidan O'Brien	FASTNET MONSOON (IRE)	Luca Cumani
BROADWAY ICON (GB)	Jeremy Noseda	FIRNAS (GB)	Charlie Appleby
BROOKE'S POINT (GB)	Charlie Appleby	FIRST START (GB)	Saeed bin Suroor
CAFOO (IRE)	Ed Dunlop	FORBIDDING (USA)	Roger Varian
CANDLE ROCKS (IRE)	Aidan O'Brien	FORESEE (GER)	A. Fabre
CANDY REAL (USA)	Mrs P. Brandt	FORTI (FR)	P. Sogorb
CARTAGO (GB)	John Gosden	FOUNDATION (IRE)	John Gosden
CAT SILVER (GB)	Sir Michael Stoute	FOUR ON EIGHT (GB)	Luca Cumani
CELTIC CHIEFTAIN (IRE)	Aidan O'Brien	FOXHAM (IRE)	
C'EST LA VIE (GER)	A. Wohler	FRENCHMAN (FR)	Charles Hills
CHANGING GUARD (IRE)	A. Fabre	FRONTIERSMAN (GB)	Charlie Appleby

HORSE	TRAINER
G K CHESTERTON (IRE)	Charlie Appleby
GALAPIAT (GB)	A. Fabre
GAMBIT (GB)	Tom Dascombe
GENERAL MACARTHUR (USA)	Aidan O'Brien
GERSHWIN (GB)	David Lanigan
GHAMAR (GB)	FH. Graffard
GLAMOUR BOY (IRE)	John M. Oxx
GOLDMEMBER (GB)	David Simcock
GOOD TRIP (IRE)	Saeed bin Suroor
GRADIENT (GB)	John Gosden
GREAT RETURN (GB)	Saeed bin Suroor
HAMMER GUN (USA)	Sir Michael Stoute
HARZAND (IRE)	D. K. Weld
HAWKER HUNTER (IRE)	Sir Michael Stoute
HAWKERLAND (IRE)	Marcus Tregoning
HEY LITTLE BOY (GER)	M. Klug
HIGH COMMAND (IRE)	Roger Varian
HIGH GROUNDS (IRE)	Charles Hills
HIGH SHIELDS (IRE)	Roger Charlton
HIGH TIDE (IRE)	Aidan O'Brien
HIGHLY PRIZED (GB)	Lady Cecil
HIT IT A BOMB (USA)	Aidan O'Brien
HOUSESOFPARLIAMENT (IRE)	Aidan O'Brien
HUDSON CANYON (IRE)	Aidan O'Brien
HUGE FUTURE (GB)	Saeed bin Suroor
ICE GALLEY (IRE)	Kevin Ryan
IDAHO (IRE)	Aidan O'Brien
IMPULSION (FR)	J. E. Pease
INEFFABLE (IRE)	Aidan O'Brien
INLAND SEA (USA)	Richard Hannon
INTERCEPTED (GB)	David Lanigan
ISTIQLAAL (GB)	Charlie Appleby
JATHAB (IRE)	John Gosden
JOHANNES VERMEER (IRE)	Aidan O'Brien
JONATHAN SWIFT (IRE)	Aidan O'Brien
JUFN (GB)	Saeed bin Suroor
KASANLI (IRE)	D. K. Weld
KELLSTORM (IRE)	Aidan O'Brien
KENTUCKY GIANT (USA)	D. K. Weld
KHAIRAAT (IRE)	Sir Michael Stoute
KHAMRY (GB)	Jean Claude Rouget
KIDD MALIBU (USA)	D. K. Weld
LACHARES (IRE)	A. de Royer Dupre
LAND OF THE FREE (IRE)	Aidan O'Brien
LANDOFHOPEANDGLORY (IRE)	Aidan O'Brien
LAQAB (IRE)	Roger Varian
LE JUGE (IRE)	A. Fabre
LE MUSEE (IRE)	A. Fabre
LE STADE (FR)	A. Fabre
LIEUTENANT GENERAL (IRE)	Aidan O'Brien
LONDON (FR)	Aidan O'Brien
LONG ISLAND SOUND (USA)	Aidan O'Brien
LORD NAPIER (IRE)	John Gosden
LOS ALAMOS (IRE)	Aidan O'Brien
LOURES (IRE)	Charlie Appleby
LOW SUN (GB)	P. Bary
LUGANO (GB)	Sir Mark Prescott Bt
LUMINARY (IRE)	Aidan O'Brien
LUSORY (GB)	Charlie Appleby
LUSTROUS LIGHT (IRE)	
MA PEEK (USA)	Brian Meehan
MADROOS (GB)	K. Prendergast
MAESTRO MAC (IRE)	Hughie Morrison
MAHFOOZ (IRE)	Charles Hills
MAINSTREAM (GB)	Sir Michael Stoute

HORSE	TRAINER
MAKE MISCHIEF (GB)	Stuart Williams
MALAGASI (GB)	Charlie Appleby
MAMBO ROCK	
MANJAAM (IRE)	Ed Dunlop
MARYLEBONE (GB)	Ed Walker
MASSAAT (IRE)	B. W. Hills
MASSAYAN (IRE)	D. K. Weld
MAYYAS (FR)	JC. Rouget
MAZAZ (IRE)	John Gosden
MEKHTAAL (GB)	JC. Rouget
MELFIT (IRE)	Richard Hannon
MEMENTO MORI (USA)	A. Fabre
MENGLI KHAN (IRE)	Hugo Palmer
MIDTERM (GB)	Sir Michael Stoute
MIND SHIFT (USA)	David Lanigan
MOKHALAD (GB)	Sir Michael Stoute
MOLTEN GOLD (GB)	Andrew Balding
MONARCH (IRE)	Aidan O'Brien
MOON ARROW (IRE)	Ismail Mohammed
MOONLIGHT MAGIC (GB)	J. S. Bolger
MORANDO (FR)	Roger Varian
MORE TO COME (GB)	Saeed bin Suroor
MOTHERLAND (IRE)	Aidan O'Brien
MR KHALID (GB)	Marco Botti
MR TURNER (GB)	Mark H. Tompkins
MUAITHER (IRE)	John Gosden
MUJAAMIL (IRE)	William Haggas
MULK (GB)	Sir Michael Stoute
MUNTAHAA (IRE)	John Gosden
MUNTAZAH (GB)	B. W. Hills
MURRAQIB (USA)	D. K. Weld
MUTADAFFEQ (IRE)	K. Prendergast
MUTARAKEM (GB)	F. Head
MUTAWAALY (IRE)	Roger Varian
NACHI FALLS (GB)	Charlie Appleby
NAZZAA (IRE)	John Gosden
NEOCLASSICAL (GB)	John Gosden
NEVER SO FEW (IRE)	Aidan O'Brien
NEW MILLENNIUM (IRE)	Aidan O'Brien
NEW WORLD POWER (JPN)	Roger Varian
NEWSMAN (IRE)	J. P. Murtagh
NEXT STAGE (GB)	Saeed bin Suroor
NICE FUTURE (IRE)	Saeed bin Suroor
OCTOBER STORM (GB)	Mick Channon
ON THE FRONT LINE (USA)	A. Fabre
PARIS BOUND (IRE)	Andrew Balding
PARKLIFE (IRE)	A. Fabre
PERSAVERANCE (GB)	Gary Moore
PERSISTENT (IRE)	A. Fabre
PHIDIAN (IRE)	P. Bary
PIETRO TESTA (IRE)	Aidan O'Brien
PIRATE'S COVE (IRE)	A. Fabre
POET'S WORD (IRE)	Sir Michael Stoute
POINT OF VIEW (IRE)	Roger Varian
PORT DOUGLAS (IRE)	Aidan O'Brien
PROCONSUL (GB)	A. Fabre
PSYCHOTIC (GB)	William Jarvis
PUMBLECHOOK (GB)	Lucy Wadham
PURE SOUL (GB)	Ismail Mohammed
QASSEM (IRE)	A. Fabre
QATAR RAINBOW (FR)	F. Head
QATARI GOLD (USA)	M. Delzangles
RACE DAY (IRE)	Saeed bin Suroor
RAS AL MAL (IRE)	Ed Dunlop
RAVENS QUEST (GB)	Hughie Morrison

HORSE	TRAINER
REAL DOMINION (USA)	Andrew Balding
REAVER (IRE)	Eve Johnson Houghton
RECORDER (GB)	William Haggas
REHEARSE (IRE)	Andrew Balding
RESOURCE (IRE)	A. Fabre
RESTIVE (IRE)	G. M. Lyons
RESTLESS RAMBLER (USA)	D. K. Weld
REUBEN JAMES (GB)	Martyn Meade
REVOLUTIONARY WAR (USA)	A. Fabre
RHINESTONE (IRE)	Aidan O'Brien
RIDE THE LIGHTNING (GB)	Brian Meehan
ROAD TO THE STARS (IRE)	Mark Johnston
ROLLER (GB)	P. Bary
ROMANESQUE (IRE)	Aidan O'Brien
ROYAL ARTILLERY (USA)	John Gosden
ROYAL RESERVE (GB)	William Muir
SAN FRANCISCO (IRE)	Aidan O'Brien
SANTA ANITA (GB)	Aidan O'Brien
SANTIAGO DE CUBA (IRE)	Aidan O'Brien
SATISH (GB)	John Gosden
SAYEDAATI SAADATI (IRE)	Kevin Ryan
SCHUBERT (USA)	Aidan O'Brien
SCOTTISH SUMMIT (IRE)	Sir Michael Stoute
SEA OF MYSTERY (IRE)	John M. Oxx
SEAN O'CASEY (IRE)	Aidan O'Brien
SHABBAH (IRE)	Sir Michael Stoute
SHABEEB (USA)	Roger Varian
SHAHRIK (USA)	M. Delzangles
SHALAKAR (FR)	M. Delzangles
SHAMSHAD (FR)	A. de Royer Dupre
SHEDED (IRE)	Richard Hannon
SHOGUN (IRE)	Aidan O'Brien
SHOW ME (FR)	A. Fabre
SHRAAOH (IRE)	Sir Michael Stoute
SILK SUIT (FR)	Luca Cumani
SIR GEORGE SOMERS (USA)	Sir Michael Stoute
SIRDAAL (USA)	B. W. Hills
SKY KINGDOM (IRE)	William Haggas
SNAN (IRE)	Richard Hannon
SOCIAL TREASURE (IRE)	D. K. Weld
SPACE MOUNTAIN (GB)	Mark Johnston
ST MICHEL (GB)	Sir Mark Prescott Bt
STERLING WORK (IRE)	Sir Michael Stoute
STRATUM (GB)	John Gosden
SUCCESSOR (IRE)	Aidan O'Brien
SUGARLOAF MOUNTAIN (IRE)	Aidan O'Brien
SUPERYACHT (IRE)	Sir Michael Stoute
SWORD FIGHTER (IRE)	Aidan O'Brien
TAAREEF (USA)	Jean Claude Rouget
TAILWIND (GB)	Roger Varian
TAKATUL (USA)	Charles Hills
TAMELLY (GB)	A. Fabre
TASHWEEQ (IRE)	John Gosden
TATHQEEF (USA)	John Gosden
TAUTOLOGY (GB)	Charlie Appleby
TAYAAR (IRE)	Richard Hannon
TEAM TALK (GB)	Saeed bin Suroor
TETRADRACHM (GB)	David Lanigan
THE GRADUATE (IRE)	Andrew Balding
THE GURKHA (IRE)	Aidan O'Brien
THE MAJOR GENERAL (IRE)	Aidan O'Brien
THE NEW MASTER (GB)	David Elsworth
THERTHAAR (GB)	Ismail Mohammed
THOMAS CROMWELL (GB)	Pat Phelan
THREE STAR GENERAL (GB)	Aidan O'Brien

HORSE	TRAINER
TIERCEL (GB)	Roger Varian
TIMEKEEPER (IRE)	David Simcock
TIPSTAFF (GB)	J. S. Bolger
TIRMIZI (FR)	D. K. Weld
TO BE WILD (IRE)	Hugo Palmer
TOGETHERNESS (IRE)	Ed Walker
TOP BEAK (IRE)	Hughie Morrison
TOPOGRAPHY (IRE)	Andreas Wohler
TORC MOUNTAIN (GB)	
TOUCHDOWN (IRE)	Sir Michael Stoute
TOWER BRIDGE (IRE)	Aidan O'Brien
TOWERING VISION (FR)	E. Libaud
TOWERLANDS PARK (IRE)	Michael Bell
TRANSMITTING (GB)	Sir Michael Stoute
TREASURE CHEST (IRE)	Aidan O'Brien
TREE OF KNOWLEDGE (IRE)	Aidan O'Brien
TRIBAL BEAT (IRE)	J. S. Bolger
TRIBALISM (USA)	A. Fabre
TRIPLICATE (IRE)	Aidan O'Brien
TYRANNICAL (GB)	Sir Mark Prescott Bt
UAE PRINCE (IRE)	Roger Varian
ULTRA (IRE)	A. Fabre
ULYSSES (IRE)	Sir Michael Stoute
UNBLINKING (GB)	A. Fabre
UNICORN (IRE)	Aidan O'Brien
US ARMY RANGER (IRE)	Aidan O'Brien
VINCENT'S FOREVER (GB)	John Gosden
VITAL SUN (FR)	P. Bary
WAIT (JPN)	
WAJEEZ (IRE)	John Gosden
WALK THE LINE (IRE)	Aidan O'Brien
WAQAAD (IRE)	B. W. Hills
WAVE REVIEWS (GB)	William Haggas
WEGO DANCING (IRE)	A. Fabre
WEST DRIVE (IRE)	Roger Varian
WINGS OF DESIRE (GB)	John Gosden
WINNING STORY (GB)	Saeed bin Suroor
ZABEEL PRINCE (IRE)	Roger Varian
ZARAK (FR)	A. de Royer Dupre
ZELZAL (FR)	JC. Rouget
ZHUI FENG (IRE)	Amanda Perrett
ZIRGON (FR)	C. Ferland
ZUBARA FORT (FR)	
EX ALSACE LORRAINE (IRE)	Roger Varian
EX GLICINE (GER)	Rodolphe Collet
EX KAMARINSKAYA (USA)	
EX KEEPERS HILL (IRE)	Roger Varian
EX MIRACOLIA (IRE)	Jeremy Gask
EX REJUVENATION (IRE)	Jeremy Gask

THE CSP
EUROPEAN FREE HANDICAP
NEWMARKET CRAVEN MEETING 2016
(ON THE ROWLEY MILE COURSE)
WEDNESDAY APRIL 13TH

The CSP European Free Handicap (Class 1) (Listed race) with total prize fund of £37,000 for two-year-olds only of 2015 which are included in the European 2-y-o Thoroughbred Rankings or which, in 2015, either ran in Great Britain or ran for a trainer who at the time was licensed by the British Horseracing Authority, and are Rated 100 or above; lowest weight 8st; highest weight 9st 7lbs.

Penalty for a winner after December 31st 2015, 5 lbs. Seven furlongs.

Rating		st	lb	Rating		st	lb
124	AIR FORCE BLUE (USA)	9	7	110	TASLEET (GB)	8	7
121	SHALAA (IRE)	9	4	110	TRUE SOLITAIRE (IRE)	8	7
120	MINDING (IRE)	9	3	110	TURRET ROCKS (IRE)	8	7
117	BURATINO (IRE)	9	0	110	YAKABA (FR)	8	7
117	EMOTIONLESS (IRE)	9	0	109	FIRST SELECTION (SPA)	8	6
116	HIT IT A BOMB (USA)	8	13	109	QUIET REFLECTION (GB)	8	6
116	LUMIERE (GB)	8	13	109	RECORDER (GB)	8	6
116	MARCEL (IRE)	8	13	108	ADVENTUROUS (IRE)	8	5
116	MASSAAT (IRE)	8	13	108	KATIE'S DIAMOND (FR)	8	5
115	ACAPULCO (USA)	8	12	107	AIR VICE MARSHAL (USA)	8	4
115	DONJUAN TRIUMPHANT (IRE)	8	12	107	BELVOIR BAY (GB)	8	4
115	GUTAIFAN (IRE)	8	12	107	BLUE BAYOU (IRE)	8	4
115	ILLUMINATE (IRE)	8	12	107	IBN MALIK (IRE)	8	4
114	AJAYA (GB)	8	11	107	PROMISING RUN (USA)	8	4
114	BESHARAH (IRE)	8	11	107	WATERLOO BRIDGE (IRE)	8	4
114	BIRCHWOOD (IRE)	8	11	106	AREEN (IRE)	8	3
113	BALLYDOYLE (IRE)	8	10	106	BING BANG BONG (IRE)	8	3
113	HERALD THE DAWN (IRE)	8	10	106	COOLMORE (IRE)	8	3
113	JOHANNES VERMEER (IRE)	8	10	106	FIELD OF VISION (IRE)	8	3
113	RIBCHESTER (IRE)	8	10	106	GRACIOUS JOHN (GB)	8	3
113	ULTRA (IRE)	8	10	106	KACHY (GB)	8	3
113	WASHINGTON DC (IRE)	8	10	106	LAWMAKING (GB)	8	3
112	ALICE SPRINGS (IRE)	8	9	106	LIL'S JOY (IRE)	8	3
112	CYMRIC (USA)	8	9	106	NO EDUCATION (GB)	8	3
112	NEMORALIA (USA)	8	9	106	RAUCOUS (GB)	8	3
112	ROBIN OF NAVAN (FR)	8	9	106	SHADEN (IRE)	8	3
112	STEADY PACE (GB)	8	9	106	TONY CURTIS (GB)	8	3
112	STORMY ANTARCTIC (GB)	8	9	105	FIREGLOW (GB)	8	2
112	TRIXIA (FR)	8	9	105	GREAT PAGE (IRE)	8	2
111	FOUNDATION (IRE)	8	8	105	HAWKSMOOR (IRE)	8	2
111	GIFTED MASTER (IRE)	8	8	105	MARENKO (IRE)	8	2
111	PAINTED CLIFFS (IRE)	8	8	105	ONLY MINE (IRE)	8	2
111	SMASH WILLIAMS (IRE)	8	8	105	PORT DOUGLAS (IRE)	8	2
110	BEACON ROCK (IRE)	8	7	105	TWIN SAILS (GB)	8	2
110	BLUE DE VEGA (GER)	8	7	104	ASHADIHAN (GB)	8	1
110	DEAUVILLE (IRE)	8	7	104	ELEGANT SUPERMODEL (GER)	8	1
110	GALILEO GOLD (GB)	8	7	104	FIRST VICTORY (IRE)	8	1
110	KING OF ROOKS (GB)	8	7	104	ROULEAU (GB)	8	1
110	LA RIOJA (GB)	8	7	104	ROUND TWO (GB)	8	1
110	LOG OUT ISLAND (IRE)	8	7	104	SQUASH (GB)	8	1
110	NATHRA (IRE)	8	7	103	BEAR CHEEK (IRE)	8	0
110	ORNATE (GB)	8	7	103	EASTON ANGEL (IRE)	8	0
110	QEMAH (IRE)	8	7	103	ELTEZAM (GB)	8	0
110	SANUS PER AQUAM (IRE)	8	7	103	LANDOFHOPEANDGLORY (IRE)	8	0
110	TASHWEEQ (IRE)	8	7	103	MIRAGE (IRE)	8	0

Rating		st	lb
103	MUNTAZAH (GB)	8	0
103	SCRUTINEER (IRE)	8	0
102	ALAMODE (GB)	7	13
102	BEAUTIFUL MORNING (GB)	7	13
102	DHAHMAAN (IRE)	7	13
102	MR LUPTON (IRE)	7	13
102	OPAL TIARA (IRE)	7	13
102	RAH RAH (GB)	7	13
102	THETIS (IRE)	7	13
102	WHATDOIWANTTHATFOR (IRE)	7	13
101	DESSERTOFLIFE (IRE)	7	12
101	DRESSED IN FUR (IRE)	7	12
101	HAALICK (IRE)	7	12
101	HUMPHREY BOGART (IRE)	7	12

Rating		st	lb
101	ROBANNE (GB)	7	12
101	SUITS YOU (FR)	7	12
101	THEY SEEK HIM HERE (IRE)	7	12
100	INDEPENDENCE DAY (IRE)	7	11
100	LIGHT UP OUR WORLD (IRE)	7	11
100	MAYFAIR LADY (GB)	7	11
100	ORVAR (IRE)	7	11
100	PALAWAN (GB)	7	11
100	RACE DAY (IRE)	7	11
100	SIXTH SENSE (IRE)	7	11
100	SPECIAL SEASON (GB)	7	11
100	THANKSFORTELLINGME (IRE)	7	11
100	TIME WARP (GB)	7	11
100	VENTURA STORM (IRE)	7	11

LONGINES WORLD'S BEST RACEHORSE RANKINGS AND EUROPEAN THOROUGHBRED RANKINGS 2015

for three-year-olds rated 115 or greater by the IFHA World's Best Racehorse Rankings Conference. Horses rated 114-110 by the European Thoroughbred Rankings Conference do not constitute a part of the World's Best Racehorse Rankings. Those ratings were compiled on behalf of the European Pattern Committee.

Rating		Trained
134	**AMERICAN PHAROAH** (USA)	USA
130	**GOLDEN HORN** (GB)	GB
124	**ORDER OF ST GEORGE** (IRE)	IRE
123	**DORTMUND** (USA)	USA
123	**FIRING LINE** (USA)	USA
123	**JACK HOBBS** (GB)	GB
123	**MUHAARAR** (GB)	GB
122	**GLENEAGLES** (IRE)	IRE
122	**KEEN ICE** (USA)	USA
122	**NEW BAY** (GB)	FR
121	**DURAMENTE** (JPN)	JPN
121	**HIGHLAND REEL** (IRE)	IRE
121	**MAKE BELIEVE** (GB)	FR
121	**RUNHAPPY** (USA)	USA
120	**ERUPT** (FR)	FR
120	**FOUND** (IRE)	IRE
120	**FROSTED** (USA)	USA
120	**HI HAPPY** (ARG)	ARG
120	**VAZIRABAD** (FR)	FR
119	**LIMATO** (IRE)	GB
119	**MUBTAAHIJ** (IRE)	UAE
119	**TERRITORIES** (IRE)	FR
118	**BONDI BEACH** (IRE)	IRE
118	**KODI BEAR** (IRE)	GB
118	**NUTAN** (IRE)	GER
118	**TIME TEST** (GB)	GB
117	**BELARDO** (IRE)	GB
117	**DARIYAN** (FR)	FR
117	**DON INC** (ARG)	ARG
117	**EXOSPHERE** (AUS)	AUS
117	**INTILAAQ** (USA)	GB
117	**KITASAN BLACK** (JPN)	JPN
117	**LADY ELI** (USA)	USA
117	**LEGATISSIMO** (IRE)	IRE
117	**MING DYNASTY** (FR)	FR
117	**RACING HISTORY** (IRE)	GB
117	**STORM THE STARS** (USA)	GB
117	**TWILIGHT SON** (GB)	GB
116	**AMPERE** (FR)	FR
116	**ARABIAN QUEEN** (IRE)	GB
116	**CARPE DIEM** (USA)	USA
116	**COVERT LOVE** (IRE)	GB
116	**DUTCH CONNECTION** (GB)	GB
116	**ENDLESS DRAMA** (IRE)	IRE
116	**INCENTIVE BOY** (ARG)	CHI
116	**KARPINO** (GER)	GER
116	**LOVELY MARIA** (USA)	USA
116	**REAL STEEL** (JPN)	JPN
116	**SATONO CROWN** (JPN)	JPN
116	**SATONO RASEN** (JPN)	JPN
116	**SIMPLE VERSE** (IRE)	GB
116	**STELLAR WIND** (USA)	USA

Rating		Trained
116	**STRATH BURN** (GB)	GB
116	**TEXAS RED** (USA)	USA
116	**XTRAVAGANT** (NZ)	NZ
115	**AMBITIOUS** (JPN)	JPN
115	**CAVORTING** (USA)	USA
115	**DANON PLATINA** (JPN)	JPN
115	**DANZIG MOON** (CAN)	USA
115	**ERVEDYA** (FR)	FR
115	**ESTIDHKAAR** (IRE)	GB
115	**FIELDS OF ATHENRY** (IRE)	IRE
115	**GOLDSTREAM** (ITY)	ITY
115	**IMPASSABLE** (IRE)	FR
115	**IVAWOOD** (IRE)	GB
115	**JAZZI TOP** (GB)	GB
115	**KARAKTAR** (IRE)	FR
115	**LIA FAIL** (JPN)	JPN
115	**MATERIALITY** (USA)	USA
115	**NIGHTFLOWER** (IRE)	GER
115	**OLD BUNCH** (ARG)	ARG
115	**PLEASCACH** (IRE)	IRE
115	**PRESS STATEMENT** (AUS)	AUS
115	**QUEEN'S JEWEL** (GB)	FR
115	**SILVERWAVE** (FR)	FR
114	**ALMANAAR** (IRE)	FR
114	**CANDARLIYA** (FR)	FR
114	**CIRCUS COUTURE** (IRE)	ITY
114	**CONSORT** (IRE)	GB
114	**DIAMONDSANDRUBIES** (IRE)	IRE
114	**FULL MAST** (USA)	FR
114	**JOURNEY** (GB)	GB
114	**LOVELYN** (GER)	GER
114	**LUCIDA** (IRE)	IRE
114	**MAGICAL MEMORY** (IRE)	GB
114	**MIGWAR** (IRE)	FR
114	**QUALIFY** (IRE)	IRE
114	**SUMBAL** (IRE)	FR
113	**ADAAY** (IRE)	GB
113	**BALIOS** (IRE)	GB
113	**ELM PARK** (GB)	GB
113	**LATHARNACH** (USA)	GB
113	**MATTMU** (GB)	GB
113	**QUASILLO** (GER)	GER
113	**SCOTTISH** (IRE)	GB
113	**STAR OF SEVILLE** (GB)	GB
113	**SUCCESS DAYS** (IRE)	IRE
113	**TANIYAR** (IRE)	FR
113	**TOSCANINI** (IRE)	IRE
113	**TURFDONNA** (GER)	GER
112	**AJALO** (FR)	GER
112	**BEAUTIFUL ROMANCE** (GB)	GB
112	**BOCCA BACIATA** (IRE)	IRE
112	**BOSSY GUEST** (IRE)	GB

Rating	Trained
112 **CURVY** (GB)	IRE
112 **JACK NAYLOR** (GB)	IRE
112 **OSAILA** (IRE)	GB
112 **PALACE PRINCE** (GER)	GER
112 **SEA CALISI** (FR)	FR
112 **THE TIN MAN** (GB)	GB
112 **TORUK** (FR)	FR
112 **VIN CHAUD** (FR)	FR
112 **WAADY** (IRE)	GB
112 **WAR DISPATCH** (USA)	FR
112 **WEDDING VOW** (IRE)	IRE
111 **AKATEA** (IRE)	FR
111 **HATHAL** (USA)	GB
111 **HOLY MOLY** (GB)	GER
111 **IRISH ROOKIE** (IRE)	GB
111 **MARKAZ** (IRE)	GB
111 **MY DREAM BOAT** (IRE)	GB
111 **PHYSIOCRATE** (FR)	FR
111 **PIMENT ROUGE** (FR)	FR
111 **TUPI** (IRE)	GB
111 **ZAWRAQ** (IRE)	IRE

Rating	Trained
110 **BOURREE** (GER)	GER
110 **CODE RED** (GB)	GB
110 **EXOSPHERE** (GB)	GB
110 **FADHAYYIL** (IRE)	GB
110 **FRENCH DRESSING** (GB)	GB
110 **GIOVANNI CANALETTO** (IRE)	IRE
110 **GOKEN** (FR)	FR
110 **HERO LOOK** (IRE)	ITY
110 **JOHNNY BARNES** (IRE)	GB
110 **KOOL KOMPANY** (IRE)	GB
110 **LET'S GO** (USA)	GB
110 **LITTLE NIGHTINGALE** (FR)	FR
110 **MEXICAN GOLD** (USA)	FR
110 **MISS TEMPLE CITY** (USA)	USA
110 **RIDE LIKE THE WIND** (IRE)	GB
110 **SARRASIN** (GB)	FR
110 **THE RIGHT MAN** (GB)	FR
110 **TIBERIAN** (FR)	FR
110 **WAR ENVOY** (USA)	IRE
110 **WEKEELA** (FR)	FR

OLDER HORSES 2015

for four-year-olds and up rated 115 or greater by the IFHA World's Best Racehorse Rankings Conference. Horses rated 114-110 by the European Thoroughbred Rankings Conference do not constitute a part of the World's Best Racehorse Rankings. Those ratings were compiled on behalf of the European Pattern Committee.

Rating		Age	Trained
126	SHARED BELIEF (USA)	4	USA
126	TREVE (FR)	5	FR
125	ABLE FRIEND (AUS)	6	HK
125	SOLOW (GB)	5	FR
123	A SHIN HIKARI (JPN)	4	JPN
123	BEHOLDER (USA)	5	USA
123	CHAUTAUQUA (AUS)	5	AUS
123	DESIGNS ON ROME (IRE)	5	HK
123	FASCINATING ROCK (IRE)	4	IRE
123	FLINTSHIRE (GB)	5	FR
123	FREE EAGLE (IRE)	4	IRE
123	HONOR CODE (USA)	4	USA
123	LANKAN RUPEE (AUS)	6	AUS
123	WINX (AUS)	4	AUS
122	LIAM'S MAP (USA)	4	USA
122	THE GREY GATSBY (IRE)	4	GB
121	AL KAZEEM (GB)	7	GB
121	BLAZING SPEED (GB)	6	HK
121	BRAZEN BEAU (AUS)	4	AUS
121	CALIFORNIA CHROME (USA)	4	USA
121	CAPTAIN OF ALL (SAF)	5	SAF
121	CIRRUS DES AIGLES (FR)	9	FR
121	LOVELY DAY (JPN)	5	JPN
121	MAURICE (JPN)	4	JPN
121	MONGOLIAN KHAN (AUS)	4	NZ
121	POSTPONED (IRE)	4	GB
121	PRINCE BISHOP (IRE)	8	UAE
120	CRITERION (NZ)	4	AUS
120	DOLNIYA (FR)	4	FR
120	EAGLE TOP (GB)	4	GB
120	EFFINEX (USA)	4	USA
120	GOLD SHIP (JPN)	6	JPN
120	STRADA COLORATO/GOLD-FUN (IRE)	6	HK
120	MECCA'S ANGEL (GB)	4	GB
120	PRIVATE ZONE (CAN)	6	USA
120	RAVE/ MILITARY ATTACK(IRE)	7	HK
120	SNOW SKY (GB)	4	GB
120	TEPIN (USA)	4	USA
120	TONALIST (USA)	4	USA
119	DUNBOYNE EXPRESS/ DAN EXCEL(IRE)	7	HK
119	ESOTERIQUE (IRE)	5	FR
119	FUTURA (SAF)	5	SAF
119	GOLD ACTOR (JPN)	4	JPN
119	HUNTER'S LIGHT (IRE)	7	UAE
119	IL CAMPIONE (CHI)	4	CHI
119	ITO (GER)	4	GER
119	LAST IMPACT (JPN)	5	JPN
119	LEA (USA)	6	USA
119	MAIN SEQUENCE (USA)	6	USA
119	PENIAPHOBIA (HK)	4	HK
119	SEA DEFENCE/ GIANT TREASURE(USA)	4	HK
119	SMOOTH ROLLER (USA)	4	USA
118	AEROVELOCITY (NZ)	7	HK
118	AROD (IRE)	4	GB
118	BIG BLUE KITTEN (USA)	7	USA
118	DISSIDENT (AUS)	5	AUS
118	KERMADEC (NZ)	4	AUS
118	MONDIALISTE (IRE)	5	GB

Rating		Age	Trained
118	NIGHT OF THUNDER (IRE)	4	GB
118	PETHER'S MOON (IRE)	5	GB
118	PRINCE GIBRALTAR (FR)	4	FR
118	REAL IMPACT (JPN)	7	JPN
118	ROCA TUMU / BEAUTY FLAME(IRE)	5	HK
118	SECOND STEP (IRE)	4	GB
118	SOLE POWER (GB)	8	IRE
118	SOUNDS OF EARTH (JPN)	4	JPN
118	SPALATO (NZ)	6	SIN
118	STAPHANOS (JPN)	4	JPN
118	TURN ME LOOSE (NZ)	4	NZ
118	UNDRAFTED (USA)	5	USA
117	AMAZING MARIA (IRE)	4	GB
117	BOBAN (AUS)	6	AUS
117	COMPLACENT (AUS)	5	AUS
117	CONTRIBUTER (IRE)	5	AUS
117	COPANO RICKEY (JPN)	5	JPN
117	COUGAR MOUNTAIN (IRE)	4	IRE
117	CUSTOM CUT (IRE)	6	GB
117	DELECTATION (AUS)	4	AUS
117	HALLOWED CROWN (AUS)	4	AUS
117	HARTNELL (GB)	4	AUS
117	JUNGLE CRUISE (JPN)	6	JPN
117	LEGAL EAGLE (SAF)	4	SAF
117	LUCKY HUSSLER (AUS)	6	AUS
117	LUCKY NINE (IRE)	8	HK
117	MANATEE (GB)	4	FR
117	MAX DYNAMITE (FR)	5	IRE
117	ONE AND ONLY (JPN)	4	JPN
117	RED RIFLE (USA)	5	USA
117	ROCK FALL (USA)	4	USA
117	SLUMBER (GB)	7	USA
117	STEPHANIE'S KITTEN (USA)	5	USA
117	STOPCHARGINGMARIA (USA)	4	USA
117	TELESCOPE (IRE)	5	GB
117	TOORMORE (IRE)	4	GB
117	UNIVERSAL LAW (BRZ)	4	BRZ
117	VERCINGETORIX (SAF)	6	UAE
117	VOLKSTOK'N'BARRELL (NZ)	4	NZ
117	WANDJINA (AUS)	4	AUS
117	WAR AFFAIR (NZ)	5	SIN
117	WESTERN HYMN (GB)	4	GB
116	ADMIRE RAKTI (JPN)	6	JPN
116	AIR PILOT (GB)	4	GB
116	BIG ORANGE (GB)	4	GB
116	CANNOCK CHASE (USA)	4	GB
116	CONQUEST TWO STEP (USA)	4	USA
116	CONSTITUTION (USA)	4	USA
116	DUNDONNELL (USA)	5	HK
116	DYLAN MOUTH (IRE)	4	ITY
116	FAME GAME (JPN)	5	JPN
116	FAVORITE TALE (USA)	4	USA
116	FAWKNER (AUS)	8	AUS
116	FIERO (JPN)	6	JPN
116	FINNEGANS WAKE (USA)	6	USA
116	GABRIEL CHARLES (USA)	5	USA
116	GAILO CHOP (FR)	4	FR
116	GOLDREAM (GB)	6	GB

Rating	Age	Trained
116 **HAKUSAN MOON** (JPN)	6	JPN
116 **HAPPY TRAILS** (AUS)	8	AUS
116 **HARD NOT TO LIKE** (CAN)	6	USA
116 **HOKKO TARUMAE** (JPN)	6	JPN
116 **HOPPERTUNITY** (USA)	4	USA
116 **ICE MACHINE** (SAF)	7	SAF
116 **ISLA BONITA** (JPN)	4	JPN
116 **IVANHOWE** (GER)	5	AUS
116 **JACK MILTON** (USA)	5	USA
116 **KIZUNA** (JPN)	5	JPN
116 **LIBERAL** (PER)	4	PER
116 **MIKKI ISLE** (JPN)	4	JPN
116 **MOURINHO** (AUS)	8	AUS
116 **NOBLE BIRD** (USA)	4	USA
116 **NOT LISTENIN'TOME** (AUS)	5	HK
116 **PORNICHET** (FR)	4	AUS
116 **PREFERMENT** (NZ)	4	AUS
116 **PROTONICO** (USA)	4	USA
116 **RACE DAY** (USA)	4	USA
116 **SAFETY CHECK** (IRE)	4	GB
116 **SECRET CIRCLE** (USA)	6	USA
116 **SHONAN PANDORA** (JPN)	4	JPN
116 **SOUND TRUE** (JPN)	5	JPN
116 **SWEET IDEA** (AUS)	5	AUS
116 **TERRAVISTA** (AUS)	6	AUS
116 **THE CORSICAN** (IRE)	4	GB
116 **TOHO JACKAL** (JPN)	4	JPN
116 **TRIP TO PARIS** (IRE)	4	GB
116 **TROPICS** (USA)	7	GB
116 **TWILIGHT ECLIPSE** (USA)	6	USA
116 **V E DAY** (USA)	4	USA
116 **VINCENNES** (JPN)	6	JPN
116 **WEDDING TOAST** (USA)	5	USA
115 **AFRICAN STORY** (GB)	8	UAE
115 **AGENT MURPHY** (GB)	4	GB
115 **ALBORAN SEA** (AUS)	4	SAF
115 **ALMA DE ACERO** (ARG)	6	ARG
115 **ALPINE EAGLE** (AUS)	4	AUS
115 **APPEALING TALE** (USA)	5	USA
115 **BAL A BALI** (BRZ)	5	USA
115 **BROWN PANTHER** (GB)	7	GB
115 **BUFFERING** (AUS)	8	AUS
115 **BUNDLE OF JOY** (AUS)	6	HK
115 **CAPTAIN AMERICA** (SAF)	5	SAF
115 **CHARLES THE GREAT** (IRE)	6	HK
115 **CHARLIE BOY** (AUS)	5	AUS
115 **CHILTON COUNTY / CONTENTMENT**(AUS)	5	HK
115 **CURREN MIROTIC** (JPN)	7	JPN
115 **DENIM AND RUBY** (JPN)	5	JPN
115 **DON OLIVER H** (URU)	5	URU
115 **EL FARAON** (CHI)	6	CHI
115 **ELBCHAUSSEE** (PER)	6	PER
115 **FIRST SEAL** (AUS)	4	AUS
115 **FLYING OFFICER** (USA)	5	GB
115 **GENERALIFE** (AUS)	6	AUS
115 **GENTLEMAN ONLY / BEAUTY ONLY**(IRE)	4	HK
115 **GOSPEL CHOIR** (GB)	6	GB
115 **GRAND ARCH** (USA)	6	USA
115 **GREEN MASK** (USA)	4	USA
115 **GUN PIT** (AUS)	5	HK
115 **HAURAKI** (AUS)	4	AUS
115 **HIELO** (BRZ)	5	URU
115 **I'M YOUR MAN / HE'S YOUR MAN**(FR)	6	AUS
115 **INCANTATION** (JPN)	5	JPN
115 **LA VERDAD** (USA)	5	USA
115 **LACHESIS** (JPN)	5	JPN
115 **LENOVO** (ARG)	5	ARG
115 **LIGHTNING SPEAR** (GB)	4	GB
115 **LINES OF BATTLE** (USA)	5	HK
115 **LLAREGYB / PACKING LLAREGYB**(IRE)	5	HK
115 **LOGOTYPE** (JPN)	5	JPN
115 **LORD OF THE SKY** (AUS)	5	AUS
115 **LUGER** (AUS)	5	HK
115 **MASOCHISTIC** (USA)	5	USA
115 **MONGOLIAN SATURDAY** (USA)	5	USA
115 **MORENO** (USA)	5	USA
115 **MUTHMIR** (IRE)	5	GB
115 **NUOVO RECORD** (JPN)	4	JPN
115 **OKIE DOKIE / SUPER JOCKEY**(NZ)	7	HK
115 **RANGALI** (AUS)	4	FR
115 **REBEL DANE** (AUS)	6	AUS
115 **RED CADEAUX** (GB)	9	GB
115 **REWARDING HERO** (GB)	6	HK
115 **RING WEEKEND** (USA)	4	USA
115 **ROYAL DESCENT** (AUS)	6	AUS
115 **SACRED STAR** (AUS)	4	NZ
115 **SATONO ALADDIN** (JPN)	4	JPN
115 **SCISSOR KICK** (AUS)	4	AUS
115 **SHEER DRAMA** (USA)	5	USA
115 **SHOOTING TO WIN** (AUS)	4	AUS
115 **SKY HUNTER** (GB)	5	GB
115 **SPIELBERG** (JPN)	6	JPN
115 **SPIRITJIM** (FR)	5	FR
115 **SRIKANDI** (AUS)	5	AUS
115 **STEPITUP** (AUS)	6	SIN
115 **SWEYNESSE** (AUS)	4	AUS
115 **TAC DE BOISTRON** (FR)	8	GB
115 **TAMARKUZ** (USA)	5	UAE
115 **THE CLEANER** (AUS)	8	AUS
115 **THE PIZZA MAN** (USA)	6	USA
115 **TIROLESCA** (ARG)	4	ARG
115 **TO THE WORLD** (JPN)	4	JPN
115 **TODO UN AMIGUITO** (ARG)	7	ARG
115 **TOSEN REVE** (JPN)	7	JPN
115 **TRIP TO HEAVEN** (SAF)	4	SAF
115 **UNTAPABLE** (USA)	4	USA
115 **WARREN'S VENEDA** (USA)	5	USA
115 **WAVELL AVENUE** (CAN)	4	USA
115 **WILD CHIEF** (GER)	4	GER
115 **WILD DUDE** (USA)	5	USA
115 **WONDER ACUTE** (JPN)	9	JPN
115 **WYLIE HALL** (AUS)	6	SAF
115 **ZAC SPIRIT** (AUS)	6	SIN
114 **CABLE BAY** (IRE)	4	GB
114 **DUBDAY** (GB)	5	QTR
114 **FRENCH NAVY** (GB)	5	GB
114 **GABRIAL** (GB)	6	GB
114 **GORDON LORD BYRON** (IRE)	7	IRE
114 **INTEGRAL** (GB)	5	GB
114 **MAGIC ARTIST** (IRE)	4	GER
114 **ODELIZ** (IRE)	5	GB
114 **RIBBONS** (GB)	5	GB
114 **ROMSDAL** (GB)	4	GB
114 **SILJAN'S SAGA** (FR)	5	FR
114 **SIRIUS** (GER)	4	GER
114 **VADAMOS** (FR)	4	FR
114 **WE ARE** (IRE)	4	FR
113 **AVENIR CERTAIN** (FR)	4	FR
113 **BAWINA** (IRE)	5	GB
113 **BRETON ROCK** (IRE)	5	GB
113 **CLEO FAN** (ITY)	4	ITY
113 **CLEVER COOKIE** (GB)	7	GB
113 **DANZENO** (GB)	4	GB
113 **EURO CHARLINE** (GB)	4	GB

Rating		Age	Trained
113	**FINTRY** (IRE)	4	FR
113	**FREE PORT LUX** (GB)	4	FR
113	**GUILIANI** (IRE)	4	GER
113	**HERE COMES WHEN** (IRE)	5	GB
113	**KINGFISHER** (IRE)	4	IRE
113	**MUSTAJEEB** (GB)	4	IRE
113	**RED DUBAWI** (IRE)	7	GER
113	**SECRET GESTURE** (GB)	5	GB
113	**SO BELOVED** (GB)	5	GB
113	**SOVEREIGN DEBT** (IRE)	6	GB
113	**TULLIUS** (IRE)	7	GB
112	**AMARON** (GB)	6	GER
112	**ARAB SPRING** (IRE)	5	GB
112	**ASTAIRE** (IRE)	4	GB
112	**AYRAD** (IRE)	4	GB
112	**BALTY BOYS** (IRE)	6	GB
112	**BELLO MATTEO** (FR)	4	FR
112	**BIG BAZ** (IRE)	5	GB
112	**EASTERN IMPACT** (IRE)	4	GB
112	**FORGOTTEN RULES** (IRE)	5	IRE
112	**GUARDINI** (IRE)	4	GB
112	**KARAKONTIE** (JPN)	4	FR
112	**LITIGANT** (GB)	7	GB
112	**LUCKY LION** (GB)	4	GER
112	**LUCKY SPEED** (IRE)	5	GER
112	**MEDICEAN MAN** (GB)	9	GB
112	**MELEAGROS** (IRE)	6	FR
112	**MILLE ET MILLE** (GB)	5	FR
112	**MISS FRANCE** (IRE)	4	FR
112	**MUTAKAYYEF** (GB)	4	GB
112	**PAS DE DEUX** (GER)	5	GER
112	**SIR MAXIMILIAN** (IRE)	6	GB
112	**SLOANE AVENUE** (USA)	4	GB
112	**SPECULATIVE BID** (IRE)	4	GB
112	**STEPPER POINT** (GB)	6	GB
112	**TAPESTRY** (IRE)	4	IRE
112	**TOP NOTCH TONTO** (IRE)	5	GB
112	**TRYSTER** (IRE)	4	GB
112	**VIF MONSIEUR** (GER)	5	GER
112	**WICKLOW BRAVE** (GB)	6	IRE
111	**AFFAIRE SOLITAIRE** (IRE)	5	FR
111	**ALEX MY BOY** (IRE)	4	GER
111	**BAINO HOPE** (FR)	4	FR
111	**BATHYRHON** (GER)	5	FR
111	**CASPAR NETSCHER** (GB)	6	GB
111	**DARK EMERALD** (IRE)	5	GB
111	**ENERGIA DAVOS** (BRZ)	7	GB
111	**FRACTIONAL** (IRE)	6	FR
111	**GRAPHIC** (IRE)	6	GB
111	**KASPERSKY** (IRE)	4	ITY
111	**LINE OF REASON** (IRE)	5	GB
111	**MAVERICK WAVE** (USA)	4	GB
111	**MIZZOU** (IRE)	4	GB
111	**PANAMA HAT** (GB)	4	IRE

Rating		Age	Trained
111	**PARISH HALL** (IRE)	6	IRE
111	**POTEMKIN** (GER)	4	GER
111	**PRETEND** (IRE)	4	GB
111	**SHEIKHZAYEDROAD** (GB)	6	GB
111	**SHINING EMERALD** (GB)	4	GER
111	**SIMENON** (IRE)	8	IRE
111	**STEPS** (IRE)	7	GB
111	**SUEDOIS** (FR)	4	FR
111	**WADI AL HATTAWI** (IRE)	5	GB
111	**WALZERTAKT** (GER)	6	GER
110	**AJAXANA** (GER)	4	GER
110	**AMY ERIA** (IRE)	4	FR
110	**ASCRIPTION** (IRE)	6	GB
110	**BASEM** (GB)	4	GB
110	**BILLABONG** (MOR)	6	FR
110	**CATCALL** (FR)	6	FR
110	**CHIL THE KITE** (GB)	6	GB
110	**CLADOCERA** (GB)	4	FR
110	**COCKTAIL QUEEN** (IRE)	5	FR
110	**CONNECTICUT** (GB)	4	GB
110	**ELLIPTIQUE** (IRE)	4	FR
110	**FATE** (FR)	6	FR
110	**FEODORA** (GER)	4	FR
110	**FIRE FIGHTING** (IRE)	4	GB
110	**FLY WITH ME** (FR)	5	FR
110	**GLASS OFFICE** (GB)	5	GB
110	**GM HOPKINS** (GB)	4	GB
110	**GOLDEN WOOD** (FR)	5	FR
110	**HILLSTAR** (GB)	5	GB
110	**KELINNI** (IRE)	7	GB
110	**LORESHO** (FR)	4	FR
110	**MAAREK** (GB)	8	IRE
110	**MAHSOOB** (GB)	4	GB
110	**MASTER CARPENTER** (IRE)	4	GB
110	**MAYHEM** (IRE)	4	FR
110	**MISS MARJURIE** (IRE)	5	GB
110	**MOOHAARIB** (IRE)	4	GB
110	**MOUNT LOGAN** (IRE)	4	GB
110	**MOVE IN TIME** (GB)	7	GB
110	**MOVIESTA** (USA)	5	IRE
110	**NORDICO** (GER)	4	GER
110	**OUT DO** (GB)	6	GB
110	**PALLASATOR** (GB)	6	GB
110	**PEARL SECRET** (GB)	6	GB
110	**QUEST FOR MORE** (IRE)	5	GB
110	**RIZEENA** (IRE)	4	GB
110	**SHIFTING POWER** (GB)	4	GB
110	**SON CESIO** (FR)	4	FR
110	**SPOIL THE FUN** (FR)	6	FR
110	**TAKE COVER** (GB)	8	GB
110	**TALMADA** (USA)	4	GB
110	**WAKE FOREST** (GER)	5	GER
110	**WATCHABLE** (GB)	5	GB

RACEFORM CHAMPIONS 2015

ONLY HORSES WHICH HAVE RUN IN EUROPE ARE INCLUDED

FOUR-YEAR-OLDS AND UP

FASCINATING ROCK	125
THE GREY GATSBY	125
TREVE	125
FLINTSHIRE	124
FREE EAGLE	124
SOLOW	124
POSTPONED	124
UNDRAFTED	123
NIGHT OF THUNDER	122
TELESCOPE	122

THREE-YEAR-OLD COLT

GOLDEN HORN	132
MUHAARAR	127
JACK HOBBS	125
ORDER OF ST GEORGE	125
GLENEAGLES	124
NEW BAY	122

THREE-YEAR-OLD FILLY

FOUND	119
ERVEDYA	118
LEGATISSIMO	118
IMPASSABLE	118
SIMPLE VERSE	118
JOURNEY	117

SPRINTER

MUHAARAR	127
UNDRAFTED	123
BRAZEN BEAU	122
MECCA'S ANGEL	121
TROPICS	121
MUTHMIR	121

STAYER

ORDER OF ST GEORGE	125
BROWN PANTHER	120
VAZIRABAD	120
BONDI BEACH	119
FIELDS OF ATHENRY	118
MAX DYNAMITE	118

TWO-YEAR-OLD COLT

AIR FORCE BLUE	125
SHALAA	120
MARCEL	118
BURATINO	117
DONJUAN TRIUMPHANT	117
EMOTIONLESS	117
MASSAAT	116

TWO-YEAR-OLD FILLY

MINDING	119
LUMIERE	114
ACAPULCO	115
BALLYDOYLE	113
ILLUMINATE	113
BESHARAH	112

MEDIAN TIMES 2015

The following Raceform median times are used in the calculation of the Split Second speed figures. They represent a true average time for the distance, which has been arrived at after looking at the winning times for all races over each distance within the past five years, except for those restricted to two or three-year-olds.

Some current race distances have been omitted as they have not yet had a sufficient number of races run over them to produce a reliable average time.

ASCOT

5f 1m 0.50	1m Straight 1m 40.80	2m 3m 29.00
6f 1m 14.50	1m 2f 2m 7.40	2m 4f 4m 24.80
7f 1m 27.60	1m 4f 2m 32.50	2m 5f 159y 4m 49.40
1m Round 1m 40.70	1m 6f 3m 1.00	

AYR

5f 59.40	1m 1m 43.80	1m 5f 13y 2m 54.00
6f 1m 12.40	1m 1f 20y 1m 57.50	1m 7f 3m 20.40
7f 50y 1m 33.40	1m 2f 2m 12.00	2m 1f 105y 3m 55.00

BATH

5f 11y 1m 2.50	1m 2f 46y 2m 11.00	1m 5f 22y 2m 52.00
5f 161y 1m 11.20	1m 3f 144y 2m 30.60	2m 1f 34y 3m 51.90
1m 5y 1m 40.80		

BEVERLEY

5f 1m 3.50	1m 100y 1m 47.60	1m 4f 16y 2m 39.80
7f 100y 1m 33.80	1m 1f 207y 2m 7.00	2m 35y 3m 39.80

BRIGHTON

5f 59y 1m 2.30	6f 209y 1m 23.10	1m 1f 209y 2m 3.60
5f 213y 1m 10.20	7f 214y 1m 36.00	1m 3f 196y 2m 32.70

CARLISLE

5f 1m 0.80	7f 200y 1m 40.00	1m 6f 32y 3m 7.50
5f 193y 1m 13.70	1m 1f 61y 1m 57.60	2m 1f 52y 3m 53.00
6f 192y 1m 27.10	1m 3f 107y 2m 23.10	

CATTERICK

5f 59.80	7f 1m 27.00	1m 5f 175y 3m 3.60
5f 212y 1m 13.60	1m 3f 214y 2m 38.90	1m 7f 177y 3m 32.00

CHELMSFORD CITY (A.W)

5f 1m 0.20	1m 1m 39.90	1m 5f 66y 2m 53.60
6f 1m 13.70	1m 1f 46y 1m 58.40	1m 6f 3m 3.20
7f 1m 27.20	1m 2f 2m 8.60	2m 3m 30.00

CHEPSTOW

5f 16y 59.30	1m 14y 1m 36.20	2m 49y 3m 38.90
6f 16y 1m 12.00	1m 2f 36y 2m 10.60	2m 2f 4m 3.60
7f 16y 1m 23.20	1m 4f 23y 2m 39.00	

CHESTER

5f 16y 1m 1.00	7f 122y 1m 33.80	1m 5f 89y 2m 52.70
5f 110y 1m 6.20	1m 75y 2m 11.20	1m 6f 91y 3m 7.00
6f 18y 1m 13.80	1m 3f 79y 2m 24.80	1m 7f 195y 3m 28.00
7f 2y 1m 26.50	1m 4f 66y 2m 38.50	2m 2f 147y 4m 4.80

DONCASTER

5f.................................... 1m 0.50	7f.................................... 1m 26.30	1m 4f.................................... 2m 34.90
5f 140y.............................. 1m 8.80	1m Straight........................ 1m 39.30	1m 6f 132y.......................... 3m 7.40
6f.................................... 1m 13.60	1m Round........................... 1m 39.70	2m 110y.............................. 3m 40.40
6f 110y.............................. 1m 19.90	1m 2f 60y............................ 2m 9.40	2m 2f.................................. 3m 55.00

EPSOM

5f.................................... 55.70	7f.................................... 1m 23.30	1m 2f 18y............................ 2m 9.70
6f.................................... 1m 9.40	1m 114y.............................. 1m 46.10	1m 4f 10y............................ 2m 38.90

FFOS LAS

5f.................................... 58.30	1m 2f.................................. 2m 9.40	1m 6f.................................. 3m 3.80
6f.................................... 1m 10.00	1m 4f.................................. 2m 37.40	2m.................................... 3m 30.00
1m.................................... 1m 41.00		

GOODWOOD

5f.................................... 1m 0.20	1m 1f.................................. 1m 56.30	1m 6f.................................. 3m 3.60
6f.................................... 1m 12.20	1m 1f 192y.......................... 2m 8.10	2m.................................... 3m 29.00
7f.................................... 1m 27.00	1m 3f.................................. 2m 26.50	2m 5f.................................. 4m 31.00
1m.................................... 1m 39.90	1m 4f.................................. 2m 38.40	

HAMILTON

5f 4y................................ 1m 0.00	1m 1f 36y............................ 1m 59.70	1m 4f 17y............................ 2m 38.60
6f 5y................................ 1m 12.20	1m 3f 16y............................ 2m 25.60	1m 5f 9y.............................. 2m 53.90
1m 65y................................ 1m 48.40		

HAYDOCK

5f.................................... 1m 0.80	7f.................................... 1m 30.70	1m 3f 200y.......................... 2m 33.80
5fI.................................... 1m 0.80	1m.................................... 1m 43.70	1m 6f.................................. 3m 2.00
6f.................................... 1m 13.80	1m 2f 95y............................ 2m 15.50	2m 45y................................ 3m 34.30
6fI.................................... 1m 13.80		

KEMPTON (A.W)

5f.................................... 1m 0.50	1m.................................... 1m 39.80	1m 4f.................................. 2m 34.50
6f.................................... 1m 13.10	1m 2f.................................. 2m 8.00	2m.................................... 3m 30.10
7f.................................... 1m 26.00	1m 3f.................................. 2m 21.90	

LEICESTER

5f 2y................................ 1m 0.00	7f 9y.................................. 1m 26.20	1m 1f 218y.......................... 2m 7.90
5f 218y.............................. 1m 13.00	1m 60y................................ 1m 45.10	1m 3f 183y.......................... 2m 33.90

LINGFIELD (TURF)

5f.................................... 58.20	7f 140y.............................. 1m 32.30	1m 3f 106y.......................... 2m 31.50
6f.................................... 1m 11.20	1m 1f.................................. 1m 56.60	1m 6f.................................. 3m 10.00
7f.................................... 1m 23.30	1m 2f.................................. 2m 10.50	

LINGFIELD (A.W)

5f 6y................................ 58.80	1m 1y................................ 1m 38.20	1m 5f.................................. 2m 46.00
6f 1y................................ 1m 11.90	1m 2f.................................. 2m 6.60	1m 7f 169y.......................... 3m 25.70
7f 1y................................ 1m 24.80	1m 4f.................................. 2m 33.00	

MUSSELBURGH

5f.................................... 1m 0.40	1m 1f.................................. 1m 53.90	1m 6f.................................. 3m 5.30
7f 30y................................ 1m 29.00	1m 4f 100y.......................... 2m 42.00	2m.................................... 3m 33.50
1m.................................... 1m 41.20	1m 5f.................................. 2m 52.00	

NEWBURY

5f 34y................................ 1m 1.40	1m Straight........................ 1m 39.70	1m 3f 5y.............................. 2m 21.20
6f 8y................................ 1m 13.00	1m 7y Round...................... 1m 38.70	1m 4f 5y.............................. 2m 35.50
6f 110y.............................. 1m 19.30	1m 1f.................................. 1m 55.50	1m 5f 61y............................ 2m 52.00
7f Straight.......................... 1m 25.70	1m 2f 6y............................ 2m 8.80	2m.................................... 3m 32.00

NEWCASTLE
Turf racing discontinued in 2016;
no AW standard times yet

NEWMARKET (ROWLEY MILE)

5f.....................................59.10	1m 1f...............................1m 51.70	1m 6f...............................2m 57.00
6f................................1m 12.20	1m 2f.................................2m 5.80	2m.................................3m 30.50
7f................................1m 25.40	1m 4f...............................2m 32.00	2m 2f..............................3m 52.00
1m................................1m 38.60		

NEWMARKET (JULY COURSE)

5f.....................................59.10	1m..................................1m 40.00	1m 5f..............................2m 44.00
6f................................1m 12.50	1m 2f.................................2m 5.50	1m 6f 175y.......................3m 8.40
7f................................1m 25.70	1m 4f...............................2m 32.90	2m 24y............................3m 27.00

NOTTINGHAM

5f 13y.............................1m 1.50	1m 75y Inner..................1m 49.00	1m 6f 15y........................3m 7.00
5f 13y Inner...................1m 1.50	1m 1f................................1m 57.60	1m 6f 15y Inner...............3m 7.00
6f 15y...........................1m 14.70	1m 2f 50y........................2m 14.30	2m 9y.............................3m 34.50
1m 75y.........................1m 49.00	1m 2f 50y Inner................2m 14.30	

PONTEFRACT

5f...................................1m 3.30	1m 2f 6y..........................2m 13.70	2m 1f 216y......................3m 56.20
6f.................................1m 16.90	1m 4f 8y..........................2m 40.80	2m 5f 122y......................4m 51.00
1m 4y...........................1m 45.90	2m 1f 22y........................3m 44.60	

REDCAR

5f.....................................58.60	1m..................................1m 36.60	1m 6f 19y........................3m 4.70
6f.................................1m 11.80	1m 1f................................1m 53.00	2m 4y.............................3m 31.40
7f.................................1m 24.50	1m 2f.................................2m 7.10	

RIPON

5f...................................1m 0.00	1m 1f................................1m 54.70	1m 4f 10y........................2m 36.70
6f.................................1m 13.00	1m 1f 170y........................2m 5.40	2m.................................3m 31.80
1m.................................1m 41.40		

SALISBURY

5f...................................1m 1.00	1m..................................1m 43.50	1m 4f..............................2m 38.00
6f.................................1m 14.80	1m 1f 198y........................2m 9.90	1m 6f 21y........................3m 7.40
6f 212y.........................1m 28.60		

SANDOWN

5f 6y.............................1m 1.60	1m 1f................................1m 55.70	1m 6f...............................3m 4.50
7f 16y...........................1m 29.50	1m 2f 7y..........................2m 10.50	2m 78y............................3m 38.70
1m 14y.........................1m 43.30		

SOUTHWELL (A.W)

5f.....................................59.70	1m..................................1m 43.70	1m 6f...............................3m 8.30
6f.................................1m 16.50	1m 3f................................2m 28.00	2m.................................3m 45.50
7f.................................1m 30.30	1m 4f...............................2m 41.00	

THIRSK

5f.....................................59.60	7f....................................1m 27.20	1m 4f..............................2m 36.20
6f.................................1m 12.70	1m..................................1m 40.10	2m.................................3m 28.30

WETHERBY
Standard times not yet available;
insufficient data

WINDSOR

5f 10y 1m 0.30	1m 67y 1m 44.70	1m 3f 135y 2m 29.50
6f 1m 13.00	1m 2f 7y 2m 8.70	

WOLVERHAMPTON (A.W)

5f 20y 1m 1.90	1m 141y 1m 50.10	1m 5f 194y 3m 4.80
5f 216y 1m 14.50	1m 1f 103y 2m 0.80	2m 119y 3m 43.70
7f 32y 1m 28.80	1m 4f 50y 2m 40.80	

YARMOUTH

5f 43y 1m 2.70	1m 3y 1m 40.60	1m 3f 101y 2m 28.70
6f 3y 1m 14.40	1m 1f 1m 55.80	1m 6f 17y 3m 7.60
7f 3y 1m 26.60	1m 2f 21y 2m 10.50	2m 3m 32.40

YORK

5f 59.30	1m 1m 39.00	1m 4f 2m 33.20
5f 89y 1m 4.10	1m 110y 1m 45.90	1m 6f 3m 0.20
6f 1m 11.90	1m 208y 1m 52.00	2m 88y 3m 34.50
7f 1m 25.30	1m 2f 88y 2m 12.50	2m 2f 3m 55.40

Join Members' Club for your definitive source of tipping, news, analysis, statistics and ratings. Membership starts from just 40p a day*

RACING POST.com/membersclub

RACEFORM RECORD TIMES (FLAT)

ASCOT

DISTANCE	TIME	AGE	WEIGHT	GOING	HORSE	DATE		
5f	58.80 secs	2	9-1	Good To Firm	NO NAY NEVER	Jun	20	2013
5f	57.44 secs	3	9-1	Good To Firm	MISS ANDRETTI	Jun	19	2007
6f	1m 12.46	2	9-1	Good To Firm	HENRYTHENAVIGATOR	Jun	19	2007
6f	1m 11.50	3	9-10	Good To Firm	MINCE	Aug	11	2012
7f	1m 26.55	2	9-0	Good To Firm	MALABAR	July	25	2014
7f	1m 24.28	4	8-11	Good To Firm	GALICIAN	July	27	2013
1m (Rnd)	1m 39.55	2	8-12	Good	JOSHUA TREE	Sep	26	2009
1m (Rnd)	1m 38.32	3	9-0	Good To Firm	GHANAATI	Jun	19	2009
1m (Str)	1m 37.09	4	9-0	Good To Firm	INTEGRAL	Jun	18	2014
1m 2f	2m 01.90	5	8-11	Good To Firm	THE FUGUE	Jun	18	2014
1m 4f	2m 24.60	4	9-7	Good	NOVELLIST	July	27	2013
2m	3m 24.12	4	8-12	Good To Firm	MIZZOU	April	29	2015
2m 4f	4m 16.92	6	9-2	Good To Firm	RITE OF PASSAGE	Jun	17	2010
2m 5f 159y	4m 45.67	7	9-2	Good To Firm	ORIENTAL FOX	Jun	20	2015

AYR

DISTANCE	TIME	AGE	WEIGHT	GOING	HORSE	DATE		
5f	56.9 secs	2	8-11	Good	BOOGIE STREET	Sep	18	2003
5f	55.68 secs	3	8-11	Good To Firm	LOOK BUSY	Jun	21	2008
6f	1m 09.7	2	7-10	Good	SIR BERT	Sep	17	1969
6f	1m 08.37	5	8-6	Good To Firm	MAISON DIEU	Jun	21	2008
7f 50y	1m 28.9	2	9-0	Good	TAFAAHUM	Sep	19	2003
7f 50y	1m 28.07	5	9-0	Good To Firm	GINGER JACK	May	30	2012
1m	1m 39.18	2	9-7	Good	MOONLIGHTNAVIGATOR	Sep	18	2014
1m	1m 36.0	4	7-13	Firm	SUFI	Sep	16	1959
1m 1f 20y	1m 50.3	4	9-3	Good	RETIREMENT	Sep	19	2003
1m 2f	2m 04.0	4	9-9	Good To Firm	ENDLESS HALL	July	17	2000
1m 5f 13y	2m 45.8	4	9-7	Good To Firm	EDEN'S CLOSE	Sep	18	1993
1m 7f	3m 13.1	3	9-4	Good	ROMANY RYE	Sep	19	1991
2m 1f 105y	3m 45.0	4	6-13	Good	CURRY	Sep	16	1955

BATH

DISTANCE	TIME	AGE	WEIGHT	GOING	HORSE	DATE		
5f 11y	59.50 secs	2	9-2	Firm	AMOUR PROPRE	July	24	2008
5f 11y	58.75 secs	3	8-12	Firm	ENTICING	May	1	2007
5f 161y	1m 08.7	2	8-12	Firm	QALAHARI	July	24	2008
5f 161y	1m 08.1	6	9-0	Firm	MADRACO	May	22	1989
1m 5y	1m 39.51	2	9-2	Firm	NATURAL CHARM	Sep	14	2014
1m 5y	1m 37.2	5	8-12	Good To Firm	ADOBE	Jun	17	2000
1m 5y	1m 37.2	3	8-7	Firm	ALASHA	Aug	18	2012
1m 2f 46y	2m 05.6	3	9-0	Good To Firm	CONNOISSEUR BAY	May	29	1998
1m 3f 144y	2m 25.74	3	9-0	Hard	TOP OF THE CHARTS	Sep	8	2005
1m 5f 22y	2m 47.2	4	10-0	Firm	FLOWN	Aug	13	1991
2m 1f 34y	3m 43.4	6	7-9	Firm	YAHESKA	Jun	14	2003

BEVERLEY

DISTANCE	TIME	AGE	WEIGHT	GOING	HORSE	DATE		
5f	1m 00.89	2	8-12	Good To Firm	LANGAVAT	Jun	8	2013
5f	1m 00.1	4	9-5	Firm	PIC UP STICKS	Apr	16	2003
7f 100y	1m 31.1	2	9-0	Firm	MAJAL	July	30	1991
7f 100y	1m 31.1	2	9-7	Good To Firm	CHAMPAGNE PRINCE	Aug	10	1995
7f 100y	1m 29.5	3	7-8	Firm	WHO'S TEF	July	30	1991
1m 100y	1m 43.3	2	9-0	Firm	ARDEN	Sep	24	1986
1m 100y	1m 42.2	3	8-4	Firm	LEGAL CASE	Jun	14	1989
1m 1f 207y	2m 01.00	3	9-7	Good To Firm	EASTERN ARIA	Aug	29	2009
1m 4f 16y	2m 33.35	5	9-2	Good To Firm	TWO JABS	April	23	2015
2m 35y	3m 29.5	4	9-2	Good To Firm	RUSHEN RAIDER	Aug	14	1996

BRIGHTON

DISTANCE	TIME	AGE	WEIGHT	GOING	HORSE	DATE		
5f 59y	1m.00.1	2	9-0	Firm	BID FOR BLUE	May	6	1993
5f 59y	59.3 secs	3	8-9	Firm	PLAY HEVER GOLF	May	26	1993
5f 213y	1m 08.1	2	8-9	Firm	SONG MIST	July	16	1996
5f 213y	1m 07.3	3	8-9	Firm	THIRD PARTY	Jun	3	1997
5f 213y	1m 07.3	5	9-1	Good To Firm	BLUNDELL LANE	May	4	2000
7f 214y	1m 32.8	2	9-7	Firm	ASIAN PETE	Oct	3	1989
7f 214y	1m 30.5	5	8-11	Firm	MYSTIC RIDGE	May	27	1999
1m 1f 209y	2m 04.7	2	9-0	Good To Soft	ESTEEMED MASTER	Nov	2	2001
1m 1f 209y	1m 57.2	3	9-0	Firm	GET THE MESSAGE	Apr	30	1984
1m 3f 196y	2m 25.8	4	8-2	Firm	NEW ZEALAND	July	4	1985

CARLISLE

DISTANCE	TIME	AGE	WEIGHT	GOING	HORSE	DATE		
5f	1m 00.1	2	8-5	Firm	LA TORTUGA	Aug	2	1999
5f	58.8 secs	3	9-8	Good To Firm	ESATTO	Aug	21	2002
5f 193y	1m 12.45	2	9-6	Good To Firm	MUSICAL GUEST	Sep	11	2005
5f 193y	1m 10.83	4	9-0	Good To Firm	BO MCGINTY	Sep	11	2005
6f 192y	1m 24.3	3	8-9	Good To Firm	MARJURITA	Aug	21	2002
7f 200y	1m 37.34	5	9-7	Good To Firm	HULA BALLEW	Aug	17	2005
1m 1f 61y	1m 53.8	3	9-0	Firm	LITTLE JIMBOB	Jun	14	2004
1m 3f 107y	2m 22.00	3	9-5	Good To Firm	TARTAN GIGHA	Jun	4	2012
1m 3f 206y	2m 29.13	5	9-8	Good To Firm	TEMPSFORD	Sep	19	2005
1m 6f 32y	3m 02.2	6	8-10	Good To Firm	EXPLOSIVE SPEED	May	26	1994

CATTERICK

DISTANCE	TIME	AGE	WEIGHT	GOING	HORSE	DATE		
5f	57.6 secs	2	9-0	Firm	H HARRISON	Oct	8	2002
5f	57.1 secs	4	8-7	Firm	KABCAST	July	7	1989
5f 212y	1m 11.4	2	9-4	Firm	CAPTAIN NICK	July	11	1978
5f 212y	1m 09.8	9	8-13	Good To Firm	SHARP HAT	May	30	2003
7f	1m 24.1	2	8-11	Firm	LINDA'S FANTASY	Sep	18	1982
7f	1m 22.5	6	8-7	Firm	DIFFERENTIAL	May	31	2003
1m 3f 214y	2m 30.5	3	8-8	Good To Firm	RAHAF	May	30	2003
1m 5f 175y	2m 54.8	3	8-5	Firm	GERYON	May	31	1984
1m 7f 177y	3m 20.8	4	7-11	Firm	BEAN BOY	July	8	1982

CHEPSTOW

DISTANCE	TIME	AGE	WEIGHT	GOING	HORSE	DATE		
5f 16y	57.6 secs	2	8-11	Firm	MICRO LOVE	July	8	1986
5f 16y	56.8 secs	3	8-4	Firm	TORBAY EXPRESS	Sep	15	1979
6f 16y	1m 08.5	2	9-2	Firm	NINJAGO	July	27	2012
6f 16y	1m 08.1	3	9-7	Firm	AMERICA CALLING	Sep	18	2001
7f 16y	1m 20.8	2	9-0	Good To Firm	ROYAL AMARETTO	Sep	12	1996
7f 16y	1m 19.3	3	9-0	Firm	TARANAKI	Sep	18	2001
1m 14y	1m 33.1	2	8-11	Good To Firm	SKI ACADEMY	Aug	28	1995
1m 14y	1m 31.6	3	8-13	Firm	STOLI	Sep	18	2001
1m 2f 36y	2m 04.1	5	8-9	Hard	LEONIDAS	July	5	1983
1m 2f 36y	2m 04.1	5	7-8	Good To Firm	IT'S VARADAN	Sep	9	1989
1m 2f 36y	2m 04.1	3	8-5	Good To Firm	ELA ATHENA	July	23	1999
1m 4f 23y	2m 31.0	3	8-9	Good To Firm	SPRITSAIL	July	13	1989
2m 49y	3m 27.7	4	9-0	Good To Firm	WIZZARD ARTIST	July	1	1989
2m 2f	3m 56.4	5	8-7	Good To Firm	LAFFAH	July	8	2000

CHELMSFORD CITY (A.W)

DISTANCE	TIME	AGE	WEIGHT	GOING	HORSE	DATE		
5f	58.72 secs	2	9-7	Standard	SUN'AQ	Nov	19	2015
5f	57.39 secs	6	9-2	Standard	LANCELOT DU LAC	Jan	2	2016
6f	1m 11.19	2	8-13	Standard	FLORENCIO	Oct	15	2015
6f	1m 10.16	4	9-4	Standard	GOLDEN AMBER	Aug	18	2015
1m	1m 37.15	2	9-3	Standard	DRAGON MALL	Sept	26	2015
1m	1m 35.46	4	9-7	Standard	MINDYOUROWNBUSINESS	Nov	23	2015
1m 2f	2m 02.33	8	9-7	Standard	BANCNUANAHEIREANN	Nov	5	2015
1m 5f 66y	2m 47.60	3	9-6	Standard	SCARLET MINSTREL	Nov	19	2015
1m 6f	2m 55.65	4	10-0	Standard	CASTLE COMBE	Sept	3	2015
2m	3m 23.27	3	8-8	Standard	DUCHESS OF MARMITE	Nov	23	2015

CHESTER

DISTANCE	TIME	AGE	WEIGHT	GOING	HORSE	DATE		
5f 16y	59.94 secs	2	9-2	Good To Firm	LEIBA LEIBA	Jun	26	2010
5f 16y	58.88 secs	3	8-7	Good To Firm	PETERKIN	July	11	2014
5f 110y	1m 6.39	2	8-7	Good To Firm	KINEMATIC	Sep	11	2014
5f 110y	1m 05.02	6	8-9	Good	BALLESTEROS	Aug	22	2015
6f 18y	1m 12.85	2	8-11	Good To Firm	FLYING EXPRESS	Aug	31	2002
6f 18y	1m 12.02	5	9-5	Good To Firm	DEAUVILLE PRINCE	June	13	2015
6f 18y	1m 12.78	6	9-2	Good	STACK ROCK	Jun	23	1993
7f 2y	1m 25.29	2	9-0	Good To Firm	DUE RESPECT	Sep	25	2002
7f 2y	1m 23.75	5	8-13	Good To Firm	THREE GRACES	July	9	2005
7f 122y	1m 32.29	2	9-0	Good To Firm	BIG BAD BOB	Sep	25	2002
7f 122y	1m 30.91	3	8-12	Good To Firm	CUPID'S GLORY	Aug	18	2005
1m 2f 75y	2m 7.15	3	8-8	Good To Firm	STOTSFOLD	Sep	23	2006
1m 3f 79y	2m 22.17	3	8-12	Good To Firm	PERFECT TRUTH	May	6	2009
1m 4f 66y	2m 33.7	3	8-10	Good To Firm	FIGHT YOUR CORNER	May	7	2002
1m 5f 89y	2m 45.4	5	8-11	Firm	RAKAPOSHI KING	May	7	1987
1m 7f 195y	3m 20.33	4	9-0	Good To Firm	GRAND FROMAGE	July	13	2002
2m 2f 147y	3m 58.59	7	9-2	Good To Firm	GREENWICH MEANTIME	May	9	2007

DONCASTER

DISTANCE	TIME	AGE	WEIGHT	GOING	HORSE	DATE		
5f	58.04 secs	2	9-1	Good	GUTAIFAN	Sep	11	2015
5f	57.2 secs	6	9-12	Good To Firm	CELTIC MILL	Sep	9	2004
5f 140y	1m 07.26	2	9-0	Good To Firm	CARTOGRAPHY	Jun	29	2003
5f 140y	1m 05.38	4	9-7	Good	MUTHMIR	Sep	13	2014
6f	1m 09.6	2	8-11	Good	CAESAR BEWARE	Sep	8	2004
6f	1m 09.56	3	8-10	Good To Firm	PROCLAIM	May	30	2009
6f 110y	1m 17.19	2	8-9	Good	MR LUPTON	Sep	10	2015
7f	1m 22.6	2	9-1	Good To Firm	LIBRETTIST	Sep	8	2004
7f	1m 21.6	3	9-4	Good To Firm	PASTORAL PURSUITS	Sep	9	2004
1m Str	1m 36.5	2	8-6	Good To Firm	SINGHALESE	Sep	9	2004
1m Rnd	1m 35.4	2	9-0	Good To Firm	PLAYFUL ACT	Sep	9	2004
1m Str	1m 34.95	6	8-9	Firm	QUICK WIT	July	18	2013
1m Rnd	1m 34.46	4	8-12	Good To Firm	STAYING ON	Apr	18	2009
1m 2f 60y	2m 13.4	2	8-8	Good	YARD BIRD	Nov	6	1981
1m 2f 60y	2m 04.81	4	8-13	Good To Firm	RED GALA	Sep	12	2007
1m 4f	2m 27.48	3	8-4	Good To Firm	SWIFT ALHAARTH	Sep	10	2011
1m 6f 132y	3m 00.44	3	9-0	Good To Firm	MASKED MARVEL	Sep	10	2011
2m 110y	3m 34.4	4	9-12	Good To Firm	FARSI	Jun	12	1992
2m 2f	3m 48.41	4	9-4	Good To Firm	SEPTIMUS	Sep	14	2007

EPSOM

DISTANCE	TIME	AGE	WEIGHT	GOING	HORSE	DATE		
5f	55.0 secs	2	8-9	Good To Firm	PRINCE ASLIA	Jun	9	1995
5f	53.6 secs	4	9-5	Firm	INDIGENOUS	Jun	2	1960
6f	1m 07.8	2	8-11	Good To Firm	SHOWBROOK	Jun	5	1991
6f	1m 07.21	5	9-13	Good To Firm	MAC GILLE EOIN	July	2	2009
7f	1m 21.3	2	8-9	Good To Firm	RED PEONY	July	29	2004
7f	1m 20.1	4	8-7	Firm	CAPISTRANO	Jun	7	1972
1m 114y	1m 42.8	2	8-5	Good To Firm	NIGHTSTALKER	Aug	30	1988
1m 114y	1m 40.7	3	8-6	Good To Firm	SYLVA HONDA	Jun	5	1991
1m 2f 18y	2m 03.5	5	7-13	Good	CROSSBOW	Jun	7	1967
1m 4f 10y	2m 31.3	3	9-0	Good To Firm	WORKFORCE	Jun	5	2010

FFOS LAS

DISTANCE	TIME	AGE	WEIGHT	GOING	HORSE	DATE		
5f	57.06 secs	2	9-3	Good To Firm	MR MAJEIKA	May	5	2011
5f	56.35 secs	5	8-8	Good	HAAJES	Sep	12	2009
6f	1m 9.00	2	9-5	Good To Firm	WONDER OF QATAR	Sep	14	2014
6f	1m 7.80	8	8-4	Good To Firm	THE JAILER	May	5	2011
1m	1m 39.36	2	9-2	Good To Firm	HALA HALA	Sep	2	2013
1m	1m 37.12	5	9-0	Good To Firm	ZEBRANO	May	5	2011
1m 2f	2m 04.85	8	8-12	Good To Firm	PELHAM CRESCENT	May	5	2011
1m 4f	2m 31.58	4	8-9	Good To Firm	MEN DON'T CRY	July	23	2013
1m 6f	2m 58.61	4	9-7	Good To Firm	LADY ECLAIR	July	12	2010
2m	3m 29.58	4	8-9	Good To Firm	ANNALUNA	July	1	2013

GOODWOOD

DISTANCE	TIME	AGE	WEIGHT	GOING	HORSE	DATE		
5f	57.30 secs	2	9-1	Good To Firm	COTAI GLORY	July	29	2014
5f	56.0 secs	5	9-0	Good To Firm	RUDI'S PET	July	27	1999
6f	1m 09.8	2	8-11	Good To Firm	BACHIR	July	28	1999
6f	1m 09.1	6	9-0	Good To Firm	TAMAGIN	Sep	12	2009
7f	1m 24.9	2	8-11	Good To Firm	EKRAAR	July	29	1999
7f	1m 23.8	3	8-7	Firm	BRIEF GLIMPSE	July	25	1995
1m	1m 37.21	2	9-0	Good	CALDRA	Sep	9	2006
1m	1m 35.61	4	8-9	Good To Firm	SPECTAIT	Aug	4	2006
1m 1f	1m 56.27	2	9-3	Good To Firm	DORDOGNE	Sep	22	2010
1m 1f	1m 52.8	3	9-6	Good	VENA	July	27	1995
1m 1f 192y	2m 02.81	3	9-3	Good To Firm	ROAD TO LOVE	Aug	3	2006
1m 3f	2m 23.0	3	8-8	Good To Firm	ASIAN HEIGHTS	May	22	2001
1m 4f	2m 31.5	3	8-10	Firm	PRESENTING	July	25	1995
1m 6f	2m 57.61	4	9-6	Good To Firm	MEEZNAH	July	28	2011
2m	3m 21.55	5	9-10	Good To Firm	YEATS	Aug	3	2006
2m 4f	4m 11.7	3	7-10	Firm	LUCKY MOON	Sep	2	1990

HAMILTON

DISTANCE	TIME	AGE	WEIGHT	GOING	HORSE	DATE		
5f 4y	57.95 secs	2	8-8	Good To Firm	ROSE BLOSSOM	May	29	2009
6f 5y	1m 10.0	2	8-12	Good To Firm	BREAK THE CODE	Aug	24	1999
6f 5y	1m 09.3	4	8-7	Firm	MARCUS GAME	July	11	1974
1m 65y	1m 45.8	2	8-11	Firm	HOPEFUL SUBJECT	Sep	24	1973
1m 65y	1m 45.46	2	9-5	Good To Firm	LAAFIRAAQ	Sep	20	2015
1m 1f 36y	1m 53.6	5	9-6	Good To Firm	REGENT'S SECRET	Aug	10	2005
1m 3f 16y	2m 19.32	3	8-1	Good To Firm	CAPTAIN WEBB	May	16	2008
1m 4f 17y	2m 30.52	5	9-10	Good To Firm	RECORD BREAKER	Jun	10	2009
1m 5f 9y	2m 45.1	6	9-6	Firm	MENTALASANYTHIN	Jun	14	1995

HAYDOCK

DISTANCE	TIME	AGE	WEIGHT	GOING	HORSE	DATE		
5f	58.56 secs	2	8-2	Good To Firm	BARRACUDA BOY	Aug	11	2012
5f	56.39 secs	5	9-4	Firm	BATED BREATH	May	26	2012
5f (Inner)	59.66 secs	2	8-12	Good	DEEDS NOT WORDS	Sep	27	2013
5f (Inner)	57.67 secs	4	9-4	Good To Firm	SOLE POWER	May	21	2011
6f	1m 09.9	4	9-0	Good To Firm	IKTAMAL	Sep	7	1996
6f	1m 10.98	4	9-9	Good To Firm	WOLFHOUND	Sep	4	1993
6f (Inner)	1m 10.72	2	9-2	Good To Firm	EASY TICKET	Sep	27	2013
6f (Inner)	1m 09.40	7	9-3	Good To Firm	MARKAB	Sep	4	2010
7f	1m 27.62	2	9-4	Good	TICKLE TIME	Aug	10	2012
7f	1m 25.79	3	8-11	Good To Firm	SAKHEE'S RETURN	June	11	2015
1m	1m 38.50	4	8-11	Good To Firm	EXPRESS HIMSELF	June	15	2015
1m 2f 95y	2m 08.25	3	9-0	Good To Firm	PRUSSIAN	Sep	7	2012
1m 3f 200y	2m 25.53	4	8-12	Good To Firm	NUMBER THEORY	May	24	2012
1m 6f	2m 55.20	5	9-9	Good To Firm	HUFF AND PUFF	Sep	7	2012
2m 45y	3m 26.98	5	8-13	Good To Firm	DE RIGUEUR	Jun	8	2013

KEMPTON (A.W)

DISTANCE	TIME	AGE	WEIGHT	GOING	HORSE	DATE		
5f	58.96	2	8-6	Standard	GLAMOROUS SPIRIT	Nov	28	2008
5f	58.33	3	9-1	Standard	EXCEEDANCE	May	7	2012
6f	1m 11.36	2	9-0	Standard	TENDU	Sep	3	2014
6f	1m 9.76	4	8-11	Standard	TRINITYELITEDOTCOM	Mar	29	2014
7f	1m 23.95	2	8-10	Standard	TAMARKUZ	Oct	10	2012
7f	1m 23.10	6	9-9	Standard	SIRIUS PROSPECT	Nov	20	2014
1m	1m 37.50	2	9-4	Standard	I'M BACK	Oct	3	2012
1m	1m 35.73	3	8-9	Standard	WESTERN ARISTOCRAT	Sep	5	2011
1m 2f	2m 2.97	5	9-0	Standard	REBELLIOUS GUEST	Mar	5	2014
1m 3f	2m 16.09	4	8-7	Standard	SALUTATION	Mar	29	2014
1m 4f	2m 28.99	6	9-3	Standard	SPRING OF FAME	Nov	7	2012
2m	3m 21.50	4	8-12	Standard	COLOUR VISION	May	2	2012

LEICESTER

DISTANCE	TIME	AGE	WEIGHT	GOING	HORSE	DATE		
5f 2y	58.4 secs	2	9-0	Firm	CUTTING BLADE	Jun	9	1986
5f 2y	57.85 secs	5	9-5	Good To Firm	THE JOBBER	Sep	18	2006
5f 218y	1m 09.99	3	9-0	Good	EL MANATI	Aug	1	2012
5f 218y	1m 09.12	6	8-12	Good To Firm	PETER ISLAND	Apr	25	2009
7f 9y	1m 22.6	2	9-0	Good To Firm	MARIE DE MEDICI	Oct	6	2009
7f 9y	1m 20.8	3	8-7	Firm	FLOWER BOWL	Jun	9	1986
1m 60y	1m 44.05	2	8-11	Good To Firm	CONGRESSIONAL	Sep	6	2005
1m 60y	1m 41.89	5	9-7	Good To Firm	VAINGLORY	Jun	18	2009
1m 1f 218y	2m 05.3	2	9-1	Good To Firm	WINDSOR CASTLE	Oct	14	1996
1m 1f 218y	2m 02.4	3	8-11	Firm	EFFIGY	Nov	4	1981
1m 1f 218y	2m 02.4	4	9-6	Good To Firm	LADY ANGHARAD	Jun	18	2000
1m 3f 183y	2m 27.1	5	8-12	Good To Firm	MURGHEM	Jun	18	2000

LINGFIELD (TURF)

DISTANCE	TIME	AGE	WEIGHT	GOING	HORSE	DATE		
5f	57.07 secs	2	9-0	Good To Firm	QUITE A THING	Jun	11	2011
5f	56.09 secs	3	9-4	Good To Firm	WHITECREST	Sep	16	2011
6f	1m 08.36	2	8-12	Good To Firm	FOLLY BRIDGE	Sep	8	2009
6f	1m 08.13	6	9-8	Firm	CLEAR PRAISE	Aug	10	2013
7f	1m 20.55	2	8-11	Good To Firm	HIKING	Aug	17	2013
7f	1m 20.05	3	8-5	Good To Firm	PERFECT TRIBUTE	May	7	2011
7f 140y	1m 29.32	2	9-3	Good To Firm	DUNDONNELL	Aug	4	2012
7f 140y	1m 26.7	3	8-6	Good To Firm	HIAAM	Jul	11	1987
1m 1f	1m 52.4	4	9-2	Good To Firm	QUANDARY	July	15	1995
1m 2f	2m 04.6	3	9-3	Firm	USRAN	July	15	1989
1m 3f 106y	2m 23.9	3	8-5	Firm	NIGHT-SHIRT	July	14	1990
1m 6f	2m 59.1	5	9-5	Firm	IBN BEY	July	1	1989
2m	3m 23.7	3	9-5	Good To Firm	LAURIES CRUSADOR	Aug	13	1988

LINGFIELD (A.W)

DISTANCE	TIME	AGE	WEIGHT	GOING	HORSE	DATE		
5f 6y	58.11 secs	2	9-5	Standard	IVORS REBEL	Sep	23	2014
5f 6y	56.67 secs	5	8-12	Standard	LADIES ARE FOREVER	Mar	16	2013
6f 1y	1m 09.99	2	8-12	Standard	SWISS DIVA	Nov	19	2008
6f 1y	1m 08.75	7	9-2	Standard	TAROOQ	Dec	18	2013
7f 1y	1m 22.67	2	9-3	Standard	COMPLICIT	Nov	23	2013
7f 1y	1m 21.92	5	9-6	Standard	GREY MIRAGE	Feb	21	2014
1m 1y	1m 35.84	2	9-5	Standard	BRAVE HERO	Nov	25	2015
1m 1y	1m 34.51	5	9-5	Standard	CAPTAIN CAT	Apr	18	2014
1m 2f	2m 00.99	5	9-0	Standard	FARRAAJ	Mar	16	2013
1m 4f	2m 27.97	4	9-3	Standard	MIDSUMMER SUN	Apr	14	2012
1m 5f	2m 39.70	3	8-10	Standard	HIDDEN GOLD	Oct	30	2014
1m 7f 169y	3m 16.73	5	9-2	Standard	ARCH VILLAIN	Jan	22	2014

MUSSELBURGH

DISTANCE	TIME	AGE	WEIGHT	GOING	HORSE	DATE		
5f	57.7 secs	2	8-2	Firm	ARASONG	May	16	1994
5f	57.1 secs	6	8-6	Good To Firm	RED BARON	Jun	13	2015
7f 30y	1m 27.46	2	8-8	Good	DURHAM REFLECTION	Sep	14	2009
7f 30y	1m 26.30	3	9-5	Firm	WALTZING WIZARD	Aug	22	2002
1m	1m 40.3	2	8-12	Good To Firm	SUCCESSION	Sep	26	2004
1m	1m 36.83	3	9-5	Good To Firm	GINGER JACK	July	13	2010
1m 1f	1m 50.42	8	8-11	Good To Firm	DHAULAR DHAR	Sep	3	2010
1m 4f 100y	2m 36.80	3	8-3	Good To Firm	HARRIS TWEED	Jun	5	2010
1m 5f	2m 46.41	3	9-5	Good To Firm	ALCAEUS	Sep	29	2013
1m 6f	2m 57.98	7	8-5	Good To Firm	JONNY DELTA	Apr	18	2014
2m	3m 25.62	4	8-3	Good To Firm	ALDRETH	June	13	2015

NEWBURY

DISTANCE	TIME	AGE	WEIGHT	GOING	HORSE	DATE		
5f 34y	59.1 secs	2	8-6	Good To Firm	SUPERSTAR LEO	July	22	2000
5f 34y	58.44 secs	5	9-1	Good To Firm	ROBOT BOY	Aug	17	2015
6f 8y	1m 11.07	2	8-4	Good To Firm	BAHATI	May	30	2009
6f 8y	1m 09.42	3	8-11	Good To Firm	NOTA BENE	May	13	2005
6f 110y	1m 18.06	2	9-5	Good To Firm	TWIN SAILS	June	11	2015
7f	1m 24.1	2	8-11	Good To Firm	HAAFHD	Aug	15	2003
7f	1m 20.80	3	9-0	Good To Firm	MUHAARAR	April	18	2015
1m	1m 37.5	2	9-1	Good To Firm	WINGED CUPID	Sep	16	2005
1m	1m 33.59	6	9-0	Firm	RAKTI	May	14	2005
1m 1f	1m 49.6	3	8-0	Good To Firm	HOLTYE	May	21	1995
1m 2f 6y	2m 1.2	3	8-7	Good To Firm	WALL STREET	July	20	1996
1m 3f 5y	2m 16.5	3	8-9	Good To Firm	GRANDERA	Sep	22	2001
1m 4f 5y	2m 28.26	4	9-7	Good To Firm	AZAMOUR	July	23	2005
1m 5f 61y	2m 44.9	5	10-0	Good To Firm	MYSTIC HILL	July	20	1996
2m	3m 25.4	8	9-12	Good To Firm	MOONLIGHT QUEST	July	19	1996

NEWCASTLE (TURF)

DISTANCE	TIME	AGE	WEIGHT	GOING	HORSE	DATE		
5f	58.8 secs	2	9-0	Firm	ATLANTIC VIKING	Jun	4	1997
5f	57.81 secs	3	9-3	Good	G FORCE	Apr	24	2014
6f	1m 11.98	2	9-3	Good	PEARL ARCH	Sep	6	2010
6f	1m 10.58	4	9-9	Good To Firm	JONNY MUDBALL	Jun	26	2010
7f	1m 24.2	2	9-0	Good To Firm	ISCAN	Aug	31	1998
7f	1m 23.3	4	9-2	Good To Firm	QUIET VENTURE	Aug	31	1998
1m 3y	1m 37.1	2	8-3	Good To Firm	HOH STEAMER	Aug	31	1998
1m 3y	1m 37.3	3	8-8	Good To Firm	IT'S MAGIC	May	27	1999
1m 1f 9y	2m 03.2	2	8-13	Soft	RESPONSE	Oct	30	1993
1m 1f 9y	1m 58.4	3	8-8	Good To Firm	INTRODUCING	Aug	6	2003
1m 2f 32y	2m 06.5	3	8-11	Firm	MISSIONARY RIDGE	July	29	1990
1m 4f 93y	2m 36.9	4	9-3	Good To Firm	LIVIA'S DREAM	Jul	27	2013
1m 6f 97y	3m 06.4	3	9-6	Good To Firm	ONE OFF	Aug	6	2003
2m 19y	3m 24.3	4	8-10	Good	FAR CRY	Jun	26	1999

NEWMARKET (ROWLEY MILE)

DISTANCE	TIME	AGE	WEIGHT	GOING	HORSE	DATE		
5f	58.76 secs	2	8-5	Good To Firm	VALIANT ROMEO	Oct	3	2002
5f	56.8 secs	6	9-2	Good To Firm	LOCHSONG	Apr	30	1994
6f	1m 09.56	3	8-12	Good To Firm	BUSHRANGER	Oct	3	2008
6f	1m 09.55	3	9-1	Good To Firm	CAPTAIN COLBY	May	16	2015
7f	1m 22.39	2	8-12	Good To Firm	ASHRAM	Oct	2	2008
7f	1m 21.98	3	9-0	Good To Firm	TUPI	May	16	2015
1m	1m 35.67	2	8-12	Good	STEELER	Sep	29	2012
1m	1m 34.07	4	9-0	Good To Firm	EAGLE MOUNTAIN	Oct	3	2008
1m 1f	1m 47.26	5	8-12	Good To Firm	MANDURO	Apr	19	2007
1m 2f	2m 04.6	2	9-4	Good	HIGHLAND CHIEFTAIN	Nov	2	1985
1m 2f	2m 00.13	3	8-12	Good	NEW APPROACH	Oct	18	2008
1m 4f	2m 26.07	3	8-9	Good To Firm	MOHEDIAN LADY	Sep	22	2011
1m 6f	2m 51.59	3	8-7	Good	ART EYES	Sep	29	2005
2m	3m 18.64	5	9-6	Good To Firm	TIMES UP	Sep	22	2011
2m 2f	3m 47.5	3	7-12	Hard	WHITEWAY	Oct	15	1947

NEWMARKET (JULY COURSE)

DISTANCE	TIME	AGE	WEIGHT	GOING	HORSE	DATE		
5f	58.5 secs	2	8-10	Good	SEDUCTRESS	July	10	1990
5f	56.09 secs	6	9-11	Good	BORDERLESCOTT	Aug	22	2008
6f	1m 10.35	2	8-11	Good	ELNAWIN	Aug	22	2008
6f	1m 09.11	4	9-5	Good To Firm	LETHAL FORCE	July	13	2013
7f	1m 23.33	2	9-1	Good To Firm	BIRCHWOOD	July	11	2015
7f	1m 22.5	3	9-7	Firm	HO LENG	July	9	1998
1m	1m 37.47	2	8-13	Good	WHIPPERS LOVE	Aug	28	2009
1m	1m 35.5	3	8-6	Good To Firm	LOVERS KNOT	July	8	1998
1m 2f	2m 00.91	3	9-5	Good To Firm	MAPUTO	July	11	2013
1m 4f	2m 25.11	3	8-11	Good	LUSH LASHES	Aug	22	2008
1m 5f	2m 40.75	5	9-10	Good	WADI AL HATTAWI	Aug	29	2015
1m 6f 175y	3m 04.2	3	8-5	Good	ARRIVE	July	11	2001
2m 24y	3m 20.2	7	9-10	Good	YORKSHIRE	July	11	2001

NOTTINGHAM

DISTANCE	TIME	AGE	WEIGHT	GOING	HORSE	DATE		
5f 13y (Inner)	59.43 secs	2	9-5	Good To Firm	BURTONWOOD	Apr	19	2014
5f 13y (Inner)	58.49 secs	4	9-2	Good To Soft	IT MUST BE FAITH	Oct	29	2014
5f 13y	57.9 secs	2	8-9	Firm	HOH MAGIC	May	13	1994
5f 13y	57.71secs	4	8-11	Good To Firm	DINKUM DIAMOND	Aug	14	2002
6f 15y	1m 11.4	2	8-11	Firm	JAMEELAPI	Aug	8	1983
6f 15y	1m 10.0	4	9-2	Firm	AJANAC	Aug	8	1988
1m 75y	1m 45.23	2	9-0	Good To Firm	TACTFULLY	Sep	28	2011
1m 75y	1m 42.25	5	9-1	Good To Firm	RIO DE LA PLATA	Jun	2	2010
1m 2f 50y	2m 07.13	5	9-8	Good To Firm	VASILY	July	19	2013
1m 2f 50y (Inner)	2m 06.66	2	9-3	Soft	LETHAL GLAZE	Oct	1	2008
1m 2f 50y (Inner)	2m 09.4	3	9-5	Good	CENTURIUS	Apr	20	2013
1m 6f 15y	2m 57.8	3	8-10	Firm	BUSTER JO	Oct	1	1985
2m 9y	3m 25.25	3	9-5	Good	BULWARK	Sep	27	2005
2m 97y (Inner)	3m 34.39	3	8-0	Good	BENOZZO GOZZOLI	Oct	28	2009

PONTEFRACT

DISTANCE	TIME	AGE	WEIGHT	GOING	HORSE	DATE		
5f	1m 01.1	2	9-0	Firm	GOLDEN BOUNTY	Sep	20	2001
5f	1m 00.8	4	8-9	Firm	BLUE MAEVE	Sep	29	2004
6f	1m 14.0	2	9-3	Firm	FAWZI	Sep	6	1983
6f	1m 12.6	3	7-13	Firm	MERRY ONE	Aug	29	1970
1m 4y	1m 42.8	2	9-13	Firm	STAR SPRAY	Sep	6	1970
1m 4y	1m 42.80	2	9-0	Firm	ALASIL	Sep	26	2002
1m 4y	1m 40.6	4	9-10	Good To Firm	ISLAND LIGHT	Apr	13	2002
1m 2f 6y	2m 10.10	2	9-0	Firm	SHANTY STAR	Oct	7	2002
1m 2f 6y	2m 08.2	4	7-8	Hard	HAPPY HECTOR	July	9	1979
1m 4f 8y	2m 33.72	3	8-7	Firm	AJAAN	Aug	8	2007
2m 1f 22y	3m 40.67	4	8-7	Good To Firm	PARADISE FLIGHT	Jun	6	2005
2m 1f 216y	3m 51.1	3	8-8	Firm	KUDZ	Sep	9	1986
2m 5f 122y	4m 47.8	4	8-4	Firm	PHYSICAL	May	14	1984

REDCAR

DISTANCE	TIME	AGE	WEIGHT	GOING	HORSE	DATE		
5f	56.88 secs	2	9-7	Good To Soft	WOLFOFWALLSTREET	Oct	27	2014
5f	56.01 secs	10	9-3	Firm	HENRY HALL	Sep	20	2006
6f	1m 08.8	2	8-3	Good To Firm	OBE GOLD	Oct	2	2004
6f	1m 08.6	3	9-2	Good To Firm	SIZZLING SAGA	Jun	21	1991
7f	1m 21.28	2	9-3	Firm	KAROO BLUE	Sep	20	2006
7f	1m 21.0	3	9-1	Firm	EMPTY QUARTER	Oct	3	1995
1m	1m 34.37	2	9-0	Firm	MASTERSHIP	Sep	20	2006
1m	1m 32.42	4	10-0	Firm	NANTON	Sep	20	2006
1m 1f	1m 52.4	2	9-0	Firm	SPEAR	Sep	13	2004
1m 1f	1m 48.5	5	8-12	Firm	MELLOTTIE	July	25	1990
1m 2f	2m 10.1	2	8-11	Good	ADDING	Nov	10	1989
1m 2f	2m 01.4	5	9-2	Firm	ERADICATE	May	28	1990
1m 3f	2m 17.2	3	8-9	Firm	PHOTO CALL	Aug	7	1990
1m 6f 19y	2m 59.81	4	9-1	Good To Firm	ESPRIT DE CORPS	Sep	11	2006
2m 4y	3m 24.9	3	9-3	Good To Firm	SUBSONIC	Oct	8	1991

RIPON

DISTANCE	TIME	AGE	WEIGHT	GOING	HORSE	DATE		
5f	57.8 secs	2	8-8	Firm	SUPER ROCKY	July	5	1991
5f	57.6 secs	5	8-5	Good	BROADSTAIRS BEAUTY	May	21	1995
6f	1m 10.9	2	9-2	Good	CUMBRIAN VENTURE	Aug	17	2002
6f	1m 09.72	4	8-9	Good	BACCARAT	Aug	17	2013
1m	1m 38.77	2	9-4	Good	GREED IS GOOD	Sep	28	2013
1m	1m 36.62	4	8-11	Good To Firm	GRANSTON	Aug	29	2005
1m 1f	1m 49.97	6	9-3	Good To Firm	GINGER JACK	Jun	20	2013
1m 2f	2m 02.6	3	9-4	Firm	SWIFT SWORD	July	20	1990
1m 4f 10y	2m 31.40	4	8-8	Good To Firm	DANDINO	Apr	16	2011
2m	3m 27.07	5	9-12	Good To Firm	GREENWICH MEANTIME	Aug	30	2005

SALISBURY

DISTANCE	TIME	AGE	WEIGHT	GOING	HORSE	DATE		
5f	59.3 secs	2	9-0	Good To Firm	AJIGOLO	May	12	2005
6f	1m 12.1	8	8-0	Good To Firm	PARISIAN LADY	Jun	10	1997
6f	1m 11.09	3	9-0	Firm	L'AMI LOUIS	May	1	2011
6f 212y	1m 25.9	2	9-0	Firm	MORE ROYAL	Jun	29	1995
6f 212y	1m 24.91	3	9-4	Firm	CHILWORTH LAD	May	1	2011
1m	1m 40.48	2	8-13	Firm	CHOIR MASTER	Sep	17	2002
1m	1m 38.29	3	8-7	Good To Firm	LAYMAN	Aug	11	2005
1m 1f 198y	2m 04.81	3	8-5	Good To Firm	PRIMEVERE	Aug	10	2011
1m 4f	2m 31.6	3	9-5	Good To Firm	ARRIVE	Jun	27	2001
1m 6f 21y	3m 0.48	7	9-2	Good To Firm	HIGHLAND CASTLE	May	23	2015

SANDOWN

DISTANCE	TIME	AGE	WEIGHT	GOING	HORSE	DATE		
5f 6y	59.4 secs	2	9-3	Firm	TIMES TIME	July	22	1982
5f 6y	58.8 secs	6	8-9	Good To Firm	PALACEGATE TOUCH	Sep	17	1996
7f 16y	1m 26.56	2	9-0	Good To Firm	RAVEN'S PASS	Sep	1	2007
7f 16y	1m 26.3	3	9-0	Firm	MAWSUFF	Jun	14	1983
1m 14y	1m 41.1	2	8-11	Firm	REFERENCE POINT	Sep	23	1986
1m 14y	1m 38.87	7	9-10	Good To Firm	PRINCE OF JOHANNE	July	6	2013
1m 1f	1m 54.6	2	8-8	Good To Firm	FRENCH PRETENDER	Sep	20	1988
1m 1f	1m 52.4	7	9-3	Good To Firm	BOURGAINVILLE	Aug	11	2005
1m 2f 7y	2m 02.1	4	8-11	Firm	KALAGLOW	May	31	1982
1m 6f	2m 56.9	4	8-7	Good To Firm	LADY ROSANNA	July	19	1989
2m 78y	3m 29.38	6	9-0	Good To Firm	CAUCUS	July	6	2013

SOUTHWELL (A.W)

DISTANCE	TIME	AGE	WEIGHT	GOING	HORSE	DATE		
5f	57.85 secs	2	9-3	Standard	ARCTIC FEELING	Mar	31	2010
5f	56.80 secs	5	9-7	Standard	GHOSTWING	Jan	3	2012
6f	1m 14.0	2	8-5	Standard	PANALO	Nov	8	1989
6f	1m 13.3	3	9-2	Standard	RAMBO EXPRESS	Dec	18	1990
7f	1m 27.1	2	8-12	Standard	WINGED ICARUS	Aug	28	2012
7f	1m 26.60	3	8-7	Standard	PHILBA	Dec	17	2015
1m	1m 38.0	2	8-9	Standard	ALPHA RASCAL	Nov	13	1990
1m	1m 38.0	4	8-10	Standard	ANDREW'S FIRST	Dec	30	1989
1m	1m 37.2	3	8-6	Standard	VALIRA	Nov	3	1990
1m 3f	2m 21.5	4	9-7	Standard	TEMPERING	Dec	5	1990
1m 4f	2m 33.9	4	9-12	Standard	FAST CHICK	Nov	8	1989
1m 6f	3m 01.6	3	7-7	Standard	QUALITAIR AVIATOR	Dec	1	1989
1m 6f	3m 01.6	3	7-8	Standard	EREVNON	Dec	29	1990
2m	3m 37.6	9	8-12	Standard	OLD HUBERT	Dec	5	1990

THIRSK

DISTANCE	TIME	AGE	WEIGHT	GOING	HORSE	DATE		
5f	57.2 secs	2	9-7	Good To Firm	PROUD BOAST	Aug	5	2000
5f	56.1 secs	7	8-0	Firm	SIR SANDROVITCH	Jun	26	2003
6f	1m 09.2	2	9-6	Good To Firm	WESTCOURT MAGIC	Aug	25	1995
6f	1m 08.8	6	9-4	Firm	JOHAYRO	July	23	1999
7f	1m 23.7	2	8-9	Firm	COURTING	July	23	1999
7f	1m 22.8	4	8-5	Firm	SILVER HAZE	May	21	1988
1m	1m 37.9	2	9-0	Good To Firm	SUNDAY SYMPHONY	Sep	4	2004
1m	1m 34.8	4	8-13	Firm	YEARSLEY	May	5	1990
1m 4f	2m 29.9	5	9-12	Firm	GALLERY GOD	Jun	4	2001
2m	3m 22.3	3	8-10	Firm	TOMASCHEK	Aug	1	1964

WETHERBY

Flat racing began in 2015; record times not yet available

WINDSOR

DISTANCE	TIME	AGE	WEIGHT	GOING	HORSE	DATE		
5f 10y	58.69 secs	2	9-0	Good To Firm	CHARLES THE GREAT	May	23	2011
5f 10y	58.08 secs	5	8-13	Good To Firm	TAURUS TWINS	Apr	4	2011
6f	1m 10.5	2	9-5	Good To Firm	CUBISM	Aug	17	1998
6f	1m 09.58	7	9-0	Good To Firm	TROPICS	June	1	2015
1m 67y	1m 42.46	2	8-9	Good To Firm	TIGER CUB	Oct	10	2011
1m 67y	1m 39.81	5	9-7	Good	FRENCH NAVY	Jun	29	2013
1m 2f 7y	2m 01.62	6	9-1	Good	AL KAZEEM	Aug	23	2014
1m 3f 135y	2m 21.5	3	9-2	Firm	DOUBLE FLORIN	May	19	1980

WOLVERHAMPTON (A.W)

Only records on Tapeta surface are included

DISTANCE	TIME	AGE	WEIGHT	GOING	HORSE	DATE		
5f 20y	59.75 secs	2	9-6	Standard	QUATRIEME AMI	Nov	13	2015
5f 20y	1m 00.25	3	8-12	Standard	BOOM THE GROOM	Nov	22	2014
5f 216y	1m 13.24	2	9-5	Standard	ENCORE D'OR	Oct	11	2014
5f 216y	1m 11.84	3	8-6	Standard	PRETEND	Dec	19	2014
7f 32y	1m 27.67	2	9-6	Standard	ALWAYS WELCOME	Dec	22	2015
7f 32y	1m 26.44	4	9-6	Standard	CAPO ROSSO	Oct	25	2014
1m 141y	1m 47.38	2	9-5	Standard	JACK HOBBS	Dec	27	2014
1m 141y	1m 46.44	6	9-8	Standard	GRAPHIC	Feb	2	2015
1m 1f 103y	1m 57.15	5	8-5	Standard	DOCS LEGACY	Nov	6	2014
1m 4f 50y	2m 37.01	5	9-10	Standard	GABRIAL'S STAR	Nov	2	2014
1m 5f 194y	2m 57.55	6	9-7	Standard	ENTIHAA	Dec	6	2014
2m 119y	3m 34.76	4	9-7	Standard	PURPLE SPECTRUM	Jan	2	2015

YARMOUTH

DISTANCE	TIME	AGE	WEIGHT	GOING	HORSE	DATE		
5f 43y	1m 00.4	2	8-6	Good To Firm	EBBA	July	26	1999
5f 43y	59.80 secs	4	8-13	Good To Firm	ROXANNE MILL	Aug	25	2002
6f 3y	1m 10.4	2	9-0	Firm	LANCHESTER	Aug	15	1988
6f 3y	1m 9.90	4	8-9	Firm	MALHUB	Jun	13	2002
7f 3y	1m 22.2	2	9-0	Good To Firm	WARRSHAN	Sep	14	1988
7f 3y	1m 22.12	4	9-4	Good To Firm	GLENBUCK	Apr	26	2007
1m 3y	1m 36.3	2	8-2	Good To Firm	OUT RUN	Sep	15	1988
1m 3y	1m 33.9	3	8-8	Firm	BONNE ETOILE	Jun	27	1995
1m 1f	1m 52.00	3	9-5	Good To Firm	TOUCH GOLD	July	5	2012
1m 2f 21y	2m 02.83	3	8-9	Firm	REUNITE	July	18	2006
1m 3f 101y	2m 23.1	3	8-9	Firm	RAHIL	July	1	1993
1m 6f 17y	2m 57.8	3	8-2	Good To Firm	BARAKAT	July	24	1990
2m	3m 26.7	4	8-2	Good To Firm	ALHESN	July	26	1999

TOP FLAT JOCKEYS IN BRITAIN 2015

(JANUARY 1st -DECEMBER 31st)

W-R	%	JOCKEY	2ND	3RD	TOTAL PRIZE	WIN PRIZE
189-1508	13%	LUKE MORRIS	208	170	1,592,953	979,881
177-1083	16%	ADAM KIRBY	136	135	1,746,941	1,095,308
155-828	19%	SILVESTRE DE SOUSA	104	95	2,235,680	1,550,020
132-938	14%	JOE FANNING	115	105	1,203,392	759,849
125-695	18%	PAUL HANAGAN	93	78	3,145,213	2,059,624
123-697	18%	GEORGE BAKER	98	81	1,335,583	950,698
121-608	20%	JAMES DOYLE	100	77	3,151,677	1,671,604
118-856	14%	JIM CROWLEY	119	110	1,674,815	761,150
113-573	20%	WILLIAM BUICK	81	75	3,297,755	1,794,042
108-952	11%	GRAHAM LEE	103	88	1,769,288	1,099,767
104-714	15%	PAT COSGRAVE	99	75	1,507,276	811,147
103-830	12%	TONY HAMILTON	97	91	1,150,065	786,976
97-751	13%	PAUL MULRENNAN	86	104	941,526	616,293
92-600	15%	PHILLIP MAKIN	69	69	1,004,040	712,570
91-729	12%	GRAHAM GIBBONS	87	85	1,017,289	671,566
91-764	12%	OISIN MURPHY	91	105	966,978	551,863
85-624	14%	JAMIE SPENCER	89	69	2,361,061	1,406,835
84-485	17%	DANIEL TUDHOPE	55	66	929,447	617,961
83-685	12%	MARTIN HARLEY	91	90	1,220,386	731,406
83-695	12%	FRANNY NORTON	78	80	817,894	519,476
82-381	22%	RYAN MOORE	74	52	5,060,509	3,233,478
82-493	17%	FREDERIK TYLICKI	64	63	734,735	499,701
82-690	12%	DAVID PROBERT	76	75	870,800	570,229
76-517	15%	ANDREA ATZENI	71	71	3,383,081	2,331,741
75-341	22%	FRANKIE DETTORI	56	38	4,947,626	3,330,334
73-517	14%	ROBERT HAVLIN	64	55	848,334	557,415
69-734	9%	P J MCDONALD	91	74	672,760	407,380
67-549	12%	DAVID ALLAN	74	77	663,137	289,014
67-602	11%	TOM MARQUAND	55	80	454,342	250,774
67-843	8%	TOM EAVES	92	74	543,878	304,012
66-509	13%	RICHARD KINGSCOTE	66	58	750,058	423,537
66-695	9%	J F EGAN	86	102	590,467	273,825
65-493	13%	SHANE GRAY	50	45	468,839	320,251
64-513	12%	BEN CURTIS	48	60	544,878	384,087
64-521	12%	PAT DOBBS	72	68	1,055,670	644,718
64-617	10%	TOM QUEALLY	61	72	793,645	505,457
63-397	16%	RICHARD HUGHES	58	58	1,368,119	690,484
62-472	13%	DANE O'NEILL	51	65	1,017,955	711,712
62-637	10%	ANDREW MULLEN	58	60	489,928	291,659
61-748	8%	LIAM KENIRY	74	81	393,301	222,537
60-453	13%	FERGAL LYNCH	52	68	523,402	306,928
58-436	13%	JACK GARRITTY	65	67	840,362	561,638
57-539	11%	MARTIN LANE	64	58	653,270	361,124
56-319	18%	HARRY BENTLEY	27	37	628,684	419,983
55-404	14%	SEAN LEVEY	47	49	651,527	360,806
54-522	10%	FERGUS SWEENEY	54	64	760,065	530,066
51-382	13%	TED DURCAN	38	45	600,245	363,651
51-509	10%	SHANE KELLY	52	43	323,051	197,818
49-512	10%	WILLIAM TWISTON-DAVIES	44	56	299,213	198,391
45-545	8%	WILLIAM CARSON	56	71	305,204	175,208

TOP FLAT TRAINERS IN BRITAIN 2015

(JANUARY 1st -DECEMBER 31st)

TRAINER	LEADING HORSE	W-R	2ND	3RD	4TH	TOTAL PRIZE	WIN PRIZE
JOHN GOSDEN	Golden Horn	133-577	101	77	59	5,277,650	3,094,711
RICHARD FAHEY	Gabrial	235-1691	220	200	219	3,846,973	2,394,305
RICHARD HANNON	Toormore	194-1382	180	173	154	3,593,428	2,027,558
A P O'BRIEN	Gleneagles	16-79	18	7	11	3,560,102	2,015,995
MARK JOHNSTON	Lumiere	204-1208	167	148	118	2,748,949	1,806,254
WILLIAM HAGGAS	Storm The Stars	113-533	87	50	63	2,364,888	1,583,672
CHARLES HILLS	Muhaarar	71-580	63	73	73	2,234,907	1,656,539
CHARLIE APPLEBY	Tryster	151-663	113	96	72	2,156,859	1,493,288
SAEED BIN SUROOR	Musaddas	105-392	67	51	37	1,725,293	1,064,512
SIR MICHAEL STOUTE	Snow Sky	80-455	63	65	58	1,719,209	1,011,552
LUCA CUMANI	Postponed	50-266	34	50	25	1,643,651	1,207,701
DAVID O'MEARA	Amazing Maria	122-931	119	105	94	1,580,568	1,024,052
RALPH BECKETT	Simple Verse	80-474	51	58	61	1,559,241	1,290,761
ROGER VARIAN	Belardo	100-474	79	66	45	1,541,464	887,554
ANDREW BALDING	Tullius	95-755	102	85	98	1,539,900	837,267
F HEAD	Solow	3-5	0	0	0	1,397,482	1,396,672
KEVIN RYAN	The Grey Gatsby	73-645	81	65	70	1,251,616	497,207
D K WELD	Fascinating Rock	2-11	1	2	0	1,148,284	1,068,274
DAVID SIMCOCK	Balios	63-396	60	57	46	1,132,601	642,234
DAVID ELSWORTH	Arabian Queen	34-219	28	25	22	1,119,043	786,808
MARCO BOTTI	Grey Mirage	54-501	65	70	64	1,095,611	525,217
HUGO PALMER	Gifted Master	34-197	32	30	22	1,042,339	646,189
MICK CHANNON	Bossy Guest	71-667	75	83	83	940,362	546,046
HENRY CANDY	Twilight Son	33-236	32	37	27	902,021	529,267
MICHAEL APPLEBY	Danzeno	94-795	95	95	83	895,918	530,955
DAVID WACHMAN	Legatissimo	3-9	2	1	1	862,880	678,705
TIM EASTERBY	Mattmu	70-691	88	80	68	791,794	354,477
ROGER CHARLTON	Time Test	46-284	52	28	39	773,768	451,174
PETER CHAPPLE-HYAM	Arod	16-124	21	13	11	761,353	388,712
ED DUNLOP	Trip To Paris	29-352	50	31	39	716,711	472,860
KEITH DALGLEISH	Tommy Docc	75-518	68	63	59	672,851	435,855
K R BURKE	Quiet Reflection	57-471	51	60	54	644,286	397,560
HUGHIE MORRISON	Chil The Kite	49-303	39	34	44	592,026	376,570
BRIAN ELLISON	Balty Boys	49-500	54	61	41	591,736	343,046
DAVID EVANS	John Reel	89-705	82	99	92	576,241	341,488
MICHAEL DODS	Mecca's Angel	45-404	45	42	50	573,403	396,261
TOM DASCOMBE	Kachy	45-424	56	42	35	570,286	311,645
SIR MARK PRESCOTT BT	Pallasator	58-307	47	23	26	560,041	370,775
DAVID BARRON	Poet's Prize	36-321	33	33	33	551,094	334,493
JAMES FANSHAWE	The Tin Man	45-254	33	38	23	544,811	335,569
BRIAN MEEHAN	Agent Murphy	40-288	35	36	27	544,059	354,689
MICHAEL BELL	Big Orange	42-371	49	52	46	541,587	396,532
CLIVE COX	Kodi Bear	44-399	42	57	55	536,855	339,043
J S BOLGER	Pleascach	4-13	3	2	0	534,953	303,866
DEAN IVORY	Tropics	36-256	20	24	24	502,097	240,086
ROBERT COWELL	Goldream	25-275	35	42	23	497,176	373,858
JAMES TATE	Lamar	43-254	40	42	27	453,151	253,853
AMANDA PERRETT	Zhui Feng	26-255	28	26	34	450,583	301,168
B W HILLS	Massaat	17-124	16	14	20	449,985	181,000
WESLEY A WARD	Undrafted	2-11	1	0	0	422,701	354,437

TOP FLAT OWNERS
IN BRITAIN IN 2015

OWNER	LEADING HORSE	W-R	2ND	3RD	4TH	TOTAL PRIZE	WIN PRIZE
GODOLPHIN	PLEASCACH	287-1194	201	161	123	5,496,892	3,624,668
HAMDAN AL MAKTOUM	MUHAARAR	137-738	125	89	79	3,420,984	2,464,150
M TABOR, D SMITH & MRS JOHN MAGNIER	LEGATISSIMO	6-20	5	1	3	1,924,227	1,148,645
A E OPPENHEIMER	GOLDEN HORN	9-43	4	3	6	1,465,857	1,210,180
WERTHEIMER & FRERE	SOLOW	3-5	0	0	1	1,412,161	1,396,672
SHEIKH HAMDAN BIN MOHAMMED AL MAKTOUM	LUMIERE	80-378	42	47	30	1,159,382	861,331
QATAR RACING LIMITED	AROD	39-277	34	31	37	1,081,050	455,371
AL SHAQAB RACING	SHALAA	45-191	20	22	17	1,055,648	807,011
SHEIKH MOHAMMED OBAID AL MAKTOUM	POSTPONED	12-83	13	18	11	1,041,581	817,513
K ABDULLAH	SNOW SKY	48-258	41	32	32	988,303	640,025
DERRICK SMITH & MRS JOHN MAGNIER & MICHAEL TABOR	MINDING	5-22	6	1	4	902,849	565,103
DR MARWAN KOUKASH	GABRIAL	35-285	33	30	28	897,929	392,333
QRL/SHEIKH SUHAIM AL THANI/ M AL KUBAISI	SIMPLE VERSE	7-22	4	3	1	824,509	807,000
MRS JOHN MAGNIER & MICHAEL TABOR & DERRICK SMITH	AIR FORCE BLUE	7-22	4	0	5	798,938	599,425
J C SMITH	ARABIAN QUEEN	17-158	18	13	12	798,738	618,691
NEWTOWN ANNER STUD FARM	FASCINATING ROCK	1-5	0	1	0	781,118	770,547
MRS FITRI HAY	BUCKSTAY	22-168	24	15	23	718,339	376,905
CHEVELEY PARK STUD	INTEGRAL	39-264	35	34	36	600,993	256,336
SHEIKH JUMA DALMOOK AL MAKTOUM	STORM THE STARS	27-147	21	13	22	570,215	275,732
LADY BAMFORD	EAGLE TOP	10-73	12	12	11	565,248	164,070
SALEH AL HOMAIZI & IMAD AL SAGAR	AJAYA	32-161	24	19	15	536,062	339,440
GEORGE STRAWBRIDGE	FLYING OFFICER	10-48	14	6	5	494,720	331,932
GODOLPHIN & PARTNERS	JACK HOBBS	1-3	1	1	0	489,671	35,160
THE QUEEN	MUSTARD	20-111	13	18	12	482,913	370,324
SHEIKH RASHID DALMOOK AL MAKTOUM	BESHARAH	22-108	10	10	13	415,872	266,128
LA GRANGE PARTNERSHIP	TRIP TO PARIS	4-8	1	1	1	395,125	342,402
F GILLESPIE	THE GREY GATSBY	5-41	7	4	2	390,945	68,927
A D SPENCE	FIRE FIGHTING	19-141	19	24	15	360,492	216,038
DR ALI RIDHA	GIFTED MASTER	6-34	3	4	2	345,435	339,206
MOYGLARE STUD FARMS LTD	FREE EAGLE	2-7	0	1	3	344,108	299,991
H H AGA KHAN	ERVEDYA	1-5	2	0	0	319,079	229,854
DAVID W ARMSTRONG	LATHOM	16-90	15	9	10	310,896	220,606
W J AND T C O GREDLEY	BIG ORANGE	11-74	7	10	13	304,369	269,003
MRS C C REGALADO-GONZALEZ	QUALIFY	5-20	4	4	2	303,440	281,911
GODFREY WILSON & CHEVELEY PARK STUD	TWILIGHT SON	1-2	1	0	0	298,179	162,190
WES WELKER & SOL KUMIN	UNDRAFTED	1-1	0	0	0	297,727	297,727
SAEED MANANA	URBAN CASTLE	40-296	38	40	36	284,250	177,417
KENNET VALLEY THOROUGHBREDS I	MAGICAL MEMORY	3-7	0	3	1	273,304	230,325
JOHN MANLEY	PETHER'S MOON	1-13	3	3	1	259,697	212,662
GODOLPHIN & PRINCE A A FAISAL	BELARDO	0-5	1	1	0	259,340	0
J SARGEANT & MRS J MORLEY	GOLDREAM	2-4	0	0	0	255,027	246,688
N D KERSHAW	MR LUPTON	2-9	3	2	0	246,720	150,451
NICHOLAS WRIGLEY & KEVIN HART	DON'T TOUCH	10-29	3	4	3	244,773	225,909
BARON EDOUARD DE ROTHSCHILD	ESOTERIQUE	1-2	1	0	0	241,539	160,914
SIR ROBERT OGDEN	AMAZING MARIA	7-31	4	3	2	239,910	218,662
THE COOL SILK PARTNERSHIP	ROYAL BAJAN	33-231	27	20	24	236,832	158,372
JOHN CONNOLLY & ODILE GRIFFITH	ZHUI FENG	5-17	1	3	2	233,211	165,042
A A BYRNE	LITIGANT	5-43	4	8	2	232,761	220,706
B E NIELSEN	INTERCEPTION	16-54	4	5	10	231,973	198,696
H R H SULTAN AHMAD SHAH	QUEST FOR MORE	5-61	15	4	9	229,163	114,560

TOP FLAT HORSES IN BRITAIN 2015

HORSE (AGE)	WIN & PLACE £	W-R	TRAINER	OWNER	BREEDER
SOLOW (5)	1,396,672	3-3	F Head	Wertheimer & Frere	Wertheimer Et Frere
GOLDEN HORN (3)	1,376,725	4-5	John Gosden	A E Oppenheimer	Hascombe And Valiant Studs
MUHAARAR (3)	906,123	4-4	Charles Hills	Hamdan Al Maktoum	Shadwell Estate Company Ltd
SIMPLE VERSE (3)	798,231	5-8	Ralph Beckett	QRL/Sheikh Suhaim Al Thani/ M Al Kubaisi	Barronstown Stud
FASCINATING ROCK (4)	772,161	1-2	D K Weld	Newtown Anner Stud Farm	Newtown Anner Stud
POSTPONED (4)	724,521	1-3	Luca Cumani	Sheikh Mohammed Obaid Al Maktoum	St Albans Bloodstock Llp
LEGATISSIMO (3)	669,521	2-3	David Wachman	Michael Tabor & Mrs John Magnier & Derrick Smith	Newsells Park Stud
ARABIAN QUEEN (3)	641,506	2-6	David Elsworth	J C Smith	Littleton Stud
JACK HOBBS (3)	533,409	2-5	John Gosden	Godolphin & Partners	Minster Stud
GLENEAGLES (3)	527,545	2-3	A P O'Brien	M Tabor, D Smith & Mrs John Magnier	You'resothrilling Syndicate
TRIP TO PARIS (4)	395,125	4-8	Ed Dunlop	La Grange Partnership	Paul Monaghan & T J Monaghan
FOUND (3)	379,273	0-2	A P O'Brien	M Tabor, D Smith & Mrs John Magnier	Roncon, Wynatt & Chelston
TWILIGHT SON (3)	373,367	3-4	Henry Candy	Godfrey Wilson & Cheveley Park Stud	Mrs C R D Wilson
AROD (4)	365,938	2-5	Peter Chapple-Hyam	Qatar Racing Ltd	Kabansk Ltd & Rathbarry Stud
GABRIAL (6)	340,410	1-13	Richard Fahey	Dr Marwan Koukash	B Kennedy
STORM THE STARS (3)	331,568	3-7	William Haggas	Sheikh Juma Dalmook Al Maktoum	Summer Wind Farm
GIFTED MASTER (2)	331,048	4-6	Hugo Palmer	Dr Ali Ridha	Tally-Ho Stud
EAGLE TOP (4)	314,165	0-4	John Gosden	Lady Bamford	Lady Bamford
AIR FORCE BLUE (2)	309,350	1-2	A P O'Brien	Mrs John Magnier & Michael Tabor & Derrick Smith	Stone Farm
THE GREY GATSBY (4)	308,011	0-3	Kevin Ryan	F Gillespie	M Parrish
MINDING (2)	302,689	1-1	A P O'Brien	Derrick Smith & Mrs John Magnier & Michael Tabor	Orpendale, Chelston & Wynatt
FREE EAGLE (4)	297,727	1-1	D K Weld	Moyglare Stud Farm	Moyglare Stud Farm Ltd
UNDRAFTED (5)	297,727	1-1	Wesley A Ward	Wes Welker & Sol Kumin	Catesby W Clay Investment LLC
MAGICAL MEMORY (3)	273,304	3-7	Charles Hills	Kennet Valley Thoroughbreds I	Wardstown Stud Ltd
TOORMORE (4)	265,480	1-3	Richard Hannon	Godolphin	BEC Bloodstock
SHALAA (2)	265,394	4-5	John Gosden	Al Shaqab Racing	Mogeely Stud
BELARDO (3)	259,340	0-5	Roger Varian	Godolphin & Prince A A Faisal	Ballylinch Stud
QUALIFY (3)	255,195	1-2	A P O'Brien	Mrs C C Regalado-Gonzalez	Whisperview Trading Ltd
GOLDREAM (6)	255,027	2-4	Robert Cowell	J Sargeant & Mrs J Morley	Tsega Breeding Limited
PLEASCACH (3)	247,621	1-2	J S Bolger	Godolphin	J S Bolger
MR LUPTON (2)	246,720	2-9	Richard Fahey	N D Kershaw	Ms E O'Neill
TRYSTER (4)	245,059	6-7	Charlie Appleby	Godolphin	Herbertstown House Stud
ESOTERIQUE (5)	241,539	1-2	A Fabre	Baron Edouard De Rothschild	Societe Civile De L'Ecurie De Meautry
PETHER'S MOON (5)	236,322	1-3	Richard Hannon	John Manley	Michael G Daly
BIG ORANGE (4)	232,200	2-5	Michael Bell	W J and T C O Gredley	Stetchworth & Middle Park Studs
FLYING OFFICER (5)	230,783	3-3	John Gosden	George Strawbridge	George Strawbridge Jr
ERVEDYA (3)	229,854	1-1	J-C Rouget	H H Aga Khan	The Aga Khan's Studs Sc
NIGHT OF THUNDER (4)	221,972	1-3	Richard Hannon	Godolphin	Frank Dunne
TASLEET (2)	219,538	3-6	William Haggas	Hamdan Al Maktoum	Whitsbury Manor Stud
MUTHMIR (5)	217,624	1-5	William Haggas	Hamdan Al Maktoum	Sunderland Holdings Ltd
SNOW SKY (4)	214,887	2-3	Sir Michael Stoute	K Abdullah	Juddmonte Farms Ltd
LITIGANT (7)	211,650	2-3	Joseph Tuite	A A Byrne	Darley
LIMATO (3)	208,570	2-4	Henry Candy	Paul G Jacobs	Seamus Phelan
BESHARAH (2)	205,758	4-7	William Haggas	Sheikh Rashid Dalmook Al Maktoum	Gerard Kerin

TOP NH JOCKEYS IN BRITAIN 2014/15

W-R	%	JOCKEY	2ND	3RD	TOTAL PRIZE
231-827	28%	A P MCCOY	149	110	2,246,905
153-861	18%	RICHARD JOHNSON	164	120	1,862,411
150-685	22%	TOM SCUDAMORE	100	83	1,478,965
145-759	19%	SAM TWISTON-DAVIES	118	99	2,474,495
106-654	16%	BRIAN HUGHES	94	82	977,372
85-477	18%	NOEL FEHILY	63	82	1,524,360
82-653	13%	AIDAN COLEMAN	78	80	956,825
73-401	18%	GAVIN SHEEHAN	47	42	699,664
72-533	14%	PAUL MOLONEY	64	70	683,894
67-442	15%	PADDY BRENNAN	64	50	917,960
64-374	17%	JASON MAGUIRE	47	51	436,282
61-467	13%	TOM O'BRIEN	61	53	576,245
60-239	25%	BARRY GERAGHTY	37	32	1,241,092
60-418	14%	WILSON RENWICK	60	54	428,353
56-361	16%	JAMES REVELEY	61	52	482,996
56-413	14%	BRIAN HARDING	37	42	483,394
55-292	19%	HARRY SKELTON	28	35	567,165
53-327	16%	DARYL JACOB	44	42	833,905
52-394	13%	TOM CANNON	48	50	426,756
51-255	20%	SEAN BOWEN	45	42	524,145
51-437	12%	NICK SCHOLFIELD	45	52	656,776
48-381	13%	JAMIE MOORE	42	54	417,910
47-378	12%	LEIGHTON ASPELL	59	56	1,234,216
46-232	20%	DAVID BASS	26	26	358,993
44-208	21%	NICO DE BOINVILLE	26	27	766,159
42-273	15%	WAYNE HUTCHINSON	51	26	587,082
40-442	9%	DOUGIE COSTELLO	60	55	341,390
38-386	10%	BRENDAN POWELL	50	52	433,054
35-300	12%	LIAM TREADWELL	32	45	476,418
34-323	11%	TREVOR WHELAN	41	58	251,152
31-186	17%	DANNY COOK	33	18	235,840
30-328	9%	ADAM WEDGE	31	49	259,448
29-239	12%	PETER BUCHANAN	31	29	326,579
29-333	9%	ANDREW THORNTON	41	35	215,371
28-291	10%	WILL KENNEDY	33	34	252,436
26-199	13%	PETER CARBERRY	20	21	140,925
25-213	12%	JAMES DAVIES	22	19	163,534
25-279	9%	CRAIG NICHOL	33	24	219,667
23-152	15%	TOM BELLAMY	17	14	159,271
23-190	12%	JOSHUA MOORE	19	17	259,623
23-228	10%	JAMES BANKS	33	33	152,805
23-245	9%	DENIS O'REGAN	48	27	300,758
22-155	14%	MICHEAL NOLAN	24	21	161,872
22-167	13%	GRAHAM WATTERS	14	24	160,572
21-162	13%	JOE COLLIVER	15	14	131,612
21-174	12%	KIELAN WOODS	20	27	205,508
21-209	10%	ANDREW TINKLER	23	28	234,592
21-225	9%	CONOR SHOEMARK	20	30	175,074
20-243	8%	RICHIE MCLERNON	30	28	338,037
20-254	8%	JAMES BEST	24	21	146,407

TOP NH TRAINERS IN BRITAIN 2014/15

TRAINER	LEADING HORSE	W-R	2ND	3RD	4TH	TOTAL PRIZE	WIN PRIZE
PAUL NICHOLLS	DODGING BULLETS	124-518	89	80	46	3,246,893	2,383,882
NICKY HENDERSON	MA FILLEULE	128-499	90	61	49	1,904,130	1,128,821
PHILIP HOBBS	MENORAH	102-552	93	77	48	1,509,917	1,020,176
W P MULLINS	FAUGHEEN	16-91	8	13	8	1,385,931	889,987
DAVID PIPE	DYNASTE	116-580	71	67	57	1,262,493	781,676
ALAN KING	UXIZANDRE	75-447	78	43	47	1,140,598	768,234
OLIVER SHERWOOD	MANY CLOUDS	31-204	43	36	22	1,041,944	894,907
JONJO O'NEILL	JOHNS SPIRIT	104-633	87	70	59	978,280	513,441
NIGEL TWISTON-DAVIES	THE NEW ONE	73-488	60	61	62	889,206	597,784
VENETIA WILLIAMS	NICEONEFRANKIE	53-441	47	61	56	859,211	490,127
TOM GEORGE	SAINT ARE	36-262	40	38	36	717,771	259,961
DAN SKELTON	BLUE HERON	73-377	47	44	50	714,164	492,905
DONALD MCCAIN	THE LAST SAMURI	98-687	96	104	65	643,729	392,869
JOHN FERGUSON	PARLOUR GAMES	56-214	49	18	18	615,184	364,771
EVAN WILLIAMS	BALLYGLASHEEN	63-410	58	65	52	608,227	346,299
GORDON ELLIOTT	DON COSSACK	35-120	22	14	11	591,751	463,167
COLIN TIZZARD	THISTLECRACK	38-294	34	41	43	560,934	319,993
WARREN GREATREX	COLE HARDEN	51-272	31	34	30	546,880	395,346
HARRY FRY	ROCK ON RUBY	36-156	21	27	16	528,346	298,416
LUCINDA RUSSELL	LIE FORRIT	47-501	64	59	58	496,580	306,547
CHARLIE LONGSDON	KILCOOLEY	50-338	50	43	35	447,715	285,689
KIM BAILEY	DARNA	61-268	32	31	29	439,192	336,774
MARK BRADSTOCK	CONEYGREE	8-24	1	3	0	436,703	429,341
GARY MOORE	VIOLET DANCER	39-312	37	33	44	425,626	271,622
NEIL MULHOLLAND	THE DRUIDS NEPHEW	51-262	38	26	26	406,956	316,649
REBECCA CURTIS	THE ROMFORD PELE	45-221	34	39	23	400,719	287,295
PETER BOWEN	ROLLING MAUL	57-373	58	66	39	399,395	245,907
SUE SMITH	WAKANDA	31-322	44	46	48	348,319	174,341
NICKY RICHARDS	GLINGERBURN	49-189	20	22	12	347,068	237,562
BRIAN ELLISON	YORKIST	35-289	55	41	23	314,239	162,770
NICK WILLIAMS	REVE DE SIVOLA	13-113	13	18	9	296,161	167,732
DR RICHARD NEWLAND	EBONY EXPRESS	35-149	23	17	16	285,744	207,556
FERGAL O'BRIEN	ALVARADO	27-247	32	29	30	270,618	152,220
EMMA LAVELLE	CLOSING CEREMONY	21-190	19	22	16	269,005	142,726
HENRY DE BROMHEAD	SPECIAL TIARA	3-15	2	2	0	268,595	179,180
LUCY WADHAM	LE REVE	19-132	19	19	13	249,796	134,039
DAVID BRIDGWATER	NO BUTS	33-184	26	26	17	247,231	165,883
NEIL KING	LIL ROCKERFELLER	29-201	28	45	29	244,476	155,301
TIM VAUGHAN	FIRST FANDANGO	38-349	38	48	30	244,260	153,164
RICHARD LEE	TOP GAMBLE	19-108	16	14	7	231,999	151,337
MICHAEL SCUDAMORE	MONBEG DUDE	13-78	10	12	10	230,569	83,399
MALCOLM JEFFERSON	CYRUS DARIUS	25-161	20	17	17	220,349	159,538
MICK CHANNON	SOMERSBY	8-54	11	1	11	218,042	47,496
CHARLIE MANN	SEVENTH SKY	23-151	19	12	28	198,000	122,833
CHRIS GORDON	LIGHTENTERTAINMENT	30-198	31	24	16	197,949	135,151
HENRY DALY	TARA MIST	21-181	42	18	15	181,957	85,338
DAVID DENNIS	ROMAN FLIGHT	32-208	12	37	26	181,307	130,881
MARTIN KEIGHLEY	ANY CURRENCY	17-210	29	27	23	180,742	117,613
JOHN QUINN	AURORE D'ESTRUVAL	20-112	30	13	7	178,453	100,156
IAN WILLIAMS	TEAK	21-191	21	17	30	174,386	115,483

TOP NH OWNERS IN BRITAIN 2014/15

OWNER	LEADING HORSE	W-R	2ND	3RD	4TH	TOTAL PRIZE	WIN PRIZE
JOHN P MCMANUS	Uxizandre	88-506	64	48	57	1,459,078	1,034,812
TREVOR HEMMINGS	Many Clouds	19-106	15	18	9	913,930	822,099
MRS S RICCI	Faugheen	7-32	2	2	6	680,968	493,076
BLOOMFIELDS.	Parlour Games	56-209	48	17	17	614,247	364,771
SIMON MUNIR & ISAAC SOUEDE.	Peace And Co	37-101	17	7	13	575,210	429,804
GIGGINSTOWN HOUSE STUD.	Don Cossack	5-50	3	8	3	517,782	305,248
CHRIS GILES & POTENSIS							
BLOODSTOCK LTD	Silviniaco Conti	7-14	2	2	1	433,689	356,406
THE MAX PARTNERSHIP.	Coneygree	4-4	0	0	0	401,930	401,930
MRS DIANA L WHATELEY	Menorah	16-63	10	6	4	386,261	296,865
MARTIN BROUGHTON & FRIENDS	Dodging Bullets	3-6	0	1	0	362,577	355,087
S SUCH & CG PALETTA	The New One	5-16	2	2	1	271,613	209,970
R S BROOKHOUSE	Cheltenian	18-83	15	11	4	249,560	158,716
PAUL & CLARE ROONEY.	The Last Samuri	43-235	32	42	23	249,223	161,744
D W FOX	Saint Are	1-6	1	3	0	240,865	7,797
MRS JILL EYNON & ROBIN EYNON	Cole Harden	4-12	2	2	1	240,314	198,419
MASTERSON HOLDINGS LIMITED.	Balder Succes	8-25	5	2	1	219,142	149,746
MRS T P RADFORD	Somersby	7-33	9	2	6	203,291	36,891
ANN & ALAN POTTS PARTNERSHIP	Goonyella	2-11	2	1	0	196,601	118,847
MRS ANGELA YEOMAN	Southfield Theatre	12-23	5	1	0	195,989	147,296
THE STEWART FAMILY.	Saphir Du Rheu	6-28	8	3	0	191,732	105,273
ROBERT WALEY-COHEN	Oscar Time	7-31	3	1	7	189,151	170,972
ANDREA & GRAHAM WYLIE	Nichols Canyon	6-43	12	5	2	185,220	71,443
J HALES.	Al Ferof	6-24	3	2	2	165,012	116,495
BROCADE RACING	Hey Big Spender	17-74	11	6	10	164,824	103,583
T J & MRS H PARROTT	Wayward Prince	2-13	2	3	0	158,553	152,085
MRS S ROWLEY-WILLIAMS.	Special Tiara	2-3	0	1	0	154,733	117,283
MRS JOHNNY DE LA HEY	Irish Saint	8-25	3	6	2	147,948	102,195
MRS GAY SMITH.	Holywell	10-47	8	5	5	142,903	60,357
WICKLOW BLOODSTOCK LIMITED	Arctic Fire	1-7	1	1	0	141,650	45,560
MR & MRS WILLIAM RUCKER.	Alvarado	6-42	11	7	3	140,216	32,165
MATT & LAUREN MORGAN	Call The Cops	5-10	2	0	3	136,521	94,900
P J MARTIN	Definitly Red	16-77	19	11	7	135,479	81,187
C G ROACH.	Hawkes Point	9-39	6	10	5	133,006	95,980
OYDUNOW	Monbeg Dude	0-6	1	2	2	132,952	0
TERRY WARNER	Lamb Or Cod	5-50	15	7	7	131,757	39,295
POTENSIS BLOODSTOCK LIMITED	All Yours	3-15	3	4	0	128,791	75,483
MR & MRS R KELVIN-HUGHES	Vaniteux	9-31	8	0	1	124,487	50,607
A BROOKS	Baradari	6-58	10	8	5	123,865	72,003
WALTERS PLANT HIRE LTD.	Whisper	11-41	3	2	7	123,308	100,288
CROSSED FINGERS PARTNERSHIP	God's Own	4-25	4	2	2	122,705	43,549
AXOM XLIII.	Vibrato Valtat	4-10	2	2	2	122,050	73,323
SIMON MUNIR	Ma Filleule	0-7	2	1	1	110,210	0
CARL HINCHY	Aurore D'Estruval	11-49	8	7	2	108,724	60,762
MRS S SMITH.	Mwaleshi	11-125	18	13	21	105,980	55,834
THE BELLAMY PARTNERSHIP	Emperor's Choice	4-25	3	2	2	105,269	80,083
CHRISTOPHER W T JOHNSTON	Johns Spirit	2-17	4	5	0	104,632	32,839
P H BETTS	Le Reve	3-21	6	4	1	104,480	47,203
DAJAM LTD	The Young Master	8-26	3	3	2	100,778	85,909
D BESSELL & GALLOPING ON THE							
SOUTH DOWNS	Violet Dancer	1-7	1	1	1	97,754	88,272
MR & MRS RAYMOND ANDERSON GREEN.	Upsilon Bleu	7-48	8	5	3	97,200	49,319

TOP NH HORSES
IN BRITAIN 2014/15

HORSE (AGE)	WIN & PLACE £	W-R	TRAINER	OWNER	BREEDER
MANY CLOUDS (8)	741,017	4-5	Oliver Sherwood	Trevor Hemmings	Aidan Aherne
CONEYGREE (8)	401,930	4-4	Mark Bradstock	The Max Partnership	Lord Oaksey
DODGING BULLETS (7)	362,577	3-4	Paul Nicholls	Martin Broughton & Friends	L Dettori
FAUGHEEN (7)	335,661	3-3	W P Mullins	Mrs S Ricci	Dr John Waldron
SILVINIACO CONTI (9)	314,023	3-5	Paul Nicholls	Chris Giles & Potensis Bloodstock Ltd	Patrick Joubert
SAINT ARE (9)	240,865	1-5	Tom George	D W Fox	Jacques Cypres
COLE HARDEN (6)	231,475	2-6	Warren Greatrex	Mrs Jill Eynon & Robin Eynon	Mrs J O'Callaghan
UXIZANDRE (7)	222,113	2-4	Alan King	John P McManus	Frederic Aimez
THE NEW ONE (7)	203,605	4-5	Nigel Twiston-Davies	S Such & Cg Paletta	R Brown & Ballylinch Stud
SAPHIR DU RHEU (6)	161,585	3-6	Paul Nicholls	The Stewart Family	Claude Duval
WAYWARD PRINCE (11)	156,266	2-6	Hilary Parrott	T J & Mrs H Parrott	M G Kilroe
SPECIAL TIARA (8)	154,733	2-3	Henry De Bromhead	Mrs S Rowley-Williams	D E M Young
DON COSSACK (8)	146,181	1-2	Gordon Elliott	Gigginstown House Stud	Gestut Etzean
BALDER SUCCES (7)	142,498	2-7	Alan King	Masterson Holdings Limited	Damien Bellanger Et Al
JEZKI (7)	134,392	1-2	Mrs John Harrington	John P McManus	Gerard M McGrath
MONBEG DUDE (10)	132,952	0-6	Michael Scudamore	Oydunow	Hilary O'Connor
MENORAH (10)	132,313	2-5	Philip Hobbs	Mrs Diana L Whateley	Mrs E Grant And Miss Anna Brislane
SOMERSBY (11)	128,481	0-6	Mick Channon	Mrs T P Radford	Miss Nicola Ann Adams
VIBRATO VALTAT (7)	122,050	4-10	Paul Nicholls	Axom XLIII	Mme C Duperret & Mlle A-M Duperret
DJAKADAM (6)	117,535	0-2	W P Mullins	Mrs S Ricci	Richard Corveller
MA FILLEULE (7)	107,829	0-4	Nicky Henderson	Simon Munir	Serge Dubois
GOONYELLA (8)	101,827	1-3	J T R Dreaper	Ann & Alan Potts Partnership	Mrs C T And Miss S Berry
PEACE AND CO (4)	101,300	3-3	Nicky Henderson	Simon Munir & Isaac Souede	S A R L Scuderia Bolgheri S R L Et Al
JOHNS SPIRIT (8)	97,870	1-5	Jonjo O'Neill	Christopher W T Johnston	Arctic Tack Stud & Crossogue Stud
VIOLET DANCER (5)	97,754	1-7	Gary Moore	D Bessell & Galloping On The South Downs	Jeremy Hinds
CAID DU BERLAIS (6)	96,470	1-5	Paul Nicholls	Donlon, Doyle, MacDonald & C Barber	Jean-Marc Lucas
ARCTIC FIRE (6)	96,090	0-3	W P Mullins	Wicklow Bloodstock Limited	U Gruning
GOD'S OWN (7)	94,948	1-6	Tom George	Crossed Fingers Partnership	Mrs Caroline O'Driscoll
JUST A PAR (8)	92,797	1-7	Paul Nicholls	Paul K Barber & C G Roach	Sean Whelan
LE REVE (7)	91,984	2-6	Lucy Wadham	P H Betts	J D Flood
CHELTENIAN (9)	90,645	1-4	Philip Hobbs	R S Brookhouse	Jean-Charles Haimet & J-Pascal Liberge
PARLOUR GAMES (7)	90,358	4-8	John Ferguson	Bloomfields	Darley
ROCK ON RUBY (10)	87,772	2-4	Harry Fry	The Festival Goers	John O'Dwyer
BAYAN (6)	87,070	1-2	Gordon Elliott	Core Syndicate	Floors Farming
LIE FORRIT (11)	86,788	3-5	Lucinda Russell	JW McNeill C McNeill Ms L Gillies	Niall McGrady
UN DE SCEAUX (7)	85,425	1-1	W P Mullins	Edward O'Connell	Haras De La Rousseliere Et Al
DON POLI (6)	85,425	1-1	W P Mullins	Gigginstown House Stud	Brian J Griffiths And John Nicholson
OSCAR TIME (14)	82,020	3-6	Robert Waley-Cohen	Robert Waley-Cohen	Edmond Coleman
GARDE LA VICTOIRE (6)	81,538	2-5	Philip Hobbs	Mrs Diana L Whateley	Mlle Laure Godet
WISHFULL THINKING (12)	80,460	2-4	Philip Hobbs	Mrs Diana L Whateley	Cobhall Court Stud
PURPLE BAY (6)	79,200	2-4	John Ferguson	Bloomfields	Darley
IRISH SAINT (6)	78,105	3-7	Paul Nicholls	Mrs Johnny de la Hey	S C É A Haras Du Ma
VIRAK (6)	77,913	4-6	Paul Nicholls	Hills Of Ledbury (Aga)	B Thierry, S Thierry & E Labataille
VYTA DU ROC (6)	77,568	4-7	Nicky Henderson	Simon Munir & Isaac Souede	Andre Le Gall
WHISPER (7)	76,767	1-3	Nicky Henderson	Walters Plant Hire Ltd	Hubert & Sandra Hosselet

LEADING SIRES OF 2015 IN GREAT BRITAIN AND IRELAND

STALLION	BREEDING	RNRS	WNRS	WINS	WIN MONEY	PLACES	PLACE MONEY	TOTAL
GALILEO (IRE)	by Sadler's Wells (USA)	216	92	123	3278819	338	2470931	5749749
DUBAWI (IRE)	by Dubai Millennium (GB)	169	81	116	2838984	263	1051266	3890250
CAPE CROSS (IRE)	by Green Desert (USA)	154	79	117	2754898	267	838328	3593226
DARK ANGEL (IRE)	by Acclamation (GB)	182	81	128	1623861	378	1218888	2842749
INVINCIBLE SPIRIT (IRE)	by Green Desert (USA)	185	92	138	1632149	413	933665	2565814
OASIS DREAM (GB)	by Green Desert (USA)	170	66	100	1824896	316	629167	2454063
TEOFILO (IRE)	by Galileo (IRE)	137	57	90	1273812	284	1085304	2359116
SHAMARDAL (USA)	by Giant's Causeway (USA)	173	82	136	1537573	333	754018	2291591
KODIAC (GB)	by Danehill (USA)	218	91	154	1584020	463	687998	2272018
FASTNET ROCK (AUS)	by Danehill (USA)	118	41	56	1809430	168	375432	2184861
DANEHILL DANCER (IRE)	by Danehill (USA)	98	36	62	1366314	170	613598	1979912
EXCEED AND EXCEL (AUS)	by Danehill (USA)	192	92	136	1137514	408	609711	1747285
HALLING (USA)	by Diesis	91	34	50	917186	178	806853	1724039
SINGSPIEL (IRE)	by In the Wings	25	9	13	1458295	56	134164	1592460
PIVOTAL (GB)	by Polar Falcon (USA)	138	60	99	753530	233	796398	1549928
ACCLAMATION (GB)	by Royal Applause (GB)	234	103	143	843628	514	684644	1528272
MASTERCRAFTSMAN (IRE)	by Danehill Dancer (IRE)	122	45	59	812853	219	670930	1483783
DUKE OF MARMALADE (IRE)	by Danehill (USA)	105	30	51	1287100	151	176059	1463159
SEA THE STARS (IRE)	by Cape Cross (IRE)	84	35	56	579999	119	774212	1354211
HIGH CHAPARRAL (IRE)	by Sadler's Wells (USA)	102	38	59	836703	164	472167	1308870
AZAMOUR (IRE)	by Night Shift (USA)	90	41	74	738682	154	538360	1277042
KYLLACHY (GB)	by Pivotal (GB)	156	57	93	779977	305	482044	1262021
IFFRAAJ (GB)	by Zafonic (USA)	158	70	100	547129	320	605876	1153004
DUTCH ART (GB)	by Medicean (GB)	138	57	85	720523	210	367120	1087643
DANSILI (GB)	by Danehill (USA)	130	54	82	632564	214	401201	1033765

LEADING SIRES OF 2015
(GREAT BRITAIN, IRELAND AND OVERSEAS)

STALLION	BREEDING	DOMESTIC WNRS	DOMESTIC WINS	WIN MONEY	OVERSEAS WNRS	OVERSEAS WINS	WIN MONEY	TOTAL
DUBAWI (IRE)	by Dubai Millennium (GB)	81	116	2833994	60	99	8082740	10921724
GALILEO (IRE)	by Sadler's Wells (USA)	92	123	3278819	60	89	4048065	7326883
CAPE CROSS (IRE)	by Green Desert (USA)	79	117	2754898	40	62	3010259	5765157
SINGSPIEL (IRE)	In the Wings	9	13	1458295	23	37	2645912	4104207
SHAMARDAL (USA)	by Giant's Causeway (USA)	82	136	1537573	78	130	2552646	4090218
AZAMOUR (IRE)	by Night Shift (USA)	41	74	738682	35	56	2867831	3606513
OASIS DREAM (GB)	by Green Desert (USA)	66	100	1824896	51	88	1484878	3309774
INVINCIBLE SPIRIT (IRE)	by Green Desert (USA)	92	138	1632149	40	65	1485861	3118010
HOLY ROMAN EMPEROR (IRE)	by Danehill (USA)	47	76	502575	82	133	2205772	2708347
DANEHILL DANCER (IRE)	by Danehill (USA)	36	62	1366314	50	68	1273407	2639721
DUKE OF MARMALADE (IRE)	by Danehill (USA)	30	51	1287100	49	77	1264749	2551849
DANSILI (GB)	by Danehill (USA)	54	82	632564	42	62	1822755	2455319
DYLAN THOMAS (IRE)	by Danehill (USA)	29	43	475947	50	87	1935525	2411472
DARK ANGEL (IRE)	by Acclamation (GB)	81	128	1623861	38	61	784867	2408728
HIGH CHAPARRAL (IRE)	by Sadler's Wells (USA)	38	59	836703	57	84	1530742	2367445
EXCEED AND EXCEL (AUS)	by Danehill (USA)	92	136	1137574	49	90	1194547	2332121
TEOFILO (IRE)	by Galileo (IRE)	41	56	1809430	16	29	475759	2285188
FASTNET ROCK (AUS)	by Danehill (USA)	57	90	1273812	43	66	866593	2140405
FOOTSTEPSINTHESAND (GB)	by Giant's Causeway (USA)	37	54	359247	82	151	1614181	1973428
KODIAC (GB)	by Danehill (USA)	91	154	1584020	26	43	346072	1930092
NEW APPROACH (IRE)	by Galileo (IRE)	43	63	547035	28	53	1227649	1774685
PIVOTAL (GB)	by Polar Falcon (USA)	60	99	753530	41	69	875998	1629528
DANDY MAN (IRE)	by Mozart (IRE)	26	43	238306	6	7	1303039	1541345
ROCK OF GIBRALTAR (IRE)	by Danehill (USA)	40	62	373807	66	100	1146935	1520742
DUTCH ART (GB)	by Medicean (GB)	57	85	720523	36	64	777314	1497837

LEADING TWO-YEAR-OLD SIRES OF 2015 IN GREAT BRITAIN AND IRELAND

STALLION	BREEDING	RNRS	WNRS	WINS	WIN MONEY	PLACES	PLACE MONEY	TOTAL
GALILEO (IRE)	by Sadler's Wells (USA)	52	21	29	1073567	48	303302	1376869
KODIAC (GB)	by Danehill (USA)	103	37	60	796185	196	277921	1074106
INVINCIBLE SPIRIT (IRE)	by Green Desert (USA)	52	23	31	606034	93	233156	839189
DARK ANGEL (IRE)	by Acclamation (GB)	65	27	37	426873	97	340049	766922
ZOFFANY (IRE)	by Dansili (GB)	64	27	38	425614	84	328151	753766
WAR FRONT (USA)	by Danzig (USA)	11	6	10	596550	10	51232	647782
SHOWCASING (GB)	by Oasis Dream (GB)	52	19	32	456904	82	140331	597234
EXCEED AND EXCEL (AUS)	by Danehill (USA)	60	29	36	288982	88	189746	478729
TEOFILO (IRE)	by Galileo (IRE)	23	11	18	224178	28	230145	454322
SHAMARDAL (USA)	by Giant's Causeway (USA)	46	20	28	311469	49	122791	434260
ACCLAMATION (GB)	by Royal Applause (GB)	81	29	35	198536	141	226534	425070
IFFRAAJ (GB)	by Zafonic (USA)	48	20	24	158366	71	224092	382457
CANFORD CLIFFS (IRE)	by Tagula (IRE)	62	26	33	255077	86	98763	353840
DREAM AHEAD (USA)	by Diktat (GB)	35	12	17	135306	52	164903	300210
ELNADIM (USA)	by Danzig (USA)	16	6	8	180698	24	110680	291377
ZEBEDEE (GB)	by Invincible Spirit (IRE)	73	23	31	120404	133	161509	281913
LAWMAN (FR)	by Invincible Spirit (IRE)	42	13	18	217377	61	57568	274945
PACO BOY (IRE)	by Desert Style (IRE)	48	16	20	208696	67	58360	267056
EQUIANO (FR)	by Acclamation (GB)	53	20	32	185807	64	76449	262256
COMPTON PLACE (GB)	by Indian Ridge	30	8	10	230899	28	21748	252647
PASTORAL PURSUITS (GB)	by Bahamian Bounty (GB)	30	12	15	61888	73	189114	251002
HOLY ROMAN EMPEROR (IRE)	by Danehill (USA)	53	16	19	141913	64	97865	239778
NEW APPROACH (IRE)	by Galileo (GB)	30	6	9	128359	30	109907	238267
DUBAWI (IRE)	by Dubai Millennium (GB)	49	20	26	169999	47	61270	231269
RAVEN'S PASS (USA)	by Elusive Quality (USA)	36	15	18	105651	52	113885	219536

LEADING FIRST CROP SIRES OF 2015 IN GREAT BRITAIN AND IRELAND

STALLION	BREEDING	RNRS	WNRS	WINS	WIN MONEY	PLACES	PLACE MONEY	TOTAL
ZOFFANY (IRE)	by Dansili (GB)	64	27	38	425614	84	328151	753766
CANFORD CLIFFS (IRE)	by Tagula (IRE)	62	26	33	255077	86	98763	353840
DREAM AHEAD (USA)	by Diktat (GB)	35	12	17	135306	52	164903	300210
LILBOURNE LAD (IRE)	by Acclamation (GB)	62	20	23	100500	87	76175	176675
RODERIC O'CONNOR (IRE)	by Galileo (IRE)	34	11	13	102977	44	70624	173602
POET'S VOICE (GB)	by Dubawi (IRE)	52	15	24	122974	48	44226	167200
POUR MOI (IRE)	by Montjeu (IRE)	20	7	8	49142	14	41591	90733
FROZEN POWER (IRE)	by Oasis Dream (GB)	51	12	13	46763	47	35558	82322
DICK TURPIN (IRE)	by Arakan (USA)	28	4	7	33962	26	47259	81221
ELUSIVE PIMPERNEL (USA)	by Elusive Quality (USA)	12	5	7	25191	12	13558	38749
TWIRLING CANDY (USA)	by Candy Ride (ARG)	1	1	2	13585	2	17681	31266
CAPE BLANCO (IRE)	by Galileo (IRE)	15	3	3	9704	14	11436	21139
ATLANTIC SPORT (USA)	by Machiavellian (USA)	6	1	1	2523	16	12053	14576
SHAKESPEAREAN (IRE)	by Shamardal (USA)	1	1	2	5951	3	2533	8484
WOOTTON BASSETT (GB)	by Iffraaj (GB)	6	0	0	0	12	7215	7215
DROSSELMEYER (USA)	by Distorted Humor (USA)	1	1	2	5499	3	1010	6509
PADDY O'PRADO (USA)	by El Prado (IRE)	3	0	0	0	5	4827	4827
GIO PONTI (USA)	by Tale of the Cat (USA)	1	0	0	0	2	3969	3969
SOUL CITY (IRE)	by Elusive City (USA)	1	1	1	2264	2	756	3020
ARCHARCHARCH (USA)	by Arch (USA)	1	0	0	0	1	1674	1674
PALAVICINI (USA)	by Giant's Causeway (USA)	1	0	0	0	1	733	733
DALGHAR (FR)	by Anabaa (USA)	1	0	0	0	1	481	481
LOVELACE (GB)	by Royal Applause (GB)	1	0	0	0	1	216	216
PRIME DEFENDER (GB)	by Bertolini (USA)	3	0	0	0	0	0	0
NATIVE RULER (GB)	by Cape Cross (IRE)	1	0	0	0	0	0	0

LEADING MATERNAL GRANDSIRES OF 2015 IN GREAT BRITAIN AND IRELAND

STALLION	BREEDING	RNRS	WNRS	WINS	WIN MONEY	PLACES	PLACE MONEY	TOTAL
DANEHILL (USA)	by Danzig (USA)	238	99	139	1969960	404	1959189	3929150
SADLER'S WELLS (USA)	by Northern Dancer	369	125	181	2304434	542	1135925	3440359
DUBAI DESTINATION (USA)	by Kingmambo (USA)	53	25	40	2664277	111	433288	3097565
PIVOTAL (GB)	by Polar Falcon (USA)	246	101	143	1126359	433	882780	2009139
MONTJEU (IRE)	by Sadler's Wells (USA)	108	49	73	1298811	180	641461	1940271
DANEHILL DANCER (IRE)	by Danehill (USA)	157	60	85	1324465	233	577294	1901759
GALILEO (IRE)	by Sadler's Wells (USA)	136	62	85	1426067	226	384855	1810922
DARSHAAN	by Shirley Heights	137	53	74	1205754	210	467359	1673114
HIGHEST HONOR (FR)	by Kenmare (FR)	40	15	24	1498281	60	104658	1602940
CADEAUX GENEREUX	by Young Generation	118	59	91	1110826	221	381026	1491852
BARATHEA (IRE)	by Sadler's Wells (USA)	153	61	85	1013467	261	426948	1440415
DANSILI (GB)	by Danehill (USA)	114	51	74	875348	213	473878	1349226
SINGSPIEL (IRE)	by In the Wings	116	57	80	580796	264	635803	1216599
LINAMIX (FR)	by Mendez (FR)	60	18	27	1074626	69	132551	1207177
INDIAN RIDGE	by Ahonoora	172	61	86	662328	341	528227	1190555
POLAR FALCON (USA)	by Nureyev (USA)	47	19	35	1001139	92	184176	1185315
STORM CAT (USA)	by Storm Bird (CAN)	52	18	26	900609	83	250650	1151259
SWAIN (IRE)	by Nashwan (USA)	21	5	8	625499	29	522403	1147902
RAINBOW QUEST (USA)	by Blushing Groom (FR)	154	50	83	552871	242	530974	1083845
KINGMAMBO (USA)	by Mr Prospector (USA)	94	41	66	604517	164	474764	1079281
ROYAL APPLAUSE (GB)	by Waajib	134	63	82	660958	262	385145	1046103
SELKIRK (USA)	by Sharpen Up	168	73	103	659055	272	344180	1003235
MARJU (IRE)	by Last Tycoon	89	39	57	717163	181	280674	997836
IN THE WINGS	by Sadler's Wells (USA)	80	29	48	391847	146	592060	983907
GREEN DESERT (USA)	by Danzig (USA)	168	58	101	566497	312	357463	923960

FLAT STALLIONS' EARNINGS FOR 2015

(includes every stallion who sired a winner on the Flat in Great Britain and Ireland in 2015)

STALLIONS	RNRS	STARTS	WNRS	WINS	PLACES	TOTAL (£)
ACCLAMATION (GB)	234	1361	103	143	514	1528271.65
ACT ONE (GB)	7	28	2	4	6	14926.92
AD VALOREM (USA)	22	161	9	20	63	133259.53
AFLEET ALEX (USA)	1	3	1	1	0	5175.20
AIR CHIEF MARSHAL (IRE)	2	16	1	1	7	16352.25
ALBANO (IRE)	1	14	1	1	7	7184.31
ALDEBARAN (USA)	1	20	1	1	7	6818.75
ALFRED NOBEL (IRE)	35	187	11	14	51	96304.04
ALHAARTH (IRE)	21	119	6	8	34	41049.75
ALKAADHEM (GB)	1	7	1	1	1	4794.57
AMADEUS WOLF (GB)	42	267	16	25	84	186156.90
AMERICAN POST (GB)	6	43	3	3	16	36093.20
ANABAA (USA)	5	20	1	1	3	3154.00
AND BEYOND (IRE)	1	12	1	6	2	15884.68
ANTONIUS PIUS (USA)	22	142	9	16	37	123513.28
A P INDY (USA)	1	5	1	2	1	7596.90
APPROVE (IRE)	71	418	22	36	141	315626.71
AQLAAM (GB)	54	238	19	30	85	241956.24
ARAAFA (IRE)	11	84	8	11	29	97780.54
ARABIAN GLEAM (GB)	14	53	2	2	12	14104.41
ARAKAN (USA)	25	101	7	8	21	311911.55
ARCANO (IRE)	87	432	40	47	155	368291.25
ARCH (USA)	24	120	8	10	48	104039.73
ARCHIPENKO (USA)	52	250	24	39	86	408695.10
AREION (GER)	7	27	2	4	8	29017.52
ARTAN (IRE)	3	19	2	2	3	12155.63
ART CONNOISSEUR (IRE)	29	147	8	10	28	64477.29
ASHKALANI (IRE)	2	13	1	1	1	3199.65
ASSERTIVE (GB)	27	154	5	5	57	52685.10
ASTRONOMER ROYAL (USA)	5	33	5	7	6	23801.48
ATLANTIC SPORT (USA)	6	32	1	1	16	14575.99
ATRAF (GB)	2	13	1	1	3	4939.95
AUCTION HOUSE (USA)	4	25	1	2	5	12379.00
AUSSIE RULES (USA)	67	376	25	37	126	306007.01
AUTHORIZED (IRE)	82	346	31	43	107	537815.29
AVONBRIDGE (GB)	42	286	15	24	88	135397.62
AZAMOUR (IRE)	90	469	41	74	154	1277042.26
BACHELOR DUKE (USA)	11	65	2	2	21	19659.85
BAHAMIAN BOUNTY (GB)	128	776	56	82	252	948378.75
BAHRI (USA)	10	48	1	4	17	23719.20
BALLET MASTER (USA)	4	23	2	3	6	14888.50
BALMONT (USA)	8	48	3	5	7	46860.13
BALTIC KING (GB)	34	196	9	13	75	135453.26
BARATHEA (IRE)	11	56	4	6	16	37671.88
BEAT ALL (USA)	3	18	1	2	10	35305.37
BEAT HOLLOW (GB)	28	147	9	12	49	292162.78
BENEFICIAL (GB)	3	17	2	2	3	10940.99
BERNARDINI (USA)	14	39	2	2	5	38411.43
BERNSTEIN (USA)	8	31	2	2	3	35551.12
BERTOLINI (USA)	51	340	14	29	89	199374.50
BIG BAD BOB (IRE)	85	379	25	34	125	502176.93
BIG BROWN (USA)	3	21	1	3	8	53337.21
BIG SHUFFLE (USA)	3	10	1	1	7	6502.05
BIRDSTONE (USA)	3	10	1	2	2	17680.24
BLACK SAM BELLAMY (IRE)	10	18	1	1	6	10778.75
BLAME (USA)	11	48	5	8	16	83694.45
BLUEGRASS CAT (USA)	3	17	1	1	8	6743.87
BLUE OCEAN (USA)	1	3	1	1	2	6755.81

STALLIONS	RNRS	STARTS	WNRS	WINS	PLACES	TOTAL (£)
BOB AND JOHN (USA)	1	11	1	2	4	14619.50
BOLLIN ERIC (GB)	3	13	1	2	4	6786.55
BROKEN VOW (USA)	1	9	1	1	2	3611.40
BUSHRANGER (IRE)	130	739	51	68	229	518727.10
BYRON (GB)	46	317	15	23	107	262986.67
CACIQUE (IRE)	13	39	3	3	9	20280.78
CADEAUX GENEREUX	11	71	2	5	28	95567.72
CAMACHO (GB)	38	286	19	30	91	243022.69
CANFORD CLIFFS (IRE)	62	246	26	33	86	353839.65
CAPE BLANCO (IRE)	15	39	3	3	14	21139.10
CAPE CROSS (IRE)	154	733	79	117	267	3593225.72
CAPTAIN AL (SAF)	1	6	1	1	1	2995.65
CAPTAIN GERRARD (IRE)	47	334	21	30	130	223424.01
CAPTAIN MARVELOUS (IRE)	13	99	6	11	32	100359.64
CAPTAIN RIO (GB)	75	487	34	46	148	461736.70
THE CARBON UNIT (USA)	12	83	4	4	34	50035.94
CATCHER IN THE RYE (IRE)	4	30	2	3	9	21921.04
CELTIC SWING (GB)	12	61	4	6	13	35305.61
CENTRAL PARK (IRE)	6	33	2	6	8	29524.45
CHAMPS ELYSEES (GB)	87	403	39	52	141	863301.07
CHEROKEE RUN (USA)	1	12	1	1	5	6241.63
CHEVALIER (IRE)	7	62	4	10	21	113207.46
CHINEUR (FR)	13	99	6	8	30	101513.88
CHOISIR (AUS)	31	189	11	18	61	238124.77
CITY ON A HILL (USA)	1	11	1	1	4	4704.35
CITY ZIP (USA)	3	19	1	2	5	13196.90
CLODOVIL (IRE)	73	428	28	43	123	459481.95
COCKNEY REBEL (IRE)	46	242	13	21	78	155399.65
COMPTON PLACE (GB)	98	558	32	49	163	650998.11
COUNTRY REEL (USA)	5	22	1	2	7	59770.50
CREACHADOIR (IRE)	1	11	1	2	3	62579.00
DAAHER (CAN)	3	18	1	1	4	7418.57
DALAKHANI (IRE)	54	265	19	24	104	570443.14
DANBIRD (AUS)	6	42	2	2	13	13073.91
DANDY MAN (IRE)	71	434	26	43	133	372554.96
DANEHILL DANCER (IRE)	98	489	36	62	170	1979911.98
DANETIME (IRE)	4	43	2	3	18	23431.31
DANROAD (AUS)	6	32	1	2	6	16861.46
DANSILI (GB)	130	574	54	82	214	1033765.27
DAPPER (GB)	2	13	1	1	6	5885.23
DARK ANGEL (IRE)	182	998	81	128	378	2842749.37
DASHING BLADE	1	8	1	3	2	7709.45
DAY FLIGHT (GB)	1	6	1	2	2	17299.80
DAYLAMI (IRE)	2	4	1	1	0	4813.95
DEFINITE ARTICLE (GB)	6	25	2	2	9	26293.53
DENOUNCE (GB)	3	26	2	2	10	119106.36
DEPORTIVO (GB)	4	9	1	1	3	21986.90
DESERT MILLENNIUM (IRE)	3	20	1	1	8	7350.95
DESERT PRINCE (IRE)	6	45	2	3	21	27543.45
DESERT STYLE (IRE)	8	66	2	4	24	29364.83
DESIDERATUM (GB)	6	35	1	2	13	12409.85
DIAMOND GREEN (FR)	22	140	6	9	35	72859.43
DICK TURPIN (IRE)	28	95	4	7	26	81221.30
DIKTAT (GB)	17	118	9	21	37	180422.15
DISCREET CAT (USA)	5	21	3	3	7	11532.47
DISCREETLY MINE (USA)	2	4	1	1	1	4129.85
DISTANT PEAK (IRE)	1	15	1	1	5	5316.90
DISTORTED HUMOR (USA)	16	58	3	3	28	76370.99
DIXIE UNION (USA)	3	21	1	2	9	16547.52
DOCTOR DINO (FR)	1	3	1	1	1	3145.05
DOYEN (IRE)	13	86	8	11	34	99811.53
DREAM AHEAD (USA)	35	118	12	17	52	300209.54
DR FONG (USA)	16	82	3	4	28	51524.83

STALLIONS	RNRS	STARTS	WNRS	WINS	PLACES	TOTAL (£)
DROSSELMEYER (USA)	1	5	1	2	3	6508.75
DUBAI DESTINATION (USA)	24	130	6	9	44	64488.12
DUBAWI (IRE)	169	625	81	116	263	3890250.29
DUKE OF MARMALADE (IRE)	105	534	30	51	151	1463159.05
DUTCH ART (GB)	138	682	57	85	210	1087642.96
DYLAN THOMAS (IRE)	90	481	29	43	180	679887.96
DYNAFORMER (USA)	16	54	8	12	18	406837.10
ECHO OF LIGHT (GB)	36	165	14	24	49	285907.59
E DUBAI (USA)	3	20	3	4	7	30688.08
EFISIO	3	34	1	1	16	49186.08
ELNADIM (USA)	45	283	20	27	90	536998.16
EL PRADO (IRE)	2	12	1	1	3	4656.77
ELUSIVE CITY (USA)	56	376	22	33	110	270844.36
ELUSIVE PIMPERNEL (USA)	12	49	5	7	12	38748.96
ELUSIVE QUALITY (USA)	34	162	16	28	53	252417.37
EMPIRE MAKER (USA)	3	15	2	2	2	79202.08
ENGLISH CHANNEL (USA)	9	25	3	6	12	48382.33
EQUIANO (FR)	104	512	43	68	176	631603.11
EREWHON (USA)	8	26	1	1	7	9380.55
ESKENDEREYA (USA)	3	9	1	2	1	6494.28
EXCEED AND EXCEL (AUS)	192	1070	92	136	408	1747284.92
EXCELLENT ART (GB)	106	598	38	56	187	549344.00
EXCHANGE RATE (USA)	9	29	3	3	6	70839.78
FALCO (USA)	4	16	1	1	5	17281.95
FANTASTIC LIGHT (USA)	11	94	5	8	32	40482.66
FASLIYEV (USA)	14	133	6	12	41	52995.57
FAST COMPANY (IRE)	88	466	38	49	150	457123.80
FASTNET ROCK (AUS)	118	472	41	56	168	2184861.21
FATH (USA)	7	45	1	1	11	9690.48
FAYRUZ	1	10	1	1	3	4581.30
FIREBREAK (GB)	42	259	15	27	75	240300.44
FIRST DEFENCE (USA)	9	34	5	5	17	82025.50
FLEMENSFIRTH (USA)	4	15	2	2	7	19918.61
FOOTSTEPSINTHESAND (GB)	91	555	37	54	198	594414.58
FRACAS (IRE)	2	8	1	2	1	39790.70
FROZEN POWER (IRE)	51	177	12	13	47	82321.53
FUSAICHI PEGASUS (USA)	1	14	1	1	0	2264.15
GALILEO (IRE)	216	800	92	123	338	5749749.48
GARUDA (IRE)	1	10	1	2	3	11419.50
GENEROUS (IRE)	5	24	1	1	7	7207.97
GENTLEMAN'S DEAL (IRE)	4	17	1	1	4	8171.65
GENTLEWAVE (IRE)	4	28	3	6	13	43197.62
GHOSTZAPPER (USA)	3	13	2	2	4	13846.23
GIANT'S CAUSEWAY (USA)	24	81	8	11	35	109653.34
GLORY OF DANCER (GB)	2	21	2	3	5	22036.10
GOLAN (IRE)	5	14	1	1	2	5833.25
GOLD AWAY (IRE)	5	44	3	6	8	25383.40
GOLDEN SNAKE (USA)	2	17	1	2	7	18147.28
GOOD REWARD (USA)	1	14	1	1	4	10523.13
GREAT EXHIBITION (USA)	3	15	1	2	4	10910.85
GREAT JOURNEY (JPN)	2	6	1	1	3	117341.35
GREEN DESERT (USA)	12	88	3	3	24	27532.37
GREEN TUNE (USA)	2	20	1	3	5	13394.45
HAAFHD (GB)	36	211	10	14	67	124404.40
HAATEF (USA)	28	176	7	13	43	70352.84
HALLING (USA)	91	484	34	50	178	1724039.40
HARD SPUN (USA)	24	113	11	17	45	231765.73
HARLAN'S HOLIDAY (USA)	2	8	1	2	4	39480.63
HAWK WING (USA)	19	91	5	8	32	83032.23
HELIOSTATIC (IRE)	4	6	2	3	0	17466.30
HELISSIO (FR)	1	6	1	2	1	59620.16
HELLVELYN (GB)	45	199	11	13	72	112008.02
HENNY HUGHES (USA)	2	17	1	2	9	31243.13

STALLIONS	RNRS	STARTS	WNRS	WINS	PLACES	TOTAL (£)
HENRYTHENAVIGATOR (USA)	43	240	22	29	80	297938.93
HERNANDO (FR)	22	119	8	9	46	174150.17
HIGH CHAPARRAL (IRE)	102	432	38	59	164	1308869.90
HOLY ROMAN EMPEROR (IRE)	120	616	47	76	212	748648.17
HUNTING LION (IRE)	1	14	1	3	3	8313.36
HURRICANE CAT (USA)	1	6	1	1	3	8810.40
HURRICANE RUN (IRE)	33	152	11	16	44	311274.33
ICEMAN (GB)	13	83	4	7	26	68188.86
IFFRAAJ (GB)	158	814	70	100	320	1153004.40
IMPERIAL DANCER (GB)	5	33	3	5	10	22923.94
INCLUDE (USA)	1	4	1	1	3	9077.00
INDESATCHEL (IRE)	17	136	8	10	40	167720.18
INDIAN CHARLIE (USA)	1	5	1	2	3	36718.40
INDIAN DANEHILL (IRE)	4	12	1	1	4	6542.69
INDIAN HAVEN (GB)	11	83	4	8	37	83052.55
INDIAN RIDGE	9	64	5	8	22	42311.96
INTENSE FOCUS (USA)	78	435	23	35	154	390399.98
INTIDAB (USA)	1	10	1	3	4	9434.03
INTIKHAB (USA)	56	324	26	38	121	379544.04
INVASOR (ARG)	5	15	1	1	4	8288.11
INVINCIBLE SPIRIT (IRE)	185	1075	92	138	413	2565814.09
ISHIGURU (USA)	23	189	10	18	75	146546.44
IVAN DENISOVICH (IRE)	8	56	2	3	17	27306.33
JAZIL (USA)	1	2	1	1	0	4546.51
JEREMY (USA)	67	359	23	37	102	374067.83
JOE BEAR (IRE)	4	15	2	2	3	6580.90
KAHYASI	2	8	1	1	2	8048.45
KAMSIN (GER)	1	1	1	1	0	3234.50
KAVAFI (IRE)	2	14	1	1	7	28308.23
KAYF TARA (GB)	9	21	2	2	8	9767.25
KENDARGENT (FR)	4	19	3	5	7	75376.85
KEY OF LUCK (USA)	9	49	3	6	18	39039.51
KHELEYF (USA)	137	848	53	83	290	682533.39
KIER PARK (IRE)	3	27	2	3	8	11445.12
KING CHARLEMAGNE (USA)	1	3	1	1	1	2674.67
KINGSALSA (USA)	5	16	1	1	4	11286.64
KING'S BEST (USA)	33	123	9	11	43	69499.89
KITTEN'S JOY (USA)	16	57	6	10	16	81717.45
KODIAC (GB)	218	1261	91	154	463	2272017.72
KONIGSTIGER (GER)	3	17	1	1	5	12367.14
KYLLACHY (GB)	156	938	57	93	305	1262020.58
LANDO (GER)	6	27	2	3	8	45482.37
LANGFUHR (CAN)	3	23	1	2	8	38672.25
LAWMAN (FR)	126	652	43	64	215	839327.25
LAYMAN (USA)	2	11	1	3	5	10311.75
LE CADRE NOIR (IRE)	8	50	1	1	16	15216.41
LE HAVRE (FR)	15	59	3	3	28	51258.45
LEMON DROP KID (USA)	11	55	5	8	28	96364.53
LEROIDESANIMAUX (BRZ)	4	40	3	6	15	43452.21
LE VIE DEI COLORI (GB)	6	39	1	2	13	115217.00
LIBRETTIST (USA)	10	61	5	11	19	46421.04
LILBOURNE LAD (IRE)	62	260	20	23	87	176675.19
LINNGARI (IRE)	5	25	1	2	8	9785.76
LION HEART (USA)	3	20	2	3	5	13172.47
LOMITAS (GB)	2	12	1	1	4	86740.95
LONHRO (AUS)	9	26	4	5	13	48624.93
LOOKIN AT LUCKY (USA)	6	38	4	5	14	55046.18
LOPE DE VEGA (IRE)	59	255	28	43	119	916705.81
LORD OF ENGLAND (GER)	6	25	3	5	8	30192.37
LORD SHANAKILL (USA)	34	175	13	19	59	175653.43
LUCARNO (USA)	3	29	2	3	9	16777.12
LUCKY STORY (USA)	29	196	12	19	79	148552.39
MAJESTIC MISSILE (IRE)	32	196	11	14	55	161873.41

STALLIONS	RNRS	STARTS	WNRS	WINS	PLACES	TOTAL (£)
MAJOR CADEAUX (GB)	39	244	15	27	73	158547.88
MAKBUL	4	27	1	1	11	10639.53
MAKFI (GB)	93	377	40	56	146	490141.82
MAMOOL (IRE)	1	3	1	1	2	6877.00
MANDURO (GER)	55	237	21	24	89	419717.25
MARJU (IRE)	20	110	7	10	41	252493.82
MARK OF ESTEEM (IRE)	4	21	2	4	7	14405.40
MARTALINE (GB)	2	9	2	2	3	17233.47
MARTINO ALONSO (IRE)	1	11	1	1	6	21393.80
MASTERCRAFTSMAN (IRE)	122	566	45	59	219	1483782.77
MASTERFUL (USA)	1	9	1	1	6	11133.63
MAWATHEEQ (USA)	19	108	10	14	32	73703.68
MEDAGLIA D'ORO (USA)	15	42	3	4	20	49973.26
MEDECIS (GB)	4	27	1	1	7	10323.39
MEDICEAN (GB)	103	554	33	54	180	668149.15
MIESQUE'S SON (USA)	1	11	1	2	5	8791.50
MILK IT MICK (GB)	11	83	2	4	31	35627.40
MILLENARY (GB)	2	12	1	1	9	18689.93
MILLKOM (GB)	5	20	1	1	6	11081.85
MIND GAMES (GB)	3	12	1	1	3	19527.70
MISU BOND (IRE)	25	155	12	21	49	104193.54
MIZZEN MAST (USA)	18	887	7	10	33	66934.93
MONSIEUR BOND (IRE)	116	612	32	45	177	597127.44
MONSUN (GER)	19	72	7	10	26	163869.02
MONTJEU (IRE)	72	299	24	37	106	364999.28
MORE THAN READY (USA)	14	78	4	5	21	52186.01
MOSS VALE (IRE)	37	301	14	29	91	258462.99
MOTIVATOR (GB)	43	172	12	18	73	386242.91
MOUNTAIN HIGH (IRE)	4	11	1	1	3	6445.74
MOUNT NELSON (GB)	69	362	25	43	140	561378.13
MUHTATHIR (GB)	11	41	2	2	18	29504.56
MUJADIL (USA)	13	87	5	6	28	69008.74
MUJAHID (USA)	3	21	1	1	10	13606.80
MULLIONMILEANHOUR (IRE)	18	84	4	9	22	58656.27
MULL OF KINTYRE (USA)	2	24	2	5	7	57210.56
MULTIPLEX (GB)	60	310	22	36	92	175465.87
MUSTAMEET (USA)	4	16	1	1	1	4527.13
MYBOYCHARLIE (IRE)	39	252	14	21	87	175284.52
NAAQOOS (GB)	12	62	4	4	16	25540.95
NAMID (GB)	11	90	4	8	29	43254.95
NAYEF (USA)	74	316	27	34	121	602076.01
NEEDWOOD BLADE (GB)	15	133	8	15	47	131186.48
NEW APPROACH (IRE)	133	481	43	63	192	1027905.42
NICARON (GER)	1	6	1	1	0	2911.05
NIGHT SHIFT (USA)	3	54	3	8	27	33680.15
NOROIT (GER)	1	6	1	1	1	3071.10
NORSE DANCER (IRE)	18	66	2	2	21	49383.87
NORWICH	2	5	1	1	0	3234.50
NOTNOWCATO (GB)	30	143	7	11	41	371665.13
NOVERRE (USA)	13	96	5	7	24	44905.49
OASIS DREAM (GB)	170	852	66	100	316	2454062.91
OBSERVATORY (USA)	20	87	2	2	18	21039.14
OFFICER (USA)	2	15	1	1	4	5632.50
OLDEN TIMES (GB)	5	26	1	2	10	18309.14
OLD VIC	3	4	1	1	1	5541.24
OLMODAVOR (USA)	1	8	1	1	1	2432.50
ONE COOL CAT (USA)	14	128	8	17	38	90602.77
ORATORIO (IRE)	56	364	26	41	138	388153.97
ORIENTATE (USA)	2	21	1	1	8	46290.80
ORIENTOR (GB)	10	67	3	3	21	81335.45
ORPEN (USA)	6	26	1	2	7	14850.95
OSORIO (GER)	1	14	1	3	3	13474.68
OVERBURY (IRE)	1	5	1	2	1	105361.63

STALLIONS	RNRS	STARTS	WNRS	WINS	PLACES	TOTAL (£)
PACO BOY (IRE)	100	501	37	53	175	649948.49
PAOLINI (GER)	1	4	1	2	1	5084.77
PAPAL BULL (GB)	21	94	4	6	25	44123.68
PARIS HOUSE (GB)	3	24	2	2	8	18682.00
PASSING GLANCE (GB)	13	50	4	7	17	47464.87
PASTERNAK (GB)	2	6	1	1	1	2780.00
PASTORAL PURSUITS (GB)	118	791	53	86	279	854313.37
PEARL OF LOVE (IRE)	1	9	1	1	2	3929.80
PEINTRE CELEBRE (USA)	25	112	11	16	36	272624.50
PENTIRE (GB)	2	4	1	1	0	31125.00
PETARDIA (GB)	1	11	1	2	7	6521.31
PETIONVILLE (USA)	1	15	1	1	7	4422.15
PHOENIX REACH (IRE)	24	110	6	9	38	135636.94
PICCOLO (GB)	74	496	26	50	164	395135.59
PIVOTAL (GB)	138	670	60	99	233	1549928.37
PLEASANTLY PERFECT (USA)	2	4	1	1	0	2911.05
POET'S VOICE (GB)	52	171	15	24	48	167199.61
POUR MOI (IRE)	20	53	7	8	14	90732.70
PRESENTING (GB)	4	6	1	1	3	7810.07
PRESIDIUM	2	13	1	1	6	5572.25
PRIMO VALENTINO (IRE)	7	61	4	5	25	214072.72
PROCLAMATION (IRE)	22	138	8	17	39	76532.53
PROUD CITIZEN (USA)	7	19	1	1	3	8430.71
PURIM (USA)	1	1	1	1	0	297727.50
PYRUS (USA)	11	62	3	4	18	24361.58
RAHY (USA)	2	7	1	1	5	7747.93
RAIL LINK (GB)	41	200	13	21	81	246332.66
RAINBOW HIGH (GB)	2	5	1	1	1	2745.15
RAISE A GRAND (IRE)	1	9	1	3	2	10754.15
RAKTI (GB)	8	54	6	11	17	96153.48
RAMONTI (FR)	5	31	1	3	17	16286.52
RAVEN'S PASS (USA)	78	310	36	46	123	756301.98
REBELLION (GB)	1	7	1	1	2	3033.74
REDBACK (GB)	13	79	2	5	21	41159.92
RED CLUBS (IRE)	29	297	20	38	126	307376.56
REDOUTE'S CHOICE (AUS)	2	10	1	3	3	17191.20
RED RANSOM (USA)	8	53	5	12	17	65381.22
RED ROCKS (IRE)	2	16	1	2	4	8151.63
REEL BUDDY (USA)	5	36	3	3	14	17506.23
REFUSE TO BEND (IRE)	41	240	15	23	88	271961.86
RESET (AUS)	4	36	2	3	6	11844.40
RESPLENDENT GLORY (IRE)	9	47	1	2	15	11320.23
REVOQUE (IRE)	2	7	1	1	2	16554.27
RIP VAN WINKLE (IRE)	89	371	33	46	135	396173.77
ROBIN DES PRES (FR)	1	3	1	1	0	2264.15
ROB ROY (USA)	4	19	1	1	4	6135.15
ROCAMADOUR (GB)	1	12	1	1	5	27926.80
ROCK HARD TEN (USA)	5	24	2	2	4	7449.52
ROCK OF GIBRALTAR (IRE)	121	649	40	62	217	663312.12
RODERIC O'CONNOR (IRE)	34	123	11	13	44	173601.59
ROYAL ACADEMY (USA)	1	16	1	1	5	4596.04
ROYAL ANTHEM (USA)	3	12	1	2	4	15453.48
ROYAL APPLAUSE (GB)	158	832	62	80	260	709049.15
SADLER'S WELLS (USA)	9	24	1	1	5	5279.99
SAKHEE (USA)	41	197	13	20	61	293350.02
SAKHEE'S SECRET (GB)	107	617	39	50	204	390987.58
SAMPOWER STAR (GB)	2	13	1	1	5	8654.15
SAMUM (GER)	4	25	3	8	7	40917.04
SCAT DADDY (USA)	13	66	8	8	35	176586.49
SEA THE STARS (IRE)	84	294	35	56	119	1354210.89
SELKIRK (USA)	32	174	12	17	54	187675.38
SEPTIEME CIEL (USA)	2	15	1	2	6	8749.53
SHAKESPEAREAN (IRE)	1	8	1	2	3	8484.48

STALLIONS	RNRS	STARTS	WNRS	WINS	PLACES	TOTAL (£)
SHAMARDAL (USA)	173	821	82	136	333	2291590.50
SHINKO FOREST (IRE)	3	19	1	1	2	3921.50
SHIROCCO (GER)	44	172	15	23	56	287684.98
SHOLOKHOV (IRE)	8	37	2	4	10	19354.98
SHOWCASING (GB)	98	483	38	60	153	816505.44
SILVER DEPUTY (CAN)	2	24	1	4	8	14393.27
SILVER FROST (IRE)	7	57	3	6	12	29207.77
SINGSPIEL (IRE)	25	141	9	13	56	1592459.59
SINNDAR (IRE)	10	35	6	7	14	250941.67
SIR PERCY (GB)	124	632	56	80	255	742871.01
SIXTIES ICON (GB)	42	249	16	22	102	260392.05
SIYOUNI (FR)	12	44	6	7	20	261774.73
SLEEPING INDIAN (GB)	55	366	21	32	134	246966.33
SMART STRIKE (CAN)	16	54	6	9	23	49332.03
SOLDIER HOLLOW (GB)	1	8	1	3	2	17156.37
SOLDIER OF FORTUNE (IRE)	9	44	3	6	17	139377.84
SOUL CITY (IRE)	1	4	1	1	2	3020.60
SOVIET STAR (USA)	12	89	5	8	29	59330.65
SPARTACUS (IRE)	5	18	1	1	7	6615.50
SPEIGHTSTOWN (USA)	23	103	12	16	29	293500.53
SPIRIT ONE (FR)	1	8	1	1	5	6283.32
STARCRAFT (NZ)	3	21	1	1	12	6335.58
STARSPANGLEDBANNER (AUS)	22	124	12	17	54	295589.35
STATUE OF LIBERTY (USA)	7	33	2	2	13	32407.49
STEPPE DANCER (IRE)	3	13	1	2	4	8282.07
STIMULATION (IRE)	38	174	10	12	48	78425.61
STORMING HOME (GB)	5	37	2	3	17	33857.09
STORMY ATLANTIC (USA)	6	34	3	4	14	28571.83
STORMY RIVER (FR)	6	28	1	1	6	8767.17
STOWAWAY (GB)	3	3	2	2	0	11767.44
STRATEGIC PRINCE (GB)	45	263	16	22	94	174828.92
STREET BOSS (USA)	4	16	1	2	4	35542.13
STREET CRY (IRE)	57	280	32	53	108	452499.59
STREET SENSE (USA)	8	32	1	1	8	9556.38
STRIKING AMBITION (GB)	12	82	3	4	14	32399.10
SUAVE (USA)	1	1	1	1	0	2393.53
SUBTLE POWER (IRE)	2	6	1	1	1	4197.00
SUCCESSFUL APPEAL (USA)	2	22	2	4	5	22458.34
SUPERIOR PREMIUM (GB)	1	11	1	2	1	13761.70
TAGULA (IRE)	57	282	18	24	96	462702.71
TALAASH (IRE)	1	5	1	1	1	2648.95
TALE OF THE CAT (USA)	3	18	1	1	6	32533.87
TAMARISK (IRE)	1	13	1	1	5	5606.68
TAMAYUZ (GB)	57	280	16	23	95	383503.26
TAMURE (IRE)	1	5	1	1	0	5883.72
TAPIT (USA)	4	6	2	2	3	46877.35
TEOFILO (IRE)	137	667	57	90	284	2359116.44
TERTULLIAN (USA)	4	17	1	4	3	10524.00
THEATRICAL	3	11	1	2	4	10550.42
THEWAYYOUARE (USA)	47	221	16	23	55	172954.98
THOUSAND WORDS (GB)	27	126	6	6	32	176632.44
THREE VALLEYS (USA)	20	106	9	11	50	96521.02
TIGER HILL (IRE)	35	176	11	15	61	127330.83
TITUS LIVIUS (FR)	6	36	4	4	14	23610.95
TIZNOW (USA)	3	23	1	2	8	17793.20
TOBOUGG (IRE)	34	179	15	23	54	176550.19
TOMBA (GB)	3	26	2	4	6	23576.60
TORRENTIAL (USA)	1	5	1	2	2	69728.60
TRADE FAIR (GB)	18	108	9	17	28	128454.54
TRADITIONALLY (USA)	3	28	3	3	12	20190.23
TRANS ISLAND (GB)	8	61	2	4	27	54701.46
TURTLE BOWL (IRE)	4	12	2	3	3	27250.42
TWIRLING CANDY (USA)	1	5	1	2	2	31266.39

STALLIONS	RNRS	STARTS	WNRS	WINS	PLACES	TOTAL (£)
UNBRIDLED'S SONG (USA)	3	15	1	2	8	9370.90
URBAN POET (USA)	2	8	1	1	2	7356.59
U S RANGER (USA)	7	33	2	2	6	9746.44
VALE OF YORK (IRE)	43	279	19	38	107	244024.24
VAL ROYAL (FR)	9	37	2	3	13	16131.89
VAN NISTELROOY (USA)	1	6	1	1	0	2749.32
VERGLAS (IRE)	67	454	29	49	130	549640.95
VETTORI (IRE)	2	10	1	1	0	3234.50
VIRTUAL (GB)	16	73	3	3	24	20997.35
VISION D'ETAT (FR)	2	10	1	5	3	37739.15
VISION OF NIGHT (GB)	1	21	1	1	9	7983.55
VITAL EQUINE (IRE)	3	27	2	2	5	20207.07
VITUS (GB)	1	9	1	1	2	3598.05
VOCALISED (USA)	30	136	7	7	38	94131.80
WAR CHANT (USA)	8	64	2	4	20	26699.88
WAR FRONT (USA)	32	95	12	17	39	818294.57
WELL CHOSEN (GB)	2	4	1	1	0	6418.60
WESTERNER (GB)	8	26	1	1	2	6240.31
WESTERN WINTER (USA)	1	2	1	1	1	28897.90
WHERE OR WHEN (IRE)	4	27	1	1	10	8265.29
WHIPPER (USA)	28	141	11	14	49	130818.08
WINDSOR KNOT (IRE)	19	100	5	7	37	88539.51
WINKER WATSON (GB)	9	59	2	3	20	20907.51
WITH APPROVAL (CAN)	3	8	1	1	2	4203.45
YEATS (IRE)	22	76	5	8	25	56594.70
YOUMZAIN (IRE)	6	22	2	2	7	85174.42
YOUNG ERN (GB)	1	8	1	1	2	3033.75
ZAFEEN (FR)	8	52	3	7	15	70074.73
ZAMBEZI SUN (GB)	1	5	1	1	2	2834.72
ZAMINDAR (USA)	62	315	18	25	104	266747.00
ZAVATA (USA)	1	10	1	2	3	5870.40
ZEBEDEE (GB)	124	702	47	66	253	833354.93
ZOFFANY (IRE)	64	247	27	38	84	753765.52

BY KIND PERMISSION OF WEATHERBYS

NH STALLIONS' EARNINGS FOR 2014/15

(includes every stallion who sired a winner over jumps in Great Britain and Ireland in 2014/2015)

STALLIONS	RNRS	STARTS	WNRS	WINS	PLACES	TOTAL (£)
ABOO HOM (GB)	6	26	2	2	8	16271.40
ACCLAMATION (GB)	17	50	3	3	20	31534.61
ACCORDION	31	88	9	13	29	209435.58
ACT ONE (GB)	25	62	4	5	23	33250.62
AD VALOREM (USA)	8	21	2	2	3	10984.35
AGENT BLEU (FR)	3	7	3	4	2	63369.30
ALAMSHAR (IRE)	3	8	1	1	1	4779.17
ALBANO (IRE)	2	14	1	2	7	16850.89
ALBERTO GIACOMETTI (IRE)	10	31	3	3	15	25635.83
ALDERBROOK (GB)	62	301	20	25	96	264309.30
ALEXIUS (IRE)	3	17	1	2	8	15153.26
ALFLORA (IRE)	113	420	34	49	159	624647.25
ALHAARTH (IRE)	27	91	9	10	22	61922.61
ALKAADHEM (GB)	14	49	2	2	14	17850.14
AL NAMIX (FR)	15	48	7	11	12	269978.82
ALZAO (USA)	1	1	1	1	0	4548.60
AMADEUS WOLF (GB)	4	16	1	1	4	6291.47
AMERICAN POST (GB)	2	17	1	3	7	20445.73
AMILYNX (FR)	10	37	3	6	12	37445.25
ANABAA (USA)	4	17	3	3	5	49374.71
ANABAA BLUE (GB)	2	10	1	1	1	2714.86
AND BEYOND (IRE)	15	72	4	6	22	34605.08
ANSHAN	53	214	11	17	71	301045.94
ANTARCTIQUE (IRE)	10	55	4	7	17	78118.40
ANTONIUS PIUS (USA)	31	150	9	14	53	125210.35
ANZILLERO (GER)	3	12	1	3	6	119190.76
APTITUDE (USA)	3	4	1	1	0	1949.40
ARAAFA (IRE)	8	32	1	1	15	13810.42
ARAKAN (USA)	14	61	5	9	26	78267.45
ARCADIO (GER)	33	117	14	20	37	160864.92
ARCH (USA)	5	16	2	3	7	9171.64
ARCHANGE D'OR (IRE)	2	11	1	1	6	35215.86
ARCHIPENKO (USA)	4	7	1	1	0	1559.52
ARKADIAN HERO (USA)	5	11	1	2	1	10683.00
ARTAN (IRE)	9	42	3	3	17	29045.74
ASHKALANI (IRE)	4	23	1	1	8	13521.20
ASSESSOR (IRE)	10	43	4	5	19	120772.53
ASTARABAD (USA)	16	72	9	11	29	261140.63
ASTRONOMER ROYAL (USA)	2	10	1	1	5	6433.43
ATRAF (GB)	7	30	2	2	11	18301.75
AUCTION HOUSE (USA)	8	30	1	1	14	13341.42
AUSSIE RULES (USA)	13	62	3	4	27	87324.32
AUTHORIZED (IRE)	39	139	15	29	63	410732.38
AVONBRIDGE (GB)	10	41	2	5	12	23639.62
AZAMOUR (IRE)	31	134	10	17	49	298568.26
BACH (IRE)	57	192	11	17	57	156931.42
BACHELOR DUKE (USA)	10	18	2	3	6	48011.89
BAHRI (USA)	6	22	4	4	7	29283.56
BALAKHERI (IRE)	4	31	3	4	10	46386.97
BAL HARBOUR (GB)	1	10	1	3	3	15478.18
BALKO (FR)	4	12	3	4	5	51441.95
BALLINGARRY (IRE)	20	84	6	8	31	146534.93
BALTIC KING (GB)	1	7	1	2	3	13143.24
BANYUMANIK (IRE)	1	4	1	1	1	2911.68
BARATHEA (IRE)	17	77	5	8	24	68513.41
BAROUD D'HONNEUR (FR)	1	7	1	2	1	16996.12
BARYSHNIKOV (AUS)	11	34	4	5	11	21548.66
BASANTA (IRE)	8	35	2	2	11	31938.06
BEAT ALL (USA)	61	194	10	14	42	74456.62
BEAT HOLLOW (GB)	38	158	9	15	52	185010.89

STALLIONS	RNRS	STARTS	WNRS	WINS	PLACES	TOTAL (£)
BEAT OF DRUMS (GB)	1	3	1	1	1	5216.40
BENEFICIAL (GB)	336	1417	106	160	513	1741375.67
BERING	7	33	1	1	17	37799.30
BERNARDINI (USA)	2	9	1	1	2	14890.37
BERNEBEAU (FR)	3	13	1	4	6	80651.14
BERTOLINI (USA)	19	73	7	11	27	165745.05
BEST OF THE BESTS (IRE)	2	13	1	1	6	10000.91
BIENAMADO (USA)	15	46	2	2	6	10263.73
BIG BAD BOB (IRE)	8	35	3	4	16	28163.90
BIG SHUFFLE (USA)	4	27	1	1	13	12240.71
BIRDSTONE (USA)	1	6	1	1	4	28806.30
BISHOP OF CASHEL (GB)	13	51	2	3	12	47829.76
BLACK MINNALOUSHE (USA)	1	11	1	1	7	7745.94
BLACK SAM BELLAMY (IRE)	30	105	9	9	43	92933.39
BLUE BRESIL (FR)	4	7	1	1	6	19237.75
BLUE OCEAN (USA)	1	9	1	2	3	25434.69
BLUEPRINT (IRE)	43	179	13	23	75	196419.78
BOB BACK (USA)	43	170	11	16	62	312528.49
BOB'S RETURN (IRE)	20	100	5	8	40	85633.91
BOLD FACT (USA)	3	9	1	1	2	3588.47
BOLLIN ERIC (GB)	30	116	8	10	35	87173.98
BONBON ROSE (FR)	5	34	1	2	11	25235.25
BONNET ROUGE (FR)	1	7	1	1	3	10076.50
BORREGO (USA)	1	5	1	1	4	9468.00
BRIAN BORU (GB)	103	415	30	47	136	436766.42
BRIER CREEK (USA)	8	60	4	10	23	54287.38
BROADWAY FLYER (USA)	15	60	5	7	22	97131.05
BULINGTON (FR)	2	13	1	2	6	16013.94
BUSHRANGER (IRE)	6	25	1	2	13	12621.49
BUSTER KING	3	16	1	2	6	14796.52
BUSY FLIGHT (GB)	6	37	4	9	12	35127.84
BYRON (GB)	16	38	5	5	13	21534.97
CABALLO RAPTOR (CAN)	4	19	2	2	6	12543.75
CADEAUX GENEREUX	4	15	1	3	8	15447.32
CADOUBEL (FR)	1	4	1	1	1	4364.94
CALIFET (FR)	10	54	4	8	23	217140.80
CAMACHO (GB)	3	16	2	3	9	19619.56
CAPE CROSS (IRE)	36	126	11	16	55	169384.09
CAPTAIN RIO (GB)	16	54	4	6	17	36774.40
CARROLL HOUSE	7	20	1	1	4	6395.68
CATCHER IN THE RYE (IRE)	48	162	9	13	40	91561.01
CELTIC SWING (GB)	14	49	4	8	15	67287.29
CENTRAL PARK (IRE)	19	64	3	5	25	40209.77
CHAMPS ELYSEES (GB)	7	28	2	5	7	34349.38
CHEVALIER (IRE)	16	70	3	5	21	38775.30
CHINEUR (FR)	8	33	1	3	10	12032.41
CHOISIR (AUS)	16	44	3	3	8	17884.93
CITY HONOURS (USA)	13	44	2	2	18	14719.23
CLASSIC CLICHE (IRE)	33	119	9	10	35	82948.96
CLERKENWELL (USA)	9	33	2	2	13	20151.31
CLODOVIL (IRE)	8	26	1	1	6	10246.40
CLOSE CONFLICT (USA)	10	45	3	6	7	39399.22
CLOUDINGS (IRE)	72	296	26	38	102	1028846.72
COCKNEY REBEL (IRE)	4	10	1	3	1	12820.08
COMMANDER COLLINS (IRE)	3	9	1	2	4	8953.84
COMPTON ADMIRAL (GB)	2	10	1	1	2	5167.62
CONILLON (GER)	1	6	1	2	1	25960.50
CORONER (IRE)	5	16	1	2	4	7547.04
CORRI PIANO (FR)	2	8	1	2	1	4752.54
CORROUGE (FR)	1	13	1	4	3	27179.16
COUNTRY REEL (USA)	2	11	2	3	2	11685.78
COURT CAVE (IRE)	67	294	18	28	90	207454.75
CRAIGSTEEL (GB)	73	300	22	34	105	214102.32
CRILLON (FR)	2	7	1	1	4	13929.12

STALLIONS	RNRS	STARTS	WNRS	WINS	PLACES	TOTAL (£)
CROCO ROUGE (IRE)	18	79	8	11	27	139539.99
CURTAIN TIME (IRE)	5	14	1	1	8	25973.98
DAI JIN (GB)	1	4	1	2	2	19518.05
DALAKHANI (IRE)	27	108	7	12	41	124786.15
DALIAPOUR (IRE)	3	14	1	1	4	16416.02
DANDY MAN (IRE)	1	4	1	2	0	7472.70
DANEHILL DANCER (IRE)	28	122	8	14	44	345378.52
DANO-MAST (GB)	1	4	1	1	0	3671.40
DANROAD (AUS)	7	23	2	2	8	17442.85
DANSILI (GB)	26	107	11	13	39	91523.01
DARK ANGEL (IRE)	14	45	4	7	16	46216.54
DARK MOONDANCER (GB)	5	20	2	2	10	22497.20
DARSI (FR)	29	133	7	12	39	83561.55
DAY FLIGHT (GB)	1	6	1	2	2	9873.72
DAYLAMI (IRE)	14	42	1	1	16	15599.72
DEFINITE ARTICLE (GB)	129	515	43	65	176	588330.89
DELLA FRANCESCA (USA)	4	13	2	2	7	11146.43
DENHAM RED (FR)	3	9	2	5	2	192317.23
DEPLOY	9	31	2	3	8	36112.96
DEPORTIVO (GB)	2	7	1	2	4	9704.52
DESERT KING (IRE)	38	136	9	11	47	79776.42
DESERT PRINCE (IRE)	13	59	3	5	27	34309.70
DESERT STYLE (IRE)	5	20	2	3	4	20021.19
DESIDERATUM (GB)	11	28	1	3	6	15453.06
DIAMOND GREEN (FR)	21	68	4	4	16	47962.73
DIESIS	2	3	1	1	1	5986.00
DIKTAT (GB)	9	41	3	3	12	21233.52
DILSHAAN (GB)	10	24	1	2	4	6932.80
DISCOVER D'AUTEUIL (FR)	9	51	2	2	20	37649.81
DISTANT MUSIC (USA)	2	11	1	3	2	9821.16
DOCTOR DINO (FR)	3	8	2	4	3	14465.40
DOLPOUR	1	4	1	2	1	13708.00
DOM ALCO (FR)	38	165	16	23	68	631432.88
DOUBLE ECLIPSE (IRE)	12	43	3	5	12	44208.86
DOUBLE TRIGGER (IRE)	29	111	7	9	40	60254.61
DOYEN (IRE)	31	135	9	13	56	129374.51
DRAGON DANCER (GB)	1	4	1	3	1	14193.30
DREAM WELL (FR)	7	28	1	7	12	68875.94
DR FONG (USA)	22	94	8	8	34	57101.53
DR MASSINI (IRE)	102	429	33	47	122	515051.08
DUBAI DESTINATION (USA)	26	82	6	9	25	67384.37
DUBAWI (IRE)	24	78	9	13	22	536870.01
DUKE OF MARMALADE (IRE)	24	63	4	5	16	28917.71
DUSHYANTOR (USA)	41	162	9	15	58	156825.37
DYLAN THOMAS (IRE)	38	152	14	19	50	139807.42
DYNAFORMER (USA)	12	63	4	5	26	87309.21
EARLY MARCH (GB)	6	22	1	1	9	22172.55
ECHO OF LIGHT (GB)	15	51	3	6	22	101232.89
ECTON PARK (USA)	1	9	1	1	1	2301.75
ELMAAMUL (USA)	3	24	2	3	13	24399.45
EL PRADO (IRE)	2	9	1	1	5	6050.56
ELUSIVE CITY (USA)	5	15	1	1	6	10652.24
EMPEROR FOUNTAIN	5	16	1	1	4	4915.08
ENCOSTA DE LAGO (AUS)	1	4	1	1	1	5073.87
ENDOLI (USA)	5	27	2	3	6	30826.04
ENRIQUE (GB)	15	63	9	11	29	133831.60
EQUERRY (USA)	3	22	2	3	9	19437.17
ERHAAB (USA)	18	69	5	7	25	43778.62
EXCEED AND EXCEL (AUS)	6	22	2	5	6	38424.64
EXCELLENT ART (GB)	14	56	2	4	10	37900.04
EXECUTIVE PERK	5	17	1	1	4	5114.70
EXIT TO NOWHERE (USA)	63	207	13	24	58	243905.66
EXPELLED (USA)	1	5	1	1	2	5618.75
FADO (FR)	1	4	1	1	1	5828.04

STALLIONS	RNRS	STARTS	WNRS	WINS	PLACES	TOTAL (£)
FAIR MIX (IRE)	61	190	8	11	55	90560.96
FALCO (USA)	2	5	1	3	0	101300.75
FANTASTIC LIGHT (USA)	8	46	2	3	19	24972.68
FANTASTIC QUEST (IRE)	3	10	1	2	1	7031.70
FANTASTIC SPAIN (USA)	2	7	1	1	2	4680.00
FATH (USA)	5	21	2	3	8	29035.95
FIREBREAK (GB)	6	24	1	1	5	4139.35
FLEETWOOD (IRE)	7	35	1	1	9	52355.14
FLEMENSFIRTH (USA)	300	1199	98	143	436	1469376.85
FLYING LEGEND (USA)	10	38	2	2	9	14953.11
FOOTSTEPSINTHESAND (GB)	13	33	3	3	11	23503.38
FOXHOUND (USA)	1	7	1	1	4	4660.08
FRAAM (GB)	12	38	2	3	14	30233.07
FRAGRANT MIX (IRE)	11	44	2	3	18	239870.67
FRENCH GLORY	1	3	1	3	0	16848.84
FRUITS OF LOVE (USA)	60	239	18	22	78	214759.82
FUNNY BABY (FR)	2	7	1	1	2	8473.26
FUSAICHI PEGASUS (USA)	1	6	1	2	3	11249.70
GALILEO (IRE)	64	244	26	35	81	383108.89
GAMUT (IRE)	54	232	14	24	69	463489.19
GARUDA (IRE)	4	22	2	3	10	24948.07
GENEROUS (IRE)	86	353	34	45	120	385176.28
GENTLEWAVE (IRE)	3	12	1	1	4	7169.08
GERMANY (USA)	15	72	5	10	14	490607.97
GIANT'S CAUSEWAY (USA)	8	25	2	2	7	49837.35
GILDORAN	1	2	1	1	1	2113.45
GLACIAL STORM (USA)	3	14	2	4	5	21417.30
GOLAN (IRE)	80	309	17	22	99	253882.79
GOLD AWAY (IRE)	4	13	2	3	6	13521.01
GOLDEN TORNADO (IRE)	8	23	1	1	6	7737.66
GOLDMARK (USA)	9	26	3	3	11	92489.50
GOLDNEYEV (USA)	4	29	4	8	12	210562.02
GOLD WELL (GB)	69	301	30	44	107	534199.30
GRAND PLAISIR (IRE)	3	6	1	1	0	12972.00
GRAND SEIGNEUR (FR)	1	4	1	1	2	6153.84
GRAND TRESOR (FR)	3	7	1	1	3	2591.75
GRAPE TREE ROAD (GB)	46	160	15	24	53	115446.56
GREAT EXHIBITION (USA)	7	25	1	1	3	6368.13
GREAT JOURNEY (JPN)	1	6	1	1	3	14003.93
GREAT PALM (USA)	31	151	11	14	45	113882.40
GREAT PRETENDER (IRE)	6	30	4	10	13	151388.25
GREEN DESERT (USA)	4	9	1	1	2	5343.00
GROOM DANCER (USA)	6	27	3	4	7	21559.66
HAAFHD (GB)	16	67	4	4	30	62795.94
HAATEF (USA)	2	8	1	1	3	4302.00
HALLING (USA)	42	173	10	14	63	222698.50
HAMAIRI (IRE)	1	4	1	2	0	13959.00
HARD SPUN (USA)	2	7	1	2	5	61750.65
HARLAN'S HOLIDAY (USA)	1	7	1	1	1	5387.50
HAWKEYE (IRE)	4	21	1	2	8	22170.63
HAWK WING (USA)	18	60	4	5	12	30488.65
HELIOSTATIC (IRE)	3	13	2	3	2	10519.08
HELISSIO (FR)	38	151	12	16	39	108282.17
HERNANDO (FR)	29	125	12	18	40	181139.12
HERON ISLAND (IRE)	95	377	37	60	124	580408.54
HIGH CHAPARRAL (IRE)	72	264	22	29	87	255145.15
HIGH-RISE (IRE)	19	65	5	5	21	42198.83
HIGH ROCK (IRE)	2	6	1	2	2	12377.42
HOLD THAT TIGER (USA)	2	12	1	2	5	7097.40
HOLY ROMAN EMPEROR (IRE)	12	30	1	1	7	7452.84
HUMBEL (USA)	8	27	2	4	7	16521.48
HURRICANE RUN (IRE)	33	114	7	12	36	78130.84
ICEMAN (GB)	11	51	4	5	14	22637.41
IDRIS (IRE)	1	6	1	3	0	11046.60

STALLIONS	RNRS	STARTS	WNRS	WINS	PLACES	TOTAL (£)
IFFRAAJ (GB)	21	68	4	6	27	62823.40
IMPERIAL BALLET (IRE)	3	20	1	2	7	7657.62
IMPERIAL DANCER (GB)	7	23	4	5	11	35243.90
INDESATCHEL (IRE)	7	31	2	4	12	43743.10
INDIAN DANEHILL (IRE)	51	220	15	21	60	152876.48
INDIAN HAVEN (GB)	19	71	4	6	27	53088.42
INDIAN RIDGE	5	24	1	1	12	7914.48
INDIAN RIVER (FR)	31	143	13	19	40	147882.14
INDIAN ROCKET (GB)	2	9	1	3	0	21470.83
INSAN (USA)	3	11	1	2	1	13127.40
INTENSE FOCUS (USA)	6	21	2	3	10	33864.52
IN THE WINGS	4	19	1	1	8	14602.73
INTIKHAB (USA)	14	54	5	5	25	42199.38
INVINCIBLE SPIRIT (IRE)	17	71	5	7	31	63784.78
IRISH WELLS (FR)	5	21	2	2	8	18618.78
ISHIGURU (GB)	10	39	3	5	13	91957.91
ISLAND HOUSE (IRE)	1	7	1	1	4	92797.80
JACKSON'S DRIFT (USA)	2	9	2	4	1	53124.49
JAMMAAL (GB)	5	25	1	1	10	24728.14
JAVA GOLD (USA)	1	8	1	2	5	10912.17
JELANI (IRE)	1	6	1	1	2	2711.34
JEREMY (USA)	42	150	13	14	56	166589.56
JEUNE HOMME (USA)	1	9	1	1	5	18189.10
JIMBLE (FR)	12	50	2	4	20	36774.07
JOHANNESBURG (USA)	4	17	1	1	8	9263.88
KADALKO (FR)	1	4	1	1	2	15464.50
KADASTROF (FR)	8	24	1	1	11	11619.15
KAHYASI	19	88	6	10	35	136955.66
KAIETEUR (USA)	2	11	1	1	3	4125.60
KALANISI (IRE)	90	301	33	43	82	276215.34
KALDOUNEVEES (FR)	2	5	1	1	2	7118.10
KALLISTO (GER)	4	13	1	1	5	7609.32
KANDIDATE (GB)	1	4	1	1	1	3535.20
KAPGARDE (FR)	36	135	13	21	58	278449.57
KARINGA BAY	64	271	16	29	92	664642.22
KASAKOV (GB)	2	11	1	1	2	8947.68
KAYF TARA (GB)	281	1041	89	129	391	1555732.07
KENTUCKY DYNAMITE (USA)	3	11	2	2	4	22974.12
KEY OF LUCK (USA)	9	53	4	4	20	44781.99
KHALKEVI (IRE)	7	27	3	5	14	63401.19
KHELEYF (USA)	22	87	3	6	31	96838.79
KIER PARK (IRE)	4	21	3	5	10	31364.29
KING CHARLEMAGNE (USA)	3	19	1	1	5	9065.73
KINGSALSA (GB)	4	15	1	2	4	40741.80
KING'S BEST (USA)	32	169	14	30	52	212561.35
KING'S THEATRE (IRE)	274	1219	126	222	452	2846760.98
KIRKWALL (GB)	10	41	2	4	11	14883.14
KODIAC (GB)	12	51	6	6	12	27608.57
KONIGSTIGER (GER)	2	11	2	4	2	24297.42
KOTASHAAN (FR)	1	6	1	1	3	6782.04
KOTKY BLEU (FR)	3	18	3	5	10	50503.60
KRIS KIN (USA)	17	71	3	7	29	42933.32
KUTUB (IRE)	14	49	2	3	22	34870.08
KYLLACHY (GB)	15	77	3	3	28	31414.36
LAHIB (USA)	24	81	7	11	28	77857.50
LANDO (GER)	13	40	4	5	13	89001.79
LAVEROCK (IRE)	2	9	1	5	2	93782.17
LAVERON (GB)	17	52	6	7	18	51993.91
LAVIRCO (GER)	16	63	5	9	31	126034.27
LAWMAN (FR)	9	29	1	2	7	40801.15
LAYMAN (USA)	5	18	1	1	4	6807.42
LE BALAFRE (FR)	3	14	1	1	7	12001.53
LE FOU (IRE)	7	28	1	1	15	58545.81
LEMON DROP KID (USA)	6	39	3	3	13	25333.32

STALLIONS	RNRS	STARTS	WNRS	WINS	PLACES	TOTAL (£)
LEND A HAND (GB)	5	23	2	3	4	21236.86
LEPORELLO (IRE)	3	16	1	1	6	8542.00
LESOTHO (USA)	2	8	1	3	4	25440.30
LET THE LION ROAR (GB)	8	15	1	1	3	5362.45
LE VIE DEI COLORI (GB)	5	15	1	1	4	5555.52
LIBRETTIST (USA)	7	29	2	4	12	18658.16
LIMNOS (JPN)	4	17	1	3	6	27208.75
LINNGARI (IRE)	1	5	1	1	1	7766.67
LION HEART (USA)	2	9	1	1	3	12713.25
LION NOIR (GB)	1	7	1	4	3	77568.84
LOMITAS (GB)	9	31	4	7	12	62303.43
LONE BID (FR)	1	5	1	1	1	8207.40
LORD AMERICO	13	41	2	3	10	77932.05
LORD OF APPEAL (GB)	6	18	1	1	5	8958.77
LORD OF ENGLAND (GER)	4	16	2	3	7	19449.36
LOST WORLD (IRE)	10	51	4	4	14	29534.79
LOUP SAUVAGE (USA)	8	25	1	2	8	10633.05
LOUP SOLITAIRE (USA)	4	22	1	1	7	5045.70
LOXIAS (FR)	1	6	1	1	2	19208.33
LUCARNO (USA)	30	90	3	3	27	20155.98
LUCKY STORY (USA)	17	50	3	4	21	27650.87
LUSO (GB)	62	231	12	15	56	107614.67
MACHIAVELLIAN (USA)	1	4	1	1	2	17687.50
MACHIAVELLIAN TSAR (FR)	1	5	1	2	3	22463.85
MAHLER (GB)	21	51	6	6	17	34861.10
MAKBUL	1	1	1	1	0	7027.35
MALINAS (GER)	7	21	2	2	9	83555.43
MAMOOL (IRE)	4	13	2	3	4	35959.14
MANDURO (GER)	19	53	6	7	12	65482.19
MANSONNIEN (FR)	4	18	1	2	5	7243.62
MARESCA SORRENTO (FR)	7	19	1	2	5	13024.01
MARJU (IRE)	13	59	4	7	24	74284.17
MARK OF ESTEEM (IRE)	8	28	1	1	11	12861.03
MARTALINE (GB)	26	87	7	9	30	163389.61
MARTILLO (GER)	1	5	1	1	2	5071.98
MASTERCRAFTSMAN (IRE)	15	48	5	7	18	71916.30
MEDAALY (GB)	9	40	1	2	16	44933.54
MEDECIS (GB)	3	11	1	1	4	7392.10
MEDICEAN (GB)	37	158	10	15	62	129303.17
MIDNIGHT LEGEND (GB)	135	557	50	78	216	536538.88
MILAN (GB)	306	1240	94	152	402	2041810.94
MILLENARY (GB)	36	145	10	14	43	123751.54
MILLKOM (GB)	5	18	2	3	4	17476.78
MISTER SACHA (FR)	3	11	1	1	2	6041.10
MONSUN (GER)	14	50	5	12	17	138639.55
MONTJEU (IRE)	48	221	17	29	95	464788.15
MONTJOY (USA)	1	6	1	2	2	16017.00
MONTMARTRE (FR)	3	11	2	3	5	140427.23
MOROZOV (USA)	26	83	8	11	32	104727.02
MORPETH (GB)	8	26	1	4	4	17575.80
MOSCOW SOCIETY (USA)	43	182	10	16	79	155915.74
MOSS VALE (IRE)	7	28	2	4	6	18470.97
MOTIVATOR (GB)	32	134	11	14	51	130422.59
MOUNTAIN HIGH (IRE)	44	153	12	18	41	111939.60
MOUNT NELSON (GB)	11	32	1	1	12	8233.65
MR COMBUSTIBLE (IRE)	16	75	5	6	34	47064.47
MR GREELEY (USA)	6	25	1	1	8	6211.42
MTOTO	5	19	3	3	9	12339.91
MUHAYMIN (USA)	3	11	2	2	2	7600.20
MUHTARRAM (USA)	11	41	6	7	13	57010.66
MUHTATHIR (GB)	12	40	6	10	15	165228.59
MUJADIL (USA)	5	23	1	1	9	8349.62
MUJAHID (USA)	1	11	1	3	4	9359.60
MULTIPLEX (GB)	40	112	6	7	32	54662.35

STALLIONS	RNRS	STARTS	WNRS	WINS	PLACES	TOTAL (£)
MUROTO	1	3	1	1	1	1699.13
MUSTAMEET (USA)	5	14	1	2	2	18759.30
MY RISK (FR)	4	11	1	1	3	35014.33
NAHEEZ (USA)	5	19	1	1	6	13425.31
NAYEF (USA)	30	112	8	10	41	68064.51
NEAR HONOR (GER)	1	5	1	1	1	3535.20
NEEDLE GUN (IRE)	25	78	2	2	26	52783.48
NEEDWOOD BLADE (GB)	17	54	4	8	17	40123.90
NETWORK (GER)	34	147	11	21	62	483149.31
NEW APPROACH (IRE)	9	29	1	1	5	8274.20
NEW FRONTIER (IRE)	10	36	1	1	14	15405.68
NEW SOUTH WALES (GB)	1	7	1	1	1	5097.00
NEXT DESERT (IRE)	1	6	1	2	2	22255.75
NICARON (GER)	3	14	1	1	4	8858.10
NICKNAME (FR)	6	17	4	5	7	84144.25
NIGHT TANGO (GER)	1	7	1	5	0	59858.33
NIKOS	1	8	1	3	3	19093.24
NOMADIC WAY (USA)	17	63	5	10	21	60995.02
NOROIT (GER)	1	6	1	1	3	5139.90
NORSE DANCER (IRE)	24	87	9	14	22	56410.89
NORWICH	20	91	1	1	27	20316.39
NOTNOWCATO (GB)	15	61	5	6	24	41302.27
NOVERRE (USA)	8	30	1	2	11	11731.56
OASIS DREAM (GB)	12	48	4	6	14	61675.06
OBSERVATORY (USA)	12	49	1	1	15	12328.23
OKAWANGO (USA)	2	9	2	3	1	75899.00
OLDEN TIMES (GB)	4	13	1	1	5	7333.20
OLD VIC	161	693	52	78	254	1039944.88
ONE COOL CAT (USA)	11	56	3	4	22	37920.48
ORATORIO (IRE)	27	91	7	8	31	48789.22
ORPEN (USA)	5	16	1	2	7	32454.87
OSCAR (IRE)	302	1221	100	154	421	1803952.94
OSCAR SCHINDLER (IRE)	14	53	3	4	19	31952.61
OSORIO (GER)	4	20	2	2	5	10757.42
OVERBURY (IRE)	92	359	27	42	141	328298.41
PANORAMIC	7	35	3	5	22	163967.04
PAPAL BULL (GB)	14	48	5	5	18	35477.44
PASSING GLANCE (GB)	19	77	7	12	24	101051.47
PASSING SALE (FR)	8	29	2	2	13	17544.60
PASTERNAK (GB)	17	52	3	4	15	41330.29
PEINTRE CELEBRE (USA)	11	36	1	2	11	31216.37
PELDER (IRE)	3	12	1	1	8	10079.76
PENTIRE (GB)	4	11	1	1	3	2557.70
PERUGINO (USA)	6	30	2	4	8	25707.23
PHANTOM BREEZE	1	12	1	2	7	16424.70
PHOENIX REACH (IRE)	12	51	1	2	17	31712.20
PIERRE (GB)	23	71	3	4	16	22330.29
PILSUDSKI (IRE)	18	73	3	4	25	33187.70
PISTOLET BLEU (IRE)	5	12	1	1	4	29051.50
PIVOTAL (GB)	23	64	4	6	16	65113.33
PLEASANTLY PERFECT (USA)	2	11	2	2	4	11824.23
POLICY MAKER (IRE)	2	7	2	3	3	25903.78
POLIGLOTE (GB)	20	82	8	16	31	327115.19
POLISH PRECEDENT (USA)	4	25	1	1	9	24000.58
PORTRAIT GALLERY (IRE)	36	156	13	17	59	151230.57
POSIDONAS (GB)	7	12	1	1	4	3170.81
PRESENTING (GB)	399	1532	134	202	524	2164351.45
PRIMITIVE RISING (USA)	2	5	1	1	3	11989.05
PRIMO VALENTINO (IRE)	7	18	1	1	5	3581.85
PRINCE DANIEL (USA)	3	11	1	2	2	2969.55
PRIOLO (USA)	3	8	1	2	2	16472.50
PROCLAMATION (IRE)	30	107	9	11	31	65189.87
PROUD CITIZEN (USA)	2	11	1	1	6	6485.31
PUIT D'OR (IRE)	1	7	1	1	3	7570.83

STALLIONS	RNRS	STARTS	WNRS	WINS	PLACES	TOTAL (£)
PURSUIT OF LOVE (GB)	6	33	1	1	12	6997.54
PUSHKIN (IRE)	8	31	2	3	9	20712.76
PYRUS (USA)	10	42	2	2	12	19493.00
QUEST FOR FAME	1	4	1	1	3	6878.46
QUWS (GB)	13	62	5	9	22	43653.73
RAHY (USA)	4	10	1	2	3	19034.95
RAIL LINK (GB)	21	69	7	7	30	43923.69
RAINBOW HIGH (GB)	6	37	2	3	14	19120.70
RAINBOW QUEST (USA)	6	29	2	4	10	39940.09
RAISE A GRAND (IRE)	6	24	1	1	11	40292.64
RAKAPOSHI KING	5	16	1	3	3	12034.08
RAKTI (GB)	18	60	5	8	18	61086.68
RASHAR (USA)	14	43	3	7	13	39686.09
RAVEN'S PASS (USA)	5	24	1	3	9	36754.80
REDBACK (GB)	9	38	2	4	9	22732.52
RED CLUBS (IRE)	11	48	3	3	16	25333.65
REDOUTE'S CHOICE (AUS)	4	13	1	1	3	6080.47
RED RANSOM (USA)	13	40	2	2	9	40516.13
REEL BUDDY (USA)	1	7	1	1	4	3289.77
REFUSE TO BEND (IRE)	25	91	8	11	32	99243.98
RELIEF PITCHER	5	13	1	1	3	11175.00
RELIGIOUSLY (USA)	1	7	1	1	3	17463.02
RESET (AUS)	5	11	2	3	1	10613.88
REVOQUE (IRE)	56	212	14	20	69	198222.64
RIDGEWOOD BEN (GB)	5	19	1	2	6	16906.20
RIGHT WIN (IRE)	3	8	1	1	3	8807.94
ROBELLINO (USA)	2	14	2	3	8	37557.50
ROBIN DES CHAMPS (FR)	53	132	16	21	54	234623.82
ROBIN DES PRES (FR)	41	143	3	5	46	43875.86
ROB ROY (IRE)	5	14	1	1	2	4680.54
ROCAMADOUR (GB)	3	13	2	4	3	30513.56
ROCK CITY	1	7	1	1	1	4559.40
ROCK HOPPER	2	12	1	1	7	9474.93
ROCK OF GIBRALTAR (IRE)	32	148	10	10	63	127811.38
ROI DE ROME (USA)	3	16	2	3	9	29008.88
ROMAN SADDLE (IRE)	1	6	1	1	3	19441.67
ROYAL ANTHEM (USA)	38	127	8	9	40	67704.61
ROYAL APPLAUSE (GB)	19	64	3	3	19	27782.58
RUDIMENTARY (USA)	27	154	12	19	54	215449.34
RUNYON (IRE)	10	37	1	2	14	11934.10
SABREHILL (USA)	4	23	1	1	6	5592.53
SADDLER MAKER (IRE)	4	18	2	2	13	93817.72
SADDLERS' HALL (IRE)	42	184	14	22	54	193196.97
SADLER'S WELLS (USA)	24	106	6	6	42	82948.06
SAFFRON WALDEN (FR)	19	111	9	15	48	153967.40
SAGAMIX (FR)	5	23	2	3	4	14976.69
SAINT DES SAINTS (FR)	24	102	15	26	41	482434.51
SAKHEE (USA)	25	103	9	14	41	103098.14
SAKHEE'S SECRET (GB)	8	19	1	1	7	6630.42
SALFORD EXPRESS (IRE)	2	7	1	2	2	22879.38
SAMRAAN (USA)	6	15	2	2	5	9017.67
SAMUM (GER)	7	19	1	3	4	26933.96
SASSANIAN (USA)	11	46	4	5	17	66094.41
SAYARSHAN (FR)	8	34	4	5	8	27243.16
SCORPION (IRE)	89	259	21	34	85	264244.67
SEA FREEDOM (GB)	2	9	1	1	3	3696.30
SEA THE STARS (IRE)	6	27	4	6	13	55203.70
SECRET SINGER (FR)	6	26	4	4	10	75499.53
SELKIRK (USA)	13	54	2	3	19	21189.12
SEPTEMBER STORM (GER)	12	36	1	1	10	10169.33
SESARO (USA)	2	9	1	2	1	7808.90
SHAANMER (IRE)	10	40	4	5	18	71547.97
SHAMARDAL (USA)	13	50	4	5	17	53800.93
SHANTOU (USA)	90	398	32	55	145	604186.06

STALLIONS	RNRS	STARTS	WNRS	WINS	PLACES	TOTAL (£)
SHERNAZAR	8	38	4	6	10	39199.72
SHIROCCO (GER)	50	169	11	16	52	156243.29
SHOLOKHOV (IRE)	15	59	4	9	25	415004.08
SILVER PATRIARCH (IRE)	35	154	11	13	59	117639.96
SINGSPIEL (IRE)	19	72	7	9	22	118921.19
SIN KIANG (FR)	2	6	1	1	2	3614.65
SINNDAR (IRE)	16	77	7	10	27	101889.50
SIR HARRY LEWIS (USA)	53	254	22	29	101	234889.65
SIR PERCY (GB)	10	28	3	3	8	10785.05
SLEEPING CAR (FR)	10	52	2	4	17	39115.21
SLICKLY (FR)	4	20	1	1	9	64353.90
SMADOUN (FR)	16	64	3	5	29	127426.58
SMART STRIKE (CAN)	3	13	1	2	3	9144.42
SNOW CAP (FR)	1	3	1	1	1	9263.57
SNURGE	23	121	14	20	40	141649.00
SOLDIER HOLLOW (GB)	2	11	1	2	8	219537.08
SOLDIER OF FORTUNE (IRE)	2	5	1	1	3	7050.24
SOLON (GER)	6	14	2	2	6	12284.31
SON OF SHARP SHOT (IRE)	1	9	1	1	3	3762.54
SONUS (IRE)	4	10	1	1	5	24204.25
SOVEREIGN WATER (FR)	4	10	1	1	4	25658.70
SOVIET STAR (USA)	10	46	4	6	9	33647.58
SPADOUN (FR)	29	127	7	13	45	115109.02
SPARTACUS (IRE)	12	53	3	6	20	40639.60
SPECTRUM (IRE)	4	23	1	2	7	18071.90
SPINNING WORLD (USA)	3	10	1	1	4	6116.66
SPIRIT ONE (FR)	3	11	2	2	4	10040.58
STARBOROUGH (GB)	3	9	2	2	2	3605.35
STATUE OF LIBERTY (USA)	6	21	1	1	10	19059.57
STERNKOENIG (IRE)	2	5	1	1	3	7891.67
ST JOVITE (USA)	8	44	3	5	16	30867.76
STORMIN FEVER (USA)	1	7	1	2	4	10231.82
STORMING HOME (GB)	13	52	4	7	14	41107.93
STORMY ATLANTIC (USA)	2	5	1	1	3	5232.96
STORMY RIVER (FR)	5	20	2	4	8	38514.58
STOWAWAY (GB)	63	266	18	25	84	422137.06
STRATEGIC CHOICE (USA)	6	26	3	4	6	53481.27
STRATEGIC PRINCE (GB)	14	57	3	3	16	39673.55
STREET CRY (IRE)	17	81	7	9	29	99688.35
SUBOTICA (FR)	1	8	1	1	4	7729.31
SUBTLE POWER (IRE)	18	77	7	10	26	151285.18
SULAMANI (IRE)	23	95	11	13	34	145535.42
SUNDAY BREAK (JPN)	3	9	1	1	2	4187.10
SUPERIOR PREMIUM (GB)	2	9	1	3	0	46363.00
SUPREME LEADER	6	26	3	4	9	33714.31
SUPREME SOUND (GB)	5	39	2	3	13	30280.59
SWIFT GULLIVER (IRE)	2	14	1	1	6	4769.01
SYLVAN EXPRESS	1	6	1	2	2	29398.80
SYSTEMATIC (GB)	4	15	2	3	5	15536.80
TAGULA (IRE)	11	35	1	1	10	55077.89
TAIPAN (IRE)	4	17	2	2	6	10367.65
TAJRAASI (USA)	5	13	1	1	1	9450.00
TAKE RISKS (FR)	4	15	1	1	6	5474.70
TALAASH (IRE)	1	10	1	1	3	4527.36
TAMAYAZ (CAN)	15	69	6	8	22	54797.71
TAMURE (IRE)	20	80	6	14	34	182621.46
TAU CETI (GB)	2	5	1	2	3	13471.22
TEN MOST WANTED (USA)	1	5	1	1	2	2831.85
TEOFILO (IRE)	25	90	10	12	46	81855.16
TERIMON	5	27	3	6	7	32241.75
TERTULLIAN (USA)	3	18	2	2	7	11104.34
THEATRICAL	3	12	1	1	5	8038.62
THOUSAND WORDS (GB)	3	13	1	1	3	4677.84
THREE VALLEYS (USA)	7	13	1	1	4	7460.70

STALLIONS	RNRS	STARTS	WNRS	WINS	PLACES	TOTAL (£)
TIGER GROOM (GB)	2	5	1	1	2	5702.40
TIGER HILL (IRE)	44	121	5	6	44	62493.96
TIKKANEN (USA)	49	189	12	18	56	134619.26
TILLERMAN (GB)	8	35	2	4	15	31463.50
TIPSY CREEK (USA)	2	10	1	2	1	5177.61
TIRAAZ (USA)	1	10	1	1	7	18557.95
TOBOUGG (IRE)	49	194	16	21	60	104194.41
TOPANOORA	3	11	1	1	3	7126.52
TOUCH OF LAND (FR)	8	34	1	1	12	10451.91
TRADE FAIR (GB)	19	81	5	9	25	69353.43
TRADITIONALLY (USA)	6	30	1	1	10	10104.84
TRANS ISLAND (GB)	37	99	4	6	18	44071.53
TREMPOLINO (USA)	9	43	3	4	22	53886.95
TURGEON (USA)	31	136	13	20	49	316127.48
TURTLE ISLAND (IRE)	58	239	18	27	87	213309.64
UNBRIDLED'S SONG (USA)	1	6	1	2	2	5769.16
UNGARO (GER)	3	8	1	1	1	3138.75
UNTIL SUNDOWN (USA)	3	10	1	1	2	6260.20
URBAN OCEAN (FR)	13	48	3	4	15	44763.13
VAL ROYAL (FR)	10	43	3	3	19	22943.16
VANGELIS (USA)	2	6	1	2	3	30346.93
VENDANGEUR (IRE)	3	8	1	2	4	12449.74
VERGLAS (IRE)	34	113	5	6	42	57181.58
VERTICAL SPEED (FR)	16	50	1	1	19	28063.33
VIKING RULER (AUS)	5	20	2	4	8	36749.93
VINNIE ROE (IRE)	88	383	33	46	134	409503.34
VIRTUAL (GB)	2	6	1	2	0	3184.02
VISIONARY (FR)	5	17	2	3	4	67813.14
VOIX DU NORD (FR)	17	101	11	29	44	517097.71
VOLOCHINE (IRE)	5	19	1	3	10	21025.54
WALK IN THE PARK (IRE)	4	14	3	6	4	149852.15
WAR CHANT (USA)	5	20	2	6	6	40261.80
WAREED (USA)	18	54	2	2	11	12787.27
WAVENEY (UAE)	3	11	1	1	2	3285.00
WELL CHOSEN (GB)	13	72	5	8	29	89581.70
WELSH LION (IRE)	2	9	1	2	4	15283.34
WESTERNER (GB)	174	764	61	92	264	1229381.82
WHERE OR WHEN (IRE)	8	31	3	4	10	32407.69
WHIPPER (USA)	14	66	5	7	22	55654.62
WHITMORE'S CONN (USA)	18	76	5	8	27	72577.07
WINDSOR CASTLE (GB)	9	34	2	5	8	22799.81
WINDSOR KNOT (IRE)	7	23	1	1	7	15304.26
WINGED LOVE (IRE)	73	279	26	34	102	378609.38
WITH APPROVAL (CAN)	9	28	1	1	8	24259.40
WITHOUT CONNEXION (IRE)	1	9	1	1	7	6447.24
WITNESS BOX (USA)	47	199	13	18	70	350126.23
WIZARD KING (GB)	7	38	1	1	10	10238.42
WOLFE TONE (IRE)	4	10	1	3	3	34081.04
WOODS OF WINDSOR (USA)	2	13	1	1	6	17575.93
XAAR (GB)	8	38	3	3	13	20827.54
YEATS (IRE)	24	51	7	7	21	37790.52
ZAFEEN (FR)	9	26	2	4	4	22473.55
ZAGREB (USA)	38	140	8	13	40	82469.61
ZAMINDAR (USA)	14	37	3	3	8	15402.34
ZAVATA (USA)	1	3	1	1	1	4316.40
ZERPOUR (IRE)	6	21	1	2	4	10219.62

BY KIND PERMISSION OF WEATHERBYS

HIGH-PRICED YEARLINGS OF 2015 AT TATTERSALLS SALES
The following yearlings realised 97,000 Guineas and over at Tattersalls Sales in 2015:-

Name and Breeding	Purchaser	Guineas
B F DUBAWI (IRE) - LOVEISALLYOUNEED (IRE)	MV MAGNIER	2100000
B F GALILEO (IRE) - A Z WARRIOR (USA)	MV MAGNIER	1300000
B C GALILEO (IRE) - ALLURING PARK (IRE)	MV MAGNIER	1250000
CH C GALILEO (IRE) - JACQUELINE QUEST (IRE)	CHINA HORSE CLUB	1200000
B C OASIS DREAM (GB) - IZZI TOP (GB)	JOHN FERGUSON BS	1100000
B F GALILEO (IRE) - LIKE A DAME (GB)	MV MAGNIER	1000000
B F DUBAWI (IRE) - BADEE'A (IRE)	CHINA HORSE CLUB	900000
B F DARK ANGEL (IRE) - FOLGA (GB)	OLIVER ST LAWRENCE BS	825000
B F STREET CRY (IRE) - SHASTYE (IRE)	C GORDON-WATSON BS	800000
B C WAR FRONT (USA) - RIVER BELLE (GB)	CHINA HORSE CLUB	775000
UAE KING (IRE) B C OASIS DREAM (GB) - CAPHENE (GB)	ROGER P VARIAN	750000
B C FRANKEL (GB) - DAR RE MI (GB)	AL SHAQAB RACING	750000
B C DUBAWI (IRE) - ALSINDI (IRE)	BLANDFORD BS	750000
DUBAWI PRINCE (GB) B C DUBAWI (IRE) - FLAWLY (GB)	A & E BS	725000
B C DUBAWI (IRE) - GOATHEMALA (GER)	JOHN FERGUSON BS	725000
B F REDOUTE'S CHOICE (AUS) - YUMMY MUMMY (GB)	MV MAGNIER	725000
B F INVINCIBLE SPIRIT (IRE) - LISCUNE (IRE)	MV MAGNIER	700000
ALWAATHEQ (IRE) CH C FRANKEL (GB) - TARIYSHA (IRE)	SHADWELL ESTATE COMPANY	700000
B F DUBAWI (IRE) - POLLY'S MARK (IRE)	JOHN FERGUSON BS	700000
B C NATHANIEL (IRE) - DANEHILL DREAMER (USA)	MV MAGNIER	675000
B C FRANKEL (GB) - MODEL QUEEN (USA)	CHINA HORSE CLUB	670000
B C SEA THE STARS (IRE) - SHAWARA (IRE)	MAYFAIR SPECULATORS	650000
BR F SHAMARDAL (USA) - RED BANDANNA (IRE)	SHAWN DUGAN, AGENT	625000
B C FRANKEL (GB) - HEAVEN SENT (GB)	JUDDMONTE FARMS	620000
B C GALILEO (IRE) - CRYSTAL VALKYRIE (IRE)	MAYFAIR SPECULATORS	600000
CH F NATHANIEL (IRE) - OUR QUEEN OF KINGS (GB)	JUDDMONTE FARMS	600000
SAMHARRY (GB) B C EXCEED AND EXCEL (AUS) - BALLYOLCA CELEBRE (IRE)	SHADWELL ESTATE COMPANY	600000
CH F DUBAWI (IRE) - WILD WIND (GER)	JOHN FERGUSON BS	580000
B C INVINCIBLE SPIRIT (IRE) - DARK PROMISE (GB)	JOHN FERGUSON BS	575000
CH F SEPOY (AUS) - DEMERGER (USA)	VENDOR	550000
B C SHAMARDAL (USA) - ASSABIYYA (IRE)	JOHN FERGUSON BS	550000
B C NATHANIEL (IRE) - KINNAIRD (IRE)	C GORDON-WATSON BS	525000
B C SHAMARDAL (USA) - BALLYBACKA LADY (IRE)	MAYFAIR SPECULATORS	525000
B F SEA THE STARS (IRE) - KITTY MATCHAM (GB)	BBA IRELAND	525000
CH F STREET CRY (IRE) - LAY TIME (GB)	SUNDERLAND HOLDING INC	520000
MURAAHIB (IRE) B C SHAMARDAL (USA) - AMATHIA (IRE)	SHADWELL ESTATE COMPANY	500000
B C FRANKEL (GB) - REACHING (GB)	VENDOR	500000
B F GALILEO (IRE) - LANDMARK (USA)	C GORDON-WATSON BS	500000
SHARJA BRIDGE (GB) B C OASIS DREAM (GB) - QUETENA (GER)	ROGER P VARIAN	500000
B C NATHANIEL (IRE) - STEEL PRINCESS (IRE)	DERMOT FARRINGTON	500000
B C SHAMARDAL (USA) - OREGON TRAIL (USA)	JOHN FERGUSON BS	475000
B C EXCELEBRATION (IRE) - LADY MILETRIAN (IRE)	MV MAGNIER	475000
B F DANSILI (GB) - CASCATA (IRE)	FRANK LYONS	470000
B F GALILEO (IRE) - HVEGER (AUS)	MAYFAIR SPECULATORS	460000
B F FRANKEL (GB) - DYNAFORCE (USA)	C GORDON-WATSON BS	450000
CH C SHAMARDAL (USA) - CELESTIAL GIRL (GB)	JOHN FERGUSON BS	450000
UAE QUEEN (GB) B F OASIS DREAM (GB) - PONGEE (GB)	ROGER P VARIAN	450000
THAAQIB (GB) GR C INVINCIBLE SPIRIT (IRE) - LIGHT SHINE (GB)	SHADWELL ESTATE COMPANY	450000
PARLANCE (IRE) B F INVINCIBLE SPIRIT (IRE) - PLEASANTRY (GB)	CHEVELEY PARK STUD	450000
B F LAWMAN (FR) - SO SILK (GB)	KERN/LILLINGSTON ASSOC	450000
CH F RAVEN'S PASS (USA) - NIGHTIME (IRE)	JOHN FERGUSON BS	450000
CH/GR C EXCEED AND EXCEL (AUS) - CLINICAL (GB)	CHINA HORSE CLUB	450000
B F LAWMAN (FR) - APPLAUDED (IRE)	MV MAGNIER	440000
B C FASTNET ROCK (AUS) - STARFISH (GB)	FORM BS	425000
BR C CAPE CROSS (IRE) - QUIET DREAM (USA)	JOHN & JAKE WARREN	425000
B C GALILEO (IRE) - PENANG PEARL (FR)	MAYFAIR SPECULATORS	425000
B F DUBAWI (IRE) - BRIGITTA (IRE)	C GORDON-WATSON BS	425000
CROSSING PATHS (IRE) B F CAPE CROSS (IRE) - REBELLINE (IRE)	HADDEN BS	420000
CH F RAVEN'S PASS (USA) - ARTISTI (GB)	TONY NERSES	420000
FAROOK (IRE) RO C RAVEN'S PASS (USA) - WRONG ANSWER (GB)	SHADWELL ESTATE COMPANY	420000
B C OASIS DREAM (GB) - SETA (GB)	BLANDFORD BS	420000
B F DUBAWI (IRE) - LADY OF EVEREST (IRE)	JOHN FERGUSON BS	420000
B F GALILEO (IRE) - MULTICOLOUR WAVE (IRE)	MAYFAIR SPECULATORS	400000
B C LOPE DE VEGA (IRE) - BRISTOL BAY (IRE)	JOHN FERGUSON BS	400000
B F GALILEO (IRE) - MOHICAN PRINCESS (GB)	CHINA HORSE CLUB	400000
B F REDOUTE'S CHOICE (AUS) - MY BRANCH (GB)	C GORDON-WATSON BS	400000
GR C OASIS DREAM (GB) - HONORLINA (FR)	JOHN & JAKE WARREN	400000
SHAJJY (IRE) B C INVINCIBLE SPIRIT (IRE) - GREENISLAND (IRE)	SHADWELL ESTATE COMPANY	400000

Name and Breeding	Purchaser	Guineas
AKHLAAQ (GB) B C NEW APPROACH (IRE) - MISHEER (GB)	SHADWELL ESTATE COMPANY	400000
B C INVINCIBLE SPIRIT (IRE) - LIXIROVA (FR)	BLANDFORD BS	380000
TEQANY (IRE) GR C DARK ANGEL (IRE) - CAPULET MONTEQUE (IRE)	SHADWELL ESTATE COMPANY	380000
BULDAN (GB) B C NEW APPROACH (IRE) - MEEZNAH (USA)	BLANDFORD BS	375000
RED LABEL (IRE) B C DUBAWI (IRE) - BORN SOMETHING (IRE)	JAMIE MCCALMONT (P.S.)	375000
B F RAVEN'S PASS (USA) - ANEEDAH (IRE)	TONY NERSES	370000
CH C NEW APPROACH (IRE) - NIGHT FROLIC (GB)	VENDOR	360000
B C KODIAC (GB) - NOVEL FUN (IRE)	AL SHAQAB RACING / DOYLE	360000
GR F GALILEO (IRE) - BEWITCHED (IRE)	JOHN & JAKE WARREN	360000
B F OASIS DREAM (GB) - ANA MARIE (FR)	AL SHAQAB RACING	350000
B C SEA THE STARS (IRE) - KELLY NICOLE (IRE)	JOHN FERGUSON BS	350000
CH C DUTCH ART (GB) - CANTAL (GB)	AL SHAQAB RACING	350000
B F EXCEED AND EXCEL (AUS) - SANTA AGATA (FR)	SUNDERLAND HOLDING INC	330000
TAWAAFOQ (GB) B C SHOWCASING (GB) - GILT LINKED (GB)	SHADWELL ESTATE COMPANY	330000
CH C SEA THE STARS (IRE) - PRIVATE LIFE (IRE)	VENDOR	330000
SAAHEQ (GB) B C INVINCIBLE SPIRIT (IRE) - BREVITY (USA)	SHADWELL ESTATE COMPANY	330000
CH F PIVOTAL (GB) - BEST TERMS (GB)	FEDERICO BARBERINI, AGENT	330000
B C DUTCH ART (GB) - SOAR (GB)	BLANDFORD BS	325000
PARADISE LAKE (IRE) B C SIYOUNI (FR) - KALANDARA (IRE)	JOHN & JAKE WARREN	320000
GREAT SOUND (IRE) B C GALILEO (IRE) - WANNA (IRE)	JOHN & JAKE WARREN	320000
B F FASTNET ROCK (AUS) - LAUREN LOUISE (GB)	HUGO LASCELLES BS	320000
B C INVINCIBLE SPIRIT (IRE) - WALLIS (GB)	JOHN & JAKE WARREN	310000
B F INVINCIBLE SPIRIT (IRE) - SALONBLUE (IRE)	CHINA HORSE CLUB	310000
FUJAIRA BRIDGE (IRE) B C SEA THE STARS (IRE) - GARANCIERE (FR)	ROGER P VARIAN	310000
B F MOTIVATOR (GB) - TURNING LEAF (IRE)	MAYFAIR SPECULATORS	300000
B F GALILEO (IRE) - BANQUISE (IRE)	SACKVILLEDONALD	300000
B C NEW APPROACH (IRE) - WILD MIMOSA (IRE)	C GORDON-WATSON BS	300000
CH C SEPOY (AUS) - PALITANA (USA)	JOHN & JAKE WARREN	300000
GR F MASTERCRAFTSMAN (IRE) - FLANDERS (IRE)	HUGO LASCELLES BS	300000
CH F FRANKEL (GB) - KIRINDA (IRE)	AL SHAQAB RACING	300000
PRINCESS DE LUNE (IRE) GR F SHAMARDAL (USA) - PRINCESS SERENA (IRE)	VENDOR	300000
B C HIGH CHAPARRAL (IRE) - ALAMOUNA (IRE)	MAYFAIR SPECULATORS	300000
B F LOPE DE VEGA (IRE) - INCHMAHOME (GB)	SUNDERLAND HOLDING INC	300000
B F INVINCIBLE SPIRIT (IRE) - DALASYLA (IRE)	AL SHAQAB RACING	300000
CH C STREET CRY (IRE) - NOMISTAKEABOUTIT (CAN)	MAYFAIR SPECULATORS (P.S.)	290000
NINGALOO (GER) B C SIYOUNI (FR) - NOTRE DAME (GER)	CRISFORD RACING	280000
CH F ZEBEDEE (GB) - HAWATTEF (IRE)	C GORDON-WATSON BS	280000
B C DUTCH ART (GB) - BAHIA EMERALD (IRE)	JOHN FERGUSON BS	280000
B C DUTCH ART (GB) - MISS QUALITY (USA)	TONY NERSES	280000
B C FRANKEL (GB) - CHRYSANTHEMUM (IRE)	VENDOR	280000
MASHAWAAR (GB) B C DANSILI (GB) - ALSACE LORRAINE (GB)	SHADWELL ESTATE COMPANY	260000
GR F OASIS DREAM (GB) - WILD SIDE (GB)	PETER & ROSS DOYLE BS	260000
B F SHAMARDAL (USA) - AKRIVI (IRE)	JOHN FERGUSON BS	260000
B C DANSILI (GB) - GIANTS PLAY (USA)	HUGO LASCELLES BS	260000
B C KODIAC (GB) - SINGITTA (GB)	HONG KONG JOCKEY CLUB	260000
B F INVINCIBLE SPIRIT (IRE) - COUNTESS FERRAMA (GB)	AL SHAQAB RACING / DOYLE	260000
B F DARK ANGEL (IRE) - GLAMOROUS AIR (IRE)	BBA IRELAND	260000
RICKRACK (IRE) B F TEOFILO (IRE) - ARAZENA (USA)	JAMIE MCCALMONT	260000
B F SHAMARDAL (USA) - CATCHLINE (USA)	JOHN FERGUSON BS	260000
B F SHAMARDAL (USA) - SCARLET BELLE (GB)	JOHN FERGUSON BS	250000
BR F TEOFILO (IRE) - PENNY POST (IRE)	SHAWN DUGAN, AGENT	250000
B C ELUSIVE CITY (USA) - AMMO (IRE)	C GORDON-WATSON BS	250000
B C INVINCIBLE SPIRIT (IRE) - DOULA (USA)	C GORDON-WATSON BS	250000
B C ROCK OF GIBRALTAR (IRE) - INCHINA (GB)	MRS A SKIFFINGTON	250000
EQTIRAAN (IRE) B C HELMET (AUS) - MIRANDA FROST (IRE)	SHADWELL ESTATE COMPANY	250000
B C LOPE DE VEGA (IRE) - KATE THE GREAT (GB)	RABBAH BS	250000
RED ENSIGN (IRE) B C DARK ANGEL (IRE) - RAYON ROUGE (IRE)	CRISFORD RACING	250000
B F EXCEED AND EXCEL (AUS) - LA CUCINA (IRE)	JOHN & JAKE WARREN	250000
BR F SEPOY (AUS) - WOSAITA (GB)	TONY NERSES	250000
B C REDOUTE'S CHOICE (AUS) - NITYA (FR)	C GORDON-WATSON BS	240000
B F SEA THE STARS (IRE) - MAMONTA (GB)	MAYFAIR SPECULATORS	240000
B C EXCEED AND EXCEL (AUS) - CHERRY ORCHARD (IRE)	SACKVILLEDONALD	240000
MARKETEER (GB) B F OASIS DREAM (GB) - BARTER (GB)	VENDOR	240000
B C ZOFFANY (IRE) - CLOSE TO THE EDGE (IRE)	HONG KONG JOCKEY CLUB	240000
B C GALILEO (IRE) - DESERT CLASSIC (IRE)	VENDOR	240000
B C CANFORD CLIFFS (IRE) - STREET STYLE (IRE)	TONY NERSES	240000
FORTITUDE (IRE) B F OASIS DREAM (GB) - SWEEPSTAKE (IRE)	JOHN & JAKE WARREN	240000
B C FRANKEL (GB) - SWISS LAKE (USA)	SUZANNE ROBERTS	235000
B F NEW APPROACH (IRE) - TIME SAVED (GB)	BALLYHANE STUD	230000
B F LAWMAN (FR) - BUFERA (IRE)	STROUD COLEMAN BS	230000
B C KITTEN'S JOY (USA) - GRANNY FRANNY (USA)	SACKVILLE DONALD	230000

Name and Breeding	Purchaser	Guineas
CH C BATED BREATH (GB) - CONDITION (GB)	C GORDON-WATSON BS	230000
CH C LOPE DE VEGA (IRE) - SAVIGNANO (GB)	JOHN & JAKE WARREN	225000
BR C DARK ANGEL (IRE) - LAN FORCE (ITY)	JOHN FERGUSON BS	220000
B C INVINCIBLE SPIRIT (IRE) - ASHLEY HALL (USA)	MV MAGNIER	220000
B F SCAT DADDY (USA) - CONNIPTION (IRE)	FRANK LYONS	220000
CH C RAVEN'S PASS (USA) - SAYYEDATI STORM (USA)	JOHN FERGUSON BS	220000
B F FASTNET ROCK (AUS) - ROSE BLOSSOM (GB)	BBA IRELAND	220000
B C INVINCIBLE SPIRIT (IRE) - LOVE EVERLASTING (GB)	VENDOR	220000
B C EXCEED AND EXCEL (AUS) - SAABIQ (USA)	HONG KONG JOCKEY CLUB	220000
B C ACCLAMATION (GB) - ENTENTE CORDIALE (IRE)	C GORDON-WATSON BS	220000
B C GALILEO (IRE) - ICE MINT (USA)	BADGERS BS	215000
CH F SPEIGHTSTOWN (USA) - MAID TO MASTER (IRE)	FORM BS	210000
B C DANSILI (GB) - LADY DARSHAAN (IRE)	JOHN FERGUSON BS	210000
B C MASTERCRAFTSMAN (IRE) - ENDURE (IRE)	A & E BS	205000
B G EXCEED AND EXCEL (AUS) - BELDARIAN (IRE)	HONG KONG JOCKEY CLUB	200000
CH C PIVOTAL (GB) - BUSH CAT (USA)	SHADWELL ESTATE COMPANY	200000
B F DUBAWI (IRE) - COYOTE (GB)	THE COOL SILK PARTNERSHIP	200000
B F CANFORD CLIFFS (IRE) - GILDED VANITY (IRE)	DEMI O'BYRNE	200000
B F SEA THE STARS (IRE) - ROYALE DANEHILL (IRE)	BLANDFORD BS	200000
B C SHAMARDAL (USA) - SCARLETT ROSE (GB)	JOHN FERGUSON BS	200000
B F ACCLAMATION (GB) - MANIEREE (IRE)	BBA IRELAND	200000
B C DREAM AHEAD (USA) - MACHEERA (IRE)	AL SHAQAB RACING	200000
B G KYLLACHY (GB) - CAPACIOUS (GB)	HONG KONG JOCKEY CLUB	200000
BEEDAA (IRE) B C DREAM AHEAD (USA) - ALEXANDER QUEEN (IRE)	SHADWELL ESTATE COMPANY	200000
BATTAASH (IRE) B C DARK ANGEL (IRE) - ANNA LAW (IRE)	SHADWELL ESTATE COMPANY	200000
B F SEA THE STARS (IRE) - CAP COZ (IRE)	MAYFAIR SPECULATORS	200000
B F POET'S VOICE (GB) - VANITY (IRE)	BLANDFORD BS	200000
SHAAQAAF (IRE) B F SEPOY (AUS) - BURKE'S ROCK (USA)	SHADWELL ESTATE COMPANY	200000
B C SHAMARDAL (USA) - PERFECT TOUCH (USA)	CHANTAL REGALADO GONZALEZ	200000
PIONEERTOWN (IRE) B C HIGH CHAPARRAL (IRE) - TEMPURA (GER)	MRS A SKIFFINGTON	200000
EAGLE CREEK (IRE) B C RAVEN'S PASS (USA) - BLUE ANGEL (IRE)	CRISFORD RACING	200000
B C HOLY ROMAN EMPEROR (IRE) - FLAMBEAU (GB)	C GORDON-WATSON BS	200000
B F GALILEO (IRE) - FAMILY (USA)	BALLYHANE STUD (P.S.)	200000
CH F SEPOY (AUS) - SOME SUNNY DAY (GB)	JOHN FERGUSON BS	200000
B C ZOFFANY (IRE) - GLYMPSE (GB)	C GORDON-WATSON BS	200000
B C ZOFFANY (IRE) - DASHING BEAUTY (IRE)	A & E BS	200000
B C TEOFILO (IRE) - JESSICA'S DREAM (IRE)	VENDOR	200000
B C INVINCIBLE SPIRIT (IRE) - ALSHAKR (GB)	C GORDON-WATSON BS	200000
B C ACCLAMATION (GB) - CARIOCA (IRE)	JOHN FERGUSON BS	200000
B F GALILEO (IRE) - RED AVIS (IRE)	BLANDFORD BS (P.S.)	200000
WARM OASIS (GB) GR C OASIS DREAM (GB) - WARLING (IRE)	THE COOL SILK PARTNERSHIP	200000
B C SEA THE STARS (IRE) - DREAM OF THE HILL (IRE)	STROUD COLEMAN BS	200000
CH F CASAMENTO (IRE) - ASHIRAH (USA)	JOHN FERGUSON BS (P.S.)	200000
AFDEEK (GB) B C BATED BREATH (GB) - SOVIET TERMS (IRE)	SHADWELL ESTATE COMPANY	200000
B C SEPOY (AUS) - MAZUNA (IRE)	MAYFAIR SPECULATORS	200000
CH C NEW APPROACH (IRE) - NIGHT FROLIC (GB)	SHADWELL ESTATE COMPANY	200000
B C INVINCIBLE SPIRIT (IRE) - ALTA MODA (GB)	MV MAGNIER	190000
TAFAAKHOR (IRE) GR C DARK ANGEL (IRE) - TELLELLE (IRE)	PETER & ROSS DOYLE BS	190000
B F HIGH CHAPARRAL (IRE) - TAKE FLIGHT (IRE)	BBA IRELAND	190000
B F LAWMAN (FR) - SMART STEP (IRE)	BLM BS	190000
SPARKLE (GB) B F OASIS DREAM (GB) - GEMSTONE (IRE)	JOHN & JAKE WARREN	190000
FLEETFOOT JACK (IRE) B C KYLLACHY (GB) - MOVE (GB)	JASON KELLY / NICK BRADLEY	185000
B C DARK ANGEL (IRE) - AND AGAIN (USA)	C GORDON-WATSON BS	180000
B C HOLY ROMAN EMPEROR (IRE) - KENTUCKY WARBLER (IRE)	BLANDFORD BS	180000
B F CACIQUE (IRE) - KATY NOWAITEE (GB)	C GORDON-WATSON BS	180000
MUHAJJAL (GB) B C CAPE CROSS (IRE) - MUQANTARA (USA)	SHADWELL ESTATE COMPANY	180000
MUTAWATHEB (IRE) GR C DARK ANGEL (IRE) - QUEEN MYRINE (IRE)	SHADWELL ESTATE COMPANY	180000
ALMOREB (IRE) B C RAVEN'S PASS (USA) - MACADAMIA (IRE)	PETER & ROSS DOYLE BS	180000
GR C DARK ANGEL (IRE) - LECEILE (USA)	GILL RICHARDSON BS	180000
FAREEQ (GB) B/GR C DARK ANGEL (IRE) - SPATE (IRE)	SHADWELL ESTATE COMPANY	180000
B F CANFORD CLIFFS (IRE) - DIVINE GRACE (IRE)	AL SHAQAB RACING / DOYLE	180000
LOYAL JUSTICE (GB) CH C TEOFILO (IRE) - SENTIMENTAL VALUE (USA)	SUN BS	180000
B F DARK ANGEL (IRE) - RED INTRIGUE (IRE)	DAVID REDVERS	180000
B F EXCEED AND EXCEL (AUS) - LADY HAWKFIELD (IRE)	ONE AGENCY	180000
B C CAPE CROSS (IRE) - OPINIONATED (IRE)	JOHN FERGUSON BS	180000
B F POWER (GB) - TARFSHI (GB)	MAYFAIR SPECULATORS	180000
B C ZOFFANY (IRE) - FLYING FLAG (IRE)	GROVE STUD	175000
B F EXCEED AND EXCEL (AUS) - ISLAND BABE (USA)	FORM BS	170000
BR C HIGH CHAPARRAL (IRE) - BEZIQUE (GB)	N A S	170000
CH C DUTCH ART (GB) - ELYSIAN (GB)	C GORDON-WATSON BS	170000
GOLCONDA KING (IRE) GR C DARK ANGEL (IRE) - VANITY'S GIRL (IRE)	AIDAN O'RYAN	170000

Name and Breeding	Purchaser	Guineas
ZIHAAM (GB) CH C DUTCH ART (GB) - HYMNSHEET (GB)	SHADWELL ESTATE COMPANY	170000
TEMERITY (IRE) B F ZOFFANY (IRE) - GAMRA (IRE)	CHEVELEY PARK STUD	170000
B F SIR PERCY (GB) - CRYSTAL GAL (IRE)	BLANDFORD BS	170000
SITAARAH (GB) B F SEA THE STARS (IRE) - EDARAAT (USA)	SHADWELL ESTATE COMPANY	170000
B F TEOFILO (IRE) - WHITE CAY (GB)	JOHN WARREN BS	160000
B F CACIQUE (IRE) - CARTIMANDUA (GB)	JOHN & JAKE WARREN	160000
B C SEPOY (AUS) - MISS BROWN TO YOU (IRE)	JOHN FERGUSON BS	160000
B F RAVEN'S PASS (USA) - ELAS DIAMOND (GB)	VENDOR	160000
SPINNAKA (IRE) B F INVINCIBLE SPIRIT (IRE) - SPINNING WELL (IRE)	FITTOCKS STUD	160000
CH C LOPE DE VEGA (IRE) - PENELOPE STAR (GER)	SACKVILLEDONALD	160000
CH C DUTCH ART (GB) - THRILL (GB)	WILLIAM R MUIR	160000
B/BR C LONHRO (AUS) - LIGHTNING LYDIA (USA)	PETER & ROSS DOYLE BS	160000
CH C LOPE DE VEGA (IRE) - PIETRA DURA (GB)	C GORDON-WATSON BS	160000
HUSHOOD (IRE) B C CHAMPS ELYSEES (GB) - COCHIN (GB)	PETER & ROSS DOYLE BS	160000
B C TEOFILO (IRE) - PELLINORE (GB)	DAVID REDVERS BS	160000
B C POWER (GB) - AL IHTITHAR (IRE)	AL SHAQAB RACING / DOYLE	160000
DISCOVERED (IRE) CH C BATED BREATH (GB) - SANDGLASS (GB)	C GORDON-WATSON BS	160000
MONAADHIL (IRE) B C DARK ANGEL (IRE) - URBAN DAYDREAM (IRE)	SHADWELL ESTATE COMPANY	160000
CH C NATHANIEL (IRE) - SPLASHDOWN (GB)	C GORDON-WATSON BS	160000
B C FASTNET ROCK (AUS) - KUSHNARENKOVO (GB)	BBA IRELAND	160000
B C FRANKEL (GB) - DORCAS LANE (GB)	VENDOR	160000
GR C SEPOY (AUS) - SERENA'S STORM (IRE)	PETER & ROSS DOYLE BS	155000
B C FOOTSTEPSINTHESAND (GB) - LUCY DIAMONDS (IRE)	BLANDFORD BS	155000
B C FASTNET ROCK (AUS) - STARSTONE (GB)	TONY NERSES	155000
GR C DARK ANGEL (IRE) - ADMIRE THE VIEW (IRE)	JOHN FERGUSON BS	150000
B C PIVOTAL (GB) - ATLANTIC DESTINY (IRE)	C GORDON-WATSON BS	150000
B F GALILEO (IRE) - DHANYATA (IRE)	STEPHEN HILLEN BS (P.S.)	150000
CH C RIP VAN WINKLE (IRE) - WHIRLY BIRD (GB)	KENJI RYOTOKUJI	150000
B C INVINCIBLE SPIRIT (IRE) - LOCH JIPP (IRE)	OAKS FARM STABLES	150000
B C DARK ANGEL (IRE) - LOVE ACTION (IRE)	JOHN FERGUSON BS	150000
B C DUTCH ART (GB) - JAMBORETTA (IRE)	C GORDON-WATSON BS	150000
GR C DARK ANGEL (IRE) - DELIRA (IRE)	PETER & ROSS DOYLE BS	150000
B F INVINCIBLE SPIRIT (IRE) - FORGOTTEN ME (IRE)	PETER & ROSS DOYLE BS	150000
CH C PIVOTAL (GB) - PARIS WINDS (IRE)	JOHN FERGUSON BS	150000
SMARTDARGENT (FR) B C KENDARGENT (FR) - LITTLE STONE (FR)	SHADWELL ESTATE COMPANY	150000
B C CASAMENTO (IRE) - ANNOUSKA (IRE)	AL SHAQAB RACING / DOYLE	150000
B C EXCEED AND EXCEL (AUS) - STARBOUND (IRE)	SUNDERLAND HOLDING INC	150000
B C DARK ANGEL (IRE) - POPPET'S PASSION (IRE)	SHADWELL ESTATE COMPANY	150000
CH C CHOISIR (AUS) - PASHMINA (IRE)	DAVID REDVERS BS	150000
B C POUR MOI (IRE) - CHATLINE (IRE)	HILLEN / TABOR	150000
LAW POWER (GB) B C LAWMAN (FR) - CLARIETTA (GB)	VENDOR	150000
B F NATHANIEL (IRE) - HAZY DANCER (GB)	JOHN & JAKE WARREN	150000
B F ELUSIVE QUALITY (USA) - SNOWGAL (IRE)	VENDOR	150000
B C KYLLACHY (GB) - WELSH ANGEL (IRE)	JOHN FERGUSON BS	150000
B C SEA THE STARS (IRE) - BITOOH (GB)	C GORDON-WATSON BS	150000
B C FRANKEL (GB) - YOU'LL BE MINE (USA)	DERMOT FARRINGTON (P.S.)	150000
B F LOPE DE VEGA (IRE) - ROSCOFF (IRE)	VENDOR	145000
CH C DISTORTED HUMOR (USA) - MOUSSE AU CHOCOLAT (USA)	VENDOR	145000
B C YOUMZAIN (IRE) - MAJESTIC ROI (USA)	ED DUNLOP RACING	145000
B C NATHANIEL (IRE) - SHESASMARTLADY (IRE)	JOHN & JAKE WARREN	145000
CH C LOPE DE VEGA (IRE) - LET IT BE ME (USA)	DAVID REDVERS BS (P.S.)	145000
UNIFIED (GB) B F OASIS DREAM (GB) - ENSEMBLE (FR)	CHEVELEY PARK STUD	145000
TAAMOL (IRE) B C HELMET (AUS) - SUPREME SEDUCTRESS (IRE)	SHADWELL ESTATE COMPANY	140000
B F KODIAC (GB) - BALTIC BELLE (GB)	TONY NERSES	140000
B C DANSILI (GB) - CRYSTAL MAZE (GB)	VENDOR	140000
B C CAMPANOLOGIST (USA) - PRAIA (GER)	BLANDFORD BS	140000
B F CAPE BLANCO (IRE) - SHERMEEN (IRE)	CORMAC MCCORMACK BS	140000
VICTORY ANGEL (IRE) B C ACCLAMATION (GB) - GOLDEN SHADOW (IRE)	ANDREW SIME	140000
B F FASTNET ROCK (AUS) - GIVE ME FIVE (GER)	VENDOR	140000
B F REDOUTE'S CHOICE (AUS) - MONAMI (GER)	JAMIE MCCALMONT	135000
DHAJEEJ (IRE) B C CAPE CROSS (IRE) - NIMBOO (USA)	SHADWELL ESTATE COMPANY	130000
CH C NATHANIEL (IRE) - AMAZON BEAUTY (IRE)	BILL GREDLEY	130000
B C BAHAMIAN BOUNTY (GB) - DARE TO DREAM (GB)	SHADWELL ESTATE COMPANY	130000
B C FRANKEL (GB) - LATIN LOVE (IRE)	RABBAH BS	130000
B C IFFRAAJ (GB) - HAZIUM (IRE)	JOHN FERGUSON BS	130000
B/BR C EXCHANGE RATE (USA) - SLOW DOWN (USA)	PEGASUS FARMS	130000
B F OASIS DREAM (GB) - HYPNOLOGY (USA)	JOHN FERGUSON BS	130000
B C DARK ANGEL (IRE) - WAGTAIL (GB)	JOHN FERGUSON BS	130000
WASM (GB) CH C EXCEED AND EXCEL (AUS) - FINCHLEY (GB)	SHADWELL ESTATE COMPANY	130000
B C LAWMAN (FR) - COMPLEXION (GB)	STROUD COLEMAN BS	130000
B C SEPOY (AUS) - FRAULEIN (GB)	BBA IRELAND	130000

Name and Breeding	Purchaser	Guineas
B F SEA THE STARS (IRE) - STYLISH ONE (IRE)	DAVID REDVERS BS	130000
B F CAPE CROSS (IRE) - FASHIONABLE (GB)	JOHN FERGUSON BS	130000
B C DARK ANGEL (IRE) - SKEHANA (IRE)	TONY NERSES	130000
B F EQUIANO (FR) - CHRISTMAS TART (IRE)	MARGARET O'TOOLE (IRE)	130000
B F TEOFILO (IRE) - WALK IN BEAUTY (IRE)	BERTRAND LE METAYER BS	130000
B C KODIAC (GB) - SHEILA BLIGE (GB)	SHADWELL ESTATE COMPANY	130000
DIYOUNI (GER) B C SIYOUNI (FR) - DUTY AND DESTINY (IRE)	BLANDFORD BS	130000
CH F PIVOTAL (GB) - SABREON (GB)	CHEVELEY PARK STUD	130000
B C MASTERCRAFTSMAN (IRE) - EUROLINK RAINDANCE (IRE)	C GORDON-WATSON BS	125000
B C HIGH CHAPARRAL (IRE) - JEWEL IN THE SAND (IRE)	JOHN & JAKE WARREN	125000
OPEN WIDE (USA) B/BR C INVINCIBLE SPIRIT (IRE) - NUNAVIK (IRE)	PETER & ROSS DOYLE BS	125000
B F KODIAC (GB) - PEARL MOUNTAIN (IRE)	STROUD COLEMAN BS	125000
B C HIGH CHAPARRAL (IRE) - MISSIONARY HYMN (USA)	MPH RACING	125000
BLAZED (IRE) GR C DARK ANGEL (IRE) - SUDDEN BLAZE (IRE)	C GORDON-WATSON BS	125000
CH F SEPOY (AUS) - FLEETING IMAGE (IRE)	PETER & ROSS DOYLE BS	125000
CH F SHAMARDAL (USA) - AIRLINE HOSTESS (IRE)	VENDOR	125000
B F KODIAC (GB) - WINDY LANE (IRE)	BLANDFORD BS	125000
B C DANSILI (GB) - LAKUTA (IRE)	VENDOR	125000
CH C EXCEED AND EXCEL (AUS) - PUTOIS PEACE (GB)	WILLIAM R MUIR	120000
B C HOLY ROMAN EMPEROR (IRE) - DISCO VOLANTE (IRE)	C GORDON-WATSON BS	120000
MELINOE (GB) B F SEA THE STARS (IRE) - PERSEFONA (IRE)	A C ELLIOTT, AGENT	120000
B C CANFORD CLIFFS (IRE) - LULAWIN (GB)	PETER & ROSS DOYLE BS	120000
B C CAPE CROSS (IRE) - SAADIAH (IRE)	RABBAH BS	120000
CH C DUTCH ART (GB) - SAFE HOUSE (IRE)	SHADWELL ESTATE COMPANY	120000
GR C DARK ANGEL (IRE) - TRINITY SCHOLAR (IRE)	BBA IRELAND	120000
B F OASIS DREAM (GB) - ALL FOR LAURA (GB)	VENDOR	120000
CH C EXCEED AND EXCEL (AUS) - FRIGID (GB)	JOHN FERGUSON BS	120000
B C HOLY ROMAN EMPEROR (IRE) - MISS ROCHESTER (USA)	MAGUS EQUINE	120000
CH C BORN TO SEA (IRE) - EMINENCE GIFT (GB)	SACKVILLEDONALD	120000
PRINCESS ROCK (GB) B F FASTNET ROCK (AUS) - QUEEN OF MEAN (GB)	STROUD COLEMAN BS (P.S.)	120000
MUTAHAADY (IRE) B C ELZAAM (AUS) - MIDNIGHT OASIS (GB)	PETER & ROSS DOYLE BS	120000
BR F CAPE CROSS (IRE) - ANALYSIS (GB)	BLANDFORD BS	120000
CH C KENDARGENT (FR) - ISPANKA (GB)	KIR/SACKVILLEDONALD	120000
MUTAWAKKED (IRE) B C KODIAC (GB) - YOUR OPINION (IRE)	SHADWELL ESTATE COMPANY	120000
B C MASTERCRAFTSMAN (IRE) - CITY OF CITIES (IRE)	MAYFAIR SPECULATORS	120000
B C NATHANIEL (IRE) - FEARLESS FLYER (IRE)	VENDOR	120000
MUMAWAJ (GB) B C BATED BREATH (GB) - POLAR CIRCLE (USA)	SHADWELL ESTATE COMPANY	120000
TRAIS FLUORS (GB) B C DANSILI (GB) - TROIS LUNES (FR)	VENDOR	120000
B C OASIS DREAM (GB) - HERONETTA (GB)	GROVE STUD	115000
B C DREAM AHEAD (USA) - MALLADORE (IRE)	MARK CROSSMAN	115000
RED GUNNER (GB) B C OASIS DREAM (GB) - BLUE MAIDEN (GB)	HIGHFLYER BS	115000
BR C DARK ANGEL (IRE) - KARLIYSHA (IRE)	SUN BS	115000
B C BATED BREATH (GB) - IWUNDER (IRE)	JOHN & JAKE WARREN	115000
CH C CHOISIR (AUS) - DAMHSA LE CHEILE (IRE)	JOHN & JAKE WARREN	115000
B C MAYSON (GB) - HYPNOTIZE (GB)	AL SHAQAB RACING	115000
B C NATHANIEL (IRE) - DASH TO THE FRONT (IRE)	VENDOR	115000
B C DYLAN THOMAS (IRE) - INSOUMISE (IRE)	CORMAC MCCORMACK BS	115000
PERSEPHONE (IRE) B F KODIAC (GB) - DEMETER (USA)	PFI COLE	115000
B F MEDICEAN (GB) - PLUCKY (GB)	RABBAH BS	115000
B C ARCHIPENKO (USA) - ALMIRANTA (GB)	BBA IRELAND	115000
ZAIN STAR (IRE) B C SHAMARDAL (USA) - ASTROLOGIE (FR)	C GORDON-WATSON BS	110000
B C EXCEED AND EXCEL (AUS) - CLOUD'S END (GB)	C GORDON-WATSON BS	110000
B C EXCEED AND EXCEL (AUS) - ADONESQUE (IRE)	HUGO PALMER	110000
B/GR F MAKFI (GB) - MISS UNIVERSE (USA)	DAVID REDVERS BS	110000
B F DARK ANGEL (IRE) - LISA'S STRONG (IRE)	AL SHAQAB RACING	110000
AZALY (IRE) CH C SEPOY (AUS) - AZZOOM (IRE)	SHADWELL ESTATE COMPANY	110000
B C LOPE DE VEGA (IRE) - CARAVAN OF DREAMS (IRE)	BBA IRELAND	110000
B F MASTERCRAFTSMAN (IRE) - IN MY LIFE (IRE)	A C ELLIOTT, AGENT	110000
B C EXCEED AND EXCEL (AUS) - MUAAMARA (GB)	BBA IRELAND	110000
GR C DARK ANGEL (IRE) - DANCE CLUB (IRE)	SHADWELL ESTATE COMPANY	110000
EKHTIYAAR (GB) B C BATED BREATH (GB) - BAYJA (IRE)	SHADWELL ESTATE COMPANY	110000
B C HIGH CHAPARRAL (IRE) - MERRY JAUNT (USA)	C GORDON-WATSON BS	110000
B C KODIAC (GB) - QUICKSTYX (GB)	STEPHEN HILLEN BS	110000
CH C LOPE DE VEGA (IRE) - INCHBERRY (GB)	MAGUS EQUINE	110000
CH C TEOFILO (IRE) - JUNO MARLOWE (IRE)	AL SHAQAB / D FARRINGTON	110000
CH C ARCHIPENKO (USA) - HERE TO ETERNITY (USA)	KIR/SACKVILLEDONALD	110000
DAIRA BRIDGE (IRE) B C DREAM AHEAD (USA) - LADY LIVIUS (IRE)	ROGER P VARIAN	110000
MEYRICK (GB) B C HELMET (AUS) - ESTEEMED LADY (IRE)	GILL RICHARDSON BS	110000
B F DARK ANGEL (IRE) - TREMPJANE (IRE)	BLANDFORD BS	110000
B F DUTCH ART (GB) - CATS EYES (GB)	RABBAH BS	110000
DAIRA PRINCE (IRE) B C DUBAWI (IRE) - CHIANG MAI (IRE)	A & E BS	110000

Name and Breeding	Purchaser	Guineas
CH C SEPOY (AUS) - CHEYENNE STAR (IRE)	JOHN FERGUSON BS	110000
CH C MASTERCRAFTSMAN (IRE) - YAQOOTAH (USA)	C GORDON-WATSON BS	110000
B/GR F MASTERCRAFTSMAN (IRE) - DANI RIDGE (IRE)	VENDOR	110000
ENFOLDING (IRE) B C FASTNET ROCK (AUS) - ALTHEA ROSE (IRE)	SUZANNE ROBERTS	110000
B C HARBOUR WATCH (IRE) - ROCK LILY (GB)	DAVID REDVERS BS	110000
B C DUTCH ART (GB) - SLIEVE MISH (GB)	WJ GREDLEY	110000
B C INVINCIBLE SPIRIT (IRE) - HIDDEN BRIEF (GB)	AL SHAQAB RACING	105000
B C DUTCH ART (GB) - TRISKEL (GB)	VENDOR	105000
B C HOLY ROMAN EMPEROR (IRE) - BAYALIKA (IRE)	JOHN & JAKE WARREN	105000
B C DALAKHANI (IRE) - WAHYLAH (IRE)	ROGER P VARIAN	105000
B C MEDICEAN (GB) - DESPATCH (GB)	BLANDFORD BS	105000
CH C RIO DE LA PLATA (USA) - GUTTER PRESS (IRE)	WJ GREDLEY	105000
B G REDOUTE'S CHOICE (AUS) - SO SQUALLY (GER)	STROUD COLEMAN BS	105000
NATHANIA (GB) CH F NATHANIEL (IRE) - GLEN ROSIE (IRE)	HILLEN & HUGHES	105000
BR C INVINCIBLE SPIRIT (IRE) - BRIGHT SNOW (USA)	BBA IRELAND	105000
CH C EXCEED AND EXCEL (AUS) - SCREEN STAR (IRE)	MARK JOHNSTON RACING	105000
B F SHOWCASING (GB) - THANKFUL (GB)	VENDOR	105000
CH C MASTERCRAFTSMAN (IRE) - SWIRLING (IRE)	DAVID REDVERS BS	105000
B F SEA THE STARS (IRE) - BEHKIYRA (IRE)	NICK BRADLEY / JASON KELLY	105000
PERFECT IN PINK (GB) CH F RAVEN'S PASS (USA) - FASHION ROCKS (IRE)	GILL RICHARDSON BS	100000
B C DARK ANGEL (IRE) - BUGIE D'AMORE (GB)	JOHN FERGUSON BS	100000
CH F NEW APPROACH (IRE) - FANN (USA)	STROUD COLEMAN BS	100000
B C IFFRAAJ (GB) - CONSENSUS (IRE)	JOHN FERGUSON BS	100000
CH C MEDICEAN (GB) - DANEHILL DESTINY (GB)	JOHN FERGUSON BS	100000
B C FASTNET ROCK (AUS) - ARABIAN MIRAGE (GB)	MV MAGNIER	100000
B C DREAM AHEAD (USA) - ROYAL ALCHEMIST (GB)	RABBAH BS	100000
GR F DARK ANGEL (IRE) - SELFARA (GB)	GL MOORE RACING	100000
CH C DUTCH ART (GB) - ROTUNDA (GB)	SHADWELL ESTATE COMPANY	100000
B C LOPE DE VEGA (IRE) - OLYMPIC MEDAL (GB)	JOHN & JAKE WARREN	100000
CH F SIR PRANCEALOT (IRE) - FUERTA VENTURA (IRE)	DAVID REDVERS BS	100000
B F TEOFILO (IRE) - MADONNA DELL'ORTO (IRE)	BBA IRELAND	100000
CORAL SEA (GB) GR F EXCELEBRATION (IRE) - TROPICAL PARADISE (IRE)	SACKVILLEDONALD	100000
B C DANSILI (GB) - LOVE TO DANCE (IRE)	VENDOR	100000
B C REQUINTO (IRE) - SANDBOX TWO (IRE)	PETER & ROSS DOYLE BS	100000
BR F KYLLACHY (GB) - LIFE RELY (USA)	RABBAH BS	100000
B C KITTEN'S JOY (USA) - ITERATION (USA)	VENDOR	100000
B C NATHANIEL (IRE) - WALK ON BYE (IRE)	BADGERS BS (P.S.)	100000
B C SEA THE STARS (IRE) - HAPPY LAND (IRE)	RICHARD KNIGHT BS AGENT	100000
B C SO YOU THINK (NZ) - FABULOUS SPEED (USA)	STROUD COLEMAN BS	100000
ORIGINAL CHOICE (IRE) CH C DRAGON PULSE (IRE) - BELLE WATLING (IRE)	JOHN & JAKE WARREN	100000
B F BORN TO SEA (IRE) - TAWAAFUR (GB)	PETER & ROSS DOYLE BS	100000
GR C ARCHIPENKO (USA) - ALVARITA (GB)	JEREMY BRUMMITT	100000
MOTAHASSEN (IRE) BR C LONHRO (AUS) - JOURNALIST (IRE)	SHADWELL ESTATE COMPANY	100000
ELERFAAN (IRE) B C SHAMARDAL (USA) - GORBAND (USA)	SHADWELL ESTATE COMPANY	100000
B C HELMET (AUS) - CAUSEWAY SONG (USA)	AL SHAQAB RACING / DOYLE	100000
B F NATHANIEL (IRE) - WHAZZAT (GB)	VENDOR	100000
ENFORCING (IRE) B C CANFORD CLIFFS (IRE) - BLACK MASCARA (IRE)	SUZANNE ROBERTS	100000
CH F NEW APPROACH (IRE) - WAKE ME UP (IRE)	VENDOR	100000
B F SEPOY (AUS) - SAMDANIYA (GB)	BLANDFORD BS	100000
ALQALSAR (IRE) CH C BAHAMIAN BOUNTY (GB) - WITH COLOUR (GB)	SHADWELL ESTATE COMPANY	100000
MAALZOOM (IRE) CH C RAVEN'S PASS - DARRFONAH (IRE)	SHADWELL ESTATE COMPANY	100000
CH C KITTEN'S JOY (USA) - QUEEN'S CAUSEWAY (USA)	SHADWELL ESTATE COMPANY	100000
B F HIGH CHAPARRAL (IRE) - MIXED BLESSING (GB)	ROB SPEERS	100000
B C SEPOY (AUS) - ZANZIBAR (IRE)	HILLEN & HUGHES	100000
B C ACCLAMATION (GB) - MISS HAWAI (FR)	HYPHEN BS	100000
B F LOPE DE VEGA (IRE) - PARDOVEN (IRE)	BBA IRELAND	100000
MOUNTAIN ANGEL (IRE) B C DARK ANGEL (IRE) - FANCIFUL DANCER (GB)	ANDREW SIME	100000
B C TEOFILO (IRE) - TWICE THE EASE (GB)	OLIVER ST LAWRENCE BS	100000
CH C DUTCH ART (GB) - ISRAAR (GB)	JOHN & JAKE WARREN	100000
B F EXCEED AND EXCEL (AUS) - NARUKO (USA)	DEMI O'BYRNE	100000
B C BORN TO SEA (IRE) - DUQUESA (IRE)	VENDOR	98000
B F INVINCIBLE SPIRIT (IRE) - SWEET STREAM (ITY)	A & K BS	97000

HIGH-PRICED YEARLINGS OF 2015 AT GOFFS
The following yearlings realised 68,000 euros and over at Goffs Sales in 2015:-

Name and Breeding	Purchaser	Euros
TOCCO D'AMORE (IRE) B F RAVEN'S PASS (USA) - SPIRIT OF TARA (IRE)	MOYGLARE STUD FARM	2000000
B F FRANKEL (GB) - ALEXANDER GOLDRUN (IRE)	CHINA HORSE CLUB	1700000
B C GALILEO (IRE) - SENT FROM HEAVEN (IRE)	DAVID REDVERS/STEVE PARKIN	1200000
B C GALILEO (IRE) - STARLIT SANDS (GB)	OLIVER ST LAWRENCE BS	1050000
B C INVINCIBLE SPIRIT (IRE) - PRIMA LUCE (IRE)	CHINA HORSE CLUB	580000
B F NEW APPROACH (IRE) - HYMN OF THE DAWN (USA)	BBA IRELAND	480000
JUMIRA PRINCE (IRE) CH C EXCEED AND EXCEL (AUS) - AOIFE ALAINN (IRE)	ROGER VARIAN	400000
ENTANGLING (IRE) B C FASTNET ROCK (AUS) - QUESTION TIMES (GB)	S A ROBERTS	380000
TIRANIA (GB) B F PIVOTAL (GB) - TIRIANA (GB)	BRIAN GRASSICK BS	370000
PINCHECK (IRE) B C INVINCIBLE SPIRIT (IRE) - ARTY CRAFTY (USA)	ANGLIA BS	370000
B F HOLY ROMAN EMPEROR (IRE) - ANOTHER STORM (USA)	NERSES	360000
BR C DREAM AHEAD (USA) - LAKE MOON (GB)	JOHN FERGUSON	360000
JAAZEM (IRE) B C DARK ANGEL (IRE) - MISS INDIGO (GB)	SHADWELL ESTATE COMPANY	360000
SORELLE DELLE ROSE (IRE) GR F DARK ANGEL (IRE) - KELSEY ROSE (IRE)	MOYGLARE STUD FARM	350000
B F INVINCIBLE SPIRIT (IRE) - LETHAL QUALITY (USA)	PETER & ROSS DOYLE	350000
B C EXCELEBRATION (IRE) - DANCE AVENUE (IRE)	SACKVILLE DONALD	340000
B C OASIS DREAM (GB) - SANJIDA (IRE)	HKJC	320000
CH C BORN TO SEA (IRE) - MASKAYA (IRE)	SACKVILLE DONALD	320000
B F GALILEO (IRE) - DANELETA (IRE)	FEDERICO BARBERINI	300000
B C ACCLAMATION (GB) - MOMENT JUSTE (GB)	HKJC	300000
B F DREAM AHEAD (USA) - LOVE AND LAUGHTER (IRE)	CHINA HORSE CLUB	290000
ESCOBAR (IRE) B C FAMOUS NAME (GB) - SAYING GRACE (IRE)	AMANDA SKIFFINGTON	280000
B F ACCLAMATION (GB) - ROO (GB)	CHINA HORSE CLUB	280000
B F LAWMAN (FR) - BREAK TIME (GB)	SHAWN DUGAN, AGENT	270000
B C GALILEO (IRE) - HEALING MUSIC (IRE)	TOWNLEY HALL BS LTD	260000
B C TEOFILO (IRE) - MILLION SPIRITS (IRE)	PETER & ROSS DOYLE	260000
CH C GALILEO (IRE) - PALE MOON RISING (IRE)	CHINA HORSE CLUB	260000
B F LONHRO (AUS) - AQUARIUS STAR (IRE)	PETER & ROSS DOYLE	250000
B C GALILEO (IRE) - FLAMES (GB)	CHINA HORSE CLUB	250000
B C FASTNET ROCK (AUS) - ANIARNOTA (IRE)	HKJC	240000
B C EXCELEBRATION (IRE) - QUIRITIS (GB)	GEORGE MOORE BS	220000
B C INVINCIBLE SPIRIT (IRE) - GAZEBO (GB)	CHINA HORSE CLUB	220000
B F GALILEO (IRE) - LA SYLVIA (IRE)	VENDOR	220000
CH F ZOFFANY (IRE) - JABROOT (IRE)	SHAWN DUGAN, AGENT	210000
WHITE MISCHIEF (IRE) GR F DARK ANGEL (IRE) - GALILEO'S STAR (IRE)	PETER & ROSS DOYLE	200000
B F FASTNET ROCK (AUS) - KIYRA WELLS (IRE)	FIONA SHAW	200000
B G HOLY ROMAN EMPEROR (IRE) - LAPLAND (FR)	HKJC	200000
B C ZOFFANY (IRE) - SNOWY PEAK (GB)	STEPHEN HILLEN	200000
CH F DUTCH ART (GB) - REQUEJADA (USA)	WILLIAM HAGGAS	200000
FURUD (IRE) GR C ZEBEDEE (GB) - KAHIRA (IRE)	SHADWELL ESTATE COMPANY	200000
TAI HANG DRAGON (IRE) B F TAMAYUZ (GB) - GIVE A WHISTLE (IRE)	SACKVILLE DONALD	200000
FIDAAHA (IRE) CH F NEW APPROACH (IRE) - CEIST EILE (IRE)	SHADWELL ESTATE COMPANY	200000
B F GALILEO (IRE) - DEVOTED TO YOU (IRE)	GATEWOOD BELL	200000
B C SHAMARDAL (USA) - NENUPHAR (IRE)	VENDOR	195000
B C FRANKEL (GB) - DRIFTING (IRE)	VENDOR	190000
B C NATHANIEL (IRE) - BAHAMA SPIRIT (IRE)	JOHN FERGUSON	190000
B F MASTERCRAFTSMAN (IRE) - ALLEGRINA (IRE)	SHAWN DUGAN, AGENT	180000
B/BR C LONHRO (AUS) - VENETIAN CAUSEWAY (USA)	JOHN FERGUSON	180000
B F ACCLAMATION (GB) - BIKINI BABE (IRE)	JOHN FERGUSON	180000
B F HIGH CHAPARRAL (IRE) - JANOUBI (GB)	FORM BS	170000
B C ZOFFANY (IRE) - KNYSNA (IRE)	TONY NERSES	160000
BR F KODIAC (GB) - MARASEM (GB)	VENDOR	160000
GR F INVINCIBLE SPIRIT (IRE) - COOLNAGREE (IRE)	CRISPIN DE MOUBRAY	160000
BR F DARK ANGEL (IRE) - TARAEFF (IRE)	BBA IRELAND	160000
B C POET'S VOICE (GB) - DUNIATTY (GB)	JOHN FERGUSON	160000
B C RIP VAN WINKLE (IRE) - TROPICAL LADY (IRE)	FEDERICO BARBERINI	160000
B F ACCLAMATION (GB) - RISING WIND (GB)	ECURIE DES MONCEAUX	160000
B ROCK OF GIBRALTAR (IRE) - TEDARSHANA (GB)	JOHN & JAKE WARREN	155000
ON HER TOES (IRE) B F KODIAC (GB) - DANCING JEST (IRE)	CHEVELEY PARK STUD	155000
B C ZOFFANY (IRE) - GEMS (GB)	PETER & ROSS DOYLE	150000
CH C NEW APPROACH (IRE) - DO THE HONOURS (IRE)	JOHN FERGUSON	150000
B C POWER (GB) - AMBER NECTAR (IRE)	M V MAGNIER	150000
B F HELMET (AUS) - ZOUMIE (IRE)	BBA IRELAND	150000
B F INVINCIBLE SPIRIT (IRE) - QUEEN OF TARA (IRE)	AMANDA SKIFFINGTON	150000
B C EXCELEBRATION (IRE) - SOMETHING EXCITING (GB)	AMANDA SKIFFINGTON	150000
B C DREAM AHEAD (USA) - EXPECTATION (IRE)	HIGHFIELD FARM LLP	145000
B/BR C KITTEN'S JOY (USA) - DEAREST GIRL (IRE)	PETER & ROSS DOYLE	145000
B F SHAMARDAL (USA) - SCARLET BELLE (GB)	EQUINE ASSOCIATES	145000

Name and Breeding	Purchaser	Euros
BORTHWEN (IRE) B F LAWMAN (FR) - APTICANTI (USA)	BBA IRELAND	140000
B F DUTCH ART (GB) - THROUGH THE FOREST (USA)	BBA IRELAND	140000
B/GR C DARK ANGEL (IRE) - SODASHY (IRE)	JOHN FERGUSON	140000
MUSTARRID (IRE) BR C ELZAAM (AUS) - SYMBOL OF PEACE (IRE)	SHADWELL ESTATE COMPANY	140000
CAPTAIN HAWK (GB) B C ACCLAMATION (GB) - VINTAGE GARDENIA (GB)	BBA IRELAND	140000
GIOVANNI ACUTO (GB) GR C REDOUTE'S CHOICE (AUS) - ALLA SPERANZA (GB)	PETER & ROSS DOYLE	140000
CH F NATHANIEL (IRE) - LADY AMIRA (USA)	JOHN & JAKE WARREN	135000
B F AZAMOUR (IRE) - KINCOB (USA)	BBA IRELAND	130000
B C CANFORD CLIFFS (IRE) - CAN DANCE (GB)	HUGO MERRY BS	130000
AJAMAN KING (IRE) CH C LOPE DE VEGA (IRE) - THIRD DIMENSION (FR)	ROGER VARIAN	130000
B F NATHANIEL (IRE) - QUAD'S MELODY (IRE)	FOZZY STACK	130000
B F HARBOUR WATCH (IRE) - CZARNA ROZA (GB)	FORM BS	130000
B C FASTNET ROCK (AUS) - GIFT FROM HEAVEN (IRE)	FIONA SHAW, AGENT	130000
CH C IFFRAAJ (GB) - ANAMARKA (GB)	JOHN FERGUSON	130000
GR C FRANKEL (GB) - DOOKUS (IRE)	MARK JOHNSTON RACING	130000
B F MUNNINGS (USA) - BROCATELLE (GB)	CHINA HORSE CLUB	130000
AQUAVIT (IRE) B C DREAM AHEAD (USA) - BAILEYS GLEAM (GB)	HARRIET JELLETT	130000
B F KODIAC (GB) - HEMARIS (IRE)	DAVID REDVERS	125000
B C KODIAC (GB) - MISTRESS MARINA (AUS)	SACKVILLE DONALD	125000
B C HARBOUR WATCH (IRE) - BLUE BEACON (GB)	DAVID REDVERS	125000
B C HENRYTHENAVIGATOR (USA) - SILVER STAR (GB)	STEPHEN HILLEN	125000
B F ZOFFANY (IRE) - SMALL SACRIFICE (IRE)	GROVE STUD	125000
CRYPTONITE (IRE) BR C DARK ANGEL (IRE) - BOWNESS (GB)	C GORDON-WATSON BS	120000
MAGILLEN (IRE) CH C LOPE DE VEGA (IRE) - LADY NATILDA (GB)	BBA IRELAND	120000
B F ROCK OF GIBRALTAR (IRE) - ZALAIYMA (FR)	M V MAGNIER	120000
B C SEA THE STARS (IRE) - PISA NO TIFFANY (USA)	VENDOR	120000
B C DRAGON PULSE (IRE) - EMSIYAH (GB)	JEREMY NOSEDA RACING LTD	120000
B C SEPOY (AUS) - KOURNIKOVA (SAF)	SACKVILLE DONALD	120000
B C BORN TO SEA (IRE) - HALLOWED PARK (IRE)	SACKVILLE DONALD	115000
B C INVINCIBLE SPIRIT (IRE) - CABARET (IRE)	BBA IRELAND	115000
B F HIGH CHAPARRAL (IRE) - URSULA MINOR (IRE)	FORM BS	110000
B F SHAMARDAL (USA) - UMSEYAT (USA)	DAVID REDVERS	110000
ENVISAGING (IRE) B C ZOFFANY (IRE) - STAR OF STARS (IRE)	S A ROBERTS	110000
B F DARK ANGEL (IRE) - RUMLINE (GB)	JOHN FERGUSON	110000
B F ACCLAMATION (GB) - CRYSTAL VIEW (IRE)	BBA IRELAND	110000
JASHMA (IRE) B C POWER (GB) - DAGANYA (IRE)	HILLEN & HUGHES	110000
B F HIGH CHAPARRAL (IRE) - TAMAZUG (GB)	DAVID WACHMAN	110000
B F DRAGON PULSE (IRE) - SILVER ARROW (USA)	VENDOR	110000
STARLIGHT ROMANCE (IRE) B F EXCELEBRATION (IRE) - TAKIZADA (IRE)	NORMAN STEEL	110000
B C BORN TO SEA (IRE) - THREE DAYS IN MAY (GB)	DAVID REDVERS	105000
CH C POWER (GB) - ARPEGE (IRE)	SACKVILLE DONALD	105000
LYNIQUE (IRE) CH F DYLAN THOMAS (IRE) - DANSE GRECQUE (IRE)	BRIAN GRASSICK BS	100000
MUCHO APPLAUSE (IRE) B C ACCLAMATION (GB) - PEDIMENT (GB)	ANDREW BALDING	100000
B F INVINCIBLE SPIRIT (IRE) - BY INVITATION (IRE)	JAMIE OSBORNE	100000
CH F DREAM AHEAD (USA) - CHOOSE ME (IRE)	SUZANNE ROBERTS	100000
B F EXCELEBRATION (IRE) - TRAGIC MOMENT (USA)	FIONA SHAW	100000
CH F SIR PRANCEALOT (IRE) - DANETIME OUT (IRE)	BBA IRELAND	100000
B/GR F MASTERCRAFTSMAN (IRE) - CANDLEHILL GIRL (IRE)	GILL RICHARDSON B/S LTD	100000
CH F DUTCH ART (GB) - PALANCA (GB)	MICHAEL O'CALLAGHAN	100000
GR C MASTERCRAFTSMAN (IRE) - EASTERN APPEAL (IRE)	BBA IRELAND	100000
TEXTURED (IRE) B F DARK ANGEL (IRE) - TIMBRE (GB)	CHEVELEY PARK STUD	100000
CH C TAMAYUZ (GB) - RAPID RANSOM (USA)	SACKVILLE DONALD	100000
B F EXCEED AND EXCEL (AUS) - NARUKO (USA)	FORM BS	100000
TWENTY TIMES (IRE) B F DREAM AHEAD (USA) - MAD EXISTENCE (IRE)	BADGERS / HUGHES	100000
BIRDS OF PREY (IRE) B C SIR PRANCEALOT (IRE) - CUTE (GB)	SACKVILLE DONALD	100000
PARYS MOUNTAIN (IRE) GR C DARK ANGEL (IRE) - MUZDAAN (IRE)	BBA IRELAND	100000
CH F SEA THE STARS (IRE) - LADY SLIPPERS (IRE)	SUNDERLAND HOLDING INC	100000
B C HOLY ROMAN EMPEROR (IRE) - SALINIA (IRE)	SACKVILLE DONALD	100000
B F POWER (GB) - RAVISH (GB)	BBA IRELAND	100000
SHERBERT (GB) B F POWER (GB) - ORIGINAL (GB)	SACKVILLE DONALD	95000
CH F TEOFILO (IRE) - HEN NIGHT (IRE)	WILLIE MCCREERY	95000
RAINBOW CHIMES (IRE) B F GALILEO (IRE) - CHIMING (IRE)	VENDOR	95000
B F SIR PRANCEALOT (IRE) - PEACE SUMMIT (IRE)	DERMOT FARRINGTON	95000
B C HOLY ROMAN EMPEROR (IRE) - CHALLOW HILLS (USA)	GEORGE MOORE BS	95000
B F EQUIANO (FR) - SENTA'S DREAM (GB)	BLANDFORD BS	92000
CH F ARCANO (IRE) - COVER GIRL (IRE)	M V MAGNIER	90000
B F SO YOU THINK (NZ) - GERMANE (GB)	J MCKEEVER	90000
B F NEW APPROACH (IRE) - OUI SAY OUI (IRE)	VENDOR	90000
BUCCANEERS COVE (IRE) B C FOOTSTEPSINTHESAND (GB) - PRIMISSIMA (GER)	NORMAN STEEL	90000
B F TEOFILO (IRE) - DEEP WINTER (GB)	GATEWOOD BELL	90000
B F FASTNET ROCK (AUS) - TRISHULI (GB)	FORM BS	90000

Name and Breeding	Purchaser	Euros
B C DUTCH ART (GB) - SULARINA (IRE)	SIMON CHRISTIAN	90000
B C CAPE CROSS (IRE) - CHANTILLY PEARL (USA)	JOHN FERGUSON	90000
CH F SHAMARDAL (USA) - KATLA (IRE)	WILLIE MCCREERY	90000
B/BR C HAT TRICK (JPN) - SUMMER CRUISE (USA)	HFTB RACING AGENCY	90000
B C LAWMAN (FR) - VIZ (IRE)	HUGO MERRY BS	90000
B C DARK ANGEL (IRE) - BEAN UASAL (IRE)	HIGHFIELD FARM LLP	90000
CH C DUTCH ART (GB) - INTIMACY (IRE)	PETER & ROSS DOYLE	90000
B C BORN TO SEA (IRE) - CHANTER (GB)	J RAILTON	90000
B C CANFORD CLIFFS (IRE) - COTE QUEST (USA)	CHINA HORSE CLUB	87000
KREB'S CYCLE (IRE) CH C HELMET (AUS) - LA NOE (GB)	PETER & ROSS DOYLE	85000
B C FAST COMPANY (IRE) - NOVA TOR (IRE)	MICHAEL O'CALLAGHAN	85000
GR C MASTERCRAFTSMAN (IRE) - KINIGI (IRE)	JAMES FANSHAWE	85000
B C CANFORD CLIFFS (IRE) - GALI GALI (IRE)	SYLVESTER KIRK	85000
B C DUTCH ART (GB) - BRAZILIAN SPIRIT (IRE)	JUNJI KAWAI	85000
PACO PUNCH (IRE) B C PACO BOY (IRE) - TRILEMMA (GB)	PETER & ROSS DOYLE	85000
B C EXCELEBRATION (IRE) - OUT OF THANKS (IRE)	BBA (IRELAND)	85000
THE LAST LION (IRE) B C CHOISIR (AUS) - MALA MALA (IRE)	MARK JOHNSTON RACING	82000
B C IFFRAAJ (GB) - EFFIGE (IRE)	BBA (IRELAND)	80000
BR F SAYIF (IRE) - LOUGH MEWIN (IRE)	RICHARD FRISBY (P.S.)	80000
CH F SEA THE STARS (IRE) - CRIMPHILL (IRE)	VENDOR	80000
B C HARBOUR WATCH (IRE) - RENOWNED (IRE)	BBA IRELAND	80000
B F INVINCIBLE SPIRIT (IRE) - FRESH MINT (IRE)	VENDOR	80000
B C IFFRAAJ (GB) - DISTINGUISH (IRE)	GRANGEBARRY	80000
BR C DARK ANGEL (IRE) - VISUAL ELEMENT (USA)	B O'RYAN/K DALGLEISH	80000
B C HARBOUR WATCH (IRE) - SPRING FASHION (IRE)	B O'RYAN/K DALGLEISH	80000
B C THE FACTOR (USA) - JIVE TALK (USA)	C GORDON-WATSON BS	80000
B C BORN TO SEA (IRE) - LA BELLE MAISON (IRE)	KARL BURKE	80000
B C SIR PRANCEALOT (IRE) - DREAM DATE (IRE)	B O'RYAN	80000
B F EXCEED AND EXCEL (AUS) - PRIVALOVA (IRE)	SALCEY FOREST STUD	80000
GR C DARK ANGEL (IRE) - SIXFIELDS FLYER (IRE)	CLIVE COX RACING	80000
B C CANFORD CLIFFS (IRE) - KAABA (GB)	HAJIME SATOMI	80000
B C ZOFFANY (IRE) - CORKLING (IRE)	MPH RACING	80000
B C CASAMENTO (IRE) - SHEBA FIVE (USA)	J RAILTON	80000
GUARDIA SVIZZERA (IRE) B C HOLY ROMAN EMPEROR (IRE) - WINGED HARRIET (IRE)	SACKVILLE DONALD	78000
QUEEN NEYLA (IRE) CH F BORN TO SEA (IRE) - STRAVINA (GER)	MAB AGENCY	78000
GIULIA (IRE) B F TEOFILO (IRE) - YES OH YES (USA)	SEELAND INTERNATIONAL (P.S.)	75000
OLLY'S FOLLY (GB) B C POET'S VOICE (GB) - PEARL DIVA (IRE)	JOHN OXX	75000
B C RODERIC O'CONNOR (IRE) - MEON MIX (GB)	PETER & ROSS DOYLE	75000
DRAKE PASSAGE (IRE) CH C DANDY MAN (IRE) - PIECE UNIQUE (GB)	SACKVILLE DONALD	75000
SPONGIE CAKE (IRE) B F LAWMAN (FR) - BELGIQUE (IRE)	PETER & ROSS DOYLE	75000
B C KODIAC (GB) - ROISIN'S STAR (IRE)	FEDERICO BARBERINI	75000
B C KODIAC (GB) - DEFINED FEATURE (IRE)	BBA IRELAND	75000
PERFORMING (IRE) CH C SHOWCASING (GB) - MANSIYA (GB)	RICHARD KNIGHT B/S / QUINN	75000
BE BE KING (IRE) B C BATED BREATH (GB) - CHAMPION PLACE (GB)	SACKVILLE DONALD	75000
CH F SHOWCASING (GB) - TAROT CARD (GB)	JEREMY BRUMMITT	75000
B F POUR MOI (IRE) - DOUBLE GREEN (IRE)	RIC WYLIE BS	75000
CH F DRAGON PULSE (IRE) - FREE LANCE (IRE)	DAVID REDVERS	75000
B F HOLY ROMAN EMPEROR (IRE) - SHARAPOVA (IRE)	D K RACING	75000
RUBIESNPEARLS (GB) B F KYLLACHY (GB) - PIECE OF CAKE (GB)	NORMAN STEEL	75000
B C ACCLAMATION (GB) - ANAM ALLTA (IRE)	VENDOR	72000
B C KODIAC (GB) - CUCA VELA (USA)	BRIGHT SIDE RACING	72000
GR F DARK ANGEL (IRE) - LA CHASSOTTE (FR)	A O'RYAN/RICHARD FAHEY	72000
B C HOLY ROMAN EMPEROR (IRE) - ROMIE'S KASTETT (GER)	JOSEPH O'BRIEN	70000
B C PIVOTAL (GB) - HIGHTIME HEROINE (IRE)	CORMAC MCCORMACK BS	70000
IL SICARIO (IRE) B C ZEBEDEE (GB) - STARRING (FR)	MARK JOHNSTON RACING	70000
B F TEOFILO (IRE) - PARAPHERNALIA (IRE)	DAVID WACHMAN	70000
BR F CAPE CROSS (IRE) - MAYBE GRACE (IRE)	JOHNNY MURTAGH	70000
B/BR C HAT TRICK (JPN) - DIVA DYNA (USA)	HFTB RACING AGENCY	70000
B F ACCLAMATION (GB) - EVENING FROST (IRE)	JAPAN HEALTH SUMMIT INC	70000
B C HOLY ROMAN EMPEROR (IRE) - TAKING LIBERTIES (IRE)	SHANE DONOHOE	70000
B C POWER (GB) - LE MONTRACHET (GB)	PETER & ROSS DOYLE	70000
CHEERFILLY (IRE) BR F EXCELEBRATION (IRE) - CLASSIC REMARK (IRE)	SACKVILLE DONALD	70000
ROYAL BLUE CARAVEL (IRE) B F HENRYTHENAVIGATOR (USA) - HOLLY BLUE (GB)	VENDOR	68000

HIGH-PRICED YEARLINGS OF 2015 AT DONCASTER

The following yearlings realised 41,904 Guineas and over at Doncaster Sales in 2015:-

Name and Breeding	Purchaser	Guineas
B F PACO BOY (IRE) - GALICUIX (GB)	T NERSES	266666
B C DARK ANGEL (IRE) - LAYLA JAMIL (IRE)	JOHN FERGUSON BS	257142
B C PIVOTAL (GB) - LORETO (IRE)	D REDVERS	238095
GR C DARK ANGEL (IRE) - GOLDEN ROSIE (IRE)	JOHN FERGUSON BS	228571
SHAWAAMEKH (GB) B C BORN TO SEA (IRE) - FRANCES STUART (IRE)	SHADWELL ESTATE CO	219047
B C KODIAC (GB) - HANNAH GREELEY (USA)	JOHN FERGUSON BS	209523
SUBHAAN (GB) CH C DUTCH ART (GB) - MAMMA MORTON (IRE)	SHADWELL ESTATE CO	195238
CH G CASAMENTO (IRE) - THREE TIMES (GB)	HKJC	190476
RAAWY (GB) B C DUTCH ART (GB) - AGE OF CHIVALRY (IRE)	SHADWELL ESTATE CO	180952
MURAAQEB (GB) B C NATHANIEL (IRE) - TESARY (GB)	SHADWELL ESTATE CO	180952
SAWLAAT (IRE) GR C CLODOVIL (IRE) - JAYWICK (UAE)	PETER & ROSS DOYLE BS	176190
GR F DARK ANGEL (IRE) - BUN PENNY (GB)	PETER & ROSS DOYLE BS	171428
WAQAAS (GB) B C SHOWCASING (GB) - RED MISCHIEF (IRE)	SHADWELL ESTATE CO	161904
THAMMIN (GB) B C DARK ANGEL (IRE) - GIMME SOME LOVIN (GB)	SHADWELL ESTATE CO	161904
B C SEPOY (AUS) - PERSARIO (GB)	T NERSES	152380
B C NATHANIEL (IRE) - RONALDSAY (GB)	HOWSON & HOULDSWORTH BS	152380
B C CANFORD CLIFFS (IRE) - MAGENA (USA)	A C ELLOI	142857
LOTHARIO (GB) GR C DARK ANGEL (IRE) - KISSES FOR ME (IRE)	PETER & ROSS DOYLE BS	142857
B C MAYSON (GB) - PIOUS (GB)	HIGHFIELD FARM	142857
CH C CASAMENTO (IRE) - OHIYESA (IRE)	BLANDFORD BS	133333
TAWAAFEEJ (IRE) GR C ZEBEDEE (GB) - ABSOLUTELY COOL (IRE)	SHADWELL ESTATE CO	133333
RUBENS DREAM (GB) CH C DUTCH ART (GB) - APACE (IRE)	HOWSON & HOULDSWORTH BS	133333
CH C POET'S VOICE (GB) - HUNTER'S FORTUNE (GB)	JOHN FERGUSON BS	133333
GR C DARK ANGEL (IRE) - MARSEILLE EXPRESS (USA)	HKJC	123809
B F ZOFFANY (IRE) - CATERINA DI CESI (GB)	F BARBERINI	119047
B C BAHAMIAN BOUNTY (GB) - TAHTHEEB (IRE)	PETER & ROSS DOYLE BS	119047
WUROOD (GB) GR F DARK ANGEL (IRE) - KEY ROSE (IRE)	SHADWELL ESTATE CO	119047
GR C DARK ANGEL (IRE) - HEEBY JEEBY (GB)	JOHN FERGUSON BS	104761
TAWALEEF (IRE) B C BAHAMIAN BOUNTY (GB) - LITERACY (USA)	SHADWELL ESTATE CO	100000
SOQRAT (GB) B C PACO BOY (IRE) - TAMARA MOON (IRE)	SHADWELL ESTATE CO	95238
MABAADY (GB) B C BATED BREATH (GB) - FIFTY (IRE)	SHADWELL ESTATE CO	95238
ALROOM (IRE) B C KODIAC (GB) - BEVERLEY MACCA (GB)	SHADWELL ESTATE CO	87619
TADWEEN (IRE) B C TAGULA (IRE) - STAINED GLASS (GB)	PETER & ROSS DOYLE BS	85714
B F DANDY MAN (IRE) - GALA STYLE (IRE)	T NERSES	80952
CH C DANDY MAN (IRE) - ZANIDA (IRE)	K BURKE	80952
B C DUTCH ART (GB) - AMICABLE TERMS (GB)	HIGHFIELD FARM	78095
B C MAYSON (GB) - CARDRONA (GB)	HIGHFIELD FARM	78095
CARAMURU (IRE) B C CASAMENTO (IRE) - ZAYNABA (IRE)	PETER & ROSS DOYLE BS	76190
B F DARK ANGEL (IRE) - KAY ES JAY (FR)	HUGO MERRY BS	76190
B F DRAGON PULSE (IRE) - QUEEN OF STARS (USA)	PETER & ROSS DOYLE BS	76190
B F ROCK OF GIBRALTAR (IRE) - MURAVKA (IRE)	MARK JOHNSTON RACING	76190
LEGENDARY LUNCH (IRE) CH C DRAGON PULSE (IRE) - TAALLUF (USA)	PETER & ROSS DOYLE BS	74285
B F ROYAL APPLAUSE (GB) - VIRGINIA HALL (GB)	J FOLEY	73333
B C BATED BREATH (GB) - CAPISTRANO DAY (USA)	BRIAN ELLISON RACING	72380
MONOSHKA (IRE) B C KODIAC (GB) - COASTAL WATERS (GB)	PETER & ROSS DOYLE BS	71428
COMPUTABLE (GB) CH C COMPTON PLACE (GB) - KUMMEL EXCESS (IRE)	T EASTERBY	71428
B C CHOISIR (AUS) - GRANDEL (GB)	BBA (IRELAND)	71428
STREET JAZZ (GB) B F ACCLAMATION (GB) - WAKE UP CALL (GB)	COOL SILK PARTNERSHIP	71428
B C COMPTON PLACE (GB) - HAKURAA (IRE)	A SKIFFINGTON	71428
TANBEEH (IRE) B C APPROVE (GB) - WHITE DAFFODIL (IRE)	SHADWELL ESTATE CO	68571
GR F CLODOVIL (IRE) - KILLINALLAN (GB)	STROUD COLEMAN BS	68571
BUSKIN RIVER (IRE) B C KODIAC (GB) - MISS SMILLA (GB)	PETER & ROSS DOYLE BS	68571
BR F BATED BREATH (GB) - DIXEY (GB)	BBA (IRELAND)	66666
GR F DARK ANGEL (IRE) - FIRST LADY (IRE)	HILLEN & BAKER	66666
CH C BAHAMIAN BOUNTY (GB) - ROYAL PUNCH (GB)	KERN LILLINGSTON	66666
HIPPOCAMPUS (IRE) B C BORN TO SEA (IRE) - TOLZEY (USA)	PETER & ROSS DOYLE BS	66666
B C EXCELEBRATION (IRE) - ALINA (IRE)	PETER & ROSS DOYLE BS	66666
CH C BAHAMIAN BOUNTY (GB) - ALIANTE (GB)	SACKVILLEDONALD	66666
OUR GRETA (GB) GR F EXCHANGE RATE (USA) - ACADEMICIENNE (CAN)	STROUD COLEMAN BS	66666
CH C CAMACHO (GB) - OBSESSIVE SECRET (USA)	B ELLISON	66666
B/BR C BATED BREATH (GB) - SALMON ROSE (IRE)	PETER & ROSS DOYLE BS	64761
CIRCULATE (GB) B F DUTCH ART (GB) - ROYAL WHISPER (GB)	CHEVELEY PARK STUD	64761
B C CASAMENTO (IRE) - COMPTON GIRL (GB)	J LEVINS	62857
HOT NATURED (IRE) B F CANFORD CLIFFS (IRE) - TEDDY BEARS PICNIC (GB)	SALCEY FOREST STUD	61904
GR F ZEBEDEE (GB) - LADY OF ROHAN (GB)	BBA (IRELAND)	61904
B C BORN TO SEA (IRE) - ALKHAWARAH (USA)	WILL EDMEADES BS	61904
B C REQUINTO (IRE) - ROYAL ESTEEM (GB)	A SKIFFINGTON	61904
B F NATHANIEL (IRE) - IMPRESSIBLE (GB)	VENDOR	61904

Name and Breeding	Purchaser	Guineas
B C LAWMAN (FR) - FRENCH FERN (IRE)	PETER & ROSS DOYLE BS	59047
B/GR C KODIAC (GB) - BYSSHE (GB)	CHURCH FARM	59047
DUSKY MAID (IRE) B F DARK ANGEL (IRE) - DREAM SCAPE (GB)	A & E BS	59047
B F BORN TO SEA (IRE) - SHAHMINA (IRE)	PETER & ROSS DOYLE BS	59047
B F HOLY ROMAN EMPEROR (IRE) - SILK DRESS (IRE)	D WACHMAN	59047
B F KODIAC (GB) - ALEXANDER WONDER (IRE)	A SKIFFINGTON	57142
BAHAMAS (IRE) B C RIP VAN WINKLE (IRE) - GWYLLION (USA)	J LLOYD	57142
SUKOOT (IRE) CH C SIR PRANCEALOT (IRE) - YANDINA (IRE)	SHADWELL ESTATE CO	57142
B C ZOFFANY (IRE) - CHELSEY JAYNE (IRE)	M V MAGNIER	57142
SWEET SIENNA (GB) CH F HARBOUR WATCH (IRE) - LOOK BUSY (IRE)	PETER & ROSS DOYLE BS	57142
DEVIL'S BRIDGE (IRE) B C CASAMENTO (IRE) - CANTALOUPE (GB)	PETER & ROSS DOYLE BS	55238
B F ACCLAMATION (GB) - MARVADA (IRE)	PETER & ROSS DOYLE BS	55238
JET SETTER (IRE) CH C FAST COMPANY (IRE) - RAVEN ONE (IRE)	SAM SANGSTER BS	54285
CH C INTIKHAB (USA) - FANTASTIC OPINION (IRE)	B O'RYAN	52380
B F KODIAC (GB) - WHEN NOT IFF (IRE)	D REDVERS	52380
B F FASTNET ROCK (AUS) - THE THRILL IS GONE (GB)	D REDVERS	52380
B F CANFORD CLIFFS - BRIERY (IRE)	PETER & ROSS DOYLE BS	51428
FULL INTENTION (GB) B C SHOWCASING (GB) - MY DELIRIUM (GB)	SACKVILLEDONALD	51428
CH C HARBOUR WATCH (IRE) - EASTERN LILY (USA)	D REDVERS	49523
B F ROYAL APPLAUSE (GB) - DUBAI BOUNTY (GB)	D BROWN	49523
B C PASTORAL PURSUITS (GB) - AMALFI (IRE)	PETER & ROSS DOYLE BS	49523
GR F DARK ANGEL (IRE) - MAHAAZEN (IRE)	A & E BS	49523
B F DARK ANGEL (IRE) - CHELSEA MORNING (USA)	BBA (IRELAND)	49523
B C ACCLAMATION (GB) - EGO (GB)	J LEVINS	49523
TIS MARVELLOUS (GB) B C HARBOUR WATCH (IRE) - MYTHICISM (GB)	CLIVE COX RACING	49523
LINALTAQY (GB) CH C MAYSON (GB) - SPANGLE (GB)	SHADWELL ESTATE CO	47619
B F DARK ANGEL (IRE) - SISTER RED (IRE)	T NERSES	47619
B F MYBOYCHARLIE (IRE) - LADY BERTA (GB)	BADGERS/HUGHES	47619
B F HELMET (AUS) - THE TERRIER (GB)	BROWN ISLAND STABLES	47619
JUAN HORSEPOWER (GB) B C FOXWEDGE (AUS) - ELYSEE (IRE)	SACKVILLEDONALD	47619
B F MAKFI (GB) - TITIVATION (GB)	KEVIN ROSS BS	47619
TADKHIRAH (GB) B F ACCLAMATION (GB) - PIN CUSHION (GB)	SHADWELL ESTATE CO	47619
B F KODIAC (GB) - DARK ARTS (USA)	STROUD COLEMAN BS	47619
CH C MAYSON (GB) - ESTONIA (GB)	B O'RYAN	47619
CH/GR F POET'S VOICE (GB) - EXPEDIENCE (USA)	T NERSES	47619
DR GOODHEAD (FR) B F ZOFFANY (IRE) - WHOOSH (FR)	BBA (IRELAND)	47619
CH F SEPOY (AUS) - FEN GUEST (GB)	GARY MUDGWAY BS	47619
B F ACCLAMATION (GB) - MEA PARVITAS (IRE)	PETER & ROSS DOYLE BS	47619
CH F MAYSON (GB) - LISIEUX ORCHID (IRE)	STROUD COLEMAN BS	47619
GR C ZEBEDEE (GB) - DERVAL (GB)	PETER & ROSS DOYLE BS	47619
B C ZEBEDEE (GB) - SWEET IRISH (GB)	B O'RYAN	47619
MY ANGEL (GB) GR F DARK ANGEL (IRE) - TANDA TULA (IRE)	M DODS	47619
MAJESTE (GB) B C ACCLAMATION (GB) - WINGED VALKYRIE (IRE)	PETER & ROSS DOYLE BS	47619
WAQT (IRE) B C ACCLAMATION (GB) - NEEDLES AND PINS (IRE)	SHADWELL ESTATE CO (P.S.)	47619
B C DARK ANGEL (IRE) - KERMANA (IRE)	R FIDDES (P.S.)	47619
B F CASPAR NETSCHER (GB) - TWIN LOVE (FR)	C WENTWORTH	47619
B/GR C DARK ANGEL (IRE) - ABBAGNATO (GB)	J LLOYD	45714
TADAWWY (IRE) B C ACCLAMATION (GB) - QALAHARI (IRE)	SHADWELL ESTATE CO	45714
B F FASTNET ROCK (AUS) - BRAZILIAN SAMBA (IRE)	HUGO MERRY BS	45714
B C ACCLAMATION (GB) - STAR NOW (GB)	BBA (IRELAND)	45714
B F MONSIEUR BOND (IRE) - FOREVER BOND (GB)	VENDOR	45714
B F KODIAC (GB) - ALEXANDER CONFRANC (IRE)	HOWSON & HOULDSWORTH BS	44761
B C SHOWCASING (GB) - REEL COOL (GB)	HARROWGATE BS	43809
B F PACO BOY (IRE) - TEGGIANO (IRE)	F BARBERINI	43809
B F DUTCH ART (GB) - SUNSEEK (GB)	OLIVER ST LAWRENCE	43809
B C IFFRAAJ (GB) - EFFIGE (IRE)	J FRETWELL	43809
SUKIWARRIOR (IRE) CH F POWER (GB) - UMNIYA (IRE)	BBA (IRELAND)	43809
PUSSY GALORE (IRE) B F HARBOUR WATCH (IRE) - GREEN CHORUS (IRE)	PETER & ROSS DOYLE BS	43809
B C PHOENIX REACH (IRE) - CHOCOLADA (IRE)	GAY KELLEWAY RACING	43809
BR F DANDY MAN (IRE) - ALJAFLIYAH (GB)	MIDDLEHAM PARK RACING	42857
B F ACCLAMATION (GB) - SOUL MOUNTAIN (IRE)	HILLEN & RYAN	42857
RUSUMAAT (IRE) B C ARCANO (GB) - QUEEN WASP (IRE)	SHADWELL ESTATE CO	42857
CH C CHOISIR (AUS) - MARGARET'S DREAM (GB)	C MCCORMACK (P.S.)	42857
CH F DUTCH ART (GB) - CARRAIGOONA (IRE)	HILLEN & RYAN	42857
B C DANDY MAN (IRE) - ROYAL MAJESTIC (GB)	SACKVILLEDONALD	42857
NORTHERN ECLIPSE (GB) B C KYLLACHY (GB) - QUADROPHENIA (GB)	J KELLY	42857
CH C FAST COMPANY (IRE) - PRINCESS BANU (IRE)	J & S QUINN	41904
CH C KYLLACHY (GB) - MA PALOMA (FR)	B O'RYAN	41904
B C DARK ANGEL (IRE) - BEATRIX POTTER (IRE)	CLIVE COX RACING	41904
CH C DREAM AHEAD (USA) - VASILIA (GB)	VENDOR	41904
B C MARTALINE (GB) - KARUMA (GER)	MOANMORE STUD	41904

HIGH-PRICED YEARLINGS OF 2015 AT TATTERSALLS IRELAND SALES

The following yearlings realised 31,000 euros and over at Tattersalls Ireland Sales in 2015:-

Name and Breeding	Purchaser	Euros
B C KODIAC (GB) - FEE ERIA (FR)	AMANDA SKIFFINGTON	130000
HARBOUR FORCE (FR) B C HARBOUR WATCH (IRE) - DAM BEAUTIFUL (GB)	HILLEN & TUITE	120000
B/BR C ELUSIVE PIMPERNEL (USA) - SPIRITVILLE (IRE)	BLM BS	120000
LARCHMONT LAD (IRE) B C FOOTSTEPSINTHESAND (GB) - FOTINI (IRE)	PETER & ROSS DOYLE	110000
CH F SEPOY (AUS) - TATIANA ROMANOVA (USA)	JOE FOLEY	90000
B C KODIAC (GB) - SWEET'N SASSY (IRE)	JC BS	88000
B C KODIAC (GB) - KATHOE (IRE)	CON MARNANE	82000
CH C SIR PRANCEALOT (IRE) - TIDES (GB)	PETER & ROSS DOYLE	82000
B C WOOTTON BASSETT (GB) - DIAMOND STAR (IRE)	BLM BS	80000
B C AVONBRIDGE (GB) - ESPAGNOLETTE (GB)	HIGHFIELD FARM	80000
COMRADE CONRAD (IRE) B C CANFORD CLIFFS (IRE) - VIEW (GB)	AMANDA SKIFFINGTON	78000
MR SCARAMANGA (GB) B C SIR PERCY (GB) - LULLA (GB)	PETER & ROSS DOYLE	78000
B F SIR PRANCEALOT (IRE) - STARTORI (GB)	EDWARD LYNAM	72000
B C DANDY MAN (IRE) - SCARLET BUTTONS (GB)	CHINOOK FARM	72000
BR C DREAM AHEAD (USA) - BOGINI (IRE)	GER LYONS	70000
CH C SAKHEE'S SECRET (GB) - SILICON STAR (IRE)	PETER & ROSS DOYLE & MPR	70000
BR/GR C DARK ANGEL (IRE) - OPHELIA'S SONG (GB)	CHURCH FARM	70000
CH C TEOFILO (IRE) - ALTESSE IMPERIALE (IRE)	SACKVILLE DONALD	68000
B F KODIAC (GB) - ZUZU (IRE)	EDWARD LYNAM	68000
B F REQUINTO (IRE) - PILLARS OF SOCIETY (IRE)	JC BS	68000
B F ROYAL APPLAUSE (GB) - NASIJ (USA)	ASHTOWN BS	67000
B C PRESENTING (GB) - REINE ANGEVINE (FR)	GARRYNACURRA STUD	65000
B C DANDY MAN (IRE) - SORANNA (IRE)	KERN/LILLINGSTON ASSOCIATION	60000
GR C CLODOVIL (IRE) - BOUCHERON (GB)	PETER & ROSS DOYLE	60000
B F COCKNEY REBEL (IRE) - VINO VERITAS (USA)	REBEL RACING	60000
B/BR G SOLDIER OF FORTUNE (IRE) - ZAINZANA (FR)	TRICKLEDOWN STUD	60000
FLEABISCUIT (IRE) B F HIGH CHAPARRAL (IRE) - BLUEBELLE DANCER (IRE)	SACKVILLE DONALD	57000
B/BR C INTENSE FOCUS (USA) - JOUEL (FR)	AMANDA SKIFFINGTON	55000
CH C POWER (GB) - ASCOT LADY (IRE)	WILLIE BROWNE	55000
B C BAHAMIAN BOUNTY (GB) - REGENT'S PARK (GB)	SACKVILLE DONALD	55000
B C JEREMY (USA) - KINGSDALE PRINXESS (IRE)	GERRY HOGAN	55000
BR C FLEMENSFIRTH (USA) - DAWN BID (IRE)	A MURPHY	55000
B C DREAM AHEAD (USA) - COXPIPPIN (IRE)	ALDUINO BOTTI	54000
B F CANFORD CLIFFS (IRE) - MARKET DAY (GB)	DAVID REDVERS	52000
CH F MEDICEAN (GB) - PIANO (GB)	SEVENTH LAP RACING	52000
B C ROBIN DES CHAMPS (FR) - SLIABH GEAL GCUA (IRE)	J O'BYRNE	52000
BR G MILAN (GB) - JOHNSALICE (IRE)	RICHARD FRISBY	50000
B C INTIKHAB (USA) - LADY MAGDALENA (IRE)	JOE FOLEY	50000
B C SEA THE STARS (IRE) - KESARA (GB)	BBA IRELAND	50000
BOBBIO (IRE) CH C CHOISIR (AUS) - BALLADIENE (IRE)	J LLOYD	50000
B C SO YOU THINK (NZ) - DESERT FANTASY (GB)	BOBBY O'RYAN/DK WELD	50000
BR F BATED BREATH (GB) - DUSTING (IRE)	AMANDA SKIFFINGTON	50000
TWIZZELL (GB) B F EQUIANO (FR) - GREENSAND (GB)	ANN DUFFIELD	50000
CH C TAGULA (IRE) - APRIL GREEN (FR)	PETER & ROSS DOYLE	50000
B C FAME AND GLORY (GB) - FULL OF BIRDS (FR)	A MURPHY	50000
B F ACCLAMATION (GB) - FATHOMING (USA)	PETER NOLAN BS	48000
CH C ROBIN DES CHAMPS (FR) - MILOGAN (IRE)	IAN FERGUSON	48000
CH F DUTCH ART (GB) - EXCELLERATOR (IRE)	STROUD COLEMAN BS	47000
B C CANFORD CLIFFS (IRE) - MAUNDAYS BAY (IRE)	RITCHIE FIDDES	46000
ONE LINER (GB) B C DELEGATOR (GB) - QUIP (GB)	AMANDA SKIFFINGTON	46000
B F KODIAC (GB) - CHICA WHOPA (IRE)	HOWSON & HOULDSWORTH BS	46000
B C HELMET (AUS) - SEEKING DUBAI (GB)	A C BS	46000
B C EQUIANO (FR) - ST ATHAN (GB)	KEVIN ROSS BS	45000
TIS WONDERFUL (IRE) B C CASAMENTO (IRE) - COSENZA (GB)	CLIVE COX RACING	45000
B G FLEMENSFIRTH (USA) - UNA SORPRESA (GER)	STROUD COLEMAN BS	45000
B C KODIAC (GB) - JACQUELIN JAG (IRE)	FEDERICO BARBERINI	44000
CH C MASTERCRAFTSMAN (IRE) - DROMOD MOUR (IRE)	BBA IRELAND	43000
B C KODIAC (GB) - RAINBOWSKIA (FR)	JC BS	43000
B G GETAWAY (GB) - CURRAGHEEN (IRE)	BROWN ISLAND STABLES	43000
B C THEWAYYOUARE (USA) - EXQUISITE NOTE (IRE)	GER LYONS	42000
BR F REQUINTO (IRE) - CANT HURRY LOVE (GB)	CHARLIE GORDON WATSON BS	42000
B F REQUINTO (IRE) - ALTOGETHER (GB)	TALLY HO STUD	42000
CH C DRAGON PULSE (IRE) - GLAMOROUS (GER)	JEREMY BRUMMITT	42000
B C ACCLAMATION (GB) - MISS WORK OF ART (GB)	HILLEN & TUITE	42000
B F KODIAC (GB) - MOJITA (IRE)	YEOMANSTOWN STUD	42000
DOUBLE DUTCH (GB) CH C DUTCH ART (GB) - DUCHESS DORA (IRE)	RICHARD KNIGHT BS	42000
B C KODIAC (GB) - MAGILINI (IRE)	CLIVE COX RACING	41000
Name and Breeding	**Purchaser**	**Euros**

B F BIG BAD BOB (IRE) - MIRACLE STEPS (CAN)	KUBLER RACING LIMITED	40000
B C ACCLAMATION (GB) - NIGHT OF DUBAI (IRE)	MAB AGENCY	40000
B F HARBOUR WATCH (IRE) - ELEKTRA MARINO (GB)	DAVID REDVERS	40000
BR F PACO BOY (IRE) - MILIANA (IRE)	D FARRINGTON	40000
B C DANDY MAN (IRE) - MY FUNNY VALENTINE (IRE)	JOE FOLEY	40000
B F REQUINTO (IRE) - FILANDRE (GB)	PETER & ROSS DOYLE	40000
LEGATO (IRE) CH C POWER (GB) - LISA GHERARDINI (IRE)	SACKVILLE DONALD	40000
CH C PIVOTAL (GB) - REGAL AURA (GB)	ALDUINO BOTTI	40000
FOXY BOY (GB) CH C FOXWEDGE (AUS) - SUZY WONG (IRE)	M DODS	40000
B C SO YOU THINK (NZ) - LAKE WINDERMERE (IRE)	JC BS	40000
B C JEREMY (USA) - BALLYGOLOGUE (IRE)	PAUL MORONEY BS	40000
CYRUS DALLIN (GB) B C RODERIC O'CONNOR (IRE) - MUNAAWASHAT (IRE)	BLANDFORD BS	40000
B G PRESENTING (GB) - THE KIDS DANTE (IRE)	IAN FERGUSON	40000
GR F DARK ANGEL (IRE) - SILVERSCREEN QUEEN (IRE)	AIDAN O'RYAN	40000
BR C STOWAWAY (GB) - ALLTHEWHILE (IRE)	C SWAN	40000
B/BR G PRESENTING (GB) - ELLA WATSON (IRE)	GARRYNACURRA STUD	38000
BR F DARK ANGEL (IRE) - SHEHIRA (FR)	GROVE STUD	38000
B C PRESENTING (GB) - LASADO (IRE)	JULIE GREEN/RACHEL JENNER	38000
B C KODIAC (GB) - PINKISTHECOLOUR (IRE)	HOWSON & HOULDSWORTH BS	38000
POND ROAD (FR) CH C NO RISK AT ALL (FR) - CALIFEA (FR)	TRICKLEDOWN STUD	38000
B F ARCANO (IRE) - HEART'S DESIRE (IRE)	HUSSEY/HARRINGTON	38000
B F FLEMENSFIRTH (USA) - DARE TO DOUBT (GB)	GERRY HOGAN BS	38000
CH C STREET BOSS (USA) - DIXIE WALTZ (USA)	ALDUINO BOTTI	37000
KICKING KATIE (IRE) BR F SHOWCASING (GB) - PROVENCE (GB)	TIM EASTERBY	37000
ESPRESSO FREDDO (IRE) B C FAST COMPANY (IRE) - SPRING BOUQUET (GB)	JEREMY BRUMMITT	36000
CH C DRAGON PULSE (IRE) - GOLD STRIKE (IRE)	ALESSANDRO BOTTI	36000
B G MILAN (GB) - FAUCON (GB)	VENDOR	36000
CH F ZEBEDEE (GB) - ELIZABELLE (IRE)	ANN DUFFIELD	36000
CH F HARBOUR WATCH (IRE) - BLONDE (IRE)	PETER & ROSS DOYLE	35000
GR C AUSSIE RULES (USA) - ALIZADORA (GB)	ALDUINO BOTTI	35000
B C SIR PRANCEALOT (IRE) - ROMANYLEI (IRE)	PD EVANS	35000
MISTER FREEZE (IRE) CH C FROZEN POWER (IRE) - BEACON OF HOPE (IRE)	CLIVE COX	35000
B F DARK ANGEL (IRE) - RIVER RAPIDS (IRE)	CHURCH FARM	35000
B F ELZAAM (AUS) - BLACK MEYEDEN (FR)	AIDAN O'RYAN / R FAHEY	35000
B G SHIROCCO (GER) - MORAR (GB)	VENDOR	35000
CH C CASAMENTO (IRE) - ELOQUENT ROSE (IRE)	EOGHAN O'NEILL	34000
B C ELZAAM (AUS) - ADAPTATION (GB)	KARL BURKE	34000
B C MAJESTIC MISSILE (IRE) - RON'S SECRET (GB)	SACKVILLE DONALD	34000
B F ELUSIVE PIMPERNEL (USA) - DEVIOUS DIVA (IRE)	F BARBERINI/N BRADLEY	34000
B C FLEMENSFIRTH (USA) - RUBY ISABEL (IRE)	FUTURERATE LIMITED	34000
CH F DANDY MAN (IRE) - ROSKEEN (IRE)	AHMAD ALDOWAISAN	33000
B B QUEEN (IRE) BR F BIG BAD BOB (IRE) - GOLD QUEEN (GB)	ALLAN BLOODLINES	33000
CH F ARCHIPENKO (USA) - MEDAILLE D'OR (GB)	STROUD COLEMAN	33000
B C SAKHEE'S SECRET (GB) - LONDON WELSH (GB)	HARROWGATE BS	32000
B C FAST COMPANY (IRE) - INVINCIBLE WOMAN (IRE)	JOHN MCCONNELL	32000
ET APRES THOU (FR) B G NETWORK (GER) - LADY THOU (FR)	AIDEN MURPHY	32000
B C ROCK OF GIBRALTAR (IRE) - AJIAAL (GB)	SALCEY FOREST STUD	32000
B F KYLLACHY (GB) - MAUGWENNA (GB)	STROUD COLEMAN BS	32000
CH F HELMET (AUS) - DEIRA DUBAI (GB)	CON MARNANE	32000
CH F DREAM AHEAD (USA) - MARIE OSORIO (GB)	JAPAN HEALTH SUMMIT INC	32000
CH G ROBIN DES CHAMPS (FR) - OUR PRIDE (GB)	GARRYNACURRA STUD	32000
SHADOW WING (IRE) CH F SAKHEE'S SECRET (GB) - GO MAGGIE GO (IRE)	SALCEY FOREST STUD	31000
B F CASAMENTO (IRE) - AVA'S WORLD (IRE)	GER LYONS	31000
RAY DONOVAN (IRE) B C ACCLAMATION (GB) - ALWAYS THE LADY (GB)	JASON KELLY	31000

TWO THOUSAND GUINEAS STAKES (3y) Newmarket 1 mile

Year	Owner	Winner and Price	Jockey	Trainer	Second	Third	Ran	Time
1974	Mme M Berger's	NONOALCO (19/2)	Y Saint Martin	F Boutin	Giacometti	Apalachee	12	39.53
1975	C d'Alessio's	BOLKONSKI (33/1)	G Dettori	H Cecil	Grundy	Dominion	24	39.53
1976	C d'Alessio's	WOLLOW (evens)	G Dettori	H Cecil	Vitiges	Thieving Demon	17	38.09
1977	N Schibbye's	NEBBIOLO (20/1)	G Curran	K Prendergast	Tachypous	The Minstrel	18	38.54
1978	J Hayter's	ROLAND GARDENS (28/1)	F Durr	D Sasse	Remainder Man	Welsh Nan	19	37.33
1979	A Shead's	TAP ON WOOD (20/1)	S Cauthen	B Hills	Kris	Young Generation	20	43.60
1980	K Abdulla's	KNOWN FACT (14/1)	W Carson	J Tree	Posse	Night Alert	14	40.46

(Nureyev finished first but was disqualified)

Year	Owner	Winner and Price	Jockey	Trainer	Second	Third	Ran	Time
1981	Mrs A Muinos's	TO-AGORI-MOU (5/2)	G Starkey	G Harwood	Mattaboy	Bel Bolide	19	41.43
1982	G Oldham's	ZINO (8/1)	F Head	F Boutin	Wind and Wuthering	Tender King	26	37.13
1983	R Sangster's	LOMOND (9/1)	Pat Eddery	V O'Brien	Tolomeo	Muscatite	16	43.87
1984	R Sangster's	EL GRAN SENOR (15/8)	Pat Eddery	V O'Brien	Chief Singer	Lear Fan	14	37.41
1985	Maktoum Al Maktoum's	SHADEED (4/5)	L Piggott	M Stoute	Bairn	Supreme Leader	14	40.00
1986	K Abdulla's	DANCING BRAVE (15/8)	G Starkey	G Harwood	Green Desert	Huntingdale	15	40.40
1987	J Horgan's	DON'T FORGET ME (9/1)	W Carson	R Hannon	Bellotto	Midyan	9	41.73
1988	H H Aga Khan's	DOYOUN (4/5)	W R Swinburn	M Stoute	Charmer	Bellefella	9	36.74
1989	Hamdan Al-Maktoum's	NASHWAN (3/1)	W Carson	R Hern	Exbourne	Danehill	14	36.44
1990	John Horgan's	TIROL (9/1)	M Kinane	R Hannon	Machiavellian	Anshan	14	35.84
1991	Lady Beaverbrook's	MYSTIKO (13/2)	M Roberts	C Brittain	Lycius	Ganges	16	37.83
1992	R Sangster's	RODRIGO DE TRIANO (6/1)	L Piggott	P Chapple-Hyam	Lucky Lindy	Pursuit of Love	16	38.37
1993	K Abdulla's	ZAFONIC (5/6)	Pat Eddery	A Fabre	Barathea	Bin Alwaad	14	35.32
1994	G R Bailey Ltd's	MISTER BAILEYS (16/1)	J Weaver	M Johnston	Grand Lodge	Colonel Collins	23	35.08
1995	Sheikh Mohammed's	PENNEKAMP (9/2)	T Jarnet	A Fabre	Celtic Swing	Bahri	11	35.16
1996	Godolphin's	MARK OF ESTEEM (8/1)	L Dettori	S Bin Suroor	Even Top	Bijou D'Inde	16	37.59
1997	M Tabor & Mrs J Magnier's	ENTREPRENEUR (11/2)	M Kinane	M Stoute	Revoque	Poteen	16	35.64
1998	M Tabor & Mrs J Magnier's	KING OF KINGS (7/2)	M Kinane	A O'Brien	Lend A Hand	Border Arrow	16	39.25
1999	Godolphin's	ISLAND SANDS (10/1)	L Dettori	S Bin Suroor	Enrique	Mujahid	16	37.14

(Run on July Course)

Year	Owner	Winner and Price	Jockey	Trainer	Second	Third	Ran	Time
2000	Saeed Suhail's	KING'S BEST (13/2)	K Fallon	Sir M Stoute	Giant's Causeway	Barathea Guest	27	37.77
2001	Lord Weinstock's	GOLAN (11/1)	K Fallon	Sir M Stoute	Tamburlaine	Frenchmans Bay	18	37.48
2002	Sir A Ferguson & Mrs J Magnier's	ROCK OF GIBRALTAR (9/1)	J Murtagh	A O'Brien	Hawk Wing	Redback	22	36.50
2003	Moyglare Stud Farm's	REFUSE TO BEND (9/2)	P J Smullen	D Weld	Zafeen	Norse Dancer	20	37.98
2004	Hamdan Al Maktoum's	HAAFHD (11/2)	R Hills	B Hills	Snow Ridge	Azamour	19	37.60
2005	Mr M Tabor & Mrs John Magnier's	FOOTSTEPSINTHESAND (13/2)	K Fallon	A O'Brien	Rebel Rebel	Kandidate	14	36.10
2006	Mrs J Magnier, Mr M Tabor & Mr D Smith's	GEORGE WASHINGTON (6/4)	J O'Brien	A O'Brien	Sir Percy	Olympian Odyssey	14	36.80
2007	P Cunningham's	COCKNEY REBEL (25/1)	O Peslier	G Huffer	Vital Equine	Dutch Art	24	35.28
2008	Mrs J Magnier's	HENRYTHENAVIGATOR (11/1)	J Murtagh	A O'Brien	New Approach	Stubbs Art	15	39.14
2009	C Tsui's	SEA THE STARS (8/1)	M Kinane	J Oxx	Delegator	Gan Amhras	15	35.88
2010	M Offerstadt's	MAKFI (1/2)	C Lemaire	M Delzangles	Dick Turpin	Canford Cliffs	19	36.35
2011	K Abdulla's	FRANKEL (1/2)	T Queally	H Cecil	Dubawi Gold	Native Khan	13	37.30
2012	D Smith, Mrs J Magnier & M Tabor's	CAMELOT (15/8)	J O'Brien	A O'Brien	French Fifteen	Hermival	18	42.46
2014	Saeed Manana's	NIGHT OF THUNDER (40/1)	K Fallon	R Hannon jnr	Kingman	Australia	14	36.61
2015	M Tabor, D Smith & Mrs J Magnier's	GLENEAGLES (4/1)	R Moore	A O'Brien	Territories	Ivawood	18	37.55

1000 GUINEAS STAKES (3y fillies) Newmarket-1 mile

Year	Owner	Winner and Price	Jockey	Trainer	Second	Third	Ran	Time
1974	The Queen's	HIGHCLERE (12/1)	J Mercer	R Hern	Polygamy	Mrs Twiggywinkle	15	1 40.32
1975	Mrs D O' Kelly's	NOCTURNAL SPREE (14/1)	J Roe	S Murless	Girl Friend	Joking Apart	16	1 41.65
1976	D Wildenstein's	FLYING WATER (2/1)	Y Saint Martin	A Penna	Konafa	Kesar Queen	25	1 37.83
1977	Mrs E Kettlewell's	MRS MCARDY (16/1)	E Hide	M W Easterby	Freeze the Secret	Sanedtki	18	1 40.07
1978	R Bonnycastle's	ENSTONE SPARK (35/1)	E Johnson	B Hills	Fair Salinia	Seraphima	16	1 41.56
1979	Helena Springfield Ltd's	ONE IN A MILLION (evens)	J Mercer	H Cecil	Abbeydale	Yanuka	17	1 43.09
1980	O Phipps's	QUICK AS LIGHTNING (12/1)	B Rouse	H Cecil	Our Home	Mrs Penny	23	1 41.89
1981	H Joel's	FAIRY FOOTSTEPS (6/4)	L Piggott	H Cecil	Tolmi	Go Leasing	14	1 40.43
1982	Sir P Oppenheimer's	ON THE HOUSE (33/1)	J Reid	Mme C Head	Time Charter	Dione	14	1 40.45
1983	Maktoum Al-Maktoum's	MA BICHE (5/2)	F Head	C Brittain	Favoridge	Habibti	15	1 41.71
1984	M Lemos's	PEBBLES (8/1)	P Robinson	C Brittain	Meis El-Reem	Desirable	18	1 39.18
1985	Sheikh Mohammed's	OH SO SHARP (2/1)	S Cauthen	H Cecil	Al Bahathri	Bella Colora	17	1 36.85
1986	H Ranier's	MIDWAY LADY (10/1)	R Cochrane	B Hanbury	Maysoon	Sonic Lady	15	1 41.54
1987	S Niarchos's	MIESQUE (15/8)	F Head	F Boutin	Milligram	Interval	14	1 38.48
1988	E Aland's	RAVINELLA (4/5)	G W Moore	Mme C Head	Dabaweyya	Diminuendo	12	1 40.88
1989	Sheikh Mohammed's	MUSICAL BLISS (7/2)	W R Swinburn	M Stoute	Kerrera	Aldbourne	7	1 42.69
1990	Hamdan Al-Maktoum's	SALSABIL (6/4)	W Carson	J Dunlop	Heart of Joy	Negligent	12	1 38.06
1991	Maktoum Al-Maktoum's	SHADAYID (4/6)	W Carson	J Dunlop	Kooyonga	Crystal Gazing	14	1 38.18
1992	Maktoum Al-Maktoum's	HATOOF (5/1)	W R Swinburn	Mme C Head	Marling	Kenbu	14	1 39.45
1993	Mohamed Obaida's	SAYYEDATI (4/1)	W R Swinburn	C Brittain	Niche	Alfan	12	1 37.34
1994	R Sangster's	LAS MENINAS (12/1)	J Reid	T Stack	Balanchine	Coup de Genie	15	1 36.71
1995	Hamdan Al-Maktoum's	HARAYIR (5/2)	R Hills	Major W R Hern	Aqaarid	Moonshell	14	1 36.72
1996	Wafic Said's	BOSRA SHAM (10/11)	Pat Eddery	H Cecil	Matiya	Bint Shadayid	13	1 37.75
1997	Greenbay Stables Ltd's	SLEEPYTIME (5/1)	K Fallon	H Cecil	Oh Nellie	Dazzle	15	1 37.66
1998	Godolphin's	CAPE VERDI (100/30)	L Dettori	S Bin Suroor	Shahtoush	Exclusive	16	1 37.86
1999	K Abdulla's	WINCE (4/1)	K Fallon	H Cecil	Wannabe Grand	Valentine Waltz	22	1 37.91

(Run on July Course)

Year	Owner	Winner and Price	Jockey	Trainer	Second	Third	Ran	Time
2000	Hamdan Al-Maktoum's	LAHAN (14/1)	R Hills	J Gosden	Princess Ellen	Petrushka	18	1 36.38
2001	Sheikh Ahmed Al Maktoum's	AMEERAT (11/1)	P Robinson	J Jarvis	Muwakelt	Toroca	15	1 36.36
2002	Godolphin's	KAZZIA (14/1)	L Dettori	S Bin Suroor	Snowfire	Alaska	17	1 37.85
2003	Cheveley Park Stud's	RUSSIAN RHYTHM (12/1)	K Fallon	Sir M Stoute	Six Perfections	Intercontinental	17	1 38.43
2004	Duke of Roxburghe's	ATTRACTION (11/2)	K Darley	M Johnston	Sundrop	Hathrah	16	1 36.70
2005	Mrs John Magnier & Mr M Tabor's	VIRGINIA WATERS (12/1)	K Fallon	A O'Brien	Maids Causeway	Vista Bella	20	1 36.50
2006	M Sly, Dr Davies & Mrs P Sly's	SPECIOSA (10/1)	M Fenton	Mrs P Sly	Confidential Lady	Nasheej	13	1 40.50
2007	M Ryan's	FINSCEAL BEO (5/4)	M Manning	J Bolger	Arch Swing	Simply Perfect	21	1 34.94
2008	S Fribory's	NATAGORA (7/1)	C Lemaire	P Bary	Spacious	Saoirse Abu	15	1 38.99
2009	Hamdan Al-Maktoum's	GHANAATI (20/1)	R Hills	B Hills	Cuis Ghaire	Super Sleuth	14	1 34.22
2010	K Abdulla's	SPECIAL DUTY (9/2)	S. Pasquier	Mme C Head-Maarek	Jacqueline Quest	Gile Na Greine	12	1 39.66

(The first two placings were reversed by the Stewards)

Year	Owner	Winner and Price	Jockey	Trainer	Second	Third	Ran	Time
2011	Godolphin's	BLUE BUNTING (16/1)	L Dettori	M Al Zarooni	Together	Maqaasid	18	1 39.27
2012	Mrs John Magnier, M Tabor & D Smith's	HOMECOMING QUEEN (25/1)	R Moore	A O'Brien	Starscope	Maybe	17	1 40.45
2013	B Keswick's	SKY LANTERN (9/1)	R Hughes	R Hannon	Just The Judge	Moth	15	1 36.38
2014	Ballymore Thoroughbred Ltd's	MISS FRANCE (7/1)	M Guyon	A Fabre	Lightning Thunder	Inimal	17	1 37.40
2015	M Tabor, D Smith & Mrs J Magnier's	LEGATISSIMO (13/2)	R Moore	D Wachman	Lucida	Tiggy Wiggy	13	1 34.60

OAKS STAKES (3y fillies) Epsom·1 mile 4 furlongs 10 yards

Year	Owner	Winner and Price	Jockey	Trainer	Second	Third	Ran	Time
1976	D Wildenstein's	PAWNEESE (6/5)	Y Saint Martin	A Penna	Roses for the Star	African Dancer	14	2 35.25
1977	The Queen's	DUNFERMLINE (6/1)	W Carson	R Hern	Freeze the Secret	Vaguely Deb	13	2 36.53
1978	S Hanson's	FAIR SALINIA (8/1)	G Starkey	M Stoute	Dancing Maid	Suni	15	2 36.82
1979	J Morrison's	SCINTILLATE (20/1)	Pat Eddery	J Tree	Bonnie Isle	Britannia's Rule	14	2 43.74
1980	R Hollingsworth's	BIREME (9/2)	W Carson	R Hern	Vielle	The Dancer	11	2 34.33
1981	Mrs B Firestone's	BLUE WIND (3/1)	L Piggott	M Weld	Madam Gay	Leap Lively	12	2 40.93
1982	R Barnett's	TIME CHARTER (12/1)	W Newnes	H Candy	Slightly Dangerous	Last Feather	15	2 34.21
1983	Sir R McAlpine's	SUN PRINCESS (6/1)	W Carson	R Hern	Acclimatise	New Coins	15	2 40.98
1984	Sir M Sobell's	CIRCUS PLUME (4/1)	L Piggott	J Dunlop	Media Luna	Poquito Queen	15	2 38.97
1985	Sheikh Mohammed's	OH SO SHARP (6/4)	S Cauthen	H Cecil	Triptych	Dubian	15	2 41.37
1986	H Ranier's	MIDWAY LADY (15/8)	R Cochrane	B Hanbury	Untold	Maysoon	15	2 37.37
1987	Sheikh Mohammed's	UNITE (11/1)	W R Swinburn	M Stoute	Bourbon Girl	Three Tails	11	2 41.60
1988	Sheikh Mohammed's	DIMINUENDO (7/4)	S Cauthen	H Cecil	Sudden Love	Animatica	11	2 38.17
1989	Saeed Maktoum Al Maktoum's	SNOW BRIDE (13/2)	S Cauthen	H Cecil	Roseate Tern	Mamaluna	9	2 35.02

(Alyisa finished first but was disqualified)

Year	Owner	Winner and Price	Jockey	Trainer	Second	Third	Ran	Time
1990	Hamdan Al-Maktoum's	SALSABIL (2/1)	W Carson	J Dunlop	Game Plan	Knight's Baroness	8	2 38.70
1991	Maktoum Al-Maktoum's	JET SKI LADY (50/1)	C Roche	J Bolger	Shamshir	Shadayid	9	2 37.30
1992	W J Gredley's	USER FRIENDLY (5/1)	G Duffield	C Brittain	All At Sea	Pearl Angel	7	2 39.77
1993	Sheikh Mohammed's	INTREPIDITY (5/1)	M Roberts	A Fabre	Royal Ballerina	Oakmead	14	2 34.19
1994	Maktoum Al Maktoum/ Godolphin's	BALANCHINE (6/1)	L Dettori	H Ibrahim	Wind In Her Hair	Hawajiss	10	2 40.37
1995	Godolphin's	MOONSHELL (3/1)	L Dettori	S Bin Suroor	Dance A Dream	Pure Grain	10	2 35.44
1996	Wafic Said's	LADY CARLA (100/30)	Pat Eddery	H Cecil	Pricket	Mezzogiorno	11	2 35.55
1997	K Abdulla's	REAMS OF VERSE (5/6)	K Fallon	H Cecil	Gazelle Royale	Crown of Light	11	2 35.59
1998	Mrs D Nagle & Mrs J Magnier's	SHAHTOUSH (12/1)	M Kinane	A O'Brien	Bahr	Midnight Line	8	2 38.23
1999	F Salman's	RAMRUMA (3/1)	K Fallon	H Cecil	Noushkey	Zahrat Dubai	10	2 38.72
2000	Lordship Stud's	LOVE DIVINE (9/4)	T Quinn	H Cecil	Kalypso Katie	Melikah	16	2 43.11
2001	Mrs D. Nagle & Mrs J Magnier's	IMAGINE (3/1)	M Kinane	A O'Brien	Flight Of Fancy	Relish The Thought	14	2 36.70
2002	Godolphin's	KAZZIA (100/30)	L Dettori	S Bin Suroor	Quarter Moon	Shadow Dancing	14	2 44.52
2003	W S Farish III's	CASUAL LOOK (10/1)	M Dwyer	E Dunlop	Yesterday	Summinville	15	2 38.07
2004	Lord Derby's	OUIJA BOARD (7/2)	K Fallon	E Dunlop	All Too Beautiful	Punctilious	15	2 35.40
2005	Hamdan Al Maktoum's	ESWARAH (11/4)	R Hills	M Jarvis	Something Exciting	Pictavia	12	2 39.00
2006	Mrs J Magnier, Mr M Tabor & Mr D Smith's	ALEXANDROVA (9/4)	K Fallon	A O'Brien	Rising Cross	Short Skirt	10	2 37.70
2007	Niarchos Family's	LIGHT SHIFT (13/2)	T Durcan	H Cecil	Peeping Fawn	All My Loving	14	2 40.38
2008	J H Richmond-Watson's	LOOK HERE (33/1)	S Sanders	R Beckett	Moonstone	Katiyra	16	2 36.89
2009	Lady Bamford's	SARISKA (9/4)	J Spencer	M Bell	Midday	High Heeled	15	2 35.28
2010	Anamoine Ltd's	SNOW FAIRY (9/1)	R Moore	E Dunlop	Remember When	Rumoush	15	2 35.77

(Meznah finished second but was disqualified)

Year	Owner	Winner and Price	Jockey	Trainer	Second	Third	Ran	Time
2011	M J & L A Taylor's	DANCING RAIN (20/1)	J Murtagh	W Haggas	Wonder of Wonders	Izzi Top	13	2 41.73
2012	D Smith, Mrs J Magnier & M Tabor's	WAS (20/1)	S Heffernan	A O'Brien	Shirocco Star	The Fugue	12	2 38.68
2013	J L Rowsell & M H Dixon's	TALENT (20/1)	R Hughes	R Beckett	Secret Gesture	The Lark	11	2 42.00
2014	Hamdan Al Maktoum's	TAGHROODA (5/1)	P Hanagan	J Gosden	Tarfasha	Volume	17	2 34.89
2015	Mrs C C Regalado - Gonzalez's	QUALIFY (50/1)	C O'Donoghue	A O'Brien	Legatissimo	Lady of Dubai	11	2 37.41

DERBY STAKES (3y) Epsom-1 mile 4 furlongs 10 yards

Year	Owner	Winner and Price	Jockey	Trainer	Second	Third	Ran	Time
1978	Lord Halifax's	SHIRLEY HEIGHTS (8/1)	G Starkey	J Dunlop	Hawaiian Sound	Remainder Man	25	2 35.30
1979	Sir M Sobell's	TROY (6/1)	W Carson	R Hern	Dickens Hill	Northern Baby	23	2 36.59
1980	Mrs A Plesch's	HENBIT (7/1)	W Carson	R Hern	Master Willie	Rankin	24	2 34.77
1981	H H Aga Khan's	SHERGAR (10/11)	W Swinburn	M Stoute	Glint of Gold	Scintillating Air	18	2 44.21
1982	R Sangster's	GOLDEN FLEECE (3/1)	Pat Eddery	M V O'Brien	Touching Wood	Silver Hawk	18	2 34.27
1983	E Moller's	TEENOSO (9/2)	L Piggott	G Wragg	Carlingford Castle	Shearwalk	21	2 49.07
1984	L Miglitti's	SECRETO (14/1)	C Roche	D O'Brien	El Gran Senor	Mighty Flutter	17	2 39.12
1985	Lord H. de Walden's	SLIP ANCHOR (9/4)	S Cauthen	H Cecil	Law Society	Damister	14	2 36.23
1986	H H Aga Khan's	SHAHRASTANI (11/2)	W Swinburn	M Stoute	Dancing Brave	Mashkour	17	2 37.13
1987	H H Aga Khan's	REFERENCE POINT (6/4)	S Cauthen	H Cecil	Most Welcome	Bellotto	19	2 33.90
1988	L Freedman's	KAHYASI (11/1)	R Cochrane	L Cumani	Glacial Storm	Doyoun	14	2 33.84
1989	H H Aga Khan's	NASHWAN (5/4)	W Carson	R Hern	Terimon	Cacoethes	12	2 34.90
1990	K Abdulla's	QUEST FOR FAME (7/1)	Pat Eddery	R Charlton	Blue Stag	Elmaamul	18	2 37.26
1991	F Salman's	GENEROUS (9/1)	A Munro	P Cole	Marju	Star of Gdansk	13	2 34.00
1992	Sidney TH Craig's	DR DEVIOUS (8/1)	J Reid	P Chapple-Hyam	St Jovite	Silver Wisp	18	2 36.19
1993	K Abdulla's	COMMANDER IN CHIEF (15/2)	M Kinane	H Cecil	Blue Judge	Blues Traveller	16	2 34.51
1994	Hamdan Al-Maktoum's	ERHAAB (7/2)	W Carson	J Dunlop	King's Theatre	Colonel Collins	25	2 34.16
1995	Saeed Maktoum Al Maktoum's	LAMMTARRA (14/1)	W Swinburn	S Bin Suroor	Tamure	Presenting	15	2 32.31
1996	K Dasmal's	SHAAMIT (12/1)	M Hills	W Haggas	Dushyantor	Shantou	20	2 35.05
1997	L Knight's	BENNY THE DIP (11/1)	W Ryan	J Gosden	Silver Patriarch	Romanov	13	2 35.77
1998	Sheikh Mohammed Obaid Al Maktoum's	HIGH-RISE (20/1)	O Pesiler	J Cumani	City Honours	Border Arrow	15	2 33.88
1999	The Thoroughbred Corporation's	OATH (13/2)	K Fallon	H Cecil	Daliapour	Beat All	16	2 37.43
2000	H H Aga Khan's	SINNDAR (7/1)	J Murtagh	J Oxx	Sakhee	Beat Hollow	15	2 36.75
2001	M Tabor & Mrs J Magnier's	GALILEO (11/4)	M Kinane	A O'Brien	Golan	Tobougg	12	2 33.27
2002	M Tabor & Mrs J Magnier's	HIGH CHAPARRAL (7/2)	J Murtagh	A O'Brien	Hawk Wing	Moon Ballad	12	2 39.45
2003	Saeed Suhail's	KRIS KIN (6/1)	K Fallon	Sir M Stoute	The Great Gatsby	Alamshar	20	2 33.35
2004	Ballymacoll Stud's	NORTH LIGHT (7/2)	K Fallon	Sir M Stoute	Rule of Law	Let The Lion Roar	14	2 33.70
2005	The Royal Ascot Racing Club's	MOTIVATOR (3/1)	J Murtagh	M Bell	Walk In The Park	Dubawi	13	2 35.60
2006	A Pakenham's	SIR PERCY (6/1)	M Dwyer	M Tregoning	Dragon Dancer	Dylan Thomas	18	2 35.20
2007	Saleh Al Homaizi & Imad Al Sagar's	AUTHORIZED (5/4)	L Dettori	P Chapple-Hyam	Eagle Mountain	Aqaleem	17	2 34.77
2008	HRH Princess Haya of Jordan's	NEW APPROACH (5/1)	K Manning	J Bolger	Tartan Bearer	Casual Conquest	16	2 36.50
2009	C Tsui's	SEA THE STARS (11/4)	M Kinane	J Oxx	Fame And Glory	Masterofthehorse	12	2 36.74
2010	K Abdulla's	WORKFORCE (6/1)	R Moore	Sir M Stoute	At First Sight	Rewilding	12	2 31.33
2011	Mrs John Magnier, M Tabor & D Smith's	POUR MOI (4/1)	M Barzalona	A Fabre	Treasure Beach	Carlton House	13	2 34.54
2012	D Smith, Mrs J Magnier & M Tabor's	CAMELOT (8/13)	J O'Brien	A O'Brien	Main Sequence	Astrology	9	2 33.90
2013	Mrs John Magnier, Michael Tabor & Derrick Smith's	RULER OF THE WORLD (7/1)	R Moore	A O'Brien	Libertarian	Galileo Rock	12	2 39.06
2014	D Smith, Mrs J Magnier, M Tabor & T Ah Khing's	AUSTRALIA (11/8)	J O'Brien	A O'Brien	Kingston Hill	Romsdal	16	2 33.63
2015	A E Oppenheimer's	GOLDEN HORN (13/8)	L Dettori	J Gosden	Jack Hobbs	Storm The Stars	12	2 32.32

ST LEGER STAKES (3y) Doncaster-1 mile 6 furlongs 132 yards

Year	Owner	Winner and Price	Jockey	Trainer	Second	Third	Ran	Time
1974	Lady Beaverbrook's	BUSTINO (11/10)	J Mercer	R Hern	Giacometti	Riboson	10	3 9.02
1975	C St George's	BRUNI (9/1)	A Murray	R Price	King Pellinore	Libra's Rib	10	3 9.02
1976	D Wildenstein's	CROW (6/1)	Y Saint-Martin	A Penna	Secret Man	Scallywag	15	3 13.17
1977	The Queen's	DUNFERMLINE (10/1)	W Carson	R Hern	Alleged	Classic Example	15	3 5.17
1978	M Lemos's	JULIO MARINER (28/1)	E Hide	C Brittain	Le Moss	M-Lolshan	14	3 4.94
1979	A Rolland's	SON OF LOVE (20/1)	A Lequeux	R Collet	Soleil Noir	Niniski	12	3 9.02
1980	H Joel's	LIGHT CAVALRY (3/1)	J Mercer	H Cecil	Water Mill	World Leader	7	3 11.48
1981	Sir J Astor's	CUT ABOVE (28/1)	J Mercer	R Hern	Glint of Gold	Bustomi	7	3 11.60
1982	Maktoum Al Maktoum's	TOUCHING WOOD (7/1)	P Cook	H T Jones	Zilos	Diamond Shoal	15	3 3.53
1983	Sir M Sobell's	SUN PRINCESS (11/2)	W Carson	R Hern	Esprit du Nord	Carlingford Castle	13	3 16.65
1984	I Allan's	COMMANCHE RUN (7/4)	L Piggott	L Cumani	Baynoun	Alphabatim	11	3 9.93
1985	Sheikh Mohammed's	OH SO SHARP (9/2)	S Cauthen	H Cecil	Phardante	Lanfranco	6	3 7.13
1986	Duchess of Norfolk's	MOON MADNESS (9/2)	Pat Eddery	J Dunlop	Celestial Storm	Untold	8	3 5.03
1987	L Freedman's	REFERENCE POINT (4/11)	S Cauthen	H Cecil	Mountain Kingdom	Dry Dock	7	3 5.91
1988	Lady Beaverbrook's	MINSTER SON (15/2)	W Carson	N A Graham	Diminuendo	Sheriff's Star	6	3 6.80
1989	C St George's (Run at Ayr)	MICHELOZZO (6/4)	S Cauthen	H Cecil	Sapience	Roseate Tern	8	3 20.72
1990	M Arbib's	SNURGE (7/2)	T Quinn	P Cole	Hellenic	River God	8	3 8.78
1991	K Abdulla's	TOULON (5/2)	Pat Eddery	A Fabre	Saddlers' Hall	Micheletti	7	3 3.12
1992	W J Gredley's	USER FRIENDLY (7/4)	G Duffield	C Brittain	Sonus	Bonny Scot	10	3 5.48
1993	Mrs G A E Smith's	BOB'S RETURN (3/1)	P Robinson	M Tompkins	Armiger	Edbaysaan	9	3 7.85
1994	Sheikh Mohammed's	MOONAX (40/1)	Pat Eddery	B Hills	Broadway Flyer	Double Trigger	8	3 4.19
1995	Godolphin's	CLASSIC CLICHE (100/30)	L Dettori	S Bin Suroor	Minds Music	Istidaad	10	3 9.74
1996	Sheikh Mohammed's	SHANTOU (8/1)	L Dettori	J Dunlop	Dushyantor	Samraan	11	3 5.10
1997	P Winfield's	SILVER PATRIARCH (5/4)	Pat Eddery	J Dunlop	Vertical Speed	The Fly	10	3 6.92
1998	Godolphin's	NEDAWI (5/2)	J Reid	S Bin Suroor	High and Low	Sunshine Street	10	3 5.61
1999	Godolphin's	MUTAFAWEQ (11/2)	T Hills	S Bin Suroor	Ramruma	Adair	9	3 2.75
2000	N Jones's	MILLENARY (11/4)	T Quinn	J Dunlop	Air Marshall	Chimes At Midnight	11	3 2.58
2001	M Tabor & Mrs J Magnier's	MILAN (13/8)	M Kinane	A O'Brien	Demophilos	Mr Combustible	10	3 5.16
2002	Sir Neil Westbrook's	BOLLIN ERIC (7/1)	K Darley	T Easterby	Highest	Bandari	8	3 2.92
2003	Mrs J Magnier's	BRIAN BORU (5/4)	J P Spencer	A O'Brien	High Accolade	Phoenix Reach	12	3 4.64
2004	Godolphin's	RULE OF LAW (3/1)	K McEvoy	S Bin Suroor	Quiff	Tycoon	9	3 6.20
2005	Mrs J Magnier & M M Tabor's	SCORPION (10/11)	L Dettori	A O'Brien	The Geezer	Tawqeet	6	3 19.00
2006	Mrs S Roy's (Run at York)	SIXTIES ICON (11/8)	L Dettori	J Noseda	The Last Drop	Red Rocks	11	2 57.20
2007	G Strawbridge's	LUCARNO (7/2)	J Fortune	J Gosden	Mahler	Honolulu	10	3 1.90
2008	Ballymacoll Stud's	CONDUIT (8/1)	L Dettori	Sir M Stoute	Unsung Heroine	Look Here	14	3 7.92
2009	Godolphin's	MASTERY (14/1)	T Durcan	S Bin Suroor	Kite Wood	Monitor Closely	8	3 4.81
2010	Ms R Hood & R Geffen's	ARCTIC COSMOS (12/1)	W Buick	J Gosden	Midas Touch	Corsica	8	3 3.12
2011	B Nielsen's	MASKED MARVEL (15/2)	W Buick	J Gosden	Brown Panther	Sea Moon	9	3 0.44
2012	Godolphin's	ENCKE (25/1)	M Barzalona	M Al Zarooni	Camelot	Michelangelo	9	3 3.81
2013	Derrick Smith & Mrs John Magnier & Michael Tabor's	LEADING LIGHT (7/2)	J O'Brien	A O'Brien	Talent	Galileo Rock	11	3 9.20
2014	Paul Smith's	KINGSTON HILL (9/4)	A Atzeni	R Varian	Romsdal	Snow Sky	12	3 5.42
2015	QRL, Sheikh Suhaim Al Thani & M Al Kubaisi's	SIMPLE VERSE (8/1)	A Atzeni	R Beckett	Bondi Beach	Fields of Athenry	7	3 7.12

KING GEORGE VI AND QUEEN ELIZABETH STAKES Ascot-1 mile 4 furlongs

Year	Owner	Winner and Price	Jockey	Trainer	Second	Third	Ran	Time
1976	D Wildenstein's	PAWNEESE 3-8-5 (9/4)	Y Saint Martin	A Penna	Bruni	Orange Bay	10	2 29.36
1977	R Sangster's	THE MINSTREL 3-8-8 (7/4)	L Piggott	V O'Brien	Orange Bay	Exceller	11	2 30.48
1978	D McCall's	ILE DE BOURBON 3-8-8 (12/1)	J Reid	F Houghton	Hawaiian Sound	Montcontour	14	2 30.53
1979	Sir M Sobell's	TROY 3-8-8 (2/5)	W Carson	R Hern	Gay Mecene	Ela-Mana-Mou	7	2 33.75
1980	S Weinstock's	ELA-MANA-MOU 4-9-7 (11/4)	W Carson	R Hern	Mrs Penny	Gregorian	10	2 35.39
1981	H H Aga Khan's	SHERGAR 3-8-8 (2/5)	W Swinburn	M Stoute	Madam Gay	Fingals Cave	9	2 35.40
1982	A Ward's	KALAGLOW 4-9-7 (13-2)	G Starkey	G Harwood	Assert	Glint of Gold	9	2 31.58
1983	R Barnett's	TIME CHARTER 4-9-4 (5/1)	J Mercer	H Candy	Diamond Shoal	Sun Princess	9	2 31.02
1984	E Moller's	TEENOSO 4-9-7 (13/2)	L Piggott	G Wragg	Sadler's Wells	Tolomeo	13	2 27.95
1985	Lady Beaverbrook's	PETOSKI 3-8-8 (12/1)	W Carson	W Hern	Oh So Sharp	Rainbow Quest	8	2 27.61
1986	K Abdulla's	DANCING BRAVE 3-8-8 (6/4)	Pat Eddery	G Harwood	Shardari	Triptych	9	2 29.49
1987	L Freedman's	REFERENCE POINT 3-8-8 (11/10)	S Cauthen	H Cecil	Celestial Storm	Triptych	9	2 34.63
1988	Sheikh Ahmed Al Maktoum	MTOTO 5-9-7 (4/1)	M Roberts	A C Stewart	Unfuwain	Tony Bin	10	2 37.33
1989	Hamdan Al-Maktoum's	NASHWAN 3-8-8 (2/9)	W Carson	R Hern	Cacoethes	Top Class	8	2 32.27
1990	Sheikh Mohammed's	BELMEZ 3-8-9 (15/2)	M Kinane	H Cecil	Old Vic	Assatis	11	2 30.76
1991	F Salman's	GENEROUS 3-8-9 (4/6)	A Munro	P Cole	Sanglamore	Rock Hopper	9	2 28.99
1992	Mrs V K Payson's	ST JOVITE 3-8-9 (4/5)	S Craine	J Bolger	Saddlers' Hall	Opera House	8	2 30.85
1993	Sheikh Mohammed's	OPERA HOUSE 5-9-7 (8/1)	M Roberts	M Stoute	White Muzzle	Commander in Chief	10	2 33.94
1994	Sheikh Mohammed's	KING'S THEATRE 3-8-9 (12/1)	M Kinane	H Cecil	White Muzzle	Wagon Master	12	2 28.92
1995	Saeed Maktoum Al Maktoum's	LAMMTARRA 3-8-9 (9/4)	L Dettori	S Bin Suroor	Pentire	Strategic Choice	7	2 31.01
1996	Mollers Racing's	PENTIRE 4-9-7 (100/30)	M Hills	G Wragg	Classic Cliche	Shaamit	8	2 28.11
1997	Godolphin's	SWAIN 5-9-7 (16/1)	J Reid	S Bin Suroor	Pilsudski	Helissio	8	2 46.45
1998	Godolphin's	SWAIN 6-9-7 (11/2)	L Dettori	S Bin Suroor	High-Rise	Royal Anthem	8	2 29.41
1999	Godolphin's	DAYLAMI 5-9-7 (3/1)	L Dettori	S Bin Suroor	Nedawi	Fruits Of Love	8	2 29.35
2000	M Tabor's	MONTJEU 4-9-7 (1/3)	M Kinane	J Hammond	Fantastic Light	Daliapour	7	2 29.98
2001	Mrs J Magnier & M Tabor's	GALILEO 3-8-9 (1/2)	M Kinane	A O'Brien	Fantastic Light	Hightori	12	2 27.71
2002	Exors of the late Lord Weinstock's	GOLAN 4-9-7 (11/2)	K Fallon	Sir M Stoute	Nayef	Zindabad	9	2 29.70
2003	H H Aga Khan	ALAMSHAR 3-8-9 (13/2)	J Murtagh	J Oxx	Sulamani	Kris Kin	12	2 33.26
2004	Godolphin's	DOYEN 4-9-7 (11/10)	L Dettori	S Bin Suroor	Hard Buck	Sulamani	11	2 33.00
2005	H H Aga Khan's (Run at Newbury)	AZAMOUR 4-9-7 (5/2)	M Kinane	J Oxx	Norse Dancer	Bago	12	2 28.20
2006	M Tabor's	HURRICANE RUN 4-9-7 (5/6)	C Soumillon	A Fabre	Electrocutionist	Heart's Cry	6	2 30.20
2007	Mrs J Magnier & M Tabor's	DYLAN THOMAS 4-9-7 (5/4)	J Murtagh	A O'Brien	Youmzain	Maraahel	7	2 31.10
2008	Mrs J Magnier & M Tabor's	DUKE OF MARMALADE 4-9-7 (4/6)	J Murtagh	A O'Brien	Papal Bull	Youmzain	8	2 27.91
2009	Ballymacoll Stud's	CONDUIT 4-9-7 (13/8)	R Moore	Sir M Stoute	Tartan Bearer	Ask	6	2 28.73
2010	Highclere Thoroughbred Racing (Adm. Rous)'s	HARBINGER 4-9-7 (4/1)	O Peslier	Sir M Stoute	Cape Blanco	Youmzain	6	2 26.78
2011	Lady Rothschild's	NATHANIEL 3-8-9 (11/2)	W Buick	J Gosden	Workforce	St Nicholas Abbey	5	2 35.07
2012	Gestut Burg Eberstein & Teruya Yoshida's	DANEDREAM 4-9-4 (9/1)	A Starke	P Schiergen	Nathaniel	St Nicholas Abbey	10	2 31.62
2013	Dr Christophe Berglar's	NOVELLIST 4-9-7 (13/2)	J Murtagh	A Wohler	Trading Leather	Hillstar	8	2 24.60
2014	Hamdan Al Maktoum's	TAGHROODA 3-8-6 (7/2)	P Hanagan	J Gosden	Telescope	Mukhadram	8	2 28.13
2015	Sheikh Mohammed Obaid Al Maktoum's	POSTPONED 4-9-7 (6/1)	A Atzeni	L Cumani	Eagle Top	Romsdal	7	2 31.25

PRIX DE L'ARC DE TRIOMPHE Longchamp-1 mile 4 furlongs

Year	Owner	Winner and Price	Jockey	Trainer	Second	Third	Ran	Time
1975	W Zeitelhack's	STAR APPEAL 5-9-6 (119/1)	G Starkey	T Grieper	On My Way	Comtesse de Loir	24	2 33.60
1976	J Wertheimer's	IVANJICA 4-9-1 (71/10)	F Head	A Head	Crow	Youth	20	2 39.40
1977	R Sangster's	ALLEGED 3-8-11 (38/10)	L Piggott	V O'Brien	Balmerino	Crystal Palace	26	2 30.60
1978	R Sangster's	ALLEGED 4-9-4 (7/5)	L Piggott	V O'Brien	Trillion	Dancing Maid	18	2 36.10
1979	Mme G Head's	THREE TROIKAS 3-8-8 (88/10)	F Head	Mme C Head	Le Marmot	Troy	22	2 28.90
1980	R Sangster's	DETROIT 3-8-8 (67/10)	Pat Eddery	A Head	Argument	Ela-Mana-Mou	14	2 28.00
1981	J Wertheimer's	GOLD RIVER 4-9-1 (53/1)	G W Moore	F Mathet	Bikala	April Run	20	2 35.20
1982	H H Aga Khan's	AKIYDA 3-8-8 (43/4)	Y Saint Martin	F Mathet	Ardross	Awaasif	17	2 37.00
1983	D Wildenstein's	ALL ALONG 4-9-1 (173/10)	W Swinburn	P Biancone	Sun Princess	Luth Enchantee	26	2 28.10
1984	D Wildenstein's	SAGACE 4-9-4 (29/10)	Y Saint Martin	P Biancone	Northern Trick	All Along	22	2 39.10
1985	K Abdulla's	RAINBOW QUEST 4-9-4 (71/10)	Pat Eddery	J Tree	Sagace	Kozana	15	2 39.50

(The first two placings were reversed by the Stewards)

Year	Owner	Winner and Price	Jockey	Trainer	Second	Third	Ran	Time
1986	K Abdulla's	DANCING BRAVE 3-8-11 (11/10)	Pat Eddery	G Harwood	Bering	Triptych	15	2 27.70
1987	P de Moussac's	TREMPOLINO 3-8-11 (20/1)	Pat Eddery	A Fabre	Tony Bin	Triptych	11	2 26.30
1988	Mrs V Gaucci del Bono's	TONY BIN 5-9-4 (14/1)	J Reid	L Camici	Mtoto	Boyatino	24	2 27.30
1989	A Balzarini's	CARROLL HOUSE 4-9-4 (19/1)	M Kinane	M Jarvis	Behera	Saint Andrews	19	2 30.80
1990	A McNall's	SAUMAREZ 3-8-11 (15/1)	G Mosse	N Clement	Epervier Bleu	Snurge	21	2 29.80
1991	B Chalhoub's	SUAVE DANCER 3-8-11 (37/10)	C Asmussen	J Hammond	Magic Night	Pistolet Bleu	14	2 31.40
1992	O Lecerf's	SUBOTICA 4-9-4 (88/10)	T Jarnet	A Fabre	User Friendly	Vert Amande	18	2 39.00
1993	Tsui's	URBAN SEA 4-9-1 (37/1)	E Saint Martin	J Lesbordes	White Muzzle	Opera House	23	2 37.90
1994	Sheikh Mohammed's	CARNEGIE 3-8-11 (3/1)	T Jarnet	A Fabre	Hernando	Apple Tree	20	2 31.10
1995	Saeed Maktoum Al Maktoum's	LAMMTARRA 3-8-11 (2/1)	L Dettori	A Fabre	Freedom Cry	Swain	16	2 31.80
1996	E Sarasola's	HELISSIO 3-8-11 (18/10)	O Peslier	E Lellouche	Pilsudski	Oscar Schindler	16	2 29.90
1997	D Wildenstein's	PEINTRE CELEBRE 3-8-11 (22/10)	O Peslier	A Fabre	Pilsudski	Borgia	16	2 24.60
1998	J-L Lagardère's	SAGAMIX 3-8-11 (5/2)	O Peslier	A Fabre	Leggera	Tiger Hill	18	2 34.50
1999	M Tabor's	MONTJEU 3-8-11 (6/4)	M Kinane	J Hammond	El Condor Pasa	Croco Rouge	14	2 38.50
2000	Godolphin's	SINNDAR 3-8-11 (6/4)	J Murtagh	J Oxx	Egyptband	Volvoreta	14	2 25.80
2001	Godolphin's	SAKHEE 4-9-5 (22/10)	L Dettori	S Bin Suroor	Aquarelliste	Sagacity	17	2 26.70
2002	Godolphin's	MARIENBARD 5-9-5 (158/10)	L Dettori	S Bin Suroor	Sulamani	High Chaparral	16	2 32.30
2003	H H Aga Khan's	DALAKHANI 3-8-11 (9/4)	C Soumillon	A De Royer-Dupre	Mubtaker	High Chaparral	13	2 32.50
2004	Niarchos Family's	BAGO 3-8-11 (10/1)	T Gillet	J E Pease	Cherry Mix	Ouija Board	13	2 25.00
2005	M Tabor's	HURRICANE RUN 3-8-11 (8/1)	K Fallon	A Fabre	Westerner	Bago	15	2 27.40
2006	K Abdulla's	RAIL LINK 3-8-11 (11/4)	S Pasquier	A Fabre	Pride	Hurricane Run	8	2 26.30

(Deep Impact disqualified from third place)

Year	Owner	Winner and Price	Jockey	Trainer	Second	Third	Ran	Time
2007	Mrs J Magnier & M Tabor's	DYLAN THOMAS 4-9-5 (11/2)	K Fallon	A O'Brien	Youmzain	Sagara	12	2 28.50
2008	H H Aga Khan's	ZARKAVA 3-8-8 (13/8)	C Soumillon	A De Royer-Dupre	Youmzain	Soldier of Fortune/It's Gino	16	2 28.80
2009	C Tsui's	SEA THE STARS 3-8-11 (4/6)	M Kinane	J Oxx	Youmzain	Cavalryman	19	2 26.30
2010	K Abdulla's	WORKFORCE 3-8-11 (6/1)	R Moore	Sir M Stoute	Nakayama Festa	Saralina	19	2 35.30
2011	Gestut Burg Eberstein & T Yoshida's	DANEDREAM 3-8-8 (20/1)	A Starke	P Schiergen	Shareta	Snow Fairy	16	2 24.49
2012	Wertheimer & Frere's	SOLEMIA 4-9-2 (33/1)	O Peslier	C Lafon-Parias	Orfevre	Masterstroke	18	2 37.68
2013	H E Sheikh Joaan Bin Hamad Al Thani's	TREVE 3-8-8 (9/2)	T Jarnet	Mme C Head-Maarek	Orfevre	Intello	17	2 32.04
2014	Al Shaqab Racing's	TREVE 4-9-2 (11/1)	T Jarnet	Mme C Head-Maarek	Flintshire	Taghrooda	20	2 26.05
2015	A E Oppenheimer's	GOLDEN HORN 3-8-11 (9/2)	L Dettori	J Gosden	Flintshire	New Bay	17	2 27.23

GRAND NATIONAL STEEPLECHASE Aintree-4m 3f 110y (4m 4f before 2013)

Year	Winner and Price	Age & Weight	Jockey	Second	Third	Ran	Time
1970	GAY TRIP (15/1)	8 11 5	P Taaffe	Vulture	Miss Hunter	28	9 38.00
1971	SPECIFY (28/1)	9 10 13	J Cook	Black Secret	Astbury	38	9 34.20
1972	WELL TO DO (14/1)	9 10 1	G Thorner	Gay Trip	Black Secret/General Symons	42	10 08.40
1973	RED RUM (9/1)	8 10 5	B Fletcher	Crisp	L'Escargot	38	9 01.90
1974	RED RUM (11/1)	9 12 0	B Fletcher	L'Escargot	Charles Dickens	42	9 20.30
1975	L'ESCARGOT (13/2)	12 11 3	T Carberry	Red Rum	Spanish Steps	31	9 31.10
1976	RAG TRADE (14/1)	10 10 12	J Burke	Red Rum	Eyecatcher	32	9 20.90
1977	RED RUM (9/1)	12 11 8	T Stack	Churchtown Boy	Eyecatcher	42	9 30.30
1978	LUCIUS (14/1)	9 10 9	B R Davies	Sebastian V	Drumman	37	9 33.90
1979	RUBSTIC (25/1)	10 10 0	M Barnes	Zongalero	Rough and Tumble	34	9 52.90
1980	BEN NEVIS (40/1)	12 10 12	Mr C Fenwick	Rough and Tumble	The Pilgarlic	30	10 17.40
1981	ALDANITI (10/1)	11 10 13	R Champion	Spartan Missile	Royal Mail	39	9 47.20
1982	GRITTAR (7/1)	9 11 5	E Saunders	Hard Outlook	Loving Words	39	9 12.60
1983	CORBIERE (13/1)	8 11 4	B de Haan	Greasepaint	Yer Man	41	9 47.04
1984	HALLO DANDY (13/1)	10 10 2	N Doughty	Greasepaint	Corbiere	40	9 21.04
1985	LAST SUSPECT (50/1)	11 10 5	H Davies	Mr Snugfit	Corbiere	40	9 42.70
1986	WEST TIP (15/2)	9 10 11	R Dunwoody	Young Driver	Classified	40	9 33.00
1987	MAORI VENTURE (28/1)	11 10 13	S C Knight	The Tsarevich	Lean Ar Aghaidh	40	9 19.30
1988	RHYME 'N' REASON (10/1)	9 11 0	B Powell	Durham Edition	Monanore	40	9 53.50
1989	LITTLE POLVEIR (28/1)	12 10 3	J Frost	West Tip	The Thinker	40	10 06.80
1990	MR FRISK (16/1)	11 10 6	Mr M Armytage	Durham Edition	Rinus	38	8 47.80
1991	SEAGRAM (12/1)	11 10 6	N Hawke	Garrison Savannah	Auntie Dot	40	9 29.90
1992	PARTY POLITICS (14/1)	8 10 7	C Llewellyn	Romany King	Laura's Beau	40	9 06.30
1993	Race Void - false start						
1994	MINNEHOMA (16/1)	11 10 8	R Dunwoody	Just So	Moorcroft Boy	36	10 18.80
1995	ROYAL ATHLETE (40/1)	12 10 6	J Titley	Party Politics	Over The Deel	35	9 04.00
1996	ROUGH QUEST (7/1)	10 10 7	M Fitzgerald	Encore Un Peu	Superior Finish	27	9 00.80
1997	LORD GYLLENE (14/1)	9 10 0	A Dobbin	Suny Bay	Camelot Knight	36	9 05.80
1998	EARTH SUMMIT (7/1)	10 10 5	C Llewellyn	Suny Bay	Samlee	37	10 51.40
1999	BOBBYJO (10/1)	9 10 0	P Carberry	Blue Charm	Call It A Day	32	9 14.00
2000	PAPILLON (10/1)	9 10 12	R Walsh	Mely Moss	Niki Dee	40	9 09.70
2001	RED MARAUDER (33/1)	11 10 11	R Guest	Smarty	Blowing Wind	40	11 00.10
2002	BINDAREE (20/1)	8 10 4	J Culloty	What's Up Boys	Blowing Wind	40	9 09.00
2003	MONTY'S PASS (16/1)	10 10 7	B J Geraghty	Supreme Glory	Amberleigh House	40	9 21.70
2004	AMBERLEIGH HOUSE (16/1)	12 10 10	G Lee	Clan Royal	Lord Atterbury	39	9 20.30
2005	HEDGEHUNTER (7/1)	9 11 1	R Walsh	Royal Auclair	Simply Gifted	40	9 20.80
2006	NUMBERSIXVALVERDE (11/1)	10 10 8	R M Power	Hedgehunter	Clan Royal	40	9 41.00
2007	SILVER BIRCH (33/1)	10 10 6	R M Murphy	McKelvey	Slim Pickings	40	9 13.60
2008	COMPLY OR DIE (7/1)	9 10 9	T Murphy	King Johns Castle	Snowy Morning	40	9 16.60
2009	MON MOME (100/1)	9 11 0	L Treadwell	Comply Or Die	My Will	40	9 32.90
2010	DON'T PUSH IT (10/1)	10 11 5	A P McCoy	Black Apalachi	State Of Play	40	9 04.60
2011	BALLABRIGGS (14/1)	10 11 0	J Maguire	Oscar Time	Don't Push It	40	9 01.20
2012	NEPTUNE COLLONGES (33/1)	11 11 6	D Jacob	Sunnyhillboy	Seabass	40	9 05.10
2013	AURORAS ENCORE (66/1)	11 10 3	R Mania	Cappa Bleu	Teaforthree	40	9 12.00
2014	PINEAU DE RE (25/1)	11 11 6	L Aspell	Balthazar King	Double Seven	40	9 09.90
2015	MANY CLOUDS (25/1)	8 11 9	L Aspell	Saint Are	Montbeg Dude	39	8 56.80

WINNERS OF GREAT RACES

LINCOLN HANDICAP

Doncaster-1m

*2006 **BLYTHE KNIGHT** 6-8-10 30
2007 **VERY WISE 5-8-11 20
2008 **SMOKEY OAKEY** 4-8-9 21
2009 **EXPRESSO STAR** 4-8-12 20
2010 **PENITENT** 4-9-2 21
2011 **SWEET LIGHTNING** 6-9-4 21
2012 **BRAE HILL** 6-9-1 22
2013 **LEVITATE** 5-8-4 22
2014 **OCEAN TEMPEST** 5-9-3 17
2015 **GABRIAL** 6-9-0 22

*Run at Redcar
**Run at Newcastle

GREENHAM STAKES (3y)

Newbury-7f

2006 **RED CLUBS** 9-0 5
2007 **MAJOR CADEAUX** 9-0 6
2008 **PACO BOY** 9-0 8
2009 **VOCALISED** 9-0 8
2010 **DICK TURPIN** 9-0 5
2011 **FRANKEL** 9-0 6
2012 **CASPAR NETSCHER** 9-0 5
2013 **OLYMPIC GLORY** 9-0 5
2014 **KINGMAN** 9-0 10
2015 **MUHAARAR** 9-0 9

EUROPEAN FREE HANDICAP (3y)

Newmarket-7f

2006 **MISU BOND** 8-13 8
2007 **PRIME DEFENDER** 9-5 7
2008 **STIMULATION** 9-3 11
2009 **OUQBA** 8-9 10
2010 **RED JAZZ** 9-6 7
2011 **PAUSANIAS** 8-12 6
2012 **TELWAAR** 8-11 7
2013 **GARSWOOD** 9-0 10
2014 **SHIFTING POWER** 9-1 6
2015 **HOME OF THE BRAVE** 8-13 5

CRAVEN STAKES (3y)

Newmarket-1m

2006 **KILLYBEGS** 8-12 9
2007 **ADAGIO** 8-12 8
2008 **TWICE OVER** 8-12 10
2009 **DELEGATOR** 8-12 7
2010 **ELUSIVE PIMPERNEL** 8-12 9
2011 **NATIVE KHAN** 8-12 6
2012 **TRUMPET MAJOR** 9-1 12
2013 **TORONADO** 9-1 4
2014 **TOORMORE** 9-3 6
2015 **KOOL KOMPANY** 9-3 7

JOCKEY CLUB STAKES

Newmarket-1m 4f

2006 **SHIROCCO** 5-9-3 7
2007 **SIXTIES ICON** 4-9-3 5
2008 **GETAWAY** 5-9-1 10
2009 **BRONZE CANNON** 4-8-12 3
2010 **JUKEBOX JURY** 4-9-3 5
2011 **DANDINO** 4-8-11 6
2012 **AL KAZEEM** 4-8-12 8
2013 **UNIVERSAL** 4-8-12 4
2014 **GOSPEL CHOIR** 5-9-0 8
2015 **SECOND STEP** 4-9-0 4

SANDOWN MILE

Sandown-1m

2006 **ROB ROY** 4-9-0 8
2007 **JEREMY** 4-9-0 9
2008 **MAJOR CADEAUX** 4-9-0 8
2009 **PACO BOY** 4-9-6 7
2010 **PACO BOY** 5-9-0 9
2011 **DICK TURPIN** 4-9-0 5
2012 **PENITENT** 6-9-0 6
2013 **TRUMPET MAJOR** 4-9-0 7
2014 **TULLIUS** 6-9-1 6
2015 **CUSTOM CUT** 6-9-5 6

CHESTER VASE (3y)

Chester-1m 4f 66yds

2006 **PAPAL BULL** 8-12 5
2007 **SOLDIER OF FORTUNE** 9-2 4
2008 **DOCTOR FREMANTLE** 8-12 8
2009 **GOLDEN SWORD** 8-12 8
2010 **TED SPREAD** 8-12 7
2011 **TREASURE BEACH** 8-12 5
2012 **MICKDAAM** 8-12 5
2013 **RULER OF THE WORLD** 8-12 4
2014 **ORCHESTRA** 9-0 8
2015 **HANS HOLBEIN** 9-0 6

CHESTER CUP

Chester-2m 2f 147yds

2006 **ADMIRAL** 5-8-1 17
2007 **GREENWICH MEANTIME** 7-9-2 17
2008 **BULWARK** 6-9-4 17
2009 **DARAAHEM** 4-9-0 17
2010 **MAMLOOK** 6-8-12 17
2011 **OVERTURN** 7-8-13 17
2012 **ILE DE RE** 6-8-11 16
2013 **ADDRESS UNKNOWN** 6-9-0 17
2014 **SUEGIOO** 5-9-4 17
2015 **TRIP TO PARIS** 4-8-9 17

OAKS TRIAL (3y fillies)

Lingfield-1m 3f 106yds

2006 **SINDIRANA** 8-10 10
2007 **KAYAH** 8-12 7
2008 **MIRACLE SEEKER** 8-12 6
2009 **MIDDAY** 8-12 9
2010 **DYNA WALTZ** 8-12 5
2011 **ZAIN AL BOLDAN** 8-12 9
*2012 **VOW** 8-12 8
2013 **SECRET GESTURE** 8-12 7
2014 **HONOR BOUND** 9-0 10
2015 **TOUJOURS L'AMOUR** 9-0 10

*Run over 1m4f on Polytrack

DERBY TRIAL (3y)

Lingfield-1m 3f 106yds

2006 **LINDA'S LAD** 9-3 5
2007 **AQALEEM** 8-12 7

2008	**ALESSANDRO VOLTA** 8-12	5
2009	**AGE OF AQUARIUS** 8-12	5
2010	**BULLET TRAIN** 8-12	7
2011	**DORDOGNE** 8-12	6
*2012	**MAIN SEQUENCE** 8-12	8
2013	**NEVIS** 8-12	4
2014	**SNOW SKY** 9-0	9
2015	**KILIMANJARO** 9-0	5

*Run over 1m4f on Polytrack

MUSIDORA STAKES (3y fillies)
York-1m 2f 88yds

2006	**SHORT SKIRT** 8-12	6
2007	**PASSAGE OF TIME** 9-1	8
2008	**LUSH LASHES** 8-12	8
2009	**SARISKA** 8-12	6
2010	**AVIATE** 8-12	8
2011	**JOVIALITY** 8-12	5
2012	**THE FUGUE** 8-12	6
2013	**LIBER NAUTICUS** 8-12	6
2014	**MADAME CHIANG** 9-0	9
2015	**STAR OF SEVILLE** 9-0	5

DANTE STAKES (3y)
York-1m 2f 88yds

2006	**SEPTIMUS** 9-0	6
2007	**AUTHORIZED** 9-0	6
2008	**TARTAN BEARER** 9-0	6
2009	**BLACK BEAR ISLAND** 9-0	10
2010	**CAPE BLANCO** 9-0	5
2011	**CARLTON HOUSE** 9-0	6
2012	**BONFIRE** 9-0	7
2013	**LIBERTARIAN** 9-0	8
2014	**THE GREY GATSBY** 9-0	6
2015	**GOLDEN HORN** 9-0	7

MIDDLETON STAKES
(fillies and mares)
York-1m 2f 88yds

2006	**STRAWBERRY DALE** 4-8-12	7
2007	**TOPATOO** 5-8-12	7
2008	**PROMISING LEAD** 4-8-12	5
2009	**CRYSTAL CAPELLA** 4-9-2	5
2010	**SARISKA** 4-8-12	4
2011	**MIDDAY** 5-9-3	8
2012	**IZZI TOP** 4-8-12	9
2013	**DALKALA** 4-9-0	8
2014	**AMBIVALENT** 5-9-0	8
2015	**SECRET GESTURE** 5-9-0	8

YORKSHIRE CUP
York-1m 6f (1m 5f 194yds before 2007)

2006	**PERCUSSIONIST** 5-8-12	7
2007	**SERGEANT CECIL** 8-9-3	10
2008	**GEORDIELAND** 7-8-12	5
2009	**ASK** 6-8-13	8
2010	**MANIFEST** 4-8-12	5
2011	**DUNCAN** 6-9-2	8
2012	**RED CADEAUX** 6-9-0	8
2013	**GLEN'S DIAMOND** 5-9-0	8
2014	**GOSPEL CHOIR** 5-9-0	12
2015	**SNOW SKY** 4-9-0	6

DUKE OF YORK STAKES
York-6f

2006	**STEENBERG** 7-9-2	16
2007	**AMADEUS WOLF** 4-9-2	17
2008	**ASSERTIVE** 5-9-7	17
2009	**UTMOST RESPECT** 5-9-7	16

2010	**PRIME DEFENDER** 6-9-7	12
2011	**DELEGATOR** 5-9-7	14
2012	**TIDDLIWINKS** 6-9-7	13
2013	**SOCIETY ROCK** 6-9-13	17
2014	**MAAREK** 7-9-13	13
2015	**GLASS OFFICE** 5-9-8	15

LOCKINGE STAKES
Newbury-1m

2006	**PEERESS** 5-8-11	9
2007	**RED EVIE** 4-8-11	8
2008	**CREACHADOIR** 4-9-0	11
2009	**VIRTUAL** 4-9-0	11
2010	**PACO BOY** 5-9-0	9
2011	**CANFORD CLIFFS** 4-9-0	7
2012	**FRANKEL** 4-9-0	6
2013	**FARHH** 5-9-0	12
2014	**OLYMPIC GLORY** 4-9-0	8
2015	**NIGHT OF THUNDER** 4-9-0	16

HENRY II STAKES
Sandown-2m 78yds

2006	**TUNGSTEN STRIKE** 5-9-2	7
2007	**ALLEGRETTO** 4-9-0	7
2008	**FINALMENTE** 6-9-2	8
2009	**GEORDIELAND** 8-9-2	7
2010	**AKMAL** 4-9-0	9
2011	**BLUE BAJAN** 9-9-2	8
2012	**OPINION POLL** 6-9-4	10
2013	**GLOOMY SUNDAY** 4-8-11	10
2014	**BROWN PANTHER** 6-9-4	11
2015	**VENT DE FORCE** 4-9-0	7

TEMPLE STAKES
Haydock-5f
(Run at Sandown before 2008)

2006	**REVERENCE** 5-9-4	12
2007	**SIERRA VISTA** 7-9-1	8
2008	**FLEETING SPIRIT** 3-8-11	12
2009	**LOOK BUSY** 4-9-1	9
2010	**KINGSGATE NATIVE** 5-9-4	9
2011	**SOLE POWER** 4-9-4	12
2012	**BATED BREATH** 5-9-4	12
2013	**KINGSGATE NATIVE** 8-9-4	10
2014	**HOT STREAK** 3-8-10	9
2015	**PEARL SECRET** 6-9-4	11

BRIGADIER GERARD STAKES
Sandown-1m 2f 7yds

2006	**NOTNOWCATO** 4-9-3	6
2007	**TAKE A BOW** 6-9-0	7
2008	**SMOKEY OAKEY** 4-9-0	14
2009	**CIMA DE TRIOMPHE** 4-9-0	12
2010	**STOTSFOLD** 7-9-0	8
2011	**WORKFORCE** 4-9-0	8
2012	**CARLTON HOUSE** 4-9-0	6
2013	**MUKHADRAM** 4-9-0	5
2014	**SHARESTAN** 6-9-0	3
2015	**WESTERN HYMN** 4-9-3	5

CORONATION CUP
Epsom-1m 4f 10yds

2006	**SHIROCCO** 5-9-0	6
2007	**SCORPION** 5-9-0	7
2008	**SOLDIER OF FORTUNE** 4-9-0	11
2009	**ASK** 6-9-0	8
2010	**FAME AND GLORY** 4-9-0	9
2011	**ST NICHOLAS ABBEY** 4-9-0	5

2012	ST NICHOLAS ABBEY 5-9-0	6
2013	ST NICHOLAS ABBEY 6-9-0	5
2014	CIRRUS DES AIGLES 8-9-0	7
2015	PETHER'S MOON 5-9-0	4

CHARITY SPRINT HANDICAP (3y)
York-6f
2006	PRINCE TAMINO 8-13	18
2007	ABANDONED	
2008	BRAVE PROSPECTOR 9-0	19
2009	SWISS DIVA 9-1	20
2010	VICTOIRE DE LYPHAR 8-7	20
2011	LEXI'S HERO 8-11	20
2012	SHOLAAN 8-7	17
2013	BODY AND SOUL 8-11	19
2014	SEE THE SUN 8-7	20
2015	TWILIGHT SON 8-10	16

QUEEN ANNE STAKES
Ascot-1m (st)
2006	AD VALOREM 4-9-0	7
2007	RAMONTI 5-9-0	8
2008	HARADASUN 5-9-0	11
2009	PACO BOY 4-9-0	9
2010	GOLDIKOVA 5-8-11	10
2011	CANFORD CLIFFS 4-9-0	7
2012	FRANKEL 4-9-0	11
2013	DECLARATION OF WAR 4-9-0	13
2014	TORONADO 4-9-0	10
2015	SOLOW 5-9-0	8

PRINCE OF WALES'S STAKES
Ascot-1m 2f
2006	OUIJA BOARD 5-8-11	7
2007	MANDURO 5-9-0	6
2008	DUKE OF MARMALADE 4-9-0	12
2009	VISION D'ETAT 4-9-0	8
2010	BYWORD 4-9-0	12
2011	REWILDING 4-9-0	7
2012	SO YOU THINK 6-9-0	11
2013	AL KAZEEM 5-9-0	11
2014	THE FUGUE 5-8-11	8
2015	FREE EAGLE 4-9-0	9

ST JAMES'S PALACE STAKES (3y)
Ascot-1m (rnd)
2006	ARAAFA 9-0	11
2007	EXCELLENT ART 9-0	8
2008	HENRYTHENAVIGATOR 9-0	8
2009	MASTERCRAFTSMAN 9-0	10
2010	CANFORD CLIFFS 9-0	9
2011	FRANKEL 9-0	9
2012	MOST IMPROVED 9-0	16
2013	DAWN APPROACH 9-0	9
2014	KINGMAN 9-0	7
2015	GLENEAGLES 9-0	5

COVENTRY STAKES (2y)
Ascot-6f
2006	HELLVELYN 9-1	21
2007	HENRYTHENAVIGATOR 9-1	20
2008	ART CONNOISSEUR 9-1	18
2009	CANFORD CLIFFS 9-1	13
2010	STRONG SUIT 9-1	13
2011	POWER 9-1	23

2012	DAWN APPROACH 9-1	22
2013	WAR COMMAND 9-1	15
2014	THE WOW SIGNAL 9-1	15
2015	BURATINO 9-1	17

KING EDWARD VII STAKES (3y)
Ascot-1m 4f
2006	PAPAL BULL 8-12	9
2007	BOSCOBEL 8-12	9
2008	CAMPANOLOGIST 8-12	9
2009	FATHER TIME 8-12	12
2010	MONTEROSSO 8-12	8
2011	NATHANIEL 8-12	10
2012	THOMAS CHIPPENDALE 8-12	5
2013	HILLSTAR 8-12	8
2014	EAGLE TOP 9-0	9
2015	BALIOS 9-0	7

JERSEY STAKES (3y)
Ascot-7f
2006	JEREMY 9-1	14
2007	TARIQ 9-1	15
2008	AQLAAM 9-1	16
2009	OUQBA 9-1	16
2010	RAINFALL 8-12	13
2011	STRONG SUIT 9-6	9
2012	ISHVANA 8-12	22
2013	GALE FORCE TEN 9-1	21
2014	MUSTAJEEB 9-4	23
2015	DUTCH CONNECTION 9-4	16

DUKE OF CAMBRIDGE STAKES (fillies & mares)
Ascot-1m (st)
(Windsor Forest Stakes before 2013)
2006	SOVIET SONG 6-8-12	10
2007	NANNINA 4-8-12	9
2008	SABANA PERDIDA 5-8-12	13
2009	SPACIOUS 4-8-12	9
2010	STRAWBERRYDAIQUIRI 4-8-12	10
2011	LOLLY FOR DOLLY 4-8-12	13
2012	JOVIALITY 4-8-12	13
2013	DUNTLE 4-8-12	9
2014	INTEGRAL 4-8-12	14
2015	AMAZING MARIA 4-9-0	6

QUEEN MARY STAKES (2y fillies)
Ascot-5f
2006	GILDED 8-12	15
2007	ELLETELLE 8-12	21
2008	LANGS LASH 8-12	17
2009	JEALOUS AGAIN 8-12	13
2010	MAQAASID 8-12	18
2011	BEST TERMS 8-12	14
2012	CEILING KITTY 8-12	27
2013	RIZEENA 8-12	23
2014	ANTHEM ALEXANDER 9-0	21
2015	ACAPULCO 9-0	20

CORONATION STAKES (3y fillies)
Ascot-1m (rnd)
2006	NANNINA 9-0	15
2007	INDIAN INK 9-0	13
2008	LUSH LASHES 9-0	11
2009	GHANAATI 9-0	10
2010	LILLIE LANGTRY 9-0	13
2011	IMMORTAL VERSE 9-0	12
2012	FALLEN FOR YOU 9-0	10

2013	**SKY LANTERN** 9-0	17
2014	**RIZEENA** 9-0	12
2015	**ERVEDYA** 9-0	9

COMMONWEALTH CUP (3y)
Ascot-6f

2015	**MUHAARAR** 9-3	18

ROYAL HUNT CUP
Ascot-1m (st)

2006	**CESARE** 5-8-8	30
2007	**ROYAL OATH** 4-9-0	26
2008	**MR AVIATOR** 4-9-5	29
2009	**FORGOTTEN VOICE** 4-9-1	25
2010	**INVISIBLE MAN** 4-8-9	29
2011	**JULIENAS** 4-8-8	28
2012	**PRINCE OF JOHANNE** 6-9-3	30
2013	**BELGIAN BILL** 5-8-11	28
2014	**FIELD OF DREAM** 7-9-1	28
2015	**GM HOPKINS** 4-9-3	30

QUEEN'S VASE (3y)
Ascot-2m

2006	**SOAPY DANGER** 9-1	11
2007	**MAHLER** 9-1	15
2008	**PATKAI** 9-1	12
2009	**HOLBERG** 9-1	14
2010	**MIKHAIL GLINKA** 9-1	12
2011	**NAMIBIAN** 9-1	11
2012	**ESTIMATE** 8-12	10
2013	**LEADING LIGHT** 9-4	15
2014	**HARTNELL** 9-3	10
2015	**ALOFT** 9-3	13

DIAMOND JUBILEE STAKES
Ascot-6f
(Golden Jubilee Stakes before 2012)

2006	**LES ARCS** 6-9-4	18
2007	**SOLDIER'S TALE** 6-9-4	21
2008	**KINGSGATE NATIVE** 3-8-11	17
2009	**ART CONNOISSEUR** 3-8-11	14
2010	**STARSPANGLEDBANNER** 4-9-4	24
2011	**SOCIETY ROCK** 4-9-4	16
2012	**BLACK CAVIAR** 6-9-1	14
2013	**LETHAL FORCE** 4-9-4	18
2014	**SLADE POWER** 5-9-4	14
2015	**UNDRAFTED** 5-9-3	15

NORFOLK STAKES (2y)
Ascot-5f

2006	**DUTCH ART** 9-1	11
2007	**WINKER WATSON** 9-1	11
2008	**SOUTH CENTRAL** 9-1	11
2009	**RADIOHEAD** 9-1	11
2010	**APPROVE** 9-1	12
2011	**BAPAK CHINTA** 9-1	15
2012	**RECKLESS ABANDON** 9-1	14
2013	**NO NAY NEVER** 9-1	14
2014	**BRAHMA ALGA** 9-1	9
2015	**WATERLOO BRIDGE** 9-1	10

GOLD CUP
Ascot-2m 4f

2006	**YEATS** 5-9-2	12
2007	**YEATS** 6-9-2	14
2008	**YEATS** 7-9-2	10
2009	**YEATS** 8-9-2	9
2010	**RITE OF PASSAGE** 6-9-2	12
2011	**FAME AND GLORY** 5-9-2	15

2012	**COLOUR VISION** 4-9-0	9
2013	**ESTIMATE** 4-8-11	14
2014	**LEADING LIGHT** 4-9-0	12
2015	**TRIP TO PARIS** 4-9-0	12

RIBBLESDALE STAKES (3y fillies)
Ascot-1m 4f

2006	**MONT ETOILE** 8-12	11
2007	**SILKWOOD** 8-12	12
2008	**MICHITA** 8-12	9
2009	**FLYING CLOUD** 8-12	10
2010	**HIBAAYEB** 8-12	11
2011	**BANIMPIRE** 8-12	12
2012	**PRINCESS HIGHWAY** 8-12	14
2013	**RIPOSTE** 8-12	9
2014	**BRACELET** 9-0	12
2015	**CURVY** 9-0	10

HARDWICKE STAKES
Ascot-1m 4f

2006	**MARAAHEL** 5-9-0	8
2007	**MARAAHEL** 6-9-0	7
2008	**MACARTHUR** 4-9-0	9
2009	**BRONZE CANNON** 4-9-3	9
2010	**HARBINGER** 4-9-0	11
2011	**AWAIT THE DAWN** 4-9-0	9
2012	**SEA MOON** 4-9-0	12
2013	**THOMAS CHIPPENDALE** 4-9-0	8
2014	**TELESCOPE** 4-9-1	10
2015	**SNOW SKY** 4-9-1	7

WOKINGHAM STAKES
Ascot-6f

2006	**BALTIC KING** 6-9-10	28
2007	**DARK MISSILE** 4-8-6	26
2008	**BIG TIMER** 4-9-2	27
2009	**HIGH STANDING** 4-8-12	26
2010	**LADDIES POKER TWO** 5-8-11	27
2011	**DEACON BLUES** 4-8-13	25
2012	**DANDY BOY** 6-9-8	28
2013	**YORK GLORY** 5-9-2	26
2014	**BACCARAT** 5-9-2	28
2015	**INTERCEPTION** 5-9-3	25

KING'S STAND STAKES
Ascot-5f

2006	**TAKEOVER TARGET** 7-9-7	28
2007	**MISS ANDRETTI** 6-9-1	20
2008	**EQUIANO** 3-8-12	13
2009	**SCENIC BLAST** 5-9-4	15
2010	**EQUIANO** 5-9-4	12
2011	**PROHIBIT** 6-9-4	19
2012	**LITTLE BRIDGE** 6-9-4	22
2013	**SOLE POWER** 6-9-4	19
2014	**SOLE POWER** 7-9-4	16
2015	**GOLDREAM** 6-9-4	18

NORTHUMBERLAND PLATE
Newcastle-2m 19yds

2006	**TOLDO** 4-8-2	20
2007	**JUNIPER GIRL** 4-8-11	20
2008	**ARC BLEU** 7-8-2	18
2009	**SOM TALA** 6-8-8	17
2010	**OVERTURN** 6-8-7	19
2011	**TOMINATOR** 4-8-5	19
2012	**ILE DE RE** 6-9-3	16
2013	**TOMINATOR** 6-9-10	18
2014	**ANGEL GABRIAL** 5-8-12	19
2015	**QUEST FOR MORE** 5-9-4	19

ECLIPSE STAKES
Sandown-1m 2f 7yds
2006	**DAVID JUNIOR** 4-9-7	9
2007	**NOTNOWCATO** 5-9-7	8
2008	**MOUNT NELSON** 4-9-7	8
2009	**SEA THE STARS** 3-8-10	10
2010	**TWICE OVER** 5-9-7	5
2011	**SO YOU THINK** 5-9-7	5
2012	**NATHANIEL** 4-9-7	9
2013	**AL KAZEEM** 5-9-7	7
2014	**MUKHADRAM** 5-9-7	9
2015	**GOLDEN HORN** 3-8-10	5

LANCASHIRE OAKS (fillies and mares)
Haydock-1m 3f 200yds
2006	**ALLEGRETTO** 3-8-6	8
*2007	**TURBO LINN** 4-9-5	12
2008	**ANNA PAVLOVA** 5-9-8	9
2009	**BARSHIBA** 5-9-5	8
2010	**BARSHIBA** 6-9-5	10
2011	**GERTRUDE BELL** 4-9-5	7
2012	**GREAT HEAVENS** 3-8-6	9
2013	**EMIRATES QUEEN** 4-9-5	8
2014	**POMOLOGY** 4-9-5	9
2015	**LADY TIANA** 4-9-5	10

*Run at Newmarket (July)

DUCHESS OF CAMBRIDGE STAKES (2y fillies)
Newmarket-6f
(Cherry Hinton Stakes before 2013)
2006	**SANDER CAMILLO** 8-12	10
2007	**YOU'RESOTHRILLING** 8-12	14
2008	**PLEASE SING** 8-12	8
2009	**MISHEER** 8-12	10
2010	**MEMORY** 8-12	7
2011	**GAMILATI** 8-12	11
2012	**SENDMYLOVETOROSE** 8-12	10
2013	**LUCKY KRISTALE** 8-12	8
2014	**ARABIAN QUEEN** 9-0	5
2015	**ILLUMINATE** 9-0	9

BUNBURY CUP
(Run as 32Red Trophy in 2010)
Newmarket-7f
2006	**MINE** 8-9-10	19
2007	**GIGANTICUS** 4-8-8	18
2008	**LITTLE WHITE LIE** 4-9-0	18
2009	**PLUM PUDDING** 6-9-10	19
2010	**ST MORITZ** 4-9-1	19
2011	**BRAE HILL** 5-9-3	20
2012	**BONNIE BRAE** 5-9-9	15
2013	**FIELD OF DREAM** 6-9-7	19
2014	**HEAVEN'S GUEST** 4-9-3	13
2015	**RENE MATHIS** 5-9-1	17

PRINCESS OF WALES'S STAKES
Newmarket-1m 4f
2006	**SOAPY DANGER** 3-8-3	4
2007	**PAPAL BULL** 4-9-2	12
2008	**LUCARNO** 4-9-7	6
2009	**DOCTOR FREMANTLE** 4-9-2	9
2010	**SANS FRONTIERES** 4-9-2	8
2011	**CRYSTAL CAPELLA** 6-8-13	8
2012	**FIORENTE** 4-9-2	7
2013	**AL KAZEEM** 4-9-5	6
2014	**CAVALRYMAN** 8-9-2	6
2015	**BIG ORANGE** 4-9-2	8

JULY STAKES (2y)
Newmarket-6f
2006	**STRATEGIC PRINCE** 8-12	9
2007	**WINKER WATSON** 9-1	13
2008	**CLASSIC BLADE** 8-12	10
2009	**ARCANO** 8-12	11
2010	**LIBRANNO** 8-12	5
2011	**FREDERICK ENGELS** 8-12	7
2012	**ALHEBAYEB** 8-12	7
2013	**ANJAAL** 8-12	11
2014	**IVAWOOD** 9-0	12
2015	**SHALAA** 9-0	9

FALMOUTH STAKES (fillies & mares)
Newmarket-1m
2006	**RAJEEM** 3-8-10	7
2007	**SIMPLY PERFECT** 3-8-10	7
2008	**NAHOODH** 3-8-10	11
2009	**GOLDIKOVA** 4-9-5	8
2010	**MUSIC SHOW** 3-8-10	8
2011	**TIMEPIECE** 4-9-5	11
2012	**GIOFRA** 4-9-5	10
2013	**ELUSIVE KATE** 4-9-5	4
2014	**INTEGRAL** 4-9-7	7
2015	**AMAZING MARIA** 4-9-7	7

SUPERLATIVE STAKES (2y)
Newmarket-7f
2006	**HALICARNASSUS** 8-11	7
2007	**HATTA FORT** 9-0	10
2008	**FIRTH OF FIFTH** 9-0	9
2009	**SILVER GRECIAN** 9-0	8
2010	**KING TORUS** 9-0	6
2011	**RED DUKE** 9-0	11
2012	**OLYMPIC GLORY** 9-0	9
2013	**GOOD OLD BOY LUKEY** 9-0	8
2014	**ESTIDHKAAR** 9-1	8
2015	**BIRCHWOOD** 9-1	8

JULY CUP
Newmarket-6f
2006	**LES ARCS** 6-9-5	15
2007	**SAKHEE'S SECRET** 3-8-13	18
2008	**MARCHAND D'OR** 5-9-5	13
2009	**FLEETING SPIRIT** 4-9-2	13
2010	**STARSPANGLEDBANNER** 4-9-5	14
2011	**DREAM AHEAD** 3-8-13	16
2012	**MAYSON** 4-9-5	12
2013	**LETHAL FORCE** 4-9-5	11
2014	**SLADE POWER** 5-9-6	13
2015	**MUHAARAR** 3-9-0	14

WEATHERBYS SUPER SPRINT (2y)
Newbury-5f 34 yds
2006	**ELHAMRI** 9-4	23
2007	ABANDONED	
2008	**JARGELLE** 8-6	23
2009	**MONSIEUR CHEVALIER** 8-12	20
2010	**TEMPLE MEADS** 8-6	24
2011	**CHARLES THE GREAT** 8-11	25
2012	**BODY AND SOUL** 7-12	22
2013	**PENIAPHOBIA** 8-8	24
2014	**TIGGY WIGGY** 9-1	24
2015	**LATHOM** 9-0	22

SUMMER MILE
Ascot-1m (rnd)
2007	CESARE 6-9-1	9
2008	ARCHIPENKO 4-9-6	7
2009	AQLAAM 4-9-1	7
2010	PREMIO LOCO 6-9-1	8
2011	DICK TURPIN 4-9-4	5
2012	FANUNALTER 6-9-1	8
2013	ALJAMAAHEER 4-9-1	11
2014	GUEST OF HONOUR 5-9-1	9
2015	AROD 4-9-1	6

PRINCESS MARGARET STAKES (2y fillies)
Ascot-6f
2006	SCARLET RUNNER 8-12	10
2007	VISIT 8-12	13
2008	AFRICAN SKIES 8-12	16
2009	LADY OF THE DESERT 8-12	9
2010	SORAAYA 8-12	11
2011	ANGELS WILL FALL 8-12	7
2012	MAUREEN 8-12	6
2013	PRINCESS NOOR 8-12	10
2014	OSAILA 9-0	8
2015	BESHARAH 9-0	6

LENNOX STAKES
Goodwood-7f
2006	IFFRAAJ 5-9-4	10
2007	TARIQ 3-8-9	13
2008	PACO BOY 3-8-9	9
2009	FINJAAN 3-8-9	8
2010	LORD SHANAKILL 4-9-2	12
2011	STRONG SUIT 3-8-9	9
2012	CHACHAMAIDEE 5-8-13	7
2013	GARSWOOD 3-8-9	10
2014	ES QUE LOVE 5-9-3	7
2015	TOORMORE 4-9-3	7

STEWARDS' CUP
Goodwood-6f
2006	BORDERLESCOTT 4-9-5	27
2007	ZIDANE 5-9-1	27
2008	CONQUEST 4-8-9	27
2009	GENKI 5-9-1	26
2010	EVENS AND ODDS 6-8-10	28
2011	HOOF IT 4-10-0	27
2012	HAWKEYETHENOO 6-9-9	27
2013	REX IMPERATOR 4-9-4	27
*2014	INTRINSIC 4-8-11	24
2015	MAGICAL MEMORY 3-8-12	27

*Run as 32Red Cup in 2014

GORDON STAKES (3y)
Goodwood-1m 4f
2006	SIXTIES ICON 9-0	7
2007	YELLOWSTONE 9-0	9
2008	CONDUIT 9-0	6
2009	HARBINGER 9-0	9
2010	REBEL SOLDIER 9-0	10
2011	NAMIBIAN 9-3	9
2012	NOBLE MISSION 9-0	7
2013	CAP O'RUSHES 9-0	7
2014	SNOW SKY 9-1	7
2015	HIGHLAND REEL 9-1	9

VINTAGE STAKES (2y)
Goodwood-7f
2006	STRATEGIC PRINCE 9-3	10
2007	RIO DE LA PLATA 9-0	7
2008	ORIZABA 9-0	9
2009	XTENSION 9-0	10
2010	KING TORUS 9-3	7
2011	CHANDLERY 9-0	7
2012	OLYMPIC GLORY 9-3	10
2013	TOORMORE 9-0	12
2014	HIGHLAND REEL 9-1	7
2015	GALILEO GOLD 9-1	8

SUSSEX STAKES
Goodwood-1m
2006	COURT MASTERPIECE 6-9-7	7
2007	RAMONTI 5-9-7	8
2008	HENRYTHENAVIGATOR 3-8-13	6
2009	RIP VAN WINKLE 3-8-13	8
2010	CANFORD CLIFFS 3-8-13	5
2011	FRANKEL 3-8-13	4
2012	FRANKEL 4-9-7	4
2013	TORONADO 3-8-13	7
2014	KINGMAN 3-9-0	4
2015	SOLOW 5-9-8	8

RICHMOND STAKES (2y)
Goodwood-6f
2006	HAMOODY 9-0	7
2007	STRIKE THE DEAL 9-0	10
2008	PROLIFIC 9-0	12
2009	DICK TURPIN 9-0	9
2010	LIBRANNO 9-3	6
2011	HARBOUR WATCH 9-0	10
2012	HEAVY METAL 9-0	10
2013	SAAYERR 9-0	10
2014	IVAWOOD 9-3	8
2015	SHALAA 9-3	8

KING GEORGE STAKES
Goodwood-5f
2006	LA CUCARACHA 5-8-11	18
2007	MOORHOUSE LAD 4-9-0	17
2008	ENTICING 4-8-11	12
2009	KINGSGATE NATIVE 4-9-0	17
2010	BORDERLESCOTT 8-9-0	15
2011	MASAMAH 5-9-0	11
2012	ORTENSIA 7-9-5	17
2013	MOVIESTA 3-8-12	15
2014	TAKE COVER 7-9-1	15
2015	MUTHMIR 5-9-6	15

GOODWOOD CUP
Goodwood-2m
2006	YEATS 5-9-10	15
2007	ALLEGRETTO 4-9-5	15
2008	YEATS 7-9-12	8
2009	SCHIAPARELLI 6-9-7	10
2010	ILLUSTRIOUS BLUE 7-9-7	10
2011	OPINION POLL 5-9-7	15
2012	SADDLER'S ROCK 4-9-7	10
2013	BROWN PANTHER 5-9-7	14
2014	CAVALRYMAN 8-9-8	8
2015	BIG ORANGE 4-9-8	11

MOLECOMB STAKES (2y)
Goodwood-5f

2006	**ENTICING** 8-11	13
2007	**FLEETING SPIRIT** 8-11	16
2008	**FINJAAN** 9-0	11
2009	**MONSIEUR CHEVALIER** 9-0	11
2010	**ZEBEDEE** 9-0	12
2011	**REQUINTO** 9-0	13
2012	**BUNGLE INTHEJUNGLE** 9-0	10
2013	**BROWN SUGAR** 9-0	8
2014	**COTAI GLORY** 9-1	8
2015	**KACHY** 9-1	10

NASSAU STAKES (fillies and mares)
Goodwood-1m 1f 192yds

2006	**OUIJA BOARD** 5-9-5	7
2007	**PEEPING FAWN** 3-8-10	8
2008	**HALFWAY TO HEAVEN** 3-8-10	9
2009	**MIDDAY** 3-8-10	10
2010	**MIDDAY** 4-9-6	7
2011	**MIDDAY** 5-9-6	6
2012	**THE FUGUE** 3-8-11	8
2013	**WINSILI** 3-8-11	14
2014	**SULTANINA** 4-9-7	6
2015	**LEGATISSIMO** 3-8-12	9

HUNGERFORD STAKES
Newbury-7f

2006	**WELSH EMPEROR** 7-9-3	7
2007	**RED EVIE** 4-9-4	10
2008	**PACO BOY** 3-9-0	9
2009	**BALTHAZAAR'S GIFT** 6-9-3	9
2010	**SHAKESPEAREAN** 3-8-11	7
2011	**EXCELEBRATION** 3-8-13	9
2012	**LETHAL FORCE** 3-8-12	9
2013	**GREGORIAN** 4-9-3	5
2014	**BRETON ROCK** 4-9-5	6
2015	**ADAAY** 3-9-2	11

GEOFFREY FREER STAKES
Newbury-1m 5f 61yds

2006	**ADMIRAL'S CRUISE** 4-9-3	5
2007	**PAPAL BULL** 4-9-7	5
2008	**SIXTIES ICON** 5-9-5	10
2009	**KITE WOOD** 3-8-8	8
2010	**SANS FRONTIERES** 4-9-8	8
2011	**CENSUS** 3-8-6	10
2012	**MOUNT ATHOS** 5-9-4	4
2013	**ROYAL EMPIRE** 4-9-4	10
2014	**SEISMOS** 6-9-4	11
2015	**AGENT MURPHY** 4-9-5	6

INTERNATIONAL STAKES
York-1m 2f 88yds

2006	**NOTNOWCATO** 4-9-5	7
2007	**AUTHORIZED** 3-8-11	7
*2008	**DUKE OF MARMALADE** 4-9-5	9
2009	**SEA THE STARS** 3-8-11	4
2010	**RIP VAN WINKLE** 4-9-5	9
2011	**TWICE OVER** 6-9-5	5
2012	**FRANKEL** 4-9-5	9
2013	**DECLARATION OF WAR** 4-9-5	6
2014	**AUSTRALIA** 3-8-12	6
2015	**ARABIAN QUEEN** 3-8-9	7

*Run at Newmarket (July) over 1m 2f

GREAT VOLTIGEUR STAKES (3y)
York-1m 4f

2006	**YOUMZAIN** 8-12	10
2007	**LUCARNO** 8-12	9
*2008	**CENTENNIAL** 8-12	5
2009	**MONITOR CLOSELY** 8-12	7
2010	**REWILDING** 8-12	10
2011	**SEA MOON** 8-12	8
2012	**THOUGHT WORTHY** 8-12	6
2013	**TELESCOPE** 8-12	9
2014	**POSTPONED** 9-0	9
2015	**STORM THE STARS** 9-0	7

*Run at Goodwood

LOWTHER STAKES (2y fillies)
York-6f

2006	**SILK BLOSSOM** 8-12	7
2007	**NAHOODH** 8-12	10
*2008	**INFAMOUS ANGEL** 8-12	7
2009	**LADY OF THE DESERT** 8-12	12
2010	**HOORAY** 8-12	8
2011	**BEST TERMS** 9-1	11
2012	**ROSDHU QUEEN** 8-12	10
2013	**LUCKY KRISTALE** 9-1	6
2014	**TIGGY WIGGY** 9-0	9
2015	**BESHARAH** 9-0	9

*Run at Newmarket (July)

YORKSHIRE OAKS (fillies and mares)
York-1m 4f

2006	**ALEXANDROVA** 3-8-11	6
2007	**PEEPING FAWN** 3-8-11	7
*2008	**LUSH LASHES** 3-8-11	6
2009	**DAR RE MI** 4-9-7	6
2010	**MIDDAY** 4-9-7	8
2011	**BLUE BUNTING** 3-8-11	8
2012	**SHARETA** 4-9-7	6
2013	**THE FUGUE** 4-9-7	7
2014	**TAPESTRY** 3-8-11	7
2015	**PLEASCACH** 3-8-11	11

*Run at Newmarket (July)

EBOR HANDICAP
York-1m 6f (1m 5f 194yds before 2007)

2006	**MUDAWIN** 5-8-4	19
2007	**PURPLE MOON** 4-9-4	19
*2008	**ALL THE GOOD** 5-9-0	20
2009	**SESENTA** 5-8-8	19
2010	**DIRAR** 5-9-1	20
2011	**MOYENNE CORNICHE** 6-8-10	20
2012	**WILLING FOE** 5-9-2	19
2013	**TIGER CLIFF** 4-9-0	14
2014	**MUTUAL REGARD** 5-9-4	19
2015	**LITIGANT** 7-9-1	19

*Run as Newburgh Handicap at Newbury over 1m 5f 61yds

GIMCRACK STAKES (2y)
York-6f

2006	**CONQUEST** 8-12	6
2007	**SIR GERRY** 8-12	8
*2008	**SHAWEEL** 8-12	12
2009	**SHOWCASING** 8-12	6
2010	**APPROVE** 9-1	11
2011	**CASPAR NETSCHER** 8-12	9
2012	**BLAINE** 8-12	8

2013	**ASTAIRE** 8-12	7
2014	**MUHAARAR** 9-0	9
2015	**AJAYA** 9-0	8

*Run at Newbury

NUNTHORPE STAKES
York-5f

2006	**REVERENCE** 5-9-11	14
2007	**KINGSGATE NATIVE** 2-8-1	16
*2008	**BORDERLESCOTT** 6-9-11	14
2009	**BORDERLESCOTT** 7-9-11	16
2010	**SOLE POWER** 3-9-9	12
2011	**MARGOT DID** 3-9-6	15
2012	**ORTENSIA** 7-9-8	19
2013	**JWALA** 4-9-6	17
2014	**SOLE POWER** 7-9-11	13
2015	**MECCA'S ANGEL** 4-9-10	19

*Run at Newmarket (July)

LONSDALE CUP
York-2m 88y (1m 7f 198y before 2006)

2006	**SERGEANT CECIL** 7 9-1	11
2007	**SEPTIMUS** 4 9-1	9
2008	ABANDONED	
2009	**ASKAR TAU** 4 9-1	5
2010	**OPINION POLL** 4 9-1	8
2011	**OPINION POLL** 5 9-4	10
2012	**TIMES UP** 6 9-1	11
2013	**AHZEEMAH** 4 9-3	7
2014	**PALE MIMOSA** 5-9-7	7
2015	**MAX DYNAMITE** 5-9-3	8

PRESTIGE STAKES (2y fillies)
Goodwood-7f

2006	**SESMEN** 9-0	10
2007	**SENSE OF JOY** 9-0	7
2008	**FANTASIA** 9-0	10
2009	**SENT FROM HEAVEN** 9-0	8
2010	**THEYSKENS' THEORY** 9-0	7
2011	**REGAL REALM** 9-0	6
2012	**OLLIE OLGA** 9-0	8
2013	**AMAZING MARIA** 9-0	7
2014	**MALABAR** 9-0	8
2015	**HAWKSMOOR** 9-0	9

CELEBRATION MILE
Goodwood-1m

2006	**CARADAK** 5-9-1	6
2007	**ECHELON** 5-8-12	8
2008	**RAVEN'S PASS** 3-8-9	5
2009	**DELEGATOR** 3-8-9	7
2010	**POET'S VOICE** 3-8-9	4
2011	**DUBAWI GOLD** 3-8-9	7
2012	**PREMIO LOCO** 8-9-1	5
2013	**AFSARE** 6-9-1	8
2014	**BOW CREEK** 3-8-12	8
2015	**KODI BEAR** 3-8-12	6

SOLARIO STAKES (2y)
Sandown-7f 16yds

2006	**DRUMFIRE** 9-0	8
2007	**RAVEN'S PASS** 9-0	9
2008	**SRI PUTRA** 9-0	11
2009	**SHAKESPEAREAN** 9-0	8
2010	**NATIVE KHAN** 9-0	6
2011	**TALWAR** 9-0	4
2012	**FANTASTIC MOON** 9-0	7

2013	**KINGMAN** 9-0	4
2014	**AKTABANTAY** 9-1	5
2015	**FIRST SELECTION** 9-1	10

SPRINT CUP
Haydock-6f

2006	**REVERENCE** 5-9-3	11
2007	**RED CLUBS** 4-9-3	14
*2008	**AFRICAN ROSE** 3-8-12	15
2009	**REGAL PARADE** 5-9-3	14
2010	**MARKAB** 7-9-3	13
2011	**DREAM AHEAD** 3-9-1	16
2012	**SOCIETY ROCK** 5-9-3	13
2013	**GORDON LORD BYRON** 5-9-3	13
2014	**G FORCE** 3-9-1	17
2015	**TWILIGHT SON** 3-9-1	15

*Run at Doncaster

SEPTEMBER STAKES
Kempton-1m 4f Polytrack

2006	**KANDIDATE** 4-9-4	6
2007	**STEPPE DANCER** 4-9-4	7
2008	**HATTAN** 6-9-7	12
2009	**KIRKLEES** 5-9-9	10
2010	**LAAHEB** 4-9-4	9
2011	**MODUN** 4-9-4	7
2012	**DANDINO** 5-9-4	9
2013	**PRINCE BISHOP** 6-9-4	10
2014	**PRINCE BISHOP** 7-9-12	7
2015	**JACK HOBBS** 3-9-3	7

MAY HILL STAKES (2y fillies)
Doncaster-1m

*2006	**SIMPLY PERFECT** 8-12	9
2007	**SPACIOUS** 8-12	12
2008	**RAINBOW VIEW** 9-1	7
2009	**POLLENATOR** 8-12	7
2010	**WHITE MOONSTONE** 8-12	7
2011	**LYRIC OF LIGHT** 8-12	8
2012	**CERTIFY** 8-12	7
2013	**IHTIMAL** 8-12	7
2014	**AGNES STEWART** 9-0	8
2015	**TURRET ROCKS** 9-0	8

*Run at York

PORTLAND HANDICAP
Doncaster-5f 140yds

*2006	**FANTASY BELIEVER** 8-8-13	19
2007	**FULLANDBY** 5-8-13	21
2008	**HOGMANEIGH** 5-9-6	21
2009	**SANTO PADRE** 5-9-1	22
2010	**POET'S PLACE** 5-9-4	22
2011	**NOCTURNAL AFFAIR** 5-9-5	21
2012	**DOC HAY** 5-8-11	20
2013	**ANGELS WILL FALL** 4-9-2	21
2014	**MUTHMIR** 4-9-7	20
2015	**STEPS** 7-9-7	20

*Run at York over 5f 89yds

PARK HILL STAKES (fillies and mares)
Doncaster-1m 6f 132yds

*2006	**RISING CROSS** 3-8-7	7
2007	**HI CALYPSO** 3-8-7	14
2008	**ALLEGRETTO** 5-9-4	8
2009	**THE MINIVER ROSE** 3-8-6	9
2010	**EASTERN ARIA** 4-9-4	12
2011	**MEEZNAH** 4-9-4	7

2012 **WILD COCO** 4-9-4 9
2013 **THE LARK** 3-8-6 9
2014 **SILK SARI** 4-9-5 13
2015 **GRETCHEN** 3-8-7 11
*Run at York

DONCASTER CUP
Doncaster-2m 2f
*2006 **SERGEANT CECIL** 7-9-4 8
2007 **SEPTIMUS** 4-9-4 8
2008 **HONOLULU** 4-9-1 9
2009 **ASKAR TAU** 4-9-4 5
2010 **SAMUEL** 6-9-1 10
2011 **SADDLER'S ROCK** 3-8-1 7
2012 **TIMES UP** 6-9-1 10
2013 **TIMES UP** 7-9-3 7
2014 **ESTIMATE** 5-9-0 12
2015 **PALLASATOR** 6-9-3 11
*Run at York

CHAMPAGNE STAKES (2y)
Doncaster-7f
*2006 **VITAL EQUINE** 8-12 8
2007 **MCCARTNEY** 8-12 10
2008 **WESTPHALIA** 8-12 7
2009 **POET'S VOICE** 8-12 7
2010 **SAAMIDD** 8-12 6
2011 **TRUMPET MAJOR** 8-12 5
2012 **TORONADO** 8-12 5
2013 **OUTSTRIP** 8-12 4
2014 **ESTIDHKAAR** 9-3 6
2015 **EMOTIONLESS** 9-0 6
*Run at York

PARK STAKES
Doncaster-7f
*2006 **IFFRAAJ** 5-9-6 9
2007 **ARABIAN GLEAM** 3-8-12 6
2008 **ARABIAN GLEAM** 4-9-4 9
2009 **DUFF** 6-9-4 6
2010 **BALTHAZAR'S GIFT** 7-9-4 12
2011 **PREMIO LOCO** 7-9-4 5
2012 **LIBRANNO** 4-9-4 8
2013 **VIZTORIA** 3-8-11 9
2014 **ANSGAR** 6-9-4 7
2015 **LIMATO** 3-9-0 15
*Run at York

FLYING CHILDERS STAKES (2y)
Doncaster-5f
*2006 **WI DUD** 9-0 9
2007 **FLEETING SPIRIT** 8-11 8
2008 **MADAME TROP VITE** 8-11 12
2009 **SAND VIXEN** 8-11 10
2010 **ZEBEDEE** 9-0 12
2011 **REQUINTO** 9-0 10
2012 **SIR PRANCEALOT** 9-0 9
2013 **GREEN DOOR** 9-0 7
2014 **BEACON** 9-1 14
2015 **GUTAIFAN** 9-1 9
*Run at York

AYR GOLD CUP
Ayr-6f
2006 **FONTHILL ROAD** 6-9-2 23
2007 **ADVANCED** 4-9-9 28
2008 **REGAL PARADE** 4-8-10 27
2009 **JIMMY STYLES** 5-9-2 26
2010 **REDFORD** 5-9-2 26

2011 **OUR JONATHAN** 4-9-6 26
2012 **CAPTAIN RAMIUS** 6-9-0 26
2013 **HIGHLAND COLORI** 5-8-13 26
2014 **LOUIS THE PIOUS** 6-9-4 27
2015 **DON'T TOUCH** 4-9-9 25

MILL REEF STAKES (2y)
Newbury-6f 8yds
2006 **EXCELLENT ART** 9-1 6
2007 **DARK ANGEL** 9-1 6
2008 **LORD SHANAKILL** 9-1 6
2009 **AWZAAN** 9-1 7
2010 **TEMPLE MEADS** 9-1 7
2011 **CASPAR NETSCHER** 9-4 7
2012 **MOOHAAJIM** 9-1 8
2013 **SUPPLICANT** 9-1 7
2014 **TOOCOOLFORSCHOOL** 9-1 6
2015 **RIBCHESTER** 9-1 6

ROYAL LODGE STAKES (2y)
Newmarket-1m (run at Ascot before 2011)
2006 **ADMIRALOFTHEFLEET** 8-12 7
2007 **CITY LEADER** 8-12 11
2008 **JUKEBOX JURY** 8-12 8
2009 **JOSHUA TREE** 8-12 10
2010 **FRANKEL** 8-12 5
2011 **DADDY LONG LEGS** 8-12 8
2012 **STEELER** 8-12 6
2013 **BERKSHIRE** 8-12 5
2014 **ELM PARK** 9-0 6
2015 **FOUNDATION** 9-0 6

CHEVELEY PARK STAKES (2y fillies)
Newmarket-6f
2006 **INDIAN INK** 8-12 11
2007 **NATAGORA** 8-12 14
2008 **SERIOUS ATTITUDE** 8-12 16
2009 **SPECIAL DUTY** 8-12 8
2010 **HOORAY** 8-12 11
2011 **LIGHTENING PEARL** 8-12 9
2012 **ROSDHU QUEEN** 8-12 11
2013 **VORDA** 8-12 7
2014 **TIGGY WIGGY** 9-0 9
2015 **LUMIERE** 9-0 8

SUN CHARIOT STAKES
(fillies and mares)
Newmarket-1m
2006 **SPINNING QUEEN** 3-8-12 5
2007 **MAJESTIC ROI** 3-8-13 9
2008 **HALFWAY TO HEAVEN** 3-8-13 10
2009 **SAHPRESA** 4-9-2 8
2010 **SAHPRESA** 5-9-2 11
2011 **SAHPRESA** 6-9-3 8
2012 **SIYOUMA** 4-9-3 8
2013 **SKY LANTERN** 3-8-13 7
2014 **INTEGRAL** 4-9-3 7
2015 **ESOTERIQUE** 5-9-3 9

CAMBRIDGESHIRE
Newmarket-1m 1f
2006 **FORMAL DECREE** 3-8-9 33
2007 **PIPEDREAMER** 3-8-12 34
2008 **TAZEEZ** 4-9-2 28
2009 **SUPASEUS** 6-9-1 32
2010 **CREDIT SWAP** 5-8-7 35
2011 **PRINCE OF JOHANNE** 5-8-9 32
2012 **BRONZE ANGEL** 3-8-8 33

2013	**EDUCATE** 4-9-9	31
2014	**BRONZE ANGEL** 5-8-8	31
2015	**THIRD TIME LUCKY** 3-8-4	34

CUMBERLAND LODGE STAKES
Ascot-1m 4f

2006	**YOUNG MICK** 4-9-0	8
2007	**ASK** 4-9-3	8
2008	**SIXTIES ICON** 5-9-3	5
2009	**MAWATHEEQ** 4-9-0	12
2010	**LAAHEB** 4-9-3	6
2011	**QUEST FOR PEACE** 3-8-7	7
2012	**HAWAAFEZ** 4-8-11	6
2013	**SECRET NUMBER** 3-8-7	7
2014	**PETHER'S MOON** 4-9-6	5
2015	**STAR STORM** 3-8-8	8

FILLIES' MILE (2y fillies)
Newmarket-1m (run at Ascot before 2011)

2006	**SIMPLY PERFECT** 8-12	8
2007	**LISTEN** 8-12	7
2008	**RAINBOW VIEW** 8-12	8
2009	**HIBAAYEB** 8-12	9
2010	**WHITE MOONSTONE** 8-12	5
2011	**LYRIC OF LIGHT** 8-12	8
2012	**CERTIFY** 8-12	6
2013	**CHRISELLIAM** 8-12	8
2014	**TOGETHER FOREVER** 9-0	7
2015	**MINDING** 9-0	10

MIDDLE PARK STAKES (2y)
Newmarket-6f

2006	**DUTCH ART** 8-12	6
2007	**DARK ANGEL** 8-12	9
2008	**BUSHRANGER** 8-12	9
2009	**AWZAAN** 8-12	5
2010	**DREAM AHEAD** 8-12	8
2011	**CRUSADE** 8-12	16
2012	**RECKLESS ABANDON** 8-12	10
2013	**ASTAIRE** 9-0	10
2014	**CHARMING THOUGHT** 9-0	6
2015	**SHALAA** 9-0	7

CHALLENGE STAKES
Newmarket-7f

2006	**SLEEPING INDIAN** 5-9-3	16
2007	**MISS LUCIFER** 3-8-12	15
2008	**STIMULATION** 3-9-1	15
2009	**ARABIAN GLEAM** 5-9-3	9
2010	**RED JAZZ** 3-9-1	14
2011	**STRONG SUIT** 3-9-5	8
2012	**FULBRIGHT** 3-9-1	11
2013	**FIESOLANA** 4-9-0	9
2014	**HERE COMES WHEN** 4-9-7	13
2015	**CABLE BAY** 4-9-3	10

DEWHURST STAKES (2y)
Newmarket-7f

2006	**TEOFILO** 9-1	15
2007	**NEW APPROACH** 9-1	13
2008	**INTENSE FOCUS** 9-1	10
2009	**BEETHOVEN** 9-1	15
2010	**FRANKEL** 9-1	6
2011	**PARISH HALL** 9-1	9
2012	**DAWN APPROACH** 9-1	6
2013	**WAR COMMAND** 9-1	6
2014	**BELARDO** 9-1	6
2015	**AIR FORCE BLUE** 9-1	7

CESAREWITCH
Newmarket-2m 2f

2006	**DETROIT CITY** 4-9-1	31
2007	**LEG SPINNER** 6-8-11	33
2008	**CARACCIOLA** 11-9-6	32
2009	**DARLEY SUN** 3-8-6	32
2010	**AIM TO PROSPER** 6-7-13	32
2011	**NEVER CAN TELL** 4-8-11	33
2012	**AIM TO PROSPER** 8-9-10	34
2013	**SCATTER DICE** 4-8-8	33
2014	**BIG EASY** 7-8-7	33
2015	**GRUMETI** 7-8-2	34

ROCKFEL STAKES (2y fillies)
Newmarket-7f

2006	**FINSCEAL BEO** 9-2	14
2007	**KITTY MATCHAM** 8-12	10
2008	**LAHALEEB** 8-12	15
2009	**MUSIC SHOW** 8-12	11
2010	**CAPE DOLLAR** 8-12	10
2011	**WADING** 8-12	9
2012	**JUST THE JUDGE** 8-12	11
2013	**AL THAKHIRA** 8-12	8
2014	**LUCIDA** 9-0	9
2015	**PROMISING RUN** 9-0	7

QIPCO BRITISH CHAMPIONS SPRINT STAKES
Ascot-6f
(run as Diadem Stakes before 2011)

2011	**DEACON BLUES** 4-9-0	16
2012	**MAAREK** 5-9-0	15
2013	**SLADE POWER** 4-9-0	14
2014	**GORDON LORD BYRON** 6-9-2	15
2015	**MUHAARAR** 3-9-1	20

QUEEN ELIZABETH II STAKES (BRITISH CHAMPIONS MILE)
Ascot-1m (st - rnd before 2011)

2006	**GEORGE WASHINGTON** 3-8-13	8
2007	**RAMONTI** 5-9-3	7
2008	**RAVEN'S PASS** 3-8-13	7
2009	**RIP VAN WINKLE** 3-8-13	4
2010	**POET'S VOICE** 3-8-13	8
2011	**FRANKEL** 3-9-0	8
2012	**EXCELEBRATION** 4-9-3	8
2013	**OLYMPIC GLORY** 3-9-0	12
2014	**CHARM SPIRIT** 3-9-1	11
2015	**SOLOW** 5-9-4	9

QIPCO BRITISH CHAMPIONS LONG DISTANCE CUP
(formerly Jockey Club Cup, run at Newmarket before 2011)
Ascot-2m

2011	**FAME AND GLORY** 5-9-0	10
2012	**RITE OF PASSAGE** 8-9-7	9
2013	**ROYAL DIAMOND** 7-9-7	12
2014	**FORGOTTEN RULES** 4-9-7	9
2015	**FLYING OFFICER** 5-9-7	13

QIPCO BRITISH CHAMPIONS FILLIES' AND MARES' STAKES
(formerly Pride Stakes, run at Newmarket before 2011)
Ascot-1m 4f

2011	**DANCING RAIN** 3-8-10	10
2012	**SAPPHIRE** 4-9-3	10
2013	**SEAL OF APPROVAL** 4-9-3	8

2014	**MADAME CHIANG** 3-8-12.................................10
2015	**SIMPLE VERSE** 3-8-12...................................12

QIPCO CHAMPION STAKES (BRITISH CHAMPIONS MIDDLE DISTANCE)

Ascot-1m 2f
(run at Newmarket before 2011)

2006	**PRIDE** 6-9-0...8
2007	**LITERATO** 3-8-12..12
2008	**NEW APPROACH** 3-8-12...............................11
2009	**TWICE OVER** 4-9-3.......................................14
2010	**TWICE OVER** 5-9-3.......................................10
2011	**CIRRUS DES AIGLES** 5-9-3............................12
2012	**FRANKEL** 4-9-3..6
2013	**FARHH** 5-9-3...10
2014	**NOBLE MISSION** 5-9-5...................................9
2015	**FASCINATING ROCK** 4-9-5............................13

CORNWALLIS STAKES (2y)

Ascot-5f

2006	**ALZERRA** 8-1..10
2007	**CAPTAIN GERRARD** 9-0.................................12
2008	**AMOUR PROPRE** 9-0.....................................19
2009	**OUR JONATHAN** 9-0......................................17
2010	**ELECTRIC WAVES** 8-11.................................14
2011	**PONTY ACCLAIM** 8-11...................................16
2012	**BUNGLE INTHEJUNGLE** 9-3.............................6
2013	**HOT STREAK** 9-0..12
2014	**ROYAL RAZALMA** 8-12...................................12
*2015	**QUIET REFLECTION** 8-12...............................11

*Run at Newmarket (Rowley Mile)

TWO-YEAR-OLD TROPHY (2y)

Redcar-6f

2006	**DANUM DANCER** 8-3......................................24
2007	**DUBAI DYNAMO** 9-2.......................................23
2008	**TOTAL GALLERY** 8-9......................................22
2009	**LUCKY LIKE** 8-6..22
2010	**LADIES ARE FOREVER** 7-12...........................22
2011	**BOGART** 8-12...22
2012	**BODY AND SOUL** 8-1......................................21
2013	**VENTURA MIST** 8-7..23
2014	**LIMATO** 8-12...23
2015	**LOG OUT ISLAND** 9-2.....................................20

HORRIS HILL STAKES (2y)

Newbury-7f

2006	**DIJEERR** 8-12..10
2007	**BEACON LODGE** 8-12.....................................11
2008	**EVASIVE** 8-12..13
2009	**CARNABY STREET** 8-12.................................14
2010	**KLAMMER** 8-12...10
2011	**TELL DAD** 8-12...14
2012	**TAWHID** 8-12...8
2013	**PIPING ROCK** 8-12..11
2014	**SMAIH** 9-0..6
2015	**CRAZY HORSE** 9-0..9

RACING POST TROPHY (2y)

Doncaster-1m

*2006	**AUTHORIZED** 9-0..14
2007	**IBN KHALDUN** 9-0...12
2008	**CROWDED HOUSE** 9-0....................................15
2009	**ST NICHOLAS ABBEY** 9-0...............................11
2010	**CASAMENTO** 9-0...10
2011	**CAMELOT** 9-0...5
2012	**KINGSBARNS** 9-0...7
2013	**KINGSTON HILL** 9-0.......................................11
2014	**ELM PARK** 9-1...8
2015	**MARCEL** 9-1..7

*Run at Newbury

NOVEMBER HANDICAP

Doncaster-1m 4f

*2006	**GROUP CAPTAIN** 4-9-5...................................20
2007	**MALT OR MASH** 3-8-10...................................21
2008	**TROPICAL STRAIT** 5-8-13...............................21
2009	**CHARM SCHOOL** 4-8-12.................................23
2010	**TIMES UP** 4-8-13..22
2011	**ZUIDER ZEE** 4-8-13.......................................23
2012	**ART SCHOLAR** 5-8-7......................................23
2013	**CONDUCT** 6-9-2..23
2014	**OPEN EAGLE** 5-8-12......................................23
2015	**LITIGANT** 7-9-10...22

*Run at Windsor

WINNERS OF PRINCIPAL RACES IN IRELAND

IRISH 2000 GUINEAS (3y)
The Curragh-1m
2006	**ARAAFA** 9-0	11
2007	**COCKNEY REBEL** 9-0	12
2008	**HENRYTHENAVIGATOR** 9-0	5
2009	**MASTERCRAFTSMAN** 9-0	9
2010	**CANFORD CLIFFS** 9-0	13
2011	**RODERIC O'CONNOR** 9-0	8
2012	**POWER** 9-0	10
2013	**MAGICIAN** 9-0	10
2014	**KINGMAN** 9-0	11
2015	**GLENEAGLES** 9-0	11

TATTERSALLS GOLD CUP
The Curragh-1m 2f 110yds
2006	**HURRICANE RUN** 4-9-0	3
2007	**NOTNOWCATO** 5-9-0	9
2008	**DUKE OF MARMALADE** 4-9-0	6
2009	**CASUAL CONQUEST** 4-9-0	5
2010	**FAME AND GLORY** 4-9-0	6
2011	**SO YOU THINK** 5-9-1	5
2012	**SO YOU THINK** 6-9-1	5
2013	**AL KAZEEM** 5-9-3	4
2014	**NOBLE MISSION** 5-9-3	5
2015	**AL KAZEEM** 7-9-3	6

IRISH 1000 GUINEAS (3y fillies)
The Curragh-1m
2006	**NIGHTIME** 9-0	15
2007	**FINSCEAL BEO** 9-0	11
2008	**HALFWAY TO HEAVEN** 9-0	13
2009	**AGAIN** 9-0	16
2010	**BETHRAH** 9-0	19
2011	**MISTY FOR ME** 9-0	15
2012	**SAMITAR** 9-0	8
2013	**JUST THE JUDGE** 9-0	15
2014	**MARVELLOUS** 9-0	11
2015	**PLEASCACH** 9-0	18

IRISH DERBY (3y)
The Curragh-1m 4f
2006	**DYLAN THOMAS** 9-0	8
2007	**SOLDIER OF FORTUNE** 9-0	11
2008	**FROZEN FIRE** 9-0	11
2009	**FAME AND GLORY** 9-0	11
2010	**CAPE BLANCO** 9-0	10
2011	**TREASURE BEACH** 9-0	8
2012	**CAMELOT** 9-0	9
2013	**TRADING LEATHER** 9-0	9
2014	**AUSTRALIA** 9-0	5
2015	**JACK HOBBS** 9-0	8

PRETTY POLLY STAKES
(fillies and mares)
Curragh-1m 2f
2006	**ALEXANDER GOLDRUN** 5-9-8	7
2007	**PEEPING FAWN** 3-8-11	9
2008	**PROMISING LEAD** 4-9-9	9
2009	**DAR RE MI** 4-9-9	7
2010	**CHINESE WHITE** 5-9-9	9
2011	**MISTY FOR ME** 3-8-12	7

2012	**IZZI TOP** 4-9-9	4
2013	**AMBIVALENT** 4-9-10	9
2014	**THISTLE BIRD** 6-9-10	8
2015	**DIAMONDSANDRUBIES** 3-8-12	9

IRISH OAKS (3y fillies)
The Curragh-1m 4f
2006	**ALEXANDROVA** 9-0	6
2007	**PEEPING FAWN** 9-0	12
2008	**MOONSTONE** 9-0	14
2009	**SARISKA** 9-0	10
2010	**SNOW FAIRY** 9-0	15
2011	**BLUE BUNTING** 9-0	9
2012	**GREAT HEAVENS** 9-0	7
2013	**CHICQUITA** 9-0	7
2014	**BRACELET** 9-0	10
2015	**COVERT LOVE** 9-0	9

PHOENIX STAKES (2y)
The Curragh-6f
2006	**HOLY ROMAN EMPEROR** 9-1	7
2007	**SAOIRSE ABU** 8-12	6
2008	**MASTERCRAFTSMAN** 9-1	5
2009	**ALFRED NOBEL** 9-1	8
2010	**ZOFFANY** 9-1	7
2011	**LA COLLINA** 8-12	9
2012	**PEDRO THE GREAT** 9-3	5
2013	**SUDIRMAN** 9-3	5
2014	**DICK WHITTINGTON** 9-3	6
2015	**AIR FORCE BLUE** 9-3	7

MATRON STAKES (fillies and mares)
Leopardstown-1m
2006	**RED EVIE** 3-8-12	8
2007	**ECHELON** 5-9-3	9
2008	**LUSH LASHES** 3-8-12	10
2009	**RAINBOW VIEW** 3-8-12	7
2010	**LILLIE LANGTRY** 3-8-12	6
2011	**EMULOUS** 4-9-5	8
*2012	**CHACHAMAIDEE** 5-9-5	11
2013	**LA COLLINA** 4-9-5	12
2014	**FIESOLANA** 5-9-5	10
2015	**LEGATISSIMO** 3-9-0	9

*Duntle disqualified from first place

IRISH CHAMPION STAKES
Leopardstown-1m 2f
2006	**DYLAN THOMAS** 3-9-0	5
2007	**DYLAN THOMAS** 4-9-7	6
2008	**NEW APPROACH** 3-9-0	8
2009	**SEA THE STARS** 3-9-0	9
2010	**CAPE BLANCO** 3-9-0	6
2011	**SO YOU THINK** 5-9-7	6
2012	**SNOW FAIRY** 5-9-4	6
2013	**THE FUGUE** 4-9-4	6
2014	**THE GREY GATSBY** 3-9-0	6
2015	**GOLDEN HORN** 3-9-0	7

IRISH CAMBRIDGESHIRE

The Curragh-1m

2006 **QUINMASTER** 4-10-1	22
2007 **JALMIRA** 6-8-13	24
2008 **TIS MIGHTY** 5-8-1	21
2009 **POET** 4-9-9	27
2010 **HUJAYLEA** 7-8-3	25
2011 **CASTLE BAR SLING** 6-8-11	21
2012 **PUNCH YOUR WEIGHT** 3-8-6	18
2013 **MORAN GRA** 6-8-13	20
2014 **SRETAW** 5-8-8	21
2015 **HINT OF A TINT** 5-9-3	22

MOYGLARE STUD STAKES (2y fillies)

The Curragh-7f

2006 **MISS BEATRIX** 8-12	12
2007 **SAOIRSE ABU** 8-12	9
2008 **AGAIN** 8-12	12
2009 **TERMAGANT** 8-12	7
2010 **MISTY FOR ME** 8-12	12
2011 **MAYBE** 9-1	8
2012 **SKY LANTERN** 9-0	13
2013 **RIZEENA** 9-0	7
2014 **CURSORY GLANCE** 9-0	10
2015 **MINDING** 9-0	9

VINCENT O'BRIEN (NATIONAL) STAKES (2y)

The Curragh-7f

2006 **TEOFILO** 9-1	6
2007 **NEW APPROACH** 9-1	9
2008 **MASTERCRAFTSMAN** 9-1	7
2009 **KINGSFORT** 9-1	6
2010 **PATHFORK** 9-1	9
2011 **POWER** 9-1	9
2012 **DAWN APPROACH** 9-3	7
2013 **TOORMORE** 9-3	5
2014 **GLENEAGLES** 9-3	5
2015 **AIR FORCE BLUE** 9-3	5

IRISH ST LEGER

The Curragh-1m 6f

2006 **KASTORIA** 5-9-7	8
2007 **YEATS** 5-9-11	9
2008 **SEPTIMUS** 5-9-11	9
2009 **ALANDI** 4-9-11	8
2010 **SANS FRONTIERES** 4-9-11	8
2011 **DUNCAN** 6-9-11 dead heated with	6
JUKEBOX JURY 5-9-11	6
2012 **ROYAL DIAMOND** 6-9-11	9
2013 **VOLEUSE DE COEURS** 4-9-8	10
2014 **BROWN PANTHER** 6-9-11	11
2015 **ORDER OF ST GEORGE** 3-9-0	11

IRISH CESAREWITCH

The Curragh-2m

2006 **IKTITAF** 5-8-8	16
2007 **SANDYMOUNT EARL** 4-9-3	21
2008 **SUAILCE** 3-8-1	28
2009 **DANI CALIFORNIA** 5-8-0	29
2010 **BRIGHT HORIZON** 3-8-7	23

2011 **MINSK** 3-8-9	19
2012 **VOLEUSE DE COEURS** 3-9-1	27
2013 **MONTEFELTRO** 5-9-4	30
2014 **EL SALVADOR** 5-9-5	21
2015 **DIGEANTA** 8-9-10	20

CORAL.IE HURDLE

Leopardstown-2m
(Pierse Hurdle 2006-9, MCR Hurdle in 2010-11, Boylesports Hurdle 2012-15)

2007 **SPRING THE QUE** 8-10-3	30
2008 **BARKER** 7-10-6	28
2009 **PENNY'S BILL** 7-9-9	29
2010 **PUYOL** 8-10-10	30
2011 **FINAL APPROACH** 5-10-9	26
2012 **CITIZENSHIP** 6-10-3	30
2013 **ABBEY LANE** 8-10-8	28
2014 **GILGAMBOA** 6-10-9	24
2015 **KATIE T** 6-10-9	24
2016 **HENRY HIGGINS** 6-10-10	23

IRISH CHAMPION HURDLE

Leopardstown-2m

2007 **HARDY EUSTACE** 10-11-10	8
2008 **SIZING EUROPE** 6-11-10	6
2009 **BRAVE INCA** 11-11-10	9
2010 **SOLWHIT** 6-11-10	7
2011 **HURRICANE FLY** 7-11-10	5
2012 **HURRICANE FLY** 8-11-10	5
2013 **HURRICANE FLY** 9-11-10	5
2014 **HURRICANE FLY** 10-11-10	4
2015 **HURRICANE FLY** 11-11-10	6
2016 **FAUGHEEN** 8-11-10	5

IRISH GOLD CUP

Leopardstown-3m
(Hennessy Gold Cup before 2016)

2006 **BEEF OR SALMON** 10-11-12	7
2007 **BEEF OR SALMON** 11-11-12	5
2008 **THE LISTENER** 9-11-10	8
2009 **NEPTUNE COLLONGES** 8-11-10	6
2010 **JONCOL** 7-11-10	7
2011 **KEMPES** 8-11-10	9
2012 **QUEL ESPRIT** 8-11-10	7
2013 **SIR DES CHAMPS** 7-11-10	4
2014 **LAST INSTALMENT** 9-11-10	7
2015 **CARLINGFORD LOUGH** 9-11-10	8
2016 **CARLINGFORD LOUGH** 10-11-10	10

IRISH GRAND NATIONAL

Fairyhouse-3m 5f

2006 **POINT BARROW** 8-10-8	26
2007 **BUTLER'S CABIN** 7-10-4	29
2008 **HEAR THE ECHO** 7-10-0	23
2009 **NICHE MARKET** 8-10-5	30
2010 **BLUESEA CRACKER** 8-10-4	26
2011 **ORGANISEDCONFUSION** 6-9-13	25
2012 **LION NA BEARNAI** 10-10-5	29
2013 **LIBERTY COUNSEL** 10-9-5	28
2014 **SHUTTHEFRONTDOOR** 7-10-13	26
2015 **THUNDER AND ROSES** 7-10-6	28

WINNERS OF PRINCIPAL RACES IN FRANCE

PRIX GANAY
Longchamp-1m 2f 110yds
2006	**CORRE CAMINOS** 4-9-2	7
2007	**DYLAN THOMAS** 4-9-2	8
2008	**DUKE OF MARMALADE** 4-9-2	6
2009	**VISION D'ETAT** 4-9-2	8
2010	**CUTLASS BAY** 4-9-2	9
2011	**PLANTEUR** 4-9-2	7
2012	**CIRRUS DES AIGLES** 6-9-2	6
2013	**PASTORIUS** 5-9-2	8
2014	**CIRRUS DES AIGLES** 8-9-2	8
2015	**CIRRUS DES AIGLES** 9-9-2	7

POULE D'ESSAI DES POULAINS (3y)
Longchamp-1m
2006	**AUSSIE RULES** 9-2	11
2007	**ASTRONOMER ROYAL** 9-2	14
2008	**FALCO** 9-2	19
2009	**SILVER FROST** 9-2	6
2010	**LOPE DE VEGA** 9-2	15
2011	**TIN HORSE** 9-2	14
2012	**LUCAYAN** 9-2	12
2013	**STYLE VENDOME** 9-2	8
2014	**KARAKONTIE** 9-2	12
2015	**MAKE BELIEVE** 9-2	18

POULE D'ESSAI DES POULICHES (3y fillies)
Longchamp-1m
*2006	**TIE BLACK** 9-0	13
2007	**DARJINA** 9-0	13
2008	**ZARKAVA** 9-0	8
2009	**ELUSIVE WAVE** 9-0	11
**2010	**SPECIAL DUTY** 9-0	10
2011	**GOLDEN LILAC** 9-0	16
2012	**BEAUTY PARLOUR** 9-0	13
2013	**FLOTILLA** 9-0	20
2014	**AVENIR CERTAIN** 9-0	16
2015	**ERVEDYA** 9-0	14

*Price Tag disqualified from first place
**Liliside disqualified from first place

PRIX SAINT-ALARY (3y fillies)
Longchamp-1m 2f
2006	**GERMANCE** 9-0	8
2007	**COQUERELLE** 9-0	6
2008	**BELLE ET CELEBRE** 9-0	7
2009	**STACELITA** 9-0	7
2010	**SARAFINA** 9-0	8
2011	**WAVERING** 9-0	12
2012	**SAGAWARA** 9-0	8
2013	**SILASOL** 9-0	8
*2014	**VAZIRA** 9-0	8
2015	**QUEEN'S JEWEL** 9-0	9

* We Are disqualified from first place

PRIX D'ISPAHAN
Longchamp-1m 1f 55yds
2006	**LAVEROCK** 4-9-2	11
2007	**MANDURO** 5-9-2	5
2008	**SAGEBURG** 4-9-2	6

2009	**NEVER ON SUNDAY** 4-9-2	9
2010	**GOLDIKOVA** 5-8-13	8
2011	**GOLDIKOVA** 6-8-13	9
2012	**GOLDEN LILAC** 4-8-13	8
2013	**MAXIOS** 5-9-2	7
2014	**CIRRUS DES AIGLES** 8-9-2	6
2015	**SOLOW** 5-9-2	4

PRIX DU JOCKEY CLUB (3y)
Chantilly-1m 2f 110yds
2006	**DARSI** 9-2	15
2007	**LAWMAN** 9-2	20
2008	**VISION D'ETAT** 9-2	20
2009	**LE HAVRE** 9-2	17
2010	**LOPE DE VEGA** 9-2	22
2011	**RELIABLE MAN** 9-2	16
2012	**SAONOIS** 9-2	20
2013	**INTELLO** 9-2	19
2014	**THE GREY GATSBY** 9-2	16
2015	**NEW BAY** 9-2	14

PRIX DE DIANE (3y fillies)
Chantilly-1m 2f 110yds
2006	**CONFIDENTIAL LADY** 9-0	16
2007	**WEST WIND** 9-0	14
2008	**ZARKAVA** 9-0	13
2009	**STACELITA** 9-0	12
2010	**SARAFINA** 9-0	9
2011	**GOLDEN LILAC** 9-0	9
2012	**VALYRA** 9-0	12
2013	**TREVE** 9-0	11
2014	**AVENIR CERTAIN** 9-0	12
2015	**STAR OF SEVILLE** 9-0	17

GRAND PRIX DE SAINT-CLOUD
Saint-Cloud-1m 4f
2006	**PRIDE** 6-8-13	6
2007	**MOUNTAIN HIGH** 5-9-2	6
2008	**YOUMZAIN** 5-9-2	10
2009	**SPANISH MOON** 5-9-2	9
2010	**PLUMANIA** 4-8-13	5
2011	**SARAFINA** 4-8-13	7
2012	**MEANDRE** 4-9-2	4
2013	**NOVELLIST** 4-9-2	11
*2014	**NOBLE MISSION** 5-9-2	7
2015	**TREVE** 5-8-13	9

*Spiritjim disqualified from first place

PRIX JEAN PRAT (3y)
Chantilly-1m
2006	**STORMY RIVER** 9-2	11
2007	**LAWMAN** 9-2	7
2008	**TAMAYUZ** 9-2	16
2009	**LORD SHANAKILL** 9-2	9
2010	**DICK TURPIN** 9-2	8
2011	**MUTUAL TRUST** 9-2	8
2012	**AESOP'S FABLES** 9-2	8
2013	**HAVANA GOLD** 9-2	12
2014	**CHARM SPIRIT** 9-2	7
2015	**TERRITORIES** 9-2	8

GRAND PRIX DE PARIS (3y)
Longchamp-1m 4f

2006	**RAIL LINK** 9-2	9
2007	**ZAMBEZI SUN** 9-2	7
2008	**MONTMARTRE** 9-2	13
2009	**CAVALRYMAN** 9-2	8
2010	**BEHKABAD** 9-2	9
2011	**MEANDRE** 9-2	7
2012	**IMPERIAL MONARCH** 9-2	9
2013	**FLINTSHIRE** 9-2	8
2014	**GALLANTE** 9-2	11
2015	**ERUPT** 9-2	6

PRIX ROTHSCHILD
(fillies and mares)
Deauville-1m
(run as Prix d'Astarte before 2008)

2006	**MANDESHA** 3-8-7	10
2007	**DARJINA** 3-8-7	12
2008	**GOLDIKOVA** 3-8-8	9
2009	**GOLDIKOVA** 4-9-0	12
2010	**GOLDIKOVA** 5-9-0	7
2011	**GOLDIKOVA** 6-9-2	9
2012	**ELUSIVE KATE** 3-8-9	5
2013	**ELUSIVE KATE** 4-9-2	12
2014	**ESOTERIQUE** 4-9-2	4
2015	**AMAZING MARIA** 4-9-2	8

PRIX MAURICE DE GHEEST
Deauville-6f 110yds

2006	**MARCHAND D'OR** 3-8-11	17
2007	**MARCHAND D'OR** 4-9-2	13
2008	**MARCHAND D'OR** 5-9-2	16
2009	**KING'S APOSTLE** 5-9-2	12
2010	**REGAL PARADE** 6-9-2	15
2011	**MOONLIGHT CLOUD** 3-8-8	13
2012	**MOONLIGHT CLOUD** 4-8-13	9
2013	**MOONLIGHT CLOUD** 5-8-13	14
2014	**GARSWOOD** 4-9-2	14
2015	**MUHAARAR** 3-8-11	12

PRIX JACQUES LE MAROIS
Deauville-1m

2006	**LIBRETTIST** 4-9-4	10
2007	**MANDURO** 5-9-4	6
2008	**TAMAYUZ** 3-8-11	8
2009	**GOLDIKOVA** 4-9-0	9
2010	**MAKFI** 3-8-11	8
2011	**IMMORTAL VERSE** 3-8-8	12
2012	**EXCELEBRATION** 4-9-4	11
2013	**MOONLIGHT CLOUD** 5-9-1	13
2014	**KINGMAN** 3-8-13	5
2015	**ESOTERIQUE** 5-9-1	9

PRIX MORNY (2y)
Deauville-6f

2006	**DUTCH ART** 9-0	7
2007	**MYBOYCHARLIE** 8-13	6
2008	**BUSHRANGER** 9-0	14
2009	**ARCANO** 9-0	5
2010	**DREAM AHEAD** 9-0	11
2011	**DABIRSIM** 9-0	7
2012	**RECKLESS ABANDON** 9-0	11
2013	**NO NAY NEVER** 9-0	10
2014	**THE WOW SIGNAL** 9-0	8
2015	**SHALAA** 9-0	5

PRIX JEAN ROMANET
(fillies and mares)
Deauville-1m 2f

2006	**SATWA QUEEN** 4-8-11	6
2007	**SATWA QUEEN** 5-8-11	9
2008	**FOLK OPERA** 4-8-12	11
2009	**ALPINE ROSE** 4-9-0	8
2010	**STACELITA** 4-9-0	8
2011	**ANNOUNCE** 4-9-0	5
*2012	**IZZI TOP** 4-9-0	6
2013	**ROMANTICA** 4-9-0	6
2014	**RIBBONS** 4-9-0	11
2015	**ODELIZ** 5-9-0	11

*Snow Fairy disqualified from first place

PRIX DU MOULIN DE LONGCHAMP
Longchamp-1m

2006	**LIBRETTIST** 4-9-2	8
2007	**DARJINA** 3-8-8	9
2008	**GOLDIKOVA** 3-8-8	11
2009	**AQLAAM** 4-9-2	6
2010	**FUISSE** 4-9-2	6
2011	**EXCELEBRATION** 3-8-11	4
2012	**MOONLIGHT CLOUD** 4-8-13	4
2013	**MAXIOS** 5-9-2	7
2014	**CHARM SPIRIT** 3-8-11	10
2015	**ERVEDYA** 3-8-9	6

PRIX VERMEILLE (fillies and mares)
Longchamp-1m 4f

2006	**MANDESHA** 3-8-7	11
2007	**MRS LINDSAY** 3-8-9	10
2008	**ZARKAVA** 3-8-8	12
*2009	**STACELITA** 3-8-8	12
2010	**MIDDAY** 4-9-3	12
2011	**GALIKOVA** 3-8-8	6
2012	**SHARETA** 4-9-2	13
2013	**TREVE** 3-8-8	10
2014	**BALTIC BARONESS** 4-9-3	9
2015	**TREVE** 5-9-3	9

*Dar Re Mi disqualified from first place

PRIX DE LA FORET
Longchamp-7f

2006	**CARADAK** 5-9-3	14
2007	**TOYLSOME** 8-9-2	13
2008	**PACO BOY** 3-9-0	8
2009	**VARENAR** 3-9-0	14
2010	**GOLDIKOVA** 5-8-13	10
2011	**DREAM AHEAD** 3-9-0	8
2012	**GORDON LORD BYRON** 4-9-2	11
2013	**MOONLIGHT CLOUD** 5-8-13	11
2014	**OLYMPIC GLORY** 4-9-2	6
2015	**MAKE BELIEVE** 3-9-0	13

PRIX DU CADRAN
Longchamp-2m 4f

2006	**SERGEANT CECIL** 7-9-2	7
2007	**LE MIRACLE** 6-9-2	6
2008	**BANNABY** 5-9-2	11
2009	**ALANDI** 4-9-2	12
2010	**GENTOO** 6-9-2	8
2011	**KASBAH BLISS** 9-9-2	10
2012	**MOLLY MALONE** 4-8-13	10
2013	**ALTANO** 7-9-2	10
2014	**HIGH JINX** 6-9-2	8
2015	**MILLE ET MILLE** 5-9-2	10

PRIX DE L'ABBAYE DE LONGCHAMP
Longchamp-5f
2006	**DESERT LORD** 6-9-11	14
2007	**BENBAUN** 6-9-11	17
*2008	**MARCHAND D'OR** 5-9-11	17
2009	**TOTAL GALLERY** 3-9-11	16
2010	**GILT EDGE GIRL** 4-9-7	21
2011	**TANGERINE TREES** 6-9-11	15
2012	**WIZZ KID** 4-9-7	18
2013	**MAAREK** 6-9-11	20
2014	**MOVE IN TIME** 6-9-11	18
2015	**GOLDREAM** 6-9-11	18

* re-run; Overdose won void first running

PRIX JEAN-LUC LAGARDERE (2y)
Longchamp-1m (7f before 2015)
2006	**HOLY ROMAN EMPEROR** 9-0	9
2007	**RIO DE LA PLATA** 9-0	8
2008	**NAAQOOS** 9-0	7
2009	**SIYOUNI** 9-0	7
2010	**WOOTTON BASSETT** 9-0	7
2011	**DABIRSIM** 9-0	8
2012	**OLYMPIC GLORY** 9-0	8
2013	**KARAKONTIE** 9-0	8
*2014	**FULL MAST** 9-0	9
2015	**ULTRA** 9-0	11

*Gleneagles disqualified from first place

PRIX MARCEL BOUSSAC (2y fillies)
Longchamp-1m
2006	**FINSCEAL BEO** 8-11	13
2007	**ZARKAVA** 8-11	10
2008	**PROPORTIONAL** 8-11	16
2009	**ROSANARA** 8-11	11
2010	**MISTY FOR ME** 8-11	8
2011	**ELUSIVE KATE** 8-11	5
2012	**SILASOL** 8-11	9
2013	**INDONESIENNE** 8-11	12
2014	**FOUND** 8-11	12
2015	**BALLYDOYLE** 8-11	8

PRIX DE L'OPERA (fillies and mares)
Longchamp-1m 2f
2006	**MANDESHA** 3-8-12	6
2007	**SATWA QUEEN** 5-9-2	11
2008	**LADY MARIAN** 3-8-11	14
2009	**SHALANAYA** 3-8-11	9

2010	**LILY OF THE VALLEY** 3-8-11	11
2011	**NAHRAIN** 3-8-11	10
2012	**RIDASIYNA** 3-8-11	13
2013	**DALKALA** 4-9-2	9
2014	**WE ARE** 3-8-11	11
2015	**COVERT LOVE** 3-8-11	13

PRIX ROYAL-OAK
Longchamp-1m 7f 110yds
2006	**MONTARE** 4-9-1	10
2007	**ALLEGRETTO** 4-9-1	11
2008	**YEATS** 7-9-4	11
2009	**ASK** 6-9-4	9
2010	**GENTOO** 6-9-4	10
2011	**BE FABULOUS** 4-9-1	14
2012	**LES BEAUFS** 3-8-9	9
2013	**TAC DE BOISTRON** 6-9-4	15
2014	**TAC DE BOISTRON** 7-9-4	13
2015	**VAZIRABAD** 3-8-10	13

CRITERIUM INTERNATIONAL (2y)
Saint-Cloud-7f (1m before 2015)
2006	**MOUNT NELSON** 9-0	10
2007	**THEWAYYOUARE** 9-0	6
2008	**ZAFISIO** 9-0	11
2009	**JAN VERMEER** 9-0	7
2010	**RODERIC O'CONNOR** 9-0	10
2011	**FRENCH FIFTEEN** 9-0	11
2012	**LOCH GARMAN** 9-0	6
2013	**ECTOT** 9-0	7
2014	**VERT DE GRECE** 9-0	9
2015	**JOHANNES VERMEER** 9-0	8

CRITERIUM DE SAINT-CLOUD (2y)
Saint-Cloud-1m 2f
2006	**PASSAGE OF TIME** 8-11	13
2007	**FULL OF GOLD** 9-0	6
2008	**FAME AND GLORY** 9-0	11
2009	**PASSION FOR GOLD** 9-0	9
2010	**RECITAL** 9-0	10
2011	**MANDAEAN** 9-0	8
2012	**MORANDI** 9-0	8
2013	**PRINCE GIBRALTAR** 9-0	12
2014	**EPICURIS** 9-0	11
2015	**ROBIN OF NAVAN** 9-0	10

WINNERS OF OTHER OVERSEAS RACES

DUBAI WORLD CUP
Meydan-1m 2f Tapeta
(Run at Nad Al Sheba on dirt before 2010)
2006	**ELECTROCUTIONIST** 5-9-0	11
2007	**INVASOR** 5-9-0	7
2008	**CURLIN** 4-9-0	12
2009	**WELL ARMED** 6-9-0	14
2010	**GLORIA DE CAMPEAO** 7-9-0	14
2011	**VICTOIRE PISA** 4-9-0	14
2012	**MONTEROSSO** 5-9-0	13
2013	**ANIMAL KINGDOM** 5-9-0	13

2014	**AFRICAN STORY** 7-9-0	16
2015	**PRINCE BISHOP** 8-9-0	9

KENTUCKY DERBY
Churchill Downs-1m 2f dirt
2006	**BARBARO** 9-0	20
2007	**STREET SENSE** 9-0	20
2008	**BIG BROWN** 9-0	20
2009	**MINE THAT BIRD** 9-0	19
2010	**SUPER SAVER** 9-0	20
2011	**ANIMAL KINGDOM** 9-0	19

2012 **I'LL HAVE ANOTHER** 9-0......................20
2013 **ORB** 9-0......................19
2014 **CALIFORNIA CHROME** 9-0......................19
2015 **AMERICAN PHAROAH** 9-0......................18

BREEDERS' CUP TURF
Various courses-1m 4f
2006 **RED ROCKS** 3-8-10......................11
2007 **ENGLISH CHANNEL** 5-9-0......................8
2008 **CONDUIT** 3-8-9......................11
2009 **CONDUIT** 4-9-0......................7
2010 **DANGEROUS MIDGE** 4-9-0......................7
2011 **ST NICHOLAS ABBEY** 4-9-0......................9
2012 **LITTLE MIKE** 4-9-0......................12
2013 **MAGICIAN** 3-8-10......................12
2014 **MAIN SEQUENCE** 5-9-0......................12
2015 **FOUND** 3-8-7......................12

BREEDERS' CUP CLASSIC
Various courses-1m 2f dirt/pro-ride
2006 **INVASOR** 4-9-0......................13
2007 **CURLIN** 3-8-9......................9
2008 **RAVEN'S PASS** 3-8-9......................12
2009 **ZENYATTA** 5-8-11......................12
2010 **BLAME** 4-9-0......................12
2011 **DROSSELMEYER** 4-9-0......................12
2012 **FORT LARNED** 4-9-0......................12
2013 **MUCHO MACHO MAN** 5-9-0......................11
2014 **BAYERN** 3-8-10......................14
2015 **AMERICAN PHAROAH** 3-8-10......................8

MELBOURNE CUP
Flemington-2m
2006 **DELTA BLUES** 5-8-11......................23
2007 **EFFICIENT** 4-8-8......................21
2008 **VIEWED** 5-8-5......................24
2009 **SHOCKING** 4-8-0......................23
2010 **AMERICAIN** 4-8-8......................23
2011 **DUNADEN** 5-8-8......................23
2012 **GREEN MOON** 5-8-6......................24
2013 **FIORENTE** 5-8-9......................24
2014 **PROTECTIONIST** 4-8-13......................22
2015 **PRINCE OF PENZANCE** 6-8-5......................24

JAPAN CUP
Tokyo-1m 4f
2006 **DEEP IMPACT** 4-9-0......................11
2007 **ADMIRE MOON** 4-9-0......................18
2008 **SCREEN HERO** 4-9-0......................17
2009 **VODKA** 5-8-10......................18
*2010 **ROSE KINGDOM** 3-8-9......................18
2011 **BUENA VISTA** 5-8-9......................16
2012 **GENTILDONNA** 3-8-5......................17
2013 **GENTILDONNA** 4-8-9......................17
2014 **EPIPHANEIA** 4-9-0......................18
2015 **SHONAN PANDORA** 4-8-9......................18
*Buena Vista disqualified from first place

WINNERS OF PRINCIPAL NATIONAL HUNT RACES

PADDY POWER GOLD CUP (HANDICAP CHASE)
Cheltenham-2m 4f 110yds
2006 **EXOTIC DANCER** 6-11-2......................16
2007 **L'ANTARTIQUE** 7-10-13......................20
2008 **IMPERIAL COMMANDER** 7-10-7......................19
2009 **TRANQUIL SEA** 7-10-13......................16
2010 **LITTLE JOSH** 8-10-5......................18
2011 **GREAT ENDEAVOUR** 7-10-3......................20
2012 **AL FEROF** 7-11-8......................18
2013 **JOHNS SPIRIT** 7-10-8......................18
2014 **CAID DU BERLAIS** 5-10-13......................18
2015 **ANNACOTTY** 7-11-0......................20

BETFAIR CHASE
Haydock-3m
2006 **KAUTO STAR** 6-11-8......................6
2007 **KAUTO STAR** 7-11-7......................7
2008 **SNOOPY LOOPY** 10-11-7......................6
2009 **KAUTO STAR** 9-11-7......................6
2010 **IMPERIAL COMMANDER** 9-11-7......................7
2011 **KAUTO STAR** 11-11-7......................6
2012 **SILVINIACO CONTI** 6-11-7......................5
2013 **CUE CARD** 7-11-7......................8
2014 **SILVINIACO CONTI** 8-11-7......................9
2015 **CUE CARD** 9-11-7......................5

HENNESSY GOLD CUP HANDICAP CHASE
Newbury-3m 2f 110yds
2006 **STATE OF PLAY** 6-11-4......................16
2007 **DENMAN** 7-11-12......................18
2008 **MADISON DU BERLAIS** 7-11-4......................15
2009 **DENMAN** 9-11-12......................19
2010 **DIAMOND HARRY** 7-10-0......................20
2011 **CARRUTHERS** 8-10-4......................18
2012 **BOBS WORTH** 7-11-6......................19
2013 **TRIOLO D'ALENE** 6-11-1......................21
2014 **MANY CLOUDS** 7-11-6......................19
2015 **SMAD PLACE** 8-11-4......................15

TINGLE CREEK CHASE
Sandown-2m
2006 **KAUTO STAR** 6-11-7......................7
2007 **TWIST MAGIC** 5-11-7......................8
2008 **MASTER MINDED** 5-11-7......................7
2009 **TWIST MAGIC** 7-11-7......................5
*2010 **MASTER MINDED** 7-11-7......................9
2011 **SIZING EUROPE** 8-11-7......................7
2012 **SPRINTER SACRE** 6-11-7......................7
2013 **SIRE DE GRUGY** 7-11-7......................7
2014 **DODGING BULLETS** 6-11-7......................10
2015 **SIRE DE GRUGY** 9-11-7......................7
*Run at Cheltenham over 2m 110yds

CHRISTMAS HURDLE
Kempton-2m

2006	JAZZ MESSENGER 6-11-7		7
2007	STRAW BEAR 6-11-7		6
2008	HARCHIBALD 9-11-7		7
2009	GO NATIVE 6-11-7		7
*2010	BINOCULAR 7-11-7		6
2011	BINOCULAR 7-11-7		5
2012	DARLAN 5-11-7		7
2013	MY TENT OR YOURS 6-11-7		6
2014	FAUGHEEN 6-11-7		6
2015	FAUGHEEN 7-11-7		5

*Run in January 2011

KING GEORGE VI CHASE
Kempton-3m

2006	KAUTO STAR 6-11-10		9
2007	KAUTO STAR 7-11-10		7
2008	KAUTO STAR 8-11-10		10
2009	KAUTO STAR 9-11-10		13
*2010	LONG RUN 6-11-10		9
2011	KAUTO STAR 11-11-10		7
2012	LONG RUN 7-11-10		9
2013	SILVINIACO CONTI 7-11-10		9
2014	SILVINIACO CONTI 8-11-10		10
2015	CUE CARD 9-11-10		9

*Run in January 2011

WELSH GRAND NATIONAL (HANDICAP CHASE)
Chepstow-3m 5f 110yds

2006	HALCON GENELARDAIS 6-11-3		18
2007	MIKO DE BEAUCHENE 7-10-5		18
2008	NOTRE PERE 7-11-10		20
2009	DREAM ALLIANCE 8-10-8		18
*2010	SYNCHRONISED 8-11-6		18
2011	LE BEAU BAI 8-10-1		20
**2012	MONBEG DUDE 8-10-1		17
2013	MOUNTAINOUS 8-10-0		20
2014	EMPEROR'S CHOICE 7-10-8		19
***2015	MOUNTAINOUS 11-10-6		20

*Run in January 2011
**Run in January 2013
***Run in January 2016

CLARENCE HOUSE CHASE
(Victor Chandler Chase before 2014)
Ascot-2m 1f

2007	ABANDONED		
2008	TAMARINBLEU 8-11-7		7
2009	MASTER MINDED 6-11-7		5
2010	TWIST MAGIC 8-11-7		7
2011	MASTER MINDED 8-11-7		9
2012	SOMERSBY 8-11-7		8
*2013	SPRINTER SACRE 7-11-7		7
2014	SIRE DE GRUGY 8-11-7		7
2015	DODGING BULLETS 7-11-7		5
2016	UN DE SCEAUX 8-11-7		5

*Run at Cheltenham over 2m 110 yds

BETFAIR H'CAP HURDLE
Newbury-2m 110yds
(Totesport Trophy 2006-2011)

2006	ABANDONED		
2007	HEATHCOTE 5-10-6		20

WINGMAN

2008	WINGMAN 6-10-0		24
2009	ABANDONED		
2010	GET ME OUT OF HERE 6-10-6		23
2011	RECESSION PROOF 5-10-8		15
2012	ZARKANDAR 5-11-1		20
2013	MY TENT OR YOURS 6-11-2		21
2014	SPLASH OF GINGE 6-10-3		20
2015	VIOLET DANCER 5-10-9		23

SUPREME NOVICES' HURDLE
Cheltenham-2m 110yds

2006	NOLAND 5-11-7		20
2007	EBAZIYAN 6-11-7		22
2008	CAPTAIN CEE BEE 7-11-7		22
2009	GO NATIVE 6-11-7		20
2010	MENORAH 5-11-7		18
2011	AL FEROF 5-11-7		15
2012	CINDERS AND ASHES 5-11-7		19
2013	CHAMPAGNE FEVER 6-11-7		12
2014	VAUTOUR 5-11-7		18
2015	DOUVAN 5-11-7		12

ARKLE CHALLENGE TROPHY (NOVICES' CHASE)
Cheltenham-2m

2006	VOY POR USTEDES 5-11-2		14
2007	MY WAY DE SOLZEN 7-11-7		13
2008	TIDAL BAY 7-11-7		14
2009	FORPADYDEPLASTERER 7-11-7		17
2010	SIZING EUROPE 8-11-7		12
2011	CAPTAIN CHRIS 7-11-7		10
2012	SPRINTER SACRE 6-11-7		6
2013	SIMONSIG 7-11-7		7
2014	WESTERN WARHORSE 6-11-4		9
2015	UN DE SCEAUX 7-11-4		11

CHAMPION HURDLE
Cheltenham-2m 110yds

2006	BRAVE INCA 8-11-10		18
2007	SUBLIMITY 7-11-10		10
2008	KATCHIT 5-11-10		15
2009	PUNJABI 6-11-10		23
2010	BINOCULAR 6-11-10		12
2011	HURRICANE FLY 7-11-10		11
2012	ROCK ON RUBY 7-11-10		10
2013	HURRICANE FLY 9-11-10		9
2014	JEZKI 6-11-10		9
2015	FAUGHEEN 7-11-10		8

QUEEN MOTHER CHAMPION CHASE
Cheltenham-2m

2006	NEWMILL 8-11-10		12
2007	VOY POR USTEDES 6-11-10		10
2008	MASTER MINDED 5-11-10		8
2009	MASTER MINDED 6-11-10		12
2010	BIG ZEB 9-11-10		9
2011	SIZING EUROPE 9-11-10		11
2012	FINIAN'S RAINBOW 9-11-10		8
2013	SPRINTER SACRE 7-11-10		7
2014	SIRE DE GRUGY 8-11-10		11
2015	DODGING BULLETS 7-11-10		11

NEPTUNE INVESTMENT MANAGEMENT NOVICES' HURDLE
(Royal & SunAlliance Hurdle until 2007,
Ballymore Hurdle 2008-9)
Cheltenham-2m 5f
2006	**NICANOR** 5-11-7	17
2007	**MASSINI'S MAGUIRE** 6-11-7	15
2008	**FIVEFORTHREE** 6-11-7	15
2009	**MIKAEL D'HAGUENET** 5-11-7	14
2010	**PEDDLERS CROSS** 5-11-7	17
2011	**FIRST LIEUTENANT** 6-11-7	12
2012	**SIMONSIG** 6-11-7	17
2013	**THE NEW ONE** 5-11-7	8
2014	**FAUGHEEN** 6-11-7	15
2015	**WINDSOR PARK** 6-11-7	10

RSA CHASE
(Royal & SunAlliance Chase before 2009)
(Cheltenham-3m
2006	**STAR DE MOHAISON** 5-10-8	15
2007	**DENMAN** 7-11-4	17
2008	**ALBERTAS RUN** 7-11-4	11
2009	**COOLDINE** 7-11-4	15
2010	**WEAPON'S AMNESTY** 7-11-4	9
2011	**BOSTONS ANGEL** 7-11-4	12
2012	**BOBS WORTH** 7-11-4	9
2013	**LORD WINDERMERE** 7-11-4	11
2014	**O'FAOLAINS BOY** 7-11-4	15
2015	**DON POLI** 6-11-4	8

WORLD HURDLE
Cheltenham-3m
2006	**MY WAY DE SOLZEN** 6-11-10	20
2007	**INGLIS DREVER** 8-11-10	14
2008	**INGLIS DREVER** 9-11-10	17
2009	**BIG BUCK'S** 6-11-10	14
2010	**BIG BUCK'S** 7-11-10	14
2011	**BIG BUCK'S** 8-11-10	13
2012	**BIG BUCK'S** 9-11-10	11
2013	**SOLWHIT** 9-11-10	13
2014	**MORE OF THAT** 6-11-10	10
2015	**COLE HARDEN** 6-11-10	16

TRIUMPH HURDLE (4y)
Cheltenham-2m 1f
2006	**DETROIT CITY** 11-0	17
2007	**KATCHIT** 11-0	23
2008	**CELESTIAL HALO** 11-0	14
2009	**ZAYNAR** 11-0	18
2010	**SOLDATINO** 11-0	17
2011	**ZARKANDAR** 11-0	23
2012	**COUNTRYWIDE FLAME** 11-0	20
2013	**OUR CONOR** 11-0	17
2014	**TIGER ROLL** 11-0	15
2015	**PEACE AND CO** 11-0	16

CHELTENHAM GOLD CUP
Cheltenham-3m 2f 110yds
2006	**WAR OF ATTRITION** 7-11-10	22
2007	**KAUTO STAR** 7-11-10	18
2008	**DENMAN** 8-11-10	12
2009	**KAUTO STAR** 9-11-10	16
2010	**IMPERIAL COMMANDER** 9-11-10	11
2011	**LONG RUN** 6-11-0	13
2012	**SYNCHRONISED** 9-11-10	14

2013	**BOBS WORTH** 8-11-10	9
2014	**LORD WINDERMERE** 8-11-10	13
2015	**CONEYGREE** 8-11-10	16

RYANAIR CHASE (FESTIVAL TROPHY)
Cheltenham-2m 5f
2006	**FONDMORT** 10-11-0	11
2007	**TARANIS** 6-11-0	9
2008	**OUR VIC** 10-11-0	9
2009	**IMPERIAL COMMANDER** 8-11-0	10
2010	**ALBERTAS RUN** 9-11-0	13
2011	**ALBERTAS RUN** 10-11-0	11
2012	**RIVERSIDE THEATRE** 8-11-0	12
2013	**CUE CARD** 7-11-0	8
2014	**DYNASTE** 8-11-0	11
2015	**UXIZANDRE** 7-11-0	14

BETFRED BOWL CHASE
(Betfair Bowl Chase 2005-8)
(Totesport Bowl Chase 2009-11)
Aintree-3m 1f
2006	**CELESTIAL GOLD** 8-11-8	9
2007	**EXOTIC DANCER** 7-11-12	5
2008	**OUR VIC** 10-11-10	5
2009	**MADISON DU BERLAIS** 8-11-10	10
2010	**WHAT A FRIEND** 7-11-7	5
2011	**NACARAT** 10-11-7	6
2012	**FOLLOW THE PLAN** 9-11-7	11
2013	**FIRST LIEUTENANT** 8-11-7	8
2014	**SILVINIACO CONTI** 8-11-7	6
2015	**SILVINIACO CONTI** 9-11-7	7

MELLING CHASE
Aintree-2m 4f
2006	**HI CLOY** 9-11-10	11
2007	**MONET'S GARDEN** 9-11-10	6
2008	**VOY POR USTEDES** 7-11-10	6
2009	**VOY POR USTEDES** 8-11-10	10
2010	**ALBERTAS RUN** 9-11-10	11
2011	**MASTER MINDED** 8-11-10	10
2012	**FINIAN'S RAINBOW** 10-11-10	8
2013	**SPRINTER SACRE** 7-11-10	6
2014	**BOSTON BOB** 9-11-10	10
2015	**DON COSSACK** 8-11-10	10

AINTREE HURDLE
Aintree-2m 4f
2006	**ASIAN MAZE** 7-11-0	9
2007	**AL EILE** 7-11-7	11
2008	**AL EILE** 8-11-7	9
2009	**SOLWHIT** 5-11-7	16
2010	**KHYBER KIM** 8-11-7	7
2011	**OSCAR WHISKY** 6-11-7	8
2012	**OSCAR WHISKY** 7-11-7	5
2013	**ZARKANDAR** 6-11-7	9
2014	**THE NEW ONE** 6-11-7	7
2015	**JEZKI** 7-11-7	6

SCOTTISH GRAND NATIONAL (H'CAP CHASE)
Ayr-4m 110 yds (4m 1f before 2007)

2006	**RUN FOR PADDY** 10-10-2	30
2007	**HOT WELD** 8-9-9	23
2008	**IRIS DE BALME** 8-9-7	24
2009	**HELLO BUD** 11-10-9	17
2010	**MERIGO** 9-10-0	30
2011	**BESHABAR** 9-10-4	28
2012	**MERIGO** 11-10-2	24
2013	**GODSMEJUDGE** 7-11-3	24
2014	**AL CO** 9-10-0	29
2015	**WAYWARD PRINCE** 11-10-1	29

BET365 GOLD CUP (H'CAP CHASE)
(Betfred Gold Cup 2005-7)
Sandown-3m 5f 110yds

2006	**LACDOUDAL** 7-11-5	18
2007	**HOT WELD** 8-10-0	10
2008	**MONKERHOSTIN** 11-10-13	19
2009	**HENNESSY** 8-10-7	14
2010	**CHURCH ISLAND** 11-10-5	19
2011	**POKER DE SIVOLA** 8-10-12	18
2012	**TIDAL BAY** 11-11-12	19
2013	**QUENTIN COLLONGES** 9-10-12	19
2014	**HADRIAN'S APPROACH** 7-11-0	19
2015	**JUST A PAR** 8-10-0	20

DISTANCE CONVERSION

5f	1,000m	10f	2,000m	15f	3,000m	20f	4,000m
6f	1,200m	11f	2,200m	16f	3,200m	21f	4,200m
7f	1,400m	12f	2,400m	17f	3,400m	22f	4,400m
8f	1,600m	13f	2,600m	18f	3,600m		
9f	1,800m	14f	2,800m	19f	3,800m		

LEADING TRAINERS ON THE FLAT: 1899-2015

1899 J Porter	1938 C Boyd-Rochfort	1977 M V O'Brien
1900 R Marsh	1939 J L Jarvis	1978 H Cecil
1901 J Huggins	1940 F Darling	1979 H Cecil
1902 R S Sievier	1941 F Darling	1980 W Hern
1903 G Blackwell	1942 F Darling	1981 M Stoute
1904 P P Gilpin	1943 W Nightingall	1982 H Cecil
1905 W T Robinson	1944 Frank Butters	1983 W Hern
1906 Hon G Lambton	1945 W Earl	1984 H Cecil
1907 A Taylor	1946 Frank Butters	1985 H Cecil
1908 C Morton	1947 F Darling	1986 M Stoute
1909 A Taylor	1948 C F N Murless	1987 H Cecil
1910 A Taylor	1949 Frank Butters	1988 H Cecil
1911 Hon G Lambton	1950 C H Semblat	1989 M Stoute
1912 Hon G Lambton	1951 J L Jarvis	1990 H Cecil
1913 R Wootton	1952 M Marsh	1991 P Cole
1914 A Taylor	1953 J L Jarvis	1992 R Hannon Snr
1915 P P Gilpin	1954 C Boyd-Rochfort	1993 H Cecil
1916 R C Dawson	1955 C Boyd-Rochfort	1994 M Stoute
1917 A Taylor	1956 C F Elsey	1995 J Dunlop
1918 A Taylor	1957 C F N Murless	1996 Saeed bin Suroor
1919 A Taylor	1958 C Boyd-Rochfort	1997 M Stoute
1920 A Taylor	1959 C F N Murless	1998 Saeed bin Suroor
1921 A Taylor	1960 C F N Murless	1999 Saeed bin Suroor
1922 A Taylor	1961 C F N Murless	2000 Sir M Stoute
1923 A Taylor	1962 W Hern	2001 A O'Brien
1924 R C Dawson	1963 P Prendergast	2002 A O'Brien
1925 A Taylor	1964 P Prendergast	2003 Sir M Stoute
1926 F Darling	1965 P Prendergast	2004 Saeed bin Suroor
1927 Frank Butters	1966 M V O'Brien	2005 Sir M Stoute
1928 Frank Butters	1967 C F N Murless	2006 Sir M Stoute
1929 R C Dawson	1968 C F N Murless	2007 A O'Brien
1930 H S Persse	1969 A M Budgett	2008 A O'Brien
1931 J Lawson	1970 C F N Murless	2009 Sir M Stoute
1932 Frank Butters	1971 I Balding	2010 R Hannon Snr
1933 F Darling	1972 W Hern	2011 R Hannon Snr
1934 Frank Butters	1973 C F N Murless	2012 J Gosden
1935 Frank Butters	1974 P Walwyn	2013 R Hannon Snr
1936 J Lawson	1975 P Walwyn	2014 R Hannon Jnr
1937 C Boyd-Rochfort	1976 H Cecil	2015 J Gosden

CHAMPION JOCKEYS ON THE FLAT: 1898-2015

1898 O Madden	161	1920 S Donoghue	143	1941 H Wragg	71
1899 S Loates	160	1921 S Donoghue	141	1942 G Richards	67
1900 L Reiff	143	1922 S Donoghue	102	1943 G Richards	65
1901 O Madden	130	1923 S Donoghue	89	1944 G Richards	88
1902 W Lane	170	C Elliott	89	1945 G Richards	104
1903 O Madden	154	1924 C Elliott	106	1946 G Richards	212
1904 O Madden	161	1925 G Richards	118	1947 G Richards	269
1905 E Wheatley	124	1926 T Weston	95	1948 G Richards	224
1906 W Higgs	149	1927 G Richards	164	1949 G Richards	261
1907 W Higgs	146	1928 G Richards	148	1950 G Richards	201
1908 D Maher	139	1929 G Richards	135	1951 G Richards	227
1909 F Wootton	165	1930 F Fox	129	1952 G Richards	231
1910 F Wootton	137	1931 G Richards	145	1953 Sir G Richards	191
1911 F Wootton	187	1932 G Richards	190	1954 D Smith	129
1912 F Wootton	118	1933 G Richards	259	1955 D Smith	168
1913 D Maher	115	1934 G Richards	212	1956 D Smith	155
1914 S Donoghue	129	1935 G Richards	217	1957 A Breasley	173
1915 S Donoghue	62	1936 G Richards	174	1958 D Smith	165
1916 S Donoghue	43	1937 G Richards	216	1959 D Smith	157
1917 S Donoghue	42	1938 G Richards	206	1960 L Piggott	170
1918 S Donoghue	66	1939 G Richards	155	1961 A Breasley	171
1919 S Donoghue	129	1940 G Richards	68	1962 A Breasley	179

1963 A Breasley 176	1981 L Piggott 179	1999 K Fallon 200
1964 L Piggott 140	1982 L Piggott 188	2000 K Darley 152
1965 L Piggott 160	1983 W Carson 159	2001 K Fallon 166
1966 L Piggott 191	1984 S Cauthen 130	2002 K Fallon 144
1967 L Piggott 117	1985 S Cauthen 195	2003 K Fallon 208
1968 L Piggott 139	1986 Pat Eddery 176	2004 L Dettori 192
1969 L Piggott 163	1987 S Cauthen 197	2005 J Spencer 163
1970 L Piggott 162	1988 Pat Eddery 183	2006 R Moore 180
1971 L Piggott 162	1989 Pat Eddery 171	2007 S Sanders 190
1972 W Carson 132	1990 Pat Eddery 209	J Spencer 190
1973 W Carson 164	1991 Pat Eddery 165	2008 R Moore 186
1974 Pat Eddery 148	1992 M Roberts 206	2009 R Moore 174
1975 Pat Eddery 164	1993 Pat Eddery 169	2010 P Hanagan 191
1976 Pat Eddery 162	1994 L Dettori 233	2011 P Hanagan 165
1977 Pat Eddery 176	1995 L Dettori 211	2012 R Hughes 172
1978 W Carson 182	1996 Pat Eddery 186	2013 R Hughes 203
1979 J Mercer 164	1997 K Fallon 196	2014 R Hughes 161
1980 W Carson 166	1998 K Fallon 185	2015 S De Sousa 132

CHAMPION APPRENTICES ON THE FLAT 1980-2015

1980 P Robinson..................59	1992 D Harrison..................56	2005 S Golam 44
1981 B Crossley..................45	1993 D Harrison..................40	H Turner 44
1982 W Newnes..................57	1994 S Davies..................45	2006 S Donohoe..................44
1983 M Hills..................39	1995 S Sanders..................61	2007 G Fairley..................65
1984 T Quinn..................62	1996 D O'Neill..................79	2008 W Buick..................50
1985 G Carter..................37	1997 R Ffrench..................77	D Probert..................50
W Ryan..................37	1998 C Lowther..................72	2009 F Tylicki..................60
1986 G Carter..................34	1999 R Winston..................49	2010 M Lane..................41
1987 G Bardwell..................27	2000 L Newman..................87	2011 M Harley..................57
1988 G Bardwell..................39	2001 C Catlin..................71	2012 A Ryan..................40
1989 L Dettori..................71	2002 P Hanagan..................81	2013 J Hart..................51
1990 J Fortune..................46	2003 R Moore..................52	2014 O Murphy 74
1991 D Holland..................79	2004 T Queally..................59	2015 T Marquand 54

LEADING OWNERS ON THE FLAT: 1896-2015

1896 Ld de Rothschild	1925 Ld Astor	1954 Her Majesty
1897 Mr J Gubbins	1926 Ld Woolavington	1955 Lady Zia Wernner
1898 Ld de Rothschild	1927 Ld Derby	1956 Maj L B Holliday
1899 Duke of Westminster	1928 Ld Derby	1957 Her Majesty
1900 H.R.H. The Prince of Wales	1929 H.H. Aga Khan	1958 Mr J McShain
1901 Sir G Blundell Maple	1930 H.H. Aga Khan	1959 Prince Aly Khan
1902 Mr R S Sievier	1931 Mr J A Dewar	1960 Sir Victor Sassoon
1903 Sir James Miller	1932 H.H. Aga Khan	1961 Maj L B Holliday
1904 Sir James Miller	1933 Ld Derby	1962 Maj L B Holliday
1905 Col W Hall Walker	1934 H.H. Aga Khan	1963 Mr J R Mullion
1906 Ld Derby (late)	1935 H.H. Aga Khan	1964 Mrs H E Jackson
1907 Col W Hall Walker	1936 Ld Astor	1965 M J Ternynck
1908 Mr J B Joel	1937 H.H. Aga Khan	1966 Lady Zia Wernher
1909 Mr "Fairie"	1938 Ld Derby	1967 Mr H J Joel
1910 Mr "Fairie"	1939 Ld Rosebery	1968 Mr Raymond R Guest
1911 Ld Derby	1940 Lord Rothermere	1969 Mr D Robinson
1912 Mr T Pilkington	1941 Ld Glanely	1970 Mr C Engelhard
1913 Mr J B Joel	1942 His Majesty	1971 Mr P Mellon
1914 Mr J B Joel	1943 Miss D Paget	1972 Mrs J Hislop
1915 Mr L Neumann	1944 H.H. Aga Khan	1973 Mr N B Hunt
1916 Mr E Hulton	1945 Ld Derby	1974 Mr N B Hunt
1917 Mr "Fairie"	1946 H.H. Aga Khan	1975 Dr C Vittadini
1918 Lady James Douglas	1947 H.H. Aga Khan	1976 Mr D Wildenstein
1919 Ld Glanely	1948 H.H. Aga Khan	1977 Mr R Sangster
1920 Sir Robert Jardine	1949 H.H. Aga Khan	1978 Mr R Sangster
1921 Mr S B Joel	1950 M M Boussac	1979 Sir M Sobell
1922 Ld Woolavington	1951 M M Boussac	1980 S Weinstock
1923 Ld Derby	1952 H.H. Aga Khan	1981 H.H. Aga Khan
1924 H.H. Aga Khan	1953 Sir Victor Sassoon	1982 Mr R Sangster

1983 Mr R Sangster
1984 Mr R Sangster
1985 Sheikh Mohammed
1986 Sheikh Mohammed
1987 Sheikh Mohammed
1988 Sheikh Mohammed
1989 Sheikh Mohammed
1990 Mr Hamdan Al-Maktoum
1991 Sheikh Mohammed
1992 Sheikh Mohammed
1993 Sheikh Mohammed

1994 Mr Hamdan Al-Maktoum
1995 Mr Hamdan Al-Maktoum
1996 Godolphin
1997 Sheikh Mohammed
1998 Godolphin
1999 Godolphin
2000 H.H. Aga Khan
2001 Godolphin
2002 Mr Hamdan Al-Maktoum
2003 K Abdullah
2004 Godolphin

2005 Mr Hamdan Al-Maktoum
2006 Godolphin
2007 Godolphin
2008 HRH Princess Haya of Jordan
2009 Mr Hamdan Al-Maktoum
2010 K Abdullah
2011 K Abdullah
2012 Godolphin
2013 Godolphin
2014 Mr Hamdan Al-Maktoum
2015 Godolphin

LEADING SIRES ON THE FLAT: 1896-2015

1896 St Simon
1897 Kendal
1898 Galopin
1899 Orme
1900 St Simon
1901 St Simon
1902 Persimmon
1903 St Frusquin
1904 Gallinule
1905 Gallinule
1906 Persimmon
1907 St Frusquin
1908 Persimmon
1909 Cyllene
1910 Cyllene
1911 Sundridge
1912 Persimmon
1913 Desmond
1914 Polymelus
1915 Polymelus
1916 Polymelus
1917 Bayardo
1918 Bayardo
1919 The Tetrarch
1920 Polymelus
1921 Polymelus
1922 Lemberg
1923 Swynford
1924 Son-in-Law
1925 Phalaris
1926 Hurry On
1927 Buchan
1928 Phalaris
1929 Tetratema
1930 Son-in-Law
1931 Pharos
1932 Gainsborough
1933 Gainsborough
1934 Blandford
1935 Blandford

1936 Fairway
1937 Solario
1938 Blandford
1939 Fairway
1940 Hyperion
1941 Hyperion
1942 Hyperion
1943 Fairway
1944 Fairway
1945 Hyperion
1946 Hyperion
1947 Nearco
1948 Big Game
1949 Nearco
1950 Fair Trial
1951 Nasrullah
1952 Tehran
1953 Chanteur II
1954 Hyperion
1955 Alycidon
1956 Court Martial
1957 Court Martial
1958 Mossborough
1959 Petition
1960 Aureole
1961 Aureole
1962 Never Say Die
1963 Ribot
1964 Chamossaire
1965 Court Harwell
1966 Charlottesville
1967 Ribot
1968 Ribot
1969 Crepello
1970 Northern Dancer
1971 Never Bend
1972 Queen's Hussar
1973 Vaguely Noble
1974 Vaguely Noble
1975 Great Nephew

1976 Wolver Hollow
1977 Northern Dancer
1978 Mill Reef (USA)
1979 Petingo
1980 Pitcairn
1981 Great Nephew
1982 Be My Guest (USA)
1983 Northern Dancer
1984 Northern Dancer
1985 Kris
1986 Nijinsky (CAN)
1987 Mill Reef (USA)
1988 Caerleon (USA)
1989 Blushing Groom (FR)
1990 Sadler's Wells (USA)
1991 Caerleon (USA)
1992 Sadler's Wells (USA)
1993 Sadler's Wells (USA)
1994 Sadler's Wells (USA)
1995 Sadler's Wells (USA)
1996 Sadler's Wells (USA)
1997 Sadler's Wells (USA)
1998 Sadler's Wells (USA)
1999 Sadler's Wells (USA)
2000 Sadler's Wells (USA)
2001 Sadler's Wells (USA)
2002 Sadler's Wells (USA)
2003 Sadler's Wells (USA)
2004 Sadler's Wells (USA)
2005 Danehill (USA)
2006 Danehill (USA)
2007 Danehill (USA)
2008 Galileo (IRE)
2009 Danehill Dancer (IRE)
2010 Galileo (IRE)
2011 Galileo (IRE)
2012 Galileo (IRE)
2013 Galileo (IRE)
2014 Galileo (IRE)
2015 Galileo (IRE)

LEADING BREEDERS ON THE FLAT: 1912-2015

1912 Col. W Hall Walker
1913 Mr J B Joel
1914 Mr J B Joel
1915 Mr L Neumann
1916 Mr E Hulton
1917 Mr "Fairie"
1918 Lady James Douglas
1919 Ld Derby

1920 Ld Derby
1921 Mr S B Joel
1922 Ld Derby
1923 Ld Derby
1924 Lady Sykes
1925 Ld Astor
1926 Ld Woolavington
1927 Ld Derby

1928 Ld Derby
1929 Ld Derby
1930 Ld Derby
1931 Ld Dewar
1932 H.H. Aga Khan
1933 Sir Alec Black
1934 H.H. Aga Khan
1935 H.H. Aga Khan

1936 Ld Astor	1962 Maj L B Holliday	1989 Mr Hamdan Al-Maktoum
1937 H.H. Aga Khan	1963 Mr H F Guggenheim	1990 Capt. Macdonald- Buchanan
1938 Ld Derby	1964 Bull Run Stud	1991 Barronstown Stud
1939 Ld Rosebery	1965 Mr J Ternynck	1992 Swettenham Stud
1940 Mr H E Morriss	1966 Someries Stud	1993 Juddmonte Farms
1941 Ld Glanely	1967 Mr H J Joel	1994 Shadwell Farm & Estate Ltd
1942 National Stud	1968 Mill Ridge Farm	1995 Shadwell Farm & Estate Ltd
1943 Miss D Paget	1969 Lord Rosebery	1996 Sheikh Mohammed
1944 Ld Rosebery	1970 Mr E P Taylor	1997 Sheikh Mohammed
1945 Ld Derby	1971 Mr P Mellon	1998 Sheikh Mohammed
1946 Lt- Col H Boyd-Rochfort	1972 Mr J Hislop	1999 H. H. The Aga Khan's Studs
1947 H.H. Aga Khan	1973 Claiborne Farm	2000 H. H. The Aga Khan's Studs
1948 H.H. Aga Khan	1974 Mr N B Hunt	2001 Shadwell Farm & Estate Ltd
1949 H.H. Aga Khan	1975 Overbury Stud	2002 Gainsborough Stud
1950 M M Boussac	1976 Dayton Ltd	2003 Juddmonte
1951 M M Boussac	1977 Mr E P Taylor	2004 Juddmonte
1952 H. H. Aga Khan	1978 Cragwood Estates Inc	2005 Shadwell Farm & Estate Ltd
1953 Mr F Darling	1979 Ballymacoll Stud	2006 Darley
1954 Maj L B Holliday	1980 P Clarke	2007 Darley
1955 Someries Stud	1981 H.H. Aga Khan	2008 Darley
1956 Maj L B Holliday	1982 Someries Stud	2009 Darley
1957 Eve Stud	1983 White Lodge Stud	2010 Juddmonte
1958 Mr R Ball	1984 Mr E P Taylor	2011 Juddmonte
1959 Prince Aly Khan and the late	1985 Dalham Stud Farms	2012 Juddmonte
H.H. Aga Khan	1986 H.H. Aga Khan	2013 Darley
1960 Eve Stud Ltd	1987 Cliveden Stud	2014 Darley
1961 Eve Stud Ltd	1988 H. H. Aga Khan	2015 Darley

LEADING TRAINERS OVER JUMPS: 1947-2015

1947-48 F T T Walwyn	1970-71 F T Winter	1993-94 D Nicholson
1948-49 F T T Walwyn	1971-72 F T Winter	1994-95 D Nicholson
1949-50 P V F Cazalet	1972-73 F T Winter	1995-96 M C Pipe
1950-51 T F Rimell	1973-74 F T Winter	1996-97 M C Pipe
1951-52 N Crump	1974-75 F T Winter	1997-98 M C Pipe
1952-53 M V O'Brien	1975-76 T F Rimell	1998-99 M C Pipe
1953-54 M V O'Brien	1976-77 F T Winter	1999-00 M C Pipe
1954-55 H R Price	1977-78 F T Winter	2000-01 M C Pipe
1955-56 W Hall	1978-79 M H Easterby	2001-02 M C Pipe
1956-57 N Crump	1979-80 M H Easterby	2002-03 M C Pipe
1957-58 F T T Walwyn	1980-81 M H Easterby	2003-04 M C Pipe
1958-59 H R Price	1981-82 M W Dickinson	2004-05 M C Pipe
1959-60 P V F Cazalet	1982-83 M W Dickinson	2005-06 P F Nicholls
1960-61 T F Rimell	1983-84 M W Dickinson	2006-07 P F Nicholls
1961-62 H R Price	1984-85 F T Winter	2007-08 P F Nicholls
1962-63 K Piggott	1985-86 N J Henderson	2008-09 P F Nicholls
1963-64 F T T Walwyn	1986-87 N J Henderson	2009-10 P F Nicholls
1964-65 P V F Cazalet	1987-88 D R C Elsworth	2010-11 P F Nicholls
1965-66 H R Price	1988-89 M C Pipe	2010-11 P F Nicholls
1966-67 H R Price	1989-90 M C Pipe	2011-12 P F Nicholls
1967-68 Denys Smith	1990-91 M C Pipe	2012-13 N J Henderson
1968-69 T F Rimell	1991-92 M C Pipe	2013-14 P F Nicholls
1969-70 T F Rimell	1992-93 M C Pipe	2014-15 P F Nicholls

CHAMPION JOCKEYS OVER JUMPS: 1902-2015

Prior to the 1925-26 season the figure relates to racing between January and December

1902	F Mason	67	1909	R Gordon	45	1916	C Hawkins	17
1903	P Woodland	54	1910	E Piggott	67	1917	W Smith	15
1904	F Mason	59	1911	W Payne	76	1918	G Duller	17
1905	F Mason	73	1912	I Anthony	78	1919	Mr H Brown	48
1906	F Mason	58	1913	E Piggott	60	1920	F B Rees	64
1907	F Mason	59	1914	Mr J R Anthony	60	1921	F B Rees	65
1908	P Cowley	65	1915	E Piggott	44	1922	J Anthony	78

1923	F B Rees	64	1953-54	R Francis	76	1983-84	J Francome	131
1924	F B Rees	108	1954-55	T Moloney	67	1984-85	J Francome	101
1925	E Foster	76	1955-56	F Winter	74	1985-86	P Scudamore	91
1925-26	T Leader	61	1956-57	F Winter	80	1986-87	P Scudamore	123
1926-27	F B Rees	59	1957-58	F Winter	82	1987-88	P Scudamore	132
1927-28	W Stott	88	1958-59	T Brookshaw	83	1988-89	P Scudamore	221
1928-29	W Stott	65	1959-60	S Mellor	68	1989-90	P Scudamore	170
1929-30	W Stott	77	1960-61	S Mellor	118	1990-91	P Scudamore	141
1930-31	W Stott	81	1961-62	S Mellor	80	1991-92	P Scudamore	175
1931-32	W Stott	77	1962-63	J Gifford	70	1992-93	R Dunwoody	173
1932-33	G Wilson	61	1963-64	J Gifford	94	1993-94	R Dunwoody	197
1933-34	G Wilson	56	1964-65	T Biddlecombe	114	1994-95	R Dunwoody	160
1934-35	G Wilson	73	1965-66	T Biddlecombe	102	1995-96	A P McCoy	175
1935-36	G Wilson	57	1966-67	J Gifford	122	1996-97	A P McCoy	190
1936-37	G Wilson	45	1967-68	J Gifford	82	1997-98	A P McCoy	253
1937-38	G Wilson	59	1968-69	B R Davies	77	1998-99	A P McCoy	186
1938-39	T F Rimell	61		T Biddlecombe	77	1999-00	A P McCoy	245
1939-40	T F Rimell	24	1969-70	B R Davies	91	2000-01	A P McCoy	191
1940-41	G Wilson	22	1970-71	G Thorner	74	2001-02	A P McCoy	289
1941-42	R Smyth	12	1971-72	B R Davies	89	2002-03	A P McCoy	256
1942-43	No racing		1972-73	R Barry	125	2003-04	A P McCoy	209
1943-44	No racing		1973-74	R Barry	94	2004-05	A P McCoy	200
1944-45	H Nicholson	15	1974-75	T Stack	82	2005-06	A P McCoy	178
	T F Rimell	15	1975-76	J Francome	96	2006-07	A P McCoy	184
1945-46	T F Rimell	54	1976-77	T Stack	97	2007-08	A P McCoy	140
1946-47	J Dowdeswell	58	1977-78	J J O'Neill	149	2008-09	A P McCoy	186
1947-48	B Marshall	66	1978-79	J Francome	95	2009-10	A P McCoy	195
1948-49	T Moloney	60	1979-80	J J O'Neill	117	2010-11	A P McCoy	218
1949-50	T Moloney	95	1980-81	J Francome	105	2011-12	A P McCoy	199
1950-51	T Moloney	83	1981-82	J Francome	120	2012-13	A P McCoy	185
1951-52	T Moloney	99		P Scudamore	120	2013-14	A P McCoy	218
1952-53	F Winter	121	1982-83	J Francome	106	2014-15	A P McCoy	231

LEADING OWNERS OVER JUMPS: 1947-2015

(Please note that prior to the 1994-95 season the leading owner was determined by win prizemoney only)

1947-48	Mr J Proctor	1970-71	Mr F Pontin	1992-93	Mrs J Mould
1948-49	Mr W F Williamson	1971-72	Capt T A Forster	1993-94	Pell-Mell Partners
1949-50	Mrs L Brotherton	1972-73	Mr N H Le Mare	1994-95	Roach Foods Limited
1950-51	Mr J Royle	1973-74	Mr N H Le Mare	1995-96	Mr A T A Wates
1951-52	Miss D Paget	1974-75	Mr R Guest	1996-97	Mr R Ogden
1952-53	Mr J H Griffin	1975-76	Mr P B Raymond	1997-98	Mr D A Johnson
1953-54	Mr J H Griffin	1976-77	Mr N H Le Mare	1998-99	Mr J P McManus
1954-55	Mrs W H E Welman	1977-78	Mrs O Jackson	1999-00	Mr R Ogden
1955-56	Mrs L Carver	1978-79	Snailwell Stud Co Ltd	2000-01	Sir R Ogden
1956-57	Mrs Geoffrey Kohn	1979-80	Mr H J Joel	2001-02	Mr D A Johnson
1957-58	Mr D J Coughlan	1980-81	Mr R J Wilson	2002-03	Mr D A Johnson
1958-59	Mr J E Bigg	1981-82	Sheikh Ali Abu Khamsin	2003-04	Mr D A Johnson
1959-60	Miss W H Wallace	1982-83	Sheikh Ali Abu Khamsin	2004-05	Mr D A Johnson
1960-61	Mr C Vaughan	1983-84	Sheikh Ali Abu Khamsin	2005-06	Mr J P McManus
1961-62	Mr N Cohen	1984-85	T Kilroe and Son Ltd	2006-07	Mr J P McManus
1962-63	Mr P B Raymond	1985-86	Sheikh Ali Abu Khamsin	2007-08	Mr D A Johnson
1963-64	Mr J K Goodman	1986-87	Mr H J Joel	2008-09	Mr J P McManus
1964-65	Mrs M Stephenson	1987-88	Miss Juliet E Reed	2009-10	Mr J P McManus
1965-66	Duchess of Westminster	1988-89	Mr R Burridge	2010-11	Mr T Hemmings
1966-67	Mr C P T Watkins	1989-90	Mrs Harry J Duffey	2011-12	Mr J P McManus
1967-68	Mr H S Alper	1990-91	Mr P Piller	2012-13	Mr J P McManus
1968-69	Mr B P Jenks	1991-92	Whitcombe Manor	2013-14	Mr J P McManus
1969-70	Mr E R Courage		Racing Stables Ltd	2014-15	Mr J P McManus

LEADING AMATEUR RIDERS OVER JUMPS: 1948-2015

1948-49	Ld Mildmay	30	1952-53	Mr A H Moralee	22		Mr A H Moralee	13
1949-50	Ld Mildmay	38	1953-54	Mr A H Moralee	22	1956-57	Mr R McCreery	23
1950-51	Mr P Chisman	13	1954-55	Mr A H Moralee	16	1957-58	Mr J Lawrence	18
1951-52	Mr C Straker	19	1955-56	Mr R McCreery	13	1958-59	Mr J Sutcliffe	18

1959-60 Mr G Kindersley............22
1960-61 Sir W Pigott-Brown......28
1961-62 Mr A Biddlecombe......30
1962-63 Sir W Pigott-Brown......20
1963-64 Mr S Davenport............32
1964-65 Mr M Gifford............15
1965-66 Mr C Collins............24
1966-67 Mr C Collins............33
1967-68 Mr R Tate............30
1968-69 Mr R Tate............17
1969-70 Mr M Dickinson 23
1970-71 Mr J Lawrence............17
1971-72 Mr W Foulkes 26
1972-73 Mr R Smith............56
1973-74 Mr A Webber 21
1974-75 Mr R Lamb 22
1975-76 Mr P Greenall 25
         Mr G Jones............25
1976-77 Mr P Greenall 27

1977-78 Mr G Sloan............23
1978-79 Mr T G Dun............26
1979-80 Mr O Sherwood 29
1980-81 Mr P Webber 32
1981-82 Mr D Browne 28
1982-83 Mr D Browne 33
1983-84 Mr S Sherwood 28
1984-85 Mr S Sherwood 30
1985-86 Mr T Thomson Jones... 25
1986-87 Mr T Thomson Jones... 19
1987-88 Mr T Thomson Jones... 15
1988-89 Mr P Fenton 18
1989-90 Mr P McMahon 15
1990-91 Mr K Johnson............24
1991-92 Mr M P Hourigan 24
1992-93 Mr A Thornton 26
1993-94 Mr J Greenall............21
1994-95 Mr D Parker 16
1995-96 Mr J Culloty 40

1996-97 Mr R Thornton 30
1997-98 Mr S Durack............41
1998-99 Mr A Dempsey............47
1999-00 Mr P Flynn............41
2000-01 Mr T Scudamore 24
2001-02 Mr D Crosse............19
2002-03 Mr C Williams............23
2003-04 Mr O Nelmes............14
2004-05 Mr T Greenall 31
2005-06 Mr T O'Brien 32
2006-07 Mr T Greenall 31
2007-08 Mr T Greenall 23
2008-09 Mr O Greenall............23
2009-10 Mr O Greenall............41
2010-11 Mr R Mahon............19
2011-12 Miss E Sayer............11
2012-13 Mr N de Boinville............16
2013-14 Mr H Bannister............11
2014-15 Mr H Bannister............15

LEADING SIRES OVER JUMPS: 1986-2015

1986 Deep Run	1995-96 Strong Gale	2005-06 Supreme Leader
1987 Deep Run	1996-97 Strong Gale	2006-07 Presenting
1988 Deep Run	1997-98 Strong Gale	2007-08 Old Vic
1989 Deep Run	1998-99 Strong Gale	2008-09 Presenting
1989-90 Deep Run	1999-00 Strong Gale	2009-10 Presenting
1990-91 Deep Run	2000-01 Be My Native (USA)	2010-11 Presenting
1991-92 Deep Run	2001-02 Be My Native (USA)	2011-12 King's Theatre
1992-93 Deep Run	2002-03 Be My Native (USA)	2012-13 Beneficial
1993-94 Strong Gale	2003-04 Be My Native (USA)	2013-14 King's Theatre
1994-95 Strong Gale	2004-05 Supreme Leader	2014-15 King's Theatre

JOCKEYS' AGENTS

Jockeys' Agents and their Contact Details

Agent	Telephone	Mobile/Email	Fax
NICKY ADAMS	01488 72004/72964	07796 547659 nickadams2594@hotmail.com	
NEIL ALLAN	01243 543870	07985 311141/07825 549081	
NIGEL BAXTER	01942 269972	07973 561521 nigelbaxter@blueyonder.co.uk	
PAUL BRIERLEY	01434 608212	07824 828750 bbjockeys@hotmail.co.uk	
CHRIS BROAD	01452 760482/447	07836 622858 chrisd.broad@yahoo.co.uk	01452 760394
ANTHONY BURKE	01638 810541	07825 330392 anyprice2001@yahoo.com	
SCOTT BUTLER		07908 591121 scottbutleragent@gmail.com	
GLORIA CHARNOCK	01653 695004	07951 576912 gloriacharnock@hotmail.com	
PAUL CLARKE	01638 660804	07885 914306 paul.clarke79@btinternet.com	
RAY COCHRANE	01223 812008	07798 651247 ray@raysagency.co.uk	
SIMON DODDS	01509 852344/852254	07974 924735 simon.dodds@btinternet.com	

Agent	Telephone	Mobile/Email	Fax
SHIPPY ELLIS	01638 668484	07860 864864 shippysjockeys@btconnect.com	01638 660946
JOHN W FORD	01954 261122	07830 294210 john.ford47@btinternet.com	
MARK FURNASS	01347 824633	07474 242332 jockeysagent@gmail.com	
MICHAEL HAGGAS	01638 660811/560505	07740 624550 mhaggas@ntlworld.com	
RICHARD HALE	01768 88699	07909 520542 richardhale77@hotmail.co.uk	
NIALL HANNITY	01677 423363	07710 141084 niallhannity@yahoo.co.uk	
ALAN HARRISON	01969 625006	07846 187991 ahjockagent60@yahoo.co.uk	0560 2729293
TONY HIND	01638 724997	07807 908599 tonyhind@jockeysagent.com	
GAVIN HORNE	01392 433610	07914 897170 gavin.horne@hotmail.co.uk	
JO HUGHES	01488 71103	07900 680189 johughes3@aol.co.uk	01488 71444
RUSS JAMES	01653 699466	07947 414001 russjames2006@btinternet.com	01653 699581
BRUCE JEFFREY	01750 21521	07747 854684 brucejeffrey@live.co.uk	
GUY JEWELL	01672 861231	07765 248859 guyjewell@btconnect.com	01672 861231

Agent	Telephone	Mobile/Email	Fax
ANDY LEWIS	01908 473812	07838 506594 andrew.lewis11@sky.com	
ANDI MAC		07958 264824 andi@andimacassociates.co.uk	
SARA-LOUISE METCALFE	01635 269647	07918 525354 troopersjockeys@hotmail.co.uk	
LOUISE MILLMAN	01884 266620	07740 932791 rod.millman@ic24.net	
PHILIP MITCHELL	01367 820299	07836 231462 philipmitchell48@gmail.com	
LEE NEWTON	01302 376370	07710 422437 newton808@btinternet.com	
CLARE NICHOLLS	07525 159431	trotandsweets@hotmail.com	
SHASHI RIGHTON	01353 688594	07825 381350 slasher74@aol.com	
DAVE ROBERTS	01737 221368/222876	07860 234342 daveroberts.racing@ntlworld.com	
PHILIP SHEA	01638 667456	07585 120297 psheajockeysagent@gmail.com	
SAM STRONGE	01488 72818	07775 727778 sam.stronge@virgin.net	01488 670378
GARY THOMSON	01642 873152	07986 607014 garythomson73@me.com	
JENNIFER WALSH	00353 45883704	00353 872528025 jennifer@ruby-walsh.com	00353 45871929

Agent	Telephone	Mobile/Email	Fax
IAN WARDLE	01793 688858	07831 865974 ian.wardlex@googlemail.com	
LAURA WAY	01704 834488	07775 777494 laura.way@btconnect.com	
IAN WOOD	01488 72324	07733 156380 ianwood@chase3c.com	

FLAT JOCKEYS

Riding weights and contact details

An index of agents appears on page 719

AHMED AJTEBI	8 - 8	07771 777010	
DAVID ALLAN	8 - 9	Mrs G. S. Charnock	
TOBY ATKINSON	8 - 5	P. C. Shea	
ANDREA ATZENI	8 - 2	Mr Paul Clarke	
GEORGE BAKER	9 - 0	Mr G. D. Jewell	
GARY BARTLEY	9 - 0	Mr R. A. Hale	
MATTIE BATCHELOR	9 - 5	Mr Dave Roberts	
CONNOR BEASLEY	8 - 4	Mr R. A. Hale	
HARRY BENTLEY	8 - 4	Mr Paul Clarke	
ADAM BESCHIZZA	8 - 4	M. Furnass	
CHARLES BISHOP	8 - 6	Mr S. T. Dodds	
IAN BRENNAN	8 - 0	Mr L. R. James	
WILLIAM BUICK	8 - 6	Mr M. R. Haggas	
DANNY BURTON	9 - 0	Mr L. R. James	
NEIL CALLAN	8 - 7	Mr S. T. Dodds	
WILLIAM CARSON	8 - 2	Mr Neil Allan	
ADAM CARTER	8 - 8	07787 415289	
CHRIS CATLIN	8 - 4	Mr G. J. Horne	
HARRY CHALLONER	9 - 4	Mr R. A. Hale	
GEORGE CHALONER	8 - 0	Mr R. A. Hale	
PAT COSGRAVE	8 - 8	Mr N. M. Adams	
MATTHEW COSHAM	8 - 4	Mr L. R. James	
DOUGIE COSTELLO	8 - 10	Mr Dave Roberts\	
		Mr N. Hannity	
STEPHEN CRAINE	8 - 12	Mr S. T. Dodds	
JIM CROWLEY	8 - 7	Mr Tony Hind	
BEN CURTIS	8 - 4	Mr S. T. Dodds	
RAUL DA SILVA	8 - 0	Andy Lewis	
GARY DERWIN	9 - 0	Mr Dave Roberts	
SILVESTRE DE SOUSA	8 - 0	07878 412342	
LEMOS DE SOUZA	8 - 6	Andy Lewis	
FRANKIE DETTORI	8 - 9	Mr R. Cochrane	
PAT DOBBS	8 - 7	Mr Tony Hind	
STEVIE DONOHOE	8 - 7	Mr L. R. James	
JAMES DOYLE	8 - 7	Mr M. R. Haggas	
STEVE DROWNE	8 - 7	Mr I. P Wardle	
TED DURCAN	8 - 6	Mr Tony Hind	
MARTIN DWYER	8 - 3	Mr S. T. Dodds	
TOM EAVES	8 - 7	Mr R. A. Hale	
JOHN EGAN	8 - 3	Mr A. D. Burke	
ANDREW ELLIOTT	8 - 4	Mr S. M. Righton	
MIKEY ENNIS	8 - 10	Mr Dave Roberts	
JOHN FAHY	8 - 6	Mr N. M. Adams	
KIEREN FALLON	8 - 6	Mrs G. S. Charnock	
JOE FANNING	8 - 2	Mr N. Hannity	
NEIL FARLEY	8 - 4	Mr Alan Harrison	
DURAN FENTIMAN	8 - 2	Mr Alan Harrison	
ROYSTON FFRENCH	8 - 4	M. Furnass	
JIMMY FORTUNE	8 - 9	Mr Tony Hind	
KIEREN FOX	8 - 2	Mr G. D. Jewell	
ANTONIO FRESU	8 - 5	Mr G. D. Jewell	
CATHY GANNON	8 - 0	Mr Neil Allan	
NATALIA GEMELOVA	7 - 12	07966910511	
GRAHAM GIBBONS	8 - 5	Mrs I. H. Way	
SALEEM GOLAM	8 - 5	M. Furnass	
IRINEU GONCALVES	8 - 2	07478 060662	
SHANE GRAY	8 - 1	Mr S. T. Dodds	
TONY HAMILTON	8 - 7	Mr N. Hannity	
PAUL HANAGAN	8 - 3	Mr R. A. Hale	
MARTIN HARLEY	8 - 9	Mr Neil Allan	
JASON HART	8 - 4	Mr Alan Harrison	
ROBERT HAVLIN	8 - 5	Mr I. P Wardle	
JOEY HAYNES	8 - 2	Mr N. Hannity	
SAM HITCHCOTT	8 - 5	Mr N. M. Adams	
SAM JAMES	8 - 6	Mrs L. H. Way	
ROSIE JESSOP	8 - 0	Mr N. A. Baxter	
LIAM JONES	8 - 2	Mr Paul Clarke	
SHANE KELLY	8 - 7	Mrs L. H. Way	
LIAM KENIRY	8 - 7	Mr N. M. Adams	
RICHARD KINGSCOTE	8 - 6	Mr G. D. Jewell	
ADAM KIRBY	9 - 0	Mr N. M. Adams	
RACHEAL KNELLER	8 - 5	Andy Lewis	
MARTIN LANE	8 - 6	Mr S. T. Dodds	
KEAGAN LATHAM	8 - 9	M. Furnass	
GRAHAM LEE	8 - 9	Mr R. A. Hale	
SEAN LEVEY	8 - 10	Mr Tony Hind	
FERGAL LYNCH	8 - 7	Mr R. A. Hale	
NICKY MACKAY	8 - 0	Mr Paul Clarke	
PHILLIP MAKIN	8 - 11	Mrs L. H. Way	
PATRICK MATHERS	8 - 2	M. Furnass	
P. J. MCDONALD	8 - 4	Mr R. A. Hale	
BARRY MCHUGH	8 - 3	Mr R. A. Hale	
ALICE MILLS	8 - 2	Mr L. R. James	
JACK MITCHELL	8 - 8	Mr Paul Clarke	
RYAN MOORE	8 - 7	Mr Tony Hind	
LUKE MORRIS	8 - 0	Mr Neil Allan	
ANDREW MULLEN	8 - 7	Mr R. A. Hale	
PAUL MULRENNAN	8 - 7	Mr R. A. Hale	
OISIN MURPHY	8 - 6	Miss S. L. Metcalfe\	
		Mr G. J. Horne	
TIMMY MURPHY	9 - 0	Mr S. T. Dodds	
D. MYLONAS	8 - 6	07979 068949	
JUSTIN NEWMAN	8 - 8	M. Furnass	
ADRIAN NICHOLLS	8 - 3	Mrs Clare Nicholls\	
		Mr L. Newton	
DAVID NOLAN	9 - 0	Mr R. A. Hale	
FRANNY NORTON	8 - 0	Mr I. P Wardle	
SLADE O'HARA	8 - 8	07745 805189	
DANE O'NEILL	8 - 2	Mr N. M. Adams	
KIERAN O'NEILL	8 - 0	Mr N. M. Adams	
SIMON PEARCE	8 - 4	07818 038770	
OSCAR PEREIRA	8 - 7	07766 658392	
PAUL PICKARD	8 - 6	01653 697225	
HARRY POULTON	8 - 9	Mr Ian Wood	
RYAN POWELL	8 - 0	Mr N. M. Adams	
DAVID PROBERT	8 - 0	Miss S. L. Metcalfe	
TOM QUEALLY	8 - 8	Mr N. Hannity	
AMIR QUINN	8 - 11	07913416683	
JIMMY QUINN	8 - 0	Mr G. J. Horne	
PAUL QUINN	8 - 0	Mr S. M. Righton	
AMY RYAN	8 - 2	Mr R. A. Hale	
SEB SANDERS	8 - 7	P. C. Shea	
VITOR SANTOS	7 - 13	07506 218446	
PAOLO SIRIGU	8 - 0	07585 308267	
RENATO SOUZA	8 - 5	Mr N. A. Baxter	
JAMIE SPENCER	8 - 7	Mr N. Hannity	

ANN STOKELL	8 - 7	07814 579982	**WILLIAM TWISTON-DAVIES** 8 - 9	Mr Neil Allan
JAMES SULLIVAN	8 - 0	Mr R. A. Hale	**FREDERIK TYLICKI** 8 - 6	Mr Paul Clarke
FERGUS SWEENEY	8 - 7	Mr G. D. Jewell	**R. P. WALSH** 7 - 5	Mr R. A. Hale
ROBERT TART	8 - 7	Mr L. R. James	**GARRY WHILLANS** 8 - 9	Mr L. R. James
DANIEL TUDHOPE	8 - 9	Mrs L. H. Way	**ROBERT WINSTON** 8 - 7	Mr L. Newton

Are your contact details missing or incorrect?
If so please update us by email:
richard.lowther@racingpost.co.uk

APPRENTICES

Riding weights and contact details

An index of agents appears on page 719

NATHAN ALISON (William Haggas)	8 - 0	c/o 07860 282281
LAMORNA BARDWELL (Seamus Mullins)	7 - 7	c/o 07702 559634
LUCY K. BARRY (Jamie Osborne)	8 - 10	Mr L. R. James
ALED BEECH (David Evans)	8 - 0	c/o 01873 890837
SAMMY JO BELL (Richard Fahey)	7 - 11	Mr R. A. Hale
CHARLIE BENNETT (Hughie Morrison)	8 - 2	P. C. Shea
SHELLEY BIRKETT (David O'Meara)	8 - 0	Mr John W. Ford
GEORGE BLACKWELL (Tim Vaughan)	9 - 0	Mr C. D. Broad
PAUL BOOTH (Dean Ivory)	8 - 2	Mr L. R. James
PADDY BRADLEY (Pat Phelan)	9 - 1	Mr L. R. James
BECKY BRISBOURNE (Mark Brisbourne)	8 - 5	c/o 07803 019651
DANNY BROCK (Jane Chapple-Hyam)	8 - 4	Mr Ian Wood
THOMAS BROWN (Ismail Mohammed)	8 - 7	Mr G. J. Horne
GEORGE BUCKELL (David Simcock)	8 - 6	M. Furnass
HARRY BURNS (Ed Dunlop)	8 - 6	c/o 01638 661998
JACOB BUTTERFIELD (Ollie Pears)	8 - 5	Mr L. Newton
LEE BYRNE (Declan Carroll)	8 - 0	c/o 01653 698517
MEGAN CARBERRY (Brian Ellison)	8 - 6	Mr R. A. Hale
LUKE CARSON (Ed Dunlop)	8 - 6	c/o 01638 661998
RYAN CLARK (Brian Meehan)	8 - 7	P. C. Shea
TIM CLARK (Martin Smith)	8 - 2	Mr N. M. Adams
SAMUEL CLARKE (Chris Wall)	8 - 5	P. C. Shea
RICHARD CONDON (Brendan Powell)	8 - 7	Mr Ian Wood
JAMES CORBETT (Susan Corbett)	9 - 0	Mr J. B. Jeffrey
GEORGIA COX (William Haggas)	8 - 2	Mr Tony Hind
STEPHEN CUMMINS (Richard Hughes)	8 - 2	c/o 01488 71198
KYLE CURRIE (Iain Jardine)	8 - 2	c/o 07944 722011
PHIL DENNIS (Michael Dods)	7 - 12	Mr R. A. Hale
GEORGE DOWNING (Tony Carroll)	8 - 7	Mr L. Newton
HOLLIE DOYLE (Richard Hannon)	7 - 7	P. C. Shea
JOSH DOYLE (David O'Meara)	8 - 2	Mr R. A. Hale
JACK DUERN (Steph Hollinshead)	8 - 5	Mr L. Newton
CHARLES EDDERY (Rae Guest)	8 - 4	Andy Lewis
MEGAN ELLINGWORTH (John Holt)	7 - 7	c/o 07850 321059
JANE ELLIOTT (Michael Appleby)	8 - 0	Mr S. M. Righton
NATHAN EVANS (Michael Easterby)	8 - 3	Mr R. A. Hale
MANUEL FERNANDES (Sir Mark Prescott Bt)	8 - 0	c/o 01638 662117
JONATHAN FISHER (Ed Dunlop)	8 - 3	c/o 01638 661998
ROB J. FITZPATRICK (Micky Hammond)	8 - 2	Mr Alan Harrison
NOEL GARBUTT (Hugo Palmer)	7 - 8	Mr L. R. James
JACK GARRITTY (Richard Fahey)	7 - 9	Mr R. A. Hale
MITCH GODWIN (Richard Hannon)	7 - 7	Miss S. L. Metcalfe
JOSEPHINE GORDON (J. S. Moore)	8 - 0	P. C. Shea
EDWARD GREATREX (Andrew Balding)	7 - 10	Miss S. L. Metcalfe
NICOLA GRUNDY (Alan Berry)	7 - 9	c/o 07880 553515
NATALIE HAMBLING (Richard Fahey)	8 - 2	M. Furnass
CAM HARDIE (Richard Hannon)	7 - 13	Mr Tony Hind
ANNA HESKETH (David Nicholls)	8 - 2	Mr R. A. Hale
RYAN HOLMES (Daniel Loughnane)	8 - 4	c/o 07805 531021
ROB HORNBY (Andrew Balding)	8 - 0	Mr N. M. Adams
LUKE INGRAM (Lucy Wadham)	8 - 7	c/o 07980 545776
RHIAIN INGRAM (Roger Ingram)	7 - 8	P. C. Shea
HAYLEY IRVINE (Richard Fahey)	7 - 11	c/o 01653 698915
STEPHANIE JOANNIDES (Richard Hughes)	7 - 12	Andy Lewis
AARON JONES (Stuart Williams)	8 - 0	Mr John W. Ford
CHRIS KELLY (Richard Hughes)	8 - 2	Andy Lewis
SOPHIE KILLORAN (David Simcock)	7 - 5	M. Furnass
GARRY LAVERY (Brian Ellison)	9 - 0	Mr L. R. James

CLIFFORD LEE (K. R. Burke)	8 - 0	Mr A. D. Burke\Mr N. Hannity
GARY MAHON (Richard Hannon)	8 - 0	Mr Tony Hind
GABRIELE MALUNE (Luca Cumani)	7 - 12	c/o 01638 665432
TOM MARQUAND (Richard Hannon)	7 - 9	Mr S. M. Righton
CIARAN MCKEE (John O'Shea)	9 - 4	Mr L. R. James
DARYL MCLAUGHLIN (David Simcock)	8 - 9	c/o 07808 954109
ADAM MCLEAN (David Elsworth)	8 - 2	P. C. Shea
ADAM MCNAMARA (Richard Fahey)	8 - 4	c/o 01653 698915
MARC MONAGHAN (Marco Botti)	8 - 6	Mr Neil Allan
DANIELLE MOONEY (Michael Easterby)	7 - 12	M. Furnass
SEAN MOONEY (Joseph Tuite)	8 - 0	Mr Ian Wood
EVA MOSCROP (Marco Botti)	8 - 5	Andy Lewis
PAULA MUIR (Patrick Holmes)	7 - 9	Mr L. R. James
MICHAEL J. M. MURPHY (John Gallagher)	8 - 6	Mr S. T. Dodds
DANIEL MUSCUTT (Marco Botti)	8 - 4	Mr A. D. Burke
MILLY NASEB (Stuart Williams)	7 - 8	c/o 01638 663984
JORDAN NASON (Ronald Thompson)	8 - 4	M. Furnass
MEGAN NICHOLLS (Richard Hannon)	8 - 0	Mr G. D. Jewell
CAMERON NOBLE (Roger Varian)	7 - 8	Mr Paul Clarke
TOMMY O'CONNOR (Owen Burrows)	8 - 0	c/o 01488 73144
PATRICK O'DONNELL (Ralph Beckett)	8 - 0	Mr S. T. Dodds
ALICE PAGANI (Marco Botti)	8 - 3	c/o 01638 662416
DAVID PARKES (Jeremy Gask)	8 - 6	c/o 01985 841166
PADDY PILLEY (Mick Channon)	7 - 9	P. C. Shea
JENNY POWELL (Henry Candy)	8 - 2	Mr L. R. James
PHILIP PRINCE (David Evans)	8 - 2	Mr S. M. Righton
JOSH QUINN (Clive Cox)	8 - 5	Mr John W. Ford
ALISTAIR RAWLINSON (Michael Appleby)	8 - 6	Mr S. M. Righton
RACHEL RICHARDSON (Tim Easterby)	7 - 13	Mr Alan Harrison
CALLUM RODRIGUEZ (Richard Ford)	8 - 0	c/o 01995 605790
BENJAMIN SANDERSON (Sylvester Kirk)	8 - 2	c/o 07768 855261
TYLER SAUNDERS (Marcus Tregoning)	8 - 2	c/o 01725 518889
EMMA SAYER (Dianne Sayer)	8 - 3	Mr R. A. Hale
ROWAN SCOTT (Ann Duffield)	8 - 0	Mr R. A. Hale
CALLUM SHEPHERD (Brian Ellison)	8 - 4	Mr N. M. Adams
KIERAN SHOEMARK (Andrew Balding)	8 - 2	Mr Tony Hind
TINA SMITH (Richard Hannon)	6 - 7	c/o 01264 850254
LULU STANFORD (George Margarson)	8 - 0	Mr Ian Wood
LOUIS STEWARD (Michael Bell)	8 - 7	Mr N. Hannity
MATHEW STILL (Antony Brittain)	7 - 10	c/o 07801 583255
LEWIS STONES (Michael Mullineaux)	8 - 7	c/o 07753 650263
KEVIN STOTT (Luca Cumani)	8 - 5	Mrs L. H. Way\Mr S. M. Righton
RYAN TATE (Clive Cox)	8 - 2	Mr G. D. Jewell
SHIRLEY TEASDALE (Heather Dalton)	7 - 10	Andy Lewis
RYAN TIMBY (David Evans)	9 - 0	Mr L. R. James
ROSS TURNER (Philip Kirby)	8 - 9	c/o 01969 624400
GEMMA TUTTY (Karen Tutty)	8 - 0	c/o 01609 883067
JORDAN UYS (Brian Meehan)	8 - 4	c/o 01672 511264
KIMBERLEY VAN DER VEGT (Daniel Kubler)	8 - 2	c/o 01488 72235
JORDAN VAUGHAN (K. R. Burke)	8 - 0	Mr R. A. Hale
PATRICK VAUGHAN (Tom Dascombe)	8 - 4	Mr G. D. Jewell
EOIN WALSH (James Tate)	8 - 4	Mr N. M. Adams
RYAN WHILE (Bill Turner)	8 - 4	c/o 07967 242404
JORDAN WILLIAMS (Paul Nicholls)	8 - 12	Mr Dave Roberts
GEORGE WOOD (James Fanshawe)	7 - 9	Mr S. M. Righton
DANIEL WRIGHT (Andrew Balding)	8 - 0	c/o 01635 298210
FLETCHER YARHAM (Hughie Morrison)	8 - 2	c/o 07836 687799

JUMP JOCKEYS

Riding weights and contact details

An index of agents appears on page 719

An index of agents appears on page 719

LUCY ALEXANDER	9 - 7		Mr R. A. Hale
LEIGHTON ASPELL	10 - 0		Mr Dave Roberts
JAMES BANKS	10 - 0		Mr L. R. James
DAVID BASS	10 - 5		Mr Dave Roberts
MATTIE BATCHELOR	10 - 0		Mr Dave Roberts
JAMES BEST	10 - 0		Mr Dave Roberts
JONATHON BEWLEY	9 - 12		01450 860651
DARAGH BOURKE	10 - 5		Mr J. B. Jeffrey
SEAN BOWEN	9 - 7		Mr Dave Roberts
PADDY BRENNAN	9 - 12		Mr Dave Roberts
HENRY BROOKE	10 - 0		Mr R. A. Hale
PETER BUCHANAN	10 - 0		Mr Paul Brierley
DANNY BURTON	10 - 0		Mr L. R. James
TOM CANNON	10 - 0		Mr Dave Roberts
PETER CARBERRY	9 - 10		Mr Dave Roberts
ALAIN CAWLEY	9 - 10		Mr Dave Roberts
HARRY CHALLONER	9 - 10		Mr R. A. Hale
AIDAN COLEMAN	9 - 10		Mr Dave Roberts
DANNY COOK	10 - 4		Mr J. B. Jeffrey
DOUGIE COSTELLO	10 - 0		Mr Dave Roberts\
			Mr N. Hannity
DAVE CROSSE	10 - 0		Mr C. D. Broad
JAMES DAVIES	10 - 0		Mr L. R. James
NICO DE BOINVILLE	9 - 11		Mr Dave Roberts
GARY DERWIN	9 - 7		Mr Dave Roberts
ROBERT DUNNE	10 - 7		Mr Dave Roberts
LEE EDWARDS	10 - 0		Mr C. D. Broad
DAVID ENGLAND	10 - 0		Mr Dave Roberts
MIKEY ENNIS	9 - 7		Mr Dave Roberts
JAN FALTEJSEK	10 - 0		07496 863637
NOEL FEHILY	10 - 4		Mr C. D. Broad
RHYS FLINT	10 - 12		Mr Dave Roberts
LUCY GARDNER	9 - 12		07814 979 699
BARRY GERAGHTY	10 - 4		Mr Dave Roberts
ANDREW GLASSONBURY	10 - 5		Mr Dave Roberts
MARC GOLDSTEIN	10 - 0		Mr Dave Roberts
MARK GRANT	10 - 0		Mr C. D. Broad
JAKE GREENALL	10 - 0		Mr Dave Roberts
BRIAN HARDING	10 - 0		Mr R. A. Hale
LIAM HEARD	10 - 2		Mr L. R. James
BRIAN HUGHES	9 - 7		Mr R. A. Hale
WAYNE HUTCHINSON	10 - 0		Mr C. D. Broad
DARYL JACOB	10 - 2		Mr C. D. Broad
KYLE JAMES	9 - 11		Mr L. R. James
ALAN JOHNS	10 - 0		Mr Dave Roberts
RICHARD JOHNSON	10 - 0		Mr Dave Roberts
KEVIN JONES	10 - 4		Mr Dave Roberts
TONY KELLY	10 - 0		Mr R. A. Hale
WILL KENNEDY	10 - 0		Mr Dave Roberts
JOHN KINGTON	10 - 0		Mr J. B. Jeffrey
ADRIAN LANE	10 - 0		Mr G. J. Thomson\
			Mr J. B. Jeffrey
JASON MAGUIRE	10 - 6		Mr C. D. Broad
RYAN MAHON	10 - 0		Mr Dave Roberts
ROB MCCARTH	9 - 12		Mr Dave Roberts
COLM MCCORMACK	10 - 2		Mr J. B. Jeffrey
RICHIE MCLERNON	9 - 10		Mr Dave Roberts
TOM MESSENGER	10 - 0		Mr J. B. Jeffrey
ALICE MILLS	8 - 2		Mr L. R. James
PAUL MOLONEY	10 - 0		Mr Dave Roberts
JAMIE MOORE	10 - 0		Mr Dave Roberts
JOSHUA MOORE	10 - 0		Mr Dave Roberts
NATHAN MOSCROP	10 - 3		Mr J. B. Jeffrey
ADAM NICOL	9 - 11		Mr R. A. Hale
MICHEAL NOLAN	10 - 0		Mr Dave Roberts
TOM O'BRIEN	10 - 0		Mr Dave Roberts
CONOR O'FARRELL	10 - 0		Mr Dave Roberts
DENIS O'REGAN	10 - 2		Mr C. D. Broad
JOSEPH PALMOWSKI	9 - 5		07713 922504
TOMMY PHELAN	9 - 13		Mr Dave Roberts
ADAM POGSON	10 - 0		07977 016155
IAN POPHAM	10 - 0		Mr Dave Roberts
BEN POSTE	9 - 7		Mr Dave Roberts
CHARLIE POSTE	10 - 0		Mr Dave Roberts
BRENDAN POWELL	9 - 7		Mr Dave Roberts
JACK QUINLAN	9 - 10		Mr Dave Roberts
MARK QUINLAN	9 - 11		Mr C. D. Broad
SEAN QUINLAN	10 - 0		Mr J. B. Jeffrey
JAMES REVELEY	10 - 4		Mr J. B. Jeffrey
GARY RUTHERFORD	9 - 2		Mr J. B. Jeffrey
NICK SCHOLFIELD	10 - 0		Mr Dave Roberts
TOM SCUDAMORE	10 - 0		Mr Dave Roberts
GAVIN SHEEHAN	10 - 0		Mr Dave Roberts
HARRY SKELTON	10 - 0		Mr Dave Roberts
ANDREW THORNTON	10 - 4		Mr Dave Roberts
ANDREW TINKLER	10 - 0		Mr Dave Roberts
BRIAN TOOMEY	9 - 7		Mr Dave Roberts
LIAM TREADWELL	10 - 0		Mr Dave Roberts
GERARD TUMELTY	10 - 0		Mr L. R. James
SAM TWISTON-DAVIES	10 - 0		Mr C. D. Broad
CHRIS WARD	9 - 9		Mr Dave Roberts
ADAM WEDGE	9 - 11		Mr Dave Roberts
TREVOR WHELAN	9 - 10		Mr Dave Roberts
CALLUM WHILLANS	9 - 11		Mr Dave Roberts
KIELAN WOODS	10 - 0		Mr C. D. Broad

CONDITIONALS

Their employer and contact details

An index of agents appears on page 719

BRIDGET ANDREWS (Dan Skelton)	9 - 3	c/o 01789 336339
JAKE BAMENT (Victor Dartnall)	10 - 0	c/o 07974 374272
HARRY BANNISTER (Warren Greatrex)	9 - 5	Mr C. D. Broad
JAMIE BARGARY (Nigel Twiston-Davies)	9 - 5	Mr C. D. Broad
ARCHIE BELLAMY (Graeme McPherson)	9 - 4	Mr Dave Roberts
TOM BELLAMY (Alan King)	10 - 0	Mr Dave Roberts
HARRISON BESWICK (Oliver Sherwood)	9 - 9	Mr C. D. Broad
CALLUM BEWLEY (Lisa Harrison)	9 - 10	Mr J. B. Jeffrey
GEORGE BLACKWELL (Tim Vaughan)	9 - 7	Mr C. D. Broad
PADDY BRADLEY (Pat Phelan)	9 - 7	Mr L. R. James
MEGAN CARBERRY (Brian Ellison)	9 - 5	Mr R. A. Hale
GRAHAM CARSON (Jamie Snowden)	9 - 10	Mr Dave Roberts
ROSS CHAPMAN (Lucinda Russell)	9 - 6	Mr R. A. Hale
THOMAS CHEESMAN (Philip Hobbs)	9 - 7	Mr Dave Roberts
ROMAIN CLAVREUL (Sarah Humphrey)	9 - 2	c/o 07774847055
HARRY COBDEN (Paul Nicholls)	9 - 0	Mr Dave Roberts
GRANT COCKBURN (Lucinda Russell)	10 - 0	Mr J. B. Jeffrey
JOE COLLIVER (Micky Hammond)	9 - 9	Mr R. A. Hale
JAMES CORBETT (Susan Corbett)	9 - 7	Mr J. B. Jeffrey
JAMES COWLEY (Donald McCain)	9 - 9	Mr R. A. Hale
PATRICK COWLEY (Jonjo O'Neill)	9 - 5	c/o 01386 584209
RYAN DAY (Nicky Richards)	9 - 10	Mr R. A. Hale
CHARLIE DEUTSCH (Venetia Williams)	10 - 0	Mr Dave Roberts
PHILIP DONOVAN (Fergal O'Brien)	9 - 7	c/o 0777 1702829
KEVIN DOWLING (Alan King)	10 - 0	c/o 01793 815009
TOMMY DOWLING (Charlie Mann)	9 - 6	c/o 01488 73118
THOMAS DOWSON (Maurice Barnes)	9 - 7	Mr J. B. Jeffrey
KIERON EDGAR (David Pipe)	9 - 7	Mr Dave Roberts
JONATHAN ENGLAND (Michael Appleby)	9 - 7	Mr J. B. Jeffrey
WILLIAM FEATHERSTONE (Alan King)	10 - 0	Mr Dave Roberts
BEN FFRENCH DAVIS (Oliver Sherwood)	10 - 0	Mr Dave Roberts
DEREK FOX (Lucinda Russell)	10 - 4	Mr J. B. Jeffrey
STEVEN FOX (Sandy Thomson)	10 - 4	Mr J. B. Jeffrey
CRAIG GALLAGHER (Brian Ellison)	9 - 7	Mr J. B. Jeffrey
THOMAS GARNER (Oliver Sherwood)	9 - 5	Mr Dave Roberts
BILLY GARRITTY (Micky Hammond)	9 - 4	c/o 01969 625223
CIARAN GETHINGS (Philip Hobbs)	9 - 12	Mr Dave Roberts
LEWIS GORDON (Evan Williams)	9 - 10	Mr Dave Roberts
GEORGE GORMAN (Gary Moore)	10 - 0	Mr Dave Roberts
MATT GRIFFITHS (Jeremy Scott)	10 - 2	Mr Dave Roberts
MIKEY HAMILL (Alexandra Dunn)	10 - 0	Mr S. J. Butler
JAMIE HAMILTON (Mark Walford)	9 - 0	Mr R. A. Hale
CHARLIE HAMMOND (Dr Richard Newland)	9 - 7	Mr Dave Roberts
RYAN HATCH (Nigel Twiston-Davies)	10 - 0	Mr C. D. Broad
GILES HAWKINS (Chris Down)	10 - 7	Mr L. R. James
MICHAEL HEARD (David Pipe)	9 - 7	Mr Dave Roberts
DANIEL HISKETT (Richard Phillips)	9 - 7	Mr Dave Roberts
JAKE HODSON (David Bridgwater)	9 - 12	Mr Dave Roberts
TOM HUMPHRIES (Charlie Longsdon)	9 - 12	c/o 07775 993263
LUKE INGRAM (Lucy Wadham)	9 - 4	c/o 07980 545776
JAMIE INSOLE (Alan King)	10 - 0	Mr L. R. James
DALE IRVING (James Ewart)	9 - 10	Mr J. B. Jeffrey
LIZZIE KELLY (Nick Williams)	10 - 0	Mr Dave Roberts
GARRY LAVERY (Brian Ellison)	9 - 7	Mr L. R. James
MAURICE LINEHAN (Ben Pauling)	10 - 0	Mr C. D. Broad
CIAN MAHER (Evan Williams)	9 - 6	c/o 01446 754069
GARETH MALONE (David Dennis)	10 - 2	Mr C. D. Broad
STEPHEN MCCARTHY (Sue Smith)	9 - 0	c/o 07903 311959

JEREMIAH MCGRATH (Nicky Henderson) .... 10 - 2   Mr Dave Roberts
LIAM MCKENNA (Harry Fry) .... 10 - 0   Mr Dave Roberts
FREDDIE MITCHELL (Nicky Henderson) .... 9 - 7   Mr Philip Mitchell\Mr Dave Roberts
KILLIAN MOORE (Sophie Leech) .... 9 - 11   Mr Dave Roberts
STEPHEN MULQUEEN (N. W. Alexander) .... 10 - 0   Mr J. B. Jeffrey
LORCAN MURTAGH (Rose Dobbin) .... 9 - 4   Mr R. A. Hale
CRAIG NICHOL (Keith Dalgleish) .... 9 - 12   Mr R. A. Hale
DAVID NOONAN (David Pipe) .... 9 - 7   Mr Dave Roberts
JASON NUTTALL (Gary Moore) .... 9 - 7   Mr John W. Ford
PAUL O'BRIEN (Colin Tizzard) .... 10 - 0   Mr C. D. Broad
RICHIE O'DEA (Emma Lavelle) .... 10 - 0   c/o 01264 735412
DIARMUID O'REGAN (Chris Grant) .... 9 - 4   Mr R. A. Hale
FINIAN O'TOOLE (Micky Hammond) .... 10 - 0   Mr R. A. Hale
FRANKIE PENFORD (David Arbuthnot) .... 9 - 7   c/o 01306 631529
DEAN PRATT (John Quinn) .... 10 - 0   Mr Paul Brierley
DAVID PRICHARD (Jeremy Scott) .... 9 - 0   Mr Dave Roberts
SHANE QUINLAN (Neil Mulholland) .... 9 - 12   Mr C. D. Broad
CONOR RING (Evan Williams) .... 9 - 10   Mr C. D. Broad
TREVOR RYAN (Sue Smith) .... 9 - 12   c/o 07903 311959
JACK SAVAGE (Jonjo O'Neill) .... 9 - 9   c/o 01386 584209
EMMA SAYER (Dianne Sayer) .... 9 - 0   Mr R. A. Hale
JACK SHERWOOD (Paul Nicholls) .... 9 - 7   Mr Dave Roberts
CONOR SHOEMARK (Fergal O'Brien) .... 10 - 0   Mr Dave Roberts
RONAN SHORT (Donald McCain) .... 9 - 0   c/o 01829 720352
NICK SLATTER (Tony Carroll) .... 9 - 7   Mr C. D. Broad
CONOR SMITH (Philip Hobbs) .... 10 - 2   Mr Dave Roberts
LEWIS STONES (Michael Mullineaux) .... 8 - 7   c/o 07753 650263
HUGO THOMPSON BROWN (Micky Hammond) .... 10 - 0   c/o 07808 572777
JOSH WALL (Trevor Wall) .... 9 - 10   Mr L. R. James
CONOR WALSH (Warren Greatrex) .... 9 - 5   Mr S. Stronge
LUKE WATSON (Alex Hales) .... 9 - 4   c/o 01295 660131
GRAHAM WATTERS (Charlie Longsdon) .... 10 - 0   Mr R. A. Hale
TOBY WHEELER (Ian Williams) .... 9 - 12   Mr C. D. Broad
RYAN WHILE (Bill Turner) .... 9 - 0   c/o 07967 242404
JORDAN WILLIAMS (Paul Nicholls) .... 8 - 12   Mr Dave Roberts
ROBERT WILLIAMS (Bernard Llewellyn) .... 9 - 12   c/o 07971 233473

AMATEUR RIDERS

Riding weights and contact details

An index of agents appears on page 719

ALEXANDER, C. 9 - 10	07799 191093
ALEXANDER, J. F. 11 - 7	0131 3328850
ALLAN, V. L. 9 - 2	07703 355878
ANDREWS, D. I. J. 10 - 5	07817 322974
ANDREWS, G. 9 - 12	Mr C. D. Broad
ANDREWS, J. 9 - 12	07889 611399
AUSTIN, E. 9 - 0	07837 781877
BAGOBAN, T. S. 7 - 5	07525 218127
BAILEY, E. W. A. 10 - 12	07972 129376
BAKER, Z. C. N. 10 - 0	Mr C. D. Broad
BANHAM, C. 9 - 5	07887 927028
BANKS, A. P. 10 - 7	07927 308486
BARBER, M. 10 - 4	Miss Andi Mac
BARLOW, A. M. E. 11 - 0	07920 714890
BARRETT, R. E. 9 - 8	07505 508740
BARTLEY, C. A. 8 - 5	07734 303862
BEAUMONT, G. 10 - 0	07535 501654
BEECH, A. J. 8 - 4	07825 652474
BENJAMIN, T. M. 9 - 6	07414 974532
BETAMBEAU, T. 11 - 3	07557 275789
BETHELL, H. 9 - 10	07733 424242
BIDDICK, W. E. T. 11 - 0	07976 556823
BINGHAM, G. F. 12 - 0	07766 204154
BIRD, R. A. 10 - 0	Mr L. R. James
BIRKETT, R. A. 10 - 0	Mr S. T. Dodds
BISHOP, T. G. H. 11 - 0	07887 612659
BISHOP-PECK, M. 8 - 2	07775 564080
BLAKEMORE, A. 9 - 0	07581 576739
BOWEN, S. L. 9 - 0	07718 069485
BOXALL, C. E. 9 - 0	01472 388438
BRACKENBURY, B. E. 10 - 5	07921 618635
BRAMLEY, F. H. 9 - 0	07882 988562
BREWER, F. 9 - 5	01347 888208
BRIDGWATER, P. K. 8 - 10	Mr S. M. Righton
BROOKE, L. 9 - 4	07786 962911
BROOME, A. 9 - 10	07891 513800
BROTHERTON, S. 8 - 12	07740 257110
BROUGHTON, T. P. 9 - 4	07769 311769
BRYAN, P. J. 10 - 7	07538 655128
BRYANT, M. P. 9 - 8	07976 217542
BRYSON, K. A. 10 - 0	Mr J. B. Jeffrey
BUCK, J. M. 9 - 9	01984 667229
BULL, P. A. 10 - 7	07968 051902
BULLOCK, E. 7 - 11	07593 951904
BURCHELL, D. G. 10 - 0	07884 263625
BURTON, S. 10 - 4	07786 438076
BUSH, A. M. 10 - 4	07966 209103
BUSHE, E. 9 - 0	07903 364953
BUTTERWORTH, E. 9 - 4	07917 717346
CARDEN, J. J. 11 - 2	07584 197366
CARR, C. 10 - 9	07734 899613
CHAMINGS, E. L. 9 - 4	07887 792980
CHANIN, I. 10 - 4	01258 817271
CHATFEILD-ROBERTS, T. 10 - 7	07794 743577
CLARK, B. E. 9 - 7	07908 250025
CLARKE, W. R. 10 - 0	07540 723993
COLES, T. B. P. 10 - 0	01638 668882
COLL, S. A. 10 - 0	07912 604950

COLLINGTON, P. P. M. 9 - 3	07946 516070
COLTHERD, S. W. 9 - 5	Mr J. B. Jeffrey
CORNOCK, H. R. L. 10 - 0	07581 675899
COSTELLO, D. 9 - 0	07538 751620
COULSON, J. T. 10 - 7	07460 471492
COWARD, J. M. 10 - 0	07919 477619
CRANE, C. R. 9 - 8	07837 965183
CRATE, G. D. 10 - 2	07717 281213
CROFT, S. 10 - 7	07809 205556
CUTHBERT, H. E. 9 - 0	01228 560700
DAGGE, R. 10 - 0	07772 136378
DALTON, A. 9 - 12	07787 501331
DAVID, E. 10 - 5	07500 383138
DAVID, T. R. 10 - 4	07866 775562
DAVIES, C. H. G. 9 - 12	07770 892085
DAVIES-THOMAS, S. 11 - 0	07769 337473
DAWSON, J. A. 10 - 0	Mr Paul Brierley
DAY, J. S. 10 - 10	07788 863067
DEAN, A. S. 9 - 7	07540 106050
DEFAGO, R. P. 10 - 0	07515 390341
DEGNAN, W. 10 - 0	07400 626696
DENIEL, A. 8 - 10	01302 861000
DINGLE, R. 9 - 3	01303 840669
DIXON, J. 9 - 7	07761 998988
DOCKER, J. M. 10 - 7	02078 444000
DODS, C. A. 8 - 7	07590 048619
DODS, S. E. 8 - 11	07590 048618
DOE, J. M. 9 - 8	07904 407258
DOGGRELL, E. 10 - 0	07773 564801
DRINKWATER, J. 9 - 0	07718 376223
DROWNE, L. 10 - 0	07506 871171
DUCKER, G. 9 - 7	07769 211642
DUKES, H. R. 9 - 2	07758 518358
DUNN, A. 9 - 7	07738 512924
DUNSDON, D. 10 - 7	07885 110826
EASTERBY, E. A. 8 - 5	07854 733689
EASTERBY, W. H. 9 - 7	07772 216507
EDDEN, M. L. 9 - 0	07773 420078
EDDERY, A. 9 - 0	07976 021285
EDWARDS, A. W. 10 - 0	07590 683295
ELEY, T. J. 9 - 0	Mr C. D. Broad
ENNIS, M. C. 9 - 4	Mr R. A. Hale
FAIRCHILD, F. D. C. 8 - 12	07936 145123
FANSHAWE, T. 8 - 7	07825 950425
FERGUSON, A. R. D. 8 - 9	07788 876161
FERGUSON, L. 9 - 7	07960 096813
FRENCH, A. 9 - 4	07776 306588
FRISWELL, G. 8 - 5	07807 959636
FROST, B. 9 - 7	078618 14643
FULLER, M. P. F. 8 - 10	Mr L. R. James
FURNIVAL, B. A. 10 - 0	077022 73729
GALLAGHER, G. R. P. 11 - 0	07546 258692
GALLIERS-PRATT, A. 9 - 9	07787 324386
GALLIGAN, M. 9 - 7	07469 969874
GEORGE, N. A. C. 10 - 7	07540 564499
GIBBS, B. 10 - 0	07818 407883
GILL, S. 11 - 2	0208 8348306
GILLAM, J. 9 - 3	07847 607391

GILLARD, T. 9 - 12.................................07824 772444
GLANVILLE, P. 10 - 5.............................07799 172784
GLENISTER, K. F. 8 - 4...........................01544 267672
GORDON, W. 9 - 0..................................07796 230473
GOSCHEN, A. 10 - 7...............................07719 611301
GOSS, J. R. 10 - 4..................................07747 514321
GOSTELOW, G. 10 - 2.............................07704 077663
GREATREX, T. 9 - 7.........................Mr Dave Roberts
GREENOCK, G. 11 - 7.............................07919 554517
GREENWAY, C. A. 9 - 5..........................07526 923647
GREENWOOD, T. O. M. 9 - 7...................07904 889779
GREGORY, F. W. 9 - 8.............................07798 572485
GREGORY, K. A. 10 - 6............................07789 394488
GRISSELL, R. L. O. 9 - 10........................07894 337241
HALL, L. 9 - 3...07972 136644
HALL, P. G. 11 - 7...................................01892 553160
HAMILTON, T. 9 - 3.........................Mr J. B. Jeffrey
HAMPSON, B. 9 - 0........................Mr L. R. James
HAMPTON, M. L. 10 - 7....................Mr Dave Roberts
HANNAFORD, D. 8 - 7.............................07976 588203
HARDING, J. 9 - 6...................................07858 783909
HARDY, P. 9 - 2......................................07949 198410
HARTE, S. A. 10 - 7................................07516 456369
HAWKER, R. 10 - 7..........................Mr Dave Roberts
HEAL, H. 8 - 3..07890 260919
HENDERSON, F. 11 - 0.............................07824 954461
HENDERSON, G. 11 - 0............................07901 716716
HENEGHAN, J. A. 10 - 2..........................07766 238711
HEPTONSTALL, R. 8 - 12.........................07725 185506
HICKMAN, H. W. W. 11 - 0.......................07841 488935
HICKS, B. 9 - 7......................................07500 703638
HOGG, R. C. 10 - 0.................................07548 934272
HOOPER, R. 9 - 12..................................07849 57211
HUGHES, J. 9 - 7....................................07884 432672
HUGHES, J. 10 - 5........................Mrs Joanna Hughes
HUGHES, R. S. 10 - 4.............................01981 250 214
HUNT, H. 8 - 9.......................................07341 847085
HUTCHINGS, O. A. 9 - 0..........................01752 842362
JACKSON-STOPS, J. 12 - 0.....................07719 443493
JAMES, B. 9 - 10....................................07544 726587
JARRETT, R. N. 10 - 7.............................07527 034069
JEWELL, C. H. 9 - 10..............................07810 334287
JOHNSON, L. 9 - 10................................01952 730722
JOHNSON, M. S. 9 - 3.............................07816 609314
KELK, S. F. 9 - 7....................................07554 173519
KELLARD, W. A. 10 - 7............................07779 008698
KENDRICK, J. 8 - 11................................07712 741793
KENDRICK, M. J. P. 9 - 7..................Mr C. D. Broad
KENT, A. 8 - 0..07733 232131
KERR, M. 9 - 7.......................................07413 375383
KILGARRIFF, L. 9 - 7...........................Andy Lewis
KINDER, H. J. 9 - 12...............................07808 551379
KING, A. M. 9 - 0....................................07710 406834
KING, J. 9 - 9...07929 831484
KING, M. 8 - 7.......................................07946516613
KNOX, J. S. 10 - 7..................................07792 196146
LAUNCHBURY, J. 11 - 0...........................07920 118627
LAWTON, N. 10 - 7.................................07525179482
LEE, S. 9 - 2...07745 327430
LEGG, M. D. 9 - 7...........................Mr Dave Roberts
LEVINSON, G. 9 - 7................................07956 223456
LEWIS, H. M. 9 - 0.................................07808 863102
LEYSHON, R. 8 - 10................................07917 545239
LOCKING, K. P. 9 - 0...............................07835 360125
LYONS, K. 9 - 10............................Mr L. R. James
LYTTLE, J. 10 - 8...................................07774 060675
MACKENZIE, E. 9 - 8..............................07702 607572
MADGWICK, L. F. 10 - 7..........................07759 301864

MAHON, L. 10 - 7...................................07961 101795
MAHOT, J. H. M. 10 - 10.........................07779 797079
MARETT, T. 9 - 0....................................07795 522162
MARGARSON, K. L. 9 - 0.................Mr Paul Brierley
MARSHALL, C. 9 - 12...............................07516 296716
MARTIN, J. I. 10 - 3................................07815 698359
MASKILL, W. G. C. 10 - 0........................07833 937472
MASON, J. L. 8 - 10........................Mr N. Hannity
MAXWELL, D. 11 - 7................................0207 5292323
MCCAIN, A. 9 - 7....................................07740 187712
MCCLOREY, T. A. 10 - 7..........................07545 073468
MCDONALD, R. M. 9 - 5...........................07494 422275
MCINERNEY, J. A. 9 - 7...........................07463 776294
MCINTYRE, M. J. 9 - 10...................Mr Dave Roberts
MCKEOWN, T. L. 9 - 7.............................07975 536617
MCLERNON, J. 9 - 7...............................07875 532791
MCMELLON, D. H. 9 - 7...........................07827 779019
MCSHARRY, F. 9 - 7...............................07554 060705
MEEHAN, C. 9 - 7...................................07710 264480
MILLER, C. 10 - 5...................................07817 455592
MILLER, S. 9 - 0.....................................07788 264066
MILLMAN, P. B. 9 - 7.........................Mr Ian Wood
MOORCROFT, B. 10 - 0............................07971 806968
MOORE, H. J. 9 - 0.................................07736 149669
MORRIS, J. 9 - 11..................................07825 599426
MORSHEAD, H. 9 - 10.............................07983 855286
MOSELEY, E. L. 9 - 7..............................07813 153264
MUIRHEAD, A. 12 - 0...............................07720 717406
MULLINEAUX, M. 8 - 7.............................01829 261440
MURRAY, S. 10 - 7..................................07813 459374
MUSPRATT, L. 10 - 0...............................07585 772198
NAILOR, J. 9 - 0.....................................07751 889859
NASH-STEER, M. 8 - 3............................07594 401124
NEWMAN, J. 9 - 7...........................Mr S. Stronge
NICHOL, R. 10 - 0...........................Mr Paul Brierley
NIXON, J. 10 - 2.....................................07456 600103
NUGENT, H. F. 9 - 7...............................07868 146696
O'BRIEN, T. M. 10 - 0......................Mr C. D. Broad
O'CONNELL, A. T. 9 - 2...........................07794 199053
O'NEILL, J. J. 10 - 0...............................07557 038016
O'SHAUGHNESSY, B. C. 9 - 7..................07565 652901
OLLIVER, J. M. 8 - 9...............................07885 412708
ORPWOOD, N. 10 - 12.............................07831 836626
ORR, C. J. 9 - 4......................................07871 142222
PAINTING, S. W. 10 - 0...........................07919 454844
PALMER, M. 9 - 2....................................07415 799212
PARIS-CROFTS, B. 9 - 4......................Andy Lewis
PARKER, N. L. 9 - 5................................07877 151521
PATRICK, R. P. 9 - 7...............................07891 968199
PAYNE, J. 9 - 8......................................07500 893516
PAYNE, S. 9 - 8......................................07596 414085
PEACOCK, S. 9 - 0.................................07775 791153
PEARCE, J. 9 - 7.............................Andy Lewis
PENDLETON, V. L. 8 - 12.............c/o 01844 353051
PETERS, D. M. 10 - 10............................07789 997367
PETTIS, W. 9 - 2....................................07908 572141
PINCHIN, L. M. 9 - 3...............................07989 425490
POOLES, R. L. 10 - 7..............................07766 244716
POWNALL, C. L. 9 - 1..............................07977 440482
PRICHARD, C. 9 - 7................................07870 291498
RANDELL, S. 9 - 7..................................07868 728440
RAWDON-MOGG, C. J. D. 11 - 5..............07759 451287
RAYBOULD, P. S. G. 9 - 0........................07576 107692
REDDINGTON, J. J. 11 - 8........................07766 767464
REED, W. H. R. 9 - 0.......................Mr J. B. Jeffrey
REYNOLDS, E. 9 - 2................................07816 531845
ROBARTS, B. A. G. 10 - 10......................07966 498559
ROBINSON, C. E. 8 - 2............................07876 123580

ROBINSON, I. P. B. 9 - 2 .... 07581 361986
ROBINSON, S. C. 12 - 0 .... 01424 204190
ROWNTREE, K. 10 - 0 .... 07714 474640
SANSOM, D. 9 - 7 .... 07821 520829
SCOTT, D. C. 9 - 4 .... 07814 147514
SCOTT, L. 10 - 0 .... 07443 597049
SHEPPARD, S. 9 - 4 .... Mr C. D. Broad
SKIPPER, P. 10 - 0 .... 07807 390203
SMITH, A. 9 - 2 .... 07462 908105
SMITH, D. J. 10 - 12 .... 07983 159367
SMITH, E. J. 9 - 7 .... 07824 158142
SMITH, J. 9 - 7 .... 07562 137956
SMITH, R. 8 - 12 .... 07716 919975
SMITH-MAXWELL, J. 11 - 4 .... 07535 459701
SPEKE, T. 10 - 3 .... 07870 813256
STEARN, R. R. P. 11 - 0 .... 07879 412414
STEPHENS, B. 9 - 4 .... 07752 208688
STIRLING, A. E. 10 - 0 .... 07557 952057
STRAWSON, T. R. F. 11 - 7 .... 07809 444373
STUCKEY, H. 8 - 5 .... 07455 265424
SWAFFIELD, C. 9 - 2 .... 07795 036047
SWAN, G. 9 - 7 .... 07966 801736
SYMES-MEINECK, D. 9 - 2 .... 07517 519786
TAYLOR, A. 9 - 4 .... 07730 872866
TEAL, H. 10 - 0 .... 07949 240199
TEAL, J. 10 - 9 .... 07984 649070
TELFER, W. 11 - 0 .... 01793 762232
TETT, F. 9 - 0 .... 07786 314587
THOMAS, J. 11 - 3 .... 07516 657526
THOMAS, P. J. 9 - 7 .... 01789 298346
TODD, E. L. 9 - 3 .... Mr Paul Brierley
TONGUE, R. 10 - 0 .... 07899 750871
TREACY, G. 10 - 7 .... 07901 199386
TREGONING, G. 9 - 7 .... 07818 441714
TUDOR, J. E. 11 - 4 .... 07950 381227
TURNER, D. I. 9 - 0 .... 07768 094908
TURNER, L. M. 10 - 0 .... 07984 531836
TUTTY, P. L. 9 - 5 .... 07815 798222

VAUGHAN-JONES, A. 11 - 7 .... 07887 567611
VOIKHANSKY, M. 9 - 12 .... 01213 772133
WADE, V. L. 9 - 8 .... 07772 925721
WAGGOTT, J. J. 10 - 0 .... 07789 465482
WALEY-COHEN, S. B. 10 - 0 .... 07887 848425
WALKER, S. A. 9 - 7 .... Mr S. T. Dodds
WALLACE, A. 9 - 0 .... 07867 923642
WALTERS, G. 8 - 7 .... 07794 652944
WALTON, C. M. 9 - 4 .... Mr J. B. Jeffrey
WALTON, J. 9 - 0 .... 07955 260235
WATSON, H. 9 - 0 .... 07793 053940
WAUGH, A. 8 - 5 .... 07761 040963
WEDMORE, O. Z. F. 9 - 10 .... 07806 517766
WELCH, H. J. 9 - 2 .... 07479 26696
WELCH, J. 7 - 8 .... 07753 254528
WEST, L. L. 9 - 7 .... 07894 733035
WHEELER, L. 10 - 0 .... 07813 969202
WILLEY, J. P. 9 - 3 .... 01909 475962
WILLIAMS, C. 9 - 10 .... 07540 858880
WILLIAMS, C. 10 - 5 .... 07495 908408
WILLIAMS, I. K. 9 - 0 .... 07714 170652
WILLIAMS, J. C. 9 - 3 .... 07841 576651
WILLIAMS, L. 10 - 0 .... 07836 327031
WILLIAMS, N. R. P. 11 - 4 .... 01308 868272
WILLIAMSON, C. L. 9 - 10 .... 07572 463468
WILSON, L. J. 8 - 10 .... 07411 902747
WILSON, R. 10 - 0 .... 07943 237205
WILSON, R. E. 9 - 0 .... 07770 732007
WINKS, R. P. 9 - 7 .... 01226 340011
WOOD, K. 9 - 10 .... 07429 078066
WORRALL, H. 8 - 0 .... 07496 658841
WORSLEY, T. 9 - 12 .... 07825 067820
WRIGHT, J. 10 - 0 .... 07787 365500
WRIGLEY, E. G. T. 10 - 7 .... 07870 699659
WYATT, C. T. 9 - 10 .... 07810 824437
YORK, P. 10 - 7 .... 07774 962168
YOUNG, E. 10 - 0 .... 07732 380913

Are your contact details missing or incorrect?
If so please update us by email:
richard.lowther@racingpost.co.uk

NOTES

NOTES

NOTES

NOTES

Rapid tests for fast horses.

Great advantages:
- Inhouse Point of Care Testing
- Easy, Rapid and Accurate
- Highly Sensitive
- Quantitative Results
- Fast on track again after illness
- Avoid spreading infection
- Follow up and access extensivness of the inflamation

Equine Haptoglobin Test Kit

LIFEASSAYS®

...e help veterinarians and trainers improve the ...rformance of their horses by offering an innovative ...lution to pick up early signs of inflammation as well ...monitoring horses under treatment. And you get ...ur Quantitative results within 12 minutes!!

...all us: +46 (0)46 286 54 00
...fo@lifeassays.com, www.lifeassays.com

LIFEASSAYS®
BLOOD ANALYSIS FOR LIFE